# Periodic Table of the Elements

**MAIN-GROUP ELEMENTS**

Legend:
- Metals (main-group)
- Metals (transition)
- Metals (inner transition)
- Metalloids
- Nonmetals

TRANSITION ELEMENTS

INNER TRANSITION ELEMENTS

As of late 2010, elements 113 through 118 had not been named.

| Period | 1A (1) | 2A (2) | 3B (3) | 4B (4) | 5B (5) | 6B (6) | 7B (7) | 8B (8) | 8B (9) | 8B (10) | 1B (11) | 2B (12) | 3A (13) | 4A (14) | 5A (15) | 6A (16) | 7A (17) | 8A (18) |
|---|---|---|---|---|---|---|---|---|---|---|---|---|---|---|---|---|---|---|
| 1 | 1 **H** 1.008 | | | | | | | | | | | | | | | | | 2 **He** 4.003 |
| 2 | 3 **Li** 6.941 | 4 **Be** 9.012 | | | | | | | | | | | 5 **B** 10.81 | 6 **C** 12.01 | 7 **N** 14.01 | 8 **O** 16.00 | 9 **F** 19.00 | 10 **Ne** 20.18 |
| 3 | 11 **Na** 22.99 | 12 **Mg** 24.31 | | | | | | | | | | | 13 **Al** 26.98 | 14 **Si** 28.09 | 15 **P** 30.97 | 16 **S** 32.07 | 17 **Cl** 35.45 | 18 **Ar** 39.95 |
| 4 | 19 **K** 39.10 | 20 **Ca** 40.08 | 21 **Sc** 44.96 | 22 **Ti** 47.88 | 23 **V** 50.94 | 24 **Cr** 52.00 | 25 **Mn** 54.94 | 26 **Fe** 55.85 | 27 **Co** 58.93 | 28 **Ni** 58.69 | 29 **Cu** 63.55 | 30 **Zn** 65.41 | 31 **Ga** 69.72 | 32 **Ge** 72.61 | 33 **As** 74.92 | 34 **Se** 78.96 | 35 **Br** 79.90 | 36 **Kr** 83.80 |
| 5 | 37 **Rb** 85.47 | 38 **Sr** 87.62 | 39 **Y** 88.91 | 40 **Zr** 91.22 | 41 **Nb** 92.91 | 42 **Mo** 95.94 | 43 **Tc** (98) | 44 **Ru** 101.1 | 45 **Rh** 102.9 | 46 **Pd** 106.4 | 47 **Ag** 107.9 | 48 **Cd** 112.4 | 49 **In** 114.8 | 50 **Sn** 118.7 | 51 **Sb** 121.8 | 52 **Te** 127.6 | 53 **I** 126.9 | 54 **Xe** 131.3 |
| 6 | 55 **Cs** 132.9 | 56 **Ba** 137.3 | 57 **La** 138.9 | 72 **Hf** 178.5 | 73 **Ta** 180.9 | 74 **W** 183.9 | 75 **Re** 186.2 | 76 **Os** 190.2 | 77 **Ir** 192.2 | 78 **Pt** 195.1 | 79 **Au** 197.0 | 80 **Hg** 200.6 | 81 **Tl** 204.4 | 82 **Pb** 207.2 | 83 **Bi** 209.0 | 84 **Po** (209) | 85 **At** (210) | 86 **Rn** (222) |
| 7 | 87 **Fr** (223) | 88 **Ra** (226) | 89 **Ac** (227) | 104 **Rf** (263) | 105 **Db** (262) | 106 **Sg** (266) | 107 **Bh** (267) | 108 **Hs** (277) | 109 **Mt** (268) | 110 **Ds** (281) | 111 **Rg** (272) | 112 **Cn** (285) | 113 (284) | 114 (289) | 115 (288) | 116 (292) | | 118 (294) |

| Inner Transition | | | | | | | | | | | | | | |
|---|---|---|---|---|---|---|---|---|---|---|---|---|---|---|
| **6 Lanthanides** | 58 **Ce** 140.1 | 59 **Pr** 140.9 | 60 **Nd** 144.2 | 61 **Pm** (145) | 62 **Sm** 150.4 | 63 **Eu** 152.0 | 64 **Gd** 157.3 | 65 **Tb** 158.9 | 66 **Dy** 162.5 | 67 **Ho** 164.9 | 68 **Er** 167.3 | 69 **Tm** 168.9 | 70 **Yb** 173.0 | 71 **Lu** 175.0 |
| **7 Actinides** | 90 **Th** 232.0 | 91 **Pa** (231) | 92 **U** 238.0 | 93 **Np** (237) | 94 **Pu** (242) | 95 **Am** (243) | 96 **Cm** (247) | 97 **Bk** (247) | 98 **Cf** (251) | 99 **Es** (252) | 100 **Fm** (257) | 101 **Md** (258) | 102 **No** (259) | 103 **Lr** (260) |

# The Elements

| Name | Symbol | Atomic Number | Atomic Mass* | Name | Symbol | Atomic Number | Atomic Mass* |
|------|--------|---------------|--------------|------|--------|---------------|--------------|
| Actinium | Ac | 89 | (227) | Mercury | Hg | 80 | 200.6 |
| Aluminum | Al | 13 | 26.98 | Molybdenum | Mo | 42 | 95.94 |
| Americium | Am | 95 | (243) | Neodymium | Nd | 60 | 144.2 |
| Antimony | Sb | 51 | 121.8 | Neon | Ne | 10 | 20.18 |
| Argon | Ar | 18 | 39.95 | Neptunium | Np | 93 | (244) |
| Arsenic | As | 33 | 74.92 | Nickel | Ni | 28 | 58.70 |
| Astatine | At | 85 | (210) | Niobium | Nb | 41 | 92.91 |
| Barium | Ba | 56 | 137.3 | Nitrogen | N | 7 | 14.01 |
| Berkelium | Bk | 97 | (247) | Nobelium | No | 102 | (253) |
| Beryllium | Be | 4 | 9.012 | Osmium | Os | 76 | 190.2 |
| Bismuth | Bi | 83 | 209.0 | Oxygen | O | 8 | 16.00 |
| Bohrium | Bh | 107 | (267) | Palladium | Pd | 46 | 106.4 |
| Boron | B | 5 | 10.81 | Phosphorus | P | 15 | 30.97 |
| Bromine | Br | 35 | 79.90 | Platinum | Pt | 78 | 195.1 |
| Cadmium | Cd | 48 | 112.4 | Plutonium | Pu | 94 | (242) |
| Calcium | Ca | 20 | 40.08 | Polonium | Po | 84 | (209) |
| Californium | Cf | 98 | (249) | Potassium | K | 19 | 39.10 |
| Carbon | C | 6 | 12.01 | Praseodymium | Pr | 59 | 140.9 |
| Cerium | Ce | 58 | 140.1 | Promethium | Pm | 61 | (145) |
| Cesium | Cs | 55 | 132.9 | Protactinium | Pa | 91 | (231) |
| Chlorine | Cl | 17 | 35.45 | Radium | Ra | 88 | (226) |
| Chromium | Cr | 24 | 52.00 | Radon | Rn | 86 | (222) |
| Cobalt | Co | 27 | 58.93 | Rhenium | Re | 75 | 186.2 |
| Copernicium | Cn | 112 | (285) | Rhodium | Rh | 45 | 102.9 |
| Copper | Cu | 29 | 63.55 | Roentgenium | Rg | 111 | (272) |
| Curium | Cm | 96 | (247) | Rubidium | Rb | 37 | 85.47 |
| Darmstadtium | Ds | 110 | (281) | Ruthenium | Ru | 44 | 101.1 |
| Dubnium | Db | 105 | (262) | Rutherfordium | Rf | 104 | (263) |
| Dysprosium | Dy | 66 | 162.5 | Samarium | Sm | 62 | 150.4 |
| Einsteinium | Es | 99 | (254) | Scandium | Sc | 21 | 44.96 |
| Erbium | Er | 68 | 167.3 | Seaborgium | Sg | 106 | (266) |
| Europium | Eu | 63 | 152.0 | Selenium | Se | 34 | 78.96 |
| Fermium | Fm | 100 | (253) | Silicon | Si | 14 | 28.09 |
| Fluorine | F | 9 | 19.00 | Silver | Ag | 47 | 107.9 |
| Francium | Fr | 87 | (223) | Sodium | Na | 11 | 22.99 |
| Gadolinium | Gd | 64 | 157.3 | Strontium | Sr | 38 | 87.62 |
| Gallium | Ga | 31 | 69.72 | Sulfur | S | 16 | 32.07 |
| Germanium | Ge | 32 | 72.61 | Tantalum | Ta | 73 | 180.9 |
| Gold | Au | 79 | 197.0 | Technetium | Tc | 43 | (98) |
| Hafnium | Hf | 72 | 178.5 | Tellurium | Te | 52 | 127.6 |
| Hassium | Hs | 108 | (277) | Terbium | Tb | 65 | 158.9 |
| Helium | He | 2 | 4.003 | Thallium | Tl | 81 | 204.4 |
| Holmium | Ho | 67 | 164.9 | Thorium | Th | 90 | 232.0 |
| Hydrogen | H | 1 | 1.008 | Thulium | Tm | 69 | 168.9 |
| Indium | In | 49 | 114.8 | Tin | Sn | 50 | 118.7 |
| Iodine | I | 53 | 126.9 | Titanium | Ti | 22 | 47.88 |
| Iridium | Ir | 77 | 192.2 | Tungsten | W | 74 | 183.9 |
| Iron | Fe | 26 | 55.85 | Uranium | U | 92 | 238.0 |
| Krypton | Kr | 36 | 83.80 | Vanadium | V | 23 | 50.94 |
| Lanthanum | La | 57 | 138.9 | Xenon | Xe | 54 | 131.3 |
| Lawrencium | Lr | 103 | (257) | Ytterbium | Yb | 70 | 173.0 |
| Lead | Pb | 82 | 207.2 | Yttrium | Y | 39 | 88.91 |
| Lithium | Li | 3 | 6.941 | Zinc | Zn | 30 | 65.41 |
| Lutetium | Lu | 71 | 175.0 | Zirconium | Zr | 40 | 91.22 |
| Magnesium | Mg | 12 | 24.31 | | | 113** | (284) |
| Manganese | Mn | 25 | 54.94 | | | 114 | (289) |
| Meitnerium | Mt | 109 | (268) | | | 115 | (288) |
| Mendelevium | Md | 101 | (256) | | | 116 | (292) |
| | | | | | | 118 | (294 |

*All atomic masses are given to four significant figures. Values in parentheses represent the mass number of the most stable isotope.
**The names and symbols for elements 113 through 116 and 118 have not yet been chosen.

## Fundamental Physical Constants (six signific

| | | |
|---|---|---|
| Avogadro's number | $N_A$ | $= 6.02214 \times 10$ |
| atomic mass unit | amu | $= 1.66054 \times 10$ |
| charge of the electron (or proton) | $e$ | $= 1.60218 \times 10$ |
| Faraday constant | $F$ | $= 9.64853 \times 10$ |
| mass of the electron | $m_e$ | $= 9.10939 \times 10$ |
| mass of the neutron | $m_n$ | $= 1.67493 \times 10$ |
| mass of the proton | $m_p$ | $= 1.67262 \times 10$ |
| Planck's constant | $h$ | $= 6.62607 \times 10$ |
| speed of light in a vacuum | $c$ | $= 2.99792 \times 10^8$ |
| standard acceleration of gravity | $g$ | $= 9.80665$ m/s$^2$ |
| universal gas constant | $R$ | $= 8.31447$ J/(m |
| | | $= 8.20578 \times 10$ (atm L)/(mol·K) |

## SI Unit Prefixes

| p | n | μ | m | c | d | k | M | G |
|---|---|---|---|---|---|---|---|---|
| pico- | nano- | micro- | milli- | centi- | deci- | kilo- | mega- | giga- |
| $10^{-12}$ | $10^{-9}$ | $10^{-6}$ | $10^{-3}$ | $10^{-2}$ | $10^{-1}$ | $10^3$ | $10^6$ | $10^9$ |

## Conversions and Relationships

### Length
**SI unit: meter, m**

| 1 km | $= 1000$ m |
|---|---|
| | $= 0.62$ mile (mi) |
| 1 inch (in) | $= 2.54$ cm |
| 1 m | $= 1.094$ yards (yd) |
| 1 pm | $= 10^{-12}$ m $= 0.01$ Å |

### Volume
**SI unit: cubic meter, m$^3$**

| 1 dm$^3$ | $= 10^{-3}$ m$^3$ |
|---|---|
| | $= 1$ liter (L) |
| | $= 1.057$ quarts (qt) |
| 1 cm$^3$ | $= 1$ mL |
| 1 m$^3$ | $= 35.3$ ft$^3$ |

### Pressure
**SI unit: pascal, Pa**

| 1 Pa | $= 1$ N/m$^2$ |
|---|---|
| | $= 1$ kg/m·s$^2$ |
| 1 atm | $= 1.01325 \times 10^5$ Pa |
| | $= 760$ torr |
| 1 bar | $= 1 \times 10^5$ Pa |

### Mass
**SI unit: kilogram, kg**

| 1 kg | $= 10^3$ g |
|---|---|
| | $= 2.205$ lb |
| 1 metric ton (t) | $= 10^3$ kg |

### Energy
**SI unit: joule, J**

| 1 J | $= 1$ kg·m$^2$/s$^2$ |
|---|---|
| | $= 1$ coulomb·volt (1 C·V) |
| 1 cal | $= 4.184$ J |
| 1 eV | $= 1.602 \times 10^{-19}$ J |

### Math relationships

$$\pi = 3.1416$$
volume of sphere $= \frac{4}{3}\pi r^3$
volume of cylinder $= \pi r^2 h$

### Temperature
**SI unit: kelvin, K**

| 0 K | $= -273.15$°C |
|---|---|
| mp of $H_2O$ | $= 0$°C (273.15 K) |
| bp of $H_2O$ | $= 100$°C (373.15 K) |
| $T$ (K) | $= T$ (°C) $+ 273.15$ |
| $T$ (°C) | $= [T$ (°F) $- 32]\frac{5}{9}$ |
| $T$ (°F) | $= \frac{9}{5}T$ (°C) $+ 32$ |

## Atomic and Molecular Properties

| | |
|---|---|
| Atomic radii | Figure 8.13, p. 309 |
| Bond energies | Table 9.2, p. 340 |
| Bond lengths | Table 9.2, p. 340 |
| Ground-state electron configurations | Figure 8.10, p. 305 |
| Electronegativity values | Figure 9.21, p. 349 |
| Ionic radii | Figure 8.29, p. 321 |
| First ionization energies | Figure 8.16, p. 312 |
| Molecular shapes | Figure 10.10, p. 379 |

## Equilibrium Constants and Thermodynamic Data

| | |
|---|---|
| $K_a$ of hydrated metal ions | Appendix C, p. A-12 |
| $K_a$ of selected acids | Appendix C, pp. A-8 to A-10 |
| Strengths of conjugate acid-base pairs | Figure 18.8, p. 731 |
| $K_b$ of amine bases | Appendix C, p. A-11 |
| $K_f$ of complex ions | Table 19.4, p. 796, and Appendix C, p. A-12 |
| $K_{sp}$ of slightly soluble ionic compounds | Appendix C, p. A-13 |
| Standard electrode potentials, $E^\circ_{half\text{-}cell}$ | Appendix D, p. A-14 |
| Standard free energies of formation, $\Delta G^\circ_f$ | Appendix B, pp. A-5 to A-7 |
| Standard heats of formation, $\Delta H^\circ_f$ | Appendix B, pp. A-5 to A-7 |
| Standard molar entropies, $S^\circ$ | Appendix B, pp. A-5 to A-7 |

## Names and Formulas

| | |
|---|---|
| Ligands | Table 23.7, p. 956 |
| Metals in complex anions | Table 23.8, p. 956 |
| Metals with more than one monatomic ion | Table 2.4, p. 62 |
| Monatomic ions | Table 2.3, p. 60 |
| Organic functional groups | Table 15.5, p. 592 |
| Polyatomic ions | Table 2.5, p. 62 |

## Properties of the Elements

| | |
|---|---|
| Group 1A(1): Alkali metals | p. 529 |
| Group 2A(2): Alkaline earth metals | p. 532 |
| Group 3A(13): Boron family | p. 534 |
| Group 4A(14): Carbon family | p. 538 |
| Group 5A(15): Nitrogen family | p. 544 |
| Group 6A(16): Oxygen family | p. 551 |
| Group 7A(17): Halogens | p. 556 |
| Group 8A(18): Noble gases | p. 562 |
| Period 4 transition metals, atomic properties | Figure 23.3, p. 948 |
| Period 4 transition metals, oxidation states | Table 23.2, p. 950 |

## Miscellaneous

| | |
|---|---|
| Rules for assigning an oxidation number | Table 4.3, p. 155 |
| SI-English equivalent quantities | Table 1.4, p. 18 |
| Solubility rules for ionic compounds in water | Table 4.1, p. 143 |
| Vapor pressure of water | Table 5.2, p. 200 |

# CHEMISTRY
## The Molecular Nature of Matter and Change

Sixth Edition

Martin S. Silberberg

For California Polytechnic State University, San Luis Obispo

 **Learning Solutions**

Boston  Burr Ridge, IL  Dubuque, IA  New York  San Francisco  St. Louis
Bangkok  Bogotá  Caracas  Lisbon  London  Madrid
Mexico City  Milan  New Delhi  Seoul  Singapore  Sydney  Taipei  Toronto

The McGraw·Hill Companies

Chemistry: The Molecular Nature of Matter and Change, Sixth Edition
For California Polytechnic State University, San Luis Obispo

This book is a McGraw-Hill Learning Solutions textbook and contains select material from *Chemistry: The Molecular Nature of Matter and Change*, Sixth Edition by Martin S. Silberberg. Copyright © 2012, 2009, 2006, 2003 by The McGraw-Hill Companies, Inc. Reprinted with permission of the publisher. Many custom published texts are modified versions or adaptations of our best-selling textbooks. Some adaptations are printed in black and white to keep prices at a minimum, while others are in color.

3 4 5 6 7 8 9 0   KNG KNG 13 12 11

ISBN-13: 978-0-07-756622-7
ISBN-10: 0-07-756622-X

*Learning Solutions Manager: Terri Harvey*
*Production Editor: Kathy Phelan*
*Printer/Binder: King Printing*
*Cover Photo Credits: Background © 2011 JupiterImages Corporation*

To Ruth and Daniel, with all my love,
and
In Memory of my Mother,
Gert Mazur,
Whose unfailing belief in me, I have finally come to realize,
has been a driving force in my life.

# BRIEF CONTENTS

# DETAILED CONTENTS

# CHAPTER 3 • Stoichiometry of Formulas and Equations 82

# CHAPTER 4 • Three Major Classes of Chemical Reactions 134

# CHAPTER 5 • Gases and the Kinetic-Molecular Theory 180

# CHAPTER 9 • Models of Chemical Bonding   328

# CHAPTER 10 • The Shapes of Molecules   362

# CHAPTER 13 • The Properties of Mixtures: Solutions and Colloids 476

# CHAPTER 14 • Periodic Patterns in the Main-Group Elements 522

# CHAPTER 17 • Equilibrium: The Extent of Chemical Reactions 676

# CHAPTER 18 • Acid-Base Equilibria 718

# CHAPTER 19 • Ionic Equilibria in Aqueous Systems 764

# CHAPTER 20 • Thermodynamics: Entropy, Free Energy, and the Direction of Chemical Reactions 810

# LIST OF SAMPLE PROBLEMS (Molecular-scene problems are shown in color.)

Martin S. Silberberg received a B.S. in Chemistry from the City University of New York and a Ph.D. in Chemistry from the University of Oklahoma. He then accepted a position as research associate in analytical biochemistry at the Albert Einstein College of Medicine in New York City, where he developed methods to study neurotransmitter metabolism in Parkinson's disease and other neurological disorders. Following six years as research associate, Dr. Silberberg joined the faculty of Bard College at Simon's Rock, a liberal arts college known for its excellence in teaching small classes of highly motivated students. As head of the Natural Sciences Major and Director of Premedical Studies, he taught courses in general chemistry, organic chemistry, biochemistry, and liberal-arts chemistry. The small class size and close student contact afforded him insights into how students learn chemistry, where they have difficulties, and what strategies can help them succeed. Dr. Silberberg decided to apply these insights in a broader context and established a textbook writing, editing, and consulting company. Before writing his own texts, he worked as a consulting and development editor on chemistry, biochemistry, and physics texts for several major college publishers. He resides with his wife Ruth and son in the Pioneer Valley near Amherst, Massachusetts, where he enjoys the rich cultural and academic life of the area and relaxes by cooking and singing.

# Preface

At the core of natural science, chemistry is so crucial to an understanding of medicine, molecular biology, genetics, pharmacology, ecology, atmospheric science, engineering, nuclear studies, materials science, and many other fields that it has become a central requirement for an increasing number of academic majors. Furthermore, chemical principles are at the core of many key societal issues, including climate change, energy options, materials recycling, diet and nutrition, and medicine and disease. Clearly, the study of chemistry plays an essential role in our world.

## WHAT SETS THIS BOOK APART

For five editions, *Chemistry: The Molecular Nature of Matter and Change* has been recognized for setting the standard among general chemistry textbooks. This sixth edition maintains that unparalleled reputation by keeping pace with the evolution of student learning. The text still contains the most accurate macroscopic-to-molecular illustrations, consistent step-by-step worked problems, and an extensive collection of end-of-chapter problems, with a wide range of difficulties and applications targeting student interests in engineering, medicine, materials, and environmental studies. Changes throughout the text have made it more succinct, the artwork more teachable and modern, and the design more open and inviting. And, while the content has certainly been updated to reflect chemistry's growing impact in the world, the mechanisms of the text—the teaching approaches that are so admired and emulated—have remained the same. Three hallmarks make this text a market leader.

### Visualizing Chemical Models— Macroscopic to Molecular

Chemistry deals with observable changes caused by unobservable atomic-scale events, requiring an understanding of a size gap of mind-boggling proportions. One of the text's goals coincides with that of so many instructors: to help the student visualize chemical events on the molecular scale. Thus, concepts are explained first at the macroscopic level and then from a molecular point of view, with the text's groundbreaking illustrations always placed next to the discussion to bring the point home for today's visually oriented students.

### Thinking Logically to Solve Problems

The problem-solving approach, based on the four-step method widely accepted by experts in chemical education, is introduced in Chapter 1 and employed *consistently* throughout the text. It encourages students to *plan* a logical approach to a problem, and only then proceed to *solve* it. Each sample problem includes a *check,* which fosters the habit of "taking a breath" to assess the reasonableness and magnitude of the answer. Finally, for *practice* and reinforcement, each sample problem is followed immediately by a similar follow-up problem, for which an abbreviated solution, not merely a numerical answer, is given at the end of the chapter. In this edition, solving problems and visualizing models have been married through an increasing number of molecular-scene problems in both worked examples and homework sets.

### Applying Ideas to the Real World

An understanding of modern chemistry influences attitudes about climate change and health care, while also explaining the spring in a running shoe and the display of a laptop screen. Today's students may enter one of the emerging chemistry-related hybrid fields—biomaterials science or planetary geochemistry, for example—and their text should point out the relevance of chemical concepts to such career directions. The *Chemical Connections* and *Tools of the Laboratory* boxed essays (which now include problems to reinforce learning), the fewer but more pedagogic margin notes, and the many applications woven into the chapter content are up-to-date, student-friendly features that complement the text content.

## REFINING THE STANDARD: AN EVOLVING LEARNING SYSTEM

Just as the field of chemistry is addressing major changes in the world, the student learning experience is changing as well—different math and reading preparation, less time for traditional studying, electronic media as part of daily lectures and homework, new challenges and options in career choices, and so on. To address these dynamic times, a modern general chemistry text supported by a suite of robust electronic tools for professor and student must continue to evolve, as this text has through all previous editions. From first to second edition, a major emphasis was placed on creating more molecular art to help students visualize chemistry at that level. The third edition incorporated many revised sample problems and a plethora of new end-of-chapter problems. The fourth edition gave birth to molecular-scene sample problems to help students understand concepts through simple molecular depictions. Molecular scenes became so popular that the fifth edition tripled the number of sample problems and doubled the number of end-of-chapter problems using them. During these revisions, major content improvements took place in limiting-reactant stoichiometry, green chemistry, biomolecular structure, kinetics and equilibrium, entropy and free energy, and nuclear chemistry, among many other areas.

With each edition, students and instructors alike have been involved in refining the text. Especially in preparation for the sixth edition, the author, together with key members of the editorial, sales, and marketing teams, consulted extensively with student and faculty users. From chapter reviews, focus groups, symposia, class tests, and one-on-one interviews with instructors, we were gratified to learn that everyone loved the pioneering, and still the most accurate, molecular art; the stepwise problem-solving approach, time-honored and consistent with decades of education research; the abundant mix of qualitative, basic quantitative, and applied end-of-chapter problems; and the thorough, student-friendly coverage of mainstream topics.

Based on this feedback, our revision for this edition focuses on "refining the standard" set earlier: distilling the writing to be concise and direct, opening up the overall appearance of pages, and improving illustrations by shortening legends and adding explanations into the art. We are delighted to introduce the sixth edition of *Chemistry: The Molecular Nature of Matter and Change,* which moves further toward perfecting content and approach in these ways:

**Chapter openings, simplified.** A familiar application and photo engage the student, followed by a bulleted list of main topics covered in the chapter.

**Writing style and content presentation.** Every line of every discussion has been revised to optimize clarity, readability, and a more direct presentation of ideas. The use of additional subheads, numbered (and titled) paragraphs, and bulleted (and titled) lists has eliminated long unbroken paragraphs. Main ideas are delineated and highlighted, making for more efficient study and lectures. As a result, the text is over 70 pages shorter, yet no key topics have been removed.

**Problem-solving format.** The much admired and duplicated four-part (plan, solution, check, practice) *Sample Problems* are displayed cleanly. Both data-based and molecular-scene problems occur throughout, and, to deepen understanding, most *Follow-Up Problems* have worked-out solutions at the back of each chapter, with a road map when appropriate, effectively doubling the number of worked problems. This edition has 15 more sample problems— many in the earlier chapters, where students need the most practice and confidence.

**Art and figure legends.** The innovative art that raised the bar in chemistry textbooks is still present, with many figures made more realistic and modern. Moreover, figure legends have been greatly shortened and their explanations added to neighboring text and the figures themselves for greater comprehension and less redundancy.

**Page design and layout.** A more open look invites the reader with cleaner margins and more white space, yet with the same attention to keeping text, figures, and tables near each other for easier viewing and studying.

**Incorporating relevance.** Applications make chemistry meaningful, so many exciting ideas from the margin notes and galleries of the fifth edition have been incorporated directly into the text, where they are more likely to be read. The boxed essays—*Chemical Connections* and *Tools of the Laboratory*—are more concise and are now accompanied by several homework problems to make them more useful for student and teacher.

**Section Summaries.** This universally approved feature is even easier to use in its new bulleted format.

**Chapter review.** Our unique *Chapter Review Guide* aids study by presenting concepts to understand and skills to master, key terms, key equations, and the multistep *Brief Solutions to Follow-Up Problems* (rather than simple numerical answers).

**End-of-chapter problem sets.** With an enhanced design to improve readability and traditional and molecular-scene problems updated and revised, these problem sets, more extensive than in most other texts, provide students and teachers with abundant choices in a wide range of difficulty and set in real-life scenarios.

## Content Changes to Individual Chapters

- Chapter 2 presents a new figure and table on molecular modeling.
- Discussion of empirical formulas has been moved from Chapter 2 to Chapter 3 so it appears just before molecular formulas.
- Within Chapter 3, some sample problems have been segmented and seven new sample problems introduced to better focus problem-solving on distinct concepts.
- Chapter 3 contains more extensive use of stoichiometry reaction tables in limiting-reactant problems.
- Chapter 4 presents a new molecular-scene sample problem on depicting an ionic compound in aqueous solution.
- Chapter 5 includes a new subsection on how gas laws apply to breathing.
- Chapter 5 also contains new short discussions on the relevance of gas density.
- Also in Chapter 5, coverage of reaction stoichiometry has been more logically grouped with other rearrangements of the ideal gas law.
- Chapter 5 contains new illustrations of diffusion and origin of pressure.
- In Chapter 5, *Chemical Connections to Atmospheric Science* uses the gas laws to explain why the troposphere has a uniform composition.
- Chapter 7 includes a new sample problem on using the Rydberg equation.
- Chapter 8 contains a new subsection covering electron configuration, chemical reactivity, and redox behavior.

- In Chapter 9, *Tools of the Laboratory: Infrared Spectroscopy* contains a new discussion of carbon dioxide in global warming.
- Chapter 11 includes a new discussion of limitations to *d*-orbital hybridization.
- Chapter 12 presents new short discussions of everyday applications of surface tension, capillarity, and viscosity.
- Chapter 13 presents everyday applications of freezing point depression and osmotic pressure.
- The fifth edition's *Interchapter* has been deleted, but key figures have been placed in relevant locations within other chapters.
- Chapter 14 provides a thorough, focused survey of main-group descriptive chemistry.
- Chapter 15 contains new art for the molecular biology of protein synthesis and DNA replication.
- Chapter 16 incorporates two of the fifth edition's boxed features—on measuring reaction rates and on enzymes—into the chapter text.
- Chapter 17 makes consistent use of benchmarks for determining when an assumption is valid.
- Chapter 17 incorporates the fifth edition's boxed feature on ammonia production into the chapter text.
- Chapter 19 incorporates the fifth edition's boxed feature on cave formation into the chapter text.

### Flexibility in Topic and Chapter Presentation

*Chemistry: The Molecular Nature of Matter and Change* has been revised to keep the mainstream topic sequence working optimally for teacher and student. But every course is unique, so flexibility has been built in: many section and subsection breaks allow topics to be rearranged with minimal loss of continuity. For example, redox balancing can be covered in Chapter 4, in Chapter 21, or, as done in the text, in both Chapter 4 (oxidation-number method) *and* Chapter 21 (half-reaction method, in preparation for electrochemistry). Likewise, several chapters can be taught in different orders. For instance, gases (Chapter 5) can be covered in sequence to explore the mathematical modeling of physical behavior or, with no loss of continuity, just before liquids and solids (Chapter 12) to show the effects of intermolecular forces on the three states of matter. In fact, feedback has indicated that many instructors move chapters, sections, and topics around, for example, covering descriptive chemistry (Chapter 14) and organic chemistry (Chapter 15) in

the more traditional placement at the end of the course. Because the topic sequence is so flexible, any instructor can feel comfortable making such changes to suit his or her course.

## KEEPING PACE WITH THE EVOLUTION OF STUDENT LEARNING

Many of us don't have the same cell phones, computers, or cars that we did just a few years ago—because technology is improving. In much the same way, the Silberberg Learning System has also been improving. The fifth edition of this text was accompanied by an online homework program called ARIS. Through careful observation of students and collaboration with instructors, the online homework tool has evolved into an online learning and engagement tool: **Connect:™ Chemistry.** The goal of Connect: Chemistry is to usher in a new era of meaningful online learning that balances the conceptual and quantitative aspect of this most vital discipline.

With this sixth edition, McGraw-Hill is offering students and instructors a greatly enhanced digital homework experience through Connect: Chemistry. Each problem formerly in the ARIS system has been carefully converted into the new program. Within Connect: Chemistry, each problem retains Silberberg's problem-solving methodology and is enhanced with specific hints, as well as feedback for common incorrect answers—all authored and accuracy-checked by teams of dedicated chemistry professors with many years of classroom experience. Several rounds of editorial revising and more expert checking, in addition to numerous instructor and student tests of all problems, ensure the accuracy and pedagogic soundness of all content.

In addition to the specific hints and feedback, many problems offer students the opportunity to engage in chemical drawing that can be assessed directly within their homework. To provide this important pedagogic experience, Connect: Chemistry has partnered with CambridgeSoft's® ChemDraw, widely considered the "gold standard" of scientific drawing programs and *the* cornerstone application for drawing and annotating molecules, reactions, and pathways. This collaboration of Connect: Chemistry and ChemDraw features an easy-to-use, intuitive, and comprehensive course management and homework system with professional-grade drawing capabilities.

# THE SILBERBERG LEARNING SYSTEM

Many pedagogic tools are woven throughout the chapters to guide students on their learning journey.

## Chapter Openers

Each chapter introduces a familiar application and photo relating to the main topic of the chapter, followed by a bulleted list of main topics. The chapter outline shows the sequence of topics and subtopics. At the top of the opposite page, *Concepts and Skills to Review* lists key material from earlier chapters that students should understand before starting to read the current one.

## Problem Solving

A worked-out *Sample Problem* appears whenever an important new concept or skill is introduced. The problem-solving step helps students think through chemistry problems logically and systematically. The universally accepted four-step approach of plan, solve, check, and practice is used consistently for every sample problem in the text. The steps are:

- **Plan** analyzes the problem so that students can use what is known to find what is unknown. This step develops the habit of thinking through the solution before performing calculations. Most quantitative problems are accompanied in the margin by a *Road Map*, a block diagram that is specific to the problem and leads students visually through the planned steps.
- **Solution** presents the calculation steps *in the same order* as they appear in the plan and in the road map.
- **Check** fosters the habit of going over one's work with a rough calculation to make sure the answer is both chemically and mathematically reasonable—a great way to avoid careless errors. In many cases, this step is followed by a *Comment* that identifies an additional insight, alternative approach, or common mistake to avoid.
- **Follow-Up Problem** presents a similar problem to provide immediate practice, with an abbreviated multistep solution appearing at the end of the chapter. Where appropriate in the first several chapters, students are asked to draw their own road map to solve the follow-up problem.

---

**Sample Problem 3.13** **Balancing an Equation from a Molecular Scene**

**Problem** The following molecular scenes depict an important reaction in nitrogen chemistry (nitrogen is blue; oxygen is red):

Write a balanced equation for this reaction.

**Plan** To write a balanced equation, we first have to determine the formulas of the molecules and obtain coefficients by counting the number of each molecule. Then, we arrange this information in the correct equation format, using the smallest whole-number coefficients and including states of matter.

**Solution** The reactant circle shows only one type of molecule. It has two N and five O atoms, so the formula is $N_2O_5$; there are four of these molecules. The product circle shows two different molecules, one with one N and two O atoms, and the other with two O atoms; there are eight $NO_2$ and two $O_2$. Thus, we have:

$$4N_2O_5 \longrightarrow 8NO_2 + 2O_2$$

Writing the balanced equation with the smallest whole-number coefficients and all substances as gases:

$$2N_2O_5(g) \longrightarrow 4NO_2(g) + O_2(g)$$

**Check** Reactant (4 N, 10 O) $\longrightarrow$ products (4 N, 8 + 2 = 10 O)

**Follow-Up Problem 3.13** Write a balanced equation for the important atmospheric reaction depicted below (carbon is black; oxygen is red):

## Three-Level Illustrations

As the art that set the standard for chemistry textbooks, these illustrations connect the macroscopic and molecular levels of reality with the symbolic level in the form of a chemical equation.

Figure 5.12 Collecting a water-insoluble gaseous product and determining its pressure.

## Annotated Figures

Modern, explanatory figures describe chemical processes through instructional labeling and realistic, three-dimensional art.

## Optimized Presentation

Text paragraphs have been made more concise, with presentation of content optimized through the use of subheads, numbered paragraphs, and lists. Main ideas are delineated, resulting in a more student-friendly study format.

## Applications

*Chemical Connections* essays show the interdisciplinary nature of chemistry by applying chemical principles directly to related scientific fields, including physiology, geology, biochemistry, engineering, and environmental science. *Tools of the Laboratory* essays describe the key instruments and techniques that chemists use in modern practice to obtain the data that underlie their theories. Both essay features now include several problems to enhance learning and relevance.

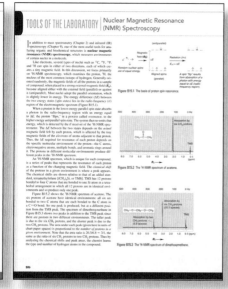

## Section Summaries

Concise, bulleted summary lists conclude each section, restating the major ideas just covered.

## Chapter Review Guide

A rich catalog of study aids ends each chapter to help students review its content.

- **Learning Objectives,** with section and/or sample problem numbers, focus on key concepts and skills.
- **Key Terms** are boldfaced and defined within the chapter and listed here by section (with page numbers), as well as being defined again in the *Glossary*.
- **Key Equations and Relationships** are screened and numbered within the chapter and listed here with page numbers.
- **Brief Solutions to Follow-Up Problems** double the number of worked problems by providing multistep calculations at the ends of the chapters, rather than just a numerical answer at the back of the book. Road maps are supplied for those follow-up problems that ask students to prepare one in planning their solution.

## End-of-Chapter Problems

An exceptionally large number of qualitative, quantitative, and molecular-scene homework problems end each chapter. Three types of problems are keyed by chapter section, with comprehensive problems following:

- **Concept Review Questions** test students' qualitative understanding of key ideas.
- **Skill-Building Exercises** are grouped in pairs that cover a similar idea, with one of each pair answered in the back of the book. These exercises begin with simple questions and increase in difficulty, gradually eliminating students' need for multistep directions.
- **Problems in Context** apply the skills learned in the skill-building exercises to interesting scenarios, including examples from industry, medicine, and the environment.
- **Comprehensive Problems,** most based on realistic applications, are more challenging and rely on concepts and skills from any section of the current chapter or from previous chapters.

# LEARNING SYSTEM RESOURCES FOR INSTRUCTORS

|CHEMISTRY

## www.mcgrawhillconnect.com/chemistry

McGraw-Hill Connect is a web-based, interactive assignment and assessment platform that incorporates cognitive science principles to customize the learning process. The chemical drawing tool found within Connect: Chemistry is CambridgeSoft's ChemDraw, which is widely considered the "gold standard" of scientific drawing programs and the cornerstone application for drawing and annotating molecules, reactions, and pathways. This combination of Connect and ChemDraw is an easy-to-use, intuitive, and comprehensive course management and homework system with professional-grade drawing capabilities.

End-of-chapter problems from this textbook are available in Connect: Chemistry for instructors to build assignments that are automatically graded and tracked through reports that export easily to Excel. Instructors can edit existing problems and write entirely new problems; track individual student performance—by problem, assignment, concept, or in relation to the class overall—with automatic grading; provide instant feedback to students; and store detailed grade reports securely online. Grade reports can be easily integrated with learning management systems such as WebCT and Blackboard. Single sign-on integration is available with the Blackboard course management system. Within Connect, instructors can also create and share materials with colleagues. Ask your McGraw-Hill representative for more information, and then check it out at www.mcgrawhillconnect.com/chemistry.

# Blackboard Course Management Integration with McGraw-Hill Content

Do More

McGraw-Hill Higher Education and Blackboard, the Web-based course-management system, have teamed up to allow students and faculty to easily use online materials and activities to complement face-to-face teaching. Blackboard features exciting social learning and teaching tools that foster more logical, visually impactful, and active learning opportunities for students. This partnership transforms closed-door classrooms into communities where students remain connected to their educational experience 24 hours a day.

This partnership allows instructors and students access to McGraw-Hill's Connect™ and Create™ from within Blackboard—with a single sign-on.

Instructors also get deep integration of McGraw-Hill content and content engines into Blackboard. Whether choosing a book for your course or building Connect™ assignments, all the tools you need are right where you want them—inside Blackboard.

Gradebooks are now seamless. When a student completes an integrated Connect™ assignment, the grade for that assignment is automatically (and instantly) fed to the Blackboard grade center.

McGraw-Hill and Blackboard now offer easy access to industry-leading technology and content, whether your campus hosts it, or we do. Be sure to ask your local McGraw-Hill representative for details.

**Presentation Center**   Accessed from your textbook's Connect website, Presentation Center is an online digital library containing McGraw-Hill owned photos, artwork, animations, and other types of media that can be used to create customized lectures, visually enhanced tests and quizzes, compelling course websites, or attractive printed support materials for classroom purposes. The visual resources in this collection include the following:

- **Art** Full-color digital files of all illustrations in the book can be readily incorporated into lecture presentations, exams, or custom-made classroom materials. In addition, all files have been inserted into PowerPoint slides for ease of lecture preparation.
- **Photos** The photo collection contains digital files of photographs from the text, which can be reproduced for multiple classroom uses.
- **Tables** Every table that appears in the text has been saved in electronic form for use in classroom presentations and/or classroom materials.

- **Animations** Numerous full-color animations illustrating important processes are also provided. Harness the visual impact of concepts in motion by importing these files into classroom presentations or online course materials.

PowerPoint materials can also be accessed through your textbook's Connect website:

- **PowerPoint Lecture Outlines** Ready-made presentations that combine art and lecture notes are provided for each chapter of the text.
- **PowerPoint Slides** For instructors who prefer to create their lectures from scratch, all illustrations, photos, sample problems, and tables have been inserted into blank Power-Point slides, arranged by chapter.

The Presentation Center library includes thousands of assets from many McGraw-Hill titles. This ever-growing resource gives instructors the power to utilize assets specific to an adopted textbook as well as content from all other books in the library. Accessed through the instructor side of your textbook's Connect website, Presentation Center's dynamic search engine allows you to explore by discipline, course, textbook chapter, asset type, or keyword. Simply browse, select, and download the files you need to build engaging course materials. To access Connect, request registration information from your McGraw-Hill sales representative.

## Mc Graw Hill ⓣegrity campus

**Digital Lecture Capture: Tegrity** McGraw-Hill *Tegrity Campus* records and distributes your lecture with just a click of a button. Students can view anytime/anywhere via computer, iPod, or mobile device. *Tegrity* indexes as it records your slideshow presentations and anything shown on your computer, so students can use keywords to find exactly what they want to study.

**Computerized Test Bank** Prepared by Walter Orchard, Professor Emeritus of Tacoma Community College, over 2300 test questions to accompany *Chemistry: The Molecular Nature of Matter and Change* are available utilizing Brownstone's Diploma testing software. *Diploma's* software allows you to quickly create a customized test using McGraw-Hill's supplied questions or by authoring your own. *Diploma* allows you to create your tests without an Internet connection—just download the software and question files directly to your computer.

**Instructor's Solutions Manual** This supplement, prepared by Patricia Amateis of Virginia Tech, contains complete, worked-out solutions for *all* the end-of-chapter problems in the text. It can be found within the Instructors Resources, on the Connect: Chemistry site.

**Content Delivery Flexibility** *Chemistry: The Molecular Nature of Matter and Change,* by Martin Silberberg, is available in other formats in addition to the traditional textbook, giving instructors and students more choices for the format of their chemistry text.

## Mc Graw Hill create

- **Customizable Textbooks: Create** McGraw-Hill Create™ is a new, self-service website that allows you to create custom course materials—print or eBook—by drawing on McGraw-Hill's comprehensive, cross-disciplinary content. Add your own content quickly and easily. Tap into other rights-secured third-party sources as well. Then, arrange the content in a way that makes the most sense for your course. Even personalize your book with your course name and information. Choose the best format for your course: color print, black-and-white print, or ebook (which is viewable on an iPad). And when you are finished customizing, you will receive a free PDF review copy in just minutes. Visit McGraw-Hill Create at www.mcgrawhillcreate.com today and begin building your perfect book.
- **ConnectPlus eBook** McGraw-Hill's ConnectPlus eBook takes digital texts beyond a simple PDF. With the same content as the printed book, but optimized for the screen, the ConnectPlus eBook has embedded media, including animations and videos, which bring concepts to life and provide "just in time" learning for students. Additionally, fully integrated homework problems allow students to interact with the problems to determine if they're gaining mastery of the content, and the problems can also be assigned by the instructor.

**Cooperative Chemistry Laboratory Manual** Prepared by Melanie Cooper of Clemson University, this innovative manual features open-ended problems designed to simulate experience in a research lab. Working in groups, students investigate one problem over a period of several weeks, so they might complete three or four projects during the semester, rather than one preprogrammed experiment per class. The emphasis is on experimental design, analytic problem solving, and communication.

# LEARNING SYSTEM RESOURCES FOR STUDENTS

**Student Study Guide**    This valuable study guide, prepared by Libby Bent Weberg, is designed to help you recognize your learning style; understand how to read, classify, and create a plan for solving a problem; and practice your problem-solving skills. For each section of each chapter, the guide provides study objectives and a summary of the corresponding text. Following the summary are sample problems with detailed solutions. Each chapter has true-false questions and a self-test, with all answers provided at the end of the chapter.

**Student Solutions Manual**    This supplement, prepared by Patricia Amateis of Virginia Tech, contains detailed solutions and explanations for all problems in the main text that have colored numbers.

**Connect: Chemistry**    With Connect: Chemistry, you can practice solving assigned homework problems using the Silberberg problem-solving methodology applied in the textbook. Algorithmic problems serve up multiple versions of similar problems for mastery of content, with hints and feedback for common incorrect answers to help you stay on track. Where appropriate, you engage in accurate, professional-grade chemical drawing through the use of CambridgeSoft's ChemDraw tool, which is implemented directly into homework problems. Check it out at www.mcgraw-hillconnect.com/chemistry.

## LearnSmart

**LearnSmart™**    This adaptive diagnostic learning system, powered by Connect: Chemistry and based on artificial intelligence, constantly assesses your knowledge of the course material. As you work within the system, LearnSmart develops a personal learning path adapted to what you have actively learned and retained. This innovative study tool also has features to allow your instructor to see exactly what you have accomplished, with a built-in assessment tool for graded assignments. You can access LearnSmart for general chemistry by going to www.mcgraw-hillconnect.com/chemistry.

**Animations for MP3/iPod**    A number of animations are available for download to your MP3/iPod through the textbook's Connect website.

# Acknowledgments

The sixth edition and its associated learning system are the culmination of numerous chapter reviews, insightful suggestions, brainstorming sessions, focus groups, interviews, and class tests. Each person involved played an important part in the revision of the text and its ancillaries.

I feel very fortunate to have a relationship with my publisher based on mutual respect, shared goals, and warm friendship. Heading the McGraw-Hill Higher Education team with their advice and support were Publisher Ryan Blankenship and Executive Editor Jeff Huettman, Developmental Editor Donna Nemmers, Director of Digital Content David Spurgeon, Digital Project Manager Daryl Bruflodt, Project Manager Peggy Selle, Designer David Hash, and Marketing Manager Tami Hodge.

Patricia Amateis, Virginia Tech, helped revise several chapters and prepared Appendix E as well as the Instructor's and Student Solutions Manuals. Krishnan Rajeshwar, University of Texas–Arlington, updated the discussion of the future of energy use.

I am very grateful to the Board of Advisors, who helped me make this text the optimum teaching tool: Debra Feakes, Texas State University–San Marcos, Derek Gragson, California Polytechnic State University–San Luis Obispo, and James Reeves, University of North Carolina–Wilmington. Also, my deepest gratitude extends to the following individuals, who attended focus groups or symposia, provided content reviews, and class-tested materials in preparation for the Sixth Edition and its associated learning system:

Patricia Amateis, *Virginia Tech*
Margaret Asirvatham, *University of Colorado—Boulder*
Yiyan Bai, *Houston Community College–Central*
Laurance Beauvais, *San Diego State University*
Thomas Bertolini, *University of Southern California*
Fereshteh Billiot, *Texas A&M University–Corpus Christi*
Deborah Booth, *University of Southern Mississippi*
Simon Bott, *University of Houston*
Stacey Lowery Bretz, *Miami University of Ohio*
Karen Brewer, *Virginia Tech*
Les Butler, *Louisiana State University*
Bindu Chakravarty, *Houston Community College–Northeast Campus*
Chris Cheatum, *University of Iowa*
Liwei Chen, *Ohio University*
Tom Clausen, *University of Alaska–Fairbanks*
Erin Dahlke, *Loras College*
Michelle Driessen, *University of Minnesota*
Jack Duff, *Southern Polytechnic State University*
Bill Durham, *University of Arkansas*
Emmanuel Ewane, *Houston Community College–Northwest*
Deborah Exton, *University of Oregon*
Paul Fazen, *Villanova University*
David Frank, *California State University–Fresno*
John Gelder, *Oklahoma State University*
Greg Gellene, *Texas Tech University*
Dimitri Giarikos, *Nova Southeastern University*

Michael Greenlief, *University of Missouri–Columbia*
Todor Gounev, *University of Missouri–Kansas City*
John Hagen, *California Polytechnic State University–San Luis Obispo*
Michael Hailu, *Columbus State Community College*
John Halpin, *New York University*
Narayan Hosmane, *Northern Illinois University*
Larry Houk, *University of Memphis*
Eihab Jaber, *Worcester State University*
Heiko Jacobsen, *Tulane University*
Richard Jarman, *College of DuPage*
Steve Keller, *University of Missouri*
San Kim, *Northern Virginia Community College*
Chuck Kirkpatrick, *St. Louis University*
Marina Koether, *Kennesaw State University*
Patric Kolniak, *Louisiana State University*
Pamela Kraemer, *Northern Virginia Community College*
Jothi Kumar, *North Carolina A&T State University*
Dorothy B. Kurland, *Emeritus, West Virginia Institute of Technology*
Anna Larsen, *Ithaca College*
Allison Long, *Georgia Southern University*
Jeanette Madea, *Broward Community College*
Diana Malone, *Clarke University*
Lisa McGaw, *University of Central Oklahoma*
Thomas McGrath, *Baylor University*
Danny McGuire, *Cameron University*
Bill McLaughlin, *Montana State University*
Lauren McMills, *Ohio University*
Joyce Miller, *San Jacinto College–South*

Kristine Miller, *Anne Arundel Community College*
Jeremy Mitchell-Koch, *Emporia State University*
Debbie Mohler, *James Madison University*
Kereen Monteyne, *University of Northern Kentucky*
Mahesh Narayan, *University of Texas–El Paso*
Jessica Orvis, *Georgia Southern University*
Jason Overby, *College of Charleston*
Richard Paselk, *Humboldt State University*
Louis Pignolet, *Emeritus, University of Minnesota*
John Pollard, *The University of Arizona*
Bernard Powell, *University of Texas–San Antonio*
William Quintana, *New Mexico State University*
Edward Quitevis, *Texas Tech University*
Jeff Rack, *Ohio University*
Lisa Reece, *Ozarks Technical Community College*
Michelle Richards-Babb, *West Virginia University*
Dawn Rickey, *Colorado State University*
Thomas Ridgway, *University of Cincinnati*
Steven Rowley, *Middlesex County College*
Raymond Sadeghi, *University of Texas–San Antonio*
Issa Salame, *The City College of New York*
Jim Satterlee, *Washington State University*
Colleen Scott, *Southern Illinois University–Carbondale*
Thomas Selegue, *Pima Community College*
Steve Shore, *Oklahoma City Community College*
Michael Sommer, *University of Wyoming*
Jie Song, *University of Michigan–Flint*

David Speckhard, *Loras College*
Rick Spinney, *Ohio State University*
Emelyn S. Q. Tan, *National University of Singapore*
Kimberly Trick, *University of Dayton*

Cyriacus Uzomba, *Austin Community College*
Debbie Warnaar, *James Madison University*
Lyle Wescott, *University of Mississippi*
Wayne Wesolowski, *The University of Arizona*

Daniel Williams, *Kennesaw State University*
Stephanie Wunder, *Temple University*
Timothy Zauche, *University of Wisconsin–Platteville*
Lin Zhu, *IUPUI*

**Connect: Chemistry** has been greatly enhanced by the efforts of Kereen Monteyne, University of Northern Kentucky; MaryKay Orgill, University of Nevada–Las Vegas; and Yasmin Patell, Kansas State University; who did a masterful job of authoring hints and feedback to augment all of the system's homework problems. The following individuals helped write and review learning goal–oriented content for **LearnSmart for General Chemistry:** Margaret Asirvatham, University of Colorado–Boulder; William Burns, Arkansas State University; Cabot-Ann Christofferson, South Dakota School of Mines; Christina Johnson, University of California–San Diego; Adam I. Keller, Columbus State Community College; Willem R. Leenstra, University of Vermont; Margaret Ruth Leslie, Kent State University; Benjamin R. Martin, Texas State University–San Marcos; Kathy Thrush Shaginaw, Particular Solutions, Inc.; and Erin Whitteck.

Several expert freelancers contributed as well. As always, Jane Hoover did an excellent copyediting of the textbook, and Francine Banwarth and Rose Kramer followed with meticulous proofreading. John Murdzek and LaurelTech exercised careful skill in accuracy-checking content within Connect: Chemistry.

Over the years and editions, I've always had the great benefit of the expertise of my "in-home" team. This time around, my son, Daniel, offered his keen artist's eye to the figures revised, the photos selected, and the cover devised. And my wife, Ruth, made this text come to fruition—literally. She worked closely with the McGraw-Hill production team and provided indispensable, detailed input to the compositor, copy editor, and proof readers. And, of course, they both kept the author going with their love and support.

CHEMISTRY

# Keys to the Study of Chemistry

## Concepts and skills to review before you study this chapter

- exponential (scientific) notation (Appendix A)

Maybe you're taking this course because chemistry is fundamental to understanding other natural sciences. Maybe it's required for your medical or engineering major. Or maybe you just want to learn more about the impact of chemistry on society or even on a personal, everyday level. For example, did you have cereal, fruit, and coffee for breakfast today? In chemical terms, you enjoyed nutrient-enriched, spoilage-retarded carbohydrate flakes mixed in a white emulsion of fats, proteins, and monosaccharides, with a piece of fertilizer-grown, pesticide-treated fruit, and a cup of hot aqueous extract of stimulating alkaloid. Earlier, you may have been awakened by the sound created as molecules aligned in the liquid-crystal display of your clock and electrons flowed to create a noise. You might have thrown off a thermal insulator of manufactured polymer and jumped in the shower to emulsify fatty substances on your skin and hair with purified water and formulated detergents. Perhaps you next adorned yourself in an array of pleasant-smelling pigmented gels, dyed polymeric fibers, synthetic footwear, and metal-alloy jewelry. After breakfast, you probably abraded your teeth with a colloidal dispersion of artificially flavored, dental-hardening agents, grabbed your laptop (an electronic device containing ultrathin, microetched semiconductor layers powered by a series of voltaic cells), collected some books (processed cellulose and plastic, electronically printed with light- and oxygen-resistant inks), hopped in your hydrocarbon-fueled, metal-vinyl-ceramic vehicle, electrically ignited a synchronized series of controlled gaseous explosions, and took off for class!

But the true impact of chemistry extends much farther than the commercial products of daily life. The truth is the most profound biological and environmental questions ultimately have chemical answers: How does an organism reproduce, grow, and age? What are the underlying explanations for health and disease? How can we sustain a planetary ecosystem in which plant, animal, and human populations thrive? Is there life on other worlds?

So, no matter what your reason for studying chemistry, you're going to learn some amazing ideas. And, this course comes with a bonus for developing two mental skills. The first, common to all science courses, is the ability to solve problems systematically. The second is specific to chemistry, for as you comprehend its ideas, you begin to view a hidden reality, one filled with incredibly minute particles moving at fantastic speeds, colliding billions of times a second, and interacting in ways that allow your brain to translate fluxes of electric charge into thoughts and that determine how all the matter inside and outside of you behaves. This chapter holds the keys to unlock and enter this new world.

**IN THIS CHAPTER . . .** We discuss some central ideas about matter and energy, the process of science, units of measurement, and how scientists handle data.
- We begin with fundamental concepts about matter and energy and their changes.
- A brief discussion of chemistry's origins, including some major missteps, leads to an overview of how scientists build models to study nature.
- We consider systematic chemical problem solving, including unit conversion and modern unit systems for mass, length, volume, density, and temperature.
- We see that data collection always includes some uncertainty and examine the distinction between accuracy and precision.

# 1.1 • SOME FUNDAMENTAL DEFINITIONS

A good place to begin our exploration of chemistry is to define it and a few central concepts. **Chemistry** is *the study of matter and its properties, the changes that matter undergoes, and the energy associated with those changes.*

## The Properties of Matter

**Matter** is the "stuff" of the universe: air, glass, planets, students—*anything that has mass and volume.* (In Section 1.5, we discuss the meanings of mass and volume in terms of how they are measured.) Chemists want to know the **composition** of matter, *the types and amounts of simpler substances that make it up.* A *substance* is a type of matter that has a defined, fixed composition.

We learn about matter by observing its **properties,** *the characteristics that give each substance its unique identity.* To identify a person, we might observe height, weight, hair and eye color, fingerprints, and, now, even DNA pattern, until we arrive at a unique identification. To identify a substance, we observe two types of properties, physical and chemical, which are closely related to two types of change that matter undergoes:

- **Physical properties** are characteristics a substance shows *by itself, without changing into or interacting with another substance.* These properties include melting point, electrical conductivity, and density. A **physical change** occurs when a substance *alters its physical properties, **not** its composition.* For example, when ice melts, several physical properties change, such as hardness, density, and ability to flow. But the composition of the sample does *not* change: it is still water. The photograph in Figure 1.1A shows what this change looks like in everyday life. The "blow-up" circles depict a magnified view of the particles making up the sample. In the icicle, the particles lie in a repeating pattern, whereas they are jumbled in the droplet, but *the particles are the same* in both forms of water.

  *Physical change (same substance before and after):*

  Water (solid form) $\longrightarrow$ water (liquid form)

- **Chemical properties** are characteristics a substance shows *as it changes into or interacts with another substance (or substances).* Chemical properties include flammability, corrosiveness, and reactivity with acids. A **chemical change,** also called a **chemical reaction,** occurs when *a substance (or substances) is converted into a different substance (or substances).* Figure 1.1B shows the chemical change (reaction) that occurs when you pass an electric current through water: the water decomposes

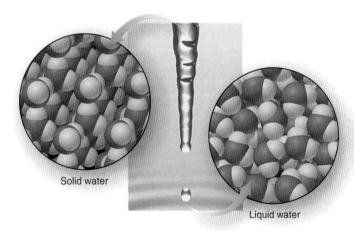

Solid water

Liquid water

Oxygen gas

Hydrogen gas

**A Physical change:**
*Solid form of water becomes liquid form. Particles before and after remain the same, which means composition did **not** change.*

**B Chemical change:**
*Electric current decomposes water into different substances (hydrogen and oxygen). Particles before and after are different, which means composition **did** change.*

**Figure 1.1** The distinction between physical and chemical change.

(breaks down) into two other substances, hydrogen and oxygen, that bubble into the tubes. The composition *has* changed: the final sample is no longer water.

*Chemical change (different substances before and after):*

$$\text{Water} \xrightarrow{\text{electric current}} \text{hydrogen} + \text{oxygen}$$

Let's work through a sample problem that uses atomic-scale scenes to distinguish between physical and chemical change.

---

**Sample Problem 1.1** | **Visualizing Change on the Atomic Scale**

**Problem** The scenes below represent an atomic-scale view of a sample of matter, A, undergoing two different changes, left to B and right to C:

Decide whether each depiction shows a physical or a chemical change.

**Plan** Given depictions of the changes, we have to determine whether each represents a physical or a chemical change. The number and colors of the little spheres that make up each particle tell its "composition." Samples with particles of the *same* composition but in a different arrangement depict a *physical* change, whereas samples with particles of a *different* composition depict a *chemical* change.

**Solution** In A, each particle consists of one blue and two red spheres. The particles in A change into two types in B, one made of red and blue spheres and the other made of two red spheres; therefore, they have undergone a   chemical change   to form different particles. The particles in C are the same as those in A, but they are closer together and arranged differently; therefore, they have undergone a   physical change.

**Follow-Up Problem 1.1** Is the following change chemical or physical? (Compare your answer with the one in Brief Solutions to Follow-Up Problems at the end of the chapter.)

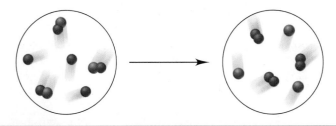

---

Like water, hydrogen, oxygen, or any other real substance, copper is also identified by *its own set* of physical and chemical properties (Table 1.1 on the next page).

## The States of Matter

Matter occurs commonly in *three physical forms* called **states:** solid, liquid, and gas. We'll define the states and see how temperature can change them.

**Defining the States** On the macroscopic scale, each state of matter is defined by the way the sample fills a container (Figure 1.2, next page, *flasks at top*):

- A **solid** has a fixed shape that does not conform to the container shape. Solids are *not* defined by rigidity or hardness: solid iron is rigid and hard, but solid lead is flexible, and solid wax is soft.

## Table 1.1   Some Characteristic Properties of Copper

| Physical Properties | | Chemical Properties | |
|---|---|---|---|
| Easily shaped into sheets (malleable) and wires (ductile) |  | Slowly forms a blue-green carbonate in moist air |  |
| Can be melted and mixed with zinc to form brass |  | Reacts with nitric or sulfuric acid |  |
| Density = 8.95 g/cm³ Melting point = 1083°C Boiling point = 2570°C | | Slowly forms deep-blue solution in aqueous ammonia |  |

- A **liquid** has a varying shape that conforms to the container shape, but only to the extent of the liquid's volume; that is, a liquid has *an upper surface.*
- A **gas** also has a varying shape that conforms to the container shape, but it fills the entire container and, thus, does *not* have a surface.

On the atomic scale, each state is defined by the relative positions of its particles (Figure 1.2, *circles at bottom*):

- In a *solid,* the particles lie next to each other in a regular, three-dimensional *array.*
- In a *liquid,* the particles also lie close together but move randomly around each other.
- In a *gas,* the particles have large distances between them and move randomly throughout the container.

**Figure 1.2** The physical states of matter.

**Solid**
*Particles are close together and organized.*

**Liquid**
*Particles are close together but disorganized.*

**Gas**
*Particles are far apart and disorganized.*

**Temperature and Changes of State** Depending on the temperature and pressure of the surroundings, many substances can exist in each of the three physical states and undergo changes in state as well. For example, as the temperature increases, solid water melts to liquid water, which boils to gaseous water (also called *water vapor*). Similarly, as the temperature drops, water vapor condenses to liquid water, and with further cooling, the liquid freezes to ice. In a steel plant, solid iron melts to liquid (molten) iron and then cools to the solid again. And, far beyond the confines of a laboratory or steel plant, lakes of molten sulfur lie on Jupiter's moon Io (*see photo*), which is capped by poles of frozen hydrogen sulfide, a gas on Earth.

The main point is that *a physical change caused by heating can generally be reversed by cooling*. This is *not* generally true for a chemical change. For example, heating iron in moist air causes a chemical reaction that yields the brown, crumbly substance known as rust. Cooling does not reverse this change; rather, another chemical change (or series of them) is required.

The following sample problem provides practice in distinguishing some familiar examples of physical and chemical change.

What common substances occur in unusual states on other worlds?

---

**Sample Problem 1.2** **Distinguishing Between Physical and Chemical Change**

**Problem** Decide whether each of the following processes is primarily a physical or a chemical change, and explain briefly:
(a) Frost forms as the temperature drops on a humid winter night.
(b) A cornstalk grows from a seed that is watered and fertilized.
(c) A match ignites to form ash and a mixture of gases.
(d) Perspiration evaporates when you relax after jogging.
(e) A silver fork tarnishes slowly in air.

**Plan** The basic question we ask to decide whether a change is chemical or physical is, "Does the substance change composition or just change form?"

**Solution** (a) Frost forming is a physical change: the drop in temperature changes water vapor (gaseous water) in humid air to ice crystals (solid water).
(b) A seed growing involves chemical change: the seed uses water, substances from air, fertilizer, and soil, and energy from sunlight to make complex changes in composition.
(c) The match burning is a chemical change: the combustible substances in the match head are converted into other substances.
(d) Perspiration evaporating is a physical change: the water in sweat changes its form, from liquid to gas, but not its composition.
(e) Tarnishing is a chemical change: silver changes to silver sulfide by reacting with sulfur-containing substances in the air.

**Follow-Up Problem 1.2** Decide whether each of the following processes is primarily a physical or a chemical change, and explain briefly (see Brief Solutions at the end of the chapter):
(a) Purple iodine vapor appears when solid iodine is warmed.
(b) Gasoline fumes are ignited by a spark in an automobile engine's cylinder.
(c) A scab forms over an open cut.

---

## The Central Theme in Chemistry

Understanding the properties of a substance and the changes it undergoes leads to the central theme in chemistry: *macroscopic-scale* properties and behavior, those we can see, are the results of *atomic-scale* properties and behavior that we cannot see. The distinction between chemical and physical change is defined by composition, which we study macroscopically. But composition ultimately depends on the makeup of substances at the atomic scale. Similarly, macroscopic properties of substances in any of the three states arise from atomic-scale behavior of their particles. Picturing a chemical event on the molecular scale, even one as common as the flame of a laboratory burner (*see margin*), helps clarify what is taking place. What is happening when water boils or copper melts? What events occur in the invisible world of minute particles that cause a seed to grow, a neon light to glow, or a nail to rust? Throughout the text, we return to this central idea:

*We study **observable** changes in matter to understand their **unobservable** causes.*

## The Importance of Energy in the Study of Matter

Physical and chemical changes are accompanied by energy changes. **Energy** is often defined as *the ability to do work.* Essentially, all work involves moving something. Work is done when your arm lifts a book, when a car's engine moves the wheels, or when a falling rock moves the ground as it lands. The object doing the work (arm, engine, rock) transfers some of the energy it possesses to the object on which the work is done (book, wheels, ground).

*The total energy an object possesses is the sum of its potential energy and its kinetic energy.*

- **Potential energy** is *the energy due to the **position** of the object relative to other objects.*
- **Kinetic energy** is *the energy due to the **motion** of the object.*

Let's examine four systems that illustrate the relationship between these two forms of energy: a weight raised above the ground, two balls attached by a spring, two electrically charged particles, and a fuel and its waste products. Two concepts central to all these cases are

1. *When energy is converted from one form to the other, it is conserved, not destroyed.*
2. *Situations of lower energy are more stable, and therefore favored, over situations of higher energy (less stable).*

The four cases are

- *A weight raised above the ground* (Figure 1.3A). The energy you exert to lift a weight against gravity, increases the weight's potential energy (energy due to its position). When you drop the weight, that additional potential energy is converted to kinetic energy (energy due to motion). The situation with the weight elevated and higher in potential energy is *less stable,* so the weight will fall when released to result in a situation that is lower in potential energy and *more stable.*
- *Two balls attached by a spring* (Figure 1.3B). When you pull the balls apart, the energy you exert to stretch the relaxed spring increases the system's potential energy. This change in potential energy is converted to kinetic energy when you release the balls. The system of balls and spring is less stable (has more potential energy) when the spring is stretched than when it is relaxed.
- *Two electrically charged particles* (Figure 1.3C). Due to interactions known as *electrostatic forces, opposite charges attract each other, and like charges repel each other.* When energy is exerted to move a positive particle away from a negative one, the potential energy of the system increases, and that increase is converted to kinetic energy when the particles are pulled together by the electrostatic attraction. Similarly, when energy is used to move two positive (or two negative) particles together, their potential energy increases and changes to kinetic energy when they are pushed apart by the electrostatic repulsion. Charged particles move naturally to a more stable situation (lower energy).
- *A fuel and its waste products* (Figure 1.3D). Matter is composed of positively and negatively charged particles. *The chemical potential energy of a substance results from the relative positions of and the attractions and repulsions among its particles.*

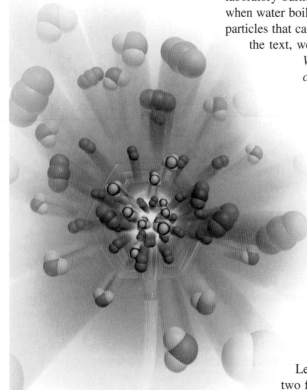

Methane and oxygen form carbon dioxide and water in the flame of a lab burner. (Carbon is black, oxygen red, and hydrogen blue.)

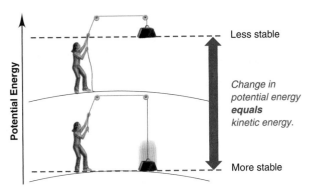

**A** **A gravitational system.** *Potential energy is gained when a weight is lifted. It is converted to kinetic energy as the weight falls.*

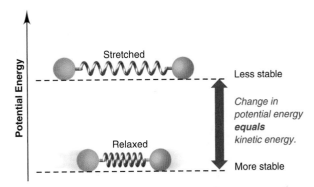

**B** **A system of two balls attached by a spring.** *Potential energy is gained when the spring is stretched. It is converted to the kinetic energy of the moving balls as the spring relaxes.*

**C** **A system of oppositely charged particles.** *Potential energy is gained when the charges are separated. It is converted to kinetic energy as the attraction pulls the charges together.*

**D** **A system of fuel and exhaust.** *A fuel is higher in chemical potential energy than the exhaust. As the fuel burns, some of its potential energy is converted to the kinetic energy of the moving car.*

**Figure 1.3** Potential energy is converted to kinetic energy. The dashed horizontal lines indicate the potential energy of each system before and after the change.

Some substances are higher in potential energy than others. For example, gasoline and oxygen have more chemical potential energy than the exhaust gases they form. This difference is converted into kinetic energy, which moves the car, heats the interior, makes the lights shine, and so on. Similarly, the difference in potential energy between the food and air we take in and the wastes we excrete enables us to move, grow, keep warm, study chemistry, and so on.

# Summary of Section 1.1

- Chemists study the composition and properties of matter and how they change.
- Each substance has a unique set of *physical* properties (attributes of the substance itself) and *chemical* properties (attributes of the substance as it interacts with or changes to other substances). Changes in matter can be *physical* (different form of the same substance) or *chemical* (different substance).
- Matter exists in three physical states—solid, liquid, and gas. The behavior of each state is due to the arrangement of the particles.
- A physical change caused by heating may be reversed by cooling. But a chemical change caused by heating can be reversed only by other chemical changes.
- Macroscopic changes result from submicroscopic changes.
- Changes in matter are accompanied by changes in energy.
- An object's potential energy is due to its position; an object's kinetic energy is due to its motion. Energy used to lift a weight, stretch a spring, or separate opposite charges increases the system's potential energy, which is converted to kinetic energy as the system returns to its original condition. Energy changes form but is conserved.
- Chemical potential energy arises from the positions and interactions of a substance's particles. When a higher energy (less stable) substance is converted into a more stable (lower energy) substance, some potential energy is converted into kinetic energy.

**Figure 1.4** Alchemical apparatus.

# 1.2 • CHEMICAL ARTS AND THE ORIGINS OF MODERN CHEMISTRY

This brief overview of early breakthroughs, and a few false directions, describes how the modern science of chemistry arose and progressed.

## Prechemical Traditions

Chemistry had its origin in a prescientific past that incorporated three overlapping traditions—alchemy, medicine, and technology:

1. *The alchemical tradition. Alchemy* was an occult study of nature that began in the 1st century AD and dominated thinking for over 1500 years. Originally influenced by the Greek idea that matter strives for "perfection," alchemists later became obsessed with converting "baser" metals, such as lead, into "purer" ones, such as gold. The alchemists' names for substances and their belief that matter could be altered magically were very difficult to correct over the centuries. Their legacy to chemistry was in technical methods. They invented distillation, percolation, and extraction and devised apparatus still used routinely today (Figure 1.4). But perhaps even more important was that alchemists encouraged observation and experimentation, which replaced the Greek approach of explaining nature solely through reason.

2. *The medical tradition.* Alchemists also influenced medical practice in medieval Europe. And ever since the 13th century, distillates and extracts of roots, herbs, and other plant matter have been used as sources of medicines. The alchemist and physician Paracelsus (1493–1541) considered the body to be a chemical system and illness an imbalance that could be restored by treatment with drugs. Although many early prescriptions were useless, later ones had increasing success. Thus began the alliance between medicine and chemistry that thrives today.

3. *The technological tradition.* For thousands of years, pottery making, dyeing, and especially metallurgy contributed greatly to people's experience with materials. During the Middle Ages and the Renaissance, books were published that described how to purify, assay, and coin silver and gold, how to use balances, furnaces, and crucibles, and how to make glass and gunpowder. Some introduced quantitative measurement, which was lacking in alchemical writings. Many creations from those times are still marveled at throughout the world. Nevertheless, the skilled artisans showed little interest in *why* a substance changes or *how to predict* its behavior.

## The Phlogiston Fiasco and the Impact of Lavoisier

Chemical investigation in the modern sense—inquiry into the causes of changes in matter—began in the late 17th century. At that time, most scientists explained **combustion,** the process of burning, with the *phlogiston theory.* It proposed that combustible materials contain *phlogiston,* an undetectable substance released when the material burns. Highly combustible materials like charcoal were thought to contain a lot of phlogiston, and slightly combustible materials like metals only a little.

But inconsistencies continuously arose.

**Phlogiston critics:** Why is air needed for combustion, and why does charcoal stop burning in a closed vessel?
**Phlogiston supporters:** Air "attracts" phlogiston out of the charcoal, and burning stops when the air in the vessel is "saturated" with phlogiston.

Critics also noted that when a metal burns, it forms its *calx,* which weighs more than the metal, leading them to ask,

**Critics:** How can the *loss* of phlogiston cause a *gain* in mass?
**Supporters:** Phlogiston has negative mass.

As ridiculous as these responses seem now, it's important to remember that, even today, scientists may dismiss conflicting evidence rather than abandon an accepted idea.

The conflict over phlogiston was resolved when the young French chemist Antoine Lavoisier (1743–1794) performed several experiments:

1. Heating mercury calx decomposed it into two products—mercury and a gas— whose *total mass equaled the starting mass of the calx*.
2. Heating mercury with the gas reformed the calx, yielded mercury and, again, *the total mass remained constant*.
3. Heating mercury in a measured volume of air yielded mercury calx and left four-fifths of the air remaining.
4. A burning candle placed in the remaining air was extinguished.

Lavoisier named the gas *oxygen* and gave metal calxes the name *metal oxides*. His explanation of his results made the phlogiston theory irrelevant:

- Oxygen, a normal component of air, combines with a substance when it burns.
- In a closed container, a combustible substance stops burning when it has combined with all the available oxygen.
- A metal calx (metal oxide) weighs more than the metal because its mass includes the mass of the oxygen.

This new theory triumphed because it relied on *quantitative, reproducible measurements*, not on strange properties of undetectable substances. Because this approach is at the heart of science, many propose that the *science* of chemistry began with Lavoisier.

## ▌Summary of Section 1.2

- Alchemy, medicine, and technology placed little emphasis on objective experimentation, focusing instead on mystical explanations or practical experience, but these traditions contributed some apparatus and methods that are still important today.
- Lavoisier overthrew the phlogiston theory by showing quantitatively that oxygen, a component of air, is required for combustion and combines with a burning substance.

## 1.3 • THE SCIENTIFIC APPROACH: DEVELOPING A MODEL

Unlike our prehistoric ancestors, who survived through *trial and error*—gradually learning which types of stone were hard enough to shape others, which plants were edible and which poisonous—we employ the *quantitative theories* of chemistry to understand materials, make better use of them, and create new ones: specialized drugs, advanced composites, synthetic polymers, and countless others (Figure 1.5).

**Figure 1.5 Modern materials in a variety of applications. A,** High-tension polymers in synthetic hip joints. **B,** Specialized polymers in clothing and sports gear. **C,** Liquid crystals and semiconductors in electronic devices. **D,** Medicinal agents in pills.

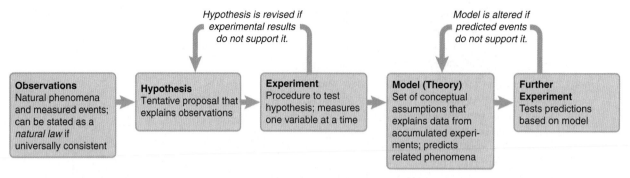

**Figure 1.6** The scientific approach to understanding nature. Hypotheses and models are mental pictures that are revised to match observations and experimental results, *not* the other way around.

To understand nature, scientists use an approach called the **scientific method.** It is not a stepwise checklist, but rather a process involving creative propositions and tests aimed at objective, verifiable discoveries. There is no single procedure, and luck often plays a key role in discovery. In general terms, the scientific approach includes the following parts (Figure 1.6):

- *Observations.* These are the facts our ideas must explain. The most useful observations are quantitative because they can be analyzed to reveal trends. Pieces of quantitative information are **data.** When the same observation is made by many investigators in many situations with no clear exceptions, it is summarized, often in mathematical terms, as a **natural law.** The observation that mass remains constant during chemical change—made by Lavoisier and numerous experimenters since—is known as the law of mass conservation (Chapter 2).
- *Hypothesis.* Whether derived from observation or from a "spark of intuition," a hypothesis is a proposal made to explain an observation. A sound hypothesis need not be correct, but it must be *testable by experiment.* Indeed, a hypothesis is often the reason for performing an experiment: if the results do not support it, the hypothesis must be revised or discarded. Hypotheses can be altered, but experimental results cannot.
- *Experiment.* A set of procedural steps that tests a hypothesis, an experiment often leads to a revised hypothesis and new experiments to test it. An experiment typically contains at least two **variables,** quantities that can have more than one value. A well-designed experiment is **controlled** in that it measures the effect of one variable on another while keeping all other variables constant. Experimental results must be *reproducible* by others. Both skill and creativity play a part in experimental design.
- *Model.* Formulating conceptual models, or **theories,** based on *experiments* that test *hypotheses* about *observations* distinguishes scientific thinking from speculation. As hypotheses are revised according to experimental results, a model emerges to explain how the phenomenon occurs. A model is a *simplified,* not an exact, representation of some aspect of nature that we use to *predict* related phenomena. Ongoing experimentation refines the model to account for new facts.

Lavoisier's overthrow of the phlogiston theory demonstrates the scientific method of thinking. *Observations* of burning and smelting led to the *hypothesis* that combustion involved the loss of phlogiston. *Experiments* showing that air is required for burning and that a metal gains mass during combustion led Lavoisier to propose a new *hypothesis,* which he tested repeatedly with quantitative *experiments.* Accumulating evidence supported his developing *model (theory)* that combustion involves combination with a component of air (oxygen). Innumerable *predictions* based on this theory have supported its validity, and Lavoisier himself extended the theory to account for animal respiration and metabolism.

# ■ Summary of Section 1.3

- The scientific method is a process designed to explain and predict phenomena.
- Observations lead to hypotheses about how or why a phenomenon occurs. When repeated with no exceptions, observations may be expressed as a natural law.
- Hypotheses are tested by controlled experiments and revised when necessary.
- If reproducible data support a hypothesis, a model (theory) can be developed to explain the observed phenomenon. A good model predicts related phenomena but must be refined whenever conflicting data appear.

---

# 1.4 • CHEMICAL PROBLEM SOLVING

In many ways, learning chemistry is learning how to solve chemistry problems, not only those in exams or homework, but the more complex ones in life and society. The sample problems in this book are designed to strengthen your skills for solving problems. In this section, we describe the problem-solving approach. Most problems include calculations, so let's first discuss how to handle measured quantities.

## Units and Conversion Factors in Calculations

All measured quantities consist of a number *and* a unit: a person's height is "5 feet, 10 inches," not "5, 10." Ratios of quantities have ratios of units, such as miles/hour. (We discuss some important units in Section 1.5.) To minimize errors, make it a habit to *include units in all calculations.*

The arithmetic operations used with quantities are the same as those used with pure numbers; that is, units can be multiplied, divided, and canceled:

- A carpet measuring 3 feet by 4 feet (ft) has an area of

$$\text{Area} = 3 \text{ ft} \times 4 \text{ ft} = (3 \times 4)(\text{ft} \times \text{ft}) = 12 \text{ ft}^2$$

- A car traveling 350 miles (mi) in 7 hours (h) has a speed of

$$\text{Speed} = \frac{350 \text{ mi}}{7 \text{ h}} = \frac{50 \text{ mi}}{1 \text{ h}} \text{ (often written } 50 \text{ mi·h}^{-1})$$

- In 3 hours, the car travels a distance of

$$\text{Distance} = 3 \text{ h} \times \frac{50 \text{ mi}}{1 \text{ h}} = 150 \text{ mi}$$

**Constructing a Conversion Factor** **Conversion factors** are *ratios used to express a quantity in different units.* Suppose we want to know the distance of that 150-mile car trip in feet. To convert miles to feet, we use *equivalent quantities,*

$$1 \text{ mi} = 5280 \text{ ft}$$

from which we can construct two conversion factors. Dividing both sides by 5280 ft gives one conversion factor (shown in blue):

$$\frac{1 \text{ mi}}{5280 \text{ ft}} = \frac{5280 \text{ ft}}{5280 \text{ ft}} = 1$$

And, dividing both sides by 1 mi gives the other conversion factor (the inverse):

$$\frac{1 \text{ mi}}{1 \text{ mi}} = \frac{5280 \text{ ft}}{1 \text{ mi}} = 1$$

Since the numerator and denominator of a conversion factor are equal, multiplying a quantity by a conversion factor is the same as multiplying by 1. Thus, *even though the number and unit change, the size of the quantity remains the same.*

To convert the distance from miles to feet, we choose the conversion factor with miles in the denominator, because it cancels miles and gives the answer in feet:

$$\text{Distance (ft)} = 150 \text{ mi} \times \frac{5280 \text{ ft}}{1 \text{ mi}} = 792{,}000 \text{ ft}$$

$$\text{mi} \quad \Rightarrow \quad \text{ft}$$

**Choosing the Correct Conversion Factor** It is easier to convert if you first decide whether the answer expressed in the new units should have a larger or smaller number. In the previous case, we know that a foot is *smaller* than a mile, so the distance in feet should have a *larger* number (792,000) than the distance in miles (150). The conversion factor has the larger number (5280) in the numerator, so it gave a larger number in the answer.

Most importantly, the *conversion factor you choose must cancel all units except those you want in the answer.* Therefore, set the unit you are converting *from* (beginning unit) in the *opposite position in the conversion factor* (numerator or denominator) so that it cancels and you are left with the unit you are converting *to* (final unit):

$$\text{beginning unit} \times \frac{\text{final unit}}{\text{beginning unit}} = \text{final unit} \qquad \text{as in} \qquad \text{mi} \times \frac{\text{ft}}{\text{mi}} = \text{ft}$$

Or, in cases that involve units raised to a power:

$$(\text{beginning unit} \times \text{beginning unit}) \times \frac{\text{final unit}^2}{\text{beginning unit}^2} = \text{final unit}^2$$

$$\text{as in} \qquad (\text{ft} \times \text{ft}) \times \frac{\text{mi}^2}{\text{ft}^2} = \text{mi}^2$$

Or, in cases that involve a ratio of units:

$$\frac{\text{beginning unit}}{\text{final unit}_1} \times \frac{\text{final unit}_2}{\text{beginning unit}} = \frac{\text{final unit}_2}{\text{final unit}_1} \qquad \text{as in} \qquad \frac{\text{mi}}{\text{h}} \times \frac{\text{ft}}{\text{mi}} = \frac{\text{ft}}{\text{h}}$$

**Converting Between Unit Systems** We use the same procedure to convert between systems of units, for example, between the English (or American) unit system and the International System (a revised metric system; Section 1.5). Suppose we know that the height of Angel Falls in Venezuela (the world's highest) is 3212 ft, and we find its height in miles as

$$\text{Height (mi)} = 3212 \text{ ft} \times \frac{1 \text{ mi}}{5280 \text{ ft}} = 0.6083 \text{ mi}$$
$$\qquad\qquad\qquad\quad \text{ft} \qquad \Rightarrow \qquad \text{mi}$$

Now, we want its height in kilometers (km). The equivalent quantities are

$$1.609 \text{ km} = 1 \text{ mi}$$

Because we are converting *from* miles *to* kilometers, we use the conversion factor with miles in the denominator in order to cancel miles:

$$\text{Height (km)} = 0.6083 \text{ mi} \times \frac{1.609 \text{ km}}{1 \text{ mi}} = 0.9788 \text{ km}$$
$$\qquad\qquad\qquad\quad \text{mi} \qquad \Rightarrow \qquad \text{km}$$

Notice that kilometers are *smaller* than miles, so this conversion factor gave us an answer with a *larger* number (0.9788 is larger than 0.6083).

If we want the height of Angel Falls in meters (m), we use the equivalent quantities 1 km = 1000 m to construct the conversion factor:

$$\text{Height (m)} = 0.9788 \text{ km} \times \frac{1000 \text{ m}}{1 \text{ km}} = 978.8 \text{ m}$$
$$\qquad\qquad\qquad\quad \text{km} \qquad \Rightarrow \qquad \text{m}$$

In longer calculations, we often string together several conversion steps:

$$\text{Height (m)} = 3212 \text{ ft} \times \frac{1 \text{ mi}}{5280 \text{ ft}} \times \frac{1.609 \text{ km}}{1 \text{ mi}} \times \frac{1000 \text{ m}}{1 \text{ km}} = 978.8 \text{ m}$$
$$\qquad\qquad\qquad\quad \text{ft} \qquad \Rightarrow \quad \text{mi} \quad \Rightarrow \quad \text{km} \quad \Rightarrow \qquad \text{m}$$

The use of conversion factors in calculations is also referred to as the factor-label method or **dimensional analysis** (because units represent physical dimensions). We use this approach throughout the text.

## A Systematic Approach to Solving Chemistry Problems

The approach used in this book to solve problems emphasizes reasoning, not memorizing, and is based on a simple idea: plan how to solve the problem *before* you try to solve it, then check your answer, and practice with a similar follow-up problem. In general, the sample problems consist of several parts:

1. **Problem.** This part states all the information you need to solve the problem, usually framed in some interesting context.

2. **Plan.** This part helps you *think* about the solution *before* juggling numbers and pressing calculator buttons. There is often more than one way to solve a problem, and the given plan is one possibility. The plan will
   - Clarify the known and unknown: what information do you have, and what are you trying to find?
   - Suggest the steps from known to unknown: what ideas, conversions, or equations are needed?
   - Present a road map (especially in early chapters), a flow diagram of the plan. The road map has a box for each intermediate result and an arrow showing the step (conversion factor or operation) used to get to the next box.

3. **Solution.** This part shows the calculation steps in the same order as in the plan (and the road map).

4. **Check.** This part helps you check that your final answer makes sense: Are the units correct? Did the change occur in the expected direction? Is it reasonable chemically? To avoid a large math error, we also often do a rough calculation and see if we get an answer "in the same ballpark" as the actual result. Here's a typical "ballpark" calculation from everyday life. You are at a music store and buy three CDs at $14.97 each. With a 5% sales tax, the bill comes to $47.16. In your mind, you know that $14.97 is about $15, and 3 times $15 is $45; with the sales tax, the cost should be a bit more. So, your quick mental calculation *is* in the same ballpark as the actual cost.

5. **Comment.** This part appears occasionally to provide an application, an alternative approach, a common mistake to avoid, or an overview.

6. **Follow-Up Problem.** This part presents a similar problem that requires you to apply concepts and/or methods used in solving the sample problem.

Of course, you can't learn to solve chemistry problems, any more than you can learn to swim, by reading about it, so here are a few suggestions:

- Follow along in the sample problem with pencil, paper, and calculator.
- Try the follow-up problem as soon as you finish the sample problem. A feature called Brief Solutions to Follow-Up Problems appears at the end of each chapter, allowing you to compare your solution steps and answer.
- Read the sample problem and text again if you have trouble.
- Try the practice quizzes in the Online Learning Center at www.mhhe.com/silberberg. For each chapter, two interactive quizzes provide conceptual and problem-solving practice and offer feedback for review.
- The end-of-chapter problems review and extend the concepts and skills in the chapter, so work as many as you can. (Answers are given in the back of the book for problems with a colored number.)

Let's apply this systematic approach in a unit-conversion problem.

## Sample Problem 1.3 | Converting Units of Length

**Problem** To wire your stereo equipment, you need 325 centimeters (cm) of speaker wire that sells for \$0.15/ft. How much does the wire cost?

**Plan** We know the length of wire in centimeters (325 cm) and the price in dollars per foot (\$0.15/ft). We can find the unknown cost of the wire by converting the length from centimeters to inches (in) and from inches to feet. The price gives us the equivalent quantities (1 ft = \$0.15) to convert feet of wire to cost in dollars. The road map starts with the known and moves through the calculation steps to the unknown.

**Solution** Converting the known length from centimeters to inches: The equivalent quantities alongside the road map arrow are needed to construct the conversion factor. We choose 1 in/2.54 cm, rather than the inverse, because it gives an answer in inches:

**Road Map**

Length (cm) of wire

2.54 cm = 1 in

Length (in) of wire

12 in = 1 ft

Length (ft) of wire

1 ft = \$0.15

Cost (\$) of wire

$$\text{Length (in)} = \text{length (cm)} \times \text{conversion factor} = 325 \ \text{cm} \times \frac{1 \ \text{in}}{2.54 \ \text{cm}} = 128 \ \text{in}$$

Converting the length from inches to feet:

$$\text{Length (ft)} = \text{length (in)} \times \text{conversion factor} = 128 \ \text{in} \times \frac{1 \ \text{ft}}{12 \ \text{in}} = 10.7 \ \text{ft}$$

Converting the length in feet to cost in dollars:

$$\text{Cost (\$)} = \text{length (ft)} \times \text{conversion factor} = 10.7 \ \text{ft} \times \frac{\$0.15}{1 \ \text{ft}} = \boxed{\$1.60}$$

**Check** The units are correct for each step. The conversion factors make sense in terms of the relative unit sizes: the number of inches is *smaller* than the number of centimeters (an inch is *larger* than a centimeter), and the number of feet is *smaller* than the number of inches. The total cost seems reasonable: a little more than 10 ft of wire at \$0.15/ft should cost a little more than \$1.50.

**Comment 1.** We could also have strung the three steps together:

$$\text{Cost (\$)} = 325 \ \text{cm} \times \frac{1 \ \text{in}}{2.54 \ \text{cm}} \times \frac{1 \ \text{ft}}{12 \ \text{in}} \times \frac{\$0.15}{1 \ \text{ft}} = \boxed{\$1.60}$$

**2.** There are usually alternative sequences in unit-conversion problems. Here, for example, we would get the same answer if we first converted the cost of wire from \$/ft to \$/cm and kept the wire length in cm. Try it yourself.

**Follow-Up Problem 1.3** A furniture factory needs 31.5 ft² of fabric to upholster one chair. Its Dutch supplier sends the fabric in bolts of exactly 200 m². How many chairs can be upholstered with 3 bolts of fabric (1 m = 3.281 ft)? Draw a road map to show how you plan the solution. (See Brief Solutions.)

## ▍Summary of Section 1.4

- A measured quantity consists of a number and a unit.
- A conversion factor is a ratio of equivalent quantities (and, thus, equal to 1) that is used to express a quantity in different units.
- The problem-solving approach used in this book has four parts: (1) plan the steps to the solution, which often includes a flow diagram (road map) of the steps, (2) perform the calculations according to the plan, (3) check to see if the answer makes sense, and (4) practice with a similar problem and compare your solution with the one at the end of the chapter.

## 1.5 • MEASUREMENT IN SCIENTIFIC STUDY

Measurement has a rich history characterized by the search for *exact, invariable standards.* Measuring for purposes of trade, building, and surveying began thousands of years ago, but for most of that time, it was based on standards that could vary: a yard was the distance from the king's nose to the tip of his outstretched arm, and an acre was the area tilled in one day by a man with a pair of oxen. Our current system of measurement began in 1790 in France, when a committee, of which Lavoisier was a member, developed the *metric system.* Then, in 1960, another committee in France revised the metric system and established the universally accepted **SI units** (from the French **S**ystème **I**nternational d'Unités).

## General Features of SI Units

The SI system is based on seven **fundamental units,** or **base units,** each identified with a physical quantity (Table 1.2). All other units are **derived units,** combinations of the seven base units. For example, the derived unit for speed, meters per second (m/s), is the base unit for length (m) divided by the base unit for time (s). (Derived units that are a ratio of base units can be used as conversion factors.) For quantities much smaller or larger than the base unit, we use decimal prefixes and exponential (scientific) notation (Table 1.3). (If you need a review of exponential notation, see Appendix A.) Because the prefixes are based on powers of 10, SI units are easier to use in calculations than English units.

## Some Important SI Units in Chemistry

Here, we discuss units for length, volume, mass, density, temperature, and time; other units are presented in later chapters. Table 1.4 (*on the next page*) shows some SI quantities for length, volume, and mass, along with their English-system equivalents.

### Table 1.2 SI Base Units

| Physical Quantity (Dimension) | Unit Name | Unit Abbreviation |
|---|---|---|
| Mass | kilogram | kg |
| Length | meter | m |
| Time | second | s |
| Temperature | kelvin | K |
| Electric current | ampere | A |
| Amount of substance | mole | mol |
| Luminous intensity | candela | cd |

### Table 1.3 Common Decimal Prefixes Used with SI Units

| Prefix* | Prefix Symbol | Word | Conventional Notation | Exponential Notation |
|---|---|---|---|---|
| tera | T | trillion | 1,000,000,000,000 | $1\times10^{12}$ |
| giga | G | billion | 1,000,000,000 | $1\times10^{9}$ |
| **mega** | M | million | 1,000,000 | $1\times10^{6}$ |
| **kilo** | k | thousand | 1,000 | $1\times10^{3}$ |
| hecto | h | hundred | 100 | $1\times10^{2}$ |
| deka | da | ten | 10 | $1\times10^{1}$ |
| — | — | one | 1 | $1\times10^{0}$ |
| **deci** | d | tenth | 0.1 | $1\times10^{-1}$ |
| **centi** | c | hundredth | 0.01 | $1\times10^{-2}$ |
| **milli** | m | thousandth | 0.001 | $1\times10^{-3}$ |
| **micro** | μ | millionth | 0.000001 | $1\times10^{-6}$ |
| **nano** | n | billionth | 0.000000001 | $1\times10^{-9}$ |
| **pico** | p | trillionth | 0.000000000001 | $1\times10^{-12}$ |
| femto | f | quadrillionth | 0.000000000000001 | $1\times10^{-15}$ |

*The prefixes most frequently used by chemists appear in bold type.

## Table 1.4 Common SI-English Equivalent Quantities

| Quantity | SI | SI Equivalents | English Equivalents | English to SI Equivalent |
|---|---|---|---|---|
| Length | 1 kilometer (km) | 1000 ($10^3$) meters | 0.6214 mile (mi) | 1 mile = 1.609 km |
| | 1 meter (m) | 100 ($10^2$) centimeters | 1.094 yards (yd) | 1 yard = 0.9144 m |
| | | 1000 millimeters (mm) | 39.37 inches (in) | 1 foot (ft) = 0.3048 m |
| | 1 centimeter (cm) | 0.10 ($10^{-2}$) meter | 0.3937 inch | 1 inch = 2.54 cm (exactly) |
| Volume | 1 cubic meter ($m^3$) | 1,000,000 ($10^6$) cubic centimeters | 35.31 cubic feet ($ft^3$) | 1 cubic foot = 0.02832 $m^3$ |
| | 1 cubic decimeter ($dm^3$) | 1000 cubic centimeters | 0.2642 gallon (gal) | 1 gallon = 3.785 $dm^3$ |
| | | | 1.057 quarts (qt) | 1 quart = 0.9464 $dm^3$ |
| | | | | 1 quart = 946.4 $cm^3$ |
| | 1 cubic centimeter ($cm^3$) | 0.001 $dm^3$ | 0.03381 fluid ounce | 1 fluid ounce = 29.57 $cm^3$ |
| Mass | 1 kilogram (kg) | 1000 grams | 2.205 pounds (lb) | 1 pound = 0.4536 kg |

**Length** The SI base unit of length is the **meter (m).** In the metric system, it was originally defined as 1/10,000,000 of the distance from the equator to the North Pole, and later as the distance between two fine lines engraved on a corrosion-resistant metal bar. More recently, the first exact, unchanging standard was adopted: 1,650,763.73 wavelengths of orange-red light from electrically excited krypton atoms. The current standard is exact and invariant: 1 meter is the distance light travels in a vacuum in 1/299,792,458 of a second.

A meter is a little longer than a yard (1 m = 1.094 yd); a centimeter ($10^{-2}$ m) is about two-fifths of an inch (1 cm = 0.3937 in; 1 in = 2.54 cm). Biological cells are often measured in micrometers (1 $\mu$m = $10^{-6}$ m). On the atomic scale, nanometers ($10^{-9}$ m) and picometers ($10^{-12}$ m) are used. Many proteins have diameters of about 2 nm; atomic diameters are about 200 pm (0.2 nm). An older unit still in use is the angstrom (1 Å = $10^{-10}$ m = 0.1 nm = 100 pm).

**Volume** Any sample of matter has a certain **volume (V),** the amount of space it occupies. The SI unit of volume is the **cubic meter ($m^3$).** In chemistry, we often use non-SI units, the **liter (L)** and the **milliliter (mL)** (note the uppercase L). Physicians and other medical practitioners measure body fluids in cubic decimeters ($dm^3$), which are equivalent to liters:

$$1\,L = 1\,dm^3 = 10^{-3}\,m^3$$

And 1 mL, or $\frac{1}{1000}$ of a liter, is equivalent to 1 cubic centimeter ($cm^3$):

$$1\,mL = 1\,cm^3 = 10^{-3}\,dm^3 = 10^{-3}\,L = 10^{-6}\,m^3$$

A liter is slightly larger than a quart (qt) (1 L = 1.057 qt; 1 qt = 946.4 mL); 1 fluid ounce ($\frac{1}{32}$ of a quart) equals 29.57 mL (29.57 $cm^3$).

Figure 1.7 is a life-size depiction of the two 1000-fold decreases in volume from 1 $dm^3$ to 1 $cm^3$ and then to 1 $mm^3$. The edge of a 1-$m^3$ cube would be about 2.5 times the width of this text opened flat.

Figure 1.8A shows some laboratory glassware for working with volumes. Erlenmeyer flasks and beakers are used to contain liquids. Graduated cylinders, pipets, and burets are used to measure and transfer them. Volumetric flasks and pipets have a fixed volume indicated by a mark on the neck. Solutions are prepared quantitatively in volumetric flasks, and specific amounts are put into cylinders, pipets, or burets to transfer to beakers or flasks for further steps. In Figure 1.8B, an automatic pipet transfers liquid accurately *and* quickly.

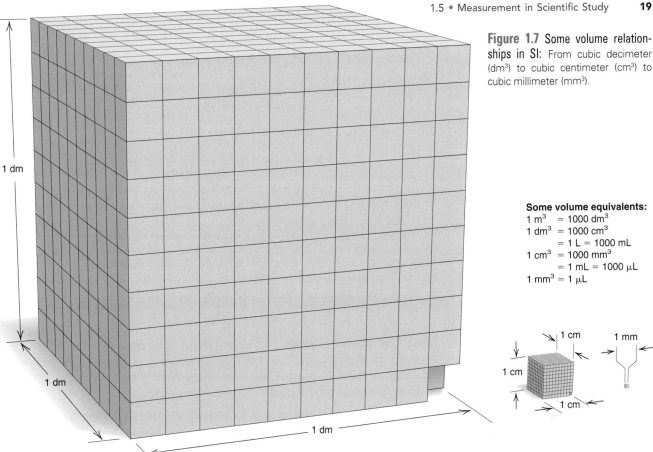

**Figure 1.7 Some volume relationships in SI:** From cubic decimeter (dm³) to cubic centimeter (cm³) to cubic millimeter (mm³).

**Some volume equivalents:**
$1\ m^3 = 1000\ dm^3$
$1\ dm^3 = 1000\ cm^3$
$\qquad = 1\ L = 1000\ mL$
$1\ cm^3 = 1000\ mm^3$
$\qquad = 1\ mL = 1000\ \mu L$
$1\ mm^3 = 1\ \mu L$

1 dm

1 dm

1 dm

1 cm

1 cm

1 cm

1 mm

**A**

**B**

**Figure 1.8 Common laboratory volumetric glassware. A,** From left to right are two graduated cylinders, a pipet being emptied into a beaker, a buret delivering liquid to an Erlenmeyer flask, and two volumetric flasks. **Inset,** In contact with the glass neck of the flask, the liquid forms a concave meniscus (curved surface). **B,** An automatic pipet delivers a given volume of liquid to each test tube.

---

## Sample Problem 1.4  Converting Units of Volume

**Problem** The volume of an irregularly shaped solid can be determined from the volume of water it displaces. A graduated cylinder contains 19.9 mL of water. When a small piece of galena, an ore of lead, is added, it sinks and the volume increases to 24.5 mL. What is the volume of the piece of galena in cm³ and in L?

**Plan** We have to find the volume of the galena from the change in volume of the cylinder contents. The volume of galena in mL is the difference before (19.9 mL) and after (24.5 mL) adding it. Since mL and cm³ represent identical volumes, the volume in mL equals the volume in cm³. We then use equivalent quantities ($1\ mL = 10^{-3}\ L$) to convert mL to L. The road map shows these steps.

**Road Map**

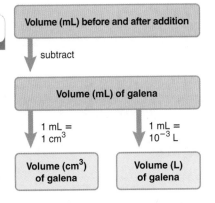

Volume (mL) before and after addition

↓ subtract

Volume (mL) of galena

$1\ mL = 1\ cm^3$

$1\ mL = 10^{-3}\ L$

Volume (cm³) of galena

Volume (L) of galena

**Solution** Finding the volume of galena:

$$\text{Volume (mL)} = \text{volume after} - \text{volume before} = 24.5 \text{ mL} - 19.9 \text{ mL} = 4.6 \text{ mL}$$

Converting the volume from mL to cm³:

$$\text{Volume (cm}^3) = 4.6 \text{ mL} \times \frac{1 \text{ cm}^3}{1 \text{ mL}} = \boxed{4.6 \text{ cm}^3}$$

Converting the volume from mL to L:

$$\text{Volume (L)} = 4.6 \text{ mL} \times \frac{10^{-3} \text{ L}}{1 \text{ mL}} = \boxed{4.6 \times 10^{-3} \text{ L}}$$

**Check** The units and magnitudes of the answers seem correct, and it makes sense that the volume in mL would have a number 1000 times larger than the same volume in L.

**Follow-Up Problem 1.4** Within a cell, proteins are synthesized on particles called ribosomes. Assuming ribosomes are spherical, what is the volume (in $dm^3$ and $\mu L$) of a ribosome whose average diameter is 21.4 nm ($V$ of a sphere $= \frac{4}{3}\pi r^3$)? Draw a road map to show how you plan the solution. (See Brief Solutions.)

**Mass** The quantity of matter an object contains is its **mass.** The SI unit of mass is the **kilogram (kg),** the only base unit whose standard is an object—a platinum-iridium cylinder kept in France—and the only one whose name has a prefix.*

The terms *mass* and *weight* have distinct meanings:

- *Mass is constant* because an object's quantity of matter cannot change.
- *Weight is variable* because it depends on the local gravitational field acting on the object.

Because the strength of the gravitational field varies with altitude, you (and other objects) weigh slightly less on a high mountain than at sea level.

Does this mean that a sample weighed on laboratory balances in Miami (sea level) and in Denver (about 1.7 km above sea level) give different results? No, because these balances measure mass, not weight. (We actually "mass" an object when we weigh it on a balance, but we don't use that term.) Mechanical balances compare the object's mass with masses built into the balance, so the local gravitational field pulls on them equally. Electronic (analytical) balances generate an electric field that counteracts the local field, and the current needed to restore the pan to zero is converted to the equivalent mass and displayed.

**Road Map**

| Length (km) of fiber |
| :---: |

$\downarrow$ 1 km = 10³ m

| Length (m) of fiber |
| :---: |

$\downarrow$ 1 m = 1.19×10⁻³ lb

| Mass (lb) of fiber |
| :---: |

$\downarrow$ 6 fibers = 1 cable

| Mass (lb) of cable |
| :---: |

$\downarrow$ 2.205 lb = 1 kg

| Mass (kg) of cable |
| :---: |

**Sample Problem 1.5** Converting Units of Mass

**Problem** Many international computer communications are carried by optical fibers in cables laid along the ocean floor. If one strand of optical fiber weighs $1.19 \times 10^{-3}$ lb/m, what is the mass (in kg) of a cable made of six strands of optical fiber, each long enough to link New York and Paris ($8.84 \times 10^3$ km)?

**Plan** We have to find the mass of cable (in kg) from the given mass/length of fiber ($1.19 \times 10^{-3}$ lb/m), number of fibers/cable (6), and length of cable ($8.84 \times 10^3$ km). Let's first find the mass of one fiber and then the mass of cable. As shown in the road map, we convert the length of one fiber from km to m and then find its mass (in lb) by converting m to lb. Then we multiply the fiber mass by 6 to get the cable mass, and finally convert lb to kg.

**Solution** Converting the fiber length from km to m:

$$\text{Length (m) of fiber} = 8.84 \times 10^3 \text{ km} \times \frac{10^3 \text{ m}}{1 \text{ km}} = 8.84 \times 10^6 \text{ m}$$

---

*The names of the other base units are used as the root words, but for units of mass we attach prefixes to the word "gram," as in "microgram" and "kilogram"; thus, we say "milligram," never "microkilogram."

Converting the length of one fiber to mass (lb):

$$\text{Mass (lb) of fiber} = 8.84\times10^{6}\ \cancel{\text{m}} \times \frac{1.19\times10^{-3}\ \text{lb}}{1\ \cancel{\text{m}}} = 1.05\times10^{4}\ \text{lb}$$

Finding the mass of the cable (lb):

$$\text{Mass (lb) of cable} = \frac{1.05\times10^{4}\ \text{lb}}{1\ \cancel{\text{fiber}}} \times \frac{6\ \cancel{\text{fibers}}}{1\ \text{cable}} = 6.30\times10^{4}\ \text{lb/cable}$$

Converting the mass of cable from lb to kg:

$$\text{Mass (kg) of cable} = \frac{6.30\times10^{4}\ \cancel{\text{lb}}}{1\ \text{cable}} \times \frac{1\ \text{kg}}{2.205\ \cancel{\text{lb}}} = \boxed{2.86\times10^{4}\ \text{kg/cable}}$$

**Check** The units are correct. Let's think through the relative sizes of the answers to see if they make sense: The number of m should be $10^{3}$ larger than the number of km. If 1 m of fiber weighs about $10^{-3}$ lb, about $10^{7}$ m should weigh about $10^{4}$ lb. The cable mass should be six times as much, or about $6\times10^{4}$ lb. Since 1 lb is about $\frac{1}{2}$ kg, the number of kg should be about half the number of lb.

**Follow-Up Problem 1.5** An intravenous nutrient solution is delivered to a hospital patient at a rate of 1.5 drops per second. If a drop of solution weighs 65 mg on average, how many kilograms are delivered in 8.0 h? Draw a road map to show how you plan the solution. (See Brief Solutions.)

Figure 1.9 shows the ranges of some common lengths, volumes, and masses.

**Figure 1.9** Some interesting quantities of length (**A**), volume (**B**), and mass (**C**). The vertical scales are exponential.

**A Length**

- $10^{12}$ m — Distance from Earth to Sun
- $10^{9}$ m
- $10^{6}$ m
- Height of Mt. Everest
- $10^{3}$ m (km)
- $10^{0}$ m (m) — Sea level
- $10^{-3}$ m (mm) — Thickness of average human hair
- $10^{-6}$ m (μm) — Diameter of average tobacco smoke particle
- $10^{-9}$ m (nm) — Diameter of largest nonradioactive atom (cesium)
- $10^{-12}$ m (pm) — Diameter of smallest atom (helium)

**B Volume**

- $10^{24}$ L — Oceans and seas of the world
- $10^{21}$ L
- $10^{18}$ L
- $10^{15}$ L
- $10^{12}$ L
- $10^{9}$ L
- $10^{6}$ L
- $10^{3}$ L — Blood in average human
- $10^{0}$ L — Normal adult breath
- $10^{-3}$ L — Baseball
- $10^{-6}$ L
- $10^{-9}$ L
- $10^{-12}$ L
- $10^{-15}$ L — Typical bacterial cell
- $10^{-18}$ L
- $10^{-21}$ L
- $10^{-24}$ L
- $10^{-27}$ L — Carbon atom
- $10^{-30}$ L

**C Mass**

- $10^{24}$ g
- $10^{21}$ g — Earth's atmosphere to 2500 km
- $10^{18}$ g
- $10^{15}$ g
- $10^{12}$ g — Ocean liner
- $10^{9}$ g — Indian elephant
- $10^{6}$ g — Average human
- $10^{3}$ g — 1.0 liter of water
- $10^{0}$ g
- $10^{-3}$ g
- $10^{-6}$ g — Grain of table salt
- $10^{-9}$ g
- $10^{-12}$ g
- $10^{-15}$ g
- $10^{-18}$ g — Typical protein
- $10^{-21}$ g — Uranium atom
- $10^{-24}$ g — Water molecule

**Table 1.5  Densities of Some Common Substances***

| Substance | Physical State | Density (g/cm³) |
|---|---|---|
| Hydrogen | gas | 0.0000899 |
| Oxygen | gas | 0.00133 |
| Grain alcohol | liquid | 0.789 |
| Water | liquid | 0.998 |
| Table salt | solid | 2.16 |
| Aluminum | solid | 2.70 |
| Lead | solid | 11.3 |
| Gold | solid | 19.3 |

*At room temperature (20°C) and normal atmospheric pressure (1 atm).

**Density**  The **density** (*d*) of an object is its mass divided by its volume:

$$\text{Density} = \frac{\text{mass}}{\text{volume}} \qquad (1.1)$$

We isolate each of these variables by treating density as a conversion factor:

$$\text{Mass} = \text{volume} \times \text{density} = \text{volume} \times \frac{\text{mass}}{\text{volume}}$$

or,

$$\text{Volume} = \text{mass} \times \frac{1}{\text{density}} = \text{mass} \times \frac{\text{volume}}{\text{mass}}$$

Because volume can change with temperature, so can density. But, at a given temperature and pressure, the *density of a substance is a characteristic physical property and, thus, has a specific value.*

The SI unit of density is kilograms per cubic meter (kg/m³), but in chemistry, density has units of g/L (g/dm³) or g/mL (g/cm³) (Table 1.5). The densities of gases are much lower than the densities of liquids or solids (see Figure 1.2).

**Sample Problem 1.6**  **Calculating Density from Mass and Volume**

**Problem**  Lithium, a soft, gray solid with the lowest density of any metal, is a key component of advanced batteries, such as the one in your laptop. A slab of lithium weighs $1.49 \times 10^3$ mg and has sides that are 20.9 mm by 11.1 mm by 11.9 mm. Find the density of lithium in g/cm³.

**Plan**  To find the density in g/cm³, we need the mass of lithium in g and the volume in cm³. The mass is $1.49 \times 10^3$ mg, so we convert mg to g. We convert the lengths of the three sides from mm to cm, and then multiply them to find the volume in cm³. Dividing the mass by the volume gives the density (see the road map).

**Road Map**

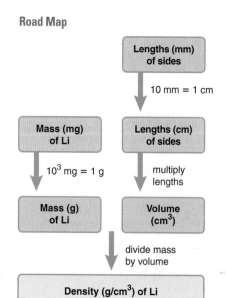

**Solution**  Converting the mass from mg to g:

$$\text{Mass (g) of lithium} = 1.49 \times 10^3 \ \text{mg} \left( \frac{10^{-3} \ \text{g}}{1 \ \text{mg}} \right) = 1.49 \ \text{g}$$

Converting side lengths from mm to cm:

$$\text{Length (cm) of one side} = 20.9 \ \text{mm} \times \frac{1 \ \text{cm}}{10 \ \text{mm}} = 2.09 \ \text{cm}$$

Similarly, the other side lengths are 1.11 cm and 1.19 cm.
Multiplying the sides to get the volume:

$$\text{Volume (cm}^3) = 2.09 \ \text{cm} \times 1.11 \ \text{cm} \times 1.19 \ \text{cm} = 2.76 \ \text{cm}^3$$

Calculating the density:

$$\text{Density of lithium} = \frac{\text{mass}}{\text{volume}} = \frac{1.49 \ \text{g}}{2.76 \ \text{cm}^3} = \boxed{0.540 \ \text{g/cm}^3}$$

**Check**  Since 1 cm = 10 mm, the number of cm in each length should be $\frac{1}{10}$ the number of mm. The units for density are correct, and the size of the answer (~0.5 g/cm³) seems correct since the number of g (1.49) is about half the number of cm³ (2.76). Also, the problem states that lithium has a very low density, so this answer makes sense.

**Follow-Up Problem 1.6** The piece of galena in Sample Problem 1.4 has a volume of 4.6 cm³. If the density of galena is 7.5 g/cm³, what is the mass (in kg) of that piece of galena? Draw a road map to show how you plan the solution. (See Brief Solutions.)

**Temperature** There is a noteworthy distinction between temperature and heat:

- **Temperature (*T*)** is *a measure* of how hot or cold one object is relative to another.
- **Heat** is *the energy* that flows from the object with the higher temperature to the object with the lower temperature. When you hold an ice cube, it feels like the "cold" flows into your hand, but actually, heat flows from your hand to the ice.

In the laboratory, we measure temperature with a **thermometer,** a narrow tube containing a fluid that expands when heated. When the thermometer is immersed in a substance hotter than itself, heat flows from the substance through the glass into the fluid, which expands and rises in the thermometer tube. If a substance is colder than the thermometer, heat flows to the substance from the fluid, which contracts and falls within the tube.

We'll consider three temperature scales: the Celsius (°C, formerly called centigrade), the Kelvin (K), and the Fahrenheit (°F) scales. The SI base unit of temperature is the **kelvin (K,** with no degree sign, °). Figure 1.10 shows some interesting temperatures in the Kelvin scale, which is preferred in scientific work (although the Celsius scale is still used frequently). In the United States, the Fahrenheit scale is used for weather reporting, body temperature, and so forth.

*The three scales differ in the size of the unit and/or the temperature of the zero point.* Figure 1.11 shows the freezing and boiling points of water in the three scales. The **Celsius scale** sets water's freezing point at 0°C and its boiling point (at normal atmospheric pressure) at 100°C. The **Kelvin (absolute) scale** uses the *same size degree* as the Celsius scale—$\frac{1}{100}$ of the difference between the freezing and boiling points of water—but it has a *different zero point;* that is, 0 K, or *absolute zero,* equals −273.15°C. Thus, in the Kelvin scale, *all temperatures are positive;* for example, water freezes at +273.15 K (0°C) and boils at +373.15 K (100°C).

**Figure 1.10** Some interesting temperatures.

Boiling point of water — 100°C — 373.15 K — 212°F

100 Celsius degrees    100 kelvins    180 Fahrenheit degrees

Freezing point of water — 0°C — 273.15 K — 32°F

0°C / 273 K / 32°F
−5°C / 268 K / 23°F

**Figure 1.11** Freezing and boiling points of water in the Celsius, Kelvin (absolute), and Fahrenheit scales. At the bottom of the figure, a portion of each of the three thermometer scales is expanded to show the sizes of the units.

## Table 1.6 The Three Temperature Scales

| Scale | Unit | Size of Degree (Relative to K) | Freezing Point of $H_2O$ | Boiling Point of $H_2O$ | $T$ at Absolute Zero | Conversion |
|---|---|---|---|---|---|---|
| Kelvin (absolute) | kelvin (K) | — | 273.15 K | 373.15 K | 0 K | to °C (Equation 1.2) |
| Celsius | Celsius degree (°C) | 1 | 0°C | 100°C | −273.15°C | to K (Equation 1.3) to °F (Equation 1.4) |
| Fahrenheit | Fahrenheit degree (°F) | $\frac{5}{9}$ | 32°F | 212°F | −459.67°F | to °C (Equation 1.5) |

We convert between the Celsius and Kelvin scales by remembering the different zero points: 0°C = 273.15 K, so

$$T \text{ (in K)} = T \text{ (in °C)} + 273.15 \tag{1.2}$$

And, therefore,

$$T \text{ (in °C)} = T \text{ (in K)} - 273.15 \tag{1.3}$$

The Fahrenheit scale differs from the other scales in its zero point *and* in the size of its degree. Water freezes at 32°F and boils at 212°F. Therefore, 180 Fahrenheit degrees (212°F − 32°F) represents the same temperature change as 100 Celsius degrees (or 100 kelvins). Because 100 Celsius degrees equal 180 Fahrenheit degrees,

$$1 \text{ Celsius degree} = \tfrac{180}{100} \text{ Fahrenheit degrees} = \tfrac{9}{5} \text{ Fahrenheit degrees}$$

To convert a temperature from °C to °F, first change the degree size and then adjust the zero point:

$$T \text{ (in °F)} = \tfrac{9}{5}T \text{ (in °C)} + 32 \tag{1.4}$$

To convert a temperature from °F to °C, do the two steps in the opposite order: adjust the zero point and then change the degree size. In other words, solve Equation 1.4 for $T$ (in °C):

$$T \text{ (in °C)} = [T \text{ (in °F)} - 32]\tfrac{5}{9} \tag{1.5}$$

Table 1.6 compares the three temperature scales.

### Sample Problem 1.7 Converting Units of Temperature

**Problem** A child has a body temperature of 38.7°C, and normal body temperature is 98.6°F. Does the child have a fever? What is the child's temperature in kelvins?

**Plan** To see if the child has a fever, we convert from °C to °F (Equation 1.4) and compare it with 98.6°F. Then, to convert the child's temperature in °C to K, we use Equation 1.2.

**Solution** Converting the temperature from °C to °F:

$$T \text{ (in °F)} = \tfrac{9}{5}T \text{ (in °C)} + 32 = \tfrac{9}{5}(38.7°C) + 32 = 101.7°F; \quad \text{yes, the child has a fever.}$$

Converting the temperature from °C to K:

$$T \text{ (in K)} = T \text{ (in °C)} + 273.15 = 38.7°C + 273.15 = \boxed{311.8 \text{ K}}$$

**Check** From everyday experience, you know that 101.7°F is a reasonable temperature for someone with a fever. In the second step, we can check for a large error as follows: 38.7°C is almost 40°C, and 40 + 273 = 313, which is close to our answer.

### Follow-Up Problem 1.7

Mercury melts at 234 K, lower than any other pure metal. What is its melting point in °C and °F?

**Time** The SI base unit of time is the **second (s),** which is now based on an atomic standard. The best pendulum clock is accurate to within 3 seconds per year, and the best quartz clock is 1000 times more accurate. The most recent version of the atomic clock is over 6000 times more accurate than that—within 1 second in 20 million years! Rather than the oscillations of a pendulum, the atomic clock measures the oscillations of microwave radiation absorbed by gaseous cesium atoms cooled to around $10^{-6}$ K: 1 second is defined as 9,192,631,770 of these oscillations. Chemists now use lasers to measure the speed of extremely fast reactions that occur in a few picoseconds ($10^{-12}$ s) or femtoseconds ($10^{-15}$ s).

**Extensive and Intensive Properties** Some variables are *dependent* on the amount of substance present; these are called **extensive properties.** On the other hand, **intensive properties** are *independent* of the amount of substance. Mass and volume, for example, are extensive properties, but density is an intensive property. Thus, a gallon of water has four times the mass of a quart of water, but it also has four times the volume, so the density, the *ratio* of mass to volume, is the same for both samples.

Another important example concerns heat, an extensive property, and temperature, an intensive property: a vat of boiling water has more heat, that is, more energy, than a cup of boiling water, but both samples have the same temperature.

## ▌Summary of Section 1.5

- The SI unit system consists of seven base units and numerous derived units.
- Exponential notation and prefixes based on powers of 10 are used to express very small and very large numbers.
- The SI base unit of length is the meter (m); on the atomic scale, the nanometer (nm) and picometer (pm) are used commonly.
- Volume (*V*) units are derived from length units, and the most important volume units are the cubic meter ($m^3$) and the liter (L).
- The *mass* of an object—the quantity of matter in it—is constant. The SI unit of mass is the kilogram (kg). The *weight* of an object varies with the gravitational field.
- Density (*d*) is a characteristic physical property of a substance and is the ratio of its mass to its volume.
- Temperature (*T*) is a measure of the relative hotness of an object. Heat is energy that flows from an object at higher *T* to one at lower *T*.
- Temperature scales differ in the size of the degree unit and/or the zero point. For scientific uses, temperature is measured in kelvins (K) or degrees Celsius (°C).
- Extensive properties, such as mass, volume, and energy, depend on the amount of a substance. Intensive properties, such as density and temperature, do not.

## 1.6 • UNCERTAINTY IN MEASUREMENT: SIGNIFICANT FIGURES

All measuring devices—balances, pipets, thermometers, and so forth—are made to limited specifications, and we use our imperfect senses and skills to read them. Therefore, we can *never* measure a quantity exactly; put another way, every measurement includes some **uncertainty.** The device we choose depends on how much uncertainty is acceptable. When you buy potatoes, a supermarket scale that measures in 0.1-kg increments is acceptable; it tells you that the mass is, for example, $2.0 \pm 0.1$ kg. The "$\pm 0.1$ kg" term expresses the uncertainty: the potatoes weigh between 1.9 and 2.1 kg. Needing more certainty than that to weigh a substance, a chemist uses a balance that measures in 0.001-kg increments and finds the substance weighs $2.036 \pm 0.001$ kg, that is, between 2.035 and 2.037 kg. The greater number of digits in this measurement means we know the mass of the substance with *more certainty* than we know the mass of potatoes.

We *always estimate the rightmost digit* of a measurement. The uncertainty can be expressed with the $\pm$ sign, but generally we drop the sign and *assume an uncertainty of one unit in the rightmost digit.* The digits we record, both the certain and the uncertain ones, are called **significant figures.** There are four significant figures in 2.036 kg

**Figure 1.12** The number of significant figures in a measurement. The thermometer on the left is graduated in increments of 0.1°C; the one on the right is graduated in increments of 1°C.

This measurement is known with more certainty because it has more significant figures.

32.33°C

32.3°C

and two in 2.0 kg. *The greater the number of significant figures, the greater is the certainty of a measurement.* Figure 1.12 shows this point for two thermometers.

## Determining Which Digits Are Significant

When you take a measurement or use one in a calculation, you must know the number of digits that are significant: *all digits are significant, except zeros used only to position the decimal point.* The following procedure applies this point:

1. Make sure the measurement has a decimal point.
2. Start at the left, and move right until you reach the first nonzero digit.
3. Count that digit and every digit to its right as significant.

A complication can arise when zeros end a number:

- If there *is* a decimal point and the zeros lie either after or before it, they *are* significant: 1.1300 g has five significant figures and 6500. has four.
- If there is *no* decimal point, we assume that the zeros are *not* significant, unless exponential notation clarifies the quantity: 5300 L is *assumed* to have two significant figures, but $5.300\times10^3$ L has four, $5.30\times10^3$ L has three, and $5.3\times10^3$ L has two.
- A terminal decimal point indicates that zeros are significant: 500 mL has one significant figure, but 500. mL has three (as do $5.00\times10^2$ mL and 0.500 L).

---

### Sample Problem 1.8 | Determining the Number of Significant Figures

**Problem** For each of the following quantities, underline the zeros that are significant figures (sf) and determine the total number of significant figures. For (d) to (f), express each quantity in exponential notation first.
**(a)** 0.0030 L          **(b)** 0.1044 g          **(c)** 53,069 mL
**(d)** 0.00004715 m      **(e)** 57,600. s          **(f)** 0.0000007160 cm$^3$

**Plan** We determine the number of significant figures by counting digits, as just presented, paying particular attention to the position of zeros in relation to the decimal point, and underline the zeros that are significant.

**Solution (a)** 0.0030 L has  2 sf
**(b)** 0.1044 g has  4 sf
**(c)** 53,069 mL has  5 sf
**(d)** 0.00004715 m, or  $4.715\times10^{-5}$  m, has  4 sf
**(e)** 57,600. s, or  $5.7600\times10^4$  s,  has  5 sf
**(f)** 0.0000007160 cm$^3$, or  $7.160\times10^{-7}$  cm$^3$, has  4 sf

**Check** Be sure that every zero counted as significant comes after nonzero digit(s) in the number.

**Follow-Up Problem 1.8** For each of the following quantities, underline the zeros that are significant figures and determine the total number of significant figures (sf). For (d) to (f), express each quantity in exponential notation first.
**(a)** 31.070 mg      **(b)** 0.06060 g      **(c)** 850.°C
**(d)** 200.0 mL      **(e)** 0.0000039 m      **(f)** 0.000401 L

## Significant Figures: Calculations and Rounding Off

Measuring several quantities typically results in data with differing numbers of significant figures. In a calculation, we keep track of the number in each quantity so that we don't have more significant figures (more certainty) in the answer than in the data. If we do have too many significant figures, we must **round off** the answer.

The general rule for rounding is that *the least certain measurement sets the limit on certainty for the entire calculation and determines the number of significant figures in the final answer.* Suppose you want to find the density of a new ceramic. You measure the mass of a piece of it on a precise laboratory balance and obtain 3.8056 g; you measure the volume as 2.5 mL by displacement of water in a graduated cylinder. The mass has five significant figures, but the volume has only two. Should you report the density as 3.8056 g/2.5 mL = 1.5222 g/mL or as 1.5 g/mL? The answer with five significant figures implies more certainty than the answer with two. But you didn't measure the volume to five significant figures, so you can't possibly know the density with that much certainty. Therefore, you report 1.5 g/mL, the answer with two significant figures.

**Rules for Arithmetic Operations** The two rules in arithmetic calculations are

1. *For multiplication and division.* The answer contains the same number of significant figures as there are in the measurement with the *fewest significant figures*. Suppose you want to find the volume of a sheet of a new graphite composite. The length (9.2 cm) and width (6.8 cm) are obtained with a ruler, and the thickness (0.3744 cm) with a set of calipers. The calculation is

$$\text{Volume (cm}^3) = 9.2 \text{ cm} \times 6.8 \text{ cm} \times 0.3744 \text{ cm} = 23.4225 \text{ cm}^3 = 23 \text{ cm}^3$$

Even though your calculator may show 23.4225 cm³, you report 23 cm³, the answer with two significant figures, the same as in the measurements with the lower number of significant figures. After all, if the length and width have two significant figures, you can't possibly know the volume with more certainty.

2. *For addition and subtraction.* The answer has the same number of decimal places as there are in the measurement with the *fewest decimal places*. Suppose you want the total volume after adding water to a protein solution: you have 83.5 mL of solution in a graduated cylinder and add 23.28 mL of water from a buret. The calculation is shown in the margin. Here the calculator shows 106.78 mL, but you report the volume as 106.8 mL, because the measurement with fewer decimal places (83.5 mL) has one decimal place (*see margin*).

> 83.5 mL
> + 23.28 mL
> ————————
> 106.78 mL
> Answer: Volume = 106.8 mL

**Rules for Rounding Off** You usually need to round off the final answer to the proper number of significant figures or decimal places. Notice that in calculating the volume of the graphite composite above, we removed the extra digits, but in calculating the total volume of the protein solution, we removed the extra digit and increased the last digit by one. The general rule for rounding is that *the least certain measurement sets the limit on the certainty of the final answer.* Here are detailed rules for rounding off:

1. If the digit removed is *more than 5*, the preceding number increases by 1: 5.379 rounds to 5.38 if you need three significant figures and to 5.4 if you need two.
2. If the digit removed is *less than 5*, the preceding number remains the same: 0.2413 rounds to 0.241 if you need three significant figures and to 0.24 if you need two.
3. If the digit removed *is 5*, the preceding number increases by 1 if it is odd and remains the same if it is even: 17.75 rounds to 17.8, but 17.65 rounds to 17.6. If the 5 is followed only by zeros, rule 3 is followed; if the 5 is followed by nonzeros, rule 1 is followed: 17.6500 rounds to 17.6, but 17.6513 rounds to 17.7.

**Figure 1.13 Significant figures and measuring devices.** The mass measurement (6.8605 g) has more significant figures than the volume measurement (68.2 mL).

4. *Always carry one or two additional significant figures through a multistep calculation and round off the final answer **only**.* Don't be concerned if you string together a calculation to check a sample or follow-up problem and find that your answer differs in the last decimal place from the one in the book. To show you the correct number of significant figures in text calculations, *we round off intermediate steps,* and that process may sometimes change the last digit.

Note that, unless you set a limit on your calculator, it gives answers with too many figures and you must round the displayed result.

**Significant Figures in the Lab** The measuring device you choose determines the number of significant figures you can obtain. Suppose an experiment requires a solution made by dissolving a solid in a liquid. You weigh the solid on an analytical balance and obtain a mass with five significant figures. It would make sense to measure the liquid with a buret or a pipet, which measures volumes to more significant figures than a graduated cylinder. If you do choose the cylinder, you would have to round off more digits, and some certainty in the mass value would be wasted (Figure 1.13). With experience, you'll choose a measuring device based on the number of significant figures you need in the final answer.

**Exact Numbers** **Exact numbers** have no uncertainty associated with them. Some are part of a unit conversion: by definition, there are exactly 60 minutes in 1 hour, 1000 micrograms in 1 milligram, and 2.54 centimeters in 1 inch. Other exact numbers result from actually counting items: there are exactly 3 coins in my hand, 26 letters in the English alphabet, and so forth. Therefore, unlike a measured quantity, *exact numbers do not limit the number of significant figures in a calculation.*

---

**Sample Problem 1.9    Significant Figures and Rounding**

**Problem** Perform the following calculations and round the answers to the correct number of significant figures:

**(a)** $\dfrac{16.3521 \text{ cm}^2 - 1.448 \text{ cm}^2}{7.085 \text{ cm}}$

**(b)** $\dfrac{(4.80\times10^4 \text{ mg})\left(\dfrac{1 \text{ g}}{1000 \text{ mg}}\right)}{11.55 \text{ cm}^3}$

**Plan** We use the rules just presented in the text: **(a)** We subtract before we divide. **(b)** We note that the unit conversion involves an exact number.

**Solution (a)** $\dfrac{16.3521 \text{ cm}^2 - 1.448 \text{ cm}^2}{7.085 \text{ cm}} = \dfrac{14.904 \text{ cm}^2}{7.085 \text{ cm}} = \boxed{2.104 \text{ cm}}$

**(b)** $\dfrac{(4.80\times10^4 \text{ mg})\left(\dfrac{1 \text{ g}}{1000 \text{ mg}}\right)}{11.55 \text{ cm}^3} = \dfrac{48.0 \text{ g}}{11.55 \text{ cm}^3} = \boxed{4.16 \text{ g/cm}^3}$

**Check** Note that in (a) we lose a decimal place in the numerator, and in (b) we retain 3 sf in the answer because there are 3 sf in 4.80. Rounding to the nearest whole number is always a good way to check: **(a)** $(16 - 1)/7 \approx 2$; **(b)** $(5\times10^4/1\times10^3)/12 \approx 4$.

**Follow-Up Problem 1.9** Perform the following calculation and round the answer to the correct number of significant figures: $\dfrac{25.65 \text{ mL} + 37.4 \text{ mL}}{73.55 \text{ s}\left(\dfrac{1 \text{ min}}{60 \text{ s}}\right)}$

---

## Precision, Accuracy, and Instrument Calibration

We may use the words "precision" and "accuracy" interchangeably in everyday speech, but for scientific measurements they have distinct meanings. **Precision,** or *reproducibility,* refers to how close the measurements in a series are to each other,

**Figure 1.14** Precision and accuracy in a laboratory calibration.

and **accuracy** refers to how close each measurement is to the actual value. These terms are related to two widespread types of error:

1. **Systematic error** produces values that are *either* all higher or all lower than the actual value. This type of error is part of the experimental system, often caused by a faulty device or by a consistent mistake in taking a reading.
2. **Random error,** in the absence of systematic error, produces values that are higher *and* lower than the actual value. Random error *always* occurs, but its size depends on the measurer's skill and the instrument's precision.

*Precise measurements have low random error,* that is, small deviations from the average. *Accurate measurements have low systematic error and, generally, low random error.* In some cases, when many measurements have a high random error, the *average* may still be accurate.

Suppose each of four students measures 25.0 mL of water in a preweighed graduated cylinder and then weighs the water *plus* cylinder on a balance. If the density of water is 1.00 g/mL at the temperature of the experiment, the *actual* mass of 25.0 mL of water is 25.0 g. Each student performs the operation four times, subtracts the mass of the empty cylinder, and obtains one of four graphs (Figure 1.14). In graphs A and B, random error is small; that is, precision is high (the weighings are reproducible). In A, however, the accuracy is high as well (all the values are close to 25.0 g), whereas in B the accuracy is low (there is a systematic error). In graphs C and D, random error is large; that is, precision is low. Note, however, that in D there is also a systematic error (all the values are high), whereas in C the average of the values is close to the actual value.

Systematic error can be taken into account through **calibration,** comparing the measuring device with a known standard. The systematic error in graph B, for example, might be caused by a poorly manufactured cylinder that reads "25.0" when it actually contains about 27 mL. If that cylinder had been calibrated, the student could have adjusted all volumes measured with it. The students also should calibrate the balance with standardized masses.

# Summary of Section 1.6

- The final digit of a measurement is always estimated. Thus, all measurements have some uncertainty, which is expressed by the number of significant figures.
- The certainty of a calculated result depends on the certainty of the data, so the answer has as many significant figures as in the least certain measurement.
- Excess digits are rounded off in the final answer with a set of rules.
- The choice of laboratory device depends on the certainty needed.
- Exact numbers have as many significant figures as the calculation requires.
- Precision refers to how close values are to each other, and accuracy refers to how close values are to the actual value.
- Systematic errors give values that are either all higher or all lower than the actual value. Random errors give some values that are higher and some that are lower than the actual value.
- Precise measurements have low random error; accurate measurements have low systematic error and low random error.
- A systematic error is often caused by faulty equipment and can be compensated for by calibration.

# CHAPTER REVIEW GUIDE

## Learning Objectives
Relevant section (§) and/or sample problem (SP) numbers appear in parentheses.

### Understand These Concepts

1. The distinction between physical and chemical properties and changes (§1.1; SPs 1.1, 1.2)
2. The defining features of the states of matter (§1.1)
3. The nature of potential and kinetic energy and their interconversion (§1.1)
4. The process of approaching a phenomenon scientifically and the distinctions between observation, hypothesis, experiment, and model (§1.3)
5. The common units of length, volume, mass, and temperature and their numerical prefixes (§1.5)
6. The distinctions between mass and weight, heat and temperature, and intensive and extensive properties (§1.5)
7. The meaning of uncertainty in measurements and the use of significant figures and rounding (§1.6)
8. The distinctions between accuracy and precision and between systematic and random error (§1.6)

### Master These Skills

1. Using conversion factors in calculations and a systematic approach of plan, solution, check, and follow-up for solving problems (§1.4; SPs 1.3–1.5)
2. Finding density from mass and volume (SP 1.6)
3. Converting among the Kelvin, Celsius, and Fahrenheit scales (SP 1.7)
4. Determining the number of significant figures (SP 1.8) and rounding to the correct number of digits (SP 1.9)

## Key Terms
Page numbers appear in parentheses.

**Section 1.1**
chemistry (4)
matter (4)
composition (4)
property (4)
physical property (4)
physical change (4)
chemical property (4)
chemical change (chemical reaction) (4)
state of matter (5)
solid (5)
liquid (6)
gas (6)
energy (8)
potential energy (8)
kinetic energy (8)

**Section 1.2**
combustion (10)

**Section 1.3**
scientific method (12)
observation (12)
data (12)
natural law (12)
hypothesis (12)
experiment (12)
variable (12)
controlled experiment (12)
model (theory) (12)

**Section 1.4**
conversion factor (13)
dimensional analysis (15)

**Section 1.5**
SI unit (17)
base (fundamental) unit (17)
derived unit (17)
meter (m) (18)
volume (V) (18)
cubic meter (m³) (18)
liter (L) (18)
milliliter (mL) (18)
mass (20)
kilogram (kg) (20)
weight (20)
density (d) (22)
temperature (T) (23)
heat (23)
thermometer (23)
kelvin (K) (23)

Celsius scale (23)
Kelvin (absolute) scale (23)
second (s) (25)
extensive property (25)
intensive property (25)

**Section 1.6**
uncertainty (25)
significant figures (25)
round off (27)
exact number (28)
precision (28)
accuracy (29)
systematic error (29)
random error (29)
calibration (29)

## Key Equations and Relationships
Page numbers appear in parentheses.

**1.1** Calculating density from mass and volume (22):

$$\text{Density} = \frac{\text{mass}}{\text{volume}}$$

**1.2** Converting temperature from °C to K (24):

$$T \text{ (in K)} = T \text{ (in °C)} + 273.15$$

**1.3** Converting temperature from K to °C (24):

$$T \text{ (in °C)} = T \text{ (in K)} - 273.15$$

**1.4** Converting temperature from °C to °F (24):

$$T \text{ (in °F)} = \tfrac{9}{5}T \text{ (in °C)} + 32$$

**1.5** Converting temperature from °F to °C (24):

$$T \text{ (in °C)} = [T \text{ (in °F)} - 32]\tfrac{5}{9}$$

## Brief Solutions to Follow-Up Problems

**1.1** Chemical. The red-and-blue and separate red particles on the left become paired red and separate blue particles on the right.

**1.2** (a) Physical. Solid iodine changes to gaseous iodine.
(b) Chemical. Gasoline burns in air to form different substances.
(c) Chemical. In contact with air, substances in torn skin and blood react to form different substances.

**1.3** No. of chairs

$$= 3 \text{ bolts} \times \frac{200 \text{ m}^2}{1 \text{ bolt}} \times \frac{(3.281)^2 \text{ ft}^2}{1 \text{ m}^2} \times \frac{1 \text{ chair}}{31.5 \text{ ft}^2}$$

$$= 205 \text{ chairs}$$

See Road Map 1.3.

**Road Map 1.3**

Fabric (bolts)

↓ 200 m² = 1 bolt

Fabric (m²)

↓ (3.281)² ft² = 1 m²

Fabric (ft²)

↓ 1 chair = 31.5 ft²

No. of chairs

**Road Map 1.4**

Diameter (dm)

↓ diameter = 2r

r (dm)

↓ $V = \frac{4}{3}\pi r^3$

V (dm³)

↓ 1 dm³ = 1 L
  1 L = 10⁶ μL

V (μL)

**Road Map 1.5**

Time (hr)

↓ 1 hr = 60 min

Time (min)

↓ 1 min = 60 s

Time (s)

↓ 1 s = 1.5 drops

No. of drops

↓ 1 drop = 65 mg

Mass (mg) of solution

↓ 10³ mg = 1 g

Mass (g) of solution

↓ 10³ g = 1 kg

Mass (kg) of solution

**Road Map 1.6**

V (cm³)

↓ multiply by density

Mass (g)

↓ 10³ g = 1 kg

Mass (kg)

**1.4** Radius of ribosome (dm) $= \dfrac{21.4 \text{ nm}}{2} \times \dfrac{1 \text{ dm}}{10^8 \text{ nm}}$

$$= 1.07 \times 10^{-7} \text{ dm}$$

Volume of ribosome (dm³) $= \frac{4}{3}\pi r^3 = \frac{4}{3}(3.14)(1.07 \times 10^{-7} \text{ dm})^3$

$$= 5.13 \times 10^{-21} \text{ dm}^3$$

Volume of ribosome (μL) $= (5.13 \times 10^{-21} \text{ dm}^3)\left(\dfrac{1 \text{ L}}{1 \text{ dm}^3}\right)\left(\dfrac{10 \text{ μL}}{1 \text{ L}}\right)$

$$= 5.13 \times 10^{-15} \text{ μL}$$

See Road Map 1.4.

**1.5** Mass (kg) of solution

$$= 8.0 \text{ h} \times \frac{60 \text{ min}}{1 \text{ h}} \times \frac{60 \text{ s}}{1 \text{ min}} \times \frac{1.5 \text{ drops}}{1 \text{ s}}$$

$$\times \frac{65 \text{ mg}}{1 \text{ drop}} \times \frac{1 \text{ g}}{10^3 \text{ mg}} \times \frac{1 \text{ kg}}{10^3 \text{ g}}$$

$$= 2.8 \text{ kg}$$

See Road Map 1.5.

**1.6** Mass (kg) of sample $= 4.6 \text{ cm}^3 \times \dfrac{7.5 \text{ g}}{1 \text{ cm}^3} \times \dfrac{1 \text{ kg}}{10^3 \text{ g}}$

$$= 0.034 \text{ kg}$$

See Road Map 1.6.

**1.7** $T$ (in °C) = 234 K − 273.15 = −39°C
$T$ (in °F) = $\frac{9}{5}$(−39°C) + 32 = −38°F
Answer contains two significant figures (see Section 1.6).

**1.8** (a) 31.0̲70 mg, 5 sf   (b) 0.0606̲0 g, 4 sf
(c) 850̲.°C, 3 sf   (d) 2.0̲00×10² mL, 4 sf
(e) 3.9×10⁻⁶ m, 2 sf   (f) 4.0̲1×10⁻⁴ L, 3 sf

**1.9** $\dfrac{25.65 \text{ mL} + 37.4 \text{ mL}}{73.55 \text{ s}\left(\dfrac{1 \text{ min}}{60 \text{ s}}\right)} = 51.4 \text{ mL/min}$

## PROBLEMS

Problems with **colored** numbers are answered in Appendix E and worked in detail in the Student Solutions Manual. Problem sections match those in the text and provide the numbers of relevant sample problems. Most offer Concept Review Questions, Skill-Building Exercises (grouped in pairs covering the same concept), and Problems in Context. The Comprehensive Problems are based on material from any section.

### Some Fundamental Definitions
(Sample Problems 1.1 and 1.2)

**Concept Review Question**

**1.1** Scenes A–D represent atomic-scale views of different samples of substances:

A    B    C    D

(a) Under one set of conditions, the substances in A and B mix, and the result is depicted in C. Does this represent a chemical or a physical change?
(b) Under a second set of conditions, the same substances mix, and the result is depicted in D. Does this represent a chemical or a physical change?
(c) Under a third set of conditions, the sample depicted in C changes to that in D. Does this represent a chemical or a physical change?
(d) After the change in part (c) has occurred, does the sample have different chemical properties? Physical properties?

**Skill-Building Exercises** (grouped in similar pairs)

**1.2** Describe solids, liquids, and gases in terms of how they fill a container. Use your descriptions to identify the physical state (at room temperature) of the following: (a) helium in a toy balloon; (b) mercury in a thermometer; (c) soup in a bowl.

**1.3** Use your descriptions from Problem 1.2 to identify the physical state (at room temperature) of the following: (a) the air in your room; (b) tablets in a bottle of vitamins; (c) sugar in a packet.

**1.4** Define *physical property* and *chemical property*. Identify each type of property in the following statements:
(a) Yellow-green chlorine gas attacks silvery sodium metal to form white crystals of sodium chloride (table salt).
(b) A magnet separates a mixture of black iron shavings and white sand.

**1.5** Define *physical change* and *chemical change*. State which type of change occurs in each of the following statements:
(a) Passing an electric current through molten magnesium chloride yields molten magnesium and gaseous chlorine.
(b) The iron in discarded automobiles slowly forms reddish brown, crumbly rust.

**1.6** Which of the following is a chemical change? Explain your reasoning: (a) boiling canned soup; (b) toasting a slice of bread; (c) chopping a log; (d) burning a log.

**1.7** Which of the following changes can be reversed by changing the temperature: (a) dew condensing on a leaf; (b) an egg turning hard when it is boiled; (c) ice cream melting; (d) a spoonful of batter cooking on a hot griddle?

**1.8** For each pair, which has higher potential energy?
(a) The fuel in your car or the gaseous products in its exhaust
(b) Wood in a fire or the ashes after the wood burns

**1.9** For each pair, which has higher kinetic energy?
(a) A sled resting at the top of a hill or a sled sliding down the hill
(b) Water above a dam or water falling over the dam

## Chemical Arts and the Origins of Modern Chemistry

**Concept Review Questions**

**1.10** The alchemical, medical, and technological traditions were precursors to chemistry. State a contribution that each made to the development of the science of chemistry.

**1.11** How did the phlogiston theory explain combustion?

**1.12** One important observation that supporters of the phlogiston theory had trouble explaining was that the calx of a metal weighs more than the metal itself. Why was that observation important? How did the phlogistonists respond?

**1.13** Lavoisier developed a new theory of combustion that overturned the phlogiston theory. What measurements were central to his theory, and what key discovery did he make?

## The Scientific Approach: Developing a Model

**Concept Review Questions**

**1.14** How are the key elements of scientific thinking used in the following scenario? While making toast, you notice it fails to pop out of the toaster. Thinking the spring mechanism is stuck, you notice that the bread is unchanged. Assuming you forgot to plug in the toaster, you check and find it is plugged in. When you take the toaster into the dining room and plug it into a different outlet, you find the toaster works. Returning to the kitchen, you turn on the switch for the overhead light and nothing happens.

**1.15** Why is a quantitative observation more useful than a non-quantitative one? Which of the following is (are) quantitative? (a) The Sun rises in the east. (b) A person weighs one-sixth as much on the Moon as on Earth. (c) Ice floats on water. (d) A hand pump cannot draw water from a well more than 34 ft deep.

**1.16** Describe the essential features of a well-designed experiment.

**1.17** Describe the essential features of a scientific model.

## Chemical Problem Solving
(Sample Problem 1.3)

**Concept Review Question**

**1.18** When you convert feet to inches, how do you decide which part of the conversion factor should be in the numerator and which in the denominator?

**Skill-Building Exercises** (grouped in similar pairs)

**1.19** Write the conversion factor(s) for
(a) $in^2$ to $m^2$          (b) $km^2$ to $cm^2$
(c) mi/h to m/s        (d) $lb/ft^3$ to $g/cm^3$

**1.20** Write the conversion factor(s) for
(a) cm/min to in/s     (b) $m^3$ to $in^3$
(c) $m/s^2$ to $km/h^2$     (d) gal/h to L/min

## Measurement in Scientific Study
(Sample Problems 1.4 to 1.7)

**Concept Review Questions**

**1.21** Describe the difference between intensive and extensive properties. Which of the following properties are intensive: (a) mass; (b) density; (c) volume; (d) melting point?

**1.22** Explain the difference between mass and weight. Why is your weight on the Moon one-sixth that on Earth?

**1.23** For each of the following cases, state whether the density of the object increases, decreases, or remains the same:
(a) A sample of chlorine gas is compressed.
(b) A lead weight is carried up a high mountain.
(c) A sample of water is frozen.
(d) An iron bar is cooled.
(e) A diamond is submerged in water.

**1.24** Explain the difference between heat and temperature. Does 1 L of water at 65°F have more, less, or the same quantity of energy as 1 L of water at 65°C?

**1.25** A one-step conversion is sufficient to convert a temperature in the Celsius scale to the Kelvin scale, but not to the Fahrenheit scale. Explain.

**Skill-Building Exercises** (grouped in similar pairs)

**1.26** The average radius of a molecule of lysozyme, an enzyme in tears, is 1430 pm. What is its radius in nanometers (nm)?

**1.27** The radius of a barium atom is $2.22 \times 10^{-10}$ m. What is its radius in angstroms (Å)?

**1.28** What is the length in inches (in) of a 100.-m soccer field?

**1.29** The center on your basketball team is 6 ft 10 in tall. How tall is the player in millimeters (mm)?

**1.30** A small hole in the wing of a space shuttle requires a 20.7-$cm^2$ patch. (a) What is the patch's area in square kilometers ($km^2$)? (b) If the patching material costs NASA $3.25/$in^2$, what is the cost of the patch?

**1.31** The area of a telescope lens is 7903 mm². (a) What is the area in square feet (ft²)? (b) If it takes a technician 45 s to polish 135 mm², how long does it take her to polish the entire lens?

**1.32** Express your body weight in kilograms (kg).

**1.33** There are $2.60 \times 10^{15}$ short tons of oxygen in the atmosphere (1 short ton = 2000 lb). How many metric tons of oxygen are present (1 metric ton = 1000 kg)?

**1.34** The average density of Earth is 5.52 g/cm³. What is its density in (a) kg/m³; (b) lb/ft³?

**1.35** The speed of light in a vacuum is $2.998 \times 10^8$ m/s. What is its speed in (a) km/h; (b) mi/min?

**1.36** The volume of a certain bacterial cell is 2.56 μm³. (a) What is its volume in cubic millimeters (mm³)? (b) What is the volume of $10^5$ cells in liters (L)?

**1.37** (a) How many cubic meters of milk are in 1 qt (946.4 mL)? (b) How many liters of milk are in 835 gal (1 gal = 4 qt)?

**1.38** An empty vial weighs 55.32 g. (a) If the vial weighs 185.56 g when filled with liquid mercury ($d$ = 13.53 g/cm³), what is its volume? (b) How much would the vial weigh if it were filled with water ($d$ = 0.997 g/cm³ at 25°C)?

**1.39** An empty Erlenmeyer flask weighs 241.3 g. When filled with water ($d$ = 1.00 g/cm³), the flask and its contents weigh 489.1 g. (a) What is the flask's volume? (b) How much does the flask weigh when filled with chloroform ($d$ = 1.48 g/cm³)?

**1.40** A small cube of aluminum measures 15.6 mm on a side and weighs 10.25 g. What is the density of aluminum in g/cm³?

**1.41** A steel ball-bearing with a circumference of 32.5 mm weighs 4.20 g. What is the density of the steel in g/cm³ ($V$ of a sphere = $\frac{4}{3}\pi r^3$; circumference of a circle = $2\pi r$)?

**1.42** Perform the following conversions:
(a) 68°F (a pleasant spring day) to °C and K
(b) −164°C (the boiling point of methane, the main component of natural gas) to K and °F
(c) 0 K (absolute zero, theoretically the coldest possible temperature) to °C and °F

**1.43** Perform the following conversions:
(a) 106°F (the body temperature of many birds) to K and °C
(b) 3410°C (the melting point of tungsten, the highest for any metallic element) to K and °F
(c) $6.1 \times 10^3$ K (the surface temperature of the Sun) to °F and °C

**Problems in Context**

**1.44** A 25.0-g sample of each of three unknown metals is added to 25.0 mL of water in graduated cylinders A, B, and C, and the final volumes are depicted in the circles below. Given their densities, identify the metal in each cylinder: zinc (7.14 g/mL), iron (7.87 g/mL), or nickel (8.91 g/mL).

**1.45** The distance between two adjacent peaks on a wave is called the *wavelength*.

(a) The wavelength of a beam of ultraviolet light is 247 nanometers (nm). What is its wavelength in meters?
(b) The wavelength of a beam of red light is 6760 pm. What is its wavelength in angstroms (Å)?

**1.46** Each of the beakers depicted below contains two liquids that do not dissolve in each other. Three of the liquids are designated A, B, and C, and water is designated W.

(a) Which of the liquids is (are) more dense than water and which less dense?
(b) If the densities of W, C, and A are 1.0 g/mL, 0.88 g/mL, and 1.4 g/mL, respectively, which of the following densities is possible for liquid B: 0.79 g/mL, 0.86 g/mL, 0.94 g/mL, or 1.2 g/mL?

**1.47** A cylindrical tube 9.5 cm high and 0.85 cm in diameter is used to collect blood samples. How many cubic decimeters (dm³) of blood can it hold ($V$ of a cylinder = $\pi r^2 h$)?

**1.48** Copper can be drawn into thin wires. How many meters of 34-gauge wire (diameter = $6.304 \times 10^{-3}$ in) can be produced from the copper in 5.01 lb of covellite, an ore of copper that is 66% copper by mass? (*Hint:* Treat the wire as a cylinder: $V$ of cylinder = $\pi r^2 h$; $d$ of copper = 8.95 g/cm³.)

## Uncertainty in Measurement: Significant Figures
(Sample Problems 1.8 and 1.9)

### Concept Review Questions

**1.49** What is an exact number? How are exact numbers treated differently from other numbers in a calculation?

**1.50** Which procedure(s) decrease(s) the random error of a measurement: (1) taking the average of more measurements; (2) calibrating the instrument; (3) taking fewer measurements? Explain.

**1.51** A newspaper reported that the attendance at Slippery Rock's home football game was 16,532. (a) How many significant figures does this number contain? (b) Was the actual number of people counted? (c) After Slippery Rock's next home game, the newspaper reported an attendance of 15,000. If you assume that this number contains two significant figures, how many people could actually have been at the game?

### Skill-Building Exercises (grouped in similar pairs)

**1.52** Underline the significant zeros in the following numbers:
(a) 0.41    (b) 0.041    (c) 0.0410    (d) $4.0100 \times 10^4$

**1.53** Underline the significant zeros in the following numbers:
(a) 5.08    (b) 508    (c) $5.080 \times 10^3$    (d) 0.05080

**1.54** Round off each number to the indicated number of significant figures (sf): (a) 0.0003554 (to 2 sf); (b) 35.8348 (to 4 sf); (c) 22.4555 (to 3 sf).

**1.55** Round off each number to the indicated number of significant figures (sf): (a) 231.554 (to 4 sf); (b) 0.00845 (to 2 sf); (c) 144,000 (to 2 sf).

**1.56** Round off each number in the following calculation to one fewer significant figure, and find the answer:

$$\frac{19 \times 155 \times 8.3}{3.2 \times 2.9 \times 4.7}$$

**1.57** Round off each number in the following calculation to one fewer significant figure, and find the answer:

$$\frac{10.8 \times 6.18 \times 2.381}{24.3 \times 1.8 \times 19.5}$$

**1.58** Carry out the following calculations, making sure that your answer has the correct number of significant figures:

(a) $\dfrac{2.795 \text{ m} \times 3.10 \text{ m}}{6.48 \text{ m}}$

(b) $V = \frac{4}{3}\pi r^3$, where $r = 17.282$ mm

(c) $1.110$ cm $+ 17.3$ cm $+ 108.2$ cm $+ 316$ cm

**1.59** Carry out the following calculations, making sure that your answer has the correct number of significant figures:

(a) $\dfrac{2.420 \text{ g} + 15.6 \text{ g}}{4.8 \text{ g}}$   (b) $\dfrac{7.87 \text{ mL}}{16.1 \text{ mL} - 8.44 \text{ mL}}$

(c) $V = \pi r^2 h$, where $r = 6.23$ cm and $h = 4.630$ cm

**1.60** Write the following numbers in scientific notation:
(a) 131,000.0    (b) 0.00047    (c) 210,006    (d) 2160.5

**1.61** Write the following numbers in scientific notation:
(a) 282.0    (b) 0.0380    (c) 4270.8    (d) 58,200.9

**1.62** Write the following numbers in standard notation. Use a terminal decimal point when needed:
(a) $5.55 \times 10^3$    (b) $1.0070 \times 10^4$    (c) $8.85 \times 10^{-7}$    (d) $3.004 \times 10^{-3}$

**1.63** Write the following numbers in standard notation. Use a terminal decimal point when needed:
(a) $6.500 \times 10^3$    (b) $3.46 \times 10^{-5}$    (c) $7.5 \times 10^2$    (d) $1.8856 \times 10^2$

**1.64** Convert the following into correct scientific notation:
(a) $802.5 \times 10^2$    (b) $1009.8 \times 10^{-6}$    (c) $0.077 \times 10^{-9}$

**1.65** Convert the following into correct scientific notation:
(a) $14.3 \times 10^1$    (b) $851 \times 10^{-2}$    (c) $7500 \times 10^{-3}$

**1.66** Carry out each calculation, paying special attention to significant figures, rounding, and units (J = joule, the SI unit of energy; mol = mole, the SI unit for amount of substance):

(a) $\dfrac{(6.626 \times 10^{-34} \text{ J·s})(2.9979 \times 10^8 \text{ m/s})}{489 \times 10^{-9} \text{ m}}$

(b) $\dfrac{(6.022 \times 10^{23} \text{ molecules/mol})(1.23 \times 10^2 \text{ g})}{46.07 \text{ g/mol}}$

(c) $(6.022 \times 10^{23} \text{ atoms/mol})(2.18 \times 10^{-18} \text{ J/atom})\left(\dfrac{1}{2^2} - \dfrac{1}{3^2}\right)$,

where the numbers 2 and 3 in the last term are exact

**1.67** Carry out each calculation, paying special attention to significant figures, rounding, and units:

(a) $\dfrac{4.32 \times 10^7 \text{ g}}{\frac{4}{3}(3.1416)(1.95 \times 10^2 \text{ cm})^3}$   (The term $\frac{4}{3}$ is exact.)

(b) $\dfrac{(1.84 \times 10^2 \text{ g})(44.7 \text{ m/s})^2}{2}$   (The term 2 is exact.)

(c) $\dfrac{(1.07 \times 10^{-4} \text{ mol/L})^2(3.8 \times 10^{-3} \text{ mol/L})}{(8.35 \times 10^{-5} \text{ mol/L})(1.48 \times 10^{-2} \text{ mol/L})^3}$

**1.68** Which statements include exact numbers?
(a) Angel Falls is 3212 ft high.
(b) There are 8 known planets in the Solar System.
(c) There are 453.59 g in 1 lb.
(d) There are 1000 mm in 1 m.

**1.69** Which of the following include exact numbers?
(a) The speed of light in a vacuum is a physical constant; to six significant figures, it is $2.99792 \times 10^8$ m/s.
(b) The density of mercury at 25°C is 13.53 g/mL.
(c) There are 3600 s in 1 h.
(d) In 2003, the United States had 50 states.

**Problems in Context**

**1.70** How long is the metal strip shown below? Be sure to answer with the correct number of significant figures.

**1.71** These organic solvents are used to clean compact discs:

| Solvent | Density (g/mL) at 20°C |
|---------|------------------------|
| Chloroform | 1.492 |
| Diethyl ether | 0.714 |
| Ethanol | 0.789 |
| Isopropanol | 0.785 |
| Toluene | 0.867 |

(a) If a 15.00-mL sample of CD cleaner weighs 11.775 g at 20°C, which solvent does the sample most likely contain?
(b) The chemist analyzing the cleaner calibrates her equipment and finds that the pipet is accurate to $\pm0.02$ mL, and the balance is accurate to $\pm0.003$ g. Is this equipment precise enough to distinguish between ethanol and isopropanol?

**1.72** A laboratory instructor gives a sample of amino-acid powder to each of four students, I, II, III, and IV, and they weigh the samples. The true value is 8.72 g. Their results for three trials are
I: 8.72 g, 8.74 g, 8.70 g      II: 8.56 g, 8.77 g, 8.83 g
III: 8.50 g, 8.48 g, 8.51 g      IV: 8.41 g, 8.72 g, 8.55 g
(a) Calculate the average mass from each set of data, and tell which set is the most accurate.
(b) Precision is a measure of the average of the deviations of each piece of data from the average value. Which set of data is the most precise? Is this set also the most accurate?
(c) Which set of data is both the most accurate and the most precise?
(d) Which set of data is both the least accurate and the least precise?

**1.73** The following dartboards illustrate the types of errors often seen in measurements. The bull's-eye represents the actual value, and the darts represent the data.

Exp. I        Exp. II        Exp. III        Exp. IV

(a) Which experiments yield the same average result?
(b) Which experiment(s) display(s) high precision?
(c) Which experiment(s) display(s) high accuracy?
(d) Which experiment(s) show(s) a systematic error?

## Comprehensive Problems

**1.74** Two blank potential energy diagrams appear below. Beneath each diagram are objects to place in the diagram. Draw the objects on the dashed lines to indicate higher or lower potential energy and label each case as more or less stable:

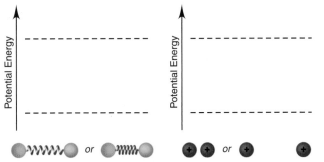

(a) Two balls attached to a relaxed *or* a compressed spring

(b) Two positive charges near *or* apart from each other

**1.75** The scenes below illustrate two different mixtures. When mixture A at 273 K is heated to 473 K, mixture B results.

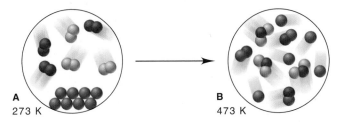

(a) How many different chemical changes occur?
(b) How many different physical changes occur?

**1.76** Bromine is used to prepare the pesticide methyl bromide and flame retardants for plastic electronic housings. It is recovered from seawater, underground brines, and the Dead Sea. The average concentrations of bromine in seawater ($d$ = 1.024 g/mL) and the Dead Sea ($d$ = 1.22 g/mL) are 0.065 g/L and 0.50 g/L, respectively. What is the mass ratio of bromine in the Dead Sea to that in seawater?

**1.77** An Olympic-size pool is 50.0 m long and 25.0 m wide. (a) How many gallons of water ($d$ = 1.0 g/mL) are needed to fill the pool to an average depth of 4.8 ft? (b) What is the mass (in kg) of water in the pool?

**1.78** At room temperature (20°C) and pressure, the density of air is 1.189 g/L. An object will float in air if its density is less than that of air. In a buoyancy experiment with a new plastic, a chemist creates a rigid, thin-walled ball that weighs 0.12 g and has a volume of 560 cm³.
(a) Will the ball float if it is evacuated?
(b) Will it float if filled with carbon dioxide ($d$ = 1.830 g/L)?
(c) Will it float if filled with hydrogen ($d$ = 0.0899 g/L)?
(d) Will it float if filled with oxygen ($d$ = 1.330 g/L)?
(e) Will it float if filled with nitrogen ($d$ = 1.165 g/L)?
(f) For any case in which the ball will float, how much weight must be added to make it sink?

**1.79** Asbestos is a fibrous silicate mineral with remarkably high tensile strength. But it is no longer used because airborne asbestos particles can cause lung cancer. Grunerite, a type of asbestos, has a tensile strength of $3.5 \times 10^2$ kg/mm² (thus, a strand of grunerite with a 1-mm² cross-sectional area can hold up to $3.5 \times 10^2$ kg). The tensile strengths of aluminum and Steel No. 5137 are $2.5 \times 10^4$ lb/in² and $5.0 \times 10^4$ lb/in², respectively. Calculate the cross-sectional areas (in mm²) of wires of aluminum and of Steel No. 5137 that have the same tensile strength as a fiber of grunerite with a cross-sectional area of 1.0 μm².

**1.80** Earth's oceans have an average depth of 3800 m, a total surface area of $3.63 \times 10^8$ km², and an average concentration of dissolved gold of $5.8 \times 10^{-9}$ g/L. (a) How many grams of gold are in the oceans? (b) How many cubic meters of gold are in the oceans? (c) Assuming the price of gold is \$370.00/troy oz, what is the value of gold in the oceans (1 troy oz = 31.1 g; $d$ of gold = 19.3 g/cm³)?

**1.81** Brass is an alloy of copper and zinc. Varying the mass percentages of the two metals produces brasses with different properties. A brass called *yellow zinc* has high ductility and strength and is 34%–37% zinc by mass. (a) Find the mass range (in g) of copper in 185 g of yellow zinc. (b) What is the mass range (in g) of zinc in a sample of yellow zinc that contains 46.5 g of copper?

**1.82** Liquid nitrogen is obtained from liquefied air and is used industrially to prepare frozen foods. It boils at 77.36 K. (a) What is this temperature in °C? (b) What is this temperature in °F? (c) At the boiling point, the density of the liquid is 809 g/L and that of the gas is 4.566 g/L. How many liters of liquid nitrogen are produced when 895.0 L of nitrogen gas is liquefied at 77.36 K?

**1.83** A jogger runs at an average speed of 5.9 mi/h. (a) How fast is she running in m/s? (b) How many kilometers does she run in 98 min? (c) If she starts a run at 11:15 am, what time is it after she covers $4.75 \times 10^4$ ft?

**1.84** Scenes A and B depict changes in matter at the atomic scale:

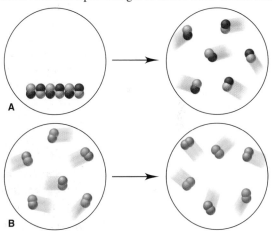

(a) Which show(s) a physical change? (b) Which show(s) a chemical change? (c) Which result(s) in different physical properties? (d) Which result(s) in different chemical properties? (e) Which result(s) in a change in state?

**1.85** If a temperature scale were based on the freezing point (5.5°C) and boiling point (80.1°C) of benzene and the temperature difference between these points was divided into 50 units (called °X), what would be the freezing and boiling points of water in °X? (See Figure 1.11, p. 23.)

**1.86** Earth's surface area is $5.10 \times 10^8$ km²; its crust has a mean thickness of 35 km and a mean density of 2.8 g/cm³. The two most abundant elements in the crust are oxygen ($4.55 \times 10^5$ g/t, where t stands for "metric ton"; 1 t = 1000 kg) and silicon ($2.72 \times 10^5$ g/t), and the two rarest nonradioactive elements are ruthenium and rhodium, each with an abundance of $1 \times 10^{-4}$ g/t. What is the total mass of each of these elements in Earth's crust?

# The Components of Matter

## Concepts and skills to review before you study this chapter

- physical and chemical change (Section 1.1)
- states of matter (Section 1.1)
- attraction and repulsion between charged particles (Section 1.1)
- meaning of a scientific model (Section 1.3)
- SI units and conversion factors (Section 1.5)
- significant figures in calculations (Section 1.6)

Look closely at almost any sample of matter—a rock, a piece of wood, a butterfly wing—and you'll see that it's made of smaller parts. With a microscope, you'll see still smaller parts. And, if you could zoom in a billion times closer, you'd find, on the atomic scale, the ultimate particles that make up all things.

Modern scientists are certainly not the first to wonder what things are made of. The philosophers of ancient Greece did too, and most believed that everything was made of one or, at most, a few elemental substances (elements), whose hotness, wetness, hardness, and other properties gave rise to the properties of everything else. Democritus (c. 460–370 BC), the father of atomism, took a different approach, and his reasoning went something like this: if you cut a piece of, say, aluminum foil smaller and smaller, you must eventually reach a particle of aluminum so small that it can no longer be cut. Therefore, matter is ultimately composed of indivisible particles with nothing but empty space between them. He called the particles *atoms* (Greek *atomos,* "uncuttable") and proclaimed: "According to convention, there is a sweet and a bitter, a hot and a cold, and . . . there is order. In truth, there are atoms and a void." But, Aristotle, one of the greatest and most influential philosophers of Western culture, said it was impossible for "nothing" to exist, and the concept of atoms was suppressed for 2000 years.

Finally, in the 17th century, the English scientist Robert Boyle argued that, by definition, an element is composed of "simple Bodies, not made of any other Bodies, of which all mixed Bodies are compounded, and into which they are ultimately resolved," a description remarkably close to our idea of an element, with atoms being the "simple Bodies." The next two centuries saw rapid progress in chemistry and the development of a "billiard-ball" image of the atom. Then, an early 20th-century burst of creativity led to our current model of an atom with a complex internal structure.

**IN THIS CHAPTER . . .** We examine the properties and composition of matter on the macroscopic and atomic scales.

- We relate the three types of matter—elements, compounds, and mixtures—to the chemical entities they consist of—atoms, ions, and molecules.
- We see how the defining properties of the types of matter relate to laws discovered in the 18th century concerning the masses of substances that react with each other.
- We examine the 19th-century atomic model proposed to explain these laws.
- We describe some 20th-century experiments that led to our current understanding of atomic structure and atomic mass.
- We focus on how the elements are organized in the periodic table and introduce the two major ways that elements combine.
- We derive names and formulas of compounds and calculate their masses.
- We examine the models chemists use to depict molecules.
- We classify mixtures and see how to separate them.
- We present a final overview of the components of matter.

## 2.1 • ELEMENTS, COMPOUNDS, AND MIXTURES: AN ATOMIC OVERVIEW

Matter can be classified into three types based on its composition—elements, compounds, and mixtures. Elements and compounds are the two kinds of substances: a **substance** is matter whose composition is fixed. Mixtures are not substances because they have a variable composition.

1. *Elements.* An **element** is the simplest type of matter with unique physical and chemical properties. *It consists of only one kind of atom* and, therefore, cannot be broken down into a simpler type of matter by any physical or chemical methods. Each element has a name, such as silicon, oxygen, or copper. A sample of silicon contains only silicon atoms. The *macroscopic* properties of a piece of silicon, such as color, density, and combustibility, are different from those of a piece of copper because the *submicroscopic* properties of silicon atoms are different from those of copper atoms; that is, *each element is unique because the properties of its atoms are unique.*

In nature, most elements exist as populations of atoms, either separated or in contact with each other, depending on the physical state. Figure 2.1A shows atoms of an element in its gaseous state. Several elements occur in molecular form: a **molecule** is an independent structure of two or more atoms bound together (Figure 2.1B). Oxygen, for example, occurs in air as *diatomic* (two-atom) molecules.

2. *Compounds.* A **compound** consists of *two or more different elements that are bonded chemically* (Figure 2.1C). That is, the elements in a compound are not just mixed together: their atoms have joined in a chemical reaction. Many compounds, such as ammonia, water, and carbon dioxide, consist of molecules. But many others, like sodium sulfate (which we'll discuss shortly) and silicon dioxide, do not. No matter what the compound, however, one defining feature is that *the elements are present in fixed parts by mass* (fixed mass ratio). This is so because *each unit of the compound consists of a fixed number of atoms of each element.* For example, consider a sample of ammonia. It is 14 parts nitrogen by mass and 3 parts hydrogen by mass *because* 1 nitrogen atom has 14 times the mass of 1 hydrogen atom, and each ammonia molecule consists of 1 nitrogen atom and 3 hydrogen atoms:

Ammonia gas is 14 parts N by mass and 3 parts H by mass.

1 N atom has 14 times the mass of 1 H atom.

*Each ammonia molecule consists of 1 N atom and 3 H atoms.*

Another defining feature of a compound is that *its properties are different from the properties of its component elements.* Table 2.1 shows a striking example: soft, silvery sodium metal and yellow-green, poisonous chlorine gas are very different from the compound they form—white, crystalline sodium chloride, common table salt!

Unlike an element, a compound *can* be broken down into simpler substances—its component elements. For example, an electric current breaks down molten sodium chloride into metallic sodium and chlorine gas. By definition, this breakdown is a *chemical change,* not a physical one.

**Figure 2.1** Elements, compounds, and mixtures on the atomic scale. The samples depicted here are gases, but the three types of matter also occur as liquids and solids.

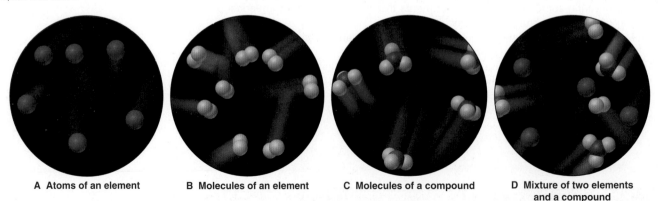

A  **Atoms of an element**          B  **Molecules of an element**          C  **Molecules of a compound**          D  **Mixture of two elements and a compound**

**Table 2.1 Some Properties of Sodium, Chlorine, and Sodium Chloride**

| Property | Sodium | + | Chlorine | ⟶ | Sodium Chloride | |
|---|---|---|---|---|---|---|
| Melting point | 97.8°C | | −101°C | | 801°C | |
| Boiling point | 881.4°C | | −34°C | | 1413°C | |
| Color | Silvery |  | Yellow-green |  | Colorless (white) |  |
| Density | 0.97 g/cm³ | | 0.0032 g/cm³ | | 2.16 g/cm³ | |
| Behavior in water | Reacts | | Dissolves slightly | | Dissolves freely | |

3. *Mixtures.* A **mixture** consists of two or more substances (elements and/or compounds) that are physically intermingled. Because a mixture is *not* a substance, in contrast to a compound, *the components of a mixture **can** vary in their parts by mass.* A mixture of the compounds sodium chloride and water, for example, can have many different parts by mass of salt to water. On the atomic scale, a mixture consists of the individual units that make up its component elements and/or compounds (Figure 2.1D). It makes sense, then, that *a mixture retains many of the properties of its components.* Saltwater, for instance, is colorless like water and tastes salty like sodium chloride.

Unlike compounds, mixtures can be separated into their components by *physical changes;* chemical changes are not needed. For example, the water in saltwater can be boiled off, a physical process that leaves behind solid sodium chloride. The following sample problem will help differentiate these types of matter.

**Sample Problem 2.1**    Distinguishing Elements, Compounds, and Mixtures at the Atomic Scale

**Problem** The scenes below represent atomic-scale views of three samples of matter:

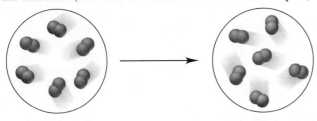

**(a)**    **(b)**    **(c)**

Describe each sample as an element, compound, or mixture.

**Plan** We have to determine the type of matter by examining the component particles. If a sample contains only one type of particle, it is either an element or a compound; if it contains more than one type, it is a mixture. Particles of an element have only one kind of atom (one color), and particles of a compound have two or more kinds of atoms.

**Solution (a)** Mixture: there are three different types of particles. Two types contain only one kind of atom, either green or purple, so they are elements, and the third type contains two red atoms for every one yellow, so it is a compound.

**(b)** Element: the sample consists of only blue atoms.

**(c)** Compound: the sample consists of molecules that each have two black and six blue atoms.

**Follow-Up Problem 2.1** Describe the following reaction in terms of elements, compounds, and mixtures. (See Brief Solutions at the end of the chapter.)

## ▮ Summary of Section 2.1

- All matter exists as either elements, compounds, or mixtures.
- Elements and compounds are substances, types of matter with a fixed composition.
- An element consists of only one type of atom and occurs as collections of individual atoms or molecules.
- A compound contains two or more elements chemically combined and exhibits different properties from its component elements. The elements occur in fixed parts by mass because each unit of the compound has a fixed number of each type of atom. Only a chemical change can break down a compound into its elements.
- A mixture consists of two or more substances mixed together, not chemically combined. The components retain their individual properties, can be present in any proportion, and can be separated by physical changes.

---

## 2.2 • THE OBSERVATIONS THAT LED TO AN ATOMIC VIEW OF MATTER

Any model of the composition of matter had to explain the *law of mass conservation* and the *law of definite (or constant) composition*. As you'll see, an atomic theory developed by John Dalton in the early 19th century explained these mass laws and another now known as the *law of multiple proportions*.

### Mass Conservation

The most fundamental chemical observation of the 18th century was the **law of mass conservation:** *the total mass of substances does not change during a chemical reaction.* The *number* of substances may change and, by definition, their properties must, but the *total amount* of matter remains constant. (Lavoisier had first stated this law on the basis of his combustion experiments.) Figure 2.2 illustrates mass conservation because the lead nitrate and sodium chromate solutions (*left*) have the same mass as the solid lead chromate in sodium nitrate solution (*right*) that forms when they react.

Even in a complex biochemical change, such as the metabolism of the sugar glucose, which involves many reactions, mass is conserved:

$$180 \text{ g glucose} + 192 \text{ g oxygen gas} \longrightarrow 264 \text{ g carbon dioxide} + 108 \text{ g water}$$
$$372 \text{ g material before} \longrightarrow 372 \text{ g material after}$$

Mass conservation means that, based on all chemical experience, *matter cannot be created or destroyed.*

To be precise about it, we now know, based on the work of Albert Einstein (1879–1955), that the mass before and after a reaction is not *exactly* the same. Some

**Figure 2.2**  The law of mass conservation.

mass is converted to energy, or vice versa, but the difference is too small to measure, even with the best balance. For example, when 100 g of carbon burns, the carbon dioxide formed weighs 0.000000036 g ($3.6 \times 10^{-8}$ g) less than the carbon and oxygen that reacted. Because the energy changes of *chemical* reactions are so small, for all practical purposes, mass *is* conserved. Later in the text, you'll see that energy changes in *nuclear* reactions are so large that mass changes are easy to measure.

## Definite Composition

The sodium chloride in your salt shaker is the same substance whether it comes from a salt mine, a salt flat, or any other source. This fact is expressed in the **law of definite (or constant) composition,** which states that *no matter what its source, a particular compound is composed of the same elements in the same parts (fractions) by mass.* The **fraction by mass (mass fraction)** is the part of the compound's mass that each element contributes. It is obtained by dividing the mass of each element by the mass of the compound. The **percent by mass (mass percent, mass %)** is the fraction by mass expressed as a percentage (multiplied by 100).

For an everyday example, consider a box that contains three types of marbles (*right*): yellow ones weigh 1.0 g each, purple 2.0 g each, and red 3.0 g each. Each type makes up a fraction of the total mass of marbles, 16.0 g. The *mass fraction* of yellow marbles is their number times their mass divided by the total mass: ($3 \times 1.0$ g)/16.0 g = 0.19. The *mass percent* (parts per 100 parts) of yellow marbles is 0.19 × 100 = 19% by mass. The purple marbles have a mass fraction of 0.25 and are 25% by mass of the total, and the red marbles have a mass fraction of 0.56 and are 56% by mass.

16.0 g marbles

Similarly, in a compound, each element has a *fixed* mass fraction (and mass percent). For example, calcium carbonate, the major compound in seashells, marble, and coral is composed of three elements—calcium, carbon, and oxygen. The following results are obtained from a mass analysis of 20.0 g of calcium carbonate:

| Analysis by Mass (grams/20.0 g) | Mass Fraction (parts/1.00 part) | Percent by Mass (parts/100 parts) |
|---|---|---|
| 8.0 g calcium | 0.40 calcium | 40% calcium |
| 2.4 g carbon | 0.12 carbon | 12% carbon |
| 9.6 g oxygen | 0.48 oxygen | 48% oxygen |
| 20.0 g | 1.00 part by mass | 100% by mass |

The mass of each element depends on the mass of the sample—that is, more than 20.0 g of compound would contain more than 8.0 g of calcium—but *the mass fraction is fixed no matter what the size of the sample.* The sum of the mass fractions (or mass percents) equals 1.00 part (or 100%) by mass. The law of definite composition tells us that pure samples of calcium carbonate, no matter where they come from, always contain 40% calcium, 12% carbon, and 48% oxygen by mass (Figure 2.3).

Because a given element always constitutes the same mass fraction of a given compound, we can use that mass fraction to find the actual mass of the element in any sample of the compound:

$$\text{Mass of element} = \text{mass of compound} \times \frac{\text{part by mass of element}}{\text{one part by mass of compound}}$$

Or, more simply, we can skip the need to find the mass fraction first and use the results of mass analysis directly:

$$\text{Mass of element in sample} = \text{mass of compound in sample} \times \frac{\text{mass of element in compound}}{\text{mass of compound}} \qquad (2.1)$$

**CALCIUM CARBONATE**
40 mass % calcium
12 mass % carbon
48 mass % oxygen

**Figure 2.3 The law of definite composition.** Calcium carbonate occurs in many forms (such as marble, *top,* and coral, *bottom*), but the mass percents of its elements are always the same.

**Road Map**

| Mass (kg) of pitchblende |
| --- |

↓ multiply by mass ratio of uranium
to pitchblende from analysis

| Mass (kg) of uranium |
| --- |

↓ 1 kg = 1000 g

| Mass (g) of uranium |
| --- |

## Sample Problem 2.2    Calculating the Mass of an Element in a Compound

**Problem** Pitchblende is the most important compound of uranium. Mass analysis of an 84.2-g sample shows that it contains 71.4 g of uranium, with oxygen the only other element. How many grams of uranium are in 102 kg of pitchblende?

**Plan** We have to find the mass of uranium in a known mass (102 kg) of pitchblende, given the mass of uranium (71.4 g) in a different mass of pitchblende (84.2 g). The mass ratio of uranium to pitchblende is the same for any sample of pitchblende. Therefore, using Equation 2.1, we multiply the mass (in kg) of the pitchblende sample by the ratio of uranium to pitchblende from the mass analysis. This gives the mass (in kg) of uranium, and we convert kilograms to grams.

**Solution** Finding the mass (kg) of uranium in 102 kg of pitchblende:

$$\text{Mass (kg) of uranium} = \text{mass (kg) of pitchblende} \times \frac{\text{mass (kg) of uranium in pitchblende}}{\text{mass (kg) of pitchblende}}$$

$$= 102 \text{ kg pitchblende} \times \frac{71.4 \text{ kg uranium}}{84.2 \text{ kg pitchblende}} = 86.5 \text{ kg uranium}$$

Converting the mass of uranium from kg to g:

$$\text{Mass (g) of uranium} = 86.5 \text{ kg uranium} \times \frac{1000 \text{ g}}{1 \text{ kg}} = \boxed{8.65 \times 10^4 \text{ g uranium}}$$

**Check** The analysis showed that most of the mass of pitchblende is due to uranium, so the large mass of uranium makes sense. Rounding off to check the math gives:

$$\sim 100 \text{ kg pitchblende} \times \frac{70}{85} = 82 \text{ kg uranium}$$

**Follow-Up Problem 2.2** How many metric tons (t) of oxygen are combined in a sample of pitchblende that contains 2.3 t of uranium? (*Hint:* Remember that oxygen is the only other element present.) See Brief Solutions.

## Multiple Proportions

An observation that applies when two elements form more than one compound is now called the **law of multiple proportions:** *if elements A and B react to form two compounds, the different masses of B that combine with a fixed mass of A can be expressed as a ratio of small whole numbers.* Consider two compounds, let's call them I and II, that carbon and oxygen form. These compounds have very different properties: the density of carbon oxide I is 1.25 g/L, whereas that of II is 1.98 g/L; I is poisonous and flammable, but II is not. Mass analysis shows that

Carbon oxide I is 57.1 mass % oxygen and 42.9 mass % carbon
Carbon oxide II is 72.7 mass % oxygen and 27.3 mass % carbon

To see the phenomenon of multiple proportions, we use the mass percents of oxygen and of carbon to find their masses in a given mass, say 100 g, of each compound. Then we divide the mass of oxygen by the mass of carbon in each compound to obtain the mass of oxygen that combines with a fixed mass of carbon:

|  | Carbon Oxide I | Carbon Oxide II |
| --- | --- | --- |
| g oxygen/100 g compound | 57.1 | 72.7 |
| g carbon/100 g compound | 42.9 | 27.3 |
| g oxygen/g carbon | $\dfrac{57.1}{42.9} = 1.33$ | $\dfrac{72.7}{27.3} = 2.66$ |

If we then divide the grams of oxygen per gram of carbon in II by that in I, we obtain a ratio of small whole numbers:

$$\frac{2.66 \text{ g oxygen/g carbon in II}}{1.33 \text{ g oxygen/g carbon in I}} = \frac{2}{1}$$

The law of multiple proportions tells us that in two compounds of the same elements, the mass fraction of one element relative to the other element changes in *increments based on ratios of small whole numbers.* In this case, the ratio is 2/1—for a given mass of carbon, compound II contains *2 times* as much oxygen as I, not 1.583 times, 1.716 times, or any other intermediate amount. In the next section, we'll explain the mass laws on the atomic scale.

## ■ Summary of Section 2.2

- The law of mass conservation states that the total mass remains constant during a chemical reaction.
- The law of definite composition states that any sample of a given compound has the same elements present in the same parts by mass.
- The law of multiple proportions states that, in different compounds of the same elements, the masses of one element that combine with a fixed mass of the other can be expressed as a ratio of small whole numbers.

---

# 2.3 • DALTON'S ATOMIC THEORY

With 200 years of hindsight, it may be easy to see how the mass laws could be explained by an atomic model—matter existing in indestructible units, each with a particular mass—but it was a major breakthrough in 1808 when John Dalton (1766–1844) presented his atomic theory of matter in *A New System of Chemical Philosophy.*

Despite having no formal education, Dalton began teaching science at age 12 and then studied color blindness, a personal affliction still known as *daltonism.* At 21, he started recording daily weather data and continued this project for the rest of his life. His results on humidity and dew point led to a key discovery about gases (Section 5.4) and eventually to his atomic theory.

## Postulates of the Atomic Theory

Dalton expressed his theory in a series of postulates. Like most great thinkers, he integrated the ideas of others into his own. As we go through the postulates, presented here in modern terms, let's see which were original and which came from others.

1. All matter consists of **atoms,** tiny indivisible particles of an element that cannot be created or destroyed. (This derives from the "eternal, indestructible atoms" proposed by Democritus more than 2000 years earlier and reflects mass conservation as stated by Lavoisier.)
2. Atoms of one element *cannot* be converted into atoms of another element. In chemical reactions, the atoms of the original substances recombine to form different substances. (This rejects the alchemical belief in the magical transmutation of elements.)
3. Atoms of an element are identical in mass and other properties and are different from atoms of any other element. (This contains Dalton's major new ideas: *unique mass and properties* for the atoms of a given element.)
4. Compounds result from the chemical combination of a specific ratio of atoms of different elements. (This follows directly from the law of definite composition.)

## How the Theory Explains the Mass Laws

Let's see how Dalton's postulates explain the mass laws:

- *Mass conservation.* Atoms cannot be created or destroyed (postulate 1) or converted into other types of atoms (postulate 2). Therefore, a chemical reaction, in which atoms are combined differently, cannot possibly result in a mass change.
- *Definite composition.* A compound is a combination of a *specific* ratio of different atoms (postulate 4), each of which has a particular mass (postulate 3). Thus, each element in a compound constitutes a fixed fraction of the total mass.
- *Multiple proportions.* Atoms of an element have the same mass (postulate 3) and are indivisible (postulate 1). The masses of element B that combine with a fixed mass of element A give a small, whole-number ratio because different numbers of B atoms combine with each A atom in different compounds.

The *simplest* arrangement consistent with the mass data for carbon oxides I and II in our earlier example is that one atom of oxygen combines with one atom of carbon in compound I (carbon monoxide) and that two atoms of oxygen combine with one atom of carbon in compound II (carbon dioxide):

Carbon oxide I
(carbon monoxide)

Carbon oxide II
(carbon dioxide)

Let's work through a sample problem that reviews the mass laws.

### Sample Problem 2.3 | Visualizing the Mass Laws

**Problem** The scenes below represent an atomic-scale view of a chemical reaction:

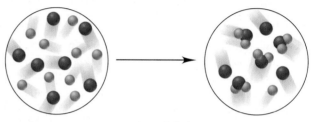

Which of the mass laws—mass conservation, definite composition, or multiple proportions—is (are) illustrated?

**Plan** From the depictions, we note the numbers, colors, and combinations of atoms (spheres) to see which mass laws pertain. If the numbers of each atom are the same before and after the reaction, the total mass did not change (mass conservation). If a compound forms that always has the same atom ratio, the elements are present in fixed parts by mass (definite composition). When the same elements form different compounds and the ratio of the atoms of one element that combine with one atom of the other element is a small whole number, the ratio of their masses is a small whole number as well (multiple proportions).

**Solution** There are seven purple and nine green atoms in each circle, so mass is conserved. The compound formed has one purple and two green atoms, so it has definite composition. Only one compound forms, so the law of multiple proportions does not pertain.

**Follow-Up Problem 2.3** Which sample(s) best display(s) the fact that compounds of bromine (orange) and fluorine (yellow) exhibit the law of multiple proportions? Explain.

A          B          C

## Summary of Section 2.3

- Dalton's atomic theory explained the mass laws by proposing that all matter consists of indivisible, unchangeable atoms of fixed, unique mass.
- Mass is conserved during a reaction because the atoms retain their identities but are combined differently.
- Each compound has a fixed mass fraction of each of its elements because it is composed of a fixed number of each type of atom.
- Different compounds of the same elements exhibit multiple proportions because they each consist of whole atoms.

# 2.4 • THE OBSERVATIONS THAT LED TO THE NUCLEAR ATOM MODEL

Dalton's model established that masses of reacting elements could be explained in terms of atoms but not why atoms bond as they do: why, for example, do two, and not three, hydrogen atoms bond with one oxygen atom in a water molecule?

Moreover, Dalton's "billiard ball" model of the atom did not predict the existence of subatomic charged particles, which were observed in later experiments that led to the discovery of *electrons* and the atomic *nucleus*. Let's examine some of these experiments and the more complex atomic model that emerged from them.

## Discovery of the Electron and Its Properties

For many years, scientists had known that matter and electric charge were related. When amber is rubbed with fur, or glass with silk, positive and negative charges form—the same charges that make your hair crackle and cling to your comb on a dry day. They also knew that an electric current could decompose certain compounds into their elements. But they did not know what a current was made of.

**Cathode Rays** To discover the nature of an electric current, some investigators tried passing current through nearly evacuated glass tubes fitted with metal electrodes. When the electric power source was turned on, a "ray" could be seen striking the phosphor-coated end of the tube and emitting a glowing spot of light. The rays were called **cathode rays** because they originated at the negative electrode (cathode) and moved to the positive electrode (anode).

Figure 2.4 shows some properties of cathode rays based on these observations. The main conclusion was that *cathode rays consist of negatively charged particles found in all matter.* The rays appear when these particles collide with the few remaining gas molecules in the evacuated tube. Cathode ray particles were later named *electrons*. There are many familiar cases of the effects of charged particles colliding with gases or hitting a phosphor-coated screen:

- In a "neon" sign, electrons collide with the gas particles in the tube, causing them to give off light.
- The aurora borealis, or northern lights (*see photo*), occurs when Earth's magnetic field bends streams of charged particles coming from the Sun, which then collide with gas particles in the atmosphere to give off light.
- In older televisions and computer monitors, the cathode ray passes back and forth over the coated screen, creating a pattern that we see as a picture.

Why do the northern lights glow?

| OBSERVATION | CONCLUSION |
|---|---|
| 1. Ray bends in magnetic field. | Consists of charged particles |
| 2. Ray bends toward positive plate in electric field. | Consists of negative particles |
| 3. Ray is identical for any cathode. | Particles found in all matter |

**Figure 2.4** Observations that established the properties of cathode rays.

**Mass and Charge of the Electron** Two classic experiments and their conclusion revealed the mass and charge of the electron:

1. *Mass/charge ratio.* In 1897, the British physicist J. J. Thomson (1856–1940) measured the ratio of the mass of a cathode ray particle to its charge. By comparing this value with the mass/charge ratio for the lightest charged particle in solution, Thomson estimated that the cathode ray particle weighed less than $\frac{1}{1000}$ as much as hydrogen, the lightest atom! He was shocked because this implied that, contrary to Dalton's atomic theory, *atoms contain even smaller particles.* Fellow scientists reacted with disbelief to Thomson's conclusion, thinking he was joking.

2. *Charge.* In 1909, the American physicist Robert Millikan (1868–1953) measured the *charge* of the electron. He did so by observing the movement of oil droplets in an apparatus that contained electrically charged plates and an x-ray source (Figure 2.5). X-rays knocked electrons from gas molecules in the air within the apparatus, and the electrons stuck to an oil droplet falling through a hole in a positively charged plate. With the electric field off, Millikan measured the mass of the droplet from its rate of fall. Then, by adjusting the field's strength, he made the droplet hang suspended in the air and, thus, measured its total charge.

**Figure 2.5** Millikan's oil-drop experiment for measuring an electron's charge. The total charge on an oil droplet is some whole-number multiple of the charge of the electron.

Fine mist of oil is sprayed into apparatus.

Oil droplets fall through hole in positively charged plate.

X-rays knock electrons from air molecules, and they stick to droplets.

Electrically charged plates influence droplet's motion.

Observer times droplet's motion and controls electric field.

X-ray source

After many tries, Millikan found that the total charge of the various droplets was always some *whole-number multiple of a minimum charge.* If different oil droplets picked up different numbers of electrons, he reasoned that this minimum charge must be the charge of the electron itself. Remarkably, the value that he calculated over a century ago was within 1% of the modern value of the electron's charge, $-1.602\times10^{-19}$ C (C stands for *coulomb,* the SI unit of charge).

3. *Conclusion: calculating the electron's mass.* The electron's mass/charge ratio from work by Thomson and others and the value for the electron's charge can be used to find the electron's mass, which is *extremely* small:

$$\text{Mass of electron} = \frac{\text{mass}}{\cancel{\text{charge}}} \times \cancel{\text{charge}} = \left(-5.686\times10^{-12}\,\frac{\text{kg}}{\cancel{\text{C}}}\right)(-1.602\times10^{-19}\,\cancel{\text{C}})$$
$$= 9.109\times10^{-31}\,\text{kg} = 9.109\times10^{-28}\,\text{g}$$

## Discovery of the Atomic Nucleus

The presence of electrons in all matter posed some major questions about the structure of atoms. Matter is electrically neutral, so atoms must be also. But if atoms contain negatively charged electrons, what positive charges balance them? And if an electron has such a tiny mass, what accounts for an atom's much larger mass? To address these issues, Thomson proposed his "plum-pudding" model—a spherical atom composed of diffuse, positively charged matter with electrons embedded like "raisins in a plum pudding."

In 1910, New Zealand–born physicist Ernest Rutherford (1871–1937) tested this model and obtained an unexpected result (Figure 2.6):

1. *Experimental design.* Figure 2.6B shows the experimental setup, in which tiny, dense, positively charged alpha ($\alpha$) particles emitted from radium are aimed at gold foil. A circular, zinc-sulfide screen registers the deflection (scattering) of the $\alpha$ particles by emitting light flashes when the particles strike it.
2. *Expected results.* With Thomson's model in mind (Figure 2.6A), Rutherford expected only minor, if any, deflections of the $\alpha$ particles because they should act as bullets and go right through the gold atoms. After all, an electron would not deflect an $\alpha$ particle any more than a Ping-Pong ball would deflect a baseball.
3. *Actual results.* Initial results were consistent with this idea, but then the unexpected happened (Figure 2.6C). As Rutherford recalled: "I remember two or three days later Geiger [one of his coworkers] coming to me in great excitement and saying, 'We have been able to get some of the $\alpha$ particles coming backwards . . .' It was quite the most incredible event that has ever happened to me in my life. It was almost as incredible as if you fired a 15-inch shell at a piece of tissue paper and it came back and hit you." In fact, very few $\alpha$ particles were deflected at all, and only 1 in 20,000 was deflected by more than 90° ("coming backwards").
4. *Rutherford's conclusion.* Rutherford concluded that these few $\alpha$ particles were being repelled by something small, dense, and positive within the gold atoms. Calculations based on the mass, charge, and velocity of the $\alpha$ particles and the proportion of these large-angle deflections showed that
   - An atom is mostly space occupied by electrons.
   - In the center is a tiny region, which Rutherford called the **nucleus,** that contains all the positive charge and essentially all the mass of the atom.

   He proposed that positive particles lay within the nucleus and called them *protons.*

Rutherford's model explained the charged nature of matter, but it could not account for all the atom's mass. After more than 20 years, in 1932, James Chadwick discovered the *neutron,* an uncharged dense particle that also resides in the nucleus.

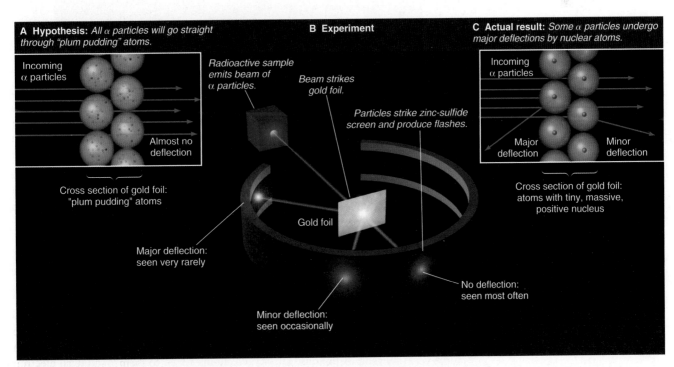

**Figure 2.6** Rutherford's $\alpha$-scattering experiment and discovery of the atomic nucleus.

## Summary of Section 2.4

- Several major discoveries at the turn of the 20th century resolved questions about Dalton's model and led to our current model of atomic structure.
- Cathode rays were shown to consist of negative particles (electrons) that exist in all matter. J. J. Thomson measured their mass/charge ratio and concluded that they are much smaller and lighter than atoms.
- Robert Millikan determined the charge of the electron, which he combined with other data to calculate its mass.
- Ernest Rutherford proposed that atoms consist of a tiny, massive, positive nucleus surrounded by electrons.

# 2.5 • THE ATOMIC THEORY TODAY

Dalton's model of an indivisible particle has given way to our current model of an atom with an elaborate internal architecture of subatomic particles. In this section, we examine that model and see how Dalton's theory stands up today.

## Structure of the Atom

An *atom* is an electrically neutral, spherical entity composed of a positively charged central nucleus surrounded by one or more negatively charged electrons (Figure 2.7). The electrons move rapidly within the available volume, held there by the attraction of the nucleus. An atom's diameter ($\sim 1 \times 10^{-10}$ m) is about 20,000 times the diameter of its nucleus ($\sim 5 \times 10^{-15}$ m). The nucleus contributes 99.97% of the atom's mass, occupies only about 1 quadrillionth of its volume, and is incredibly dense: about $10^{14}$ g/mL! ●

**The Tiny, Massive Nucleus** A few analogies can help you grasp the incredible properties of the atomic nucleus. A nucleus the size of the period at the end of a sentence would weigh about 100 tons, as much as 50 cars! An atom the size of the Houston Astrodome would have a nucleus the size of a green pea that would contain virtually all its mass. If the nucleus were the size depicted at the right in Figure 2.7 (about 1 cm across), the atom would be about 200 m across, or more than the length of two football fields!

**Figure 2.7** General features of the atom.

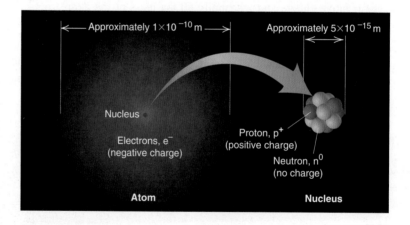

An *atomic nucleus consists of protons and neutrons* (the only exception is the simplest hydrogen nucleus, which is a single proton). The **proton (p⁺)** has a positive charge, and the **neutron (n⁰)** has no charge; thus, the positive charge of the nucleus results from its protons. The *magnitudes* of the charges possessed by a proton and by an **electron (e⁻)** are equal, but the *signs* of the charges are opposite. *An atom is neutral because the number of protons in the nucleus equals the number of electrons surrounding the nucleus.* Some properties of these three subatomic particles are listed in Table 2.2 on the next page.

## Atomic Number, Mass Number, and Atomic Symbol

The **atomic number (Z)** of an element equals the number of protons in the nucleus of each of its atoms. *All atoms of an element have the same atomic number, and the atomic number of each element is different from that of any other element.* All carbon atoms (Z = 6) have 6 protons, all oxygen atoms (Z = 8) have 8 protons, and all

## Table 2.2 Properties of the Three Key Subatomic Properties

| Name (Symbol) | Charge | | Mass | | Location in Atom |
|---|---|---|---|---|---|
| | Relative | Absolute (C)* | Relative (amu)† | Absolute (g) | |
| Proton ($p^+$) | 1+ | $+1.60218\times10^{-19}$ | 1.00727 | $1.67262\times10^{-24}$ | Nucleus |
| Neutron ($n^0$) | 0 | 0 | 1.00866 | $1.67493\times10^{-24}$ | Nucleus |
| Electron ($e^-$) | 1− | $-1.60218\times10^{-19}$ | 0.00054858 | $9.10939\times10^{-24}$ | Outside nucleus |

*The coulomb (C) is the SI unit of charge.
†The atomic mass unit (amu) equals $1.66054\times10^{-24}$ g; discussed later in this section.

**Figure 2.8** The $_{Z}^{A}X$ notations and spherical representations for four atoms. (The nuclei are not drawn to scale.)

uranium atoms ($Z = 92$) have 92 protons. There are currently 117 known elements, of which 90 occur in nature and 27 have been synthesized by nuclear scientists.

The **mass number ($A$)** is the total number of protons and neutrons in the nucleus of an atom. Each proton and each neutron contributes one unit to the mass number. Thus, a carbon atom with 6 protons and 6 neutrons in its nucleus has a mass number of 12, and a uranium atom with 92 protons and 146 neutrons in its nucleus has a mass number of 238.

The **atomic symbol** (or *element symbol*) of an element is based on its English, Latin, or Greek name, such as C for carbon, S for sulfur, and Na for sodium (Latin *natrium*). Often written with the symbol are the atomic number ($Z$) as a left *sub*script and the mass number ($A$) as a left *super*script, so element X would be $_{Z}^{A}X$. Since the mass number is the sum of protons and neutrons, the number of neutrons ($N$) equals the mass number minus the atomic number:

$$\text{Number of neutrons} = \text{mass number} - \text{atomic number,} \quad \text{or} \quad N = A - Z \quad \textbf{(2.2)}$$

Thus, a chlorine atom, symbolized $_{17}^{35}Cl$, has $A = 35$, $Z = 17$, and $N = 35 - 17 = 18$. Because each element has its own atomic number, we also know the atomic number given the symbol. For example, instead of writing $_{6}^{12}C$ for carbon with mass number 12, we can write $^{12}C$ (spoken "carbon twelve"), with $Z = 6$ understood. Another way to name this atom is carbon-12.

### Isotopes

*All atoms of an element have the same atomic number but not the same mass number.* **Isotopes** of an element are atoms that have *different numbers of neutrons* and therefore different mass numbers. For example, all carbon atoms ($Z = 6$) have 6 protons and 6 electrons, but only 98.89% of naturally occurring carbon atoms have 6 neutrons ($A = 12$). A small percentage (1.11%) have 7 neutrons ($A = 13$), and even fewer (less than 0.01%) have 8 ($A = 14$). These are carbon's three naturally occurring isotopes—$^{12}C$, $^{13}C$, and $^{14}C$. *A natural sample of carbon has these three isotopes in these relative proportions.* Five other carbon isotopes—$^{9}C$, $^{10}C$, $^{11}C$, $^{15}C$, and $^{16}C$—have been created in the laboratory. Figure 2.8 depicts the atomic number, mass number, and symbol for four atoms, two of which are isotopes of the element uranium.

The chemical properties of an element are primarily determined by the number of electrons, so *all isotopes of an element have nearly identical chemical behavior,* even though they have different masses.

## Sample Problem 2.4  Determining the Number of Subatomic Particles in the Isotopes of an Element

**Problem** Silicon (Si) is a major component of semiconductor chips. It has three naturally occurring isotopes: $^{28}Si$, $^{29}Si$, and $^{30}Si$. Determine the numbers of protons, neutrons, and electrons in each silicon isotope.

**Plan** The mass number ($A$; left superscript) of each of the three isotopes is given, which is the sum of protons and neutrons. From the elements list on the text's inside front cover, we find the atomic number ($Z$, number of protons), which equals the number of electrons. We obtain the number of neutrons by subtracting $Z$ from $A$ (Equation 2.2).

**Solution** From the elements list, the atomic number of silicon is 14. Therefore,

$$^{28}\text{Si has } 14\text{p}^+, 14\text{e}^-, \text{ and } 14\text{n}^0 (28 - 14)$$
$$^{29}\text{Si has } 14\text{p}^+, 14\text{e}^-, \text{ and } 15\text{n}^0 (29 - 14)$$
$$^{30}\text{Si has } 14\text{p}^+, 14\text{e}^-, \text{ and } 16\text{n}^0 (30 - 14)$$

**Follow-Up Problem 2.4** How many protons, neutrons, and electrons are in **(a)** $^{11}_{5}\text{Q}$? **(b)** $^{41}_{20}\text{R}$? **(c)** $^{131}_{53}\text{X}$? What elements do Q, R, and X represent?

## Atomic Masses of the Elements

The mass of an atom is measured *relative* to the mass of an atomic standard. The modern standard is the carbon-12 atom, whose mass is defined as *exactly* 12 atomic mass units. Thus, the **atomic mass unit (amu)** is $\frac{1}{12}$ the mass of a carbon-12 atom. Based on this standard, the $^1\text{H}$ atom has a mass of 1.008 amu; in other words, a $^{12}\text{C}$ atom has almost 12 times the mass of an $^1\text{H}$ atom. We will continue to use the term *atomic mass unit* in the text, although the name of the unit has been changed to the **dalton (Da)**; thus, one $^{12}\text{C}$ atom has a mass of 12 daltons (12 Da, or 12 amu). The atomic mass unit is a unit of relative mass, but it has an absolute mass of $1.66054 \times 10^{-24}$ g.

The isotopic makeup of an element is determined by **mass spectrometry,** a method for measuring the relative masses and abundances of atomic-scale particles very precisely (which we discuss in the Tools of the Laboratory essay). For example, using a mass spectrometer, we measure the mass ratio of $^{28}\text{Si}$ to $^{12}\text{C}$ as

$$\frac{\text{Mass of } ^{28}\text{Si atom}}{\text{Mass of } ^{12}\text{C standard}} = 2.331411$$

From this mass ratio, we find the **isotopic mass** of the $^{28}\text{Si}$ atom, the relative mass of this silicon isotope:

$$\text{Isotopic mass of } ^{28}\text{Si} = \text{measured mass ratio} \times \text{mass of } ^{12}\text{C}$$
$$= 2.331411 \times 12 \text{ amu} = 27.97693 \text{ amu}$$

Along with the isotopic mass, the mass spectrometer gives the relative abundance as a percentage (or fraction) of each isotope in a sample of the element. For example, the relative abundance of $^{28}\text{Si}$ is 92.23% (or 0.9223).

From such data, we can obtain the **atomic mass** (also called *atomic weight*) of an element, the *average* of the masses of its naturally occurring isotopes weighted according to their abundances. Each naturally occurring isotope of an element contributes a certain portion to the atomic mass. For instance, multiplying the isotopic mass of $^{28}\text{Si}$ by its fractional abundance gives the portion of the atomic mass of Si contributed by $^{28}\text{Si}$:

$$\text{Portion of Si atomic mass from } ^{28}\text{Si} = 27.97693 \text{ amu} \times 0.9223 = 25.8031 \text{ amu}$$
$$\text{(retaining two additional significant figures)}$$

Similar calculations give the portions contributed by $^{29}\text{Si}$ (28.976495 amu $\times$ 0.0467 = 1.3532 amu) and by $^{30}\text{Si}$ (29.973770 amu $\times$ 0.0310 = 0.9292 amu). Adding the three portions together (rounding to two decimal places at the end) gives the atomic mass of silicon:

$$\text{Atomic mass of Si} = 25.8031 \text{ amu} + 1.3532 \text{ amu} + 0.9292 \text{ amu}$$
$$= 28.0855 \text{ amu} = 28.09 \text{ amu}$$

The atomic mass is an average value; thus, while no individual silicon atom has a mass of 28.09 amu, in the laboratory, we consider a sample of silicon to consist of atoms with this average mass.

# TOOLS OF THE LABORATORY | Mass Spectrometry

Mass spectrometry is a powerful technique for measuring the mass and abundance of charged particles from their mass/charge ratio (*m/e*). When a high-energy electron collides with a particle, say, an atom of neon-20, one of the atom's electrons is knocked away and the resulting particle has one positive charge, $Ne^+$ (Figure B2.1). Thus, its *m/e* equals the mass divided by 1+.

Figure B2.2, part A, depicts the core of one type of mass spectrometer. The sample is introduced (and vaporized if liquid or solid), then bombarded by high-energy electrons to form positively charged particles, in this case, of the different neon isotopes. These are attracted toward a series of negatively charged plates with slits in them. Some particles pass through the slits into an evacuated tube exposed to a magnetic field. As the particles enter this region, their paths are bent, the lightest particles (lowest *m/e*) are deflected most and the heaviest particles (highest *m/e*) least. At the end of the magnetic region, the particles strike a detector, which records their relative positions and abundances (Figure B2.2, parts B and C).

Mass spectrometry is now employed to measure the mass of virtually any atom, molecule, or molecular fragment. The technique is being used to study catalyst surfaces, forensic materials, fuel mixtures, medicinal agents, and many other samples, especially proteins (Figure B2.2, part D); in fact, John B. Fenn and Koichi Tanaka shared part of the 2002 Nobel Prize in chemistry for developing methods to study proteins by mass spectrometry.

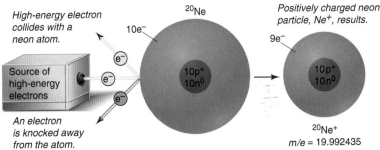

**Figure B2.1** Formation of a positively charged neon particle ($Ne^+$).

## Problems

**B2.1** Chlorine has two naturally occurring isotopes, $^{35}Cl$ (abundance 76%) and $^{37}Cl$ (abundance 24%), and it occurs as diatomic (two-atom) molecules. In a mass spectrum, peaks are seen for the molecule and for the separated atoms.
(a) How many peaks are in the mass spectrum?
(b) What is the *m/e* value of the heaviest particle and of the lightest particle?

**B2.2** When a sample of pure carbon is analyzed by mass spectrometry, peaks X, Y, and Z are obtained. Peak Y is taller than X and Z, and Z is taller than X. What is the *m/e* value of the isotope responsible for peak Z?

**Figure B2.2** The mass spectrometer and its data. **A,** Particles are separated by their *m/e* values. **B,** The relative abundances of three Ne isotopes. **C,** The percent abundance of each isotope. **D,** The mass spectrum of a protein molecule. Each peak represents a molecular fragment.

**Sample Problem 2.5**  Calculating the Atomic Mass of an Element

**Problem**  Silver (Ag; $Z = 47$) has 46 known isotopes, but only two occur naturally, $^{107}Ag$ and $^{109}Ag$. Given the following data, calculate the atomic mass of Ag:

| Isotope | Mass (amu) | Abundance (%) |
|---------|-----------|---------------|
| $^{107}Ag$ | 106.90509 | 51.84 |
| $^{109}Ag$ | 108.90476 | 48.16 |

**Plan**  From the mass and abundance of the two Ag isotopes, we have to find the atomic mass of Ag (weighted average of the isotopic masses). We divide each percent abundance by 100 to get the fractional abundance and then multiply that by each isotopic mass to find the portion of the atomic mass contributed by each isotope. The sum of the isotopic portions is the atomic mass.

**Solution**  Finding the fractional abundances:

Fractional abundance of $^{107}Ag = 51.84/100 = 0.5184$; similarly, $^{109}Ag = 0.4816$

Finding the portion of the atomic mass from each isotope:

Portion of atomic mass from $^{107}Ag$ = isotopic mass × fractional abundance
$$= 106.90509 \text{ amu} \times 0.5184 = 55.42 \text{ amu}$$
Portion of atomic mass from $^{109}Ag = 108.90476 \text{ amu} \times 0.4816 = 52.45 \text{ amu}$

Finding the atomic mass of silver:

Atomic mass of Ag = 55.42 amu + 52.45 amu =  107.87 amu

**Check**  The individual portions seem right: ~100 amu × 0.50 = 50 amu. The portions should be almost the same because the two isotopic abundances are almost the same. We rounded each portion to four significant figures because that is the number of significant figures in the abundance values. This is the correct atomic mass (to two decimal places); in the list of elements (inside front cover), it is rounded to 107.9 amu.

**Follow-Up Problem 2.5**  Boron (B; $Z = 5$) has two naturally occurring isotopes. Find the percent abundances of $^{10}B$ and $^{11}B$ given these data: atomic mass of B = 10.81 amu, isotopic mass of $^{10}B$ = 10.0129 amu, and isotopic mass of $^{11}B$ = 11.0093 amu. (*Hint:* The sum of the fractional abundances is 1. If $x$ = abundance of $^{10}B$, then $1 - x$ = abundance of $^{11}B$.)

**Road Map**

| Mass (g) of each isotope |

multiply by fractional abundance of each isotope

| Portion of atomic mass from each isotope |

add isotopic portions

| Atomic mass |

## ▍Summary of Section 2.5

- An atom has a central nucleus, which contains positively charged protons and uncharged neutrons and is surrounded by negatively charged electrons. An atom is neutral because the number of electrons equals the number of protons.
- An atom is represented by the notation $^{A}_{Z}X$, in which $Z$ is the atomic number (number of protons), $A$ the mass number (sum of protons and neutrons), and X the atomic symbol.
- An element occurs naturally as a mixture of isotopes, atoms with the same number of protons but different numbers of neutrons. Each isotope has a mass relative to the $^{12}C$ mass standard.
- The atomic mass of an element is the average of its isotopic masses weighted according to their natural abundances and is determined using modern instruments, especially the mass spectrometer.

## 2.6 • ELEMENTS: A FIRST LOOK AT THE PERIODIC TABLE

At the end of the 18th century, Lavoisier compiled a list of the 23 elements known at that time; by 1870, 65 were known; by 1925, 88; today, there are 117 and still counting! By the mid-19th century, enormous amounts of information concerning reactions, properties, and atomic masses of the elements had been accumulated. Several researchers noted recurring, or *periodic,* patterns of behavior and proposed schemes to organize the elements according to some fundamental property.

In 1871, the Russian chemist Dmitri Mendeleev (1836–1907) published the most successful of these organizing schemes as a table of the elements listed by increasing atomic mass and arranged so that elements with similar chemical properties fell in the same column. The modern **periodic table of the elements,** based on Mendeleev's version (but arranged by *atomic number,* not mass), is one of the great classifying schemes in science and an indispensable tool to chemists—and chemistry students.

**Organization of the Periodic Table**  One common version of the modern periodic table appears in Figure 2.9 (and inside the front cover). It is formatted as follows:

1. Each element has a box that contains its atomic number, atomic symbol, and atomic mass. (A mass in parentheses is the mass number of the most stable isotope of that element.) The boxes lie, from left to right, in order of *increasing atomic number* (number of protons in the nucleus).
2. The boxes are arranged into a grid of **periods** (horizontal rows) and **groups** (vertical columns). Each period has a number from 1 to 7. Each group has a number from 1 to 8 *and* either the letter A or B. A newer system, with group numbers from 1 to 18 but no letters, appears in parentheses under the number-letter designations. (The text uses the number-letter system and shows the newer numbering system in parentheses.)
3. The eight A groups (two on the left and six on the right) contain the *main-group elements.* The ten B groups, located between Groups 2A(2) and 3A(13), contain the *transition elements.* Two horizontal series of *inner transition elements,* the lanthanides and the actinides, fit *between* the elements in Group 3B(3) and Group 4B(4) and are placed below the main body of the table.

**Figure 2.9** The modern periodic table. As of mid-2010, elements 113–116 and 118 had not been named.

**Classifying the Elements**  One of the clearest ways to classify the elements is as metals, nonmetals, and metalloids. The "staircase" line that runs from the top of Group 3A(13) to the bottom of Group 6A(16) is a dividing line:

- The **metals** (three shades of blue in Figure 2.9) lie in the large lower-left portion of the table. About three-quarters of the elements are metals, including many main-group elements and all the transition and inner transition elements. They are generally shiny solids at room temperature (mercury is the only liquid) that conduct heat and electricity well. They can be tooled into sheets (are malleable) and wires (are ductile).
- The **nonmetals** (yellow) lie in the small upper-right portion of the table. They are generally gases or dull, brittle solids at room temperature (bromine is the only liquid) and conduct heat and electricity poorly.
- The **metalloids** (green; also called **semimetals**), which lie along the staircase line, have properties between those of metals and nonmetals.

Figure 2.10 shows examples of these three classes of elements.

**Figure 2.10**  Some metals, metalloids, and nonmetals.

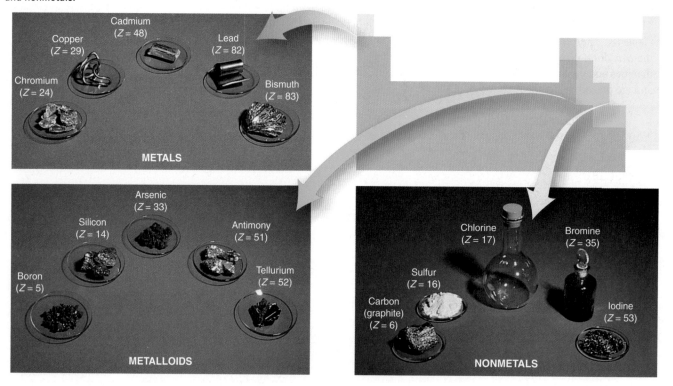

Two major points to keep in mind:

1. In general, elements in a group have **similar** chemical properties and elements in a period have **different** chemical properties.
2. Despite this classification of three types of elements, in reality, there is a gradation in properties from left to right and top to bottom.

It is important to learn some of the group (family) names. Group 1A(1), except for hydrogen, consists of the *alkali metals,* and Group 2A(2) consists of the *alkaline earth metals.* Both groups consist of highly reactive elements. The *halogens,* Group 7A(17), are highly reactive nonmetals, whereas the *noble gases,* Group 8A(18), are relatively unreactive nonmetals. Other main groups [3A(13) to 6A(16)] are often named for the first element in the group; for example, Group 6A(16) is the *oxygen family.*

Two of the major branches of chemistry have traditionally been defined by the elements that each studies. *Organic chemistry* studies the compounds of carbon, specifically those that contain hydrogen and often oxygen, nitrogen, and a few other elements. This branch is concerned with fuels, drugs, dyes, and the like. *Inorganic chemistry,* on the other hand, focuses on the compounds of all the other elements and is concerned with catalysts, electronic materials, metal alloys, mineral salts, and the like. With the explosive growth in biomedical and materials sciences, the line between these branches has all but disappeared.

## ◼ Summary of Section 2.6

- In the periodic table, the elements are arranged by atomic number into horizontal periods and vertical groups.
- Nonmetals appear in the upper-right portion of the table, metalloids lie along a staircase line, and metals fill the rest of the table.
- Elements within a group have similar behavior, whereas elements within a period have dissimilar behavior.

## 2.7 • COMPOUNDS: INTRODUCTION TO BONDING

Only a few elements occur free in nature. The noble gases—helium (He), neon (Ne), argon (Ar), krypton (Kr), xenon (Xe), and radon (Rn)—occur in air as separate atoms. In addition to occurring in compounds, oxygen (O), nitrogen (N), and sulfur (S) occur in their most common elemental form as the molecules $O_2$, $N_2$, and $S_8$, and carbon (C) occurs in vast, nearly pure deposits of coal. And some metals—copper (Cu), silver (Ag), gold (Au), and platinum (Pt)—are also sometimes found uncombined. But, aside from these few exceptions, *the overwhelming majority of elements occur in compounds combined with other elements.*

Elements combine in two general ways and both involve *the electrons of the atoms of interacting elements:*

1. *Transferring electrons* from one element to another to form **ionic compounds**
2. *Sharing electrons* between atoms of different elements to form **covalent compounds**

These processes generate **chemical bonds,** the forces that hold the atoms together in a compound. This section introduces compound formation, which we'll discuss in much more detail in later chapters.

### The Formation of Ionic Compounds

Ionic compounds are composed of **ions,** charged particles that form when an atom (or small group of atoms) gains or loses one or more electrons. The simplest type of ionic compound is a **binary ionic compound,** one composed of two elements. It typically forms *when a metal reacts with a nonmetal:*

- Each metal atom *loses* one or more electrons and becomes a **cation,** a positively charged ion.
- Each nonmetal atom *gains* one or more of the electrons lost by the metal atom and becomes an **anion,** a negatively charged ion.

In effect, the metal atoms *transfer electrons* to the nonmetal atoms. The resulting large numbers of cations and anions attract each other and form the ionic compound. A cation or anion derived from a single atom is called a **monatomic ion;** we'll discuss polyatomic ions, those derived from a small group of atoms, later.

### The Case of Sodium Chloride

*All binary ionic compounds are solid arrays of oppositely charged ions.* The formation of the binary ionic compound sodium chloride, common table salt, from its elements is depicted in Figure 2.11. In the electron transfer, a sodium atom *loses* one electron and forms a sodium cation, $Na^+$. (The charge on the ion is written as a *right superscript.*) A chlorine atom *gains* the electron and becomes a chloride anion, $Cl^-$. (The name change when the nonmetal atom becomes an anion is discussed in the next section.) The oppositely charged ions ($Na^+$ and $Cl^-$) attract each other, and the similarly charged ions ($Na^+$ and $Na^+$, or $Cl^-$ and $Cl^-$) repel each other. The resulting solid aggregation is a regular array of alternating $Na^+$ and $Cl^-$ ions that extends in all three dimensions. Even the tiniest visible grain of table salt contains an enormous number of sodium and chloride ions.

### Coulomb's Law

The strength of the ionic bonding depends to a great extent on the net strength of these attractions and repulsions and is described by *Coulomb's law,* which can be expressed as follows: *the energy of attraction (or repulsion) between two particles is directly proportional to the product of the charges and inversely proportional to the distance between them.*

$$\text{Energy} \propto \frac{\text{charge 1} \times \text{charge 2}}{\text{distance}}$$

In other words, as is summarized in Figure 2.12,

- Ions with higher charges attract (or repel) each other more strongly than ions with lower charges.
- Smaller ions attract (or repel) each other more strongly than larger ions, because their charges are closer together.

### Predicting the Number of Electrons Lost or Gained

*Ionic compounds are neutral* because they contain equal numbers of positive and negative *charges.* Thus, there are equal numbers of $Na^+$ and $Cl^-$ ions in sodium chloride, because both ions are singly charged. But there are two $Na^+$ ions for each oxide ion, $O^{2-}$, in sodium oxide because two $1+$ ions balance one $2-$ ion.

Can we predict the number of electrons a given atom will lose or gain when it forms an ion? For A-group elements, we usually find that metal atoms lose electrons and nonmetal atoms gain electrons to *form ions with the same number of electrons as in an atom of the nearest noble gas* [Group 8A(18)]. Noble gases have a stability that is related to their number (and arrangement) of electrons. Thus, a sodium atom ($11e^-$) can attain the stability of a neon atom ($10e^-$), the nearest noble gas, by

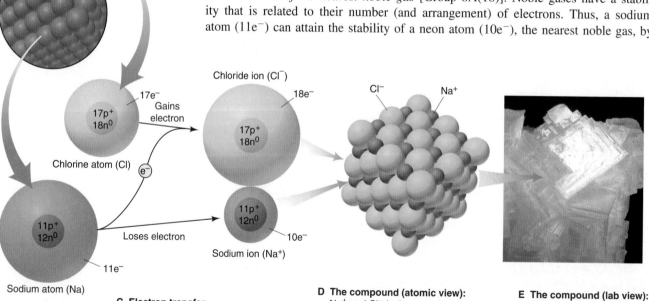

**Figure 2.11 The formation of an ionic compound. A,** The two elements as seen in the laboratory. **B,** The elements on the atomic scale. **C,** The electron transfer from Na atom to Cl atom to form $Na^+$ and $Cl^-$ ions.

**D,** Countless $Na^+$ and $Cl^-$ ions attract each other and form a regular three-dimensional array. **E,** Crystalline NaCl occurs naturally as the mineral halite.

losing one electron. Similarly, a chlorine atom ($17e^-$) attains the stability of an argon atom ($18e^-$), its nearest noble gas, by gaining one electron. Thus, in general, when an element located near a noble gas forms a monatomic ion,

- *Metals lose electrons:* elements in Group 1A(1) lose one electron, elements in Group 2A(2) lose two, and aluminum in Group 3A(13) loses three.
- *Nonmetals gain electrons:* elements in Group 7A(17) gain one electron, oxygen and sulfur in Group 6A(16) gain two, and nitrogen in Group 5A(15) gains three.

In the periodic table in Figure 2.9, it looks like the elements in Group 7A(17) are "closer" to the noble gases than the elements in Group 1A(1). In truth, both groups are only one electron away from the number of electrons in the nearest noble gas. Figure 2.13 shows a periodic table of monatomic ions that is cut and rejoined as a cylinder. Note that fluorine (F; $Z = 9$) has one electron *fewer* than the noble gas neon (Ne; $Z = 10$) and sodium (Na; $Z = 11$) has one electron *more;* thus, they form the $F^-$ and $Na^+$ ions. Similarly, oxygen (O; $Z = 8$) gains two electrons and magnesium (Mg; $Z = 12$) loses two to form the $O^{2-}$ and $Mg^{2+}$ ions and attain the same number of electrons as neon. In Figure 2.13, species in a row have the same number of electrons.

**Figure 2.12** Factors that influence the strength of ionic bonding.

**Figure 2.13** The relationship between ion formed and the nearest noble gas.

---

## Sample Problem 2.6 — Predicting the Ion an Element Forms

**Problem** What monatomic ions do the following elements form?
**(a)** Iodine ($Z = 53$)    **(b)** Calcium ($Z = 20$)    **(c)** Aluminum ($Z = 13$)

**Plan** We use the given $Z$ value to find the element in the periodic table and see where its group lies relative to the noble gases. Elements in Groups 1A, 2A, and 3A *lose* electrons to attain the same number as the nearest noble gas and become positive ions; those in Groups 5A, 6A, and 7A *gain* electrons and become negative ions.

**Solution (a)** $I^-$ Iodine ($_{53}I$) is in Group 7A(17), the halogens. Like any member of this group, it gains 1 electron to attain the same number as the nearest Group 8A(18) member, in this case, $_{54}Xe$.
**(b)** $Ca^{2+}$ Calcium ($_{20}Ca$) is in Group 2A(2), the alkaline earth metals. Like any Group 2A member, it loses 2 electrons to attain the same number as the nearest noble gas, $_{18}Ar$.
**(c)** $Al^{3+}$ Aluminum ($_{13}Al$) is a metal in the boron family [Group 3A(13)] and thus loses 3 electrons to attain the same number as its nearest noble gas, $_{10}Ne$.

**Follow-Up Problem 2.6** What monatomic ion does each of the following elements form: **(a)** $_{16}S$; **(b)** $_{37}Rb$; **(c)** $_{56}Ba$?

Atoms far apart: *No interactions.*

**Atoms closer:** *Attractions* (green arrows) *between nucleus of one atom and electron of the other increase. Repulsions between nuclei and between electrons are very weak.*

**Optimum distance:** *H₂ molecule forms because attractions* (green arrows) *balance repulsions* (red arrows).

**Figure 2.14** Formation of a covalent bond between two H atoms.

## The Formation of Covalent Compounds

*Covalent compounds form when elements share electrons, which usually occurs between nonmetals.* The simplest case of electron sharing occurs not in a compound but between two hydrogen atoms (H; $Z = 1$). Imagine two separated H atoms approaching each other (Figure 2.14). As they get closer, the nucleus of each atom attracts the electron of the other atom more and more strongly. As the separated atoms begin to interpenetrate each other, repulsions between the nuclei and between the electrons begin to increase. At some optimum distance between the nuclei, the two atoms form a **covalent bond,** a pair of electrons mutually attracted by the two nuclei. The result is a hydrogen molecule, in which each electron no longer "belongs" to a particular H atom: the two electrons are *shared* by the two nuclei. A sample of hydrogen gas consists of these diatomic molecules ($H_2$)—pairs of atoms that are chemically bound and behave as an independent unit—*not* separate H atoms. Figure 2.15 shows other nonmetals that exist as molecules at room temperature.

**Figure 2.15** Elements that occur as molecules.

*Atoms of different elements share electrons to form the molecules of a covalent compound.* A sample of hydrogen fluoride, for example, consists of molecules in which one H atom forms a covalent bond with one F atom; water consists of molecules in which one O atom forms covalent bonds with two H atoms:

Hydrogen fluoride, HF      Water, $H_2O$

**Distinguishing the Entities in Covalent and Ionic Substances** There is a key distinction between the chemical entities in covalent substances and in ionic substances. *Most covalent substances consist of molecules.* A cup of water, for example, consists of individual water molecules lying near each other. In contrast, under ordinary conditions, *there are no molecules in an ionic compound.* A piece of sodium chloride, for example, is a continuous array in three dimensions of oppositely charged sodium and chloride ions, *not* a collection of individual sodium chloride "molecules."

Another key distinction between covalent and ionic substances concerns the nature of the particles attracting each other. Covalent bonding involves the mutual attraction between two (positively charged) nuclei and the two (negatively charged) electrons that reside between them. Ionic bonding involves the mutual attraction between positive and negative ions.

**Polyatomic Ions: Covalent Bonds Within Ions** Many ionic compounds contain **polyatomic ions,** which consist of two or more atoms bonded *covalently* and have a net positive or negative charge. For example, Figure 2.16 shows that a crystalline form of calcium carbonate (*left*) occurs on the atomic scale as an array of polyatomic carbonate anions and monatomic calcium cations (*center*). The carbonate ion (*right*) consists of a carbon atom covalently bonded to three oxygen atoms, and two additional electrons give the ion its 2− charge. In many reactions, the polyatomic ion stays together as a unit.

**Figure 2.16** The carbonate ion in calcium carbonate.

Carbonate ion
$CO_3^{2-}$

## ◼ Summary of Section 2.7

- Although a few elements occur uncombined in nature, the great majority exist in compounds.
- Ionic compounds form when a metal *transfers* electrons to a nonmetal, and the resulting positive and negative ions attract each other to form a three-dimensional array. In many cases, metal atoms lose and nonmetal atoms gain enough electrons to attain the same number of electrons as in atoms of the nearest noble gas.
- Covalent compounds form when elements, usually nonmetals, *share* electrons. Each covalent bond is an electron pair mutually attracted by two atomic nuclei.
- Monatomic ions are derived from single atoms. Polyatomic ions consist of two or more covalently bonded atoms that have a net positive or negative charge due to a deficit or excess of electrons.

## 2.8 • FORMULAS, NAMES, AND MASSES OF COMPOUNDS

In a **chemical formula,** element symbols and, often, numerical subscripts show the type and number of each atom in the smallest unit of the substance. In this section, you'll learn how to write the names and formulas of ionic and simple covalent compounds, how to calculate the mass of a compound from its formula, and how to visualize molecules with three-dimensional models. To make learning the names and formula of compounds easier, we'll rely on various rules, so be prepared for a bit of memorization and a lot of practice.

### Binary Ionic Compounds

Let's begin with two general rules:

- For *all* ionic compounds, *names and formulas give the positive ion (cation) first and the negative ion (anion) second.*
- For all *binary* ionic compounds, *the name of the cation is the name of the metal, and the name of the anion has the suffix -ide added to the root of the name of the nonmetal.*

For example, the anion formed from brom*ine* is named brom*ide* (brom+ide). Therefore, the compound formed from the metal calcium and the nonmetal bromine is named *calcium bromide.*

## Table 2.3 Common Monatomic Ions*

| Charge | Formula | Name |
|--------|---------|------|
| **Cations** | | |
| 1+ | $H^+$ | hydrogen |
| | **$Li^+$** | **lithium** |
| | **$Na^+$** | **sodium** |
| | **$K^+$** | **potassium** |
| | $Cs^+$ | cesium |
| | **$Ag^+$** | **silver** |
| 2+ | **$Mg^{2+}$** | **magnesium** |
| | **$Ca^{2+}$** | **calcium** |
| | $Sr^{2+}$ | strontium |
| | **$Ba^{2+}$** | **barium** |
| | **$Zn^{2+}$** | **zinc** |
| | $Cd^{2+}$ | cadmium |
| 3+ | **$Al^{3+}$** | **aluminum** |
| **Anions** | | |
| 1− | $H^-$ | hydride |
| | **$F^-$** | **fluoride** |
| | **$Cl^-$** | **chloride** |
| | **$Br^-$** | **bromide** |
| | **$I^-$** | **iodide** |
| 2− | **$O^{2-}$** | **oxide** |
| | **$S^{2-}$** | **sulfide** |
| 3− | $N^{3-}$ | nitride |

*Listed by charge; those in **boldface** are most common.

In general, if the metal of a binary ionic compound is a main-group element (A groups) it usually forms a single type of ion; if it is a transition element (B groups), it often forms more than one. We discuss each case in turn.

**Compounds of Elements That Form One Ion** The periodic table presents some key points about the formulas of main-group monatomic ions:

- Monatomic ions of main-group elements have the same ionic charge; the alkali metals—Li, Na, K, Rb, Cs, and Fr—form ions with a 1+ charge; the halogens—F, Cl, Br, and I—form ions with a 1− charge; and so forth.
- For cations, ion charge equals A-group number: Na is in Group 1A and forms $Na^+$, Ba is in Group 2A and forms $Ba^{2+}$. (Exceptions in Figure 2.17 are $Sn^{2+}$ and $Pb^{2+}$.)
- For anions, ion charge equals A-group number minus 8; for example, S is in Group 6A ($6 - 8 = -2$) and thus forms $S^{2-}$.

Try to memorize the A-group monatomic ions in Table 2.3 (all of these listed except $Ag^+$, $Zn^{2+}$, and $Cd^{2+}$) according to their positions in Figure 2.17. These ions have *the same number of electrons as an atom of the nearest noble gas.*

Because an ionic compound consists of an array of ions rather than separate molecules, its formula represents the **formula unit,** the *relative* numbers of cations and anions in the compound. The compound has zero net charge, so the positive charges of the cations balance the negative charges of the anions. For example, calcium bromide is composed of $Ca^{2+}$ ions and $Br^-$ ions, so two $Br^-$ balance each $Ca^{2+}$. The formula is $CaBr_2$, not $Ca_2Br$. In this and all other formulas,

- The subscript refers to the element *preceding* it.
- The *subscript 1 is understood* from the presence of the element symbol alone (that is, we do not write $Ca_1Br_2$).
- The charge (without the sign) of one ion becomes the subscript of the other:

$$Ca^{2+} \quad Br^{1-} \qquad \text{gives} \qquad Ca_1Br_2 \quad \text{or} \quad CaBr_2$$

- Reduce the subscripts to the smallest whole numbers that retain the ratio of ions. Thus, for example, for the $Ca^{2+}$ and $O^{2-}$ ions in calcium oxide, we get $Ca_2O_2$, which we reduce to the formula CaO.*

---

*Compounds of the mercury(I) ion, such as $Hg_2Cl_2$, and peroxides of the alkali metals, such as $Na_2O_2$, are the only two common exceptions to this step; in fact, reducing the subscripts for these compounds would give the incorrect formulas HgCl and NaO.

**Figure 2.17 Some common monatomic ions of the elements.** Most main-group elements form one monatomic ion. Most transition elements form two monatomic ions. ($Hg_2^{2+}$ is a diatomic ion but is included for comparison with $Hg^{2+}$.)

The following two sample problems apply these rules. In Sample Problem 2.7, we name the compound from its elements, and in Sample Problem 2.8, we find the formula.

## Sample Problem 2.7 | Naming Binary Ionic Compounds

**Problem** Name the ionic compound formed from the following pairs of elements:
**(a)** Magnesium and nitrogen
**(b)** Iodine and cadmium
**(c)** Strontium and fluorine
**(d)** Sulfur and cesium

**Plan** The key to naming a binary ionic compound is to recognize which element is the metal and which is the nonmetal. When in doubt, check the periodic table. We place the cation name first, add the suffix -*ide* to the nonmetal root, and place the anion name last.

**Solution** **(a)** Magnes*ium* is the metal; *nitr-* is the nonmetal root:  magnesium nitride
**(b)** Cadm*ium* is the metal; *iod-* is the nonmetal root: cadmium iodide
**(c)** Stront*ium* is the metal; *fluor-* is the nonmetal root: strontium fluoride (Note the spelling is flu*o*ride, not fl*o*uride.)
**(d)** Ces*ium* is the metal; *sulf-* is the nonmetal root: cesium sulfide

**Follow-Up Problem 2.7** For the following ionic compounds, give the name and periodic table group number of each element present:
**(a)** Zinc oxide
**(b)** Silver bromide
**(c)** Lithium chloride
**(d)** Aluminum sulfide

## Sample Problem 2.8 | Determining Formulas of Binary Ionic Compounds

**Problem** Write formulas for the compounds named in Sample Problem 2.7.

**Plan** We write the formula by finding the smallest number of each ion that gives the neutral compound. These numbers appear as *right subscripts* to the element symbol.

**Solution**
**(a)** $Mg^{2+}$ and $N^{3-}$; three $Mg^{2+}$ ions (6+) balance two $N^{3-}$ ions (6−):  $Mg_3N_2$
**(b)** $Cd^{2+}$ and $I^-$; one $Cd^{2+}$ ion (2+) balances two $I^-$ ions (2−):  $CdI_2$
**(c)** $Sr^{2+}$ and $F^-$; one $Sr^{2+}$ ion (2+) balances two $F^-$ ions (2−):  $SrF_2$
**(d)** $Cs^+$ and $S^{2-}$; two $Cs^+$ ions (2+) balance one $S^{2-}$ ion (2−):  $Cs_2S$

**Comment 1.** The subscript 1 is understood and so not written; thus, in (b), we do *not* write $Cd_1I_2$.
**2.** Ion charges do *not* appear in the compound formula; thus, in (c), we do *not* write $Sr^{2+}F_2^-$.

**Follow-Up Problem 2.8** Write the formulas of the compounds named in Follow-Up Problem 2.7.

**Compounds with Metals That Form More Than One Ion** As noted earlier, many metals, particularly the transition elements (B groups), can form more than one ion. Table 2.4 on the next page lists some examples; see Figure 2.17 for their placement in the periodic table. Names of compounds containing these elements include a *Roman numeral within parentheses* immediately after the metal ion's name to indicate its ionic charge. For example, iron can form $Fe^{2+}$ and $Fe^{3+}$ ions. The two compounds that iron forms with chlorine are $FeCl_2$, named iron(II) chloride (spoken "iron two chloride"), and $FeCl_3$, named iron(III) chloride.

## Table 2.4 Some Metals That Form More Than One Monatomic Ion*

| Element | Ion Formula | Systematic Name | Common (Trivial) Name |
|---|---|---|---|
| Chromium | $Cr^{2+}$ | chromium(II) | chromous |
| | **$Cr^{3+}$** | **chromium(III)** | chromic |
| Cobalt | $Co^{2+}$ | cobalt(II) | |
| | $Co^{3+}$ | cobalt(III) | |
| Copper | **$Cu^+$** | **copper(I)** | cuprous |
| | **$Cu^{2+}$** | **copper(II)** | cupric |
| Iron | **$Fe^{2+}$** | **iron(II)** | ferrous |
| | **$Fe^{3+}$** | **iron(III)** | ferric |
| Lead | **$Pb^{2+}$** | **lead(II)** | |
| | $Pb^{4+}$ | lead(IV) | |
| Mercury | $Hg_2^{2+}$ | mercury(I) | mercurous |
| | **$Hg^{2+}$** | **mercury(II)** | mercuric |
| Tin | **$Sn^{2+}$** | **tin(II)** | stannous |
| | $Sn^{4+}$ | tin(IV) | stannic |

*Listed alphabetically by metal name; the ions in **boldface** are most common.

We are focusing here on systematic names, but some common (trivial) names are still used. In common names for certain metal ions, the Latin root of the metal is followed by either of two suffixes (see Table 2.4):

- The suffix *-ous* for the ion with the lower charge
- The suffix *-ic* for the ion with the higher charge

Thus, iron(II) chloride is also called ferr*ous* chloride and iron(III) chloride is ferr*ic* chloride. (Memory aid: there is an *o* in *-ous* and *lower,* and an *i* in *-ic* and *higher.*)

## Table 2.5 Common Polyatomic Ions*

| Formula | Name |
|---|---|
| **Cations** | |
| $NH_4^+$ | **ammonium** |
| $H_3O^+$ | **hydronium** |
| **Anions** | |
| $CH_3COO^-$ | **acetate** |
| (or $C_2H_3O_2^-$) | |
| $CN^-$ | cyanide |
| $OH^-$ | **hydroxide** |
| $ClO^-$ | hypochlorite |
| $ClO_2^-$ | chlorite |
| $ClO_3^-$ | **chlorate** |
| $ClO_4^-$ | **perchlorate** |
| $NO_2^-$ | nitrite |
| $NO_3^-$ | **nitrate** |
| $MnO_4^-$ | **permanganate** |
| $CO_3^{2-}$ | **carbonate** |
| $HCO_3^-$ | **hydrogen carbonate** (or **bicarbonate**) |
| $CrO_4^{2-}$ | chromate |
| $Cr_2O_7^{2-}$ | **dichromate** |
| $O_2^{2-}$ | peroxide |
| $PO_4^{3-}$ | **phosphate** |
| $HPO_4^{2-}$ | hydrogen phosphate |
| $H_2PO_4^-$ | dihydrogen phosphate |
| $SO_3^{2-}$ | sulfite |
| $SO_4^{2-}$ | **sulfate** |
| $HSO_4^-$ | hydrogen sulfate (or bisulfate) |

*Boldface ions are most common.

### Sample Problem 2.9  Determining Names and Formulas of Ionic Compounds of Metals That Form More Than One Ion

**Problem** Give the systematic names for the formulas or the formulas for the names of the following compounds:
**(a)** Tin(II) fluoride  **(b)** $CrI_3$  **(c)** Ferric oxide  **(d)** CoS

**Solution** **(a)** Tin(II) ion is $Sn^{2+}$; fluoride is $F^-$. Two $F^-$ ions balance one $Sn^{2+}$ ion: tin(II) fluoride is $SnF_2$. (The common name is stannous fluoride.)
**(b)** The anion is $I^-$, iodide, and the formula shows three $I^-$. Therefore, the cation must be $Cr^{3+}$, chromium(III) ion: $CrI_3$ is chromium(III) iodide. (The common name is chromic iodide.)
**(c)** *Ferric* is the common name for iron(III) ion, $Fe^{3+}$; oxide ion is $O^{2-}$. To balance the charges, the formula is $Fe_2O_3$. [The systematic name is iron(III) oxide.]
**(d)** The anion is sulfide, $S^{2-}$, which requires that the cation be $Co^{2+}$. The name is cobalt(II) sulfide.

**Follow-Up Problem 2.9** Give the systematic names for the formulas or the formulas for the names of the following compounds:
**(a)** Lead(IV) oxide  **(b)** $Cu_2S$  **(c)** $FeBr_2$  **(d)** Mercuric chloride

## Compounds That Contain Polyatomic Ions

Many ionic compounds contain polyatomic ions. Table 2.5 shows some common polyatomic ions. Remember that *the polyatomic ion stays together as a charged unit.* The formula for potassium nitrate is $KNO_3$: each $K^+$ balances one $NO_3^-$. The formula for sodium carbonate is $Na_2CO_3$: two $Na^+$ balance one $CO_3^{2-}$. *When two or more of the same polyatomic ion are present in the formula unit, that ion appears in parentheses with the subscript written outside.* For example, calcium nitrate contains one $Ca^{2+}$ and two $NO_3^-$ ions and has the formula $Ca(NO_3)_2$. Parentheses and a subscript are *only* used if *more than one* of a given polyatomic ion is present; thus, sodium nitrate is $NaNO_3$, *not* $Na(NO_3)$.

**Families of Oxoanions**  As Table 2.5 shows, most polyatomic ions are **oxoanions** (or *oxyanions*), those in which an element, usually a nonmetal, is bonded to one or more oxygen atoms. There are several families of two or four oxoanions that differ only in the number of oxygen atoms. The following simple naming conventions are used with these ions.

With two oxoanions in the family:

- The ion with *more* O atoms takes the nonmetal root and the suffix *-ate*.
- The ion with *fewer* O atoms takes the nonmetal root and the suffix *-ite*.

For example, $SO_4^{2-}$ is the sulf*ate* ion, and $SO_3^{2-}$ is the sulf*ite* ion; similarly, $NO_3^-$ is nitr*ate*, and $NO_2^-$ is nitr*ite*.

With four oxoanions in the family (a halogen bonded to O) (Figure 2.18):

- The ion with *most* O atoms has the prefix *per-*, the nonmetal root, and the suffix *-ate*.
- The ion with *one fewer* O atom has just the root and the suffix *-ate*.
- The ion with *two fewer* O atoms has just the root and the suffix *-ite*.
- The ion with *least (three fewer)* O atoms has the prefix *hypo-*, the root, and the suffix *-ite*.

For example, for the four chlorine oxoanions,

$ClO_4^-$ is *per*chlor*ate*,   $ClO_3^-$ is chlor*ate*,   $ClO_2^-$ is chlor*ite*,   $ClO^-$ is *hypo*chlor*ite*

**Hydrated Ionic Compounds**  Ionic compounds called **hydrates** have a specific number of water molecules in each formula unit, which is shown after a centered dot in the formula and noted in the name by a Greek numerical prefix before the word *hydrate*. Table 2.6 shows these prefixes. For example, Epsom salt has seven water molecules in each formula unit: the formula is $MgSO_4·7H_2O$, and the name is magnesium sulfate *hepta*hydrate. Similarly, the mineral gypsum has the formula $CaSO_4·2H_2O$ and the name calcium sulfate *di*hydrate. The water molecules, referred to as "waters of hydration," are part of the hydrate's structure. Heating can remove some or all of them, leading to a different substance. For example, when heated strongly, blue copper(II) sulfate pentahydrate ($CuSO_4·5H_2O$) is converted to white copper(II) sulfate ($CuSO_4$).

**Figure 2.18 Naming oxoanions.** Prefixes and suffixes indicate the number of O atoms in the anion.

| | Prefix | Root | Suffix |
|---|---|---|---|
| | per | *root* | ate |
| | | *root* | ate |
| | | *root* | ite |
| | hypo | *root* | ite |

No. of O atoms ↑

**Table 2.6 Numerical Prefixes for Hydrates and Binary Covalent Compounds**

| Number | Prefix |
|---|---|
| 1 | mono- |
| 2 | di- |
| 3 | tri- |
| 4 | tetra- |
| 5 | penta- |
| 6 | hexa- |
| 7 | hepta- |
| 8 | octa- |
| 9 | nona- |
| 10 | deca- |

**Sample Problem 2.10    Determining Names and Formulas of Ionic Compounds Containing Polyatomic Ions**

**Problem**  Give the systematic names for the formulas or the formulas for the names of the following compounds:
**(a)** $Fe(ClO_4)_2$    **(b)** Sodium sulfite    **(c)** $Ba(OH)_2·8H_2O$

**Solution**  **(a)** $ClO_4^-$ is perchlorate, which has a $1-$ charge, so the cation must be $Fe^{2+}$. The name is iron(II) perchlorate. (The common name is ferrous perchlorate.)
**(b)** Sodium is $Na^+$; sulfite is $SO_3^{2-}$, and two $Na^+$ ions balance one $SO_3^{2-}$ ion. The formula is $Na_2SO_3$.
**(c)** $Ba^{2+}$ is barium; $OH^-$ is hydroxide. There are eight (*octa-*) water molecules in each formula unit. The name is barium hydroxide octahydrate.

**Follow-Up Problem 2.10**  Give the systematic names for the formulas or the formulas for the names of the following compounds:
**(a)** Cupric nitrate trihydrate    **(b)** Zinc hydroxide    **(c)** LiCN

**Sample Problem 2.11** Recognizing Incorrect Names and Formulas of Ionic Compounds

**Problem** Explain what is wrong with the name or formula at the end of each statement, and correct it:
(a) $Ba(C_2H_3O_2)_2$ is called barium diacetate.
(b) Sodium sulfide has the formula $(Na)_2SO_3$.
(c) Iron(II) sulfate has the formula $Fe_2(SO_4)_3$.
(d) Cesium carbonate has the formula $Cs_2(CO_3)$.

**Solution** (a) The charge of the $Ba^{2+}$ ion *must* be balanced by *two* $C_2H_3O_2^-$ ions, so the prefix *di-* is unnecessary. For ionic compounds, we do not indicate the number of ions with numerical prefixes. The correct name is barium acetate.
(b) Two mistakes occur here. The sodium ion is monatomic, so it does *not* require parentheses. The sulfide ion is $S^{2-}$, *not* $SO_3^{2-}$ (which is sulfite). The correct formula is $Na_2S$.
(c) The Roman numeral refers to the charge of the ion, *not* the number of ions in the formula. $Fe^{2+}$ is the cation, so it requires one $SO_4^{2-}$ to balance its charge. The correct formula is $FeSO_4$. [$Fe_2(SO_4)_3$ is the formula for iron(III) sulfate.]
(d) Parentheses are *not* required when only one polyatomic ion of a kind is present. The correct formula is $Cs_2CO_3$.

**Follow-Up Problem 2.11** State why the formula or name at the end of each statement is incorrect, and correct it:
(a) Ammonium phosphate is $(NH_3)_4PO_4$.
(b) Aluminum hydroxide is $AlOH_3$.
(c) $Mg(HCO_3)_2$ is manganese(II) carbonate.
(d) $Cr(NO_3)_3$ is chromic(III) nitride.
(e) $Ca(NO_2)_2$ is cadmium nitrate.

## Acid Names from Anion Names

Acids are an important group of hydrogen-containing compounds that have been used in chemical reactions since before alchemical times. In the laboratory, acids are typically used in water solution. When naming them and writing their formulas, we consider acids as anions that are connected to the number of hydrogen ions ($H^+$) needed for charge neutrality. The two common types of acids are binary acids and oxoacids:

1. *Binary acid* solutions form when certain gaseous compounds dissolve in water. For example, when gaseous hydrogen chloride (HCl) dissolves in water, it forms hydrochloric acid, that is,

    Prefix *hydro-* + nonmetal *root* + suffix *-ic* + separate word *acid*
    hydro + chlor + ic + acid

    or *hydrochloric acid.* This naming pattern holds for many compounds in which hydrogen combines with an anion that has an *-ide* suffix.

2. *Oxoacid* names are similar to those of the oxoanions, except for two suffix changes:
    • *-ate* in the anion becomes *-ic* in the acid
    • *-ite* in the anion becomes *-ous* in the acid
    The oxoanion prefixes *hypo-* and *per-* are retained. Thus,

    $BrO_4^-$ is *per*brom*ate*, and $HBrO_4$ is *per*brom*ic* acid.
    $IO_2^-$ is iod*ite*, and $HIO_2$ is iod*ous* acid.

## Sample Problem 2.12   Determining Names and Formulas of Anions and Acids

**Problem** Name each of the following anions and give the name and formula of the acid derived from it: **(a)** $Br^-$ **(b)** $IO_3^-$ **(c)** $CN^-$ **(d)** $SO_4^{2-}$ **(e)** $NO_2^-$.

**Solution** **(a)** The anion is bromide; the acid is hydrobromic acid, HBr.
**(b)** The anion is iodate; the acid is iodic acid, $HIO_3$.
**(c)** The anion is cyanide; the acid is hydrocyanic acid, HCN.
**(d)** The anion is sulfate; the acid is sulfuric acid, $H_2SO_4$. (In this case, the suffix is added to the element name *sulfur,* not to the root, *sulf-.*)
**(e)** The anion is nitrite; the acid is nitrous acid, $HNO_2$.

**Comment** We must add *two* $H^+$ ions to the sulfate ion to obtain sulfuric acid because $SO_4^{2-}$ has a 2− charge.

**Follow-Up Problem 2.12** Write the formula for the name or name for the formula of each acid: **(a)** chloric acid **(b)** HF **(c)** acetic acid **(d)** sulfurous acid **(e)** HBrO.

## Binary Covalent Compounds

**Binary covalent compounds** are typically formed by the combination of two non-metals. Some are so familiar that we use their common names, such as ammonia ($NH_3$), methane ($CH_4$), and water ($H_2O$), but most are named systematically:

• The element with the lower group number in the periodic table comes first in the name. The element with the higher group number comes second and is named with its root and the suffix *-ide*. For example, nitrogen [Group 5A(15)] and fluorine [Group 7A(17)] form a compound that has three fluorine atoms for every nitrogen atom. The name and formula are nitrogen trifluoride, $NF_3$ (*Exception:* When the compound contains oxygen and any of the halogens chlorine, bromine, or iodine, the halogen is named first.)
• If both elements are in the same group, the one with the higher period number is named first. Thus, the Group 6A(16) elements sulfur (Period 3) and oxygen (Period 2) form sulfur dioxide, $SO_2$.
• Covalent compounds use Greek numerical prefixes (see Table 2.6) to indicate the number of atoms of each element. The first element in the name has a prefix *only* when more than one atom of it is present; the second element *usually* has a prefix.

## Sample Problem 2.13   Determining Names and Formulas of Binary Covalent Compounds

**Problem** **(a)** What is the formula of carbon disulfide?
**(b)** What is the name of $PCl_5$?
**(c)** Give the name and formula of the compound whose molecules each consist of two N atoms and four O atoms.

**Solution** **(a)** The prefix *di-* means "two." The formula is $CS_2$.
**(b)** P is the symbol for phosphorus; there are five chlorine atoms, which is indicated by the prefix *penta-*. The name is phosphorus pentachloride.
**(c)** Nitrogen (N) comes first in the name (lower group number). The compound is dinitrogen tetraoxide, $N_2O_4$.

**Follow-Up Problem 2.13** Give the name or formula for **(a)** $SO_3$; **(b)** $SiO_2$; **(c)** dinitrogen monoxide; **(d)** selenium hexafluoride.

**Problem** Explain what is wrong with the name or formula at the end of each statement, and correct it: **(a)** $SF_4$ is monosulfur pentafluoride. **(b)** Dichlorine heptaoxide is $Cl_2O_6$. **(c)** $N_2O_3$ is dinitrotrioxide.

**Solution** **(a)** There are two mistakes. *Mono-* is not needed if there is only one atom of the first element, and the prefix for four is *tetra-*, not *penta-*. The correct name is sulfur tetrafluoride.
**(b)** The prefix *hepta-* indicates seven, not six. The correct formula is $Cl_2O_7$.
**(c)** The full name of the first element is needed, and a space separates the two element names. The correct name is dinitrogen trioxide.

**Follow-Up Problem 2.14** Explain what is wrong with the name or formula at the end of each statement, and correct it: **(a)** $S_2Cl_2$ is disulfurous dichloride. **(b)** Nitrogen monoxide is $N_2O$. **(c)** $BrCl_3$ is trichlorine bromide.

| Table **2.7** The First 10 Straight-Chain Alkanes | |
| --- | --- |
| **Name (Formula)** | **Model** |
| Methane ($CH_4$) | |
| Ethane ($C_2H_6$) | |
| Propane ($C_3H_8$) | |
| Butane ($C_4H_{10}$) | |
| Pentane ($C_5H_{12}$) | |
| Hexane ($C_6H_{14}$) | |
| Heptane ($C_7H_{16}$) | |
| Octane ($C_8H_{18}$) | |
| Nonane ($C_9H_{20}$) | |
| Decane ($C_{10}H_{22}$) | |

## The Simplest Organic Compounds: Straight-Chain Alkanes

Organic compounds typically have complex structures that consist of chains, branches, and/or rings of carbon atoms bonded to hydrogen atoms and, often, to atoms of oxygen, nitrogen, and a few other elements. At this point, we'll lay the groundwork for naming organic compounds by focusing on the simplest ones. Rules for naming more complex ones are detailed in Chapter 15.

*Hydrocarbons,* the simplest type of organic compound, contain *only* carbon and hydrogen. *Alkanes* are the simplest type of hydrocarbon; many function as important fuels, such as methane, propane, butane, and the mixture that makes up gasoline. The simplest alkanes to name are the *straight-chain alkanes* because the carbon chains have no branches. Alkanes are named with a *root,* based on the number of C atoms in the chain, followed by the suffix *-ane.* Table 2.7 gives the names, molecular formulas, and space-filling models (discussed shortly) of the first 10 straight-chain alkanes. Note that the roots of the four smallest ones are new, but those for the larger ones are the same as the Greek prefixes shown in Table 2.6.

## Molecular Masses from Chemical Formulas

In Section 2.5, we calculated the atomic mass of an element. Using the periodic table and the formula of a compound, we calculate the **molecular mass** (also called *molecular weight*) of a formula unit of the compound as the sum of the atomic masses:

$$\text{Molecular mass} = \text{sum of atomic masses} \tag{2.3}$$

The molecular mass of a water molecule (using atomic masses to four significant figures from the periodic table) is

$$\text{Molecular mass of } H_2O = (2 \times \text{atomic mass of H}) + (1 \times \text{atomic mass of O})$$
$$= (2 \times 1.008 \text{ amu}) + 16.00 \text{ amu} = 18.02 \text{ amu}$$

Ionic compounds don't consist of molecules, so the mass of a formula unit is termed the **formula mass** instead of *molecular mass.* To calculate the formula mass of a compound with a polyatomic ion, *the number of atoms of each element inside the parentheses is multiplied by the subscript outside the parentheses.* For barium nitrate, $Ba(NO_3)_2$,

Formula mass of $Ba(NO_3)_2$

$$= (1 \times \text{atomic mass of Ba}) + (2 \times \text{atomic mass of N}) + (6 \times \text{atomic mass of O})$$
$$= 137.3 \text{ amu} + (2 \times 14.01 \text{ amu}) + (6 \times 16.00 \text{ amu}) = 261.3 \text{ amu}$$

We can use atomic masses, not ionic masses, because electron loss equals electron gain, so electron mass is balanced. In the next two sample problems, the name or molecular depiction is used to find a compound's molecular or formula mass.

| **Sample Problem 2.15** | **Calculating the Molecular Mass of a Compound** |

**Problem** Using the periodic table, calculate the molecular (or formula) mass of
**(a)** Tetraphosphorus trisulfide    **(b)** Ammonium nitrate

**Plan** We first write the formula, then multiply the number of atoms (or ions) of each element by its atomic mass (from the periodic table), and find the sum.

**Solution (a)** The formula is $P_4S_3$.

Molecular mass = (4 × atomic mass of P) + (3 × atomic mass of S)

= (4 × 30.97 amu) + (3 × 32.07 amu) =  220.09 amu

**(b)** The formula is $NH_4NO_3$. We count the total number of N atoms even though they belong to different ions:

Formula mass

= (2 × atomic mass of N) + (4 × atomic mass of H) + (3 × atomic mass of O)

= (2 × 14.01 amu) + (4 × 1.007 amu) + (3 × 16.00 amu) =  80.05 amu

**Check** You can often find large errors by rounding atomic masses to the nearest 5 and adding: **(a)** (4 × 30) + (3 × 30) = 210 ≈ 220.09. The sum has two decimal places because the atomic masses have two. **(b)** (2 × 15) + 4 + (3 × 15) = 79 ≈ 80.05.

**Follow-Up Problem 2.15** What is the molecular (or formula) mass of
**(a)** Hydrogen peroxide    **(b)** Cesium chloride
**(c)** Sulfuric acid    **(d)** Potassium sulfate?

| **Sample Problem 2.16** | **Using Molecular Depictions to Determine Formula, Name, and Mass** |

**Problem** Each scene represents a binary compound. Determine its formula, name, and molecular (or formula) mass.

**Plan** Each of the compounds contains only two elements, so to find the formula, we find the simplest whole-number ratio of one atom to the other. From the formula, we determine the name and the molecular (or formula) mass.

**Solution (a)** There is one brown sphere (sodium) for each green sphere (fluorine), so the formula is NaF. A metal and nonmetal form an ionic compound, in which the metal is named first: sodium fluoride.

Formula mass = (1 × atomic mass of Na) + (1 × atomic mass of F)

= 22.99 amu + 19.00 amu =  41.99 amu

**(b)** There are three green spheres (fluorine) for each blue sphere (nitrogen), so the formula is $NF_3$. Two nonmetals form a covalent compound. Nitrogen has a lower group number, so it is named first: nitrogen trifluoride.

Molecular mass = (1 × atomic mass of N) + (3 × atomic mass of F)

= 14.01 amu + (3 × 19.00) =  71.01 amu

**Check (a)** For binary ionic compounds, we predict ionic charges from the periodic table (see Figure 2.13). Na forms a 1+ ion, and F forms a 1− ion, so the charges balance with one $Na^+$ per $F^-$. Also, ionic compounds are solids, consistent with the picture. **(b)** Covalent compounds often occur as individual molecules, as in the picture. Rounding in (a) gives 25 + 20 = 45; in (b), we get 15 + (3 × 20) = 75, so there are no large errors.

**Follow-Up Problem 2.16** Each scene represents a binary compound. Determine its name, formula, and molecular (or formula) mass.

**(a)**     **(b)**

- sodium
- oxygen
- nitrogen

## Representing Molecules with Formulas and Models

In order to represent objects too small to see, chemists employ a variety of formulas and models. Each conveys different information, as shown for water below:

- A **molecular formula** uses element symbols and, often, numerical subscripts to give the *actual* number of atoms of each element in a molecule of the compound. (Recall that, for ionic compounds, the *formula unit* gives the *relative* number of each type of ion.) The molecular formula of water is $H_2O$: there are two H atoms and one O atom in each molecule.

$$H_2O$$

- A **structural formula** shows the relative placement and connections of atoms in the molecule. It uses symbols for the atoms *and* either a pair of dots (*electron-dot formula*) or a line (*bond-line formula*) to show the bonds between the atoms. In water, each H atom is bonded to the O atom, but not to the other H atom.

H:O:H

H—O—H

In models, colored balls represent atoms (*see margin*).

Hydrogen, H    Phosphorus, P

Carbon, C    Sulfur, S

Nitrogen, N    Chlorine, Cl

Oxygen, O    Group 8A(18), e.g., neon, Ne

Group 1A(1), e.g., lithium, Li

- A *ball-and-stick model* shows atoms as balls and bonds as sticks, and the angles between the bonds are accurate. Note that water is a bent molecule (with a bond angle of 104.5°). This type of model doesn't show the bonded atoms overlapping (see Figure 2.14) or their relative sizes, so it exaggerates the distance between them.

- A *space-filling model* is an accurately scaled-up image of the molecule, so it shows the relative sizes of the atoms, the relative distances between the nuclei (centers of the spheres), and the angles between the bonds. However, bonds are not shown, and it can be difficult to see each atom in a complex molecule.

Every molecule is minute, but the range of molecular sizes, and thus molecular masses, is enormous. Table 2.8 shows some diatomic and small polyatomic molecules, and, at the other end of the size range two extremely large molecules, called *macromolecules*, deoxyribonucleic acid (DNA) and nylon.

## ■ Summary of Section 2.8

- An ionic compound is named with cation first and anion second. For metals that can form more than one ion, the charge is shown with a Roman numeral.
- Oxoanions have suffixes, and sometimes prefixes, attached to the root of the element name to indicate the number of oxygen atoms.
- Names of hydrates have a numerical prefix indicating the number of associated water molecules.
- Acid names are based on anion names.
- For binary covalent compounds, the first word of the name is the element farther left or lower down in the periodic table, and prefixes show the numbers of each atom.
- The molecular (or formula) mass of a compound is the sum of the atomic masses.
- Chemical formulas give the number of atoms (molecular) or the arrangement of atoms (structural) of one unit of a compound.
- Molecular models convey information about bond angles (ball-and-stick) and relative atomic sizes and distances between atoms (space-filling).

## Table **2.8** Representing Molecules

| Name | Molecular Formula (Molecular Mass, in amu) | Bond-Line Formula | Ball-and-Stick Model | Space-Filling Model |
|---|---|---|---|---|
| Carbon monoxide | CO (28.01) | | | |
| Nitrogen dioxide | $NO_2$ (46.01) | | | |
| Butane | $C_4H_{10}$ (58.12) | | | |
| Aspirin (acetylsalicylic acid) | $C_9H_8O_4$ (180.15) | | | |

Deoxyribonucleic acid (DNA ∼10,000,000 amu)

Nylon-66 (∼15,000 amu)

## 2.9 • MIXTURES: CLASSIFICATION AND SEPARATION

In the natural world, *matter usually occurs as mixtures.* A sample of clean air, for example, consists of many elements and compounds physically mixed together, including $O_2$, $N_2$, $CO_2$, the noble gases [Group 8A(18)], and water vapor ($H_2O$). The oceans are complex mixtures of dissolved ions and covalent substances, including $Na^+$, $Mg^{2+}$, $Cl^-$, $SO_4^{2-}$, $O_2$, $CO_2$, and of course $H_2O$. Rocks and soils are mixtures of numerous compounds, including calcium carbonate ($CaCO_3$), silicon dioxide ($SiO_2$), aluminum oxide ($Al_2O_3$), and iron(III) oxide ($Fe_2O_3$). And living things contain thousands of substances—carbohydrates, lipids, proteins, nucleic acids, and many simpler ionic and covalent compounds.

There are two broad classes of mixtures:

- A **heterogeneous mixture** has one or more visible boundaries between the components. Thus, its composition is *not* uniform, but rather varies from one region to another. Many rocks are heterogeneous, having individual grains of different minerals. In some heterogeneous mixtures, such as milk and blood, the boundaries can be seen only with a microscope.
- A **homogeneous mixture** (or **solution**) has no visible boundaries because the components are individual atoms, ions, or molecules. Thus, its composition *is* uniform. A mixture of sugar dissolved in water is homogeneous, for example, because the sugar molecules and water molecules are uniformly intermingled on the molecular level. We have no way to tell visually whether a sample of matter is a substance (element or compound) or a homogeneous mixture.

Although we usually think of solutions as liquid, they can exist in all three physical states. For example, air is a gaseous solution of mostly oxygen and nitrogen molecules, and wax is a solid solution of several fatty substances. Solutions in water, called **aqueous solutions,** are especially important in the chemistry lab and comprise a major portion of the environment and of all organisms.

Recall that mixtures differ from compounds in three major ways:

1. The proportions of the components can vary.
2. The individual properties of the components are observable.
3. The components can be separated by physical means.

The difference between a mixture and a compound is well illustrated using iron and sulfur as components (Figure 2.19). Any proportion of iron metal filings and powdered sulfur forms a mixture. The components can be separated with a magnet because iron metal is magnetic. But if we heat the container strongly, the components form the compound iron(II) sulfide (FeS). The magnet can no longer remove the iron because it exists as $Fe^{2+}$ ions chemically bound to $S^{2-}$ ions.

Chemists have devised many procedures for separating a mixture into its components, and the Tools of the Laboratory essay describes some common ones.

### An Overview of the Components of Matter

Understanding matter at the observable and atomic scales is the essence of chemistry. Figure 2.20 is a visual overview of many key terms and ideas in this chapter.

**Figure 2.19** **The distinction between mixtures and compounds. A,** A *mixture* of iron and sulfur consists of the two elements. **B,** The *compound* iron(II) sulfide consists of an array of $Fe^{2+}$ and $S^{2-}$ ions.

### Summary of Section 2.9

- Heterogeneous mixtures have visible boundaries between the components.
- Homogeneous mixtures (solutions) have no visible boundaries because mixing occurs at the molecular level. They can occur in any physical state.
- Components of mixtures (unlike those of compounds) can have variable proportions, can be separated physically, and retain their properties.
- Separation methods are based on differences in physical properties and include filtration (particle size), crystallization (solubility), distillation (volatility), and chromatography (solubility).

Some of the most challenging laboratory procedures involve separating mixtures and purifying the components. All of the techniques described here depend on the *physical properties* of the substances in the mixture; no chemical changes occur.

**Filtration** is based on *differences in particle size* and is often used to separate a solid from a liquid, which flows through the tiny holes in filter paper as the solid is retained. In vacuum filtration, reduced pressure speeds the flow of the liquid through the filter. Filtration is used in the purification of tap water.

**Crystallization** is based on *differences in solubility*. The *solubility* of a substance is the amount that dissolves in a fixed volume of solvent at a given temperature. Since solubility often increases with temperature, the impure solid is dissolved in hot solvent and when the solution cools, the purified compound crystallizes. A key component of computer chips is purified by a type of crystallization.

**Distillation** separates components through *differences in volatility,* the tendency of a substance to become a gas. *Simple* distillation separates components with *large* differences in volatility, such as water from dissolved ionic compounds (Figure B2.3). As the mixture boils, the vapor is richer in the more volatile component, in this case, water, which is condensed and collected separately. *Fractional* distillation uses many vaporization-condensation steps to separate components with small volatility differences, such as those in petroleum (discussed in Chapter 13).

**Chromatography** is also based on *differences in solubility*. The mixture is dissolved in a gas or liquid, and the components are

**Figure B2.4** Procedure for column chromatography.

Ink mixture is placed on stationary phase.

Solvent (mobile phase)

Fresh solvent flows through column.

Components move at different rates.

Stationary phase packed in column

Component most soluble in mobile phase (least soluble in stationary phase) moves fastest.

Later time

Collecting flasks

Components are collected separately.

separated as this solution, called the *mobile phase,* flows through a solid (or viscous liquid) called the *stationary phase.* A component with lower solubility in the stationary phase moves through it faster than a component with a higher solubility. Figure B2.4 depicts the separation of inks by *column chromatography.*

In a related technique called *gas-liquid chromatography (GLC),* the mobile phase is an inert gas, such as helium, that carries a gaseous mixture of components into a long tube packed with the stationary phase (Figure B2.5, part A). The components emerge separately and reach a detector. A chromatogram has numerous peaks, each representing the amount of a specific component (Figure B2.5, part B). *High-performance (high-pressure) liquid chromatography (HPLC)* is similar to GLC, but the mixture need not be vaporized, so more diverse mixtures can be separated.

## Problem

**B2.3** Name the technique(s) and briefly describe the procedure for separating each of the following mixtures into pure components: (a) table salt and pepper; (b) drinking water contaminated with soot; (c) crushed ice and crushed glass; (d) table sugar dissolved in ethanol; (e) two pigments (chlorophyll *a* and chlorophyll *b*) from spinach leaves.

Thermometer

Mixture is heated and volatile component vaporizes.

Vapors in contact with cool glass condense to form pure liquid distillate.

Water-cooled condenser

Distilling flask

Water out to sink

Water in

Distillate collected in separate flask.

**Figure B2.3** Distillation.

He gas

He gas

Time
• • •

He gas

He gas

**A** *Gaseous mixture (blue and red) is carried into column with mobile phase.*

*Component (blue) that is more soluble in stationary phase moves slower.*

**Solubility in stationary phase**

Detector response

20
18
16
14
12
10
8
6
4
2
0

22   24   26   28   30   32   34   36
Time (minutes)

**B**

**Figure B2.5** Principle of gas-liquid chromatography (GLC). The stationary phase is shown as a viscous liquid *(gray circles)* coating the solid beads *(yellow)* of an inert packing.

# MATTER
- Anything with mass and volume
- Exists in three physical states: solid, liquid, gas

## MIXTURES
- Two or more elements or compounds in variable proportions
- Components retain their properties

### Heterogeneous Mixtures
- Visible parts
- Differing regional composition

### Homogeneous Mixtures (Solutions)
- No visible parts
- Same composition throughout

PHYSICAL CHANGES

- Filtration
- Crystallization
- Distillation
- Chromatography

## SUBSTANCES
- Fixed composition throughout

### Elements
- Composed of one type of atom
- Classified as metal, nonmetal, or metalloid
- Simplest type of matter that retains characteristic properties
- May occur as individual atoms or diatomic or polyatomic molecules
- Atomic mass is average of isotopic masses weighted by abundance

### Compounds
- Two or more elements combined in fixed parts by mass
- Properties differ from those of component elements
- Molecular mass is sum of atomic masses

CHEMICAL CHANGES

### Atoms
- Protons ($p^+$) and neutrons ($n^0$) in tiny, massive, positive nucleus
- Atomic number ($Z$) = no. of $p^+$
- Mass number ($A$) = no. of $p^+$ + no. of $n^0$
- Electrons ($e^-$) occupy surrounding volume; no. of $p^+$ = no. of $e^-$

### Ionic
- Ions arise through $e^-$ transfer from metal to nonmetal
- Solids composed of array of mutually attracting cations and anions
- Formula unit represents the fixed cation/anion ratio

### Covalent
- Often consist of separate molecules
- Atoms (usually nonmetals) bonded by $e^-$ pair mutually attracted (shared) by both nuclei

**Figure 2.20**  The classification of matter from a chemical point of view.

# CHAPTER REVIEW GUIDE

## Understand These Concepts

1. The defining characteristics of the three types of matter—element, compound, and mixture—on the macroscopic and atomic levels (§2.1)
2. The significance of the three mass laws—mass conservation, definite composition, and multiple proportions (§2.2)
3. The postulates of Dalton's atomic theory and how it explains the mass laws (§2.3)
4. The major contribution of experiments by Thomson, Millikan, and Rutherford to our understanding of atomic structure (§2.4)
5. The structure of the atom, the main features of the subatomic particles, and the importance of isotopes (§2.5)
6. The format of the periodic table and general location and characteristics of metals, metalloids, and nonmetals (§2.6)
7. The essential features of ionic and covalent compounds and the distinction between them (§2.7)
8. The types of mixtures and their properties (§2.9)

## Master These Skills

1. Distinguishing elements, compounds, and mixtures at the atomic scale (SP 2.1)
2. Using the mass ratio of element to compound to find the mass of an element in a compound (SP 2.2)
3. Visualizing the mass laws (SP 2.3)
4. Using atomic notation to express the subatomic makeup of an isotope (SP 2.4)
5. Calculating an atomic mass from isotopic composition (SP 2.5)
6. Predicting the monatomic ion formed from a main-group element (SP 2.6)
7. Naming and writing the formula of an ionic compound formed from the ions in Tables 2.3 to 2.5 (SPs 2.7–2.12, 2.16)
8. Naming and writing the formula of a binary covalent compound (SPs 2.13, 2.14, 2.16)
9. Calculating the molecular or formula mass of a compound (SP 2.15)

**Section 2.1**
substance (38)
element (38)
molecule (38)
compound (38)
mixture (39)

**Section 2.2**
law of mass conservation (40)
law of definite (or constant) composition (41)
fraction by mass (mass fraction) (41)
percent by mass (mass percent, mass %) (41)
law of multiple proportions (42)

**Section 2.3**
atom (43)

**Section 2.4**
cathode ray (45)
nucleus (47)

**Section 2.5**
proton ($p^+$) (48)
neutron ($n^0$) (48)
electron ($e^-$) (48)
atomic number ($Z$) (48)
mass number ($A$) (49)
atomic symbol (49)
isotope (49)
atomic mass unit (amu) (50)
dalton (Da) (50)
mass spectrometry (50)
isotopic mass (50)
atomic mass (50)

**Section 2.6**
periodic table of the elements (53)

period (53)
group (53)
metal (54)
nonmetal (54)
metalloid (semimetal) (54)

**Section 2.7**
ionic compound (55)
covalent compound (55)
chemical bond (55)
ion (55)
binary ionic compound (55)
cation (55)
anion (55)
monatomic ion (55)
covalent bond (58)
polyatomic ion (59)

**Section 2.8**
chemical formula (59)
formula unit (60)

oxoanion (63)
hydrate (63)
binary covalent compound (65)
molecular mass (66)
formula mass (66)
molecular formula (68)
structural formula (68)

**Section 2.9**
heterogeneous mixture (70)
homogeneous mixture (solution) (70)
aqueous solution (70)
filtration (71)
crystallization (71)
distillation (71)
volatility (71)
chromatography (71)

**2.1** Finding the mass of an element in a given mass of compound (41):

Mass of element in sample

$$= \text{mass of compound in sample} \times \frac{\text{mass of element}}{\text{mass of compound}}$$

**2.2** Calculating the number of neutrons in an atom (49):

Number of neutrons = mass number − atomic number

or $$N = A - Z$$

**2.3** Determining the molecular mass of a formula unit of a compound (66):

Molecular mass = sum of atomic masses

## Brief Solutions to Follow-Up Problems

**2.1** There are two types of particles reacting (left circle), one with two blue atoms and the other with two orange; the depiction shows a mixture of two elements. In the product (right circle), all the particles have one blue atom and one orange; this is a compound.

**2.2** Mass (t) of pitchblende

$$= 2.3 \text{ t uranium} \times \frac{84.2 \text{ t pitchblende}}{71.4 \text{ t uranium}} = 2.7 \text{ t pitchblende}$$

Mass (t) of oxygen

$$= 2.7 \text{ t pitchblende} \times \frac{(84.2 - 71.4 \text{ t oxygen})}{84.2 \text{ t pitchblend}} = 0.41 \text{ t oxygen}$$

**2.3** Sample B. Two bromine-fluorine compounds appear. In one, there are three fluorine atoms for each bromine; in the other, there is one fluorine for each bromine. Therefore, in the two compounds, the ratio of fluorines combining with one bromine is 3/1.

**2.4** (a) $5p^+$, $6n^0$, $5e^-$; Q = B
(b) $20p^+$, $21n^0$, $20e^-$; R = Ca
(c) $53p^+$, $78n^0$, $53e^-$; X = I

**2.5** $10.0129x + [11.0093(1 - x)] = 10.81$; $0.9964x = 0.1993$; $x = 0.2000$ and $1 - x = 0.8000$; % abundance of $^{10}$B = 20.00%; % abundance of $^{11}$B = 80.00%

**2.6** (a) $S^{2-}$; (b) $Rb^+$; (c) $Ba^{2+}$

**2.7** (a) Zinc [Group 2B(12)] and oxygen [Group 6A(16)]
(b) Silver [Group 1B(11)] and bromine [Group 7A(17)]
(c) Lithium [Group 1A(1)] and chlorine [Group 7A(17)]
(d) Aluminum [Group 3A(13)] and sulfur [Group 6A(16)]

**2.8** (a) ZnO; (b) AgBr; (c) LiCl; (d) $Al_2S_3$

**2.9** (a) $PbO_2$; (b) copper(I) sulfide (cuprous sulfide); (c) iron(II) bromide (ferrous bromide); (d) $HgCl_2$

**2.10** (a) $Cu(NO_3)_2 \cdot 3H_2O$; (b) $Zn(OH)_2$; (c) lithium cyanide

**2.11** (a) $(NH_4)_3PO_4$; ammonium is $NH_4^+$ and phosphate is $PO_4^{3-}$.
(b) $Al(OH)_3$; parentheses are needed around the polyatomic ion $OH^-$.
(c) Magnesium hydrogen carbonate; $Mg^{2+}$ is magnesium and can have only a 2+ charge, so it does not need (II); $HCO_3^-$ is hydrogen carbonate (or bicarbonate).
(d) Chromium(III) nitrate; the -ic ending is not used with Roman numerals; $NO_3^-$ is nitrate.
(e) Calcium nitrite; $Ca^{2+}$ is calcium and $NO_2^-$ is nitrite.

**2.12** (a) $HClO_3$; (b) hydrofluoric acid; (c) $CH_3COOH$ (or $HC_2H_3O_2$); (d) $H_2SO_3$; (e) hypobromous acid

**2.13** (a) Sulfur trioxide; (b) silicon dioxide; (c) $N_2O$; (d) $SeF_6$

**2.14** (a) Disulfur dichloride; the -ous suffix is not used.
(b) NO; the name indicates one nitrogen.
(c) Bromine trichloride; Br is in a higher period in Group 7A(17), so it is named first.

**2.15** (a) $H_2O_2$, 34.02 amu; (b) CsCl, 168.4 amu; (c) $H_2SO_4$, 98.09 amu; (d) $K_2SO_4$, 174.27 amu

**2.16** (a) $Na_2O$. This is an ionic compound, so the name is sodium oxide.

Formula mass

$= (2 \times$ atomic mass of Na$) + (1 \times$ atomic mass of O$)$

$= (2 \times 22.99 \text{ amu}) + 16.00 \text{ amu} = 61.98 \text{ amu}$

(b) $NO_2$. This is a covalent compound, and N has the lower group number, so the name is nitrogen dioxide.

Molecular mass

$= (1 \times$ atomic mass of N$) + (2 \times$ atomic mass of O$)$

$= 14.01 \text{ amu} + (2 \times 16.00 \text{ amu}) = 46.01 \text{ amu}$

## PROBLEMS

Problems with **colored** numbers are answered in Appendix E and worked in detail in the Student Solutions Manual. Problem sections match those in the text and provide the numbers of relevant sample problems. Most offer Concept Review Questions, Skill-Building Exercises (grouped in pairs covering the same concept), and Problems in Context. The Comprehensive Problems are based on material from any section or previous chapter.

### Elements, Compounds, and Mixtures: An Atomic Overview
(Sample Problem 2.1)

**Concept Review Questions**

**2.1** What is the key difference between an element and a compound?

**2.2** List two differences between a compound and a mixture.

**2.3** Which of the following are pure substances? Explain.
(a) Calcium chloride, used to melt ice on roads, consists of two elements, calcium and chlorine, in a fixed mass ratio.

(b) Sulfur consists of sulfur atoms combined into octatomic molecules.
(c) Baking powder, a leavening agent, contains 26% to 30% sodium hydrogen carbonate and 30% to 35% calcium dihydrogen phosphate by mass.
(d) Cytosine, a component of DNA, consists of H, C, N, and O atoms bonded in a specific arrangement.

**2.4** Classify each substance in Problem 2.3 as an element, compound, or mixture, and explain your answers.

**2.5** Explain the following statement: The smallest particles unique to an element may be atoms or molecules.

**2.6** Explain the following statement: The smallest particles unique to a compound cannot be atoms.

**2.7** Can the relative amounts of the components of a mixture vary? Can the relative amounts of the components of a compound vary? Explain.

**Problems in Context**

**2.8** The tap water found in many areas of the United States leaves white deposits when it evaporates. Is this tap water a mixture or a compound? Explain.

**2.9** Each scene below represents a mixture. Describe each one in terms of the number(s) of elements and/or compounds present.

**2.10** Samples of illicit "street" drugs often contain an inactive component, such as ascorbic acid (vitamin C). After obtaining a sample of cocaine, government chemists calculate the mass of vitamin C per gram of drug sample, and use it to track the drug's distribution. For example, if different samples of cocaine obtained on the streets of New York, Los Angeles, and Paris all contain 0.6384 g of vitamin C per gram of sample, they very likely come from a common source. Do these street samples consist of a compound, element, or mixture? Explain.

**The Observations That Led to an Atomic View of Matter**
(Sample Problem 2.2)

**Concept Review Questions**

**2.11** Why was it necessary for separation techniques and methods of chemical analysis to be developed before the laws of definite composition and multiple proportions could be formulated?

**2.12** To which classes of matter—element, compound, and/or mixture—do the following apply: (a) law of mass conservation; (b) law of definite composition; (c) law of multiple proportions?

**2.13** In our modern view of matter and energy, is the law of mass conservation still relevant to chemical reactions? Explain.

**2.14** Identify the mass law that each of the following observations demonstrates, and explain your reasoning:
(a) A sample of potassium chloride from Chile contains the same percent by mass of potassium as one from Poland.
(b) A flashbulb contains magnesium and oxygen before use and magnesium oxide afterward, but its mass does not change.
(c) Arsenic and oxygen form one compound that is 65.2 mass % arsenic and another that is 75.8 mass % arsenic.

**2.15** Which of the following scenes illustrate(s) the fact that compounds of chlorine (green) and oxygen (red) exhibit the law of multiple proportions? Name the compounds.

**2.16** (a) Does the percent by mass of each element in a compound depend on the amount of compound? Explain.

(b) Does the mass of each element in a compound depend on the amount of compound? Explain.

**2.17** Does the percent by mass of each element in a compound depend on the amount of that element used to make the compound? Explain.

**Skill-Building Exercises** (grouped in similar pairs)

**2.18** State the mass law(s) demonstrated by the following experimental results, and explain your reasoning:

Experiment 1: A student heats 1.00 g of a blue compound and obtains 0.64 g of a white compound and 0.36 g of a colorless gas.

Experiment 2: A second student heats 3.25 g of the same blue compound and obtains 2.08 g of a white compound and 1.17 g of a colorless gas.

**2.19** State the mass law(s) demonstrated by the following experimental results, and explain your reasoning:

Experiment 1: A student heats 1.27 g of copper and 3.50 g of iodine to produce 3.81 g of a white compound; 0.96 g of iodine remains.

Experiment 2: A second student heats 2.55 g of copper and 3.50 g of iodine to form 5.25 g of a white compound, and 0.80 g of copper remains.

**2.20** Fluorite, a mineral of calcium, is a compound of the metal with fluorine. Analysis shows that a 2.76-g sample of fluorite contains 1.42 g of calcium. Calculate the (a) mass of fluorine in the sample; (b) mass fractions of calcium and fluorine in fluorite; (c) mass percents of calcium and fluorine in fluorite.

**2.21** Galena, a mineral of lead, is a compound of the metal with sulfur. Analysis shows that a 2.34-g sample of galena contains 2.03 g of lead. Calculate the (a) mass of sulfur in the sample; (b) mass fractions of lead and sulfur in galena; (c) mass percents of lead and sulfur in galena.

**2.22** Magnesium oxide (MgO) forms when the metal burns in air.
(a) If 1.25 g of MgO contains 0.754 g of Mg, what is the mass ratio of magnesium to oxide?
(b) How many grams of Mg are in 534 g of MgO?

**2.23** Zinc sulfide (ZnS) occurs in the zinc blende crystal structure.
(a) If 2.54 g of ZnS contains 1.70 g of Zn, what is the mass ratio of zinc to sulfide?
(b) How many kilograms of Zn are in 3.82 kg of ZnS?

**2.24** A compound of copper and sulfur contains 88.39 g of metal and 44.61 g of nonmetal. How many grams of copper are in 5264 kg of compound? How many grams of sulfur?

**2.25** A compound of iodine and cesium contains 63.94 g of metal and 61.06 g of nonmetal. How many grams of cesium are in 38.77 g of compound? How many grams of iodine?

**2.26** Show, with calculations, how the following data illustrate the law of multiple proportions:
Compound 1: 47.5 mass % sulfur and 52.5 mass % chlorine
Compound 2: 31.1 mass % sulfur and 68.9 mass % chlorine

**2.27** Show, with calculations, how the following data illustrate the law of multiple proportions:
Compound 1: 77.6 mass % xenon and 22.4 mass % fluorine
Compound 2: 63.3 mass % xenon and 36.7 mass % fluorine

**Problems in Context**

**2.28** Dolomite is a carbonate of magnesium and calcium. Analysis shows that 7.81 g of dolomite contains 1.70 g of Ca. Calculate the mass percent of Ca in dolomite. On the basis of the mass percent of Ca, and neglecting all other factors, which is the richer source of Ca, dolomite or fluorite (see Problem 2.20)?

**2.29** The mass percent of sulfur in a sample of coal is a key factor in the environmental impact of the coal because the sulfur combines with oxygen when the coal is burned and the oxide can then be incorporated into acid rain. Which of the following coals would have the smallest environmental impact?

|              | Mass (g) of Sample | Mass (g) of Sulfur in Sample |
|--------------|:------------------:|:----------------------------:|
| Coal A       | 378                | 11.3                         |
| Coal B       | 495                | 19.0                         |
| Coal C       | 675                | 20.6                         |

## Dalton's Atomic Theory
(Sample Problem 2.3)

**Concept Review Questions**

**2.30** Which of Dalton's postulates about atoms are inconsistent with later observations? Do these inconsistencies mean that Dalton was wrong? Is Dalton's model still useful? Explain.

**2.31** Use Dalton's theory to explain why potassium nitrate from India or Italy has the same mass percents of K, N, and O.

## The Observations That Led to the Nuclear Atom Model

**Concept Review Questions**

**2.32** Thomson was able to determine the mass/charge ratio of the electron but not its mass. How did Millikan's experiment allow determination of the electron's mass?

**2.33** The following charges on individual oil droplets were obtained during an experiment similar to Millikan's. Determine a charge for the electron (in C, coulombs), and explain your answer: $-3.204 \times 10^{-19}$ C; $-4.806 \times 10^{-19}$ C; $-8.010 \times 10^{-19}$ C; $-1.442 \times 10^{-18}$ C.

**2.34** Describe Thomson's model of the atom. How might it account for the production of cathode rays?

**2.35** When Rutherford's coworkers bombarded gold foil with $\alpha$ particles, they obtained results that overturned the existing (Thomson) model of the atom. Explain.

## The Atomic Theory Today
(Sample Problems 2.4 and 2.5)

**Concept Review Questions**

**2.36** Define *atomic number* and *mass number*. Which can vary without changing the identity of the element?

**2.37** Choose the correct answer. The difference between the mass number of an isotope and its atomic number is (a) directly related to the identity of the element; (b) the number of electrons; (c) the number of neutrons; (d) the number of isotopes.

**2.38** Even though several elements have only one naturally occurring isotope and all atomic nuclei have whole numbers of protons and neutrons, no atomic mass is a whole number. Use the data from Table 2.2 to explain this fact.

**Skill-Building Exercises** (grouped in similar pairs)

**2.39** Argon has three naturally occurring isotopes, $^{36}$Ar, $^{38}$Ar, and $^{40}$Ar. What is the mass number of each? How many protons, neutrons, and electrons are present in each?

**2.40** Chlorine has two naturally occurring isotopes, $^{35}$Cl and $^{37}$Cl. What is the mass number of each isotope? How many protons, neutrons, and electrons are present in each?

**2.41** Do both members of the following pairs have the same number of protons? Neutrons? Electrons?
(a) $^{16}_{8}$O and $^{17}_{8}$O    (b) $^{40}_{18}$Ar and $^{41}_{19}$K    (c) $^{60}_{27}$Co and $^{60}_{28}$Ni
Which pair(s) consist(s) of atoms with the same $Z$ value? $N$ value? $A$ value?

**2.42** Do both members of the following pairs have the same number of protons? Neutrons? Electrons?
(a) $^{3}_{1}$H and $^{3}_{2}$He    (b) $^{14}_{6}$C and $^{15}_{7}$N    (c) $^{19}_{9}$F and $^{18}_{9}$F
Which pair(s) consist(s) of atoms with the same $Z$ value? $N$ value? $A$ value?

**2.43** Write the $^{A}_{Z}$X notation for each atomic depiction:

(a)          (b)          (c)

**2.44** Write the $^{A}_{Z}$X notation for each atomic depiction:

(a)          (b)          (c)

**2.45** Draw atomic depictions similar to those in Problem 2.43 for (a) $^{48}_{22}$Ti; (b) $^{79}_{34}$Se; (c) $^{11}_{5}$B.

**2.46** Draw atomic depictions similar to those in Problem 2.43 for (a) $^{207}_{82}$Pb; $^{9}_{4}$Be; $^{75}_{33}$As.

**2.47** Gallium has two naturally occurring isotopes, $^{69}$Ga (isotopic mass = 68.9256 amu, abundance = 60.11%) and $^{71}$Ga (isotopic mass = 70.9247 amu, abundance = 39.89%). Calculate the atomic mass of gallium.

**2.48** Magnesium has three naturally occurring isotopes, $^{24}$Mg (isotopic mass = 23.9850 amu, abundance = 78.99%), $^{25}$Mg (isotopic mass = 24.9858 amu, abundance = 10.00%), and $^{26}$Mg (isotopic mass = 25.9826 amu, abundance = 11.01%). Calculate the atomic mass of magnesium.

**2.49** Chlorine has two naturally occurring isotopes, $^{35}$Cl (isotopic mass = 34.9689 amu) and $^{37}$Cl (isotopic mass = 36.9659 amu). If chlorine has an atomic mass of 35.4527 amu, what is the percent abundance of each isotope?

**2.50** Copper has two naturally occurring isotopes, $^{63}$Cu (isotopic mass = 62.9396 amu) and $^{65}$Cu (isotopic mass = 64.9278 amu). If copper has an atomic mass of 63.546 amu, what is the percent abundance of each isotope?

## Elements: A First Look at the Periodic Table

### Concept Review Questions

**2.51** How can iodine ($Z = 53$) have a higher atomic number yet a lower atomic mass than tellurium ($Z = 52$)?

**2.52** Correct each of the following statements:
(a) In the modern periodic table, the elements are arranged in order of increasing atomic mass.
(b) Elements in a period have similar chemical properties.
(c) Elements can be classified as either metalloids or nonmetals.

**2.53** What class of elements lies along the "staircase" line in the periodic table? How do the properties of these elements compare with those of metals and nonmetals?

**2.54** What are some characteristic properties of elements to the left of the elements along the "staircase"? To the right?

**2.55** The elements in Groups 1A(1) and 7A(17) are all quite reactive. What is a major difference between them?

### Skill-Building Exercises (grouped in similar pairs)

**2.56** Give the name, atomic symbol, and group number of the element with each $Z$ value, and classify it as a metal, metalloid, or nonmetal:
(a) $Z = 32$   (b) $Z = 15$   (c) $Z = 2$   (d) $Z = 3$   (e) $Z = 42$

**2.57** Give the name, atomic symbol, and group number of the element with each $Z$ value, and classify it as a metal, metalloid, or nonmetal:
(a) $Z = 33$   (b) $Z = 20$   (c) $Z = 35$   (d) $Z = 19$   (e) $Z = 13$

**2.58** Fill in the blanks:
(a) The symbol and atomic number of the heaviest alkaline earth metal are _____ and _____.
(b) The symbol and atomic number of the lightest metalloid in Group 4A(14) are _____ and _____.
(c) Group 1B(11) consists of the *coinage metals*. The symbol and atomic mass of the coinage metal whose atoms have the fewest electrons are _____ and _____.
(d) The symbol and atomic mass of the halogen in Period 4 are _____ and _____.

**2.59** Fill in the blanks:
(a) The symbol and atomic number of the heaviest nonradioactive noble gas are _____ and _____.
(b) The symbol and group number of the Period 5 transition element whose atoms have the fewest protons are _____ and _____.
(c) The elements in Group 6A(16) are sometimes called the *chalcogens*. The symbol and atomic number of the first metallic chalcogen are _____ and _____.
(d) The symbol and number of protons of the Period 4 alkali metal atom are _____ and _____.

## Compounds: Introduction to Bonding
(Sample Problem 2.6)

### Concept Review Questions

**2.60** Describe the type and nature of the bonding that occurs between reactive metals and nonmetals.

**2.61** Describe the type and nature of the bonding that often occurs between two nonmetals.

**2.62** How can ionic compounds be neutral if they consist of positive and negative ions?

**2.63** Given that the ions in LiF and in MgO are of similar size, which compound has stronger ionic bonding? Use Coulomb's law in your explanation.

**2.64** Are molecules present in a sample of $BaF_2$? Explain.

**2.65** Are ions present in a sample of $P_4O_6$? Explain.

**2.66** The monatomic ions of Groups 1A(1) and 7A(17) are all singly charged. In what major way do they differ? Why?

**2.67** Describe the formation of solid magnesium chloride ($MgCl_2$) from large numbers of magnesium and chlorine atoms.

**2.68** Describe the formation of solid potassium sulfide ($K_2S$) from large numbers of potassium and sulfur atoms.

**2.69** Does potassium nitrate ($KNO_3$) incorporate ionic bonding, covalent bonding, or both? Explain.

### Skill-Building Exercises (grouped in similar pairs)

**2.70** What monatomic ions do potassium ($Z = 19$) and iodine ($Z = 53$) form?

**2.71** What monatomic ions do barium ($Z = 56$) and selenium ($Z = 34$) form?

**2.72** For each ionic depiction, give the name of the parent atom, its mass number, and its group and period numbers:

**2.73** For each ionic depiction, give the name of the parent atom, its mass number, and its group and period numbers:

**2.74** An ionic compound forms when lithium ($Z = 3$) reacts with oxygen ($Z = 8$). If a sample of the compound contains $8.4 \times 10^{21}$ lithium ions, how many oxide ions does it contain?

**2.75** An ionic compound forms when calcium ($Z = 20$) reacts with iodine ($Z = 53$). If a sample of the compound contains $7.4 \times 10^{21}$ calcium ions, how many iodide ions does it contain?

**2.76** The radii of the sodium and potassium ions are 102 pm and 138 pm, respectively. Which compound has stronger ionic attractions, sodium chloride or potassium chloride?

**2.77** The radii of the lithium and magnesium ions are 76 pm and 72 pm, respectively. Which compound has stronger ionic attractions, lithium oxide or magnesium oxide?

## Formulas, Names, and Masses of Compounds
(Sample Problems 2.7 to 2.16)

### Concept Review Questions

**2.78** What information about the relative numbers of ions and the percent mass of elements is in the formula $MgF_2$?

**2.79** How is a structural formula similar to a molecular formula? How is it different?

**2.80** Consider a mixture of 10 billion $O_2$ molecules and 10 billion $H_2$ molecules. In what way is this mixture similar to a sample containing 10 billion hydrogen peroxide ($H_2O_2$) molecules? In what way is it different?

**2.81** For what type(s) of compound do we use Roman numerals in the names?

**2.82** For what type(s) of compound do we use Greek numerical prefixes in the names?

**2.83** For what type of compound are we unable to write a molecular formula?

### Skill-Building Exercises (grouped in similar pairs)

**2.84** Give the name and formula of the compound formed from the following elements: (a) sodium and nitrogen; (b) oxygen and strontium; (c) aluminum and chlorine.

**2.85** Give the name and formula of the compound formed from the following elements: (a) cesium and bromine; (b) sulfur and barium; (c) calcium and fluorine.

**2.86** Give the name and formula of the compound formed from the following elements:
(a) $_{12}L$ and $_9M$     (b) $_{30}L$ and $_{16}M$     (c) $_{17}L$ and $_{38}M$

**2.87** Give the name and formula of the compound formed from the following elements:
(a) $_{37}Q$ and $_{35}R$     (b) $_8Q$ and $_{13}R$     (c) $_{20}Q$ and $_{53}R$

**2.88** Give the systematic names for the formulas or the formulas for the names: (a) tin(IV) chloride; (b) $FeBr_3$; (c) cuprous bromide; (d) $Mn_2O_3$.

**2.89** Give the systematic names for the formulas or the formulas for the names: (a) $Na_2HPO_4$; (b) potassium carbonate dihydrate; (c) $NaNO_2$; (d) ammonium perchlorate.

**2.90** Give the systematic names for the formulas or the formulas for the names: (a) CoO; (b) mercury(I) chloride; (c) $Pb(C_2H_3O_2)_2 \cdot 3H_2O$; (d) chromic oxide.

**2.91** Give the systematic names for the formulas or the formulas for the names: (a) $Sn(SO_3)_2$; (b) potassium dichromate; (c) $FeCO_3$; (d) copper(II) nitrate.

**2.92** Correct each of the following formulas:
(a) Barium oxide is $BaO_2$
(b) Iron(II) nitrate is $Fe(NO_3)_3$
(c) Magnesium sulfide is $MnSO_3$

**2.93** Correct each of the following names:
(a) CuI is cobalt(II) iodide
(b) $Fe(HSO_4)_3$ is iron(II) sulfate
(c) $MgCr_2O_7$ is magnesium dichromium heptaoxide

**2.94** Give the name and formula for the acid derived from each of the following anions:
(a) hydrogen sulfate     (b) $IO_3^-$     (c) cyanide     (d) $HS^-$

**2.95** Give the name and formula for the acid derived from each of the following anions:
(a) perchlorate     (b) $NO_3^-$     (c) bromite     (d) $F^-$

**2.96** Many chemical names are similar at first glance. Give the formulas of the species in each set:
(a) Ammonium ion and ammonia
(b) Magnesium sulfide, magnesium sulfite, and magnesium sulfate
(c) Hydrochloric acid, chloric acid, and chlorous acid
(d) Cuprous bromide and cupric bromide

**2.97** Give the formulas of the compounds in each set:
(a) Lead(II) oxide and lead(IV) oxide
(b) Lithium nitride, lithium nitrite, and lithium nitrate
(c) Strontium hydride and strontium hydroxide
(d) Magnesium oxide and manganese(II) oxide

**2.98** Give the name and formula of the compound whose molecules consist of two sulfur atoms and four fluorine atoms.

**2.99** Give the name and formula of the compound whose molecules consist of two chlorine atoms and one oxygen atom.

**2.100** Correct the name to match the formula of the following compounds: (a) calcium(II) dichloride, $CaCl_2$; (b) Copper(II) oxide, $Cu_2O$; (c) Stannous tetrafluoride, $SnF_4$; (d) Hydrogen chloride acid, HCl.

**2.101** Correct the formula to match the name of the following compounds: (a) iron(III) oxide, $Fe_3O_4$; (b) chloric acid, HCl; (c) mercuric oxide, $Hg_2O$; (d) dichlorine heptaoxide, $Cl_2O_6$.

**2.102** Give the number of atoms of the specified element in a formula unit of each of the following compounds, and calculate the molecular (formula) mass:
(a) Oxygen in aluminum sulfate, $Al_2(SO_4)_3$
(b) Hydrogen in ammonium hydrogen phosphate, $(NH_4)_2HPO_4$
(c) Oxygen in the mineral azurite, $Cu_3(OH)_2(CO_3)_2$

**2.103** Give the number of atoms of the specified element in a formula unit of each of the following compounds, and calculate the molecular (formula) mass:
(a) Hydrogen in ammonium benzoate, $C_6H_5COONH_4$
(b) Nitrogen in hydrazinium sulfate, $N_2H_6SO_4$
(c) Oxygen in the mineral leadhillite, $Pb_4SO_4(CO_3)_2(OH)_2$

**2.104** Write the formula of each compound, and determine its molecular (formula) mass: (a) ammonium sulfate; (b) sodium dihydrogen phosphate; (c) potassium bicarbonate.

**2.105** Write the formula of each compound, and determine its molecular (formula) mass: (a) sodium dichromate; (b) ammonium perchlorate; (c) magnesium nitrite trihydrate.

**2.106** Calculate the molecular (formula) mass of each compound: (a) dinitrogen pentaoxide; (b) lead(II) nitrate; (c) calcium peroxide.

**2.107** Calculate the molecular (formula) mass of each compound: (a) iron(II) acetate tetrahydrate; (b) sulfur tetrachloride; (c) potassium permanganate.

**2.108** Give the formula, name, and molecular mass of the following molecules:

(a)    (b)

**2.109** Give the formula, name, and molecular mass of the following molecules:

(a)    (b)

### Problems in Context

**2.110** Before the use of systematic names, many compounds had common names. Give the systematic name for each of the following:
(a) Blue vitriol, $CuSO_4 \cdot 5H_2O$
(b) Slaked lime, $Ca(OH)_2$
(c) Oil of vitriol, $H_2SO_4$
(d) Washing soda, $Na_2CO_3$
(e) Muriatic acid, HCl
(f) Epsom salt, $MgSO_4 \cdot 7H_2O$
(g) Chalk, $CaCO_3$
(h) Dry ice, $CO_2$
(i) Baking soda, $NaHCO_3$
(j) Lye, NaOH

**2.111** Each circle contains a representation of a binary compound. Determine its name, formula, and molecular (formula) mass.

(a)    (b)

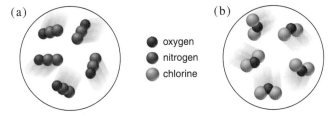

- oxygen
- nitrogen
- chlorine

## Mixtures: Classification and Separation

### Concept Review Questions

**2.112** In what main way is separating the components of a mixture different from separating the components of a compound?

**2.113** What is the difference between a homogeneous and a heterogeneous mixture?

**2.114** Is a solution a homogeneous or a heterogeneous mixture? Give an example of an aqueous solution.

### Skill-Building Exercises (grouped in similar pairs)

**2.115** Classify each of the following as a compound, a homogeneous mixture, or a heterogeneous mixture: (a) distilled water; (b) gasoline; (c) beach sand; (d) wine; (e) air.

**2.116** Classify each of the following as a compound, a homogeneous mixture, or a heterogeneous mixture: (a) orange juice; (b) vegetable soup; (c) cement; (d) calcium sulfate; (e) tea.

### Problems in Context

**2.117** Which separation method is operating in each of the following procedures?
(a) Pouring a mixture of cooked pasta and boiling water into a colander

(b) Removing colored impurities from raw sugar to make refined sugar

**2.118** A quality-control laboratory analyzes a product mixture using gas-liquid chromatography. The separation of components is more than adequate, but the process takes too long. Suggest two ways, other than changing the stationary phase, to shorten the analysis time.

## Comprehensive Problems

**2.119** Helium is the lightest noble gas and the second most abundant element (after hydrogen) in the universe.
(a) The radius of a helium atom is $3.1 \times 10^{-11}$ m; the radius of its nucleus is $2.5 \times 10^{-15}$ m. What fraction of the spherical atomic volume is occupied by the nucleus ($V$ of a sphere $= \frac{4}{3}\pi r^3$)?
(b) The mass of a helium-4 atom is $6.64648 \times 10^{-24}$ g, and each of its two electrons has a mass of $9.10939 \times 10^{-28}$ g. What fraction of this atom's mass is contributed by its nucleus?

**2.120** From the following ions (with their radii in pm), choose the pair that forms the strongest ionic bond and the pair that forms the weakest:

| Ion:    | $Mg^{2+}$ | $K^+$ | $Rb^+$ | $Ba^{2+}$ | $Cl^-$ | $O^{2-}$ | $I^-$ |
|---------|------|-----|-----|------|-----|-----|-----|
| Radius: | 72   | 138 | 152 | 135  | 181 | 140 | 220 |

**2.121** Give the molecular mass of each compound depicted below, and provide a correct name for any that are named incorrectly.

(a) boron fluoride    (b) monosulfur dichloride

(c) phosphorus trichloride    (d) dinitride pentaoxide

**2.122** Polyatomic ions are named by patterns that apply to elements in a given group. Using the periodic table and Table 2.5, give the name of each of the following: (a) $SeO_4^{2-}$; (b) $AsO_4^{3-}$; (c) $BrO_2^-$; (d) $HSeO_4^-$; (e) $TeO_3^{2-}$.

**2.123** Ammonium dihydrogen phosphate, formed from the reaction of phosphoric acid with ammonia, is used as a crop fertilizer as well as a component of some fire extinguishers. (a) What are the mass percentages of N and P in the compound? (b) How much ammonia is incorporated into 100. g of the compound?

**2.124** Nitrogen forms more oxides than any other element. The percents by mass of N in three different nitrogen oxides are (I) 46.69%; (II) 36.85%; (III) 25.94%. For each compound, determine (a) the simplest whole-number ratio of N to O, and (b) the number of grams of oxygen per 1.00 g of nitrogen.

**2.125** The number of atoms in 1 $dm^3$ of aluminum is nearly the same as the number of atoms in 1 $dm^3$ of lead, but the densities of these metals are very different (see Table 1.5). Explain.

**2.126** You are working in the laboratory preparing sodium chloride. Consider the following results for three preparations of the compound:

Case 1: 39.34 g Na + 60.66 g $Cl_2$ ⟶ 100.00 g NaCl
Case 2: 39.34 g Na + 70.00 g $Cl_2$ ⟶
    100.00 g NaCl + 9.34 g $Cl_2$
Case 3: 50.00 g Na + 50.00 g $Cl_2$ ⟶
    82.43 g NaCl + 17.57 g Na

Explain these results in terms of the laws of conservation of mass and definite composition.

**2.127** Scenes A–I depict various types of matter on the atomic scale. Choose the correct scene(s) for each of the following:
(a) A mixture that fills its container
(b) A substance that cannot be broken down into simpler ones
(c) An element with a very high resistance to flow
(d) A homogeneous mixture
(e) An element that conforms to the walls of its container and displays an upper surface
(f) A gas consisting of diatomic particles
(g) A gas that can be broken down into simpler substances
(h) A substance with a 2/1 ratio of its component atoms
(i) Matter that can be separated into its component substances by physical means
(j) A heterogeneous mixture
(k) Matter that obeys the law of definite composition

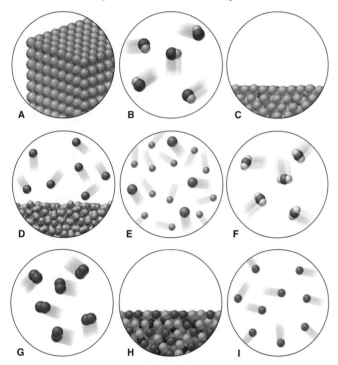

**2.128** The seven most abundant ions in seawater make up more than 99% by mass of the dissolved compounds. Here are their abundances in units of mg ion/kg seawater: chloride 18,980; sodium 10,560; sulfate 2650; magnesium 1270; calcium 400; potassium 380; hydrogen carbonate 140.
(a) What is the mass % of each ion in seawater?
(b) What percent of the total mass of ions is sodium ion?
(c) How does the total mass % of alkaline earth metal ions compare with the total mass % of alkali metal ions?
(d) Which make up the larger mass fraction of dissolved components, anions or cations?

**2.129** The scenes below represent a mixture of two monatomic gases undergoing a reaction when heated. Which mass law(s) is (are) illustrated by this change?

**2.130** When barium (Ba) reacts with sulfur (S) to form barium sulfide (BaS), each Ba atom reacts with an S atom. If 2.50 cm³ of Ba reacts with 1.75 cm³ of S, are there enough Ba atoms to react with the S atoms ($d$ of Ba = 3.51 g/cm³; $d$ of S = 2.07 g/cm³)?

**2.131** Succinic acid (*below*) is an important metabolite in biological energy production. Give the molecular formula, molecular mass, and the mass percent of each element in succinic acid.

**2.132** Fluoride ion is poisonous in relatively low amounts: 0.2 g of F⁻ per 70 kg of body weight can cause death. Nevertheless, in order to prevent tooth decay, F⁻ ions are added to drinking water at a concentration of 1 mg of F⁻ ion per L of water. How many liters of fluoridated drinking water would a 70-kg person have to consume in one day to reach this toxic level? How many kilograms of sodium fluoride would be needed to treat a $8.50 \times 10^7$-gal reservoir?

**2.133** Antimony has many uses, for example, in infrared devices and as part of an alloy in lead storage batteries. The element has two naturally occurring isotopes, one with mass 120.904 amu, the other with mass 122.904 amu. (a) Write the $^A_Z X$ notation for each isotope. (b) Use the atomic mass of antimony from the periodic table to calculate the natural abundance of each isotope.

**2.134** Dinitrogen monoxide ($N_2O$; nitrous oxide) is a greenhouse gas that enters the atmosphere principally from natural fertilizer breakdown. Some studies have shown that the isotope ratios of $^{15}N$ to $^{14}N$ and of $^{18}O$ to $^{16}O$ in $N_2O$ depend on the source, which can thus be determined by measuring the relative abundance of molecular masses in a sample of $N_2O$.
(a) What different molecular masses are possible for $N_2O$?
(b) The percent abundance of $^{14}N$ is 99.6%, and that of $^{16}O$ is 99.8%. Which molecular mass of $N_2O$ is least common, and which is most common?

**2.135** Use the box color(s) in the periodic table below to identify the element(s) described by each of the following:

(a) Four elements that are nonmetals
(b) Two elements that are metals
(c) Three elements that are gases at room temperature
(d) Three elements that are solid at room temperature
(e) One pair of elements likely to form a covalent compound
(f) Another pair of elements likely to form a covalent compound
(g) One pair of elements likely to form an ionic compound with formula MX
(h) Another pair of elements likely to form an ionic compound with formula MX
(i) Two elements likely to form an ionic compound with formula $M_2X$
(j) Two elements likely to form an ionic compound with formula $MX_2$

(k) An element that forms no compounds

(l) A pair of elements whose compounds exhibit the law of multiple proportions

**2.136** The two isotopes of potassium with significant abundance in nature are $^{39}K$ (isotopic mass 38.9637 amu, 93.258%) and $^{41}K$ (isotopic mass 40.9618 amu, 6.730%). Fluorine has only one naturally occurring isotope, $^{19}F$ (isotopic mass 18.9984 amu). Calculate the formula mass of potassium fluoride.

**2.137** Boron trifluoride is used as a catalyst in the synthesis of organic compounds. When this compound is analyzed by mass spectrometry (see Tools of the Laboratory, p. 51), several different 1+ ions form, including ions representing the whole molecule as well as molecular fragments formed by the loss of one, two, and three F atoms. Given that boron has two naturally occurring isotopes, $^{10}B$ and $^{11}B$, and fluorine has one, $^{19}F$, calculate the masses of all possible 1+ ions.

**2.138** Nitrogen monoxide (NO) is a bioactive molecule in blood. Low NO concentrations cause respiratory distress and the formation of blood clots. Doctors prescribe nitroglycerin, $C_3H_5N_3O_9$, and isoamyl nitrate, $(CH_3)_2CHCH_2CH_2ONO_2$, to increase NO. If each compound releases one molecule of NO per atom of N it contains, calculate the mass percent of NO in each.

**2.139** TNT (trinitrotoluene; *below*) is used as an explosive in construction. Calculate the mass of each element in 1.00 lb of TNT.

**2.140** Nuclei differ in their stability, and some are so unstable that they undergo radioactive decay. The ratio of the number of neutrons to number of protons ($N/Z$) in a nucleus correlates with its stability. Calculate the $N/Z$ ratio for (a) $^{144}Sm$; (b) $^{56}Fe$; (c) $^{20}Ne$; (d) $^{107}Ag$. (e) The radioactive isotope $^{238}U$ decays in a series of nuclear reactions that includes another uranium isotope, $^{234}U$, and three lead isotopes, $^{214}Pb$, $^{210}Pb$, and $^{206}Pb$. How many neutrons, protons, and electrons are in each of these five isotopes?

**2.141** The anticancer drug Platinol (Cisplatin), $Pt(NH_3)_2Cl_2$, reacts with the cancer cell's DNA and interferes with its growth. (a) What is the mass % of platinum (Pt) in Platinol? (b) If Pt costs \$32/g, how many grams of Platinol can be made for \$1.00 million (assume that the cost of Pt determines the cost of the drug)?

**2.142** In the periodic table below, give the name, symbol, atomic number, atomic mass, period number, and group number of (a) the *building-block elements (red),* which occur in nearly every biological molecule, and (b) the *macronutrients (green),* which are either essential ions in cell fluids or are part of many biomolecules.

**2.143** The block diagram below classifies the components of matter on the macroscopic scale. Identify blocks (a)–(d).

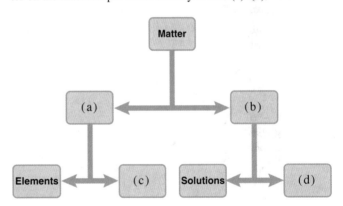

**2.144** Which of the following steps in an overall process involve(s) a physical change and which involve(s) a chemical change?

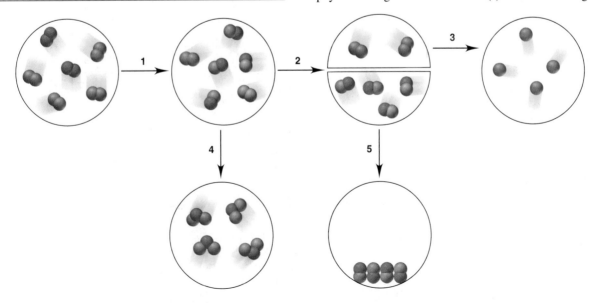

# Stoichiometry of Formulas and Equations

## Concepts and skills to review before you study this chapter

- atomic mass (Section 2.5)
- names and formulas of compounds (Section 2.8)
- molecular (or formula) mass (Section 2.8)
- molecular and structural formulas, and ball-and-stick and space-filling models (Section 2.8)

hemistry is, above all, a practical science. Imagine that you're a biochemist who has extracted a substance with medicinal activity from a tropical plant: what is its formula, and what quantity of metabolic products will establish a safe dosage level? In 1785, the cardiac drug digitoxin was extracted from the foxglove (*photo*). (Since then, thousands of other biologically active compounds have been found in plants and many are used in modern medicines.) Or, suppose you're a chemical engineer studying rocket-fuel thrust: what amount of propulsive gases will a fuel produce? Perhaps you're on a team of environmental chemists examining coal samples: what quantity of air pollutants will a sample produce when burned? Or, maybe you're a polymer chemist preparing a plastic with unusual properties: how much of this new material will the polymerization reaction yield? You can answer countless questions like these with a knowledge of **stoichiometry** (pronounced "stoy-key-AHM-uh-tree"; from the Greek *stoicheion*, "element or part," and *metron*, "measure"), the study of the quantitative aspects of formulas and reactions.

**IN THIS CHAPTER** . . . We relate the mass of a substance to the number of chemical entities comprising it (atoms, ions, molecules, or formula units) and apply this relationship to formulas and equations.
- We discuss the *mole*, the chemist's unit for amount of a substance, and use it to convert between mass and number of entities.
- We also use it to derive a chemical formula from the results of mass analysis.
- We see whether two key types of formulas relate to molecular structures.
- We learn how to write chemical equations and how to balance them in terms of the amounts of substances reacting and produced.
- We calculate the amounts of reactants and products in a reaction and see why one of the reactants limits the amount of product that can form and, thus, the reaction yield.
- We discuss concentration and apply stoichiometry to reactions in solution.

## 3.1 • THE MOLE

In daily life, we often measure things by counting or by weighing: we weigh beans or rice, but we count eggs or pencils. And we use counting units (a dozen pencils) or mass units (a kilogram of beans) to express the amount. Similarly, daily life in the laboratory involves measuring substances. We want to know the numbers of chemical entities—atoms, ions, molecules, or formula units—that react with each other, but how can we possibly count or weigh such minute objects? As you'll see, chemists have devised a unit, called the *mole*, to *count chemical entities by weighing them.*

### Defining the Mole

The **mole** (abbreviated **mol**) is the SI unit for *amount of substance*. It is defined as *the amount of a substance that contains the same number of entities as the number of atoms in 12 g of carbon-12*. This number, called **Avogadro's number** (in honor of the 19th-century Italian physicist Amedeo Avogadro), is enormous: ●

One mole (1 mol) contains $6.022 \times 10^{23}$ entities (to four significant figures)     **(3.1)**

● **Imagine a Mole of . . .** A mole of any ordinary object is a staggering amount: a mole of periods (.) lined up side by side would equal the radius of our galaxy; a mole of marbles stacked tightly together would cover the United States 70 miles deep. However, atoms and molecules are not ordinary objects: you can swallow a mole of water molecules (about 18 mL) in one gulp!

A counting unit, like *dozen,* tells you the number of objects but not their mass; a mass unit, like *kilogram,* tells you the mass of the objects but not their number. The mole tells you both—the *number* of objects in a given *mass* of substance:

1 mol of carbon-12 contains $6.022 \times 10^{23}$ carbon-12 atoms *and* has a mass of 12 g

What does it mean that the mole unit allows you to count entities by weighing the sample? Suppose you have a sample of carbon-12 and want to know the number of atoms present. You find that the sample weighs 6 g, so it is 0.5 mol of carbon-12 and contains $3.011 \times 10^{23}$ atoms:

6 g of carbon-12 is 0.5 mol of carbon-12 and contains $3.011 \times 10^{23}$ atoms

Knowing the amount (in moles), the mass (in grams), and the number of entities becomes very important when we mix different substances to run a reaction. The central relationship between masses on the atomic scale and on the macroscopic scale is the same for elements and compounds:

- *Elements.* The mass in **atomic mass units (amu)** of one atom of an element is the *same numerically* as the mass in **grams (g)** of 1 mole of atoms of the element. Recall from Chapter 2 that each atom of an element is considered to have the *atomic mass* given in the periodic table *(see margin).* Thus,

| 16 |
|:--:|
| **S** |
| 32.07 |

1 atom of S   has a mass of   32.07 amu   and   1 mol ($6.022 \times 10^{23}$ atoms) of S   has a mass of   32.07 g
1 atom of Fe   has a mass of   55.85 amu   and   1 mol ($6.022 \times 10^{23}$ atoms) of Fe   has a mass of   55.85 g

Note, also, that since atomic masses are relative, 1 Fe atom weighs 55.85/32.07 as much as 1 S atom, and 1 mol of Fe weighs 55.85/32.07 as much as 1 mol of S.

- *Compounds.* The mass in **atomic mass units (amu)** of one molecule (or formula unit) of a compound is the *same numerically* as the mass in **grams (g)** of 1 mole of the compound. Thus, for example,

1 molecule of $H_2O$   has a mass of   18.02 amu   and   1 mol ($6.022 \times 10^{23}$ molecules) of $H_2O$   has a mass of   18.02 g
1 formula unit of NaCl   has a mass of   58.44 amu   and   1 mol ($6.022 \times 10^{23}$ formula units) of NaCl   has a mass of   58.44 g

Here, too, because masses are relative, 1 $H_2O$ molecule weighs 18.02/58.44 as much as 1 NaCl formula unit, and 1 mol of $H_2O$ weighs 18.02/58.44 as much as 1 mol of NaCl.

The two key points to remember about the importance of the mole unit are

- The *mole* lets us relate the *number* of entities to the *mass* of a sample of those entities.
- The mole maintains the *same numerical relationship* between mass on the atomic scale (atomic mass units, amu) and mass on the macroscopic scale (grams, g).

In everyday terms, a grocer *does not* know there are 1 dozen eggs from their weight or that there is 1 kilogram of beans from their count, because eggs and beans do not have fixed masses. But, by weighing out 63.55 g (1 mol) of copper, a chemist *does* know that there are $6.022 \times 10^{23}$ copper atoms, because all copper atoms have an atomic mass of 63.55 amu. Figure 3.1 shows 1 mole of some familiar elements and compounds.

## Determining Molar Mass

The **molar mass** ($\mathcal{M}$) of a substance is the mass per mole of its entities (atoms, molecules, or formula units) and has units of grams per mole (g/mol). The periodic table is indispensable for calculating molar mass:

1. *Elements.* To find the molar mass, look up the atomic mass and note whether the element is monatomic or molecular.
- *Monatomic elements.* The molar mass is the periodic-table value in grams per mole.* For example, the molar mass of neon is 20.18 g/mol, and the molar mass of gold is 197.0 g/mol.

**Figure 3.1 One mole ($6.022 \times 10^{23}$ entities) of some familiar substances.** From left to right: 1 mol of copper (63.55 g), of liquid $H_2O$ (18.02 g), of sodium chloride (table salt, 58.44 g), of sucrose (table sugar, 342.3 g), and of aluminum (26.98 g).

*The mass value in the periodic table has no units because it is a *relative* atomic mass, given by the atomic mass (in amu) divided by 1 amu ($\frac{1}{12}$ mass of one $^{12}C$ atom in amu):

$$\text{Relative atomic mass} = \frac{\text{atomic mass (amu)}}{\frac{1}{12} \text{ mass of } ^{12}C \text{ (amu)}}$$

Therefore, you use the same number for the atomic mass and for the molar mass.

• *Molecular elements.* You must know the formula to determine the molar mass (see Figure 2.15). For example, in air, oxygen exists most commonly as diatomic molecules, so the molar mass of $O_2$ is twice that of O:

$$\text{Molar mass } (\mathcal{M}) \text{ of } O_2 = 2 \times \mathcal{M} \text{ of } O = 2 \times 16.00 \text{ g/mol} = 32.00 \text{ g/mol}$$

The most common form of sulfur exists as octatomic molecules, $S_8$:

$$\mathcal{M} \text{ of } S_8 = 8 \times \mathcal{M} \text{ of } S = 8 \times 32.07 \text{ g/mol} = 256.6 \text{ g/mol}$$

2. *Compounds. The molar mass is the sum of the molar masses of the atoms in the formula.* Thus, from the formula of sulfur dioxide, $SO_2$, we know that 1 mol of $SO_2$ molecules contains 1 mol of S atoms and 2 mol of O atoms:

$$\mathcal{M} \text{ of } SO_2 = \mathcal{M} \text{ of } S + (2 \times \mathcal{M} \text{ of } O) = 32.07 \text{ g/mol} + (2 \times 16.00 \text{ g/mol}) = 64.07 \text{ g/mol}$$

Similarly, for ionic compounds, such as potassium sulfide ($K_2S$), we have

$$\mathcal{M} \text{ of } K_2S = (2 \times \mathcal{M} \text{ of } K) + \mathcal{M} \text{ of } S = (2 \times 39.10 \text{ g/mol}) + 32.07 \text{ g/mol} = 110.27 \text{ g/mol}$$

Thus, *subscripts in a formula refer to individual atoms (or ions) as well as to moles of atoms (or ions).* Table 3.1 summarizes these ideas for glucose, $C_6H_{12}O_6$ *(see margin),* the essential sugar in energy metabolism.

Glucose

| Table **3.1** Information Contained in the Chemical Formula of Glucose, $C_6H_{12}O_6$ ($\mathcal{M}$ = 180.16 g/mol) | | | |
|---|---|---|---|
| | **Carbon (C)** | **Hydrogen (H)** | **Oxygen (O)** |
| Atoms/molecule of compound | 6 atoms | 12 atoms | 6 atoms |
| Moles of atoms/mole of compound | 6 mol of atoms | 12 mol of atoms | 6 mol of atoms |
| Atoms/mole of compound | $6(6.022\times10^{23})$ atoms | $12(6.022\times10^{23})$ atoms | $6(6.022\times10^{23})$ atoms |
| Mass/molecule of compound | $6(12.01 \text{ amu}) = 72.06$ amu | $12(1.008 \text{ amu}) = 12.10$ amu | $6(16.00 \text{ amu}) = 96.00$ amu |
| Mass/mole of compound | 72.06 g | 12.10 g | 96.00 g |

## Converting Between Amount, Mass, and Number of Chemical Entities

One of the most common skills in the lab—and on exams—is converting between amount (mol), mass (g), and number of entities of a substance.

1. *Converting between amount and mass.* If you know the amount of a substance, you can find its mass, and vice versa. The molar mass ($\mathcal{M}$), which expresses the equivalence between 1 mole of a substance and its mass in grams, is the conversion factor.
   • *From amount (mol) to mass (g),* multiply by the molar mass:

$$\text{Mass (g)} = \text{amount (mol)} \times \frac{\text{no. of grams}}{1 \text{ mol}} \qquad \text{(3.2)}$$

   • *From mass (g) to amount (mol),* divide by the molar mass (multiply by $1/\mathcal{M}$):

$$\text{Amount (mol)} = \text{mass (g)} \times \frac{1 \text{ mol}}{\text{no. of grams}} \qquad \text{(3.3)}$$

2. *Converting between amount and number.* Similarly, if you know the amount (mol), you can find the number of entities, and vice versa. Avogadro's number, which expresses the equivalence between 1 mole of a substance and the number of entities it contains, is the conversion factor.
   • *From amount (mol) to number of entities,* multiply by Avogadro's number:

$$\text{No. of entities} = \text{amount (mol)} \times \frac{6.022\times10^{23} \text{ entities}}{1 \text{ mol}} \qquad \text{(3.4)}$$

   • *From number of entities to amount (mol),* divide by Avogadro's number:

$$\text{Amount (mol)} = \text{no. of entities} \times \frac{1 \text{ mol}}{6.022\times10^{23} \text{ entities}} \qquad \text{(3.5)}$$

**Amount-Mass-Number Conversions Involving Elements** We begin with amount-mass-number relationships of elements. As Figure 3.2 shows, *convert mass or number of entities to amount (mol) first.*

**Figure 3.2 Mass-mole-number relation-ships for elements.** To find the number of atoms (or molecules) in a given mass, or vice versa, convert to amount (mol) first. For molecular elements, Avogadro's number gives *molecules* per mole.

Let's work through a series of sample problems that show these conversions for both elements and compounds.

---

**Sample Problem 3.1** | **Calculating the Mass of a Given Amount of an Element**

**Problem** Silver (Ag) is used in jewelry and tableware but no longer in U.S. coins. How many grams of Ag are in 0.0342 mol of Ag?

**Plan** We know the amount of Ag (0.0342 mol) and have to find the mass (g). To convert units of *moles* of Ag to *grams* of Ag, we multiply by the *molar mass* of Ag, which we find in the periodic table (see the road map).

**Solution** Converting from amount (mol) of Ag to mass (g):

$$\text{Mass (g) of Ag} = 0.0342 \text{ mol Ag} \times \frac{107.9 \text{ g Ag}}{1 \text{ mol Ag}} = \boxed{3.69 \text{ g Ag}}$$

**Road Map**

**Check** We rounded the mass to three significant figures because the amount (mol) has three. The units are correct. About 0.03 mol × 100 g/mol gives 3 g; the small mass makes sense because 0.0342 is a small fraction of a mole.

**Follow-Up Problem 3.1** Graphite is the crystalline form of carbon used in "lead" pencils. How many moles of carbon are in 315 mg of graphite? Include a road map that shows how you planned the solution. (See Brief Solutions at the end of the chapter for solutions to this and all other follow-up problems.)

---

**Sample Problem 3.2** | **Calculating the Number of Entities in a Given Amount of an Element**

**Problem** Gallium (Ga) is a key element in solar panels, calculators, and other light-sensitive electronic devices. How many Ga atoms are in $2.85 \times 10^{-3}$ mol of gallium?

**Plan** We know the amount of gallium ($2.85 \times 10^{-3}$ mol) and need the number of Ga atoms. We multiply amount (mol) by Avogadro's number to find number of atoms (see the road map).

**Solution** Converting from amount (mol) of Ga to number of atoms:

$$\text{No. of Ga atoms} = 2.85 \times 10^{-3} \; \cancel{\text{mol Ga}} \times \frac{6.022 \times 10^{23} \text{ Ga atoms}}{1 \; \cancel{\text{mol Ga}}}$$

$$= \boxed{1.72 \times 10^{21} \text{ Ga atoms}}$$

**Check** The number of atoms has three significant figures because the number of moles does. When we round amount (mol) of Ga and Avogadro's number, we have $\sim(3 \times 10^{-3} \text{ mol})(6 \times 10^{23} \text{ atoms/mol}) = 18 \times 10^{20}$, or $1.8 \times 10^{21}$ atoms, so our answer seems correct.

**Follow-Up Problem 3.2** At rest, a person inhales $9.72 \times 10^{21}$ nitrogen molecules in an average breath of air. How many moles of nitrogen atoms are inhaled? (*Hint:* In air, nitrogen occurs as a diatomic molecule.) Include a road map that shows how you planned the solution.

**Road Map**

| Amount (mol) of Ga |
|---|

↓ multiply by
$6.022 \times 10^{23}$ atoms/mol

| Number of Ga atoms |
|---|

For the next problem, note that mass and number of entities relate directly to amount (mol), but *not* to each other. Therefore, *to convert between mass and number, first convert to amount.*

---

**Sample Problem 3.3** | **Calculating the Number of Entities in a Given Mass of an Element**

**Problem** Iron (Fe) is the main component of steel and, thus, the most important metal in industrial society; it is also essential in the body. How many Fe atoms are in 95.8 g of Fe?

**Plan** We know the mass of Fe (95.8 g) and need the number of Fe atoms. We cannot convert directly from mass to number, so we first convert to amount (mol) by dividing mass of Fe by its molar mass. Then, we multiply amount (mol) by Avogadro's number to find number of atoms (see the road map).

**Solution** Converting from mass (g) of Fe to amount (mol):

$$\text{Moles of Fe} = 95.8 \; \cancel{\text{g Fe}} \times \frac{1 \text{ mol Fe}}{55.85 \; \cancel{\text{g Fe}}} = 1.72 \text{ mol Fe}$$

Converting from amount (mol) of Fe to number of Fe atoms:

$$\text{No. of Fe atoms} = 1.72 \; \cancel{\text{mol Fe}} \times \frac{6.022 \times 10^{23} \text{ atoms Fe}}{1 \; \cancel{\text{mol Fe}}}$$

$$= 10.4 \times 10^{23} \text{ atoms Fe}$$

$$= \boxed{1.04 \times 10^{24} \text{ atoms Fe}}$$

**Check** Rounding the mass and the molar mass of Fe, we have $\sim 100 \text{ g}/(\sim 60 \text{ g/mol}) = 1.7$ mol. Therefore, the number of atoms should be a bit less than twice Avogadro's number: $<2(6 \times 10^{23}) = <1.2 \times 10^{24}$, so the answer seems correct.

**Follow-Up Problem 3.3** Manganese (Mn) is a transition element essential for the growth of bones. What is the mass in grams of $3.22 \times 10^{20}$ Mn atoms, the number found in 1 kg of bone? Include a road map that shows how you planned the solution.

**Road Map**

| Mass (g) of Fe |
|---|

↓ divide by ℳ of Fe

| Amount (mol) of Fe |
|---|

↓ multiply by $6.022 \times 10^{23}$ atoms/mol

| Number of Fe atoms |
|---|

**Amount-Mass-Number Conversions Involving Compounds** Only one new step is needed to solve amount-mass-number problems involving compounds: we need the chemical formula to find the molar mass and the amount of each element in the compound. The relationships are shown in Figure 3.3 on the next page, and Sample Problems 3.4 and 3.5 apply them to compounds with simple and more complicated formulas, respectively.

**Figure 3.3 Amount-mass-number relationships for compounds.** Use the chemical formula to find the amount (mol) of each element in a compound.

---

**Road Map**

**Problem** Nitrogen dioxide is a component of urban smog that forms from gases in car exhaust. How many molecules are in 8.92 g of nitrogen dioxide?

**Plan** We know the mass of compound (8.92 g) and need to find the number of molecules. As you just saw in Sample Problem 3.3, to convert mass to number of entities, we have to find the amount (mol). To do so, we divide the mass by the molar mass ($\mathcal{M}$), which we calculate from the molecular formula (see Sample Problem 2.15). Once we have the amount (mol), we multiply by Avogadro's number to find the number of molecules (see the road map).

**Solution** The formula is $NO_2$. Calculating the molar mass:

$$\mathcal{M} = (1 \times \mathcal{M} \text{ of N}) + (2 \times \mathcal{M} \text{ of O})$$
$$= 14.01 \text{ g/mol} + (2 \times 16.00 \text{ g/mol})$$
$$= 46.01 \text{ g/mol}$$

Converting from mass (g) of $NO_2$ to amount (mol):

$$\text{Amount (mol) of } NO_2 = 8.92 \text{ g } NO_2 \times \frac{1 \text{ mol } NO_2}{46.01 \text{ g } NO_2}$$
$$= 0.194 \text{ mol } NO_2$$

Converting from amount (mol) of $NO_2$ to number of molecules:

$$\text{No. of molecules} = 0.194 \text{ mol } NO_2 \times \frac{6.022 \times 10^{23} \text{ } NO_2 \text{ molecules}}{1 \text{ mol } NO_2}$$
$$= 1.17 \times 10^{23} \text{ } NO_2 \text{ molecules}$$

**Check** Rounding, we get $(\sim 0.2 \text{ mol})(6 \times 10^{23}) = 1.2 \times 10^{23}$, so the answer seems correct.

**Follow-Up Problem 3.4** Fluoride ion is added to drinking water to prevent tooth decay. What is the mass (g) of sodium fluoride in a liter of water that contains $1.19 \times 10^{19}$ formula units of the compound? Include a road map that shows how you planned the solution.

## Sample Problem 3.5 Calculating the Number of Chemical Entities in a Given Mass of a Compound II

**Problem** Ammonium carbonate is a white solid that decomposes with warming. It has many uses, for example, as a component in baking powder, fire extinguishers, and smelling salts.
**(a)** How many formula units are in 41.6 g of ammonium carbonate?
**(b)** How many O atoms are in this sample?

**Plan (a)** We know the mass of compound (41.6 g) and need to find the number of formula units. As in Sample Problem 3.4, we find the amount (mol) and then multiply by Avogadro's number to find the number of formula units. [The road map shows the steps for part (a).] **(b)** To find the number of O atoms, we multiply the number of formula units by the number of O atoms in one formula unit.

**Solution (a)** The formula is $(NH_4)_2CO_3$ (see Table 2.5). Calculating the molar mass:

$$\mathcal{M} = (2 \times \mathcal{M} \text{ of N}) + (8 \times \mathcal{M} \text{ of H}) + (1 \times \mathcal{M} \text{ of C}) + (3 \times \mathcal{M} \text{ of O})$$
$$= (2 \times 14.01 \text{ g/mol N}) + (8 \times 1.008 \text{ g/mol H}) + 12.01 \text{ g/mol C}$$
$$+ (3 \times 16.00 \text{ g/mol O})$$
$$= 96.09 \text{ g/mol } (NH_4)_2CO_3$$

Converting from mass (g) to amount (mol):

$$\text{Amount (mol) of } (NH_4)_2CO_3 = 41.6 \text{ g } (NH_4)_2CO_3 \times \frac{1 \text{ mol } (NH_4)_2CO_3}{96.09 \text{ g } (NH_4)_2CO_3}$$
$$= 0.433 \text{ mol } (NH_4)_2CO_3$$

Converting from amount (mol) to formula units:

$$\text{Formula units of } (NH_4)_2CO_3 = 0.433 \text{ mol } (NH_4)_2CO_3$$
$$\times \frac{6.022 \times 10^{23} \text{ formula units } (NH_4)_2CO_3}{1 \text{ mol } (NH_4)_2CO_3}$$
$$= 2.61 \times 10^{23} \text{ formula units } (NH_4)_2CO_3$$

**(b)** Finding the number of O atoms:

$$\text{No. of O atoms} = 2.61 \times 10^{23} \text{ formula units } (NH_4)_2CO_3 \times \frac{3 \text{ O atoms}}{1 \text{ formula unit } (NH_4)_2CO_3}$$
$$= 7.83 \times 10^{23} \text{ O atoms}$$

**Check** In (a), the units are correct. Since the mass is less than half the molar mass ($\sim42/96 < 0.5$), the number of formula units should be less than half Avogadro's number ($\sim2.6 \times 10^{23}/6.0 \times 10^{23} < 0.5$).

**Comment** A *common mistake* is to forget the subscript 2 outside the parentheses in $(NH_4)_2CO_3$, which would give a much lower molar mass.

## Follow-Up Problem 3.5
Tetraphosphorus decaoxide reacts with water to form phosphoric acid, a major industrial acid. In the laboratory, the oxide is a drying agent.
**(a)** What is the mass (g) of $4.65 \times 10^{22}$ molecules of tetraphosphorus decaoxide?
**(b)** How many P atoms are present in this sample?

**Road Map**

| Mass (g) of $(NH_4)_2CO_3$ |
| :-: |

divide by $\mathcal{M}$ (g/mol)

| Amount (mol) of $(NH_4)_2CO_3$ |
| :-: |

multiply by $6.022 \times 10^{23}$ formula units/mol

| Number of formula units of $(NH_4)_2CO_3$ |
| :-: |

# The Importance of Mass Percent

For many purposes, it is important to know how much of an element is present in a given amount of compound. A biochemist may want the ionic composition of a mineral nutrient; an atmospheric chemist may be studying the amount of carbon in a fuel; a materials scientist may want the metalloid composition of a semiconductor. In this section, we find the composition of a compound in terms of mass percent and use it to find the mass of each element in the compound.

**Determining Mass Percent from a Chemical Formula** Each element contributes a fraction of a compound's mass, and that fraction multiplied by 100 gives the element's mass percent. Finding the mass percent is similar on the molecular and molar scales:

- *For a molecule (or formula unit) of compound,* use the molecular (or formula) mass and chemical formula to find the mass percent of any element X in the compound:

$$\text{Mass \% of element X} = \frac{\text{atoms of X in formula} \times \text{atomic mass of X(amu)}}{\text{molecular (or formula) mass of compound (amu)}} \times 100$$

- *For a mole of compound,* use the molar mass and formula to find the mass percent of each element on a mole basis:

$$\text{Mass \% of element X} = \frac{\text{moles of X in formula} \times \text{molar mass of X (g/mol)}}{\text{mass (g) of 1 mol of compound}} \times 100 \qquad \textbf{(3.6)}$$

As always, the individual mass percents add up to 100% (within rounding). In Sample Problem 3.6, we determine the mass percent of each element in a compound.

---

**Sample Problem 3.6**    **Calculating the Mass Percent of Each Element in a Compound from the Formula**

**Problem** In mammals, lactose (milk sugar) is metabolized to glucose ($C_6H_{12}O_6$), the key nutrient for generating chemical potential energy. What is the mass percent of each element in glucose?

**Plan** We know the relative amounts (mol) of the elements from the formula (6 C, 12 H, 6 O), and we have to find the mass % of each element. We multiply the amount of each by its molar mass to find its mass. Dividing each mass by the mass of 1 mol of glucose gives the mass fraction of each element, and multiplying by 100 gives each mass %. The calculation steps for any element (X) are shown in the road map.

**Solution** Converting amount (mol) of C to mass (g):
We have 6 mol of C in 1 mol of glucose, so

$$\text{Mass (g) of C} = 6 \text{ mol C} \times \frac{12.01 \text{ g C}}{1 \text{ mol C}} = 72.06 \text{ g C}$$

Calculating the mass of 1 mol of glucose ($C_6H_{12}O_6$):

$$\mathcal{M} = (6 \times \mathcal{M} \text{ of C}) + (12 \times \mathcal{M} \text{ of H}) + (6 \times \mathcal{M} \text{ of O})$$
$$= (6 \times 12.01 \text{ g/mol C}) + (12 \times 1.008 \text{ g/mol H}) + (6 \times 16.00 \text{ g/mol O})$$
$$= 180.16 \text{ g/mol } C_6H_{12}O_6$$

Finding the mass fraction of C in glucose:

$$\text{Mass fraction of C} = \frac{\text{total mass of C}}{\text{mass of 1 mol glucose}} = \frac{72.06 \text{ g C}}{180.16 \text{ g glucose}} = 0.4000$$

Changing to mass %:

$$\text{Mass \% of C} = \text{mass fraction of C} \times 100 = 0.4000 \times 100$$
$$= \boxed{40.00 \text{ mass \% C}}$$

Combining the steps for each of the other elements in glucose:

$$\text{Mass \% of H} = \frac{\text{mol H} \times \mathcal{M} \text{ of H}}{\text{mass of 1 mol glucose}} \times 100 = \frac{12 \text{ mol H} \times \frac{1.008 \text{ g H}}{1 \text{ mol H}}}{180.16 \text{ g glucose}} \times 100$$
$$= \boxed{6.714 \text{ mass \% H}}$$

$$\text{Mass \% of O} = \frac{\text{mol O} \times \mathcal{M} \text{ of O}}{\text{mass of 1 mol glucose}} \times 100 = \frac{6 \text{ mol O} \times \frac{16.00 \text{ g O}}{1 \text{ mol O}}}{180.16 \text{ g glucose}} \times 100$$
$$= \boxed{53.29 \text{ mass \% O}}$$

**Road Map**

Amount (mol) of element X in 1 mol of glucose

↓ multiply by $\mathcal{M}$ (g/mol) of X

Mass (g) of X in 1 mol of glucose

↓ divide by mass (g) of 1 mol of compound

Mass fraction of X in glucose

↓ multiply by 100

Mass % of X in glucose

**Check** The answers make sense: even though there are equal numbers of moles of O and of C in the compound, the mass % of O is greater than the mass % of C because the molar mass of O is greater than the molar mass of C. The mass % of H is small because the molar mass of H is small. The sum of the mass percents is 100.00%.

**Comment** From here on, you should be able to determine the molar mass of a compound, so that calculation will no longer be shown.

**Follow-Up Problem 3.6** Agronomists base the effectiveness of fertilizers on their nitrogen content. Ammonium nitrate is a common fertilizer. Calculate the mass percent of N in ammonium nitrate.

**Determining the Mass of an Element from Its Mass Percent** Sample Problem 3.6 shows that *an element always constitutes the same fraction of the mass of a given compound.* We obtained that fraction by dividing the total mass of element in a formula unit by the mass of one mole of the compound (see Equation 3.6). We can use that ratio directly to find the mass of element in any mass of a compound:

$$\text{Mass of element} = \text{mass of compound} \times \frac{\text{mass of element in 1 mol of compound}}{\text{mass of 1 mol of compound}} \quad \text{(3.7)}$$

For example, to find the mass of oxygen in 15.5 g of nitrogen dioxide, we have

$$\text{Mass (g) of O} = 15.5 \text{ g NO}_2 \times \frac{2 \text{ mol} \times M \text{ of O (g/mol)}}{\text{mass (g) of 1 mol NO}_2}$$

$$= 15.5 \text{ g NO}_2 \times \frac{32.00 \text{ g O}}{46.01 \text{ g NO}_2} = 10.8 \text{ g O}$$

---

**Sample Problem 3.7** | **Calculating the Mass of an Element in a Compound**

**Problem** Use the information in Sample Problem 3.6 to determine the mass (g) of carbon in 16.55 g of glucose.

**Plan** To find the mass of C in the sample of glucose, we multiply the mass of the sample by the mass of 6 mol of C divided by the mass of 1 mol of glucose.

**Solution** Finding the mass of C in a given mass of glucose:

$$\text{Mass (g) of C} = \text{mass (g) of glucose} \times \frac{6 \text{ mol C} \times M \text{ of C (g/mol)}}{\text{mass (g) of 1 mol glucose}}$$

$$= 16.55 \text{ g glucose} \times \frac{72.06 \text{ g C}}{180.16 \text{ g glucose}} = \boxed{6.620 \text{ g C}}$$

**Check** Rounding shows that the answer is "in the right ballpark": 16 g times less than 0.5 parts by mass should be less than 8 g.

**Follow-Up Problem 3.7** Use the information in Follow-Up Problem 3.6 to find the mass (g) of N in 35.8 kg of ammonium nitrate.

---

## ■ Summary of Section 3.1

- A mole of substance is the amount that contains Avogadro's number ($6.022 \times 10^{23}$) of chemical entities (atoms, molecules, or formula units).
- The mass (in grams) of a mole of the entity has the same numerical value as the mass (in amu) of the individual entity. Thus, the mole allows us to count entities by weighing them.
- Using the molar mass ($M$, g/mol) of an element (or compound) and Avogadro's number as conversion factors, we can convert among amount (mol), mass (g), and number of entities.
- The mass fraction of element X in a compound is used to find the mass of X in a given amount of the compound.

# 3.2 • DETERMINING THE FORMULA OF AN UNKNOWN COMPOUND

In Sample Problems 3.6 and 3.7, we used a compound's formula to find the mass percent (or mass fraction) of each element in it *and* the mass of each element in any size sample of it. In this section, we do the reverse: we use the masses of elements in a compound to find the formula. Then, we look briefly at the relationship between molecular formula and molecular structure.

Let's compare three common types of formula, using hydrogen peroxide as an example:

- The **empirical formula** is derived from mass analysis. It shows the *lowest* whole number of moles, and thus the *relative* number of atoms, of each element in the compound. For example, in hydrogen peroxide, there is 1 part by mass of hydrogen for every 16 parts by mass of oxygen. Because the atomic mass of hydrogen is 1.008 amu and that of oxygen is 16.00 amu, there is one H atom for every O atom. Thus, the empirical formula is HO.

Recall from Section 2.8, p. 59, that

- The **molecular formula** shows the *actual* number of atoms of each element in a molecule: the molecular formula is $H_2O_2$, twice the empirical formula.
- The **structural formula** shows the relative *placement and connections of atoms* in the molecule: the structural formula is H—O—O—H.

Let's see how to determine empirical and molecular formulas.

## Empirical Formulas

A chemist studying an unknown compound goes through a three-step process to find the empirical formula:

1. Determine the mass (g) of each component element.
2. Convert each mass (g) to amount (mol), and write a preliminary formula.
3. Convert the amounts (mol) mathematically to whole-number (integer) subscripts. To accomplish this math conversion,
   - Divide each subscript by the smallest subscript, and
   - If necessary, multiply through by the *smallest integer* that turns all subscripts into integers.

Sample Problem 3.8 demonstrates these math steps.

---

**Sample Problem 3.8**  **Determining an Empirical Formula from Amounts of Elements**

**Road Map**

> Amount (mol) of each element

> use nos. of moles as subscripts

> Preliminary formula

> change to integer subscripts

> Empirical formula

**Problem** A sample of an unknown compound contains 0.21 mol of zinc, 0.14 mol of phosphorus, and 0.56 mol of oxygen. What is the empirical formula?

**Plan** We are given the amount (mol) of each element as fractions. We use these fractional amounts directly in a preliminary formula as subscripts of the element symbols. Then, we convert the fractions to whole numbers.

**Solution** Using the fractions to write a preliminary formula, with the symbols Zn for zinc, P for phosphorus, and O for oxygen:

$$Zn_{0.21}P_{0.14}O_{0.56}$$

Converting the fractions to whole numbers:
1. Divide each subscript by the smallest one, which in this case is 0.14:

$$Zn_{\frac{0.21}{0.14}}P_{\frac{0.14}{0.14}}O_{\frac{0.56}{0.14}} \longrightarrow Zn_{1.5}P_{1.0}O_{4.0}$$

2. Multiply through by the *smallest integer* that turns all subscripts into integers. We multiply by 2 to make 1.5 (the subscript for Zn) into an integer:

$$Zn_{(1.5 \times 2)}P_{(1.0 \times 2)}O_{(4.0 \times 2)} \longrightarrow Zn_{3.0}P_{2.0}O_{8.0}, \quad \text{or} \quad \boxed{Zn_3P_2O_8}$$

**Check** The integer subscripts must be the smallest integers with the same ratio as the original fractional numbers of moles: 3/2/8 is *the same ratio* as 0.21/0.14/0.56.

**Comment** A more conventional way to write this formula is $Zn_3(PO_4)_2$; this compound is zinc phosphate, formerly used widely as a dental cement.

**Follow-Up Problem 3.8** A sample of a white solid contains 0.170 mol of boron and 0.255 mol of hydrogen. What is the empirical formula?

---

Sample Problems 3.9–3.11 show how other types of compositional data are used to determine chemical formulas.

---

**Sample Problem 3.9** | **Determining an Empirical Formula from Masses of Elements**

**Problem** Analysis of a sample of an ionic compound yields 2.82 g of Na, 4.35 g of Cl, and 7.83 g of O. What is the empirical formula and the name of the compound?

**Plan** This problem is similar to Sample Problem 3.8, except that we are given element *masses* that we must convert into integer subscripts. We first divide each mass by the element's molar mass to find amount (mol). Then we construct a preliminary formula and convert the amounts (mol) to integers.

**Solution** Finding amount (mol) of each element:

$$\text{Amount (mol) of Na} = 2.82 \text{ g Na} \times \frac{1 \text{ mol Na}}{22.99 \text{ g Na}} = 0.123 \text{ mol Na}$$

$$\text{Amount (mol) of Cl} = 4.35 \text{ g Cl} \times \frac{1 \text{ mol Cl}}{35.45 \text{ g Cl}} = 0.123 \text{ mol Cl}$$

$$\text{Amount (mol) of O} = 7.83 \text{ g O} \times \frac{1 \text{ mol O}}{16.00 \text{ g O}} = 0.489 \text{ mol O}$$

Constructing a preliminary formula: $Na_{0.123}Cl_{0.123}O_{0.489}$

Converting to integer subscripts (dividing all by the smallest subscript):

$$Na_{\frac{0.123}{0.123}}Cl_{\frac{0.123}{0.123}}O_{\frac{0.489}{0.123}} \longrightarrow Na_{1.00}Cl_{1.00}O_{3.98} \approx Na_1Cl_1O_4, \quad \text{or} \quad NaClO_4$$

The empirical formula is $\boxed{NaClO_4}$; the name is $\boxed{\text{sodium perchlorate.}}$

**Check** The numbers of moles seem correct because the masses of Na and Cl are slightly more than 0.1 of their molar masses. The mass of O is greatest and its molar mass is smallest, so it should have the greatest number of moles. The ratio of subscripts, 1/1/4, is the same as the ratio of moles, 0.123/0.123/0.489 (within rounding).

**Follow-Up Problem 3.9** An unknown metal M reacts with sulfur to form a compound with the formula $M_2S_3$. If 3.12 g of M reacts with 2.88 g of S, what are the names of M and $M_2S_3$? [*Hint:* Determine the amount (mol) of S and use the formula to find the amount (mol) of M.]

---

## Molecular Formulas

If we know the molar mass of a compound, we can use the empirical formula to obtain the molecular formula, which uses as subscripts the *actual* numbers of moles of each element in 1 mol of compound. For some compounds, such as water ($H_2O$), ammonia ($NH_3$), and methane ($CH_4$), the empirical and molecular formulas are identical, but for many others, the molecular formula is a *whole-number multiple* of the empirical formula. As you saw, hydrogen peroxide has the empirical formula HO. Dividing the molar mass of hydrogen peroxide (34.02 g/mol) by the empirical formula mass of HO (17.01 g/mol) gives the whole-number multiple:

$$\text{Whole-number multiple} = \frac{\text{molar mass (g/mol)}}{\text{empirical formula mass (g/mol)}} = \frac{34.02 \ \cancel{\text{g/mol}}}{17.01 \ \cancel{\text{g/mol}}} = 2.000 = 2$$

Multiplying the empirical formula subscripts by 2 gives the molecular formula:

$$H_{(1\times2)}O_{(1\times2)} \text{ gives } H_2O_2$$

Instead of giving compositional data as masses of each element, analytical laboratories provide mass percents. To find the molecular formula, we first determine the empirical formula and then the whole-number multiple:

1. Assume 100.0 g of compound to express each mass percent directly as mass (g).
2. Convert each mass (g) to amount (mol).
3. Derive the empirical formula.
4. Divide the compound's molar mass by the empirical formula mass to find the whole-number multiple.
5. Multiply each subscript in the empirical formula by the multiple.

### Sample Problem 3.10 | Determining a Molecular Formula from Elemental Analysis and Molar Mass

**Problem** During excessive physical activity, lactic acid ($\mathcal{M}$ = 90.08 g/mol) forms in muscle tissue and is responsible for muscle soreness. Elemental analysis shows that this compound contains 40.0 mass % C, 6.71 mass % H, and 53.3 mass % O.
**(a)** Determine the empirical formula of lactic acid.
**(b)** Determine the molecular formula.

**(a) Determining the empirical formula**

**Plan** We know the mass % of each element and must convert each to an integer subscript. The mass of the sample of lactic acid is not given, but the mass percents are the same for any sample of it. Therefore, we assume there is 100.0 g of lactic acid and express each mass % as a number of grams. Then, we construct the empirical formula as in Sample Problem 3.9.

**Solution** Expressing mass % as mass (g) by assuming 100.0 g of lactic acid:

$$\text{Mass (g) of C} = \frac{40.0 \text{ parts C by mass}}{100 \text{ parts by mass}} \times 100.0 \text{ g} = 40.0 \text{ g C}$$

Similarly, we have 6.71 g of H and 53.3 g of O.

Converting from mass (g) of each element to amount (mol):

$$\text{Amount (mol) of C} = \text{mass of C} \times \frac{1}{\mathcal{M} \text{ of C}} = 40.0 \ \cancel{\text{g C}} \times \frac{1 \text{ mol C}}{12.01 \ \cancel{\text{g C}}} = 3.33 \text{ mol C}$$

Similarly, we have 6.66 mol of H and 3.33 mol of O.

Constructing the preliminary formula: $C_{3.33}H_{6.66}O_{3.33}$

Converting to integer subscripts:

$$C_{\frac{3.33}{3.33}}H_{\frac{6.66}{3.33}}O_{\frac{3.33}{3.33}} \longrightarrow C_{1.00}H_{2.00}O_{1.00} = C_1H_2O_1, \text{ the empirical formula is } \boxed{CH_2O}$$

**Check** The numbers of moles seem correct: the masses of C and O are each slightly more than 3 times their molar masses (e.g., for C, 40 g/(12 g/mol) > 3 mol), and the mass of H is over 6 times its molar mass of 1.

**(b) Determining the molecular formula**

**Plan** The molecular formula subscripts are whole-number multiples of the empirical formula subscripts. To find this multiple, we divide the given molar mass (90.08 g/mol) by the empirical formula mass, which we find from the sum of the elements' molar masses. Then we multiply each subscript in the empirical formula by the multiple.

**Solution** The empirical formula mass is 30.03 g/mol. Finding the whole-number multiple:

$$\text{Whole-number multiple} = \frac{\mathcal{M} \text{ of lactic acid}}{\mathcal{M} \text{ of empirical formula}} = \frac{90.08 \ \cancel{\text{g/mol}}}{30.03 \ \cancel{\text{g/mol}}} = 3.000 = 3$$

Determining the molecular formula:

$$C_{(1\times3)}H_{(2\times3)}O_{(1\times3)} = \boxed{C_3H_6O_3}$$

**Check** The calculated molecular formula has the same ratio of moles of elements (3/6/3) as the empirical formula (1/2/1) and corresponds to the given molar mass:

$\mathcal{M}$ of lactic acid $= (3 \times \mathcal{M} \text{ of C}) + (6 \times \mathcal{M} \text{ of H}) + (3 \times \mathcal{M} \text{ of O})$

$\qquad = (3 \times 12.01 \text{ g/mol}) + (6 \times 1.008 \text{ g/mol}) + (3 \times 16.00 \text{ g/mol})$

$\qquad = 90.08 \text{ g/mol}$

**Follow-Up Problem 3.10** One of the most widespread environmental carcinogens (cancer-causing agents) is benzo[*a*]pyrene ($\mathcal{M} = 252.30$ g/mol). It is found in coal dust, cigarette smoke, and even charcoal-grilled meat. Analysis of this hydrocarbon shows 95.21 mass % C and 4.79 mass % H. What is the molecular formula of benzo[*a*]pyrene?

**Combustion Analysis of Organic Compounds** Still another type of compositional data is obtained through **combustion analysis,** used to measure the amounts of carbon and hydrogen in a combustible organic compound. The unknown compound is burned in an excess of pure $O_2$, and the $H_2O$ and $CO_2$ that form are absorbed in separate containers (Figure 3.4). By weighing the absorbers before and after combustion, we find the masses of $CO_2$ and $H_2O$ and use them to find the masses of C and H in the compound; from these results, we find the empirical formula. Many organic compounds also contain oxygen, nitrogen, or a halogen. As long as the third element doesn't interfere with the absorption of $H_2O$ and $CO_2$, we calculate its mass by subtracting the masses of C and H from the original mass of the compound.

**Figure 3.4 Combustion apparatus for determining formulas of organic compounds.** A sample of an organic compound is burned in a stream of $O_2$. The resulting $H_2O$ is absorbed by $Mg(ClO_4)_2$, and the $CO_2$ is absorbed by NaOH on asbestos.

Stream of $O_2$

$H_2O$ absorber

$CO_2$ absorber

Other substances not absorbed

Sample of compound containing C, H, and other elements

| **Sample Problem 3.11** | **Determining a Molecular Formula from Combustion Analysis** |
|---|---|

**Problem** Vitamin C ($\mathcal{M} = 176.12$ g/mol) is a compound of C, H, and O found in many natural sources, especially citrus fruits. When a 1.000-g sample of vitamin C is burned in a combustion apparatus, the following data are obtained:

Mass of $CO_2$ absorber after combustion = 85.35 g

Mass of $CO_2$ absorber before combustion = 83.85 g

Mass of $H_2O$ absorber after combustion = 37.96 g

Mass of $H_2O$ absorber before combustion = 37.55 g

What is the molecular formula of vitamin C?

**Plan** We find the masses of $CO_2$ and $H_2O$ by subtracting the masses of the absorbers before and after the combustion. From the mass of $CO_2$, we use Equation 3.7 to find the mass of C. Similarly, we find the mass of H from the mass of $H_2O$. The mass of vitamin C (1.000 g) minus the sum of the masses of C and H gives the mass of O, the third element present. Then, we proceed as in Sample Problem 3.10: calculate amount (mol) of each element using its molar mass, construct the empirical formula, determine the whole-number multiple from the given molar mass, and construct the molecular formula.

**Solution** Finding the masses of combustion products:

$$\text{Mass (g) of } CO_2 = \text{mass of } CO_2 \text{ absorber after} - \text{mass before}$$
$$= 85.35 \text{ g} - 83.85 \text{ g} = 1.50 \text{ g } CO_2$$
$$\text{Mass (g) of } H_2O = \text{mass of } H_2O \text{ absorber after} - \text{mass before}$$
$$= 37.96 \text{ g} - 37.55 \text{ g} = 0.41 \text{ g } H_2O$$

Calculating masses (g) of C and H using Equation 3.7:

$$\text{Mass of element} = \text{mass of compound} \times \frac{\text{mass of element in 1 mol of compound}}{\text{mass of 1 mol of compound}}$$

$$\text{Mass (g) of C} = \text{mass of } CO_2 \times \frac{1 \text{ mol C} \times \mathcal{M} \text{ of C}}{\text{mass of 1 mol } CO_2} = 1.50 \text{ g } CO_2 \times \frac{12.01 \text{ g C}}{44.01 \text{ g } CO_2}$$
$$= 0.409 \text{ g C}$$

$$\text{Mass (g) of H} = \text{mass of } H_2O \times \frac{2 \text{ mol H} \times \mathcal{M} \text{ of H}}{\text{mass of 1 mol } H_2O} = 0.41 \text{ g } H_2O \times \frac{2.016 \text{ g H}}{18.02 \text{ g } H_2O}$$
$$= 0.046 \text{ g H}$$

Calculating mass (g) of O:

$$\text{Mass (g) of O} = \text{mass of vitamin C sample} - (\text{mass of C} + \text{mass of H})$$
$$= 1.000 \text{ g} - (0.409 \text{ g} + 0.046 \text{ g}) = 0.545 \text{ g O}$$

Finding the amounts (mol) of elements: Dividing the mass (g) of each element by its molar mass gives 0.0341 mol of C, 0.046 mol of H, and 0.0341 mol of O.

Constructing the preliminary formula: $C_{0.0341}H_{0.046}O_{0.0341}$

Determining the empirical formula: Dividing through by the smallest subscript gives

$$C_{\frac{0.0341}{0.0341}}H_{\frac{0.046}{0.0341}}O_{\frac{0.0341}{0.0341}} = C_{1.00}H_{1.3}O_{1.00}$$

We find that 3 is the smallest integer that makes all subscripts into integers:

$$C_{(1.00\times3)}H_{(1.3\times3)}O_{(1.00\times3)} = C_{3.00}H_{3.9}O_{3.00} \approx C_3H_4O_3$$

Determining the molecular formula:

$$\text{Whole-number multiple} = \frac{\mathcal{M} \text{ of vitamin C}}{\mathcal{M} \text{ of empirical formula}} = \frac{176.12 \text{ g/mol}}{88.06 \text{ g/mol}} = 2.000 = 2$$
$$C_{(3\times2)}H_{(4\times2)}O_{(3\times2)} = \boxed{C_6H_8O_6}$$

**Check** The element masses seem correct: carbon makes up slightly more than 0.25 of the mass of $CO_2$ (12 g/44 g > 0.25), as do the masses in the problem (0.409 g/1.50 g > 0.25). Hydrogen makes up slightly more than 0.10 of the mass of $H_2O$ (2 g/18 g > 0.10), as do the masses in the problem (0.046 g/0.41 g > 0.10). The molecular formula has the same ratio of subscripts (6/8/6) as the empirical formula (3/4/3) and the preliminary formula (0.0341/0.046/0.0341), and it gives the known molar mass:

$$(6 \times \mathcal{M} \text{ of C}) + (8 \times \mathcal{M} \text{ of H}) + (6 \times \mathcal{M} \text{ of O}) = \mathcal{M} \text{ of vitamin C}$$
$$(6 \times 12.01 \text{ g/mol}) + (8 \times 1.008 \text{ g/mol}) + (6 \times 16.00 \text{ g/mol}) = 176.12 \text{ g/mol}$$

**Comment** The subscript we calculated for H was 3.9, which we rounded to 4. But, if we had strung the calculation steps together, we would have obtained 4.0:

$$\text{Subscript of H} = 0.41 \text{ g } H_2O \times \frac{2.016 \text{ g H}}{18.02 \text{ g } H_2O} \times \frac{1 \text{ mol H}}{1.008 \text{ g H}} \times \frac{1}{0.0341 \text{ mol}} \times 3 = 4.0$$

**Follow-Up Problem 3.11** A dry-cleaning solvent ($\mathcal{M} = 146.99$ g/mol) that contains C, H, and Cl is suspected to be a cancer-causing agent. When a 0.250-g sample was studied by combustion analysis, 0.451 g of $CO_2$ and 0.0617 g of $H_2O$ formed. Find the molecular formula.

## Chemical Formulas and Molecular Structures; Isomers

*A formula represents a real, three-dimensional object.* The structural formula makes this point, with its relative placement of atoms, but do empirical and molecular formulas contain structural information?

**Table 3.2 Some Compounds with Empirical Formula CH₂O (Composition by Mass: 40.0% C, 6.71% H, 53.3% O)**

| Name | Molecular Formula | Whole-Number Multiple | $\mathscr{M}$ (g/mol) | Use or Function |
|---|---|---|---|---|
| Formaldehyde | $CH_2O$ | 1 | 30.03 | Disinfectant; biological preservative |
| Acetic acid | $C_2H_4O_2$ | 2 | 60.05 | Acetate polymers; vinegar (5% solution) |
| Lactic acid | $C_3H_6O_3$ | 3 | 90.08 | Causes milk to sour; forms in muscles during exercise |
| Erythrose | $C_4H_8O_4$ | 4 | 120.10 | Forms during sugar metabolism |
| Ribose | $C_5H_{10}O_5$ | 5 | 150.13 | Component of many nucleic acids and vitamin $B_2$ |
| Glucose | $C_6H_{12}O_6$ | 6 | 180.16 | Major nutrient for energy in cells |

$CH_2O$ $\qquad$ $C_2H_4O_2$ $\qquad$ $C_3H_6O_3$ $\qquad$ $C_4H_8O_4$ $\qquad$ $C_5H_{10}O_5$ $\qquad$ $C_6H_{12}O_6$

1. *Different compounds with the same empirical formula.* The empirical formula tells nothing about molecular structure because it is based solely on mass analysis. In fact, different compounds can have the *same* empirical formula. $NO_2$ and $N_2O_4$ are inorganic cases, and there are numerous organic ones. For example, many compounds have the empirical formula $CH_2$ (the general formula is $C_nH_{2n}$, with $n$ an integer greater than or equal to 2), such as ethylene ($C_2H_4$) and propylene ($C_3H_6$), starting materials for two common plastics. Table 3.2 shows some biological compounds with the same empirical formula.

2. *Isomers: Different compounds with the same molecular formula.* A molecular formula also tells nothing about structure. Different compounds can have the *same* molecular formula because their atoms can bond in different arrangements to give more than one *structural formula*. **Isomers** are compounds with the same molecular formula, and thus molar mass, but different properties. *Constitutional,* or *structural, isomers,* occur when the atoms link together in different arrangements. Table 3.3 shows two pairs of examples. The left pair, butane and 2-methylpropane, share the molecular formula $C_4H_{10}$. One has a four-C chain and the other a one-C branch off a three-C chain. Both are small alkanes, so their properties are similar, but not identical. The two compounds with the molecular formula $C_2H_6O$ have very different properties; indeed, they are different classes of organic compound—one is an alcohol and the other an ether.

**Table 3.3 Two Pairs of Constitutional Isomers**

| Property | $C_4H_{10}$ | | $C_2H_6O$ | |
|---|---|---|---|---|
| | Butane | 2-Methylpropane | Ethanol | Dimethyl Ether |
| $\mathscr{M}$ (g/mol) | 58.12 | 58.12 | 46.07 | 46.07 |
| Boiling point | −0.5°C | −11.6°C | 78.5°C | −25°C |
| Density (at 20°C) | 0.579 g/mL (gas) | 0.549 g/mL | 0.789 g/mL (liquid) | 0.00195 g/mL (gas) |
| Structural formula | | | | |
| Space-filling model | | | | |

**Figure 3.5** The antibiotic ampicillin.

As the number and kinds of atoms increase, the number of constitutional isomers—that is, the number of structural formulas that can be written for a given molecular formula—also increases: $C_2H_6O$ has two structural formulas (Table 3.3), $C_3H_8O$ has three, and $C_4H_{10}O$ seven. Imagine how many there are for $C_{16}H_{19}N_3O_4S$! Of all the possible isomers, only one is the antibiotic ampicillin (Figure 3.5). We'll discuss these and other types of isomerism fully later in the text.

## ▌Summary of Section 3.2

- From the masses of elements in a compound, their relative numbers of moles are found, which gives the empirical formula.
- If the molar mass of the compound is known, the molecular formula, the actual numbers of moles of each element, can also be determined.
- Combustion analysis provides data on the masses of C and H in an organic compound, which are used to obtain the formula.
- Atoms can bond in different arrangements (structural formulas). Two or more compounds with the same molecular formula are constitutional isomers.

---

## 3.3 • WRITING AND BALANCING CHEMICAL EQUATIONS

Thinking in terms of amounts, rather than masses, allows us to view reactions as large populations of interacting particles rather than as grams of material. For example, for the formation of HF from $H_2$ and $F_2$, if we weigh the substances, we find that

*Macroscopic level (grams):* 2.016 g of $H_2$ and 38.00 g of $F_2$ react to form 40.02 g of HF

This information tells us little except that mass is conserved. However, if we convert these masses (g) to amounts (mol), we find that

*Macroscopic level (moles):* 1 mol of $H_2$ and 1 mol of $F_2$ react to form 2 mol of HF

This information reveals that an enormous number of $H_2$ molecules react with just as many $F_2$ molecules to form twice as many HF molecules. Dividing by Avogadro's number shows the reaction between individual molecules:

*Molecular level:* 1 molecule of $H_2$ and 1 molecule of $F_2$ react to form 2 molecules of HF

Thus, *the macroscopic (molar) change corresponds to the submicroscopic (molecular) change* (Figure 3.6). This information forms the essence of a **chemical equation,** a statement that uses formulas to express the identities and quantities of substances in a chemical or physical change.

**Figure 3.6** The formation of HF on the macroscopic and molecular levels.

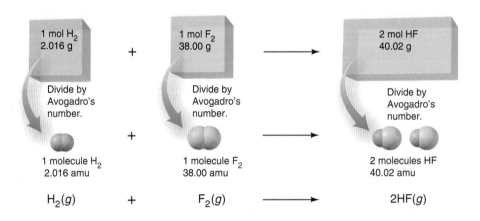

**Steps for Balancing an Equation** To present a chemical change quantitatively, the equation must be *balanced: the same number of each type of atom must appear on both sides.* As an example, here is a description of a chemical change that occurs in many fireworks and in a common lecture demonstration: a magnesium strip burns in oxygen gas to yield powdery magnesium oxide. (Light and heat are also produced, but we are concerned here only with substances.) Converting this description into a balanced equation involves the following steps:

1. *Translating the statement.* We first translate the chemical statement into a "skeleton" equation: the substances present *before* the change, called **reactants,** are placed to the left of a yield arrow, which points to the substances produced *during* the change, called **products:**

$$\underbrace{\_Mg + \_O_2}_{\text{magnesium and oxygen}} \xrightarrow[\text{yield}]{} \underset{\text{magnesium oxide}}{\_MgO}$$

   At the beginning of the balancing process, we put a blank *in front of* each formula to remind us that we have to account for its atoms.

2. *Balancing the atoms.* By shifting our attention back and forth, we *match the numbers of each type of atom on the left and the right of the yield arrow.* In each blank, we place a **balancing (stoichiometric) coefficient,** a numerical multiplier of *all the atoms* in the formula that follows it. In general, balancing is easiest when we
   • Start with the most complex substance, the one with the largest number of different types of atoms.
   • End with the least complex substance, such as an element by itself.
   In this case, MgO is the most complex, so we place a coefficient 1 in that blank:

   $$\_Mg + \_O_2 \longrightarrow \underline{1}\,MgO$$

   To balance the Mg in MgO, we place a 1 in front of Mg on the left:

   $$\underline{1}\,Mg + \_O_2 \longrightarrow \underline{1}\,MgO$$

   The O atom in MgO must be balanced by one O atom on the left. One-half an $O_2$ molecule provides one O atom:

   $$\underline{1}\,Mg + \tfrac{1}{2}\,O_2 \longrightarrow \underline{1}\,MgO$$

   In terms of numbers of each type of atom, the equation is balanced.

3. *Adjusting the coefficients.* There are several conventions about the final coefficients:
   • In most cases, *the smallest whole-number coefficients are preferred.* In this case, one-half of an $O_2$ molecule cannot exist, so we multiply the equation by 2:

   $$2Mg + 1O_2 \longrightarrow 2MgO$$

   • We used the coefficient 1 to remind us to balance each substance. But, a coefficient of 1 is implied by the presence of the formula, so we don't write it:

   $$2Mg + O_2 \longrightarrow 2MgO$$

   (This convention is similar to not writing a subscript 1 in a formula.)

4. *Checking.* After balancing and adjusting the coefficients, always check that the equation is balanced:

   $$\text{Reactants (2 Mg, 2 O)} \longrightarrow \text{products (2 Mg, 2 O)}$$

5. *Specifying the states of matter.* The final equation also indicates the physical state of each substance or whether it is dissolved in water. The abbreviations used for these states are shown in the margin. From the original statement, we know that a Mg "strip" is solid, $O_2$ is a gas, and "powdery" MgO is also solid. The balanced equation, therefore, is

   $$2Mg(s) + O_2(g) \longrightarrow 2MgO(s)$$

*g*   for gas
*l*   for liquid
*s*   for solid
*aq*  for aqueous solution

As you saw in Figure 3.6, *balancing coefficients refer to both individual chemical entities and moles of entities.* Thus,

2 atoms of Mg and 1 molecule of $O_2$ yield 2 formula units of MgO

2 moles of Mg and 1 mole of $O_2$    yield 2 moles of MgO

Figure 3.7 depicts this reaction on three levels:

- *Macroscopic level (photos),* as it appears in the laboratory
- *Molecular level (blow-up circles),* as chemists imagine it (with darker colored atoms representing the stoichiometry)
- *Symbolic level,* in the form of the balanced chemical equation

Keep in mind several key points about the balancing process:

- A coefficient operates on *all* the atoms in the formula that follows it:

    2MgO    *means* $2 \times (MgO)$,    or 2 Mg atoms + 2 O atoms

    $2Ca(NO_3)_2$ *means* $2 \times [Ca(NO_3)_2]$, or 2 Ca atoms + 4 N atoms + 12 O atoms

- Chemical formulas *cannot* be altered. In step 2 of the example, we *cannot* balance the O atoms by changing MgO to $MgO_2$ because $MgO_2$ is a different compound.
- Other reactants or products *cannot* be added. Thus, we *cannot* balance the O atoms by changing the reactant from $O_2$ molecules to O atoms or by adding an O atom to the products. The description of the reaction mentions oxygen gas, which consists of $O_2$ molecules, *not* separate O atoms.
- A balanced equation remains balanced if you multiply all the coefficients by the same number. For example,

$$4Mg(s) + 2O_2(g) \longrightarrow 4MgO(s)$$

is also balanced because the coefficients have just been multiplied by 2. However, *by convention,* we balance an equation with the *smallest* whole-number coefficients.

**Figure 3.7** A three-level view of the reaction between magnesium and oxygen.

## Sample Problem 3.12 Balancing Chemical Equations

**Problem** Within the cylinders of a car's engine, the hydrocarbon octane ($C_8H_{18}$), one of many components of gasoline, mixes with oxygen from the air and burns to form carbon dioxide and water vapor. Write a balanced equation for this reaction.

**Solution 1.** *Translate* the statement into a skeleton equation (with coefficient blanks). Octane and oxygen are reactants; "oxygen from the air" implies molecular oxygen, $O_2$. Carbon dioxide and water vapor are products:

$$\underline{\phantom{1}}C_8H_{18} + \underline{\phantom{1}}O_2 \longrightarrow \underline{\phantom{1}}CO_2 + \underline{\phantom{1}}H_2O$$

**2.** *Balance the atoms.* Start with the most complex substance, $C_8H_{18}$, and balance $O_2$ last:

$$\underline{1}\,C_8H_{18} + \underline{\phantom{1}}O_2 \longrightarrow \underline{\phantom{1}}CO_2 + \underline{\phantom{1}}H_2O$$

The C atoms in $C_8H_{18}$ end up in $CO_2$. Each $CO_2$ contains one C atom, so 8 molecules of $CO_2$ are needed to balance the 8 C atoms in each $C_8H_{18}$:

$$\underline{1}\,C_8H_{18} + \underline{\phantom{1}}O_2 \longrightarrow \underline{8}\,CO_2 + \underline{\phantom{1}}H_2O$$

The H atoms in $C_8H_{18}$ end up in $H_2O$. The 18 H atoms in $C_8H_{18}$ require the coefficient 9 in front of $H_2O$:

$$\underline{1}\,C_8H_{18} + \underline{\phantom{1}}O_2 \longrightarrow \underline{8}\,CO_2 + \underline{9}\,H_2O$$

There are 25 atoms of O on the right (16 in $8CO_2$ plus 9 in $9H_2O$), so we place the coefficient $\frac{25}{2}$ in front of $O_2$:

$$\underline{1}\,C_8H_{18} + \frac{25}{2}\,O_2 \longrightarrow \underline{8}\,CO_2 + \underline{9}\,H_2O$$

**3.** *Adjust the coefficients.* Multiply through by 2 to obtain whole numbers:

$$2C_8H_{18} + 25O_2 \longrightarrow 16CO_2 + 18H_2O$$

**4.** *Check* that the equation is balanced:

$$\text{Reactants (16 C, 36 H, 50 O)} \longrightarrow \text{products (16 C, 36 H, 50 O)}$$

**5.** *Specify* states of matter. $C_8H_{18}$ is liquid; $O_2$, $CO_2$, and $H_2O$ vapor are gases:

$$2C_8H_{18}(l) + 25O_2(g) \longrightarrow 16CO_2(g) + 18H_2O(g)$$

**Comment** This is an example of a combustion reaction. *Any* compound containing C and H that burns in an excess of air produces $CO_2$ and $H_2O$.

### Follow-Up Problem 3.12 Write a balanced equation for each of the following:
**(a)** A characteristic reaction of Group 1A(1) elements: chunks of sodium react violently with water to form hydrogen gas and sodium hydroxide solution.
**(b)** The destruction of marble statuary by acid rain: aqueous nitric acid reacts with calcium carbonate to form carbon dioxide, water, and aqueous calcium nitrate.
**(c)** Halogen compounds exchanging bonding partners: phosphorus trifluoride is prepared by the reaction of phosphorus trichloride and hydrogen fluoride; hydrogen chloride is the other product. The reaction involves gases only.
**(d)** Explosive decomposition of dynamite: liquid nitroglycerine ($C_3H_5N_3O_9$) explodes to produce a mixture of gases—carbon dioxide, water vapor, nitrogen, and oxygen.

**Visualizing a Reaction with a Molecular Scene** A great way to focus on the rearrangement of atoms from reactants to products is by visualizing an equation as a molecular scene. Here's a representation of the combustion of octane we just balanced:

$$2C_8H_{18}(l) \quad + \quad 25O_2(g) \quad \longrightarrow \quad 16CO_2(g) \quad + \quad 18H_2O(g)$$

Now let's work through a sample problem to do the reverse—derive a balanced equation from a molecular scene.

---

**Sample Problem 3.13**  **Balancing an Equation from a Molecular Scene**

**Problem** The following molecular scenes depict an important reaction in nitrogen chemistry (nitrogen is blue; oxygen is red):

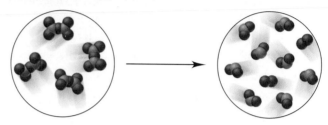

Write a balanced equation for this reaction.

**Plan** To write a balanced equation, we first have to determine the formulas of the molecules and obtain coefficients by counting the number of each molecule. Then, we arrange this information in the correct equation format, using the smallest whole-number coefficients and including states of matter.

**Solution** The reactant circle shows only one type of molecule. It has two N and five O atoms, so the formula is $N_2O_5$; there are four of these molecules. The product circle shows two different molecules, one with one N and two O atoms, and the other with two O atoms; there are eight $NO_2$ and two $O_2$. Thus, we have:

$$4N_2O_5 \longrightarrow 8NO_2 + 2O_2$$

Writing the balanced equation with the smallest whole-number coefficients and all substances as gases:

$$2N_2O_5(g) \longrightarrow 4NO_2(g) + O_2(g)$$

**Check** Reactant (4 N, 10 O) $\longrightarrow$ products (4 N, 8 + 2 = 10 O)

**Follow-Up Problem 3.13** Write a balanced equation for the important atmospheric reaction depicted below (carbon is black; oxygen is red):

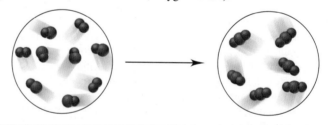

---

## Summary of Section 3.3

- A chemical equation has reactant formulas on the left of a yield arrow and product formulas on the right.
- A balanced equation has the same number of each type of atom on both sides.
- Balancing coefficients are integer multipliers for *all* the atoms in a formula and apply to the individual entity or to moles of entities.

---

# 3.4 • CALCULATING QUANTITIES OF REACTANT AND PRODUCT

A balanced equation is essential for all calculations involving chemical change: *if you know the number of moles of one substance, the balanced equation tells you the number of moles of the others.*

# Stoichiometrically Equivalent Molar Ratios from the Balanced Equation

In a balanced equation, *the amounts (mol) of substances are stoichiometrically equivalent to each other,* which means that a specific amount of one substance is formed from, produces, or reacts with a specific amount of the other. The quantitative relationships are expressed as *stoichiometrically equivalent molar ratios* that we use as conversion factors to calculate the amounts. For example, consider the equation for the combustion of propane, a hydrocarbon fuel used in cooking and water heating:

$$C_3H_8(g) + 5O_2(g) \longrightarrow 3CO_2(g) + 4H_2O(g)$$

If we view the reaction quantitatively in terms of $C_3H_8$, we see that

> 1 mol of $C_3H_8$ reacts with 5 mol of $O_2$
> 1 mol of $C_3H_8$ produces    3 mol of $CO_2$
> 1 mol of $C_3H_8$ produces    4 mol of $H_2O$

Therefore, in this reaction,

> 1 mol of $C_3H_8$ is stoichiometrically equivalent to 5 mol of $O_2$
> 1 mol of $C_3H_8$ is stoichiometrically equivalent to 3 mol of $CO_2$
> 1 mol of $C_3H_8$ is stoichiometrically equivalent to 4 mol of $H_2O$

We chose to look at $C_3H_8$, but any two of the substances are stoichiometrically equivalent to each other. Thus,

> 3 mol of $CO_2$ is stoichiometrically equivalent to 4 mol of $H_2O$
> 5 mol of $O_2$   is stoichiometrically equivalent to 3 mol of $CO_2$

and so on. A balanced equation contains a wealth of quantitative information relating individual chemical entities, amounts (mol) of substances, and masses of substances, and Table 3.4 presents the quantitative information contained in this equation.

Here's a typical problem that shows how stoichiometric equivalence is used to create conversion factors: in the combustion of propane, how many moles of $O_2$ are consumed when 10.0 mol of $H_2O$ are produced? To solve this problem, we have to find the molar ratio between $O_2$ and $H_2O$. From the balanced equation, we see that for every 5 mol of $O_2$ consumed, 4 mol of $H_2O$ is formed:

> 5 mol of $O_2$ is stoichiometrically equivalent to 4 mol of $H_2O$

| Table **3.4** Information Contained in a Balanced Equation | | | | |
|---|---|---|---|---|
| **Viewed in Terms of** | **Reactants** $C_3H_8(g)$ + $5O_2(g)$ | | $\longrightarrow$ $\longrightarrow$ | **Products** $3CO_2(g)$ + $4H_2O(g)$ |
| Molecules | 1 molecule $C_3H_8$ + 5 molecules $O_2$ | | $\longrightarrow$ | 3 molecules $CO_2$ + 4 molecules $H_2O$ |
| | 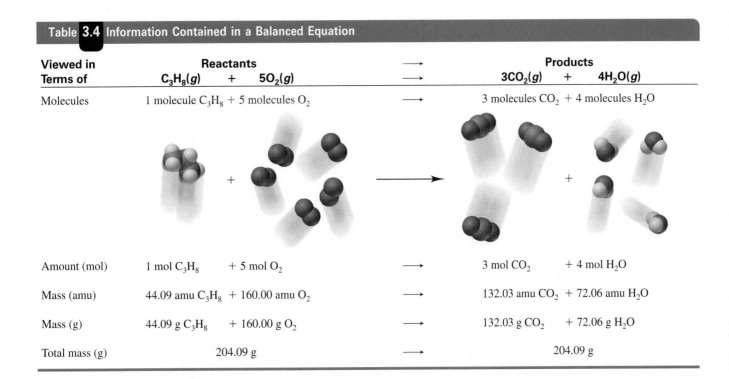 | | | |
| Amount (mol) | 1 mol $C_3H_8$ + 5 mol $O_2$ | | $\longrightarrow$ | 3 mol $CO_2$ + 4 mol $H_2O$ |
| Mass (amu) | 44.09 amu $C_3H_8$ + 160.00 amu $O_2$ | | $\longrightarrow$ | 132.03 amu $CO_2$ + 72.06 amu $H_2O$ |
| Mass (g) | 44.09 g $C_3H_8$ + 160.00 g $O_2$ | | $\longrightarrow$ | 132.03 g $CO_2$ + 72.06 g $H_2O$ |
| Total mass (g) | 204.09 g | | $\longrightarrow$ | 204.09 g |

As with any equivalent quantities, we can construct two conversion factors, depending on the quantity we want to find:

$$\frac{5 \text{ mol O}_2}{4 \text{ mol H}_2\text{O}} \quad \text{or} \quad \frac{4 \text{ mol H}_2\text{O}}{5 \text{ mol O}_2}$$

Since we want to find amount (mol) of $O_2$ and we know amount (mol) of $H_2O$, we choose "5 mol $O_2$/4 mol $H_2O$" to cancel "mol $H_2O$":

$$\text{Amount (mol) of O}_2 \text{ consumed} = 10.0 \text{ mol H}_2\text{O} \times \frac{5 \text{ mol O}_2}{4 \text{ mol H}_2\text{O}} = 12.5 \text{ mol O}_2$$

$$\underset{\text{mol H}_2\text{O}}{\phantom{x}} \xrightarrow[\substack{\text{molar ratio as} \\ \text{conversion factor}}]{} \underset{\text{mol O}_2}{\phantom{x}}$$

*You **cannot** solve this type of problem without the balanced equation.* Here is an approach for solving *any* stoichiometry problem that involves a reaction:

1. Write the balanced equation.
2. When necessary, convert the known mass (or number of entities) of one substance to amount (mol) using its molar mass (or Avogadro's number).
3. Use the molar ratio to calculate the unknown amount (mol) of the other substance.
4. When necessary, convert the amount of that other substance to the desired mass (or number of entities) using its molar mass (or Avogadro's number).

Figure 3.8 summarizes the possible relationships among quantities of substances in a reaction, and Sample Problems 3.14–3.16 apply three of them in the first chemical step of converting copper ore to copper metal.

**Figure 3.8** Summary of amount-mass-number relationships in a chemical equation. Start at any box (known) and move to any other (unknown) by using the conversion factor on the arrow. As always, convert to amount (mol) first.

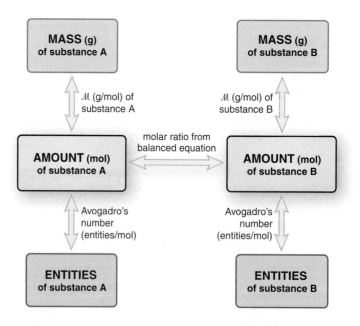

---

| Sample Problem 3.14 | Calculating Quantities of Reactants and Products: Amount (mol) to Amount (mol) |

**Problem** In a lifetime, the average American uses 1750 lb (794 kg) of copper in coins, plumbing, and wiring. Copper is obtained from sulfide ores, such as chalcocite [copper(I) sulfide] by a multistep process. After grinding the ore, it is "roasted" (heated strongly with oxygen gas) to form powdered copper(I) oxide and gaseous sulfur dioxide. How many moles of oxygen are required to roast 10.0 mol of copper(I) sulfide?

**Plan** We *always* write the balanced equation first. The formulas of the reactants are $Cu_2S$ and $O_2$, and the formulas of the products are $Cu_2O$ and $SO_2$, so we have

$$2Cu_2S(s) + 3O_2(g) \longrightarrow 2Cu_2O(s) + 2SO_2(g)$$

We know the amount of $Cu_2S$ (10.0 mol) and must find the amount (mol) of $O_2$ that is needed to roast it. The balanced equation shows that 3 mol of $O_2$ is needed for 2 mol of $Cu_2S$, so the conversion factor for finding amount (mol) of $O_2$ is "3 mol $O_2$/2 mol $Cu_2S$" (see the road map).

**Road Map**

Amount (mol) of $Cu_2S$

↓ molar ratio

Amount (mol) of $O_2$

**Solution** Calculating the amount of $O_2$:

$$\text{Amount (mol) of } O_2 = 10.0 \ \cancel{\text{mol } Cu_2S} \times \frac{3 \text{ mol } O_2}{2 \ \cancel{\text{mol } Cu_2S}} = 15.0 \text{ mol } O_2$$

**Check** The units are correct, and the answer is reasonable because this molar ratio of $O_2$ to $Cu_2S$ (15/10) is identical to the ratio in the balanced equation (3/2).

**Comment** A *common mistake* is to invert the conversion factor; that calculation would be

$$\text{Amount (mol) of } O_2 = 10.0 \text{ mol } Cu_2S \times \frac{2 \text{ mol } Cu_2S}{3 \text{ mol } O_2} = \frac{6.67 \text{ mol}^2 \ Cu_2S}{1 \text{ mol } O_2}$$

The strange units should alert you that an error was made in setting up the conversion factor. Also note that this answer, 6.67, is *less* than 10.0, whereas the equation shows that there should be *more* moles of $O_2$ (3 mol) than moles of $Cu_2S$ (2 mol). Be sure to think through the calculation when setting up the conversion factor and canceling units.

**Follow-Up Problem 3.14** Thermite is a mixture of iron(III) oxide and aluminum powders that was once used to weld railroad tracks. It undergoes a spectacular reaction to yield solid aluminum oxide and molten iron. How many moles of iron(III) oxide are needed to form $3.60 \times 10^3$ mol of iron? Include a road map that shows how you planned the solution.

---

**Sample Problem 3.15** | **Calculating Quantities of Reactants and Products: Amount (mol) to Mass (g)**

**Problem** During the roasting process, how many grams of sulfur dioxide form when 10.0 mol of copper(I) sulfide reacts?

**Plan** Referring to the balanced equation in Sample Problem 3.14, here we are given amount of reactant (10.0 mol of $Cu_2S$) and need the mass (g) of product ($SO_2$) that forms. We find the amount (mol) of $SO_2$ using the molar ratio (2 mol $SO_2$/2 mol $Cu_2S$) and then multiply by its molar mass (64.07 g/mol) to find mass (g) of $SO_2$ (see the road map).

**Road Map**

Amount (mol) of $Cu_2S$

↓ molar ratio

Amount (mol) of $SO_2$

↓ multiply by $\mathcal{M}$ (g/mol)

Mass (g) of $SO_2$

**Solution** Combining the two conversion steps into one calculation, we have

$$\text{Mass (g) of } SO_2 = 10.0 \ \cancel{\text{mol } Cu_2S} \times \frac{2 \ \cancel{\text{mol } SO_2}}{2 \ \cancel{\text{mol } Cu_2S}} \times \frac{64.07 \text{ g } SO_2}{1 \ \cancel{\text{mol } SO_2}} = 641 \text{ g } SO_2$$

**Check** The answer makes sense, since the molar ratio shows that 10.0 mol of $SO_2$ is formed and each mole weighs about 64 g. We rounded to three significant figures.

**Follow-Up Problem 3.15** In the thermite reaction, what amount (mol) of iron forms when $1.85 \times 10^{25}$ formula units of aluminum oxide reacts? Write a road map to show how to plan the solution.

---

**Sample Problem 3.16** | **Calculating Quantities of Reactants and Products: Mass to Mass**

**Problem** During the roasting of chalcocite, how many kilograms of oxygen are required to form 2.86 kg of copper(I) oxide?

**Plan** In this problem, we know the mass of the product, $Cu_2O$ (2.86 kg), and we need the mass (kg) of $O_2$ that reacts to form it. Therefore, we must convert from mass of product to amount of product to amount of reactant to mass of reactant. We convert the mass of $Cu_2O$ from kg to g and then to amount (mol). Then, we use the molar ratio (3 mol $O_2$/2 mol $Cu_2O$) to find the amount (mol) of $O_2$ required. Finally, we convert amount of $O_2$ to g and then kg (see the road map on the next page).

**Road Map**

```
┌─────────────────────────────┐
│    Mass (kg) of Cu₂O         │
└─────────────────────────────┘
        │ 1 kg = 10³ g
        ▼
┌─────────────────────────────┐
│    Mass (g) of Cu₂O          │
└─────────────────────────────┘
        │ divide by 𝓜 (g/mol)
        ▼
┌─────────────────────────────┐
│    Amount (mol) of Cu₂O      │
└─────────────────────────────┘
        │ molar ratio
        ▼
┌─────────────────────────────┐
│    Amount (mol) of O₂        │
└─────────────────────────────┘
        │ multiply by 𝓜 (g/mol)
        ▼
┌─────────────────────────────┐
│    Mass (g) of O₂            │
└─────────────────────────────┘
        │ 10³ g = 1 kg
        ▼
┌─────────────────────────────┐
│    Mass (kg) of O₂           │
└─────────────────────────────┘
```

**Solution** Converting from kilograms of $Cu_2O$ to moles of $Cu_2O$: Combining the mass unit conversion with the mass-to-amount conversion gives

$$\text{Amount (mol) of } Cu_2O = 2.86 \text{ kg } Cu_2O \times \frac{10^3 \text{ g}}{1 \text{ kg}} \times \frac{1 \text{ mol } Cu_2O}{143.10 \text{ g } Cu_2O} = 20.0 \text{ mol } Cu_2O$$

Converting from moles of $Cu_2O$ to moles of $O_2$:

$$\text{Amount (mol) of } O_2 = 20.0 \text{ mol } Cu_2O \times \frac{3 \text{ mol } O_2}{2 \text{ mol } Cu_2O} = 30.0 \text{ mol } O_2$$

Converting from moles of $O_2$ to kilograms of $O_2$: Combining the amount-to-mass conversion with the mass unit conversion gives

$$\text{Mass (kg) of } O_2 = 30.0 \text{ mol } O_2 \times \frac{32.00 \text{ g } O_2}{1 \text{ mol } O_2} \times \frac{1 \text{ kg}}{10^3 \text{ g}} = \boxed{0.960 \text{ kg } O_2}$$

**Check** The units are correct. Rounding to check the math, for example, in the final step, $\sim 30 \text{ mol} \times 30 \text{ g/mol} \times 1 \text{ kg}/10^3 \text{ g} = 0.90 \text{ kg}$. The answer seems reasonable: even though the amount (mol) of $O_2$ is greater than the amount (mol) of $Cu_2O$, the mass of $O_2$ is less than the mass of $Cu_2O$ because $\mathcal{M}$ of $O_2$ is less than $\mathcal{M}$ of $Cu_2O$.

**Comment** The three related sample problems (3.14–3.16) highlight the main point for solving stoichiometry problems: *convert the information given into amount (mol).* Then, use the appropriate molar ratio and any other conversion factors to complete the solution.

**Follow-Up Problem 3.16** During the thermite reaction, how many atoms of aluminum react for every 1.00 g of aluminum oxide that forms? Include a road map that shows how you planned the solution.

## Reactions That Occur in a Sequence

In many situations, a product of one reaction becomes a reactant for the next in a sequence of reactions. For stoichiometric purposes, when the same (common) substance forms in one reaction and reacts in the next, we eliminate it in an **overall (net) equation**. The steps to writing the overall equation are

1. Write the sequence of balanced equations.
2. Adjust the equations arithmetically to cancel the common substance.
3. Add the adjusted equations together to obtain the overall balanced equation.

Sample Problem 3.17 shows the approach by continuing with the copper recovery process that started in Sample Problem 3.14.

### Sample Problem 3.17  Writing an Overall Equation for a Reaction Sequence

**Problem** Roasting is the first step in extracting copper from chalcocite. In the next step, copper(I) oxide reacts with powdered carbon to yield copper metal and carbon monoxide gas. Write a balanced overall equation for the two-step sequence.

**Plan** To obtain the overall equation, we write the individual equations in sequence, adjust coefficients to cancel the common substance (or substances), and add the equations together. In this case, only $Cu_2O$ appears as a product in one equation and a reactant in the other, so it is the common substance.

**Solution** Writing the individual balanced equations:

$$2Cu_2S(s) + 3O_2(g) \longrightarrow 2Cu_2O(s) + 2SO_2(g) \text{ [equation 1; see Sample Problem 3.14]}$$
$$Cu_2O(s) + C(s) \longrightarrow 2Cu(s) + CO(g) \quad \text{[equation 2]}$$

Adjusting the coefficients: Since 2 mol of $Cu_2O$ forms in equation 1 but 1 mol of $Cu_2O$ reacts in equation 2, we double *all* the coefficients in equation 2 to use up the $Cu_2O$:

$$2Cu_2S(s) + 3O_2(g) \longrightarrow 2Cu_2O(s) + 2SO_2(g) \text{ [equation 1]}$$
$$2Cu_2O(s) + 2C(s) \longrightarrow 4Cu(s) + 2CO(g) \quad \text{[equation 2, doubled]}$$

Adding the two equations and canceling the common substance: We keep the reactants of both equations on the left and the products of both equations on the right:

$$2Cu_2S(s) + 3O_2(g) + \cancel{2Cu_2O(s)} + 2C(s) \longrightarrow \cancel{2Cu_2O(s)} + 2SO_2(g) + 4Cu(s) + 2CO(g)$$

or, $\quad 2Cu_2S(s) + 3O_2(g) + 2C(s) \longrightarrow 2SO_2(g) + 4Cu(s) + 2CO(g)$

**Check** Reactants (4 Cu, 2 S, 6 O, 2 C) $\longrightarrow$ products (4 Cu, 2 S, 6 O, 2 C)

**Comment 1.** Even though $Cu_2O$ *does* participate in the chemical change, it is not involved in the reaction stoichiometry. An overall equation *may not* show which substances actually react; for example, $C(s)$ and $Cu_2S(s)$ do not interact directly in this reaction sequence, even though both are shown as reactants.
**2.** The $SO_2$ formed in copper recovery contributes to acid rain, so chemists have devised microbial and electrochemical methods to extract metals without roasting sulfide ores. Such methods are examples of *green chemistry;* we'll discuss another on page 113.
**3.** These reactions were shown to explain how to obtain an overall equation. The actual extraction of copper is more complex, as you'll see in Chapter 22.

**Follow-Up Problem 3.17** The $SO_2$ formed in copper recovery reacts in air with oxygen and forms sulfur trioxide. This gas, in turn, reacts with water to form a sulfuric acid solution that falls in rain. Write a balanced overall equation for this process.

**Reaction Sequences in Organisms** Multistep reaction sequences called *metabolic pathways* occur throughout biological systems. (We discuss them again in Chapter 17.) For example, in most cells, the chemical energy in glucose is released through a sequence of about 30 individual reactions. The product of each reaction step is the reactant of the next, so that all the common substances cancel, and the overall equation is

$$C_6H_{12}O_6(aq) + 6O_2(g) \longrightarrow 6CO_2(g) + 6H_2O(l)$$

We eat food that contains glucose, inhale $O_2$, and excrete $CO_2$ and $H_2O$. In our cells, these reactants and products are many steps apart: $O_2$ never reacts *directly* with glucose, and $CO_2$ and $H_2O$ are formed at various, often distant, steps along the sequence of reactions. Even so, the molar ratios in the overall equation are the same as if the glucose burned in a combustion chamber filled with $O_2$ and formed $CO_2$ and $H_2O$ directly (Figure 3.9).

**Figure 3.9** An overall equation equals the sum of the individual steps.

## Reactions That Involve a Limiting Reactant

In problems up to now, the amount of *one* reactant was given, and we assumed there was enough of the other reactants to react with it completely. For example, suppose we want the amount (mol) of $SO_2$ that forms when 5.2 mol of $Cu_2S$ reacts with $O_2$:

$$2Cu_2S(s) + 3O_2(g) \longrightarrow 2Cu_2O(s) + 2SO_2(g) \quad \text{[equation 1; see Sample Problem 3.14]}$$

We assume the 5.2 mol of $Cu_2S$ reacts with as much $O_2$ as needed. Because all the $Cu_2S$ reacts, its initial amount of 5.2 mol determines, or *limits*, the amount of $SO_2$ that can form, no matter how much more $O_2$ is present. In this situation, we call $Cu_2S$ the **limiting reactant** (or *limiting reagent*).

Suppose, however, you know the amounts of both $Cu_2S$ *and* $O_2$ and need to find out how much $SO_2$ forms. You first have to determine whether $Cu_2S$ or $O_2$ is the limiting reactant—that is, which one is completely used up—because it limits how much $SO_2$ can form. The reactant that is *not* limiting is present *in excess*, which means the amount that doesn't react is left over. ● To determine which is the limiting reactant, we use the molar ratios in the balanced equation to perform a series of calculations to see *which reactant forms less product.*

**Determining the Limiting Reactant** Let's clarify these ideas in a much more appetizing situation. Suppose you have a job making ice cream sundaes. Each sundae requires two scoops (12 oz) of ice cream, one cherry, and 50 mL of syrup:

$$2 \text{ scoops } (12 \text{ oz}) + 1 \text{ cherry} + 50 \text{ mL syrup} \longrightarrow 1 \text{ sundae}$$

● **Limiting "Reactants" in Everyday Life**
Limiting-"reactant" situations arise in business all the time. A car assembly-plant manager must order more tires if there are 1500 car bodies and only 4000 tires, and a clothes manufacturer must cut more sleeves if there are 320 sleeves for 170 shirt bodies. You've probably faced such situations in daily life as well. A muffin recipe calls for 2 cups of flour and 1 cup of sugar, but you have 3 cups of flour and only $\frac{3}{4}$ cup of sugar. Clearly, the flour is in excess and the sugar limits the number of muffins you can make. Or, you're in charge of making cheeseburgers for a picnic, and you have 10 buns, 12 meat patties, and 15 slices of cheese. Here, the number of buns limits how many cheeseburgers you can make. Or, there are 26 students and only 23 microscopes in a cell biology lab. You'll find that limiting-"reactant" situations are almost limitless.

**Figure 3.10 An ice cream sundae analogy for limiting reactants.**
**A,** The "reactants" form the "product" (sundae). **B,** Only two sundaes can be made before all the syrup is used up, so syrup is the limiting "reactant"; four scoops of ice cream and four cherries are "in excess."

A mob of 25 ravenous school kids enters, and each one wants a sundae with vanilla ice cream and chocolate syrup. You have 300 oz of vanilla ice cream (at 6 oz per scoop), 30 cherries, and 1 L of syrup: can you feed them all? A series of calculations based on the balanced equation shows the number of sundaes you can make from each ingredient:

$$\text{Ice cream: No. of sundaes} = 300 \ \cancel{\text{oz}} \times \frac{1 \ \cancel{\text{scoop}}}{6 \ \cancel{\text{oz}}} \times \frac{1 \ \text{sundae}}{2 \ \cancel{\text{scoops}}} = 25 \ \text{sundaes}$$

$$\text{Cherries: No. of sundaes} = 30 \ \cancel{\text{cherries}} \times \frac{1 \ \text{sundae}}{1 \ \cancel{\text{cherry}}} = 30 \ \text{sundaes}$$

$$\text{Syrup: No. of sundaes} = 1000 \ \cancel{\text{mL syrup}} \times \frac{1 \ \text{sundae}}{50 \ \cancel{\text{mL syrup}}} = 20 \ \text{sundaes}$$

Of the reactants (ice cream, cherry, syrup), the syrup forms the *least* product (sundaes), so it is the limiting "reactant." When all the syrup has been used up, some ice cream and cherries are "unreacted" so they are in excess:

300 oz (50 scoops) + 30 cherries + 1 L syrup ⟶

**20 sundaes** + 60 oz (10 scoops) + 10 cherries

Figure 3.10 shows a similar example with different initial (starting) quantities.

**Using Reaction Tables in Limiting-Reactant Problems**   A good way to keep track of the quantities in a limiting-reactant problem is with a *reaction table*. The balanced equation appears at the top for the column heads. The table shows the

- *Initial* quantities of reactants and products *before* the reaction
- *Change* in the quantities of reactants and products *during* the reaction
- *Final* quantities of reactants and products remaining *after* the reaction

For example, for the ice-cream sundae "reaction," the reaction table would be

| Quantity | 12 oz (2 scoops) | + 1 cherry | + 50 mL syrup | ⟶ 1 sundae |
|---|---|---|---|---|
| Initial | 300 oz (50 scoops) | 30 cherries | 1000 mL syrup | 0 sundaes |
| Change | −240 oz (40 scoops) | −20 cherries | −1000 mL syrup | +20 sundaes |
| Final | 60 oz (10 scoops) | 10 cherries | 0 mL syrup | 20 sundaes |

The body of the table shows the following important points:

- In the Initial line, "product" has not yet formed, so the entry is "0 sundaes."
- In the Change line, since the reactants (ice cream, cherries, syrup) are used during the reaction, their quantities decrease, so the changes in their quantities have a *negative* sign. At the same time, the quantity of product (sundaes) increases, so the change in its quantity has a *positive* sign.
- For the Final line, we *add* the Change and Initial lines. Notice that some reactants (ice cream and cherries) are in excess, while the limiting reactant (syrup) is used up.

**Solving Limiting-Reactant Problems**  In limiting-reactant problems, *the quantities of two (or more) reactants are given, and we first determine which is limiting.* To do this, just as we did with the ice cream sundaes, we use the balanced equation to solve a series of calculations to see how much product forms from the given quantity of each reactant: the limiting reactant is the one that yields the *least* quantity of product.

The following problems examine these ideas from several aspects. In Sample Problem 3.18, we solve the problem by looking at a molecular scene; in Sample Problem 3.19, we start with the amounts (mol) of two reactants, and in Sample Problem 3.20, we start with masses of two reactants.

---

**Sample Problem 3.18**  **Using Molecular Depictions in a Limiting-Reactant Problem**

**Problem**  Nuclear engineers use chlorine trifluoride to prepare uranium fuel for power plants. The compound is formed as a gas by the reaction of elemental chlorine and fluorine. The circle in the margin shows a representative portion of the reaction mixture before the reaction starts (chlorine is *green;* fluorine is *yellow*).
**(a)** Find the limiting reactant.
**(b)** Write a reaction table for the process.
**(c)** Draw a representative portion of the mixture after the reaction is complete. (*Hint:* The $ClF_3$ molecule has Cl bonded to three individual F atoms.)

**Plan (a)** We have to find the limiting reactant. The first step is to write the balanced equation, so we need the formulas and states of matter. From the name, chlorine trifluoride, we know the product consists of one Cl atom bonded to three F atoms, or $ClF_3$. Elemental chlorine and fluorine are the diatomic molecules $Cl_2$ and $F_2$, and all three substances are gases. To find the limiting reactant, we find the number of molecules of product that would form from the numbers of molecules of each reactant: whichever forms less product is the limiting reactant. **(b)** We use these numbers of molecules to write a reaction table. **(c)** We use the numbers in the Final line of the table to draw the scene.

**Solution (a)** The balanced equation is

$$Cl_2(g) + 3F_2(g) \longrightarrow 2ClF_3(g)$$

For $Cl_2$: Molecules of $ClF_3$ = 3 ~~molecules of $Cl_2$~~ × $\dfrac{2 \text{ molecules of } ClF_3}{1 \text{ ~~molecule of $Cl_2$~~}}$

$$= 6 \text{ molecules of } ClF_3$$

For $F_2$: Molecules of $ClF_3$ = 6 ~~molecules of $F_2$~~ × $\dfrac{2 \text{ molecules of } ClF_3}{3 \text{ ~~molecules of $F_2$~~}}$

$$= \tfrac{12}{3} \text{ molecules of } ClF_3 = 4 \text{ molecules of } ClF_3$$

Because it forms less product, $F_2$ is the limiting reactant.
**(b)** Since $F_2$ is the limiting reactant, all of it (6 molecules) is used in the "Change" line of the reaction table:

| Molecules | $Cl_2(g)$ | + | $3F_2(g)$ | $\longrightarrow$ | $2ClF_3(g)$ |
|-----------|-----------|---|-----------|--------------------|-------------|
| Initial   | 3         |   | 6         |                    | 0           |
| Change    | −2        |   | −6        |                    | +4          |
| Final     | 1         |   | 0         |                    | 4           |

**(c)** The representative portion of the final reaction mixture (*see margin*) includes 1 molecule of $Cl_2$ (the reactant in excess) and 4 molecules of product $ClF_3$.

**Check** The equation is balanced: reactants (2 Cl, 6 F) ⟶ products (2 Cl, 6 F). And, as shown in the circles, the numbers of each type of atom before and after the reaction are equal. Let's think through our choice of limiting reactant. From the equation, one $Cl_2$ needs three $F_2$ to form two $ClF_3$. Therefore, the three $Cl_2$ molecules in the circle depicting reactants need nine ($3 \times 3$) $F_2$. But there are only six $F_2$, so there is not enough $F_2$ to react with the available $Cl_2$; or put the other way, there is too much $Cl_2$ to react with the available $F_2$. From either point of view, $F_2$ is the limiting reactant.

**Follow-Up Problem 3.18**  $B_2$ (B is *red*) reacts with AB as shown below:

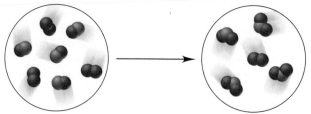

Write a balanced equation for the reaction, and determine the limiting reactant.

---

**Sample Problem 3.19**  **Calculating Quantities in a Limiting-Reactant Problem: Amount to Amount**

**Problem**  In another preparation of $ClF_3$ (see Sample Problem 3.18), 0.750 mol of $Cl_2$ reacts with 3.00 mol of $F_2$. **(a)** Find the limiting reactant. **(b)** Write a reaction table.

**Plan**  **(a)** We find the limiting reactant by calculating the amount (mol) of $ClF_3$ formed from the amount (mol) of each reactant: the reactant that forms fewer moles of $ClF_3$ is limiting. **(b)** We enter those values into the reaction table.

**Solution**  **(a)** Determining the limiting reactant:
Finding amount (mol) of $ClF_3$ from amount (mol) of $Cl_2$:

$$\text{Amount (mol) of } ClF_3 = 0.750 \text{ mol } Cl_2 \times \frac{2 \text{ mol } ClF_3}{1 \text{ mol } Cl_2} = 1.50 \text{ mol } ClF_3$$

Finding amount (mol) of $ClF_3$ from amount (mol) of $F_2$:

$$\text{Amount (mol) of } ClF_3 = 3.00 \text{ mol } F_2 \times \frac{2 \text{ mol } ClF_3}{3 \text{ mol } F_2} = 2.00 \text{ mol } ClF_3$$

In this case, $Cl_2$ is limiting because it forms fewer moles of $ClF_3$.
**(b)** Writing the reaction table, with $Cl_2$ limiting:

| Amount (mol) | $Cl_2(g)$ | + | $3F_2(g)$ | ⟶ | $2ClF_3(g)$ |
|---|---|---|---|---|---|
| Initial | 0.750 | | 3.00 | | 0 |
| Change | −0.750 | | −2.25 | | +1.50 |
| Final | 0 | | 0.75 | | 1.50 |

**Check**  Let's check that $Cl_2$ is the limiting reactant by assuming, for the moment, that $F_2$ is limiting. If that were true, all 3.00 mol of $F_2$ would react to form 2.00 mol of $ClF_3$. However, based on the balanced equation, obtaining 2.00 mol of $ClF_3$ would require 1.00 mol of $Cl_2$, and only 0.750 mol of $Cl_2$ is present. Thus, $Cl_2$ must be the limiting reactant.

**Comment**  A major point to note from Sample Problems 3.18 and 3.19 is that the relative quantities of reactants *do not* determine which is limiting, but rather the quantity of product formed, which is based on the *molar ratio in the balanced equation*. In both problems, there is more $F_2$ than $Cl_2$. However,
• Sample Problem 3.18 has an $F_2/Cl_2$ ratio of 6/3, or 2/1, which is less than the required molar ratio of 3/1, so $F_2$ is limiting and $Cl_2$ is in excess.
• Sample Problem 3.19 has an $F_2/Cl_2$ ratio of 3.00/0.750, which is greater than the required molar ratio of 3/1, so $Cl_2$ is limiting and $F_2$ is in excess.

**Follow-Up Problem 3.19**  For the reaction in Follow-Up Problem 3.18, how many moles of product form from 1.5 mol of each reactant?

**Sample Problem 3.20**  **Calculating Quantities in a Limiting-Reactant Problem: Mass to Mass**

**Problem**  A fuel mixture used in the early days of rocketry consisted of two liquids, hydrazine ($N_2H_4$) and dinitrogen tetraoxide ($N_2O_4$), which ignite on contact to form nitrogen gas and water vapor.
**(a)** How many grams of nitrogen gas form when $1.00\times10^2$ g of $N_2H_4$ and $2.00\times10^2$ g of $N_2O_4$ are mixed?
**(b)** Write a reaction table for this process.

**Plan**  The amounts of two reactants are given, which means this is a limiting-reactant problem. **(a)** To determine the mass of product formed, we must find the limiting reactant by calculating which of the given masses of reactant forms *less* nitrogen gas. As always, we first write the balanced equation. We convert the grams of each reactant to moles using its molar mass and then use the molar ratio from the balanced equation to find the number of moles of $N_2$ each reactant forms. Next, we convert the lower amount of $N_2$ to mass (see the road map). **(b)** We use the values based on the limiting reactant for the reaction table.

**Road Map**

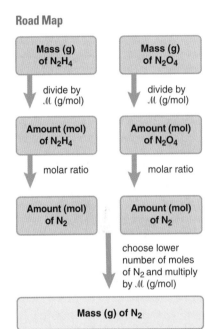

**Solution**  **(a)** Writing the balanced equation:

$$2N_2H_4(l) + N_2O_4(l) \longrightarrow 3N_2(g) + 4H_2O(g)$$

Finding the amount (mol) of $N_2$ from the amount (mol) of each reactant

For $N_2H_4$:  $\text{Amount (mol) of } N_2H_4 = 1.00\times10^2 \text{ g } N_2H_4 \times \dfrac{1 \text{ mol } N_2H_4}{32.05 \text{ g } N_2H_4} = 3.12 \text{ mol } N_2H_4$

$$\text{Amount (mol) of } N_2 = 3.12 \text{ mol } N_2H_4 \times \dfrac{3 \text{ mol } N_2}{2 \text{ mol } N_2H_4} = 4.68 \text{ mol } N_2$$

For $N_2O_4$:  $\text{Amount (mol) of } N_2O_4 = 2.00\times10^2 \text{ g } N_2O_4 \times \dfrac{1 \text{ mol } N_2O_4}{92.02 \text{ g } N_2O_4} = 2.17 \text{ mol } N_2O_4$

$$\text{Amount (mol) of } N_2 = 2.17 \text{ mol } N_2O_4 \times \dfrac{3 \text{ mol } N_2}{1 \text{ mol } N_2O_4} = 6.51 \text{ mol } N_2$$

Thus, $N_2H_4$ is the limiting reactant because it yields less $N_2$.
Converting from amount (mol) of $N_2$ to mass (g):

$$\text{Mass (g) of } N_2 = 4.68 \text{ mol } N_2 \times \dfrac{28.02 \text{ g } N_2}{1 \text{ mol } N_2} = \boxed{131 \text{ g } N_2}$$

**(b)** With $N_2H_4$ as the limiting reactant, the reaction table is

| Amount (mol) | $2N_2H_4(g)$ + | $N_2O_4(g)$ $\longrightarrow$ | $3N_2(g)$ + | $4H_2O(g)$ |
|---|---|---|---|---|
| Initial | 3.12 | 2.17 | 0 | 0 |
| Change | −3.12 | −1.56 | +4.68 | +6.24 |
| Final | 0 | 0.61 | 4.68 | 6.24 |

**Check**  The number of grams of $N_2O_4$ is more than that of $N_2H_4$, but there are fewer moles of $N_2O_4$ because its $M$ is much higher. Rounding for $N_2H_4$: 100 g $N_2H_4$ × 1 mol/32 g ≈ 3 mol; ~3 mol × $\frac{3}{2}$ ≈ 4.5 mol $N_2$; ~4.5 mol × 30 g/mol ≈ 135 g $N_2$.

**Comment 1.** Recall this *common mistake* in solving limiting-reactant problems: The limiting reactant is not the *reactant* present in fewer moles (or grams). Rather, it is the reactant that forms fewer moles (or grams) of *product*.
**2.** An *alternative approach* to finding the limiting reactant compares "How much is needed?" with "How much is given?" That is, based on the balanced equation,
• Find the amount (mol) of each reactant needed to react with the other reactant.
• Compare that *needed* amount with the *given* amount in the problem statement. There will be *more* than enough of one reactant (excess) and *less* than enough of the other (limiting). For example, the balanced equation for this problem shows that 2 mol of $N_2H_4$ reacts with 1 mol of $N_2O_4$. The amount (mol) of $N_2O_4$ needed to react with the given 3.12 mol of $N_2H_4$ is

$$\text{Amount (mol) of } N_2O_4 \text{ needed} = 3.12 \text{ mol } N_2H_4 \times \dfrac{1 \text{ mol } N_2O_4}{2 \text{ mol } N_2H_4} = 1.56 \text{ mol } N_2O_4$$

The amount of $N_2H_4$ needed to react with the given 2.17 mol of $N_2O_4$ is

$$\text{Amount (mol) of } N_2H_4 \text{ needed} = 2.17 \text{ mol } N_2O_4 \times \dfrac{2 \text{ mol } N_2H_4}{1 \text{ mol } N_2O_4} = 4.34 \text{ mol } N_2H_4$$

We are given 2.17 mol of $N_2O_4$, which is *more* than the 1.56 mol of $N_2O_4$ needed, and we are given 3.12 mol of $N_2H_4$, which is *less* than the 4.34 mol of $N_2H_4$ needed. Therefore, $N_2H_4$ is limiting, and $N_2O_4$ is in excess.

**Follow-Up Problem 3.20** How many grams of solid aluminum sulfide can be prepared by the reaction of 10.0 g of aluminum and 15.0 g of sulfur? How many grams of the nonlimiting reactant are in excess?

## Theoretical, Actual, and Percent Reaction Yields

Up until now, we've assumed that 100% of the limiting reactant becomes product, that ideal methods exist for isolating the product, and that we have perfect lab technique and collect all the product. In theory, this may happen, but in reality, it doesn't, and chemists recognize three types of reaction yield:

1. *Theoretical yield.* The amount of product calculated from the molar ratio in the balanced equation is the **theoretical yield.** But, there are several reasons why the theoretical yield is *never* obtained:
   - Reactant mixtures often proceed through **side reactions** that form different products (Figure 3.11). In the rocket fuel reaction in Sample Problem 3.20, for example, the reactants might form some NO in the following side reaction:

     $$N_2H_4(l) + 2N_2O_4(l) \longrightarrow 6NO(g) + 2H_2O(g)$$

     This reaction decreases the amounts of reactants available for $N_2$ production.
   - Even more important, many reactions seem to stop before they are complete, so some limiting reactant is unused. (We'll see why in Chapter 4.)
   - Physical losses occur in every step of a separation (see Tools of the Laboratory, Section 2.9): some solid clings to filter paper, some distillate evaporates, and so forth. With careful technique, you can minimize, but never eliminate, such losses.

2. *Actual yield.* Given these reasons for obtaining less than the theoretical yield, the amount of product actually obtained is the **actual yield.** Theoretical and actual yields are expressed in units of amount (moles) or mass (grams).

3. *Percent yield.* The **percent yield (% yield)** is the actual yield expressed as a percentage of the theoretical yield:

$$\% \text{ yield} = \frac{\text{actual yield}}{\text{theoretical yield}} \times 100 \qquad (3.8)$$

By definition, the actual yield is less than the theoretical yield, so the percent yield is *always* less than 100%.

**Road Map**

**Figure 3.11** The effect of a side reaction on the yield of the main product.

### Sample Problem 3.21 | Calculating Percent Yield

**Problem** Silicon carbide (SiC) is an important ceramic material made by reacting sand (silicon dioxide, $SiO_2$) with powdered carbon at a high temperature. Carbon monoxide is also formed. When 100.0 kg of sand is processed, 51.4 kg of SiC is recovered. What is the percent yield of SiC from this process?

**Plan** We are given the actual yield of SiC (51.4 kg), so we need the theoretical yield to calculate the percent yield. After writing the balanced equation, we convert the given mass of $SiO_2$ (100.0 kg) to amount (mol). We use the molar ratio to find the amount of SiC formed and convert it to mass (kg) to obtain the theoretical yield. Then, we use Equation 3.8 to find the percent yield (see the road map).

**Solution** Writing the balanced equation:

$$SiO_2(s) + 3C(s) \longrightarrow SiC(s) + 2CO(g)$$

Converting from mass (kg) of $SiO_2$ to amount (mol):

$$\text{Amount (mol) of } SiO_2 = 100.0 \text{ kg } SiO_2 \times \frac{1000 \text{ g}}{1 \text{ kg}} \times \frac{1 \text{ mol } SiO_2}{60.09 \text{ g } SiO_2} = 1664 \text{ mol } SiO_2$$

Converting from amount (mol) of $SiO_2$ to amount (mol) of SiC:
The molar ratio is 1 mol SiC/1 mol $SiO_2$, so

$$\text{Amount (mol) of } SiO_2 = \text{moles of SiC} = 1664 \text{ mol SiC}$$

Converting from amount (mol) of SiC to mass (kg):

$$\text{Mass (kg) of SiC} = 1664 \text{ mol SiC} \times \frac{40.10 \text{ g SiC}}{1 \text{ mol SiC}} \times \frac{1 \text{ kg}}{1000 \text{ g}} = 66.73 \text{ kg SiC}$$

Calculating the percent yield:

$$\text{\% yield of SiC} = \frac{\text{actual yield}}{\text{theoretical yield}} \times 100 = \frac{51.4 \text{ kg SiC}}{66.73 \text{ kg SiC}} \times 100 = \boxed{77.0\%}$$

**Check** Rounding shows that the mass of SiC seems correct: ~1500 mol × 40 g/mol × 1 kg/1000 g = 60 kg. The molar ratio of $SiC/SiO_2$ is 1/1, and $\mathcal{M}$ of SiC is about two-thirds ($\sim\frac{40}{60}$) of $\mathcal{M}$ of $SiO_2$, so 100 kg of $SiO_2$ should form about 66 kg of SiC.

**Follow-Up Problem 3.21** Marble (calcium carbonate) reacts with hydrochloric acid solution to form calcium chloride solution, water, and carbon dioxide. Find the percent yield of carbon dioxide if 3.65 g is collected when 10.0 g of marble reacts.

**Yields in Multistep Syntheses** In the multistep synthesis of a complex compound, the overall yield can be surprisingly low, even if the yield of each step is high. For example, suppose a six-step synthesis has a 90.0% yield for each step. To find the overall percent yield, *express the yield of each step as a decimal, multiply them together, and then convert back to percent*. The overall recovery is only slightly more than 50%:

$$\text{Overall \% yield} = (0.900 \times 0.900 \times 0.900 \times 0.900 \times 0.900 \times 0.900) \times 100 = 53.1\%$$

Such multistep sequences are common in laboratory syntheses of medicines, dyes, pesticides, and many other organic compounds. For example, the antidepressant Sertraline is prepared from a simple starting compound in six steps, with yields of 80%, 80%, 50%, 100%, 48%, and 30%, respectively, and an overall percent yield of only 4.6% (Figure 3.12). Because a typical synthesis begins with large amounts of inexpensive, simple reactants and ends with small amounts of expensive, complex products, the overall yield greatly influences the commercial potential of a product.

**Atom Economy: A Green Chemistry Perspective on Yield** In the relatively new field of **green chemistry,** academic, industrial, and government chemists develop methods that reduce or prevent the release of harmful substances into the environment and the wasting of energy resources.

One way that green chemists evaluate a synthetic route is to focus on its *atom economy,* the proportion of reactant atoms that end up in the desired product. The efficiency of a synthesis is quantified in terms of the *percent atom economy:*

$$\text{\% atom economy} = \frac{\text{no. of moles} \times \text{molar mass of desired product}}{\text{sum of (no. of moles} \times \text{molar mass) for all products}} \times 100$$

Consider two synthetic routes—one starting with benzene ($C_6H_6$), the other with butane ($C_4H_{10}$)—for the production of maleic anhydride ($C_4H_2O_3$), a key substance in the manufacture of polymers, dyes, medicines, pesticides, and other products:

Route 1.    $2C_6H_6(l) + 9O_2(g) \rightarrow \cdots \rightarrow 2C_4H_2O_3(l) + 4H_2O(l) + 4CO_2(g)$

Route 2.    $2C_4H_{10}(g) + 7O_2(g) \rightarrow \cdots \rightarrow 2C_4H_2O_3(l) + 8H_2O(l)$

Let's compare the efficiency of these routes in terms of percent atom economy:

Route 1.

$$\text{\% atom economy} = \frac{2 \times \mathcal{M} \text{ of } C_4H_2O_3}{(2 \times \mathcal{M} \text{ of } C_4H_2O_3) + (4 \times \mathcal{M} \text{ of } H_2O) + (4 \times \mathcal{M} \text{ of } CO_2)} \times 100$$

$$= \frac{2 \times 98.06 \text{ g}}{(2 \times 98.06 \text{ g}) + (4 \times 18.02 \text{ g}) + (4 \times 44.01 \text{ g})} \times 100$$

$$= 44.15\%$$

Starting with 100 g
of 1,2-dichlorobenzene,

↓ 80%
↓ 80%
↓ 50%
↓ 100%
↓ 48%
↓ 30%

Sertraline

the yield of Sertraline is only 4.6 g.

**Figure 3.12** Low overall yield for a multistep biomedical synthesis.

Route 2.

$$\% \text{ atom economy} = \frac{2 \times \mathcal{M} \text{ of } C_4H_2O_3}{(2 \times \mathcal{M} \text{ of } C_4H_2O_3) + (8 \times \mathcal{M} \text{ of } H_2O)} \times 100$$

$$= \frac{2 \times 98.06 \text{ g}}{(2 \times 98.06 \text{ g}) + (8 \times 18.02 \text{ g})} \times 100$$

$$= 57.63\%$$

From the perspective of atom economy, route 2 is preferable because a larger percentage of reactant atoms end up in the desired product. It is also a "greener" approach than route 1 because it avoids the use of the toxic reactant benzene and does not produce $CO_2$, a gas that contributes to global warming.

## ■ Summary of Section 3.4

- The substances in a balanced equation are related to each other by stoichiometrically equivalent molar ratios, which are used as conversion factors to find the amount (mol) of one substance given the amount of another.
- In limiting-reactant problems, the quantities of two (or more) reactants are given, and the limiting reactant is the one that forms the lower quantity of product. Reaction tables show the initial and final quantities of all reactants and products, as well as the changes in those quantities.
- In practice, side reactions, incomplete reactions, and physical losses result in an actual yield of product that is less than the theoretical yield (the quantity based on the molar ratio from the balanced equation), giving a percent yield less than 100%. In multistep reaction sequences, the overall yield is found by multiplying the yields for each step.
- Atom economy, or the proportion of reactant atoms found in the product, is one criterion for choosing a "greener" reaction process.

## 3.5 • FUNDAMENTALS OF SOLUTION STOICHIOMETRY

In popular media, you may see a chemist in a lab coat, surrounded by glassware, mixing colored solutions that froth and give off billowing fumes. Most reactions in solution are not this dramatic, and good technique requires safer mixing procedures; however, it is true that aqueous solution chemistry is central to laboratory chemistry. Liquid solutions are easier to store than gases and easier to mix than solids, and the amounts of substances in solution can be measured precisely. Many environmental reactions and almost all biochemical reactions occur in solution.

We know the amounts of pure substances by converting their masses into number of moles. But for dissolved substances, we need the *concentration*—the number of moles per volume of solution—to find the volume that contains a given number of moles. In this section, we first discuss *molarity*, the most common way to express concentration (Chapter 13 covers others). Then, we see how to prepare a solution of a specific molarity and how to use solutions in stoichiometric calculations.

### Expressing Concentration in Terms of Molarity

A solution consists of a smaller quantity of one substance, the **solute,** dissolved in a larger quantity of another, the **solvent.** When it dissolves, the solute's chemical entities become evenly dispersed throughout the solvent. The **concentration** of a solution is often expressed as *the quantity of solute dissolved in a given quantity of solution.*

Concentration is an *intensive* property (like density or temperature; Section 1.5) and thus is independent of the solution volume: a 50-L tank of a solution has the *same concentration* (solute quantity/solution quantity) as a 50-mL beaker of the solution. **Molarity (*M*)** expresses the concentration in units of *moles of solute per liter of solution:*

$$\text{Molarity} = \frac{\text{moles of solute}}{\text{liters of solution}} \quad \text{or} \quad M = \frac{\text{mol solute}}{\text{L soln}} \tag{3.9}$$

## Sample Problem 3.22 | Calculating the Molarity of a Solution

**Problem** Glycine has the simplest structure of the 20 amino acids that make up proteins. What is the molarity of a solution that contains 0.715 mol of glycine in 495 mL?

**Plan** The molarity is the number of moles of solute in each liter of solution. We divide the number of moles (0.715 mol) by the volume (495 mL) and convert the volume to liters to find the molarity (see the road map).

**Solution**    $\text{Molarity} = \dfrac{0.715 \text{ mol glycine}}{495 \text{ mL soln}} \times \dfrac{1000 \text{ mL}}{1 \text{ L}} = 1.44 \; M \text{ glycine}$

**Check** A quick look at the math shows about 0.7 mol of glycine in about 0.5 L of solution, so the concentration should be about 1.4 mol/L, or 1.4 $M$.

**Follow-Up Problem 3.22** How many moles of KI are in 84 mL of 0.50 $M$ KI? Include a road map that shows how you planned the solution.

**Road Map**

> **Amount (mol) of glycine**
>
>    ↓ divide by volume (mL)
>
> **Concentration (mol/mL) of glycine**
>
>    ↓ $10^3$ mL = 1 L
>
> **Molarity (mol/L) of glycine**

## Amount-Mass-Number Conversions Involving Solutions

Like many intensive properties, molarity can be used as a *conversion factor* between volume (L) of solution and amount (mol) of solute, from which we can find the mass or the number of entities of solute (Figure 3.13), as applied in Sample Problem 3.23.

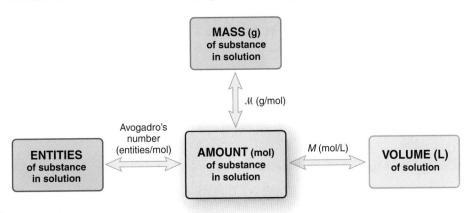

**Figure 3.13  Summary of amount-mass-number relationships in solution.** The amount (mol) of a substance in solution is related to the volume (L) of solution through the molarity (*M*; mol/L). As always, convert the given quantity to amount (mol) first.

## Sample Problem 3.23 | Calculating Mass of Solute in a Given Volume of Solution

**Problem** Biochemists often study reactions in solutions containing phosphate ion, commonly found in cells. How many grams of solute are in 1.75 L of 0.460 $M$ sodium hydrogen phosphate?

**Plan** We need the mass (g) of solute, so we multiply the known solution volume (1.75 L) by the known molarity (0.460 $M$) to find the amount (mol) of solute and convert it to mass (g) using the solute's molar mass (see the road map).

**Solution** Calculating amount (mol) of solute in solution:

$\text{Amount (mol) of } Na_2HPO_4 = 1.75 \text{ L soln} \times \dfrac{0.460 \text{ mol } Na_2HPO_4}{1 \text{ L soln}} = 0.805 \text{ mol } Na_2HPO_4$

Converting from amount (mol) of solute to mass (g):

$\text{Mass (g) } Na_2HPO_4 = 0.805 \text{ mol } Na_2HPO_4 \times \dfrac{141.96 \text{ g } Na_2HPO_4}{1 \text{ mol } Na_2HPO_4} = 114 \text{ g } Na_2HPO_4$

**Check** The answer seems to be correct: ~1.8 L of 0.5 mol/L solution contains 0.9 mol, and 150 g/mol × 0.9 mol = 135 g, which is close to 114 g of solute.

**Follow-Up Problem 3.23** In biochemistry laboratories, solutions of sucrose (table sugar, $C_{12}H_{22}O_{11}$) are used in high-speed centrifuges to separate the parts of a biological cell. How many liters of 3.30 $M$ sucrose contain 135 g of solute? Include a road map that shows how you planned the solution.

**Road Map**

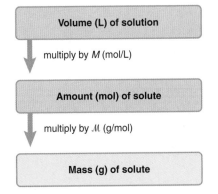

## Preparing and Diluting Molar Solutions

Notice that the volume term in the denominator of the molarity expression in Equation 3.9 is the *solution* volume, **not** the *solvent* volume. This means that you *cannot* dissolve 1 mol of solute in 1 L of solvent to make a 1 *M* solution. Because the solute volume adds to the solvent volume, the total volume (solute + solvent) would be *more* than 1 L, so the concentration would be *less* than 1 *M*.

Step 2
Step 3
Step 4

**Figure 3.14** Laboratory preparation of molar solutions.

**Preparing a Solution** Correctly preparing a solution of a solid solute requires four steps. Let's prepare 0.500 L of 0.350 *M* nickel(II) nitrate hexahydrate [$Ni(NO_3)_2\cdot6H_2O$]:

1. *Weigh the solid.* Calculate the mass of solid needed by converting from volume (L) to amount (mol) and then to mass (g):

$$\text{Mass (g) of solute} = 0.500 \text{ L soln} \times \frac{0.350 \text{ mol } Ni(NO_3)_2\cdot6H_2O}{1 \text{ L soln}}$$
$$\times \frac{290.82 \text{ g } Ni(NO_3)_2\cdot6H_2O}{1 \text{ mol } Ni(NO_3)_2\cdot6H_2O}$$
$$= 50.9 \text{ g } Ni(NO_3)_2\cdot6H_2O$$

2. *Transfer the solid.* We need 0.500 L of solution, so we choose a 500-mL volumetric flask, add enough distilled water to fully dissolve the solute (usually about half the final volume, or 250 mL of distilled water in this case), and transfer the solute. Wash down any solid clinging to the neck with some solvent.

3. *Dissolve the solid.* Swirl the flask until all the solute is dissolved. If necessary, wait until the solution is at room temperature. (As we discuss in Chapter 13, the solution process may be accompanied by heating or cooling.)

4. *Add solvent to the final volume.* Add distilled water to bring the solution volume to the line on the flask neck; cover and mix thoroughly again.

Figure 3.14 shows the last three steps.

**Diluting a Solution** A concentrated solution (higher molarity) is converted to a dilute solution (lower molarity) by adding solvent, which means the solution volume increases but the amount (mol) of solute stays the same. As a result, the dilute solution contains *fewer solute particles per unit volume* and, thus, has a lower concentration than the concentrated solution (Figure 3.15). If you need several different dilute solutions, prepare a concentrated solution *(stock solution)* and store it and dilute it as needed.

**Figure 3.15** Converting a concentrated solution to a dilute solution.

Solvent added to double volume →

**Concentrated solution:** *More solute particles are present per unit volume.*

**Dilute solution:** *Fewer solute particles are present per unit volume.*

## Sample Problem 3.24    Preparing a Dilute Solution from a Concentrated Solution

**Problem** Isotonic saline is 0.15 $M$ aqueous NaCl. It simulates the total concentration of ions in many cellular fluids, and its uses range from cleaning contact lenses to washing red blood cells. How would you prepare 0.80 L of isotonic saline from a 6.0 $M$ stock solution?

**Plan** To dilute a concentrated solution, we add only solvent, so the *moles of solute are the same in both solutions.* We know the volume (0.80 L) and molarity (0.15 $M$) of the dilute (dil) NaCl solution needed, so we find the amount (mol) of NaCl it contains. Then, we find the volume (L) of concentrated (conc; 6.0 $M$) NaCl solution that contains the same amount (mol). We add solvent *up to* the final volume (see the road map).

**Solution** Finding amount (mol) of solute in dilute solution:

$$\text{Amount (mol) of NaCl in dil soln} = 0.80 \text{ L soln} \times \frac{0.15 \text{ mol NaCl}}{1 \text{ L soln}}$$
$$= 0.12 \text{ mol NaCl}$$

Finding amount (mol) of solute in concentrated solution:

Because we add only solvent to dilute the solution,

$$\text{Amount (mol) of NaCl in dil soln} = \text{amount (mol) of NaCl in conc soln}$$
$$= 0.12 \text{ mol NaCl}$$

Finding the volume (L) of concentrated solution that contains 0.12 mol of NaCl:

$$\text{Volume (L) of conc NaCl soln} = 0.12 \text{ mol NaCl} \times \frac{1 \text{ L soln}}{6.0 \text{ mol NaCl}}$$
$$= 0.020 \text{ L soln}$$

To prepare 0.80 L of dilute solution, place 0.020 L of 6.0 $M$ NaCl in a 1.0-L graduated cylinder, add distilled water (~780 mL) to the 0.80-L mark, and stir thoroughly.

**Check** The answer seems reasonable because a small volume of concentrated solution is used to prepare a large volume of dilute solution. Also, the ratio of volumes (0.020 L/0.80 L) is the same as the ratio of concentrations (0.15 $M$/6.0 $M$).

**Follow-Up Problem 3.24** A chemical engineer dilutes a stock solution of sulfuric acid by adding 25.0 $m^3$ of 7.50 $M$ acid to enough water to make 500. $m^3$. What is the concentration of sulfuric acid in the diluted solution in g/mL?

**Road Map**

| Volume (L) of dilute solution |
|---|

multiply by $M$ (mol/L) of dilute solution

| Amount (mol) of NaCl in dilute solution = Amount (mol) of NaCl in concentrated solution |
|---|

divide by $M$ (mol/L) of concentrated solution

| Volume (L) of concentrated solution |
|---|

**Solving Dilution Problems** To solve dilution problems and others involving a change in concentration, apply the following relationship:

$$M_{\text{dil}} \times V_{\text{dil}} = \text{amount (mol)} = M_{\text{conc}} \times V_{\text{conc}} \qquad \text{(3.10)}$$

where $M$ and $V$ are the molarity and volume of the *dil*ute (subscript "dil") and *conc*entrated (subscript "conc") solutions. Using the values in Sample Problem 3.24, for example, and solving Equation 3.10 for $V_{\text{conc}}$ gives

$$V_{\text{conc}} = \frac{M_{\text{dil}} \times V_{\text{dil}}}{M_{\text{conc}}} = \frac{0.15 \, M \times 0.80 \text{ L}}{6.0 \, M}$$
$$= 0.020 \text{ L}$$

Notice that Sample Problem 3.24 had the same calculation broken into two parts:

$$V_{\text{conc}} = 0.80 \text{ L} \times \frac{0.15 \text{ mol NaCl}}{1 \text{ L}} \times \frac{1 \text{ L}}{6.0 \text{ mol NaCl}}$$
$$= 0.020 \text{ L}$$

In the next sample problem, we use a variation of this relationship, with molecular scenes showing numbers of particles, to visualize changes in concentration.

**(a)**

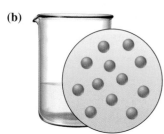

**(b)**

## Sample Problem 3.25 | Visualizing Changes in Concentration

**Problem** The top circle at left represents a unit volume of a solution. Draw a circle representing a unit volume of the solution after each of these changes:
**(a)** For every 1 mL of solution, 1 mL of solvent is added.
**(b)** One-third of the solvent is boiled off.

**Plan** Given the starting solution, we have to find the number of solute particles in a unit volume after each change. The number of particles per unit volume, $N$, is directly related to the number of moles per unit volume, $M$, so we can use a relationship similar to Equation 3.10 to find the number of particles. **(a)** The volume increases, so the final solution is more dilute—fewer particles per unit volume. **(b)** Some solvent is lost, so the final solution is more concentrated—more particles per unit volume.

**Solution** **(a)** Finding the number of particles in the dilute solution, $N_{dil}$:

$$N_{dil} \times V_{dil} = N_{conc} \times V_{conc}$$

thus,

$$N_{dil} = N_{conc} \times \frac{V_{conc}}{V_{dil}} = 8 \text{ particles} \times \frac{1 \text{ mL}}{2 \text{ mL}} = 4 \text{ particles}$$

**(b)** Finding the number of particles in the concentrated solution, $N_{conc}$:

$$N_{dil} \times V_{dil} = N_{conc} \times V_{conc}$$

thus,

$$N_{conc} = N_{dil} \times \frac{V_{dil}}{V_{conc}} = 8 \text{ particles} \times \frac{1 \text{ mL}}{\frac{2}{3} \text{ mL}} = 12 \text{ particles}$$

**Check** In (a), the volume is doubled (from 1 mL to 2 mL), so the number of particles should be halved; $\frac{1}{2}$ of 8 is 4. In (b), the volume is $\frac{2}{3}$ of the original, so the number of particles should be $\frac{3}{2}$ of the original; $\frac{3}{2}$ of 8 is 12.

**Comment** In (b), we assumed that only solvent boils off. This is true with nonvolatile solutes, such as ionic compounds, but in Chapter 13, we'll encounter solutions in which both solvent *and* solute are volatile.

**Follow-Up Problem 3.25** The circle labeled A represents a unit volume of a solution. Explain the changes that must be made to A to obtain the unit volumes in B and C.

A          B          C

## Stoichiometry of Reactions in Solution

Solving stoichiometry problems for reactions in solution requires the additional step of converting the volume of reactant or product in solution to amount (mol):

1. Balance the equation.
2. Find the amount (mol) of one substance from the volume and molarity.
3. Relate it to the stoichiometrically equivalent amount of another substance.
4. Convert to the desired units.

## Sample Problem 3.26 | Calculating Quantities of Reactants and Products for a Reaction in Solution

**Problem** Specialized cells in the stomach release HCl to aid digestion. If they release too much, the excess can be neutralized with an antacid. A common antacid contains magnesium hydroxide, which reacts with the acid to form water and magnesium chloride solution. As a government chemist testing commercial antacids, you use 0.10 *M* HCl to simulate the acid concentration in the stomach. How many liters of "stomach acid" react with a tablet containing 0.10 g of magnesium hydroxide?

**Plan** We are given the mass (0.10 g) of magnesium hydroxide, $Mg(OH)_2$, that reacts with the acid. We also know the acid concentration (0.10 *M*) and must find the acid volume. After writing the balanced equation, we convert the mass (g) of $Mg(OH)_2$ to amount (mol) and use the molar ratio to find the amount (mol) of HCl that reacts with it. Then, we use the molarity of HCl to find the volume (L) that contains this amount (see the road map).

**Solution** Writing the balanced equation:

$$Mg(OH)_2(s) + 2HCl(aq) \longrightarrow MgCl_2(aq) + 2H_2O(l)$$

Converting from mass (g) of $Mg(OH)_2$ to amount (mol):

$$\text{Amount (mol) of } Mg(OH)_2 = 0.10 \text{ g } Mg(OH)_2 \times \frac{1 \text{ mol } Mg(OH)_2}{58.33 \text{ g } Mg(OH)_2} = 1.7 \times 10^{-3} \text{ mol } Mg(OH)_2$$

Converting from amount (mol) of $Mg(OH)_2$ to amount (mol) of HCl:

$$\text{Amount (mol) of HCl} = 1.7 \times 10^{-3} \text{ mol } Mg(OH)_2 \times \frac{2 \text{ mol HCl}}{1 \text{ mol } Mg(OH)_2} = 3.4 \times 10^{-3} \text{ mol HCl}$$

Converting from amount (mol) of HCl to volume (L):

$$\text{Volume (L) of HCl} = 3.4 \times 10^{-3} \text{ mol HCl} \times \frac{1 \text{ L}}{0.10 \text{ mol HCl}} = \boxed{3.4 \times 10^{-2} \text{ L}}$$

**Check** The size of the answer seems reasonable: a small volume of dilute acid (0.034 L of 0.10 *M*) reacts with a small amount of antacid (0.0017 mol).

**Comment** In Chapter 4, you'll see that this equation is an oversimplification, because HCl and $MgCl_2$ exist in solution as separated ions.

**Follow-Up Problem 3.26** Another active ingredient in some antacids is aluminum hydroxide. Which is more effective at neutralizing stomach acid, magnesium hydroxide or aluminum hydroxide? [*Hint:* "Effectiveness" refers to the amount of acid that reacts with a given mass of antacid. You already know the effectiveness of 0.10 g of $Mg(OH)_2$.]

**Road Map**

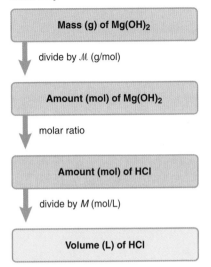

Except for the additional step of finding amounts (mol) in solution, limiting-reactant problems for reactions in solution are handled just like other such problems.

## Sample Problem 3.27 | Solving Limiting-Reactant Problems for Reactions in Solution

**Problem** Mercury and its compounds have uses from fillings for teeth (as a mixture with silver, copper, and tin) to the production of chlorine. Because of their toxicity, however, soluble mercury compounds, such as mercury(II) nitrate, must be removed from industrial wastewater. One removal method reacts the wastewater with sodium sulfide solution to produce solid mercury(II) sulfide and sodium nitrate solution. In a laboratory simulation, 0.050 L of 0.010 *M* mercury(II) nitrate reacts with 0.020 L of 0.10 *M* sodium sulfide. **(a)** How many grams of mercury(II) sulfide form? **(b)** Write a reaction table for this process.

**Plan** This is a limiting-reactant problem because *the quantities of two reactants are given*. After balancing the equation, we determine the limiting reactant. From the molarity and volume of each solution, we calculate the amount (mol) of each reactant. Then, we use the molar ratio to find the amount of product (HgS) that each reactant forms. The limiting reactant forms fewer moles of HgS, which we convert to mass (g) of HgS using its molar mass (see the road map). We use the amount of HgS formed from the limiting reactant in the reaction table.

**Solution (a)** Writing the balanced equation:

$$Hg(NO_3)_2(aq) + Na_2S(aq) \longrightarrow HgS(s) + 2NaNO_3(aq)$$

Finding the amount (mol) of HgS formed from $Hg(NO_3)_2$: Combining the steps gives

$$\text{Amount (mol) of HgS} = 0.050 \text{ L soln} \times \frac{0.010 \text{ mol } Hg(NO_3)_2}{1 \text{ L soln}} \times \frac{1 \text{ mol HgS}}{1 \text{ mol } Hg(NO_3)_2}$$

$$= \mathbf{5.0 \times 10^{-4} \text{ mol HgS}}$$

**Road Map**

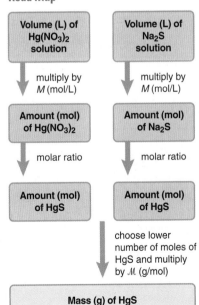

Finding the amount (mol) of HgS from $Na_2S$: Combining the steps gives

$$\text{Amount (mol) of HgS} = 0.020 \, \cancel{\text{L soln}} \times \frac{0.10 \, \cancel{\text{mol } Na_2S}}{1 \, \cancel{\text{L soln}}} \times \frac{1 \, \text{mol HgS}}{1 \, \cancel{\text{mol } Na_2S}} = 2.0 \times 10^{-3} \, \text{mol HgS}$$

$Hg(NO_3)_2$ is the limiting reactant because it forms fewer moles of HgS.
Converting the amount (mol) of HgS formed from $Hg(NO_3)_2$ to mass (g):

$$\text{Mass (g) of HgS} = 5.0 \times 10^{-4} \, \cancel{\text{mol HgS}} \times \frac{232.7 \, \text{g HgS}}{1 \, \cancel{\text{mol HgS}}} = \boxed{0.12 \, \text{g HgS}}$$

**(b)** With $Hg(NO_3)_2$ as the limiting reactant, the reaction table is

| Amount (mol) | $Hg(NO_3)_2(aq)$ + | $Na_2S(aq)$ $\longrightarrow$ | HgS(s) + | $2NaNO_3(aq)$ |
|---|---|---|---|---|
| Initial | $5.0 \times 10^{-4}$ | $2.0 \times 10^{-3}$ | 0 | 0 |
| Change | $-5.0 \times 10^{-4}$ | $-5.0 \times 10^{-4}$ | $+5.0 \times 10^{-4}$ | $+1.0 \times 10^{-3}$ |
| Final | 0 | $1.5 \times 10^{-3}$ | $5.0 \times 10$ | $1.0 \times 10^{-3}$ |

A large excess of $Na_2S$ remains after the reaction. Note that the amount of $NaNO_3$ formed is twice the amount of $Hg(NO_3)_2$ consumed, as the balanced equation shows.

**Check** As a check on our choice of the limiting reactant, let's use the alternative method in Sample Problem 3.20 (see Comment, p. 111).
Finding amount (mol) of reactants given:

$$\text{Amount (mol) of } Hg(NO_3)_2 = 0.050 \, \cancel{\text{L soln}} \times \frac{0.010 \, \text{mol } Hg(NO_3)_2}{1 \, \cancel{\text{L soln}}} = 5.0 \times 10^{-4} \, \text{mol } Hg(NO_3)_2$$

$$\text{Amount (mol) of } Na_2S = 0.020 \, \cancel{\text{L soln}} \times \frac{0.10 \, \text{mol } Na_2S}{1 \, \cancel{\text{L soln}}} = 2.0 \times 10^{-3} \, \text{mol } Na_2S$$

The molar ratio of the reactants is 1 $Hg(NO_3)_2$/1 $Na_2S$. Therefore, $Hg(NO_3)_2$ is limiting because there is less of it than we would need to react with all of the available $Na_2S$.

**Follow-Up Problem 3.27** Despite the toxicity of lead, many of its compounds are still used to make pigments. **(a)** When 268 mL of 1.50 *M* lead(II) acetate reacts with 130. mL of 3.40 *M* sodium chloride, how many grams of solid lead(II) chloride can form? (Sodium acetate solution also forms.) **(b)** Using the abbreviation "Ac" for the acetate ion, write a reaction table for the process.

**Figure 3.16** An overview of amount-mass-number stoichiometric relationships.

Figure 3.16 provides a visual review of all the stoichiometric relationships we've discussed in this chapter.

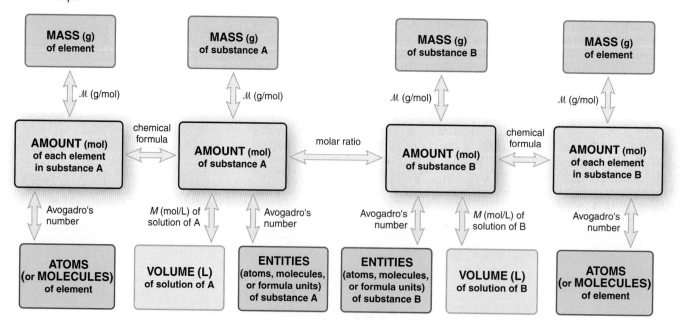

# Summary of Section 3.5

- When reactions occur in solution, amounts of reactants and products are given in terms of concentration and volume.
- Molarity is the number of moles of solute dissolved in one liter of solution. A concentrated solution (higher molarity) is converted to a dilute solution (lower molarity) by adding solvent.
- By using molarity as a conversion factor, we can apply the principles of stoichiometry to reactions in solution.

# CHAPTER REVIEW GUIDE

**Learning Objectives**    Relevant section (§) and/or sample problem (SP) numbers appear in parentheses.

## Understand These Concepts

1. The definition of the mole unit (§3.1)
2. Relation between the mass of a chemical entity (in amu) and the mass of a mole of the entities (in g) (§3.1)
3. The relations among amount of substance (in mol), mass (in g), and number of chemical entities (§3.1)
4. Mole-mass-number information in a chemical formula (§3.1)
5. The difference between empirical and molecular formulas of a compound (§3.2)
6. How more than one substance can have the same empirical formula and the same molecular formula (isomers) (§3.2)
7. The importance of balancing equations for the quantitative study of chemical reactions (§3.3)
8. Mole-mass-number information in a balanced equation (§3.4)
9. The relation between amounts of reactants and amounts of products (§3.4)
10. Why one reactant limits the amount of product (§3.4)
11. The causes of lower-than-expected yields and the distinction between theoretical and actual yields (§3.4)
12. The meanings of concentration and molarity (§3.5)
13. The effect of dilution on the concentration of solute (§3.5)
14. How reactions in solution differ from reactions of pure reactants (§3.5)

## Master These Skills

1. Calculating the molar mass of any substance (§3.1; SPs 3.5, 3.6)
2. Converting between amount of substance (in moles), mass (in grams), and number of chemical entities (SPs 3.1–3.5)
3. Using mass percent to find the mass of an element in a given mass of compound (SPs 3.6, 3.7)
4. Determining empirical and molecular formulas of a compound from mass percents and molar masses of elements (SPs 3.8–3.10)
5. Determining a molecular formula from combustion analysis (SP 3.11)
6. Converting a chemical statement or a molecular depiction into a balanced equation (SPs 3.12, 3.13)
7. Using stoichiometrically equivalent molar ratios to convert between amounts of reactants and products in reactions of pure and dissolved substances (SPs 3.14–3.16, 3.26)
8. Writing an overall equation from a series of equations (SP 3.17)
9. Solving limiting-reactant problems for reactions of pure and dissolved substances (SPs 3.18–3.20, 3.27)
10. Calculating percent yield (SP 3.21)
11. Calculating molarity and mass of solute in solution (SPs 3.22, 3.23)
12. Preparing a dilute solution from a concentrated one (SP 3.24)
13. Using molecular depictions to understand changes in concentration (SP 3.25)

**Key Terms**    Page numbers appear in parentheses.

stoichiometry (83)

**Section 3.1**
mole (mol) (83)
Avogadro's number (83)
molar mass ($\mathcal{M}$) (84)

**Section 3.2**
empirical formula (92)
molecular formula (92)

structural formula (92)
combustion analysis (95)
isomer (97)

**Section 3.3**
chemical equation (98)
reactant (99)
product (99)
balancing (stoichiometric) coefficient (99)

**Section 3.4**
overall (net) equation (106)
limiting reactant (107)
theoretical yield (112)
side reaction (112)
actual yield (112)
percent yield (% yield) (112)
green chemistry (113)

**Section 3.5**
solute (114)
solvent (114)
concentration (114)
molarity ($M$) (114)

## Key Equations and Relationships     Page numbers appear in parentheses.

**3.1** Number of entities in one mole (83):

1 mol contains $6.022 \times 10^{23}$ entities (to 4 sf)

**3.2** Converting amount (mol) to mass (g) using $\mathcal{M}$ (85):

$$\text{Mass (g)} = \text{amount (mol)} \times \frac{\text{no. of grams}}{1 \text{ mol}}$$

**3.3** Converting mass (g) to amount (mol) using $1/\mathcal{M}$ (85):

$$\text{Amount (mol)} = \text{mass (g)} \times \frac{1 \text{ mol}}{\text{no. of grams}}$$

**3.4** Converting amount (mol) to number of entities (85):

$$\text{No. of entities} = \text{amount (mol)} \times \frac{6.022 \times 10^{23} \text{ entities}}{1 \text{ mol}}$$

**3.5** Converting number of entities to amount (mol) (85):

$$\text{Amount (mol)} = \text{no. of entities} \times \frac{1 \text{ mol}}{6.022 \times 10^{23} \text{ entities}}$$

**3.6** Calculating mass % (90):

Mass % of element X

$$= \frac{\text{moles of X in formula} \times \text{molar mass of X (g/mol)}}{\text{mass (g) of 1 mol of compound}} \times 100$$

**3.7** Finding the mass of an element in any mass of compound (91):

Mass of element = mass of compound

$$\times \frac{\text{mass of element in 1 mol of compound}}{\text{mass of 1 mol of compound}}$$

**3.8** Calculating percent yield (112):

$$\% \text{ yield} = \frac{\text{actual yield}}{\text{theoretical yield}} \times 100$$

**3.9** Defining molarity (114):

$$\text{Molarity} = \frac{\text{moles of solute}}{\text{liters of solution}} \quad \text{or} \quad M = \frac{\text{mol solute}}{\text{L soln}}$$

**3.10** Diluting a concentrated solution (117):

$$M_{\text{dil}} \times V_{\text{dil}} = \text{amount (mol)} = M_{\text{conc}} \times V_{\text{conc}}$$

## Brief Solutions to Follow-Up Problems

**3.1**

$$\text{Amount (mol) of C} = 315 \text{ mg C} \times \frac{1 \text{ g}}{10^3 \text{ mg}} \times \frac{1 \text{ mol C}}{12.01 \text{ g C}}$$
$$= 2.62 \times 10^{-2} \text{ mol C}$$

**3.2**

$$\text{Amount (mol) of N} = 9.72 \times 10^{21} \text{ N}_2 \text{ molecules}$$
$$\times \frac{1 \text{ mol N}_2}{6.022 \times 10^{23} \text{ N}_2 \text{ molecules}} \times \frac{2 \text{ mol N}}{1 \text{ mol N}_2}$$
$$= 3.23 \times 10^{-2} \text{ mol N}$$

**3.3**

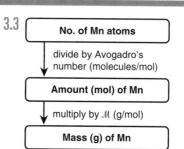

$$\text{Mass (g) of Mn} = 3.22 \times 10^{20} \text{ Mn atoms}$$
$$\times \frac{1 \text{ mol Mn}}{6.022 \times 10^{23} \text{ Mn atoms}} \times \frac{54.94 \text{ g Mn}}{1 \text{ mol Mn}}$$
$$= 2.94 \times 10^{-2} \text{ g Mn}$$

**3.4**

$$\mathcal{M} = (1 \times \mathcal{M} \text{ of Na}) + (1 \times \mathcal{M} \text{ of F})$$
$$= 22.99 \text{ g/mol} + 19.00 \text{ g/mol} = 41.99 \text{ g/mol}$$

$$\text{Mass (g) of NaF} = 1.19 \times 10^{19} \text{ NaF formula units}$$
$$\times \frac{1 \text{ mol NaF}}{6.022 \times 10^{23} \text{ NaF formula units}}$$
$$\times \frac{41.99 \text{ g NaF}}{1 \text{ mol NaF}} = 8.30 \times 10^{-4} \text{ NaF}$$

**3.5** (a) Mass (g) of $P_4O_{10}$

$$= 4.65\times10^{22} \text{ molecules } P_4O_{10}$$
$$\times \frac{1 \text{ mol } P_4O_{10}}{6.022\times10^{23} \text{ molecules } P_4O_{10}} \times \frac{283.88 \text{ g } P_4O_{10}}{1 \text{ mol } P_4O_{10}}$$
$$= 21.9 \text{ g } P_4O_{10}$$

(b) No. of P atoms $= 4.65\times10^{22}$ molecules $P_4O_{10}$

$$\times \frac{4 \text{ atoms P}}{1 \text{ molecule } P_4O_{10}}$$
$$= 1.86\times10^{23} \text{ P atoms}$$

**3.6** Mass % of N $= \dfrac{2 \text{ mol N} \times \dfrac{14.01 \text{ g N}}{1 \text{ mol N}}}{80.05 \text{ g } NH_4NO_3} \times 100$

$$= 35.00 \text{ mass \% N}$$

**3.7** Mass (g) of N $= 35.8 \text{ kg } NH_4NO_3 \times \dfrac{10^3 \text{ g}}{1 \text{ kg}} \times \dfrac{0.3500 \text{ g N}}{1 \text{ g } NH_4NO_3}$

$$= 1.25\times10^4 \text{ g N}$$

**3.8** Preliminary formula: $B_{0.170}O_{0.255}$

Divide by smaller subscript: $B_{\frac{0.170}{0.170}}O_{\frac{0.255}{0.170}} = B_{1.00}O_{1.50}$

Multiply by 2: $B_{2\times1.00}O_{2\times1.50} = B_{2.00}O_{3.00} = B_2O_3$

**3.9** Amount (mol) of S $= 2.88 \text{ g S} \times \dfrac{1 \text{ mol S}}{32.07 \text{ g S}} = 0.0898 \text{ mol S}$

Amount (mol) of M $= 0.0898 \text{ mol S} \times \dfrac{2 \text{ mol M}}{3 \text{ mol S}} = 0.0599 \text{ mol M}$

Molar mass of M $= \dfrac{3.12 \text{ g M}}{0.0599 \text{ mol M}} = 52.1 \text{ g/mol}$

M is chromium, and $M_2S_3$ is chromium(III) sulfide.

**3.10** Assuming 100.00 g of compound, we have 95.21 g of C and 4.79 g of H:

Amount (mol) of C $= 95.21 \text{ g C} \times \dfrac{1 \text{ mol C}}{12.01 \text{ g C}} = 7.928 \text{ mol C}$

Similarly, there is 4.75 mol H.

Preliminary formula: $C_{7.928}H_{4.75} \approx C_{1.67}H_{1.00}$

Empirical formula: $C_5H_3$

Whole-number multiple $= \dfrac{252.30 \text{ g/mol}}{63.07 \text{ g/mol}} = 4$

Molecular formula: $C_{20}H_{12}$

**3.11** Mass (g) of C $= 0.451 \text{ g } CO_2 \times \dfrac{12.01 \text{ g C}}{44.01 \text{ g } CO_2}$

$$= 0.123 \text{ g C}$$

Similarly, there is 0.00690 g H.

Mass (g) of Cl $= 0.250 \text{ g} - (0.123 \text{ g} + 0.00690 \text{ g}) = 0.120 \text{ g Cl}$

Amount (mol) of elements: 0.0102 mol C; 0.00685 mol H; 0.00339 mol Cl

Empirical formula: $C_3H_2Cl$

Whole-number multiple $= 2$

Molecular formula: $C_6H_4Cl_2$

**3.12** (a) $2Na(s) + 2H_2O(l) \longrightarrow H_2(g) + 2NaOH(aq)$

(b) $2HNO_3(aq) + CaCO_3(s) \longrightarrow$
$$CO_2(g) + H_2O(l) + Ca(NO_3)_2(aq)$$

(c) $PCl_3(g) + 3HF(g) \longrightarrow PF_3(g) + 3HCl(g)$

(d) $4C_3H_5N_3O_9(l) \longrightarrow$
$$12CO_2(g) + 10H_2O(g) + 6N_2(g) + O_2(g)$$

**3.13** From the depiction, we have

$$6CO + 3O_2 \longrightarrow 6CO_2$$

Or,

$$2CO(g) + O_2(g) \longrightarrow 2CO_2(g)$$

**3.14**

| Amount (mol) of Fe |
|---|

↓ molar ratio

| Amount (mol) of Fe₂O₃ |
|---|

$$Fe_2O_3(s) + 2Al(s) \longrightarrow Al_2O_3(s) + 2Fe(l)$$

Amount (mol) of $Fe_2O_3 = 3.60\times10^3 \text{ mol Fe} \times \dfrac{1 \text{ mol } Fe_2O_3}{2 \text{ mol Fe}}$

$$= 1.80\times10^3 \text{ mol } Fe_2O_3$$

**3.15**

| No. of formula units of Al₂O₃ |
|---|

↓ divide by Avogadro's number (formula units/mol)

| Amount (mol) of Al₂O₃ |
|---|

↓ molar ratio

| Amount (mol) of Fe |
|---|

Amount (mol) of Fe $= 1.85\times10^{25} \text{ } Al_2O_3 \text{ f.u.}$

$$\times \frac{1 \text{ mol } Al_2O_3}{6.022\times10^{23} \text{ } Al_2O_3 \text{ f.u.}} \times \frac{2 \text{ mol Fe}}{1 \text{ mol } Al_2O_3}$$
$$= 61.4 \text{ mol Fe}$$

**3.16**

| Mass (g) of Al₂O₃ |
|---|

↓ divide by $\mathcal{M}$ (g/mol)

| Amount (mol) of Al₂O₃ |
|---|

↓ molar ratio

| Amount (mol) of Al |
|---|

↓ multiply by Avogadro's number (atoms/mol)

| No. of Al atoms |
|---|

No. of Al atoms $= 1.00 \text{ g } Al_2O_3 \times \dfrac{1 \text{ mol } Al_2O_3}{101.96 \text{ g } Al_2O_3}$

$$\times \frac{2 \text{ mol Al}}{1 \text{ mol } Al_2O_3} \times \frac{6.022\times10^{23} \text{ Al atoms}}{1 \text{ mol Al}}$$
$$= 1.18\times10^{22} \text{ Al atoms}$$

**3.17**
$$2SO_2(g) + O_2(g) \longrightarrow 2SO_3(g)$$
$$\underline{2SO_3(g) + 2H_2O(l) \longrightarrow 2H_2SO_4(aq)}$$
$$2SO_2(g) + O_2(g) + 2H_2O(l) \longrightarrow 2H_2SO_4(aq)$$

**3.18** $4AB + 2B_2 \longrightarrow 4AB_2$, or $2AB(g) + B_2(g) \longrightarrow 2AB_2(g)$

For AB: Molecules of $AB_2 = 4AB \times \dfrac{2AB_2}{2AB} = 4AB_2$

For $B_2$: Molecules of $AB_2 = 3B_2 \times \dfrac{2AB_2}{1B_2} = 6AB_2$

Thus, $AB_2$ is the limiting reactant; one $B_2$ molecule is in excess.

**3.19**

Amount (mol) of $AB_2 = 1.5\ \text{mol AB} \times \dfrac{2\ \text{mol } AB_2}{2\ \text{mol AB}} = 1.5\ \text{mol } AB_2$

Amount (mol) of $AB_2 = 1.5\ \text{mol } B_2 \times \dfrac{2\ \text{mol } AB_2}{1\ \text{mol } B_2} = 3.0\ \text{mol } AB_2$

Therefore, 1.5 mol of $AB_2$ can form.

**3.20** $2Al(s) + 3S(s) \longrightarrow Al_2S_3(s)$

Mass (g) of $Al_2S_3$ formed from 10.0 g of Al

$= 10.0\ \text{g Al} \times \dfrac{1\ \text{mol Al}}{26.98\ \text{g Al}} \times \dfrac{1\ \text{mol } Al_2S_3}{2\ \text{mol Al}} \times \dfrac{150.17\ \text{g } Al_2S_3}{1\ \text{mol } Al_2S_3}$

$= 27.8\ \text{g } Al_2S_3$

Similarly, mass (g) of $Al_2S_3$ formed from 15.0 g of S $= 23.4$ g $Al_2S_3$. Thus, S is the limiting reactant, and 23.4 g of $Al_2S_3$ forms.

Mass (g) of Al in excess

$=$ total mass of Al $-$ mass of Al used

$= 10.0\ \text{g Al}$

$- \left( 15.0\ \text{g S} \times \dfrac{1\ \text{mol S}}{32.07\ \text{g S}} \times \dfrac{2\ \text{mol Al}}{3\ \text{mol S}} \times \dfrac{26.98\ \text{g Al}}{1\ \text{mol Al}} \right)$

$= 1.6\ \text{g Al}$

(We would obtain the same answer if sulfur were shown more correctly as $S_8$.)

**3.21** $CaCO_3(s) + 2HCl(aq) \longrightarrow CaCl_2(aq) + H_2O(l) + CO_2(g)$

Theoretical yield (g) of $CO_2 = 10.0\ \text{g CaCO}_3 \times \dfrac{1\ \text{mol CaCO}_3}{100.09\ \text{g CaCO}_3}$

$\times \dfrac{1\ \text{mol } CO_2}{1\ \text{mol CaCO}_3} \times \dfrac{44.01\ \text{g } CO_2}{1\ \text{mol } CO_2} = 4.40\ \text{g } CO_2$

% yield $= \dfrac{3.65\ \text{g } CO_2}{4.40\ \text{g } CO_2} \times 100 = 83.0\%$

**3.22**

Amount (mol) of KI $= 84\ \text{mL soln} \times \dfrac{1\ \text{L}}{10^3\ \text{mL}} \times \dfrac{0.50\ \text{mol KI}}{1\ \text{L soln}}$

$= 0.042\ \text{mol KI}$

**3.23**

Volume (L) of sucrose soln

$= 135\ \text{g sucrose} \times \dfrac{1\ \text{mol sucrose}}{342.30\ \text{g sucrose}} \times \dfrac{1\ \text{L soln}}{3.30\ \text{mol sucrose}}$

$= 0.120\ \text{L soln}$

**3.24** $M_{dil}$ of $H_2SO_4 = \dfrac{7.50\ M \times 25.0\ \text{m}^3}{500.\ \text{m}^3} = 0.375\ M\ H_2SO_4$

Mass (g) of $H_2SO_4$/mL soln

$= \dfrac{0.375\ \text{mol } H_2SO_4}{1\ \text{L soln}} \times \dfrac{1\ \text{L}}{10^3\ \text{mL}} \times \dfrac{98.09\ \text{g } H_2SO_4}{1\ \text{mol } H_2SO_4}$

$= 3.68 \times 10^{-2}\ \text{g/mL soln}$

**3.25** To obtain B, the total volume of sol A was reduced by half:

$V_{conc} = V_{dil} \times \dfrac{N_{dil}}{N_{conc}} = 1.0\ \text{mL} \times \dfrac{6\ \text{particles}}{12\ \text{particles}} = 0.50\ \text{mL}$

To obtain C, $\frac{1}{2}$ of a volume of solvent was added for every volume of A:

$V_{dil} = V_{conc} \times \dfrac{N_{conc}}{N_{dil}} = 1.0\ \text{mL} \times \dfrac{6\ \text{particles}}{4\ \text{particles}} = 1.5\ \text{mL}$

**3.26** $Al(OH)_3(s) + 3HCl(aq) \longrightarrow AlCl_3(aq) + 3H_2O(l)$

Volume (L) of HCl neutralized

$= 0.10\ \text{g Al(OH)}_3 \times \dfrac{1\ \text{mol Al(OH)}_3}{78.00\ \text{g Al(OH)}_3}$

$\times \dfrac{3\ \text{mol HCl}}{1\ \text{mol Al(OH)}_3} \times \dfrac{1\ \text{L soln}}{0.10\ \text{mol HCl}}$

$= 3.8 \times 10^{-2}\ \text{L soln}$

Therefore, $Al(OH)_3$ is more effective than $Mg(OH)_2$.

**3.27** (a) For $Pb(C_2H_3O_2)_2$:

Amount (mol) of $Pb(C_2H_3O_2)_2 = 0.268\ \text{L} \times \dfrac{1.50\ \text{mol } Pb(C_2H_3O_2)_2}{1\ \text{L}}$

$= 0.402\ \text{mol } Pb(C_2H_3O_2)_2$

Amount (mol) of $PbCl_2 = 0.402\ \text{mol } Pb(C_2H_3O_2)_2$

$\times \dfrac{1\ \text{mol } PbCl_2}{1\ \text{mol } Pb(C_2H_3O_2)_2} = 0.402\ \text{mol } PbCl_2$

For NaCl: Amount (mol) of NaCl $= \dfrac{3.40\ \text{mol NaCl}}{1\ \text{L}} \times 0.130\ \text{L}$

$= 0.442\ \text{mol NaCl}$

Amount (mol) of $PbCl_2 = 0.442\ \text{mol NaCl} \times \dfrac{1\ \text{mol } PbCl_2}{2\ \text{mol NaCl}}$

$= 0.221\ \text{mol } PbCl_2$

Thus, NaCl is the limiting reactant.

Mass (g) of $PbCl_2 = 0.22\ \text{mol } PbCl_2 \times \dfrac{278.1\ \text{g } PbCl_2}{1\ \text{mol } PbCl_2}$

$= 61.5\ \text{g } PbCl_2$

(b) Using "Ac" for acetate ion and with NaCl limiting:

| Amount (mol) | $Pb(Ac)_2$ | + | $2NaCl$ | $\longrightarrow$ | $PbCl_2$ | + | $2NaAc$ |
|---|---|---|---|---|---|---|---|
| Initial | 0.402 | | 0.442 | | 0 | | 0 |
| Change | $-0.221$ | | $-0.442$ | | $+0.221$ | | $+0.442$ |
| Final | 0.181 | | 0 | | 0.221 | | 0.442 |

# PROBLEMS

Problems with **colored** numbers are answered in Appendix E and worked in detail in the Student Solutions Manual. Problem sections match those in the text and provide the numbers of relevant sample problems. Most offer Concept Review Questions, Skill-Building Exercises (grouped in pairs covering the same concept), and Problems in Context. The Comprehensive Problems are based on material from any section or previous chapter.

## The Mole
(Sample Problems 3.1 to 3.7)

### Concept Review Questions

**3.1** The atomic mass of Cl is 35.45 amu, and the atomic mass of Al is 26.98 amu. What are the masses in grams of 3 mol of Al atoms and of 2 mol of Cl atoms?

**3.2** (a) How many moles of C atoms are in 1 mol of sucrose ($C_{12}H_{22}O_{11}$)?
(b) How many C atoms are in 2 mol of sucrose?

**3.3** Why might the expression "1 mol of chlorine" be confusing? What change would remove any uncertainty? For what other elements might a similar confusion exist? Why?

**3.4** How is the molecular mass of a compound the same as the molar mass, and how is it different?

**3.5** What advantage is there to using a counting unit (the mole) for amount of substance rather than a mass unit?

**3.6** You need to calculate the number of $P_4$ molecules that can form from 2.5 g of $Ca_3(PO_4)_2$. Draw a road map for solving this and write a Plan, without doing any calculations.

**3.7** Each of the following balances weighs the indicated numbers of atoms of two elements:

For each balance, which element—left, right, or neither,
(a) Has the higher molar mass?
(b) Has more atoms per gram?
(c) Has fewer atoms per gram?
(d) Has more atoms per mole?

### Skill-Building Exercises (grouped in similar pairs)

**3.8** Calculate the molar mass of each of the following:
(a) $Sr(OH)_2$      (b) $N_2O_3$      (c) $NaClO_3$      (d) $Cr_2O_3$

**3.9** Calculate the molar mass of each of the following:
(a) $(NH_4)_3PO_4$   (b) $CH_2Cl_2$   (c) $CuSO_4\cdot5H_2O$   (d) $BrF_3$

**3.10** Calculate the molar mass of each of the following:
(a) SnO    (b) $BaF_2$    (c) $Al_2(SO_4)_3$    (d) $MnCl_2$

**3.11** Calculate the molar mass of each of the following:
(a) $N_2O_4$    (b) $C_4H_9OH$    (c) $MgSO_4\cdot7H_2O$    (d) $Ca(C_2H_3O_2)_2$

**3.12** Calculate each of the following quantities:
(a) Mass (g) of 0.68 mol of $KMnO_4$
(b) Amount (mol) of O atoms in 8.18 g of $Ba(NO_3)_2$
(c) Number of O atoms in $7.3\times10^{-3}$ g of $CaSO_4\cdot2H_2O$

**3.13** Calculate each of the following quantities:
(a) Mass (kg) of $4.6\times10^{21}$ molecules of $NO_2$
(b) Amount (mol) of Cl atoms in 0.0615 g of $C_2H_4Cl_2$
(c) Number of $H^-$ ions in 5.82 g of $SrH_2$

**3.14** Calculate each of the following quantities:
(a) Mass (g) of $6.44\times10^{-2}$ mol of $MnSO_4$
(b) Amount (mol) of compound in 15.8 kg of $Fe(ClO_4)_3$
(c) Number of N atoms in 92.6 mg of $NH_4NO_2$

**3.15** Calculate each of the following quantities:
(a) Total number of ions in 38.1 g of $SrF_2$
(b) Mass (kg) of 3.58 mol of $CuCl_2\cdot2H_2O$
(c) Mass (mg) of $2.88\times10^{22}$ formula units of $Bi(NO_3)_3\cdot5H_2O$

**3.16** Calculate each of the following quantities:
(a) Mass (g) of 8.35 mol of copper(I) carbonate
(b) Mass (g) of $4.04\times10^{20}$ molecules of dinitrogen pentaoxide
(c) Amount (mol) and number of formula units in 78.9 g of sodium perchlorate
(d) Number of sodium ions, perchlorate ions, chlorine atoms, and oxygen atoms in the mass of compound in part (c)

**3.17** Calculate each of the following quantities:
(a) Mass (g) of 8.42 mol of chromium(III) sulfate decahydrate
(b) Mass (g) of $1.83\times10^{24}$ molecules of dichlorine heptaoxide
(c) Amount (mol) and number of formula units in 6.2 g of lithium sulfate
(d) Number of lithium ions, sulfate ions, sulfur atoms, and oxygen atoms in the mass of compound in part (c)

**3.18** Calculate each of the following:
(a) Mass % of H in ammonium bicarbonate
(b) Mass % of O in sodium dihydrogen phosphate heptahydrate

**3.19** Calculate each of the following:
(a) Mass % of I in strontium periodate
(b) Mass % of Mn in potassium permanganate

**3.20** Calculate each of the following:
(a) Mass fraction of C in cesium acetate
(b) Mass fraction of O in uranyl sulfate trihydrate (the uranyl ion is $UO_2^{2+}$)

**3.21** Calculate each of the following:
(a) Mass fraction of Cl in calcium chlorate
(b) Mass fraction of N in dinitrogen trioxide

### Problems in Context

**3.22** Oxygen is required for the metabolic combustion of foods. Calculate the number of atoms in 38.0 g of oxygen gas, the amount absorbed from the lungs at rest in about 15 min.

**3.23** Cisplatin (*right*), or Platinol, is used in the treatment of certain cancers. Calculate (a) the amount (mol) of compound in 285.3 g of cisplatin; (b) the number of hydrogen atoms in 0.98 mol of cisplatin.

**3.24** Allyl sulfide (*below*) gives garlic its characteristic odor. Calculate (a) the mass (g) of 2.63 mol of allyl sulfide; (b) the number of carbon atoms in 35.7 g of allyl sulfide.

**3.25** Iron reacts slowly with oxygen and water to form a compound commonly called rust ($Fe_2O_3 \cdot 4H_2O$). For 45.2 kg of rust, calculate (a) moles of compound; (b) moles of $Fe_2O_3$; (c) grams of Fe.

**3.26** Propane is widely used in liquid form as a fuel for barbecue grills and camp stoves. For 85.5 g of propane, calculate (a) moles of compound; (b) grams of carbon.

**3.27** The effectiveness of a nitrogen fertilizer is determined mainly by its mass % N. Rank the following fertilizers, most effective first: potassium nitrate; ammonium nitrate; ammonium sulfate; urea, $CO(NH_2)_2$.

**3.28** The mineral galena is composed of lead(II) sulfide and has an average density of 7.46 g/cm$^3$. (a) How many moles of lead(II) sulfide are in 1.00 ft$^3$ of galena? (b) How many lead atoms are in 1.00 dm$^3$ of galena?

**3.29** Hemoglobin, a protein in red blood cells, carries $O_2$ from the lungs to the body's cells. Iron (as ferrous ion, $Fe^{2+}$) makes up 0.33 mass % of hemoglobin. If the molar mass of hemoglobin is $6.8 \times 10^4$ g/mol, how many $Fe^{2+}$ ions are in one molecule?

### Determining the Formula of an Unknown Compound
(Sample Problems 3.8 to 3.11)

**Concept Review Questions**

**3.30** What is the difference between an empirical formula and a molecular formula? Can they ever be the same?

**3.31** List three ways compositional data may be given in a problem that involves finding an empirical formula.

**3.32** Which of the following sets of information allows you to obtain the molecular formula of a covalent compound? In each case that allows it, explain how you would proceed (draw a road map and write a Plan for a solution).
(a) Number of moles of each type of atom in a given sample of the compound
(b) Mass % of each element and the total number of atoms in a molecule of the compound
(c) Mass % of each element and the number of atoms of one element in a molecule of the compound
(d) Empirical formula and mass % of each element
(e) Structural formula

**3.33** Is $MgCl_2$ an empirical or a molecular formula for magnesium chloride? Explain.

**Skill-Building Exercises** (grouped in similar pairs)

**3.34** What is the empirical formula and empirical formula mass for each of the following compounds?
(a) $C_2H_4$    (b) $C_2H_6O_2$    (c) $N_2O_5$    (d) $Ba_3(PO_4)_2$    (e) $Te_4I_{16}$

**3.35** What is the empirical formula and empirical formula mass for each of the following compounds?
(a) $C_4H_8$    (b) $C_3H_6O_3$    (c) $P_4O_{10}$    (d) $Ga_2(SO_4)_3$    (e) $Al_2Br_6$

**3.36** Give the name, empirical formula, and molar mass of the compound depicted in Figure P3.36.

**3.37** Give the name, empirical formula, and molar mass of the compound depicted in Figure P3.37.

Figure P3.36          Figure P3.37

**3.38** What is the molecular formula of each compound?
(a) Empirical formula $CH_2$ ($\mathcal{M}$ = 42.08 g/mol)
(b) Empirical formula $NH_2$ ($\mathcal{M}$ = 32.05 g/mol)
(c) Empirical formula $NO_2$ ($\mathcal{M}$ = 92.02 g/mol)
(d) Empirical formula $CHN$ ($\mathcal{M}$ = 135.14 g/mol)

**3.39** What is the molecular formula of each compound?
(a) Empirical formula $CH$ ($\mathcal{M}$ = 78.11 g/mol)
(b) Empirical formula $C_3H_6O_2$ ($\mathcal{M}$ = 74.08 g/mol)
(c) Empirical formula $HgCl$ ($\mathcal{M}$ = 472.1 g/mol)
(d) Empirical formula $C_7H_4O_2$ ($\mathcal{M}$ = 240.20 g/mol)

**3.40** Find the empirical formula of the following compounds:
(a) 0.063 mol of chlorine atoms combined with 0.22 mol of oxygen atoms
(b) 2.45 g of silicon combined with 12.4 g of chlorine
(c) 27.3 mass % carbon and 72.7 mass % oxygen

**3.41** Find the empirical formula of the following compounds:
(a) 0.039 mol of iron atoms combined with 0.052 mol of oxygen atoms
(b) 0.903 g of phosphorus combined with 6.99 g of bromine
(c) A hydrocarbon with 79.9 mass % carbon

**3.42** An oxide of nitrogen contains 30.45 mass % N. (a) What is the empirical formula of the oxide? (b) If the molar mass is $90 \pm 5$ g/mol, what is the molecular formula?

**3.43** A chloride of silicon contains 79.1 mass % Cl. (a) What is the empirical formula of the chloride? (b) If the molar mass is 269 g/mol, what is the molecular formula?

**3.44** A sample of 0.600 mol of a metal M reacts completely with excess fluorine to form 46.8 g of $MF_2$.
(a) How many moles of F are in the sample of $MF_2$ that forms?
(b) How many grams of M are in this sample of $MF_2$?
(c) What element is represented by the symbol M?

**3.45** A 0.370-mol sample of a metal oxide ($M_2O_3$) weighs 55.4 g.
(a) How many moles of O are in the sample?
(b) How many grams of M are in the sample?
(c) What element is represented by the symbol M?

## Problems in Context

**3.46** Nicotine is a poisonous, addictive compound found in tobacco. A sample of nicotine contains 6.16 mmol of C, 8.56 mmol of H, and 1.23 mmol of N [1 mmol (1 millimole) = $10^{-3}$ mol]. What is the empirical formula of nicotine?

**3.47** Cortisol ($\mathcal{M} = 362.47$ g/mol) is a steroid hormone involved in protein synthesis. Medically, it has a major use in reducing inflammation from rheumatoid arthritis. Cortisol is 69.6% C, 8.34% H, and 22.1% O by mass. What is its molecular formula?

**3.48** Acetaminophen (*below*) is a popular nonaspirin pain reliever. What is the mass % of each element in acetaminophen?

**3.49** Menthol ($\mathcal{M} = 156.3$ g/mol), the strong-smelling substance in many cough drops, is a compound of carbon, hydrogen, and oxygen. When 0.1595 g of menthol was burned in a combustion apparatus, 0.449 g of $CO_2$ and 0.184 g of $H_2O$ formed. What is menthol's molecular formula?

## Writing and Balancing Chemical Equations
(Sample Problems 3.12 and 3.13)

### Concept Review Questions

**3.50** What three types of information does a balanced chemical equation provide? How?

**3.51** How does a balanced chemical equation apply the law of conservation of mass?

**3.52** In the process of balancing the equation
$$Al + Cl_2 \longrightarrow AlCl_3$$
Student I writes: $Al + Cl_2 \longrightarrow AlCl_2$
Student II writes: $Al + Cl_2 + Cl \longrightarrow AlCl_3$
Student III writes: $2Al + 3Cl_2 \longrightarrow 2AlCl_3$
Is the approach of Student I valid? Student II? Student III? Explain.

**3.53** The scenes below represent a chemical reaction between elements A (red) and B (green):

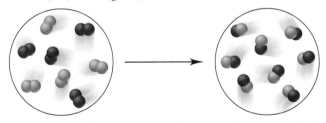

Which best represents the balanced equation for the reaction?
(a) $2A + 2B \longrightarrow A_2 + B_2$          (b) $A_2 + B_2 \longrightarrow 2AB$
(c) $B_2 + 2AB \longrightarrow 2B_2 + A_2$     (d) $4A_2 + 4B_2 \longrightarrow 8AB$

### Skill-Building Exercises (grouped in similar pairs)

**3.54** Write balanced equations for each of the following by inserting the correct coefficients in the blanks:
(a) __Cu(s) + __S₈(s) ⟶ __Cu₂S(s)
(b) __P₄O₁₀(s) + __H₂O(l) ⟶ __H₃PO₄(l)
(c) __B₂O₃(s) + __NaOH(aq) ⟶ __Na₃BO₃(aq) + __H₂O(l)

(d) __CH₃NH₂(g) + __O₂(g) ⟶
$$\_\_CO_2(g) + \_\_H_2O(g) + \_\_N_2(g)$$

**3.55** Write balanced equations for each of the following by inserting the correct coefficients in the blanks:
(a) __Cu(NO₃)₂(aq) + __KOH(aq) ⟶
$$\_\_Cu(OH)_2(s) + \_\_KNO_3(aq)$$
(b) __BCl₃(g) + __H₂O(l) ⟶ __H₃BO₃(s) + __HCl(g)
(c) __CaSiO₃(s) + __HF(g) ⟶
$$\_\_SiF_4(g) + \_\_CaF_2(s) + \_\_H_2O(l)$$
(d) __(CN)₂(g) + __H₂O(l) ⟶ __H₂C₂O₄(aq) + __NH₃(g)

**3.56** Write balanced equations for each of the following by inserting the correct coefficients in the blanks:
(a) __SO₂(g) + __O₂(g) ⟶ __SO₃(g)
(b) __Sc₂O₃(s) + __H₂O(l) ⟶ __Sc(OH)₃(s)
(c) __H₃PO₄(aq) + __NaOH(aq) ⟶
$$\_\_Na_2HPO_4(aq) + \_\_H_2O(l)$$
(d) __C₆H₁₀O₅(s) + __O₂(g) ⟶ __CO₂(g) + __H₂O(g)

**3.57** Write balanced equations for each of the following by inserting the correct coefficients in the blanks:
(a) __As₄S₆(s) + __O₂(g) ⟶ __As₄O₆(s) + __SO₂(g)
(b) __Ca₃(PO₄)₂(s) + __SiO₂(s) + __C(s) ⟶
$$\_\_P_4(g) + \_\_CaSiO_3(l) + \_\_CO(g)$$
(c) __Fe(s) + __H₂O(g) ⟶ __Fe₃O₄(s) + __H₂(g)
(d) __S₂Cl₂(l) + __NH₃(g) ⟶
$$\_\_S_4N_4(s) + \_\_S_8(s) + \_\_NH_4Cl(s)$$

**3.58** Convert the following into balanced equations:
(a) When gallium metal is heated in oxygen gas, it melts and forms solid gallium(III) oxide.
(b) Liquid hexane burns in oxygen gas to form carbon dioxide gas and water vapor.
(c) When solutions of calcium chloride and sodium phosphate are mixed, solid calcium phosphate forms and sodium chloride remains in solution.

**3.59** Convert the following into balanced equations:
(a) When lead(II) nitrate solution is added to potassium iodide solution, solid lead(II) iodide forms and potassium nitrate solution remains.
(b) Liquid disilicon hexachloride reacts with water to form solid silicon dioxide, hydrogen chloride gas, and hydrogen gas.
(c) When nitrogen dioxide is bubbled into water, a solution of nitric acid forms and gaseous nitrogen monoxide is released.

### Problem in Context

**3.60** Loss of atmospheric ozone has led to an ozone "hole" over Antarctica. The loss occurs in part through three consecutive steps:
(1) Chlorine atoms react with ozone ($O_3$) to form chlorine monoxide and molecular oxygen.
(2) Chlorine monoxide forms ClOOCl.
(3) ClOOCl absorbs sunlight and breaks into chlorine atoms and molecular oxygen.
(a) Write a balanced equation for each step.
(b) Write an overall balanced equation for the sequence.

## Calculating Quantities of Reactant and Product
(Sample Problems 3.14 to 3.21)

### Concept Review Questions

**3.61** What does the term *stoichiometrically equivalent molar ratio* mean, and how is it applied in solving problems?

**3.62** The circle below represents a mixture of $A_2$ and $B_2$ before they react to form $AB_3$.

(a) What is the limiting reactant?
(b) How many molecules of product can form?

**3.63** Percent yields are generally calculated from masses. Would the result be the same if amounts (mol) were used instead? Why?

**Skill-Building Exercises** (grouped in similar pairs)

**3.64** Reactants A and B form product C. Draw a road map and write a Plan to find the mass (g) of C when 25 g of A reacts with excess B.

**3.65** Reactants D and E form product F. Draw a road map and write a Plan to find the mass (g) of F when 27 g of D reacts with 31 g of E.

**3.66** Chlorine gas can be made in the laboratory by the reaction of hydrochloric acid and manganese(IV) oxide:

$$4HCl(aq) + MnO_2(s) \longrightarrow MnCl_2(aq) + 2H_2O(g) + Cl_2(g)$$

When 1.82 mol of HCl reacts with excess $MnO_2$, how many (a) moles of $Cl_2$ and (b) grams of $Cl_2$ form?

**3.67** Bismuth oxide reacts with carbon to form bismuth metal:

$$Bi_2O_3(s) + 3C(s) \longrightarrow 2Bi(s) + 3CO(g)$$

When 283 g of $Bi_2O_3$ reacts with excess carbon, how many (a) moles of $Bi_2O_3$ react and (b) moles of Bi form?

**3.68** Potassium nitrate decomposes on heating, producing potassium oxide and gaseous nitrogen and oxygen:

$$4KNO_3(s) \longrightarrow 2K_2O(s) + 2N_2(g) + 5O_2(g)$$

To produce 56.6 kg of oxygen, how many (a) moles of $KNO_3$ and (b) grams of $KNO_3$ must be heated?

**3.69** Chromium(III) oxide reacts with hydrogen sulfide ($H_2S$) gas to form chromium(III) sulfide and water:

$$Cr_2O_3(s) + 3H_2S(g) \longrightarrow Cr_2S_3(s) + 3H_2O(l)$$

To produce 421 g of $Cr_2S_3$, how many (a) moles of $Cr_2O_3$ and (b) grams of $Cr_2O_3$ are required?

**3.70** Calculate the mass (g) of each product formed when 43.82 g of diborane ($B_2H_6$) reacts with excess water:

$$B_2H_6(g) + H_2O(l) \longrightarrow H_3BO_3(s) + H_2(g) \text{ [unbalanced]}$$

**3.71** Calculate the mass (g) of each product formed when 174 g of silver sulfide reacts with excess hydrochloric acid:

$$Ag_2S(s) + HCl(aq) \longrightarrow AgCl(s) + H_2S(g) \text{ [unbalanced]}$$

**3.72** Elemental phosphorus occurs as tetratomic molecules, $P_4$. What mass (g) of chlorine gas is needed to react completely with 455 g of phosphorus to form phosphorus pentachloride?

**3.73** Elemental sulfur occurs as octatomic molecules, $S_8$. What mass (g) of fluorine gas is needed to react completely with 17.8 g of sulfur to form sulfur hexafluoride?

**3.74** Solid iodine trichloride is prepared in two steps: first, a reaction between solid iodine and gaseous chlorine to form solid iodine monochloride; then, treatment with more chlorine.

(a) Write a balanced equation for each step.
(b) Write a balanced equation for the overall reaction.
(c) How many grams of iodine are needed to prepare 2.45 kg of final product?

**3.75** Lead can be prepared from galena [lead(II) sulfide] by first roasting the galena in oxygen gas to form lead(II) oxide and sulfur dioxide. Heating the metal oxide with more galena forms the molten metal and more sulfur dioxide.
(a) Write a balanced equation for each step.
(b) Write an overall balanced equation for the process.
(c) How many metric tons of sulfur dioxide form for every metric ton of lead obtained?

**3.76** Many metals react with oxygen gas to form the metal oxide. For example, calcium reacts as follows:

$$2Ca(s) + O_2(g) \longrightarrow 2CaO(s)$$

You wish to calculate the mass (g) of calcium oxide that can be prepared from 4.20 g of Ca and 2.80 g of $O_2$.
(a) What amount (mol) of CaO can be produced from the given mass of Ca?
(b) What amount (mol) of CaO can be produced from the given mass of $O_2$?
(c) Which is the limiting reactant?
(d) How many grams of CaO can be produced?

**3.77** Metal hydrides react with water to form hydrogen gas and the metal hydroxide. For example,

$$SrH_2(s) + 2H_2O(l) \longrightarrow Sr(OH)_2(s) + 2H_2(g)$$

You wish to calculate the mass (g) of hydrogen gas that can be prepared from 5.70 g of $SrH_2$ and 4.75 g of $H_2O$.
(a) What amount (mol) of $H_2$ can be produced from the given mass of $SrH_2$?
(b) What amount (mol) of $H_2$ can be produced from the given mass of $H_2O$?
(c) Which is the limiting reactant?
(d) How many grams of $H_2$ can be produced?

**3.78** Calculate the maximum numbers of moles and grams of iodic acid ($HIO_3$) that can form when 635 g of iodine trichloride reacts with 118.5 g of water:

$$ICl_3 + H_2O \longrightarrow ICl + HIO_3 + HCl \text{ [unbalanced]}$$

How many grams of the excess reactant remains?

**3.79** Calculate the maximum numbers of moles and grams of $H_2S$ that can form when 158 g of aluminum sulfide reacts with 131 g of water:

$$Al_2S_3 + H_2O \longrightarrow Al(OH)_3 + H_2S \text{ [unbalanced]}$$

How many grams of the excess reactant remain?

**3.80** When 0.100 mol of carbon is burned in a closed vessel with 8.00 g of oxygen, how many grams of carbon dioxide can form? Which reactant is in excess, and how many grams of it remain after the reaction?

**3.81** A mixture of 0.0375 g of hydrogen and 0.0185 mol of oxygen in a closed container is sparked to initiate a reaction. How many grams of water can form? Which reactant is in excess, and how many grams of it remain after the reaction?

**3.82** Aluminum nitrite and ammonium chloride react to form aluminum chloride, nitrogen, and water. How many grams of each substance are present after 72.5 g of aluminum nitrite and 58.6 g of ammonium chloride react completely?

**3.83** Calcium nitrate and ammonium fluoride react to form calcium fluoride, dinitrogen monoxide, and water vapor. How many grams of each substance are present after 16.8 g of calcium nitrate and 17.50 g of ammonium fluoride react completely?

**3.84** Two successive reactions, A ⟶ B and B ⟶ C, have yields of 73% and 68%, respectively. What is the overall percent yield for conversion of A to C?

**3.85** Two successive reactions, D ⟶ E and E ⟶ F, have yields of 48% and 73%, respectively. What is the overall percent yield for conversion of D to F?

**3.86** What is the percent yield of a reaction in which 45.5 g of tungsten(VI) oxide ($WO_3$) reacts with excess hydrogen gas to produce metallic tungsten and 9.60 mL of water ($d = 1.00$ g/mL)?

**3.87** What is the percent yield of a reaction in which 200. g of phosphorus trichloride reacts with excess water to form 128 g of HCl and aqueous phosphorous acid ($H_3PO_3$)?

**3.88** When 20.5 g of methane and 45.0 g of chlorine gas undergo a reaction that has a 75.0% yield, what mass (g) of chloromethane ($CH_3Cl$) forms? Hydrogen chloride also forms.

**3.89** When 56.6 g of calcium and 30.5 g of nitrogen gas undergo a reaction that has a 93.0% yield, what mass (g) of calcium nitride forms?

**Problems in Context**

**3.90** Cyanogen, $(CN)_2$, has been observed in the atmosphere of Titan, Saturn's largest moon, and in the gases of interstellar nebulas. On Earth, it is used as a welding gas and a fumigant. In its reaction with fluorine gas, carbon tetrafluoride and nitrogen trifluoride gases are produced. What mass (g) of carbon tetrafluoride forms when 60.0 g of each reactant is used?

**3.91** Gaseous dichlorine monoxide decomposes readily to chlorine and oxygen gases. (a) Which of the following circles best depicts the product mixture after the decomposition?

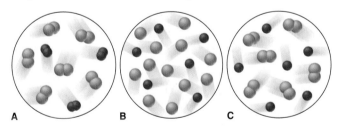

**A**          **B**          **C**

(b) Write the balanced equation for the decomposition.
(c) If each oxygen atom represents 0.050 mol, how many molecules of dichlorine monoxide were present before the decomposition?

**3.92** An intermediate step in the production of nitric acid involves the reaction of ammonia with oxygen gas to form nitrogen monoxide and water. How many grams of nitrogen monoxide can form in the reaction of 485 g of ammonia with 792 g of oxygen?

**3.93** Butane gas is compressed and used as a liquid fuel in disposable cigarette lighters and lightweight camping stoves. Suppose a lighter contains 5.50 mL of butane ($d = 0.579$ g/mL).
(a) How many grams of oxygen are needed to burn the butane completely?
(b) How many moles of $H_2O$ form when all the butane burns?
(c) How many total molecules of gas form when the butane burns completely?

**3.94** Sodium borohydride ($NaBH_4$) is used industrially in many organic syntheses. One way to prepare it is by reacting sodium hydride with gaseous diborane ($B_2H_6$). Assuming an 88.5% yield,

how many grams of $NaBH_4$ can be prepared by reacting 7.98 g of sodium hydride and 8.16 g of diborane?

**Fundamentals of Solution Stoichiometry**
(Sample Problems 3.22 to 3.27)

**Concept Review Questions**

**3.95** Box A represents a unit volume of a solution. Choose from boxes B and C the one representing the same unit volume of solution that has (a) more solute added; (b) more solvent added; (c) higher molarity; (d) lower concentration.

**A**          **B**          **C**

**3.96** A mathematical equation useful for dilution calculations is $M_{dil} \times V_{dil} = M_{conc} \times V_{conc}$. (a) What does each symbol mean, and why does the equation work? (b) Given the volume and molarity of a $CaCl_2$ solution, how do you determine the amount (mol) and the mass (g) of solute?

**3.97** Six different aqueous solutions (with solvent molecules omitted for clarity) are represented in the beakers below, and their total volumes are noted.

**A**          **B**          **C**
**D**          **E**          **F**

(a) Which solution has the highest molarity? (b) Which solutions have the same molarity? (c) If you mix solutions A and C, does the resulting solution have a higher, a lower, or the same molarity as solution B? (d) After 50. mL of water is added to solution D, is its molarity higher, lower, or the same as the molarity of solution F after 75 mL is added to it? (e) How much solvent must be evaporated from solution E for it to have the same molarity as solution A?

**3.98** Are the following instructions for diluting a 10.0 $M$ solution to a 1.00 $M$ solution correct: "Take 100.0 mL of the 10.0 $M$ solution and add 900.0 mL water"? Explain.

**Skill-Building Exercises** (grouped in similar pairs)

**3.99** Calculate each of the following quantities:
(a) Mass (g) of solute in 185.8 mL of 0.267 $M$ calcium acetate
(b) Molarity of 500. mL of solution containing 21.1 g of potassium iodide
(c) Amount (mol) of solute in 145.6 L of 0.850 $M$ sodium cyanide

**3.100** Calculate each of the following quantities:
(a) Volume (mL) of 2.26 $M$ potassium hydroxide that contains 8.42 g of solute
(b) Number of $Cu^{2+}$ ions in 52 L of 2.3 $M$ copper(II) chloride
(c) Molarity of 275 mL of solution containing 135 mmol of glucose

**3.101** Calculate each of the following quantities:
(a) Mass (g) of solute needed to make 475 mL of $5.62 \times 10^{-2}$ $M$ potassium sulfate
(b) Molarity of a solution that contains 7.25 mg of calcium chloride in each milliliter
(c) Number of $Mg^{2+}$ ions in each milliliter of 0.184 $M$ magnesium bromide

**3.102** Calculate each of the following quantities:
(a) Molarity of the solution resulting from dissolving 46.0 g of silver nitrate in enough water to give a final volume of 335 mL
(b) Volume (L) of 0.385 $M$ manganese(II) sulfate that contains 63.0 g of solute
(c) Volume (mL) of $6.44 \times 10^{-2}$ $M$ adenosine triphosphate (ATP) that contains 1.68 mmol of ATP

**3.103** Calculate each of the following quantities:
(a) Molarity of a solution prepared by diluting 37.00 mL of 0.250 $M$ potassium chloride to 150.00 mL
(b) Molarity of a solution prepared by diluting 25.71 mL of 0.0706 $M$ ammonium sulfate to 500.00 mL
(c) Molarity of sodium ion in a solution made by mixing 3.58 mL of 0.348 $M$ sodium chloride with 500. mL of $6.81 \times 10^{-2}$ $M$ sodium sulfate (assume volumes are additive)

**3.104** Calculate each of the following quantities:
(a) Volume (L) of 2.050 $M$ copper(II) nitrate that must be diluted with water to prepare 750.0 mL of a 0.8543 $M$ solution
(b) Volume (L) of 1.63 $M$ calcium chloride that must be diluted with water to prepare 350. mL of a $2.86 \times 10^{-2}$ $M$ chloride ion solution
(c) Final volume (L) of a 0.0700 $M$ solution prepared by diluting 18.0 mL of 0.155 $M$ lithium carbonate with water

**3.105** A sample of concentrated nitric acid has a density of 1.41 g/mL and contains 70.0% $HNO_3$ by mass.
(a) What mass (g) of $HNO_3$ is present per liter of solution?
(b) What is the molarity of the solution?

**3.106** Concentrated sulfuric acid (18.3 $M$) has a density of 1.84 g/mL.
(a) How many moles of $H_2SO_4$ are in each milliliter of solution?
(b) What is the mass % of $H_2SO_4$ in the solution?

**3.107** How many milliliters of 0.383 $M$ HCl are needed to react with 16.2 g of $CaCO_3$?
$$2HCl(aq) + CaCO_3(s) \longrightarrow CaCl_2(aq) + CO_2(g) + H_2O(l)$$

**3.108** How many grams of $NaH_2PO_4$ are needed to react with 43.74 mL of 0.285 $M$ NaOH?
$$NaH_2PO_4(s) + 2NaOH(aq) \longrightarrow Na_3PO_4(aq) + 2H_2O(l)$$

**3.109** How many grams of solid barium sulfate form when 35.0 mL of 0.160 $M$ barium chloride reacts with 58.0 mL of 0.065 $M$ sodium sulfate? Aqueous sodium chloride forms also.

**3.110** How many moles of excess reactant are present when 350. mL of 0.210 $M$ sulfuric acid reacts with 0.500 L of 0.196 $M$ sodium hydroxide to form water and aqueous sodium sulfate?

**Problems in Context**

**3.111** Ordinary household bleach is an aqueous solution of sodium hypochlorite. What is the molarity of a bleach solution that contains 20.5 g of sodium hypochlorite in 375 mL?

**3.112** Muriatic acid, an industrial grade of concentrated HCl, is used to clean masonry and cement. Its concentration is 11.7 $M$.

(a) Write instructions for diluting the concentrated acid to make 3.0 gallons of 3.5 $M$ acid for routine use (1 gal = 4 qt; 1 qt = 0.946 L). (b) How many milliliters of the muriatic acid solution contain 9.66 g of HCl?

**3.113** A sample of impure magnesium was analyzed by allowing it to react with excess HCl solution:
$$Mg(s) + 2HCl(aq) \longrightarrow MgCl_2(aq) + H_2(g)$$
After 1.32 g of the impure metal was treated with 0.100 L of 0.750 $M$ HCl, 0.0125 mol of HCl remained. Assuming the impurities do not react, what is the mass % of Mg in the sample?

**Comprehensive Problems**

**3.114** The mole is defined in terms of the carbon-12 atom. Use the definition to find (a) the mass in grams equal to 1 atomic mass unit; (b) the ratio of the gram to the atomic mass unit.

**3.115** The first sulfur-nitrogen compound was prepared in 1835 and has been used to synthesize many others. In the early 1980s, researchers made another such compound that conducts electricity like a metal. Mass spectrometry of the compound shows a molar mass of 184.27 g/mol, and analysis shows it to contain 2.288 g of S for every 1.000 g of N. What is its molecular formula?

**3.116** Hydroxyapatite, $Ca_5(PO_4)_3(OH)$, is the main mineral component of dental enamel, dentin, and bone. Coating the compound on metallic implants (such as titanium alloys and stainless steels) helps the body accept the implant. When placed in bone voids, the powder encourages natural bone to grow into the void. Hydroxyapatite is prepared by adding aqueous phosphoric acid to a dilute slurry of calcium hydroxide. (a) Write a balanced equation for this preparation. (b) What mass (g) of hydroxyapatite could form from 100. g of 85% phosphoric acid and 100. g of calcium hydroxide?

**3.117** Narceine is a narcotic in opium that crystallizes from solution as a hydrate that contains 10.8 mass % water and has a molar mass of 499.52 g/mol. Determine $x$ in narceine·$x$H$_2$O.

**3.118** Hydrogen-containing fuels have a "fuel value" based on their mass % H. Rank the following compounds from highest fuel value to lowest: ethane, propane, benzene, ethanol, cetyl palmitate (whale oil, $C_{32}H_{64}O_2$).

ethane    propane    benzene

ethanol

**3.119** Serotonin ($\mathcal{M}$ = 176 g/mol) transmits nerve impulses between neurons. It contains 68.2% C, 6.86% H, 15.9% N, and 9.08% O by mass. What is its molecular formula?

**3.120** In 1961, scientists agreed that the atomic mass unit (amu) would be defined as $\frac{1}{12}$ the mass of an atom of $^{12}$C. Before then, it was defined as $\frac{1}{16}$ the *average* mass of an atom of naturally occurring oxygen (a mixture of $^{16}$O, $^{17}$O, and $^{18}$O). The current atomic mass of oxygen is 15.9994 amu. (a) Did Avogadro's number change after the definition of an amu changed and, if so, in what direction? (b) Did the definition of the mole change? (c) Did the mass of a mole of a substance change? (d) Before 1961, was Avogadro's number $6.02 \times 10^{23}$ (to three significant figures), as it is today?

**3.121** Convert the following descriptions into balanced equations:
(a) In a gaseous reaction, hydrogen sulfide burns in oxygen to form sulfur dioxide and water vapor.
(b) When crystalline potassium chlorate is heated to just above its melting point, it reacts to form two different crystalline compounds, potassium chloride and potassium perchlorate.
(c) When hydrogen gas is passed over powdered iron(III) oxide, iron metal and water vapor form.
(d) The combustion of gaseous ethane in air forms carbon dioxide and water vapor.
(e) Iron(II) chloride is converted to iron(III) fluoride by treatment with chlorine trifluoride gas. Chlorine gas is also formed.

**3.122** Isobutylene is a hydrocarbon used in the manufacture of synthetic rubber. When 0.847 g of isobutylene was subjected to combustion analysis, the gain in mass of the $CO_2$ absorber was 2.657 g and that of the $H_2O$ absorber was 1.089 g. What is the empirical formula of isobutylene?

**3.123** The multistep smelting of ferric oxide to form elemental iron occurs at high temperatures in a blast furnace. In the first step, ferric oxide reacts with carbon monoxide to form $Fe_3O_4$. This substance reacts with more carbon monoxide to form iron(II) oxide, which reacts with still more carbon monoxide to form molten iron. Carbon dioxide is also produced in each step. (a) Write an overall balanced equation for the iron-smelting process. (b) How many grams of carbon monoxide are required to form 45.0 metric tons of iron from ferric oxide?

**3.124** One of the compounds used to increase the octane rating of gasoline is toluene (*right*). Suppose 20.0 mL of toluene ($d = 0.867$ g/mL) is consumed when a sample of gasoline burns in air.
(a) How many grams of oxygen are needed for complete combustion of the toluene? (b) How many total moles of gaseous products form? (c) How many molecules of water vapor form?

**3.125** During studies of the reaction in Sample Problem 3.20,

$$2N_2H_4(l) + N_2O_4(l) \longrightarrow 3N_2(g) + 4H_2O(g)$$

a chemical engineer measured a less-than-expected yield of $N_2$ and discovered that the following side reaction occurs:

$$N_2H_4(l) + 2N_2O_4(l) \longrightarrow 6NO(g) + 2H_2O(g)$$

In one experiment, 10.0 g of NO formed when 100.0 g of each reactant was used. What is the highest percent yield of $N_2$ that can be expected?

**3.126** A 0.652-g sample of a pure strontium halide reacts with excess sulfuric acid. The solid strontium sulfate formed is separated, dried, and found to weigh 0.755 g. What is the formula of the original halide?

**3.127** The following circles represent a chemical reaction between $AB_2$ and $B_2$:

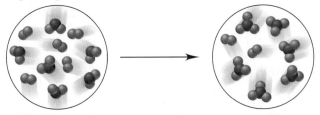

(a) Write a balanced equation for the reaction. (b) What is the limiting reactant? (c) How many moles of product can be made

from 3.0 mol of $B_2$ and 5.0 mol of $AB_2$? (d) How many moles of excess reactant remain after the reaction in part (c)?

**3.128** Calculate each of the following quantities:
(a) Volume (L) of 18.0 $M$ sulfuric acid that must be added to water to prepare 2.00 L of a 0.429 $M$ solution
(b) Molarity of the solution obtained by diluting 80.6 mL of 0.225 $M$ ammonium chloride to 0.250 L
(c) Volume (L) of water added to 0.130 L of 0.0372 $M$ sodium hydroxide to obtain a 0.0100 $M$ solution (assume the volumes are additive at these low concentrations)
(d) Mass (g) of calcium nitrate in each milliliter of a solution prepared by diluting 64.0 mL of 0.745 $M$ calcium nitrate to a final volume of 0.100 L

**3.129** Which of the following models represent compounds having the same empirical formula? What is the molecular mass of this common empirical formula?

**3.130** The zirconium oxalate $K_2Zr(C_2O_4)_3(H_2C_2O_4)\cdot H_2O$ was synthesized by mixing 1.68 g of $ZrOCl_2\cdot 8H_2O$ with 5.20 g of $H_2C_2O_4\cdot 2H_2O$ and an excess of aqueous KOH. After 2 months, 1.25 g of crystalline product was obtained, along with aqueous KCl and water. Calculate the percent yield.

**3.131** Seawater is approximately 4.0% by mass dissolved ions, 85% of which are from NaCl. (a) Find the mass % of NaCl in seawater. (b) Find the mass % of $Na^+$ ions and of $Cl^-$ ions in seawater. (c) Find the molarity of NaCl in seawater at 15°C ($d$ of seawater at 15°C = 1.025 g/mL).

**3.132** Is each of the following statements true or false? Correct any that are false.
(a) A mole of one substance has the same number of atoms as a mole of any other substance.
(b) The theoretical yield for a reaction is based on the balanced chemical equation.
(c) A limiting-reactant problem is being stated when the available quantity of one of the reactants is given in moles.
(d) To prepare 1.00 L of 3.00 $M$ NaCl, weigh 175.5 g of NaCl and dissolve it in 1.00 L of distilled water.
(e) The concentration of a solution is an intensive property, but the amount of solute in a solution is an extensive property.

**3.133** Box A represents one unit volume of solution A. Which box—B, C, or D—represents one unit volume after adding enough solvent to solution A to (a) triple its volume; (b) double its volume; (c) quadruple its volume?

**3.134** In each pair, choose the larger of the indicated quantities or state that the samples are equal:
(a) Entities: 0.4 mol of $O_3$ molecules or 0.4 mol of O atoms
(b) Grams: 0.4 mol of $O_3$ molecules or 0.4 mol of O atoms

(c) Moles: 4.0 g of $N_2O_4$ or 3.3 g of $SO_2$

(d) Grams: 0.6 mol of $C_2H_4$ or 0.6 mol of $F_2$

(e) Total ions: 2.3 mol of sodium chlorate or 2.2 mol of magnesium chloride

(f) Molecules: 1.0 g of $H_2O$ or 1.0 g of $H_2O_2$

(g) $Na^+$ ions: 0.500 L of 0.500 $M$ NaBr or 0.0146 kg of NaCl

(h) Grams: $6.02\times10^{23}$ atoms of $^{235}U$ or $6.02\times10^{23}$ atoms of $^{238}U$

**3.135** For the reaction between solid tetraphosphorus trisulfide and oxygen gas to form solid tetraphosphorus decaoxide and sulfur dioxide gas, write a balanced equation. Show the equation (see Table 3.4) in terms of (a) molecules, (b) moles, and (c) grams.

**3.136** Hydrogen gas is considered a clean fuel because it produces only water vapor when it burns. If the reaction has a 98.8% yield, what mass (g) of hydrogen forms 105 kg of water?

**3.137** Solar winds composed of free protons, electrons, and α particles bombard Earth constantly, knocking gas molecules out of the atmosphere. In this way, Earth loses about 3.0 kg of matter per second. It is estimated that the atmosphere will be gone in about 50 billion years. Use this estimate to calculate (a) the mass (kg) of Earth's atmosphere and (b) the amount (mol) of nitrogen, which makes up 75.5 mass % of the atmosphere.

**3.138** Calculate each of the following quantities:

(a) Amount (mol) of 0.588 g of ammonium bromide

(b) Number of potassium ions in 88.5 g of potassium nitrate

(c) Mass (g) of 5.85 mol of glycerol ($C_3H_8O_3$)

(d) Volume (L) of 2.85 mol of chloroform ($CHCl_3$; $d = 1.48$ g/mL)

(e) Number of sodium ions in 2.11 mol of sodium carbonate

(f) Number of atoms in 25.0 μg of cadmium

(g) Number of atoms in 0.0015 mol of fluorine gas

**3.139** Elements X (green) and Y (purple) react according to the following equation: $X_2 + 3Y_2 \longrightarrow 2XY_3$. Which molecular scene represents the product of the reaction?

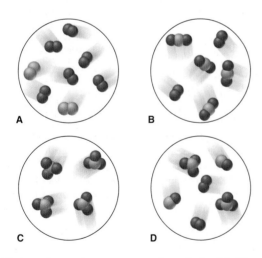

**3.140** Hydrocarbon mixtures are used as fuels. (a) How many grams of $CO_2(g)$ are produced by the combustion of 200. g of a mixture that is 25.0% $CH_4$ and 75.0% $C_3H_8$ by mass? (b) A 252-g gaseous mixture of $CH_4$ and $C_3H_8$ burns in excess $O_2$, and 748 g of $CO_2$ gas is collected. What is the mass % of $CH_4$ in the mixture?

**3.141** To 1.35 L of 0.325 $M$ HCl, you add 3.57 L of a second HCl solution of unknown concentration. The resulting solution is 0.893 $M$ HCl. Assuming the volumes are additive, calculate the molarity of the second HCl solution.

**3.142** Nitrogen (N), phosphorus (P), and potassium (K) are the main nutrients in plant fertilizers. By industry convention, the numbers on a label refer to the mass percents of N, $P_2O_5$, and $K_2O$, in that order.

Calculate the N/P/K ratio of a 30/10/10 fertilizer in terms of moles of each element, and express it as x/y/1.0.

**3.143** What mass percents of ammonium sulfate, ammonium hydrogen phosphate, and potassium chloride would you use to prepare 10/10/10 plant fertilizer (see Problem 3.142)?

**3.144** Ferrocene, synthesized in 1951, was the first organic iron compound with Fe—C bonds. An understanding of the structure of ferrocene gave rise to new ideas about chemical bonding and led to the preparation of many useful compounds. In the combustion analysis of ferrocene, which contains only Fe, C, and H, a 0.9437-g sample produced 2.233 g of $CO_2$ and 0.457 g of $H_2O$. What is the empirical formula of ferrocene?

**3.145** When carbon-containing compounds are burned in a limited amount of air, some $CO(g)$ as well as $CO_2(g)$ is produced. A gaseous product mixture is 35.0 mass % CO and 65.0 mass % $CO_2$. What is the mass % of C in the mixture?

**3.146** Write a balanced equation for the reaction depicted below:

| | |
|---|---|
| Si | ● |
| N | ● |
| F | ● |
| H | ● |

If each reactant molecule represents $1.25\times10^{-2}$ mol and the reaction yield is 87%, how many grams of Si-containing product form?

**3.147** Citric acid (*right*) is concentrated in citrus fruits and plays a central metabolic role in nearly every animal and plant cell. (a) What are the molar mass and formula of citric acid? (b) How many moles of citric acid are in 1.50 qt of lemon juice ($d = 1.09$ g/mL) that is 6.82% citric acid by mass?

**3.148** Various nitrogen oxides, as well as sulfur oxides, contribute to acidic rainfall through complex reaction sequences. Nitrogen and oxygen combine during high-temperature combustion of fuels in air to form nitrogen monoxide gas, which reacts with more oxygen to form nitrogen dioxide gas. In contact with water vapor, nitrogen dioxide forms aqueous nitric acid and more nitrogen monoxide. (a) Write balanced equations for these reactions. (b) Use the equations to write one overall balanced equation that does *not* include nitrogen monoxide and nitrogen dioxide. (c) How many metric tons (t) of nitric acid form when 1350 t of atmospheric nitrogen is consumed (1 t = 1000 kg)?

**3.149** Nitrogen monoxide reacts with elemental oxygen to form nitrogen dioxide. The scene at right represents an initial mixture of reactants. If the reaction has a 66% yield, which of the scenes below (A, B, or C) best represents the final product mixture?

**3.150** Fluorine is so reactive that it forms compounds with several of the noble gases.
(a) When 0.327 g of platinum is heated in fluorine, 0.519 g of a dark red, volatile solid forms. What is its empirical formula?
(b) When 0.265 g of this red solid reacts with excess xenon gas, 0.378 g of an orange-yellow solid forms. What is the empirical formula of this compound, the first to contain a noble gas?
(c) Fluorides of xenon can be formed by direct reaction of the elements at high pressure and temperature. Under conditions that produce only the tetra- and hexafluorides, $1.85 \times 10^{-4}$ mol of xenon reacted with $5.00 \times 10^{-4}$ mol of fluorine, and $9.00 \times 10^{-6}$ mol of xenon was found in excess. What are the mass percents of each xenon fluoride in the product mixture?

**3.151** Hemoglobin is 6.0% heme ($C_{34}H_{32}FeN_4O_4$) by mass. To remove the heme, hemoglobin is treated with acetic acid and NaCl, which forms hemin ($C_{34}H_{32}N_4O_4FeCl$). A blood sample from a crime scene contains 0.65 g of hemoglobin. (a) How many grams of heme are in the sample? (b) How many moles of heme? (c) How many grams of Fe? (d) How many grams of hemin could be formed for a forensic chemist to measure?

**3.152** Manganese is a key component of extremely hard steel. The element occurs naturally in many oxides. A 542.3-g sample of a manganese oxide has an Mn/O ratio of 1.00/1.42 and consists of braunite ($Mn_2O_3$) and manganosite (MnO). (a) How many grams of braunite and of manganosite are in the ore? (b) What is the $Mn^{3+}/Mn^{2+}$ ratio in the ore?

**3.153** The human body excretes nitrogen in the form of urea, $NH_2CONH_2$. The key step in its biochemical formation is the reaction of water with arginine to produce urea and ornithine:

Arginine    Water    Urea    Ornithine

(a) What is the mass % of nitrogen in urea, in arginine, and in ornithine? (b) How many grams of nitrogen can be excreted as urea when 135.2 g of ornithine is produced?

**3.154** Aspirin (acetylsalicylic acid, $C_9H_8O_4$) is made by reacting salicylic acid ($C_7H_6O_3$) with acetic anhydride [$(CH_3CO)_2O$]:

$$C_7H_6O_3(s) + (CH_3CO)_2O(l) \longrightarrow C_9H_8O_4(s) + CH_3COOH(l)$$

In one preparation, 3.077 g of salicylic acid and 5.50 mL of acetic anhydride react to form 3.281 g of aspirin. (a) Which is the limiting reactant ($d$ of acetic anhydride = 1.080 g/mL)? (b) What is the percent yield of this reaction? (c) What is the percent atom economy of this reaction?

**3.155** The rocket fuel hydrazine ($N_2H_4$) is made by the three-step Raschig process, which has the following overall equation:

$$NaOCl(aq) + 2NH_3(aq) \longrightarrow N_2H_4(aq) + NaCl(aq) + H_2O(l)$$

What is the percent atom economy of this process?

**3.156** Lead(II) chromate ($PbCrO_4$) is used as the yellow pigment for marking traffic lanes but is banned from house paint because of the risk of lead poisoning. It is produced from chromite ($FeCr_2O_4$), an ore of chromium:

$$4FeCr_2O_4(s) + 8K_2CO_3(aq) + 7O_2(g) \longrightarrow$$
$$2Fe_2O_3(s) + 8K_2CrO_4(aq) + 8CO_2(g)$$

Lead(II) ion then replaces the $K^+$ ion. If a yellow paint is to have 0.511% $PbCrO_4$ by mass, how many grams of chromite are needed per kilogram of paint?

**3.157** Ethanol ($CH_3CH_2OH$), the intoxicant in alcoholic beverages, is also used to make other organic compounds. In concentrated sulfuric acid, ethanol forms diethyl ether and water:

$$2CH_3CH_2OH(l) \longrightarrow CH_3CH_2OCH_2CH_3(l) + H_2O(g)$$

In a side reaction, some ethanol forms ethylene and water:

$$CH_3CH_2OH(l) \longrightarrow CH_2CH_2(g) + H_2O(g)$$

(a) If 50.0 g of ethanol yields 35.9 g of diethyl ether, what is the percent yield of diethyl ether? (b) If 45.0% of the ethanol that did not produce the ether reacts by the side reaction, what mass (g) of ethylene is produced?

**3.158** When powdered zinc is heated with sulfur, a violent reaction occurs, and zinc sulfide forms:

$$Zn(s) + S_8(s) \longrightarrow ZnS(s) \text{ [unbalanced]}$$

Some of the reactants also combine with oxygen in air to form zinc oxide and sulfur dioxide. When 83.2 g of Zn reacts with 52.4 g of $S_8$, 104.4 g of ZnS forms.
(a) What is the percent yield of ZnS?
(b) If all the remaining reactants combine with oxygen, how many grams of each of the two oxides form?

**3.159** Cocaine ($C_{17}H_{21}O_4N$) is a natural substance found in coca leaves, which have been used for centuries as a local anesthetic and stimulant. Illegal cocaine arrives in the United States either as the pure compound or as the hydrochloride salt ($C_{17}H_{21}O_4NHCl$). At 25°C, the salt is very soluble in water (2.50 kg/L), but cocaine is much less so (1.70 g/L).
(a) What is the maximum mass (g) of the salt that can dissolve in 50.0 mL of water?
(b) If this solution is treated with NaOH, the salt is converted to cocaine. How much more water (L) is needed to dissolve it?

**3.160** High-temperature superconducting oxides hold great promise in the utility, transportation, and computer industries.
(a) One superconductor is $La_{2-x}Sr_xCuO_4$. Calculate the molar masses of this oxide when $x = 0$, $x = 1$, and $x = 0.163$.
(b) Another common superconducting oxide is made by heating a mixture of barium carbonate, copper(II) oxide, and yttrium(III) oxide, followed by further heating in $O_2$:

$$4BaCO_3(s) + 6CuO(s) + Y_2O_3(s) \longrightarrow$$
$$2YBa_2Cu_3O_{6.5}(s) + 4CO_2(g) \quad 2YBa_2Cu_3O_{6.5}(s) + \tfrac{1}{2}O_2(g) \longrightarrow$$
$$2YBa_2Cu_3O_7(s)$$

When equal masses of the three reactants are heated, which reactant is limiting?
(c) After the product in part (b) is removed, what is the mass % of each reactant in the remaining solid mixture?

# Three Major Classes of Chemical Reactions

## Concepts and skills to review before you study this chapter

- names and formulas of compounds (Section 2.8)
- nature of ionic and covalent bonding (Section 2.7)
- amount-mass-number conversions (Section 3.1)
- molarity and amount-mass-number conversions in solution (Section 3.5)
- balancing chemical equations (Section 3.3)
- calculating quantities of reactants and products (Section 3.4)

Rapid chemical changes occur among gas molecules as sunlight bathes the atmosphere or lightning rips through a stormy sky and strikes the sea. Aqueous reactions occur unceasingly in the gigantic containers we know as oceans. And, in every cell of your body, thousands of reactions taking place right now enable you to function. Indeed, the amazing variety in nature is largely a consequence of the amazing variety of chemical reactions. With millions of reactions occurring in and around you, it would be impossible to describe them all. Fortunately, it isn't necessary because, when we survey even a small percentage of reactions, especially those in aqueous solution, a few major classes emerge.

**IN THIS CHAPTER . . .** We examine the underlying nature of three classes of reactions and the complex part that water plays in aqueous chemistry.
- We visualize the molecular structure of water to learn its role as solvent, how it interacts with ionic and covalent compounds, and the nature of electrolytes.
- We write ionic equations that represent the species in solution and the actual change that occurs when ionic compounds dissolve and react in water.
- We describe precipitation reactions and learn how to predict when they will occur.
- We see how acids and bases act as electrolytes and how they neutralize each other. We view acid-base reactions as proton-transfer processes and discuss how to quantify these reactions through titration.
- We examine oxidation-reduction (redox) reactions in the formation of ionic and covalent substances. We learn how to determine oxidation numbers and use them to balance redox equations and how to quantify these reactions through titration. We describe several important types of redox reactions, one of which is used to predict the relative reactivity of metals.
- An introduction to the reversible nature of all chemical change and the nature of equilibrium previews coverage of this central topic in later chapters.

# 4.1 • THE ROLE OF WATER AS A SOLVENT

For any reaction in solution, the solvent plays a key role that depends on its chemical nature. Some solvents passively disperse the substances into individual molecules. But water is much more active, interacting strongly with the substances and even reacting with them in some cases. Let's focus on how the water molecule interacts with both ionic and covalent solutes.

## The Polar Nature of Water

On the atomic scale, water's great solvent power arises from the *uneven distribution of electron charge* and its *bent molecular shape,* which create a *polar molecule:*

1. *Uneven charge distribution.* Recall from Section 2.7 that the electrons in a covalent bond are shared between the atoms. In a bond between identical atoms—as in $H_2$, $Cl_2$, $O_2$—the sharing is equal and electron charge is distributed evenly between the two nuclei (symmetrical shading in the space-filling model of Figure 4.1A on the next page). In covalent bonds between different atoms, the sharing is uneven because one atom attracts the electron pair more strongly than the other atom does.

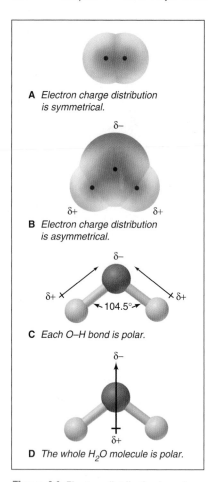

A *Electron charge distribution is symmetrical.*

B *Electron charge distribution is asymmetrical.*

C *Each O–H bond is polar.*

D *The whole H₂O molecule is polar.*

**Figure 4.1** Electron distribution in molecules of $H_2$ and $H_2O$.

For example, in each O—H bond of water, the shared electrons are closer to the O atom because an O atom attracts electrons more strongly than an H atom does. (We'll discuss the reasons in Chapter 9.) This uneven charge distribution creates a *polar bond,* one with partially charged "poles." In Figure 4.1B, the asymmetrical shading shows this distribution, and the δ symbol indicates a partial charge. The O end is partially negative, represented by red shading and δ−, and the H end is partially positive, represented by blue shading and δ+. In the ball-and-stick model of Figure 4.1C, the *polar arrow* points to the negative pole, and the tail, shaped like a plus sign, marks the positive pole.

2. *Bent molecular shape.* The sequence of the H—O—H atoms in water is not linear: the water molecule is bent with a bond angle of 104.5° (Figure 4.1C).

3. *Molecular polarity.* The combination of polar bonds and bent shape makes water a **polar molecule:** the region near the O atom is partially negative, and the region between the H atoms is partially positive (Figure 4.1D).

## Ionic Compounds in Water

In this subsection, we consider two closely related aspects of aqueous solutions of ionic compounds—how they occur and how they behave. We also use a compound's formula to calculate the amount (mol) of each ion in solution.

**How Ionic Compounds Dissolve: Replacement of Charge Attractions** In an ionic solid, oppositely charged ions are held together by electrostatic attractions (see Figure 1.3C and Section 2.7). Water separates the ions by *replacing these attractions with stronger ones between several water molecules and each ion.* Picture a granule of a soluble ionic compound in water: the negative ends of some water molecules are attracted to the cations, and the positive ends of other water molecules are attracted to the anions (Figure 4.2). Dissolution occurs because the *attractions between each type of ion and several water molecules outweigh the attractions between the ions.* Gradually, all the ions separate (dissociate), become **solvated**—surrounded closely by solvent molecules—and then move randomly in the solution.

For an ionic compound that doesn't dissolve in water, the attraction between ions is greater than the attraction between the ions and water. Actually, these so-called insoluble substances *do* dissolve to a very small extent, usually several orders of magnitude less than so-called soluble substances. For example, NaCl (a "soluble" compound) is over $4\times10^4$ times more soluble than AgCl (an "insoluble" compound):

Solubility of NaCl in $H_2O$ at 20°C = 365 g/L

Solubility of AgCl in $H_2O$ at 20°C = 0.009 g/L

**Figure 4.2** An ionic compound dissolving in water. The inset shows the polar arrow and partial charges (not shown in the rest of the scene) of each water molecule.

**A** *Distilled water does not conduct a current.*

**B** *Positive and negative ions fixed in a solid do not conduct a current.*

**C** *In solution, positive and negative ions move and conduct a current.*

To (+) electrode

To (−) electrode

**Figure 4.3** The electrical conductivity of ionic solutions.

In Chapter 13, you'll see that dissolving involves more than a contest between the relative attractions of ions for each other or for water. It also occurs because it frees ions from the solid to disperse randomly through the solution.

**How Ionic Solutions Behave: Electrolytes and Electrical Conductivity** When an ionic compound dissolves, the solution's *electrical conductivity,* the flow of electric current, increases dramatically. When electrodes are immersed in distilled water (Figure 4.3A) or pushed into an ionic solid (Figure 4.3B), no current flows, as shown by the unlit bulb. But in an aqueous solution of the compound, a large current flows, as shown by the lit bulb (Figure 4.3C). Current flow implies the *movement of charged particles:* when the ionic compound dissolves, the separate solvated ions move toward the electrode of opposite charge. A substance that conducts a current when dissolved in water is an **electrolyte.** Soluble ionic compounds are *strong* electrolytes because they dissociate completely and conduct a large current.

**Calculating the Amount (mol) of Ions in Solution** *The formula of the soluble ionic compound tells the number of moles of the component ions in solution.* For example, the equation for dissolving KBr in water to form solvated ions is

$$KBr(s) \xrightarrow{\text{H}_2\text{O}} K^+(aq) + Br^-(aq)$$

("$H_2O$" above the arrow means that water is the solvent, not a reactant.) Note that 1 mol of KBr dissociates into 2 mol of ions—1 mol of $K^+$ and 1 mol of $Br^-$. Sample Problems 4.1 and 4.2 apply these ideas, first with molecular scenes and then in calculations.

## Sample Problem 4.1    Using Molecular Scenes to Depict an Ionic Compound in Aqueous Solution

**Problem** The beakers contain aqueous solutions of the strong electrolyte potassium sulfate.
**(a)** Which beaker best represents the compound in solution (water molecules are not shown)?
**(b)** If each particle represents 0.1 mol, what is the total number of particles in solution?

A        B        C        D

**Plan (a)** We determine the formula and write an equation for 1 mol of compound dissociating into ions. Potassium sulfate is a strong electrolyte, so it dissociates completely, but, in general, *polyatomic ions remain intact in solution*. **(b)** We count the number of separate particles, and then multiply by 0.1 mol and by Avogadro's number.

**Solution (a)** The formula is $K_2SO_4$, so the equation is

$$K_2SO_4(s) \xrightarrow{H_2O} 2K^+(aq) + SO_4^{2-}(aq)$$

There are two separate 1+ particles for every 2− particle, so   beaker C is best.
**(b)** There are 9 particles, so the total amount (mol) of particles is 0.9 mol, and we have

$$\text{No. of particles} = 0.9 \text{ mol} \times \frac{6.022 \times 10^{23} \text{ particles}}{1 \text{ mol}} = \boxed{5.420 \times 10^{23} \text{ particles}}$$

**Check** Rounding to check the math in (b) gives $0.9 \times 6 = 5.4$, so the answer seems correct. The number of particles is an exact number since we actually counted them; thus, the answer can have as many significant figures as in Avogadro's number.

**Follow-Up Problem 4.1 (a)** Which strong electrolyte is dissolved in water (water molecules not shown) in the beaker at left: LiBr, $Cs_2CO_3$, or $BaCl_2$?
**(b)** If each particle represents 0.05 mol, what mass (g) of compound was dissolved?

## Sample Problem 4.2    Determining Amount (mol) of Ions in Solution

**Problem** What amount (mol) of each ion is in each solution?
**(a)** 5.0 mol of ammonium sulfate dissolved in water
**(b)** 78.5 g of cesium bromide dissolved in water
**(c)** $7.42 \times 10^{22}$ formula units of copper(II) nitrate dissolved in water
**(d)** 35 mL of 0.84 *M* zinc chloride

**Plan** We write an equation that shows 1 mol of compound dissociating into ions.
**(a)** We multiply the number of moles of ions by 5.0. **(b)** We first convert grams to moles. **(c)** We first convert formula units to moles. **(d)** We first convert molarity and volume to moles.

**Solution (a)** $(NH_4)_2SO_4(s) \xrightarrow{H_2O} 2NH_4^+(aq) + SO_4^{2-}(aq)$

Calculating amount (mol) of $NH_4^+$ ions:

$$\text{Amount (mol) of } NH_4^+ = 5.0 \text{ mol } (NH_4)_2SO_4 \times \frac{2 \text{ mol } NH_4^+}{1 \text{ mol } (NH_4)_2SO_4} = \boxed{10. \text{ mol } NH_4^+}$$

The formula shows 1 mol of $SO_4^{2-}$ per mole of $(NH_4)_2SO_4$, so   5.0 mol of $SO_4^{2-}$   is also present.

**(b)** $CsBr(s) \xrightarrow{H_2O} Cs^+(aq) + Br^-(aq)$

Converting from mass (g) to amount (mol):

$$\text{Amount (mol) of CsBr} = 78.5 \text{ g CsBr} \times \frac{1 \text{ mol CsBr}}{212.8 \text{ g CsBr}} = 0.369 \text{ mol CsBr}$$

Thus, $\boxed{0.369 \text{ mol of } Cs^+ \text{ and } 0.369 \text{ mol of } Br^-}$ are present.

**(c)** $Cu(NO_3)_2(s) \xrightarrow{H_2O} Cu^{2+}(aq) + 2NO_3^-(aq)$

Converting from formula units to amount (mol):

$$\text{Amount (mol) of Cu(NO}_3)_2 = 7.42 \times 10^{22} \text{ formula units Cu(NO}_3)_2$$

$$\times \frac{1 \text{ mol Cu(NO}_3)_2}{6.022 \times 10^{23} \text{ formula units Cu(NO}_3)_2}$$

$$= 0.123 \text{ mol Cu(NO}_3)_2$$

$$\text{Amount (mol) of NO}_3^- = 0.123 \text{ mol Cu(NO}_3)_2 \times \frac{2 \text{ mol NO}_3^-}{1 \text{ mol Cu(NO}_3)_2} = \boxed{0.246 \text{ mol NO}_3^-}$$

$\boxed{0.123 \text{ mol of } Cu^{2+}}$ is also present.

**(d)** $ZnCl_2(aq) \longrightarrow Zn^{2+}(aq) + 2Cl^-(aq)$

Converting from volume (mL) and molarity (mol/L) to amount (mol):

$$\text{Amount (mol) of ZnCl}_2 = 35 \text{ mL} \times \frac{1 \text{ L}}{10^3 \text{ mL}} \times \frac{0.84 \text{ mol ZnCl}_2}{1 \text{ L}} = 2.9 \times 10^{-2} \text{ mol ZnCl}_2$$

$$\text{Amount (mol) of Cl}^- = 2.9 \times 10^{-2} \text{ mol ZnCl}_2 \times \frac{2 \text{ mol Cl}^-}{1 \text{ mol ZnCl}_2} = \boxed{5.8 \times 10^{-2} \text{ mol Cl}^-}$$

$\boxed{2.9 \times 10^{-2} \text{ mol of } Zn^{2+}}$ is also present.

**Check** Round off to check the math and see if the relative numbers of moles of ions are consistent with the formula. For instance, in (a), 10 mol $NH_4^+$/5.0 mol $SO_4^{2-}$ = 2 $NH_4^+$/ 1 $SO_4^{2-}$, or $(NH_4)_2SO_4$. In (d), 0.029 mol $Zn^{2+}$/0.058 mol $Cl^-$ = 1 $Zn^{2+}$/2 $Cl^-$, or $ZnCl_2$.

**Follow-Up Problem 4.2** What amount (mol) of each ion is in each solution?
**(a)** 2 mol of potassium perchlorate dissolved in water
**(b)** 354 g of magnesium acetate dissolved in water
**(c)** $1.88 \times 10^{24}$ formula units of ammonium chromate dissolved in water
**(d)** 1.32 L of 0.55 $M$ sodium bisulfate

## Covalent Compounds in Water

Water dissolves many covalent (molecular) compounds also. Table sugar (sucrose, $C_{12}H_{22}O_{11}$), beverage (grain) alcohol (ethanol, $CH_3CH_2OH$), and automobile antifreeze (ethylene glycol, $HOCH_2CH_2OH$) are some familiar examples. All contain their own polar bonds, which interact with the bonds of water. However, most soluble covalent substances *do not* separate into ions, but remain intact molecules. For example,

$$HOCH_2CH_2OH(l) \xrightarrow{H_2O} HOCH_2CH_2OH(aq)$$

As a result, their aqueous solutions do not conduct an electric current, and these substances are **nonelectrolytes.** (As you'll see shortly, however, a small group of H-containing molecules that act as acids in aqueous solution *do* dissociate into ions.) Many other covalent substances, such as benzene ($C_6H_6$) and octane ($C_8H_{18}$), do not contain polar bonds, and these substances do not dissolve appreciably in water.

## ■ Summary of Section 4.1

- Because of polar bonds and a bent shape, the water molecule is polar, and water dissolves many ionic and covalent compounds.
- When an ionic compound dissolves, the attraction between each ion and water replaces the attraction between ions. Soluble ionic compounds are electrolytes because the ions are free to move and, thus, the solution conducts electricity.

- The formula of a soluble ionic compound shows the number of moles of each ion in solution per mole of compound dissolved.
- Water dissolves many covalent substances with polar bonds. These compounds are nonelectrolytes because the molecules remain intact and, thus, the solution does not conduct electricity.

## 4.2 • WRITING EQUATIONS FOR AQUEOUS IONIC REACTIONS

Chemists use three types of equations to represent aqueous ionic reactions. Let's examine a reaction to see what each type shows. When solutions of silver nitrate and sodium chromate are mixed, brick-red, solid silver chromate ($Ag_2CrO_4$) forms. Figure 4.4 depicts the reaction at the macroscopic level *(photos),* the atomic level *(blow-up circles),* and the symbolic level with the three types of equations (reacting ions are in red type):

- The **molecular equation** *(top)* reveals the least about the species that are actually in solution because *it shows all the reactants and products as if they were intact, undissociated compounds.* Only the designation for solid, *(s),* tells that a change has occurred:

$$2AgNO_3(aq) + Na_2CrO_4(aq) \longrightarrow Ag_2CrO_4(s) + 2NaNO_3(aq)$$

**Figure 4.4** An aqueous ionic reaction and the three types of equations.

- The **total ionic equation** (*middle*) is much more accurate because *it shows all the soluble ionic substances dissociated into ions.* The $Ag_2CrO_4(s)$ stands out as the only undissociated substance:

$$2Ag^+(aq) + 2NO_3^-(aq) + 2Na^+(aq) + CrO_4^{2-}(aq) \longrightarrow$$
$$Ag_2CrO_4(s) + 2Na^+(aq) + 2NO_3^-(aq)$$

The charges also balance: four positive and four negative for a net zero charge on the left side, and two positive and two negative for a net zero charge on the right.

   Notice that $Na^+(aq)$ and $NO_3^-(aq)$ appear unchanged on both sides of the equation. These are called **spectator ions** (shown with pale colors in the atomic-level scenes). They are not involved in the actual chemical change but are present only as part of the reactants; that is, we can't add an $Ag^+$ ion without also adding an anion, in this case, the $NO_3^-$ ion.

- The **net ionic equation** (*bottom*) is very useful because *it eliminates the spectator ions and shows only the actual chemical change:*

$$2Ag^+(aq) + CrO_4^{2-}(aq) \longrightarrow Ag_2CrO_4(s)$$

The formation of solid silver chromate from silver ions and chromate ions *is* the only change. To make that point clearly, suppose we had mixed solutions of potassium chromate, $K_2CrO_4(aq)$, and silver acetate, $AgC_2H_3O_2(aq)$, instead of sodium chromate and silver nitrate. The three ionic equations would be

Molecular:   $2AgC_2H_3O_2(aq) + K_2CrO_4(aq) \longrightarrow Ag_2CrO_4(s) + 2KC_2H_3O_2(aq)$

Total ionic:   $2Ag^+(aq) + 2C_2H_3O_2^-(aq) + 2K^+(aq) + CrO_4^{2-}(aq) \longrightarrow$
$$Ag_2CrO_4(s) + 2K^+(aq) + 2C_2H_3O_2(aq)$$

Net ionic:   $2Ag^+(aq) + CrO_4^{2-}(aq) \longrightarrow Ag_2CrO_4(s)$

Thus, the same change would have occurred, and only the spectator ions would differ—$K^+(aq)$ and $C_2H_3O_2^-(aq)$ instead of $Na^+(aq)$ and $NO_3^-(aq)$.

Next, we'll apply these types of equations to three important classes of chemical reactions—precipitation, acid-base, and oxidation-reduction.

## ▮ Summary of Section 4.2

- A molecular equation shows all substances intact and undissociated into ions.
- A total ionic equation shows all soluble ionic compounds as separate, solvated ions. Spectator ions appear unchanged on both sides of the equation.
- A net ionic equation eliminates the spectator ions and, thus, shows only the actual chemical change.

## 4.3 • PRECIPITATION REACTIONS

Precipitation reactions occur commonly in both nature and commerce. Coral reefs and some gems and minerals form, in part, through this process. And the chemical industry employs precipitation methods to make several important inorganic compounds.

### The Key Event: Formation of a Solid from Dissolved Ions

In a **precipitation reaction,** two soluble ionic compounds react to form an insoluble product, a **precipitate.** The reaction you saw between silver nitrate and sodium chromate is one example. Precipitates form for the same reason that some ionic compounds don't dissolve: the electrostatic attraction between the ions outweighs the tendency of the ions to remain solvated and move throughout the solution. When the two solutions are mixed, the ions collide and stay together, and a solid product "comes out of solution." Thus, the key event in a precipitation reaction is *the formation of an insoluble product through the net removal of ions from solution.* Figure 4.5 (*on the next page*) shows the process for calcium fluoride.

**Figure 4.5 The precipitation of calcium fluoride.** When aqueous solutions of NaF (from pipet) and $CaCl_2$ (in test tube) react, solid $CaF_2$ forms (water molecules are omitted for clarity).

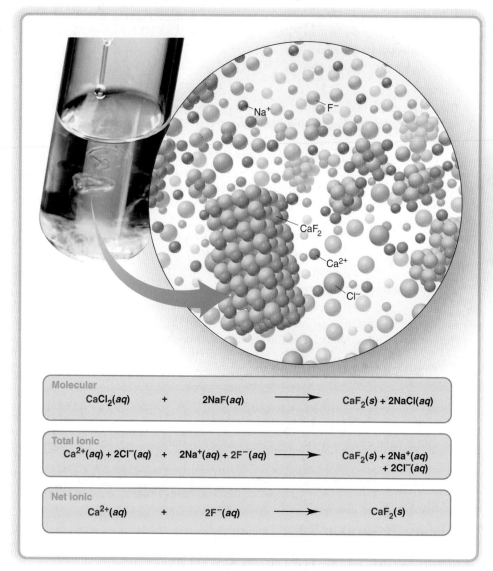

**Molecular**

$$CaCl_2(aq) \ + \ 2NaF(aq) \ \longrightarrow \ CaF_2(s) + 2NaCl(aq)$$

**Total ionic**

$$Ca^{2+}(aq) + 2Cl^-(aq) \ + \ 2Na^+(aq) + 2F^-(aq) \ \longrightarrow \ CaF_2(s) + 2Na^+(aq) + 2Cl^-(aq)$$

**Net ionic**

$$Ca^{2+}(aq) \ + \ 2F^-(aq) \ \longrightarrow \ CaF_2(s)$$

## Predicting Whether a Precipitate Will Form

To predict whether a precipitate will form when you mix two aqueous ionic solutions, we refer to the short list of solubility rules in Table 4.1. Let's see how to apply these rules. When sodium iodide and potassium nitrate are each dissolved in water, their solutions consist of solvated, dispersed ions:

$$NaI(s) \xrightarrow{H_2O} Na^+(aq) + I^-(aq)$$
$$KNO_3(s) \xrightarrow{H_2O} K^+(aq) + NO_3^-(aq)$$

Three steps help us predict if a precipitate forms:

1. *Note the ions in the reactants.* The reactant ions are

$$Na^+(aq) + I^-(aq) + K^+(aq) + NO_3^-(aq) \longrightarrow ?$$

2. *Consider all possible cation-anion combinations.* In addition to NaI and $KNO_3$, which we know are soluble, the other cation-anion combinations are $NaNO_3$ and KI.

3. *Decide whether any combination is insoluble.* According to Table 4.1, no reaction occurs because all the combinations—NaI, $KNO_3$, $NaNO_3$, and KI—are soluble: Rules 1 and 2 say all compounds of Group 1A(1) ions and all nitrates are soluble.

Now, what happens if we substitute a solution of lead(II) nitrate, $Pb(NO_3)_2$, for the $KNO_3$ solution? The reactant ions are $Na^+$, $I^-$, $Pb^{2+}$, and $NO_3^-$. In addition to the two soluble reactants, NaI and $Pb(NO_3)_2$, the other two possible cation-anion combinations are $NaNO_3$ and $PbI_2$. According to Table 4.1, $NaNO_3$ is soluble

| Table **4.1** Solubility Rules for Ionic Compounds in Water | |
| --- | --- |
| **Soluble Ionic Compounds** | **Insoluble Ionic Compounds** |
| 1. All common compounds of Group 1A(1) ions ($Li^+$, $Na^+$, $K^+$, etc.) and ammonium ion ($NH_4^+$) are soluble.<br>2. All common nitrates ($NO_3^-$), acetates ($CH_3COO^-$ or $C_2H_3O_2^-$), and most perchlorates ($ClO_4^-$) are soluble.<br>3. All common chlorides ($Cl^-$), bromides ($Br^-$), and iodides ($I^-$) are soluble, *except* those of $Ag^+$, $Pb^{2+}$, $Cu^+$, and $Hg_2^{2+}$. All common fluorides ($F^-$) are soluble, *except* those of $Pb^{2+}$ and Group 2A(2).<br>4. All common sulfates ($SO_4^{2-}$) are soluble, except those of $Ca^{2+}$, $Sr^{2+}$, $Ba^{2+}$, $Ag^+$, and $Pb^{2+}$. | 1. All common metal hydroxides are insoluble, *except* those of Group 1A(1) and the larger members of Group 2A(2) (beginning with $Ca^{2+}$).<br>2. All common carbonates ($CO_3^{2-}$) and phosphates ($PO_4^{3-}$) are insoluble, *except* those of Group 1A(1) and $NH_4^+$.<br>3. All common sulfides are insoluble except those of Group 1A(1), Group 2A(2), and $NH_4^+$. |

(Rule 1), but $PbI_2$ is *not* (Rule 3). The total ionic equation shows the reaction that occurs as $Pb^{2+}$ and $I^-$ ions collide and form a precipitate:

$$2Na^+(aq) + 2I^-(aq) + Pb^{2+}(aq) + 2NO_3^-(aq) \longrightarrow 2Na^+(aq) + 2NO_3^-(aq) + PbI_2(s)$$

And the net ionic equation confirms it:

$$Pb^{2+}(aq) + 2I^-(aq) \longrightarrow PbI_2(s)$$

**Metathesis Reactions** The molecular equation for the reaction between $Pb(NO_3)_2$ and NaI shows *the ions exchanging partners* (Figure 4.6):

$$2NaI(aq) + Pb(NO_3)_2(aq) \longrightarrow PbI_2(s) + 2NaNO_3(aq)$$

Such reactions are called *double-displacement reactions,* or **metathesis** (pronounced *meh-TA-thuh-sis*) **reactions.** Several are important in industry, including the preparation of silver bromide for the manufacture of black-and-white film:

$$AgNO_3(aq) + KBr(aq) \longrightarrow AgBr(s) + KNO_3(aq)$$

The reactions that form $Ag_2CrO_4$ (Figure 4.4) and $CaF_2$ (Figure 4.5) are metathesis, too. Sample Problems 4.2 and 4.3 provide practice in predicting if a precipitate forms.

$2NaI(aq) + Pb(NO_3)_2(aq) \longrightarrow$
$PbI_2(s) + 2NaNO_3(aq)$

**Figure 4.6** The precipitation of $PbI_2$, a metathesis reaction.

| **Sample Problem 4.3** | **Predicting Whether a Precipitation Reaction Occurs; Writing Ionic Equations** |
| --- | --- |

**Problem** Does a reaction occur when each of these pairs of solutions is mixed? If so, write balanced molecular, total ionic, and net ionic equations, and identify the spectator ions.
**(a)** Potassium fluoride(*aq*) + strontium nitrate(*aq*) $\longrightarrow$
**(b)** Ammonium perchlorate(*aq*) + sodium bromide(*aq*) $\longrightarrow$

**Plan** We note the reactant ions, write the cation-anion combinations, and refer to Table 4.1 to see if any are insoluble. For the molecular equation, we predict the products and write them all as intact compounds. For the total ionic equation, we write the soluble compounds as separate ions. For the net ionic equation, we eliminate the spectator ions.

**Solution (a)** In addition to the reactants, the two other ion combinations are strontium fluoride and potassium nitrate. Table 4.1 shows that strontium fluoride is insoluble, so a reaction *does* occur. Writing the molecular equation:

$$2KF(aq) + Sr(NO_3)_2(aq) \longrightarrow SrF_2(s) + 2KNO_3(aq)$$

Writing the total ionic equation:

$$2K^+(aq) + 2F^-(aq) + Sr^{2+}(aq) + 2NO_3^-(aq) \longrightarrow SrF_2(s) + 2K^+(aq) + 2NO_3^-(aq)$$

Writing the net ionic equation:

$$Sr^{2+}(aq) + 2F^-(aq) \longrightarrow SrF_2(s)$$

The spectator ions are $K^+$ and $NO_3^-$.

**(b)** The other ion combinations are ammonium bromide and sodium perchlorate. Table 4.1 shows that all ammonium, sodium, and most perchlorate compounds are soluble, and all bromides are soluble except those of $Ag^+$, $Pb^{2+}$, $Cu^+$, and $Hg_2^{2+}$. Therefore, **no reaction occurs.** The compounds remain as solvated ions.

**Follow-Up Problem 4.3** Predict whether a reaction occurs, and if so, write balanced total and net ionic equations:
**(a)** Iron(III) chloride(*aq*) + cesium phosphate(*aq*) $\longrightarrow$
**(b)** Sodium hydroxide(*aq*) + cadmium nitrate(*aq*) $\longrightarrow$
**(c)** Magnesium bromide(*aq*) + potassium acetate(*aq*) $\longrightarrow$
**(d)** Silver nitrate(*aq*) + barium chloride(*aq*) $\longrightarrow$

---

**Sample Problem 4.4**    **Using Molecular Depictions in Precipitation Reactions**

**Problem** The molecular views below show reactant solutions for a precipitation reaction (with ions shown as colored spheres and water omitted for clarity):

A          +          B

**(a)** Which compound is dissolved in beaker A: KCl, $Na_2SO_4$, $MgBr_2$, or $Ag_2SO_4$?
**(b)** Which compound is dissolved in beaker B: $NH_4NO_3$, $MgSO_4$, $Ba(NO_3)_2$, or $CaF_2$?
**(c)** Name the precipitate and the spectator ions when solutions A and B are mixed, and write balanced molecular, total ionic, and net ionic equations for any reaction.
**(d)** If each particle represents 0.010 mol of ions, what is the maximum mass (g) of precipitate that can form (assuming complete reaction)?

**Plan** **(a)** and **(b)** From the depictions, we note the charge and number of each kind of ion and use Table 4.1 to determine the ion combinations that are soluble. **(c)** Once we know the combinations, Table 4.1 tells which two ions form the solid, so the other two are spectator ions. **(d)** This part is a limiting-reactant problem because the amounts of two species are involved. We count the number of each kind of ion that formed the solid. We multiply the number of each reactant ion by 0.010 mol and calculate the amount (mol) of product formed from each. Whichever ion forms less is limiting, so we use the molar mass of the precipitate to find mass (g).

**Solution** **(a)** In solution A, there are two 1+ particles for each 2− particle. Therefore, the dissolved compound cannot be KCl or $MgBr_2$. Of the remaining two choices, $Ag_2SO_4$ is insoluble, so the dissolved compound must be $Na_2SO_4$.
**(b)** In solution B, there are two 1− particles for each 2+ particle. Therefore, the dissolved compound cannot be $NH_4NO_3$ or $MgSO_4$. Of the remaining two choices, $CaF_2$ is insoluble, so the dissolved compound must be $Ba(NO_3)_2$.
**(c)** Of the two possible ion combinations, $BaSO_4$ and $NaNO_3$, $BaSO_4$ is insoluble, so $Na^+$ and $NO_3^-$ are spectator ions.

| | |
|---|---|
| Molecular: | $Ba(NO_3)_2(aq) + Na_2SO_4(aq) \longrightarrow BaSO_4(s) + 2NaNO_3(aq)$ |
| Total ionic: | $Ba^{2+}(aq) + 2NO_3^-(aq) + 2Na^+(aq) + SO_4^{2-}(aq) \longrightarrow$ |
| | $\qquad\qquad\qquad\qquad BaSO_4(s) + 2NO_3^-(aq) + 2Na^+(aq)$ |
| Net ionic: | $Ba^{2+}(aq) + SO_4^{2-}(aq) \longrightarrow BaSO_4(s)$ |

**(d)** Finding the ion that is the limiting reactant:

For $Ba^{2+}$:

$$\text{Amount (mol) of } BaSO_4 = 4 \ \cancel{Ba^{2+} \text{ particles}} \times \frac{0.010 \ \text{mol } \cancel{Ba^{2+} \text{ ion}}}{1 \ \cancel{\text{particle}}} \times \frac{1 \ \text{mol } BaSO_4}{1 \ \cancel{\text{mol } Ba^{2+} \text{ ions}}}$$

$$= 0.040 \ \text{mol } BaSO_4$$

For $SO_4^{2-}$:

$$\text{Amount (mol) of BaSO}_4 = 5\ \overline{SO_4^{2-}\text{ particles}} \times \frac{0.010\ \overline{\text{mol SO}_4^{2-}\text{ ions}}}{1\ \overline{\text{particle}}} \times \frac{1\ \text{mol BaSO}_4}{1\ \overline{\text{mol SO}_4^{2-}\text{ ions}}}$$

$$= 0.050\ \text{mol BaSO}_4$$

Therefore, $Ba^{2+}$ ion is the limiting reactant.

Calculating the mass (g) of product ($\mathcal{M}$ of $BaSO_4 = 233.4$ g/mol):

$$\text{Mass (g) of BaSO}_4 = 0.040\ \overline{\text{mol BaSO}_4} \times \frac{233.4\ \text{g BaSO}_4}{1\ \overline{\text{mol BaSO}_4}} = \boxed{9.3\ \text{g BaSO}_4}$$

**Check** Counting the number of $Ba^{2+}$ ions allows a more direct calculation for a check: four $Ba^{2+}$ particles means the maximum mass of $BaSO_4$ that can form is

$$\text{Mass (g) of BaSO}_4 = 4\ \overline{Ba^{2+}\text{ particles}} \times \frac{0.010\ \overline{\text{mol Ba}^{2+}\text{ ions}}}{1\ \overline{\text{particle}}} \times \frac{1\ \overline{\text{mol BaSO}_4}}{1\ \overline{\text{mol Ba}^{2+}\text{ ions}}} \times \frac{233.4\ \text{g BaSO}_4}{1\ \overline{\text{mol}}} = 9.3\ \text{g BaSO}_4$$

**Follow-Up Problem 4.4** Molecular views of the reactant solutions for a precipitation reaction are shown below (with ions represented as spheres and water molecules omitted):

**(a)** Which compound is dissolved in beaker A: $Zn(NO_3)_2$, KCl, $Na_2SO_4$, or $PbCl_2$?
**(b)** Which compound is dissolved in beaker B: $(NH_4)_2SO_4$, $Cd(OH)_2$, $Ba(OH)_2$, or $KNO_3$?
**(c)** Name the precipitate and the spectator ions when solutions A and B are mixed, and write balanced molecular, total ionic, and net ionic equations for the reaction.
**(d)** If each particle represents 0.050 mol of ions, what is the maximum mass (g) of precipitate that can form (assuming complete reaction)?

## ■ Summary of Section 4.3

- In a precipitation reaction, an insoluble ionic compound forms when solutions of two soluble ones are mixed. The electrostatic attraction between certain pairs of solvated ions is strong enough to overcome the attraction of each ion for water.
- Based on a set of solubility rules, we can predict the formation of a precipitate by noting which of all possible cation-anion combinations is insoluble.

## 4.4 • ACID-BASE REACTIONS

Aqueous acid-base reactions occur in processes as diverse as the metabolic action of proteins, the industrial production of fertilizer, and the revitalization of lakes damaged by acid rain.

*These reactions involve water as reactant or product*, in addition to its common role as solvent. Of course, an **acid-base reaction** (also called a **neutralization reaction**) occurs when an acid reacts with a base, but the definitions of these terms and the scope of this reaction class have changed over the years. For our purposes at this point, we'll use definitions that apply to substances found commonly in the lab:

- *An **acid** is a substance that produces $H^+$ ions when dissolved in water.*

$$HX \xrightarrow{H_2O} H^+(aq) + X^-(aq)$$

- *A **base** is a substance that produces $OH^-$ ions when dissolved in water.*

$$MOH \xrightarrow{H_2O} M^+(aq) + OH^-(aq)$$

(Other definitions are presented later in this section and in Chapter 18.)

**Acids and the Solvated Proton** *Acidic solutions arise when certain covalent H-containing molecules dissociate into ions in water.* In every case, these molecules contain a *polar bond to H* in which the other atom pulls much more strongly on the electron pair. A good example is HBr. The Br end of the H—Br bond is partially negative, and the H end is partially positive. When hydrogen bromide gas dissolves in water, the poles of $H_2O$ molecules are attracted to the oppositely charged poles of the HBr. The bond breaks, with H becoming the solvated cation $H^+(aq)$ and Br becoming the solvated anion $Br^-(aq)$:

$$HBr(g) \xrightarrow{H_2O} H^+(aq) + Br^-(aq)$$

The solvated $H^+$ ion is a very unusual species. The H atom is a proton surrounded by an electron, so $H^+$ is just a proton. With a full positive charge concentrated in such a tiny volume, $H^+$ attracts the negative pole of water molecules so strongly that it forms a covalent bond to one of them. We can show this interaction by writing the solvated $H^+$ ion as an $H_3O^+$ ion (hydronium ion) that also is solvated:

$$HBr(g) \quad + \quad H_2O(l) \quad \longrightarrow \quad H_3O^+(aq) + \quad Br^-(aq)$$

The hydronium ion, which we write as $H_3O^+$ [or $(H_2O)H^+$], associates with other water molecules to give species such as $H_5O_2^+$ [or $(H_2O)_2H^+$], $H_7O_3^+$ [or $(H_2O)_3H^+$], $H_9O_4^+$ [or $(H_2O)_4H^+$], and so forth. Figure 4.7 shows $H_7O_3^+$, an $H_3O^+$ ion associated *(dotted lines)* with two $H_2O$ molecules. As a general notation for these various species, we write $H^+(aq)$, but later in this chapter and in much of the text, we'll use $H_3O^+(aq)$.

**Figure 4.7** The $H^+$ ion as a solvated hydronium ion.

**Acids and Bases as Electrolytes** Acids and bases are categorized in terms of their "strength," the degree to which they dissociate into ions in water (Table 4.2):

• *Strong acids and strong bases dissociate completely into ions.* Therefore, like soluble ionic compounds, they are *strong* electrolytes and conduct a large current, as shown by the brightly lit bulb (Figure 4.8A).

• *Weak acids and weak bases dissociate very little into ions.* Most of their molecules remain intact. Therefore, they are *weak* electrolytes, which means they conduct a small current (Figure 4.8B).

Because a strong acid (or strong base) dissociates completely, we can find the molarity of $H^+$ (or $OH^-$) and the amount (mol) or number of each ion in solution. (You'll see how to determine these quantities for weak acids in Chapter 18.)

**Table 4.2 Strong and Weak Acids and Bases**

**Acids**

**Strong**
Hydrochloric acid, HCl
Hydrobromic acid, HBr
Hydriodic acid, HI
Nitric acid, $HNO_3$
Sulfuric acid, $H_2SO_4$
Perchloric acid, $HClO_4$

**Weak (a few of many examples)**
Hydrofluoric acid, HF
Phosphoric acid, $H_3PO_4$
Acetic acid, $CH_3COOH$ (or $HC_2H_3O_2$)

**Bases**

**Strong**
*Group 1A(1) hydroxides:*
Lithium hydroxide, LiOH
Sodium hydroxide, NaOH
Potassium hydroxide, KOH
Rubidium hydroxide, RbOH
Cesium hydroxide, CsOH

*Heavy Group 2A(2) hydroxides:*
Calcium hydroxide, $Ca(OH)_2$
Strontium hydroxide, $Sr(OH)_2$
Barium hydroxide, $Ba(OH)_2$

**Weak (one of many examples)**
Ammonia, $NH_3$

**A** Strong acid (or base) = strong electrolyte

**B** Weak acid (or base) = weak electrolyte

**Figure 4.8** Acids and bases as electrolytes.

## Sample Problem 4.5  Determining the Number of H⁺ (or OH⁻) Ions in Solution

**Problem** Nitric acid is a major chemical in the fertilizer and explosives industries. How many $H^+(aq)$ ions are in 25.3 mL of 1.4 $M$ nitric acid?

**Plan** We know the volume (25.3 mL) and molarity (1.4 $M$) of nitric acid, and we need the number of $H^+(aq)$. We convert from mL to L and multiply by the molarity to find the amount (mol) of acid. Table 4.2 shows that nitric acid is a strong acid, so it dissociates completely. With the formula, we write a dissociation equation, which shows the amount (mol) of $H^+$ ions per mole of acid. We multiply that amount by Avogadro's number to find the number of $H^+(aq)$ ions (see the road map).

**Solution** Finding the amount (mol) of nitric acid:

$$\text{Amount (mol) of HNO}_3 = 25.3 \ \cancel{\text{mL}} \times \frac{1 \ \cancel{\text{L}}}{1000 \ \cancel{\text{mL}}} \times \frac{1.4 \ \text{mol}}{1 \ \cancel{\text{L}}} = 0.035 \ \text{mol}$$

Nitric acid is $HNO_3$, so we have:

$$HNO_3(l) \xrightarrow{H_2O} H^+(aq) + NO_3^-(aq)$$

Finding the number of $H^+$ ions:

$$\text{No. of H}^+ \text{ ions} = 0.035 \ \cancel{\text{mol HNO}_3} \times \frac{1 \ \cancel{\text{mol H}^+}}{1 \ \cancel{\text{mol HNO}_3}} \times \frac{6.022 \times 10^{23} \ H^+ \ \text{ions}}{1 \ \cancel{\text{mol H}^+}}$$

$$= 2.1 \times 10^{22} \ H^+ \ \text{ions}$$

**Check** The number of moles seems correct: $0.025 \ L \times 1.4 \ \text{mol/L} = 0.035 \ \text{mol}$, and multiplying by $6 \times 10^{23}$ ions/mol gives $2 \times 10^{22}$ ions.

**Follow-Up Problem 4.5** How many moles of $OH^-(aq)$ are present in 451 mL of 1.20 $M$ potassium hydroxide?

**Road Map**

| Volume (mL) of HNO₃ |
|---|

$10^3$ mL = 1 L

| Volume (L) of HNO₃ |
|---|

multiply by $M$ (mol/L)

| Amount (mol) of HNO₃ |
|---|

mol of $H^+$/mol of $HNO_3$

| Amount (mol) of H⁺ ions |
|---|

multiply by Avogadro's number

| No. of H⁺ ions |
|---|

### Structural Features of Acids and Bases
A key structural feature appears in common laboratory acids and bases:

- *Acids.* Strong acids, such as $HNO_3$ and $H_2SO_4$, and weak acids, such as HF and $H_3PO_4$, have one or more H atoms as part of their structure, which are either completely released (strong) or partially released (weak) as protons in water.
- *Bases.* Strong bases have either $OH^-$ (e.g., NaOH) or $O^{2-}$ (e.g., $K_2O$) as part of their structure. The oxide ion is not stable in water and reacts to form $OH^-$ ion:

$$O^{2-}(s) + H_2O(l) \longrightarrow 2OH^-(aq) \quad \text{so} \quad K_2O(s) + H_2O(l) \longrightarrow 2K^+(aq) + 2OH^-(aq)$$

Weak bases, such as ammonia, do not contain $OH^-$ ions, but, as you'll see in later chapters, they all have an electron pair on N. Weak bases produce $OH^-$ ions in a reaction that occurs to a small extent in water:

$$NH_3(g) + H_2O(l) \rightleftharpoons NH_4^+(aq) + OH^-(aq)$$

(The reaction arrow in the preceding equation indicates that the reaction proceeds in both directions; we'll discuss this important idea further in Section 4.7.)

## The Key Event: Formation of H₂O from H⁺ and OH⁻

To see the key event in acid-base reactions, we'll write the three types of aqueous ionic equations (with color) and focus on the reaction between the strong acid HCl and the strong base $Ba(OH)_2$:

- The molecular equation is

$$2HCl(aq) + Ba(OH)_2(aq) \longrightarrow BaCl_2(aq) + 2H_2O(l)$$

- HCl and $Ba(OH)_2$ dissociate completely, so the total ionic equation is

$$2H^+(aq) + 2Cl^-(aq) + Ba^{2+}(aq) + 2OH^-(aq) \longrightarrow Ba^{2+}(aq) + 2Cl^-(aq) + 2H_2O(l)$$

- In the net ionic equation, we eliminate the spectator ions, $Ba^{2+}(aq)$ and $Cl^-(aq)$:

$$2H^+(aq) + 2OH^-(aq) \longrightarrow 2H_2O(l) \quad \text{or} \quad H^+(aq) + OH^-(aq) \longrightarrow H_2O(l)$$

Thus, *the key event in aqueous reactions between a strong acid and a strong base is that an $H^+$ ion from the acid and an $OH^-$ ion from the base form a water molecule.* Only the spectator ions differ from one strong acid–strong base reaction to another.

Like precipitation reactions, acid-base reactions occur through *the electrostatic attraction of ions and their removal from solution as the product.* In this case, rather than an insoluble ionic solid, the product is $H_2O$, which consists almost entirely of undissociated molecules. Actually, water molecules dissociate *very* slightly (which, as you'll see in Chapter 18, is very important), but the formation of water in an acid-base reaction results in an enormous net removal of $H^+$ and $OH^-$ ions.

The molecular and total ionic equations above show that if you evaporate the water, the spectator ions remain: the ionic compound that results from the reaction of an acid and a base is called a **salt,** which in this case is barium chloride. Thus, in an aqueous neutralization reaction, *an acid and a base form a salt solution and water:*

$$\underset{\text{acid}}{HX(aq)} + \underset{\text{base}}{MOH(aq)} \longrightarrow \underset{\text{salt}}{MX(aq)} + \underset{\text{water}}{H_2O(l)}$$

Note that *the cation of the salt comes from the base and the anion from the acid.*

Acid-base reactions, like precipitation reactions, are metathesis (double-displacement) reactions. The reaction of aluminum hydroxide, the active ingredient in some antacids, with HCl, the major component of stomach acid, is another example:

$$3HCl(aq) + Al(OH)_3(s) \longrightarrow AlCl_3(aq) + 3H_2O(l)$$

---

**Sample Problem 4.6** | **Writing Ionic Equations for Acid-Base Reactions**

**Problem** Write balanced molecular, total ionic, and net ionic equations for each of the following acid-base reactions and identify the spectator ions:
**(a)** Hydrochloric acid(*aq*) + potassium hydroxide(*aq*) $\longrightarrow$
**(b)** Strontium hydroxide(*aq*) + perchloric acid(*aq*) $\longrightarrow$
**(c)** Barium hydroxide(*aq*) + sulfuric acid(*aq*) $\longrightarrow$

**Plan** All are strong acids and bases (see Table 4.2), so the actual reaction is between $H^+$ and $OH^-$. The products are $H_2O$ and a salt solution of spectator ions. In (c), we note that the salt ($BaSO_4$) is insoluble (see Table 4.1), so there are no spectator ions.

**Solution (a)** Writing the molecular equation:

$$HCl(aq) + KOH(aq) \longrightarrow KCl(aq) + H_2O(l)$$

Writing the total ionic equation:

$$H^+(aq) + Cl^-(aq) + K^+(aq) + OH^-(aq) \longrightarrow K^+(aq) + Cl^-(aq) + H_2O(l)$$

Writing the net ionic equation:

$$H^+(aq) + OH^-(aq) \longrightarrow H_2O(l)$$

$K^+(aq)$ and $Cl^-(aq)$ are the spectator ions.

**(b)** Writing the molecular equation:

$$Sr(OH)_2(aq) + 2HClO_4(aq) \longrightarrow Sr(ClO_4)_2(aq) + 2H_2O(l)$$

Writing the total ionic equation:

$$Sr^{2+}(aq) + 2OH^-(aq) + 2H^+(aq) + 2ClO_4^-(aq) \longrightarrow$$
$$Sr^{2+}(aq) + 2ClO_4^-(aq) + 2H_2O(l)$$

Writing the net ionic equation:

$$2OH^-(aq) + 2H^+(aq) \longrightarrow 2H_2O(l) \quad \text{or} \quad OH^-(aq) + H^+(aq) \longrightarrow H_2O(l)$$

$Sr^{2+}(aq)$ and $ClO_4^-(aq)$ are the spectator ions.

**(c)** Writing the molecular equation:

$$Ba(OH)_2(aq) + H_2SO_4(aq) \longrightarrow BaSO_4(s) + 2H_2O(l)$$

Writing the total ionic equation:

$$Ba^{2+}(aq) + 2OH^-(aq) + 2H^+(aq) + SO_4^{2-}(aq) \longrightarrow BaSO_4(s) + 2H_2O(l)$$

This is a neutralization *and* a precipitation reaction, so the net ionic equation is the same as the total ionic. There are no spectator ions, because they appear in the solid.

**Follow-Up Problem 4.6** Write balanced molecular, total ionic, and net ionic equations for the reaction between aqueous solutions of calcium hydroxide and nitric acid.

## Proton Transfer in Acid-Base Reactions

When we take a closer look (with color) at the reaction between a strong acid and strong base, as well as several related reactions, a unifying pattern appears. Let's examine three types of reaction to gain insight about this pattern.

**Reaction Between Strong Acid and Strong Base** When HCl gas dissolves in water, the $H^+$ ion ends up bonded to a water molecule. Thus, hydrochloric acid actually consists of solvated $H_3O^+$ and $Cl^-$ ions:

$$HCl(g) + H_2O(l) \longrightarrow H_3O^+(aq) + Cl^-(aq)$$

If we add NaOH solution, the total ionic equation shows that $H_3O^+$ *transfers a proton* to $OH^-$ (leaving a water molecule written as $H_2O$, and forming a water molecule written as HOH):

$$\overbrace{[H_3O^+(aq) + Cl^-(aq)] + [Na^+(aq) + OH^-(aq)]}^{\text{H}^+ \text{ transfer}} \longrightarrow$$
$$H_2O(l) + Cl^-(aq) + Na^+(aq) + HOH(l)$$

Without the spectator ions, the net ionic equation shows more clearly the *transfer of a proton* from $H_3O^+$ to $OH^-$:

$$\overbrace{H_3O^+(aq) + OH^-(aq)}^{\text{H}^+ \text{ transfer}} \longrightarrow H_2O(l) + HOH(l) \quad [\text{or } 2H_2O(l)]$$

This equation is identical to the one we saw earlier (see p. 147),

$$H^+(aq) + OH^-(aq) \longrightarrow H_2O(l)$$

with the additional $H_2O$ molecule left over from the $H_3O^+$. Figure 4.9 shows this process on the atomic level and also shows that, if the water is evaporated, the spectator ions, $Cl^-$ and $Na^+$, crystallize as the salt NaCl.

**Figure 4.9** An aqueous strong acid–strong base reaction as a proton-transfer process.

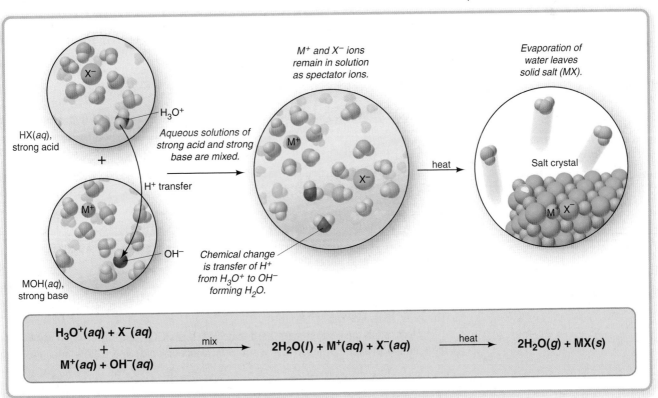

$$\begin{array}{c} H_3O^+(aq) + X^-(aq) \\ + \\ M^+(aq) + OH^-(aq) \end{array} \xrightarrow{\text{mix}} 2H_2O(l) + M^+(aq) + X^-(aq) \xrightarrow{\text{heat}} 2H_2O(g) + MX(s)$$

Thus, *an acid-base reaction is a proton-transfer process.* In the early 20th century, the chemists Johannes Brønsted and Thomas Lowry stated:

- *An acid is a molecule (or ion) that donates a proton.*
- *A base is a molecule (or ion) that accepts a proton.*

Therefore, in an aqueous reaction between strong acid and strong base, $H_3O^+$ *ion acts as the acid and donates a proton to* $OH^-$ *ion, which acts as the base and accepts it.* (We discuss the Brønsted-Lowry concept thoroughly in Chapter 18.)

**Gas-Forming Reactions: Acids with Carbonates (or Sulfites)** When an ionic carbonate, such as $K_2CO_3$, is treated with an acid, such as HCl, one of the products is carbon dioxide, as the molecular equation shows:

$$2HCl(aq) + K_2CO_3(aq) \longrightarrow 2KCl(aq) + [H_2CO_3(aq)]$$
$$[H_2CO_3(aq)] \longrightarrow H_2O(l) + CO_2(g)$$

Square brackets around a species, in this case, $H_2CO_3$, mean it is very unstable: $H_2CO_3$ decomposes immediately into water and carbon dioxide. Combining these two equations (see Sample Problem 3.17, p. 106) cancels $[H_2CO_3]$ and gives the overall equation:

$$2HCl(aq) + K_2CO_3(aq) \longrightarrow 2KCl(aq) + H_2O(l) + CO_2(g)$$

Writing the total ionic equation with $H_3O^+$ ions from the HCl shows the actual species in solution and the key event in a gas-forming reaction, *removal of ions from solution through formation of both a gas and water:*

$$2H_3O^+(aq) + 2Cl^-(aq) + 2K^+(aq) + CO_3^{2-}(aq) \longrightarrow$$
$$2Cl^-(aq) + 2K^+(aq) + CO_2(g) + H_2O(l) + 2H_2O(l) \quad [or\ 3H_2O(l)]$$

Writing the net ionic equation, with the intermediate formation of $H_2CO_3$, eliminates the spectator ions, $Cl^-$ and $K^+$, and makes it easier to see that *proton transfer* takes place as each of the two $H_3O^+$ ions transfers one proton to the carbonate ion:

$$\overset{\frown\ 2H^+\ \text{transfer}\ \searrow}{2H_3O^+(aq) + CO_3^{2-}(aq)} \longrightarrow [H_2CO_3(aq)] + 2H_2O(l) \longrightarrow$$
$$CO_2(g) + H_2O(l) + 2H_2O(l) \quad [or\ 3H_2O(l)]$$

In essence, this is an acid-base reaction with carbonate ion accepting the protons and, thus, acting as the base.

Ionic sulfites react similarly to form water and gaseous $SO_2$; the net ionic equation, in which $SO_3^{2-}$ acts as the base and forms the unstable $H_2SO_3$, is

$$\overset{\frown\ 2H^+\ \text{transfer}\ \searrow}{2H_3O^+(aq) + SO_3^{2-}(aq)} \longrightarrow [H_2SO_3(aq)] + 2H_2O(l) \longrightarrow$$
$$SO_2(g) + H_2O(l) + 2H_2O(l) \quad [or\ 3H_2O(l)]$$

**Reactions of Weak Acids with Bases** When solutions of sodium hydroxide and the weak acid acetic acid ($CH_3COOH$, Table 4.2) are mixed, the molecular equation is

$$CH_3COOH(aq) + NaOH(aq) \longrightarrow CH_3COONa(aq) + H_2O(l)$$

The total ionic equation is written differently for the reaction of a weak acid. Because acetic acid is weak and, thus, dissociates very little, it appears as *undissociated, intact molecules:*

$$CH_3COOH(aq) + Na^+(aq) + OH^-(aq) \longrightarrow CH_3COO^-(aq) + Na^+(aq) + H_2O(l)$$

The net ionic equation reveals that proton transfer occurs here as well, but directly from the weak acid rather than from $H_3O^+$:

$$\overset{\frown\ H^+\ \text{transfer}\ \searrow}{CH_3COOH(aq) + OH^-(aq)} \longrightarrow CH_3COO^-(aq) + H_2O(l)$$

The only spectator ion is $Na^+(aq)$.

Weak acids also react with carbonates to form $CO_2$, as Figure 4.10 shows for the reaction between vinegar (a 5% solution of acetic acid) and baking soda (sodium

**Figure 4.10  A gas-forming reaction with a weak acid.** Note that the two ionic equations include acetic acid because it does *not* dissociate appreciably into ions.

hydrogen carbonate) solution. In fact, when stomach acid (mostly HCl) builds up, your duodenum releases the hormone secretin, which stimulates your pancreas to release $HCO_3^-$ ions that react with the excess acid in an analogous reaction.

---

**Sample Problem 4.7    Writing Proton-Transfer Equations for Acid-Base Reactions**

**Problem**  Write balanced total and net ionic equations for the following reactions and use curved arrows to show how the proton transfer occurs. For (a), give the name and formula of the salt present when the water evaporates. For (b), note that propionic acid $(CH_3CH_2COOH)$ is a weak acid and identify the spectator ion(s).
**(a)** Hydriodic acid(*aq*) + calcium hydroxide(*aq*) $\longrightarrow$
**(b)** Potassium hydroxide(*aq*) + propionic acid(*aq*) $\longrightarrow$

**Plan**  **(a)** The reactants are a strong acid and a strong base (Table 4.2), so the acidic species is $H_3O^+$, which transfers a proton to the $OH^-$ from the base. The products are $H_2O$ and a solution of spectator ions that becomes a solid salt when the water evaporates.
**(b)** Since the acid is weak, it occurs as intact molecules in solution and transfers its proton to the $OH^-$ from the base. The only spectator ion is the cation of the base.

**Solution**  **(a)** Writing the total ionic equation:

$$2H_3O^+(aq) + 2I^-(aq) + Ca^{2+}(aq) + 2OH^-(aq) \longrightarrow 2I^-(aq) + Ca^{2+}(aq) + 4H_2O(l)$$

Writing the net ionic equation:

$$2H_3O^+(aq) + 2OH^-(aq) \longrightarrow 4H_2O(l) \quad \text{or} \quad H_3O^+(aq) + OH^-(aq) \longrightarrow 2H_2O(l)$$

$I^-(aq)$ and $Ca^{2+}(aq)$ are spectator ions, so the salt is  calcium iodide, $CaI_2$.
**(b)** Writing the total ionic equation:

$$K^+(aq) + OH^-(aq) + CH_3CH_2COOH(aq) \longrightarrow K^+(aq) + H_2O(l) + CH_3CH_2COO^-(aq)$$

Writing the net ionic equation:

$$OH^-(aq) + CH_3CH_2COOH(aq) \longrightarrow H_2O(l) + CH_3CH_2COO^-(aq)$$

$K^+(aq)$ is the only spectator ion.

**Follow-Up Problem 4.7**  Write balanced total and net ionic equations for the reaction between aqueous solutions of calcium hydrogen carbonate and hydrobromic acid. Use a curved arrow in the net ionic equation to show the proton transfer. Give the name and formula of the salt that is present when the water evaporates.

**Figure 4.11** An acid-base titration.

A  Before titration        B  Near end point        C  At end point

$$H^+(aq) + X^-(aq) + M^+(aq) + OH^-(aq) \longrightarrow H_2O(l) + M^+(aq) + X^-(aq)$$

## Quantifying Acid-Base Reactions by Titration

In any **titration,** *the known concentration of one solution is used to determine the unknown concentration of another.* In a typical acid-base titration, a *standardized* solution of base, one whose concentration is *known,* is added to a solution of acid whose concentration is *unknown (or vice versa).*

Figure 4.11A shows the laboratory setup for an acid-base titration with a known volume of acid and a few drops of indicator in a flask. An *acid-base indicator* is a substance whose color is different in acid than in base; the indicator used in the figure is phenolphthalein, which is pink in base and colorless in acid. (We examine indicators in Chapters 18 and 19.) Base is added from a buret, and the $OH^-$ ions react with the $H^+$ ions. As the titration nears its end (Figure 4.11B), the drop of added base creates a temporary excess of $OH^-$, causing some indicator molecules to change to the basic color; they return to the acidic color when the flask is swirled. There are two key stages in the titration:

- The **equivalence point** occurs when *the amount (mol) of $H^+$ ions in the original volume of acid has reacted with the same amount (mol) of $OH^-$ ions from the buret:*

    Amount (mol) of $H^+$ (originally in flask) = amount (mol) of $OH^-$ (added from buret)

- The **end point** occurs when a tiny excess of $OH^-$ ions changes the indicator permanently to its basic color (Figure 4.11C).

In calculations, such as in Sample Problem 4.8, we assume that this tiny excess of $OH^-$ ions is insignificant and that *the amount of base needed to reach the end point is the same as the amount needed to reach the equivalence point.*

---

**Sample Problem 4.8**    **Finding the Concentration of an Acid from a Titration**

**Problem** To standardize an HCl solution, you put 50.00 mL of it in a flask with a few drops of indicator and put 0.1524 *M* NaOH in a buret. The buret reads 0.55 mL at the start and 33.87 mL at the end point. Find the molarity of the HCl solution.

**Plan** We have to find the molarity of the acid from the volume of acid (50.00 mL), the initial (0.55 mL) and final (33.87 mL) volumes of base, and the molarity of the base (0.1524 *M*). First, we balance the equation. The volume of added base is the difference in buret readings, and we use the base's molarity to calculate the amount (mol) of base. Then, we use the molar ratio from the balanced equation to find the amount (mol) of acid originally present and divide by the acid's original volume to find the molarity (see the road map).

**Solution** Writing the balanced equation:

$$NaOH(aq) + HCl(aq) \longrightarrow NaCl(aq) + H_2O(l)$$

Finding the volume (L) of NaOH solution added:

$$\text{Volume (L) of solution} = (33.87 \text{ mL soln} - 0.55 \text{ mL soln}) \times \frac{1 \text{ L}}{1000 \text{ mL}}$$

$$= 0.03332 \text{ L soln}$$

Finding the amount (mol) of NaOH added:

$$\text{Amount (mol) of NaOH} = 0.03332 \text{ L soln} \times \frac{0.1524 \text{ mol NaOH}}{1 \text{ L soln}}$$

$$= 5.078 \times 10^{-3} \text{ mol NaOH}$$

Finding the amount (mol) of HCl originally present: Since the molar ratio is 1/1,

$$\text{Amount (mol) of HCl} = 5.078 \times 10^{-3} \text{ mol NaOH} \times \frac{1 \text{ mol HCl}}{1 \text{ mol NaOH}} = 5.078 \times 10^{-3} \text{ mol HCl}$$

Calculating the molarity of HCl:

$$\text{Molarity of HCl} = \frac{5.078 \times 10^{-3} \text{ mol HCl}}{50.00 \text{ mL}} \times \frac{1000 \text{ mL}}{1 \text{ L}} = \boxed{0.1016 \ M \text{ HCl}}$$

**Check** The answer makes sense: a large volume of less concentrated acid neutralized a small volume of more concentrated base. With rounding, the numbers of moles of $H^+$ and $OH^-$ are about equal: 50 mL $\times$ 0.1 $M$ $H^+$ = 0.005 mol = 33 mL $\times$ 0.15 $M$ $OH^-$.

**Follow-Up Problem 4.8** What volume of 0.1292 $M$ $Ba(OH)_2$ would neutralize 50.00 mL of the HCl solution standardized in Sample Problem 4.8?

**Road Map**

## ■ Summary of Section 4.4

- In an acid-base (neutralization) reaction between an acid (an $H^+$-yielding substance) and a base (an $OH^-$-yielding substance), $H^+$ and $OH^-$ ions form $H_2O$.
- Strong acids and bases dissociate completely in water (strong electrolytes); weak acids and bases dissociate slightly (weak electrolytes).
- An acid-base reaction involves the transfer of a proton from an acid (a species that donates an $H^+$) to a base (a species that accepts an $H^+$).
- A gas-forming acid-base reaction occurs when an acid transfers a proton to a carbonate (or sulfite), forming water and a gas that leaves the reaction mixture.
- Since weak acids dissociate very little, ionic equations show a weak acid as an intact molecule transferring its proton to the base.
- In a titration, the known concentration of one solution is used to determine the concentration of the other.

# 4.5 • OXIDATION-REDUCTION (REDOX) REACTIONS

Oxidation-reduction (redox) reactions include the formation of a compound from its elements (and the reverse process), all combustion processes, the generation of electricity in batteries, the production of cellular energy, and many others. In fact, redox reactions are so widespread that many do not occur in aqueous solution. In this section, we examine the key event in the redox process, discuss important terminology, see one way to balance redox equations, and learn how to quantify them.

## The Key Event: Movement of Electrons Between Reactants

The key chemical event in an **oxidation-reduction** (or **redox**) **reaction** is the *net movement of electrons from one reactant to another*. The movement occurs from the reactant (or atom in the reactant) with *less* attraction for electrons to the reactant (or atom) with *more* attraction for electrons.

**Figure 4.12** The redox process in the formation of (A) ionic and (B) covalent compounds from their elements.

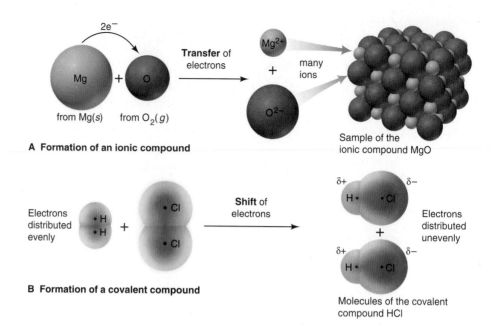

**A Formation of an ionic compound**

**B Formation of a covalent compound**

This process occurs in the formation of both ionic and covalent compounds:

- *Ionic compounds: transfer of electrons.* In the reaction that forms MgO from its elements (see Figure 3.7, p. 100), the balanced equation is

$$2Mg(s) + O_2(g) \longrightarrow 2MgO(s)$$

Figure 4.12A shows that each Mg atom loses two electrons and each O atom gains them. This loss and gain is a ***transfer*** *of electrons* away from each Mg atom to each O atom. The resulting $Mg^{2+}$ and $O^{2-}$ ions aggregate into an ionic solid.

- *Covalent compounds: shift of electrons.* During the formation of a covalent compound from its elements, there is more of a ***shift*** *of electrons* than a full transfer. Thus, *ions do not form.* Consider the formation of HCl gas:

$$H_2(g) + Cl_2(g) \longrightarrow 2HCl(g)$$

To see the electron movement, we'll compare the electron distribution in reactant and product. As Figure 4.12B shows, in $H_2$ and $Cl_2$, the electrons are shared equally between the atoms *(symmetrical shading)*. Because the Cl atom attracts electrons more than the H atom, in HCl, the electrons are shared unequally *(asymmetrical shading)*. Electrons shift away from H and toward Cl, so the Cl atom has more negative charge *(red and δ−)* than it had in $Cl_2$, and the H atom has less negative charge *(blue and δ+)* than it had in $H_2$.

## Some Essential Redox Terminology

Certain key terms describe the process and explain the name of this reaction class:

- **Oxidation** is the *loss* of electrons.
- **Reduction** is the *gain* of electrons.

During the formation of MgO, Mg undergoes oxidation (loss of electrons), and $O_2$ undergoes reduction (gain of electrons). The loss and gain are simultaneous, but we can imagine them occurring separately:

Oxidation (electron loss by Mg):     $Mg \longrightarrow Mg^{2+} + 2e^-$

Reduction (electron gain by $O_2$): $\frac{1}{2}O_2 + 2e^- \longrightarrow O^{2-}$

(Throughout the chapter, blue type indicates oxidation, and red type reduction.)

- The **oxidizing agent** is the species doing the oxidizing (causing the electron loss).
- The **reducing agent** is the species doing the reducing (causing the electron gain).

One reactant acts on the other. During the reaction that forms MgO, *$O_2$ oxidizes Mg,* so $O_2$ is the oxidizing agent, and *Mg reduces $O_2$,* so Mg is the reducing agent.

Note the give and take of electrons: $O_2$ takes the electrons that Mg gives up, or, put the other way around, Mg gives up the electrons that $O_2$ takes. This means that

- *The oxidizing agent is reduced:* it takes electrons (and, thus, gains them).
- *The reducing agent is oxidized:* it gives up electrons (and, thus, loses them).

In the formation of HCl, *$Cl_2$ oxidizes $H_2$* (H loses some electron charge and Cl gains it), which is the same as saying that *$H_2$ reduces $Cl_2$.* The reducing agent, $H_2$, is oxidized, and the oxidizing agent, $Cl_2$, is reduced.

## Using Oxidation Numbers to Monitor Electron Charge

Chemists have devised a "bookkeeping" system to monitor which atom loses electron charge and which atom gains it: each atom in a molecule (or formula unit) is assigned an **oxidation number (O.N.),** or *oxidation state,* which is the charge the atom would have *if* electrons were transferred completely, not shared.

Each element in a binary *ionic* compound has a full charge because the atom transferred its electron(s), and so the atom's oxidation number equals the ionic charge. But, each element in a *covalent* compound (or in a polyatomic ion) has a partial charge because the electrons shifted away from one atom and toward the other. For these cases, we determine oxidation number by a set of rules (Table 4.3; you'll learn the atomic basis of the rules in Chapters 8 and 9).

An O.N. has the sign *before* the number (e.g., +2), whereas an ionic charge has the sign *after* the number (e.g., 2+). Also, unlike a unitary ionic charge, as in $Na^+$ or $Cl^-$, an O.N. of +1 or −1 retains the numeral. For example, we don't write the sodium ion as $Na^{+1}$, but the O.N. of the $Na^+$ ion is +1, not +.

---

### Table 4.3  Rules for Assigning an Oxidation Number (O.N.)

#### General Rules

1. For an atom in its elemental form (Na, $O_2$, $Cl_2$, etc.): O.N. = 0
2. For a monatomic ion: O.N. = ion charge (with the sign *before* the numeral)
3. The sum of O.N. values for the atoms in a molecule or formula unit of a compound equals zero. The sum of O.N. values for the atoms in a polyatomic ion equals the ion's charge.

#### Rules for Specific Atoms or Periodic Table Groups

| | |
|---|---|
| 1. For Group 1A(1): | O.N. = +1 in all compounds |
| 2. For Group 2A(2): | O.N. = +2 in all compounds |
| 3. For hydrogen: | O.N. = +1 in combination with nonmetals |
| | O.N. = −1 in combination with metals and boron |
| 4. For fluorine: | O.N. = −1 in all compounds |
| 5. For oxygen: | O.N. = −1 in peroxides |
| | O.N. = −2 in all other compounds (except with F) |
| 6. For Group 7A(17): | O.N. = −1 in combination with metals, nonmetals (except O), and other halogens lower in the group |

---

### Sample Problem 4.9   Determining the Oxidation Number of Each Element in a Compound (or Ion)

**Problem** Determine the oxidation number (O.N.) of each element in these species:
**(a)** Zinc chloride    **(b)** Sulfur trioxide    **(c)** Nitric acid    **(d)** Dichromate ion

**Plan** We determine the formulas and consult Table 4.3, including the general rules that the O.N. values for a compound add up to zero and those for a polyatomic ion add up to the ion's charge.

**Solution** **(a)** $ZnCl_2$. The sum of O.N.s must equal zero. The O.N. of the $Zn^{2+}$ ion is +2, so the O.N. of each $Cl^-$ ion is −1, for a total of −2.
**(b)** $SO_3$. The O.N. of each oxygen is −2, for a total of −6. The O.N.s must add up to zero, so the O.N. of S is +6.

(c) $HNO_3$. The O.N. of H is $+1$, so the O.N.s of the atoms in $NO_3^-$ must add up to $-1$ to equal the charge of the polyatomic ion and give zero for the compound. The O.N. of each O is $-2$, for a total of $-6$. Therefore, the O.N. of N is $+5$.

(d) $Cr_2O_7^{2-}$. The O.N. of each O is $-2$, so the total for seven O atoms is $-14$. Therefore, each Cr must have an O.N. of $+6$ in order for the sum of the O.N.s to equal the charge of the ion: $+12 + (-14) = -2$.

**Follow-Up Problem 4.9** Determine the O.N. of each element in the following:
(a) Scandium oxide $(Sc_2O_3)$      (b) Gallium chloride $(GaCl_3)$
(c) Hydrogen phosphate ion      (d) Iodine trifluoride

**Using O.N.s to Identify Redox Reactions** A redox reaction is defined as one in which the oxidation numbers of the species change. Sample Problem 4.10 introduces the *tie-line*, a useful device for keeping track of these changes.

---

**Sample Problem 4.10**    **Identifying Redox Reactions**

**Problem** Use oxidation numbers to decide whether each of the following is a redox reaction:
(a) $CaO(s) + CO_2(g) \longrightarrow CaCO_3(s)$
(b) $4KNO_3(s) \longrightarrow 2K_2O(s) + 2N_2(g) + 5O_2(g)$
(c) $H_2SO_4(aq) + 2NaOH(aq) \longrightarrow Na_2SO_4(aq) + 2H_2O(l)$

**Plan** To determine whether a reaction is an oxidation-reduction process, we use Table 4.3 to assign an O.N. to each atom. If an O.N. changes during the reaction, we draw a tie-line from the atom on the left side to the one on the right and note the change.

**Solution** (a)

$$
\underset{CaO(s)}{\overset{+2}{|}\underset{-2}{|}} + \underset{CO_2(g)}{\overset{+4}{|}\underset{-2}{|}} \longrightarrow \underset{CaCO_3(s)}{\overset{+4}{\overset{+2}{|}}\underset{-2}{|}}
$$

Because each atom in the product has the same O.N. that it had in the reactants, we conclude that this is *not* a redox reaction.

(b)

O.N. decreased: *reduction*

$$
\underset{4KNO_3(s)}{\overset{+5}{\overset{+1}{|}\underset{-2}{|}}} \longrightarrow \underset{2K_2O(s)}{\overset{+1 \, -2}{|}} + \underset{2N_2(g)}{\overset{0}{|}} + \underset{5O_2(g)}{\overset{0}{|}}
$$

O.N. increased: *oxidation*

In this case, the O.N. of N changes from $+5$ to 0, and the O.N. of O changes from $-2$ to 0, so this *is* a redox reaction.

(c)

$$
\underset{H_2SO_4(aq)}{\overset{+6}{\overset{+1}{|}\underset{-2}{|}}} + \underset{2NaOH(aq)}{\overset{+1 \, -2}{|}} \longrightarrow \underset{Na_2SO_4(aq)}{\overset{+6}{\overset{+1}{|}\underset{-2}{|}}} + \underset{2H_2O(l)}{\overset{+1-2}{|}}
$$

The O.N. values do not change, so this is *not* a redox reaction.

**Comment** The reaction in (c) is an acid-base reaction in which $H_2SO_4$ transfers two $H^+$ ions to two $OH^-$ ions to form two $H_2O$ molecules. In the net ionic equation,

$$
\underset{H^+(aq)}{\overset{+1}{|}} + \underset{OH^-(aq)}{\overset{+1}{\overset{-2}{|}}} \longrightarrow \underset{H_2O(l)}{\overset{+1-2}{|}}
$$

we see that the O.N. values remain the same on both sides of the equation. Therefore, an acid-base reaction is **not** a redox reaction.

**Follow-Up Problem 4.10** Use oxidation numbers to decide which, if any, of the following equations represents a redox reaction:
(a) $NCl_3(l) + 3H_2O(l) \longrightarrow NH_3(aq) + 3HOCl(aq)$
(b) $AgNO_3(aq) + NH_4I(aq) \longrightarrow AgI(s) + NH_4NO_3(aq)$
(c) $2H_2S(g) + 3O_2(g) \longrightarrow 2SO_2(g) + 2H_2O(g)$

**Using O.N.s to Identify Oxidizing and Reducing Agents** By assigning an oxidation number to each atom, we can see which species was oxidized and which reduced and, thus, which is the oxidizing agent and which the reducing agent:

- If an atom has a higher (more positive or less negative) O.N. in the product than it had in the reactant, the reactant that contains that atom was oxidized (lost electrons) and is the reducing agent. Thus, *oxidation is shown by an increase in O.N.*
- If an atom has a lower (more negative or less positive) O.N. in the product than it had in the reactant, the reactant that contains that atom was reduced (gained electrons) and is the oxidizing agent. Thus, *reduction is shown by a decrease in O.N.*

---

**Sample Problem 4.11**   **Identifying Oxidizing and Reducing Agents**

**Problem** Identify the oxidizing agent and the reducing agent in each of the following:
**(a)** $2Al(s) + 3H_2SO_4(aq) \longrightarrow Al_2(SO_4)_3(aq) + 3H_2(g)$
**(b)** $PbO(s) + CO(g) \longrightarrow Pb(s) + CO_2(g)$
**(c)** $2H_2(g) + O_2(g) \longrightarrow 2H_2O(g)$

**Plan** We assign an O.N. to each atom (or ion). The reducing agent contains an atom that is oxidized (O.N. *increased* from left to right in the equation). The oxidizing agent contains an atom that is reduced (O.N. *decreased*). We mark the changes with tie-lines.

**Solution (a)** Assigning oxidation numbers:

$$\underset{\text{reduction}}{\overset{\text{oxidation}}{2\overset{0}{Al}(s) + 3\overset{+1}{H_2}\overset{+6}{S}\overset{-2}{O_4}(aq) \longrightarrow \overset{+3}{Al_2}(\overset{+6}{S}\overset{-2}{O_4})_3(aq) + 3\overset{0}{H_2}(g)}}$$

The O.N. of Al increased from 0 to +3 (Al lost electrons), so Al was oxidized;
Al is the reducing agent.
The O.N. of H decreased from +1 to 0 (H gained electrons), so $H^+$ was reduced;
$H_2SO_4$ is the oxidizing agent.

**(b)** Assigning oxidation numbers:

$$\underset{\text{reduction}}{\overset{\text{oxidation}}{\overset{+2}{P}\overset{-2}{b}O(s) + \overset{+2}{C}\overset{-2}{O}(g) \longrightarrow \overset{0}{Pb}(s) + \overset{+4}{C}\overset{-2}{O_2}(g)}}$$

Pb decreased its O.N. from +2 to 0, so PbO was reduced; PbO is the oxidizing agent.
C increased its O.N. from +2 to +4, so CO was oxidized; CO is the reducing agent.
When a reactant (in this case, CO) becomes a product with more O atoms ($CO_2$), it is oxidized; when a reactant (PbO) becomes a product with fewer O atoms (Pb), it is reduced.

**(c)** Assigning oxidation numbers:

$$\underset{\text{reduction}}{\overset{\text{oxidation}}{2\overset{0}{H_2}(g) + \overset{0}{O_2}(g) \longrightarrow 2\overset{+1}{H_2}\overset{-2}{O}(g)}}$$

$O_2$ was reduced (O.N. of O decreased from 0 to −2); $O_2$ is the oxidizing agent.
$H_2$ was oxidized (O.N. of H increased from 0 to +1); $H_2$ is the reducing agent.
Oxygen is always the oxidizing agent in a combustion reaction.

**Follow-Up Problem 4.11** Identify each oxidizing agent and each reducing agent:
**(a)** $2Fe(s) + 3Cl_2(g) \longrightarrow 2FeCl_3(s)$   **(b)** $2C_2H_6(g) + 7O_2(g) \longrightarrow 4CO_2(g) + 6H_2O(g)$
**(c)** $5CO(g) + I_2O_5(s) \longrightarrow I_2(s) + 5CO_2(g)$

---

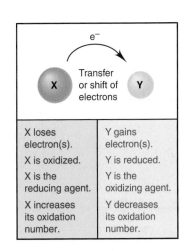

**Figure 4.13** A summary of terminology for redox reactions.

Be sure to remember that *transferred electrons are never free because the reducing agent loses electrons and the oxidizing agent gains them* **simultaneously.** In other words, a complete reaction *cannot* be "an oxidation" *or* "a reduction"; it must be an oxidation-reduction. Figure 4.13 summarizes redox terminology.

## Balancing Redox Equations

We balance a redox reaction by making sure that *the number of electrons lost by the reducing agent equals the number of electrons gained by the oxidizing agent.*

Two methods used to balance redox equations are the *oxidation number* method and the *half-reaction* method. This section describes the oxidation number method; the half-reaction method is covered in Chapter 21. (If your professor chooses to cover the half-reaction method here as well, it is easily transferable.)

The **oxidation number method** consists of five steps that use the changes in oxidation numbers to generate balancing coefficients. The first two steps are identical to those in Sample Problem 4.11:

*Step 1.*    Assign O.N.s to all atoms.
*Step 2.*    From the changes in O.N.s, identify the oxidized and reduced reactants.
*Step 3.*    Compute the numbers of electrons lost in the oxidation and gained in the reduction, and draw tie-lines from the reactant atom to the product atom to show the change.
*Step 4.*    Multiply the numbers of electrons by factor(s) that make the electrons lost equal the electrons gained, and use the factor(s) as balancing coefficients.
*Step 5.*    Complete the balancing by inspection and add states of matter.

---

**Sample Problem 4.12**    **Balancing Redox Equations by the Oxidation Number Method**

**Problem** Use the oxidation number method to balance the following equations:
**(a)** $Cu(s) + HNO_3(aq) \longrightarrow Cu(NO_3)_2(aq) + NO_2(g) + H_2O(l)$
**(b)** $PbS(s) + O_2(g) \longrightarrow PbO(s) + SO_2(g)$

**(a) Reaction of copper and nitric acid**

**Solution** *Step 1.* Assign oxidation numbers to all atoms:

$$\overset{0}{Cu} + \overset{+1}{H}\overset{+5}{N}\overset{-2}{O_3} \longrightarrow \overset{+2}{Cu}(\overset{+5}{N}\overset{-2}{O_3})_2 + \overset{+4}{N}\overset{-2}{O_2} + \overset{+1}{H_2}\overset{-2}{O}$$

*Step 2.* Identify oxidized and reduced reactants. The O.N. of Cu increased from 0 (in Cu metal) to +2 (in $Cu^{2+}$), so Cu was oxidized. The O.N. of N decreased from +5 (in $HNO_3$) to +4 (in $NO_2$), so $HNO_3$ was reduced. Note that some $NO_3^-$ also acts as a spectator ion, appearing unchanged in $Cu(NO_3)_2$.
*Step 3.* Compute $e^-$ lost and $e^-$ gained and draw tie-lines. In the oxidation, $2e^-$ were lost from Cu. In the reduction, $1e^-$ was gained by N:

$$\overset{\text{loses } 2e^-}{Cu + HNO_3 \longrightarrow Cu(NO_3)_2 + NO_2 + H_2O}$$
$$\text{gains } 1e^-$$

*Step 4.* Multiply by factor(s) to make $e^-$ lost equal $e^-$ gained, and use the factor(s) as coefficients. Cu lost $2e^-$, so the $1e^-$ gained by N should be multiplied by 2. We put the coefficient 2 before *both* $NO_2$ and $HNO_3$:

$$Cu + 2HNO_3 \longrightarrow Cu(NO_3)_2 + 2NO_2 + H_2O$$

*Step 5.* Complete the balancing by inspection. Balancing N atoms requires a 4 in front of $HNO_3$ because two additional N atoms are in the $NO_3^-$ ions in $Cu(NO_3)_2$:

$$Cu + 4HNO_3 \longrightarrow Cu(NO_3)_2 + 2NO_2 + H_2O$$

Then, balancing H atoms requires a 2 in front of $H_2O$, and we add states of matter:

$$Cu(s) + 4HNO_3(aq) \longrightarrow Cu(NO_3)_2(aq) + 2NO_2(g) + 2H_2O(l)$$

**Check**

Reactants (1 Cu, 4 H, 4 N, 12 O) $\longrightarrow$ products [1 Cu, 4 H, (2 + 2) N, (6 + 4 + 2) O]

Copper in nitric acid.

**Comment** We often find that some of a species reacts and the rest doesn't. In this case, 2 mol of $NO_3^-$ are reduced to $NO_2$, and 2 mol of $NO_3^-$ are spectator ions.

### (b) Reaction of lead(II) sulfide and oxygen

**Solution** *Step 1.* Assign oxidation numbers to all atoms:

$$\overset{+2}{\underset{}{Pb}}\overset{-2}{\underset{}{S}} + \overset{0}{O_2} \longrightarrow \overset{+2}{\underset{}{Pb}}\overset{-2}{\underset{}{O}} + \overset{+4}{\underset{}{S}}\overset{-2}{\underset{}{O_2}}$$

*Step 2.* Identify oxidized and reduced reactants. The O.N. of S increased from −2 in PbS to +4 in $SO_2$, so PbS was oxidized. The O.N. of O decreased from 0 in $O_2$ to −2 in both PbO and $SO_2$, so $O_2$ was reduced.

*Step 3.* Compute $e^-$ lost and $e^-$ gained and draw tie-lines. In the oxidation, the S lost $6e^-$. In the reduction, each O gained $2e^-$:

$$PbS + O_2 \longrightarrow PbO + SO_2$$

loses $6e^-$
gains $2e^-$
gains $2e^-$

*Step 4.* Multiply by factor(s) to make $e^-$ lost equal $e^-$ gained. The S atom loses $6e^-$, and each O in $O_2$ gains $2e^-$, for a total gain of $4e^-$. Placing the coefficient $\frac{3}{2}$ before $O_2$ gives 3 O atoms that each gain $2e^-$, for a total gain of $6e^-$:

$$PbS + \tfrac{3}{2}O_2 \longrightarrow PbO + SO_2$$

*Step 5.* Complete the balancing by inspection. The atoms are balanced, but we multiply all coefficients by 2 to obtain integers and add states of matter:

$$2PbS(s) + 3O_2(g) \longrightarrow 2PbO(s) + 2SO_2(g)$$

**Check** Reactants (2 Pb, 2 S, 6 O) $\longrightarrow$ products [2 Pb, 2 S, (2 + 4) O]

**Follow-Up Problem 4.12** Use the oxidation number method to balance the following equation: $K_2Cr_2O_7(aq) + HI(aq) \longrightarrow KI(aq) + CrI_3(aq) + I_2(s) + H_2O(l)$.

## Quantifying Redox Reactions by Titration

In an acid-base titration, a known concentration of a base is used to find an unknown concentration of an acid (or vice versa). Similarly, in a redox titration, a known concentration of oxidizing agent is used to find an unknown concentration of reducing agent (or vice versa). This kind of titration has many applications, from measuring the iron content in drinking water to quantifying vitamin C in fruits and vegetables.

The permanganate ion, $MnO_4^-$, is a common oxidizing agent because it is deep purple, and so also serves as an indicator. In Figure 4.14, $MnO_4^-$ is used to determine oxalate ion ($C_2O_4^{2-}$) concentration. As long as $C_2O_4^{2-}$ is present, it reduces the added $MnO_4^-$ to faint pink (nearly colorless) $Mn^{2+}$ (Figure 4.14, *left*). When all the $C_2O_4^{2-}$ has been oxidized, the next drop of $MnO_4^-$ turns the solution light purple (Figure 4.14, *right*). This color change indicates the *end point,* which we assume is the same as the *equivalence point,* the point at which the electrons lost by the oxidized species ($C_2O_4^{2-}$) equal the electrons gained by the reduced species ($MnO_4^-$). We can calculate the $C_2O_4^{2-}$ concentration from the known volume of $Na_2C_2O_4$ solution and the known volume and concentration of $KMnO_4$ solution.

Before titration — $KMnO_4(aq)$

$Na_2C_2O_4(aq)$

At end point

Net ionic equation:

$$2\overset{+7}{Mn}O_4^-(aq) + 5\overset{+3}{C_2}O_4^{2-}(aq) + 16H^+(aq) \longrightarrow 2\overset{+2}{Mn}{}^{2+}(aq) + 10\overset{+4}{C}O_2(g) + 8H_2O(l)$$

**Figure 4.14** The redox titration of $C_2O_4^{2-}$ with $MnO_4^-$.

**Sample Problem 4.13** Finding the Amount of Reducing Agent by Titration

**Problem** Calcium ion ($Ca^{2+}$) is necessary for the clotting of blood and many other physiological processes. To measure the $Ca^{2+}$ concentration in 1.00 mL of human blood, $Na_2C_2O_4$ solution is added, which precipitates the $Ca^{2+}$ as $CaC_2O_4$. This solid is dissolved in dilute $H_2SO_4$ to release $C_2O_4^{2-}$, and 2.05 mL of $4.88\times10^{-4}$ $M$ $KMnO_4$ is required to reach the end point. The balanced equation is

$$2KMnO_4(aq) + 5CaC_2O_4(s) + 8H_2SO_4(aq) \longrightarrow$$
$$2MnSO_4(aq) + K_2SO_4(aq) + 5CaSO_4(s) + 10CO_2(g) + 8H_2O(l)$$

Calculate the amount (mol) of $Ca^{2+}$ in 1.00 mL of blood.

**Plan** We have to find the amount (mol) of $Ca^{2+}$ from the volume (2.05 mL) and concentration ($4.88\times10^{-4}$ $M$) of $KMnO_4$ used to oxidize the $CaC_2O_4$ precipitated from 1.00 mL of blood. We find the amount (mol) of $KMnO_4$ needed to reach the end point and use the molar ratio to find the amount (mol) of $CaC_2O_4$. Then we use the chemical formula, which shows 1 mol of $Ca^{2+}$ for every mol of $CaC_2O_4$.

**Solution** Converting volume (mL) and concentration ($M$) to amount (mol) of $KMnO_4$:

$$\text{Amount (mol) of } KMnO_4 = 2.05 \text{ mL soln} \times \frac{1 \text{ L}}{1000 \text{ mL}} \times \frac{4.88\times10^{-4} \text{ mol } KMnO_4}{1 \text{ L soln}}$$
$$= 1.00\times10^{-6} \text{ mol } KMnO_4$$

Using the molar ratio to convert amount (mol) of $KMnO_4$ to amount (mol) of $CaC_2O_4$:

$$\text{Amount (mol) of } CaC_2O_4 = 1.00\times10^{-6} \text{ mol } KMnO_4 \times \frac{5 \text{ mol } CaC_2O_4}{2 \text{ mol } KMnO_4}$$
$$= 2.50\times10^{-6} \text{ mol } CaC_2O_4$$

Finding the amount (mol) of $Ca^{2+}$:

$$\text{Amount (mol) of } Ca^{2+} = 2.50\times10^{-6} \text{ mol } CaC_2O_4 \times \frac{1 \text{ mol } Ca^{2+}}{1 \text{ mol } CaC_2O_4} = \boxed{2.50\times10^{-6} \text{ mol } Ca^+}$$

**Check** A very small volume of dilute $KMnO_4$ is needed, so $10^{-6}$ mol of $KMnO_4$ seems reasonable. The molar ratio of $CaC_2O_4$ to $KMnO_4$ is 5/2, which gives $2.5\times10^{-6}$ mol of $CaC_2O_4$ and thus $2.5\times10^{-6}$ mol of $Ca^{2+}$.

**Comment 1.** When blood is donated, the receiving bag contains $Na_2C_2O_4$ solution, which precipitates the $Ca^{2+}$ ion to prevent clotting.
**2.** Normal $Ca^{2+}$ concentration in human adult blood is 9.0 to 11.5 mg $Ca^{2+}$/100 mL. If we multiply the amount of $Ca^{2+}$ in 1 mL by 100 and then multiply by the molar mass of Ca (40.08 g/mol), we get $1.0\times10^{-2}$ g, or 10.0 mg $Ca^{2+}$ in 100 mL:

$$\text{Mass (mg) of } Ca^{2+} = \frac{2.50\times10^{-6} \text{ mol } Ca^{2+}}{1 \text{ mL}} \times 100 \text{ mL} \times \frac{40.08 \text{ g } Ca^{2+}}{1 \text{ mol } Ca^{2+}} \times \frac{1000 \text{ mg}}{1 \text{ g}}$$
$$= 10.0 \text{ mg } Ca^{2+}$$

**Follow-Up Problem 4.13** When 2.50 mL of low-fat milk was treated with sodium oxalate and the precipitate dissolved in $H_2SO_4$, 6.53 mL of $4.56\times10^{-3}$ $M$ $KMnO_4$ was required to reach the end point. **(a)** Calculate the molarity of $Ca^{2+}$ in the milk sample. **(b)** What is the concentration of $Ca^{2+}$ in g/L? Is this value consistent with the typical value for milk of about 1.2 g $Ca^{2+}$/L?

**Road Map**

| Volume (mL) of $KMnO_4$ solution |
| :---: |

↓ $10^3$ mL = 1 L

| Volume (L) of $KMnO_4$ solution |
| :---: |

↓ multiply by $M$ (mol/L)

| Amount (mol) of $KMnO_4$ |
| :---: |

↓ molar ratio

| Amount (mol) of $CaC_2O_4$ |
| :---: |

↓ ratio of elements in chemical formula

| Amount (mol) of $Ca^{2+}$ |
| :---: |

# Summary of Section 4.5

- When one reactant has a greater attraction for electrons than another, there is a net movement of electrons, and a redox reaction takes place. Electron gain (reduction) and electron loss (oxidation) occur simultaneously.
- Assigning oxidation numbers to all atoms in a reaction is a method for identifying a redox reaction. The species that is oxidized (contains an atom that increases in oxidation number) is the reducing agent; the species that is reduced (contains an atom that decreases in oxidation number) is the oxidizing agent.
- We balance redox reactions by keeping track of the changes in oxidation number.
- A redox titration determines the concentration of an oxidizing agent from the known concentration of the reducing agent (or vice versa).

# 4.6 • ELEMENTS IN REDOX REACTIONS

In many redox reactions, such as those in Sample Problems 4.11 and 4.12, *atoms occur as an element on one side of an equation and as part of a compound on the other.*\* One way to classify these is by comparing the *numbers* of reactants and products. With that approach, we have three types—*combination, decomposition,* and *displacement;* one other type involving elements is *combustion.* In this section, we survey each type with several examples.

## Combination Redox Reactions

*In a combination redox reaction,* two or more reactants, at least one of which is an element, form a compound:

$$X + Y \longrightarrow Z$$

**Combining Two Elements**  Two elements may react to form binary ionic or covalent compounds. Here are some important examples:

1. *Metal and nonmetal form an ionic compound.* Figure 4.15 shows a typical example, the reaction between the alkali metal potassium and the halogen chlorine, on the macroscopic, atomic, and symbolic levels. Note the change in oxidation numbers in the balanced equation: K is oxidized, so it is the reducing agent; $Cl_2$ is reduced, so it is the oxidizing agent. In fact, whenever a binary ionic compound forms from its elements, *the metal is the reducing agent and the nonmetal is the oxidizing agent.*

---

\*Many other redox reactions, however, do *not* involve elements (see Sample Problem 4.13).

**Figure 4.15** Combining elements to form an ionic compound: potassium metal and chlorine gas form solid potassium chloride. Darker atoms in the atomic view indicate the stoichiometry.

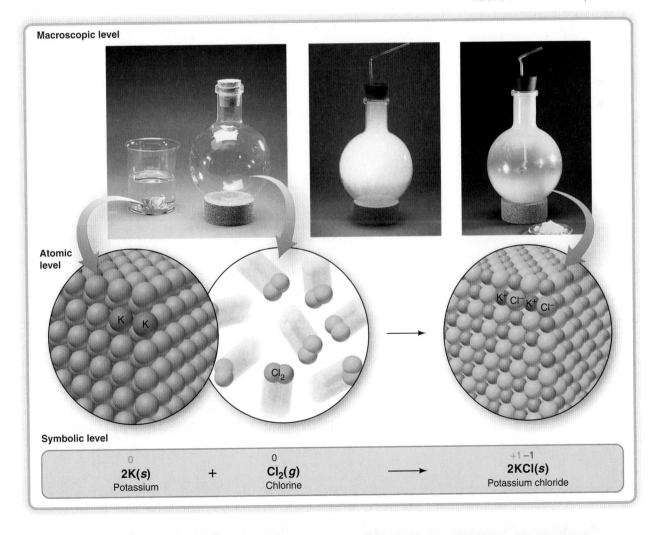

Macroscopic level

Atomic level

K   K

$Cl_2$

$K^+$ $Cl^-$ $K^+$ $Cl^-$

Symbolic level

$$\overset{0}{2K(s)} \quad + \quad \overset{0}{Cl_2(g)} \quad \longrightarrow \quad \overset{+1 \; -1}{2KCl(s)}$$

Potassium       Chlorine            Potassium chloride

Aluminum reacts with $O_2$, as does nearly every metal, to form an ionic oxide:

$$\overset{0}{4Al}(s) + \overset{0}{3O_2}(g) \longrightarrow \overset{+3\,-2}{2Al_2O_3}(s)$$

The $Al_2O_3$ layer on the surface of an aluminum pot prevents oxygen from reacting with the next layer of Al atoms, thus protecting the metal from further oxidation.

2. *Two nonmetals form a covalent compound.* In one of thousands of examples, ammonia forms from nitrogen and hydrogen in a reaction that occurs in industry on an enormous scale:

$$\overset{0}{N_2}(g) + \overset{0}{3H_2}(g) \longrightarrow \overset{-3\;+1}{2NH_3}(g)$$

Halogens react with many other nonmetals, as in the formation of phosphorus trichloride, a reactant in the production of pesticides and other organic compounds:

$$\overset{0}{P_4}(s) + \overset{0}{6Cl_2}(g) \longrightarrow \overset{+3\;-1}{4PCl_3}(l)$$

Nearly every nonmetal reacts with $O_2$ to form a covalent oxide, as when nitrogen monoxide forms from the nitrogen and oxygen in air at the very high temperatures created by lightning and in a car's engine:

$$\overset{0}{N_2}(g) + \overset{0}{O_2}(g) \longrightarrow \overset{+2\;-2}{2NO}(g)$$

**Combining Compound and Element** Many binary covalent compounds react with nonmetals to form larger compounds. Many nonmetal oxides react with additional $O_2$ to form "higher" oxides (those with more O atoms in each molecule). For example,

$$\overset{+2\;-2}{2NO}(g) + \overset{0}{O_2}(g) \longrightarrow \overset{+4\;-2}{2NO_2}(g)$$

Similarly, many nonmetal halides combine with additional halogen to form "higher" halides:

$$\overset{+3\;-1}{PCl_3}(l) + \overset{0}{Cl_2}(g) \longrightarrow \overset{+5\;-1}{PCl_5}(s)$$

## Decomposition Redox Reactions

In a *decomposition redox reaction,* a compound forms two or more products, at least one of which is an element:

$$Z \longrightarrow X + Y$$

In any decomposition reaction, the reactant absorbs enough energy for one or more bonds to break. The energy can take several forms, but the most important are decomposition by heat (thermal) and by electricity (electrolytic). The products are either elements or elements and smaller compounds.

**Thermal Decomposition** When the energy absorbed is heat, the reaction is called a *thermal decomposition.* (A Greek delta, $\Delta$, above the yield arrow indicates strong heating is required.) Many metal oxides, chlorates, and perchlorates release oxygen when strongly heated. Heating potassium chlorate is a method for forming small amounts of oxygen in the laboratory; the same reaction occurs in some explosives and fireworks:

$$\overset{+1\;+5\;-2}{2KClO_3}(s) \overset{\Delta}{\longrightarrow} \overset{+1\;-1}{2KCl}(s) + \overset{0}{3O_2}(g)$$

$$\overset{+2\,-2}{2HgO(s)} \xrightarrow{\Delta} \overset{0}{2Hg(l)} + \overset{0}{O_2(g)}$$

Mercury(II) oxide     Mercury    Oxygen

The decomposition of mercury(II) oxide, used by Lavoisier in his classic experiments, is shown in Figure 4.16. Notice that, in these cases, the lone reactant is the oxidizing *and* the reducing agent. For example, with the reactant HgO, the $O^{2-}$ ion reduces the $Hg^{2+}$ ion, and at the same time, $Hg^{2+}$ oxidizes $O^{2-}$.

**Electrolytic Decomposition** In the process of electrolysis, a compound absorbs electrical energy and decomposes into its elements. In the early 19th century, the observation of the electrolysis of water was crucial for establishing atomic masses:

$$\overset{+1\,-2}{2H_2O(l)} \xrightarrow{\text{electricity}} \overset{0}{2H_2(g)} + \overset{0}{O_2(g)}$$

Many active metals, such as sodium, magnesium, and calcium, are produced industrially by electrolysis of their molten halides:

$$\overset{+2\,-1}{MgCl_2(l)} \xrightarrow{\text{electricity}} \overset{0}{Mg(l)} + \overset{0}{Cl_2(g)}$$

(We examine the details of electrolysis in Chapter 21 and its role in the industrial recovery of several elements in Chapter 22.)

## Displacement Redox Reactions and Activity Series

In any *displacement reaction,* the number of substances on the two sides of the equation remains the same, but atoms (or ions) exchange places. There are two types:

1. In *double*-displacement (metathesis) reactions, such as precipitation and acid-base reactions (Sections 4.3 and 4.4), atoms (or ions) of two *compounds* exchange places; these reactions are *not* redox processes:

$$AB + CD \longrightarrow AC + BD$$

2. In *single*-displacement reactions, one of the substances is an *element;* therefore, *all single-displacement reactions **are** redox processes:*

$$X + YZ \longrightarrow XZ + Y$$

*In solution, single-displacement reactions occur when an atom of one element displaces the ion of another:* if the displacement involves metals, the atom *reduces* the

**Figure 4.17** The active metal lithium displaces hydrogen from water. Only water molecules involved as products of the reaction are red and blue.

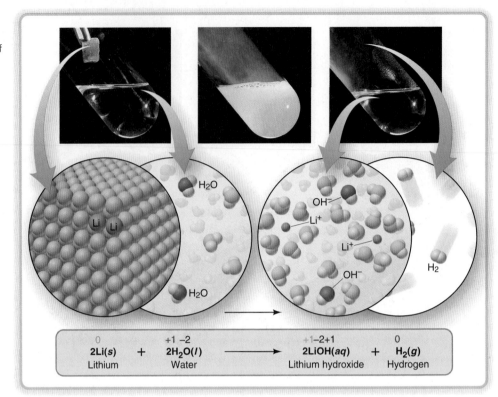

$$\underset{\substack{0 \\ \textbf{2Li}(s) \\ \text{Lithium}}}{} + \underset{\substack{+1\ -2 \\ \textbf{2H}_2\textbf{O}(l) \\ \text{Water}}}{} \longrightarrow \underset{\substack{+1\ -2\ +1 \\ \textbf{2LiOH}(aq) \\ \text{Lithium hydroxide}}}{} + \underset{\substack{0 \\ \textbf{H}_2(g) \\ \text{Hydrogen}}}{}$$

ion; if it involves nonmetals (specifically halogens), the atom *oxidizes* the ion. In two *activity series*—one for metals and one for halogens—the elements are ranked in order of their ability to displace hydrogen (for metals) and one another.

**The Activity Series of the Metals** Metals are ranked by their ability to displace $H_2$ from various sources and another metal from solution. In all displacements of $H_2$, the metal is the reducing agent (O.N. increases), and water or acid is the oxidizing agent (O.N. of H decreases). The activity series of the metals is based on these facts:

- *The most reactive metals displace $H_2$ from liquid water.* Group 1A(1) metals and Ca, Sr, and Ba from Group 2A(2) displace $H_2$ from water (Figure 4.17).
- *Slightly less reactive metals displace $H_2$ from steam.* Heat supplied by steam is needed for less reactive metals such as Al and Zn to displace $H_2$:

$$\underset{\substack{0}}{2Al(s)} + \underset{\substack{+1\ -2}}{6H_2O(g)} \overset{\Delta}{\longrightarrow} \underset{\substack{+3\ -2\ +1}}{2Al(OH)_3(s)} + \underset{\substack{0}}{3H_2(g)}$$

- *Still less reactive metals displace $H_2$ from acids.* The higher concentration of $H^+$ in acid solutions is needed for even less reactive metals such as Ni and Sn to displace $H_2$ (Figure 4.18). For nickel, the net ionic equation is

$$\underset{\substack{0}}{Ni(s)} + \underset{\substack{+1}}{2H^+(aq)} \longrightarrow \underset{\substack{+2}}{Ni^{2+}(aq)} + \underset{\substack{0}}{H_2(g)}$$

- *The least reactive metals cannot displace $H_2$ from any source.* Fortunately, precious metals, such as silver, gold, and platinum, do *not* react with water or acid.
- *An atom of one metal displaces the ion of another.* Comparisons of metal reactivity show, for example, that Zn metal displaces $Cu^{2+}$ ion from aqueous $CuSO_4$:

$$\underset{\substack{+2}}{Cu^{2+}(aq)} + \underset{\substack{+6\ -2}}{SO_4^{2-}(aq)} + \underset{\substack{0}}{Zn(s)} \longrightarrow \underset{\substack{0}}{Cu(s)} + \underset{\substack{+2}}{Zn^{2+}(aq)} + \underset{\substack{+6\ -2}}{SO_4^{2-}(aq)}$$

**Figure 4.18** The displacement of $H_2$ from acid by nickel.

And Figure 4.19 shows that Cu metal displaces silver ($Ag^+$) ion from solution; therefore, zinc is more reactive than copper, which is more reactive than silver.

**Figure 4.19** A more reactive metal (Cu) displacing the ion of a less reactive metal ($Ag^+$) from solution.

Many such reactions form the basis of the **activity series of the metals.** Note these two points from Figure 4.20:

- Elements higher on the list are stronger reducing agents than elements lower down; in other words, any metal can reduce the ions of metals below it.
- From higher to lower, a metal can displace $H_2$ (reduce $H^+$) from water, steam, acid, or not at all.

**Figure 4.20** The activity series of the metals. The most active metal (strongest reducing agent) is at the top, and the least active metal (weakest reducing agent) is at the bottom.

**The Activity Series of the Halogens** Reactivity of the elements decreases down Group 7A(17), so we have

$$F_2 > Cl_2 > Br_2 > I_2$$

A halogen higher in the group is a stronger oxidizing agent than one lower down. Thus, elemental chlorine can oxidize bromide ions (*below*) or iodide ions from solution, and elemental bromine can oxidize iodide ions:

$$\overset{-1}{2Br^-}(aq) + \overset{0}{Cl_2}(aq) \longrightarrow \overset{0}{Br_2}(aq) + \overset{-1}{2Cl^-}(aq)$$

## Combustion Reactions

*Combustion* is the process of combining with oxygen, most commonly with the release of heat and the production of light, as in a flame. Combustion reactions are not classified by the number of reactants and products, but *all of these reactions are redox processes* because elemental oxygen is a reactant:

$$2CO(g) + O_2(g) \longrightarrow 2CO_2(g)$$

The combustion reactions that we commonly use to produce energy involve coal, petroleum, gasoline, natural gas, or wood as a reactant. These mixtures consist of substances with many C—C and C—H bonds, which break during the reaction, and each C and H atom combines with oxygen to form $CO_2$ and $H_2O$. The combustion of butane is typical:

$$2C_4H_{10}(g) + 13O_2(g) \longrightarrow 8CO_2(g) + 10H_2O(g)$$

Biological *respiration* is a multistep combustion process that occurs within our cells when we "burn" foodstuffs, such as glucose, for energy:

$$C_6H_{12}O_6(s) + 6O_2(g) \longrightarrow 6CO_2(g) + 6H_2O(g) + \text{energy}$$

---

**Sample Problem 4.14** | **Identifying the Type of Redox Reaction**

**Problem** Classify each of the following redox reactions as a combination, decomposition, or displacement reaction, write a balanced molecular equation for each, as well as total and net ionic equations for part (c), and identify the oxidizing and reducing agents:
**(a)** Magnesium(*s*) + nitrogen(*g*) $\longrightarrow$ magnesium nitride(*s*)
**(b)** Hydrogen peroxide(*l*) $\longrightarrow$ water + oxygen gas
**(c)** Aluminum(*s*) + lead(II) nitrate(*aq*) $\longrightarrow$ aluminum nitrate(*aq*) + lead(*s*)

**Plan** To decide on reaction type, recall that combination reactions produce fewer products than reactants, decomposition reactions produce more products, and displacement reactions have the same number of reactants and products. The oxidation number (O.N.) becomes more positive for the reducing agent and less positive for the oxidizing agent.

**Solution (a)** Combination: two substances form one. This reaction occurs, along with formation of magnesium oxide, when magnesium burns in air, which is mostly $N_2$:

$$\overset{0}{3Mg}(s) + \overset{0}{N_2}(g) \longrightarrow \overset{+2\ -3}{Mg_3N_2}(s)$$

Mg is the reducing agent; $N_2$ is the oxidizing agent.

**(b)** Decomposition: one substance forms two. Because hydrogen peroxide is very unstable and breaks down from heat, light, or just shaking, this reaction occurs within every bottle of this common household antiseptic:

$$\overset{+1\ -1}{2H_2O_2}(l) \longrightarrow \overset{+1\ -2}{2H_2O}(l) + \overset{0}{O_2}(g)$$

$H_2O_2$ is both the oxidizing *and* the reducing agent. The O.N. of O in peroxides is $-1$. It is shown in blue *and* red because it both increases to 0 in $O_2$ and decreases to $-2$ in $H_2O$.

**(c)** Displacement: two substances form two others. As Figure 4.20 shows, Al is more active than Pb and, thus, displaces it from aqueous solution:

$$2Al(s) + 3Pb(NO_3)_2(aq) \longrightarrow 2Al(NO_3)_3(aq) + 3Pb(s)$$

Al is the reducing agent; $Pb(NO_3)_2$ is the oxidizing agent.

The total ionic equation is

$$2Al(s) + 3Pb^{2+}(aq) + 6NO_3^-(aq) \longrightarrow 2Al^{3+}(aq) + 6NO_3^-(aq) + 3Pb(s)$$

The net ionic equation is

$$2Al(s) + 3Pb^{2+}(aq) \longrightarrow 2Al^{3+}(aq) + 3Pb(s)$$

**Follow-Up Problem 4.14** Classify each of the following redox reactions as a combination, decomposition, or displacement reaction, write a balanced molecular equation for each, as well as total and net ionic equations for parts (b) and (c), and identify the oxidizing and reducing agents:

**(a)** $S_8(s) + F_2(g) \longrightarrow SF_4(g)$
**(b)** $CsI(aq) + Cl_2(aq) \longrightarrow CsCl(aq) + I_2(aq)$
**(c)** $Ni(NO_3)_2(aq) + Cr(s) \longrightarrow Ni(s) + Cr(NO_3)_3(aq)$

## ■ Summary of Section 4.6

- A reaction that has an element as reactant or product is a redox reaction.
- In combination redox reactions, elements combine to form a compound, or a compound and an element combine.
- In decomposition redox reactions, compounds break down by absorption of heat or electricity into elements or into a compound and an element.
- In displacement redox reactions, one element displaces the ion of another from solution.
- Activity series rank elements in order of ability to displace each other. A more reactive metal can displace (reduce) hydrogen ion or the ion of a less reactive metal from solution. A more reactive halogen can displace (oxidize) the ion of a less reactive halogen from solution.
- Combustion releases heat through a redox reaction of a substance with $O_2$.

## 4.7 • THE REVERSIBILITY OF REACTIONS AND THE EQUILIBRIUM STATE

So far, we have viewed reactions as transformations of reactants into products that proceed until they are complete, that is, until the limiting reactant is used up. However, many reactions stop before this happens because two opposing reactions are taking place simultaneously: the forward (left-to-right) reaction continues, but the reverse (right-to-left) reaction occurs just as fast (at the same rate). At this point, *no further changes appear in the amounts of reactants or products,* and the reaction mixture has reached **dynamic equilibrium.** On the macroscopic level, the reaction is *static,* but it is *dynamic* on the molecular level.

In principle, *every reaction is reversible and will reach dynamic equilibrium if all the reactants and products are present.* Consider the reversible breakdown and formation of calcium carbonate. When heated, it breaks down to calcium oxide and carbon dioxide:

$$CaCO_3(s) \xrightarrow{\Delta} CaO(s) + CO_2(g) \text{ [breakdown]}$$

And it forms when calcium oxide and carbon dioxide react:

$$CaO(s) + CO_2(g) \longrightarrow CaCO_3(s) \text{ [formation]}$$

Let's study this process with two experiments:

1. We place $CaCO_3$ in an *open* steel container and heat it to approximately 900°C (Figure 4.21A). The $CaCO_3$ starts breaking down to $CaO$ and $CO_2$, and the $CO_2$ escapes from the open container. The reaction goes to completion because the reverse reaction (formation) cannot occur in the absence of $CO_2$.

2. We perform the same experiment in a *closed* container (Figure 4.21B). The breakdown (forward reaction) starts as before, but soon the $CaO$ and $CO_2$ start reacting with each other (formation). Gradually, with time, as the amounts of $CaO$ and $CO_2$ increase, the formation reaction speeds up. Eventually, the reverse reaction (formation) occurs as fast as the forward reaction (breakdown), and the amounts of $CaCO_3$, $CaO$, and $CO_2$ no longer change: the system has reached a state of equilibrium. We indicate this condition with a pair of arrows pointing in opposite directions:

$$CaCO_3(s) \rightleftharpoons CaO(s) + CO_2(g)$$

In contrast to the reaction in the open container, equilibrium *is* reached because *all the substances remain in contact with each other.*

**A Nonequilibrium system**

**B Equilibrium system**

**Figure 4.21 The equilibrium state. A,** In an *open* container, $CaCO_3$ breaks down completely because $CO_2$ escapes. **B,** In a *closed* container, $CaCO_3$ breakdown and formation reach equilibrium.

Reaction reversibility applies to other systems as well:

1. *Weak acids in water.* Weak acids dissociate very little into ions in water because the dissociation becomes balanced by a reassociation of $H_3O^+$ with the anion to re-form the weak acid and water. For example, when acetic acid dissolves, some $CH_3COOH$ molecules transfer a proton to $H_2O$ and form $H_3O^+$ and $CH_3COO^-$ ions. As more ions form, the ions react with each other more often to re-form acetic acid and water:

$$CH_3COOH(aq) + H_2O(l) \rightleftharpoons H_3O^+(aq) + CH_3COO^-(aq)$$

In fact, in 0.1 $M$ $CH_3COOH$ at 25°C, only about 1.3% of acid molecules are dissociated! Each weak acid dissociates to its own extent. For example, under the same conditions, propionic acid ($CH_3CH_2COOH$) is 1.1% dissociated, and hydrofluoric acid (HF) is 8.6% dissociated.

2. *Weak bases in water.* Similarly, the weak base ammonia reacts with water to form $NH_4^+$ and $OH^-$ ions. As more ions form, they interact more often to re-form ammonia and water, and the rates of the forward and reverse reactions soon balance:

$$NH_3(aq) + H_2O(l) \rightleftharpoons NH_4^+(aq) + OH^-(aq)$$

The weak base methylamine ($CH_3NH_2$) reacts with water to a greater extent than ammonia does before reaching equilibrium, and the weak base aniline ($C_6H_5NH_2$) reacts to a lesser extent.

3. *Gas-forming reactions.* When an acid reacts with a carbonate, the reaction goes to completion in an open container because the $CO_2$ escapes. But, if the container is closed to keep the $CO_2$ present, the reverse reaction takes place and the mixture reaches equilibrium.

4. *Other acid-base and precipitation reactions.* These processes seem to "go to completion" because the ions become tied up in the product, either as water (acid-base) or as an insoluble solid (precipitation), and are not available to re-form reactants. In truth, though, water and ionic precipitates do dissociate to an extremely small extent, so these reactions also reach equilibrium, but the final reaction mixture consists of *almost* all product.

Thus, some reactions proceed very little before reaching equilibrium, others proceed almost to completion, and still others reach equilibrium with significant amounts of both reactants *and* products present. In Chapter 20, we'll examine the factors that determine to what extent a reaction proceeds.

Dynamic equilibrium occurs in many natural systems, from the cycling of water in the environment to the nuclear processes occurring in stars. We examine equilibrium in chemical and physical systems in Chapters 12, 13, and 17 through 21.

## ▌ Summary of Section 4.7

- Every reaction is reversible if all the substances involved are present.
- As the amounts of products increase, the reactants begin to re-form. When the reverse reaction occurs as rapidly as the forward reaction, the amounts of the substances no longer change, and the reaction mixture has reached dynamic equilibrium.
- Weak acids and bases reach equilibrium in water with a very small proportion of their molecules dissociated.
- An aqueous ionic reaction "goes to completion" because a product is removed (gas) or products are formed that react very slightly in a reverse reaction (water or precipitate).

# CHAPTER REVIEW GUIDE

**Learning Objectives** Relevant section (§) and/or sample problem (SP) numbers appear in parentheses.

## Understand These Concepts

1. Why water is a polar molecule and how it dissociates ionic compounds into ions (§4.1)
2. The differing nature of the species present when ionic and covalent compounds dissolve in water (§4.1)
3. The distinctions among strong electrolytes, weak electrolytes, and nonelectrolytes (§4.1, §4.4)
4. The three types of equations that specify the species and the chemical change in an aqueous ionic reaction (§4.2)
5. The key event in three classes of aqueous ionic reactions (§4.3–§4.5)
6. How to decide whether a precipitation reaction occurs (§4.3)
7. The distinction between strong and weak aqueous acids and bases (§4.4)
8. How acid-base reactions are proton transfers; how carbonates (and sulfites) act as bases in gas-forming reactions (§4.4)
9. The distinction between a transfer and a shift of electrons in the formation of ionic and covalent compounds (§4.5)
10. The relation between change in oxidation number and identity of oxidizing and reducing agents (§4.5)
11. The presence of elements in combination, decomposition, and displacement redox reactions; the meaning of an activity series (§4.6)
12. The balance between forward and reverse reactions in dynamic equilibrium; why some acids and bases are weak (§4.7)

## Master These Skills

1. Using molecular scenes to depict a soluble ionic compound in water (SP 4.1)
2. Using the formula of a compound to find the number of moles of ions in solution (SP 4.2)
3. Predicting whether a precipitation reaction occurs (SP 4.3)
4. Using molecular depictions to understand a precipitation reaction (SP 4.4)
5. Determining the number of $H^+$ (or $OH^-$) ions in an aqueous acid (or base) solution (SP 4.5)
6. Writing ionic equations to describe precipitation and acid-base reactions (SPs 4.3, 4.4, 4.6)
7. Writing acid-base equations as proton transfers (SP 4.7)
8. Calculating an unknown concentration from an acid-base or redox titration (SPs 4.8, 4.13)
9. Determining the oxidation number of any element in a compound (SP 4.9)
10. Identifying redox reactions from changes in O.N.s (SP 4.10)
11. Identifying the oxidizing and reducing agents in a redox reaction (SP 4.11)
12. Balancing redox reactions by the oxidation number method (SP 4.12)
13. Distinguishing among combination, decomposition, and displacement redox reactions (SP 4.14)
14. Predicting the products of a single-dissociation reaction based on an activity series (§4.6)

## Key Terms    Page numbers appear in parentheses.

**Section 4.1**
polar molecule (136)
solvated (136)
electrolyte (137)
nonelectrolyte (139)

**Section 4.2**
molecular equation (140)
total ionic equation (141)
spectator ion (141)
net ionic equation (141)

**Section 4.3**
precipitation reaction (141)
precipitate (141)
metathesis reaction (143)

**Section 4.4**
acid-base (neutralization) reaction (145)
acid (145)
base (145)
salt (148)

titration (152)
equivalence point (152)
end point (152)

**Section 4.5**
oxidation-reduction (redox) reaction (153)
oxidation (154)
reduction (154)
oxidizing agent (154)
reducing agent (154)

oxidation number (O.N.) (or oxidation state) (155)
oxidation number method (158)

**Section 4.6**
activity series of the metals (165)

**Section 4.7**
dynamic equilibrium (167)

## Brief Solutions to Follow-Up Problems

**4.1** The compound is $BaCl_2$.

$$\text{Mass (g) of } BaCl_2 = 9 \text{ particles} \times \frac{0.05 \text{ mol particles}}{1 \text{ particle}}$$
$$\times \frac{1 \text{ mol } BaCl_2}{3 \text{ mol particles}} \times \frac{208.2 \text{ g } BaCl_2}{1 \text{ mol } BaCl_2}$$
$$= 31.2 \text{ g } BaCl_2$$

**4.2** (a) $KClO_4(s) \xrightarrow{H_2O} K^+(aq) + ClO_4^-(aq)$;
2 mol of $K^+$ and 2 mol of $ClO_4^-$

(b) $Mg(C_2H_3O_2)_2(s) \xrightarrow{H_2O} Mg^{2+}(aq) + 2C_2H_3O_2^-(aq)$;
2.49 mol of $Mg^{2+}$ and 4.97 mol of $C_2H_3O_2^-$

(c) $(NH_4)_2CrO_4(s) \xrightarrow{H_2O} 2NH_4^+(aq) + CrO_4^{2-}(aq)$;
6.24 mol of $NH_4^+$ and 3.12 mol of $CrO_4^{2-}$

(d) $NaHSO_4(s) \xrightarrow{H_2O} Na^+(aq) + HSO_4^-(aq)$;
0.73 mol of $Na^+$ and 0.73 mol of $HSO_4^-$

**4.3** (a) $Fe^{3+}(aq) + 3Cl^-(aq) + 3Cs^+(aq) + PO_4^{3-}(aq) \longrightarrow$
$$FePO_4(s) + 3Cl^-(aq) + 3Cs^+(aq)$$
$Fe^{3+}(aq) + PO_4^{3-}(aq) \longrightarrow FePO_4(s)$

(b) $2Na^+(aq) + 2OH^-(aq) + Cd^{2+}(aq) + 2NO_3^-(aq) \longrightarrow$
$$2Na^+(aq) + 2NO_3^-(aq) + Cd(OH)_2(s)$$
$2OH^-(aq) + Cd^{2+}(aq) \longrightarrow Cd(OH)_2(s)$
(c) No reaction occurs
(d) $2Ag^+(aq) + 2NO_3^-(aq) + Ba^{2+}(aq) + 2Cl^-(aq) \longrightarrow$
$$2AgCl(s) + 2NO_3^-(aq) + Ba^{2+}(aq)$$
$Ag^+(aq) + Cl^-(aq) \longrightarrow AgCl(s)$

**4.4** (a) Beaker A contains a solution of $Zn(NO_3)_2$.
(b) Beaker B contains a solution of $Ba(OH)_2$.
(c) The precipitate is zinc hydroxide, and the spectator ions are $Ba^{2+}$ and $NO_3^-$.
Molecular: $Zn(NO_3)_2(aq) + Ba(OH)_2(aq) \longrightarrow$
$$Zn(OH)_2(s) + Ba(NO_3)_2(aq)$$
Total ionic:
$Zn^{2+}(aq) + 2NO_3^-(aq) + Ba^{2+}(aq) + 2OH^-(aq) \longrightarrow$
$$Zn(OH)_2(s) + Ba^{2+}(aq) + 2NO_3^-(aq)$$
Net ionic: $Zn^{2+}(aq) + 2OH^-(aq) \longrightarrow Zn(OH)_2(s)$
(d) The $OH^-$ ion is limiting.
Mass (g) of $Zn(OH)_2$

$$= 6 \text{ OH}^- \text{ particles} \times \frac{0.050 \text{ mol OH}^- \text{ ions}}{1 \text{ OH}^- \text{ particle}}$$
$$\times \frac{1 \text{ mol Zn(OH)}_2}{2 \text{ mol OH}^- \text{ ions}} \times \frac{99.43 \text{ g Zn(OH)}_2}{1 \text{ mol Zn(OH)}_2}$$
$$= 15 \text{ g Zn(OH)}_2$$

**4.5** No. of $OH^-$ ions $= 451 \text{ mL} \times \dfrac{1 \text{ L}}{10^3 \text{ mL}}$

$$\times \frac{1.20 \text{ mol KOH}}{1 \text{ L soln}} \times \frac{1 \text{ mol OH}^-}{1 \text{ mol KOH}}$$
$$\times \frac{6.022 \times 10^{23} \text{ OH}^- \text{ ions}}{1 \text{ mol OH}^-}$$
$$= 3.26 \times 10^{23} \text{ OH}^-$$

**4.6** $Ca(OH)_2(aq) + 2HNO_3(aq) \longrightarrow Ca(NO_3)_2(aq) + 2H_2O(l)$
$Ca^{2+}(aq) + 2OH^-(aq) + 2H^+(aq) + 2NO_3^-(aq) \longrightarrow$
$$Ca^{2+}(aq) + 2NO_3^-(aq) + 2H_2O(l)$$
$H^+(aq) + OH^-(aq) \longrightarrow H_2O(l)$

**4.7** $2H_3O^+(aq) + 2Br^-(aq) + Ca^{2+}(aq) + 2HCO_3^-(aq) \longrightarrow$
$$2CO_2(g) + 4H_2O(l) + 2Br^-(aq) + Ca^{2+}(aq)$$
or $H_3O^+(aq) + HCO_3^-(aq) \longrightarrow CO_2(g) + 2H_2O(l)$
The salt is calcium bromide, $CaBr_2$.

**4.8** $Ba(OH)_2(aq) + 2HCl(aq) \longrightarrow BaCl_2(aq) + 2H_2O(l)$
Volume (L) of soln

$$= 50.00 \text{ mL HCl soln} \times \frac{1 \text{ L}}{10^3 \text{ mL}} \times \frac{0.1016 \text{ mol HCl}}{1 \text{ L soln}}$$
$$\times \frac{1 \text{ mol Ba(OH)}_2}{2 \text{ mol HCl}} \times \frac{1 \text{ L soln}}{0.1292 \text{ mol Ba(OH)}_2}$$
$$= 0.01966 \text{ L}$$

**4.9** (a) O.N. of Sc $= +3$; O.N. of O $= -2$
(b) O.N. of Ga $= +3$; O.N. of Cl $= -1$
(c) O.N. of H $= +1$; O.N. of P $= +5$; O.N. of O $= -2$
(d) O.N. of I $= +3$; O.N. of F $= -1$

**4.10**
(a) $NCl_3(l) + 3H_2O(l) \longrightarrow NH_3(aq) + 3HOCl(aq)$
Redox; O.N. of N decreases, and O.N. of Cl increases.

(b) $AgNO_3(aq) + NH_4I(aq) \longrightarrow AgI(s) + NH_4NO_3(aq)$
Not redox; no changes in O.N. values.

(c) $2H_2S(g) + 3O_2(g) \longrightarrow 2SO_2(g) + 2H_2O(g)$
Redox; O.N. of S increases, and O.N. of O decreases.

**4.11** (a) Fe is the reducing agent; $Cl_2$ is the oxidizing agent.
(b) $C_2H_6$ is the reducing agent; $O_2$ is the oxidizing agent.
(c) CO is the reducing agent; $I_2O_5$ is the oxidizing agent.

**4.12** $K_2Cr_2O_7(aq) + 14HI(aq) \longrightarrow$
$$2KI(aq) + 2CrI_3(aq) + 3I_2(s) + 7H_2O(l)$$

**4.13** (a) Amount (mol) of $Ca^{2+}$

$$= 6.53 \text{ mL soln} \times \frac{1 \text{ L}}{10^3 \text{ mL}} \times \frac{4.56 \times 10^{-3} \text{ mol KMnO}_4}{1 \text{ L soln}}$$
$$\times \frac{5 \text{ mol CaC}_2O_4}{2 \text{ mol KMnO}_4} \times \frac{1 \text{ mol Ca}^{2+}}{1 \text{ mol CaC}_2O_4}$$
$$= 7.44 \times 10^{-5} \text{ mol Ca}^{2+}$$

Molarity of $Ca^{2+} = \dfrac{7.44 \times 10^{-2} \text{ mol Ca}^{2+}}{2.50 \text{ mL milk}} \times \dfrac{10^3 \text{ mL}}{1 \text{ L}}$
$$= 2.98 \times 10^{-2} \text{ M Ca}^{2+}$$

(b) Conc. of $Ca^{2+}$ (g/L) $= \dfrac{2.98 \times 10^{-2} \text{ mol Ca}^{2+}}{1 \text{ L}} \times \dfrac{40.08 \text{ g Ca}^{2+}}{1 \text{ mol Ca}^{2+}}$
$$= \frac{1.19 \text{ g Ca}^{2+}}{1 \text{ L}}$$

Yes, the calculated value is close to the typical value.

**4.14** (a) Combination: $S_8(s) + 16F_2(g) \longrightarrow 8SF_4(g)$
$S_8$ is the reducing agent; $F_2$ is the oxidizing agent.
(b) Displacement:
$2CsI(aq) + Cl_2(aq) \longrightarrow 2CsCl(aq) + I_2(aq)$
$2Cs^+(aq) + 2I^-(aq) + Cl_2(aq) \longrightarrow 2Cs^+(aq) + 2Cl^-(aq) + I_2(aq)$
$2I^-(aq) + Cl_2(aq) \longrightarrow 2Cl^-(aq) + I_2(aq)$
$Cl_2$ is the oxidizing agent; CsI is the reducing agent.
(c) Displacement:
$3Ni(NO_3)_2(aq) + 2Cr(s) \longrightarrow 3Ni(s) + 2Cr(NO_3)_3(aq)$
$3Ni^{2+}(aq) + 6NO_3^-(aq) + 2Cr(s) \longrightarrow$
$$3Ni(s) + 2Cr^{3+}(aq) + 6NO_3^-(aq)$$
$3Ni^{2+}(aq) + 2Cr(s) \longrightarrow 3Ni(s) + 2Cr^{3+}(aq)$
Cr is the reducing agent; $Ni(NO_3)_2$ is the oxidizing agent.

## PROBLEMS

Problems with **colored** numbers are answered in Appendix E and worked in detail in the Student Solutions Manual. Problem sections match those in the text and provide the numbers of relevant sample problems. Most offer Concept Review Questions, Skill-Building Exercises (grouped in pairs covering the same concept), and Problems in Context. The Comprehensive Problems are based on material from any section or previous chapter.

### The Role of Water as a Solvent
(Sample Problems 4.1 and 4.2)

**Concept Review Questions**

**4.1** What two factors cause water to be polar?

**4.2** What types of substances are most likely to be soluble in water?

**4.3** What must be present in an aqueous solution for it to conduct an electric current? What general classes of compounds form solutions that conduct?

**4.4** What occurs on the molecular level when an ionic compound dissolves in water?

**4.5** Which of the following scenes best represents how the ions occur in an aqueous solution of: (a) $CaCl_2$; (b) $Li_2SO_4$; (c) $NH_4Br$?

**4.6** Which of the following scenes best represents a volume from a solution of magnesium nitrate?

= magnesium ion     = nitrate ion

**4.7** Why are some ionic compounds soluble in water and others are not?

**4.8** Why are some covalent compounds soluble in water and others are not?

**4.9** Some covalent compounds dissociate into ions in water. What atom do these compounds have in their structures? What type of solution do they form? Name three examples of such a solution.

**Skill-Building Exercises** (grouped in similar pairs)

**4.10** Is each of the following very soluble in water? Explain.
(a) Benzene, $C_6H_6$          (b) Sodium hydroxide
(c) Ethanol, $CH_3CH_2OH$       (d) Potassium acetate

**4.11** Is each of the following very soluble in water? Explain.
(a) Lithium nitrate            (b) Glycine, $H_2NCH_2COOH$
(c) Pentane                    (d) Ethylene glycol, $HOCH_2CH_2OH$

**4.12** Does an aqueous solution of each of the following conduct an electric current? Explain.
(a) Cesium bromide          (b) Hydrogen iodide

**4.13** Does an aqueous solution of each of the following conduct an electric current? Explain.
(a) Potassium sulfate          (b) Sucrose, $C_{12}H_{22}O_{11}$

**4.14** How many total moles of ions are released when each of the following dissolves in water?
(a) 0.32 mol of $NH_4Cl$        (b) 25.4 g of $Ba(OH)_2·8H_2O$
(c) $3.55×10^{19}$ formula units of LiCl

**4.15** How many total moles of ions are released when each of the following dissolves in water?
(a) 0.805 mol of $Rb_2SO_4$      (b) $3.85×10^{-3}$ g of $Ca(NO_3)_2$
(c) $4.03×10^{19}$ formula units of $Sr(HCO_3)_2$

**4.16** How many total moles of ions are released when each of the following dissolves in water?
(a) 0.75 mol of $K_3PO_4$        (b) $6.88×10^{-3}$ g of $NiBr_2·3H_2O$
(c) $2.23×10^{22}$ formula units of $FeCl_3$

**4.17** How many total moles of ions are released when each of the following dissolves in water?
(a) 0.734 mol of $Na_2HPO_4$      (b) 3.86 g of $CuSO_4·5H_2O$
(c) $8.66×10^{20}$ formula units of $NiCl_2$

**4.18** How many moles and how many ions of each type are present in each of the following?
(a) 130. mL of 0.45 $M$ aluminum chloride
(b) 9.80 mL of a solution containing 2.59 g lithium sulfate/L
(c) 245 mL of a solution containing $3.68×10^{22}$ formula units of potassium bromide per liter

**4.19** How many moles and how many ions of each type are present in each of the following?
(a) 88 mL of 1.75 $M$ magnesium chloride
(b) 321 mL of a solution containing 0.22 g aluminum sulfate/L
(c) 1.65 L of a solution containing $8.83×10^{21}$ formula units of cesium nitrate per liter

**4.20** How many moles of $H^+$ ions are present in the following aqueous solutions?
(a) 1.40 L of 0.25 $M$ perchloric acid
(b) 6.8 mL of 0.92 $M$ nitric acid
(c) 2.6 L of 0.085 $M$ hydrochloric acid

**4.21** How many moles of $H^+$ ions are present in the following aqueous solutions?
(a) 1.4 mL of 0.75 $M$ hydrobromic acid
(b) 2.47 mL of 1.98 $M$ hydriodic acid
(c) 395 mL of 0.270 $M$ nitric acid

**Problems in Context**

**4.22** To study a marine organism, a biologist prepares a 1.00-kg sample to simulate the ion concentrations in seawater. She mixes 26.5 g of NaCl, 2.40 g of $MgCl_2$, 3.35 g of $MgSO_4$, 1.20 g of $CaCl_2$, 1.05 g of KCl, 0.315 g of $NaHCO_3$, and 0.098 g of NaBr in distilled water. (a) If the density of the solution is 1.025 $g/cm^3$, what is the molarity of each ion? (b) What is the total molarity of alkali metal ions? (c) What is the total molarity of alkaline earth metal ions? (d) What is the total molarity of anions?

**4.23** Water "softeners" remove metal ions such as $Ca^{2+}$ and $Fe^{3+}$ by replacing them with enough $Na^+$ ions to maintain the same number of positive charges in the solution. If $1.0 \times 10^3$ L of "hard" water is 0.015 $M$ $Ca^{2+}$ and 0.0010 $M$ $Fe^{3+}$, how many moles of $Na^+$ are needed to replace these ions?

## Writing Equations for Aqueous Ionic Reactions

### Concept Review Questions

**4.24** Which ions do not appear in a net ionic equation? Why?

**4.25** Write two sets of equations (both molecular and total ionic) with different reactants that have the same net ionic equation as the following equation:

$$Ba(NO_3)_2(aq) + Na_2CO_3(aq) \longrightarrow BaCO_3(s) + 2NaNO_3(aq)$$

## Precipitation Reactions

(Sample Problems 4.3 and 4.4)

### Concept Review Questions

**4.26** Why do some pairs of ions precipitate and others do not?

**4.27** Use Table 4.1 to determine which of the following combinations leads to a precipitation reaction. How can you identify the spectator ions in the reaction?
(a) Calcium nitrate(*aq*) + sodium chloride(*aq*) $\longrightarrow$
(b) Potassium chloride(*aq*) + lead(II) nitrate(*aq*) $\longrightarrow$

**4.28** The beakers represent the aqueous reaction of $AgNO_3$ and NaCl. Silver ions are gray. What colors are used to represent $NO_3^-$, $Na^+$, and $Cl^-$? Write molecular, total ionic, and net ionic equations for the reaction.

**Skill-Building Exercises** (grouped in similar pairs)

**4.29** Complete the following precipitation reactions with balanced molecular, total ionic, and net ionic equations:
(a) $Hg_2(NO_3)_2(aq) + KI(aq) \longrightarrow$
(b) $FeSO_4(aq) + Sr(OH)_2(aq) \longrightarrow$

**4.30** Complete the following precipitation reactions with balanced molecular, total ionic, and net ionic equations:
(a) $CaCl_2(aq) + Cs_3PO_4(aq) \longrightarrow$
(b) $Na_2S(aq) + ZnSO_4(aq) \longrightarrow$

**4.31** When each of the following pairs of aqueous solutions is mixed, does a precipitation reaction occur? If so, write balanced molecular, total ionic, and net ionic equations:
(a) Sodium nitrate + copper(II) sulfate
(b) Ammonium bromide + silver nitrate

**4.32** When each of the following pairs of aqueous solutions is mixed, does a precipitation reaction occur? If so, write balanced molecular, total ionic, and net ionic equations:
(a) Potassium carbonate + barium hydroxide
(b) Aluminum nitrate + sodium phosphate

**4.33** When each of the following pairs of aqueous solutions is mixed, does a precipitation reaction occur? If so, write balanced molecular, total ionic, and net ionic equations.
(a) Potassium chloride + iron(III) nitrate
(b) Ammonium sulfate + barium chloride

**4.34** When each of the following pairs of aqueous solutions is mixed, does a precipitation reaction occur? If so, write balanced molecular, total ionic, and net ionic equations:
(a) Sodium sulfide + nickel(II) sulfate
(b) Lead(II) nitrate + potassium bromide

**4.35** If 38.5 mL of lead(II) nitrate solution reacts completely with excess sodium iodide solution to yield 0.628 g of precipitate, what is the molarity of lead(II) ion in the original solution?

**4.36** If 25.0 mL of silver nitrate solution reacts with excess potassium chloride solution to yield 0.842 g of precipitate, what is the molarity of silver ion in the original solution?

**4.37** With ions shown as spheres and solvent molecules omitted for clarity, the circle (*right*) illustrates the solid formed when a solution containing $K^+$, $Mg^{2+}$, $Ag^+$, or $Pb^{2+}$ (*blue*) is mixed with one containing $ClO_4^-$, $NO_3^-$, or $SO_4^{2-}$ (*yellow*). (a) Identify the solid. (b) Write a balanced net ionic equation for the reaction. (c) If each sphere represents $5.0 \times 10^{-4}$ mol of ion, what mass of product forms?

**4.38** The precipitation reaction between 25.0 mL of a solution containing a cation (*purple*) and 35.0 mL of a solution containing an anion (*green*) is depicted below (with ions shown as spheres and solvent molecules omitted for clarity).

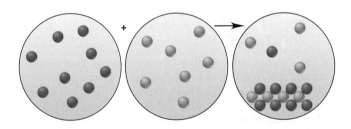

(a) Given the following choices of reactants, write balanced total ionic and net ionic equations that best represent the reaction:
(1) $KNO_3(aq) + CuCl_2(aq) \longrightarrow$
(2) $NaClO_4(aq) + CaCl_2(aq) \longrightarrow$
(3) $Li_2SO_4(aq) + AgNO_3(aq) \longrightarrow$
(4) $NH_4Br(aq) + Pb(CH_3COO)_2(aq) \longrightarrow$
(b) If each sphere represents $2.5 \times 10^{-3}$ mol of ion, find the total number of ions present.
(c) What is the mass of solid formed?

**4.39** A 1.50-g sample of an unknown alkali-metal carbonate was dissolved in water, and 31.10 mL of 0.350 $M$ $CaCl_2$ was required to precipitate all the carbonate ions as $CaCO_3$. Give the name and formula of the unknown compound.

**4.40** A 0.750-g sample of a compound that might be iron(II) chloride, nickel(II) chloride, or zinc chloride is dissolved in water, and 22.40 mL of 0.515 $M$ $AgNO_3$ is required to completely precipitate all the chloride ion as AgCl. Name the compound, and write its formula.

**Problems in Context**

**4.41** The mass percent of $Cl^-$ in a seawater sample is determined by titrating 25.00 mL of seawater with $AgNO_3$ solution, causing a precipitation reaction. An indicator is used to detect the end point, which occurs when free $Ag^+$ ion is present in solution after all the $Cl^-$ has reacted. If 53.63 mL of 0.2970 $M$ $AgNO_3$ is required to reach the end point, what is the mass percent of $Cl^-$ in the seawater ($d$ of seawater = 1.024 g/mL)?

**4.42** Aluminum sulfate, known as *cake alum,* has a wide range of uses, from dyeing leather and cloth to purifying sewage. In aqueous solution, it reacts with base to form a white precipitate. (a) Write balanced total and net ionic equations for its reaction with aqueous NaOH. (b) What mass of precipitate forms when 185.5 mL of 0.533 $M$ NaOH is added to 627 mL of a solution that contains 15.8 g of aluminum sulfate per liter?

## Acid-Base Reactions

(Sample Problems 4.5 to 4.8)

**Concept Review Questions**

**4.43** Is the total ionic equation the same as the net ionic equation when $Sr(OH)_2(aq)$ and $H_2SO_4(aq)$ react? Explain.

**4.44** State a general equation for a neutralization reaction.

**4.45** (a) Name three common strong acids. (b) Name three common strong bases. (c) What is a characteristic behavior of a strong acid or a strong base?

**4.46** (a) Name three common weak acids. (b) Name one common weak base. (c) What is the major difference between a weak acid and a strong acid or between a weak base and a strong base, and what experiment would you perform to observe it?

**4.47** Do either of the following reactions go to completion? If so, what factor(s) cause(s) each to do so?
(a) $MgSO_3(s) + 2HCl(aq) \longrightarrow MgCl_2(aq) + SO_2(g) + H_2O(l)$
(b) $3Ba(OH)_2(aq) + 2H_3PO_4(aq) \longrightarrow Ba_3(PO_4)_2(s) + 6H_2O(l)$

**4.48** (a) The net ionic equation for the aqueous neutralization reaction between acetic acid and sodium hydroxide is different from that for the reaction between hydrochloric acid and sodium hydroxide. Explain by writing balanced net ionic equations. (b) For a solution of acetic acid in water, list the major species in decreasing order of concentration.

**Skill-Building Exercises** (grouped in similar pairs)

**4.49** Complete the following acid-base reactions with balanced molecular, total ionic, and net ionic equations:
(a) Potassium hydroxide($aq$) + hydrobromic acid($aq$) $\longrightarrow$
(b) Ammonia($aq$) + hydrochloric acid($aq$) $\longrightarrow$

**4.50** Complete the following acid-base reactions with balanced molecular, total ionic, and net ionic equations:
(a) Cesium hydroxide($aq$) + nitric acid($aq$) $\longrightarrow$
(b) Calcium hydroxide($aq$) + acetic acid($aq$) $\longrightarrow$

**4.51** Limestone (calcium carbonate) is insoluble in water but dissolves when a hydrochloric acid solution is added. Write balanced total ionic and net ionic equations, showing hydrochloric acid as it actually exists in water and the reaction as a proton-transfer process.

**4.52** Zinc hydroxide is insoluble in water but dissolves when a nitric acid solution is added. Why? Write balanced total ionic and net ionic equations, showing nitric acid as it actually exists in water and the reaction as a proton-transfer process.

**4.53** If 25.98 mL of 0.1180 $M$ KOH solution reacts with 52.50 mL of $CH_3COOH$ solution, what is the molarity of the acid solution?

**4.54** If 26.25 mL of 0.1850 $M$ NaOH solution reacts with 25.00 mL of $H_2SO_4$, what is the molarity of the acid solution?

**Problems in Context**

**4.55** An auto mechanic spills 88 mL of 2.6 $M$ $H_2SO_4$ solution from an auto battery. How many milliliters of 1.6 $M$ $NaHCO_3$ must be poured on the spill to react completely with the sulfuric acid?

**4.56** Sodium hydroxide is used extensively in acid-base titrations because it is a strong, inexpensive base. A sodium hydroxide solution was standardized by titrating 25.00 mL of 0.1528 $M$ standard hydrochloric acid. The initial buret reading of the sodium hydroxide was 2.24 mL, and the final reading was 39.21 mL. What was the molarity of the base solution?

**4.57** An unknown amount of acid can often be determined by adding an excess of base and then "back-titrating" the excess. A 0.3471-g sample of a mixture of oxalic acid, which has two ionizable protons, and benzoic acid, which has one, is treated with 100.0 mL of 0.1000 $M$ NaOH. The excess NaOH is titrated with 20.00 mL of 0.2000 $M$ HCl. Find the mass % of benzoic acid.

**4.58** One of the first steps in the enrichment of uranium for use in nuclear power plants involves a displacement reaction between $UO_2$ and aqueous HF:

$$UO_2(s) + HF(aq) \longrightarrow UF_4(s) + H_2O(l) \text{ [unbalanced]}$$

How many liters of 2.40 $M$ HF will react with 2.15 kg of $UO_2$?

**4.59** A mixture of bases can sometimes be the active ingredient in antacid tablets. If 0.4826 g of a mixture of $Al(OH)_3$ and $Mg(OH)_2$ is neutralized with 17.30 mL of 1.000 $M$ $HNO_3$, what is the mass % of $Al(OH)_3$ in the mixture?

## Oxidation-Reduction (Redox) Reactions

(Sample Problems 4.9 to 4.13)

**Concept Review Questions**

**4.60** Describe how to determine the oxidation number of sulfur in (a) $H_2S$ and (b) $SO_3^{2-}$.

**4.61** Is the following a redox reaction? Explain.

$$NH_3(aq) + HCl(aq) \longrightarrow NH_4Cl(aq)$$

**4.62** Explain why an oxidizing agent undergoes reduction.

**4.63** Why must every redox reaction involve an oxidizing agent and a reducing agent?

**4.64** In which of the following equations does sulfuric acid act as an oxidizing agent? In which does it act as an acid? Explain.
(a) $4H^+(aq) + SO_4^{2-}(aq) + 2NaI(s) \longrightarrow$
$\qquad 2Na^+(aq) + I_2(s) + SO_2(g) + 2H_2O(l)$
(b) $BaF_2(s) + 2H^+(aq) + SO_4^{2-}(aq) \longrightarrow 2HF(aq) + BaSO_4(s)$

**4.65** Identify the oxidizing agent and the reducing agent in the following reaction, and explain your answer:

$$8NH_3(g) + 6NO_2(g) \longrightarrow 7N_2(g) + 12H_2O(l)$$

**Skill-Building Exercises** (grouped in similar pairs)

**4.66** Give the oxidation number of carbon in the following:
(a) $CF_2Cl_2$      (b) $Na_2C_2O_4$      (c) $HCO_3^-$      (d) $C_2H_6$

**4.67** Give the oxidation number of bromine in the following:
(a) KBr      (b) $BrF_3$      (c) $HBrO_3$      (d) $CBr_4$

**4.68** Give the oxidation number of nitrogen in the following:
(a) $NH_2OH$      (b) $N_2F_4$      (c) $NH_4^+$      (d) $HNO_2$

**4.69** Give the oxidation number of sulfur in the following:
(a) $SOCl_2$      (b) $H_2S_2$      (c) $H_2SO_3$      (d) $Na_2S$

**4.70** Give the oxidation number of arsenic in the following:
(a) $AsH_3$      (b) $H_2AsO_4^-$      (c) $AsCl_3$

**4.71** Give the oxidation number of phosphorus in the following:
(a) $H_2P_2O_7^{2-}$      (b) $PH_4^+$      (c) $PCl_5$

**4.72** Give the oxidation number of manganese in the following:
(a) $MnO_4^{2-}$      (b) $Mn_2O_3$      (c) $KMnO_4$

**4.73** Give the oxidation number of chromium in the following:
(a) $CrO_3$      (b) $Cr_2O_7^{2-}$      (c) $Cr_2(SO_4)_3$

**4.74** Identify the oxidizing and reducing agents in the following:
(a) $5H_2C_2O_4(aq) + 2MnO_4^-(aq) + 6H^+(aq) \longrightarrow$
$$2Mn^{2+}(aq) + 10CO_2(g) + 8H_2O(l)$$
(b) $3Cu(s) + 8H^+(aq) + 2NO_3^-(aq) \longrightarrow$
$$3Cu^{2+}(aq) + 2NO(g) + 4H_2O(l)$$

**4.75** Identify the oxidizing and reducing agents in the following:
(a) $Sn(s) + 2H^+(aq) \longrightarrow Sn^{2+}(aq) + H_2(g)$
(b) $2H^+(aq) + H_2O_2(aq) + 2Fe^{2+}(aq) \longrightarrow$
$$2Fe^{3+}(aq) + 2H_2O(l)$$

**4.76** Identify the oxidizing and reducing agents in the following:
(a) $8H^+(aq) + 6Cl^-(aq) + Sn(s) + 4NO_3^-(aq) \longrightarrow$
$$SnCl_6^{2-}(aq) + 4NO_2(g) + 4H_2O(l)$$
(b) $2MnO_4^-(aq) + 10Cl^-(aq) + 16H^+(aq) \longrightarrow$
$$5Cl_2(g) + 2Mn^{2+}(aq) + 8H_2O(l)$$

**4.77** Identify the oxidizing and reducing agents in the following:
(a) $8H^+(aq) + Cr_2O_7^{2-}(aq) + 3SO_3^{2-}(aq) \longrightarrow$
$$2Cr^{3+}(aq) + 3SO_4^{2-}(aq) + 4H_2O(l)$$
(b) $NO_3^-(aq) + 4Zn(s) + 7OH^-(aq) + 6H_2O(l) \longrightarrow$
$$4Zn(OH)_4^{2-}(aq) + NH_3(aq)$$

**4.78** Use the oxidation number method to balance the following equations. Identify the reducing and oxidizing agents:
(a) $HNO_3(aq) + K_2CrO_4(aq) + Fe(NO_3)_2(aq) \longrightarrow$
$$KNO_3(aq) + Fe(NO_3)_3(aq) + Cr(NO_3)_3(aq) + H_2O(l)$$
(b) $HNO_3(aq) + C_2H_6O(l) + K_2Cr_2O_7(aq) \longrightarrow$
$$KNO_3(aq) + C_2H_4O(l) + H_2O(l) + Cr(NO_3)_3(aq)$$
(c) $HCl(aq) + NH_4Cl(aq) + K_2Cr_2O_7(aq) \longrightarrow$
$$KCl(aq) + CrCl_3(aq) + N_2(g) + H_2O(l)$$
(d) $KClO_3(aq) + HBr(aq) \longrightarrow Br_2(l) + H_2O(l) + KCl(aq)$

**4.79** Use the oxidation number method to balance the following equations. Identify the reducing and oxidizing agents:
(a) $HCl(aq) + FeCl_2(aq) + H_2O_2(aq) \longrightarrow FeCl_3(aq) + H_2O(l)$
(b) $I_2(s) + Na_2S_2O_3(aq) \longrightarrow Na_2S_4O_6(aq) + NaI(aq)$
(c) $HNO_3(aq) + KI(aq) \longrightarrow$
$$NO(g) + I_2(s) + H_2O(l) + KNO_3(aq)$$
(d) $PbO(s) + NH_3(aq) \longrightarrow N_2(g) + H_2O(l) + Pb(s)$

**Problems in Context**

**4.80** The active agent in many hair bleaches is hydrogen peroxide. The amount of $H_2O_2$ in 14.8 g of hair bleach was determined by titration with a standard potassium permanganate solution:

$2MnO_4^-(aq) + 5H_2O_2(aq) + 6H^+(aq) \longrightarrow$
$$5O_2(g) + 2Mn^{2+}(aq) + 8H_2O(l)$$

(a) How many moles of $MnO_4^-$ were required for the titration if 43.2 mL of 0.105 $M$ $KMnO_4$ was needed to reach the end point?

(b) How many moles of $H_2O_2$ were present in the 14.8-g sample of bleach?
(c) How many grams of $H_2O_2$ were in the sample?
(d) What is the mass percent of $H_2O_2$ in the sample?
(e) What is the reducing agent in the redox reaction?

**4.81** A person's blood alcohol ($C_2H_5OH$) level can be determined by titrating a sample of blood plasma with a potassium dichromate solution. The balanced equation is

$16H^+(aq) + 2Cr_2O_7^{2-}(aq) + C_2H_5OH(aq) \longrightarrow$
$$4Cr^{3+}(aq) + 2CO_2(g) + 11H_2O(l)$$

If 35.46 mL of 0.05961 $M$ $Cr_2O_7^{2-}$ is required to titrate 28.00 g of plasma, what is the mass percent of alcohol in the blood?

## Elements in Redox Reactions
(Sample Problem 4.14)

**Concept Review Questions**

**4.82** Which type of redox reaction leads to each of the following?
(a) An increase in the number of substances
(b) A decrease in the number of substances
(c) No change in the number of substances

**4.83** Why do decomposition redox reactions typically have compounds as reactants, whereas combination redox and displacement redox reactions have one or more elements?

**4.84** Which of the types of reactions discussed in Section 4.6 commonly produce more than one compound?

**4.85** Are all combustion reactions redox reactions? Explain.

**4.86** Give one example of a combination reaction that is a redox reaction and another that is not a redox reaction.

**Skill-Building Exercises** (grouped in similar pairs)

**4.87** Balance each of the following redox reactions and classify it as a combination, decomposition, or displacement reaction:
(a) $Ca(s) + H_2O(l) \longrightarrow Ca(OH)_2(aq) + H_2(g)$
(b) $NaNO_3(s) \longrightarrow NaNO_2(s) + O_2(g)$
(c) $C_2H_2(g) + H_2(g) \longrightarrow C_2H_6(g)$

**4.88** Balance each of the following redox reactions and classify it as a combination, decomposition, or displacement reaction:
(a) $HI(g) \longrightarrow H_2(g) + I_2(g)$
(b) $Zn(s) + AgNO_3(aq) \longrightarrow Zn(NO_3)_2(aq) + Ag(s)$
(c) $NO(g) + O_2(g) \longrightarrow N_2O_4(l)$

**4.89** Balance each of the following redox reactions and classify it as a combination, decomposition, or displacement reaction:
(a) $Sb(s) + Cl_2(g) \longrightarrow SbCl_3(s)$
(b) $AsH_3(g) \longrightarrow As(s) + H_2(g)$
(c) $Zn(s) + Fe(NO_3)_2(aq) \longrightarrow Zn(NO_3)_2(aq) + Fe(s)$

**4.90** Balance each of the following redox reactions and classify it as a combination, decomposition, or displacement reaction:
(a) $Mg(s) + H_2O(g) \longrightarrow Mg(OH)_2(s) + H_2(g)$
(b) $Cr(NO_3)_3(aq) + Al(s) \longrightarrow Al(NO_3)_3(aq) + Cr(s)$
(c) $PF_3(g) + F_2(g) \longrightarrow PF_5(g)$

**4.91** Predict the product(s) and write a balanced equation for each of the following redox reactions:
(a) $Sr(s) + Br_2(l) \longrightarrow$
(b) $Ag_2O(s) \xrightarrow{\Delta}$
(c) $Mn(s) + Cu(NO_3)_2(aq) \longrightarrow$

**4.92** Predict the product(s) and write a balanced equation for each of the following redox reactions:

(a) $Mg(s) + HCl(aq) \longrightarrow$

(b) $LiCl(l) \xrightarrow{electricity}$

(c) $SnCl_2(aq) + Co(s) \longrightarrow$

**4.93** Predict the product(s) and write a balanced equation for each of the following redox reactions:

(a) $N_2(g) + H_2(g) \longrightarrow$

(b) $NaClO_3(s) \xrightarrow{\Delta}$

(c) $Ba(s) + H_2O(l) \longrightarrow$

**4.94** Predict the product(s) and write a balanced equation for each of the following redox reactions:

(a) $Fe(s) + HClO_4(aq) \longrightarrow$

(b) $S_8(s) + O_2(g) \longrightarrow$

(c) $BaCl_2(l) \xrightarrow{electricity}$

**4.95** Predict the product(s) and write a balanced equation for each of the following redox reactions:

(a) Cesium + iodine $\longrightarrow$

(b) Aluminum + aqueous manganese(II) sulfate $\longrightarrow$

(c) Sulfur dioxide + oxygen $\longrightarrow$

(d) Butane and oxygen $\longrightarrow$

(e) Write a balanced net ionic equation for (b).

**4.96** Predict the product(s) and write a balanced equation for each of the following redox reactions:

(a) Pentane ($C_5H_{12}$) + oxygen $\longrightarrow$

(b) Phosphorus trichloride + chlorine $\longrightarrow$

(c) Zinc + hydrobromic acid $\longrightarrow$

(d) Aqueous potassium iodide + bromine $\longrightarrow$

(e) Write a balanced net ionic equation for (d).

**4.97** How many grams of $O_2$ can be prepared from the thermal decomposition of 4.27 kg of HgO? Name and calculate the mass (in kg) of the other product.

**4.98** How many grams of chlorine gas can be produced from the electrolytic decomposition of 874 g of calcium chloride? Name and calculate the mass (in g) of the other product.

**4.99** In a combination reaction, 1.62 g of lithium is mixed with 6.50 g of oxygen.
(a) Which reactant is present in excess?
(b) How many moles of product are formed?
(c) After reaction, how many grams of each reactant and product are present?

**4.100** In a combination reaction, 2.22 g of magnesium is heated with 3.75 g of nitrogen.
(a) Which reactant is present in excess?
(b) How many moles of product are formed?
(c) After reaction, how many grams of each reactant and product are present?

**4.101** A mixture of $KClO_3$ and KCl with a mass of 0.950 g was heated to produce $O_2$. After heating, the mass of residue was 0.700 g. Assuming all the $KClO_3$ decomposed to KCl and $O_2$, calculate the mass percent of $KClO_3$ in the original mixture.

**4.102** A mixture of $CaCO_3$ and CaO weighing 0.693 g was heated to produce gaseous $CO_2$. After heating, the remaining solid weighed 0.508 g. Assuming all the $CaCO_3$ broke down to CaO and $CO_2$, calculate the mass percent of $CaCO_3$ in the original mixture.

**Problems in Context**

**4.103** Before arc welding was developed, a displacement reaction involving aluminum and iron(III) oxide was commonly used to

produce molten iron (the thermite process). This reaction was used, for example, to connect sections of iron rails for train tracks. Calculate the mass of molten iron produced when 1.50 kg of aluminum reacts with 25.0 mol of iron(III) oxide.

**4.104** Iron reacts rapidly with chlorine gas to form a reddish brown, ionic compound (A), which contains iron in the higher of its two common oxidation states. Strong heating decomposes compound A to compound B, another ionic compound, which contains iron in the lower of its two oxidation states. When compound A is formed by the reaction of 50.6 g of Fe and 83.8 g of $Cl_2$ and then heated, how much compound B forms?

## The Reversibility of Reactions and the Equilibrium State

**Concept Review Questions**

**4.105** Why is the equilibrium state called "dynamic"?

**4.106** In a decomposition reaction involving a gaseous product, what must be done for the reaction to reach equilibrium?

**4.107** Describe what happens on the molecular level when acetic acid dissolves in water.

**4.108** When either a mixture of NO and $Br_2$ or pure nitrosyl bromide (NOBr) is placed in a reaction vessel, the product mixture contains NO, $Br_2$, and NOBr. Explain.

**Problem in Context**

**4.109** Ammonia is produced by the millions of tons annually for use as a fertilizer. It is commonly made from $N_2$ and $H_2$ by the Haber process. Because the reaction reaches equilibrium before going completely to product, the stoichiometric amount of ammonia is not obtained. At a particular temperature and pressure, 10.0 g of $H_2$ reacts with 20.0 g of $N_2$ to form ammonia. When equilibrium is reached, 15.0 g of $NH_3$ has formed. (a) Calculate the percent yield. (b) How many moles of $N_2$ and $H_2$ are present at equilibrium?

## Comprehensive Problems

**4.110** Nutritional biochemists have known for decades that acidic foods cooked in cast-iron cookware can supply significant amounts of dietary iron (ferrous ion). (a) Write a balanced net ionic equation, with oxidation numbers, that supports this fact. (b) Measurements show an increase from 3.3 mg of iron to 49 mg of iron per $\frac{1}{2}$-cup (125-g) serving during the slow preparation of tomato sauce in a cast-iron pot. How many ferrous ions are present in a 26-oz (737-g) jar of the tomato sauce?

**4.111** Limestone ($CaCO_3$) is used to remove acidic pollutants from smokestack flue gases. It is heated to form lime (CaO), which reacts with sulfur dioxide to form calcium sulfite. Assuming a 70.% yield in the overall reaction, what mass of limestone is required to remove all the sulfur dioxide formed by the combustion of $8.5 \times 10^4$ kg of coal that is 0.33 mass % sulfur?

**4.112** The brewing industry uses yeast to convert glucose to ethanol. The baking industry uses the carbon dioxide produced in the same reaction to make bread rise:

$$C_6H_{12}O_6(s) \xrightarrow{yeast} 2C_2H_5OH(l) + 2CO_2(g)$$

How many grams of ethanol can be produced from 100. g of glucose? What volume of $CO_2$ is produced? (Assume 1 mol of gas occupies 22.4 L at the conditions used.)

**4.113** A chemical engineer determines the mass percent of iron in an ore sample by converting the Fe to $Fe^{2+}$ in acid and then titrating the $Fe^{2+}$ with $MnO_4^-$. A 1.1081-g sample was dissolved in acid and then titrated with 39.32 mL of 0.03190 $M$ KMnO$_4$. The balanced equation is

$$8H^+(aq) + 5Fe^{2+}(aq) + MnO_4^-(aq) \longrightarrow$$
$$5Fe^{3+}(aq) + Mn^{2+}(aq) + 4H_2O(l)$$

Calculate the mass percent of iron in the ore.

**4.114** Mixtures of CaCl$_2$ and NaCl are used to melt ice on roads. A dissolved 1.9348-g sample of such a mixture was analyzed by using excess Na$_2$C$_2$O$_4$ to precipitate the Ca$^{2+}$ as CaC$_2$O$_4$. The CaC$_2$O$_4$ was dissolved in sulfuric acid, and the resulting H$_2$C$_2$O$_4$ was titrated with 37.68 mL of 0.1019 $M$ KMnO$_4$ solution.
(a) Write the balanced net ionic equation for the precipitation reaction.
(b) Write the balanced net ionic equation for the titration reaction. (See Sample Problem 4.13.)
(c) What is the oxidizing agent?
(d) What is the reducing agent?
(e) Calculate the mass percent of CaCl$_2$ in the original sample.

**4.115** You are given solutions of HCl and NaOH and must determine their concentrations. You use 27.5 mL of NaOH to titrate 100. mL of HCl and 18.4 mL of NaOH to titrate 50.0 mL of 0.0782 $M$ H$_2$SO$_4$. Find the unknown concentrations.

**4.116** The flask (*right*) represents the products of the titration of 25 mL of sulfuric acid with 25 mL of sodium hydroxide.
(a) Write balanced molecular, total ionic, and net ionic equations for the reaction.
(b) If each orange sphere represents 0.010 mol of sulfate ion, how many moles of acid and of base reacted?
(c) What are the molarities of the acid and the base?

**4.117** To find the mass percent of dolomite [CaMg(CO$_3$)$_2$] in a soil sample, a geochemist titrates 13.86 g of soil with 33.56 mL of 0.2516 $M$ HCl. What is the mass percent of dolomite in the soil?

**4.118** On a lab exam, you have to find the concentrations of the monoprotic (one proton per molecule) acids HA and HB. You are given 43.5 mL of HA solution in one flask. A second flask contains 37.2 mL of HA, and you add enough HB solution to it to reach a final volume of 50.0 mL. You titrate the first HA solution with 87.3 mL of 0.0906 $M$ NaOH and the mixture of HA and HB in the second flask with 96.4 mL of the NaOH solution. Calculate the molarity of the HA and HB solutions.

**4.119** Nitric acid, a major industrial and laboratory acid, is produced commercially by the multistep Ostwald process, which begins with the oxidation of ammonia:

*Step 1.* $\quad 4NH_3(g) + 5O_2(g) \longrightarrow 4NO(g) + 6H_2O(l)$
*Step 2.* $\quad 2NO(g) + O_2(g) \longrightarrow 2NO_2(g)$
*Step 3.* $\quad 3NO_2(g) + H_2O(l) \longrightarrow 2HNO_3(l) + NO(g)$

(a) What are the oxidizing and reducing agents in each step?
(b) Assuming 100% yield in each step, what mass (in kg) of ammonia must be used to produce $3.0\times10^4$ kg of HNO$_3$?

**4.120** Various data can be used to find the composition of an alloy (a metallic mixture). Show that calculating the mass % of Mg in a magnesium-aluminum alloy ($d = 2.40$ g/cm$^3$) using each of the following pieces of data gives the same answer (within rounding): (a) a sample of the alloy has a mass of 0.263 g ($d$ of Mg = 1.74 g/cm$^3$; $d$ of Al = 2.70 g/cm$^3$); (b) an identical sample reacting with excess aqueous HCl forms $1.38\times10^{-2}$ mol of H$_2$; (c) an identical sample reacting with excess O$_2$ forms 0.483 g of oxide.

**4.121** Use the oxidation number method to balance the following equations by placing coefficients in the blanks. Identify the reducing and oxidizing agents:
(a) __KOH($aq$) + __H$_2$O$_2$($aq$) + __Cr(OH)$_3$($s$) $\longrightarrow$
$\quad\quad\quad\quad$ __K$_2$CrO$_4$($aq$) + __H$_2$O($l$)
(b) __MnO$_4^-$($aq$) + __ClO$_2^-$($aq$) + __H$_2$O($l$) $\longrightarrow$
$\quad\quad\quad\quad$ __MnO$_2$($s$) + __ClO$_4^-$($aq$) + __OH$^-$($aq$)
(c) __KMnO$_4$($aq$) + __Na$_2$SO$_3$($aq$) + __H$_2$O($l$) $\longrightarrow$
$\quad\quad\quad\quad$ __MnO$_2$($s$) + __Na$_2$SO$_4$($aq$) + __KOH($aq$)
(d) __CrO$_4^{2-}$($aq$) + __HSnO$_2^-$($aq$) + __H$_2$O($l$) $\longrightarrow$
$\quad\quad\quad\quad$ __CrO$_2^-$($aq$) + __HSnO$_3^-$($aq$) + __OH$^-$($aq$)
(e) __KMnO$_4$($aq$) + __NaNO$_2$($aq$) + __H$_2$O($l$) $\longrightarrow$
$\quad\quad\quad\quad$ __MnO$_2$($s$) + __NaNO$_3$($aq$) + __KOH($aq$)
(f) __I$^-$($aq$) + __O$_2$($g$) + __H$_2$O($l$) $\longrightarrow$ __I$_2$($s$) + __OH$^-$($aq$)

**4.122** In 1995, Mario Molina, Paul Crutzen, and F. Sherwood Rowland shared the Nobel Prize in chemistry for their work on atmospheric chemistry. One reaction sequence they proposed for the role of chlorine in the decomposition of stratospheric ozone (we'll see another sequence in Chapter 16) is
(1) Cl($g$) + O$_3$($g$) $\longrightarrow$ ClO($g$) + O$_2$($g$)
(2) ClO($g$) + ClO($g$) $\longrightarrow$ Cl$_2$O$_2$($g$)
(3) Cl$_2$O$_2$($g$) $\xrightarrow{\text{light}}$ 2Cl($g$) + O$_2$($g$)
Over the tropics, O atoms are more common in the stratosphere:
(4) ClO($g$) + O($g$) $\longrightarrow$ Cl($g$) + O$_2$($g$)
(a) Which, if any, of these are oxidation-reduction reactions?
(b) Write an overall equation combining reactions 1–3.

**4.123** Sodium peroxide (Na$_2$O$_2$) is often used in self-contained breathing devices, such as those used in fire emergencies, because it reacts with exhaled CO$_2$ to form Na$_2$CO$_3$ and O$_2$. How many liters of respired air can react with 80.0 g of Na$_2$O$_2$ if each liter of respired air contains 0.0720 g of CO$_2$?

**4.124** A student forgets to weigh a mixture of sodium bromide dihydrate and magnesium bromide hexahydrate. Upon strong heating, the sample loses 252.1 mg of water. The mixture of anhydrous salts reacts with excess AgNO$_3$ solution to form $6.00\times10^{-3}$ mol of solid AgBr. Find the mass % of each compound in the original mixture.

**4.125** A typical formulation for window glass is 75% SiO$_2$, 15% Na$_2$O, and 10.% CaO by mass. What masses of sand (SiO$_2$), sodium carbonate, and calcium carbonate must be combined to produce 1.00 kg of glass after carbon dioxide is driven off by thermal decomposition of the carbonates?

**4.126** The quantity of dissolved oxygen (DO) in natural waters is an essential parameter for monitoring survival of most aquatic life. DO is affected by temperature and the amount of organic waste. An earlier method for determining DO involved a two-step process:

1. The water sample is treated with KI,

$$O_2(aq) + 4KI(aq) + 2H_2SO_4(aq) \longrightarrow$$
$$2I_2(aq) + 2H_2O(l) + 2K_2SO_4(aq)$$

2. The I$_2$ is titrated with sodium thiosulfate,

$$I_2(aq) + 2Na_2S_2O_3(aq) \longrightarrow Na_2S_4O_6(aq) + 2NaI(aq)$$

A 50.0-mL water sample is treated with KI, and then 15.75 mL of 0.0105 $M$ Na$_2$S$_2$O$_3$ is required to reach the end point.
(a) Which substance is oxidized in step 1, and which is reduced in step 2?
(b) What mass (g) of O$_2$ is dissolved in the water sample?

**4.127** Physicians who specialize in sports medicine routinely treat athletes and dancers. Ethyl chloride, a local anesthetic commonly used for simple injuries, is the product of the combination of ethylene with hydrogen chloride:

$$C_2H_4(g) + HCl(g) \longrightarrow C_2H_5Cl(g)$$

If 0.100 kg of $C_2H_4$ and 0.100 kg of HCl react: (a) How many molecules of gas (reactants plus products) are present when the reaction is complete? (b) How many moles of gas are present when half the product forms?

**4.128** Thyroxine ($C_{15}H_{11}I_4NO_4$) is a hormone synthesized by the thyroid gland and used to control many metabolic functions in the body. A physiologist determines the mass percent of thyroxine in a thyroid extract by igniting 0.4332 g of extract with sodium carbonate, which converts the iodine to iodide. The iodide is dissolved in water, and bromine and hydrochloric acid are added, which convert the iodide to iodate.

(a) How many moles of iodate form per mole of thyroxine?
(b) Excess bromine is boiled off and more iodide is added, which reacts as shown in the following *unbalanced* equation:

$$IO_3^-(aq) + H^+(aq) + I^-(aq) \longrightarrow I_2(aq) + H_2O(l)$$

How many moles of iodine are produced per mole of thyroxine? (*Hint:* Be sure to balance the charges as well as the atoms.) What are the oxidizing and reducing agents in the reaction?
(c) The iodine reacts completely with 17.23 mL of 0.1000 *M* thiosulfate as shown in the following *unbalanced* equation:

$$I_2(aq) + S_2O_3^{2-}(aq) \longrightarrow I^-(aq) + S_4O_6^{2-}(aq)$$

What is the mass percent of thyroxine in the thyroid extract?

**4.129** Over time, as their free fatty acid (FFA) content increases, edible fats and oils become rancid. To measure rancidity, the fat or oil is dissolved in ethanol, and any FFA present is titrated with KOH dissolved in ethanol. In a series of tests on olive oil, a stock solution of 0.050 *M* ethanolic KOH was prepared at 25°C, stored at 0°C, and then placed in a 100-mL buret to titrate oleic acid [an FFA with formula $CH_3(CH_2)_7CH{=}CH(CH_2)_7COOH$] in the oil. Each of four 10.00-g samples of oil took several minutes to titrate: the first required 19.60 mL, the second 19.80 mL, and the third and fourth 20.00 mL of the ethanolic KOH.
(a) What is the apparent acidity of each sample, in terms of mass % of oleic acid? (*Note:* As the ethanolic KOH warms in the buret, its volume increases by a factor of 0.00104/°C.)
(b) Is the variation in acidity a random or systematic error? Explain.
(c) What is the actual acidity? How would you demonstrate this?

**4.130** A chemist mixes solid AgCl, $CuCl_2$, and $MgCl_2$ in enough water to give a final volume of 50.0 mL.
(a) With ions shown as spheres and solvent molecules omitted for clarity, which scene best represents the resulting mixture?

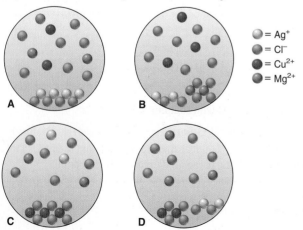

= Ag$^+$
= Cl$^-$
= Cu$^{2+}$
= Mg$^{2+}$

(b) If each sphere represents $5.0{\times}10^{-3}$ mol of ions, what is the total concentration of *dissolved* (separated) ions?
(c) What is the total mass of solid?

**4.131** Calcium dihydrogen phosphate, $Ca(H_2PO_4)_2$, and sodium hydrogen carbonate, $NaHCO_3$, are ingredients of baking powder that react to produce $CO_2$, which causes dough or batter to rise:

$$Ca(H_2PO_4)_2(s) + NaHCO_3(s) \longrightarrow$$
$$CO_2(g) + H_2O(g) + CaHPO_4(s) + Na_2HPO_4(s)$$
[unbalanced]

If the baking powder contains 31% $NaHCO_3$ and 35% $Ca(H_2PO_4)_2$ by mass:
(a) How many moles of $CO_2$ are produced from 1.00 g of baking powder?
(b) If 1 mol of $CO_2$ occupies 37.0 L at 350°F (a typical baking temperature), what volume of $CO_2$ is produced from 1.00 g of baking powder?

**4.132** In a titration of $HNO_3$, you add a few drops of phenolphthalein indicator to 50.00 mL of acid in a flask. You quickly add 20.00 mL of 0.0502 *M* NaOH but overshoot the end point, and the solution turns deep pink. Instead of starting over, you add 30.00 mL of the acid, and the solution turns colorless. Then, it takes 3.22 mL of the NaOH to reach the end point.
(a) What is the concentration of the $HNO_3$ solution?
(b) How many moles of NaOH were in excess after the first addition?

**4.133** The active compound in Pepto-Bismol contains C, H, O, and Bi.
(a) When 0.22105 g of it was burned in excess $O_2$, 0.1422 g of bismuth(III) oxide, 0.1880 g of carbon dioxide, and 0.02750 g of water were formed. What is the empirical formula of this compound?
(b) Given a molar mass of 1086 g/mol, determine the molecular formula.
(c) Complete and balance the acid-base reaction between bismuth(III) hydroxide and salicylic acid ($HC_7H_5O_3$), which is used to form this compound.
(d) A dose of Pepto-Bismol contains 0.600 mg of active ingredient. If the yield of the reaction in part (c) is 88.0%, what mass (in mg) of bismuth(III) hydroxide is required to prepare one dose?

**4.134** Two aqueous solutions contain the ions indicated below.

250. mL      +      250. mL

= Na$^+$
= CO$_3^{2-}$
= Ca$^{2+}$
= Cl$^-$

(a) Write balanced molecular, total ionic, and net ionic equations for the reaction that occurs when the solutions are mixed.
(b) If each sphere represents 0.050 mol of ion, what mass (in g) of precipitate forms, assuming 100% yield?
(c) What is the concentration of each ion in solution after reaction?

**4.135** In 1997 and 2009, at United Nations conferences on climate change, many nations agreed to expand their research efforts to develop renewable sources of carbon-based fuels. For more than a quarter century, Brazil has been engaged in a program to replace gasoline with ethanol derived from the root crop manioc (cassava).

(a) Write separate balanced equations for the complete combustion of ethanol ($C_2H_5OH$) and of gasoline (represented by the formula $C_8H_{18}$).

(b) What mass of oxygen is required to burn completely 1.00 L of a mixture that is 90.0% gasoline ($d = 0.742$ g/mL) and 10.0% ethanol ($d = 0.789$ g/mL) by volume?

(c) If 1.00 mol of $O_2$ occupies 22.4 L, what volume of $O_2$ is needed to burn 1.00 L of the mixture?

(d) Air is 20.9% $O_2$ by volume. What volume of air is needed to burn 1.00 L of the mixture?

**4.136** In a car engine, gasoline (represented by $C_8H_{18}$) does not burn completely, and some CO, a toxic pollutant, forms along with $CO_2$ and $H_2O$. If 5.0% of the gasoline forms CO:

(a) What is the ratio of $CO_2$ to CO molecules in the exhaust?

(b) What is the mass ratio of $CO_2$ to CO?

(c) What percentage of the gasoline must form CO for the mass ratio of $CO_2$ to CO to be exactly 1/1?

**4.137** The amount of ascorbic acid (vitamin C; $C_6H_8O_6$) in tablets is determined by reaction with bromine and then titration of the hydrobromic acid with standard base:

$$C_6H_8O_6(aq) + Br_2(aq) \longrightarrow C_6H_6O_6(aq) + 2HBr(aq)$$
$$HBr(aq) + NaOH(aq) \longrightarrow NaBr(aq) + H_2O(l)$$

A certain tablet is advertised as containing 500 mg of vitamin C. One tablet was dissolved in water and reacted with $Br_2$. The solution was then titrated with 43.20 mL of 0.1350 $M$ NaOH. Did the tablet contain the advertised quantity of vitamin C?

**4.138** In the process of *salting-in*, protein solubility in a dilute salt solution is increased by adding more salt. Because the protein solubility depends on the total ion concentration as well as the ion charge, salts containing doubly charged ions are often more effective than those containing singly charged ions.

(a) How many grams of $MgCl_2$ must dissolve to equal the ion concentration of 12.4 g of NaCl?

(b) How many grams of CaS must dissolve?

(c) Which of the three salt solutions would dissolve the most protein?

**4.139** At liftoff, a space shuttle uses a solid mixture of ammonium perchlorate and aluminum powder to obtain great thrust from the volume change of solid to gas. In the presence of a catalyst, the mixture forms solid aluminum oxide and aluminum trichloride and gaseous water and nitrogen monoxide.

(a) Write a balanced equation for the reaction, and identify the reducing and oxidizing agents.

(b) How many total moles of gas (water vapor and nitrogen monoxide) are produced when 50.0 kg of ammonium perchlorate reacts with a stoichiometric amount of Al?

(c) What is the change in volume from this reaction? ($d$ of $NH_4ClO_4 = 1.95$ g/cc, Al $= 2.70$ g/cc, $Al_2O_3 = 3.97$ g/cc, and $AlCl_3 = 2.44$ g/cc; assume 1 mol of gas occupies 22.4 L.)

**4.140** A *reaction cycle* for an element is a series of reactions beginning and ending with that element. In the following copper reaction cycle, copper has either a 0 or a +2 oxidation state. Write balanced molecular and net ionic equations for each step.

(1) Copper metal reacts with aqueous bromine to produce a green-blue solution.

(2) Adding aqueous sodium hydroxide forms a blue precipitate.

(3) The precipitate is heated and turns black (water is released).

(4) The black solid dissolves in nitric acid to give a blue solution.

(5) Adding aqueous sodium phosphate forms a green precipitate.

(6) The precipitate forms a blue solution in sulfuric acid.

(7) Copper metal is recovered from the blue solution when zinc metal is added.

**4.141** Two 25.0-mL aqueous solutions, labeled A and B, contain the ions indicated:

(a) If each sphere represents $1.0 \times 10^{-3}$ mol of ion, will the equivalence point have been reached when all of B has been added to A?

(b) What is the molarity of B?

(c) What additional volume (mL) of B must be added to reach the equivalence point?

# Gases and the Kinetic-Molecular Theory

## Concepts and skills to review before you study this chapter

- physical states of matter (Section 1.1)
- SI unit conversions (Section 1.5)
- mole-mass-number conversions (Section 3.1)

Amazing as it may seem, what actually occurs when you drink through a straw is that you suck the air out of the straw and the weight of Earth's atmosphere pushes down on the liquid and forces it into your mouth! Other remarkable properties of gases are at work in the rising of a loaf of bread, the operation of a car engine, and, as we'll discuss later in the chapter, even in the act of breathing. People have been studying the behavior of gases and the other states of matter throughout history; in fact, three of the four "elements" of the ancient Greeks were air (gas), water (liquid), and earth (solid). Yet, despite millennia of observations, many questions remain. In this chapter and its companion, Chapter 12, we examine the physical states and their interrelations. Here, we highlight the gaseous state, the one we understand best.

Gases are everywhere. Our atmosphere is a colorless, odorless mixture of 18 gases, some of which—$O_2$, $N_2$, $H_2O$ vapor, and $CO_2$—take part in life-sustaining cycles of redox reactions throughout the environment. And several other gases, such as chlorine and ammonia, have essential roles in industry. Yet, in this chapter, we put aside the *chemical* behavior unique to any particular gas and focus instead *on the **physical** behavior common to all gases.*

**IN THIS CHAPTER** . . . We explore the physical behavior of gases and the theory that explains it. In the process, we see how scientists use mathematics to model nature.
- We compare the behaviors of gases, liquids, and solids.
- We discuss laboratory methods for measuring gas pressure.
- We consider laws that describe the behavior of a gas in terms of how its volume changes with a change in (1) pressure, (2) temperature, or (3) amount. We focus on the ideal gas law, which encompasses these three laws, and apply it to solve gas law problems.
- We rearrange the ideal gas law to determine the density and molar mass of an unknown gas, the partial pressure of any gas in a mixture, and the amounts of gaseous reactants and products in a chemical change.
- We see how the kinetic-molecular theory explains the gas laws and accounts for other important behaviors of gas particles.
- We apply key ideas about gas behavior to Earth's atmosphere.
- We find that the behavior of real, not ideal, gases, especially under extreme conditions, requires refinements of the ideal gas law and the kinetic-molecular theory.

## 5.1 • AN OVERVIEW OF THE PHYSICAL STATES OF MATTER

*Most substances can exist as a solid, a liquid, or a gas* under appropriate conditions of pressure and temperature. In Chapter 1, we used the relative position and motion of the particles of a substance to distinguish how each state fills a container (see Figure 1.2, p. 6):

**Figure 5.1** The three states of matter. Many pure substances, such as bromine (Br₂), can exist under appropriate conditions of pressure and temperature as a gas, liquid, or solid.

**Gas:** *Particles are far apart, move freely, and fill the available space.*

**Liquid:** *Particles are close together but move around one another.*

**Solid:** *Particles are close together in a regular array and do not move around one another.*

- A gas adopts the container shape and fills it, because its particles are far apart and move randomly.
- A liquid adopts the container shape to the extent of its volume, because its particles are close together but free to move around each other.
- A solid has a fixed shape regardless of the container shape, because its particles are close together and held rigidly in place.

Figure 5.1 focuses on the three states of bromine.

Several other aspects of their behaviors distinguish gases from liquids and solids:

1. *Gas volume changes significantly with pressure.* When a sample of gas is confined to a container of variable volume, such as a cylinder with a piston, *increasing* the force on the piston *decreases* the gas volume. Removing the external force allows the volume to increase again. Gases under pressure can do a lot of work: rapidly expanding compressed air in a jackhammer breaks rock and cement; compressed air in tires lifts the weight of a car. In contrast, the volume of a liquid or a solid does not change significantly under pressure.

2. *Gas volume changes significantly with temperature.* When a sample of gas is heated, it expands; when it is cooled, it shrinks. This volume change is 50 to 100 times greater for gases than for liquids or solids. The expansion that occurs when gases are rapidly heated can have dramatic effects, like lifting a rocket into space, and everyday ones, like popping corn.

3. *Gases flow very freely.* Gases flow much more freely than liquids and solids. This behavior allows gases to be transported more easily through pipes, but it also means they leak more rapidly out of small holes and cracks.

4. *Gases have relatively low densities.* Gas density is usually measured in units of grams per liter (g/L), whereas liquid and solid densities are in grams per milliliter (g/mL), about 1000 times as dense (see Table 1.5, p. 22). For example, at 20°C and normal atmospheric pressure, the density of $O_2(g)$ is 1.3 g/**L,** whereas the density of $H_2O(l)$ is 1.0 g/**mL** and the density of NaCl(s) is 2.2 g/**mL.** When a gas cools, its density *increases* because its volume *decreases:* on cooling from 20°C to 0°C, the density of $O_2(g)$ increases from 1.3 to 1.4 g/L.

5. *Gases form a solution in any proportions.* Air is a solution of 18 gases. Two liquids, however, may or may not form a solution: water and ethanol do, but water and gasoline do not. Two solids generally do not form a solution unless they are melted and mixed while liquids, then allowed to solidify (as is done to make the alloy bronze from copper and tin).

Like the way a gas completely fills a container, these macroscopic properties—changing volume with pressure or temperature, great ability to flow, low density, and ability to form solutions—arise because the particles in a gas are much farther apart than those in either a liquid or a solid.

## Summary of Section 5.1

- The volume of a gas can be altered significantly by changing the applied force or the temperature. Corresponding changes for liquids and solids are *much* smaller.
- Gases flow more freely and have much lower densities than liquids and solids.
- Gases mix in any proportions to form solutions; liquids and solids generally do not.
- Differences in the physical states are due to the greater average distance between particles in a gas than in a liquid or a solid.

# 5.2 • GAS PRESSURE AND ITS MEASUREMENT

You can blow up a balloon or pump up a tire because *a gas exerts pressure on the walls of its container.* **Pressure (P)** is defined as the force exerted per unit of surface area:

$$\text{Pressure} = \frac{\text{force}}{\text{area}}$$

Earth's gravity attracts the atmospheric gases, and they exert a force uniformly on *all* surfaces. The force, or *weight,* of these gases creates a pressure of about 14.7 pounds per square inch (lb/in²; psi) of surface. Thus, a pressure of 14.7 lb/in² exists on the outside of your room (or your body), and it equals the pressure on the inside. What would happen if the pressures were *not* equal? Consider the empty can attached to a vacuum pump in Figure 5.2. With the pump off (*left*) the can maintains its shape because the pressure on the outside is equal to the pressure on the inside. With the pump on (*right*), much of the air inside is removed, decreasing the internal pressure greatly, and the pressure of the atmosphere easily crushes the can. The vacuum-filtration flasks and tubing that you may have used in the lab have thick walls that withstand the relatively higher external pressure.

## Laboratory Devices for Measuring Gas Pressure

The **barometer** is used to measure atmospheric pressure. The device is still essentially the same as it was when invented in 1643 by the Italian physicist Evangelista Torricelli:

Vacuum off:
Pressure outside = pressure inside

Vacuum on:
Pressure outside >> pressure inside

**Figure 5.2** Effect of atmospheric pressure on a familiar object.

Vacuum above Hg column

Pressure due to weight of mercury ($P_{Hg}$)

Pressure due to weight of atmosphere ($P_{atm}$)

$\Delta h = 760$ mmHg

Dish filled with Hg

**Figure 5.3** A mercury barometer. The pressure of the atmosphere, $P_{atm}$, balances the pressure of the mercury column, $P_{Hg}$.

a tube about 1 m long, closed at one end, filled with mercury (atomic symbol, Hg), and inverted into a dish containing more mercury. When the tube is inverted, some of the mercury flows out into the dish, and a vacuum forms above the mercury remaining in the tube (Figure 5.3). At sea level, under ordinary atmospheric conditions, the mercury stops flowing out when the surface of the mercury in the tube is about 760 mm above the surface of the mercury in the dish. At that height, the column of mercury exerts the same pressure (weight/area) on the mercury surface in the dish as the atmosphere does: $P_{Hg} = P_{atm}$. Likewise, if you evacuate a closed tube and invert it into a dish of mercury, the atmosphere pushes the mercury up to a height of about 760 mm.

Notice that we did not specify the diameter of the barometer tube. If the mercury in a 1-cm diameter tube rises to a height of 760 mm, the mercury in a 2-cm diameter tube will rise to that height also. The *weight* of mercury is greater in the wider tube, but so is the area; thus, the *pressure,* the *ratio* of weight to area, is the same.

Because the pressure of the mercury column is directly proportional to its height, a unit commonly used for pressure is millimeters of mercury (mmHg). We discuss other units of pressure shortly. *At sea level and 0°C, normal atmospheric pressure is 760 mmHg;* at the top of Mt. Everest (elevation 29,028 ft, or 8848 m), the atmospheric pressure is only about 270 mmHg. Thus, *pressure decreases with altitude:* the column of air above the sea is taller, so it weighs more than the column of air above Mt. Everest.

Laboratory barometers contain mercury because its high density allows a barometer to be a convenient size. If a barometer contained water instead, it would have to be more than 34 ft high, because the pressure of the atmosphere equals the pressure of a column of water about 10,300 mm (almost 34 ft) high. For a given pressure, the ratio of heights ($h$) of the liquid columns is inversely related to the ratio of the densities ($d$) of the liquids:

$$\frac{h_{H_2O}}{h_{Hg}} = \frac{d_{Hg}}{d_{H_2O}}$$

Interestingly, several centuries ago, people thought a vacuum had mysterious "suction" powers, and they didn't understand why a suction pump could remove water from a well only to a depth of 34 feet. We know now, as the great 17th-century scientist Galileo explained, that a vacuum does not suck mercury up into a barometer tube, a suction pump does not suck water up from a well, the vacuum pump in Figure 5.2 does not suck in the walls of the crushed can, and the vacuum you create in a straw does not suck the drink into your mouth. Only matter—in this case, the atmospheric gases—can exert a force.

**Manometers** are devices used to measure the pressure of a gas in an experiment. Figure 5.4 shows two types of manometer. In the *closed-end manometer (left side),* a

**Closed-end manometer**

Closed end

Vacuum

Hg levels equal

Evacuated flask

$\Delta h$

$P_{gas}$

The Hg levels are equal because both arms of the U tube are evacuated.

A gas in the flask pushes the Hg level down in the left arm, and the difference in levels, $\Delta h$, equals the gas pressure, $P_{gas}$.

**Open-end manometer**

$P_{atm}$

Open end

$P_{atm}$

$P_{gas}$

$\Delta h$

$P_{gas}$

$\Delta h$

When $P_{gas}$ is less than $P_{atm}$, subtract $\Delta h$ from $P_{atm}$:
$P_{gas} < P_{atm}$
$P_{gas} = P_{atm} - \Delta h$

When $P_{gas}$ is greater than $P_{atm}$, add $\Delta h$ to $P_{atm}$:
$P_{gas} > P_{atm}$
$P_{gas} = P_{atm} + \Delta h$

**Figure 5.4** Two types of manometer.

mercury-filled, curved tube is *closed* at one end and attached to a flask at the other. When the flask is evacuated, the mercury levels in the two arms of the tube are the same because no gas exerts pressure on either mercury surface. When a gas is in the flask, it pushes down the mercury level in the near arm, causing the level to rise in the far arm. The *difference* in column heights ($\Delta h$) equals the gas pressure.

The *open-end manometer* (*right side* of Figure 5.4) also consists of a curved tube filled with mercury, but one end of the tube is *open* to the atmosphere and the other is connected to the gas sample. The atmosphere pushes on one mercury surface, and the gas pushes on the other. Again, $\Delta h$ equals the difference between two pressures. But, when using this type of manometer, we must measure the atmospheric pressure with a barometer and either add or subtract $\Delta h$ from that value.

## Units of Pressure

Pressure results from a force exerted on an area. The SI unit of force is the newton (N): $1 \text{ N} = 1 \text{ kg·m/s}^2$ (about the weight of an apple). The SI unit of pressure is the **pascal (Pa),** which equals a force of one newton exerted on an area of one square meter:

$$1 \text{ Pa} = 1 \text{ N/m}^2$$

A much larger unit is the **standard atmosphere (atm),** the average atmospheric pressure measured at sea level and 0°C. It is defined in terms of the pascal:

$$1 \text{ atm} = 101.325 \text{ kilopascals (kPa)} = 1.01325 \times 10^5 \text{ Pa}$$

Another common unit is the **millimeter of mercury (mmHg),** mentioned earlier; in honor of Torricelli, this unit has been renamed the **torr:**

$$1 \text{ torr} = 1 \text{ mmHg} = \frac{1}{760} \text{ atm} = \frac{101.325}{760} \text{ kPa} = 133.322 \text{ Pa}$$

The *bar* is coming into more common use in chemistry:

$$1 \text{ bar} = 1 \times 10^2 \text{ kPa} = 1 \times 10^5 \text{ Pa}$$

Despite a gradual change to SI units, many chemists still express pressure in torrs and atmospheres, so those units are used in this book, with reference to pascals and bars. Table 5.1 lists some important pressure units with the corresponding values for normal atmospheric pressure.

| Table **5.1** Common Units of Pressure | |
|---|---|
| **Unit** | **Normal Atmospheric Pressure at Sea Level and 0°C** |
| pascal (Pa); kilopascal (kPa) | $1.01325 \times 10^5$ Pa; 101.325 kPa |
| atmosphere (atm) | 1 atm* |
| millimeters of mercury (mmHg) | 760 mmHg* |
| torr | 760 torr* |
| pounds per square inch (lb/in² or psi) | 14.7 lb/in² |
| bar | 1.01325 bar |

*This is an exact quantity; in calculations, we use as many significant figures as necessary.

## Sample Problem 5.1    Converting Units of Pressure

**Problem** A geochemist heats a limestone ($CaCO_3$) sample and collects the $CO_2$ released in an evacuated flask attached to a closed-end manometer. After the system comes to room temperature, $\Delta h = 291.4$ mmHg. Calculate the $CO_2$ pressure in torrs, atmospheres, and kilopascals.

**Plan** The $CO_2$ pressure is given in units of mmHg, so we construct conversion factors from Table 5.1 to find the pressure in the other units.

**Solution**  Converting from mmHg to torr:

$$P_{CO_2} \text{ (torr)} = 291.4 \text{ mmHg} \times \frac{1 \text{ torr}}{1 \text{ mmHg}} = \boxed{291.4 \text{ torr}}$$

Converting from torr to atm:

$$P_{CO_2} \text{ (atm)} = 291.4 \text{ torr} \times \frac{1 \text{ atm}}{760 \text{ torr}} = \boxed{0.3834 \text{ atm}}$$

Converting from atm to kPa:

$$P_{CO_2} \text{ (kPa)} = 0.3834 \text{ atm} \times \frac{101.325 \text{ kPa}}{1 \text{ atm}} = \boxed{38.85 \text{ kPa}}$$

**Check**  There are 760 torr in 1 atm, so ~300 torr should be <0.5 atm. There are ~100 kPa in 1 atm, so <0.5 atm should be <50 kPa.

**Comment 1.** In the conversion from torr to atm, we retained four significant figures because this unit conversion factor involves *exact* numbers; that is, 760 torr has as many significant figures as the calculation requires (see the footnote on Table 5.1).
**2.** From here on, except in particularly complex situations, *unit canceling will no longer be shown.*

**Follow-Up Problem 5.1**  The $CO_2$ released from another mineral sample was collected in an evacuated flask connected to an open-end manometer. If the barometer reading is 753.6 mmHg and $P_{gas}$ is less than $P_{atm}$ to give a $\Delta h$ of 174.0 mmHg, calculate $P_{CO_2}$ in torrs, pascals, and lb/in$^2$.

## Summary of Section 5.2

- Gases exert pressure (force/area) on all surfaces they contact.
- A barometer measures atmospheric pressure based on the height of a mercury column that the atmosphere can support (760 mmHg at sea level and 0°C).
- Closed-end and open-end manometers are used to measure the pressure of a gas sample.
- Pressure units include the atmosphere (atm), torr (identical to mmHg), and pascal (Pa, the SI unit).

# 5.3 • THE GAS LAWS AND THEIR EXPERIMENTAL FOUNDATIONS

The physical behavior of a sample of gas can be described completely by four variables: pressure ($P$), volume ($V$), temperature ($T$), and amount (number of moles, $n$). The variables are interdependent, which means that *any one of them can be determined by measuring the other three.* Three key relationships exist among the four gas variables—Boyle's, Charles's, and Avogadro's laws. Each of these *gas laws expresses the effect of one variable on another, with the remaining two variables held constant.* Because gas volume is so easy to measure, the laws are expressed as the effect on gas volume of a change in the pressure, temperature, or amount of the gas.

The individual gas laws are special cases of a unifying relationship called the *ideal gas law,* which quantitatively describes the behavior of an **ideal gas,** one that exhibits linear relationships among volume, pressure, temperature, and amount. Although *no ideal gas actually exists,* most simple gases, such as $N_2$, $O_2$, $H_2$, and the noble gases, behave nearly ideally at ordinary temperatures and pressures. We discuss the ideal gas law after the three individual laws.

## The Relationship Between Volume and Pressure: Boyle's Law

Following Torricelli's invention of the barometer, the great 17th-century English chemist Robert Boyle studied the effect of pressure on the volume of a sample of gas.

1. *The experiment.* Figure 5.5 illustrates the setup Boyle might have used in his experiments (parts A and B), the data he might have collected (part C), and graphs of

**Figure 5.5** Boyle's law, the relationship between the volume and pressure of a gas.

the data (parts D and E). Boyle sealed the shorter leg of a J-shaped glass tube and poured mercury into the longer open leg, thereby trapping some air (the gas in the experiment) in the shorter leg. He calculated the gas volume ($V_{gas}$) from the height of the trapped air and the diameter of the tube. The total pressure, $P_{total}$, applied to the trapped gas is the pressure of the atmosphere, $P_{atm}$ (760 mm, measured with a barometer), plus the difference in the heights of the mercury columns ($\Delta h$) in the two legs of the J tube, 20 mm (Figure 5.5A); thus, $P_{total}$ is 780 torr. By adding mercury, Boyle increased $P_{total}$, and the gas volume decreased. In Figure 5.5B, more mercury has been added to the original $\Delta h$ of 20 mm, so $P_{total}$ doubles to 1560 torr; note that $V_{gas}$ is halved from 20 mL to 10 mL. In this way, by keeping the temperature and amount of gas constant, Boyle was able to measure the effect of the applied pressure on gas volume.

Note the following results in Figure 5.5:

- The product of corresponding $P$ and $V$ values is a constant (part C, rightmost column).
- $V$ is *inversely* proportional to $P$ (part D).
- $V$ is *directly* proportional to $1/P$ (part E), and a plot of $V$ versus $1/P$ is linear. This *linear relationship between two gas variables* is a hallmark of ideal gas behavior.

2. *Conclusion and statement of the law.* The generalization of Boyle's observations is known as **Boyle's law:** *at constant temperature, the volume occupied by a fixed amount of gas is **inversely** proportional to the applied (external) pressure,* or

$$V \propto \frac{1}{P} \qquad [T \text{ and } n \text{ fixed}] \qquad \textbf{(5.1)}$$

This relationship can also be expressed as

$$PV = \text{constant} \qquad \text{or} \qquad V = \frac{\text{constant}}{P} \qquad [T \text{ and } n \text{ fixed}]$$

That is, at fixed $T$ and $n$,       $P\uparrow, V\downarrow$    and    $P\downarrow, V\uparrow$

The constant is the same for most simple gases under ordinary conditions. Thus, tripling the external pressure reduces the volume of a gas to a third of its initial value; halving the pressure doubles the volume; and so forth.

The wording of Boyle's law focuses on *external* pressure. But, notice that the mercury level rises as mercury is added, until the pressure of the trapped gas *on* the mercury increases enough to stop its rise. At that point, the pressure exerted *on* the gas equals the pressure exerted *by* the gas ($P_{gas}$). Thus, in general, if $V_{gas}$ increases, $P_{gas}$ decreases, and vice versa.

## The Relationship Between Volume and Temperature: Charles's Law

Boyle's work showed that the pressure-volume relationship holds only at constant temperature, but why should that be so? It would take more than a century, until the work of French scientists J. A. C. Charles and J. L. Gay-Lussac, for the relationship between gas volume and temperature to be understood.

1. *The experiment.* Let's examine this relationship by measuring the volume at different temperatures of a fixed amount of a gas under constant pressure. A straight tube, closed at one end, traps a fixed amount of gas (air) under a small mercury plug. The tube is immersed in a water bath that is warmed with a heater or cooled with ice. After each change of temperature, we measure the length of the gas column, which is proportional to its volume. The total pressure exerted on the gas is constant because the mercury plug and the atmospheric pressure do not change (Figure 5.6, parts A and B).

Figure 5.6C shows some typical data. Consider the red line, which shows how the volume of 0.04 mol of gas at 1 atm pressure changes with temperature. Extrapolating that line to lower temperatures (dashed portion) shows that, in theory, the gas occupies zero volume at −273.15°C (the intercept on the temperature axis). Plots for a different amount of gas (green) or a different gas pressure (blue) have different slopes, but they all converge at −273.15°C. William Thomson (Lord Kelvin) later used this linear relation between gas volume and temperature to devise the absolute temperature scale (Section 1.5).

2. *Conclusion and statement of the law.* Above all, note that *the volume-temperature relationship is linear,* but, unlike volume and pressure, volume and temperature are *directly* proportional. This behavior is incorporated into the modern statement of the volume-temperature relationship, which is known as **Charles's law:** *at constant pressure, the volume occupied by a fixed amount of gas is* **directly** *proportional to its absolute (Kelvin) temperature,* or

$$V \propto T \qquad [P \text{ and } n \text{ fixed}] \tag{5.2}$$

This relationship can also be expressed as

$$\frac{V}{T} = \text{constant} \qquad \text{or} \qquad V = \text{constant} \times T \qquad [P \text{ and } n \text{ fixed}]$$

That is, at fixed $P$ and $n$, $\quad T\uparrow, V\uparrow \quad$ and $\quad T\downarrow, V\downarrow$

If $T$ increases, $V$ increases, and vice versa. Once again, for any given $P$ and $n$, the constant is the same for most simple gases under ordinary conditions.

**Figure 5.6** Charles's law, the relationship between the volume and temperature of a gas.

**A** Ice water bath (0°C, or 273 K)  **B** Boiling water bath (100°C, or 373 K)  **C**

Absolute zero (0 K or −273.15°C) is the temperature at which an ideal gas would have zero volume. (Absolute zero has never been reached, but physicists have attained $10^{-9}$ K.) In reality, no sample of matter can have zero volume, and every real gas condenses to a liquid at some temperature higher than 0 K. Nevertheless, the linear dependence of volume on absolute temperature holds for most common gases over a wide temperature range. This dependence of gas volume on the *absolute* temperature adds a practical requirement for chemists (and chemistry students): *the Kelvin scale must be used in gas law calculations.* For instance, if the temperature changes from 200 K to 400 K, the volume of gas doubles. But, if the temperature changes from 200°C to 400°C, the volume increases by a factor of 1.42; that is,

$$\left(\frac{400°C + 273.15}{200°C + 273.15}\right) = \frac{673}{473} = 1.42$$

### Other Relationships Based on Boyle's and Charles's Laws
Two other important relationships arise from Boyle's and Charles's laws:

1. *The pressure-temperature relationship.* Charles's law is expressed as the effect of temperature on gas *volume* at constant pressure. But volume and pressure are interdependent, so a similar relationship can be expressed for the effect of temperature on pressure (sometimes referred to as *Amontons's law*). Measure the pressure in your car or bike tires before and after a long ride, and you'll find that it increases. Heating due to friction between the tires and the road increases the air temperature inside the tires, but since a tire's volume can't increase very much, the air pressure does. Thus, *at constant volume, the pressure exerted by a fixed amount of gas is directly proportional to the absolute temperature:*

$$P \propto T \qquad [V \text{ and } n \text{ fixed}] \qquad (5.3)$$

or

$$\frac{P}{T} = \text{constant} \qquad \text{or} \qquad P = \text{constant} \times T$$

That is, at fixed $V$ and $n$, $\qquad T\uparrow, P\uparrow \qquad$ and $\qquad T\downarrow, P\downarrow$

2. *The combined gas law.* Combining Boyle's and Charles's laws gives the *combined gas law,* which applies to cases when changes in *two* of the three variables ($V$, $P$, $T$) affect the third:

$$V \propto \frac{T}{P} \qquad \text{or} \qquad V = \text{constant} \times \frac{T}{P} \qquad \text{or} \qquad \frac{PV}{T} = \text{constant}$$

### The Relationship Between Volume and Amount: Avogadro's Law

Let's see why both Boyle's and Charles's laws specify a fixed amount of gas.

1. *The experiment.* Figure 5.7 shows an experiment that involves two small test tubes, each fitted to a much larger piston-cylinder assembly. We add 0.10 mol (4.4 g) of dry ice (solid $CO_2$) to the first tube (A) and 0.20 mol (8.8 g) to the second tube (B). As the solid $CO_2$ warms to room temperature, it changes to gaseous $CO_2$, and the volume increases until $P_{gas} = P_{atm}$. At constant temperature, when all the solid has changed to gas, cylinder B has twice the volume of cylinder A.

**Figure 5.7** The relationship between the volume and amount of a gas.

2. *Conclusion and statement of the law.* Thus, *at fixed temperature and pressure, the volume occupied by a gas is directly proportional to the amount (mol) of gas:*

$$V \propto n \qquad [P \text{ and } T \text{ fixed}] \qquad \text{(5.4)}$$

That is, as *n* increases, *V* increases, and vice versa. This relationship is also expressed as

$$\frac{V}{n} = \text{constant} \qquad \text{or} \qquad V = \text{constant} \times n$$

That is, at fixed *P* and *T*, $n\uparrow, V\uparrow$ and $n\downarrow, V\downarrow$

The constant is the same for all simple gases at ordinary temperature and pressure. This relationship is another way of expressing **Avogadro's law,** which states that *at fixed temperature and pressure, equal volumes of **any** ideal gas contain equal numbers of particles (or moles).*

### Familiar Applications of the Gas Laws

The gas laws apply to countless familiar phenomena. In a car engine, a reaction occurs in which fewer moles of gasoline and $O_2$ form more moles of $CO_2$ and $H_2O$ vapor, and heat is released. The increase in *n* (Avogadro's law) and *T* (Charles's law) increases *V*, and the piston is pushed back. Dynamite is a solid that forms more moles of hot gases very rapidly when it reacts (Avogadro's and Charles's laws). Dough rises because yeast digests sugar, which creates bubbles of $CO_2$ (Avogadro's law); the dough expands more as the bread bakes in a hot oven (Charles's law).

No application of the gas laws can be more vital or familiar than breathing (Figure 5.8). When you inhale, muscles move your diaphragm down and your rib cage out (*blue*). This coordinated movement increases the volume of your lungs, which decreases the air pressure inside them (Boyle's law). The inside pressure is 1–3 torr *less* than atmospheric pressure, so air rushes in. The greater amount of air stretches the elastic tissue of the lungs and expands the volume further (Avogadro's law). The air also expands as it warms from the external temperature to your body temperature (Charles's law). When you exhale, the diaphragm moves up and the rib cage moves in, so your lung volume decreases (*red*). The inside pressure becomes 1–3 torr *more* than the outside pressure (Boyle's law), so air rushes out.

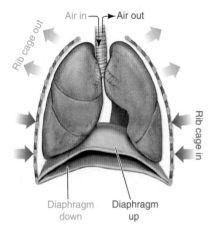

**Figure 5.8** The process of breathing applies the gas laws.

### Gas Behavior at Standard Conditions

To better understand the factors that influence gas behavior, chemists have assigned a baseline set of *standard conditions* called **standard temperature and pressure (STP):**

$$\text{STP:} \quad 0°C \text{ (273.15 K) and 1 atm (760 torr)} \qquad \text{(5.5)}$$

Under these conditions, the volume of 1 mol of an ideal gas is called the **standard molar volume:**

$$\text{Standard molar volume} = 22.4141 \text{ L or } 22.4 \text{ L } [\text{to 3 sf}] \qquad \text{(5.6)}$$

At STP, helium (He), nitrogen ($N_2$), oxygen ($O_2$), and other simple gases behave nearly ideally (Figure 5.9). Note that the mass, and thus the density (*d*), depend on the specific gas, but 1 mol of any of them occupies 22.4 L at STP. Figure 5.10 compares the volumes of some familiar objects with the standard molar volume of an ideal gas.

### The Ideal Gas Law

Each of the three gas laws shows how one of the three other gas variables affects gas volume:

- Boyle's law focuses on pressure ($V \propto 1/P$).
- Charles's law focuses on temperature ($V \propto T$).
- Avogadro's law focuses on amount (mol) of gas ($V \propto n$).

| n = 1 mol | n = 1 mol | n = 1 mol |
|---|---|---|
| P = 1 atm (760 torr) | P = 1 atm (760 torr) | P = 1 atm (760 torr) |
| T = 0°C (273 K) | T = 0°C (273 K) | T = 0°C (273 K) |
| V = 22.4 L | V = 22.4 L | V = 22.4 L |
| Number of gas particles = $6.022 \times 10^{23}$ | Number of gas particles = $6.022 \times 10^{23}$ | Number of gas particles = $6.022 \times 10^{23}$ |
| Mass = 4.003 g | Mass = 28.02 g | Mass = 32.00 g |
| d = 0.179 g/L | d = 1.25 g/L | d = 1.43 g/L |

**Figure 5.9 Standard molar volume.** One mole of an ideal gas occupies 22.4 L at STP (0°C and 1 atm).

**Figure 5.10** The volumes of 1 mol (22.4 L) of an ideal gas and of some familiar objects: 1 gal of milk (3.79 L), a basketball (7.50 L), and 2.00 L of a carbonated drink.

By combining these individual effects, we obtain the **ideal gas law** (or *ideal gas equation*):

$$V \propto \frac{nT}{P} \quad \text{or} \quad PV \propto nT \quad \text{or} \quad \frac{PV}{nT} = R$$

where $R$ is a proportionality constant known as the **universal gas constant.** Rearranging gives the most common form of the ideal gas law:

$$PV = nRT \tag{5.7}$$

We obtain a value of $R$ by measuring the volume, temperature, and pressure of a given amount of gas and substituting the values into the ideal gas law. For example, using standard conditions for the gas variables and 1 mol of gas, we have

$$R = \frac{PV}{nT} = \frac{1 \text{ atm} \times 22.4141 \text{ L}}{1 \text{ mol} \times 273.15 \text{ K}} = 0.082058 \frac{\text{atm} \cdot \text{L}}{\text{mol} \cdot \text{K}} = 0.0821 \frac{\text{atm} \cdot \text{L}}{\text{mol} \cdot \text{K}} \, [3 \text{ sf}] \tag{5.8}$$

This numerical value of $R$ corresponds to $P$, $V$, and $T$ expressed *in these units; $R$ has a different numerical value when different units are used.* For example, on p. 209, $R$ has the value 8.314 J/mol·K (J stands for joule, the SI unit of energy).

Figure 5.11 on the next page makes a central point: the ideal gas law *becomes* one of the individual gas laws when two of the four variables are kept constant. When initial conditions (subscript 1) change to final conditions (subscript 2), we have

$$P_1V_1 = n_1RT_1 \quad \text{and} \quad P_2V_2 = n_2RT_2$$

Thus, $\quad \dfrac{P_1V_1}{n_1T_1} = R \quad \text{and} \quad \dfrac{P_2V_2}{n_2T_2} = R, \quad \text{so} \quad \dfrac{P_1V_1}{n_1T_1} = \dfrac{P_2V_2}{n_2T_2}$

Notice that if, for example, the two variables $P$ and $T$ remain constant, then $P_1 = P_2$ and $T_1 = T_2$, and we obtain an expression for Avogadro's law:

$$\frac{P_1V_1}{n_1T_1} = \frac{P_2V_2}{n_2T_2} \quad \text{or} \quad \frac{V_1}{n_1} = \frac{V_2}{n_2}$$

# IDEAL GAS LAW

Figure 5.11 The individual gas laws as special cases of the ideal gas law.

As you'll see next, you can use a similar approach to solve gas law problems. Thus, by keeping track of the initial and final values of the gas variables, you avoid the need to memorize the three individual gas laws.

## Solving Gas Law Problems

Gas law problems are phrased in many ways but can usually be grouped into two types:

   1. *A change in one of the four variables causes a change in another, while the two other variables remain constant.* In this type, the ideal gas law reduces to one of the individual gas laws, and you solve for the new value of the affected variable. Units must be consistent and *T* must always be in kelvins, but *R* is not involved. Sample Problems 5.2 to 5.4 and 5.6 are of this type. [A variation on this type involves the combined gas law (p. 189) when simultaneous changes in two of the variables cause a change in a third.]
   2. *One variable is unknown, but the other three are known and no change occurs.* In this type, exemplified by Sample Problem 5.5, you apply the ideal gas law directly to find the unknown, and the units must conform to those in *R*.

Solving these problems requires a systematic approach:

• Summarize the changing gas variables—knowns and unknown—and those held constant.
• Convert units, if necessary.
• Rearrange the ideal gas law to obtain the needed relationship of variables, and solve for the unknown.

**Road Map**

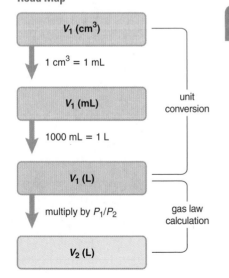

## Sample Problem 5.2 Applying the Volume-Pressure Relationship

**Problem** Boyle's apprentice finds that the air trapped in a J tube occupies 24.8 cm³ at 1.12 atm. By adding mercury to the tube, he increases the pressure on the trapped air to 2.64 atm. Assuming constant temperature, what is the new volume of air (in L)?

**Plan** We must find the final volume ($V_2$) in liters, given the initial volume ($V_1$), initial pressure ($P_1$), and final pressure ($P_2$). The temperature and amount of gas are fixed. We convert the units of $V_1$ from cm³ to mL and then to L, rearrange the ideal gas law to the appropriate form, and solve for $V_2$. (Note that the road map has two parts.)

**Solution** Summarizing the gas variables:

$$P_1 = 1.12 \text{ atm} \qquad\qquad P_2 = 2.64 \text{ atm}$$
$$V_1 = 24.8 \text{ cm}^3 \text{ (convert to L)} \qquad V_2 = \text{unknown} \qquad T \text{ and } n \text{ remain constant}$$

Converting $V_1$ from cm³ to L:

$$V_1 = 24.8 \text{ cm}^3 \times \frac{1 \text{ mL}}{1 \text{ cm}^3} \times \frac{1 \text{ L}}{1000 \text{ mL}} = 0.0248 \text{ L}$$

Rearranging the ideal gas law and solving for $V_2$: At fixed $n$ and $T$, we have

$$\frac{P_1V_1}{n_1T_1} = \frac{P_2V_2}{n_2T_2} \quad \text{or} \quad P_1V_1 = P_2V_2$$

$$V_2 = V_1 \times \frac{P_1}{P_2} = 0.0248 \text{ L} \times \frac{1.12 \text{ atm}}{2.64 \text{ atm}} = \boxed{0.0105 \text{ L}}$$

**Check** The relative values of $P$ and $V$ can help us check the math: $P$ more than doubled, so $V_2$ should be less than $\frac{1}{2}V_1$ ($0.0105/0.0248 < \frac{1}{2}$).

**Comment** Predicting the direction of the change provides another check on the problem setup: Since $P$ increases, $V$ will decrease; thus, $V_2$ should be less than $V_1$. To make $V_2 < V_1$, we must multiply $V_1$ by a number *less than* 1. This means the ratio of pressures must be *less than* 1, so the larger pressure ($P_2$) must be in the denominator, or $P_1/P_2$.

**Follow-Up Problem 5.2** A sample of argon gas occupies 105 mL at 0.871 atm. If the temperature remains constant, what is the volume (in L) at 26.3 kPa?

---

**Sample Problem 5.3** | **Applying the Pressure-Temperature Relationship**

**Problem** A steel tank used for fuel delivery is fitted with a safety valve that opens if the internal pressure exceeds $1.00 \times 10^3$ torr. It is filled with methane at 23°C and 0.991 atm and placed in boiling water 100.°C. Will the safety valve open?

**Plan** The question "Will the safety valve open?" translates to "Is $P_2$ greater than $1.00 \times 10^3$ torr at $T_2$?" Thus, $P_2$ is the unknown, and $T_1$, $T_2$, and $P_1$ are given, with $V$ (steel tank) and $n$ fixed. We convert both $T$ values to kelvins and $P_1$ to torrs in order to compare $P_2$ with the safety-limit pressure. We rearrange the ideal gas law and solve for $P_2$.

**Road Map**

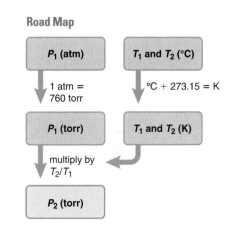

**Solution** Summarizing the gas variables:

$$P_1 = 0.991 \text{ atm (convert to torr)} \quad P_2 = \text{unknown}$$
$$T_1 = 23°C \text{ (convert to K)} \quad T_2 = 100.°C \text{ (convert to K)}$$
$$V \text{ and } n \text{ remain constant}$$

Converting $T$ from °C to K:

$$T_1 \text{ (K)} = 23°C + 273.15 = 296 \text{ K} \quad T_2 \text{ (K)} = 100.°C + 273.15 = 373 \text{ K}$$

Converting $P$ from atm to torr:

$$P_1 \text{ (torr)} = 0.991 \text{ atm} \times \frac{760 \text{ torr}}{1 \text{ atm}} = 753 \text{ torr}$$

Rearranging the ideal gas law and solving for $P_2$: At fixed $n$ and $V$, we have

$$\frac{P_1V_1}{n_1T_1} = \frac{P_2V_2}{n_2T_2} \quad \text{or} \quad \frac{P_1}{T_1} = \frac{P_2}{T_2}$$

$$P_2 = P_1 \times \frac{T_2}{T_1} = 753 \text{ torr} \times \frac{373 \text{ K}}{296 \text{ K}} = 949 \text{ torr}$$

$P_2$ is less than $1.00 \times 10^3$ torr, so $\boxed{\text{the valve will *not* open.}}$

**Check** Let's predict the change to check the math: Because $T_2 > T_1$, we expect $P_2 > P_1$. Thus, the temperature ratio should be $>1$ ($T_2$ in the numerator). The $T$ ratio is about 1.25 (373/296), so the $P$ ratio should also be about 1.25 (950/750 $\approx$ 1.25).

**Follow-Up Problem 5.3** An engineer pumps air at 0°C into a newly designed piston-cylinder assembly. The volume measures 6.83 cm³. At what temperature (in K) will the volume be 9.75 cm³?

## Road Map

**n₁ (mol) of He**

↓ multiply by $V_2/V_1$

**n₂ (mol) of He**

↓ subtract $n_1$

**n_add'l (mol) of He**

↓ multiply by $\mathcal{M}$ (g/mol)

**Mass (g) of He**

---

**Sample Problem 5.4**    **Applying the Volume-Amount Relationship**

**Problem**  A scale model of a blimp rises when it is filled with helium to a volume of 55.0 dm³. When 1.10 mol of He is added to the blimp, the volume is 26.2 dm³. How many more grams of He must be added to make it rise? Assume constant $T$ and $P$.

**Plan**  We are given the initial amount of helium ($n_1$), the initial volume of the blimp ($V_1$), and the volume needed for it to rise ($V_2$), and we need the additional mass of helium to make it rise. So we first need to find $n_2$. We rearrange the ideal gas law to the appropriate form, solve for $n_2$, subtract $n_1$ to find the additional amount ($n_{add'l}$), and then convert moles to grams.

**Solution**  Summarizing the gas variables:

$$n_1 = 1.10 \text{ mol} \qquad n_2 = \text{unknown (find, and then subtract } n_1)$$
$$V_1 = 26.2 \text{ dm}^3 \qquad V_2 = 55.0 \text{ dm}^3$$
$$P \text{ and } T \text{ remain constant}$$

Rearranging the ideal gas law and solving for $n_2$: At fixed $P$ and $T$, we have

$$\frac{P_T V_1}{n_1 T_T} = \frac{P_2 V_2}{n_2 T_2} \qquad \text{or} \qquad \frac{V_1}{n_1} = \frac{V_2}{n_2}$$

$$n_2 = n_1 \times \frac{V_2}{V_1} = 1.10 \text{ mol He} \times \frac{55.0 \text{ dm}^3}{26.2 \text{ dm}^3}$$

$$= 2.31 \text{ mol He}$$

Finding the additional amount of He:

$$n_{add'l} = n_2 - n_1 = 2.31 \text{ mol He} - 1.10 \text{ mol He}$$

$$= 1.21 \text{ mol He}$$

Converting amount (mol) of He to mass (g):

$$\text{Mass (g) of He} = 1.21 \text{ mol He} \times \frac{4.003 \text{ g He}}{1 \text{ mol He}}$$

$$= \boxed{4.84 \text{ g He}}$$

**Check**  We predict that $n_2 > n_1$ because $V_2 > V_1$: since $V_2$ is about twice $V_1$ (55/26 ≈ 2), $n_2$ should be about twice $n_1$ (2.3/1.1 ≈ 2). Since $n_2 > n_1$, we were right to multiply $n_1$ by a number >1 (that is, $V_2/V_1$). About 1.2 mol × 4 g/mol ≈ 4.8 g.

**Comment 1.**  A different sequence of steps will give you the same answer: first find the additional volume ($V_{add'l} = V_2 - V_1$), and then solve directly for $n_{add'l}$. Try it for yourself.
**2.**  You saw that Charles's law ($V \propto T$ at fixed $P$ and $n$) becomes a similar relationship between $P$ and $T$ at fixed $V$ and $n$. The follow-up problem demonstrates that Avogadro's law ($V \propto n$ at fixed $P$ and $T$) becomes a similar relationship at fixed $V$ and $T$.

**Follow-Up Problem 5.4**  A rigid plastic container holds 35.0 g of ethylene gas ($C_2H_4$) at a pressure of 793 torr. What is the pressure if 5.0 g of ethylene is removed at constant temperature?

---

**Sample Problem 5.5**    **Solving for an Unknown Gas Variable at Fixed Conditions**

**Problem**  A steel tank has a volume of 438 L and is filled with 0.885 kg of $O_2$. Calculate the pressure of $O_2$ at 21°C.

**Plan**  We are given $V$, $T$, and the mass of $O_2$, and we must find $P$. Since conditions are not changing, we apply the ideal gas law without rearranging it. We use the given $V$ in liters, convert $T$ to kelvins and mass (kg) of $O_2$ to amount (mol), and solve for $P$.

**Solution** Summarizing the gas variables:

$V = 438$ L $\qquad\qquad\qquad\qquad$ $T = 21°C$ (convert to K)

$n = 0.885$ kg $O_2$ (convert to mol) $\qquad$ $P = $ unknown

Converting $T$ from °C to K:

$$T\,(K) = 21°C + 273.15 = 294\ K$$

Converting from mass (g) of $O_2$ to amount (mol):

$$n = \text{mol of } O_2 = 0.885 \text{ kg } O_2 \times \frac{1000\ g}{1\ kg} \times \frac{1\ \text{mol } O_2}{32.00\ g\ O_2} = 27.7\ \text{mol } O_2$$

Solving for $P$ (note the unit canceling here):

$$P = \frac{nRT}{V} = \frac{27.7\ \cancel{\text{mol}} \times 0.0821\ \dfrac{\text{atm·}\cancel{L}}{\cancel{\text{mol·K}}} \times 294\ \cancel{K}}{438\ \cancel{L}}$$

$$= \boxed{1.53\ \text{atm}}$$

**Check** The amount of $O_2$ seems correct: $\sim900$ g/(30 g/mol) = 30 mol. To check the approximate size of the final calculation, round off the values, including that for $R$:

$$P = \frac{30\ \text{mol } O_2 \times 0.1\ \dfrac{\text{atm·L}}{\text{mol·K}} \times 300\ K}{450\ L} = 2\ \text{atm}$$

which is reasonably close to 1.53 atm.

**Follow-Up Problem 5.5** The tank in the sample problem develops a slow leak that is discovered and sealed. The new pressure is 1.37 atm. How many grams of $O_2$ remain?

---

Finally, in a picture problem, we apply the gas laws to determine the balanced equation for a gaseous reaction.

## Sample Problem 5.6 — Using Gas Laws to Determine a Balanced Equation

**Problem** The piston-cylinder below is depicted before and after a gaseous reaction that is carried out in it at constant pressure: the temperature is 150 K before and 300 K after the reaction. (Assume the cylinder is insulated.)

Which of the following balanced equations describes the reaction?

(1) $A_2(g) + B_2(g) \longrightarrow 2AB(g)$ $\qquad\qquad$ (2) $2AB(g) + B_2(g) \longrightarrow 2AB_2(g)$

(3) $A(g) + B_2(g) \longrightarrow AB_2(g)$ $\qquad\qquad$ (4) $2AB_2(g) \longrightarrow A_2(g) + 2B_2(g)$

**Plan** We are shown a depiction of the volume and temperature of a gas mixture before and after a reaction and must deduce the balanced equation. The problem says that $P$ is constant, and the picture shows that, when $T$ doubles, $V$ stays the same. If $n$ were also constant, Charles's law tells us that $V$ should double when $T$ doubles. But, since $V$ does not change, $n$ cannot be constant. From Avogadro's law, the only way to maintain $V$ constant, with $P$ constant and $T$ doubling, is for $n$ to be halved. So we examine the four balanced equations and count the number of moles on each side to see in which equation $n$ is halved.

**Solution** In equation (1), $n$ does not change, so doubling $T$ would double $V$.
In equation (2), $n$ decreases from 3 mol to 2 mol, so doubling $T$ would increase $V$ by one-third.
In equation (3), $n$ decreases from 2 mol to 1 mol. Doubling $T$ would exactly balance the decrease from halving $n$, so $V$ would stay the same.
In equation (4), $n$ increases, so doubling $T$ would more than double $V$.
Therefore, equation (3) is correct:

$$A(g) + B_2(g) \longrightarrow AB_2(g)$$

**Follow-Up Problem 5.6** The piston-cylinder below shows the volumes of a gaseous reaction mixture before and after a reaction that takes place at constant pressure and an initial temperature of $-73°C$.

If the *unbalanced* equation is $CD(g) \longrightarrow C_2(g) + D_2(g)$, what is the final temperature (in °C)?

---

## Summary of Section 5.3

- Four interdependent variables define the physical behavior of an ideal gas: volume ($V$), pressure ($P$), temperature ($T$), and amount (number of moles, $n$).
- Most simple gases display nearly ideal behavior at ordinary temperatures and pressures.
- Boyle's, Charles's, and Avogadro's laws refer to the linear relationships between the volume of a gas and the pressure, temperature, and amount of gas, respectively.
- At STP (0°C and 1 atm), 1 mol of an ideal gas occupies 22.4 L.
- The ideal gas law incorporates the individual gas laws into one equation: $PV = nRT$, where $R$ is the universal gas constant.

---

# 5.4 • REARRANGEMENTS OF THE IDEAL GAS LAW

In this section, we mathematically rearrange the ideal gas law to find gas density, molar mass, the partial pressure of each gas in a mixture, and the amount of gaseous reactant or product in a reaction.

## The Density of a Gas

One mole of any gas behaving ideally occupies the same volume at a given temperature and pressure, so differences in gas density ($d = m/V$) depend on differences in molar mass (see Figure 5.9, p. 191). For example, at STP, 1 mol of $O_2$ occupies the same volume as 1 mol of $N_2$; however, $O_2$ is denser because each $O_2$ molecule has a greater mass (32.00 amu) than each $N_2$ molecule (28.02 amu). Thus, $d$ of $O_2$ is $\dfrac{32.00}{28.02} \times d$ of $N_2$.

We can rearrange the ideal gas law to calculate the density of a gas from its molar mass. Recall that the number of moles ($n$) is the mass ($m$) divided by the molar mass ($\mathcal{M}$), $n = m/\mathcal{M}$. Substituting for $n$ in the ideal gas law gives

$$PV = \frac{m}{\mathcal{M}}RT$$

Rearranging to isolate $m/V$ gives

$$\frac{m}{V} = d = \frac{\mathcal{M} \times P}{RT} \tag{5.9}$$

Two important ideas are expressed by Equation 5.9:

- *The density of a gas is directly proportional to its molar mass.* The volume of a given amount of a heavier gas equals the volume of the same amount of a lighter gas (Avogadro's law), so the density of the heavier gas is higher (as you just saw for $O_2$ and $N_2$).
- *The density of a gas is inversely proportional to the temperature.* As the volume of a gas increases with temperature (Charles's law), the same mass occupies more space, so the density of the gas is lower.

We use Equation 5.9 to find the density of a gas at any temperature and pressure near standard conditions.

---

## Sample Problem 5.7    Calculating Gas Density

**Problem**  To apply a green chemistry approach, a chemical engineer uses waste $CO_2$ from a manufacturing process, instead of chlorofluorocarbons, as a "blowing agent" in the production of polystyrene. Find the density (in g/L) of $CO_2$ and the number of molecules per liter **(a)** at STP (0°C and 1 atm) and **(b)** at room conditions (20.°C and 1.00 atm).

**Plan**  We must find the density ($d$) and the number of molecules of $CO_2$, given two sets of $P$ and $T$ data. We find $\mathcal{M}$, convert $T$ to kelvins, and calculate $d$ with Equation 5.9. Then we convert the mass per liter to molecules per liter with Avogadro's number.

**Solution**  **(a)** Density and molecules per liter of $CO_2$ at STP. Summary of gas properties:

$$T = 0°C + 273.15 = 273 \text{ K} \qquad P = 1 \text{ atm} \qquad \mathcal{M} \text{ of } CO_2 = 44.01 \text{ g/mol}$$

Calculating density (note the unit canceling here):

$$d = \frac{\mathcal{M} \times P}{RT} = \frac{44.01 \text{ g/\cancel{mol}} \times 1.00 \text{ \cancel{atm}}}{0.0821 \frac{\cancel{atm} \cdot L}{\cancel{mol} \cdot \cancel{K}} \times 273 \text{ \cancel{K}}} = \boxed{1.96 \text{ g/L}}$$

Converting from mass/L to molecules/L:

$$\text{Molecules } CO_2/L = \frac{1.96 \text{ g } CO_2}{1 \text{ L}} \times \frac{1 \text{ mol } CO_2}{44.01 \text{ g } CO_2} \times \frac{6.022 \times 10^{23} \text{ molecules } CO_2}{1 \text{ mol } CO_2}$$

$$= \boxed{2.68 \times 10^{22} \text{ molecules } CO_2/L}$$

**(b)** Density and molecules of $CO_2$ per liter at room conditions. Summary of gas properties:

$$T = 20.°C + 273.15 = 293 \text{ K} \qquad P = 1.00 \text{ atm} \qquad \mathcal{M} \text{ of } CO_2 = 44.01 \text{ g/mol}$$

Calculating density:

$$d = \frac{\mathcal{M} \times P}{RT} = \frac{44.01 \text{ g/mol} \times 1.00 \text{ atm}}{0.0821 \frac{atm \cdot L}{mol \cdot K} \times 293 \text{ K}} = \boxed{1.83 \text{ g/L}}$$

Converting from mass/L to molecules/L:

$$\text{Molecules } CO_2/L = \frac{1.83 \text{ g } CO_2}{1 \text{ L}} \times \frac{1 \text{ mol } CO_2}{44.01 \text{ g } CO_2} \times \frac{6.022 \times 10^{23} \text{ molecules } CO_2}{1 \text{ mol } CO_2}$$

$$= \boxed{2.50 \times 10^{22} \text{ molecules } CO_2/L}$$

**Check**  Round off to check the density values; for example, in (a), at STP:

$$\frac{50 \text{ g/mol} \times 1 \text{ atm}}{0.1 \frac{atm \cdot L}{mol \cdot K} \times 250 \text{ K}} = 2 \text{ g/L} \approx 1.96 \text{ g/L}$$

At the higher temperature in (b), the density should decrease, which can happen only if there are fewer molecules per liter, so the answer is reasonable.

**Comment 1.** An *alternative approach* for finding the density of most simple gases, but *at STP only,* is to divide the molar mass by the standard molar volume, 22.4 L:

$$d = \frac{\mathcal{M}}{V} = \frac{44.01 \text{ g/mol}}{22.4 \text{ L/mol}} = 1.96 \text{ g/L}$$

Once you know the density at one temperature (0°C), you can find it at any other temperature with the following relationship: $d_1/d_2 = T_2/T_1$.
**2.** Note that we have different numbers of significant figures for the pressure values. In (a), "1 atm" is part of the definition of STP, so it is an exact number. In (b), we specified "1.00 atm" to allow three significant figures in the answer.

**Follow-Up Problem 5.7** Compare the density of $CO_2$ at 0°C and 380. torr with its density at STP.

**Gas Density and the Human Condition** A few applications demonstrate the wide-ranging relevance of gas density:

- *Engineering.* Architectural designers and heating engineers place heating ducts near the floor so that the warmer, and thus less dense, air coming from the ducts will rise and mix with the cooler room air.
  - *Safety and air pollution.* In the absence of mixing, a less dense gas will lie above a more dense one. Fire extinguishers that release $CO_2$ are effective because this gas is heavier than air: it sinks onto the fire and keeps more $O_2$ from reaching the fuel. The dense gases in smog that blankets urban centers, such as Mexico City, Los Angeles, and Beijing, contribute to respiratory illnesses.
  - *Toxic releases.* During World War I, poisonous phosgene gas ($COCl_2$) was used against ground troops because it was dense enough to sink into their trenches. In 1984, the accidental release of poisonous methylisocyanate gas from a Union Carbide plant in India killed thousands of people as it blanketed nearby neighborhoods. In 1986, $CO_2$ released naturally from Lake Nyos in Cameroon suffocated thousands of people as it flowed down valleys into villages. Some paleontologists suggest that the release of $CO_2$ from volcanic lakes may have contributed to widespread dying off of dinosaurs.
- *Ballooning.* When the gas in a hot-air balloon is heated, its volume increases and the balloon inflates. Further heating causes some of the gas to escape. Thus, the gas density decreases and the balloon rises. In 1783, Jacques Charles (of Charles's law) made one of the first balloon flights, and 20 years later, Joseph Gay-Lussac (who studied the pressure-temperature relationship) set a solo altitude record that held for 50 years.

## The Molar Mass of a Gas

Through another rearrangement of the ideal gas law, we can determine the molar mass of an unknown gas or a volatile liquid (one that is easily vaporized):

$$n = \frac{m}{\mathcal{M}} = \frac{PV}{RT} \qquad \text{so} \qquad \mathcal{M} = \frac{mRT}{PV} \qquad \text{(5.10)}$$

Notice that this equation is just a rearrangement of Equation 5.9.

---

**Sample Problem 5.8** **Finding the Molar Mass of a Volatile Liquid**

**Problem** An organic chemist isolates a colorless liquid from a petroleum sample. She places the liquid in a preweighed flask and puts the flask in boiling water, which vaporizes the liquid and fills the flask with gas. She closes the flask and reweighs it. She obtains the following data:

| | | |
|---|---|---|
| Volume ($V$) of flask = 213 mL | $T$ = 100.0°C | $P$ = 754 torr |
| Mass of flask + gas = 78.416 g | Mass of flask = 77.834 g | |

Calculate the molar mass of the liquid.

**Plan** We are given $V$, $T$, $P$, and mass data and must find the molar mass ($M$) of the liquid. We convert $V$ to liters, $T$ to kelvins, and $P$ to atmospheres, find the mass of gas by subtracting the mass of the flask from the mass of the flask plus gas, and use Equation 5.10 to calculate $M$.

**Solution** Summarizing and converting the gas variables:

$$V\ (L) = 213\ mL \times \frac{1\ L}{1000\ mL} = 0.213\ L \qquad T\ (K) = 100.0°C + 273.15 = 373.2\ K$$

$$P\ (atm) = 754\ torr \times \frac{1\ atm}{760\ torr} = 0.992\ atm \qquad m = 78.416\ g - 77.834\ g = 0.582\ g$$

Calculating $M$:

$$M = \frac{mRT}{PV} = \frac{0.582\ g \times 0.0821\ \dfrac{atm \cdot L}{mol \cdot K} \times 373.2\ K}{0.992\ atm \times 0.213\ L} = \boxed{84.4\ g/mol}$$

**Check** Rounding to check the arithmetic, we have

$$\frac{0.6\ g \times 0.08\ \dfrac{atm \cdot L}{mol \cdot K} \times 375\ K}{1\ atm \times 0.2\ L} = 90\ g/mol \qquad \text{(which is close to 84.4 g/mol)}$$

**Follow-Up Problem 5.8** An empty 149-mL flask weighs 68.322 g before a sample of volatile liquid is added. The flask is then placed in a hot (95.0°C) water bath; the barometric pressure is 740. torr. The liquid vaporizes and the gas fills the flask. After cooling, flask and condensed liquid together weigh 68.697 g. What is the molar mass of the liquid?

## The Partial Pressure of Each Gas in a Mixture of Gases

The gas behaviors we've discussed so far were observed in experiments with air, which is a mixture of gases; thus, the ideal gas law holds for virtually any gas at ordinary conditions, whether pure or a mixture, because

- Gases mix homogeneously (form a solution) in any proportions.
- Each gas in a mixture behaves as if it were the only gas present (assuming no chemical interactions).

**Dalton's Law of Partial Pressures** The second point above was discovered by John Dalton during his lifelong study of humidity. He observed that when water vapor is added to dry air, the total air pressure increases by the pressure of the water vapor:

$$P_{\text{humid air}} = P_{\text{dry air}} + P_{\text{added water vapor}}$$

He concluded that each gas in the mixture exerts a **partial pressure** equal to the pressure it would exert *by itself*. Stated as **Dalton's law of partial pressures,** his discovery was that *in a mixture of unreacting gases, the total pressure is the sum of the partial pressures of the individual gases:*

$$P_{\text{total}} = P_1 + P_2 + P_3 + \cdots \tag{5.11}$$

As an example, suppose we have a tank of fixed volume that contains nitrogen gas at a certain pressure, and we introduce a sample of hydrogen gas into the tank. Each gas behaves independently, so we can write an ideal gas law expression for each:

$$P_{N_2} = \frac{n_{N_2}RT}{V} \qquad \text{and} \qquad P_{H_2} = \frac{n_{H_2}RT}{V}$$

Because each gas occupies the same total volume and is at the same temperature, the pressure of each gas depends only on its amount, $n$. Thus, the total pressure is

$$P_{\text{total}} = P_{N_2} + P_{H_2} = \frac{n_{N_2}RT}{V} + \frac{n_{H_2}RT}{V} = \frac{(n_{N_2} + n_{H_2})RT}{V} = \frac{n_{\text{total}}RT}{V}$$

where $n_{\text{total}} = n_{N_2} + n_{H_2}$.

Each component in a mixture contributes a fraction of the total number of moles in the mixture; this portion is the **mole fraction ($X$)** of that component. Multiplying $X$ by 100 gives the mole percent. The sum of the mole fractions of all components must be 1, and the sum of the mole percents must be 100%. For $N_2$ in our mixture, the mole fraction is

$$X_{N_2} = \frac{n_{N_2}}{n_{total}} = \frac{n_{N_2}}{n_{N_2} + n_{H_2}}$$

If the total pressure is due to the total number of moles, the partial pressure of gas A is the total pressure multiplied by the mole fraction of A, $X_A$:

$$P_A = X_A \times P_{total} \tag{5.12}$$

Equation 5.12 is a very useful result. To see that it is valid for the mixture of $N_2$ and $H_2$, we recall that $X_{N_2} + X_{H_2} = 1$; then we obtain

$$P_{total} = P_{N_2} + P_{H_2} = (X_{N_2} \times P_{total}) + (X_{H_2} \times P_{total}) = (X_{N_2} + X_{H_2})P_{total} = 1 \times P_{total}$$

---

**Sample Problem 5.9**    **Applying Dalton's Law of Partial Pressures**

**Problem** In a study of $O_2$ uptake by muscle at high altitude, a physiologist prepares an atmosphere consisting of 79 mole % $N_2$, 17 mole % $^{16}O_2$, and 4.0 mole % $^{18}O_2$. (The isotope $^{18}O$ will be measured to determine $O_2$ uptake.) The total pressure is 0.75 atm to simulate high altitude. Calculate the mole fraction and partial pressure of $^{18}O_2$ in the mixture.

**Plan** We must find $X_{^{18}O_2}$ and $P_{^{18}O_2}$ from $P_{total}$ (0.75 atm) and the mole % of $^{18}O_2$ (4.0). Dividing the mole % by 100 gives the mole fraction, $X_{^{18}O_2}$. Then, using Equation 5.12, we multiply $X_{^{18}O_2}$ by $P_{total}$ to find $P_{^{18}O_2}$.

**Solution** Calculating the mole fraction of $^{18}O_2$:

$$X_{^{18}O_2} = \frac{4.0 \text{ mol } \% \; ^{18}O_2}{100} = \boxed{0.040}$$

Solving for the partial pressure of $^{18}O_2$:

$$P_{^{18}O_2} = X_{^{18}O_2} \times P_{total} = 0.040 \times 0.75 \text{ atm} = \boxed{0.030 \text{ atm}}$$

**Check** $X_{^{18}O_2}$ is small because the mole % is small, so $P_{^{18}O_2}$ should be small also.

**Comment** At high altitudes, specialized brain cells that are sensitive to $O_2$ and $CO_2$ levels in the blood trigger an increase in rate and depth of breathing for several days, until a person becomes acclimated.

**Follow-Up Problem 5.9** To prevent the presence of air, noble gases are placed over highly reactive chemicals to act as inert "blanketing" gases. A chemical engineer places a mixture of noble gases consisting of 5.50 g of He, 15.0 g of Ne, and 35.0 g of Kr in a piston-cylinder assembly at STP. Calculate the partial pressure of each gas.

---

**Road Map**

Mole % of $^{18}O_2$

divide by 100

Mole fraction, $X_{^{18}O_2}$

multiply by $P_{total}$

Partial pressure, $P_{^{18}O_2}$

---

**Table 5.2 Vapor Pressure of Water ($P_{H_2O}$) at Different $T$**

| $T$ (°C) | $P_{H_2O}$ (torr) | $T$ (°C) | $P_{H_2O}$ (torr) |
|---|---|---|---|
| 0 | 4.6 | 40 | 55.3 |
| 5 | 6.5 | 45 | 71.9 |
| 10 | 9.2 | 50 | 92.5 |
| 12 | 10.5 | 55 | 118.0 |
| 14 | 12.0 | 60 | 149.4 |
| 16 | 13.6 | 65 | 187.5 |
| 18 | 15.5 | 70 | 233.7 |
| 20 | 17.5 | 75 | 289.1 |
| 22 | 19.8 | 80 | 355.1 |
| 24 | 22.4 | 85 | 433.6 |
| 26 | 25.2 | 90 | 525.8 |
| 28 | 28.3 | 95 | 633.9 |
| 30 | 31.8 | 100 | 760.0 |
| 35 | 42.2 | | |

**Collecting a Gas over Water** Whenever a gas is in contact with water, some of the water vaporizes into the gas. The water vapor that mixes with the gas contributes the *vapor pressure,* a portion of the total pressure that depends only on the water temperature (Table 5.2). A common use of the law of partial pressures is to determine the yield of a water-insoluble gas formed in a reaction: the gaseous product bubbles through water, some water vaporizes into the bubbles, and the mixture of product gas and water vapor is collected into an inverted container (Figure 5.12).

To determine the yield, we look up the vapor pressure ($P_{H_2O}$) at the temperature of the experiment in Table 5.2 and subtract it from the total gas pressure ($P_{total}$, corrected for barometric pressure) to get the partial pressure of the gaseous product ($P_{gas}$). With $V$ and $T$ known, we can calculate the amount of product.

The vapor pressure ($P_{H_2O}$) adds to $P_{gas}$ to give $P_{total}$. Here, the water level in the vessel is above the level in the beaker, so $P_{total} < P_{atm}$.

Molecules of $H_2O$ enter bubbles of gas.

Water-insoluble gaseous product bubbles through water into collection vessel.

After all the gas has been collected, $P_{total}$ is made equal to $P_{atm}$ by adjusting the height of the collection vessel until the water level in it equals the level in the beaker.

$P_{total}$ equals $P_{gas}$ plus $P_{H_2O}$ at the temperature of the experiment. Therefore, $P_{gas} = P_{total} - P_{H_2O}$.

**Figure 5.12** Collecting a water-insoluble gaseous product and determining its pressure.

---

## Sample Problem 5.10 | Calculating the Amount of Gas Collected over Water

**Problem** Acetylene ($C_2H_2$), an important fuel in welding, is produced in the laboratory when calcium carbide ($CaC_2$) reacts with water:

$$CaC_2(s) + 2H_2O(l) \longrightarrow C_2H_2(g) + Ca(OH)_2(aq)$$

For a sample of acetylene collected over water, total gas pressure (adjusted to barometric pressure) is 738 torr and the volume is 523 mL. At the temperature of the gas (23°C), the vapor pressure of water is 21 torr. How many grams of acetylene are collected?

**Plan** In order to find the mass of $C_2H_2$, we first need to find the number of moles of $C_2H_2$, $n_{C_2H_2}$, which we can obtain from the ideal gas law by calculating $P_{C_2H_2}$. The barometer reading gives us $P_{total}$, which is the sum of $P_{C_2H_2}$ and $P_{H_2O}$, and we are given $P_{H_2O}$, so we subtract to find $P_{C_2H_2}$. We are also given $V$ and $T$, so we convert to consistent units, and find $n_{C_2H_2}$ from the ideal gas law. Then we convert moles to grams using the molar mass from the formula, as shown in the road map.

**Road Map**

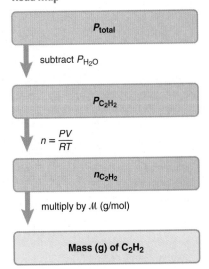

$P_{total}$

subtract $P_{H_2O}$

$P_{C_2H_2}$

$n = \dfrac{PV}{RT}$

$n_{C_2H_2}$

multiply by $\mathcal{M}$ (g/mol)

**Mass (g) of $C_2H_2$**

**Solution** Summarizing and converting the gas variables:

$$P_{C_2H_2} \text{ (torr)} = P_{total} - P_{H_2O} = 738 \text{ torr} - 21 \text{ torr} = 717 \text{ torr}$$

$$P_{C_2H_2} \text{ (atm)} = 717 \text{ torr} \times \frac{1 \text{ atm}}{760 \text{ torr}} = 0.943 \text{ atm}$$

$$V \text{ (L)} = 523 \text{ mL} \times \frac{1 \text{ L}}{1000 \text{ mL}} = 0.523 \text{ L}$$

$$T \text{ (K)} = 23°C + 273.15 = 296 \text{ K}$$

$$n_{C_2H_2} = \text{unknown}$$

Solving for $n_{C_2H_2}$:

$$n_{C_2H_2} = \frac{PV}{RT} = \frac{0.943 \text{ atm} \times 0.523 \text{ L}}{0.0821 \dfrac{\text{atm·L}}{\text{mol·K}} \times 296 \text{ K}} = 0.0203 \text{ mol}$$

Converting $n_{C_2H_2}$ to mass (g):

$$\text{Mass (g) of } C_2H_2 = 0.0203 \text{ mol } C_2H_2 \times \frac{26.04 \text{ g } C_2H_2}{1 \text{ mol } C_2H_2}$$

$$= \boxed{0.529 \text{ g } C_2H_2}$$

**Check** Rounding to one significant figure, a quick arithmetic check for $n$ gives

$$n \approx \frac{1 \text{ atm} \times 0.5 \text{ L}}{0.08 \frac{\text{atm·L}}{\text{mol·K}} \times 300 \text{ K}} = 0.02 \text{ mol} \approx 0.0203 \text{ mol}$$

**Comment** The $C_2^{2-}$ ion (called the *carbide,* or *acetylide, ion*) is an interesting anion. It is simply $^-C\equiv C^-$, which acts as a base in water, removing an $H^+$ ion from two $H_2O$ molecules to form acetylene, $H-C\equiv C-H$.

**Follow-Up Problem 5.10** A small piece of zinc reacts with dilute HCl to form $H_2$, which is collected over water at 16°C into a large flask. The total pressure is adjusted to barometric pressure (752 torr), and the volume is 1495 mL. Use Table 5.2 to help calculate the partial pressure and mass of $H_2$.

## The Ideal Gas Law and Reaction Stoichiometry

As you saw in Chapters 3 and 4, and in the preceding discussion of collecting a gas over water, many reactions involve gases as reactants or products. From the balanced equation for such a reaction, you can calculate the amounts (mol) of reactants and products and convert these quantities into masses or numbers of molecules. Figure 5.13 shows how you use the ideal gas law to convert between gas variables ($P$, $T$, and $V$) and amounts (mol) of gaseous reactants and products. In effect, you combine a gas law problem with a stoichiometry problem, as you'll see in Sample Problems 5.11 and 5.12.

**Figure 5.13** The relationships among the amount (mol, $n$) of gaseous reactant (or product) and the gas pressure ($P$), volume ($V$), and temperature ($T$).

**Sample Problem 5.11** Using Gas Variables to Find Amounts of Reactants or Products I

**Problem** Engineers use copper in absorbent beds to react with and remove oxygen impurities in ethylene used to make polyethylene. The beds are regenerated when hot $H_2$ reduces the copper(II) oxide, forming the pure metal and $H_2O$. On a laboratory scale, what volume of $H_2$ at 765 torr and 225°C is needed to reduce 35.5 g of copper(II) oxide?

**Plan** This is a stoichiometry *and* gas law problem. To find $V_{H_2}$, we first need $n_{H_2}$. We write and balance the equation. Next, we convert the given mass (35.5 g) of copper(II) oxide, CuO, to amount (mol) and use the molar ratio to find amount (mol) of $H_2$ needed (stoichiometry portion). Then, we use the ideal gas law to convert moles of $H_2$ to liters (gas law portion). A road map is shown, but you are familiar with all the steps.

**Solution** Writing the balanced equation:

$$CuO(s) + H_2(g) \longrightarrow Cu(s) + H_2O(g)$$

Calculating $n_{H_2}$:

$$n_{H_2} = 35.5 \text{ g CuO} \times \frac{1 \text{ mol CuO}}{79.55 \text{ g CuO}} \times \frac{1 \text{ mol } H_2}{1 \text{ mol CuO}} = 0.446 \text{ mol } H_2$$

Summarizing and converting other gas variables:

$$V = \text{unknown} \qquad P \text{ (atm)} = 765 \text{ torr} \times \frac{1 \text{ atm}}{760 \text{ torr}} = 1.01 \text{ atm}$$

$$T \text{ (K)} = 225°C + 273.15 = 498 \text{ K}$$

**Road Map**

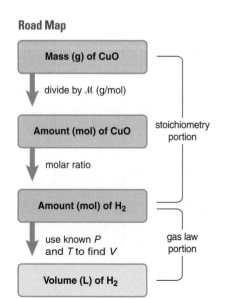

Solving for $V_{H_2}$:

$$V = \frac{nRT}{P} = \frac{0.446 \text{ mol} \times 0.0821 \dfrac{\text{atm·L}}{\text{mol·K}} \times 498 \text{ K}}{1.01 \text{ atm}} = \boxed{18.1 \text{ L}}$$

**Check** One way to check the answer is to compare it with the molar volume of an ideal gas at STP (22.4 L at 273.15 K and 1 atm). One mole of $H_2$ at STP occupies about 22 L, so less than 0.5 mol occupies less than 11 L. $T$ is less than twice 273 K, so $V$ should be less than twice 11 L.

**Comment** The main point here is that the stoichiometry provides one gas variable ($n$), two more are given, and the ideal gas law is used to find the fourth.

**Follow-Up Problem 5.11** Sulfuric acid reacts with sodium chloride to form aqueous sodium sulfate and hydrogen chloride gas. How many milliliters of gas form at STP when 0.117 kg of sodium chloride reacts with excess sulfuric acid?

---

**Sample Problem 5.12** | **Using Gas Variables to Find Amounts of Reactants or Products II**

**Problem** The alkali metals [Group 1A(1)] react with the halogens [Group 7A(17)] to form ionic metal halides. What mass of potassium chloride forms when 5.25 L of chlorine gas at 0.950 atm and 293 K reacts with 17.0 g of potassium (*see photo*)?

**Plan** The amounts of two reactants are given, so this is a limiting-reactant problem. The only difference between this and previous limiting-reactant problems (see Sample Problem 3.20, p. 111) is that here we use the ideal gas law to find the amount ($n$) of gaseous reactant from the known $V$, $P$, and $T$. We first write the balanced equation and then use it to find the limiting reactant and the amount and mass of product.

**Solution** Writing the balanced equation:

$$2K(s) + Cl_2(g) \longrightarrow 2KCl(s)$$

Summarizing the gas variables:

$$P = 0.950 \text{ atm} \qquad V = 5.25 \text{ L}$$
$$T = 293 \text{ K} \qquad n = \text{unknown}$$

Chlorine gas reacting with potassium.

Solving for $n_{Cl_2}$:

$$n_{Cl_2} = \frac{PV}{RT} = \frac{0.950 \text{ atm} \times 5.25 \text{ L}}{0.0821 \dfrac{\text{atm·L}}{\text{mol·K}} \times 293 \text{ K}} = 0.207 \text{ mol}$$

Converting from mass (g) of potassium (K) to amount (mol):

$$\text{Amount (mol) of K} = 17.0 \text{ g K} \times \frac{1 \text{ mol K}}{39.10 \text{ g K}} = 0.435 \text{ mol K}$$

Determining the limiting reactant: If $Cl_2$ is limiting,

$$\text{Amount (mol) of KCl} = 0.207 \text{ mol Cl}_2 \times \frac{2 \text{ mol KCl}}{1 \text{ mol Cl}_2} = 0.414 \text{ mol KCl}$$

If K is limiting,

$$\text{Amount (mol) of KCl} = 0.435 \text{ mol K} \times \frac{2 \text{ mol KCl}}{2 \text{ mol K}} = 0.435 \text{ mol KCl}$$

$Cl_2$ is the limiting reactant because it forms less KCl.
Converting from amount (mol) of KCl to mass (g):

$$\text{Mass (g) of KCl} = 0.414 \text{ mol KCl} \times \frac{74.55 \text{ g KCl}}{1 \text{ mol KCl}} = \boxed{30.9 \text{ g KCl}}$$

**Check** The gas law calculation seems correct. At STP, 22 L of $Cl_2$ gas contains about 1 mol, so a 5-L volume will contain a bit less than 0.25 mol of $Cl_2$. Moreover, since *P* (in numerator) is slightly lower than STP, and *T* (in denominator) is slightly higher than STP, these should lower the calculated *n* further below the ideal value. The mass of KCl seems correct: less than 0.5 mol of KCl gives <0.5 mol × $\mathcal{M}$ (~75 g/mol), and 30.9 g < 0.5 mol × 75 g/mol.

**Follow-Up Problem 5.12** Ammonia and hydrogen chloride gases react to form solid ammonium chloride. A 10.0-L reaction flask contains ammonia at 0.452 atm and 22°C, and 155 mL of hydrogen chloride gas at 7.50 atm and 271 K is introduced. After the reaction occurs and the temperature returns to 22°C, what is the pressure inside the flask? (Neglect the volume of the solid product.)

## ▌Summary of Section 5.4

- Gas density is inversely related to temperature: higher *T* causes lower *d*, and vice versa. At the same *P* and *T*, gases with larger $\mathcal{M}$ have higher *d*.
- In a mixture of gases, each component contributes its partial pressure to the total pressure (Dalton's law of partial pressures). The mole fraction of each component is the ratio of its partial pressure to the total pressure.
- When a gaseous reaction product is collected by bubbling it through water, the total pressure is the sum of the gas pressure and the vapor pressure of water at the given temperature.
- By converting the variables *P*, *V*, and *T* for a gaseous reactant (or product) to amount (*n*, mol), we can solve stoichiometry problems for gaseous reactions.

# 5.5 • THE KINETIC-MOLECULAR THEORY: A MODEL FOR GAS BEHAVIOR

The **kinetic-molecular theory** is the model that accounts for macroscopic gas behavior at the level of individual particles (atoms or molecules). Developed by some of the great scientists of the 19th century, most notably James Clerk Maxwell and Ludwig Boltzmann, the theory was able to explain the gas laws that some of the great scientists of the 18th century had arrived at empirically. The theory draws quantitative conclusions based on a few postulates (assumptions), but our discussion will be largely qualitative.

## How the Kinetic-Molecular Theory Explains the Gas Laws

Let's address some questions the theory must answer, then state the postulates, and draw conclusions that explain the gas laws and related phenomena.

**Questions Concerning Gas Behavior** Observing gas behavior at the macroscopic level, we must derive a molecular model that explains it:

1. *Origin of pressure.* Pressure is a measure of the force a gas exerts on a surface. How do individual gas particles create this force?
2. *Boyle's law (V ∝ 1/P).* A change in gas pressure in one direction causes a change in gas volume in the other. What happens to the particles when external pressure compresses the gas volume? And why aren't liquids and solids compressible?
3. *Dalton's law ($P_{total} = P_1 + P_2 + P_3 + \cdots$).* The pressure of a gas mixture is the sum of the pressures of the individual gases. Why does each gas contribute to the total pressure in proportion to its number of particles?
4. *Charles's law (V ∝ T).* A change in temperature causes a corresponding change in volume. What effect does higher temperature have on gas particles that increases gas volume? This question raises a more fundamental one: what does temperature measure on the molecular scale?
5. *Avogadro's law (V ∝ n).* Gas volume depends on the number of moles present, not on the chemical nature of the gas. But shouldn't 1 mol of heavier particles exert more pressure, and thus take up more space, than 1 mol of lighter ones?

**Postulates of the Kinetic-Molecular Theory** The theory is based on three postulates:

Postulate 1. *Particle volume.* A gas consists of a large collection of individual particles with empty space between them. The volume of each particle is so small compared with the volume of the whole sample that it is assumed to be zero; each particle is essentially a point of mass.

Postulate 2. *Particle motion.* The particles are in constant, random, straight-line motion, except when they collide with the container walls or with each other.

Postulate 3. *Particle collisions.* The collisions are *elastic,* which means that, like minute billiard balls, the colliding molecules exchange energy but do not lose any energy through friction. Thus, *their total kinetic energy ($E_k$) is constant.* Between collisions, the molecules do not influence each other by attractive or repulsive forces.

Imagine what a sample of gas in a container looks like. Countless minute particles move in every direction, smashing into the container walls and each other. Any given particle changes its speed often—at one moment standing still from a head-on collision and the next moment zooming away from a smash on the side.

In the sample as a whole, *each particle has a molecular speed (u); most are moving near the most probable speed, but some are much faster and others much slower.* Figure 5.14 depicts this distribution of molecular speeds for $N_2$ gas at three temperatures.

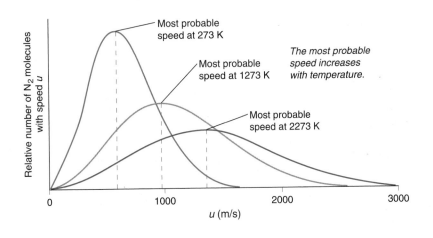

Most probable speed at 273 K

Most probable speed at 1273 K

*The most probable speed increases with temperature.*

Most probable speed at 2273 K

Relative number of $N_2$ molecules with speed $u$

$u$ (m/s)

**Figure 5.14** Distribution of molecular speeds for $N_2$ at three temperatures.

Note that the curves flatten and spread at higher temperatures and that the *most probable speed (the peak of each curve) increases as the temperature increases.* This increase occurs because the average kinetic energy of the molecules, which is related to the most probable speed, is proportional to the absolute temperature: $\overline{E_k} \propto T$, or $\overline{E_k} = c \times T$, where $\overline{E_k}$ is the average kinetic energy of the molecules (an overbar indicates the average value of a quantity) and $c$ is a constant that is the same for any gas. (We'll return to this equation shortly.) Thus, a major conclusion based on the distribution of speeds, which arises directly from postulate 3, is that *at a given temperature, all gases have the same average kinetic energy.*

**A Molecular View of the Gas Laws** Let's keep visualizing gas particles in a container to see how the theory explains the macroscopic behavior of gases and answers the questions we posed above:

1. *Origin of pressure* (Figure 5.15). From postulates 1 and 2, each gas particle (point of mass) colliding with the container walls (and bottom of piston) exerts a force. Countless collisions over the inner surface of the container result in a pressure. The greater the number of particles, the more frequently they collide with the container, and so the greater the pressure.

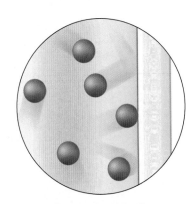

**Figure 5.15** Pressure arises from countless collisions between gas particles and walls.

2. *Boyle's law* ($V \propto 1/P$) (Figure 5.16). The particles in a gas are points of mass with empty space between them (postulate 1). Before any change in pressure, the pressure exerted *by* the gas ($P_{gas}$) equals the pressure exerted *on* the gas ($P_{ext}$), and there is some average distance ($d_1$) between the particles and the container walls. As $P_{ext}$ increases at constant temperature, the average distance ($d_2$) between the particles and the walls decreases (that is, $d_2 < d_1$), and so the sample volume decreases. Collisions of the particles with the walls become more frequent over the shorter average distance, which causes $P_{gas}$ to increase until it again equals $P_{ext}$. The fact that liquids and solids cannot be compressed implies there is little, if any, free space between their particles.

**Figure 5.16** A molecular view of Boyle's law.

At any $T$, $P_{gas} = P_{ext}$ as particles hit the walls from an average distance, $d_1$.

$P_{ext}$ increases, $T$ and $n$ fixed

Higher $P_{ext}$ causes lower $V$, which results in more collisions, because particles hit the walls from a shorter average distance ($d_2 < d_1$). As a result, $P_{gas} = P_{ext}$ again.

3. *Dalton's law of partial pressures* ($P_{total} = P_A + P_B$) (Figure 5.17). Adding a given amount (mol) of gas A to a given amount of gas B causes an increase in the total number of particles, in proportion to the particles of A added. This increase causes a corresponding increase in the total number of collisions with the walls per second (postulate 2), which causes a corresponding increase in the total pressure of the gas mixture ($P_{total}$). Each gas exerts a fraction of $P_{total}$ in proportion to its fraction of the total number of particles (or equivalently, its fraction of the total number of moles, that is, the mole fraction).

**Figure 5.17** A molecular view of Dalton's law.

When gases A and B are separate, each exerts the total pressure in its own container.

Gas A

Gas B

Closed

Stopcock opened, piston depressed at fixed $T$

Mixture of A and B

Open

When gas A is mixed with gas B, $P_{total} = P_A + P_B$ and the numbers of collisions of particles of each gas with the container walls are in proportion to the amount (mol) of that gas.

$P_A = P_{total}$
$= 1.0$ atm
$n_A = 0.60$ mol

$P_B = P_{total}$
$= 0.50$ atm
$n_B = 0.30$ mol

$P_{total} = P_A + P_B = 1.5$ atm
$n_{total} = 0.90$ mol
$X_A = 0.67$ mol  $X_B = 0.33$ mol

4. *Charles's law* ($V \propto T$) (Figure 5.18). At some starting temperature, $T_1$, the external (atmospheric) pressure ($P_{atm}$) equals the pressure of the gas ($P_{gas}$). When the gas is heated and the temperature increases to $T_2$, the most probable molecular speed and the average kinetic energy increase (postulate 3). Thus, the particles hit the walls more frequently *and* more energetically. This change temporarily increases $P_{gas}$. As a result, the piston moves up, which increases the volume and lowers the collision frequency until $P_{atm}$ and $P_{gas}$ are again equal.

**Figure 5.18** A molecular view of Charles's law.

At $T_1$, $P_{gas}$ = $P_{atm}$.

*Higher T increases collision frequency, so $P_{gas}$ > $P_{atm}$.*

*Thus, V increases until $P_{gas}$ = $P_{atm}$ at $T_2$.*

T increases
fixed n

V increases

5. *Avogadro's law* ($V \propto n$) (Figure 5.19). At some starting amount, $n_1$, of gas, $P_{atm}$ equals $P_{gas}$. When more gas is added from the attached tank, the amount increases to $n_2$. Thus, more particles hit the walls more frequently, which temporarily increases $P_{gas}$. As a result, the piston moves up, which increases the volume and lowers the collision frequency until $P_{atm}$ and $P_{gas}$ are again equal.

**Figure 5.19** A molecular view of Avogadro's law.

*For a given amount, $n_1$, of gas, $P_{gas}$ = $P_{atm}$.*

*When gas is added to reach $n_2$ the collision frequency of the particles increases, so $P_{gas}$ > $P_{atm}$.*

*As a result, V increases until $P_{gas}$ = $P_{atm}$ again.*

n increases
fixed T

V increases

**The Central Importance of Kinetic Energy** Recall from Chapter 1 that the kinetic energy of an object is the energy associated with its motion. It is key to explaining some implications of Avogadro's law and, most importantly, the meaning of temperature.

1. *Implications of Avogadro's law.* As we just saw, Avogadro's law says that, at any given $T$ and $P$, the volume of a gas depends only on the number of moles—that is, number of particles—in the sample. The law doesn't mention the chemical nature of the gas, so equal numbers of particles of any two gases, say $O_2$ and $H_2$, should occupy the same volume. But, why don't the heavier $O_2$ molecules exert more pressure on the container walls, and thus take up more volume, than the lighter $H_2$ molecules? To answer this, we'll show one way to express kinetic energy mathematically:

$$E_k = \tfrac{1}{2}\text{mass} \times \text{speed}^2$$

This equation says that, for a given $E_k$, an object's mass and speed are inversely related, which means that *a heavier object moving slower can have the same kinetic energy as a lighter object moving faster.* Figure 5.20 on the next page shows that, for several gases, *the most probable speed (top of each curve) increases as the molar mass (number in parentheses) decreases.*

As we saw earlier, postulate 3 of the kinetic-molecular theory directly implies that, at a given $T$, all gases have the same average kinetic energy. From Figure 5.20, we see

**Figure 5.20 The relationship between molar mass and molecular speed.** At a given temperature, gases with lower molar masses (numbers in parentheses) have higher most probable speeds (peak of each curve).

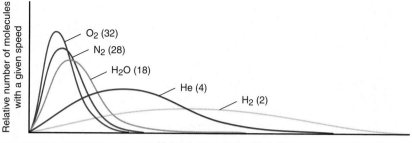

that $O_2$ molecules move more slowly, on average, than $H_2$ molecules. With their higher most probable speed, $H_2$ molecules collide with the walls of a container more often than $O_2$ molecules do, but their lower mass means that each collision has less force. Therefore, at a given $T$, equimolar samples of $H_2$ and $O_2$ (or any other gas) exert the same pressure and, thus, occupy the same volume because, on average, *their molecules hit the walls with the same kinetic energy.*

2. *The meaning of temperature.* Closely related to these ideas is the central relation between kinetic energy and temperature. Earlier we said that the average kinetic energy of the particles ($\overline{E_k}$) equals the absolute temperature times a constant; that is, $\overline{E_k} = c \times T$. Using definitions of velocity, momentum, force, and pressure, we can also express this relationship by the following equation:

$$\overline{E_k} = \tfrac{3}{2}\left(\frac{R}{N_A}\right)T$$

where $R$ is the gas constant and $N_A$ is the symbol for Avogadro's number. This equation makes the essential point that *temperature is a **measure** of the average kinetic energy of the particles:* as $T$ increases, $\overline{E_k}$ increases, and vice versa. Temperature is an intensive property (Section 1.5), so it is not related to the *total* energy of motion of the particles, which depends on the size of the sample, but to the *average* energy.

Thus, for example, in the macroscopic world, we heat a beaker of water over a flame and see the mercury rise inside a thermometer we put in the beaker. We see this because, in the molecular world, kinetic energy transfers, in turn, from higher energy gas particles in the flame to lower energy particles in the beaker glass, the water molecules, the particles in the thermometer glass, and the atoms of mercury.

**Root-Mean-Square Speed** Finally, let's derive an expression for the speed of a gas particle that has the average kinetic energy of the particles in a sample. From the general expression for kinetic energy of an object,

$$E_k = \tfrac{1}{2}\text{mass} \times \text{speed}^2$$

the average kinetic energy of each particle in a large population is

$$\overline{E_k} = \tfrac{1}{2}m\overline{u^2}$$

where $m$ is the particle's mass (atomic or molecular) and $\overline{u^2}$ is the average of the squares of the molecular speeds. Setting this expression for average kinetic energy equal to the earlier one gives

$$\tfrac{1}{2}m\overline{u^2} = \tfrac{3}{2}\left(\frac{R}{N_A}\right)T$$

Multiplying through by Avogadro's number, $N_A$, gives the average kinetic energy for a mole of gas particles:

$$\tfrac{1}{2}N_A\,m\overline{u^2} = \tfrac{3}{2}RT$$

Avogadro's number times the molecular mass, $N_A \times m$, is the molar mass, $\mathcal{M}$, and solving for $\overline{u^2}$, we have

$$\overline{u^2} = \frac{3RT}{\mathcal{M}}$$

The square root of $\overline{u^2}$ is the root-mean-square speed, or **rms speed ($u_{rms}$):** *a particle moving at this speed has the average kinetic energy.*\* That is, taking the square root of both sides of the previous equation gives

$$u_{rms} = \sqrt{\frac{3RT}{M}} \qquad (5.13)$$

where $R$ is the gas constant, $T$ is the absolute temperature, and $M$ is the molar mass. (Because we want $u$ in m/s and $R$ includes the joule, which has units of kg·m²/s², we use the value 8.314 J/mol·K for $R$ and express $M$ in kg/mol.)

Thus, as an example, the root-mean-square speed of an $O_2$ molecule ($M = 3.200 \times 10^{-2}$ kg/mol) at room temperature (20°C, or 293 K) in the air you're breathing right now is

$$u_{rms} = \sqrt{\frac{3RT}{M}} = \sqrt{\frac{3(8.314 \text{ J/mol·K})(293 \text{ K})}{3.200 \times 10^{-2} \text{ kg/mol}}}$$

$$= \sqrt{\frac{3(8.314 \text{ kg·m}^2/\text{s}^2/\text{mol·K})(293 \text{ K})}{3.200 \times 10^{-2} \text{ kg/mol}}}$$

$$= 478 \text{ m/s (about 1070 mi/hr)}$$

## Effusion and Diffusion

The movement of a gas into a vacuum and the movement of gases through one another are phenomena with some vital applications.

**The Process of Effusion** One of the early triumphs of the kinetic-molecular theory was an explanation of **effusion,** the process by which a gas escapes through a tiny hole in its container into an evacuated space. In 1846, Thomas Graham studied the effusion rate of a gas, the number of molecules escaping per unit time, and found that it was inversely proportional to the square root of the gas density. But, density is directly related to molar mass, so **Graham's law of effusion** is stated as follows: *the rate of effusion of a gas is inversely proportional to the square root of its molar mass,* or

$$\text{Rate of effusion} \propto \frac{1}{\sqrt{M}}$$

Argon (Ar) is lighter than krypton (Kr), so it effuses faster, assuming equal pressures of the two gases (Figure 5.21). Thus, the ratio of the rates is

$$\frac{\text{Rate}_{Ar}}{\text{Rate}_{Kr}} = \frac{\sqrt{M_{Kr}}}{\sqrt{M_{Ar}}} \quad \text{or, in general,} \quad \frac{\text{Rate}_A}{\text{Rate}_B} = \frac{\sqrt{M_B}}{\sqrt{M_A}} = \sqrt{\frac{M_B}{M_A}} \qquad (5.14)$$

The kinetic-molecular theory explains that, at a given temperature and pressure, *the gas with the lower molar mass effuses faster because the rms speed of its molecules is higher; therefore, more molecules reach the hole and escape per unit time.*

**Figure 5.21 Effusion.** Lighter (*black*) particles effuse faster than heavier (*red*) particles.

| Sample Problem 5.13 | Applying Graham's Law of Effusion |

**Problem** A mixture of helium (He) and methane ($CH_4$) is placed in an effusion apparatus. Calculate the ratio of their effusion rates.

**Plan** The effusion rate is inversely proportional to $\sqrt{M}$, so we find the molar mass of each substance from the formula and take its square root. The inverse of the ratio of the square roots is the ratio of the effusion rates.

**Solution**

$$M \text{ of } CH_4 = 16.04 \text{ g/mol} \qquad M \text{ of He} = 4.003 \text{ g/mol}$$

---

\*The rms speed, $u_{rms}$, is proportional to, but slightly higher than, the most probable speed; for an ideal gas, $u_{rms} = 1.09 \times$ average speed.

Calculating the ratio of the effusion rates:

$$\frac{\text{Rate}_{\text{He}}}{\text{Rate}_{\text{CH}_4}} = \sqrt{\frac{\mathcal{M}_{\text{CH}_4}}{\mathcal{M}_{\text{He}}}} = \sqrt{\frac{16.04 \text{ g/mol}}{4.003 \text{ g/mol}}} = \sqrt{4.007} = \boxed{2.002}$$

**Check** A ratio $>1$ makes sense because the lighter He should effuse faster than the heavier $CH_4$. Because the molar mass of $CH_4$ is about four times the molar mass of He, He should effuse about twice as fast as $CH_4$ ($\sqrt{4}$).

**Follow-Up Problem 5.13** If it takes 1.25 min for 0.010 mol of He to effuse, how long will it take for the same amount of ethane ($C_2H_6$) to effuse?

**Applications of Effusion** The process of effusion has two important uses.

1. *Determination of molar mass.* We can also use Graham's law to *determine the molar mass of an unknown gas.* By comparing the effusion rate of gas X with that of a known gas, such as He, we can solve for the molar mass of X:

$$\frac{\text{Rate}_X}{\text{Rate}_{\text{He}}} = \sqrt{\frac{\mathcal{M}_{\text{He}}}{\mathcal{M}_X}}$$

Squaring both sides and solving for the molar mass of X gives

$$\mathcal{M}_X = \mathcal{M}_{\text{He}} \times \left(\frac{\text{rate}_{\text{He}}}{\text{rate}_X}\right)^2$$

2. *Preparation of nuclear fuel.* By far the most important application of Graham's law is in the preparation of fuel for nuclear energy reactors. The process of *isotope enrichment* increases the proportion of fissionable, but rarer, $^{235}U$ (only 0.7% by mass of naturally occurring uranium) to the nonfissionable, more abundant $^{238}U$ (99.3% by mass). Because the two isotopes have identical chemical properties, they are extremely difficult to separate chemically. But, one way to separate them takes advantage of a difference in a physical property—the effusion rate of gaseous compounds. Uranium ore is treated with fluorine to yield a gaseous mixture of $^{238}UF_6$ and $^{235}UF_6$ that is pumped through a series of chambers separated by porous barriers. Molecules of $^{235}UF_6$ are slightly lighter ($\mathcal{M} = 349.03$) than molecules of $^{238}UF_6$ ($\mathcal{M} = 352.04$), so they move slightly faster and effuse through each barrier 1.0043 times faster. Many passes must be made, each one increasing the fraction of $^{235}UF_6$, until the mixture obtained is 3–5% by mass $^{235}UF_6$. This process was developed during the latter years of World War II and produced enough $^{235}U$ for two of the world's first atomic bombs. Today, a less expensive centrifuge process is used more often. The ability to enrich uranium has become a key international concern, as more countries aspire to develop nuclear energy and nuclear arms.

**The Process of Diffusion** Closely related to effusion is the process of gaseous **diffusion,** the movement of one gas through another. Diffusion rates are also described generally by Graham's law:

$$\text{Rate of diffusion} \propto \frac{1}{\sqrt{\mathcal{M}}}$$

For two gases at equal pressures, such as $NH_3$ and $HCl$, moving through another gas or a mixture of gases, such as air, we find

$$\frac{\text{Rate}_{\text{NH}_3}}{\text{Rate}_{\text{HCl}}} = \sqrt{\frac{\mathcal{M}_{\text{HCl}}}{\mathcal{M}_{\text{NH}_3}}}$$

The reason for this dependence on molar mass is the same as for effusion rates: *lighter molecules have higher average speeds than heavier molecules, so they move farther in a given time.*

If gas molecules move at hundreds of meters per second (see Figure 5.14), why does it take a second or two after you open a bottle of perfume to smell it? Although convection plays an important role in this process, another reason for the time lag is

**Figure 5.22 Diffusion of gases.** When different gases (*black*, from the left, and *green*, from the right) move through each other, they mix. For simplicity, the complex path of only one black particle is shown (in *red*). In reality, all the particles have similar paths.

that a gas particle does not travel very far before it collides with another particle (Figure 5.22). Thus, a perfume molecule travels slowly because it collides with countless molecules in the air. The presence of so many other particles means that *diffusion rates are much lower than effusion rates.* Imagine how much quicker you can walk through an empty room than through a room crowded with other moving people.

Diffusion also occurs when a gas enters a liquid (and even to a small extent a solid). However, the average distances between molecules are so much shorter in a liquid that collisions are much more frequent; thus, diffusion of a gas through a liquid is *much* slower than through a gas. Nevertheless, this type of diffusion is a vital process in biological systems, for example, in the movement of $O_2$ from lungs to blood.

## The Chaotic World of Gases: Mean Free Path and Collision Frequency

Refinements of the basic kinetic-molecular theory provide a view into the chaotic molecular world of gases. Try to visualize an "average" $N_2$ molecule in the room you are in now. It is continually changing speed as it collides with other molecules—at one instant, going 2500 mi/h, and at another, standing still. But these extreme speeds are *much* less likely than the most probable one and those near it (see Figure 5.14). At 20°C and 1 atm pressure, the $N_2$ molecule is hurtling at an average speed of 470 m/s (rms speed = 510 m/s), or nearly 1100 mi/h!

**Mean Free Path** From a particle's diameter, we can obtain the **mean free path,** the average distance it travels between collisions at a given temperature and pressure. An $N_2$ molecule ($3.7\times10^{-10}$ m in diameter) has a mean free path of $6.6\times10^{-8}$ m, which means it travels an average of 180 molecular diameters before smashing into a fellow traveler. (An $N_2$ molecule the size of a billiard ball would travel an average of about 30 ft before hitting another.) Therefore, even though gas molecules are *not* points of mass, it is still valid to assume that a gas sample *is* nearly all empty space. Mean free path is a key factor in the rate of diffusion and the rate of heat flow through a gas.

**Collision Frequency** Divide the most probable speed (meters per second) by the mean free path (meters per collision) and you obtain the **collision frequency,** the average number of collisions per second that each particle undergoes. As you can see, the $N_2$ molecule experiences, on average, an enormous number of collisions every second: ●

$$\text{Collision frequency} = \frac{4.7\times10^2 \text{ m/s}}{6.6\times10^{-8} \text{ m/collision}} = 7.0\times10^9 \text{ collision/s}$$

Distribution of speed (and kinetic energy) and collision frequency are essential ideas for understanding the speed of a reaction, as you'll see in Chapter 16. As the Chemical Connections essay shows, many of the concepts we've discussed so far apply directly to our planet's atmosphere.

● **Danger in a Molecular Amusement Park** To really appreciate the astounding events in the molecular world, let's use a two-dimensional analogy to compare the moving $N_2$ molecule with a bumper car you are driving in an enormous amusement park ride. To match the collision frequency of the $N_2$ molecule, you would need to be traveling 2.8 billion mi/s (4.5 billion km/s, much faster than the speed of light!) and would smash into another bumper car every 700 yd (640 m).

An **atmosphere** is the envelope of gases that extends continuously from a planet's surface outward, thinning gradually until it is identical with outer space. A sample of clean, dry air at sea level on Earth contains 18 gases (Table B5.1). Under standard conditions, they behave nearly ideally, so volume percent equals mole percent (Avogadro's law), and the mole fraction of a component relates directly to its partial pressure (Dalton's law). Let's see how the gas laws and kinetic-molecular theory apply to our atmosphere, first with regard to variations in pressure and temperature, and then as explanations of some very familiar phenomena.

### Table B5.1 Composition of Clean, Dry Air at Sea Level

| Component | Mole Fraction |
| --- | --- |
| Nitrogen ($N_2$) | 0.78084 |
| Oxygen ($O_2$) | 0.20946 |
| Argon (Ar) | 0.00934 |
| Carbon dioxide ($CO_2$) | 0.00933 |
| Neon (Ne) | $1.818 \times 10^{-5}$ |
| Helium (He) | $5.24 \times 10^{-6}$ |
| Methane ($CH_4$) | $2 \times 10^{-6}$ |
| Krypton (Kr) | $1.14 \times 10^{-6}$ |
| Hydrogen ($H_2$) | $5 \times 10^{-7}$ |
| Dinitrogen monoxide ($N_2O$) | $5 \times 10^{-7}$ |
| Carbon monoxide (CO) | $1 \times 10^{-7}$ |
| Xenon (Xe) | $8 \times 10^{-8}$ |
| Ozone ($O_3$) | $2 \times 10^{-8}$ |
| Ammonia ($NH_3$) | $6 \times 10^{-9}$ |
| Nitrogen dioxide ($NO_2$) | $6 \times 10^{-9}$ |
| Nitrogen monoxide (NO) | $6 \times 10^{-10}$ |
| Sulfur dioxide ($SO_2$) | $2 \times 10^{-10}$ |
| Hydrogen sulfide ($H_2S$) | $2 \times 10^{-10}$ |

## The Smooth Variation in Pressure with Altitude

Because gases are compressible (Boyle's law), the pressure of the atmosphere *increases* smoothly as we approach Earth's surface, with a more rapid increase at lower altitudes (Figure B5.1, *left*). No boundary delineates the beginning of the atmosphere from the end of outer space, but the densities and compositions are identical at an altitude of about 10,000 km (6000 mi). Yet, about 99% of the atmosphere's mass lies within 30 km (almost 19 mi) of the surface, and 75% lies within the lowest 11 km (almost 7 mi).

## The Zig-Zag Variation in Temperature with Altitude

Unlike pressure, temperature does *not* change smoothly with altitude above Earth's surface. The atmosphere is classified into regions based on the direction of temperature change, and we'll start at the surface (Figure B5.1, *right*).

1. *The troposphere.* In the troposphere, which extends from the surface to between 7 km (23,000 ft) at the poles and 17 km (60,000 ft) at the equator, the temperature *drops* 7°C per kilometer to −55°C (218 K). This region contains about 80% of the total mass of the atmosphere, with 50% of the mass in the lower 5.6 km (18,500 ft). All weather occurs in this region, and nearly all, except supersonic, aircraft fly here.

2. *The stratosphere and the ozone layer.* In the stratosphere, the temperature *rises* from −55°C to about 7°C (280 K) at 50 km. This rise is due to a variety of complex reactions, mostly involving ozone, and is caused by the absorption of solar radiation. Most high-energy radiation is absorbed by upper levels of the atmosphere, but some that reaches the stratosphere breaks $O_2$ into O atoms. The energetic O atoms collide with more $O_2$ to form ozone ($O_3$), another molecular form of oxygen:

$$O_2(g) \xrightarrow{\text{high-energy radiation}} 2O(g)$$

$$M + O(g) + O_2(g) \longrightarrow O_3(g) + M + heat$$

where M is any particle that can carry away excess energy. This reaction releases heat, which is why stratospheric temperatures increase with altitude. Over 90% of atmospheric ozone remains in a thin layer within the stratosphere, its thickness varying both geographically (greatest at the poles) and seasonally (greatest in spring in the Northern Hemisphere and in fall in the Southern). Stratospheric ozone is vital to life because it absorbs over 95% of the harmful ultraviolet (UV) solar radiation that would otherwise reach the surface. In Chapter 16, we'll discuss the destructive effect of certain industrial chemicals on the ozone layer.

3. *The mesosphere.* In the mesosphere, the temperature *drops* again to −93°C (180 K) at around 80 km.

4. *The outer atmosphere.* Within the *thermosphere,* which extends to around 500 km, the temperature *rises* again, but varies between 700 and 2000 K, depending on the intensity of solar radiation and sunspot activity. The *exosphere,* the outermost region, maintains these temperatures and merges with outer space.

What does it actually mean to have a temperature of 2000 K at 500 km (300 mi) above Earth's surface? Would a piece of iron (melting point = 1808 K) glow red-hot within a minute or so and melt in the thermosphere, as it does if heated to 2000 K in the troposphere? The answer involves the relation between temperature and the time it takes to transfer kinetic energy. Our use of the words "hot" and "cold" refers to measurements near the surface. There, the collision frequency of gas particles with a thermometer is enormous, and so the transfer of their kinetic energy is very fast. But, at an altitude of 500 km, where the density of gas particles is a million times *less,* collision frequency is extremely low, and a thermometer, or any object, experiences *very slow transfer of kinetic energy.* Thus, the object would not become "hot" in the usual sense in any reasonable time. But the high-energy solar radiation that *is* transferred to the few particles present in these regions makes their average kinetic energy extremely high, as indicated by the high absolute temperature.

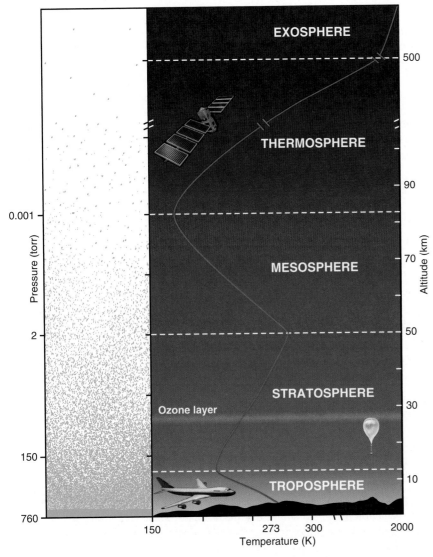

**Figure B5.1** Variations in pressure and temperature with altitude in Earth's atmosphere.

## Convection in the Lower Atmosphere

Why must you take more breaths per minute on a high mountaintop than at sea level? Because at the higher elevation, there is a smaller *amount* of $O_2$ in each breath. However, the *proportion* (mole percent) of $O_2$ throughout the lower atmosphere remains about 21%. This uniform composition arises from *vertical (convective) mixing,* and the gas laws explain how it occurs.

Let's follow an air mass from ground level, as solar heating of Earth's surface warms it. The warmer air mass expands (Charles's law), which makes it less dense, so it rises. As it does so, the pressure on it decreases, making it expand further (Boyle's law). Pushing against the surrounding air requires energy, so the temperature of the air mass decreases and thus the air mass shrinks slightly (Charles's law). But, as its temperature drops, its water vapor condenses (or solidifies), and these changes of state release heat; therefore, the air mass becomes warmer and rises further. Meanwhile, the cooler, and thus denser, air that was above it sinks, becomes warmer through contact with the surface, and goes through the same process as the first air mass. As a result of this vertical mixing, the composition of the lower atmosphere remains uniform.

Warm air rising from the ground, called a *thermal,* is used by soaring birds and glider pilots to stay aloft. Convection helps clean the air in urban areas, because the rising air carries up pollutants, which are dispersed by winds. Under certain conditions, however, a warm air mass remains stationary over a cool one. The resulting *temperature inversion* blocks normal convection, and harmful pollutants build up, causing severe health problems.

## Problems

**B5.1** Suggest a reason why supersonic aircraft are kept well below their maximum speeds until they reach their highest altitudes.

**B5.2** Gases behave nearly ideally under Earth's conditions. Elsewhere in the Solar System, however, conditions are very different. On which would you expect atmospheric gases to deviate most from ideal behavior, Saturn ($4 \times 10^6$ atm and 130 K) or Venus (90 atm and 730 K)? Explain.

**B5.3** What is the volume percent and partial pressure (in torr) of argon in a sample of dry air at sea level?

**B5.4** Earth's atmosphere is estimated to have a mass of $5.14 \times 10^{15}$ t (1 t = 1000 kg).
(a) If the average molar mass of air is 28.8 g/mol, how many moles of gas are in the atmosphere?
(b) How many liters would the atmosphere occupy at 25°C and 1 atm?

## ▌Summary of Section 5.5

- The kinetic-molecular theory postulates that gas particles have no volume, move in straight-line paths between elastic (energy-conserving) collisions, and have average kinetic energies proportional to the absolute temperature of the gas.
- This theory explains the gas laws in terms of changes in distances between particles and the container walls, changes in molecular speed, and the energy of collisions.
- Temperature is a measure of the average kinetic energy of the particles.
- Effusion and diffusion rates are *inversely* proportional to the square root of the molar mass (Graham's law) because they are *directly* proportional to molecular speed.
- Molecular motion is characterized by a temperature-dependent, most probable speed (within a range of speeds), which affects mean free path and collision frequency.
- The atmosphere is a complex mixture of gases that exhibits variations in pressure and temperature with altitude. High temperatures in the upper atmosphere result from absorption of high-energy solar radiation. The lower atmosphere has a uniform composition as a result of convective mixing.

## 5.6 • REAL GASES: DEVIATIONS FROM IDEAL BEHAVIOR

A fundamental principle of science is that simpler models are more useful than complex ones, as long as they explain the data. With only a few postulates, the kinetic-molecular theory explains the behavior of most gases under ordinary conditions. But, two of the postulates are useful approximations that do not reflect reality:

1. *Gas particles are **not** points of mass* but have volumes determined by the sizes of their atoms and the lengths and directions of their bonds.
2. *Attractive and repulsive forces **do** exist among gas particles* because atoms contain charged subatomic particles and many bonds are polar. (As you'll see in Chapter 12, such forces lead to changes of physical state.)

These two features cause deviations from ideal behavior under *extreme conditions of low temperature and high pressure.* These deviations mean that we must alter the simple model and the ideal gas law to predict the behavior of real gases.

### Effects of Extreme Conditions on Gas Behavior

At ordinary conditions—relatively high temperatures and low pressures—most real gases exhibit nearly ideal behavior. Yet, even at STP (0°C and 1 atm), gases deviate *slightly* from ideal behavior. Table 5.3 shows that the standard molar volumes of several gases, when measured to five significant figures, do not equal the ideal value. Note that the deviations increase as the boiling point rises.

The phenomena that cause slight deviations under standard conditions exert more influence as temperature decreases and pressure increases. Figure 5.23 shows a plot of $PV/RT$ versus external pressure ($P_{ext}$) for 1 mol of several real gases and an ideal gas. The $PV/RT$ values range from normal (at $P_{ext} = 1$ atm, $PV/RT = 1$) to very high (at $P_{ext} \approx$ 1000 atm, $PV/RT \approx$ 1.6 to 2.3). For the *ideal* gas, $PV/RT$ is 1 at any $P_{ext}$.

The $PV/RT$ curve for methane ($CH_4$) is typical of most gases: it decreases *below* the ideal value at moderately high $P_{ext}$ and then rises *above* the ideal value as $P_{ext}$ increases to very high values. This shape arises from two overlapping effects:

- At moderately high $P_{ext}$, $PV/RT$ values are lower than ideal values (less than 1) because of *interparticle attractions.*
- At very high $P_{ext}$, $PV/RT$ values are greater than ideal values (more than 1) because of *particle volume.*

Let's examine these effects on the molecular level:

1. *Effect of interparticle attractions.* Interparticle attractions occur between separate atoms or molecules and are caused by imbalances in electron distributions. They are important only over *very* short distances and are *much* weaker than the covalent bonding forces that hold a molecule together. At normal $P_{ext}$, the spaces between the particles are so large that attractions are negligible and the gas behaves nearly ideally.

**Table 5.3** Molar Volume of Some Common Gases at STP (0°C and 1 atm)

| Gas | Molar Volume (L/mol) | Boiling Point (°C) |
|---|---|---|
| He | 22.435 | −268.9 |
| $H_2$ | 22.432 | −252.8 |
| Ne | 22.422 | −246.1 |
| **Ideal gas** | **22.414** | — |
| Ar | 22.397 | −185.9 |
| $N_2$ | 22.396 | −195.8 |
| $O_2$ | 22.390 | −183.0 |
| CO | 22.388 | −191.5 |
| $Cl_2$ | 22.184 | −34.0 |
| $NH_3$ | 22.079 | −33.4 |

**Figure 5.23** Deviations from ideal behavior with increasing external pressure. The horizontal line shows that, for 1 mol of ideal gas, $PV/RT = 1$ at all $P_{ext}$. At very high $P_{ext}$, real gases deviate significantly from ideal behavior, but small deviations appear even at ordinary pressures (expanded portion).

As $P_{ext}$ rises, the volume of the sample decreases and the particles get closer together, so interparticle attractions have a greater effect. As a particle approaches the container wall under these higher pressures, nearby particles attract it, which lessens the force of its impact (Figure 5.24). *Repeated throughout the sample, this effect results in decreased gas pressure and, thus, a smaller numerator in PV/RT.* Similarly, lowering the temperature slows the particles, so they attract each other for a longer time.

*At ordinary $P_{ext}$, particles are too far apart to interact.*

*At moderately high $P_{ext}$, particles are close enough to interact.*

*Interparticle attractions (red arrows) lower the force of collisions with the container wall.*

**Figure 5.24** The effect of interparticle attractions on measured gas pressure.

2. *Effect of particle volume.* At normal $P_{ext}$, the space between particles (free volume) is enormous compared with the volume of the particles *themselves* (particle volume); thus, the free volume is essentially equal to $V$, the container volume in $PV/RT$. At *moderately* high $P_{ext}$ and as free volume decreases, the particle volume makes up an increasing proportion of the container volume (Figure 5.25). At *extremely* high pressures, the space taken up by the particles themselves makes the free volume significantly *less* than the container volume. Nevertheless, we continue to use the container volume for $V$ in $PV/RT$, which causes the numerator, and thus the ratio, to become

*At ordinary $P_{ext}$, free volume ≈ container volume because particle volume is an insignificant portion of container volume.*

*At very high $P_{ext}$, free volume < container volume because particle volume becomes a significant portion of container volume.*

**Figure 5.25** The effect of particle volume on measured gas volume.

artificially high. This particle volume effect increases as $P_{ext}$ increases, eventually outweighing the effect of interparticle attractions and causing $PV/RT$ to rise above the ideal value.

In Figure 5.23, note that the $H_2$ and He curves do not show the typical dip at moderate pressures. These gases consist of particles with such weak interparticle attractions that the particle volume effect predominates at all pressures.

## The van der Waals Equation: Adjusting the Ideal Gas Law

To describe real gas behavior more accurately, we need to adjust the ideal gas equation in two ways:

1. Adjust $P$ *up* by adding a factor that accounts for interparticle attractions.
2. Adjust $V$ *down* by subtracting a factor that accounts for particle volume.

In 1873, Johannes van der Waals revised the ideal gas equation to account for the behavior of real gases. The **van der Waals equation** for $n$ moles of a real gas is

$$\left(P + \frac{n^2a}{V^2}\right)(V - nb) = nRT \qquad \text{(5.15)}$$

$$\underset{\substack{\text{adjusts}\\P\text{ up}}}{} \qquad \underset{\substack{\text{adjusts}\\V\text{ down}}}{}$$

where $P$ is the measured pressure, $V$ is the known container volume, $n$ and $T$ have their usual meanings, and $a$ and $b$ are **van der Waals constants,** experimentally determined and specific for a given gas (Table 5.4). The constant $a$ depends on the number and distribution of electrons, which relates to the complexity of a particle and the strength of its interparticle attractions. The constant $b$ relates to particle volume. For instance, $CO_2$ is both more complex and larger than $H_2$, and the values of their constants reflect this.

Here is a typical application of the van der Waals equation. A 1.98-L vessel contains 215 g (4.89 mol) of dry ice. After standing at 26°C (299 K), the $CO_2(s)$ changes to $CO_2(g)$. The pressure is measured ($P_{real}$) and then calculated by the ideal gas law ($P_{IGL}$) and, using the appropriate values of $a$ and $b$, by the van der Waals equation ($P_{VDW}$). The results are revealing:

$$P_{real} = 44.8 \text{ atm} \qquad P_{IGL} = 60.6 \text{ atm} \qquad P_{VDW} = 45.9 \text{ atm}$$

Comparing the real value with each calculated value shows that $P_{IGL}$ is 35.3% greater than $P_{real}$, but $P_{VDW}$ is only 2.5% greater than $P_{real}$. At these conditions, $CO_2$ deviates so much from ideal behavior that the ideal gas law is not very useful.

A key point to realize: According to kinetic-molecular theory, the constants $a$ and $b$ are zero for an ideal gas because the gas particles do not attract each other and have no volume. Yet, even in a real gas at ordinary pressures, the particles are very far apart. This large average interparticle distance has two consequences:

- Attractive forces are miniscule, so $P + \frac{n^2a}{V^2} \approx P$.

- The particle volume is a minute fraction of the container volume, so $V - nb \approx V$.

Therefore, *at ordinary conditions, the van der Waals equation* **becomes** *the ideal gas equation.*

| Table 5.4 Van der Waals Constants for Some Common Gases | | |
|---|---|---|
| **Gas** | $a\left(\dfrac{\text{atm}\cdot\text{L}^2}{\text{mol}^2}\right)$ | $b\left(\dfrac{\text{L}}{\text{mol}}\right)$ |
| He | 0.034 | 0.0237 |
| Ne | 0.211 | 0.0171 |
| Ar | 1.35 | 0.0322 |
| Kr | 2.32 | 0.0398 |
| Xe | 4.19 | 0.0511 |
| $H_2$ | 0.244 | 0.0266 |
| $N_2$ | 1.39 | 0.0391 |
| $O_2$ | 1.36 | 0.0318 |
| $Cl_2$ | 6.49 | 0.0562 |
| $CH_4$ | 2.25 | 0.0428 |
| CO | 1.45 | 0.0395 |
| $CO_2$ | 3.59 | 0.0427 |
| $NH_3$ | 4.17 | 0.0371 |
| $H_2O$ | 5.46 | 0.0305 |

## ▌Summary of Section 5.6

- At very high $P$ or low $T$, all gases deviate significantly from ideal behavior.
- As external pressure increases, most real gases exhibit first a lower and then a higher $PV/RT$; for 1 mol of an ideal gas, this ratio remains constant at 1.
- The deviations from ideal behavior are due to (1) attractions between particles, which lower the pressure (and decrease $PV/RT$), and (2) the volume of the particles themselves, which takes up an increasingly larger fraction of the container volume (and increases $PV/RT$).
- The van der Waals equation includes constants specific for a given gas to correct for deviations from ideal behavior. At ordinary $P$ and $T$, the van der Waals equation reduces to the ideal gas equation.

# CHAPTER REVIEW GUIDE

**Learning Objectives**   Relevant section (§) and/or sample problem (SP) numbers appear in parentheses.

## Understand These Concepts

1. How gases differ in their macroscopic properties from liquids and solids (§5.1)
2. The meaning of pressure and the operation of a barometer and a manometer (§5.2)
3. The relations among gas variables expressed by Boyle's, Charles's, and Avogadro's laws (§5.3)
4. How the individual gas laws are incorporated into the ideal gas law (§5.3)
5. How the ideal gas law can be used to study gas density, molar mass, and amounts of gases in reactions (§5.4)
6. The relation between the density and the temperature of a gas (§5.4)
7. The meaning of Dalton's law and the relation between partial pressure and mole fraction of a gas; how Dalton's law applies to collecting a gas over water (§5.4)
8. How the postulates of the kinetic-molecular theory are applied to explain the origin of pressure and the gas laws (§5.5)
9. The relations among molecular speed, average kinetic energy, and temperature (§5.5)
10. The meanings of *effusion* and *diffusion* and how their rates are related to molar mass (§5.5)
11. The relations among mean free path, molecular speed, and collision frequency (§5.5)
12. Why intermolecular attractions and molecular volume cause gases to deviate from ideal behavior at low temperatures and high pressures (§5.6)
13. How the van der Waals equation corrects the ideal gas law for extreme conditions (§5.6)

## Master These Skills

1. Interconverting among the units of pressure (atm, mmHg, torr, pascal, lb/in$^2$) (SP 5.1)
2. Reducing the ideal gas law to the individual gas laws (SPs 5.2–5.5)
3. Applying gas laws to choose the correct chemical equation (SP 5.6)
4. Rearranging the ideal gas law to calculate gas density (SP 5.7) and molar mass of a volatile liquid (SP 5.8)
5. Calculating the mole fraction and the partial pressure of a gas (SP 5.9)
6. Using the vapor pressure of water to correct for the amount of a gas collected over water (SP 5.10)
7. Applying stoichiometry and gas laws to calculate amounts of reactants and products (SPs 5.11, 5.12)
8. Using Graham's law to solve problems of gaseous effusion (SP 5.13)

**Key Terms**   Page numbers appear in parentheses.

**Section 5.2**
pressure ($P$) (183)
barometer (183)
manometer (184)
pascal (Pa) (185)
standard atmosphere (atm) (185)
millimeter of mercury (mmHg) (185)
torr (185)

**Section 5.3**
ideal gas (186)
Boyle's law (187)
Charles's law (188)
Avogadro's law (190)
standard temperature and pressure (STP) (190)
standard molar volume (190)
ideal gas law (191)
universal gas constant ($R$) (191)

**Section 5.4**
partial pressure (199)
Dalton's law of partial pressures (199)
mole fraction ($X$) (200)

**Section 5.5**
kinetic-molecular theory (204)
rms speed ($u_{rms}$) (209)
effusion (209)
Graham's law of effusion (209)

diffusion (210)
mean free path (211)
collision frequency (211)
atmosphere (212)

**Section 5.6**
van der Waals equation (216)
van der Waals constants (216)

**Key Equations and Relationships**   Page numbers appear in parentheses.

**5.1** Expressing the volume-pressure relationship (Boyle's law) (187):

$$V \propto \frac{1}{P} \quad \text{or} \quad PV = \text{constant} \quad [T \text{ and } n \text{ fixed}]$$

**5.2** Expressing the volume-temperature relationship (Charles's law) (188):

$$V \propto T \quad \text{or} \quad \frac{V}{T} = \text{constant} \quad [P \text{ and } n \text{ fixed}]$$

**5.3** Expressing the pressure-temperature relationship (Amontons's law) (189):

$$P \propto T \quad \text{or} \quad \frac{P}{T} = \text{constant} \quad [V \text{ and } n \text{ fixed}]$$

**5.4** Expressing the volume-amount relationship (Avogadro's law) (190):

$$V \propto n \quad \text{or} \quad \frac{V}{n} = \text{constant} \quad [P \text{ and } T \text{ fixed}]$$

**5.5** Defining standard temperature and pressure (190):

STP: 0°C (273.15 K) and 1 atm (760 torr)

**5.6** Defining the volume of 1 mol of an ideal gas at STP (190):

Standard molar volume = 22.4141 L = 22.4 L [3 sf]

**5.7** Relating volume to pressure, temperature, and amount (ideal gas law) (191):

$$PV = nRT \quad \text{and} \quad \frac{P_1V_1}{n_1T_1} = \frac{P_2V_2}{n_2T_2}$$

**5.8** Calculating the value of $R$ (191):

$$R = \frac{PV}{nT} = \frac{1 \text{ atm} \times 22.4141 \text{ L}}{1 \text{ mol} \times 273.15 \text{ K}}$$

$$= 0.082058 \frac{\text{atm·L}}{\text{mol·K}} = 0.0821 \frac{\text{atm·L}}{\text{mol·K}} \quad [3 \text{ sf}]$$

**5.9** Rearranging the ideal gas law to find gas density (196):

$$PV = \frac{m}{\mathcal{M}} RT$$

so

$$\frac{m}{V} = d = \frac{\mathcal{M} \times P}{RT}$$

**5.10** Rearranging the ideal gas law to find molar mass (198):

$$n = \frac{m}{\mathcal{M}} = \frac{PV}{RT} \quad \text{so} \quad \mathcal{M} = \frac{mRT}{PV}$$

**5.11** Relating the total pressure of a gas mixture to the partial pressures of the components (Dalton's law of partial pressures) (199):

$$P_{\text{total}} = P_1 + P_2 + P_3 + \cdots$$

**5.12** Relating partial pressure to mole fraction (200):

$$P_A = X_A \times P_{\text{total}}$$

**5.13** Defining rms speed as a function of molar mass and temperature (209):

$$u_{\text{rms}} = \sqrt{\frac{3RT}{\mathcal{M}}}$$

**5.14** Applying Graham's law of effusion (209):

$$\frac{\text{Rate}_A}{\text{Rate}_B} = \frac{\sqrt{\mathcal{M}_B}}{\sqrt{\mathcal{M}_A}} = \sqrt{\frac{\mathcal{M}_B}{\mathcal{M}_A}}$$

**5.15** Applying the van der Waals equation to find the pressure or volume of a gas under extreme conditions (216):

$$\left(P + \frac{n^2a}{V^2}\right)(V - nb) = nRT$$

## Brief Solutions to Follow-Up Problems

**5.1** $P_{CO_2}$ (torr) = (753.6 mmHg − 174.0 mmHg) × $\frac{1 \text{ torr}}{1 \text{ mmHg}}$

$= 579.6$ torr

$P_{CO_2}$ (Pa) = 579.6 torr × $\frac{1 \text{ atm}}{760 \text{ torr}}$ × $\frac{1.01325 \times 10^5 \text{ Pa}}{1 \text{ atm}}$

$= 7.727 \times 10^4$ Pa

$P_{CO_2}$ (lb/in$^2$) = 579.6 torr × $\frac{1 \text{ atm}}{760 \text{ torr}}$ × $\frac{14.7 \text{ lb/in}^2}{1 \text{ atm}}$

$= 11.2$ lb/in$^2$

**5.2** $P_2$ (atm) = 26.3 kPa × $\frac{1 \text{ atm}}{101.325 \text{ kPa}}$ = 0.260 atm

$V_2$ (L) = 105 mL × $\frac{1 \text{ L}}{1000 \text{ mL}}$ × $\frac{0.871 \text{ atm}}{0.260 \text{ atm}}$ = 0.352 L

**5.3** $T_2$ (K) = 273 K × $\frac{9.75 \text{ cm}^3}{6.83 \text{ cm}^3}$ = 390. K

**5.4** $P_2$ (torr) = 793 torr × $\frac{35.0 \text{ g} - 5.0 \text{ g}}{35.0 \text{ g}}$ = 680. torr

(There is no need to convert mass to moles because the ratio of masses equals the ratio of moles.)

**5.5** $n = \frac{PV}{RT} = \dfrac{1.37 \text{ atm} \times 438 \text{ L}}{0.0821 \dfrac{\text{atm·L}}{\text{mol·K}} \times 294 \text{ K}}$ = 24.9 mol O$_2$

Mass (g) of O$_2$ = 24.9 mol O$_2$ × $\frac{32.00 \text{ g O}_2}{1 \text{ mol O}_2}$ = $7.97 \times 10^2$ g O$_2$

**5.6** The balanced equation is $2CD(g) \longrightarrow C_2(g) + D_2(g)$, so $n$ does not change. Therefore, given constant $P$, the temperature, $T$, must double: $T_1 = -73°C + 273.15 = 200$ K; so $T_2 = 400$ K, or 400 K − 273.15 = 127°C.

**5.7** $d$ (at 0°C and 380 torr) = $\dfrac{44.01 \text{ g/mol} \times \dfrac{380 \text{ torr}}{760 \text{ torr/atm}}}{0.0821 \dfrac{\text{atm·L}}{\text{mol·K}} \times 273 \text{ K}}$

$= 0.982$ g/L

The density is lower at the smaller $P$ because $V$ is larger. In this case, $d$ is lowered by one-half because $P$ is one-half as much.

**5.8**

$\mathcal{M} = \dfrac{(68.697 \text{ g} - 68.322 \text{ g}) \times 0.0821 \dfrac{\text{atm·L}}{\text{mol·K}} \times (273.15 + 95.0) \text{ K}}{\dfrac{740. \text{ torr}}{760 \text{ torr/atm}} \times \dfrac{149 \text{ mL}}{1000 \text{ mL/L}}}$

$= 78.1$ g/mol

**5.9** $n_{total} = \left(5.50 \text{ g He} \times \dfrac{1 \text{ mol He}}{4.003 \text{ g He}}\right)$

$+ \left(15.0 \text{ g Ne} \times \dfrac{1 \text{ mol Ne}}{20.18 \text{ g Ne}}\right)$

$+ \left(35.0 \text{ g Kr} \times \dfrac{1 \text{ mol Kr}}{83.80 \text{ g Kr}}\right)$

$= 2.53 \text{ mol}$

$P_{He} = \left(\dfrac{5.50 \text{ g He} \times \dfrac{1 \text{ mol He}}{4.003 \text{ g He}}}{2.53 \text{ mol}}\right) \times 1 \text{ atm} = 0.543 \text{ atm}$

$P_{Ne} = 0.294 \text{ atm} \qquad P_{Kr} = 0.165 \text{ atm}$

**5.10** $P_{H_2} = 752 \text{ torr} - 13.6 \text{ torr} = 738 \text{ torr}$

Mass (g) of $H_2 = \left(\dfrac{\dfrac{738 \text{ torr}}{760 \text{ torr/atm}} \times 1.495 \text{ L}}{0.0821 \dfrac{\text{atm·L}}{\text{mol·K}} \times 289 \text{ K}}\right) \times \dfrac{2.016 \text{ g } H_2}{1 \text{ mol } H_2}$

$= 0.123 \text{ g } H_2$

**5.11** $H_2SO_4(aq) + 2NaCl(s) \longrightarrow Na_2SO_4(aq) + 2HCl(g)$

$n_{HCl} = 0.117 \text{ kg NaCl} \times \dfrac{10^3 \text{ g}}{1 \text{ kg}} \times \dfrac{1 \text{ mol NaCl}}{58.44 \text{ g NaCl}} \times \dfrac{2 \text{ mol HCl}}{2 \text{ mol NaCl}}$

$= 2.00 \text{ mol HCl}$

At STP, $V \text{ (mL)} = 2.00 \text{ mol} \times \dfrac{22.4 \text{ L}}{1 \text{ mol}} \times \dfrac{10^3 \text{ mL}}{1 \text{ L}}$

$= 4.48 \times 10^4 \text{ mL}$

**5.12** $NH_3(g) + HCl(g) \longrightarrow NH_4Cl(s)$

$n_{NH_3} = 0.187 \text{ mol}$ and $n_{HCl} = 0.0522 \text{ mol}$; thus, HCl is the limiting reactant.

$n_{NH_3}$ after reaction

$= 0.187 \text{ mol } NH_3 - \left(0.0522 \text{ mol HCl} \times \dfrac{1 \text{ mol } NH_3}{1 \text{ mol HCl}}\right)$

$= 0.135 \text{ mol } NH_3$

$P = \dfrac{0.135 \text{ mol} \times 0.0821 \dfrac{\text{atm·L}}{\text{mol·K}} \times 295 \text{ K}}{10.0 \text{ L}} = 0.327 \text{ atm}$

**5.13** $\dfrac{\text{Rate of He}}{\text{Rate of } C_2H_6} = \sqrt{\dfrac{30.07 \text{ g/mol}}{4.003 \text{ g/mol}}} = 2.741$

Time for $C_2H_6$ to effuse $= 1.25 \text{ min} \times 2.741 = 3.43 \text{ min}$

---

# PROBLEMS

Problems with **colored** numbers are answered in Appendix E and worked in detail in the Student Solutions Manual. Problem sections match those in the text and provide the numbers of relevant sample problems. Most offer Concept Review Questions, Skill-Building Exercises (grouped in pairs covering the same concept), and Problems in Context. The Comprehensive Problems are based on material from any section or previous chapter.

## An Overview of the Physical States of Matter

### Concept Review Questions

**5.1** How does a sample of gas differ in its behavior from a sample of liquid in each of the following situations?
(a) The sample is transferred from one container to a larger one.
(b) The sample is heated in an expandable container, but no change of state occurs.
(c) The sample is placed in a cylinder with a piston, and an external force is applied.

**5.2** Are the particles in a gas farther apart or closer together than the particles in a liquid? Use your answer to explain each of the following general observations:
(a) Gases are more compressible than liquids.
(b) Gases have lower viscosities than liquids.
(c) After thorough stirring, all gas mixtures are solutions.
(d) The density of a substance in the gas state is lower than in the liquid state.

## Gas Pressure and Its Measurement
(Sample Problem 5.1)

### Concept Review Questions

**5.3** How does a barometer work? Is the column of mercury in a barometer shorter when it is on a mountaintop or at sea level? Explain.

**5.4** How can a unit of length such as millimeter of mercury (mmHg) be used as a unit of pressure, which has the dimensions of force per unit area?

**5.5** In a closed-end manometer, the mercury level in the arm attached to the flask can never be higher than the mercury level in the other arm, whereas in an open-end manometer, it *can* be higher. Explain.

### Skill-Building Exercises (grouped in similar pairs)

**5.6** On a cool, rainy day, the barometric pressure is 730 mmHg. Calculate the barometric pressure in centimeters of water ($cmH_2O$) ($d$ of Hg = 13.5 g/mL; $d$ of $H_2O$ = 1.00 g/mL).

**5.7** A long glass tube, sealed at one end, has an inner diameter of 10.0 mm. The tube is filled with water and inverted into a pail of water. If the atmospheric pressure is 755 mmHg, how high (in $mmH_2O$) is the column of water in the tube ($d$ of Hg = 13.5 g/mL; $d$ of $H_2O$ = 1.00 g/mL)?

**5.8** Convert the following:
(a) 0.745 atm to mmHg
(b) 992 torr to bar
(c) 365 kPa to atm
(d) 804 mmHg to kPa

**5.9** Convert the following:
(a) 76.8 cmHg to atm
(b) 27.5 atm to kPa
(c) 6.50 atm to bar
(d) 0.937 kPa to torr

**5.10** In Figure P5.10, what is the pressure of the gas in the flask (in atm) if the barometer reads 738.5 torr?

**5.11** In Figure P5.11, what is the pressure of the gas in the flask (in kPa) if the barometer reads 765.2 mmHg?

**Figure P5.10**     **Figure P5.11**

**5.12** If the sample flask in Figure P5.12 is open to the air, what is the atmospheric pressure (in atm)?

**5.13** What is the pressure (in Pa) of the gas in the flask in Figure P5.13?

**Figure P5.12**     **Figure P5.13**

**Problems in Context**

**5.14** Convert each of the pressures described below to atm:
(a) At the peak of Mt. Everest, atmospheric pressure is only $2.75 \times 10^2$ mmHg.
(b) A cyclist fills her bike tires to 86 psi.
(c) The surface of Venus has an atmospheric pressure of $9.15 \times 10^6$ Pa.
(d) At 100 ft below sea level, a scuba diver experiences a pressure of $2.54 \times 10^4$ torr.

**5.15** The gravitational force exerted by an object is given by $F = mg$, where $F$ is the force in newtons, $m$ is the mass in kilograms, and $g$ is the acceleration due to gravity (9.81 m/s²).
(a) Use the definition of the pascal to calculate the mass (in kg) of the atmosphere above 1 m² of ocean.
(b) Osmium ($Z = 76$) is a transition metal in Group 8B(8) and has the highest density of any element (22.6 g/mL). If an osmium column is 1 m² in area, how high must it be for its pressure to equal atmospheric pressure? [Use the answer from part (a) in your calculation.]

## The Gas Laws and Their Experimental Foundations
(Sample Problems 5.2 to 5.6)

### Concept Review Questions

**5.16** A student states Boyle's law as follows: "The volume of a gas is inversely proportional to its pressure." How is this statement incomplete? Give a correct statement of Boyle's law.

**5.17** In the following relationships, which quantities are variables and which are fixed: (a) Charles's law; (b) Avogadro's law; (c) Amontons's law?

**5.18** Boyle's law relates gas volume to pressure, and Avogadro's law relates gas volume to amount (mol). State a relationship between gas pressure and amount (mol).

**5.19** Each of the following processes caused the gas volume to double, as shown. For each process, tell how the remaining gas variable changed or state that it remained fixed:
(a) $T$ doubles at fixed $P$.
(b) $T$ and $n$ are fixed.
(c) At fixed $T$, the reaction is $CD_2(g) \longrightarrow C(g) + D_2(g)$.
(d) At fixed $P$, the reaction is $A_2(g) + B_2(g) \longrightarrow 2AB(g)$.

### Skill-Building Exercises (grouped in similar pairs)

**5.20** What is the effect of the following on the volume of 1 mol of an ideal gas?
(a) The pressure is tripled (at constant $T$).
(b) The absolute temperature is increased by a factor of 3.0 (at constant $P$).
(c) Three more moles of the gas are added (at constant $P$ and $T$).

**5.21** What is the effect of the following on the volume of 1 mol of an ideal gas?
(a) The pressure is reduced by a factor of 4 (at constant $T$).
(b) The pressure changes from 760 torr to 202 kPa, and the temperature changes from 37°C to 155 K.
(c) The temperature changes from 305 K to 32°C, and the pressure changes from 2 atm to 101 kPa.

**5.22** What is the effect of the following on the volume of 1 mol of an ideal gas?
(a) Temperature decreases from 800 K to 400 K (at constant $P$).
(b) Temperature increases from 250°C to 500°C (at constant $P$).
(c) Pressure increases from 2 atm to 6 atm (at constant $T$).

**5.23** What is the effect of the following on the volume of 1 mol of an ideal gas?
(a) Half the gas escapes (at constant $P$ and $T$).
(b) The initial pressure is 722 torr, and the final pressure is 0.950 atm; the initial temperature is 32°F, and the final temperature is 273 K.
(c) Both the pressure and temperature decrease to one-fourth of their initial values.

**5.24** A sample of sulfur hexafluoride gas occupies 9.10 L at 198°C. Assuming that the pressure remains constant, what temperature (in °C) is needed to reduce the volume to 2.50 L?

**5.25** A 93-L sample of dry air cools from 145°C to −22°C while the pressure is maintained at 2.85 atm. What is the final volume?

**5.26** A sample of Freon-12 ($CF_2Cl_2$) occupies 25.5 L at 298 K and 153.3 kPa. Find its volume at STP.

**5.27** A sample of carbon monoxide occupies 3.65 L at 298 K and 745 torr. Find its volume at −14°C and 367 torr.

**5.28** A sample of chlorine gas is confined in a 5.0-L container at 328 torr and 37°C. How many moles of gas are in the sample?

**5.29** If $1.47 \times 10^{-3}$ mol of argon occupies a 75.0-mL container at 26°C, what is the pressure (in torr)?

**5.30** You have 357 mL of chlorine trifluoride gas at 699 mmHg and 45°C. What is the mass (in g) of the sample?

**5.31** A 75.0-g sample of dinitrogen monoxide is confined in a 3.1-L vessel. What is the pressure (in atm) at 115°C?

### Problems in Context

**5.32** In preparation for a demonstration, your professor brings a 1.5-L bottle of sulfur dioxide into the lecture hall before class to allow the gas to reach room temperature. If the pressure gauge reads 85 psi and the temperature in the hall is 23°C, how many moles of sulfur dioxide are in the bottle? (*Hint:* The gauge reads zero when 14.7 psi of gas remains.)

**5.33** A gas-filled weather balloon with a volume of 65.0 L is released at sea-level conditions of 745 torr and 25°C. The balloon can expand to a maximum volume of 835 L. When the balloon rises to an altitude at which the temperature is −5°C and the pressure is 0.066 atm, will it reach its maximum volume?

### Rearrangements of the Ideal Gas Law
(Sample Problems 5.7 to 5.12)

### Concept Review Questions
**5.34** Why is moist air less dense than dry air?

**5.35** To collect a beaker of $H_2$ gas by displacing the air already in the beaker, would you hold the beaker upright or inverted? Why? How would you hold the beaker to collect $CO_2$?

**5.36** Why can we use a gas mixture, such as air, to study the general behavior of an ideal gas under ordinary conditions?

**5.37** How does the partial pressure of gas A in a mixture compare to its mole fraction in the mixture? Explain.

**5.38** The scene at right represents a portion of a mixture of four gases A (*purple*), B (*black*), C (*green*), and $D_2$ (*orange*).
(a) Which has the highest partial pressure?
(b) Which has the lowest partial pressure?
(c) If the total pressure is 0.75 atm, what is the partial pressure of $D_2$?

### Skill-Building Exercises (grouped in similar pairs)
**5.39** What is the density of Xe gas at STP?

**5.40** Find the density of Freon-11 ($CFCl_3$) at 120°C and 1.5 atm.

**5.41** How many moles of gaseous arsine ($AsH_3$) occupy 0.0400 L at STP? What is the density of gaseous arsine?

**5.42** The density of a noble gas is 2.71 g/L at 3.00 atm and 0°C. Identify the gas.

**5.43** Calculate the molar mass of a gas at 388 torr and 45°C if 206 ng occupies 0.206 μL.

**5.44** When an evacuated 63.8-mL glass bulb is filled with a gas at 22°C and 747 mmHg, the bulb gains 0.103 g in mass. Is the gas $N_2$, Ne, or Ar?

**5.45** After 0.600 L of Ar at 1.20 atm and 227°C is mixed with 0.200 L of $O_2$ at 501 torr and 127°C in a 400-mL flask at 27°C, what is the pressure in the flask?

**5.46** A 355-mL container holds 0.146 g of Ne and an unknown amount of Ar at 35°C and a total pressure of 626 mmHg. Calculate the number of moles of Ar present.

**5.47** How many grams of phosphorus react with 35.5 L of $O_2$ at STP to form tetraphosphorus decaoxide?

$$P_4(s) + 5O_2(g) \longrightarrow P_4O_{10}(s)$$

**5.48** How many grams of potassium chlorate decompose to potassium chloride and 638 mL of $O_2$ at 128°C and 752 torr?

$$2KClO_3(s) \longrightarrow 2KCl(s) + 3O_2(g)$$

**5.49** How many grams of phosphine ($PH_3$) can form when 37.5 g of phosphorus and 83.0 L of hydrogen gas react at STP?

$$P_4(s) + H_2(g) \longrightarrow PH_3(g) \quad [\text{unbalanced}]$$

**5.50** When 35.6 L of ammonia and 40.5 L of oxygen gas at STP burn, nitrogen monoxide and water form. After the products return to STP, how many grams of nitrogen monoxide are present?

$$NH_3(g) + O_2(g) \longrightarrow NO(g) + H_2O(l) \quad [\text{unbalanced}]$$

**5.51** Aluminum reacts with excess hydrochloric acid to form aqueous aluminum chloride and 35.8 mL of hydrogen gas over water at 27°C and 751 mmHg. How many grams of aluminum reacted?

**5.52** How many liters of hydrogen gas are collected over water at 18°C and 725 mmHg when 0.84 g of lithium reacts with water? Aqueous lithium hydroxide also forms.

### Problems in Context

**5.53** The air in a hot-air balloon at 744 torr is heated from 17°C to 60.0°C. Assuming that the amount (mol) of air and the pressure remain constant, what is the density of the air at each temperature? (The average molar mass of air is 28.8 g/mol.)

**5.54** On a certain winter day in Utah, the average atmospheric pressure is 650. torr. What is the molar density (in mol/L) of the air if the temperature is −25°C?

**5.55** A sample of a liquid hydrocarbon known to consist of molecules with five carbon atoms is vaporized in a 0.204-L flask by immersion in a water bath at 101°C. The barometric pressure is 767 torr, and the remaining gas weighs 0.482 g. What is the molecular formula of the hydrocarbon?

**5.56** A sample of air contains 78.08% nitrogen, 20.94% oxygen, 0.05% carbon dioxide, and 0.93% argon, by volume. How many molecules of each gas are present in 1.00 L of the sample at 25°C and 1.00 atm?

**5.57** An environmental chemist sampling industrial exhaust gases from a coal-burning plant collects a $CO_2$-$SO_2$-$H_2O$ mixture in a 21-L steel tank until the pressure reaches 850. torr at 45°C.
(a) How many moles of gas are collected?

(b) If the $SO_2$ concentration in the mixture is $7.95 \times 10^3$ parts per million by volume (ppmv), what is its partial pressure? [*Hint:* ppmv = (volume of component/volume of mixture) × $10^6$.]

**5.58** "Strike anywhere" matches contain the compound tetraphosphorus trisulfide, which burns to form tetraphosphorus decaoxide and sulfur dioxide gas. How many milliliters of sulfur dioxide, measured at 725 torr and 32°C, can be produced from burning 0.800 g of tetraphosphorus trisulfide?

**5.59** Freon-12 ($CF_2Cl_2$), widely used as a refrigerant and aerosol propellant, is a dangerous air pollutant. In the troposphere, it traps heat 25 times as effectively as $CO_2$, and in the stratosphere, it participates in the breakdown of ozone. Freon-12 is prepared industrially by reaction of gaseous carbon tetrachloride with hydrogen fluoride. Hydrogen chloride gas also forms. How many grams of carbon tetrachloride are required for the production of 16.0 $dm^3$ of Freon-12 at 27°C and 1.20 atm?

**5.60** Xenon hexafluoride was one of the first noble gas compounds synthesized. The solid reacts rapidly with the silicon dioxide in glass or quartz containers to form liquid $XeOF_4$ and gaseous silicon tetrafluoride. What is the pressure in a 1.00-L container at 25°C after 2.00 g of xenon hexafluoride reacts? (Assume that silicon tetrafluoride is the only gas present and that it occupies the entire volume.)

**5.61** In the four cylinder-piston assemblies below, the reactant in the left cylinder is about to undergo a reaction at constant *T* and *P*:

Which of the other three depictions best represents the products of the reaction?

**5.62** Roasting galena [lead(II) sulfide] is a step in the industrial isolation of lead. How many liters of sulfur dioxide, measured at STP, are produced by the reaction of 3.75 kg of galena with 228 L of oxygen gas at 220°C and 2.0 atm? Lead(II) oxide also forms.

**5.63** In one of his most critical studies into the nature of combustion, Lavoisier heated mercury(II) oxide and isolated elemental mercury and oxygen gas. If 40.0 g of mercury(II) oxide is heated in a 502-mL vessel and 20.0% (by mass) decomposes, what is the pressure (in atm) of the oxygen that forms at 25.0°C? (Assume that the gas occupies the entire volume.)

## The Kinetic-Molecular Theory: A Model for Gas Behavior
(Sample Problem 5.13)

**Concept Review Questions**

**5.64** Use the kinetic-molecular theory to explain the change in gas pressure that results from warming a sample of gas.

**5.65** How does the kinetic-molecular theory explain why 1 mol of krypton and 1 mol of helium have the same volume at STP?

**5.66** Is the rate of effusion of a gas higher than, lower than, or equal to its rate of diffusion? Explain. For two gases with molecules of approximately the same size, is the ratio of their effusion rates higher than, lower than, or equal to the ratio of their diffusion rates? Explain.

**5.67** Consider two 1-L samples of gas: one is $H_2$ and the other is $O_2$. Both are at 1 atm and 25°C. How do the samples compare in terms of (a) mass, (b) density, (c) mean free path, (d) average molecular kinetic energy, (e) average molecular speed, and (f) time for a given fraction of molecules to effuse?

**5.68** Three 5-L flasks, fixed with pressure gauges and small valves, each contain 4 g of gas at 273 K. Flask A contains $H_2$, flask B contains He, and flask C contains $CH_4$. Rank the flask contents in terms of (a) pressure, (b) average molecular kinetic energy, (c) diffusion rate after the valve is opened, (d) total kinetic energy of the molecules, (e) density, and (f) collision frequency.

**Skill-Building Exercises** (grouped in similar pairs)

**5.69** What is the ratio of effusion rates for the lightest gas, $H_2$, and the heaviest known gas, $UF_6$?

**5.70** What is the ratio of effusion rates for $O_2$ and Kr?

**5.71** The graph below shows the distribution of molecular speeds for argon and helium at the same temperature.

(a) Does curve 1 or 2 better represent the behavior of argon?
(b) Which curve represents the gas that effuses more slowly?
(c) Which curve more closely represents the behavior of fluorine gas? Explain.

**5.72** The graph below shows the distribution of molecular speeds for a gas at two different temperatures.

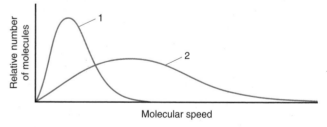

(a) Does curve 1 or 2 better represent the behavior of the gas at the lower temperature?
(b) Which curve represents the gas when it has a higher $\overline{E_k}$?
(c) Which curve is consistent with a higher diffusion rate?

**5.73** At a given pressure and temperature, it takes 4.85 min for a 1.5-L sample of He to effuse through a membrane. How long does it take for 1.5 L of $F_2$ to effuse under the same conditions?

**5.74** A sample of an unknown gas effuses in 11.1 min. An equal volume of $H_2$ in the same apparatus under the same conditions effuses in 2.42 min. What is the molar mass of the unknown gas?

**Problems in Context**

**5.75** White phosphorus melts and then vaporizes at high temperature. The gas effuses at a rate that is 0.404 times that of neon in the same apparatus under the same conditions. How many atoms are in a molecule of gaseous white phosphorus?

**5.76** Helium (He) is the lightest noble gas component of air, and xenon (Xe) is the heaviest. [For this problem, use $R = 8.314$ J/(mol·K) and $\mathcal{M}$ in kg/mol.] (a) Find the rms speed of He in winter (0.°C) and in summer (30.°C). (b) Compare the rms speed of He with that of Xe at 30.°C. (c) Find the average kinetic energy per mole of He and of Xe at 30.°C. (d) Find the average kinetic energy per molecule of He at 30.°C.

**5.77** A mixture of gaseous disulfur difluoride, dinitrogen tetrafluoride, and sulfur tetrafluoride is placed in an effusion apparatus. (a) Rank the gases in order of increasing effusion rate. (b) Find the ratio of effusion rates of disulfur difluoride and dinitrogen tetrafluoride. (c) If gas X is added, and it effuses at 0.935 times the rate of sulfur tetrafluoride, find the molar mass of X.

## Real Gases: Deviations from Ideal Behavior

**Skill-Building Exercises** (grouped in similar pairs)

**5.78** Do interparticle attractions cause negative or positive deviations from the *PV/RT* ratio of an ideal gas? Use Table 5.3 to rank Kr, $CO_2$, and $N_2$ in order of increasing magnitude of these deviations.

**5.79** Does particle volume cause negative or positive deviations from the *PV/RT* ratio of an ideal gas? Use Table 5.3 to rank $Cl_2$, $H_2$, and $O_2$ in order of increasing magnitude of these deviations.

**5.80** Does $N_2$ behave more ideally at 1 atm or at 500 atm? Explain.

**5.81** Does $SF_6$ (boiling point = 16°C at 1 atm) behave more ideally at 150°C or at 20°C? Explain.

## Comprehensive Problems

**5.82** An "empty" gasoline can with dimensions 15.0 cm by 40.0 cm by 12.5 cm is attached to a vacuum pump and evacuated. If the atmospheric pressure is 14.7 lb/in², what is the total force (in pounds) on the outside of the can?

**5.83** Hemoglobin is the protein that transports $O_2$ through the blood from the lungs to the rest of the body. In doing so, each molecule of hemoglobin combines with four molecules of $O_2$. If 1.00 g of hemoglobin combines with 1.53 mL of $O_2$ at 37°C and 743 torr, what is the molar mass of hemoglobin?

**5.84** A baker uses sodium hydrogen carbonate (baking soda) as the leavening agent in a banana-nut quickbread. The baking soda decomposes in either of two possible reactions:

(1) $2NaHCO_3(s) \longrightarrow Na_2CO_3(s) + H_2O(l) + CO_2(g)$

(2) $NaHCO_3(s) + H^+(aq) \longrightarrow H_2O(l) + CO_2(g) + Na^+(aq)$

Calculate the volume (in mL) of $CO_2$ that forms at 200.°C and 0.975 atm per gram of $NaHCO_3$ by each of the reaction processes.

**5.85** A weather balloon containing 600. L of He is released near the equator at 1.01 atm and 305 K. It rises to a point where conditions are 0.489 atm and 218 K and eventually lands in the northern hemisphere under conditions of 1.01 atm and 250 K. If one-fourth of the helium leaked out during this journey, what is the volume (in L) of the balloon at landing?

**5.86** Chlorine is produced from sodium chloride by the electrochemical chlor-alkali process. During the process, the chlorine is collected in a container that is isolated from the other products to prevent unwanted (and explosive) reactions. If a 15.50-L container holds 0.5950 kg of $Cl_2$ gas at 225°C, calculate:

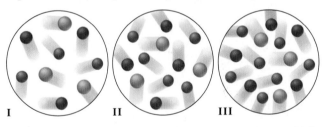

(a) $P_{IGL}$ $\qquad$ (b) $P_{VDW}$ $\left(\text{use } R = 0.08206 \dfrac{\text{atm·L}}{\text{mol·K}}\right)$

**5.87** In a certain experiment, magnesium boride ($Mg_3B_2$) reacted with acid to form a mixture of four boron hydrides ($B_xH_y$), three as liquids (labeled I, II, and III) and one as a gas (IV).
(a) When a 0.1000-g sample of each liquid was transferred to an evacuated 750.0-mL container and volatilized at 70.00°C, sample I had a pressure of 0.05951 atm; sample II, 0.07045 atm; and sample III, 0.05767 atm. What is the molar mass of each liquid?
(b) Boron is 85.63% by mass in sample I, 81.10% in II, and 82.98% in III. What is the molecular formula of each sample?
(c) Sample IV was found to be 78.14% boron. Its rate of effusion was compared to that of sulfur dioxide; under identical conditions, 350.0 mL of sample IV effused in 12.00 min and 250.0 mL of sulfur dioxide effused in 13.04 min. What is the molecular formula of sample IV?

**5.88** Three equal volumes of gas mixtures, all at the same *T*, are depicted below (with gas A *red,* gas B *green,* and gas C *blue*):

I $\qquad\qquad$ II $\qquad\qquad$ III

(a) Which sample, if any, has the highest partial pressure of A?
(b) Which sample, if any, has the lowest partial pressure of B?
(c) In which sample, if any, do the gas particles have the highest average kinetic energy?

**5.89** Will the volume of a gas increase, decrease, or remain unchanged for each of the following sets of changes?
(a) The pressure is decreased from 2 atm to 1 atm, while the temperature is decreased from 200°C to 100°C.
(b) The pressure is increased from 1 atm to 3 atm, while the temperature is increased from 100°C to 300°C.
(c) The pressure is increased from 3 atm to 6 atm, while the temperature is increased from −73°C to 127°C.
(d) The pressure is increased from 0.2 atm to 0.4 atm, while the temperature is decreased from 300°C to 150°C.

**5.90** When air is inhaled, it enters the alveoli of the lungs, and varying amounts of the component gases exchange with dissolved gases in the blood. The resulting alveolar gas mixture is quite different from the atmospheric mixture. The following table presents selected data on the composition and partial pressure of four gases in the atmosphere and in the alveoli:

| | Atmosphere (sea level) | | Alveoli | |
|---|---|---|---|---|
| Gas | Mole % | Partial Pressure (torr) | Mole % | Partial Pressure (torr) |
| $N_2$ | 78.6 | — | — | 569 |
| $O_2$ | 20.9 | — | — | 104 |
| $CO_2$ | 00.04 | — | — | 40 |
| $H_2O$ | 00.46 | — | — | 47 |

If the total pressure of each gas mixture is 1.00 atm, calculate:
(a) The partial pressure (in torr) of each gas in the atmosphere
(b) The mole % of each gas in the alveoli
(c) The number of $O_2$ molecules in 0.50 L of alveolar air (volume of an average breath of a person at rest) at 37°C

**5.91** Radon (Rn) is the heaviest, and only radioactive, member of Group 8A(18) (noble gases). It is a product of the disintegration of heavier radioactive nuclei found in minute concentrations in many common rocks used for building and construction. In recent years, health concerns about the cancers caused from inhaled residential radon have grown. If $1.0 \times 10^{15}$ atoms of radium (Ra) produce an average of $1.373 \times 10^4$ atoms of Rn per second, how many liters of Rn, measured at STP, are produced per day by 1.0 g of Ra?

**5.92** At 1450. mmHg and 286 K, a skin diver exhales a 208-mL bubble of air that is 77% $N_2$, 17% $O_2$, and 6.0% $CO_2$ by volume.
(a) How many milliliters would the volume of the bubble be if it were exhaled at the surface at 1 atm and 298 K?
(b) How many moles of $N_2$ are in the bubble?

**5.93** Nitrogen dioxide is used industrially to produce nitric acid, but it contributes to acid rain and photochemical smog. What volume (in L) of nitrogen dioxide is formed at 735 torr and 28.2°C by reacting 4.95 cm³ of copper ($d = 8.95$ g/cm³) with 230.0 mL of nitric acid ($d = 1.42$ g/cm³, 68.0% $HNO_3$ by mass)?

$$Cu(s) + 4HNO_3(aq) \longrightarrow Cu(NO_3)_2(aq) + 2NO_2(g) + 2H_2O(l)$$

**5.94** In the average adult male, the residual volume (RV) of the lungs, the volume of air remaining after a forced exhalation, is 1200 mL. (a) How many moles of air are present in the RV at 1.0 atm and 37°C? (b) How many molecules of gas are present under these conditions?

**5.95** In a bromine-producing plant, how many liters of gaseous elemental bromine at 300°C and 0.855 atm are formed by the reaction of 275 g of sodium bromide and 175.6 g of sodium bromate in aqueous acid solution? (Assume no $Br_2$ dissolves.)

$$5NaBr(aq) + NaBrO_3(aq) + 3H_2SO_4(aq) \longrightarrow$$
$$3Br_2(g) + 3Na_2SO_4(aq) + 3H_2O(g)$$

**5.96** In a collision of sufficient force, automobile air bags respond by electrically triggering the explosive decomposition of sodium azide ($NaN_3$) to its elements. A 50.0-g sample of sodium azide was decomposed, and the nitrogen gas generated was collected over water at 26°C. The total pressure was 745.5 mmHg. How many liters of dry $N_2$ were generated?

**5.97** An anesthetic gas contains 64.81% carbon, 13.60% hydrogen, and 21.59% oxygen, by mass. If 2.00 L of the gas at 25°C and 0.420 atm weighs 2.57 g, what is the molecular formula of the anesthetic?

**5.98** Aluminum chloride is easily vaporized above 180°C. The gas escapes through a pinhole 0.122 times as fast as helium at the same conditions of temperature and pressure in the same apparatus. What is the molecular formula of aluminum chloride gas?

**5.99** (a) What is the total volume (in L) of gaseous *products,* measured at 350°C and 735 torr, when an automobile engine burns 100. g of $C_8H_{18}$ (a typical component of gasoline)?
(b) For part (a), the source of $O_2$ is air, which is 78% $N_2$, 21% $O_2$, and 1.0% Ar by volume. Assuming all the $O_2$ reacts, but no $N_2$ or Ar does, what is the total volume (in L) of gaseous *exhaust?*

**5.100** An atmospheric chemist studying the pollutant $SO_2$ places a mixture of $SO_2$ and $O_2$ in a 2.00-L container at 800. K and 1.90 atm. When the reaction occurs, gaseous $SO_3$ forms, and the pressure falls to 1.65 atm. How many moles of $SO_3$ form?

**5.101** The thermal decomposition of ethylene occurs during the compound's transit in pipelines and during the formation of polyethylene. The decomposition reaction is

$$CH_2{=}CH_2(g) \longrightarrow CH_4(g) + C(graphite)$$

If the decomposition begins at 10°C and 50.0 atm with a gas density of 0.215 g/mL and the temperature increases by 950 K,
(a) What is the final pressure of the confined gas (ignore the volume of graphite and use the van der Waals equation)?
(b) How does the *PV/RT* value of $CH_4$ compare to that in Figure 5.23? Explain.

**5.102** Ammonium nitrate, a common fertilizer, was used by terrorists in the tragic explosion in Oklahoma City in 1995. How many liters of gas at 307°C and 1.00 atm are formed by the explosive decomposition of 15.0 kg of ammonium nitrate to nitrogen, oxygen, and water vapor?

**5.103** An environmental engineer analyzes a sample of air contaminated with sulfur dioxide. To a 500.-mL sample at 700. torr and 38°C, she adds 20.00 mL of 0.01017 *M* aqueous iodine, which reacts as follows:

$$SO_2(g) + I_2(aq) + H_2O(l) \longrightarrow$$
$$HSO_4^-(aq) + I^-(aq) + H^+(aq) \quad \text{[unbalanced]}$$

Excess $I_2$ reacts with 11.37 mL of 0.0105 *M* sodium thiosulfate:

$$I_2(aq) + S_2O_3^{2-}(aq) \longrightarrow I^-(aq) + S_4O_6^{2-}(aq) \quad \text{[unbalanced]}$$

What is the volume % of $SO_2$ in the air sample?

**5.104** Canadian chemists have developed a modern variation of the 1899 Mond process for preparing extremely pure metallic nickel. A sample of impure nickel reacts with carbon monoxide at 50°C to form gaseous nickel carbonyl, $Ni(CO)_4$.
(a) How many grams of nickel can be converted to the carbonyl with 3.55 m³ of CO at 100.7 kPa?
(b) The carbonyl is then decomposed at 21 atm and 155°C to pure (>99.95%) nickel. How many grams of nickel are obtained per cubic meter of the carbonyl?
(c) The released carbon monoxide is cooled and collected for reuse by passing it through water at 35°C. If the barometric pressure is 769 torr, what volume (in m³) of CO is formed per cubic meter of carbonyl?

**5.105** Analysis of a newly discovered gaseous silicon-fluorine compound shows that it contains 33.01 mass % silicon. At 27°C, 2.60 g of the compound exerts a pressure of 1.50 atm in a 0.250-L vessel. What is the molecular formula of the compound?

**5.106** A gaseous organic compound containing only carbon, hydrogen, and nitrogen is burned in oxygen gas, and the volume of each reactant and product is measured under the same conditions of temperature and pressure. Reaction of four volumes of the compound produces four volumes of $CO_2$, two volumes of $N_2$, and ten volumes of water vapor. (a) How many volumes of $O_2$ were required? (b) What is the empirical formula of the compound?

**5.107** Containers A, B, and C are attached by closed stopcocks of negligible volume.

If each particle shown in the picture represents $10^6$ particles,
(a) How many blue particles and black particles are in B after the stopcocks are opened and the system reaches equilibrium?
(b) How many blue particles and black particles are in A after the stopcocks are opened and the system reaches equilibrium?
(c) If the pressure in C, $P_C$, is 750 torr before the stopcocks are opened, what is $P_C$ afterward? (d) What is $P_B$ afterward?

**5.108** Combustible vapor-air mixtures are flammable over a limited range of concentrations. The minimum volume % of vapor that gives a combustible mixture is called the *lower flammable limit* (LFL). Generally, the LFL is about half the stoichiometric mixture, the concentration required for complete combustion of the vapor in air. (a) If oxygen is 20.9 vol % of air, estimate the LFL for *n*-hexane, $C_6H_{14}$. (b) What volume (in mL) of *n*-hexane *(d = 0.660 g/cm³)* is required to produce a flammable mixture of hexane in 1.000 m³ of air at STP?

**5.109** By what factor would a scuba diver's lungs expand if she ascended rapidly to the surface from a depth of 125 ft without inhaling or exhaling? If an expansion factor greater than 1.5 causes lung rupture, how far could she safely ascend from 125 ft without breathing? Assume constant temperature (*d* of seawater = 1.04 g/mL; *d* of Hg = 13.5 g/mL).

**5.110** When 15.0 g of fluorite ($CaF_2$) reacts with excess sulfuric acid, hydrogen fluoride gas is collected at 744 torr and 25.5°C. Solid calcium sulfate is the other product. What gas temperature is required to store the gas in an 8.63-L container at 875 torr?

**5.111** Dilute aqueous hydrogen peroxide is used as a bleaching agent and for disinfecting surfaces and small cuts. Its concentration is sometimes given as a certain number of "volumes hydrogen peroxide," which refers to the number of volumes of $O_2$ gas, measured at STP, that a given volume of hydrogen peroxide solution will release when it decomposes to $O_2$ and liquid $H_2O$. How many grams of hydrogen peroxide are in 0.100 L of "20 volumes hydrogen peroxide" solution?

**5.112** At a height of 300 km above Earth's surface, an astronaut finds that the atmospheric pressure is about $10^{-8}$ mmHg and the temperature is 500 K. How many molecules of gas are there per milliliter at this altitude?

**5.113** (a) What is the rms speed of $O_2$ at STP? (b) If the mean free path of $O_2$ molecules at STP is $6.33\times10^{-8}$ m, what is their collision frequency? [Use $R = 8.314$ J/(mol·K) and $\mathcal{M}$ in kg/mol.]

**5.114** Acrylic acid ($CH_2{=}CHCOOH$) is used to prepare polymers, adhesives, and paints. The first step in making acrylic acid involves the vapor-phase oxidation of propylene ($CH_2{=}CHCH_3$) to acrolein ($CH_2{=}CHCHO$). This step is carried out at 330°C and 2.5 atm in a large bundle of tubes around which circulates a heat-transfer agent. The reactants spend an average of 1.8 s in the tubes, which have a void space of 100 ft³. How many pounds of propylene must be added per hour in a mixture whose mole fractions are 0.07 propylene, 0.35 steam, and 0.58 air?

**5.115** Standard conditions are based on relevant environmental conditions. If normal average surface temperature and pressure on Venus are 730. K and 90 atm, respectively, what is the standard molar volume of an ideal gas on Venus?

**5.116** A barometer tube is $1.00\times10^2$ cm long and has a cross-sectional area of 1.20 cm². The height of the mercury column is 74.0 cm, and the temperature is 24°C. A small amount of $N_2$ is introduced into the evacuated space above the mercury, which causes the mercury level to drop to a height of 64.0 cm. How many grams of $N_2$ were introduced?

**5.117** What is the molarity of the cleaning solution formed when 10.0 L of ammonia gas at 33°C and 735 torr dissolves in enough water to give a final volume of 0.750 L?

**5.118** The Hawaiian volcano Kilauea emits an average of $1.5\times10^3$ m³ of gas each day, when corrected to 298 K and 1.00 atm. The mixture contains gases that contribute to global warming and acid rain, and some are toxic. An atmospheric chemist analyzes a sample and finds the following mole fractions: 0.4896 $CO_2$, 0.0146 CO, 0.3710 $H_2O$, 0.1185 $SO_2$, 0.0003 $S_2$, 0.0047 $H_2$, 0.0008 HCl, and 0.0003 $H_2S$. How many metric tons (t) of each gas are emitted per year (1 t = 1000 kg)?

**5.119** To study a key fuel-cell reaction, a chemical engineer has 20.0-L tanks of $H_2$ and of $O_2$ and wants to use up both tanks to form 28.0 mol of water at 23.8°C. (a) Use the ideal gas law to find the pressure needed in each tank. (b) Use the van der Waals equation to find the pressure needed in each tank. (c) Compare the results from the two equations.

**5.120** For each of the following, which shows the greater deviation from ideal behavior at the same set of conditions? Explain.
(a) Argon or xenon            (b) Water vapor or neon
(c) Mercury vapor or radon   (d) Water vapor or methane

**5.121** How many liters of gaseous hydrogen bromide at 29°C and 0.965 atm will a chemist need if she wishes to prepare 3.50 L of 1.20 *M* hydrobromic acid?

**5.122** A mixture consisting of 7.0 g of CO and 10.0 g of $SO_2$, two atmospheric pollutants, has a pressure of 0.33 atm when placed in a sealed container. What is the partial pressure of CO?

**5.123** Sulfur dioxide is used to make sulfuric acid. One method of producing it is by roasting mineral sulfides, for example,

$$FeS_2(s) + O_2(g) \xrightarrow{\Delta} SO_2(g) + Fe_2O_3(s) \quad [unbalanced]$$

A production error leads to the sulfide being placed in a 950-L vessel with insufficient oxygen. Initially, the partial pressure of $O_2$ is 0.64 atm, and the total pressure is 1.05 atm, with the balance due to $N_2$. The reaction is run until 85% of the $O_2$ is consumed, and the vessel is then cooled to its initial temperature. What is the total pressure and the partial pressure of each gas in the vessel?

**5.124** A mixture of $CO_2$ and Kr weighs 35.0 g and exerts a pressure of 0.708 atm in its container. Since Kr is expensive, you wish to recover it from the mixture. After the $CO_2$ is completely removed by absorption with $NaOH(s)$, the pressure in the container is 0.250 atm. How many grams of $CO_2$ were originally present? How many grams of Kr can you recover?

**5.125** When a car accelerates quickly, the passengers feel a force that presses them back into their seats, but a balloon filled with helium floats forward. Why?

**5.126** Gases such as CO are gradually oxidized in the atmosphere, not by $O_2$ but by the hydroxyl radical, $\cdot OH$, a species with one fewer electron than a hydroxide ion. At night, the $\cdot OH$ concentration is nearly zero, but it increases to $2.5 \times 10^{12}$ molecules/m$^3$ in polluted air during the day. At daytime conditions of 1.00 atm and 22°C, what is the partial pressure and mole percent of $\cdot OH$ in air?

**5.127** Aqueous sulfurous acid ($H_2SO_3$) was made by dissolving 0.200 L of sulfur dioxide gas at 19°C and 745 mmHg in water to yield 500.0 mL of solution. The acid solution required 10.0 mL of sodium hydroxide solution to reach the titration end point. What was the molarity of the sodium hydroxide solution?

**5.128** In the 19$^{th}$ century, J. B. A. Dumas devised a method for finding the molar mass of a volatile liquid from the volume, temperature, pressure, and mass of its vapor. He placed a sample of such a liquid in a flask that was closed with a stopper fitted with a narrow tube, immersed the flask in a hot water bath to vaporize the liquid, and then cooled the flask. Find the molar mass of a volatile liquid from the following:
Mass of empty flask = 65.347 g
Mass of flask filled with water at 25°C = 327.4 g
Density of water at 25°C = 0.997 g/mL
Mass of flask plus condensed unknown liquid = 65.739 g
Barometric pressure = 101.2 kPa
Temperature of water bath = 99.8°C

**5.129** During World War II, a portable source of hydrogen gas was needed for weather balloons, and solid metal hydrides were the most convenient form. Many metal hydrides react with water to generate the metal hydroxide and hydrogen. Two candidates were lithium hydride and magnesium hydride. What volume (in L) of gas is formed from 1.00 lb of each hydride reacting with excess water at 750. torr and 27°C?

**5.130** The lunar surface reaches 370 K at midday. The atmosphere consists of neon, argon, and helium at a total pressure of only $2 \times 10^{-14}$ atm. Calculate the rms speed of each component in the lunar atmosphere. [Use $R = 8.314$ J/(mol·K) and $\mathcal{M}$ in kg/mol.]

**5.131** A person inhales air richer in $O_2$ and exhales air richer in $CO_2$ and water vapor. During each hour of sleep, a person exhales a total of about 300 L of this $CO_2$-enriched and $H_2O$-enriched air. (a) If the partial pressures of $CO_2$ and $H_2O$ in exhaled air are each 30.0 torr at 37.0°C, calculate the mass (g) of $CO_2$ and of $H_2O$ exhaled in 1 h of sleep. (b) How many grams of body mass does the person lose in an 8-h sleep if all the $CO_2$ and $H_2O$ exhaled come from the metabolism of glucose?

$$C_6H_{12}O_6(s) + 6O_2(g) \longrightarrow 6CO_2(g) + 6H_2O(g)$$

**5.132** Popcorn pops because the horny endosperm, a tough, elastic material, resists gas pressure within the heated kernel until it reaches explosive force. A 0.25-mL kernel has a water content of 1.6% by mass, and the water vapor reaches 170°C and 9.0 atm before the kernel ruptures. Assume that water vapor can occupy 75% of the kernel's volume. (a) What is the mass (in g) of the kernel? (b) How many milliliters would this amount of water vapor occupy at 25°C and 1.00 atm?

**5.133** Sulfur dioxide emissions from coal-burning power plants are removed by *flue-gas desulfurization*. The flue gas passes through a scrubber, and a slurry of wet calcium carbonate reacts with it to form carbon dioxide and calcium sulfite. The calcium sulfite then reacts with oxygen to form calcium sulfate, which is sold as gypsum. (a) If the sulfur dioxide concentration is 1000 times higher than its mole fraction in clean dry air ($2 \times 10^{-10}$), how much calcium sulfate (kg) can be made from scrubbing 4 GL of flue gas (1 GL = $1 \times 10^9$ L)? A state-of-the-art scrubber removes at least 95% of the sulfur dioxide. (b) If the mole fraction of oxygen in air is 0.209, what volume (L) of air at 1.00 atm and 25°C is needed to react with all the calcium sulfite?

**5.134** Many water treatment plants use chlorine gas to kill microorganisms before the water is released for residential use. A plant engineer has to maintain the chlorine pressure in a tank below the 85.0-atm rating and, to be safe, decides to fill the tank to 80.0% of this maximum pressure. (a) How many moles of $Cl_2$ gas can be kept in an 850.-L tank at 298 K if she uses the ideal gas law in the calculation? (b) What is the tank pressure if she uses the van der Waals equation for this amount of gas? (c) Did the engineer fill the tank to the desired pressure?

**5.135** At 10.0°C and 102.5 kPa, the density of dry air is 1.26 g/L. What is the average "molar mass" of dry air at these conditions?

**5.136** In A, the picture shows a cylinder with 0.1 mol of a gas that behaves ideally. Choose the cylinder (B, C, or D) that correctly represents the volume of the gas after each of the following changes. If none of the cylinders is correct, specify "none."
(a) $P$ is doubled at fixed $n$ and $T$.
(b) $T$ is reduced from 400 K to 200 K at fixed $n$ and $P$.
(c) $T$ is increased from 100°C to 200°C at fixed $n$ and $P$.
(d) 0.1 mol of gas is added at fixed $P$ and $T$.
(e) 0.1 mol of gas is added and $P$ is doubled at fixed $T$.

A          B          C          D

**5.137** Ammonia is essential to so many industries that, on a molar basis, it is the most heavily produced substance in the world. Calculate $P_{IGL}$ and $P_{VDW}$ (in atm) of 51.1 g of ammonia in a 3.000-L container at 0°C and 400.°C, the industrial temperature. (See Table 5.4 for the values of the van der Waals constants.)

**5.138** A 6.0-L flask contains a mixture of methane ($CH_4$), argon, and helium at 45°C and 1.75 atm. If the mole fractions of helium and argon are 0.25 and 0.35, respectively, how many molecules of methane are present?

**5.139** A large portion of metabolic energy arises from the biological combustion of glucose:

$$C_6H_{12}O_6(s) + 6O_2(g) \longrightarrow 6CO_2(g) + 6H_2O(g)$$

(a) If this reaction is carried out in an expandable container at 37°C and 780. torr, what volume of $CO_2$ is produced from 20.0 g of glucose and excess $O_2$? (b) If the reaction is carried out at the same conditions with the stoichiometric amount of $O_2$, what is the partial pressure of each gas when the reaction is 50% complete (10.0 g of glucose remains)?

**5.140** What is the average kinetic energy and rms speed of $N_2$ molecules at STP? Compare these values with those of $H_2$ molecules at STP. [Use $R = 8.314$ J/(mol·K) and $\mathcal{M}$ in kg/mol.]

**5.141** According to government standards, the *8-h threshold limit value* is 5000 ppmv for $CO_2$ and 0.1 ppmv for $Br_2$ (1 ppmv is 1 part by volume in $10^6$ parts by volume). Exposure to either gas for 8 h above these limits is unsafe. At STP, which of the following would be unsafe for 8 h of exposure?
(a) Air with a partial pressure of 0.2 torr of $Br_2$
(b) Air with a partial pressure of 0.2 torr of $CO_2$
(c) 1000 L of air containing 0.0004 g of $Br_2$ gas
(d) 1000 L of air containing $2.8 \times 10^{22}$ molecules of $CO_2$

**5.142** One way to prevent emission of the pollutant NO from industrial plants is by a catalyzed reaction with $NH_3$:

$$4NH_3(g) + 4NO(g) + O_2(g) \xrightarrow{\text{catalyst}} 4N_2(g) + 6H_2O(g)$$

(a) If the NO has a partial pressure of $4.5 \times 10^{-5}$ atm in the flue gas, how many liters of $NH_3$ are needed per liter of flue gas at 1.00 atm? (b) If the reaction takes place at 1.00 atm and 365°C, how many grams of $NH_3$ are needed per kL of flue gas?

**5.143** An equimolar mixture of Ne and Xe is accidentally placed in a container that has a tiny leak. After a short while, a very small proportion of the mixture has escaped. What is the mole fraction of Ne in the effusing gas?

**5.144** From the relative rates of effusion of $^{235}UF_6$ and $^{238}UF_6$, find the number of steps needed to produce a sample of the enriched fuel used in many nuclear reactors, which is 3.0 mole % $^{235}U$. The natural abundance of $^{235}U$ is 0.72%.

**5.145** A slight deviation from ideal behavior exists even at normal conditions. If it behaved ideally, 1 mol of CO would occupy 22.414 L and exert 1 atm pressure at 273.15 K. Calculate $P_{VDW}$ for 1.000 mol of CO at 273.15 K. $\left(\text{Use } R = 0.08206 \dfrac{\text{atm·L}}{\text{mol·K}}.\right)$

**5.146** In preparation for a combustion demonstration, a professor fills a balloon with equal molar amounts of $H_2$ and $O_2$, but the demonstration has to be postponed until the next day. During the night, both gases leak through pores in the balloon. If 35% of the $H_2$ leaks, what is the $O_2/H_2$ ratio in the balloon the next day?

**5.147** Phosphorus trichloride is important in the manufacture of insecticides, fuel additives, and flame retardants. Phosphorus has only one naturally occurring isotope, $^{31}P$, whereas chlorine has two, $^{35}Cl$ (75%) and $^{37}Cl$ (25%). (a) What different molecular masses (in amu) can be found for $PCl_3$? (b) Which is the most abundant? (c) What is the ratio of the effusion rates of the heaviest and the lightest $PCl_3$ molecules?

**5.148** A truck tire has a volume of 218 L and is filled with air to 35.0 psi at 295 K. After a drive, the air heats up to 318 K. (a) If the tire volume is constant, what is the pressure (in psi)? (b) If the tire volume increases 2.0%, what is the pressure (in psi)? (c) If the tire leaks 1.5 g of air per minute and the temperature is constant, how many minutes will it take for the tire to reach the original pressure of 35.0 psi ($\mathcal{M}$ of air = 28.8 g/mol)?

**5.149** Allotropes are different molecular forms of an element, such as dioxygen ($O_2$) and ozone ($O_3$). (a) What is the density of each oxygen allotrope at 0°C and 760 torr? (b) Calculate the ratio of densities, $d_{O_3}/d_{O_2}$, and explain the significance of this number.

**5.150** When gaseous $F_2$ and solid $I_2$ are heated to high temperatures, the $I_2$ sublimes and gaseous iodine heptafluoride forms. If 350. torr of $F_2$ and 2.50 g of solid $I_2$ are put into a 2.50-L container at 250. K and the container is heated to 550. K, what is the final pressure (in torr)? What is the partial pressure of $I_2$ gas?

# Thermochemistry: Energy Flow and Chemical Change

## Concepts and skills to review before you study this chapter

- energy and its interconversion (Section 1.1)
- distinction between heat and temperature (Section 1.5)
- nature of chemical bonding (Section 2.7)
- calculations of reaction stoichiometry (Section 3.4)
- properties of the gaseous state (Section 5.1)
- relation between kinetic energy and temperature (Section 5.5)

All matter contains energy, so *whenever matter undergoes a change, the quantity of energy that the matter contains also changes.* When a burning candle melts a piece of ice, both chemical and physical changes occur. In the chemical change, the higher energy reactants (wax and $O_2$) form lower energy products ($CO_2$ and $H_2O$), and the difference in energy is *released* as heat and light. Then, during the physical change, some of that heat is *absorbed* when lower energy ice becomes higher energy water. In a thunderstorm, the changes in energy are reversed: lower energy $N_2$ and $O_2$ *absorb* energy from lightning to form higher energy NO, and higher energy water vapor *releases* energy as it condenses to lower energy liquid water that falls as rain.

This interplay of matter and energy is profoundly important and has an enormous impact on society. On an everyday level, many familiar materials release, absorb, or alter the flow of energy. Fuels such as oil and wood release energy to warm our homes or power our vehicles. Fertilizers help crops convert solar energy into food. Metal wires increase the flow of electrical energy, and polymer fibers in winter clothing limit the flow of thermal energy away from our bodies.

**Thermodynamics** is the study of energy and its transformations, and two chapters in this text address this central topic. Our focus here is on **thermochemistry,** the branch of thermodynamics that deals with heat in chemical and physical change. In Chapter 20, we consider the fundamental question of *why* reactions occur.

**IN THIS CHAPTER . . .** We see how heat, or thermal energy, flows when matter changes, how to measure the quantity of heat for a given change, and how to determine the heat flow accompanying any reaction.

- We see that energy always flows between a system and its surroundings in the form of heat or work, so the total energy is conserved.
- We discuss the units of energy and show that the total size of an energy change does not depend on how the change occurs.
- We identify the heat of a reaction in an open container as a change in enthalpy, which can be negative (exothermic reaction) or positive (endothermic reaction).
- We describe how a calorimeter measures heat and how the quantity of heat in a reaction is proportional to the amounts of substances.
- We define standard conditions to compare enthalpies of reactions and see how to obtain the change in enthalpy for any reaction.
- We discuss some current and future energy sources and describe the critical relation between energy demand and climate change.

## 6.1 • FORMS OF ENERGY AND THEIR INTERCONVERSION

In Chapter 1, we saw that all energy is either potential or kinetic, and that these forms are interconvertible. An object has potential energy by virtue of its position and kinetic energy by virtue of its motion. Let's re-examine these ideas by considering a weight raised above the ground. As your muscles or a motor raise the weight, its potential energy increases; this energy is converted to kinetic energy as the weight falls (see Figure 1.3, p. 9). When it hits the ground, some of that kinetic energy appears as *work* done when the weight moves the soil and pebbles slightly, and some appears as *heat* when it warms them slightly. Thus, in this situation, *potential energy is converted to kinetic energy, which appears as work and heat.*

Several other forms of energy—solar, electrical, nuclear, and chemical—are examples of potential and kinetic energy on the atomic scale. No matter what the form of energy or the situation, *when energy is transferred from one object to another, it appears as work and/or heat.* In this section, we examine this idea in terms of the release or absorption of energy during a chemical or physical change.

## Defining the System and Its Surroundings

In any thermodynamic study, including measuring a change in energy, the first step is to define the **system**—the part of the universe we are focusing on. And the moment we define the system, everything else is defined as the **surroundings.**

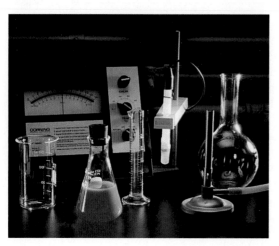

**Figure 6.1** A chemical system and its surroundings.

Figure 6.1 shows a typical chemical system—the contents of a flask; the flask itself, other equipment, and perhaps the rest of the laboratory are the surroundings. In principle, the rest of the universe is the surroundings, but in practice, we consider only the parts that are relevant to the system: it's not likely that a thunderstorm in central Asia or a methane blizzard on Neptune will affect the contents of the flask, but the temperature and pressure of the lab might. Thus, the experimenter defines the system and the relevant surroundings. An astronomer defines a galaxy as the system and nearby galaxies as the surroundings; a microbiologist defines a given cell as the system and neighboring cells and the extracellular fluid as the surroundings; and so forth.

## Energy Transfer to and from a System

Each particle in a system has potential energy and kinetic energy, and the sum of all these energies is the **internal energy, $E$,** of the system (some texts use the symbol $U$). When the reactants in a chemical system change to products, the system's internal energy has changed. This change, $\Delta E$, is the difference between the internal energy *after* the change ($E_{\text{final}}$) and *before* the change ($E_{\text{initial}}$):

$$\Delta E = E_{\text{final}} - E_{\text{initial}} = E_{\text{products}} - E_{\text{reactants}} \tag{6.1}$$

where $\Delta$ (Greek *delta*) means "change (or difference) in" and refers to the *final state* **minus** the *initial state*. Thus, $\Delta E$ is the final quantity of energy of the system **minus** the initial quantity.

Because the universe consists of only system and surroundings, *a change in the energy of the system must be accompanied by an **equal** and **opposite** change in the energy of the surroundings.* In an *energy diagram,* the final and initial states are horizontal lines along a vertical energy axis, with $\Delta E$ the difference in the heights of the lines. A system can change its internal energy in one of two ways:

• By releasing some energy in a transfer *to* the surroundings (Figure 6.2A):

$$E_{\text{final}} < E_{\text{initial}} \qquad \text{so} \qquad \Delta E < 0$$

• By absorbing some energy in a transfer *from* the surroundings (Figure 6.2B):

$$E_{\text{final}} > E_{\text{initial}} \qquad \text{so} \qquad \Delta E > 0$$

Thus, $\Delta E$ is a *transfer* of energy from system to surroundings, or vice versa.

## Heat and Work: Two Forms of Energy Transfer

Energy transferred from system to surroundings or vice versa appears in two forms:

1. *Heat.* **Heat** or *thermal energy* (symbolized by $q$) is the energy transferred as a result of a difference in temperature between the system and the surroundings. For example, energy in the form of heat is transferred from hot soup (system) to the bowl, air, and table (surroundings) because they are at a lower temperature.

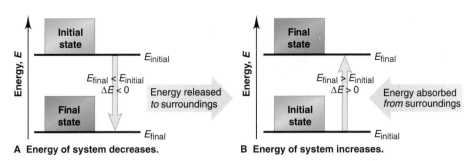

**A** Energy of system decreases.

**B** Energy of system increases.

**Figure 6.2** Energy diagrams for the transfer of internal energy ($E$) between a system and its surroundings. **A,** When the system releases energy, $\Delta E$ ($E_{final} - E_{initial}$) is negative. **B,** When the system absorbs energy, $\Delta E$ ($E_{final} - E_{initial}$) is positive. (The vertical yellow arrow always has its tail at the initial state.)

2. *Work.* All other forms of energy transfer involve some type of **work (*w*),** the energy transferred when an object is moved by a force. When you (system) kick a football, energy is transferred as work because the force of the kick moves the ball and air (surroundings). When you pump up a ball, energy is transferred as work because the added air (system) exerts a force on the inner wall of the ball (surroundings) and moves it outward.

The total change in a system's internal energy is the sum of the energy transferred as heat and/or work:

$$\Delta E = q + w \qquad (6.2)$$

The values of $q$ and $w$ (and, therefore, of $\Delta E$) can have either a positive or negative sign. *We define the sign of the energy change from the **system's** perspective:*

- Energy transferred *into* the system is *positive* because the *system ends up with more energy.*
- Energy transferred *out from* the system is *negative,* because the *system ends up with less* energy.

Innumerable combinations of heat and/or work can change a system's internal energy. In the rest of this subsection, we'll examine the four simplest cases—two that involve only heat and two that involve only work.

**Energy Transferred as Heat Only** For a system that transfers energy only as heat ($q$) and does no work ($w = 0$), we have, from Equation 6.2, $\Delta E = q + 0 = q$. There are two ways this transfer can happen:

1. *Heat flowing **out** from a system.* Suppose hot water is the system, and the beaker holding it and the rest of the lab are the surroundings. The water transfers energy as heat outward until the temperature of the water and the surroundings are equal. Since heat flows *out* from the system, the final energy of the system is less than the initial energy. Heat was released, so *q is negative,* and therefore $\Delta E$ *is negative* (Figure 6.3A).

2. *Heat flowing **into** a system.* If the system consists of ice water, the surroundings transfer energy as heat *into* the system, once again until the ice melts and the temperature of the water and the surroundings become equal. In this case, heat flows *in,* so the final energy of the system is higher than its initial energy. Heat was absorbed, so *q is positive,* and therefore $\Delta E$ *is positive* (Figure 6.3B). ●

● **Thermodynamics in the Kitchen** A new view of two familiar kitchen appliances can clarify the sign of $q$. The air in a refrigerator (surroundings) has a lower temperature than a newly added piece of food (system), so the food releases energy as heat to the refrigerator air, $q < 0$. The air in a hot oven (surroundings) has a higher temperature than a newly added piece of food (system), so the food absorbs energy as heat from the oven air, $q > 0$.

**A** Energy released as heat.

**B** Energy absorbed as heat.

**Figure 6.3** The two cases where energy is transferred as heat only. **A,** The system releases heat. **B,** The system absorbs heat.

**A  Energy released as work.**

**B  Energy absorbed as work.**

**Figure 6.4** The two cases where energy is transferred as work only. **A,** The system does work *on* the surroundings. **B,** The system has work done on it *by* the surroundings.

**Energy Transferred as Work Only** For a system that transfers energy only as work, $q = 0$; therefore, $\Delta E = 0 + w = w$. There are two ways this transfer can happen:

1. *Work done **by** a system* (Figure 6.4A). Consider an aqueous reaction of a gray metal (for example, Zn) and a strong acid (for example, HCl) that takes place in a nearly evacuated (narrow $P_{sys}$ arrow), insulated container attached to a piston-cylinder assembly and that has a gas (e.g., $H_2$) as one of the products. (The container is insulated so that heat does not flow.) We define the system as the reaction mixture, and the container, piston-cylinder, outside air, and so forth as the surroundings. In the initial state, the internal energy is the energy of the reactants, and in the final state, it is the energy of the products. As the gas forms, it pushes back the piston. Thus, energy is transferred as work done *by* the system *on* the surroundings. Since the system releases energy as work, *w is negative;* the final energy of the system is less than the initial energy, so $\Delta E$ is negative.*

2. *Work done **on** a system* (Figure 6.4B). Suppose that, after the reaction is over, we increase the pressure of the surroundings (wider $P_{surr}$ arrow) so that the piston moves in. Energy is transferred as work done *by* the surroundings *on* the system, so *w is positive*. The final energy of the system is greater than the initial energy, so $\Delta E$ *is positive*.

Table 6.1 summarizes the sign conventions for $q$ and $w$ and their effect on the sign of $\Delta E$.

---

*The system shown in Figure 6.4A is not doing very useful work because it just pushes back the piston and outside air. But, if the reaction mixture is gasoline and oxygen and the surroundings are an automobile engine, much of the internal energy is transferred as the work done to move a car.

**Table 6.1  The Sign Conventions* for $q$, $w$, and $\Delta E$**

| $q$ | + | $w$ | = | $\Delta E$ |
|:---:|:---:|:---:|:---:|:---|
| + |  | + |  | + |
| + |  | − |  | Depends on the sizes of $q$ and $w$ |
| − |  | + |  | Depends on the sizes of $q$ and $w$ |
| − |  | − |  | − |

*For $q$: + means system *absorbs* heat; − means system *releases* heat.
*For $w$: + means work done *on* system; − means work done *by* system.

## The Law of Energy Conservation

As you've seen, when a system absorbs energy, the surroundings release it, and when a system releases energy, the surroundings absorb it. Energy transferred between system and surroundings can be in the form of heat and/or various types of work—mechanical, electrical, radiant, chemical, and so forth.

Indeed, energy is often converted from one form to another during transfers. For example, when gasoline burns in a car engine, the reaction releases energy that is transferred as heat and work. The heat warms the car parts, passenger compartment, and surrounding air. The work is done when mechanical energy turns the car's wheels and belts. That energy is converted into the electrical energy of the sound system, the radiant energy of the headlights, the chemical energy of the battery, and so forth. The sum of all these forms equals the change in energy between reactants and products as the gasoline is burned.

Complex biological processes exhibit the same general pattern. During photosynthesis, green plants convert solar energy into the chemical energy of the bonds in starch and $O_2$; when you digest starch, the bonds in the compound are converted into the muscular (mechanical) energy needed to run a marathon.

The most important point to realize in these, and all other situations, is that the energy changes form but does not simply appear or disappear—energy cannot be created or destroyed. Put another way, *energy is conserved: the total energy of the system plus the surroundings remains constant.* The **law of conservation of energy,** also known as the **first law of thermodynamics,** restates this basic observation: *the total energy of the universe is constant.* It is expressed mathematically as

$$\Delta E_{universe} = \Delta E_{system} + \Delta E_{surroundings} = 0 \qquad (6.3)$$

This law applies, as far as we know, to all systems, from a burning match to continental drift, from the pumping of your heart to the formation of the Solar System.

## Units of Energy

The SI unit of energy is the **joule (J),** a derived unit composed of three base units:

$$1 \text{ J} = 1 \text{ kg·m}^2/\text{s}^2$$

Both heat and work are expressed in joules. Let's see why the joule is the unit for work. The work ($w$) done on a mass is the force ($F$) times the distance ($d$) that the mass moves: $w = F \times d$. A *force* changes the velocity of a mass over time; that is, a force *accelerates* a mass. Velocity has units of meters per second (m/s), so acceleration ($a$) has units of meters per second per second (m/s²). Force, therefore, has units of mass ($m$, in kilograms) times acceleration:

$$F = m \times a \quad \text{has units of} \quad \text{kg·m/s}^2$$

Therefore, $\quad w = F \times d \quad$ has units of $\quad (\text{kg·m/s}^2) \times \text{m} = \text{kg·m}^2/\text{s}^2 = \text{J}$

The **calorie (cal)** is an older unit defined originally as the quantity of energy needed to raise the temperature of 1 g of water by 1°C (from 14.5°C to 15.5°C). The calorie is now defined in terms of the joule:

$$1 \text{ cal} \equiv 4.184 \text{ J} \quad \text{or} \quad 1 \text{ J} = \frac{1}{4.184} \text{ cal} = 0.2390 \text{ cal}$$

Since the quantities of energy involved in chemical reactions are usually quite large, chemists use the kilojoule (kJ), or, in earlier sources, the kilocalorie (kcal):

$$1 \text{ kJ} = 1000 \text{ J} = 0.2390 \text{ kcal} = 239.0 \text{ cal}$$

The nutritional Calorie (note the capital C), the unit that shows the energy available from food, is actually a kilocalorie.

The *British thermal unit (Btu),* a unit that you may have seen used for the energy output of appliances, is the quantity of energy required to raise the temperature of 1 lb of water by 1°F; *1 Btu is equivalent to 1055 J.* In general, the SI unit (J or kJ) is used in this text. Some interesting quantities of energy appear in Figure 6.5.

| | |
|---|---|
| $10^{24}$ J | |
| $10^{21}$ J | Daily solar energy falling on Earth |
| $10^{18}$ J | Energy of a strong earthquake |
| $10^{15}$ J | Daily electrical output of Hoover Dam |
| $10^{12}$ J | 1000 tons of coal burned |
| $10^{9}$ J | 1 ton of TNT exploded |
| $10^{6}$ J | 1 kilowatt-hour of electrical energy |
| | Combustion of 1 mol of glucose |
| $10^{3}$ J | |
| $10^{0}$ J | 1 calorie (4.184 J) |
| $10^{-3}$ J | |
| $10^{-6}$ J | |
| $10^{-9}$ J | Heat absorbed during division of one bacterial cell |
| $10^{-12}$ J | Energy from fission of one $^{235}$U atom |
| $10^{-15}$ J | |
| $10^{-18}$ J | |
| $10^{-21}$ J | Average kinetic energy of a molecule in air at 300 K |

**Figure 6.5 Some quantities of energy.** The vertical scale is exponential.

## Sample Problem 6.1    Determining the Change in Internal Energy of a System

**Problem** When gasoline burns in a car engine, the heat released causes the products $CO_2$ and $H_2O$ to expand, which pushes the pistons outward. Excess heat is removed by the car's radiator. If the expanding gases do 451 J of work on the pistons and the system releases 325 J to the surroundings as heat, calculate the change in energy ($\Delta E$) in J, kJ, and kcal.

**Plan** We must define system and surroundings to choose signs for $q$ and $w$, and then we calculate $\Delta E$ with Equation 6.2. The system is the reactants and products, and the surroundings are the pistons, the radiator, and the rest of the car. Heat is released by the system, so $q$ is negative. Work is done by the system to push the pistons outward, so $w$ is also negative. We obtain the answer in J and then convert it to kJ and kcal.

**Solution** Calculating $\Delta E$ (from Equation 6.2) in J:

$$q = -325 \text{ J}$$
$$w = -451 \text{ J}$$
$$\Delta E = q + w = -325 \text{ J} + (-451 \text{ J}) = \boxed{-776 \text{ J}}$$

Converting from J to kJ:

$$\Delta E = -776 \text{ J} \times \frac{1 \text{ kJ}}{1000 \text{ J}} = \boxed{-0.776 \text{ kJ}}$$

Converting from kJ to kcal:

$$\Delta E = -0.776 \text{ kJ} \times \frac{1 \text{ kcal}}{4.184 \text{ kJ}} = \boxed{-0.185 \text{ kcal}}$$

**Check** The answer is reasonable: combustion of gasoline releases energy from the system, so $E_{final} < E_{initial}$ and $\Delta E$ should be negative. Rounding shows that, since 4 kJ ≈ 1 kcal, nearly 0.8 kJ should be nearly 0.2 kcal.

**Follow-Up Problem 6.1** In a reaction, gaseous reactants form a liquid product. The heat absorbed by the surroundings is 26.0 kcal, and the work done on the system is 15.0 Btu. Calculate $\Delta E$ (in kJ).

## State Functions and the Path Independence of the Energy Change

The internal energy ($E$) of a system is called a **state function,** a property dependent only on the *current* state of the system (its composition, volume, pressure, and temperature), *not* on the path the system takes to reach that state. The energy change of a system can occur by countless combinations of heat ($q$) and/or work ($w$). However, because $E$ is a state function, the overall $\Delta E$ is the same no matter what the specific combination may be. That is, $\Delta E$ does **not** depend on how the change takes place, but only on the **difference** between the final and initial states.

As an example, let's define a system in its initial state as 1 mol of octane (a component of gasoline) together with enough $O_2$ to burn it. In its final state, the system is the $CO_2$ and $H_2O$ that form:

$$C_8H_{18}(l) + \tfrac{25}{2}O_2(g) \longrightarrow 8CO_2(g) + 9H_2O(g)$$

initial state ($E_{initial}$)                    final state ($E_{final}$)

Energy is transferred *out* from the system as heat and/or work, so $\Delta E$ is negative. Figure 6.6 shows just two of the many ways the change can occur. If we burn the octane in an open container (*left*), $\Delta E$ is transferred almost completely as heat (with a small amount of work done to push back the atmosphere). If we burn it in a car engine (*right*), a much larger portion (~30%) of $\Delta E$ is transferred as work that moves the car, with the rest released as heat that warms the car, exhaust gases, and surrounding air. If we burn the octane in a lawn mower or a plane, $\Delta E$ appears as other combinations of work and heat. Thus, $q$ and $w$ are *not* state functions because their values *do* depend on the path the system takes, but $\Delta E$ (the *sum* of $q$ and $w$) *does not*. ●

● **Your Personal Financial State Function** The *balance* in your checkbook is a state function of your personal financial system. You can open a new checking account with a birthday gift of $50, or you can open one with a deposit of a $100 paycheck and then write two $25 checks. The two paths to the balance are different, but the balance (current state) is the same.

**Figure 6.6** Two different paths for the energy change of a system. Even though $q$ and $w$ for the two paths are different, $\Delta E$ is the same.

Pressure ($P$), volume ($V$), and temperature ($T$) are some other state functions. Path independence means that *changes in state functions—$\Delta E$, $\Delta P$, $\Delta V$, and $\Delta T$—depend only on the initial and final states.*

### ▌ Summary of Section 6.1

- Internal energy ($E$) is transferred as heat ($q$) when system and surroundings are at different temperatures or as work ($w$) when an object is moved by a force.
- Heat or work absorbed by a system ($q > 0$; $w > 0$) increases its $E$; heat or work released by the system ($q < 0$; $w < 0$) decreases its $E$. The change in the internal energy is the sum of the heat and work: $\Delta E = q + w$. Heat and work are measured in joules (J).
- Energy is always conserved: it can change from one form to another and move into or out of the system, but the total quantity of energy in the universe (system *plus* surroundings) is constant.
- The internal energy of a system is a state function and, thus, is independent of how the system attained that energy; therefore, the same overall $\Delta E$ can occur through any combination of $q$ and $w$.

## 6.2 • ENTHALPY: CHEMICAL CHANGE AT CONSTANT PRESSURE

Most physical and chemical changes occur at nearly constant atmospheric pressure—a reaction in an open flask, the freezing of a lake, a biochemical process in an organism. In this section, we discuss *enthalpy,* a thermodynamic variable that relates directly to energy changes at constant pressure.

### The Meaning of Enthalpy

To determine $\Delta E$, we must measure both heat and work. The two most important types of chemical work are electrical work, done by moving charged particles (Chapter 21), and **pressure-volume work (*PV* work),** the mechanical work done when the volume of the system changes in the presence of an external pressure ($P$). The quantity of $PV$ work equals $P$ times the change in volume ($\Delta V$, or $V_{final} - V_{initial}$). In an open flask (or in a cylinder with a weightless, frictionless piston) (Figure 6.7), a system of an expanding gas does $PV$ work *on* the surroundings, so it has a negative sign:

$$w = -P\Delta V \qquad (6.4)$$

For reactions *at constant pressure,* a thermodynamic variable called **enthalpy (*H*)** eliminates the need to measure $PV$ work. The enthalpy of a system is defined as the internal energy *plus* the product of the pressure and volume:

$$H = E + PV$$

The **change in enthalpy ($\Delta H$)** is the change in internal energy *plus* the product of the pressure, which is constant, and the change in volume ($\Delta V$):

$$\Delta H = \Delta E + P\Delta V \qquad (6.5)$$

**Surroundings**

**Figure 6.7** Pressure-volume work. An expanding gas pushing back the atmosphere does $PV$ work ($w = -P\Delta V$).

Combining Equations 6.2 ($\Delta E = q + w$) and 6.4 ($w = -P\Delta V$) gives

$$\Delta E = q + w = q + (-P\Delta V) = q - P\Delta V$$

At constant pressure, we denote $q$ as $q_P$, giving $\Delta E = q_P - P\Delta V$, which we can use to solve for $q_P$:

$$q_P = \Delta E + P\Delta V$$

Notice that the right sides of this equation and of Equation 6.5 are the same:

$$q_P = \Delta E + P\Delta V = \Delta H \tag{6.6}$$

Thus, *the change in enthalpy equals the heat absorbed or released at **constant** pressure.* For most changes occurring at constant pressure, $\Delta H$ is more relevant than $\Delta E$ and easier to obtain: *to find $\Delta H$, measure $q_P$.* We discuss the laboratory method in Section 6.3.

## Comparing $\Delta E$ and $\Delta H$

Knowing the *enthalpy* change of a system tells us a lot about its *energy* change as well. In fact, because many reactions involve little (if any) $PV$ work, most (or all) of the energy change occurs as a transfer of heat. Here are three cases:

1. *Reactions that do not involve gases.* Gases do not appear in precipitation, many acid-base, many redox reactions, and so forth. For example,

$$2KOH(aq) + H_2SO_4(aq) \longrightarrow K_2SO_4(aq) + 2H_2O(l)$$

   Because liquids and solids undergo *very* small volume changes, $\Delta V \approx 0$; thus $P\Delta V \approx 0$ and $\Delta H \approx \Delta E$.

2. *Reactions in which the amount (mol) of gas does **not** change.* When the total amount of gaseous reactants equals the total amount of gaseous products, the volume is constant, $\Delta V = 0$, so $P\Delta V = 0$ and $\Delta H = \Delta E$. For example,

$$N_2(g) + O_2(g) \longrightarrow 2NO(g)$$

3. *Reactions in which the amount (mol) of gas **does** change.* In these cases, $P\Delta V \neq 0$. However, $q_P$ is usually *much* larger than $P\Delta V$, so $\Delta H$ is still very close to $\Delta E$. For instance, in the combustion of $H_2$, 3 mol of gas yields 2 mol of gas:

$$2H_2(g) + O_2(g) \longrightarrow 2H_2O(g)$$

   In this reaction, $\Delta H = -483.6$ kJ and $P\Delta V = -2.5$ kJ, so (from Equation 6.5),

   $$\Delta H = \Delta E + P\Delta V \quad \text{and} \quad \Delta E = \Delta H - P\Delta V = -483.6 \text{ kJ} - (-2.5 \text{ kJ}) = -481.1 \text{ kJ}$$

   Since most of $\Delta E$ occurs as energy transferred as heat, $\Delta H \approx \Delta E$.

Thus, *for most reactions, $\Delta H$ equals, or is very close to, $\Delta E$.*

## Exothermic and Endothermic Processes

Because $H$ is a combination of the three state functions $E$, $P$, and $V$, it is also a state function. Therefore, $\Delta H$ equals $H_{\text{final}}$ *minus* $H_{\text{initial}}$. For a reaction, $H_{\text{final}}$ is $H_{\text{products}}$ and $H_{\text{initial}}$ is $H_{\text{reactants}}$, so the enthalpy change of a reaction is

$$\Delta H = H_{\text{final}} - H_{\text{initial}} = H_{\text{products}} - H_{\text{reactants}}$$

Since $H_{\text{products}}$ can be either more or less than $H_{\text{reactants}}$, the *sign* of $\Delta H$ indicates whether heat is absorbed or released during the reaction. We determine the sign of $\Delta H$ by imagining the heat as "reactant" or "product." The two possibilities are

1. *Exothermic process.* An **exothermic** ("heat out") **process** *releases* heat and results in a *decrease* in the enthalpy of the system:

$$\text{Exothermic:} \quad H_{\text{products}} < H_{\text{reactants}} \quad \text{so} \quad \Delta H < 0$$

For example, when methane burns in air, heat flows *out of* the system into the surroundings, so we show it as a product:

$$CH_4(g) + 2O_2(g) \longrightarrow CO_2(g) + 2H_2O(g) + \textit{heat}$$

**Figure 6.8** Enthalpy diagrams for exothermic and endothermic processes. **A,** The combustion of methane is exothermic: $\Delta H < 0$. **B,** The melting of ice is endothermic: $\Delta H > 0$.

**A Exothermic process**

**B Endothermic process**

The reactants (1 mol of $CH_4$ and 2 mol of $O_2$) release heat during the reaction, so they originally had more enthalpy than the products (1 mol of $CO_2$ and 2 mol of $H_2O$):

$$H_{reactants} > H_{products} \quad \text{so} \quad \Delta H\,(H_{products} - H_{reactants}) < 0$$

This exothermic change is shown in the **enthalpy diagram** in Figure 6.8A.

2. *Endothermic process.* An **endothermic** ("heat in") **process** *absorbs* heat and results in an *increase* in the enthalpy of the system:

$$\text{Endothermic:} \quad H_{products} > H_{reactants} \quad \text{so} \quad \Delta H > 0$$

When ice melts, for instance, heat flows *into* the ice from the surroundings, so we show the heat as a reactant:

$$heat + H_2O(s) \longrightarrow H_2O(l)$$

Because heat is absorbed, the enthalpy of the product (water) must be higher than that of the reactant (ice):

$$H_{water} > H_{ice} \quad \text{so} \quad \Delta H\,(H_{water} - H_{ice}) > 0$$

This endothermic change is shown in Figure 6.8B. (In general, the value of an enthalpy change is determined with reactants and products at the same temperature.)

---

**Sample Problem 6.2**    **Drawing Enthalpy Diagrams and Determining the Sign of $\Delta H$**

**Problem** In each of the following cases, determine the sign of $\Delta H$, state whether the reaction is exothermic or endothermic, and draw an enthalpy diagram:
**(a)** $H_2(g) + \frac{1}{2}O_2(g) \longrightarrow H_2O(l) + 285.8 \text{ kJ}$
**(b)** $40.7 \text{ kJ} + H_2O(l) \longrightarrow H_2O(g)$

**Plan** From each equation, we note whether heat is a "product" (exothermic; $\Delta H < 0$) or a "reactant" (endothermic; $\Delta H > 0$). For exothermic reactions, reactants are above products on the enthalpy diagram; for endothermic reactions, reactants are below products. The $\Delta H$ arrow *always* points from reactants to products.

**Solution (a)** Heat is a product (on the right), so $\Delta H < 0$ and the reaction is exothermic. The enthalpy diagram appears in the margin (*top*).
**(b)** Heat is a reactant (on the left), so $\Delta H > 0$ and the reaction is endothermic. The enthalpy diagram appears in the margin (*bottom*).

**Check** Substances that are on the same side of the equation as the heat have less enthalpy than substances on the other side, so make sure those substances are placed on the lower line of the diagram.

**Follow-Up Problem 6.2** When nitroglycerine decomposes, the reaction creates a violent explosion and releases $5.72 \times 10^3$ kJ of heat per mole:

$$C_3H_5(NO_3)_3(l) \longrightarrow 3CO_2(g) + \tfrac{5}{2}H_2O(g) + \tfrac{1}{4}O_2(g) + \tfrac{3}{2}N_2(g)$$

Is the decomposition of nitroglycerine exothermic or endothermic? Draw an enthalpy diagram for the process.

## ■ Summary of Section 6.2

- Enthalpy ($H$) is a state function, so any change in enthalpy ($\Delta H$) is independent of how the change occurred. At constant $P$, the value of $\Delta H$ equals $\Delta E + PV$ work, which occurs when the volume of the system changes in the presence of an external pressure.
- $\Delta H$ equals $q_P$, the heat released or absorbed during a chemical or physical change that takes place at constant pressure.
- In most cases, $\Delta H$ is equal, or very close, to $\Delta E$.
- A change that releases heat is exothermic ($\Delta H < 0$); a change that absorbs heat is endothermic ($\Delta H > 0$).

# 6.3 • CALORIMETRY: MEASURING THE HEAT OF A CHEMICAL OR PHYSICAL CHANGE

Data about energy content and usage are everywhere—the caloric value of a slice of bread, the energy efficiency of a dishwasher, the gas mileage of a new car. In this section, we'll see how these values are determined.

## Specific Heat Capacity

To find the energy change during a process, we measure the quantity of heat released or absorbed by relating it to the change in temperature. You know from everyday experience that the more you heat an object, the higher its temperature, and the more you cool it, the lower its temperature; in other words, the quantity of heat ($q$) absorbed or released by an object is proportional to its temperature change:

$$q \propto \Delta T \qquad \text{or} \qquad q = \text{constant} \times \Delta T \qquad \text{or} \qquad \frac{q}{\Delta T} = \text{constant}$$

What you might not know is that the temperature change depends on the object. Every object has its own **heat capacity,** the quantity of heat required to change its temperature by 1 K. Heat capacity is the proportionality constant in the preceding equation:

$$\text{Heat capacity} = \frac{q}{\Delta T} \quad [\text{in units of J/K}]$$

A related property is **specific heat capacity ($c$),** the quantity of heat required to change the temperature of 1 *gram* of an object by 1 K:

$$\text{Specific heat capacity } (c) = \frac{q}{\text{mass} \times \Delta T} \quad [\text{in units of J/g·K}]$$

If we know $c$ of the object being heated (or cooled), we can measure the mass and the temperature change and calculate the heat absorbed (or released):

$$q = c \times \text{mass} \times \Delta T \qquad\qquad (6.7)$$

Equation 6.7 says that when an object gets hotter, that is, when $\Delta T$ ($T_{\text{final}} - T_{\text{initial}}$) is positive, $q > 0$ (the sample absorbs heat). And when an object gets cooler, that is, when $\Delta T$ is negative, $q < 0$ (the sample releases heat). Table 6.2 lists the specific heat capacities of some representative substances and materials. Notice that metals have relatively low values of $c$ and water has a very high value: for instance, it takes over 30 times as much energy to increase the temperature of a gram of water by 1 K as it does a gram of gold!

Closely related to the specific heat capacity (but reserved for substances) is the **molar heat capacity ($C$;** note the capital letter), the quantity of heat required to change the temperature of 1 *mole* of a substance by 1 K:

$$\text{Molar heat capacity } (C) = \frac{q}{\text{amount (mol)} \times \Delta T} \quad [\text{in units of J/mol·K}]$$

**Table 6.2 Specific Heat Capacities ($c$) of Some Elements, Compounds, and Materials**

| Substance | $c$ (J/g·K)* |
|---|---|
| **Elements** | |
| Aluminum, Al | 0.900 |
| Graphite, C | 0.711 |
| Iron, Fe | 0.450 |
| Copper, Cu | 0.387 |
| Gold, Au | 0.129 |
| **Compounds** | |
| Water, $H_2O(l)$ | 4.184 |
| Ethyl alcohol, $C_2H_5OH(l)$ | 2.46 |
| Ethylene glycol, $(CH_2OH)_2(l)$ | 2.42 |
| Carbon tetracholoride, $CCl_4(l)$ | 0.862 |
| **Solid Materials** | |
| Wood | 1.76 |
| Cement | 0.88 |
| Glass | 0.84 |
| Granite | 0.79 |
| Steel | 0.45 |

*At 298 K (25°C)

To find $C$ of liquid $H_2O$, we multiply $c$ of liquid $H_2O$ (4.184 J/g·K) by the molar mass of $H_2O$ (18.02 g/mol):

$$C \text{ of } H_2O(l) = 4.184 \frac{J}{g \cdot K} \times \frac{18.02 \text{ g}}{1 \text{ mol}} = 75.40 \frac{J}{mol \cdot K}$$

Liquid water has a *very* high specific heat capacity (~4.2 J/g·K), about six times that of rock (~0.7 J/g·K). If Earth had no oceans (*see margin*), it would take one-sixth as much energy for the Sun to heat the rocky surface, and the surface would give off six times as much heat after sundown. Days would be scorching and nights frigid.

What if Earth had no oceans?

---

**Sample Problem 6.3** | **Finding the Quantity of Heat from a Temperature Change**

**Problem** A layer of copper welded to the bottom of a skillet weighs 125 g. How much heat is needed to raise the temperature of the copper layer from 25°C to 300.°C? The specific heat capacity (*c*) of Cu is given in Table 6.2.

**Plan** We know the mass (125 g) and $c$ (0.387 J/g·K) of Cu and can find $\Delta T$ in °C, which equals $\Delta T$ in K. We then use Equation 6.7 to calculate the heat.

**Solution** Calculating $\Delta T$ and then $q$:

$$\Delta T = T_{final} - T_{initial} = 300.°C - 25°C = 275°C = 275 \text{ K}$$

$$q = c \times \text{mass (g)} \times \Delta T = 0.387 \text{ J/g·K} \times 125 \text{ g} \times 275 \text{ K} = \boxed{1.33 \times 10^4 \text{ J}}$$

**Check** Heat is absorbed by the copper bottom (system), so $q$ is positive. Rounding shows the arithmetic is reasonable: $q \approx 0.4 \text{ J/g·K} \times 100 \text{ g} \times 300 \text{ K} = 1.2 \times 10^4 \text{ J}$.

**Follow-Up Problem 6.3** Find the heat released (in kJ) when 5.50 L of ethylene glycol ($d = 1.11$ g/mL; see Table 6.2) in a car radiator cools from 37.0°C to 25.0°C.

---

## The Two Major Types of Calorimetry

How do we know the heat of an acid-base reaction or the Calories in a teaspoon of sugar? We construct "surroundings" that retain the heat as reactants change to products, and then note the temperature change. In the laboratory, these "surroundings" take the form of a **calorimeter,** a device used to measure the heat released (or absorbed) by a physical or chemical process. Let's look at two types of calorimeter—one designed to measure the heat at constant pressure and the other at constant volume.

**Constant-Pressure Calorimetry** For processes that take place at constant pressure, the heat transferred ($q_P$) is often measured in a *coffee-cup calorimeter* (Figure 6.9). This simple apparatus is often used to find the heat of an aqueous reaction or the heat accompanying the dissolving of a salt.

A coffee-cup calorimeter can also be used to find the specific heat capacity of a solid, as long as it does not react with or dissolve in water. The solid (the system) is weighed, heated to some known temperature, and added to a known mass and temperature of water (surroundings) in the calorimeter. After stirring, the final water temperature is measured, which is also the final temperature of the solid. Assuming no heat escapes the calorimeter, the heat released by the system ($-q_{sys}$, or $-q_{solid}$) is equal in magnitude but opposite in sign to the heat absorbed by the surroundings ($+q_{surr}$, or $+q_{H_2O}$):

$$-q_{solid} = q_{H_2O}$$

Substituting from Equation 6.7 on each side of this equation gives

$$-(c_{solid} \times \text{mass}_{solid} \times \Delta T_{solid}) = c_{H_2O} \times \text{mass}_{H_2O} \times \Delta T_{H_2O}$$

All the quantities are known or measured except $c_{solid}$:

$$c_{solid} = -\frac{c_{H_2O} \times \text{mass}_{H_2O} \times \Delta T_{H_2O}}{\text{mass}_{solid} \times \Delta T_{solid}}$$

**Figure 6.9 Coffee-cup calorimeter.** This device measures the heat transferred at constant pressure ($q_P$).

Stirrer — Thermometer — Cork stopper — Nested Styrofoam cups (insulation) — Water (surroundings) — Sample (system)

## Sample Problem 6.4 — Determining the Specific Heat Capacity of a Solid

**Problem** You heat 22.05 g of a solid in a test tube to 100.00°C and add it to 50.00 g of water in a coffee-cup calorimeter. The water temperature changes from 25.10°C to 28.49°C. Find the specific heat capacity of the solid.

**Plan** We are given the masses of the solid (22.05 g) and of $H_2O$ (50.00 g), and we can find the temperature changes of the water and of the solid by subtracting the given values, always using $T_{final} - T_{initial}$. Using Equation 6.7, we set the heat released by the solid ($-q_{solid}$) equal to the heat absorbed by the water ($q_{water}$). The specific heat of water is known, and we solve for $c_{solid}$.

**Solution** Finding $\Delta T_{solid}$ and $\Delta T_{water}$:

$$\Delta T_{water} = T_{final} - T_{initial} = (28.49°C - 25.10°C) = 3.39°C = 3.39 \text{ K}$$
$$\Delta T_{solid} = T_{final} - T_{initial} = (28.49°C - 100.00°C) = -71.51°C = -71.51 \text{ K}$$

Solving for $c_{solid}$:

$$c_{solid} = -\frac{c_{H_2O} \times \text{mass}_{H_2O} \times \Delta T_{H_2O}}{\text{mass}_{solid} \times \Delta T_{solid}} = -\frac{4.184 \text{ J/g·K} \times 50.00 \text{ g} \times 3.39 \text{ K}}{22.05 \text{ g} \times (-71.51 \text{ K})} = \boxed{0.450 \text{ J/g·K}}$$

**Check** Rounding gives $-4$ J/g·K $\times 50$ g $\times 3$ K/[20 g $\times (-70°C)$] $= 0.4$ J/g·K, so the answer seems correct.

**Follow-Up Problem 6.4** A 12.18-g sample of a shiny, orange-brown metal is heated to 65.00°C in a controlled water bath. The metal is then added to 25.00 g of water in a coffee-cup calorimeter, and the water temperature changes from 25.55°C to 27.25°C. What is the unknown metal (see Table 6.2)?

In the next sample problem, the calorimeter is used to study the change in heat during an aqueous acid-base reaction. Recall that, if a reaction takes place at constant pressure, the heat of the reaction ($q_{rxn}$) is equal to its enthalpy change ($\Delta H$).

## Sample Problem 6.5 — Determining the Enthalpy Change of an Aqueous Reaction

**Problem** You place 50.0 mL of 0.500 $M$ NaOH in a coffee-cup calorimeter at 25.00°C and add 25.0 mL of 0.500 $M$ HCl, also at 25.00°C. After stirring, the final temperature is 27.21°C. [Assume that the total volume is the sum of the individual volumes and that the final solution has the same density (1.00 g/mL) and specific heat capacity (Table 6.2) as water.] **(a)** Calculate $q_{soln}$ (in J). **(b)** Calculate the change in enthalpy, $\Delta H$, of the reaction (in kJ/mol of $H_2O$ formed).

**(a) Calculate $q_{soln}$**
**Plan** The solution is the surroundings, and as the reaction takes place, heat flows into the solution. To find $q_{soln}$, we use Equation 6.7, so we need the mass of solution, the change in temperature, and the specific heat capacity. We know the solutions' volumes (25.0 mL and 50.0 mL), so we find their masses with the given density (1.00 g/mL). Then, to find $q_{soln}$, we multiply the total mass by the given $c$ (4.184 J/g·K) and the change in $T$, which we find from $T_{final} - T_{initial}$.

**Solution** Finding $\text{mass}_{soln}$ and $\Delta T_{soln}$:

$$\text{Total mass (g) of solution} = (25.0 \text{ mL} + 50.0 \text{ mL}) \times 1.00 \text{ g/mL} = 75.0 \text{ g}$$
$$\Delta T = 27.21°C - 25.00°C = 2.21°C = 2.21 \text{ K}$$

Finding $q_{soln}$:

$$q_{soln} = c_{soln} \times \text{mass}_{soln} \times \Delta T_{soln} = (4.184 \text{ J/g·K})(75.0 \text{ g})(2.21 \text{ K}) = \boxed{693 \text{ J}}$$

**Check** Rounding to check $q_{soln}$ gives 4 J/g·K $\times 75$ g $\times 2$ K $= 600$ J, which is close to the answer.

**(b) Calculate the change in enthalpy ($\Delta H$)**
**Plan** To find $\Delta H$, we write the balanced equation for the acid-base reaction and use the volumes and the concentrations (0.500 $M$) to find amount (mol) of each reactant ($H^+$ and $OH^-$). Since the amounts of two reactants are given, we determine which is limiting, that is, which gives less product ($H_2O$). The heat of the surroundings is $q_{soln}$, and it is the negative of the heat of the reaction ($q_{rxn}$), which equals $\Delta H$. And dividing $q_{rxn}$ by the amount (mol) of water formed gives $\Delta H$ in kJ/mol of water formed.

**Solution** Writing the balanced equation:

$$HCl(aq) + NaOH(aq) \longrightarrow H_2O(l) + NaCl(aq)$$

Finding amount (mol) of reactants:

Amount (mol) of HCl = 0.500 mol HCl/L × 0.0250 L = 0.0125 mol HCl

Amount (mol) of NaOH = 0.500 mol NaOH/L × 0.0500 L = 0.0250 mol NaOH

Finding the amount (mol) of product: All the coefficients in the equation are 1, which means that the amount (mol) of reactant yields that amount of product. Therefore, HCl is limiting because it yields less product: 0.0125 mol of $H_2O$.

Finding $\Delta H$: Heat absorbed by the solution was released by the reaction; that is,

$$q_{soln} = -q_{rxn} = 693 \text{ J} \qquad \text{so} \qquad q_{rxn} = -693 \text{ J}$$

$$\Delta H \text{ (kJ/mol)} = \frac{q_{rxn}}{\text{mol } H_2O} \times \frac{1 \text{ kJ}}{1000 \text{ J}} = \frac{-693 \text{ J}}{0.0125 \text{ mol } H_2O} \times \frac{1 \text{ kJ}}{1000 \text{ J}} = \boxed{-55.4 \text{ kJ/mol } H_2O}$$

**Check** We check for the limiting reactant: The volume of $H^+$ is half the volume of $OH^-$, but they have the same concentration and a 1:1 stoichiometric ratio. Therefore, the amount (mol) of $H^+$ determines the amount of product. Rounding and taking the negative of $q_{soln}$ to find $\Delta H$ gives $-600$ J/0.012 mol = $-5 \times 10^4$ J/mol, or $-50$ kJ/mol, so the answer seems correct.

**Follow-Up Problem 6.5** After 50.0 mL of 0.500*M* Ba(OH)₂ and the same volume and concentration of HCl react in a coffee-cup calorimeter, you find $q_{soln}$ to be 1.386 kJ. Calculate $\Delta H$ of the reaction in kJ/mol of $H_2O$ formed.

**Constant-Volume Calorimetry** Constant-volume calorimetry is often carried out in a *bomb calorimeter*, a device commonly used to measure the heat of combustion reactions, such as for fuels and foods. In the coffee-cup calorimeter, we assume all the heat is absorbed by the water, but in reality, some must be absorbed by the stirrer, thermometer, and so forth. With the much more precise bomb calorimeter, the *heat capacity of the entire calorimeter* is known (or can be determined).

Figure 6.10 depicts the preweighed combustible sample in a metal-walled chamber (the bomb), which is filled with oxygen gas and immersed in an insulated water bath fitted with motorized stirrer and thermometer. A heating coil connected to an electrical source ignites the sample, and the heat released raises the temperature of the bomb, water, and other calorimeter parts. Because we know the mass of the sample and the heat capacity of the entire calorimeter, we can use the measured $\Delta T$ to calculate the heat released.

**Figure 6.10 A bomb calorimeter.** This device measures the heat released at constant volume ($q_V$). It is often used to study combustion reactions.

Note that the steel bomb is tightly sealed, not open to the atmosphere as is the coffee cup, so the pressure is *not* constant. And the volume of the bomb is fixed, so $\Delta V = 0$, and thus $P\Delta V = 0$. Thus, the energy change measured is the *heat released at constant volume* ($q_V$), which equals $\Delta E$, not $\Delta H$:

$$\Delta E = q + w = q_V + 0 = q_V$$

Recall from Section 6.2, however, that even though the number of moles of gas may change, $P\Delta V$ is usually *much* less than $\Delta E$, so $\Delta H$ is very close to $\Delta E$. For example, $\Delta H$ is only 0.5% larger than $\Delta E$ for the combustion of $H_2$ and only 0.2% smaller than $\Delta E$ for the combustion of octane.

---

### Sample Problem 6.6 | Calculating the Heat of a Combustion Reaction

**Problem** A manufacturer claims that its new dietetic dessert has "fewer than 10 Calories per serving." To test the claim, a chemist at the Department of Consumer Affairs places one serving in a bomb calorimeter and burns it in $O_2$. The initial temperature is 21.862°C and the temperature rises to 26.799°C. If the heat capacity of the calorimeter is 8.151 kJ/K, is the manufacturer's claim correct?

**Plan** When the dessert (system) burns, the heat released is absorbed by the calorimeter:

$$-q_{\text{system}} = q_{\text{calorimeter}}$$

The claim is correct if the heat of the system is less than 10 Calories. To find the heat, we multiply the given heat capacity of the calorimeter (8.151 kJ/K) by $\Delta T$ and then convert to Calories.

**Solution** Finding $\Delta T$:

$$\Delta T = T_{\text{final}} - T_{\text{initial}} = 26.799°C - 21.862°C = 4.937°C = 4.937 \text{ K}$$

Calculating the heat absorbed by the calorimeter:

$$q_{\text{calorimeter}} = \text{heat capacity} \times \Delta T = 8.151 \text{ kJ/K} \times 4.937 \text{ K} = 40.24 \text{ kJ}$$

Recall that 1 Calorie = 1 kcal = 4.184 kJ. Therefore, 10 Calories = 41.84 kJ, so the claim is correct.

**Check** A quick math check shows that the answer is reasonable: 8 kJ/K × 5 K = 40 kJ.

### Follow-Up Problem 6.6 A chemist burns 0.8650 g of graphite (a form of carbon) in a new bomb calorimeter, and $CO_2$ forms. If 393.5 kJ of heat is released per mole of graphite and $\Delta T$ is 2.613 K, what is the heat capacity of the bomb calorimeter?

---

### ■ Summary of Section 6.3

- We calculate $\Delta H$ of a process by measuring the energy transferred as heat at constant pressure ($q_P$). To do this, we determine $\Delta T$ and multiply it by the mass of the substance and by its specific heat capacity ($c$), which is the quantity of energy needed to raise the temperature of 1 g of the substance by 1 K.
- Calorimeters measure the heat released (or absorbed) during a process either at constant pressure (coffee cup; $q_P = \Delta H$) or at constant volume (bomb; $q_V = \Delta E$).

---

## 6.4 • STOICHIOMETRY OF THERMOCHEMICAL EQUATIONS

A **thermochemical equation** is a balanced equation that includes the enthalpy change of the reaction ($\Delta H$). Keep in mind that a given $\Delta H$ refers only to the *amounts (mol) of substances* **and** *their states of matter in that equation.* The enthalpy change of any process has two aspects:

- *Sign.* The sign of $\Delta H$ depends on whether the reaction is exothermic ($-$) or endothermic ($+$). A forward reaction has the *opposite* sign of the reverse reaction.
  Decomposition of 2 mol of water to its elements (endothermic):

$$2H_2O(l) \longrightarrow 2H_2(g) + O_2(g) \quad \Delta H = 572 \text{ kJ}$$

Formation of 2 mol of water from its elements (exothermic):

$$2H_2(g) + O_2(g) \longrightarrow 2H_2O(l) \quad \Delta H = -572 \text{ kJ}$$

• *Magnitude.* The magnitude of $\Delta H$ is *proportional to the amount of substance.* Formation of 1 mol of water from its elements (half the preceding amount):

$$H_2(g) + \tfrac{1}{2}O_2(g) \longrightarrow H_2O(l) \quad \Delta H = -286 \text{ kJ}$$

Two key points to understand about thermochemical equations are as follows:

1. *Balancing coefficients.* When necessary, we use fractional coefficients to balance an equation, because we are specifying the magnitude of $\Delta H$ for a *particular amount,* often 1 mol, *of substance:*

$$\tfrac{1}{8}S_8(s) + O_2(g) \longrightarrow SO_2(g) \quad \Delta H = -296.8 \text{ kJ}$$

2. *Thermochemical equivalence.* For a *particular reaction,* a certain amount of substance is thermochemically equivalent to a certain quantity of energy. For example, in the preceding reaction,

> 296.8 kJ is thermochemically equivalent to $\tfrac{1}{8}$ mol of $S_8(s)$
>
> 286  kJ is thermochemically equivalent to $\tfrac{1}{2}$ mol of $O_2(g)$
>
> 286  kJ is thermochemically equivalent to 1 mol of $H_2O(l)$

Just as we use stoichiometrically equivalent molar ratios to find amounts of substances, we use thermochemically equivalent quantities to find the $\Delta H$ of a reaction for a given amount of substance. Also, just as we use molar mass (in g/mol) to convert an amount (mol) of a substance to mass (g), we use the $\Delta H$ (in kJ/mol) to convert an amount of a substance to an equivalent quantity of heat (in kJ). Figure 6.11 shows this new relationship, and Sample Problem 6.7 applies it.

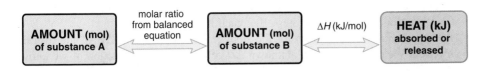

**Figure 6.11** The relationship between amount (mol) of substance and the energy (kJ) transferred as heat during a reaction.

---

**Sample Problem 6.7**  |  **Using the Enthalpy Change of a Reaction ($\Delta H$) to Find Amounts of Substance**

**Problem** The major source of aluminum in the world is bauxite (mostly aluminum oxide). Its thermal decomposition can be written as

$$Al_2O_3(s) \xrightarrow{\Delta} 2Al(s) + \tfrac{3}{2}O_2(g) \quad \Delta H = 1676 \text{ kJ}$$

If aluminum is produced this way (see Comment), how many grams of aluminum can form when $1.000 \times 10^3$ kJ of heat is transferred?

**Plan** From the balanced equation and the enthalpy change, we see that 2 mol of Al forms when 1676 kJ of heat is absorbed. With this equivalent quantity, we convert the given number of kJ to amount (mol) formed and then convert amount to mass (g).

**Solution** Combining steps to convert from heat transferred to mass of Al:

$$\text{Mass (g) of Al} = (1.000 \times 10^3 \text{ kJ}) \times \frac{2 \text{ mol Al}}{1676 \text{ kJ}} \times \frac{26.98 \text{ g Al}}{1 \text{ mol Al}} = \boxed{32.20 \text{ g Al}}$$

**Check** The mass of aluminum seems correct: ~1700 kJ forms about 2 mol of Al (54 g), so 1000 kJ should form a bit more than half that amount (27 g).

**Comment** In practice, aluminum is not obtained by heating bauxite but by supplying electrical energy (as you'll see in Chapter 22). Because $H$ is a state function, however, the total energy required for the change, $\Delta H$, is the same no matter how it occurs.

**Road Map**

**Follow-Up Problem 6.7** Hydrogenation reactions, in which $H_2$ and an "unsaturated" organic compound combine, are used in the food, fuel, and polymer industries. In the simplest case, ethene ($C_2H_4$) and $H_2$ form ethane ($C_2H_6$). If 137 kJ is given off per mole of $C_2H_4$ reacting, how much heat is released when 15.0 kg of $C_2H_6$ forms?

## ▌Summary of Section 6.4

- A thermochemical equation shows a balanced reaction *and* its $\Delta H$ value. The sign of $\Delta H$ for a forward reaction is opposite that for the reverse reaction. The magnitude of $\Delta H$ is specific for the given equation.
- The amount of a substance and the quantity of heat specified by the balanced equation are thermochemically equivalent and act as conversion factors to find the quantity of heat transferred when any amount of the substance reacts.

---

# 6.5 • HESS'S LAW: FINDING $\Delta H$ OF ANY REACTION

In some cases, a reaction is difficult, even impossible, to carry out individually: it may be part of a complex biochemical process, or take place under extreme conditions, or require a change in conditions to occur. Even if we can't run a reaction in the lab, we can still find its enthalpy change. In fact, the state-function property of enthalpy ($H$) allows us to find $\Delta H$ of *any* reaction for which we can write an equation.

This application is based on **Hess's law:** *the enthalpy change of an overall process is the sum of the enthalpy changes of its individual steps:*

$$\Delta H_{\text{overall}} = \Delta H_1 + \Delta H_2 + \cdots + \Delta H_n \qquad \text{(6.8)}$$

This law follows from the fact that $\Delta H$ for a process depends only on the difference between the final and initial states. We apply Hess's law by

- Imagining that an overall reaction occurs through a series of individual reaction steps, whether or not it actually does. Adding the steps must give the overall reaction.
- Choosing individual reaction steps that each has a known $\Delta H$.
- Adding the known $\Delta H$ values for the steps to get the unknown $\Delta H$ of the overall reaction. We can also find an unknown $\Delta H$ of any step by subtraction, if we know the $\Delta H$ values for the overall reaction and all the other steps.

Let's apply Hess's law to the oxidation of sulfur to sulfur trioxide, the key change in the industrial production of sulfuric acid and in the formation of acid rain. (To introduce this approach, we'll use S as the formula for sulfur, rather than the more correct $S_8$.) When we burn S in an excess of $O_2$, sulfur dioxide ($SO_2$) forms, *not* sulfur trioxide ($SO_3$) (Equation 1). After a change in conditions, we add more $O_2$ and oxidize $SO_2$ to $SO_3$ (Equation 2). Thus, we cannot put S and $O_2$ in a calorimeter and find $\Delta H$ for the overall reaction of S to $SO_3$ (Equation 3). But, we *can* find it with Hess's law. The three equations are

Equation 1:     $S(s) + O_2(g) \longrightarrow SO_2(g)$     $\Delta H_1 = -296.8 \text{ kJ}$

Equation 2: $2SO_2(g) + O_2(g) \longrightarrow 2SO_3(g)$     $\Delta H_2 = -198.4 \text{ kJ}$

Equation 3:     $S(s) + \frac{3}{2}O_2(g) \longrightarrow SO_3(g)$     $\Delta H_3 = ?$

If we can manipulate Equation 1 and/or Equation 2, *along with their $\Delta H$ value(s),* so the equations add up to Equation 3, their $\Delta H$ values will add up to the unknown $\Delta H_3$.

First, we identify our "target" equation, the one whose $\Delta H$ we want to find, and note the amount (mol) of each reactant and product; our "target" is Equation 3. Then, we manipulate Equations 1 and/or 2 to make them add up to Equation 3:

- Equations 3 and 1 have the same amount of S, so we don't change Equation 1.
- Equation 3 has half as much $SO_3$ as Equation 2, so we multiply Equation 2, *and $\Delta H_2$,* by $\frac{1}{2}$; that is, we always treat the equation and its $\Delta H$ value the same.
- With the targeted amounts of reactants and products present, we add Equation 1 to the halved Equation 2 and cancel terms that appear on both sides:

Equation 1:                  $S(s) + O_2(g) \longrightarrow SO_2(g)$     $\Delta H_1 = -296.8 \text{ kJ}$

$\frac{1}{2}$(Equation 2):           $SO_2(g) + \frac{1}{2}O_2(g) \longrightarrow SO_3(g)$   $\frac{1}{2}(\Delta H_2) = -99.2 \text{ kJ}$

Equation 3: $S(s) + O_2(g) + \cancel{SO_2(g)} + \frac{1}{2}O_2(g) \longrightarrow \cancel{SO_2(g)} + SO_3(g)$

or,

                             $S(s) + \frac{3}{2}O_2(g) \longrightarrow SO_3(g)$     $\Delta H_3 = -396.0 \text{ kJ}$

Because $\Delta H$ depends only on the difference between $H_{\text{final}}$ and $H_{\text{initial}}$, Hess's law tells us that the difference between the enthalpies of the reactants (1 mol of S and $\frac{3}{2}$ mol of $O_2$) and the product (1 mol of $SO_3$) is the same, whether S is oxidized directly to $SO_3$ (impossible) or through the intermediate formation of $SO_2$ (actual).

To summarize, calculating an unknown $\Delta H$ involves three steps:

1. Identify the target equation, the step whose $\Delta H$ is unknown, and note the amount (mol) of each reactant and product.
2. Manipulate each equation with known $\Delta H$ values so that the target amount (mol) of each substance is on the correct side of the equation. Remember to:
   • Change the sign of $\Delta H$ when you reverse an equation.
   • Multiply amount (mol) and $\Delta H$ by the same factor.
3. Add the manipulated equations and their resulting $\Delta H$ values to get the target equation and its $\Delta H$. All substances except those in the target equation must cancel.

## Sample Problem 6.8    Using Hess's Law to Calculate an Unknown ΔH

**Problem** Two pollutants that form in auto exhaust are CO and NO. An environmental chemist must convert these pollutants to less harmful gases through the following:

$$CO(g) + NO(g) \longrightarrow CO_2(g) + \tfrac{1}{2}N_2(g) \quad \Delta H = ?$$

Given the following information, calculate the unknown $\Delta H$:

> Equation A:  $CO(g) + \tfrac{1}{2}O_2(g) \longrightarrow CO_2(g)$     $\Delta H = -283.0 \text{ kJ}$
> Equation B:  $N_2(g) + O_2(g) \longrightarrow 2NO(g)$     $\Delta H = 180.6 \text{ kJ}$

**Plan** We note the amount (mol) of each substance and on which side each appears in the target equation. We manipulate Equations A and/or B *and* their $\Delta H$ values as needed and add them together to obtain the target equation and the unknown $\Delta H$.

**Solution** Noting substances in the target equation: For reactants, there are 1 mol of CO and of NO; for products, there are 1 mol of $CO_2$ and $\tfrac{1}{2}$ mol of $N_2$. Manipulating the given equations:

• Equation A has the same amounts of CO and $CO_2$ on the same sides of the arrow as in the target, so we leave it as written.
• Equation B has twice as much $N_2$ and NO as the target, and they are on the opposite sides in the target. Thus, we reverse Equation B, change the sign of its $\Delta H$, and multiply both by $\tfrac{1}{2}$:

$$\tfrac{1}{2}[2NO(g) \longrightarrow N_2(g) + O_2(g)] \quad \Delta H = -\tfrac{1}{2}(\Delta H) = -\tfrac{1}{2}(180.6 \text{ kJ})$$

or    $NO(g) \longrightarrow \tfrac{1}{2}N_2(g) + \tfrac{1}{2}O_2(g)$    $\Delta H = -90.3 \text{ kJ}$

Adding the manipulated equations to obtain the target equation:

| | | |
|---|---|---|
| Equation A: | $CO(g) + \tfrac{1}{2}\cancel{O_2(g)} \longrightarrow CO_2(g)$ | $\Delta H = -283.0 \text{ kJ}$ |
| $\tfrac{1}{2}$(Equation B reversed) | $NO(g) \longrightarrow \tfrac{1}{2}N_2(g) + \tfrac{1}{2}\cancel{O_2(g)}$ | $\Delta H = \phantom{-}-90.3 \text{ kJ}$ |
| Target equation: | $CO(g) + NO(g) \longrightarrow CO_2(g) + \tfrac{1}{2}N_2(g)$ | $\Delta H = -373.3 \text{ kJ}$ |

**Check** Obtaining the desired target equation is a sufficient check. Be sure to remember to change the *sign* of $\Delta H$ for any equation you reverse.

**Follow-Up Problem 6.8** Nitrogen oxides undergo many reactions in the environment and in industry. Given the following information, calculate $\Delta H$ for the overall equation, $2NO_2(g) + \tfrac{1}{2}O_2(g) \longrightarrow N_2O_5(s)$:

$$N_2O_5(s) \longrightarrow 2NO(g) + \tfrac{3}{2}O_2(g) \quad \Delta H = 223.7 \text{ kJ}$$
$$NO(g) + \tfrac{1}{2}O_2(g) \longrightarrow NO_2(g) \quad \Delta H = -57.1 \text{ kJ}$$

## ▌Summary of Section 6.5

• Because $H$ is a state function, we can use Hess's law to determine $\Delta H$ of any reaction by assuming that it is the sum of other reactions.
• After manipulating the equations of those reactions and their $\Delta H$ values to match the substances in the target equation, we add the manipulated $\Delta H$ values to find the unknown $\Delta H$.

## Table 6.3 Selected Standard Enthalpies of Formation at 25°C (298 K)

| Formula | $\Delta H_f^\circ$ (kJ/mol) |
|---|---|
| **Calcium** | |
| Ca(s) | 0 |
| CaO(s) | −635.1 |
| CaCO$_3$(s) | −1206.9 |
| **Carbon** | |
| C(graphite) | 0 |
| C(diamond) | 1.9 |
| CO(g) | −110.5 |
| CO$_2$(g) | −393.5 |
| CH$_4$(g) | −74.9 |
| CH$_3$OH(l) | −238.6 |
| HCN(g) | 135 |
| CS$_2$(l) | 87.9 |
| **Chlorine** | |
| Cl(g) | 121.0 |
| Cl$_2$(g) | 0 |
| HCl(g) | −92.3 |
| **Hydrogen** | |
| H(g) | 218.0 |
| H$_2$(g) | 0 |
| **Nitrogen** | |
| N$_2$(g) | 0 |
| NH$_3$(g) | −45.9 |
| NO(g) | 90.3 |
| **Oxygen** | |
| O$_2$(g) | 0 |
| O$_3$(g) | 143 |
| H$_2$O(g) | −241.8 |
| H$_2$O(l) | −285.8 |
| **Silver** | |
| Ag(s) | 0 |
| AgCl(s) | −127.0 |
| **Sodium** | |
| Na(s) | 0 |
| Na(g) | 107.8 |
| NaCl(s) | −411.1 |
| **Sulfur** | |
| S$_8$(rhombic) | 0 |
| S$_8$(monoclinic) | 0.3 |
| SO$_2$(g) | −296.8 |
| SO$_3$(g) | −396.0 |

# 6.6 • STANDARD ENTHALPIES OF REACTION ($\Delta H_{rxn}^\circ$)

In this section, we see how Hess's law is used to determine the $\Delta H$ values of an enormous number of reactions. Thermodynamic variables, such as $\Delta H$, vary somewhat with conditions. Therefore, in order to study and compare reactions, chemists have established a set of specific conditions called **standard states:**

- For a *gas,* the standard state is 1 atm* and ideal behavior.
- For a substance in *aqueous solution,* the standard state is 1 *M* concentration.
- For a *pure substance* (element or compound), the standard state is usually the most stable form of the substance at 1 atm and the temperature of interest. In this text (and in most thermodynamic tables), that temperature is usually 25°C (298 K).

The standard-state symbol (shown as a degree sign) indicates that the variable has been measured with *all the substances in their standard states.* For example, when the enthalpy change of a reaction is measured at the standard state, it is the **standard enthalpy of reaction, $\Delta H_{rxn}^\circ$** (also called *standard heat of reaction;* "rxn" stands for reaction).

## Formation Equations and Their Standard Enthalpy Changes

In a **formation equation,** 1 mol of a compound forms from its elements. The **standard enthalpy of formation ($\Delta H_f^\circ$;** or *standard heat of formation*) is the enthalpy change for the formation equation when all the substances are in their standard states. For instance, the formation equation for methane (CH$_4$) is

$$\text{C(graphite)} + 2\text{H}_2(g) \longrightarrow \text{CH}_4(g) \quad \Delta H_f^\circ = -74.9 \text{ kJ}$$

Fractional coefficients are often used with reactants to obtain 1 mol of the product:

$$\text{Na}(s) + \tfrac{1}{2}\text{Cl}_2(g) \longrightarrow \text{NaCl}(s) \quad \Delta H_f^\circ = -411.1 \text{ kJ}$$

$$2\text{C(graphite)} + 3\text{H}_2(g) + \tfrac{1}{2}\text{O}_2(g) \longrightarrow \text{C}_2\text{H}_5\text{OH}(l) \quad \Delta H_f^\circ = -277.6 \text{ kJ}$$

Standard enthalpies of formation have been tabulated for many substances. Table 6.3 shows several, and a much more extensive table appears in Appendix B. The values in Table 6.3 make two points:

1. *For an element in its standard state, $\Delta H_f^\circ = 0$.*
   - The standard state for metals, like sodium, is the solid ($\Delta H_f^\circ = 0$); it takes 107.8 kJ of heat to form 1 mol of gaseous Na ($\Delta H_f^\circ = 107.8$ kJ/mol).
   - The standard state for molecular elements, such as the halogens, is the molecular form, not separate atoms: for Cl$_2$, $\Delta H_f^\circ = 0$, but for Cl, $\Delta H_f^\circ = 121.0$ kJ/mol.
   - Some elements exist in different forms (called *allotropes;* Chapter 14), but only one is the standard state. The standard state of carbon is graphite ($\Delta H_f^\circ = 0$), not diamond ($\Delta H_f^\circ = 1.9$ kJ/mol), the standard state of oxygen is O$_2$ ($\Delta H_f^\circ = 0$), not ozone (O$_3$; $\Delta H_f^\circ = 143$ kJ/mol), and the standard state of sulfur is S$_8$ in its rhombic crystal form ($\Delta H_f^\circ = 0$), not in its monoclinic form ($\Delta H_f^\circ = 0.3$ kJ/mol).

2. *Most compounds have a negative $\Delta H_f^\circ$.* That is, most compounds have exothermic formation reactions: *under standard conditions, heat is released when most compounds form from their elements.*

## Sample Problem 6.9    Writing Formation Equations

**Problem** Write a balanced formation equation for each of the following and include the value of $\Delta H_f^\circ$:
**(a)** AgCl(s)          **(b)** CaCO$_3$(s)          **(c)** HCN(g)

**Plan** We write the elements as the reactants and 1 mol of the compound as the product, being sure all substances are in their standard states. Then, we balance the equations and find the $\Delta H_f^\circ$ values in Table 6.3 or Appendix B.

---

*The definition of the standard state for gases has been changed to 1 bar, a slightly lower pressure than the 1 atm standard on which the data in this book are based (1 atm = 101.3 kPa = 1.013 bar). For most purposes, this makes very little difference in the standard enthalpy values.

**Solution  (a)** $Ag(s) + \frac{1}{2}Cl_2(g) \longrightarrow AgCl(s)$     $\Delta H^\circ_f = -127.0 \text{ kJ}$

**(b)** $Ca(s) + C(graphite) + \frac{3}{2}O_2(g) \longrightarrow CaCO_3(s)$     $\Delta H^\circ_f = -1206.9 \text{ kJ}$

**(c)** $\frac{1}{2}H_2(g) + C(graphite) + \frac{1}{2}N_2(g) \longrightarrow HCN(g)$     $\Delta H^\circ_f = 135 \text{ kJ}$

**Follow-Up Problem 6.9** Write a balanced formation equation for each of the following and include its $\Delta H^\circ_f$: **(a)** $CH_3OH(l)$, **(b)** $CaO(s)$, **(c)** $CS_2(l)$.

## Determining $\Delta H^\circ_{rxn}$ from $\Delta H^\circ_f$ Values for Reactants and Products

We can use $\Delta H^\circ_f$ values to determine $\Delta H^\circ_{rxn}$ for any reaction. By applying Hess's law, we can imagine the reaction occurring in two steps (Figure 6.12):

*Step 1.* Each reactant decomposes to its elements. This is the *reverse* of the formation reaction for the *reactant,* so the standard enthalpy change is $-\Delta H^\circ_f$.

*Step 2.* Each product forms from its elements. This step *is* the formation reaction for the *product,* so the standard enthalpy change is $\Delta H^\circ_f$.

$$\Delta H^\circ_{rxn} = \Sigma m \Delta H^\circ_{f(products)} - \Sigma n \Delta H^\circ_{f(reactants)}$$

**Figure 6.12** The two-step process for determining $\Delta H^\circ_{rxn}$ from $\Delta H^\circ_f$ values.

According to Hess's law, we add the enthalpy changes for these steps to obtain the overall enthalpy change for the reaction ($\Delta H^\circ_{rxn}$). Suppose we want $\Delta H^\circ_{rxn}$ for

$$TiCl_4(l) + 2H_2O(g) \longrightarrow TiO_2(s) + 4HCl(g)$$

We write this equation as though it were the sum of four individual equations, one for each compound. The first two show step 1, the decomposition of the reactants to their elements (*reverse* of their formation); the second two show step 2, the formation of the products from their elements:

$$TiCl_4(l) \longrightarrow Ti(s) + 2Cl_2(g) \qquad -\Delta H^\circ_f[TiCl_4(l)]$$
$$2H_2O(g) \longrightarrow 2H_2(g) + O_2(g) \qquad -2\Delta H^\circ_f[H_2O(g)]$$
$$Ti(s) + O_2(g) \longrightarrow TiO_2(s) \qquad \Delta H^\circ_f[TiO_2(s)]$$
$$2H_2(g) + 2Cl_2(g) \longrightarrow 4HCl(g) \qquad 4\Delta H^\circ_f[HCl(g)]$$

$TiCl_4(l) + 2H_2O(g) + \cancel{Ti(s)} + \cancel{O_2(g)} + \cancel{2H_2(g)} + \cancel{2Cl_2(g)} \longrightarrow$
$$\cancel{Ti(s)} + \cancel{2Cl_2(g)} + \cancel{2H_2(g)} + \cancel{O_2(g)} + TiO_2(s) + 4HCl(g)$$

or     $TiCl_4(l) + 2H_2O(g) \longrightarrow TiO_2(s) + 4HCl(g)$

It's important to realize that when titanium(IV) chloride and water react, the reactants don't *actually* decompose to their elements, which then recombine to form the products. But the great usefulness of Hess's law and the state-function concept is that $\Delta H^\circ_{rxn}$ is the difference between two state functions, $H^\circ_{products}$ minus $H^\circ_{reactants}$, so it doesn't matter how the reaction *actually* occurs. We add the individual enthalpy changes to find $\Delta H^\circ_{rxn}$:

$$\Delta H^\circ_{rxn} = \Delta H^\circ_f[TiO_2(s)] + 4\Delta H^\circ_f[HCl(g)] + \{-\Delta H^\circ_f[TiCl_4(l)]\} + \{-2\Delta H^\circ_f[H_2O(g)]\}$$
$$= \{\Delta H^\circ_f[TiO_2(s)] + 4\Delta H^\circ_f[HCl(g)]\} - \{\Delta H^\circ_f[TiCl_4(l)] + 2\Delta H^\circ_f[H_2O(g)]\}$$

$\underbrace{\qquad\qquad\qquad\qquad\qquad}_{\text{Products}}$     $\underbrace{\qquad\qquad\qquad\qquad\qquad}_{\text{Reactants}}$

The arithmetic in this case gives $\Delta H^\circ_{rxn} = -25.39$ kJ, but more importantly, when we generalize the pattern, we see that *the standard enthalpy of reaction is the sum of the standard enthalpies of formation of the **products** minus the sum of the standard enthalpies of formation of the **reactants*** (see Figure 6.12):

$$\Delta H^\circ_{rxn} = \Sigma m\Delta H^\circ_{f(products)} - \Sigma n\Delta H^\circ_{f(reactants)} \qquad (6.9)$$

where $\Sigma$ means "sum of," and $m$ and $n$ are the amounts (mol) of the products and reactants given by the coefficients in the balanced equation.

---

**Sample Problem 6.10** | **Calculating $\Delta H^\circ_{rxn}$ from $\Delta H^\circ_f$ Values**

**Problem** Nitric acid is used to make many products, including fertilizers, dyes, and explosives. The first step in its production is the oxidation of ammonia:

$$4NH_3(g) + 5O_2(g) \longrightarrow 4NO(g) + 6H_2O(g)$$

Calculate $\Delta H^\circ_{rxn}$ from $\Delta H^\circ_f$ values.

**Plan** We use values from Table 6.3 (or Appendix B) and apply Equation 6.9.

**Solution** Calculating $\Delta H^\circ_{rxn}$:

$$\Delta H^\circ_{rxn} = \Sigma m\Delta H^\circ_{f(products)} - \Sigma n\Delta H^\circ_{f(reactants)}$$
$$= \{4\Delta H^\circ_f[NO(g)] + 6\Delta H^\circ_f[H_2O(g)]\} - \{4\Delta H^\circ_f[NH_3(g)] + 5\Delta H^\circ_f[O_2(g)]\}$$
$$= (4 \text{ mol})(90.3 \text{ kJ/mol}) + (6 \text{ mol})(-241.8 \text{ kJ/mol})$$
$$\quad -[(4 \text{ mol})(-45.9 \text{ kJ/mol}) + (5 \text{ mol})(0 \text{ kJ/mol})]$$
$$= 361 \text{ kJ} - 1451 \text{ kJ} + 184 \text{ kJ} - 0 \text{ kJ} = \boxed{-906 \text{ kJ}}$$

**Check** We write formation equations, with $\Delta H^\circ_f$ values for the amounts of each compound, in the correct direction (forward for products and reverse for reactants) and find the sum:

| | | |
|---|---|---|
| $4NH_3(g) \longrightarrow \cancel{2N_2(g)} + \cancel{6H_2(g)}$ | $-4\Delta H^\circ_f = -4(-45.9 \text{ kJ}) =$ | $184 \text{ kJ}$ |
| $\cancel{2N_2(g)} + 2O_2(g) \longrightarrow 4NO(g)$ | $4\Delta H^\circ_f = 4(90.3 \text{ kJ}) =$ | $361 \text{ kJ}$ |
| $\cancel{6H_2(g)} + 3O_2(g) \longrightarrow 6H_2O(g)$ | $6\Delta H^\circ_f = 6(-241.8 \text{ kJ}) =$ | $-1451 \text{ kJ}$ |
| $4NH_3(g) + 5O_2(g) \longrightarrow 4NO(g) + 6H_2O(g)$ | $\Delta H^\circ_{rxn} =$ | $-906 \text{ kJ}$ |

**Comment** In this problem, we know the individual $\Delta H^\circ_f$ values and find the sum, $\Delta H^\circ_{rxn}$. In the follow-up problem, we know the sum and want to find one of the $\Delta H^\circ_f$ values.

**Follow-Up Problem 6.10** Use the following to find $\Delta H^\circ_f$ of methanol [$CH_3OH(l)$]:

$$CH_3OH(l) + \tfrac{3}{2}O_2(g) \longrightarrow CO_2(g) + 2H_2O(g) \qquad \Delta H^\circ_{rxn} = -638.5 \text{ kJ}$$
$$\Delta H^\circ_f \text{ of } CO_2(g) = -393.5 \text{ kJ/mol}$$
$$\Delta H^\circ_f \text{ of } H_2O(g) = -241.8 \text{ kJ/mol}$$

---

The Chemical Connections essay applies ideas from this chapter to new approaches for energy utilization.

## ■ Summary of Section 6.6

- Standard states are a set of specific conditions used for determining thermodynamic variables for all substances.
- When 1 mol of a compound forms from its elements with all substances in their standard states, the enthalpy change is the standard enthalpy of formation, $\Delta H^\circ_f$.
- Hess's law allows us to picture a reaction as the decomposition of the reactants to their elements followed by the formation of the products from their elements.
- We use tabulated $\Delta H^\circ_f$ values to find $\Delta H^\circ_{rxn}$ or use known $\Delta H^\circ_{rxn}$ and $\Delta H^\circ_f$ values to find an unknown $\Delta H^\circ_f$.
- Because of major concerns about climate change, chemists are developing energy alternatives, including coal and biomass conversion, hydrogen fuel, and noncombustible energy sources.

Out of necessity, we must rethink our global use of energy. The dwindling supplies of our most common fuels and the environmental impact of their combustion products threaten human well-being and the survival of many other species. Energy production presents scientists, engineers, and political leaders with some of the greatest challenges of our time.

A changeover in energy sources from wood to coal and then petroleum took place over the past century. The **fossil fuels**—coal, petroleum, and natural gas—remain our major sources, but they are *nonrenewable* because natural processes form them many orders of magnitude slower than we consume them. In the United States, ongoing research seeks new approaches to using coal and nuclear energy, and utilizing *renewable* sources—biomass, hydrogen, sunlight, wind, geothermal heat, and tides—is the subject of intensive efforts as well.

In this discussion, we focus on converting coal and biomass to cleaner fuels, understanding the effect of carbon-based fuels on climate, developing hydrogen as a fuel, utilizing solar energy, and conserving energy.

## Converting Coal to Cleaner Fuels

U.S. reserves of coal are enormous, but the burning of coal, in addition to forming $CO_2$, produces $SO_2$ and particulates, and releases mercury. Exposure to $SO_2$ and particulates causes respiratory disease, and $SO_2$ can be oxidized to $H_2SO_4$, the key component of acid rain (Chapter 19). The trace amounts of Hg, a neurotoxin, spread as Hg vapor and bioaccumulate in fish.

Two processes reduce the amounts of $SO_2$:

*Desulfurization.* The removal of sulfur dioxide from flue gases is done with devices called *scrubbers* that heat powdered limestone ($CaCO_3$) or spray lime-water slurries [$Ca(OH)_2$]:

$$CaCO_3(s) + SO_2(g) \xrightarrow{\Delta} CaSO_3(s) + CO_2(g)$$
$$2CaSO_3(s) + O_2(g) + 4H_2O(l) \longrightarrow 2CaSO_4 \cdot 2H_2O(s; \text{gypsum})$$
$$2Ca(OH)_2(aq) + 2SO_2(g) + O_2(g) + 2H_2O(l) \longrightarrow$$
$$2CaSO_4 \cdot 2H_2O(s)$$

A wallboard (drywall) plant built next to the power plant sells the gypsum (1 ton per customer each year); about 20% of the drywall produced each year is made with synthetic gypsum.

*Gasification.* In **coal gasification,** solid coal is converted to sulfur-free gaseous fuels. In this process, the sulfur in the coal is reduced to $H_2S$, which is removed through an acid-base reaction with a base, such as ethanolamine ($HOCH_2CH_2NH_2$). The resulting salt is heated to release $H_2S$, which is converted to elemental sulfur by the Claus process (Chapter 22) and sold. Several reactions yield mixtures with increasing fuel value, that is, with a lower C/H ratio:

- Pulverized coal reacts with limited $O_2$ and water at 800–1500°C to form approximately a 2/1 mixture of $CO/H_2$.
- Alternatively, in the *water-gas reaction* (or *steam-carbon reaction*), an exothermic oxidation of C to CO is followed by the endothermic reaction of C with steam to form a nearly 1/1 mixture of $CO/H_2$ called *water gas:*

$$C(s) + \tfrac{1}{2}O_2(g) \longrightarrow CO(g) \qquad \Delta H^\circ_{rxn} = -110 \text{ kJ}$$
$$C(s) + H_2O(g) \longrightarrow CO(g) + H_2(g) \quad \Delta H^\circ_{rxn} = 131 \text{ kJ}$$

However, water gas has a much lower fuel value than methane ($CH_4$). For example, a mixture of 0.5 mol of CO and 0.5 mol of $H_2$ releases about one-third as much energy as 1.0 mol of methane ($\Delta H = -802$ kJ/mol):

$$\tfrac{1}{2}H_2(g) + \tfrac{1}{4}O_2(g) \longrightarrow \tfrac{1}{2}H_2O(g) \qquad \Delta H^\circ_{rxn} = -121 \text{ kJ}$$
$$\tfrac{1}{2}CO(g) + \tfrac{1}{4}O_2(g) \longrightarrow \tfrac{1}{2}CO_2(g) \qquad \Delta H^\circ_{rxn} = -142 \text{ kJ}$$
$$\tfrac{1}{2}H_2(g) + \tfrac{1}{2}CO(g) + \tfrac{1}{2}O_2(g) \longrightarrow \tfrac{1}{2}H_2O(g) + \tfrac{1}{2}CO_2(g)$$
$$\Delta H^\circ_{rxn} = -263 \text{ kJ}$$

- In the *CO-shift* (or *water-gas shift*) reaction, the $H_2$ content of water gas is increased to produce synthesis gas (*syngas*):

$$CO(g) + H_2O(g) \longrightarrow CO_2(g) + H_2(g) \quad \Delta H^\circ_{rxn} = -41 \text{ kJ}$$

- To produce $CH_4$, a syngas that is a 3/1 mixture of $H_2/CO$ from which the $CO_2$ has been removed, is employed:

$$CO(g) + 3H_2(g) \longrightarrow CH_4(g) + H_2O(g) \quad \Delta H^\circ_{rxn} = -206 \text{ kJ}$$

Drying the product gives **synthetic natural gas (SNG).**

Syngas is used is some newer methods as well. In *integrated gasification combined cycle (IGCC),* electricity is produced in two ways—when syngas is burned in a combustion turbine and when the hot product gases generate steam to power a steam turbine. In the *Fischer-Tropsch process,* syngas is used to form liquid hydrocarbon fuels that have higher molar masses than methane:

$$nCO(g) + (2n + 1)H_2(g) \longrightarrow C_nH_{2n+2}(l) + nH_2O(g)$$

## Converting Biomass to Fuels

Nearly half the world's people rely on wood for energy. In principle, wood is renewable, but widespread deforestation has resulted from its use for fuel, lumber, and paper. Therefore, great emphasis has been placed on **biomass conversion** of vegetable and animal waste. In one process, chemical and/or microbial methods convert vegetable (sugarcane, corn, switchgrass) and tree waste into fuel, mainly ethanol ($C_2H_5OH$). In the United States, ethanol is mixed with gasoline to form *gasohol;* in Brazil, it substitutes directly for gasoline.

**Methanogenesis** forms methane by anaerobic (oxygen-free) biodegradation of organic sources such as manure and vegetable waste or wastewater. China's biogas-generating facilities apply this technique, and similar ones in the U.S. use garbage and sewage. In addition to producing methane, the process yields residues that improve soil; it also prevents the wastes from polluting natural waters.

Another biomass conversion process changes vegetable oils (soybean, cottonseed, sunflower, canola, and even used cooking oil) into a mixture called *biodiesel,* whose combustion produces less CO, $SO_2$, and particulate matter than fossil-fuel-based diesel. The $CO_2$ produced in combustion of biodiesel has minimal impact on the net atmospheric amount because the carbon is taken up by the plants grown as sources of the vegetable oils.

## The Greenhouse Effect and Global Warming

Combustion of all carbon-based fuels releases $CO_2$, and over the past two decades, it has become clear that the atmospheric build-up of this gas from our increased use of these fuels is changing the climate. Throughout Earth's history, $CO_2$ has played a key

*(continued)*

temperature-regulating role in the atmosphere. Much of the sunlight that shines on Earth is absorbed by the land and oceans and converted to heat (IR radiation; Figure B6.1). Like the glass of a greenhouse, $CO_2$ does not absorb visible light from the Sun, but it absorbs and re-emits some of the heat radiating from Earth's surface and, thus, helps warm the atmosphere. This process is called the *natural greenhouse effect* (Figure B6.1, *left*).

Over several billion years, due to the spread of plant life, which uses $CO_2$ in photosynthesis, the amount of $CO_2$ originally present (from volcanic activity) decreased to 0.028% by volume. With this amount, Earth's average temperature was about 14°C (57°F); without $CO_2$, it would be −17°C (2°F)! However, as a result of intensive use of fossil fuels for the past 150 years, this amount increased to 0.039%. Thus, although the same quantity of solar energy passes through the atmosphere, more is being trapped as heat, which has created an *enhanced greenhouse effect* that is changing the climate through *global warming* (Figure B6.1, *right*). Based on current trends, $CO_2$ amounts will increase to between 0.049% and 0.126% by 2100 (Figure B6.2).

If this projected increase in $CO_2$ occurs, two closely related questions arise: (1) How much will the temperature rise? (2) How will this rise affect life on Earth? Despite constantly improving models, answers are difficult to obtain. Natural fluctuations in temperature must be taken into account, as well as cyclic changes in solar activity. Moreover, as the amount of $CO_2$ increases from fossil-fuel burning, so do the amounts of particulate matter and $SO_2$, which may block sunlight and have a cooling effect. Water vapor also traps heat, and as temperatures rise, more water evaporates. The increased amounts of water vapor may thicken the cloud cover and lead to cooling as well.

Despite such opposing factors, all of the best models predict net warming, and scientists are observing the effects. The average temperature has increased by 0.6±0.2°C since the late 19th century and 0.2–0.3°C over the past 25 years. Globally, the decade from 2001 to 2010 was the warmest on record. Snow cover and glacial size in the northern hemisphere and floating ice in the Arctic Ocean have decreased dramatically. Antarctica is also experiencing widespread breakup of icebound regions. Globally, sea level has risen an average of 17 cm (6.7 in) over the past century, and flooding and other extreme weather events have increased.

Fifteen years ago, the best models predicted a temperature rise of 1.0–3.5°C; today, their predictions are more than 50% higher. Such increases would alter rainfall patterns and crop yields throughout the world and increase sea level as much as 1 meter, thus flooding regions such as the Netherlands, half of Florida, much of southern Asia, coastal New England and New York, and many Pacific island nations. To make matters worse, as we burn fossil fuels that *release* $CO_2$, we cut down forests that *absorb* it.

In addition to ways to reduce fossil-fuel consumption, researchers are studying methods of *carbon capture and storage (CCS),* including *$CO_2$ sequestration,* both naturally by maintaining forests and jungles and industrially by liquefying $CO_2$ formed and either burying it underground or using it to produce mineral carbonates.

The 1997 United Nations Conference on Climate Change in Kyoto, Japan, created a treaty with legally binding targets to limit greenhouse gases. It was ratified by 189 countries, but not by the United States, the largest emitter. The 2009 conference in Copenhagen, Denmark, was attended by representatives from 192 countries (including the U.S.), but did not result in legally binding emission targets or financial commitments.

**Figure B6.1 The trapping of heat by the atmosphere.** Of the total sunlight reaching Earth, some is reflected and some is absorbed and converted to IR radiation (heat). Some heat emitted by the surface is trapped by atmospheric $CO_2$, creating a *natural* greenhouse effect (*left*) that has been essential to life. But, largely as a result of human activity in the past 150 years, and especially the past several decades, the buildup of $CO_2$ and several other greenhouse gases (*pie chart*) has created an *enhanced* greenhouse effect (*right*).

A

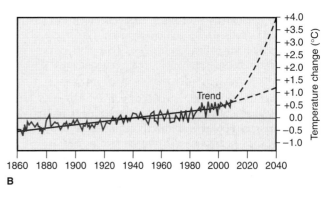

B

**Figure B6.2 Evidence for the enhanced greenhouse effect. A,** Since the mid-19th century, atmospheric $CO_2$ has increased. **B,** Since the mid-19th century, average global temperature has risen 0.6°C. (Zero is the average from 1957 to 1970.) The projections in the graphs (*dashed lines*) assume that current fossil fuel consumption and deforestation continue (*upper line*) or slow (*lower line*).

**Hydrogen** The use of $H_2$ as an energy source holds great promise but presents several problems. The simplest element and most plentiful gas in the universe always occurs on Earth in compounds, most importantly with oxygen in water and carbon in hydrocarbons. Once freed, however, $H_2$ is an excellent energy source because of several properties:

- It has the highest energy content per *mass* unit of any fuel—nearly three times as much as gasoline.
- Its energy content per *volume* unit is low at STP but increases greatly when the $H_2$ is liquefied under extremely high $P$ and low $T$.
- Its combustion does not produce $CO_2$, particulates, or sulfur oxides. It is such a clean energy source that $H_2$-fuel cells operate electrical systems aboard the space shuttles, and the crews drink the pure water product.

A hydrogen-based economy is the dream of many because, even though combustion of $H_2$ ($\Delta H^{\circ}_{rxn} = -242$ kJ/mol) produces less than one-third as much energy per mole as combustion of $CH_4$ ($\Delta H^{\circ}_{rxn} = -802$ kJ/mol), it yields nonpolluting water vapor. The keys to realizing the dream, however, involve major improvements in both production of $H_2$ and its transportation and storage.

*Production of $H_2$.* Hydrogen is produced by a number of methods, some more widely used than others.

- *Fossil-fuel byproduct.* In the United States today, almost all $H_2$ is produced by the *steam-reforming process,* in which methane or natural gas is treated with steam in high-temperature reactions (Chapter 22).
- *Electrolysis of liquid water.* Formation of $H_2$ from the decomposition of liquid water is endothermic ($\Delta H^{\circ}_{rxn} = 286$ kJ/mol), and most direct methods that utilize electricity are costly. However, energy from flowing water, wind, and geothermal sources can provide the needed electricity. An exciting new *photoelectrochemical approach* uses a photovoltaic panel coupled to an electrolysis unit: the energy of sunlight powers the decomposition of water.
- *Biological methods.* Green algae and cyanobacteria store the energy of sunlight in the form of starch or glycogen for their own metabolism. Under certain conditions, however, these

microbes can be made to produce $H_2$ gas instead of these large organic molecules. For example, eliminating sulfur from the diet of green algae activates a long dormant gene and the cells produce $H_2$. But, major improvements in yields are needed to make this method cost-effective.

*Transportation and storage of $H_2$.* The absence of an infrastructure for transporting and storing large quantities of hydrogen is still a roadblock to realizing a hydrogen-based economy. Currently, the cost of energy to cool and compress the gas to liquefy it is very high. Hydrogen is carried in pipelines, but its ability to escape through metals and make them brittle requires more expensive piping. Storage in the form of solid metal hydrides has been explored, but heating the hydrides to release the stored hydrogen requires energy. Use of $H_2$ in fuel cells is a major area of electrochemical research (Chapter 21). Tests are underway to commercialize fuel-cell technology using the hydrogen that is a byproduct of the petrochemical and coal industries.

**Solar Energy** The Sun's energy drives global winds and ocean currents, the cycle of evaporation and condensation, and many biological processes, especially photosynthesis. More energy falls on Earth's surface as sunlight in 1 h [$1.2 \times 10^5$ TW (terawatts); 1 TW = $1 \times 10^{12}$ W] than is used in all human activity in 1 year. Solar energy is, however, a dilute source (only 1 kW/m² at noon); in 1 h, about 600–1000 TW strikes land at sites suitable for collecting. Nevertheless, covering 0.16% of that land with today's photovoltaic systems would provide 20 TW/h, equivalent to the output of 20,000 nuclear power plants producing 1 GW (gigawatt) each. Clearly, solar energy is the largest carbon-free option among renewable sources.

Three important ways to utilize solar energy are with electronic materials, biomass, and thermal systems:

*Electronic materials.* A **photovoltaic cell** converts sunlight directly into electricity by employing certain combinations of elements (usually metalloids; we discuss the behavior of elements with *semiconductor* properties in Chapter 12). Early cells relied primarily on crystalline silicon, but their *yield,* the proportion of electrical energy produced relative to the radiant energy supplied, was only about 10%. More recent devices have achieved much higher yields by using thin films of polycrystalline materials that

*(continued)*

251

incorporate combinations of other elements, such as cadmium telluride (CdTe cells, 16%), gallium arsenide (GaAs cells, 18%), and copper indium gallium selenide (CIGS cells, 20%). And ongoing research on nanometer-sized semiconductor devices, called *quantum dots,* suggests yields as high as 70%.

*Biomass.* Solar energy is used to convert $CO_2$ and water via photosynthesis to plant material (carbohydrate) and oxygen. Plant biomass can be burned directly as a fuel or converted to other fuels, such as ethanol or hydrogen (see p. 249).

*Thermal systems.* The operation of a photovoltaic cell creates a buildup of heat, which lowers its efficiency. A *photovoltaic thermal (PVT) hybrid cell* thus combines such a cell with conductive metal piping (filled with water or antifreeze) that transfers the heat from the cell to a domestic hot-water system.

Because sunlight is typically available only 6 to 8 hours a day and is greatly reduced in cloudy weather, another thermal system focuses on storing solar energy during the day and releasing it at night. When an ionic hydrate, such as $Na_2SO_4 \cdot 10H_2O$, is warmed by sunlight to over 32°C, the 3 mol of ions dissolve in the 10 mol of water in an endothermic process:

$$Na_2SO_4(aq) \cdot 10H_2O(s) \xrightarrow{\geq 32°C} Na_2SO_4(aq) \quad \Delta H^\circ_{rxn} = 354 \text{ kJ}$$

When cooled below 32°C after sunset, the solution recrystallizes, releasing the absorbed energy for heating:

$$Na_2SO_4(aq) \xrightarrow{\leq 32°C} Na_2SO_4(aq) \cdot 10H_2O(s) \quad \Delta H^\circ_{rxn} = -354 \text{ kJ}$$

Unfortunately, as of the end of the first decade of the 21$^{st}$ century, solar energy is not yet competitive with highly subsidized fossil fuels. Nevertheless, changes in economic policy as well as improvements in photovoltaic technology and biomass processing should greatly increase solar energy's contribution to a carbon-free energy future.

## Nuclear Energy
Despite ongoing problems with disposal of radioactive waste, energy from nuclear *fission*—the splitting of large, unstable atomic nuclei—is used extensively, especially in France and other parts of northern Europe. Nuclear *fusion*—the combining of small atomic nuclei—avoids the problems of fission but has been achieved so far only with a net consumption of power. (We'll discuss these processes in detail in Chapter 24.)

## Energy Conservation: More from Less
All systems, whether organisms or factories, waste energy, which is, in effect, a waste of fuel. For example, the production of one aluminum beverage can requires energy equivalent to burning 0.25 L of gasoline. Energy conservation lowers costs, extends our fuel supply, and reduces the effects of climate change. Following are three examples of conservation.

*Passive solar design.* Heating and cooling costs can be reduced by as much as 50% when buildings are constructed with large windows and materials that absorb the Sun's heat in the day and release it slowly at night.

*Residential heating systems.* A high-efficiency gas-burning furnace channels hot waste gases through a system of baffles to transfer more heat to the room and then to an attached domestic hot-water system. While moving through the system, the gases cool to 100°C, so the water vapor condenses, thus releasing about 10% more heat:

$$CH_4(g) + 2O_2(g) \longrightarrow CO_2(g) + 2H_2O(g) \quad \Delta H^\circ_{rxn} = -802 \text{ kJ}$$
$$2H_2O(g) \longrightarrow 2H_2O(l) \quad \Delta H^\circ_{rxn} = -88 \text{ kJ}$$
$$\overline{CH_4(g) + 2O_2(g) \longrightarrow CO_2(g) + 2H_2O(l) \quad \Delta H^\circ_{rxn} = -890 \text{ kJ}}$$

*Modern lighting.* Incandescent bulbs give off light when the material in their filament reaches a high temperature. They are very inefficient because less than 7% of the electrical energy is converted to light, the rest being wasted as heat. *Compact fluorescent lamps (CFLs)* have an efficiency of about 18% and are having a major economic impact: in many parts of Europe, incandescent bulbs are no longer sold. *Light-emitting diodes (LEDs)* are even more efficient (about 30%) and are already being used in car indicator lamps and tail lights. Light-emitting devices based on organic semiconductors (OLEDs) are used in flat-panel displays, and recent use of Al-In-Ga-P materials and Ga and In nitrides in LEDs has increased brightness and improved color richness. Over 20% of electricity generated in the U.S. is used for lighting, and burning of fossil fuels in power plants creates smog, particulates, and $CO_2$. By 2020, use of these devices for lighting can cut electricity usage by 50%, eliminating the emission of $2.8 \times 10^7$ metric tons of carbon per year.

Engineers and chemists will continue to explore alternatives for energy production and use, but a more hopeful energy future ultimately depends on our dedication to conserving planetary resources.

## Problems

**B6.1** To make use of an ionic hydrate for storing solar energy, you place 500.0 kg of sodium sulfate decahydrate on your house roof. Assuming complete reaction and 100% efficiency of heat transfer, how much heat (in kJ) is released to your house at night?

**B6.2** In one step of coal gasification, coal reacts with superheated steam:

$$C(coal) + H_2O(g) \longrightarrow CO(g) + H_2(g) \quad \Delta H^\circ_{rxn} = 129.7 \text{ kJ}$$

(a) Use this reaction and the following two to write an overall reaction for the production of methane:

$$CO(g) + H_2O(g) \longrightarrow CO_2(g) + H_2(g) \quad \Delta H^\circ_{rxn} = -41 \text{ kJ}$$
$$CO(g) + 3H_2(g) \longrightarrow CH_4(g) + H_2O(g) \quad \Delta H^\circ_{rxn} = -206 \text{ kJ}$$

(b) Calculate $\Delta H^\circ_{rxn}$ for this overall change.

(c) Using the value from part (b) and a calculated value of $\Delta H^\circ_{rxn}$ for the combustion of methane, find the total $\Delta H$ for gasifying 1.00 kg of coal and burning the methane formed (assume water forms as a gas and $M$ of coal = 12.00 g/mol).

# CHAPTER REVIEW GUIDE

## Learning Objectives    Relevant section (§) and/or sample problem (SP) numbers appear in parentheses.

### Understand These Concepts

1. The distinction between a system and its surroundings (§6.1)
2. The transfer of energy to or from a system as heat and/or work (§6.1)
3. The relation of internal energy change, heat, and work (§6.1)
4. The meaning of energy conservation (§6.1)
5. The meaning of a state function and why $\Delta E$ is constant even though $q$ and $w$ vary (§6.1)
6. The meaning of enthalpy and the relation between $\Delta E$ and $\Delta H$ (§6.2)
7. The meaning of $\Delta H$ and the distinction between exothermic and endothermic reactions (§6.2)
8. The relation between specific heat capacity and heat (§6.3)
9. How constant-pressure (coffee-cup) and constant-volume (bomb) calorimeters work (§6.3)
10. The relation between $\Delta H$ and amount of substance (§6.4)
11. The calculation of $\Delta H$ values with Hess's law (§6.5)

12. The meaning of a formation equation and the standard enthalpy of formation (§6.6)
13. How a reaction can be viewed as the decomposition of reactants followed by the formation of products (§6.6)

### Master These Skills

1. Determining the change in a system's internal energy in different units (SP 6.1)
2. Drawing enthalpy diagrams for chemical and physical changes (SP 6.2)
3. Solving problems involving specific heat capacity and heat transferred in a reaction (SPs 6.3–6.6)
4. Relating the heat transferred in a reaction to the amounts of substances changing (SP 6.7)
5. Using Hess's law to find an unknown $\Delta H$ (SP 6.8)
6. Writing formation equations and using $\Delta H_f^\circ$ values to find $\Delta H_{rxn}^\circ$ (SPs 6.9, 6.10)

## Key Terms    Page numbers appear in parentheses.

thermodynamics (229)
thermochemistry (229)

**Section 6.1**
system (230)
surroundings (230)
internal energy ($E$) (230)
heat ($q$) (230)
work ($w$) (231)
law of conservation of energy (first law of thermodynamics) (233)
joule (J) (233)

calorie (cal) (233)
state function (234)

**Section 6.2**
pressure-volume work ($PV$ work) (235)
enthalpy ($H$) (235)
change in enthalpy ($\Delta H$) (235)
exothermic process (236)
enthalpy diagram (237)
endothermic process (237)

**Section 6.3**
heat capacity (238)
specific heat capacity ($c$) (238)
molar heat capacity ($C$) (238)
calorimeter (239)

**Section 6.4**
thermochemical equation (242)

**Section 6.5**
Hess's law (244)

**Section 6.6**
standard state (246)
standard enthalpy of reaction ($\Delta H_{rxn}^\circ$) (246)
formation equation (246)
standard enthalpy of formation ($\Delta H_f^\circ$) (246)
fossil fuel (249)
coal gasification (249)
synthetic natural gas (SNG) (249)
biomass conversion (249)
methanogenesis (249)
photovoltaic cell (251)

## Key Equations and Relationships    Page numbers appear in parentheses.

**6.1** Defining the change in internal energy (230):
$$\Delta E = E_{final} - E_{initial} = E_{products} - E_{reactants}$$

**6.2** Expressing the change in internal energy in terms of heat and work (231):
$$\Delta E = q + w$$

**6.3** Stating the first law of thermodynamics (law of conservation of energy) (233):
$$\Delta E_{universe} = \Delta E_{system} + \Delta E_{surroundings} = 0$$

**6.4** Determining the work due to a change in volume at constant pressure ($PV$ work) (235):
$$w = -P\Delta V$$

**6.5** Relating the enthalpy change to the internal energy change at constant pressure (235):
$$\Delta H = \Delta E + P\Delta V$$

**6.6** Identifying the enthalpy change with the heat absorbed or released at constant pressure (236):
$$q_P = \Delta E + P\Delta V = \Delta H$$

**6.7** Calculating the heat absorbed or released when a substance undergoes a temperature change or a reaction occurs (238):
$$q = c \times \text{mass} \times \Delta T$$

**6.8** Calculating the overall enthalpy change of a reaction (Hess's law) (244):
$$\Delta H_{overall} = \Delta H_1 + \Delta H_2 + \cdots + \Delta H_n$$

**6.9** Calculating the standard enthalpy of reaction (248):
$$\Delta H_{rxn}^\circ = \Sigma m \Delta H_{f(products)}^\circ - \Sigma n \Delta H_{f(reactants)}^\circ$$

## Brief Solutions to Follow-Up Problems

**6.1** $\Delta E = q + w$

$$= \left(-26.0 \text{ kcal} \times \frac{4.184 \text{ kJ}}{1 \text{ kcal}}\right) + \left(15.0 \text{ Btu} \times \frac{1.055 \text{ kJ}}{1 \text{ Btu}}\right)$$

$$= -93 \text{ kJ}$$

**6.2** The reaction is exothermic.

**6.3** $\Delta T = 25.0°C - 37.0°C = -12.0°C = -12.0 \text{ K}$

Mass (g) $= 1.11 \text{ g/mL} \times \dfrac{1000 \text{ mL}}{1 \text{ L}} \times 5.50 \text{ L} = 6.10 \times 10^3 \text{ g}$

$q = c \times \text{mass} \times \Delta T$

$$= (2.42 \text{ J/g·K})\left(\frac{1 \text{ kJ}}{1000 \text{ J}}\right)(6.10 \times 10^3 \text{ g})(-12.0 \text{ K}) = -177 \text{ kJ}$$

**6.4** $c_{\text{solid}} = -\dfrac{4.184 \text{ J/g·K} \times 25.00 \text{ g} \times 1.70 \text{ K}}{12.18 \text{ g} \times (-37.75 \text{ K})} = 0.387 \text{ J/g·K}$

From Table 6.2, the metal is copper.

**6.5** $2HCl(aq) + Ba(OH)_2(aq) \longrightarrow 2H_2O(l) + BaCl_2(aq)$

Amount (mol) of HCl $= 0.500 \text{ mol HCl/L} \times 0.0500 \text{ L} = 0.0250 \text{ mol HCl}$

Similarly, we have 0.0250 mol $BaCl_2$.

Finding the limiting reactant from the balanced equation:

Amount (mol) of $H_2O = 0.0250 \text{ mol HCl} \times \dfrac{2 \text{ mol } H_2O}{2 \text{ mol HCl}}$

$$= 0.0250 \text{ mol } H_2O$$

Amount (mol) of $H_2O = 0.0250 \text{ mol Ba(OH)}_2 \times \dfrac{2 \text{ mol } H_2O}{1 \text{ mol Ba(OH)}_2}$

$$= 0.0500 \text{ mol } H_2O$$

Thus, HCl is limiting.

$$\Delta H \text{ (kJ/mol } H_2O) = \frac{q_{\text{rxn}}}{\text{mol } H_2O} = \frac{-1.386 \text{ kJ}}{0.0250 \text{ mol } H_2O}$$

$$= -55.4 \text{ kJ/mol } H_2O$$

**6.6** $-q_{\text{sample}} = q_{\text{calorimeter}}$

$$-(0.8650 \text{ g C})\left(\frac{1 \text{ mol C}}{12.01 \text{ g C}}\right)(-393.5 \text{ kJ/mol C}) = (2.613 \text{ K})x$$

$$x = 10.85 \text{ kJ/K}$$

**6.7** $C_2H_4(g) + H_2(g) \longrightarrow C_2H_6(g) + 137 \text{ kJ}$

Heat (kJ) $= 15.0 \text{ kg} \times \dfrac{1000 \text{ g}}{1 \text{ kg}} \times \dfrac{1 \text{ mol } C_2H_6}{30.07 \text{ g } C_2H_6} \times \dfrac{137 \text{ kJ}}{1 \text{ mol}}$

$$= 6.83 \times 10^4 \text{ kJ}$$

**6.8**

$2NO(g) + \frac{3}{2}O_2(g) \longrightarrow N_2O_5(s) \qquad \Delta H = -223.7 \text{ kJ}$

$\underline{2NO_2(g) \longrightarrow 2NO(g) + O_2(g) \quad \Delta H = 114.2 \text{ kJ}}$

$\cancel{2NO(g)} + \frac{1}{2}\cancel{\frac{3}{2}}O_2(g) + 2NO_2(g) \longrightarrow$

$$N_2O_5(s) + \cancel{2NO(g)} + \cancel{O_2(g)}$$

$2NO_2(g) + \frac{1}{2}O_2(g) \longrightarrow N_2O_5(s) \qquad \Delta H = -109.5 \text{ kJ}$

**6.9** (a) $C(\text{graphite}) + 2H_2(g) + \frac{1}{2}O_2(g) \longrightarrow CH_3OH(l)$

$$\Delta H_f^\circ = -238.6 \text{ kJ}$$

(b) $Ca(s) + \frac{1}{2}O_2(g) \longrightarrow CaO(s) \quad \Delta H_f^\circ = -635.1 \text{ kJ}$

(c) $C(\text{graphite}) + \frac{1}{4}S_8(\text{rhombic}) \longrightarrow CS_2(l) \quad \Delta H_f^\circ = 87.9 \text{ kJ}$

**6.10** $\Delta H_f^\circ$ of $CH_3OH(l)$

$$= -\Delta H_{\text{rxn}}^\circ + 2\Delta H_f^\circ[H_2O(g)] + \Delta H_f^\circ[CO_2(g)]$$

$$= 638.5 \text{ kJ} + (2 \text{ mol})(-241.8 \text{ kJ/mol})$$

$$+ (1 \text{ mol})(-393.5 \text{ kJ/mol})$$

$$= -238.6 \text{ kJ}$$

---

## PROBLEMS

Problems with **colored** numbers are answered in Appendix E and worked in detail in the Student Solutions Manual. Problem sections match those in the text and provide the numbers of relevant sample problems. Most offer Concept Review Questions, Skill-Building Exercises (grouped in pairs covering the same concept), and Problems in Context. The Comprehensive Problems are based on material from any section or previous chapter.

### Forms of Energy and Their Interconversion
(Sample Problem 6.1)

**Concept Review Questions**

**6.1** Why do heat ($q$) and work ($w$) have positive values when entering a system and negative values when leaving?

**6.2** If you feel warm after exercising, have you increased the internal energy of your body? Explain.

**6.3** An *adiabatic* process is one that involves no heat transfer. What is the relationship between work and the change in internal energy in an adiabatic process?

**6.4** State two ways that you increase the internal energy of your body and two ways that you decrease it.

**6.5** Name a common device used to accomplish each change:
(a) Electrical energy to thermal energy
(b) Electrical energy to sound energy
(c) Electrical energy to light energy
(d) Mechanical energy to electrical energy
(e) Chemical energy to electrical energy

**6.6** In winter, an electric heater uses a certain amount of electrical energy to heat a room to 20°C. In summer, an air conditioner uses the same amount of electrical energy to cool the room to 20°C. Is the change in internal energy of the heater larger, smaller, or the same as that of the air conditioner? Explain.

**6.7** You lift your textbook and drop it onto a desk. Describe the energy transformations (from one form to another) that occur, moving backward in time from a moment after impact.

**Skill-Building Exercises** (grouped in similar pairs)

**6.8** A system receives 425 J of heat from and delivers 425 J of work to its surroundings. What is the change in internal energy of the system (in J)?

**6.9** A system conducts 255 cal of heat to the surroundings and delivers 428 cal of work. What is the change in internal energy of the system (in cal)?

**6.10** What is the change in internal energy (in J) of a system that releases 675 J of thermal energy to its surroundings and has 530 cal of work done on it?

**6.11** What is the change in internal energy (in J) of a system that absorbs 0.615 kJ of heat from its surroundings and has 0.247 kcal of work done on it?

**6.12** Complete combustion of 2.0 metric tons of coal to gaseous carbon dioxide releases $6.6 \times 10^{10}$ J of heat. Convert this energy to (a) kilojoules; (b) kilocalories; (c) British thermal units.

**6.13** Thermal decomposition of 5.0 metric tons of limestone to lime and carbon dioxide absorbs $9.0 \times 10^6$ kJ of heat. Convert this energy to (a) joules; (b) calories; (c) British thermal units.

**Problems in Context**

**6.14** The nutritional calorie (Calorie) is equivalent to 1 kcal. One pound of body fat is equivalent to about $4.1 \times 10^3$ Calories. Express this quantity of energy in joules and kilojoules.

**6.15** If an athlete expends 1950 kJ/h, how long does it take her to work off 1.0 lb of body fat? (See Problem 6.14.)

## Enthalpy: Chemical Change at Constant Pressure
(Sample Problem 6.2)

**Concept Review Questions**

**6.16** Why is the work done when a system expands against a constant external pressure assigned a negative sign?

**6.17** Why is it often more convenient to measure $\Delta H$ than $\Delta E$?

**6.18** "Hot packs" used by skiers use the crystallization of sodium acetate from a concentrated solution. What is the sign of $\Delta H$ for this crystallization? Is the reaction exothermic or endothermic?

**6.19** Classify the following processes as exothermic or endothermic: (a) freezing of water; (b) boiling of water; (c) digestion of food; (d) a person running; (e) a person growing; (f) wood being chopped; (g) heating with a furnace.

**6.20** What are the two main components of the internal energy of a substance? On what are they based?

**6.21** For each process, state whether $\Delta H$ is less than (more negative), equal to, or greater than $\Delta E$ of the system. Explain.
(a) An ideal gas is cooled at constant pressure.
(b) A gas mixture reacts exothermically at fixed volume.
(c) A solid reacts exothermically to yield a mixture of gases in a container of variable volume.

**Skill-Building Exercises** (grouped in similar pairs)

**6.22** Draw an enthalpy diagram for a general exothermic reaction; label the axis, reactants, products, and $\Delta H$ with its sign.

**6.23** Draw an enthalpy diagram for a general endothermic reaction; label the axis, reactants, products, and $\Delta H$ with its sign.

**6.24** Write a balanced equation and draw an approximate enthalpy diagram for: (a) combustion of 1 mol of ethane; (b) freezing of liquid water.

**6.25** Write a balanced equation and draw an approximate enthalpy diagram for (a) formation of 1 mol of sodium chloride from its elements (heat is released); (b) vaporization of liquid benzene.

**6.26** Write a balanced equation and draw an approximate enthalpy diagram for (a) combustion of 1 mol of liquid methanol ($CH_3OH$); (b) formation of 1 mol of $NO_2$ from its elements (heat is absorbed).

**6.27** Write a balanced equation and draw an approximate enthalpy diagram for (a) sublimation of dry ice [conversion of $CO_2(s)$ directly to $CO_2(g)$]; (b) reaction of 1 mol of $SO_2$ with $O_2$.

**6.28** The circles represent a phase change at constant temperature:

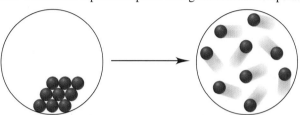

Is the value of each of the following positive (+), negative (−), or zero: (a) $q_{sys}$; (b) $\Delta E_{sys}$; (c) $\Delta E_{univ}$?

**6.29** The scenes below represent a physical change taking place in a piston-cylinder assembly:

(a) Is $w_{sys}$ +, −, or 0? (b) Is $\Delta H_{sys}$ +, −, or 0? (c) Can you determine whether $\Delta E_{surr}$ is +, −, or 0? Explain.

## Calorimetry: Measuring the Heat of a Chemical or Physical Change
(Sample Problems 6.3 to 6.6)

**Concept Review Questions**

**6.30** Which is larger, the specific heat capacity or the molar heat capacity of a substance? Explain.

**6.31** What data do you need to determine the specific heat capacity of a substance?

**6.32** Is the specific heat capacity of a substance an intensive or extensive property? Explain.

**6.33** Distinguish between specific heat capacity, molar heat capacity, and heat capacity.

**6.34** Both a coffee-cup calorimeter and a bomb calorimeter can be used to measure the heat transferred in a reaction. Which measures $\Delta E$ and which measures $\Delta H$? Explain.

**Skill-Building Exercises** (grouped in similar pairs)

**6.35** Find $q$ when 22.0 g of water is heated from 25.0°C to 100.°C.

**6.36** Calculate $q$ when 0.10 g of ice is cooled from 10.°C to −75°C ($c_{ice} = 2.087$ J/g·K).

**6.37** A 295-g aluminum engine part at an initial temperature of 13.00°C absorbs 75.0 kJ of heat. What is the final temperature of the part ($c$ of Al = 0.900 J/g·K)?

**6.38** A 27.7-g sample of the radiator coolant ethylene glycol releases 688 J of heat. What was the initial temperature of the sample if the final temperature is 32.5°C ($c$ of ethylene glycol = 2.42 J/g·K)?

**6.39** Two iron bolts of equal mass—one at 100.°C, the other at 55°C—are placed in an insulated container. Assuming the heat capacity of the container is negligible, what is the final temperature inside the container ($c$ of iron = 0.450 J/g·K)?

**6.40** One piece of copper jewelry at 105°C has twice the mass of another piece at 45°C. Both are placed in a calorimeter of negligible heat capacity. What is the final temperature inside the calorimeter ($c$ of copper = 0.387 J/g·K)?

**6.41** When 155 mL of water at 26°C is mixed with 75 mL of water at 85°C, what is the final temperature? (Assume that no heat is released to the surroundings; $d$ of water is 1.00 g/mL.)

**6.42** An unknown volume of water at 18.2°C is added to 24.4 mL of water at 35.0°C. If the final temperature is 23.5°C, what was the unknown volume? (Assume that no heat is released to the surroundings; $d$ of water is 1.00 g/mL.)

**6.43** A 455-g piece of copper tubing is heated to 89.5°C and placed in an insulated vessel containing 159 g of water at 22.8°C. Assuming no loss of water and a heat capacity of 10.0 J/K for the vessel, what is the final temperature ($c$ of copper = 0.387 J/g·K)?

**6.44** A 30.5-g sample of an alloy at 93.0°C is placed into 50.0 g of water at 22.0°C in an insulated coffee cup with a heat capacity of 9.2 J/K. If the final temperature of the system is 31.1°C, what is the specific heat capacity of the alloy?

**Problems in Context**
**6.45** High-purity benzoic acid ($C_6H_5COOH$; $\Delta H$ for combustion = −3227 kJ/mol) is used to calibrate bomb calorimeters. A 1.221-g sample burns in a calorimeter (heat capacity = 1365 J/°C) that contains 1.200 kg of water. What is the temperature change?

**6.46** Two aircraft rivets, one iron and the other copper, are placed in a calorimeter that has an initial temperature of 20.°C. The data for the rivets are as follows:

|  | Iron | Copper |
|---|---|---|
| Mass (g) | 30.0 | 20.0 |
| Initial $T$ (°C) | 0.0 | 100.0 |
| $c$ (J/g·K) | 0.450 | 0.387 |

(a) Will heat flow from Fe to Cu or from Cu to Fe?
(b) What other information is needed to correct any measurements in an actual experiment?
(c) What is the maximum final temperature of the system (assuming the heat capacity of the calorimeter is negligible)?

**6.47** A chemical engineer placed 1.520 g of a hydrocarbon in the bomb of a calorimeter (see Figure 6.10, p. 241). The bomb was immersed in 2.550 L of water and the sample was burned. The water temperature rose from 20.00°C to 23.55°C. If the calorimeter (excluding the water) had a heat capacity of 403 J/K, what was the heat released ($q_V$) per gram of hydrocarbon?

**6.48** When 25.0 mL of 0.500 $M$ $H_2SO_4$ is added to 25.0 mL of 1.00 $M$ KOH in a coffee-cup calorimeter at 23.50°C, the temperature rises to 30.17°C. Calculate $\Delta H$ of this reaction. (Assume the total volume is the sum of the volumes and the density and specific heat capacity of the solution are the same as for water.)

## Stoichiometry of Thermochemical Equations
(Sample Problem 6.7)

**Concept Review Questions**
**6.49** Does a negative $\Delta H$ mean that the heat should be treated as a reactant or as a product?

**6.50** Would you expect $O_2(g) \longrightarrow 2O(g)$ to have a positive or a negative $\Delta H$? Explain.

**6.51** Is $\Delta H$ positive or negative when 1 mol of water vapor condenses to liquid water? Why? How does this value compare with $\Delta H$ for the vaporization of 2 mol of liquid water to water vapor?

**Skill-Building Exercises** (grouped in similar pairs)
**6.52** Consider the following balanced thermochemical equation for a reaction sometimes used for $H_2S$ production:

$$\tfrac{1}{8}S_8(s) + H_2(g) \longrightarrow H_2S(g) \quad \Delta H = -20.2 \text{ kJ}$$

(a) Is this an exothermic or endothermic reaction?
(b) What is $\Delta H$ for the reverse reaction?
(c) What is $\Delta H$ when 2.6 mol of $S_8$ reacts?
(d) What is $\Delta H$ when 25.0 g of $S_8$ reacts?

**6.53** Consider the following balanced thermochemical equation for the decomposition of the mineral magnesite:

$$MgCO_3(s) \longrightarrow MgO(s) + CO_2(g) \quad \Delta H = 117.3 \text{ kJ}$$

(a) Is heat absorbed or released in the reaction?
(b) What is $\Delta H$ for the reverse reaction?
(c) What is $\Delta H$ when 5.35 mol of $CO_2$ reacts with excess MgO?
(d) What is $\Delta H$ when 35.5 g of $CO_2$ reacts with excess MgO?

**6.54** When 1 mol of NO($g$) forms from its elements, 90.29 kJ of heat is absorbed. (a) Write a balanced thermochemical equation. (b) What is $\Delta H$ when 3.50 g of NO decomposes to its elements?

**6.55** When 1 mol of KBr($s$) decomposes to its elements, 394 kJ of heat is absorbed. (a) Write a balanced thermochemical equation. (b) What is $\Delta H$ when 10.0 kg of KBr forms from its elements?

**Problems in Context**
**6.56** Liquid hydrogen peroxide, an oxidizing agent in many rocket fuel mixtures, releases oxygen gas on decomposition:

$$2H_2O_2(l) \longrightarrow 2H_2O(l) + O_2(g) \quad \Delta H = -196.1 \text{ kJ}$$

How much heat is released when 652 kg of $H_2O_2$ decomposes?

**6.57** Compounds of boron and hydrogen are remarkable for their unusual bonding (described in Section 14.5) and also for their reactivity. With the more reactive halogens, for example, diborane ($B_2H_6$) forms trihalides even at low temperatures:

$$B_2H_6(g) + 6Cl_2(g) \longrightarrow 2BCl_3(g) + 6HCl(g)$$
$$\Delta H = -755.4 \text{ kJ}$$

What is $\Delta H$ per kilogram of diborane that reacts?

**6.58** Deterioration of buildings, bridges, and other structures through the rusting of iron costs millions of dollars a day. The actual process requires water, but a simplified equation is

$$4Fe(s) + 3O_2(g) \longrightarrow 2Fe_2O_3(s) \quad \Delta H = -1.65\times10^3 \text{ kJ}$$

(a) How much heat is released when 0.250 kg of iron rusts?
(b) How much rust forms when $4.85\times10^3$ kJ of heat is released?

**6.59** A mercury mirror forms inside a test tube as a result of the thermal decomposition of mercury(II) oxide:

$$2HgO(s) \longrightarrow 2Hg(l) + O_2(g) \quad \Delta H = 181.6 \text{ kJ}$$

(a) How much heat is absorbed to decompose 555 g of the oxide?
(b) If 275 kJ of heat is absorbed, how many grams of Hg form?

**6.60** Most ethylene ($C_2H_4$), the starting material for producing polyethylene, comes from petroleum processing. It also occurs naturally as a fruit-ripening hormone and as a component of natural gas. (a) The heat transferred during combustion of $C_2H_4$ is −1411 kJ/mol. Write a balanced thermochemical equation. (b) How many grams of $C_2H_4$ must burn to give 70.0 kJ of heat?

**6.61** Sucrose ($C_{12}H_{22}O_{11}$, table sugar) is oxidized in the body by $O_2$ via a complex set of reactions that produces $CO_2(g)$ and $H_2O(g)$ and releases $5.64 \times 10^3$ kJ/mol of sucrose. (a) Write a balanced thermochemical equation for the overall process. (b) How much heat is released per gram of sucrose oxidized?

### Hess's Law: Finding $\Delta H$ of Any Reaction
(Sample Problem 6.8)

#### Concept Review Questions
**6.62** Express Hess's law in your own words.

**6.63** What is the main application of Hess's law?

**6.64** When carbon burns in a deficiency of $O_2$, a mixture of CO and $CO_2$ forms. Carbon burns in excess $O_2$ to form only $CO_2$, and CO burns in excess $O_2$ to form only $CO_2$. Use $\Delta H$ values of the latter two reactions (from Appendix B) to calculate $\Delta H$ for

$$C(\text{graphite}) + \tfrac{1}{2}O_2(g) \longrightarrow CO(g)$$

#### Skill-Building Exercises (grouped in similar pairs)
**6.65** Calculate $\Delta H$ for

$$Ca(s) + \tfrac{1}{2}O_2(g) + CO_2(g) \longrightarrow CaCO_3(s)$$

given the following reactions:

$$Ca(s) + \tfrac{1}{2}O_2(g) \longrightarrow CaO(s) \qquad \Delta H = -635.1 \text{ kJ}$$
$$CaCO_3(s) \longrightarrow CaO(s) + CO_2(g) \qquad \Delta H = 178.3 \text{ kJ}$$

**6.66** Calculate $\Delta H$ for

$$2NOCl(g) \longrightarrow N_2(g) + O_2(g) + Cl_2(g)$$

given the following reactions:

$$\tfrac{1}{2}N_2(g) + \tfrac{1}{2}O_2(g) \longrightarrow NO(g) \qquad \Delta H = 90.3 \text{ kJ}$$
$$NO(g) + \tfrac{1}{2}Cl_2(g) \longrightarrow NOCl(g) \qquad \Delta H = -38.6 \text{ kJ}$$

**6.67** Write the balanced overall equation (equation 3) for the following process, calculate $\Delta H_{\text{overall}}$, and match the number of each equation with the letter of the appropriate arrow in Figure P6.67:

| | | |
|---|---|---|
| (1) | $N_2(g) + O_2(g) \longrightarrow 2NO(g)$ | $\Delta H = 180.6$ kJ |
| (2) | $2NO(g) + O_2(g) \longrightarrow 2NO_2(g)$ | $\Delta H = -114.2$ kJ |
| (3) | | $\Delta H_{\text{overall}} = ?$ |

**6.68** Write the balanced overall equation (equation 3) for the following process, calculate $\Delta H_{\text{overall}}$, and match the number of each equation with the letter of the appropriate arrow in Figure P6.68:

| | | |
|---|---|---|
| (1) | $P_4(s) + 6Cl_2(g) \longrightarrow 4PCl_3(g)$ | $\Delta H = -1148$ kJ |
| (2) | $4PCl_3(g) + 4Cl_2(g) \longrightarrow 4PCl_5(g)$ | $\Delta H = -460$ kJ |
| (3) | | $\Delta H_{\text{overall}} = ?$ |

**Figure P6.67**

**Figure P6.68**

**6.69** At a given set of conditions, 241.8 kJ of heat is given off when 1 mol of $H_2O(g)$ forms from its elements. Under the same conditions, 285.8 kJ is given off when 1 mol of $H_2O(l)$ forms from its elements. Find $\Delta H$ for the vaporization of water at these conditions.

**6.70** When 1 mol of $CS_2(l)$ forms from its elements at 1 atm and 25°C, 89.7 kJ of heat is absorbed, and it takes 27.7 kJ to vaporize 1 mol of the liquid. How much heat is absorbed when 1 mol of $CS_2(g)$ forms from its elements at these conditions?

#### Problems in Context
**6.71** Diamond and graphite are two crystalline forms of carbon. At 1 atm and 25°C, diamond changes to graphite so slowly that the enthalpy change of the process must be obtained indirectly. Using equations from the numbered list below, determine $\Delta H$ for

$$C(\text{diamond}) \longrightarrow C(\text{graphite})$$

| | | |
|---|---|---|
| (1) | $C(\text{diamond}) + O_2(g) \longrightarrow CO_2(g)$ | $\Delta H = -395.4$ kJ |
| (2) | $2CO_2(g) \longrightarrow 2CO(g) + O_2(g)$ | $\Delta H = 566.0$ kJ |
| (3) | $C(\text{graphite}) + O_2(g) \longrightarrow CO_2(g)$ | $\Delta H = -393.5$ kJ |
| (4) | $2CO(g) \longrightarrow C(\text{graphite}) + CO_2(g)$ | $\Delta H = -172.5$ kJ |

### Standard Enthalpies of Reaction ($\Delta H^{\circ}_{\text{rxn}}$)
(Sample Problems 6.9 and 6.10)

#### Concept Review Questions
**6.72** What is the difference between the standard enthalpy of formation and the standard enthalpy of reaction?

**6.73** How are $\Delta H^{\circ}_{\text{f}}$ values used to calculate $\Delta H^{\circ}_{\text{rxn}}$?

**6.74** Make any changes needed in each of the following equations to make the enthalpy change equal to $\Delta H^{\circ}_{\text{f}}$ for the compound:
(a) $Cl(g) + Na(s) \longrightarrow NaCl(s)$
(b) $H_2O(g) \longrightarrow 2H(g) + \tfrac{1}{2}O_2(g)$
(c) $\tfrac{1}{2}N_2(g) + \tfrac{3}{2}H_2(g) \longrightarrow NH_3(g)$

#### Skill-Building Exercises (grouped in similar pairs)
**6.75** Use Table 6.3 or Appendix B to write a balanced formation equation at standard conditions for each of the following compounds: (a) $CaCl_2$; (b) $NaHCO_3$; (c) $CCl_4$; (d) $HNO_3$.

**6.76** Use Table 6.3 or Appendix B to write a balanced formation equation at standard conditions for each of the following compounds: (a) HI; (b) $SiF_4$; (c) $O_3$; (d) $Ca_3(PO_4)_2$.

**6.77** Calculate $\Delta H^{\circ}_{\text{rxn}}$ for each of the following:
(a) $2H_2S(g) + 3O_2(g) \longrightarrow 2SO_2(g) + 2H_2O(g)$
(b) $CH_4(g) + Cl_2(g) \longrightarrow CCl_4(l) + HCl(g)$ [unbalanced]

**6.78** Calculate $\Delta H^{\circ}_{\text{rxn}}$ for each of the following:
(a) $SiO_2(s) + 4HF(g) \longrightarrow SiF_4(g) + 2H_2O(l)$
(b) $C_2H_6(g) + O_2(g) \longrightarrow CO_2(g) + H_2O(g)$ [unbalanced]

**6.79** Copper(I) oxide can be oxidized to copper(II) oxide:

$$Cu_2O(s) + \tfrac{1}{2}O_2(g) \longrightarrow 2CuO(s) \quad \Delta H^{\circ}_{\text{rxn}} = -146.0 \text{ kJ}$$

Given $\Delta H^{\circ}_{\text{f}}$ of $Cu_2O(s) = -168.6$ kJ/mol, find $\Delta H^{\circ}_{\text{f}}$ of $CuO(s)$.

**6.80** Acetylene burns in air by the following equation:

$$C_2H_2(g) + \tfrac{5}{2}O_2(g) \longrightarrow 2CO_2(g) + H_2O(g)$$
$$\Delta H^{\circ}_{\text{rxn}} = -1255.8 \text{ kJ}$$

Given $\Delta H^{\circ}_{\text{f}}$ of $CO_2(g) = -393.5$ kJ/mol and $\Delta H^{\circ}_{\text{f}}$ of $H_2O(g) = -241.8$ kJ/mol, find $\Delta H^{\circ}_{\text{f}}$ of $C_2H_2(g)$.

#### Problems in Context
**6.81** The common lead-acid car battery produces a large burst of current, even at low temperatures, and is rechargeable. The reaction that occurs while recharging a "dead" battery is

$$2PbSO_4(s) + 2H_2O(l) \longrightarrow Pb(s) + PbO_2(s) + 2H_2SO_4(l)$$

(a) Use $\Delta H^{\circ}_{\text{f}}$ values from Appendix B to calculate $\Delta H^{\circ}_{\text{rxn}}$.
(b) Use the following equations to check your answer to part (a):

(1) $Pb(s) + PbO_2(s) + 2SO_3(g) \longrightarrow 2PbSO_4(s)$

$$\Delta H^\circ_{rxn} = -768 \text{ kJ}$$

(2) $SO_3(g) + H_2O(l) \longrightarrow H_2SO_4(l)$ $\quad \Delta H^\circ_{rxn} = -132 \text{ kJ}$

## Comprehensive Problems

**6.82** Stearic acid ($C_{18}H_{36}O_2$) is a fatty acid, a molecule with a long hydrocarbon chain and an organic acid group (COOH) at the end. It is used to make cosmetics, ointments, soaps, and candles and is found in animal tissue as part of many saturated fats. In fact, when you eat meat, you are ingesting some fats containing stearic acid. (a) Write a balanced equation for the combustion of stearic acid to gaseous products. (b) Calculate $\Delta H^\circ_{rxn}$ for this combustion ($\Delta H^\circ_f$ of $C_{18}H_{36}O_2 = -948 \text{ kJ/mol}$). (c) Calculate the heat ($q$) released in kJ and kcal when 1.00 g of stearic acid is burned completely. (d) A candy bar contains 11.0 g of fat and 100. Cal from fat; is this consistent with your answer for part (c)?

**6.83** Diluting sulfuric acid with water is highly exothermic:

$$H_2SO_4(l) \xrightarrow{H_2O} H_2SO_4(aq) + heat$$

(a) Use Appendix B to find $\Delta H^\circ_{rxn}$ for diluting 1.00 mol of $H_2SO_4(l)$ ($d = 1.83 \text{ g/mL}$) to 1 L of 1.00 $M$ $H_2SO_4(aq)$ ($d = 1.060 \text{ g/mL}$). (b) Suppose you carry out the dilution in a calorimeter. The initial $T$ is 25.0°C, and the specific heat capacity of the final solution is 3.50 J/g·K. What is the final $T$? (c) Use the ideas of density and heat capacity to explain why you should add acid to water rather than water to acid.

**6.84** A balloonist begins a trip in a helium-filled balloon in early morning when the temperature is 15°C. By mid-afternoon, the temperature is 30.°C. Assuming the pressure remains at 1.00 atm, for each mole of helium, calculate the following: (a) The initial and final volumes (b) The change in internal energy, $\Delta E$ (*Hint:* Helium behaves like an ideal gas, so $E = \frac{3}{2}nRT$. Be sure the units of $R$ are consistent with those of $E$.) (c) The work ($w$) done by the helium (in J) (d) The heat ($q$) transferred (in J) (e) $\Delta H$ for the process (in J) (f) Explain the relationship between the answers to parts (d) and (e).

**6.85** In winemaking, the sugars in grapes undergo *fermentation* by yeast to yield $CH_3CH_2OH$ and $CO_2$. During cellular *respiration* (combustion), sugar and ethanol yield water vapor and $CO_2$. (a) Using $C_6H_{12}O_6$ for sugar, calculate $\Delta H^\circ_{rxn}$ of fermentation and of respiration. (b) Write a combustion reaction for ethanol. Which has a higher $\Delta H^\circ_{rxn}$ for combustion per mole of C, sugar or ethanol?

**6.86** Three of the reactions that occur when the paraffin of a candle (typical formula $C_{21}H_{44}$) burns are as follows: (1) Complete combustion forms $CO_2$ and water vapor. (2) Incomplete combustion forms CO and water vapor. (3) Some wax is oxidized to elemental C (soot) and water vapor. (a) Find $\Delta H^\circ_{rxn}$ of each reaction ($\Delta H^\circ_f$ of $C_{21}H_{44} = -476 \text{ kJ/mol}$; use graphite for elemental carbon). (b) Find $q$ (in kJ) when a 254-g candle burns completely. (c) Find $q$ (in kJ) when 8.00% by mass of the candle burns incompletely and 5.00% by mass of it undergoes soot formation.

**6.87** Ethylene oxide (EO) is prepared by the vapor-phase oxidation of ethylene. Its main uses are in the preparation of the antifreeze ethylene glycol and in the production of poly(ethylene terephtha-late), which is used to make beverage bottles and fibers. Pure EO vapor can decompose explosively:

Liquid EO has $\Delta H^\circ_f = -77.4 \text{ kJ/mol}$ and $\Delta H^\circ$ for its vaporization = 569.4 J/g. (a) Calculate $\Delta H^\circ_{rxn}$ for the gas-phase reaction. (b) External heating causes the vapor to decompose at 10 bar and 93°C in a distillation column. What is the final temperature if the average specific heat capacity of the products is 2.5 J/g·°C?

**6.88** The following scenes represent a gaseous reaction between compounds of nitrogen (blue) and oxygen (red) at 298 K:

(a) Write a balanced equation and use Appendix B to calculate $\Delta H^\circ_{rxn}$. (b) If each molecule of product represents $1.50 \times 10^{-2}$ mol, what quantity of heat (in J) is released or absorbed?

**6.89** Isooctane ($C_8H_{18}$; $d = 0.692 \text{ g/mL}$) is used as the fuel in a test of a new automobile drive train. (a) How much energy (in kJ) is released by combustion of 20.4 gal of isooctane to gases ($\Delta H^\circ_{rxn} = -5.44 \times 10^3 \text{ kJ/mol}$)? (b) The energy delivered to the wheels at 65 mph is $5.5 \times 10^4$ kJ/h. Assuming *all* the energy is transferred as work to the wheels, how far (in km) can the car travel on the 20.4 gal of fuel? (c) If the actual range is 455 miles, explain your answer to (b).

**6.90** Four 50.-g samples of different colorless liquids are placed in beakers at $T_{initial} = 25.00°C$. Each liquid is heated until 450. J of heat has been absorbed; $T_{final}$ is shown on each beaker below. Rank the liquids in order of increasing specific heat capacity.

| 27.15°C | 35.59°C | 28.96°C | 30.29°C |
|---------|---------|---------|---------|
| A | B | C | D |

**6.91** Reaction of gaseous ClF with $F_2$ yields liquid $ClF_3$, an important fluorinating agent. Use the following thermochemical equations to calculate $\Delta H^\circ_{rxn}$ for this reaction: (1) $2ClF(g) + O_2(g) \longrightarrow Cl_2O(g) + OF_2(g)$ $\quad \Delta H^\circ_{rxn} = 167.5 \text{ kJ}$ (2) $2F_2(g) + O_2(g) \longrightarrow 2OF_2(g)$ $\quad \Delta H^\circ_{rxn} = -43.5 \text{ kJ}$ (3) $2ClF_3(l) + 2O_2(g) \longrightarrow Cl_2O(g) + 3OF_2(g)$

$$\Delta H^\circ_{rxn} = 394.1 \text{ kJ}$$

**6.92** Silver bromide is used to coat ordinary black-and-white photographic film, while high-speed film uses silver iodide. (a) When 50.0 mL of 5.0 g/L $AgNO_3$ is added to a coffee-cup calorimeter containing 50.0 mL of 5.0 g/L NaI, with both solutions at 25°C, what mass of AgI forms? (b) Use Appendix B to find $\Delta H^\circ_{rxn}$. (c) What is $\Delta T_{soln}$ (assuming the volumes are additive and the solution has the density and specific heat capacity of water)?

**6.93** The calorie (4.184 J) is defined as the quantity of energy needed to raise the temperature of 1.00 g of liquid water 1.00°C. The British thermal unit (Btu) is defined as the quantity of energy needed to raise the temperature of 1.00 lb of liquid water 1.00°F.
(a) How many joules are in 1.00 Btu (1 lb = 453.6 g; 1.0°C = 1.8°F)?
(b) The *therm* is a unit of energy consumption and is defined as 100,000 Btu. How many joules are in 1.00 therm?
(c) How many moles of methane must be burned to give 1.00 therm of energy? (Assume water forms as a gas.)
(d) If natural gas costs $0.66 per therm, what is the cost per mole of methane? (Assume natural gas is pure methane.)
(e) How much would it cost to warm 318 gal of water in a hot tub from 15.0°C to 42.0°C by burning methane (1 gal = 3.78 L)?

**6.94** When organic matter decomposes under oxygen-free (anaerobic) conditions, methane is one of the products. Thus, enormous deposits of natural gas, which is almost entirely methane, serve as a major source of fuel for home and industry.
(a) Known deposits of natural gas can produce 5600 EJ of energy (1 EJ = $10^{18}$ J). Current total global energy usage is $4.0 \times 10^2$ EJ per year. Find the mass (in kg) of known deposits of natural gas ($\Delta H^\circ_{rxn}$ for the combustion of $CH_4 = -802$ kJ/mol).
(b) At current rates of usage, for how many years could these deposits supply the world's total energy needs?
(c) What volume (in $ft^3$) of natural gas, measured at STP, is required to heat 1.00 qt of water from 25.0°C to 100.0°C (*d* of $H_2O$ = 1.00 g/mL; *d* of $CH_4$ at STP = 0.72 g/L)?
(d) The fission of 1 mol of uranium (about $4 \times 10^{-4}$ $ft^3$) in a nuclear reactor produces $2 \times 10^{13}$ J. What volume (in $ft^3$) of natural gas would produce the same amount of energy?

**6.95** A reaction takes place in a steel vessel within a chamber filled with argon gas. Shown below are molecular views of the argon adjacent to the surface of the reaction vessel before and after the reaction. Was the reaction exothermic or endothermic? Explain.

**6.96** An aqueous waste stream with a maximum concentration of 0.50 *M* $H_2SO_4$ (*d* = 1.030 g/mL at 25°C) is neutralized by controlled addition of 40% NaOH (*d* = 1.430 g/L) before it goes to the process sewer and then to the chemical plant waste treatment facility. A safety review finds that the waste stream could meet a small stream of an immiscible organic compound, which could form a flammable vapor in air at 40.°C. The maximum temperature reached by the NaOH solution and the waste stream is 31°C. Could the temperature increase due to the heat transferred by the neutralization cause the organic vapor to explode? Assume the specific heat capacity of each solution is 4.184 J/g·K.

**6.97** Kerosene, a common space-heater fuel, is a mixture of hydrocarbons whose "average" formula is $C_{12}H_{26}$.
(a) Write a balanced equation, using the simplest whole-number coefficients, for the complete combustion of kerosene to gases.
(b) If $\Delta H^\circ_{rxn} = -1.50 \times 10^4$ kJ for the combustion equation as written in part (a), determine $\Delta H^\circ_f$ of kerosene.
(c) Calculate the heat released by combustion of 0.50 gal of kerosene (*d* of kerosene = 0.749 g/mL).

(d) How many gallons of kerosene must be burned for a kerosene furnace to produce 1250. Btu (1 Btu = 1.055 kJ)?

**6.98** Silicon tetrachloride is produced annually on the multikiloton scale and used in making transistor-grade silicon. It can be produced directly from the elements (reaction 1) or, more cheaply, by heating sand and graphite with chlorine gas (reaction 2). If water is present in reaction 2, some tetrachloride may be lost in an unwanted side reaction (reaction 3):
(1) $Si(s) + 2Cl_2(g) \longrightarrow SiCl_4(g)$
(2) $SiO_2(s) + 2C(graphite) + 2Cl_2(g) \longrightarrow SiCl_4(g) + 2CO(g)$
(3) $SiCl_4(g) + 2H_2O(g) \longrightarrow SiO_2(s) + 4HCl(g)$
$$\Delta H^\circ_{rxn} = -139.5 \text{ kJ}$$
(a) Use reaction 3 to calculate the standard enthalpies of reaction of reactions 1 and 2. (b) What is the standard enthalpy of reaction for a fourth reaction that is the sum of reactions 2 and 3?

**6.99** One mole of nitrogen gas confined within a cylinder by a piston is heated from 0°C to 819°C at 1.00 atm.
(a) Calculate the work done by the expanding gas in joules (1 J = $9.87 \times 10^{-3}$ atm·L). Assume all the energy is used to do work.
(b) What would be the temperature change if the gas were heated using the same amount of energy in a container of fixed volume? (Assume the specific heat capacity of $N_2$ is 1.00 J/g·K.)

**6.100** The chemistry of nitrogen oxides is very versatile. Given the following reactions and their standard enthalpy changes,
(1) $NO(g) + NO_2(g) \longrightarrow N_2O_3(g)$   $\Delta H^\circ_{rxn} = -39.8$ kJ
(2) $NO(g) + NO_2(g) + O_2(g) \longrightarrow N_2O_5(g)$   $\Delta H^\circ_{rxn} = -112.5$ kJ
(3) $2NO_2(g) \longrightarrow N_2O_4(g)$   $\Delta H^\circ_{rxn} = -57.2$ kJ
(4) $2NO(g) + O_2(g) \longrightarrow 2NO_2(g)$   $\Delta H^\circ_{rxn} = -114.2$ kJ
(5) $N_2O_5(s) \longrightarrow N_2O_5(g)$   $\Delta H^\circ_{rxn} = 54.1$ kJ
calculate the standard enthalpy of reaction for
$$N_2O_3(g) + N_2O_5(s) \longrightarrow 2N_2O_4(g)$$

**6.101** Electric generating plants transport large amounts of hot water through metal pipes, and oxygen dissolved in the water can cause a major corrosion problem. Hydrazine ($N_2H_4$) added to the water avoids the problem by reacting with the oxygen:
$$N_2H_4(aq) + O_2(g) \longrightarrow N_2(g) + 2H_2O(l)$$
About $4 \times 10^7$ kg of hydrazine is produced every year by reacting ammonia with sodium hypochlorite in the *Raschig process*:
$$2NH_3(aq) + NaOCl(aq) \longrightarrow N_2H_4(aq) + NaCl(aq) + H_2O(l)$$
$$\Delta H^\circ_{rxn} = -151 \text{ kJ}$$
(a) If $\Delta H^\circ_f$ of NaOCl(aq) = $-346$ kJ/mol, find $\Delta H^\circ_f$ of $N_2H_4(aq)$.
(b) What is the heat released when aqueous $N_2H_4$ is added to $5.00 \times 10^3$ L of water that is $2.50 \times 10^{-4}$ *M* $O_2$?

**6.102** Liquid methanol ($CH_3OH$) can be used as an alternative fuel in pickup and SUV engines. An industrial method for preparing it involves the catalytic hydrogenation of carbon monoxide:
$$CO(g) + 2H_2(g) \xrightarrow{catalyst} CH_3OH(l)$$
How much heat (in kJ) is released when 15.0 L of CO at 85°C and 112 kPa reacts with 18.5 L of $H_2$ at 75°C and 744 torr?

**6.103** (a) How much heat is released when 25.0 g of methane burns in excess $O_2$ to form gaseous $CO_2$ and $H_2O$?
(b) Calculate the temperature of the product mixture if the methane and air are both at an initial temperature of 0.0°C. Assume a stoichiometric ratio of methane to oxygen from the air, with air being 21% $O_2$ by volume (*c* of $CO_2$ = 57.2 J/mol·K; *c* of $H_2O(g)$ = 36.0 J/mol·K; *c* of $N_2$ = 30.5 J/mol·K).

# Quantum Theory and Atomic Structure

## Concepts and skills to review before you study this chapter

- discovery of the electron and atomic nucleus (Section 2.4)
- major features of atomic structure (Section 2.5)
- changes in the energy state of a system (Section 6.1)

Over a few remarkable decades—from around 1890 to 1930—a number of revolutions took place in Western science and culture. ● One concerned our view of matter and energy, and you demonstrate it with every flick of a light switch (*photo*). That new view is essential for understanding TV screens, fireworks, and neon signs, not to mention the structure of the atom! But revolutions in science are not the violent upheavals of political overthrow. Flaws appear in a model due to conflicting evidence, a startling discovery widens the flaws into cracks, and the theoretical structure crumbles. Then, new insight, verified by experiment, builds a model more consistent with reality. So it was when Lavoisier's theory of combustion overthrew the phlogiston model, when Dalton's atomic theory established the idea of individual units of matter, and when Rutherford's model substituted nuclear atoms for "billiard balls" or "plum puddings." You will see this process unfold again as we discuss the development of modern atomic theory.

**IN THIS CHAPTER . . .** We discuss quantum mechanics, the theory that explains the fundamental nature of energy and matter and accounts for atomic structure.
- We consider the classical distinction between the wave properties of energy and the particle properties of matter.
- We then examine two observations—blackbody radiation and the photoelectric effect—whose explanations led to a *quantized*, or particulate, model of light.
- We see that light emitted by excited atoms—an *atomic spectrum*—suggests an atom with distinct energy levels, and we apply spectra to chemical analysis.
- We see how wave-particle duality, which shows that matter and energy have similar properties, and the uncertainty principle, which proposes that electron behavior can never be known exactly, led to the current model of the H atom.
- We present quantum numbers, which specify the size, shape, and orientation of atomic orbitals, the regions an electron occupies in the H atom. (In Chapter 8, we'll examine quantum numbers for atoms with more than one electron.)

● **A Time of Revolution** Here are some of the revolutionary discoveries and events witnessed by the Western world during those decades:

1895 Röntgen: discovery of x-rays
1896 Becquerel: discovery of radioactivity
1897 Thomson: discovery of the electron
1900 Freud: theory of the unconscious
1900 Planck: quantum theory
1901 Marconi: invention of the radio
1903 Wright brothers: flight of a plane
1905 Ford: assembly line to build cars
1905 Rutherford: radioactivity explained
1905 Einstein: relativity/photon theories
1906 St. Denis: modern dance
1908 Matisse/Picasso: modern art
1909 Schoenberg/Berg: modern music
1911 Rutherford: nuclear model
1913 Bohr: atomic spectra and new model
1914–1918: World War I
1923 Compton: photon momentum
1924 De Broglie: wave theory of matter
1926 Schrödinger: wave equation
1927 Heisenberg: uncertainty principle

# 7.1 • THE NATURE OF LIGHT

Visible light, x-rays, and microwaves are some of the types of **electromagnetic radiation** (also called *electromagnetic energy* or *radiant energy*). All electromagnetic radiation consists of energy propagated by electric and magnetic fields that increase and decrease in intensity as they move through space. This *classical wave model* explains why rainbows form, how magnifying glasses work, and many other familiar observations. But, it cannot explain observations on the very *un*familiar atomic scale. In this section, we describe some properties of electromagnetic radiation and note how they are distinguished from the properties of matter. But, then, we see that some other properties blur that distinction and require a new model to explain them.

## The Wave Nature of Light

The wave properties of electromagnetic radiation are described by three variables and one constant (Figure 7.1, *next page*):

1. *Frequency* ($\nu$, Greek *nu*). The **frequency** of a wave is the number of cycles it undergoes per second, expressed by the unit 1/second [$s^{-1}$; also called a *hertz* (Hz)].

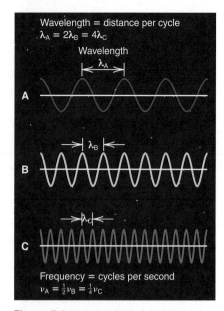

**Figure 7.1** The reciprocal relationship of frequency and wavelength.

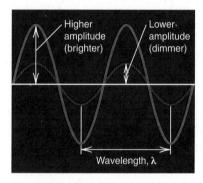

**Figure 7.2** Differing amplitude (brightness, or intensity) of a wave.

2. *Wavelength* ($\lambda$, Greek *lambda*). The **wavelength** is the distance between any point on a wave and the corresponding point on the next crest (or trough) of the wave, that is, the distance the wave travels during one cycle. Wavelength has units of meters or, for very short wavelengths, nanometers (nm, $10^{-9}$ m), picometers (pm, $10^{-12}$ m), or the non-SI unit angstroms (Å, $10^{-10}$ m).

3. *Speed*. The speed of a wave is the distance it moves per unit time (meters per second), the product of its frequency (cycles per second) and wavelength (meters per cycle):

$$\text{Units for speed of wave:} \quad \frac{\cancel{\text{cycles}}}{\text{s}} \times \frac{\text{m}}{\cancel{\text{cycle}}} = \frac{\text{m}}{\text{s}}$$

In a vacuum, electromagnetic radiation moves at $2.99792458 \times 10^8$ m/s ($3.00 \times 10^8$ m/s to three significant figures), a *physical constant* called the **speed of light** ($c$):

$$c = \nu \times \lambda \tag{7.1}$$

Since the product of $\nu$ and $\lambda$ is a constant, they have a reciprocal relationship—*radiation with a high frequency has a short wavelength, and vice versa*:

$$\nu \uparrow \lambda \downarrow \quad \text{and} \quad \nu \downarrow \lambda \uparrow$$

4. *Amplitude*. The **amplitude** of a wave is the height of the crest (or depth of the trough). For an electromagnetic wave, the amplitude is related to the *intensity* of the radiation, or its brightness in the case of visible light. Light of a particular color has a specific frequency (and thus, wavelength) but, as Figure 7.2 shows, it can be dimmer (lower amplitude, less intense) or brighter (higher amplitude, more intense).

**The Electromagnetic Spectrum** Visible light represents a small region of the **electromagnetic spectrum** (Figure 7.3). *All waves in the spectrum travel at the same speed through a vacuum but differ in frequency and, therefore, wavelength.*

The spectrum is a *continuum of radiant energy,* so each region meets the next. For instance, the **infrared (IR)** region meets the *microwave* region on one end and the *visible* region on the other. We perceive different wavelengths (or frequencies) of visible light as colors, from red ($\lambda \approx 750$ nm) to violet ($\lambda \approx 400$ nm). Light of a single wavelength is called *monochromatic* (Greek, "one color"), whereas light of many wavelengths is *polychromatic*. White light is polychromatic. The region adjacent to visible light on the short-wavelength end consists of **ultraviolet (UV)** radiation (also called *ultraviolet light*). Still shorter wavelengths (higher frequencies) make up the x-ray and gamma ($\gamma$) ray regions.

Some types of electromagnetic radiation are utilized by familiar devices; for example, long-wavelength, low-frequency radiation is used by microwave ovens, radios, and cell phones. But electromagnetic emissions are everywhere: coming from

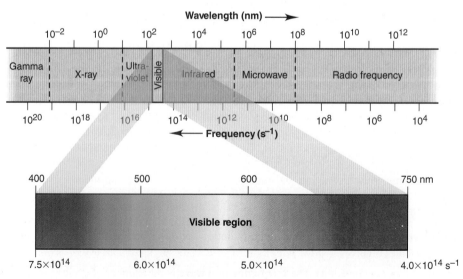

**Figure 7.3** Regions of the electromagnetic spectrum. The visible region is expanded (and the scale made linear) to show the component colors.

human artifacts such as lightbulbs, x-ray equipment, and car motors, and from natural sources such as the Sun, lightning, radioactivity, and even the glow of fireflies! Our knowledge of the universe comes from radiation entering our eyes and our light, x-ray, and radio telescopes.

---

## Sample Problem 7.1   Interconverting Wavelength and Frequency

**Problem**  A dental hygienist uses x-rays ($\lambda = 1.00$ Å) to take a series of dental radiographs while the patient listens to a radio station ($\lambda = 325$ cm) and looks out the window at the blue sky ($\lambda = 473$ nm). What is the frequency (in $s^{-1}$) of the electromagnetic radiation from each source? (Assume that the radiation travels at the speed of light, $3.00 \times 10^8$ m/s.)

**Plan**  We are given the wavelengths, so we use Equation 7.1 to find the frequencies. However, we must first convert the wavelengths to meters because $c$ has units of m/s.

**Solution**  For the x-rays: Converting from angstroms to meters,

$$\lambda = 1.00 \text{ Å} \times \frac{10^{-10} \text{ m}}{1 \text{ Å}} = 1.00 \times 10^{-10} \text{ m}$$

Calculating the frequency:

$$\nu = \frac{c}{\lambda} = \frac{3.00 \times 10^8 \text{ m/s}}{1.00 \times 10^{-10} \text{ m}} = \boxed{3.00 \times 10^{18} \text{ s}^{-1}}$$

For the radio signal: Combining steps to calculate the frequency,

$$\nu = \frac{c}{\lambda} = \frac{3.00 \times 10^8 \text{ m/s}}{325 \text{ cm} \times \dfrac{10^{-2} \text{ m}}{1 \text{ cm}}} = \boxed{9.23 \times 10^7 \text{ s}^{-1}}$$

For the blue sky: Combining steps to calculate the frequency,

$$\nu = \frac{c}{\lambda} = \frac{3.00 \times 10^8 \text{ m/s}}{473 \text{ nm} \times \dfrac{10^{-9} \text{ m}}{1 \text{ nm}}} = \boxed{6.34 \times 10^{14} \text{ s}^{-1}}$$

**Check**  The orders of magnitude are correct for the regions of the electromagnetic spectrum (see Figure 7.3): x-rays ($10^{19}$ to $10^{16}$ $s^{-1}$), radio waves ($10^9$ to $10^4$ $s^{-1}$), and visible light ($7.5 \times 10^{14}$ to $4.0 \times 10^{14}$ $s^{-1}$).

**Comment**  The radio station here is broadcasting at $92.3 \times 10^6$ $s^{-1}$, or 92.3 million Hz (92.3 MHz), about midway in the FM range.

**Road Map**

Wavelength (given units)

↓  $1 \text{ Å} = 10^{-10}$ m
$1 \text{ cm} = 10^{-2}$ m
$1 \text{ nm} = 10^{-9}$ m

Wavelength (m)

↓  $\nu = \dfrac{c}{\lambda}$

Frequency ($s^{-1}$, or Hz)

**Follow-Up Problem 7.1**  Some diamonds appear yellow because they contain nitrogen compounds that absorb purple light of frequency $7.23 \times 10^{14}$ Hz. Calculate the wavelength (in nm and Å) of the absorbed light.

---

**The Classical Distinction Between Energy and Matter**  In our everyday world, matter comes in chunks you can hold and weigh, and you can change the quantity of matter piece by piece. In contrast, energy is "massless," and its quantity can change continuously. Matter moves in specific paths, whereas radiant energy (light) travels in diffuse waves. Let's examine some distinctions between the behavior of waves of energy and particles of matter.

1. *Refraction and dispersion.* Light of a given wavelength travels at different speeds through various transparent media—vacuum, air, water, quartz, and so forth. Therefore, when a light wave passes from one medium into another, the speed of the wave changes. Figure 7.4A on the next page shows the phenomenon known as **refraction.** If the wave strikes the boundary between media, say, between air and water, at an angle other than 90°, the change in speed causes a change in direction, and the wave continues at a different angle. The angle of refraction depends on the two media and the wavelength of the light. In the related process of *dispersion,* white light separates (disperses) into its component colors when it passes through a prism (or other refracting object) because each incoming wave is refracted at a slightly different angle.

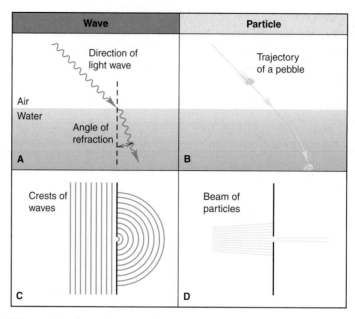

**Figure 7.4 Different behaviors of waves and particles. A,** Refraction: The speed of a light wave passing between media changes immediately, which bends its path. **B,** The speed of a particle continues changing gradually. **C,** Diffraction: A wave bends around both edges of a small opening, forming a semicircular wave. **D,** Particles either enter a small opening or not.

*In contrast* to a wave of light, a particle of matter, like a pebble, does not undergo refraction. If you throw a pebble through the air into a pond, it continues to slow down gradually along a curved path after entering the water (Figure 7.4B).

Two of many familiar applications of refraction and dispersion involve rainbows and diamonds. You see a rainbow when sunlight entering the near surface of a droplet is dispersed and reflected off the far surface. Red light is bent least, so it appears higher in the sky and violet lower *(see photo).* A diamond's color sparkles because its facets disperse and reflect the incoming light.

2. *Diffraction and interference.* When a wave strikes the edge of an object, it bends around it in a phenomenon called **diffraction.** If the wave passes through a slit about as wide as its wavelength, it bends around both edges of the slit and forms a semicircular wave on the other side of the opening (Figure 7.4C).

*In contrast,* when you throw a collection of particles, like a handful of sand, at a small opening, some particles hit the edge, while others go through the opening and continue in a narrower group (Figure 7.4D).

When waves of light pass through two adjacent slits, the nearby emerging circular waves interact through the process of *interference.* If the crests of the waves coincide *(in phase),* they interfere *constructively*—the amplitudes add together to form a brighter region. If crests coincide with troughs *(out of phase),* they interfere *destructively*—the amplitudes cancel to form a darker region. The result is a *diffraction pattern* (Figure 7.5).

*In contrast,* particles passing through adjacent openings continue in straight paths, some colliding and moving at different angles.

How does wave theory explain rainbows?

## The Particle Nature of Light

Three observations involving matter and light confounded physicists at the turn of the 20th century: blackbody radiation, the photoelectric effect, and atomic spectra. Explaining these phenomena required a radically new picture of energy. We discuss the first two of them here and the third in Section 7.2.

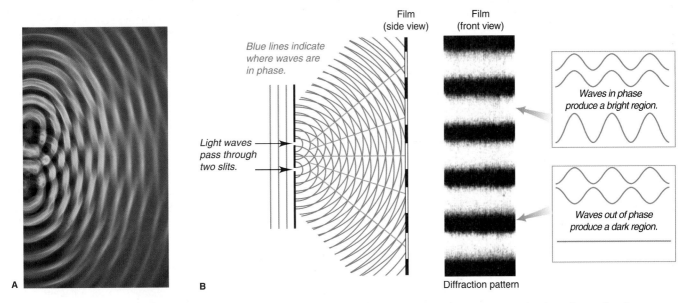

Film (side view)

Film (front view)

Blue lines indicate where waves are in phase.

Light waves pass through two slits.

Waves in phase produce a bright region.

Waves out of phase produce a dark region.

Diffraction pattern

**Figure 7.5 Formation of a diffraction pattern. A,** Constructive interference and destructive interference occur as water waves pass through two adjacent slits. **B,** Light waves passing through two slits also emerge as circular waves and create a diffraction pattern.

**Blackbody Radiation and the Quantum Theory of Energy** The first of the puzzling observations involved the light given off by an object being heated.

- *Observation: blackbody radiation.* When a solid object is heated to about 1000 K, it begins to emit visible light, as you can see in the red glow of smoldering coal (Figure 7.6A). At about 1500 K, the light is brighter and more orange, like that from an electric heating coil (Figure 7.6B). At temperatures greater than 2000 K, the light is still brighter and whiter, like that emitted by the filament of a lightbulb (Figure 7.6C). These changes in intensity and wavelength of emitted light as an object is heated are characteristic of *blackbody radiation,* light given off by a hot *blackbody.** All attempts to account for these changes by applying classical electromagnetic theory failed.
- *Explanation: the quantum theory.* In 1900, the German physicist Max Planck (1858–1947) developed a formula that fit the data perfectly. To find a physical explanation for his formula, Planck assumed, in a self-proclaimed "act of despair," that the hot, glowing object could emit (or absorb) only *certain* quantities of energy:

$$E = nh\nu$$

---

*A blackbody is an idealized object that absorbs all the radiation incident on it. A hollow cube with a small hole in one wall approximates a blackbody.

**A Smoldering coal**

**B Electric heating element**

**C Lightbulb filament**

**Figure 7.6** Familiar examples of light emission related to blackbody radiation.

where $E$ is the energy of the radiation, $\nu$ is its frequency, $n$ is a positive integer (1, 2, 3, and so on) called a **quantum number,** and $h$ is **Planck's constant.** With energy in joules (J) and frequency in $s^{-1}$, $h$ has units of J·s:

$$h = 6.62606876 \times 10^{-34} \text{ J·s} = 6.626 \times 10^{-34} \text{ J·s} \quad \text{(4 sf)}$$

Since the hot object emits only certain quantities of energy, and the energy must be emitted by the object's atoms, this means that each atom *emits* only certain quantities of energy. It follows, then, that each atom *has* only certain quantities of energy. Thus, the energy of an atom is *quantized:* it occurs in fixed quantities, rather than being continuous. Each change in an atom's energy occurs when the atom absorbs or emits one or more "packets," or definite amounts, of energy. Each energy packet is called a **quantum** ("fixed quantity"; plural, *quanta*). A quantum of energy is equal to $h\nu$. Thus, *an atom changes its energy state by emitting (or absorbing) one or more quanta,* and the energy of the emitted (or absorbed) radiation is equal to the *difference in the atom's energy states:*

$$\Delta E_{\text{atom}} = E_{\text{emitted (or absorbed) radiation}} = \Delta n h\nu$$

Because the atom can change its energy only by integer multiples of $h\nu$, the smallest change occurs when an atom in a given energy state changes to an adjacent state, that is, when $\Delta n = 1$:

$$\Delta E = h\nu \qquad \text{(7.2)}$$

**The Photoelectric Effect and the Photon Theory of Light** Despite the idea of quantization, physicists still pictured energy as traveling in waves. But, the wave model could not explain the second confusing observation, the flow of current when light strikes a metal.

- *Observation: the **photoelectric effect.*** When monochromatic light of sufficient frequency shines on a metal plate, a current flows (Figure 7.7). It was thought that the current arises because light transfers energy that frees electrons from the metal surface. However, the effect had two confusing features, the presence of a threshold frequency and the absence of a time lag:
  1. *Presence of a threshold frequency.* For current to flow, the light shining on the metal must have a minimum, or threshold, *frequency,* and different metals have different minimum frequencies. But, the wave theory associates the energy of light with its *amplitude* (intensity), not its frequency (color). Thus, the theory predicts that an electron would break free when it absorbed enough energy from light of *any* color.
  2. *Absence of a time lag.* Current flows the moment light of the minimum frequency shines on the metal, regardless of the light's intensity. But the wave theory predicts that with dim light there would be a time lag before the current flows, because the electrons would have to absorb enough energy to break free.

- *Explanation: the photon theory.* Building on Planck's ideas, Einstein proposed that light itself is particulate, quantized into tiny "bundles" of energy, later called **photons.** Each atom changes its energy, $\Delta E_{\text{atom}}$, when it absorbs or emits one photon, one "particle" of light, whose energy is related to its *frequency,* not its amplitude:

$$E_{\text{photon}} = h\nu = \Delta E_{\text{atom}}$$

Let's see how the photon theory explains the two features of the photoelectric effect:

1. *Why there is a threshold frequency.* A beam of light consists of an enormous number of photons. The intensity (brightness) is related to the *number* of photons, but *not* to the energy of each. Therefore, a photon of a certain *minimum* energy must be absorbed to free an electron from the surface (see Figure 7.7). Since energy depends on frequency ($h\nu$), the theory predicts a threshold frequency.
2. *Why there is no time lag.* An electron breaks free when it absorbs a photon of *enough* energy; it cannot break free by "saving up" energy from several photons, each having less than the minimum energy. The current is weak in dim light because fewer photons of enough energy can free fewer electrons per unit time, but some current flows *as soon as* light of sufficient energy (frequency) strikes the metal. ●

Incoming light strikes the metal surface.

Evacuated tube

$h\nu$

Freed electrons travel to the electrode and produce a current.

Metal plate

Positive electrode

Battery

Current meter

**Figure 7.7** The photoelectric effect.

● **Ping-Pong Photons** This analogy helps explain why light of *insufficient* energy *cannot* free an electron from the metal surface. If one Ping-Pong ball doesn't have enough energy to knock a book off a shelf, neither does a series of Ping-Pong balls, because the book can't save up the energy from the individual impacts. But one baseball traveling at the same speed does have enough energy.

## Sample Problem 7.2   Calculating the Energy of Radiation from Its Wavelength

**Problem**  A student uses a microwave oven to heat a meal. The wavelength of the radiation is 1.20 cm. What is the energy of one photon of this microwave radiation?

**Plan**  We know $\lambda$ in centimeters (1.20 cm) so we convert to meters, find the frequency with Equation 7.1, and then find the energy of one photon with Equation 7.2.

**Solution**  Combining steps to find the energy of a photon:

$$E = h\nu = \frac{hc}{\lambda} = \frac{(6.626 \times 10^{-34} \text{ J·s})(3.00 \times 10^8 \text{ m/s})}{(1.20 \text{ cm})\left(\dfrac{10^{-2} \text{ m}}{1 \text{ cm}}\right)} = 1.66 \times 10^{-23} \text{ J}$$

**Check**  Checking the order of magnitude gives

$$\frac{10^{-33} \text{ J·s} \times 10^8 \text{ m/s}}{10^{-2} \text{ m}} = 10^{-23} \text{ J}$$

**Follow-Up Problem 7.2**  Calculate the energy of one photon of **(a)** ultraviolet light ($\lambda = 1 \times 10^{-8}$ m); **(b)** visible light ($\lambda = 5 \times 10^{-7}$ m); and **(c)** infrared light ($\lambda = 1 \times 10^{-4}$ m). What do the answers indicate about the relationship between the wavelength and energy of light?

## ■ Summary of Section 7.1

- Electromagnetic radiation travels in waves characterized by a given wavelength ($\lambda$) and frequency ($\nu$).
- Electromagnetic waves travel through a vacuum at the speed of light, $c$ ($3.00 \times 10^8$ m/s), which equals $\nu \times \lambda$. Therefore, wavelength and frequency have a reciprocal relationship.
- The intensity (brightness) of light is related to the amplitude of its waves.
- The electromagnetic spectrum ranges from very long radio waves to very short gamma rays and includes the visible region between wavelengths 750 nm (red) and 400 nm (violet).
- Refraction (change in a wave's speed when entering a different medium) and diffraction (bend of a wave around an edge of an object) indicate that energy is wavelike, with properties distinct from those of particles of mass.
- Blackbody radiation and the photoelectric effect, however, are consistent with energy occurring in discrete packets, like particles.
- Light exists as photons (quanta) whose energy is proportional to the frequency.
- According to quantum theory, an atom has only certain quantities of energy ($E = nh\nu$), and it can change its energy only by absorbing or emitting a photon whose energy equals the change in the atom's energy.

## 7.2 • ATOMIC SPECTRA

The third confusing observation about matter and energy involved the light emitted when an element is vaporized and then excited electrically. In this section, we discuss the nature of that light and see why it created a problem for the existing atomic model and how a new model solved the problem.

### Line Spectra and the Rydberg Equation

When light from electrically excited gaseous atoms passes through a slit and is refracted by a prism, it does not create a *continuous spectrum,* or rainbow, as sunlight does. Instead, it creates a **line spectrum,** a series of fine lines at specific frequencies separated by black spaces. Figure 7.8A on the next page shows the apparatus and the line spectrum of atomic hydrogen. Figure 7.8B shows that each spectrum is *characteristic* of the element producing it.

**Figure 7.8** The line spectra of several elements. **A,** The line spectrum of atomic hydrogen. **B,** Unlike the continuous spectrum of white light, emission spectra of elements, such as mercury and strontium, appear as characteristic series of colored lines.

**Features of the Rydberg Equation** Spectroscopists studying atomic hydrogen identified several series of spectral lines in different regions of the electromagnetic spectrum. Figure 7.9 shows three of them. Using data, not theory, the Swedish physicist Johannes Rydberg developed a relationship, called the *Rydberg equation,* that predicted the position and wavelength of any line in a given series:

$$\frac{1}{\lambda} = R\left(\frac{1}{n_1^2} - \frac{1}{n_2^2}\right) \tag{7.3}$$

where $\lambda$ is the wavelength of the line, $n_1$ and $n_2$ are positive integers with $n_2 > n_1$, and $R$ is the Rydberg constant ($1.096776 \times 10^7$ m$^{-1}$). For the visible series, $n_1 = 2$:

$$\frac{1}{\lambda} = R\left(\frac{1}{2^2} - \frac{1}{n_2^2}\right), \quad \text{with } n_2 = 3, 4, 5, \ldots$$

(Problems 7.23 and 7.24 are two of several that apply the Rydberg equation.)

**Figure 7.9** Three series of spectral lines of atomic hydrogen.

**Problems with Rutherford's Nuclear Model** Almost as soon as Rutherford proposed his nuclear model (described in Chapter 2), a major problem arose. A positive nucleus and a negative electron attract each other, and for them to stay apart, the kinetic energy of the electron's motion must counterbalance the potential energy of attraction. However, the laws of classical physics say that a negative particle moving in a curved path around a positive particle *must* emit radiation and thus lose energy. If the orbiting electrons behaved in that way, they would spiral into the nucleus, and all atoms would collapse! The laws of classical physics also say that the frequency of the emitted radiation should change smoothly as the negative particle spirals inward and, thus, create a continuous spectrum, not a line spectrum. The behavior of subatomic particles seemed to violate real-world experience and accepted principles.

## The Bohr Model of the Hydrogen Atom

Two years after the nuclear model was proposed, Niels Bohr (1885–1962), a young Danish physicist working in Rutherford's laboratory, suggested a model for the H atom that *did* predict the existence of line spectra.

**Postulates of the Model** In his model, Bohr used Planck's and Einstein's ideas about quantized energy and proposed three postulates:

1. *The H atom has only certain energy levels,* which Bohr called **stationary states.** Each state is associated with a fixed circular orbit of the electron around the nucleus. The higher the energy level, the farther the orbit is from the nucleus.
2. *The atom does **not** radiate energy while in one of its stationary states.* Even though it violates principles of classical physics, the atom does not change energy while the electron moves *within* an orbit.
3. *The atom changes to another stationary state* (the electron moves to another orbit) *only by absorbing or emitting a photon. The energy of the photon (hν) equals the difference in the energies of the two states:*

$$E_{\text{photon}} = \Delta E_{\text{atom}} = E_{\text{final}} - E_{\text{initial}} = h\nu$$

**Features of the Model** The model has several key features:

- *Quantum numbers and electron orbit.* The quantum number $n$ is a positive integer (1, 2, 3, . . .) associated with the radius of an electron orbit, which is directly related to the electron's energy: *the lower the n value, the smaller the radius of the orbit, and the lower the energy level.*
- *Ground state.* When the electron is in the first orbit ($n = 1$), it is closest to the nucleus, and the H atom is in its lowest (first) energy level, called the **ground state.**
- *Excited states.* If the electron is in any orbit farther from the nucleus, the atom is in an **excited state.** With the electron in the second orbit ($n = 2$), the atom is in the first excited state; when it's in the third orbit ($n = 3$), the atom is in the second excited state, and so forth.
- *Absorption.* If an H atom *absorbs* a photon whose energy equals the *difference* between lower and higher energy levels, the electron moves to the outer (higher energy) orbit.
- *Emission.* If an H atom in a higher energy level (electron in farther orbit) returns to a lower energy level (electron in closer orbit), the atom *emits* a photon whose energy equals the difference between the two levels. Figure 7.10 shows an analogy that illustrates absorption and emission.

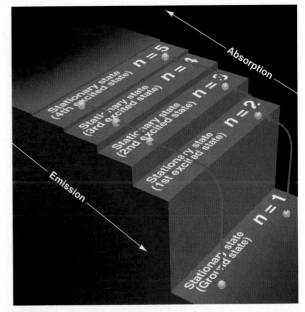

**Figure 7.10 A quantum "staircase" as an analogy for atomic energy levels.** Note that the electron can move up or down one or more steps at a time but cannot lie *between* steps.

**How the Model Explains Line Spectra**   A spectral line results because a photon of specific energy (and thus frequency) is *emitted*. The emission occurs when the electron moves to an orbit closer to the nucleus as the atom's energy changes from a higher state to a lower one. Therefore, *an atomic spectrum is not continuous because the atom's energy is not continuous, but rather has only certain states.*

Figure 7.11A shows how Bohr's model accounts for three series of spectral lines of hydrogen. When a sample of gaseous H atoms is excited, the atoms absorb different quantities of energy. Each atom has one electron, but there are so many atoms in the whole sample that all the energy levels (orbits) have electrons. When electrons drop from outer orbits to the $n = 3$ orbit (second excited state), the emitted photons create the *infrared* series of lines. The *visible* series arises when electrons drop to the $n = 2$ orbit (first excited state), and the *ultraviolet* series arises when electrons drop to the $n = 1$ orbit (ground state). Figure 7.11B shows how the specific lines in the ultraviolet series appear.

**Limitations of the Model**   Despite its great success in accounting for the spectral lines of the H atom, the Bohr model failed to predict the spectrum of any other atom. The reason is that it is a *one-electron model:* it works beautifully for the H atom and for other one-electron species, such as $He^+$ $(Z = 2)$, $Li^{2+}$ $(Z = 3)$, and $Be^{3+}$ $(Z = 4)$. It fails completely for atoms with more than one electron because the electron-electron repulsions and additional nucleus-electron attractions that are present create much more complex interactions. But, even more fundamentally, as we'll see in Section 7.4, *electrons do not move in fixed, defined orbits.* Even though, as a picture of the atom, the Bohr model is incorrect, we still use the terms "ground state" and "excited state" and retain the central idea that *the energy of an atom occurs in discrete levels and it changes energy by absorbing or emitting a photon of specific energy.*

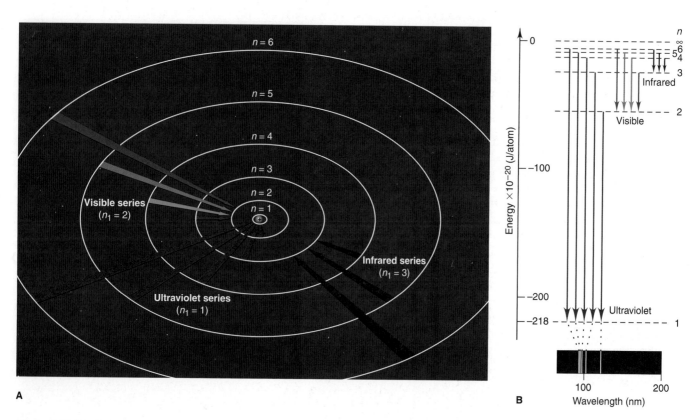

**A**

**B**

**Figure 7.11**   The Bohr explanation of three series of spectral lines emitted by the H atom. **A,** In a given series, the outer electron drops to the same inner orbit (the same value of $n_1$ in the Rydberg equation). **B,** An energy diagram shows how the ultraviolet series arises.

## The Energy Levels of the Hydrogen Atom

Bohr's work leads to an equation for calculating the energy levels of an atom:

$$E = -2.18 \times 10^{-18} \text{ J} \left( \frac{Z^2}{n^2} \right)$$

where $Z$ is the charge of the nucleus. For the H atom, $Z = 1$, so we have

$$E = -2.18 \times 10^{-18} \text{ J} \left( \frac{1^2}{n^2} \right) = -2.18 \times 10^{-18} \text{ J} \left( \frac{1}{n^2} \right)$$

Therefore, the energy of the ground state ($n = 1$) of the H atom is

$$E = -2.18 \times 10^{-18} \text{ J} \left( \frac{1}{1^2} \right) = -2.18 \times 10^{-18} \text{ J}$$

The negative sign for the energy (also used on the axis in Figure 7.11B) appears because we *define* the zero point of the atom's energy when *the electron is completely removed from the nucleus.* Thus, $E = 0$ when $n = \infty$, so $E < 0$ for any smaller $n$. ●

### Applying Bohr's Equation for the Energy Levels of an Atom
We can use the equation for the energy levels in several ways:

1. *Finding the difference in energy between two levels.* By subtracting the initial energy level of the atom from its final energy level, we find the change in energy when the electron moves between the two levels:

$$\Delta E = E_{\text{final}} - E_{\text{initial}} = -2.18 \times 10^{-18} \text{ J} \left( \frac{1}{n_{\text{final}}^2} - \frac{1}{n_{\text{initial}}^2} \right) \qquad \textbf{(7.4)}$$

Note that, since $n$ is in the denominator,

- *When the atom emits energy,* the electron moves closer to the nucleus ($n_{\text{final}} < n_{\text{initial}}$), so the atom's final energy is a *larger* negative number and $\Delta E$ is negative.
- *When the atom absorbs energy,* the electron moves away from the nucleus ($n_{\text{final}} > n_{\text{initial}}$), so the atom's final energy is a *smaller* negative number and $\Delta E$ is positive. (Analogously, in Chapter 6, you saw that, when the system releases heat, $\Delta H$ is negative, and when it absorbs heat, $\Delta H$ is positive.)

2. *Finding the energy needed to ionize the H atom.* We can also find the energy needed to remove the electron completely, that is, find $\Delta E$ for the following change:

$$\text{H}(g) \longrightarrow \text{H}^+(g) + \text{e}^-$$

We substitute $n_{\text{final}} = \infty$ and $n_{\text{initial}} = 1$ into Equation 7.4 and obtain

$$\Delta E = E_{\text{final}} - E_{\text{initial}} = -2.18 \times 10^{-18} \text{ J} \left( \frac{1}{\infty^2} - \frac{1}{1^2} \right)$$

$$= -2.18 \times 10^{-18} \text{ J} (0 - 1) = 2.18 \times 10^{-18} \text{ J}$$

Energy must be *absorbed* to remove the electron from the nucleus, so $\Delta E$ is positive.

The *ionization energy* of hydrogen is the energy required to form 1 mol of gaseous H$^+$ ions from 1 mol of gaseous H atoms. Thus, for 1 mol of H atoms,

$$\Delta E = \left( 2.18 \times 10^{-18} \frac{\text{J}}{\text{atom}} \right) \left( 6.022 \times 10^{23} \frac{\text{atoms}}{\text{mol}} \right) \left( \frac{1 \text{ kJ}}{10^3 \text{ J}} \right) = 1.31 \times 10^3 \text{ kJ/mol}$$

Ionization energy is a key atomic property, and we'll return to it in Chapter 8.

3. *Finding the wavelength of a spectral line.* Once we know $\Delta E$ from Equation 7.4, we find the wavelengths of the spectral lines of the H atom by combining the relation between frequency and wavelength (Equation 7.1) with Planck's expression for the change in energy of an atom (Equation 7.2) and solving for $\lambda$:

$$\Delta E = h\nu = \frac{hc}{\lambda} \quad \text{or} \quad \lambda = \frac{hc}{\Delta E}$$

In Sample Problem 7.3, we find the energy change when an H atom absorbs a photon.

● **A tabletop analogy for defining the energy of a system.** If you define the zero point of your textbook's potential energy when the book is on a table, the energy is negative when it's on the floor.

## Sample Problem 7.3 — Determining $\Delta E$ and $\lambda$ of an Electron Transition

**Problem** A hydrogen atom absorbs a photon of UV light (see Figure 7.11), and its electron enters the $n = 4$ energy level. Calculate (a) the change in energy of the atom and (b) the wavelength (in nm) of the photon.

**Plan** (a) The H atom absorbs energy, so $E_{final} > E_{initial}$. We are given $n_{final} = 4$, and Figure 7.11 shows that $n_{initial} = 1$ because a UV photon is absorbed. We apply Equation 7.4 to find $\Delta E$. (b) Once we know $\Delta E$, we find the frequency with Equation 7.2 and the wavelength (in m) with Equation 7.1. Then we convert from meters to nanometers.

**Solution** (a) Substituting the known values into Equation 7.4:

$$\Delta E = -2.18 \times 10^{-18} \text{ J} \left( \frac{1}{n_{final}^2} - \frac{1}{n_{initial}^2} \right)$$

$$= -2.18 \times 10^{-18} \text{ J} \left( \frac{1}{4^2} - \frac{1}{1^2} \right) = -2.18 \times 10^{-18} \text{ J} \left( \frac{1}{16} - \frac{1}{1} \right)$$

$$= 2.04 \times 10^{-18} \text{ J}$$

(b) Using Equations 7.2 and 7.1 to solve for $\lambda$:

$$\Delta E = h\nu = \frac{hc}{\lambda}$$

therefore,

$$\lambda = \frac{hc}{\Delta E} = \frac{(6.626 \times 10^{-34} \text{ J·s})(3.00 \times 10^8 \text{ m/s})}{2.04 \times 10^{-18} \text{ J}} = 9.74 \times 10^{-8} \text{ m}$$

Converting m to nm:

$$\lambda = 9.74 \times 10^{-8} \text{ m} \times \frac{1 \text{ nm}}{10^{-9} \text{ m}} = 97.4 \text{ nm}$$

**Check** (a) The energy change is positive, which is consistent with absorption.
(b) The wavelength is within the UV region (about 10–380 nm).

**Comment** In the follow-up problem, note that if $\Delta E$ is negative (the atom loses energy), we use its absolute value, $|\Delta E|$, because $\lambda$ must have a positive value.

**Follow-Up Problem 7.3** A hydrogen atom with its electron in the $n = 6$ energy level emits a photon of IR light. Calculate (a) the change in energy of the atom and (b) the wavelength (in Å) of the photon.

---

Spectrometric analysis of the H atom led to the Bohr model, the first step toward our current model of the atom. From its use by 19th-century chemists as a means of identifying elements and compounds, spectrometry has developed into a major tool of modern chemistry (see Tools of the Laboratory).

## ■ Summary of Section 7.2

- Unlike sunlight, light emitted by electrically excited atoms of elements appears as separate spectral lines.
- Spectroscopists use an empirical formula (the Rydberg equation) to determine the wavelength of a spectral line. Atomic hydrogen displays several series of spectral lines.
- To explain the existence of line spectra, Bohr proposed that an electron moves in fixed orbits. It moves from one orbit to another when the atom absorbs or emits a photon whose energy equals the difference in energy levels (orbits).
- Bohr's model predicts only the spectrum of the H atom and other one-electron species. Despite this, Bohr was correct that an atom's energy is quantized.
- Spectrometry is an instrumental technique that uses emission and absorption spectra to identify substances and measure their concentrations.

The use of spectral data to identify and quantify substances is essential to modern chemical analysis. The terms *spectroscopy* and **spectrometry** refer to a large group of instrumental techniques that obtain spectra to gather data on a substance's atomic and molecular energy levels.

## Types of Spectra

Emission and absorption spectra are two important types:

1. An **emission spectrum,** such as the H atom line spectrum, occurs when atoms in an excited state *emit* photons as they return to a lower energy state. Some elements produce an intense spectral line (or several closely spaced ones) that is evidence of their presence. **Flame tests,** performed by placing a granule of an ionic compound or a drop of its solution in a flame, rely on these intense emissions (Figure B7.1, part A), and some colors of

**Figure B7.1 Flame tests and fireworks. A,** The flame's color is due to intense emission by the element of light of a particular wavelength. **B,** Fireworks display emissions similar to those seen in flame tests.

**Figure B7.2 Emission and absorption spectra of sodium atoms.** The wavelengths of the bright emission lines correspond to those of the dark absorption lines because both are created by the same energy change: $\Delta E_{\text{emission}} = -\Delta E_{\text{absorption}}$. (Only the two most intense lines in the Na spectra are shown.)

fireworks are due to the same elements (Figure B7.1, part B). The colors of sodium-vapor and mercury-vapor streetlamps are due to intense emissions lines in these elements' spectra.

2. An **absorption spectrum** is produced when atoms *absorb* photons of certain wavelengths and become excited. When white light passes through sodium vapor, for example, the absorption spectrum shows dark lines at the same wavelengths as the yellow-orange lines in sodium's emission spectrum (Figure B7.2).

## Basic Instrumentation

Instruments based on absorption spectra are much more common than those based on emission spectra because many substances absorb relatively few wavelengths so their spectra are more characteristic, and absorption is less destructive of fragile molecules.

Design differences depend on the region of the electromagnetic spectrum used to irradiate the sample, but all modern spectrometers have components that perform the same basic functions (Figure B7.3). (We discuss infrared spectroscopy and nuclear magnetic resonance spectroscopy in later chapters.)

*(continued)*

**Source** produces radiation in the region of interest. In most cases, the source emits many wavelengths.

**Lenses/slits/ collimators** narrow and align the beam.

**Monochromator** (wavelength selector) disperses the incoming radiation into its component wavelengths.

**Sample** in the compartment absorbs a characteristic amount of incoming wavelength.

**Detector** converts the transmitted radiation into an amplified electrical signal.

**Computer** converts the signal into displayed data.

**Figure B7.3** Components of a typical spectrometer.

## Identifying and Quantifying a Substance

In chemical analysis, spectra are used to identify a substance and/or quantify the amount in a sample. Visible light is often used for colored substances, because they absorb only some of the wavelengths. A leaf looks green, for example, because its chlorophyll absorbs red and blue light strongly but green light weakly, so most of the green light is reflected.

Figure B7.4 shows the visible absorption spectrum of chlorophyll *a* in ether solution. The shape of the curve and the wavelengths of the major peaks are characteristic of chlorophyll *a*. The curve varies in height because chlorophyll *a* absorbs light of different wavelengths to different extents. The absorptions appear as broad bands, rather than as the distinct lines seen on absorption spectra of elements, because there are greater numbers and types of energy levels within a molecule and between molecules and solvent.

In addition to identifying a substance, a spectrometer can be used to measure its concentration because *absorbance,* the quantity of light of a given wavelength absorbed by a substance, is *proportional to the number of molecules.* Suppose you want to determine the concentration of chlorophyll *a* in a leaf extract. You select a strongly absorbed wavelength from the compound's spectrum (such as 663 nm in Figure B7.4, part A), measure the absorbance of the *unknown* solution, and compare it with the absorbances of a series of solutions of *known* concentration (Figure B7.4, part B).

### Problems

**B7.1** The sodium salt of 2-quinizarinsulfonic acid forms a complex with $Al^{3+}$ that absorbs strongly at 560 nm. (a) Use the data below to draw a plot of absorbance vs. concentration of the complex in solution and find the slope and *y*-intercept:

| Concentration (*M*) | Absorbance (560 nm) |
|---|---|
| $1.0 \times 10^{-5}$ | 0.131 |
| $1.5 \times 10^{-5}$ | 0.201 |
| $2.0 \times 10^{-5}$ | 0.265 |
| $2.5 \times 10^{-5}$ | 0.329 |
| $3.0 \times 10^{-5}$ | 0.396 |

(b) When 20.0 mL of a solution of this complex is diluted with water to 150. mL, its absorbance is 0.236. Find the concentrations of the diluted solution and of the original solution.

**B7.2** In fireworks displays, flame tests, and other emission events, light of a given wavelength often indicates the presence of a particular element or ion. What are the frequency and color of the light associated with each of the following?
(a) Li, $\lambda = 671$ nm
(b) $Cs^+$, $\lambda = 453$ nm
(c) Na, $\lambda = 589$ nm

**A,** The spectrometer is set to measure the strong absorption at 663 nm

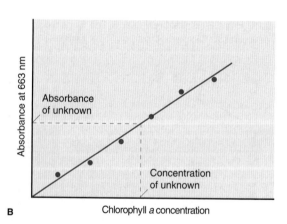

**Figure B7.4 Measuring chlorophyll *a* concentration in leaf extract.**
in the chlorophyll *a* spectrum. **B,** The absorbance from the leaf extract is compared to a series of known standards.

# 7.3 • THE WAVE-PARTICLE DUALITY OF MATTER AND ENERGY

The year 1905 was a busy one for Albert Einstein. He had just presented the photon theory and explained the photoelectric effect. A friend remembered him in his small apartment, rocking his baby in its carriage with one hand, while scribbling with the other ideas for a new branch of physics—the theory of relativity. One of its revelations was that *matter and energy are alternate forms of the same entity*. This idea is embodied in his famous equation $E = mc^2$, relating the quantity of energy equivalent to a given mass. Some results that showed energy to be particle-like had to coexist with others that showed matter to be wavelike. These remarkable ideas are the key to understanding our modern atomic model.

## The Wave Nature of Electrons and the Particle Nature of Photons

Bohr's model was a perfect case of fitting theory to data: he *assumed* that an atom has only certain energy levels in order to *explain* line spectra. However, Bohr had no theoretical basis for the assumption. Several breakthroughs in the early 1920s provided that basis and blurred the distinction between matter (chunky and massive) and energy (diffuse and massless).

**The Wave Nature of Electrons** Attempting to explain why an atom has fixed energy levels, a French physics student, Louis de Broglie, considered other systems that display only certain allowed motions, such as the vibrations of a plucked guitar string. Figure 7.12 shows that, because the end of the string is fixed, only certain vibrational frequencies (and wavelengths) are allowable to create a note. De Broglie proposed that *if energy is particle-like, perhaps matter is wavelike*. He reasoned that *if electrons have wavelike motion* in orbits of fixed radii, they would have only certain allowable frequencies and energies.

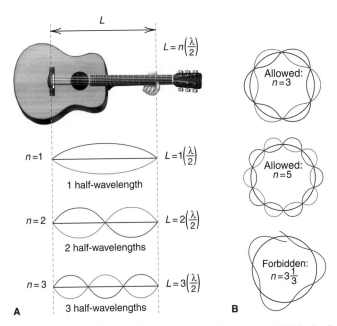

**Figure 7.12 Wave motion in restricted systems. A,** One half-wavelength ($\lambda/2$) is the "quantum" of the guitar string's vibration. With string length $L$ fixed by a finger on the fret, allowed vibrations occur when $L$ is a whole-number multiple ($n$) of $\lambda/2$. **B,** In a circular electron orbit, only whole numbers of wavelengths are allowed ($n = 3$ and $n = 5$ are shown). A wave with a fractional number of wavelengths (such as $n = 3\frac{1}{3}$) is "forbidden" because it dies out through overlap of crests and troughs.

Combining the equations for mass-energy equivalence ($E = mc^2$) and energy of a photon ($E = h\nu = hc/\lambda$), de Broglie derived an equation for the wavelength of any particle of mass $m$—whether planet, baseball, or electron—moving at speed $u$:

$$\lambda = \frac{h}{mu} \tag{7.5}$$

According to this equation for the **de Broglie wavelength,** *matter behaves as though it moves in a wave.* An object's wavelength is *inversely* proportional to its mass, so heavy objects such as planets and baseballs have wavelengths *many* orders of magnitude smaller than the object itself (Table 7.1).

**Table 7.1 The de Broglie Wavelengths of Several Objects**

| Substance | Mass (g) | Speed (m/s) | $\lambda$ (m) |
|---|---|---|---|
| Slow electron | $9 \times 10^{-28}$ | 1.0 | $7 \times 10^{-4}$ |
| Fast electron | $9 \times 10^{-28}$ | $5.9 \times 10^{6}$ | $1 \times 10^{-10}$ |
| Alpha particle | $6.6 \times 10^{-24}$ | $1.5 \times 10^{7}$ | $7 \times 10^{-15}$ |
| 1-gram mass | 1.0 | 0.01 | $7 \times 10^{-29}$ |
| Baseball | 142 | 40.0 | $1 \times 10^{-34}$ |
| Earth | $6.0 \times 10^{27}$ | $3.0 \times 10^{4}$ | $4 \times 10^{-63}$ |

**Sample Problem 7.4    Calculating the de Broglie Wavelength of an Electron**

**Problem** Find the de Broglie wavelength of an electron with a speed of $1.00 \times 10^6$ m/s (electron mass = $9.11 \times 10^{-31}$ kg; $h = 6.626 \times 10^{-34}$ kg·m²/s).

**Plan** We know the speed ($1.00 \times 10^6$ m/s) and mass ($9.11 \times 10^{-31}$ kg) of the electron, so we substitute these into Equation 7.5 to find $\lambda$.

**Solution**

$$\lambda = \frac{h}{mu} = \frac{6.626 \times 10^{-34} \text{ kg·m}^2/\text{s}}{(9.11 \times 10^{-31} \text{ kg})(1.00 \times 10^6 \text{ m/s})} = 7.27 \times 10^{-10} \text{ m}$$

**Check** The order of magnitude and units seem correct:

$$\lambda \approx \frac{10^{-33} \text{ kg·m}^2/\text{s}}{(10^{-30} \text{ kg})(10^6 \text{ m/s})} = 10^{-9} \text{ m}$$

**Comment** As you'll see in the upcoming discussion, such fast-moving electrons, with wavelengths in the range of atomic sizes, exhibit remarkable properties.

**Follow-Up Problem 7.4** What is the speed of an electron that has a de Broglie wavelength of 100. nm?

If electrons travel in waves, they should exhibit diffraction and interference. A fast-moving electron has a wavelength of about $10^{-10}$ m, so a beam of such electrons should be diffracted by the spaces between atoms in a crystal—about $10^{-10}$ m. In 1927, C. Davisson and L. Germer guided a beam of x-rays and then a beam of electrons at a nickel crystal and obtained two diffraction patterns; Figure 7.13 shows these patterns for aluminum. Thus, electrons—particles with mass and charge—create diffraction patterns, just as electromagnetic waves do.

A major application of electrons traveling in waves is the *electron microscope.* Its great advantage over light microscopes is that high-speed electrons have much smaller wavelengths than visible light, which allow much higher resolution. A transmission electron microscope focuses a beam of electrons through a lens, and the beam then passes through a thin section of the specimen to a second and then third lens. In this instrument, these "lenses" are electromagnetic fields, which can result in up to 200,000-fold magnification. In a scanning electron microscope, the beam scans the

**Figure 7.13** Diffraction patterns of aluminum with x-rays (*top*) and electrons (*bottom*).

specimen, knocking electrons from it that create a current, which generates an image that looks like the object's surface (Figure 7.14).

**The Particle Nature of Photons** If electrons have properties of energy, do photons have properties of matter? The de Broglie equation suggests that we can calculate the momentum ($p$), the product of mass and speed, for a photon. Substituting the speed of light ($c$) for speed $u$ in Equation 7.5 and solving for $p$ gives

$$\lambda = \frac{h}{mc} = \frac{h}{p} \quad \text{and} \quad p = \frac{h}{\lambda}$$

The inverse relationship between $p$ and $\lambda$ in this equation means that shorter wavelength (higher energy) photons have greater momentum. Thus, a decrease in a photon's momentum should appear as an increase in its wavelength. In 1923, Arthur Compton directed a beam of x-ray photons at graphite and observed an increase in the wavelength of the reflected photons. Thus, just as billiard balls transfer momentum when they collide, the photons transferred momentum to the electrons in the carbon atoms of the graphite. In this experiment, photons behaved as particles.

**Wave-Particle Duality** Classical experiments had shown matter to be particle-like and energy to be wavelike. But, results on the atomic scale show electrons moving in waves and photons having momentum. Thus, every property of matter was also a property of energy. The truth is that *both* matter and energy show *both* behaviors: each possesses both "faces." In some experiments, we observe one face; in other experiments, we observe the other face. Our everyday distinction between matter and energy is meaningful in the macroscopic world, *not* in the atomic world. The distinction is in our minds and the limited definitions we have created, not inherent in nature. This dual character of matter and energy is known as the **wave-particle duality.** Figure 7.15 summarizes the theories and observations that led to this new understanding.

**Figure 7.14** False-color scanning electron micrograph of blood cells (x1200).

**Figure 7.15** Major observations and theories leading from classical theory to quantum theory.

CLASSICAL THEORY

| Matter | Energy |
|---|---|
| particulate, massive | continuous, wavelike |

Since **matter** is discontinuous and particulate, perhaps **energy** is discontinuous and particulate.

*Observation*

Blackbody radiation ⟶
Photoelectric effect ⟶
Atomic line spectra ⟶

*Theory*

Planck: Energy is quantized; only certain values allowed.
Einstein: Light has particulate behavior (photons).
Bohr: Energy of atoms is quantized; photon is emitted when electron changes orbit.

Since **energy** is wavelike, perhaps **matter** is wavelike.

*Observation*

Davisson/Germer: Electron beam is diffracted by metal crystal. ⟵

*Theory*

de Broglie: All matter travels in waves: energy of atom is quantized due to wave motion of electrons.

Since **matter** has mass, perhaps **energy** has mass.

*Observation*

Compton: Photon's wavelength increases (momentum decreases) after colliding with electron. ⟵

*Theory*

Einstein/de Broglie: Mass and energy are equivalent: particles have wavelength and photons have momentum.

QUANTUM THEORY

**Energy** *and* **Matter**
particulate, massive, wavelike

# Heisenberg's Uncertainty Principle

In classical physics, a moving particle has a definite location at any instant, whereas a wave is spread out in space. If an electron has the properties of *both* a particle and a wave, can we determine its position in the atom? In 1927, the German physicist Werner Heisenberg postulated the **uncertainty principle,** which states that it is impossible to know simultaneously the position *and* momentum (mass times speed) of a particle. For a particle with constant mass $m$, the principle is expressed mathematically as

$$\Delta x \cdot m \Delta u \geq \frac{h}{4\pi} \tag{7.6}$$

where $\Delta x$ is the uncertainty in position, $\Delta u$ is the uncertainty in speed, and $h$ is Planck's constant. The more accurately we know the position of the particle (smaller $\Delta x$), the less accurately we know its speed (larger $\Delta u$), and vice versa. The best-case scenario is that we know the product of these uncertainties, which is equal to $h/4\pi$.

For a macroscopic object like a baseball, $\Delta x$ and $\Delta u$ are insignificant because the mass is enormous compared with $h/4\pi$. Thus, by knowing the position and speed of a pitched baseball, we can use the laws of motion to predict its trajectory and whether it will be a ball or a strike. However, using the position and speed of an electron to find its trajectory is a very different proposition, as Sample Problem 7.5 demonstrates.

---

## Sample Problem 7.5 | Applying the Uncertainty Principle

**Problem** An electron moving near an atomic nucleus has a speed of $6 \times 10^6$ m/s $\pm$ 1%. What is the uncertainty in its position ($\Delta x$)?

**Plan** The uncertainty in the speed ($\Delta u$) is given as 1%, so we multiply $u$ ($6 \times 10^6$ m/s) by 0.01 to calculate the value of $\Delta u$, substitute it into Equation 7.6, and solve for the uncertainty in position ($\Delta x$).

**Solution** Finding the uncertainty in speed, $\Delta u$:

$$\Delta u = 1\% \text{ of } u = 0.01(6 \times 10^6 \text{ m/s}) = 6 \times 10^4 \text{ m/s}$$

Calculating the uncertainty in position, $\Delta x$:

$$\Delta x \cdot m \Delta u \geq \frac{h}{4\pi}$$

Thus,

$$\Delta x \geq \frac{h}{4\pi m \Delta u} \geq \frac{6.626 \times 10^{-34} \text{ kg} \cdot \text{m}^2/\text{s}}{4\pi (9.11 \times 10^{-31} \text{ kg})(6 \times 10^4 \text{ m/s})} \geq \boxed{1 \times 10^{-9} \text{ m}}$$

**Check** Be sure to round off and check the order of magnitude of the answer:

$$\Delta x \geq \frac{10^{-33} \text{ kg} \cdot \text{m}^2/\text{s}}{(10^1)(10^{-30} \text{ kg})(10^5 \text{ m/s})} = 10^{-9} \text{ m}$$

**Comment** The uncertainty in the electron's position is about 10 times greater than the diameter of the entire atom ($10^{-10}$ m)! Therefore, we have no precise idea where in the atom the electron is located. In the follow-up problem, you'll see if an umpire has any better idea about the position of a baseball.

**Follow-Up Problem 7.5** How accurately can an umpire know the position of a baseball (mass = 0.142 kg) moving at 100.0 mi/h $\pm$ 1.00% (44.7 m/s $\pm$ 1.00%)?

# ■ Summary of Section 7.3

- As a result of Planck's quantum theory and Einstein's theory of relativity, we no longer view matter and energy as distinct entities.
- The de Broglie wavelength is based on the idea that an electron (or any object) has wavelike motion. Allowed atomic energy levels are related to allowed wavelengths of the electron's motion.
- Electrons exhibit diffraction, just as light waves do, and photons exhibit transfer of momentum, just as objects do. This wave-particle duality of matter and energy is observable only on the atomic scale.
- According to the uncertainty principle, we can never know the position and speed of an electron simultaneously.

# 7.4 • THE QUANTUM-MECHANICAL MODEL OF THE ATOM

Acceptance of the dual nature of matter and energy and of the uncertainty principle culminated in the field of **quantum mechanics,** which examines the wave nature of objects on the atomic scale. In 1926, Erwin Schrödinger derived an equation that is the basis for the *quantum-mechanical model* of the H atom. The model describes an atom with specific quantities of energy that result from allowed frequencies of its electron's wavelike motion. The electron's position can only be known within a certain probability. Key features of the model are described in the following subsections.

## The Atomic Orbital and the Probable Location of the Electron

Two central aspects of the quantum-mechanical model concern the atomic orbital and the electron's probable location.

**The Schrödinger Equation and the Atomic Orbital** The electron's matter-wave occupies the space near the nucleus and is continuously influenced by it. The **Schrödinger equation** is quite complex but can be represented in simpler form as

$$\mathscr{H}\psi = E\psi$$

where $E$ is the energy of the atom. The symbol $\psi$ (Greek *psi*, pronounced "sigh") is called a **wave function (or atomic orbital),** a mathematical description of the electron's matter-wave in three dimensions. The symbol $\mathscr{H}$, called the Hamiltonian operator, represents a set of mathematical operations that, when carried out with a particular $\psi$, yields one of the allowed energy states of the atom.* Thus, *each solution of the equation gives an energy state associated with a given atomic orbital.*

An important point to keep in mind throughout this discussion is that an "orbital" in the quantum-mechanical model *bears no resemblance* to an "orbit" in the Bohr model: an *orbit* is an electron's actual path around the nucleus, whereas an *orbital* is a mathematical function that describes the electron's matter-wave but has no physical meaning.

**The Probable Location of the Electron** While we cannot know *exactly* where the electron is at any moment, we can know where it *probably* is, that is, where it spends most of its time. We get this information by squaring the wave function. Thus, even

---

*The complete form of the Schrödinger equation in terms of the three linear axes is

$$\left[ -\frac{h^2}{8\pi^2 m_e}\left( \frac{d^2}{dx^2} + \frac{d^2}{dy^2} + \frac{d^2}{dz^2} \right) + V(x, y, z) \right]\psi(x, y, z) = E\psi(x, y, z)$$

where $\psi$ is the wave function; $m_e$ is the electron's mass; $E$ is the total quantized energy of the atomic system; and $V$ is the potential energy at point $(x, y, z)$.

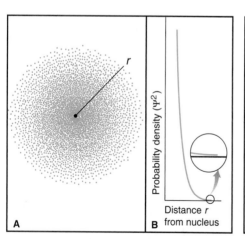

Distance from trunk

● **A Radial Probability Distribution of Apples** An analogy might clarify why the curve in the radial probability distribution plot peaks and then falls off. Picture fallen apples around the base of an apple tree: the density of apples is greatest near the trunk and decreases with distance. Divide the ground under the tree into foot-wide concentric rings and collect the apples within each ring. Apple density is greatest in the first ring, but the area of the second ring is larger, and so it contains a greater *total* number of apples. Farther out near the edge of the tree, rings have more area but lower apple "density," so the total number of apples decreases. A plot of "number of apples in each ring" vs. "distance from trunk" shows a peak at some distance close to the trunk, as in Figure 7.16D.

though ψ has no physical meaning, ψ² does and is called the *probability density,* a measure of the probability of finding the electron in some tiny volume of the atom. We depict the electron's probable location in several ways, which we'll look at first for the H atom's *ground state:*

1. *Probability of the electron being in some tiny volume of the atom.* For each energy level, we can create an *electron probability density diagram,* or more simply, an **electron density diagram.** The value of ψ² for a given volume is shown with dots: the greater the density of dots, the higher the probability of finding the electron in that volume. Note, that for the ground state of the H atom, *the electron probability density decreases with distance from the nucleus* along a line, r (Figure 7.16A).

These diagrams are also called **electron cloud depictions** because, if we *could* take a time-exposure photograph of the electron in wavelike motion around the nucleus, it would appear as a "cloud" of positions. The electron cloud is an *imaginary* picture of the electron changing its position rapidly over time; it does *not* mean that an electron is a diffuse cloud of charge.

Figure 7.16B shows a plot of ψ² vs. r. Due to the thickness of the printed line, the curve appears to touch the axis; however, in the blow-up circle, we see that *the probability of the electron being far from the nucleus is very small, but not zero.*

2. *Total probability density at some distance from the nucleus.* To find *radial probability distribution,* that is, the *total* probability of finding the electron at some distance r from the nucleus, we first mentally divide the volume around the nucleus into thin, concentric, spherical layers, like the layers of an onion (shown in cross section in Figure 7.16C). Then, we find the *sum of ψ² values* in each layer to see which is most likely to contain the electron.

The falloff in probability density with distance has an important effect. Near the nucleus, *the volume of each layer increases faster than its density of dots decreases.* The result of these opposing effects is that the *total* probability peaks in a layer *near,* but not *at,* the nucleus. For example, the total probability in the second layer is higher than in the first, but this result disappears with greater distance. Figure 7.16D shows this result as a **radial probability distribution plot.** ●

3. *Probability contour and the size of the atom.* How far away from the nucleus can we find the electron? This is the same as asking "How big is the H atom?" Recall from Figure 7.16B that the probability of finding the electron far from the nucleus

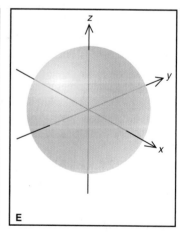

**Figure 7.16** Electron probability density in the ground-state H atom. **A,** In the electron density diagram, the density of dots represents the probability of the electron within a tiny volume and decreases with distance, r, from the nucleus. **B,** The probability density (ψ²) decreases with r but does not reach zero (*blow-up circle*). **C,** Count- ing dots within each layer gives the total probability of the electron being in that layer. **D,** A radial probability distribution plot shows that total electron density peaks *near,* but not *at,* the nucleus. **E,** A 90% probability contour for the ground state of the H atom.

is not zero. Therefore, we *cannot* assign a definite volume to an atom. However, we can visualize an atom with a 90% **probability contour:** the electron is somewhere within that volume 90% of the time (Figure 7.16E).

As you'll see later in this section, each atomic orbital has a distinctive radial probability distribution and 90% probability contour.

## Quantum Numbers of an Atomic Orbital

*An atomic orbital is specified by three quantum numbers* (Table 7.2) that are part of the solution of the Schrödinger equation and indicate the size, shape, and orientation in space of the orbital.*

1. The **principal quantum number (*n*)** *is a positive integer* (1, 2, 3, and so forth). It indicates the relative *size* of the orbital and therefore the relative *distance from the nucleus* of the peak in the radial probability distribution plot. The principal quantum number specifies the *energy level* of the H atom: *the higher the n value, the higher the energy level.* When the electron occupies an orbital with $n = 1$, the H atom is in its ground state and has its lowest energy. When the electron occupies an orbital with $n = 2$ (first excited state), the atom has more energy.

2. The **angular momentum quantum number (*l*)** *is an integer from 0 to* $n - 1$. It is related to the *shape* of the orbital. Note that the principal quantum number sets a limit on the angular momentum quantum number: *n* limits *l*. For an orbital with $n = 1$, *l* can have only one value, 0. For orbitals with $n = 2$, *l* can have two values, 0 or 1. For orbitals with $n = 3$, *l* can have three values, 0, 1, or 2; and so forth. Thus, the number of possible *l* values equals the value of *n*.

3. The **magnetic quantum number ($m_l$)** *is an integer from* $-l$ *through 0 to* $+l$. It prescribes the three-dimensional *orientation* of the orbital in the space around the nucleus. The angular momentum quantum number sets a limit on the magnetic quantum number: *l* limits $m_l$. An orbital with $l = 0$ can have only $m_l = 0$. However, an orbital with $l = 1$ can have one of three $m_l$ values, $-1$, 0, or $+1$; that is, there are three possible orbitals with $l = 1$, each with its own orientation. Note that the number of $m_l$ values *equals* $2l + 1$, which is the number of orbitals for a given *l*. The total number of $m_l$ values, that is, the total number of orbitals, for a given *n* value is $n^2$.

---

*For ease in discussion, chemists often refer to the size, shape, and orientation of an "atomic orbital," although we really mean the size, shape, and orientation of an "atomic orbital's radial probability distribution."

**Table 7.2 The Hierarchy of Quantum Numbers for Atomic Orbitals**

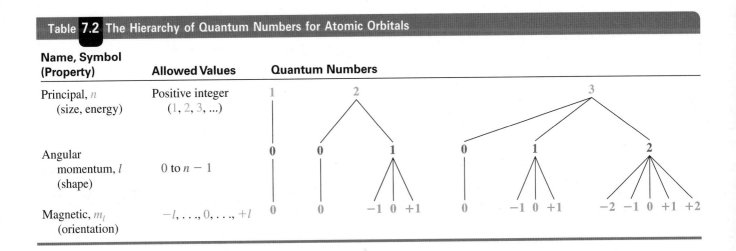

| Name, Symbol (Property) | Allowed Values | Quantum Numbers |
|---|---|---|
| Principal, $n$ (size, energy) | Positive integer $(1, 2, 3, ...)$ | 1    2    3 |
| Angular momentum, $l$ (shape) | 0 to $n - 1$ | 0    0  1    0  1  2 |
| Magnetic, $m_l$ (orientation) | $-l, ..., 0, ..., +l$ | 0    0  $-1\ 0\ +1$    0  $-1\ 0\ +1$  $-2\ -1\ 0\ +1\ +2$ |

**Problem** What values of the angular momentum ($l$) and magnetic ($m_l$) quantum numbers are allowed for a principal quantum number ($n$) of 3? How many orbitals are allowed?

**Plan** We determine allowable quantum numbers with the rules from the text: $l$ values are integers from 0 to $n - 1$, and $m_l$ values are integers from $-l$ to 0 to $+l$. One $m_l$ value is assigned to each orbital, so the number of $m_l$ values gives the number of orbitals.

**Solution** Determining $l$ values: for $n = 3$, $l = 0, 1, 2$.
Determining $m_l$ for each $l$ value:

$$\text{For } l = 0, \quad m_l = 0$$
$$\text{For } l = 1, \quad m_l = -1, 0, +1$$
$$\text{For } l = 2, \quad m_l = -2, -1, 0, +1, +2$$

There are nine $m_l$ values, so there are nine orbitals with $n = 3$.

**Check** Table 7.2 shows that we are correct. As we saw, the total number of orbitals for a given $n$ value is $n^2$, and for $n = 3$, $n^2 = 9$.

**Follow-Up Problem 7.6** What are the possible $l$ and $m_l$ values for $n = 4$?

## Quantum Numbers and Energy Levels

The energy states and orbitals of the atom are described with specific terms and are associated with one or more quantum numbers:

1. *Level.* The atom's energy **levels,** or *shells,* are given by the $n$ value: the smaller the $n$ value, the lower the energy level and the greater the probability that the electron is closer to the nucleus.

2. *Sublevel.* The atom's levels are divided into **sublevels,** or *subshells,* that are given by the $l$ value. Each designates the orbital shape with a letter:

$l = 0$ is an $s$ sublevel.
$l = 1$ is a $p$ sublevel.
$l = 2$ is a $d$ sublevel.
$l = 3$ is an $f$ sublevel.

(The letters derive from names of spectroscopic lines: *s*harp, *p*rincipal, *d*iffuse, and *f*undamental.) Sublevels with $l$ values greater than 3 are designated by consecutive letters after $f$: $g$ sublevel, $h$ sublevel, and so on. A sublevel is named with its $n$ value and letter designation; for example, the sublevel (subshell) with $n = 2$ and $l = 0$ is called the $2s$ sublevel. We discuss orbital shapes below.

3. *Orbital.* Each combination of $n$, $l$, and $m_l$ specifies the size (energy), shape, and spatial orientation of one of the atom's orbitals. We know the quantum numbers of the orbitals in a sublevel from the sublevel name and the quantum-number hierarchy. For example, any orbital in the $2s$ sublevel has $n = 2$ and $l = 0$, and given that $l$ value, it can have only $m_l = 0$; thus, the $2s$ sublevel has only one orbital. Any orbital in the $3p$ sublevel has $n = 3$ and $l = 1$, and given that $l$ value, one orbital has $m_l = -1$, another has $m_l = 0$, and a third has $m_l = +1$; thus, the $3p$ sublevel has three orbitals.

## Sample Problem 7.7 | Determining Sublevel Names and Orbital Quantum Numbers

**Problem** Give the name, magnetic quantum numbers, and number of orbitals for each sublevel with the given $n$ and $l$ quantum numbers:

(a) $n = 3, l = 2$
(b) $n = 2, l = 0$
(c) $n = 5, l = 1$
(d) $n = 4, l = 3$

**Plan** We name the sublevel (subshell) with the $n$ value and the letter designation of the $l$ value. From the $l$ value, we find the number of possible $m_l$ values, which equals the number of orbitals in that sublevel.

**Solution**

| $n$ | $l$ | Sublevel Name | Possible $m_l$ Values | No. of Orbitals |
|-----|-----|---------------|-----------------------|-----------------|
| (a) 3 | 2 | $3d$ | $-2, -1, 0, +1, +2$ | 5 |
| (b) 2 | 0 | $2s$ | $0$ | 1 |
| (c) 5 | 1 | $5p$ | $-1, 0, +1$ | 3 |
| (d) 4 | 3 | $4f$ | $-3, -2, -1, 0, +1, +2, +3$ | 7 |

**Check** Check the number of orbitals in each sublevel using

$$\text{No. of orbitals} = \text{no. of } m_l \text{ values} = 2l + 1$$

**Follow-Up Problem 7.7** What are the $n$, $l$, and possible $m_l$ values for the $2p$ and $5f$ sublevels?

## Sample Problem 7.8 | Identifying Incorrect Quantum Numbers

**Problem** What is wrong with each of the following quantum number designations and/or sublevel names?

| $n$ | $l$ | $m_l$ | Name |
|-----|-----|-------|------|
| (a) 1 | 1 | 0 | $1p$ |
| (b) 4 | 3 | +1 | $4d$ |
| (c) 3 | 1 | -2 | $3p$ |

**Solution** (a) A sublevel with $n = 1$ can have only $l = 0$, not $l = 1$. The only possible sublevel name is $1s$.

(b) A sublevel with $l = 3$ is an $f$ sublevel, not a $d$ sublevel. The name should be $4f$.

(c) A sublevel with $l = 1$ can have only $-1, 0,$ or $+1$ for $m_l$, not $-2$.

**Check** Check that $l$ is always less than $n$, and $m_l$ is always $\geq -l$ and $\leq +l$.

**Follow-Up Problem 7.8** Supply the missing quantum numbers and sublevel names.

| $n$ | $l$ | $m_l$ | Name |
|-----|-----|-------|------|
| (a) ? | ? | 0 | $4p$ |
| (b) 2 | 1 | 0 | ? |
| (c) 3 | 2 | -2 | ? |
| (d) ? | ? | ? | $2s$ |

## Shapes of Atomic Orbitals

Each sublevel of the H atom consists of a set of orbitals with characteristic shapes. As you'll see in Chapter 8, orbitals for the other atoms have similar shapes.

**The s Orbital** An orbital with $l = 0$ has a *spherical* shape with the nucleus at its center and is called an **s orbital.** Because a sphere has only one orientation, an *s* orbital has only one $m_l$ value: for any *s* orbital, $m_l = 0$.

1. *The 1s orbital* holds the electron in the H atom's ground state. *The electron probability density is highest at the nucleus.* Figure 7.17A shows this graphically (*top*), and an electron density *relief map (inset)* depicts the graph's curve in three dimensions. Note the quarter-section of a three-dimensional electron cloud depiction (*middle*) has the darkest shading at the nucleus. For reasons discussed earlier (see Figure 7.16D and the margin note, p. 280), the radial probability distribution plot

**Figure 7.17 The 1s, 2s, and 3s orbitals.** For each of the *s* orbitals, a plot of probability density vs. distance (*top*, with the relief map, *inset*, showing the plot in three dimensions) lies above a quarter section of an electron cloud depiction of the 90% probability contour (*middle*), which lies above a radial probability distribution plot (*bottom*). **A,** The 1*s* orbital. **B,** The 2*s* orbital. **C,** The 3*s* orbital.

(*bottom*) is highest slightly out from the nucleus. Both plots fall off smoothly with distance.

2. *The 2s orbital* (Figure 7.17B) has two regions of higher electron density. The radial probability distribution (Figure 7.17B, *bottom*) of the more distant region is *higher* than that of the closer one because the sum of $\psi^2$ for it is taken over a much larger volume. Between the two regions is a spherical **node,** where the probability of finding the electron drops to zero ($\psi^2 = 0$ at the node, analogous to zero amplitude of a wave exactly between the peak and trough). Because the 2s orbital is larger than the 1s, an electron in the 2s spends more time farther from the nucleus (in the larger of the two regions) than it does when it occupies the 1s.

3. *The 3s orbital* (Figure 7.17C) has three regions of high electron density and two nodes. Here again, the highest radial probability is at the greatest distance from the nucleus. This pattern of more nodes and higher probability with distance from the nucleus continues with the 4s, 5s, and so forth.

**The *p* Orbital** An orbital with $l = 1$ is called a ***p* orbital** and has two regions (lobes) of high probability, one on *either side* of the nucleus (Figure 7.18). The *nucleus lies at the nodal plane* of this dumbbell-shaped orbital. Since the maximum value of $l$ is $n - 1$, only levels with $n = 2$ or higher have a p orbital: the lowest energy p orbital (the one closest to the nucleus) is the 2p. One p orbital consists of *two* lobes, and the electron spends *equal* time in both. Similar to the pattern for s orbitals, a 3p orbital is larger than a 2p, a 4p is larger than a 3p, and so forth.

Unlike s orbitals, p orbitals *have* different spatial orientations. The three possible $m_l$ values of $-1$, 0, and $+1$ refer to three *mutually perpendicular* orientations; that is, while identical in size, shape, and energy, the three p orbitals differ in orientation. We associate p orbitals with the $x$, $y$, and $z$ axes: the $p_x$ orbital lies along the $x$ axis, the $p_y$ along the $y$ axis, and the $p_z$ along the $z$ axis. (There is no relationship between a particular axis and a given $m_l$ value.)

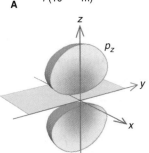

**A**

**Figure 7.18 The 2p orbitals. A,** A radial probability distribution plot of the 2p orbital shows a peak much farther from the nucleus than for the 1s. **B,** Cross section of an electron cloud depiction of the 90% probability contour of the $2p_z$ orbital shows a nodal plane. **C,** An accurate representation of the $2p_z$ probability contour. **D,** The stylized depiction of the 2p probability contour used in the text. **E,** The three (stylized) 2p orbitals occupy mutually perpendicular regions of space, contributing to the atom's overall spherical shape.

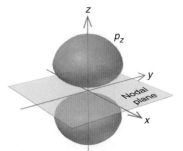

**B  Cross section of electron cloud depiction**

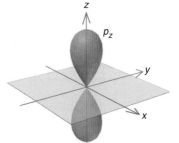

**C  Accurate probability contour**

**D  Stylized probability contour**

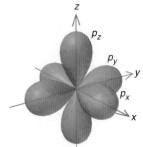

**E  The three *p* orbitals**

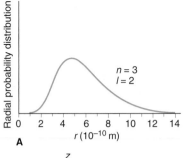

**A**

**Figure 7.19** The 3*d* orbitals. **A,** A radial probability distribution plot. **B,** Cross section of an electron cloud depiction of the $3d_{yz}$ orbital probability contour shows two mutually perpendicular nodal planes and lobes lying *between* the axes. **C,** An accurate representation of the $3d_{yz}$ orbital probability contour. **D,** The stylized depiction of the $3d_{yz}$ orbital used in the text. **E,** The $3d_{xz}$ orbital. **F,** The $3d_{xy}$ orbital. **G,** The lobes of the $d_{x^2-y^2}$ orbital lie *along* the x and y axes. **H,** The $d_{z^2}$ orbital has two lobes and a central, donut-shaped region. **I,** A composite of the five 3*d* (stylized) orbitals shows how they contribute to the atom's spherical shape.

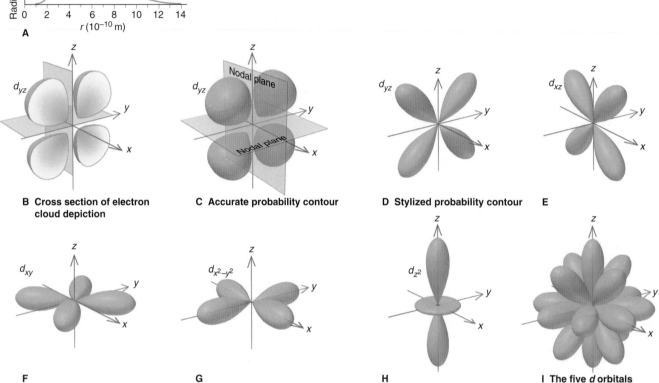

**B Cross section of electron cloud depiction**  **C Accurate probability contour**  **D Stylized probability contour**  **E**

**F**  **G**  **H**  **I The five *d* orbitals**

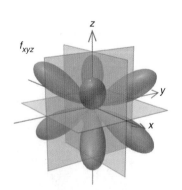

**Figure 7.20** The $4f_{xyz}$ orbital, one of the seven 4*f* orbitals.

**The *d* Orbital** An orbital with $l = 2$ is called a ***d* orbital.** There are five possible $m_l$ values for $l = 2$: $-2$, $-1$, 0, $+1$, and $+2$. Thus, a *d* orbital has any one of five orientations (Figure 7.19). Four of the five *d* orbitals have four lobes (a cloverleaf shape) with two mutually perpendicular nodal planes between them and the nucleus at the junction of the lobes (Figure 7.19C). (The orientation of the nodal planes always lies between the orbital lobes.) Three of these orbitals lie in the *xy, xz,* and *yz* planes, with their lobes *between* the axes, and are called the $d_{xy}$, $d_{xz}$, and $d_{yz}$ orbitals. A fourth, the $d_{x^2-y^2}$ orbital, also lies in the *xy* plane, but its lobes are *along* the axes. The fifth *d* orbital, the $d_{z^2}$, has two major lobes *along* the *z* axis, and a donut-shaped region girdles the center. An electron in a *d* orbital spends equal time in all of its lobes.

In keeping with the quantum-number hierarchy, a *d* orbital ($l = 2$) must have a principal quantum number of $n = 3$ or higher, so 3*d* is the lowest energy *d* sublevel. Orbitals in the 4*d* sublevel are larger (extend farther from the nucleus) than the 3*d*, and the 5*d* are larger still.

**Orbitals with Higher *l* Values** Orbitals with $l = 3$ are *f* orbitals and have a principal quantum number of at least $n = 4$. Figure 7.20 shows one of the seven *f* orbitals ($2l + 1 = 7$); each *f* orbital has a complex, multilobed shape with several nodal planes. Orbitals with $l = 4$ are *g* orbitals, but they play no known role in chemical bonding.

## The Special Case of Energy Levels in the H Atom

With regard to energy levels and sublevels, the H atom is a special case. When an H atom gains energy, its electron occupies an orbital of higher $n$ value, which is (on average) farther from the nucleus. But, because it has just one electron, *hydrogen is the only atom whose energy state depends completely on the principal quantum number, n.* As you'll see in Chapter 8, because of additional nucleus-electron attractions and electron-electron repulsions, the energy states of all other atoms depend on the $n$ *and* $l$ values of the occupied orbitals. Thus, *for the H atom only,* all four $n = 2$ orbitals (one 2s and three 2p) have the same energy, all nine $n = 3$ orbitals (one 3s, three 3p, and five 3d) have the same energy (Figure 7.21), and so forth.

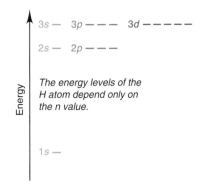

*The energy levels of the H atom depend only on the n value.*

**Figure 7.21** Energy levels of the H atom.

## ■ Summary of Section 7.4

- The atomic orbital ($\psi$, wave function) is a mathematical description of the electron's wavelike behavior in an atom. The Schrödinger equation converts each allowed wave function to one of the atom's energy states.
- The probability density of finding the electron at a particular location is represented by $\psi^2$. For a given energy level, an electron density diagram and a radial probability distribution plot show how the electron occupies the space near the nucleus.
- An atomic orbital is described by three quantum numbers: size ($n$), shape ($l$), and orientation ($m_l$): $n$ limits $l$ to $n - 1$ values, and $l$ limits $m_l$ to $2l + 1$ values.
- An energy level has sublevels with the same $n$ value; a sublevel has orbitals with the same $n$ and $l$ values but differing $m_l$ values.
- A sublevel with $l = 0$ has a spherical ($s$) orbital; a sublevel with $l = 1$ has three, two-lobed ($p$) orbitals; and a sublevel with $l = 2$ has five multilobed ($d$) orbitals.
- In the special case of the H atom, the energy levels depend only on the $n$ value.

# CHAPTER REVIEW GUIDE

**Learning Objectives**    Relevant section (§) and/or sample problem (SP) numbers appear in parentheses.

### Understand These Concepts

1. The wave characteristics of light (the interrelations of frequency, wavelength, and speed; the meaning of amplitude) and the general regions of the electromagnetic spectrum (§7.1)
2. How particles and waves differ in terms of the phenomena of refraction, diffraction, and interference (§7.1)
3. The quantization of energy and how an atom changes its energy by emitting or absorbing quanta of radiation (§7.1)
4. How the photon theory explains the photoelectric effect (§7.1)
5. How Bohr's theory explained the line spectra of the H atom; why the theory is wrong and which ideas we retain (§7.2)
6. The wave-particle duality of matter and energy and the relevant theories and experiments that led to it (de Broglie wavelength, electron diffraction, and photon momentum) (§7.3)
7. The meaning of the uncertainty principle and how uncertainty limits our knowledge of electron properties (§7.3)
8. The distinction between $\psi$ (wave function, or atomic orbital) and $\psi^2$ (probability density) (§7.4)
9. How electron density diagrams and radial probability distribution plots depict the electron's location within the atom (§7.4)

10. The hierarchy of the quantum numbers that describe the size ($n$, energy), shape ($l$), and orientation ($m_l$) of an orbital (§7.4)
11. The distinction between energy level (shell), sublevel (subshell), and orbital (§7.4)
12. The shapes of $s$, $p$, and $d$ orbitals (§7.4)

### Master These Skills

1. Interconverting wavelength and frequency (SP 7.1)
2. Calculating the energy of a photon from its wavelength (SP 7.2)
3. Finding the energy change and wavelength of the photon absorbed or emitted when an H atom changes its energy level (SP 7.3)
4. Applying de Broglie's equation to find the wavelength of an electron (SP 7.4)
5. Applying the uncertainty principle to see that the location and speed of a particle cannot be determined simultaneously (SP 7.5)
6. Determining quantum numbers and sublevel designations (SPs 7.6–7.8)

## Key Terms    Page numbers appear in parentheses.

**Section 7.1**
electromagnetic radiation (261)
frequency ($\nu$) (261)
wavelength ($\lambda$) (262)
speed of light ($c$) (262)
amplitude (262)
electromagnetic spectrum (262)
infrared (IR) (262)
ultraviolet (UV) (262)
refraction (263)
diffraction (264)
quantum number (266)

Planck's constant ($h$) (266)
quantum (266)
photoelectric effect (266)
photon (266)

**Section 7.2**
line spectrum (267)
stationary state (269)
ground state (269)
excited state (269)
spectrometry (273)
emission spectrum (273)
flame test (273)
absorption spectrum (273)

**Section 7.3**
de Broglie wavelength (276)
wave-particle duality (277)
uncertainty principle (278)

**Section 7.4**
quantum mechanics (279)
Schrödinger equation (279)
atomic orbital (wave function) (279)
electron density diagram (280)
electron cloud depiction (280)
radial probability distribution plot (280)

probability contour (281)
principal quantum number ($n$) (281)
angular momentum quantum number ($l$) (281)
magnetic quantum number ($m_l$) (281)
level (shell) (282)
sublevel (subshell) (282)
$s$ orbital (284)
node (285)
$p$ orbital (285)
$d$ orbital (286)

## Key Equations and Relationships    Page numbers appear in parentheses.

**7.1** Relating the speed of light to its frequency and wavelength (262):

$$c = \nu \times \lambda$$

**7.2** Determining the smallest change in an atom's energy (266):

$$\Delta E = h\nu$$

**7.3** Calculating the wavelength of any line in the H atom spectrum (Rydberg equation) (268):

$$\frac{1}{\lambda} = R\left(\frac{1}{n_1^2} - \frac{1}{n_2^2}\right)$$

where $n_1$ and $n_2$ are positive integers and $n_2 > n_1$

**7.4** Finding the difference between two energy levels in the H atom (271):

$$\Delta E = E_{\text{final}} - E_{\text{initial}} = -2.18\times10^{-18}\ \text{J}\left(\frac{1}{n_{\text{final}}^2} - \frac{1}{n_{\text{initial}}^2}\right)$$

**7.5** Calculating the wavelength of any moving particle (de Broglie wavelength) (276):

$$\lambda = \frac{h}{mu}$$

**7.6** Finding the uncertainty in position or speed of a particle (Heisenberg's uncertainty principle) (278):

$$\Delta x \cdot m\Delta u \geq \frac{h}{4\pi}$$

## Brief Solutions to Follow-Up Problems

**7.1**  $\lambda\ (\text{nm}) = \dfrac{3.00\times10^8\ \text{m/s}}{7.23\times10^{14}\ \text{s}^{-1}} \times \dfrac{10^9\ \text{nm}}{1\ \text{m}} = 415\ \text{nm}$

$\lambda\ (\text{Å}) = 415\ \text{nm} \times \dfrac{10\ \text{Å}}{1\ \text{nm}} = 4150\ \text{Å}$

**7.2** (a) UV: $E = hc/\lambda$

$= \dfrac{(6.626\times10^{-34}\ \text{J·s})(3.00\times10^8\ \text{m/s})}{1\times10^{-8}\ \text{m}}$

$= 2\times10^{-17}\ \text{J}$

(b) Visible: $E = 4\times10^{-19}\ \text{J}$; (c) IR: $E = 2\times10^{-21}\ \text{J}$
As $\lambda$ increases, $E$ decreases.

**7.3** (a) With $n_{\text{final}} = 3$ for an IR photon:

$\Delta E = -2.18\times10^{-18}\ \text{J}\left(\dfrac{1}{n_{\text{final}}^2} - \dfrac{1}{n_{\text{initial}}^2}\right)$

$= -2.18\times10^{-18}\ \text{J}\left(\dfrac{1}{3^2} - \dfrac{1}{6^2}\right)$

$= -2.18\times10^{-18}\ \text{J}\left(\dfrac{1}{9} - \dfrac{1}{36}\right) = -1.82\times10^{-19}\ \text{J}$

(b)  $\lambda = \dfrac{hc}{|\Delta E|} = \dfrac{(6.626\times10^{-34}\ \text{J·s})(3.00\times10^8\ \text{m/s})}{1.82\times10^{-19}\ \text{J}} \times \dfrac{1\ \text{Å}}{10^{-10}\ \text{m}}$

$= 1.09\times10^4\ \text{Å}$

**7.4**  $u = \dfrac{h}{m\lambda} = \dfrac{6.626\times10^{-34}\ \text{kg·m}^2\text{/s}}{(9.11\times10^{-31}\ \text{kg})\left(100\ \text{nm} \times \dfrac{1\ \text{m}}{10^9\ \text{nm}}\right)}$

$= 7.27\times10^3\ \text{m/s}$

**7.5**  $\Delta x \geq \dfrac{6.626\times10^{-34}\ \text{kg·m}^2\text{/s}}{4\pi\,(0.142\ \text{kg})(0.447\ \text{m/s})} \geq 8.31\times10^{-34}\ \text{m}$

**7.6**  $n = 4$, so $l = 0, 1, 2, 3$. In addition to the nine $m_l$ values in Sample Problem 7.6 there are those for $l = 3$:
$$m_l = -3, -2, -1, 0, +1, +2, +3$$

**7.7**  For 2p: $n = 2$, $l = 1$, $m_l = -1, 0, +1$
For 5f: $n = 5$, $l = 3$, $m_l = -3, -2, -1, 0, +1, +2, +3$

**7.8** (a) $n = 4$, $l = 1$; (b) name is 2p; (c) name is 3d; (d) $n = 2$, $l = 0$, $m_l = 0$

# PROBLEMS

Problems with **colored** numbers are answered in Appendix E and worked in detail in the Student Solutions Manual. Problem sections match those in the text and provide numbers of relevant sample problems. Most offer Concept Review Questions, Skill-Building Exercises (grouped in pairs covering the same concept), and Problems in Context. Comprehensive Problems are based on material from any section or previous chapter.

## The Nature of Light
(Sample Problems 7.1 and 7.2)

### Concept Review Questions

**7.1** In what ways are microwave and ultraviolet radiation the same? In what ways are they different?

**7.2** Consider the following types of electromagnetic radiation:
(1) Microwave    (2) Ultraviolet    (3) Radio waves
(4) Infrared    (5) X-ray    (6) Visible
(a) Arrange them in order of increasing wavelength.
(b) Arrange them in order of increasing frequency.
(c) Arrange them in order of increasing energy.

**7.3** Define each of the following wave phenomena, and give an example of where each occurs: (a) refraction; (b) diffraction; (c) dispersion; (d) interference.

**7.4** In the 17th century, Newton proposed that light was a stream of particles. The wave-particle debate continued for over 250 years until Planck and Einstein presented their ideas. Give two pieces of evidence for the wave model and two for the particle model.

**7.5** Portions of electromagnetic waves A, B, and C are represented below (not drawn to scale):

Rank them in order of (a) increasing frequency; (b) increasing energy; (c) increasing amplitude. (d) If wave B just barely fails to cause a current when shining on a metal, is wave A or C more likely to do so? (e) If wave B represents visible radiation, is wave A or C more likely to be IR radiation?

**7.6** What new idea about light did Einstein use to explain the photoelectric effect? Why does the photoelectric effect exhibit a threshold frequency but not a time lag?

### Skill-Building Exercises (grouped in similar pairs)

**7.7** An AM station broadcasts rock music at "950 on your radio dial." Units for AM frequencies are given in kilohertz (kHz). Find the wavelength of the station's radio waves in meters (m), nanometers (nm), and angstroms (Å).

**7.8** An FM station broadcasts music at 93.5 MHz (megahertz, or $10^6$ Hz). Find the wavelength (in m, nm, and Å) of these waves.

**7.9** A radio wave has a frequency of $3.8 \times 10^{10}$ Hz. What is the energy (in J) of one photon of this radiation?

**7.10** An x-ray has a wavelength of 1.3 Å. Calculate the energy (in J) of one photon of this radiation.

**7.11** Rank these photons in terms of increasing energy: (a) blue ($\lambda = 453$ nm); (b) red ($\lambda = 660$ nm); (c) yellow ($\lambda = 595$ nm).

**7.12** Rank these photons in terms of decreasing energy: (a) IR ($\nu = 6.5 \times 10^{13}$ s$^{-1}$); (b) microwave ($\nu = 9.8 \times 10^{11}$ s$^{-1}$); (c) UV ($\nu = 8.0 \times 10^{15}$ s$^{-1}$).

### Problems in Context

**7.13** Police often monitor traffic with "K-band" radar guns, which operate in the microwave region at 22.235 GHz (1 GHz = $10^9$ Hz). Find the wavelength (in nm and Å) of this radiation.

**7.14** Covalent bonds in a molecule absorb radiation in the IR region and vibrate at characteristic frequencies.
(a) The C—O bond absorbs radiation of wavelength 9.6 μm. What frequency (in s$^{-1}$) corresponds to that wavelength?
(b) The H—Cl bond has a frequency of vibration of $8.652 \times 10^{13}$ Hz. What wavelength (in μm) corresponds to that frequency?

**7.15** Cobalt-60 is a radioactive isotope used to treat cancers. A gamma ray emitted by this isotope has an energy of 1.33 MeV (million electron volts; 1 eV = $1.602 \times 10^{-19}$ J). What is the frequency (in Hz) and the wavelength (in m) of this gamma ray?

**7.16** (a) Ozone formation in the upper atmosphere starts when oxygen molecules absorb UV radiation of wavelengths $\leq 242$ nm. Find the frequency and energy of the least energetic of these photons. (b) Ozone absorbs radiation of wavelengths 2200–2900 Å, thus protecting organisms from this radiation. Find the frequency and energy of the most energetic of these photons.

## Atomic Spectra
(Sample Problem 7.3)

### Concept Review Questions

**7.17** How is $n_1$ in the Rydberg equation (Equation 7.3) related to the quantum number $n$ in the Bohr model?

**7.18** What key assumption of Bohr's model would a "Solar System" model of the atom violate? What was the theoretical basis for this assumption?

**7.19** Distinguish between an absorption spectrum and an emission spectrum. With which did Bohr work?

**7.20** Which of these electron transitions correspond to absorption of energy and which to emission?
(a) $n = 2$ to $n = 4$    (b) $n = 3$ to $n = 1$
(c) $n = 5$ to $n = 2$    (d) $n = 3$ to $n = 4$

**7.21** Why couldn't the Bohr model predict spectra for atoms other than hydrogen?

**7.22** The H atom and the $Be^{3+}$ ion each have one electron. Would you expect the Bohr model to predict their spectra accurately? Would you expect their spectra to be identical? Explain.

### Skill-Building Exercises (grouped in similar pairs)

**7.23** Use the Rydberg equation to find the wavelength (in nm) of the photon emitted when an H atom undergoes a transition from $n = 5$ to $n = 2$.

**7.24** Use the Rydberg equation to find the wavelength (in Å) of the photon absorbed when an H atom undergoes a transition from $n = 1$ to $n = 3$.

**7.25** What is the wavelength (in nm) of the least energetic spectral line in the infrared series of the H atom?

**7.26** What is the wavelength (in nm) of the least energetic spectral line in the visible series of the H atom?

**7.27** Calculate the energy difference ($\Delta E$) for the transition in Problem 7.23 for 1 mol of H atoms.

**7.28** Calculate the energy difference ($\Delta E$) for the transition in Problem 7.24 for 1 mol of H atoms.

**7.29** Arrange the following H atom electron transitions in order of *increasing* frequency of the photon absorbed or emitted:
(a) $n = 2$ to $n = 4$       (b) $n = 2$ to $n = 1$
(c) $n = 2$ to $n = 5$       (d) $n = 4$ to $n = 3$

**7.30** Arrange the following H atom electron transitions in order of *decreasing* wavelength of the photon absorbed or emitted:
(a) $n = 2$ to $n = \infty$       (b) $n = 4$ to $n = 20$
(c) $n = 3$ to $n = 10$       (d) $n = 2$ to $n = 1$

**7.31** The electron in a ground-state H atom absorbs a photon of wavelength 97.20 nm. To what energy level does it move?

**7.32** An electron in the $n = 5$ level of an H atom emits a photon of wavelength 1281 nm. To what energy level does it move?

### Problems in Context

**7.33** In addition to continuous radiation, fluorescent lamps emit some visible lines from mercury. A prominent line has a wavelength of 436 nm. What is the energy (in J) of one photon of it?

**7.34** A Bohr-model representation of the H atom is shown below with several electron transitions depicted by arrows:

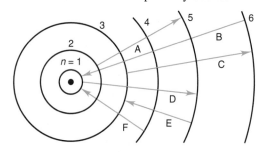

(a) Which transitions are absorptions and which are emissions?
(b) Rank the emissions in terms of increasing energy. (c) Rank the absorptions in terms of increasing wavelength of light emitted.

### The Wave-Particle Duality of Matter and Energy
(Sample Problems 7.4 and 7.5)

#### Concept Review Questions

**7.35** In what sense is the wave motion of a guitar string analogous to the motion of an electron in an atom?

**7.36** What experimental support did de Broglie's concept receive?

**7.37** If particles have wavelike motion, why don't we observe that motion in the macroscopic world?

**7.38** Why can't we overcome the uncertainty predicted by Heisenberg's principle by building more precise instruments to reduce the error in measurements below the $h/4\pi$ limit?

#### Skill-Building Exercises (grouped in similar pairs)

**7.39** A 232-lb fullback runs 40 yd at $19.8 \pm 0.1$ mi/h.
(a) What is his de Broglie wavelength (in meters)?
(b) What is the uncertainty in his position?

**7.40** An alpha particle (mass $= 6.6\times10^{-24}$ g) emitted by a radium isotope travels at $3.4\times10^7 \pm 0.1\times10^7$ mi/h.
(a) What is its de Broglie wavelength (in meters)?
(b) What is the uncertainty in its position?

**7.41** How fast must a 56.5-g tennis ball travel to have a de Broglie wavelength equal to that of a photon of green light (5400 Å)?

**7.42** How fast must a 142-g baseball travel to have a de Broglie wavelength equal to that of an x-ray photon with $\lambda = 100.$ pm?

**7.43** A sodium flame has a characteristic yellow color due to emissions of wavelength 589 nm. What is the mass equivalence of one photon of this wavelength (1 J $= 1$ kg·m²/s²)?

**7.44** A lithium flame has a characteristic red color due to emissions of wavelength 671 nm. What is the mass equivalence of 1 mol of photons of this wavelength (1 J $= 1$ kg·m²/s²)?

### The Quantum-Mechanical Model of the Atom
(Sample Problems 7.6 to 7.8)

#### Concept Review Questions

**7.45** What physical meaning is attributed to $\psi^2$?

**7.46** What does "electron density in a tiny volume of space" mean?

**7.47** Explain what it means for the peak in the radial probability distribution plot for the $n = 1$ level of an H atom to be at 0.529 Å. Is the probability of finding an electron at 0.529 Å from the nucleus greater for the 1s or the 2s orbital?

**7.48** What feature of an orbital is related to each of the following?
(a) Principal quantum number ($n$)
(b) Angular momentum quantum number ($l$)
(c) Magnetic quantum number ($m_l$)

#### Skill-Building Exercises (grouped in similar pairs)

**7.49** How many orbitals in an atom can have each of the following designations: (a) 1s; (b) 4d; (c) 3p; (d) $n = 3$?

**7.50** How many orbitals in an atom can have each of the following designations: (a) 5f; (b) 4p; (c) 5d; (d) $n = 2$?

**7.51** Give all possible $m_l$ values for orbitals that have each of the following: (a) $l = 2$; (b) $n = 1$; (c) $n = 4, l = 3$.

**7.52** Give all possible $m_l$ values for orbitals that have each of the following: (a) $l = 3$; (b) $n = 2$; (c) $n = 6, l = 1$.

**7.53** Draw 90% probability contours (with axes) for each of the following orbitals: (a) $s$; (b) $p_x$.

**7.54** Draw 90% probability contours (with axes) for each of the following orbitals: (a) $p_z$; (b) $d_{xy}$.

**7.55** For each of the following, give the sublevel designation, the allowable $m_l$ values, and the number of orbitals:
(a) $n = 4, l = 2$       (b) $n = 5, l = 1$       (c) $n = 6, l = 3$

**7.56** For each of the following, give the sublevel designation, the allowable $m_l$ values, and the number of orbitals:
(a) $n = 2, l = 0$       (b) $n = 3, l = 2$       (c) $n = 5, l = 1$

**7.57** For each of the following sublevels, give the $n$ and $l$ values and the number of orbitals: (a) 5s; (b) 3p; (c) 4f.

**7.58** For each of the following sublevels, give the $n$ and $l$ values and the number of orbitals: (a) 6g; (b) 4s; (c) 3d.

**7.59** Are the following combinations allowed? If not, show two ways to correct them:
(a) $n = 2; l = 0; m_l = -1$    (b) $n = 4; l = 3; m_l = -1$
(c) $n = 3; l = 1; m_l = 0$    (d) $n = 5; l = 2; m_l = +3$

**7.60** Are the following combinations allowed? If not, show two ways to correct them:
(a) $n = 1; l = 0; m_l = 0$    (b) $n = 2; l = 2; m_l = +1$
(c) $n = 7; l = 1; m_l = +2$    (d) $n = 3; l = 1; m_l = -2$

## Comprehensive Problems

**7.61** The orange color of carrots and orange peel is due mostly to β-carotene, an organic compound insoluble in water but soluble in benzene and chloroform. Describe an experiment to determine the concentration of β-carotene in the oil from orange peel.

**7.62** The quantum-mechanical treatment of the H atom gives the energy, $E$, of the electron as a function of $n$:

$$E = -\frac{h^2}{8\pi^2 m_e a_0^2 n^2} \qquad (n = 1, 2, 3, \ldots)$$

where $h$ is Planck's constant, $m_e$ is the electron mass, and $a_0$ is $52.92 \times 10^{-12}$ m.
(a) Write the expression in the form $E = -(\text{constant})(1/n^2)$, evaluate the constant (in J), and compare it with the corresponding expression from Bohr's theory.
(b) Use the expression to find $\Delta E$ between $n = 2$ and $n = 3$.
(c) Calculate the wavelength of the photon that corresponds to this energy change.

**7.63** The photoelectric effect is illustrated in a plot of the kinetic energies of electrons ejected from the surface of potassium metal or silver metal at different frequencies of incident light.

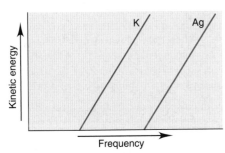

(a) Why don't the lines begin at the origin? (b) Why don't the lines begin at the same point? (c) From which metal will light of shorter wavelength eject an electron? (d) Why are the slopes equal?

**7.64** The optic nerve needs a minimum of $2.0 \times 10^{-17}$ J of energy to trigger a series of impulses that eventually reach the brain.
(a) How many photons of red light (700. nm) are needed? (b) How many photons of blue light (475 nm)?

**7.65** One reason carbon monoxide (CO) is toxic is that it binds to the blood protein hemoglobin more strongly than oxygen does. The bond between hemoglobin and CO absorbs radiation of 1953 cm$^{-1}$. (The units are the reciprocal of the wavelength in centimeters.) Calculate the wavelength (in nm and Å) and the frequency (in Hz) of the absorbed radiation.

**7.66** A metal ion $M^{n+}$ has a single electron. The highest energy line in its emission spectrum has a frequency of $2.961 \times 10^{16}$ Hz. Identify the ion.

**7.67** Compare the wavelengths of an electron (mass $= 9.11 \times 10^{-31}$ kg) and a proton (mass $= 1.67 \times 10^{-27}$ kg), each having (a) a speed of $3.4 \times 10^6$ m/s; (b) a kinetic energy of $2.7 \times 10^{-15}$ J.

**7.68** Five lines in the H atom spectrum have these wavelengths (in Å): (a) 1212.7; (b) 4340.5; (c) 4861.3; (d) 6562.8; (e) 10,938. Three lines result from transitions to $n_{\text{final}} = 2$ (visible series). The other two result from transitions in different series, one with $n_{\text{final}} = 1$ and the other with $n_{\text{final}} = 3$. Identify $n_{\text{initial}}$ for each line.

**7.69** In his explanation of the threshold frequency in the photoelectric effect, Einstein reasoned that the absorbed photon must have a minimum energy to dislodge an electron from the metal surface. This energy is called the *work function* (φ) of that metal. What is the longest wavelength of radiation (in nm) that could cause the photoelectric effect in each of these metals: (a) calcium, $\phi = 4.60 \times 10^{-19}$ J; (b) titanium, $\phi = 6.94 \times 10^{-19}$ J; (c) sodium, $\phi = 4.41 \times 10^{-19}$ J?

**7.70** Refractometry is based on the difference in the speed of light through a substance ($v$) and through a vacuum ($c$). In the procedure, light of known wavelength passes through a fixed thickness of the substance at a known temperature. The index of refraction equals $c/v$. Using yellow light ($\lambda = 589$ nm) at 20°C, for example, the index of refraction of water is 1.33 and that of diamond is 2.42. Calculate the speed of light in (a) water and (b) diamond.

**7.71** A laser (*light amplification by stimulated emission of radiation*) provides nearly monochromatic high-intensity light. Lasers are used in eye surgery, CD/DVD players, basic research, and many other areas. Some dye lasers can be "tuned" to emit a desired wavelength. Fill in the blanks in the following table of the properties of some common lasers:

| Type | λ (nm) | $\nu$ (s$^{-1}$) | $E$ (J) | Color |
|------|--------|------------------|---------|-------|
| He-Ne | 632.8 | ? | ? | ? |
| Ar | ? | $6.148 \times 10^{14}$ | ? | ? |
| Ar-Kr | ? | ? | $3.499 \times 10^{-19}$ | ? |
| Dye | 663.7 | ? | ? | ? |

**7.72** The following combinations are not allowed. If $n$ and $m_l$ are correct, change the $l$ value to create an allowable combination:
(a) $n = 3; l = 0; m_l = -1$    (b) $n = 3; l = 3; m_l = +1$
(c) $n = 7; l = 2; m_l = +3$    (d) $n = 4; l = 1; m_l = -2$

**7.73** A ground-state H atom absorbs a photon of wavelength 94.91 nm, and its electron attains a higher energy level. The atom then emits two photons: one of wavelength 1281 nm to reach an intermediate energy level, and a second to return to the ground state.
(a) What higher level did the electron reach?
(b) What intermediate level did the electron reach?
(c) What was the wavelength of the second photon emitted?

**7.74** Ground-state ionization energies of some one-electron species are

H $= 1.31 \times 10^3$ kJ/mol      He$^+ = 5.24 \times 10^3$ kJ/mol
Li$^{2+} = 1.18 \times 10^4$ kJ/mol

(a) Write a general expression for the ionization energy of any one-electron species. (b) Use your expression to calculate the ionization energy of $B^{4+}$. (c) What is the minimum wavelength required to remove the electron from the $n = 3$ level of $He^+$? (d) What is the minimum wavelength required to remove the electron from the $n = 2$ level of $Be^{3+}$?

**7.75** Use the relative size of the $3s$ orbital below to answer the following questions about orbitals A–D.

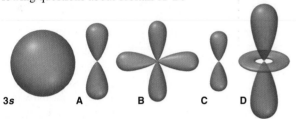

$3s$      A      B      C      D

(a) Which orbital has the highest value of $n$? (b) Which orbital(s) have a value of $l = 1$? $l = 2$? (c) How many other orbitals with the same value of $n$ have the same shape as orbital B? Orbital C? (d) Which orbital has the highest energy? Lowest energy?

**7.76** In the course of developing his model, Bohr arrived at the following formula for the radius of the electron's orbit: $r_n = n^2h^2\epsilon_0/\pi m_e e^2$, where $m_e$ is the electron mass, $e$ is its charge, and $\epsilon_0$ is a constant related to charge attraction in a vacuum. Given that $m_e = 9.109 \times 10^{-31}$ kg, $e = 1.602 \times 10^{-19}$ C, and $\epsilon_0 = 8.854 \times 10^{-12}$ $C^2/J \cdot m$, calculate the following:
(a) The radius of the first ($n = 1$) orbit in the H atom
(b) The radius of the tenth ($n = 10$) orbit in the H atom

**7.77** (a) Find the Bohr radius of an electron in the $n = 3$ orbit of an H atom (see Problem 7.76). (b) What is the energy (in J) of the atom in part (a)? (c) What is the energy of an $Li^{2+}$ ion with its electron in the $n = 3$ orbit? (d) Why are the answers to (b) and (c) different?

**7.78** Enormous numbers of microwave photons are needed to warm macroscopic samples of matter. A portion of soup containing 252 g of water is heated in a microwave oven from 20.°C to 98°C, with radiation of wavelength $1.55 \times 10^{-2}$ m. How many photons are absorbed by the water in the soup?

**7.79** The quantum-mechanical treatment of the hydrogen atom gives this expression for the wave function, $\psi$, of the $1s$ orbital:

$$\psi = \frac{1}{\sqrt{\pi}} \left(\frac{1}{a_0}\right)^{3/2} e^{-r/a_0}$$

where $r$ is the distance from the nucleus and $a_0$ is 52.92 pm. The probability of finding the electron in a tiny volume at distance $r$ from the nucleus is proportional to $\psi^2$. The total probability of finding the electron at all points at distance $r$ from the nucleus is proportional to $4\pi r^2\psi^2$. Calculate the values (to three significant figures) of $\psi$, $\psi^2$, and $4\pi r^2\psi^2$ to fill in the following table and sketch a plot of each set of values versus $r$. Compare the latter two plots with those in Figure 7.17A, p. 284:

| $r$ (pm) | $\psi$ $(pm^{-3/2})$ | $\psi^2$ $(pm^{-3})$ | $4\pi r^2\psi^2$ $(pm^{-1})$ |
|---|---|---|---|
| 0 | | | |
| 50 | | | |
| 100 | | | |
| 200 | | | |

**7.80** Lines in one spectral series can overlap lines in another. (a) Does the range of wavelengths in the $n_1 = 1$ series for the H atom overlap the range in the $n_1 = 2$ series? (b) Does the range in the $n_1 = 3$ series overlap the range in the $n_1 = 4$ series? (c) How many lines in the $n_1 = 4$ series lie in the range of the $n_1 = 5$ series? (d) What does this overlap imply about the H atom line spectrum at longer wavelengths?

**7.81** The following values are the only energy levels of a hypothetical one-electron atom:

| | |
|---|---|
| $E_6 = -2 \times 10^{-19}$ J | $E_5 = -7 \times 10^{-19}$ J |
| $E_4 = -11 \times 10^{-19}$ J | $E_3 = -15 \times 10^{-19}$ J |
| $E_2 = -17 \times 10^{-19}$ J | $E_1 = -20 \times 10^{-19}$ J |

(a) If the electron were in the $n = 3$ level, what would be the highest frequency (and minimum wavelength) of radiation that could be emitted? (b) What is the ionization energy (in kJ/mol) of the atom in its ground state? (c) If the electron were in the $n = 4$ level, what would be the shortest wavelength (in nm) of radiation that could be absorbed without causing ionization?

**7.82** Photoelectron spectroscopy applies the principle of the photoelectric effect to study orbital energies of atoms and molecules. High-energy radiation (usually UV or x-ray) is absorbed by a sample and an electron is ejected. The orbital energy can be calculated from the known energy of the radiation and the measured energy of the electron lost. The following energy differences were determined for several electron transitions:

| | |
|---|---|
| $\Delta E_{2 \rightarrow 1} = 4.098 \times 10^{-17}$ J | $\Delta E_{3 \rightarrow 1} = 4.854 \times 10^{-17}$ J |
| $\Delta E_{5 \rightarrow 1} = 5.242 \times 10^{-17}$ J | $\Delta E_{4 \rightarrow 2} = 1.024 \times 10^{-17}$ J |

Calculate $\Delta E$ and $\lambda$ of a photon emitted in the following transitions: (a) level 3 $\longrightarrow$ 2; (b) level 4 $\longrightarrow$ 1; (c) level 5 $\longrightarrow$ 4.

**7.83** Horticulturists know that, for many plants, dark green leaves are associated with low light levels and pale green with high levels. (a) Use the photon theory to explain this behavior. (b) What change in leaf composition might account for this difference?

**7.84** In order to comply with the requirement that energy be conserved, Einstein showed in the photoelectric effect that the energy of a photon ($h\nu$) absorbed by a metal is the sum of the work function ($\phi$), the minimum energy needed to dislodge an electron from the metal's surface, and the kinetic energy ($E_k$) of the electron: $h\nu = \phi + E_k$. When light of wavelength 358.1 nm falls on the surface of potassium metal, the speed ($u$) of the dislodged electron is $6.40 \times 10^5$ m/s. (a) What is $E_k$ ($\frac{1}{2}mu^2$) of the dislodged electron? (b) What is $\phi$ (in J) of potassium?

**7.85** For any microscope, the smallest object observable is one-half the wavelength of the radiation used. For example, the smallest object observable with light of 400 nm is $2 \times 10^{-7}$ m. (a) What is the smallest object observable with an electron microscope using electrons moving at $5.5 \times 10^4$ m/s? (b) At $3.0 \times 10^7$ m/s?

**7.86** In fireworks, the heat of the reaction of an oxidizing agent, such as $KClO_4$, with an organic compound excites certain salts, which emit specific colors. Strontium salts have an intense emission at 641 nm, and barium salts have one at 493 nm. (a) What colors do these emissions produce? (b) What is the energy (in kJ) of these emissions for 5.00 g each of the chloride salts of Sr and Ba? (Assume that all the heat produced is converted to emitted light.)

**7.87** Atomic hydrogen produces several series of spectral lines. Each series fits the Rydberg equation with its own particular $n_1$ value. Calculate the value of $n_1$ (by trial and error if necessary) that would produce a series of lines in which:
(a) The *highest* energy line has a wavelength of 3282 nm.
(b) The *lowest* energy line has a wavelength of 7460 nm.

**7.88** Fish-liver oil is a good source of vitamin A, whose concentration is measured spectrometrically at a wavelength of 329 nm. (a) Suggest a reason for using this wavelength. (b) In what region of the spectrum does this wavelength lie? (c) When 0.1232 g of fish-liver oil is dissolved in 500. mL of solvent, the absorbance is 0.724 units. When $1.67 \times 10^{-3}$ g of vitamin A is dissolved in 250. mL of solvent, the absorbance is 1.018 units. Calculate the vitamin A concentration in the fish-liver oil.

**7.89** Many calculators use photocells as their energy source. Find the maximum wavelength needed to remove an electron from silver ($\phi = 7.59 \times 10^{-19}$ J). Is silver a good choice for a photocell that uses visible light? [The concept of the work function ($\phi$) is explained in Problem 7.69.]

**7.90** In a game of "Clue," Ms. White is killed in the conservatory. A spectrometer in each room records who is present to help find the murderer. For example, if someone wearing yellow is in a room, light at 580 nm is reflected. The suspects are Col. Mustard, Prof. Plum, Mr. Green, Ms. Peacock (blue), and Ms. Scarlet. At the time of the murder, the spectrometer in the dining room shows a reflection at 520 nm, those in the lounge and study record lower frequencies, and the one in the library records the shortest possible wavelength. Who killed Ms. White? Explain.

**7.91** Technetium (Tc; $Z = 43$) is a synthetic element used as a radioactive tracer in medical studies. A Tc atom emits a beta particle (electron) with a kinetic energy ($E_k$) of $4.71 \times 10^{-15}$ J. What is the de Broglie wavelength of this electron ($E_k = \frac{1}{2}mv^2$)?

**7.92** Electric power is measured in watts (1 W = 1 J/s). About 95% of the power output of an incandescent bulb is converted to heat and 5% to light. If 10% of that light shines on your chemistry text, how many photons per second shine on the book from a 75-W bulb? (Assume the photons have a wavelength of 550 nm.)

**7.93** The flame tests for sodium and potassium are based on the emissions at 589 nm and 404 nm, respectively. When both elements are present, the $Na^+$ emission is so strong that the $K^+$ emission can only be seen by looking through a cobalt-glass filter. (a) What are the colors of these $Na^+$ and $K^+$ emissions?

(b) What does the cobalt-glass filter do? (c) Why is $KClO_4$ used as an oxidizing agent in fireworks rather than $NaClO_4$?

**7.94** The net change during photosynthesis involves $CO_2$ and $H_2O$ forming glucose ($C_6H_{12}O_6$) and $O_2$. Chlorophyll absorbs light in the 600–700 nm region. (a) Write a balanced thermochemical equation for formation of 1.00 mol of glucose. (b) What is the minimum number of photons with $\lambda = 680$. nm needed to form 1.00 mol of glucose?

**7.95** Only certain transitions are allowed from one energy level to another. In one-electron species, the change in $l$ of an allowed transition is $\pm 1$. For example, a $3p$ electron can move to a $2s$ orbital but not to a $2p$. Thus, in the UV series, where $n_{final} = 1$, allowed transitions can start in a $p$ orbital ($l = 1$) of $n = 2$ or higher, not in an $s$ ($l = 0$) or $d$ ($l = 2$) orbital of $n = 2$ or higher. From what orbital do each of the allowed transitions start for the first four emission lines in the visible series ($n_{final} = 2$)?

**7.96** The discharge of phosphate in detergents to the environment has led to imbalances in the life cycle of freshwater lakes. A chemist uses a spectrometric method to measure total phosphate and obtains the following data for known standards:

| Absorbance (880 nm) | Concentration (mol/L) |
|---|---|
| 0 | $0.0 \times 10^{-5}$ |
| 0.10 | $2.5 \times 10^{-5}$ |
| 0.16 | $3.2 \times 10^{-5}$ |
| 0.20 | $4.4 \times 10^{-5}$ |
| 0.25 | $5.6 \times 10^{-5}$ |
| 0.38 | $8.4 \times 10^{-5}$ |
| 0.48 | $10.5 \times 10^{-5}$ |
| 0.62 | $13.8 \times 10^{-5}$ |
| 0.76 | $17.0 \times 10^{-5}$ |
| 0.88 | $19.4 \times 10^{-5}$ |

(a) Draw a curve of absorbance vs. phosphate concentration. (b) If a sample of lake water has an absorbance of 0.55, what is its phosphate concentration?

# Electron Configuration and Chemical Periodicity

## Concepts and skills to review before you study this chapter

- format of the periodic table (Section 2.6)
- characteristics of metals and nonmetals (Section 2.6)
- attractions, repulsions, and Coulomb's law (Section 2.7)
- characteristics of acids and bases (Section 4.4)
- rules for assigning quantum numbers (Section 7.4)

W e have become expert at measuring recurring patterns in nature—day and night, the seasons, solar and lunar eclipses, even the swirl in a shell or the rhythm of a heartbeat. Elements exhibit recurring patterns in properties because their atoms do, and we can measure these patterns, too.

The outpouring of scientific creativity by early 20th-century physicists that led to the new quantum-mechanical model of the atom was preceded by countless hours of laboratory work by 19th-century chemists who were exploring the nature of electrolytes, the kinetic-molecular theory, and chemical thermodynamics. The fields of organic chemistry and biochemistry were born in the 19th century, as were the fertilizer, explosives, glassmaking, soapmaking, bleaching, and dyestuff industries. And, for the first time, chemistry became a subject in universities in Europe and America.

Condensed from all these efforts, an enormous body of facts emerged about the elements, which became organized into the periodic table:

- *The original periodic table.* In 1870, the Russian chemist Dmitri Mendeleev arranged the 65 elements known at the time into a table and summarized their behavior in the **periodic law:** when arranged by *atomic mass,* the elements exhibit a periodic recurrence of similar properties. Mendeleev left blank spaces in his table and was even able to *predict* the properties of several elements, for example, germanium, that were not discovered until later.
- *The modern periodic table.* Today's table *(inside front cover)* includes 52 elements not known in 1870 and, most importantly, arranges the elements by *atomic number* (number of protons) *not* atomic mass. This change is based on the work of the British physicist Henry G. J. Moseley, who obtained x-ray spectra of various metals by bombarding the metals with electrons. Moseley found that the largest x-ray peak for each metal was related to the nuclear charge, which increased by 1 for each successive element.

The great test for the new atomic model was to answer one of the central questions in chemistry: *why* do the elements behave as they do? Or, rephrasing to fit the main topic of this chapter, how does the **electron configuration** of an element—*the distribution of electrons within the levels and sublevels of its atoms*—relate to its chemical and physical properties?

**IN THIS CHAPTER . . .** We explore recurring patterns of electron distributions in atoms to see how they account for the recurring behavior of the elements.
- We describe a new quantum number and a restriction on the number of electrons in an orbital, which allows us to define a unique set of quantum numbers for each electron in an atom of any element.
- We explore electrostatic effects that lead to splitting of atomic energy levels into sublevels and give rise to the order in which orbitals fill with electrons. This filling order correlates with the order of elements in the periodic table.
- We examine the reasons for periodic trends in three atomic properties.
- We see how these trends account for chemical reactivity with regard to metallic and redox behavior, oxide acidity, ion formation, and magnetic behavior.

# 8.1 • CHARACTERISTICS OF MANY-ELECTRON ATOMS

The Schrödinger equation (introduced in Chapter 7) does not give *exact* solutions for the energy levels of *many-electron atoms,* those with more than one electron—that is, all atoms except hydrogen. However, unlike the Bohr model, it gives excellent *approximate* solutions. Three additional features become important in many-electron atoms: (1) a fourth quantum number, (2) a limit on the number of electrons in an orbital, and (3) a splitting of energy levels into sublevels.

## The Electron-Spin Quantum Number

The three quantum numbers $n$, $l$, and $m_l$ describe the size (energy), shape, and orientation, respectively, of an atomic orbital. An additional quantum number describes a property called *spin,* which is a property of the electron and not the orbital.

When a beam of atoms that have one or more lone electrons passes through a nonuniform magnetic field (created by magnet faces with different shapes), it splits into two beams; Figure 8.1 shows this for a beam of H atoms. Each electron behaves like a spinning charge and generates a tiny magnetic field, which can have one of two values of *spin*. The two electron fields have opposing directions, so half of the electrons are *attracted* by the large external magnetic field while the other half are *repelled* by it.

**Figure 8.1 The effect of electron spin.** A beam of H atoms splits because each atom's electron has one of the two possible values of spin.

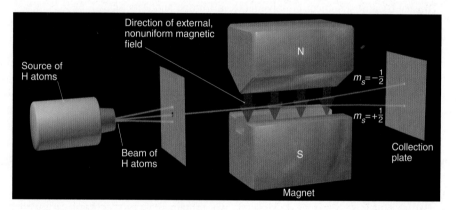

Corresponding to the two directions of the electron's field, the **spin quantum number ($m_s$)** has two possible values, $+\frac{1}{2}$ or $-\frac{1}{2}$. Thus, *each electron in an atom is described completely by a set of **four** quantum numbers: the first three describe its orbital, and the fourth describes its spin.* The quantum numbers are summarized in Table 8.1.

Now we can write a set of four quantum numbers for any electron in the ground state of any atom. For example, the set of quantum numbers for the lone electron in hydrogen (H; $Z = 1$) is $n = 1$, $l = 0$, $m_l = 0$, and $m_s = +\frac{1}{2}$. (The spin quantum number could just as well have been $-\frac{1}{2}$, but by convention, we assign $+\frac{1}{2}$ to the first electron in an orbital.)

| Table **8.1** Summary of Quantum Numbers of Electrons in Atoms | | | |
|---|---|---|---|
| **Name** | **Symbol** | **Permitted Values** | **Property** |
| Principal | $n$ | Positive integers (1, 2, 3, . . .) | Orbital energy (size) |
| Angular momentum | $l$ | Integers from 0 to $n - 1$ | Orbital shape (the $l$ values 0, 1, 2, and 3 correspond to $s$, $p$, $d$, and $f$ orbitals, respectively.) |
| Magnetic | $m_l$ | Integers from $-l$ to 0 to $+l$ | Orbital orientation |
| Spin | $m_s$ | $+\frac{1}{2}$ or $-\frac{1}{2}$ | Direction of $e^-$ spin |

## The Exclusion Principle

The element after hydrogen is helium (He; $Z = 2$), the first with atoms having more than one electron. The first electron in the He ground state has the same set of quantum numbers as the electron in the H atom, but the second He electron does not. Based on observations of excited states, the Austrian physicist Wolfgang Pauli formulated the **exclusion principle:** *no two electrons in the same atom can have the same four quantum numbers.* Therefore, the second He electron occupies the same orbital as the first but has an opposite spin: $n = 1$, $l = 0$, $m_l = 0$, and $m_s = -\frac{1}{2}$. ●

The major consequence of the exclusion principle is that *an atomic orbital can hold a maximum of two electrons and they must have opposing spins.* We say that the $1s$ orbital in He is *filled* and that the electrons have *paired spins.* Thus, a beam of He atoms is not split in an experiment like that in Figure 8.1.

> ● **Baseball Quantum Numbers**
> The unique set of quantum numbers that describes an electron is analogous to the unique location of a box seat at a baseball game. The stadium (atom) is divided into section ($n$, level), box ($l$, sublevel), row ($m_l$, orbital), and seat ($m_s$, spin). Only one person (electron) can have this particular set of stadium "quantum numbers."

## Electrostatic Effects and Energy-Level Splitting

Electrostatic effects—attraction of opposite charges and repulsion of like charges—play a major role in determining the energy states of many-electron atoms. Unlike the H atom, in which there is only the attraction between nucleus and electron and the energy state is determined *only* by the $n$ value, the energy states of many-electron atoms are also affected by electron-electron repulsions. You'll see shortly how these additional interactions give rise to *the splitting of energy levels into sublevels of differing energies: the energy of an orbital in a many-electron atom depends mostly on its n value (size) and to a lesser extent on its l value (shape).*

Our first encounter with energy-level splitting occurs with lithium (Li; $Z = 3$). The first two electrons of Li fill its $1s$ orbital, so the third Li electron must go into the $n = 2$ level. But, this level has $2s$ *and* $2p$ sublevels: which does the third electron enter? For reasons we discuss below, the $2s$ is lower in energy than the $2p$, so the ground state of Li has its third electron in the $2s$.

This energy difference arises from three factors—*nuclear attraction, electron repulsions,* and *orbital shape* (i.e., radial probability distribution). Their interplay leads to two phenomena—*shielding* and *penetration*—that occur in all atoms *except* hydrogen. [In the following discussion, keep in mind that more energy is needed to remove an electron from a more stable (lower energy) sublevel than from a less stable (higher energy) sublevel.]

### The Effect of Nuclear Charge (Z) on Sublevel Energy

Higher charges interact more strongly than lower charges (Coulomb's law, Section 2.7). Therefore, *a higher nuclear charge increases nucleus-electron attractions and, thus, lowers sublevel energy (stabilizes the atom).* We see this effect by comparing the $1s$ sublevel energies of three species with one electron—H atom ($Z = 1$), He$^+$ ion ($Z = 2$), and Li$^{2+}$ ion ($Z = 3$). Figure 8.2 shows that the $1s$ sublevel in H is the least stable (highest energy), so the least energy is needed to remove its electron; and the $1s$ sublevel in Li$^{2+}$ is the most stable, so the most energy is needed to remove its electron.

### Shielding: The Effect of Electron Repulsions on Sublevel Energy

In many-electron atoms, each electron "feels" not only the attraction to the nucleus but also repulsions from other electrons. Repulsions counteract the nuclear attraction somewhat, making each electron easier to remove by, in effect, helping to push it away. We speak of each electron "shielding" the other electrons to some extent from the nuclear charge. **Shielding** (also called *screening*) reduces the full nuclear charge to an **effective nuclear charge** ($Z_{\text{eff}}$), the nuclear charge an electron *actually experiences,* and *this lower nuclear charge makes the electron easier to remove.*

1. *Shielding by other electrons in a given energy level.* Electrons in the *same* energy level shield each other somewhat. Compare the He atom and He$^+$ ion: both have a 2+ nuclear charge, but He has two electrons in the $1s$ sublevel and He$^+$ has

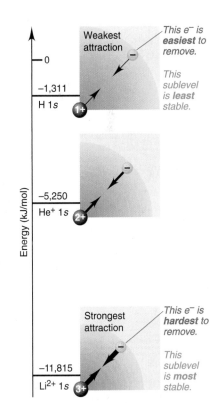

**Figure 8.2 The effect of nuclear charge on sublevel energy.** Greater nuclear charge lowers sublevel energy (to a more negative number), which makes the electron harder to remove. (The strength of attraction is indicated by the thickness of the black arrows.)

**Figure 8.3** Shielding and energy levels. **A,** Within an energy level, each electron shields *(red arrows)* other electrons from the full nuclear charge *(black arrows),* so they experience a lower $Z_{eff}$. **B,** Inner electrons shield outer electrons *much* more effectively than electrons in the same energy level.

only one (Figure 8.3A). It takes less than half as much energy to remove an electron from He (2372 kJ/mol) than from He$^{+}$ (5250 kJ/mol) because the second electron in He repels the first, in effect causing a lower $Z_{eff}$.

2. *Shielding by electrons in inner energy levels.* Because inner electrons spend nearly all their time *between* the outer electrons and the nucleus, they cause a *much* lower $Z_{eff}$ than do electrons in the same level. We can see this by comparing two atomic systems with the same nucleus, one *with* inner electrons and the other *without.* The ground-state Li atom has two inner ($1s$) electrons and one outer ($2s$) electron, while the Li$^{2+}$ ion has only one electron, which occupies the $2s$ orbital in the first excited state (Figure 8.3B). It takes about one-sixth as much energy to remove the $2s$ electron from the Li atom (520 kJ/mol) as it takes to remove it from the Li$^{2+}$ ion (2954 kJ/mol), because the *inner electrons shield very effectively.*

**Penetration: The Effect of Orbital Shape on Sublevel Energy** To see why the third Li electron occupies the $2s$ sublevel rather than the $2p$, we have to consider orbital shapes, that is, radial probability distributions (Figure 8.4). A $2p$ orbital *(orange curve)* is slightly closer to the nucleus, on average, than the major portion of the $2s$ orbital *(blue curve).* But a small portion of the $2s$ radial probability distribution peaks within the $1s$ region. Thus, an electron in the $2s$ orbital spends part of its time "penetrating" very close to the nucleus. **Penetration** has two effects:

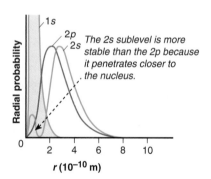

**Figure 8.4** Penetration and sublevel energy.

• It *increases the nuclear attraction* for a $2s$ electron over that for a $2p$ electron.
• It *decreases the shielding* of a $2s$ electron by the $1s$ electrons.

Thus, since it takes more energy to remove a $2s$ electron (520 kJ/mol) than a $2p$ (341 kJ/mol), the $2s$ sublevel is lower in energy than the $2p$.

**Splitting of Levels into Sublevels** In general, *penetration and the resulting effects on shielding cause an energy level to split into sublevels of differing energy.* The lower the $l$ value of a sublevel, the more its electrons penetrate, and so the greater their attraction to the nucleus. Therefore, *for a given n value, a lower l value indicates a more stable (lower energy) sublevel:*

$$\text{Order of sublevel energies: } s < p < d < f \qquad \textbf{(8.1)}$$

Thus, the $2s$ ($l = 0$) is lower in energy than the $2p$ ($l = 1$), the $3p$ ($l = 1$) is lower than the $3d$ ($l = 2$), and so forth.

Figure 8.5 shows the general energy order of levels ($n$ value) and how they are split into sublevels ($l$ values) of differing energies. (Compare this with the H atom energy levels in Figure 7.21, p. 287.) Next, we'll use this energy order to construct a periodic table of ground-state atoms.

# Summary of Section 8.1

- Identifying electrons in many-electron atoms requires four quantum numbers: three ($n$, $l$, $m_l$) describe the orbital, and a fourth ($m_s$) describes electron spin.
- The exclusion principle requires each electron to have a unique set of four quantum numbers; therefore, an orbital can hold no more than two electrons, and their spins must be paired (opposite).
- Electrostatic interactions determine sublevel energies as follows:
  1. Greater nuclear charge lowers sublevel energy, making electrons harder to remove.
  2. Electron-electron repulsions raise sublevel energy, making electrons easier to remove. Repulsions shield electrons from the full nuclear charge, reducing it to an effective nuclear charge, $Z_{eff}$. Inner electrons shield outer electrons very effectively.
  3. Penetration makes an electron harder to remove because nuclear attraction increases and shielding decreases. As a result, an energy level is split into sublevels with the energy order $s < p < d < f$.

# 8.2 • THE QUANTUM-MECHANICAL MODEL AND THE PERIODIC TABLE

Quantum mechanics provides the theoretical foundation for the experimentally based periodic table. In this section, we fill the table by determining the ground-state electron configuration of each element—*the lowest-energy distribution of electrons in the sublevels of its atoms*. Note especially the *recurring pattern in electron configurations, which is the basis for recurring patterns in chemical behavior.*

A useful way to determine electron configurations is based on the **aufbau principle** (German *aufbauen,* "to build up"). We start at the beginning of the periodic table and add one proton to the nucleus and one electron to the *lowest energy sublevel available.* (Of course, one or more neutrons are also added to the nucleus.)

There are two common ways to indicate the distribution of electrons:

- *The electron configuration.* This shorthand notation consists of the principal energy level ($n$ value), the letter designation of the sublevel ($l$ value), and the number of electrons (#) in the sublevel, written as a superscript: $nl^{\#}$.
- *The orbital diagram.* An **orbital diagram** consists of a box (or circle, or just a line) for each orbital in a given energy level, grouped by sublevel (with $nl$ designation shown beneath), with an arrow representing an electron *and* its spin: ↑ is $+\frac{1}{2}$ and ↓ is $-\frac{1}{2}$. (Throughout the text, orbital occupancy is also indicated by color intensity: no color is empty, pale color is half-filled, and full color is filled.)

## Building Up Period 1

Let's begin by applying the aufbau principle to Period 1, whose ground-state elements have only the $n = 1$ level and, thus, only the $1s$ sublevel, which consists of only the $1s$ orbital. We'll also assign a set of four quantum numbers to each element's *last added* electron.

1. *Hydrogen.* For the electron in H, as you've seen, the set of quantum numbers is H ($Z = 1$): $n = 1, l = 0, m_l = 0, m_s = +\frac{1}{2}$. The electron configuration (spoken "one-ess-one") and orbital diagram are

$$\text{H } (Z = 1) \quad 1s^1 \quad \boxed{\uparrow}$$
$$1s$$

2. *Helium.* Recall that the first electron in He has the same quantum numbers as the electron in H, but the second He electron has opposing spin (exclusion principle) He ($Z = 2$): $n = 1, l = 0, m_l = 0, m_s = -\frac{1}{2}$. The electron configuration (spoken "one-ess-two," *not* "one-ess-squared") and orbital diagram are

$$\text{He } (Z = 2) \quad 1s^2 \quad \boxed{\uparrow\downarrow}$$
$$1s$$

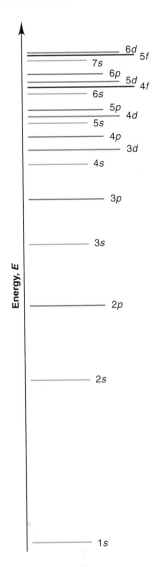

**Figure 8.5 Order for filling energy sublevels with electrons.** In general, energies of sublevels increase with the principal quantum number $n$ ($1 < 2 < 3$, etc.) and the angular momentum quantum number $l$ ($s < p < d < f$). As $n$ increases, some sublevels overlap; for example, the $4s$ sublevel is lower in energy than the $3d$. (Line color indicates sublevel type.)

## Building Up Period 2

The exclusion principle says an orbital can hold no more than two electrons. Therefore, with He, the $1s$ orbital, the $1s$ sublevel, the $n = 1$ level, and Period 1 are filled. Filling the $n = 2$ level builds up Period 2 and begins with the $2s$ sublevel, which is the next lowest in energy (see Figure 8.4) and consists of only the $2s$ orbital. When the $2s$ sublevel is filled, we proceed to fill the $2p$.

1. *Lithium.* The first two electrons in Li fill the $1s$ sublevel, and the last added Li electron has quantum numbers $n = 2$, $l = 0$, $m_l = 0$, $m_s = +\frac{1}{2}$. The electron configuration and orbital diagram are

**Figure 8.6** A vertical orbital diagram for the Li ground state.

$$\text{Energy, } E \longrightarrow$$

Li ($Z = 3$)  $1s^2 2s^1$  [↑↓] [↑] [ ][ ][ ]
                           $1s$   $2s$   $2p$

(Note that a complete orbital diagram shows all the orbitals for the given $n$ value, whether or not they are occupied.) To save space on a page, orbital diagrams are written horizontally, with *the sublevel energy increasing left to right*. But Figure 8.6 highlights the energy increase with a vertical orbital diagram for lithium.

2. *Beryllium.* The $2s$ orbital is only half-filled in Li, and the fourth electron of beryllium fills it with the electron's spin paired: $n = 2$, $l = 0$, $m_l = 0$, $m_s = -\frac{1}{2}$.

Be ($Z = 4$)  $1s^2 2s^2$  [↑↓] [↑↓] [ ][ ][ ]
                           $1s$   $2s$   $2p$

3. *Boron.* The next lowest energy sublevel is the $2p$. A $p$ sublevel has $l = 1$, so the $m_l$ (orientation) values can be $-1$, $0$, or $+1$. The three orbitals in the $2p$ sublevel have *equal energy* (same $n$ and $l$ values), which means that the fifth electron of boron can go into *any one of the $2p$ orbitals*. For convenience, let's label the boxes from left to right: $-1$, $0$, $+1$. By convention, we start on the left and place the fifth electron in the $m_l = -1$ orbital: $n = 2$, $l = 1$, $m_l = -1$, $m_s = +\frac{1}{2}$.

$$-1 \quad 0 \quad +1$$

B ($Z = 5$)  $1s^2 2s^2 2p^1$  [↑↓] [↑↓] [↑][ ][ ]
                               $1s$   $2s$   $2p$

4. *Carbon.* To minimize electron-electron repulsions, the sixth electron of carbon enters one of the *unoccupied* $2p$ orbitals; by convention, we place it in the $m_l = 0$ orbital. Experiment shows that the spin of this electron is *parallel* to (the same as) the spin of the other $2p$ electron. This result exemplifies **Hund's rule:** *when orbitals of equal energy are available, the electron configuration of lowest energy has the maximum number of unpaired electrons with parallel spins.* Thus, the sixth electron has $n = 2$, $l = 1$, $m_l = 0$, and $m_s = +\frac{1}{2}$.

C ($Z = 6$)  $1s^2 2s^2 2p^2$  [↑↓] [↑↓] [↑][↑][ ]
                               $1s$   $2s$   $2p$

5. *Nitrogen.* Based on Hund's rule, nitrogen's seventh electron enters the last empty $2p$ orbital, with its spin parallel to the other two: $n = 2$, $l = 1$, $m_l = +1$, $m_s = +\frac{1}{2}$.

N ($Z = 7$)  $1s^2 2s^2 2p^3$  [↑↓] [↑↓] [↑][↑][↑]
                               $1s$   $2s$   $2p$

6. *Oxygen.* The eighth electron in oxygen must enter one of the three half-filled $2p$ orbitals and "pair up" with (oppose the spin of) the electron present. We place the electron in a half-filled $2p$ orbital: $n = 2$, $l = 1$, $m_l = -1$, $m_s = -\frac{1}{2}$.

O ($Z = 8$)  $1s^2 2s^2 2p^4$  [↑↓] [↑↓] [↑↓][↑][↑]
                               $1s$   $2s$   $2p$

7. *Fluorine.* Fluorine's ninth electron enters the next of the two remaining half-filled 2p orbitals: $n = 2$, $l = 1$, $m_l = 0$, $m_s = -\frac{1}{2}$.

F (Z = 9)   $1s^2 2s^2 2p^5$

8. *Neon.* Only one unfilled 2p orbital remains, so the tenth electron of neon occupies it: $n = 2$, $l = 1$, $m_l = +1$, $m_s = -\frac{1}{2}$. With neon, the $n = 2$ level is filled.

Ne (Z = 10)   $1s^2 2s^2 2p^6$

---

### Sample Problem 8.1 | Determining Quantum Numbers from Orbital Diagrams

**Problem** Use the orbital diagram shown above to write the set of quantum numbers for the third electron and the set for the eighth electron of the F atom.

**Plan** Referring to the orbital diagram, we identify the electron of interest and note its level ($n$), sublevel ($l$), orbital ($m_l$), and spin ($m_s$).

**Solution** The third electron is in the 2s orbital. The upward arrow indicates a spin of $+\frac{1}{2}$:

$$n = 2, l = 0, m_l = 0, m_s = +\tfrac{1}{2}$$

The eighth electron is in the first 2p orbital, which is designated $m_l = -1$, and has a downward arrow:

$$n = 2, l = 1, m_l = -1, m_s = -\tfrac{1}{2}$$

**Follow-Up Problem 8.1** Use the periodic table to identify the element with the electron configuration $1s^2 2s^2 2p^4$. Write its orbital diagram and the set of quantum numbers for its sixth electron.

---

With our attention on these notations, it's easy to forget that atoms are real objects and electrons occupy volumes with specific shapes and orientations. Figure 8.7 shows orbital contours for the first 10 elements arranged in periodic table format.

Even now, we can make an important correlation: *elements in the same group have similar outer electron configurations and similar patterns of reactivity.* As an example, helium (He) and neon (Ne) in Group 8A(18) both have filled outer sublevels—$1s^2$ for helium and $2s^2 2p^6$ for neon—and neither element forms compounds. Filled outer sublevels make elements much more stable and unreactive.

**Figure 8.7 Depicting orbital occupancy for the first 10 elements.** In addition to atomic number, atomic symbol, and ground-state electron configuration, each box shows the probability contours of the atom's orbitals. Orbital occupancy is indicated by lighter shading for half-filled (one e⁻) orbitals and darker shading for filled (two e⁻) orbitals.

**Table 8.2    Partial Orbital Diagrams and Electron Configurations\* for the Elements in Period 3**

| Atomic Number | Element | Partial Orbital Diagram (3s and 3p Sublevels Only) | Full Electron Configuration† | Condensed Electron Configuration |
|---|---|---|---|---|
| | | 3s          3p | | |
| 11 | Na | [↑] [ ][ ][ ] | $[1s^2 2s^2 2p^6]\, 3s^1$ | $[Ne]\, 3s^1$ |
| 12 | Mg | [↑↓] [ ][ ][ ] | $[1s^2 2s^2 2p^6]\, 3s^2$ | $[Ne]\, 3s^2$ |
| 13 | Al | [↑↓] [↑][ ][ ] | $[1s^2 2s^2 2p^6]\, 3s^2 3p^1$ | $[Ne]\, 3s^2 3p^1$ |
| 14 | Si | [↑↓] [↑][↑][ ] | $[1s^2 2s^2 2p^6]\, 3s^2 3p^2$ | $[Ne]\, 3s^2 3p^2$ |
| 15 | P | [↑↓] [↑][↑][↑] | $[1s^2 2s^2 2p^6]\, 3s^2 3p^3$ | $[Ne]\, 3s^2 3p^3$ |
| 16 | S | [↑↓] [↑↓][↑][↑] | $[1s^2 2s^2 2p^6]\, 3s^2 3p^4$ | $[Ne]\, 3s^2 3p^4$ |
| 17 | Cl | [↑↓] [↑↓][↑↓][↑] | $[1s^2 2s^2 2p^6]\, 3s^2 3p^5$ | $[Ne]\, 3s^2 3p^5$ |
| 18 | Ar | [↑↓] [↑↓][↑↓][↑↓] | $[1s^2 2s^2 2p^6]\, 3s^2 3p^6$ | $[Ne]\, 3s^2 3p^6$ |

\*Colored type indicates the sublevel to which the last electron is added.

†The full configuration is not usually written with square brackets; they are included here to show how the [Ne] designation arises.

## Building Up Period 3

The Period 3 elements, Na through Ar, lie directly under the Period 2 elements, Li through Ne. That is, even though the $n = 3$ level splits into 3s, 3p, and 3d sublevels, Period 3 fills only 3s and 3p; as you'll see shortly, the 3d is filled in Period 4. Table 8.2 introduces two ways to present electron distributions more concisely:

- *Partial orbital diagrams* show only the sublevels being filled, here the 3s and 3p.
- *Condensed electron configurations (rightmost column)* have the element symbol of the previous noble gas in brackets, to stand for its configuration, followed by the electron configuration of filled inner sublevels and the energy level being filled. For example, the condensed electron configuration of sulfur is [Ne] $3s^2 3p^4$, where [Ne] stands for $1s^2 2s^2 2p^6$.

In Na (the second alkali metal) and Mg (the second alkaline earth metal), electrons are added to the 3s sublevel, which contains only the 3s orbital; this is directly comparable to the filling of the 2s sublevel in Li and Be in Period 2. Then, in the same way as the 2p orbitals of B, C, and N in Period 2 are half-filled, the last electrons added to Al, Si, and P in Period 3 half-fill successive 3p orbitals with spins parallel (Hund's rule). The last electrons added to S, Cl, and Ar then successively pair up to fill those 3p orbitals, which fills the 3p sublevel.

## Similar Electron Configurations Within Groups

One of the central points in chemistry is that *similar outer electron configurations correlate with similar chemical behavior*. Figure 8.8 shows the condensed electron configurations of the first 18 elements. Note the similarity within each group. Here are examples from three of the groups:

- In Group 1A(1), Li and Na have the outer electron configuration $ns^1$ (where $n$ is the quantum number of the highest energy level), as do the other alkali metals (K, Rb, Cs, and Fr). All are highly reactive metals whose atoms lose the outer electron when they form ionic compounds with nonmetals, and all react vigorously with water to displace $H_2$ (Figure 8.9A).
- In Group 7A(17), F and Cl have the outer electron configuration $ns^2 np^5$, as do the other halogens (Br, I, and At). All are reactive nonmetals that occur as diatomic

| | 1A (1) | | | | | | | | 8A (18) |
|---|---|---|---|---|---|---|---|---|---|
| 1 | 1 **H** $1s^1$ | 2A (2) | 3A (13) | 4A (14) | 5A (15) | 6A (16) | 7A (17) | | 2 **He** $1s^2$ |
| 2 | 3 **Li** [He] $2s^1$ | 4 **Be** [He] $2s^2$ | 5 **B** [He] $2s^22p^1$ | 6 **C** [He] $2s^22p^2$ | 7 **N** [He] $2s^22p^3$ | 8 **O** [He] $2s^22p^4$ | 9 **F** [He] $2s^22p^5$ | | 10 **Ne** [He] $2s^22p^6$ |
| 3 | 11 **Na** [Ne] $3s^1$ | 12 **Mg** [Ne] $3s^2$ | 13 **Al** [Ne] $3s^23p^1$ | 14 **Si** [Ne] $3s^23p^2$ | 15 **P** [Ne] $3s^23p^3$ | 16 **S** [Ne] $3s^23p^4$ | 17 **Cl** [Ne] $3s^23p^5$ | | 18 **Ar** [Ne] $3s^23p^6$ |

Period (left axis label)

**Figure 8.8 Condensed electron configurations in the first three periods.** Elements in a group have similar outer electron configurations (*color*).

molecules ($X_2$), and all form ionic compounds with metals (KX, $MgX_2$) in which the ion charge is $1-$ (Figure 8.9B), covalent compounds with hydrogen (HX) that yield acidic solutions in water, and covalent compounds with carbon ($CX_4$).

- In Group 8A(18), He has the electron configuration $ns^2$, and all the other elements in the group have the outer configuration $ns^2np^6$. Consistent with their *filled* energy levels, all the members are very unreactive monatomic gases.

To summarize the major connection between quantum mechanics and chemical periodicity: *sublevels are filled in order of increasing energy, which leads to outer electron configurations that recur periodically, which leads to chemical properties that recur periodically.*

A

B

**Figure 8.9 Similar reactivities in a group. A,** Potassium reacting with water. **B,** Chlorine reacting with potassium.

## Building Up Period 4: The First Transition Series

Period 4 contains the first series of **transition elements,** those in which *d* orbitals are being filled. Let's examine three factors that affect the filling pattern in a period with a transition series.

1. *Effects of shielding and penetration on sublevel energy.* The 3*d* sublevel is filled in Period 4, but *the 4s sublevel is filled first.* This switch in filling order is due to shielding and penetration effects. Based on the 3*d* radial probability distribution (see Figure 7.19, p. 286), a 3*d* electron spends most of the time outside the filled inner $n = 1$ and $n = 2$ levels, so it is shielded very effectively from the nuclear charge. However, the outermost 4*s* electron penetrates close to the nucleus part of the time, so it is subject to a greater attraction. As a result, the 4*s* orbital is slightly *lower* in energy than the 3*d* and fills first. In any period, *the ns sublevel fills before the*

*(n − 1)d sublevel.* Other variations in the filling pattern occur at higher values of $n$ because sublevel energies become very close together (see Figure 8.5).

2. *Filling the 4s and 3d sublevels.* Table 8.3 shows the partial orbital diagrams and full and condensed electron configurations for the 18 elements in Period 4. The first two elements, K and Ca, are the next alkali and alkaline earth metals, respectively; the last electron of K half-fills and that of Ca fills the $4s$ sublevel. The last electron of scandium (Sc; $Z = 21$), the first transition element, occupies any one of the five $3d$ orbitals because they are equal in energy; Sc has the electron configuration [Ar] $4s^2 3d^1$. Filling of the $3d$ orbitals proceeds one electron at a time, as with the $p$ orbitals, except in two cases, chromium (Cr; $Z = 24$) and copper (Cu; $Z = 29$), discussed next.

3. *Stability of half-filled and filled sublevels.* Vanadium (V; $Z = 23$) has three half-filled $d$ orbitals ([Ar] $4s^2 3d^3$). However, the last electron of the next element, Cr, does not enter a fourth empty $d$ orbital to give [Ar] $4s^2 3d^4$; instead, Cr has one electron in the $4s$ sublevel and five in the $3d$ sublevel, making both sublevels half filled: [Ar] $4s^1 3d^5$ *(see margin)*. In the next element, manganese (Mn; $Z = 25$), the $4s$ sublevel is filled again ([Ar] $4s^2 3d^5$).

Cr (Z = 24)  [Ar] $4s^1 3d^5$

## Table 8.3  Partial Orbital Diagrams and Electron Configurations* for the Elements in Period 4

| Atomic Number | Element | Partial Orbital Diagram (4s, 3d, and 4p Sublevels Only) | Full Electron Configuration | Condensed Electron Configuration |
|---|---|---|---|---|
| | | 4s / 3d / 4p | | |
| 19 | K | 4s: ↑ | $1s^2 2s^2 2p^6 3s^2 3p^6 4s^1$ | [Ar] $4s^1$ |
| 20 | Ca | 4s: ↑↓ | $1s^2 2s^2 2p^6 3s^2 3p^6 4s^2$ | [Ar] $4s^2$ |
| 21 | Sc | 4s: ↑↓  3d: ↑ | $1s^2 2s^2 2p^6 3s^2 3p^6 4s^2 3d^1$ | [Ar] $4s^2 3d^1$ |
| 22 | Ti | 4s: ↑↓  3d: ↑ ↑ | $1s^2 2s^2 2p^6 3s^2 3p^6 4s^2 3d^2$ | [Ar] $4s^2 3d^2$ |
| 23 | V | 4s: ↑↓  3d: ↑ ↑ ↑ | $1s^2 2s^2 2p^6 3s^2 3p^6 4s^2 3d^3$ | [Ar] $4s^2 3d^3$ |
| 24 | Cr | 4s: ↑  3d: ↑ ↑ ↑ ↑ ↑ | $1s^2 2s^2 2p^6 3s^2 3p^6 4s^1 3d^5$ | [Ar] $4s^1 3d^5$ |
| 25 | Mn | 4s: ↑↓  3d: ↑ ↑ ↑ ↑ ↑ | $1s^2 2s^2 2p^6 3s^2 3p^6 4s^2 3d^5$ | [Ar] $4s^2 3d^5$ |
| 26 | Fe | 4s: ↑↓  3d: ↑↓ ↑ ↑ ↑ ↑ | $1s^2 2s^2 2p^6 3s^2 3p^6 4s^2 3d^6$ | [Ar] $4s^2 3d^6$ |
| 27 | Co | 4s: ↑↓  3d: ↑↓ ↑↓ ↑ ↑ ↑ | $1s^2 2s^2 2p^6 3s^2 3p^6 4s^2 3d^7$ | [Ar] $4s^2 3d^7$ |
| 28 | Ni | 4s: ↑↓  3d: ↑↓ ↑↓ ↑↓ ↑ ↑ | $1s^2 2s^2 2p^6 3s^2 3p^6 4s^2 3d^8$ | [Ar] $4s^2 3d^8$ |
| 29 | Cu | 4s: ↑  3d: ↑↓ ↑↓ ↑↓ ↑↓ ↑↓ | $1s^2 2s^2 2p^6 3s^2 3p^6 4s^1 3d^{10}$ | [Ar] $4s^1 3d^{10}$ |
| 30 | Zn | 4s: ↑↓  3d: ↑↓ ↑↓ ↑↓ ↑↓ ↑↓ | $1s^2 2s^2 2p^6 3s^2 3p^6 4s^2 3d^{10}$ | [Ar] $4s^2 3d^{10}$ |
| 31 | Ga | 4s: ↑↓  3d: ↑↓ ↑↓ ↑↓ ↑↓ ↑↓  4p: ↑ | $1s^2 2s^2 2p^6 3s^2 3p^6 4s^2 3d^{10} 4p^1$ | [Ar] $4s^2 3d^{10} 4p^1$ |
| 32 | Ge | 4s: ↑↓  3d: ↑↓ ↑↓ ↑↓ ↑↓ ↑↓  4p: ↑ ↑ | $1s^2 2s^2 2p^6 3s^2 3p^6 4s^2 3d^{10} 4p^2$ | [Ar] $4s^2 3d^{10} 4p^2$ |
| 33 | As | 4s: ↑↓  3d: ↑↓ ↑↓ ↑↓ ↑↓ ↑↓  4p: ↑ ↑ ↑ | $1s^2 2s^2 2p^6 3s^2 3p^6 4s^2 3d^{10} 4p^3$ | [Ar] $4s^2 3d^{10} 4p^3$ |
| 34 | Se | 4s: ↑↓  3d: ↑↓ ↑↓ ↑↓ ↑↓ ↑↓  4p: ↑↓ ↑ ↑ | $1s^2 2s^2 2p^6 3s^2 3p^6 4s^2 3d^{10} 4p^4$ | [Ar] $4s^2 3d^{10} 4p^4$ |
| 35 | Br | 4s: ↑↓  3d: ↑↓ ↑↓ ↑↓ ↑↓ ↑↓  4p: ↑↓ ↑↓ ↑ | $1s^2 2s^2 2p^6 3s^2 3p^6 4s^2 3d^{10} 4p^5$ | [Ar] $4s^2 3d^{10} 4p^5$ |
| 36 | Kr | 4s: ↑↓  3d: ↑↓ ↑↓ ↑↓ ↑↓ ↑↓  4p: ↑↓ ↑↓ ↑↓ | $1s^2 2s^2 2p^6 3s^2 3p^6 4s^2 3d^{10} 4p^6$ | [Ar] $4s^2 3d^{10} 4p^6$ |

*Colored type indicates sublevel(s) whose occupancy changes when the last electron is added.

Because it follows nickel (Ni; [Ar] $4s^23d^8$), copper would be expected to have the configuration [Ar] $4s^23d^9$. Instead, the $4s$ sublevel of Cu is *half-filled* with 1 electron, and the $3d$ sublevel is *filled* with 10 (*see margin*). From these two exceptions, Cr and Cu, we conclude that *half-filled and filled sublevels are unexpectedly stable (low in energy)*; we see this pattern with many other elements.

With zinc (Zn; $Z = 30$), the $4s$ sublevel is filled ([Ar] $4s^23d^{10}$), and the first transition series ends. The $4p$ sublevel is filled by the next six elements, and Period 4 ends with the noble gas krypton (Kr; $Z = 36$).

Cu ($Z = 29$)    [Ar] $4s^13d^{10}$

$\underset{4s}{} \qquad \underset{3d}{} \qquad \underset{4p}{}$

## General Principles of Electron Configurations

Figure 8.10 shows the partial (highest energy sublevels being filled) ground-state electron configurations of the 117 known elements. Let's highlight some key relationships among them.

**Similar Outer Electron Configurations Within a Group** Among the main-group elements (A groups)—the *s*-block and *p*-block elements—outer electron configurations within a group are identical. Some variations in the transition elements (B groups, *d* block) and inner transition elements (*f* block) occur, as we'll see.

**Orbital Filling Order** When the elements are "built up" by filling levels and sublevels in order of increasing energy, we obtain the sequence in the periodic table. Reading the table from left to right, like words on a page, gives the energy order

**Figure 8.10** A periodic table of partial ground-state electron configurations.

**Figure 8.11  Orbital filling and the periodic table.** This form of the periodic table shows the sublevel blocks. *Pale green inset:* A summary of the sublevel filling order.

● **Aid to memorizing sublevel filling order.** List the sublevels as shown, and read from $1s$, following the direction of the arrows. Note that the
- $n$ value is constant horizontally
- $l$ value is constant vertically
- $n + l$ is constant diagonally

of levels and sublevels (Figure 8.11); the margin note is a memory aid for sublevel filling order when a periodic table is not available. ●

**Categories of Electrons** Atoms have three categories of electrons:

1. **Inner (core) electrons** are those an atom has in common with the previous noble gas and any *completed* transition series. They fill all the *lower energy levels* of an atom.
2. **Outer electrons** are those in the *highest energy level* (highest $n$ value). They spend most of their time farthest from the nucleus.
3. **Valence electrons** are those involved in forming compounds:
   - For main-group elements, the *valence electrons **are** the outer electrons.*
   - For transition elements, in addition to the outer $ns$ electrons, the $(n - 1)d$ electrons are also valence electrons, though the metals Fe ($Z = 26$) through Zn ($Z = 30$) may use only a few, if any, of their $d$ electrons in bonding.

**Group and Period Numbers** Key information is embedded in the periodic table:

- Among the main-group elements (A groups), *the A number equals the number of outer electrons* (those with the highest $n$); thus, chlorine (Cl; Group **7**A) has 7 outer electrons, and so forth.
- *The period number is the $n$ value of the highest energy level.*
- For an energy level, the $n$ value squared ($n^2$) is the number of *orbitals*, and $2n^2$ is the maximum number of *electrons* (or elements). For example, consider the $n = 3$ level. The number of orbitals is $n^2 = 9$: one $3s$, three $3p$, and five $3d$. The number of electrons is $2n^2 = 18$: two $3s$ and six $3p$ electrons for the eight elements of Period 3, and ten $3d$ electrons for the ten transition elements of Period 4.

### Intervening Series: Transition and Inner Transition Elements

As Figure 8.11 shows, the $d$ block and $f$ block occur between the main-group $s$ and $p$ blocks.

1. *Transition series.* Periods 4, 5, 6, and 7 incorporate the $3d$, $4d$, $5d$, and $6d$ sublevels, respectively. As you've seen, the general pattern is that the $(n - 1)d$ sublevel is filled between the $ns$ and $np$ sublevels. Thus, in Period 5, the filling order is $5s$, then $4d$, and then $5p$.

2. *Inner transition series.* In Period 6, the first of two series of **inner transition elements,** those in which $f$ orbitals are being filled, appears (Figure 8.11). The $f$ orbitals have $l = 3$, so the possible $m_l$ values are $-3, -2, -1, 0, +1, +2,$ and $+3$; that is, there are seven $f$ orbitals, for a total of 14 elements in *each* of the two inner transition series:

- The Period 6 inner transition series, called the **lanthanides** (or **rare earths**), occurs after lanthanum (La; $Z = 57$), and the $4f$ orbitals are filled.
- The Period 7 inner transition series, called the **actinides,** occurs after actinium (Ac; $Z = 89$), and the $5f$ orbitals are filled.

Thus, in Periods 6 and 7, the filling sequence is

$ns$, first of the $(n - 1)d$, all $(n - 2)f$, remainder of the $(n - 1)d$, and $np$

Period 6 ends with the $6p$ sublevel. Period 7 is incomplete because only five elements with $7p$ electrons are known at this time; element 117 has not yet been synthesized.

3. *Irregular filling patterns.* Irregularities in the filling pattern, such as those for Cr and Cu in Period 4, occur in the $d$ and $f$ blocks because the sublevel energies in these larger atoms differ very little. Even though occasional deviations occur in the $d$ block, the sum of $ns$ electrons and $(n - 1)d$ electrons always equals the new group number (in parentheses). For instance, despite variations in Group 6B(**6**)—Cr, Mo, W, and Sg—the sum of $ns$ and $(n - 1)d$ electrons is 6; for Group 8B(**10**)—Ni, Pd, Pt, and Ds—the sum is 10.

## Sample Problem 8.2 — Determining Electron Configurations

**Problem** Using the periodic table (not Figure 8.10 or Table 8.3) and assuming a regular filling pattern, give the full and condensed electron configurations, partial orbital diagrams showing valence electrons only, and number of inner electrons for the following elements:
**(a)** Potassium (K; $Z = 19$)    **(b)** Technetium (Tc; $Z = 43$)    **(c)** Lead (Pb; $Z = 82$)

**Plan** The atomic number tells us the number of electrons, and the periodic table shows the order for filling sublevels. In the partial orbital diagrams, we include all electrons added after the previous noble gas *except* those in *filled* inner sublevels. The number of inner electrons is the sum of those in the previous noble gas and in filled $d$ and $f$ sublevels.

**Solution** **(a)** For K ($Z = 19$), the full electron configuration is $1s^2 2s^2 2p^6 3s^2 3p^6 4s^1$. The condensed configuration is $[Ar]\, 4s^1$.
The partial orbital diagram showing valence electrons is

K is a main-group element in Group 1A(1) and Period 4, so there are 18 inner electrons.
**(b)** For Tc ($Z = 43$), assuming the expected pattern, the full electron configuration is $1s^2 2s^2 2p^6 3s^2 3p^6 4s^2 3d^{10} 4p^6 5s^2 4d^5$.
The condensed electron configuration is $[Kr]\, 5s^2 4d^5$.
The partial orbital diagram showing valence electrons is

Tc is a transition element in Group 7B(7) and Period 5, so there are 36 inner electrons.
**(c)** For Pb ($Z = 82$), the full electron configuration is
$1s^2 2s^2 2p^6 3s^2 3p^6 4s^2 3d^{10} 4p^6 5s^2 4d^{10} 5p^6 6s^2 4f^{14} 5d^{10} 6p^2$.

The condensed electron configuration is $[Xe]\, 6s^2 4f^{14} 5d^{10} 6p^2$.
The partial orbital diagram showing valence electrons (no filled inner sublevels) is

Pb is a main-group element in Group 4A(14) and Period 6, so there are 54 (in Xe) + 14 (in the $4f$ sublevel) + 10 (in the $5d$ sublevel) = 78 inner electrons.

**Check** Be sure that the sum of the superscripts (numbers of electrons) in the full electron configuration equals the atomic number and that the number of *valence* electrons in the condensed configuration equals the number of electrons in the partial orbital diagram.

**Follow-Up Problem 8.2** Without referring to Table 8.3 or Figure 8.10, give full and condensed electron configurations, partial orbital diagrams showing valence electrons only, and the number of inner electrons for the following elements:
**(a)** Ni ($Z = 28$)    **(b)** Sr ($Z = 38$)    **(c)** Po ($Z = 84$)

## ▌Summary of Section 8.2

- By the aufbau principle, one electron is added to an atom of each successive element in accord with the exclusion principle (no two electrons can have the same set of quantum numbers) and Hund's rule (orbitals of equal energy become half-filled, with electron spins parallel, before any pairing of spins occurs).
- The elements of a group have similar outer electron configurations and similar chemical behavior.
- For the main-group elements, valence electrons (those involved in reactions) are in the outer (highest energy) level only. For transition elements, $(n - 1)d$ electrons are also considered valence electrons.
- Because of shielding of $d$ electrons by electrons in inner sublevels and penetration by the $ns$ electron, the $(n - 1)d$ sublevel fills after the $ns$ and before the $np$ sublevels.
- In Periods 6 and 7, $(n - 2)f$ orbitals fill between the first and second $(n - 1)d$ orbitals.

---

# 8.3 • TRENDS IN THREE ATOMIC PROPERTIES

In this section, we focus on three atomic properties directly influenced by electron configuration and effective nuclear charge: atomic size, ionization energy, and electron affinity. Most importantly, these properties are *periodic,* which means they generally exhibit consistent changes, or *trends,* within a group or period.

## Trends in Atomic Size

Recall from Chapter 7 that we often represent atoms with spherical contours in which the electrons spend 90% of their time. We *define* atomic size (the extent of the contour) in terms of how closely one atom lies next to another. But, in practice, as we discuss in Chapter 12, we measure the distance between atomic nuclei in a sample of an element and divide that distance in half. Because atoms do not have hard surfaces, the size of an atom in a given compound depends somewhat on the atoms near it. In other words, *atomic size varies slightly from substance to substance.*

Figure 8.12 shows two common definitions of atomic size:

1. **Metallic radius.** Used mostly for *metals,* it is one-half the shortest distance between nuclei of adjacent, individual atoms in a crystal of the element (Figure 8.12A).
2. **Covalent radius.** Used for elements occurring as molecules, mostly *nonmetals,* it is one-half the shortest distance between nuclei of bonded atoms (Figure 8.12B).

Radii measured for some elements are used to determine the radii of other elements from distances between atoms in compounds. For instance, in a carbon-chlorine compound, the distance between nuclei in a C—Cl bond is 177 pm. Using the known covalent radius of Cl (100 pm), we find the covalent radius of C (177 pm − 100 pm = 77 pm) (Figure 8.12C).

**Main-Group Elements** Figure 8.13 shows the atomic radii of the main-group elements and most of the transition elements. Among the main-group elements, atomic size varies within both groups and periods as a result of two opposing influences:

1. *Changes in n.* As the principal quantum number ($n$) increases, the probability that outer electrons spend most of their time farther from the nucleus increases as well; thus, atomic size increases.
2. *Changes in $Z_{eff}$.* As the effective nuclear charge ($Z_{eff}$) increases, outer electrons are pulled closer to the nucleus; thus, atomic size decreases.

The net effect of these influences depends on how effectively the inner electrons shield the increasing nuclear charge:

1. *Down a group, n dominates.* As we move down a main group, each member has *one more level of inner electrons that shield the outer electrons very effectively.* Even though additional protons do moderately increase $Z_{eff}$ for the outer electrons, the atoms get larger as a result of the increasing $n$ value:

   *Atomic radius generally **increases** down a group.*

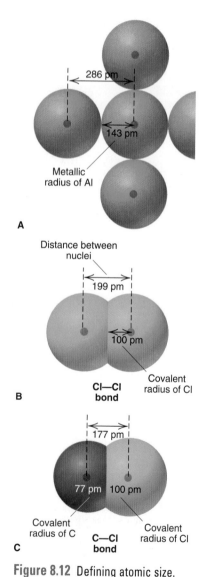

**Figure 8.12 Defining atomic size. A,** The metallic radius of aluminum. **B,** The covalent radius of chlorine. **C,** Known covalent radii and distances between nuclei can be used to find unknown radii.

2. *Across a period, $Z_{eff}$ dominates.* Across a period from left to right, electrons are added to the *same* outer level, so the shielding by inner electrons does not change. Despite greater electron repulsions, outer electrons shield each other only slightly, so $Z_{eff}$ rises significantly, and the outer electrons are pulled closer to the nucleus:

*Atomic radius generally* **decreases** *across a period.*

**Transition Elements** As Figure 8.13 shows, size trends are *not* as consistent for the transition elements:

1. *Down a transition group, n increases,* but shielding by an additional level of inner electrons results in only a small size increase from Period 4 to 5 and none from 5 to 6.

2. *Across a transition series,* atomic size shrinks through the first two or three elements because of the increasing nuclear charge. But, from then on, *size remains relatively constant* because shielding by the inner *d* electrons counteracts the increase in $Z_{eff}$. Thus, for example, in Period 4, the third transition element, vanadium (V; $Z = 23$), has the same radius as the last, zinc (Zn; $Z = 30$). This pattern also appears in Periods 5 and 6 in the transition and both inner transition series.

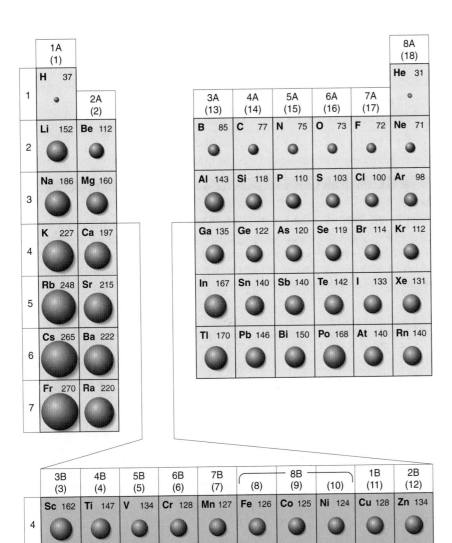

**Figure 8.13 Atomic radii of the main-group and transition elements.** Atomic radii (in picometers) are shown for the main-group elements (*tan*) and the transition elements (*blue*). (Values for the noble gases are calculated.)

3. *A transition series affects atomic size in neighboring main groups.* Shielding by *d* electrons causes a *major size decrease from Group 2A(2) to Group 3A(13)* in Periods 4 through 6. Because the *np* sublevel has more penetration than the $(n - 1)d$, the first *np* electron [added in Group 3A(13)] "feels" a much greater $Z_{eff}$, due to all the protons added in the intervening transition elements. The greatest decrease occurs in Period 4: calcium (Ca; $Z = 20$) in Group 2A(2) is nearly 50% larger than gallium (Ga; $Z = 31$) in 3A(13). In fact, *d*-orbital shielding causes gallium to be slightly *smaller* than aluminum (Al; $Z = 13$), the element above it!

---

### Sample Problem 8.3 | Ranking Elements by Atomic Size

**Problem** Using only the periodic table (not Figure 8.13), rank each set of main-group elements in order of *decreasing* atomic size:
**(a)** Ca, Mg, Sr    **(b)** K, Ga, Ca    **(c)** Br, Rb, Kr    **(d)** Sr, Ca, Rb

**Plan** To rank the elements by atomic size, we find them in the periodic table. They are main-group elements, so size increases down a group and decreases across a period.

**Solution (a)** Sr > Ca > Mg. These three elements are in Group 2A(2), and size decreases up the group.
**(b)** K > Ca > Ga. These three elements are in Period 4, and size decreases across a period.
**(c)** Rb > Br > Kr. Rb is largest because it has one more energy level (Period 5) and is farthest to the left. Kr is smaller than Br because Kr is farther to the right in Period 4.
**(d)** Rb > Sr > Ca. Ca is smallest because it has one fewer energy level. Sr is smaller than Rb because it is farther to the right.

**Check** From Figure 8.13, we see that the rankings are correct.

**Follow-Up Problem 8.3** Using only the periodic table, rank the elements in each set in order of *increasing* size: **(a)** Se, Br, Cl; **(b)** I, Xe, Ba.

---

**Periodicity of Atomic Size** Figure 8.14 shows the variation in atomic size with atomic number. Note the up-and-down pattern as size drops across a period to the noble gas (*purple*) and then leaps up to the alkali metal (*brown*) that begins the next period. Also note the deviations from the smooth size decrease in each transition (*blue*) and inner transition (*green*) series.

**Figure 8.14** Periodicity of atomic radius.

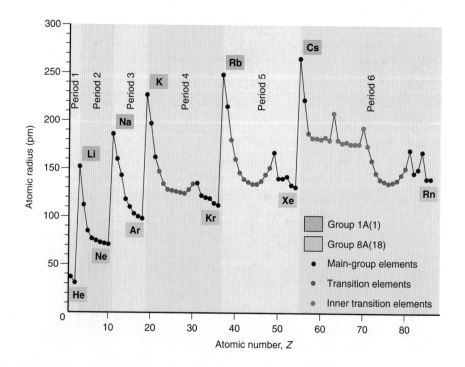

# Trends in Ionization Energy

The **ionization energy (IE)** is the energy required for the *complete removal* of 1 mol of electrons from 1 mol of gaseous atoms or ions. Pulling an electron away from a nucleus *requires* energy to overcome their electrostatic attraction. Because energy flows *into* the system, the ionization energy is always positive (like $\Delta H$ of an endothermic reaction). (Chapter 7 viewed the ionization energy of the H atom as the energy difference between $n = 1$ and $n = \infty$, where the electron is completely removed.) The ionization energy is a key factor in an element's reactivity:

- *Atoms with a low IE tend to form cations during reactions.*
- *Atoms with a high IE (except the noble gases) tend to form anions.*

Many-electron atoms can lose more than one electron. The *first* ionization energy ($IE_1$) removes an outermost electron (highest energy sublevel) from a gaseous atom:

$$\text{Atom}(g) \longrightarrow \text{ion}^+(g) + e^- \quad \Delta E = IE_1 > 0 \qquad (8.2)$$

The *second* ionization energy ($IE_2$) removes a second electron. Since this electron is pulled away from a positive ion, $IE_2$ is always larger than $IE_1$:

$$\text{Ion}^+(g) \longrightarrow \text{ion}^{2+}(g) + e^- \quad \Delta E = IE_2 \,(\text{always} > IE_1)$$

**Periodicity of First Ionization Energy** Figure 8.15 shows the variation in first ionization energy with atomic number. This up-and-down pattern—$IE_1$ rising across a period to the noble gas (*purple*) and then dropping down to the next alkali metal (*brown*)—is the *inverse* of the variation in atomic size (Figure 8.14): *as size decreases, it takes more energy to remove an electron because the nucleus is closer, so $IE_1$ increases.*

Let's examine the group and period trends and their exceptions:

1. *Down a group.* As we move *down* a main group, the $n$ value increases, so atomic size does as well. As the distance from nucleus to outer electron increases, their attraction lessens, so the electron is easier to remove (Figure 8.16, *next page*):

*Ionization energy generally **decreases** down a group.*

The only significant exception occurs in Group 3A(13): $IE_1$ decreases from boron (B) to aluminum (Al), but not for the rest of the group. Filling the transition series in Periods 4, 5, and 6 causes a much higher $Z_{eff}$ and an unusually small change in size, so outer electrons in the larger Group 3A members are held tighter.

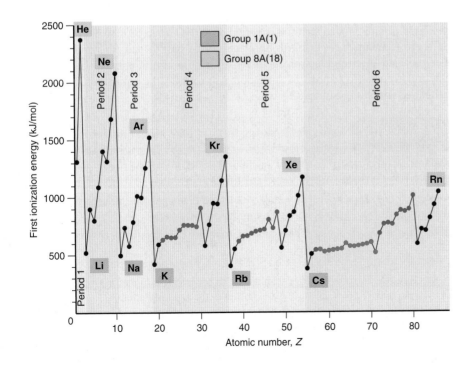

**Figure 8.15** Periodicity of first ionization energy ($IE_1$). This trend is the *inverse* of the trend in atomic size (see Figure 8.14).

**Figure 8.16** First ionization energies of the main-group elements.

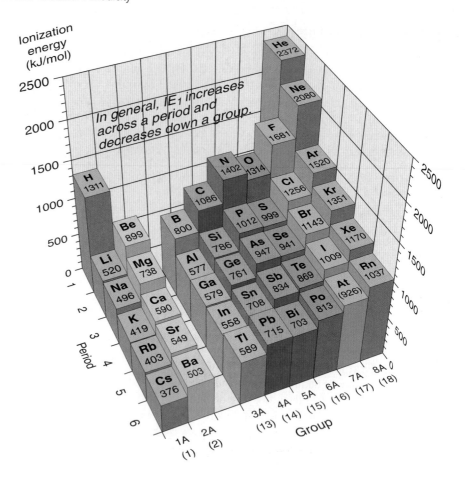

2. *Across a period.* As we move left to right across a period, $Z_{eff}$ increases and atomic size decreases. The attraction between nucleus and outer electron increases, so the electron is harder to remove:

*Ionization energy generally **increases** across a period.*

There are two exceptions to the otherwise smooth increase in $IE_1$ across periods:

- In Periods 2 and 3, there are dips at the Group 3A(13) elements, B and Al. These elements have the first *np* electrons, which are removed more easily because the resulting ion has a filled (stable) *ns* sublevel.
- In Periods 2 and 3, once again, there are dips at the Group 6A(16) elements, O and S. These elements have a fourth *np* electron, the first to pair up with another *np* electron, and electron-electron repulsions raise the orbital energy. The fourth *np* electron is easier to remove because doing so relieves the repulsions and leaves a half-filled (stable) *np* sublevel.

---

**Sample Problem 8.4**    **Ranking Elements by First Ionization Energy**

**Problem** Using the periodic table only, rank the elements in each set in order of *decreasing* $IE_1$: **(a)** Kr, He, Ar; **(b)** Sb, Te, Sn; **(c)** K, Ca, Rb; **(d)** I, Xe, Cs.

**Plan** We find the elements in the periodic table and then apply the general trends of decreasing $IE_1$ down a group and increasing $IE_1$ across a period.

**Solution** **(a)** He > Ar > Kr. These are in Group 8A(18), and $IE_1$ decreases down a group.

**(b)** Te > Sb > Sn. These are in Period 5, and $IE_1$ increases across a period.

**(c)** Ca > K > Rb. $IE_1$ of K is larger than $IE_1$ of Rb because K is higher in Group 1A(1). $IE_1$ of Ca is larger than $IE_1$ of K because Ca is farther to the right in Period 4.

**(d)** Xe > I > Cs. $IE_1$ of I is smaller than $IE_1$ of Xe because I is farther to the left. $IE_1$ of I is larger than $IE_1$ of Cs because I is farther to the right and in the previous period.

**Check** Because trends in IE$_1$ are generally the opposite of the trends in size, you can rank the elements by size and check that you obtain the reverse order.

**Follow-Up Problem 8.4** Rank the elements in each set in order of *increasing* IE$_1$: **(a)** Sb, Sn, I; **(b)** Sr, Ca, Ba.

**Successive Ionization Energies** For a given element, IE$_1$, IE$_2$, and so on, increase because each electron is pulled away from a species with a higher positive charge. This increase includes an enormous jump *after* the outer (valence) electrons have been removed because *much* more energy is needed to remove an inner (core) electron (Figure 8.17).

Table 8.4 shows successive ionization energies for Period 2 and the first element in Period 3. Move across the values for any element, and you reach a point that separates relatively low from relatively high IE values *(shaded area)*. For example, follow the values for boron (B): IE$_1$ (0.80 MJ) is lower than IE$_2$ (2.43 MJ), which is lower than IE$_3$ (3.66 MJ), which is *much* lower than IE$_4$ (25.02 MJ). From this jump, we know that boron has three electrons in the highest energy level ($1s^2 2s^2 2p^1$). Because they are so difficult to remove, *core electrons are not involved in reactions.*

**Figure 8.17 The first three ionization energies of beryllium.** Beryllium has two valence electrons, so IE$_3$ is much larger than IE$_2$.

---

**Sample Problem 8.5**    **Identifying an Element from Its Ionization Energies**

**Problem** Name the Period 3 element with the following ionization energies (kJ/mol), and write its full electron configuration:

| IE$_1$ | IE$_2$ | IE$_3$ | IE$_4$ | IE$_5$ | IE$_6$ |
|---|---|---|---|---|---|
| 1012 | 1903 | 2910 | 4956 | 6278 | 22,230 |

**Plan** We look for a large jump in the IE values, which occurs after all valence electrons have been removed. Then we refer to the periodic table to find the Period 3 element with this number of valence electrons and write its electron configuration.

**Solution** The large jump occurs after IE$_5$, indicating that the element has five valence electrons and, thus, is in Group 5A(15). This Period 3 element is phosphorus (P; Z = 15). Its electron configuration is $1s^2 2s^2 2p^6 3s^2 3p^3$.

**Follow-Up Problem 8.5** Element Q is in Period 3 and has the following ionization energies (in kJ/mol):

| IE$_1$ | IE$_2$ | IE$_3$ | IE$_4$ | IE$_5$ | IE$_6$ |
|---|---|---|---|---|---|
| 577 | 1816 | 2744 | 11,576 | 14,829 | 18,375 |

Name element Q, and write its full electron configuration.

---

| Table **8.4** | Successive Ionization Energies of the Elements Lithium Through Sodium | | | | | | | | | | |
|---|---|---|---|---|---|---|---|---|---|---|---|
| | | **Number of Valence Electrons** | **Ionization Energy (MJ/mol)\*** | | | | | | | | |
| **Z** | **Element** | | **IE$_1$** | **IE$_2$** | **IE$_3$** | **IE$_4$** | **IE$_5$** | **IE$_6$** | **IE$_7$** | **IE$_8$** | **IE$_9$** | **IE$_{10}$** |
| 3 | Li | 1 | 0.52 | 7.30 | 11.81 | | | **CORE ELECTRONS** | | | | |
| 4 | Be | 2 | 0.90 | 1.76 | 14.85 | 21.01 | | | | | | |
| 5 | B | 3 | 0.80 | 2.43 | 3.66 | 25.02 | 32.82 | | | | | |
| 6 | C | 4 | 1.09 | 2.35 | 4.62 | 6.22 | 37.83 | 47.28 | | | | |
| 7 | N | 5 | 1.40 | 2.86 | 4.58 | 7.48 | 9.44 | 53.27 | 64.36 | | | |
| 8 | O | 6 | 1.31 | 3.39 | 5.30 | 7.47 | 10.98 | 13.33 | 71.33 | 84.08 | | |
| 9 | F | 7 | 1.68 | 3.37 | 6.05 | 8.41 | 11.02 | 15.16 | 17.87 | 92.04 | 106.43 | |
| 10 | Ne | 8 | 2.08 | 3.95 | 6.12 | 9.37 | 12.18 | 15.24 | 20.00 | 23.07 | 115.38 | 131.43 |
| 11 | Na | 1 | 0.50 | 4.56 | 6.91 | 9.54 | 13.35 | 16.61 | 20.11 | 25.49 | 28.93 | 141.37 |

\*MJ/mol, or megajoules per mole = $10^3$ kJ/mol.

## Trends in Electron Affinity

The **electron affinity (EA)** is the energy change (kJ/mol) accompanying the *addition* of 1 mol of electrons to 1 mol of gaseous atoms or ions. The *first electron affinity* ($EA_1$) refers to the formation of 1 mol of monovalent (1−) gaseous anions:

$$\text{Atom}(g) + e^- \longrightarrow \text{ion}^-(g) \qquad \Delta E = EA_1$$

As with ionization energy, there is a first electron affinity, a second, and so forth. The first electron is *attracted* by the atom's nucleus, so in most cases, $EA_1$ *is negative* (energy is released), analogous to the negative $\Delta H$ for an exothermic reaction.* But, the second electron affinity ($EA_2$) is always positive because energy must be *absorbed* to overcome electrostatic repulsions and add another electron to a negative ion.

Factors other than $Z_{eff}$ and atomic size affect electron affinities, so trends are not regular, as are those for size and $IE_1$. The many exceptions arise from changes in sublevel energy and electron-electron repulsion:

- *Down a group.* We might expect a smooth decrease (smaller negative number) down a group because size increases, and the nucleus is farther away from an electron being added. But only Group 1A(1) exhibits this behavior (Figure 8.18).

- *Across a period.* We might expect a regular increase (larger negative number) across a period because size decreases, and higher $Z_{eff}$ should attract the electron being added more strongly. There is an overall left-to-right increase, but it is not at all regular.

**Figure 8.18** Electron affinities of the main-group elements (in kJ/mol). Values for Group 8A(18) are estimates, which is indicated by parentheses.

Despite these irregularities, relative values of IE and EA show three general behavior patterns:

1. *Reactive nonmetals.* Members of Group 6A(16) and especially Group 7A(17) (the halogens) have high IEs and highly negative (exothermic) EAs: these elements lose electrons with difficulty but attract them strongly. Therefore, *in their ionic compounds, they form negative ions.*
2. *Reactive metals.* Members of Groups 1A(1) and 2A(2) have low IEs and slightly negative (exothermic) EAs: they lose electrons easily but attract them weakly, if at all. Therefore, *in their ionic compounds, they form positive ions.*
3. *Noble gases.* Members of Group 8A(18) have very high IEs and slightly positive (endothermic) EAs: *they tend **not** to lose or gain electrons.* In fact, only the larger members of the group (Kr, Xe, and Rn) form compounds at all.

## ▌ Summary of Section 8.3

- Trends in three atomic properties are summarized in Figure 8.19.
- Atomic size (half the distance between nuclei of adjacent atoms) increases down a main group and decreases across a period. In a transition series, size remains relatively constant.
- First ionization energy (the energy required to remove the outermost electron from a mole of gaseous atoms) is inversely related to atomic size: $IE_1$ decreases down a main group and increases across a period.
- Successive ionization energies of an element show a very large increase after all valence electrons have been removed, because the first inner (core) electron is in an orbital of much lower energy and so is held very tightly.
- Electron affinity (the energy involved in adding an electron to a mole of gaseous atoms) shows many variations from expected trends.
- Based on the relative sizes of IEs and EAs, Group 1A(1) and 2A(2) elements tend to form cations and Group 6A(16) and 7A(17) elements tend to form anions in ionic compounds. Group 8A(18) elements are very unreactive.

**Figure 8.19** Trends in three atomic properties. For electron affinity, the dashed arrows indicate that there are numerous exceptions to expected trends.

---

*Some tables of $EA_1$ list them as positive values because energy would be *absorbed* to remove an electron from the anion.

# 8.4 • ATOMIC PROPERTIES AND CHEMICAL REACTIVITY

*All physical and chemical behaviors of the elements and their compounds are based on electron configuration and effective nuclear charge.* In this section, you'll see how atomic properties determine metallic behavior and the properties of ions.

## Trends in Metallic Behavior

The three general classes of elements have distinguishing properties:

- *Metals,* found in the left and lower three-quarters of the periodic table, are typically shiny solids, have moderate to high melting points, are good conductors of heat and electricity, can be machined into wires and sheets, and lose electrons to nonmetals.
- *Nonmetals,* found in the upper right quarter of the table, are typically not shiny, have relatively low melting points, are poor conductors, are mostly crumbly solids or gases, and tend to gain electrons from metals.
- *Metalloids,* found between the other two classes, have intermediate properties.

Thus, *metallic behavior decreases left-to-right across a period and increases down a group in the periodic table* (Figure 8.20).

Remember, though, that some elements don't fit these categories: as graphite, nonmetallic carbon is a good electrical conductor; the nonmetal iodine is shiny; metallic gallium melts in your hand; mercury is a liquid; and iron is brittle. Despite such exceptions, in this discussion, we'll make several generalizations about metallic behavior and its applications to redox behavior and the acid-base properties of oxides.

**Figure 8.20** Trends in metallic behavior. (Hydrogen appears next to helium.)

**Relative Tendency to Lose or Gain Electrons** Metals tend to lose electrons to nonmetals during reactions:

1. *Down a main group.* The increase in metallic behavior down a group is consistent with an increase in size and a decrease in IE and is most obvious in groups with more than one class of element, such as Group 5A(15) (Figure 8.21, *vertical*): *elements at the top can form anions, and*

**Figure 8.21** Metallic behavior in Group 5A(15) and Period 3. Moving down from N to Bi, there is an *increase* in metallic behavior. Moving across from Na to Cl, there is a *decrease* in metallic behavior.

*those at the bottom can form cations.* Nitrogen (N) is a gaseous nonmetal, and phosphorus (P) is a soft nonmetal; both occur occasionally as 3− anions in their compounds. Arsenic (As) and antimony (Sb) are metalloids, with Sb the more metallic, and neither forms ions readily. Bismuth (Bi) is a typical metal, forming a 3+ cation in its mostly ionic compounds. Groups 3A(13), 4A(14), and 6A(16) show a similar trend. But even in Group 2A(2), which contains only metals, the tendency to form cations increases down the group: beryllium (Be) forms covalent compounds with nonmetals, whereas all compounds of barium (Ba) are ionic.

2. *Across a period.* The decrease in metallic behavior across a period is consistent with a decrease in size, an increase in IE, and a more favorable (more negative) EA. Consider Period 3 (Figure 8.21, *horizontal*): *elements at the left tend to form cations, and those at the right tend to form anions.* Sodium and magnesium are metals that occur as $Na^+$ and $Mg^{2+}$ in seawater, minerals, and organisms. Aluminum is metallic physically and occurs as $Al^{3+}$ in some compounds, but it bonds covalently in most others. Silicon (Si) is a shiny metalloid that does not occur as

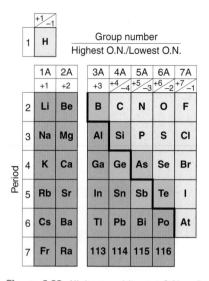

**Figure 8.22** Highest and lowest O.N.s of reactive main-group elements.

a monatomic ion. Phosphorus is a white, waxy nonmetal that occurs rarely as $P^{3-}$, whereas crumbly, yellow sulfur forms $S^{2-}$ in many compounds, and gaseous, yellow-green chlorine occurs in nature almost always as $Cl^-$.

**Redox Behavior of the Main-Group Elements** Closely related to an element's tendency to lose or gain electrons is its redox behavior—that is, whether it behaves as an oxidizing or reducing agent and the associated changes in its oxidation number (O.N.). You can find the highest and lowest oxidation numbers of many main-group elements from the periodic table (Figure 8.22):

- For most elements, the A-group number is the *highest* oxidation number (always positive) of any element in the group. The exceptions are O and F (see Table 4.3).
- For nonmetals and some metalloids, the A-group number minus 8 is the *lowest* oxidation number (always negative) of any element in the group.

For example, the highest oxidation number of S (Group 6A) is +6, as in $SF_6$, and the lowest is $6 - 8$, or $-2$, as in FeS and other metal sulfides.

Redox behavior is closely related to atomic properties:

- With their low IEs and small EAs, the members of Groups 1A(1) and 2A(2) lose electrons readily, so they are *strong reducing agents* and become oxidized.
- With their high IEs and large EAs, nonmetals in Groups 6A(16) and 7A(17) gain electrons readily, so they are *strong oxidizing agents* and become reduced.

**Acid-Base Behavior of Oxides** Metals are also distinguished from nonmetals by the acid-base behavior of their oxides in water:

- Most main-group metals *transfer* electrons to oxygen, so their *oxides are ionic. In water, these oxides act as bases,* producing $OH^-$ ions from $O^{2-}$ and reacting with acids. Calcium oxide is an example (Figure 8.23, *left*).
- Nonmetals *share* electrons with oxygen, so *nonmetal oxides are covalent. They react with water to form acids,* producing $H^+$ ions and reacting with bases. Tetraphosphorus decaoxide is an example (Figure 8.23, *right*).

Some metals and many metalloids form oxides that are **amphoteric:** they can act as acids *or* bases in water.

Figure 8.24 shows the acid-base behavior of some common oxides of elements in Group 5A(15) and Period 3 with a gradient from blue (basic) to red (acidic):

1. *As elements become more metallic down a group (larger size and smaller IE), their oxides become more basic.* In Group 5A(15), dinitrogen pentaoxide, $N_2O_5$, forms the strong acid $HNO_3$:

$$N_2O_5(s) + H_2O(l) \longrightarrow 2HNO_3(aq)$$

Tetraphosphorus decaoxide, $P_4O_{10}$, forms the weaker acid $H_3PO_4$:

$$P_4O_{10}(s) + 6H_2O(l) \longrightarrow 4H_3PO_4(aq)$$

The oxide of the metalloid arsenic is weakly acidic, whereas that of the metalloid antimony is weakly basic. Bismuth, the most metallic of the group, forms a basic oxide that is insoluble in water but reacts with acid to yield a salt and water:

$$Bi_2O_3(s) + 6HNO_3(aq) \longrightarrow 2Bi(NO_3)_3(aq) + 3H_2O(l)$$

**Figure 8.23 Oxide acidity.** In water, metal oxides are basic (*left*), and nonmetal oxides are acidic (*right*). The colors are due to the presence of acid-base indicators.

**Figure 8.24** Acid-base behavior of some element oxides.

2. *As the elements become less metallic across a period (smaller size and higher IE), their oxides become more acidic.* In Period 3, $Na_2O$ and $MgO$ are strongly basic, and amphoteric aluminum oxide ($Al_2O_3$) reacts with acid or with base:

$$Al_2O_3(s) + 6HCl(aq) \longrightarrow 2AlCl_3(aq) + 3H_2O(l)$$

$$Al_2O_3(s) + 2NaOH(aq) + 3H_2O(l) \longrightarrow 2NaAl(OH)_4(aq)$$

Silicon dioxide is weakly acidic, forming a salt and water with base:

$$SiO_2(s) + 2NaOH(aq) \longrightarrow Na_2SiO_3(aq) + H_2O(l)$$

The common oxides of phosphorus, sulfur, and chlorine form acids of increasing strength: $H_3PO_4$, $H_2SO_4$, and $HClO_4$.

## Properties of Monatomic Ions

So far we have focused on the reactants—the atoms—in the process of electron loss and gain. Now we focus on the products—the ions—considering their electron configurations, magnetic properties, and sizes.

**Electron Configurations of Main-Group Ions** Why does an ion have a particular charge: $Na^+$ not $Na^{2+}$, or $F^-$ not $F^{2-}$? Why do some metals form two ions, such as $Sn^{2+}$ and $Sn^{4+}$? The answer relates to the location of the element in the periodic table and the energy associated with losing or gaining electrons:

1. *Ions with a noble gas configuration.* Atoms of the noble gases have very low reactivity because their highest energy level is *filled* ($ns^2np^6$). Thus, *when elements at either end of a period form ions, they attain a filled outer level—a noble gas configuration.* These elements lie on either side of Group 8A(18), and their ions are **isoelectronic** (Greek *iso,* "same") with the nearest noble gas (Figure 8.25; see also Figure 2.13, p. 57).

- Elements in Groups 1A(1) and 2A(2) *lose* electrons and become isoelectronic with the *previous* noble gas. The $Na^+$ ion, for example, is isoelectronic with neon (Ne):

$$Na(1s^22s^22p^63s^1) \longrightarrow e^- + Na^+([He]2s^22p^6) \text{ [isoelectronic with Ne}([He]2s^22p^6)]$$

- Elements in Groups 6A(16) and 7A(17) *gain* electrons and become isoelectronic with the *next* noble gas. The $Br^-$ ion, for example, is isoelectronic with krypton (Kr):

$$Br ([Ar] 4s^23d^{10}4p^5) + e^- \longrightarrow Br^- ([Ar] 4s^23d^{10}4p^6)$$
$$\text{[isoelectronic with Kr ([Ar] } 4s^23d^{10}4p^6)]$$

The energy needed to remove electrons from metals or add them to nonmetals determines the charges of the resulting ions:

- *Cations.* Removing another electron from $Na^+$ or from $Mg^{2+}$ means removing a core electron, which requires too much energy: thus, $NaCl_2$ and $MgF_3$ do *not* exist.
- *Anions.* Similarly, adding another electron to $F^-$ or to $O^{2-}$ means putting it into the next higher energy level ($n = 3$). With 10 electrons ($1s^22s^22p^6$) acting as inner electrons, the nuclear charge would be shielded very effectively, and adding an outer electron would require too much energy: thus, we never see $Na_2F$ or $Mg_3O_2$.

2. *Ions without a noble gas configuration.* Except for aluminum, the metals of Groups 3A(13) to 5A(15) do not form ions with noble gas configurations. Instead, they form cations with two different stable configurations:

- *Pseudo–noble gas configuration.* If the metal atom empties its highest energy level, it attains the stability of empty $ns$ and $np$ sublevels and filled inner $(n - 1)d$ sublevel. This $(n - 1)d^{10}$ configuration is called a **pseudo–noble gas configuration.** For example, tin (Sn; $Z = 50$) loses four electrons to form the tin(IV) ion ($Sn^{4+}$), which has empty $5s$ and $5p$ sublevels and a filled inner $4d$ sublevel:

$$Sn ([Kr] 5s^24d^{10}5p^2) \longrightarrow Sn^{4+} ([Kr] 4d^{10}) + 4e^-$$

- *Inert pair configuration.* Alternatively, the metal atom loses just its $np$ electrons and attains a stable configuration with filled $ns$ and $(n - 1)d$ sublevels. The retained $ns^2$ electrons are sometimes called an *inert pair.* For example, in the more

**Figure 8.25** Main-group elements whose ions have noble gas electron configurations.

common tin(II) ion ($Sn^{2+}$), the atom loses the two $5p$ electrons and has filled $5s$ and $4d$ sublevels:

$$Sn \ ([Kr] \ 5s^2 4d^{10} 5p^2) \longrightarrow Sn^{2+} \ ([Kr] \ 5s^2 4d^{10}) + 2e^-$$

Thallium, lead, and bismuth, the largest and, thus, most metallic members of Groups 3A(13) to 5A(15), form ions that retain the $ns^2$ pair: $Tl^+$, $Pb^{2+}$, and $Bi^{3+}$.

Once again, energy considerations explain these configurations. It would be energetically impossible for metals in Groups 3A(13) to 5A(15) to achieve noble gas configurations: tin, for example, would have to lose 14 electrons—ten $4d$ in addition to the two $5p$ and two $5s$—to be isoelectronic with krypton (Kr; $Z = 36$), the previous noble gas.

---

### Sample Problem 8.6 | Writing Electron Configurations of Main-Group Ions

**Problem** Using condensed electron configurations, write equations representing the formation of the ion(s) of the following elements:
**(a)** Iodine ($Z = 53$)    **(b)** Potassium ($Z = 19$)    **(c)** Indium ($Z = 49$)

**Plan** We identify the element's position in the periodic table and recall that
- Ions of elements in Groups 1A(1), 2A(2), 6A(16), and 7A(17) are isoelectronic with the nearest noble gas.
- Metals in Groups 3A(13) to 5A(15) lose the $ns$ and $np$ electrons or just the $np$.

**Solution** **(a)** Iodine is in Group 7A(17), so it gains one electron, and $I^-$ is isoelectronic with xenon:

$$I \ ([Kr] \ 5s^2 4d^{10} 5p^5) + e^- \longrightarrow I^- \ ([Kr] \ 5s^2 4d^{10} 5p^6) \quad \text{(same as Xe)}$$

**(b)** Potassium is in Group 1A(1), so it loses one electron; $K^+$ is isoelectronic with argon:

$$K \ ([Ar] \ 4s^1) \longrightarrow K^+ \ ([Ar]) + e^-$$

**(c)** Indium is in Group 3A(13), so it loses either three electrons to form $In^{3+}$ (with a pseudo–noble gas configuration) or one to form $In^+$ (with an inert pair):

$$In \ ([Kr] \ 5s^2 4d^{10} 5p^1) \longrightarrow In^{3+} \ ([Kr] \ 4d^{10}) + 3e^-$$

$$In \ ([Kr] \ 5s^2 4d^{10} 5p^1) \longrightarrow In^+ \ ([Kr] \ 5s^2 4d^{10}) + e^-$$

**Check** Be sure that the number of electrons in the ion's electron configuration, plus the number gained or lost to form the ion, equals $Z$.

**Follow-Up Problem 8.6** Using condensed electron configurations, write equations representing the formation of the ion(s) of the following elements:
**(a)** Ba ($Z = 56$)    **(b)** O ($Z = 8$)    **(c)** Pb ($Z = 82$)

---

**Electron Configurations of Transition Metal Ions** In contrast to many main-group ions, *transition metal ions rarely attain a noble gas configuration.* Aside from the Period 4 elements scandium, which forms $Sc^{3+}$, and titanium, which occasionally forms $Ti^{4+}$, *a transition element typically forms more than one cation by losing all of its ns and some of its (n − 1)d electrons.*

The reason, once again, is that energy costs are too high. Let's consider again the filling of Period 4. At the beginning of Period 4 (the same point holds in other periods), penetration makes the $4s$ sublevel *more stable* than the $3d$. Therefore, the first and second electrons added enter the $4s$, which is the outer sublevel. But, the $3d$ is an *inner* sublevel, so as it begins to fill, its electrons are not well shielded from the increasing nuclear charge.

A *crossover in sublevel energy* results: the $3d$ becomes *more stable* than the $4s$ in the transition series (Figure 8.26). This crossover has a major effect on the formation of Period 4 transition metal ions: because the $3d$ electrons are held tightly and shield those in the outer sublevel, *the 4s electrons of a transition metal are lost **before** the*

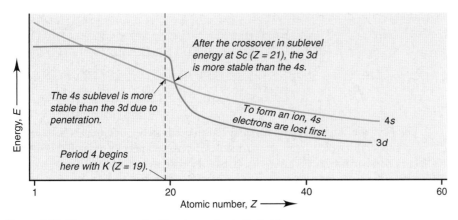

**Figure 8.26** The crossover of sublevel energies in Period 4.

*3d electrons.* Thus, 4s electrons are added before 3d electrons to form the *atom* and are lost before them to form the *ion,* the so-called "first-in, first-out" rule.

**Ion Formation: A Summary of Electron Loss or Gain** The various ways that cations form have one point in common—*outer electrons are removed first.* Here is a summary of the rules for formation of any main-group or transition metal ion:

- Main-group *s*-block metals lose all electrons with the highest *n* value.
- Main-group *p*-block metals lose *np* electrons before *ns* electrons.
- Transition (*d*-block) metals lose *ns* electrons before $(n - 1)d$ electrons.
- Nonmetals gain electrons in the *p* orbitals of highest *n* value.

**Magnetic Properties of Transition Metal Ions** We learn a great deal about an element's electron configuration from atomic spectra, and magnetic studies provide additional evidence.

Recall that electron spin generates a tiny magnetic field, which causes a beam of H atoms to split in an external magnetic field (see Figure 8.1). Only a beam of a species (atoms, ions, or molecules) with one or more *unpaired* electrons will split. A beam of silver atoms (Ag; Z = 47) was used in the original 1921 experiment:

$$\text{Ag } (Z = 47) \quad [\text{Kr}] \, 5s^1 4d^{10} \quad \boxed{\uparrow} \quad \boxed{\uparrow\downarrow\ \uparrow\downarrow\ \uparrow\downarrow\ \uparrow\downarrow\ \uparrow\downarrow} \quad \boxed{\ \ \ }$$
$$\qquad\qquad\qquad\qquad\qquad\qquad\quad 5s \qquad\qquad 4d \qquad\qquad\qquad 5p$$

Note the unpaired 5s electron. A beam of cadmium atoms (Cd; Z = 48) is not split because their 5s electrons are *paired* ([Kr] $5s^2 4d^{10}$).

A species with unpaired electrons exhibits **paramagnetism:** it is attracted by an external field. A species with all of its electrons paired exhibits **diamagnetism:** it is not attracted (and is slightly repelled) by the field (Figure 8.27). Many transition metals and their compounds are paramagnetic because their atoms and ions have unpaired electrons.

Let's see three examples of how magnetic studies might provide evidence for a proposed electron configuration:

1. *The $Ti^{2+}$ ion.* Spectral analysis of titanium metal yields the electron configuration [Ar] $4s^2 3d^2$, and experiment shows that the metal is paramagnetic, which indicates the presence of unpaired electrons. Spectral analysis shows that the $Ti^{2+}$ ion is [Ar] $3d^2$, indicating loss of the 4s electrons. In support of the spectra, magnetic studies show that $Ti^{2+}$ compounds are paramagnetic. If Ti had lost its 3d electrons to form $Ti^{2+}$, its compounds would be diamagnetic:

$$\text{Ti ([Ar] } 4s^2 3d^2) \longrightarrow \text{Ti}^{2+} \text{ ([Ar] } 3d^2) + 2e^-$$

**Figure 8.27 Measuring the magnetic behavior of a sample.** The substance is weighed with the external magnetic field "off." **A,** If the substance is diamagnetic (has all *paired* electrons), its apparent mass is unaffected (or slightly reduced) with the field "on." **B,** If the substance is paramagnetic (has *unpaired* electrons), its apparent mass increases.

The partial orbital diagrams are

2. *The $Fe^{3+}$ ion.* An increase in paramagnetism occurs when iron metal (Fe) becomes $Fe^{3+}$ in compounds, which indicates an increase in the number of unpaired electrons. This fact is consistent with Fe losing its $4s$ pair and one electron of a $3d$ pair:

$$Fe\ ([Ar]\ 4s^23d^6) \longrightarrow Fe^{3+}\ ([Ar]\ 3d^5) + 3e^-$$

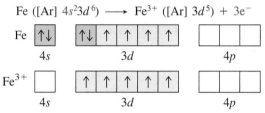

3. *The $Cu^+$ and $Zn^{2+}$ ions.* Copper (Cu) metal is paramagnetic, but zinc (Zn) is diamagnetic. The $Cu^+$ and $Zn^{2+}$ ions are diamagnetic, too. These observations are consistent with the ions being isoelectronic, which means $4s$ electrons were lost:

$$Cu\ ([Ar]\ 4s^13d^{10}) \longrightarrow Cu^+\ ([Ar]\ 3d^{10}) + e^-$$
$$Zn\ ([Ar]\ 4s^23d^{10}) \longrightarrow Zn^{2+}\ ([Ar]\ 3d^{10}) + 2e^-$$

---

**Sample Problem 8.7** | **Writing Electron Configurations and Predicting Magnetic Behavior of Transition Metal Ions**

**Problem** Use condensed electron configurations to write an equation for the formation of each transition metal ion, and predict whether it is paramagnetic:
**(a)** $Mn^{2+}$ ($Z = 25$)    **(b)** $Cr^{3+}$ ($Z = 24$)    **(c)** $Hg^{2+}$ ($Z = 80$)

**Plan** We first write the condensed electron configuration of the atom, recalling the irregularity for Cr. Then we remove electrons, beginning with $ns$ electrons, to attain the ion charge. If unpaired electrons are present, the ion is paramagnetic.

**Solution** **(a)** $Mn\ ([Ar]\ 4s^23d^5) \longrightarrow Mn^{2+}\ ([Ar]\ 3d^5) + 2e^-$
There are five unpaired $e^-$, so $Mn^{2+}$ is paramagnetic.

**(b)** $Cr\ ([Ar]\ 4s^13d^5) \longrightarrow Cr^{3+}\ ([Ar]\ 3d^3) + 3e^-$

There are three unpaired $e^-$, so $Cr^{3+}$ is paramagnetic.

**(c)** $Hg\ ([Xe]\ 6s^24f^{14}5d^{10}) \longrightarrow Hg^{2+}\ ([Xe]\ 4f^{14}5d^{10}) + 2e^-$
The $4f$ and $5d$ sublevels are filled, so there are no unpaired $e^-$: $Hg^{2+}$ is *not* paramagnetic.

**Check** We removed the $ns$ electrons first, and the sum of the lost electrons and those in the electron configuration of the ion equals $Z$.

**Follow-Up Problem 8.7** Write the condensed electron configuration of each transition metal ion, and predict whether it is paramagnetic:
**(a)** $V^{3+}$ ($Z = 23$)    **(b)** $Ni^{2+}$ ($Z = 28$)    **(c)** $La^{3+}$ ($Z = 57$)

---

**Figure 8.28 Ionic radius.** Cation radius ($r^+$) and anion radius ($r^-$) together make up the distance between nuclei.

**Ionic Size vs. Atomic Size** The **ionic radius** is a measure of the size of an ion and is obtained from the distance between the nuclei of adjacent ions in a crystalline ionic compound (Figure 8.28). From the relation between effective nuclear charge ($Z_{eff}$) and atomic size, we can predict the size of an ion relative to its parent atom:

- *Cations are smaller than parent atoms.* When a cation forms, electrons are *removed from* the outer level. The resulting decrease in shielding and value of *nl* allows the nucleus to pull the remaining electrons closer.
- *Anions are larger than parent atoms.* When an anion forms, electrons are *added to* the outer level. The increases in shielding and electron repulsions means the electrons occupy more space.

Figure 8.29 shows the radii of some main-group ions and their parent atoms:

1. *Down a group, ionic size increases* because *n* increases.
2. *Across a period,* for instance, Period 3, the pattern is complex:
   - *Among cations,* the increase in $Z_{eff}$ from left to right makes $Na^+$ larger than $Mg^{2+}$, which is larger than $Al^{3+}$.
   - *From last cation to first anion,* a great jump in size occurs: we are *adding* electrons rather than removing them, so repulsions increase sharply. For instance, $P^{3-}$ has eight more electrons than $Al^{3+}$.
   - *Among anions,* the increase in $Z_{eff}$ from left to right makes $P^{3-}$ larger than $S^{2-}$, which is larger than $Cl^-$.
   - *Within an isoelectronic series,* these factors have striking results. Within the dashed outline in Figure 8.29, the ions are isoelectronic with neon. Period 2 anions are much larger than Period 3 cations because the same number of electrons are attracted by an increasing nuclear charge. The pattern is

$$3- > 2- > 1- > 1+ > 2+ > 3+$$

3. *Cation size decreases with charge.* When a metal forms more than one cation, *the greater the ionic charge, the smaller the ionic radius.* With the two ions of iron, for example, $Fe^{3+}$ has one fewer electron, so shielding is reduced somewhat, and the same nucleus is attracting fewer electrons. As a result, $Z_{eff}$ increases, so $Fe^{3+}$ is smaller than $Fe^{2+}$.

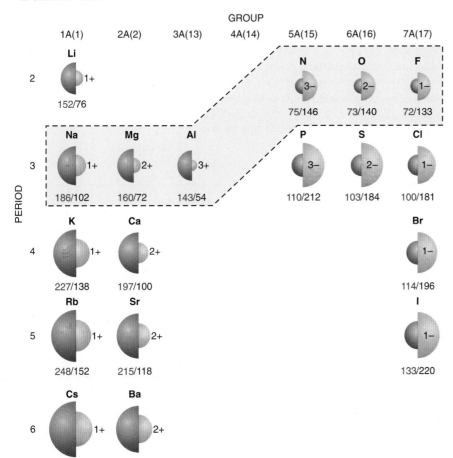

**Figure 8.29 Ionic vs. atomic radii.** Atomic radii (*color*) and ionic radii (*gray*) are given in picometers. Metal atoms (*blue*) form *smaller* positive ions, and nonmetal atoms (*red*) form *larger* negative ions. Ions in the dashed outline are *isoelectronic* with neon.

**Sample Problem 8.8** Ranking Ions by Size

**Problem** Rank each set of ions in order of *decreasing* size, and explain your ranking:
**(a)** $Ca^{2+}$, $Sr^{2+}$, $Mg^{2+}$ **(b)** $K^+$, $S^{2-}$, $Cl^-$ **(c)** $Au^+$, $Au^{3+}$

**Plan** We find the position of each element in the periodic table and apply the ideas presented in the text.

**Solution** **(a)** $Mg^{2+}$, $Ca^{2+}$, and $Sr^{2+}$ are all from Group 2A(2), so their sizes decrease up the group: $Sr^{2+} > Ca^{2+} > Mg^{2+}$.
**(b)** The ions $K^+$, $S^{2-}$, and $Cl^-$ are isoelectronic. $S^{2-}$ has a lower $Z_{eff}$ than $Cl^-$, so it is larger. $K^+$ is a cation and has the highest $Z_{eff}$, so it is smallest: $S^{2-} > Cl^- > K^+$.
**(c)** $Au^+$ has a lower charge than $Au^{3+}$, so it is larger: $Au^+ > Au^{3+}$.

**Follow-Up Problem 8.8** Rank the ions in each set in order of *increasing* size:
**(a)** $Cl^-$, $Br^-$, $F^-$ **(b)** $Na^+$, $Mg^{2+}$, $F^-$ **(c)** $Cr^{2+}$, $Cr^{3+}$

## ▌ Summary of Section 8.4

- Metallic behavior correlates with large atomic size and low ionization energy. Thus, metallic behavior increases down a group and decreases across a period.
- Elements in Groups 1A(1) and 2A(2) are strong reducing agents; nonmetals in Groups 6A(16) and 7A(17) are strong oxidizing agents.
- Within the main groups, metal oxides are basic and nonmetal oxides acidic. Thus, oxides become more acidic across a period and more basic down a group.
- Many main-group elements form ions that are isoelectronic with the nearest noble gas. Removing (or adding) more electrons than needed to attain the noble gas configuration requires a prohibitive amount of energy.
- Metals in Groups 3A(13) to 5A(15) lose either their *np* electrons or both their *ns* and *np* electrons.
- Transition metals lose *ns* electrons before $(n - 1)d$ electrons and commonly form more than one ion.
- Many transition metals and their compounds are paramagnetic because their atoms (or ions) have unpaired electrons.
- Cations are smaller and anions larger than their parent atoms. Ionic radius increases down a group. Across a period, ionic radii generally decrease, but a large increase occurs from the last cation to the first anion.

# CHAPTER REVIEW GUIDE

**Learning Objectives** Relevant section (§) and/or sample problem (SP) numbers appear in parentheses.

## Understand These Concepts

1. The meaning of the periodic law and the arrangement of elements by atomic number (Introduction)
2. The reason for the spin quantum number and its two possible values (§8.1)
3. How the exclusion principle applies to orbital filling (§8.1)
4. The effects of nuclear charge, shielding, and penetration on the splitting of energy levels; the meaning of effective nuclear charge (§8.1)
5. How the arrrangement of the periodic table is based on the order of sublevel energies (§8.2)
6. How sublevels are filled in main-group and transition elements; the importance of Hund's rule (§8.2)
7. How outer electron configuration within a group is related to chemical behavior (§8.2)
8. The distinction among inner, outer, and valence electrons (§8.2)
9. The meaning of atomic radius, ionization energy, and electron affinity (§8.3)

10. How $n$ value and effective nuclear charge give rise to the periodic trends of atomic size and ionization energy (§8.3)
11. The importance of core electrons to the pattern of successive ionization energies (§8.3)
12. How atomic properties relate to the tendency to form ions (§8.3)
13. The general properties of metals and nonmetals (§8.4)
14. How vertical and horizontal trends in metallic behavior are related to ion formation and oxide acidity (§8.4)
15. How atomic size and IE relate to redox behavior (§8.4)
16. Why main-group ions are either isoelectronic with the nearest noble gas or have a pseudo–noble gas electron configuration (§8.4)
17. Why transition elements lose *ns* electrons first (§8.4)
18. The origin of paramagnetic and diamagnetic behavior (§8.4)
19. The relation between ionic and atomic size and the trends in ionic size (§8.4)

## Master These Skills

1. Using orbital diagrams to determine the set of quantum numbers for any electron in an atom (SP 8.1)
2. Writing full and condensed electron configurations for an element (SP 8.2)
3. Using periodic trends to rank elements by atomic size and first ionization energy (SPs 8.3, 8.4)
4. Identifying an element from its successive ionization energies (SP 8.5)
5. Writing electron configurations of main-group and transition metal ions (SPs 8.6, 8.7)
6. Using periodic trends to rank ions by size (SP 8.8)

## Key Terms    Page numbers appear in parentheses.

**Introduction**
periodic law (295)
electron configuration (295)

**Section 8.1**
spin quantum number ($m_s$) (296)
exclusion principle (297)
shielding (297)
effective nuclear charge ($Z_{eff}$) (297)
penetration (298)

**Section 8.2**
aufbau principle (299)
orbital diagram (299)
Hund's rule (300)
transition elements (303)
inner (core) electrons (306)
outer electrons (306)
valence electrons (306)
inner transition elements (306)

lanthanides (rare earths) (306)
actinides (306)

**Section 8.3**
metallic radius (308)
covalent radius (308)
ionization energy (IE) (311)
electron affinity (EA) (314)

**Section 8.4**
amphoteric (316)
isoelectronic (317)
pseudo–noble gas configuration (317)
paramagnetism (319)
diamagnetism (319)
ionic radius (320)

## Key Equations and Relationships    Page numbers appear in parentheses.

**8.1** Defining the energy order of sublevels in terms of the angular momentum quantum number ($l$ value) (298):

Order of sublevel energies: $s < p < d < f$

**8.2** Meaning of the first ionization energy (311):

$$\text{Atom}(g) \longrightarrow \text{ion}^+(g) + e^- \qquad \Delta E = \text{IE}_1 > 0$$

## Brief Solutions to Follow-Up Problems

**8.1** The element has eight electrons, so $Z = 8$: oxygen.

Sixth electron: $n = 2$, $l = 1$, $m_l = 0$, $+\frac{1}{2}$

**8.2** (a) For Ni, $1s^2 2s^2 2p^6 3s^2 3p^6 4s^2 3d^8$; [Ar] $4s^2 3d^8$

Ni has 18 inner electrons.
(b) For Sr, $1s^2 2s^2 2p^6 3s^2 3p^6 4s^2 3d^{10} 4p^6 5s^2$; [Kr] $5s^2$

Sr has 36 inner electrons.

(c) For Po, $1s^2 2s^2 2p^6 3s^2 3p^6 4s^2 3d^{10} 4p^6 5s^2 4d^{10} 5p^6 6s^2 4f^{14} 5d^{10} 6p^4$; [Xe] $6s^2 4f^{14} 5d^{10} 6p^4$

Po has 78 inner electrons.

**8.3** (a) Cl < Br < Se; (b) Xe < I < Ba

**8.4** (a) Sn < Sb < I; (b) Ba < Sr < Ca

**8.5** Q is aluminum: $1s^2 2s^2 2p^6 3s^2 3p^1$

**8.6** (a) Ba ([Xe] $6s^2$) $\longrightarrow$ Ba$^{2+}$ ([Xe]) + 2e$^-$
(b) O ([He] $2s^2 2p^4$) + 2e$^-$ $\longrightarrow$ O$^{2-}$ ([He] $2s^2 2p^6$) (same as Ne)
(c) Pb ([Xe] $6s^2 4f^{14} 5d^{10} 6p^2$) $\longrightarrow$ Pb$^{2+}$ ([Xe] $6s^2 4f^{14} 5d^{10}$) + 2e$^-$
Pb ([Xe] $6s^2 4f^{14} 5d^{10} 6p^2$) $\longrightarrow$ Pb$^{4+}$ ([Xe] $4f^{14} 5d^{10}$) + 4e$^-$

**8.7** (a) V$^{3+}$: [Ar] $3d^2$; paramagnetic
(b) Ni$^{2+}$: [Ar] $3d^8$; paramagnetic
(c) La$^{3+}$: [Xe]; not paramagnetic (diamagnetic)

**8.8** (a) F$^-$ < Cl$^-$ < Br$^-$
(b) Mg$^{2+}$ < Na$^+$ < F$^-$
(c) Cr$^{3+}$ < Cr$^{2+}$

# PROBLEMS

Problems with **colored** numbers are answered in Appendix E and worked in detail in the Student Solutions Manual. Problem sections match those in the text and provide the numbers of relevant sample problems. Most offer Concept Review Questions, Skill-Building Exercises (grouped in pairs covering the same concept), and Problems in Context. The Comprehensive Problems are based on material from any section or previous chapter.

## Introduction

### Concept Review Questions

**8.1** What would be your reaction to a claim that a new element had been discovered and it fit between tin (Sn) and antimony (Sb) in the periodic table?

**8.2** Based on results of his study of atomic x-ray spectra, Moseley discovered a relationship that replaced atomic mass as the criterion for ordering the elements. By what criterion are the elements now ordered in the periodic table? Give an example of a sequence of element order that was confirmed by Moseley's findings.

### Skill-Building Exercises (grouped in similar pairs)

**8.3** Before Mendeleev published his periodic table, Döbereiner grouped elements with similar properties into "triads," in which the unknown properties of one member could be predicted by averaging known values of the properties of the others. To test this idea, predict the values of the following quantities:
(a) The atomic mass of K from the atomic masses of Na and Rb
(b) The melting point of $Br_2$ from the melting points of $Cl_2$ ($-101.0°C$) and $I_2$ ($113.6°C$) (actual value $= -7.2°C$)

**8.4** To test Döbereiner's idea (Problem 8.3), predict:
(a) The boiling point of HBr from the boiling points of HCl ($-84.9°C$) and HI ($-35.4°C$) (actual value $= -67.0°C$)
(b) The boiling point of $AsH_3$ from the boiling points of $PH_3$ ($-87.4°C$) and $SbH_3$ ($-17.1°C$) (actual value $= -55°C$)

## Characteristics of Many-Electron Atoms

### Concept Review Questions

**8.5** Summarize the rules for the allowable values of the four quantum numbers of an electron in an atom.

**8.6** Which of the quantum numbers relate(s) to the electron only? Which relate(s) to the orbital?

**8.7** State the exclusion principle. What does it imply about the number and spin of electrons in an atomic orbital?

**8.8** What is the key distinction between sublevel energies in one-electron species, such as the H atom, and those in many-electron species, such as the C atom? What factors lead to this distinction? Would you expect the pattern of sublevel energies in $Be^{3+}$ to be more like that in H or that in C? Explain.

**8.9** Define *shielding* and *effective nuclear charge*. What is the connection between the two?

**8.10** What is penetration? How is it related to shielding? Use the penetration effect to explain the difference in relative orbital energies of a $3p$ and a $3d$ electron in the same atom.

### Skill-Building Exercises (grouped in similar pairs)

**8.11** How many electrons in an atom can have each of the following quantum number or sublevel designations?
(a) $n = 2, l = 1$     (b) $3d$     (c) $4s$

**8.12** How many electrons in an atom can have each of the following quantum number or sublevel designations?
(a) $n = 2, l = 1, m_l = 0$     (b) $5p$     (c) $n = 4, l = 3$

**8.13** How many electrons in an atom can have each of the following quantum number or sublevel designations?
(a) $4p$     (b) $n = 3, l = 1, m_l = +1$     (c) $n = 5, l = 3$

**8.14** How many electrons in an atom can have each of the following quantum number or sublevel designations?
(a) $2s$     (b) $n = 3, l = 2$     (c) $6d$

## The Quantum-Mechanical Model and the Periodic Table

(Sample Problems 8.1 and 8.2)

### Concept Review Questions

**8.15** State the periodic law, and explain its relation to electron configuration. (Use Na and K in your explanation.)

**8.16** State Hund's rule in your own words, and show its application in the orbital diagram of the nitrogen atom.

**8.17** How does the aufbau principle, in connection with the periodic law, lead to the format of the periodic table?

**8.18** For main-group elements, are outer electron configurations similar or different within a group? Within a period? Explain.

**8.19** For which blocks of elements are outer electrons the same as valence electrons? For which are $d$ electrons often included among the valence electrons?

**8.20** What is the electron capacity of the $n$th energy level? What is the capacity of the fourth energy level?

### Skill-Building Exercises (grouped in similar pairs)

**8.21** Write a full set of quantum numbers for the following:
(a) The outermost electron in an Rb atom
(b) The electron gained when an $S^-$ ion becomes an $S^{2-}$ ion
(c) The electron lost when an Ag atom ionizes
(d) The electron gained when an $F^-$ ion forms from an F atom

**8.22** Write a full set of quantum numbers for the following:
(a) The outermost electron in an Li atom
(b) The electron gained when a Br atom becomes a $Br^-$ ion
(c) The electron lost when a Cs atom ionizes
(d) The highest energy electron in the ground-state B atom

**8.23** Write the full ground-state electron configuration for each:
(a) Rb     (b) Ge     (c) Ar

**8.24** Write the full ground-state electron configuration for each:
(a) Br     (b) Mg     (c) Se

**8.25** Write the full ground-state electron configuration for each:
(a) Cl     (b) Si     (c) Sr

**8.26** Write the full ground-state electron configuration for each:
(a) S     (b) Kr     (c) Cs

**8.27** Draw a partial (valence-level) orbital diagram, and write the condensed ground-state electron configuration for each:
(a) Ti     (b) Cl     (c) V

**8.28** Draw a partial (valence-level) orbital diagram, and write the condensed ground-state electron configuration for each:
(a) Ba     (b) Co     (c) Ag

**8.29** Draw a partial (valence-level) orbital diagram, and write the condensed ground-state electron configuration for each:
(a) Mn          (b) P          (c) Fe

**8.30** Draw a partial (valence-level) orbital diagram, and write the condensed ground-state electron configuration for each:
(a) Ga          (b) Zn          (c) Sc

**8.31** Draw the partial (valence-level) orbital diagram, and write the symbol, group number, and period number of the element:
(a) [He] $2s^2 2p^4$     (b) [Ne] $3s^2 3p^3$

**8.32** Draw the partial (valence-level) orbital diagram, and write the symbol, group number, and period number of the element:
(a) [Kr] $5s^2 4d^{10}$     (b) [Ar] $4s^2 3d^8$

**8.33** Draw the partial (valence-level) orbital diagram, and write the symbol, group number, and period number of the element:
(a) [Ne] $3s^2 3p^5$     (b) [Ar] $4s^2 3d^{10} 4p^3$

**8.34** Draw the partial (valence-level) orbital diagram, and write the symbol, group number, and period number of the element:
(a) [Ar] $4s^2 3d^5$     (b) [Kr] $5s^2 4d^2$

**8.35** From each partial (valence-level) orbital diagram, write the condensed electron configuration and group number:

**8.36** From each partial (valence-level) orbital diagram, write the condensed electron configuration and group number:

**8.37** How many inner, outer, and valence electrons are present in an atom of each of the following elements?
(a) O          (b) Sn          (c) Ca          (d) Fe          (e) Se

**8.38** How many inner, outer, and valence electrons are present in an atom of each of the following elements?
(a) Br          (b) Cs          (c) Cr          (d) Sr          (e) F

**8.39** Identify each element below, and give the symbols of the other elements in its group:
(a) [He] $2s^2 2p^1$          (b) [Ne] $3s^2 3p^4$          (c) [Xe] $6s^2 5d^1$

**8.40** Identify each element below, and give the symbols of the other elements in its group:
(a) [Ar] $4s^2 3d^{10} 4p^4$     (b) [Xe] $6s^2 4f^{14} 5d^2$     (c) [Ar] $4s^2 3d^5$

**8.41** Identify each element below, and give the symbols of the other elements in its group:
(a) [He] $2s^2 2p^2$          (b) [Ar] $4s^2 3d^3$          (c) [Ne] $3s^2 3p^3$

**8.42** Identify each element below, and give the symbols of the other elements in its group:
(a) [Ar] $4s^2 3d^{10} 4p^2$     (b) [Ar] $4s^2 3d^7$     (c) [Kr] $5s^2 4d^5$

**Problems in Context**

**8.43** After an atom in its ground state absorbs energy, it exists in an excited state. Spectral lines are produced when the atom returns to its ground state. The yellow-orange line in the sodium spectrum, for example, is produced by the emission of energy when excited sodium atoms return to their ground state. Write the electron configuration and the orbital diagram of the first excited state of sodium. (*Hint:* The outermost electron is excited.)

**8.44** One reason spectroscopists study excited states is to gain information about the energies of orbitals that are unoccupied in an atom's ground state. Each of the following electron configurations represents an atom in an excited state. Identify the element, and write its condensed ground-state configuration:
(a) $1s^2 2s^2 2p^6 3s^1 3p^1$          (b) $1s^2 2s^2 2p^6 3s^2 3p^4 4s^1$
(c) $1s^2 2s^2 2p^6 3s^2 3p^6 4s^2 3d^4 4p^1$          (d) $1s^2 2s^2 2p^5 3s^1$

## Trends in Three Atomic Properties
(Sample Problems 8.3 to 8.5)

**Concept Review Questions**

**8.45** If the exact outer limit of an isolated atom cannot be measured, what criterion can we use to determine atomic radii? What is the difference between a covalent radius and a metallic radius?

**8.46** Given the following partial (valence-level) electron configurations, (a) identify each element, (b) rank the four elements in order of increasing atomic size, and (c) rank them in order of increasing ionization energy:

**8.47** In what region of the periodic table will you find elements with relatively high IEs? With relatively low IEs?

**8.48** (a) Why do successive IEs of a given element always increase? (b) When the difference between successive IEs of a given element is exceptionally large (for example, between $IE_1$ and $IE_2$ of K), what do we learn about its electron configuration? (c) The bars represent the relative magnitudes of the first five ionization energies of an atom:

Identify the element and write its complete electron configuration, assuming it comes from (a) Period 2; (b) Period 3; (c) Period 4.

**8.49** In a plot of $IE_1$ for the Period 3 elements (see Figure 8.15, p. 311), why do the values for elements in Groups 3A(13) and 6A(16) drop slightly below the generally increasing trend?

**8.50** Which group in the periodic table has elements with high (endothermic) $IE_1$ and very negative (exothermic) first electron affinities ($EA_1$)? Give the charge on the ions these atoms form.

**8.51** The $EA_2$ of an oxygen atom is positive, even though its $EA_1$ is negative. Why does this change of sign occur? Which other elements exhibit a positive $EA_2$? Explain.

**8.52** How does *d*-electron shielding influence atomic size among the Period 4 transition elements?

**Skill-Building Exercises** (grouped in similar pairs)

**8.53** Arrange each set in order of *increasing* atomic size:
(a) Rb, K, Cs        (b) C, O, Be        (c) Cl, K, S        (d) Mg, K, Ca

**8.54** Arrange each set in order of *decreasing* atomic size:
(a) Ge, Pb, Sn        (b) Sn, Te, Sr        (c) F, Ne, Na        (d) Be, Mg, Na

**8.55** Arrange each set of atoms in order of *increasing* $IE_1$:
(a) Sr, Ca, Ba        (b) N, B, Ne        (c) Br, Rb, Se        (d) As, Sb, Sn

**8.56** Arrange each set of atoms in order of *decreasing* $IE_1$:
(a) Na, Li, K        (b) Be, F, C        (c) Cl, Ar, Na        (d) Cl, Br, Se

**8.57** Write the full electron configuration of the Period 2 element with the following successive IEs (in kJ/mol):

$IE_1 = 801$        $IE_2 = 2427$        $IE_3 = 3659$

$IE_4 = 25,022$        $IE_5 = 32,822$

**8.58** Write the full electron configuration of the Period 3 element with the following successive IEs (in kJ/mol):

$IE_1 = 738$        $IE_2 = 1450$        $IE_3 = 7732$

$IE_4 = 10,539$        $IE_5 = 13,628$

**8.59** Which element in each of the following sets would you expect to have the *highest* $IE_2$?
(a) Na, Mg, Al        (b) Na, K, Fe        (c) Sc, Be, Mg

**8.60** Which element in each of the following sets would you expect to have the *lowest* $IE_3$?
(a) Na, Mg, Al        (b) K, Ca, Sc        (c) Li, Al, B

## Atomic Properties and Chemical Reactivity
(Sample Problems 8.6 to 8.8)

**Concept Review Questions**

**8.61** List three ways in which metals and nonmetals differ.

**8.62** Summarize the trend in metallic character as a function of position in the periodic table. Is it the same as the trend in atomic size? The trend in ionization energy?

**8.63** Explain the relationship between atomic size and reducing strength in Group 1A(1). Explain the relationship between IE and oxidizing strength in Group 7A(17).

**8.64** Summarize the acid-base behavior of the main-group metal and nonmetal oxides in water. How does oxide acidity in water change down a group and across a period?

**8.65** What ions are possible for the two largest stable elements in Group 4A(14)? How does each arise?

**8.66** What is a pseudo–noble gas configuration? Give an example of one ion from Group 3A(13) that has it.

**8.67** How are measurements of paramagnetism used to support electron configurations derived spectroscopically? Use Cu(I) and Cu(II) chlorides as examples.

**8.68** The charges of a set of isoelectronic ions vary from 3+ to 3−. Place the ions in order of increasing size.

**Skill-Building Exercises** (grouped in similar pairs)

**8.69** Which element would you expect to be *more* metallic?
(a) Ca or Rb        (b) Mg or Ra        (c) Br or I

**8.70** Which element would you expect to be *more* metallic?
(a) S or Cl        (b) In or Al        (c) As or Br

**8.71** Which element would you expect to be *less* metallic?
(a) Sb or As        (b) Si or P        (c) Be or Na

**8.72** Which element would you expect to be *less* metallic?
(a) Cs or Rn        (b) Sn or Te        (c) Se or Ge

**8.73** Does the reaction of a main-group nonmetal oxide in water produce an acidic or a basic solution? Write a balanced equation for the reaction of a Group 6A(16) nonmetal oxide with water.

**8.74** Does the reaction of a main-group metal oxide in water produce an acidic or a basic solution? Write a balanced equation for the reaction of a Group 2A(2) oxide with water.

**8.75** Write the charge and full ground-state electron configuration of the monatomic ion most likely to be formed by each:
(a) Cl        (b) Na        (c) Ca

**8.76** Write the charge and full ground-state electron configuration of the monatomic ion most likely to be formed by each:
(a) Rb        (b) N        (c) Br

**8.77** Write the charge and full ground-state electron configuration of the monatomic ion most likely to be formed by each:
(a) Al        (b) S        (c) Sr

**8.78** Write the charge and full ground-state electron configuration of the monatomic ion most likely to be formed by each:
(a) P        (b) Mg        (c) Se

**8.79** How many unpaired electrons are present in a ground-state atom from each of the following groups?
(a) 2A(2)        (b) 5A(15)        (c) 8A(18)        (d) 3A(13)

**8.80** How many unpaired electrons are present in a ground-state atom from each of the following groups?
(a) 4A(14)        (b) 7A(17)        (c) 1A(1)        (d) 6A(16)

**8.81** Which of these are paramagnetic in their ground state?
(a) Ga        (b) Si        (c) Be        (d) Te

**8.82** Are compounds of these ground-state ions paramagnetic?
(a) $Ti^{2+}$        (b) $Zn^{2+}$        (c) $Ca^{2+}$        (d) $Sn^{2+}$

**8.83** Write the condensed ground-state electron configurations of these transition metal ions, and state which are paramagnetic:
(a) $V^{3+}$        (b) $Cd^{2+}$        (c) $Co^{3+}$        (d) $Ag^+$

**8.84** Write the condensed ground-state electron configurations of these transition metal ions, and state which are paramagnetic:
(a) $Mo^{3+}$        (b) $Au^+$        (c) $Mn^{2+}$        (d) $Hf^{2+}$

**8.85** Palladium (Pd; $Z = 46$) is diamagnetic. Draw partial orbital diagrams to show which of the following electron configurations is consistent with this fact:
(a) $[Kr]\,5s^2 4d^8$        (b) $[Kr]\,4d^{10}$        (c) $[Kr]\,5s^1 4d^9$

**8.86** Niobium (Nb; $Z = 41$) has an anomalous ground-state electron configuration for a Group 5B(5) element: $[Kr]\,5s^1 4d^4$. What is the expected electron configuration for elements in this group? Draw partial orbital diagrams to show how paramagnetic measurements could support niobium's actual configuration.

**8.87** Rank the ions in each set in order of *increasing* size, and explain your ranking:
(a) $Li^+$, $K^+$, $Na^+$        (b) $Se^{2-}$, $Rb^+$, $Br^-$        (c) $O^{2-}$, $F^-$, $N^{3-}$

**8.88** Rank the ions in each set in order of *decreasing* size, and explain your ranking:
(a) $Se^{2-}$, $S^{2-}$, $O^{2-}$        (b) $Te^{2-}$, $Cs^+$, $I^-$        (c) $Sr^{2+}$, $Ba^{2+}$, $Cs^+$

## Comprehensive Problems

**8.89** Name the element described in each of the following:
(a) Smallest atomic radius in Group 6A(16)
(b) Largest atomic radius in Period 6
(c) Smallest metal in Period 3
(d) Highest $IE_1$ in Group 4A(14)
(e) Lowest $IE_1$ in Period 5
(f) Most metallic in Group 5A(15)
(g) Group 3A(13) element that forms the most basic oxide
(h) Period 4 element with highest energy level filled
(i) Condensed ground-state electron configuration of [Ne] $3s^23p^2$
(j) Condensed ground-state electron configuration of [Kr] $5s^24d^6$
(k) Forms 2+ ion with electron configuration [Ar] $3d^3$
(l) Period 5 element that forms 3+ ion with pseudo–noble gas configuration
(m) Period 4 transition element that forms 3+ diamagnetic ion
(n) Period 4 transition element that forms 2+ ion with a half-filled $d$ sublevel
(o) Heaviest lanthanide
(p) Period 3 element whose 2− ion is isoelectronic with Ar
(q) Alkaline earth metal whose cation is isoelectronic with Kr
(r) Group 5A(15) metalloid with the most acidic oxide

**8.90** Use electron configurations to account for the stability of the lanthanide ions $Ce^{4+}$ and $Eu^{2+}$.

**8.91** When a nonmetal oxide reacts with water, it forms an oxoacid with the same oxidation number as the nonmetal. Give the name and formula of the oxide used to prepare each of these oxoacids:
(a) hypochlorous acid; (b) chlorous acid; (c) chloric acid; (d) perchloric acid; (e) sulfuric acid; (f) sulfurous acid; (g) nitric acid; (h) nitrous acid; (i) carbonic acid; (j) phosphoric acid.

**8.92** A fundamental relationship of electrostatics states that the energy required to separate opposite charges of magnitudes $Q_1$ and $Q_2$ that are a distance $d$ apart is proportional to $\dfrac{Q_1 \times Q_2}{d}$.
Use this relationship and any other factors to explain the following: (a) the $IE_2$ of He ($Z = 2$) is *more* than twice the $IE_1$ of H ($Z = 1$); (b) the $IE_1$ of He is *less* than twice the $IE_1$ of H.

**8.93** The energy difference between the $5d$ and $6s$ sublevels in gold accounts for its color. Assuming this energy difference is about 2.7 eV (electron volt; 1 eV = $1.602 \times 10^{-19}$ J), explain why gold has a warm yellow color.

**8.94** Write the formula and name of the compound formed from the following ionic interactions: (a) The 2+ ion and the 1− ion are both isoelectronic with the atoms of a chemically unreactive Period 4 element. (b) The 2+ ion and the 2− ion are both isoelectronic with the Period 3 noble gas. (c) The 2+ ion is the smallest with a filled $d$ sublevel; the anion forms from the smallest halogen. (d) The ions form from the largest and smallest ionizable atoms in Period 2.

**8.95** The energy changes for many unusual reactions can be determined using Hess's law (Section 6.5).
(a) Calculate $\Delta E$ for the conversion of $F^-(g)$ into $F^+(g)$.
(b) Calculate $\Delta E$ for the conversion of $Na^+(g)$ into $Na^-(g)$.

**8.96** Discuss each conclusion from a study of redox reactions:
(a) The sulfide ion functions only as a reducing agent.
(b) The sulfate ion functions only as an oxidizing agent.
(c) Sulfur dioxide functions as an oxidizing or a reducing agent.

**8.97** The hot glowing gases around the Sun, the *corona*, can reach millions of degrees Celsius, high enough to remove many electrons from gaseous atoms. Iron ions with charges as high as 14+ have been observed in the corona. Which ions from $Fe^+$ to $Fe^{14+}$ are paramagnetic? Which would be most strongly attracted to a magnetic field?

**8.98** There are some exceptions to the trends of first and successive ionization energies. For each of the following pairs, explain which ionization energy would be higher:
(a) $IE_1$ of Ga or $IE_1$ of Ge    (b) $IE_2$ of Ga or $IE_2$ of Ge
(c) $IE_3$ of Ga or $IE_3$ of Ge    (d) $IE_4$ of Ga or $IE_4$ of Ge

**8.99** Use Figure 8.16, p. 312, to find: (a) the longest wavelength of electromagnetic (EM) radiation that can ionize an alkali metal atom; (b) the longest wavelength of EM radiation that can ionize an alkaline earth metal atom; (c) the elements, other than the alkali and alkaline earth metals, that could also be ionized by the radiation of part (b); (d) the region of the EM spectrum in which these photons are found.

**8.100** Rubidium and bromine atoms are depicted at right. (a) What monatomic ions do they form? (b) What electronic feature characterizes this pair of ions, and which noble gas are they related to? (c) Which pair best represents the relative ionic sizes?

**A**    **B**    **C**    **D**

**8.101** Partial (valence-level) electron configurations for four different ions are shown below:

Identify the elements from which the ions are derived, and write the formula of the oxide each ion forms.

**8.102** Data from the planet Zog for some main-group elements are shown below (Zoggian units are linearly related to Earth units but are not shown). Radio signals from Zog reveal that balloonium is a monatomic gas with two positive nuclear charges. Use the data to deduce the names that Earthlings give to these elements:

| Name | Atomic Radius | $IE_1$ | $EA_1$ |
|---|---|---|---|
| Balloonium | 10 | 339 | 0 |
| Inertium | 24 | 297 | +4.1 |
| Allotropium | 34 | 143 | −28.6 |
| Brinium | 63 | 70.9 | −7.6 |
| Canium | 47 | 101 | −15.3 |
| Fertilium | 25 | 200 | 0 |
| Liquidium | 38 | 163 | −46.4 |
| Utilium | 48 | 82.4 | −6.1 |
| Crimsonium | 72 | 78.4 | −2.9 |

# Models of Chemical Bonding

## Concepts and skills to review before you study this chapter

- characteristics of ionic and covalent compounds; Coulomb's law (Section 2.7)
- polar covalent bonds and the polarity of water (Section 4.1)
- Hess's law, $\Delta H^{\circ}_{rxn}$, and $\Delta H^{\circ}_{f}$ (Sections 6.5 and 6.6)
- atomic and ionic electron configurations (Sections 8.2 and 8.4)
- trends in atomic properties and metallic behavior (Sections 8.3 and 8.4)

Why do substances behave as they do? That is, why is table salt (or any other ionic substance) a hard, brittle, high-melting solid that conducts a current only when molten or dissolved in water? Why is candle wax (along with most covalent substances) low melting, soft, and nonconducting, even though diamond (and a few others of this type of covalent substance) is high melting and extremely hard? And why is copper (and most other metals) shiny, malleable, and able to conduct a current whether molten or solid? The answers lie in the *type of bonding within the substance*. In Chapter 8, we examined the properties of individual atoms and ions. But the behavior of matter really depends on how those atoms and ions bond.

**IN THIS CHAPTER . . .** We examine how atomic properties give rise to three models of chemical bonding—ionic, covalent, and metallic—and how each model explains the behavior of substances.

- We see how metals and nonmetals combine via three types of bonding and learn how to depict atoms and ions with Lewis symbols.
- We detail the steps in the formation of an ionic solid and focus on the importance of lattice energy.
- Covalent bonding occurs in the vast majority of compounds, so we look at how a bond forms and discuss the relations among bond order, energy, and length.
- We explore the relationship between bond energy and the enthalpy change of a reaction, with a focus on fuels and foods.
- We examine periodic trends in electronegativity and learn its role in the range of bonding, from pure covalent to ionic, and in bond polarity.
- We consider a simple bonding model that explains the properties of metals.

# 9.1 • ATOMIC PROPERTIES AND CHEMICAL BONDS

Before we examine the types of chemical bonding, we should start with the most fundamental question: why do atoms bond at all? In general, *bonding lowers the potential energy between positive and negative particles* (see Figure 1.3, p. 9), whether they are oppositely charged ions or nuclei and electron pairs. Just as the electron configuration and the strength of nucleus-electron attractions determine the properties of an atom, the type and strength of chemical bonds determine the properties of a substance.

## Types of Bonding: Three Ways Metals and Nonmetals Combine

In general, there is a gradation from atoms of more metallic elements to atoms of more nonmetallic elements across a period *and* up a group (Figure 9.1, *next page*). Three types of bonding result from the three ways these two types of atoms can combine:

**Figure 9.1** A comparison of metals and nonmetals. **A,** Location within the periodic table. **B,** Relative magnitudes of some atomic properties across a period.

| PROPERTY | METAL ATOM | NONMETAL ATOM |
|---|---|---|
| **Atomic size** | Larger | Smaller |
| $Z_{eff}$ | Lower | Higher |
| **IE** | Lower | Higher |
| **EA** | Less negative | More negative |

1. *Metal with nonmetal: electron transfer and ionic bonding* (Figure 9.2A). We observe **ionic bonding** between atoms with large differences in their tendencies to lose or gain electrons. Such differences occur between reactive metals [Groups 1A(1) and 2A(2)] and nonmetals [Group 7A(17) and the top of Group 6A(16)]. A metal atom (low IE) loses its one or two valence electrons, and a nonmetal atom (highly negative EA) gains the electron(s). *Electron transfer* from metal to nonmetal occurs, and each atom forms an ion with a noble gas electron configuration. The electrostatic attractions between these positive and negative ions draw them into a three-dimensional array to form an ionic solid. Note that the chemical formula of an ionic compound is the *empirical formula* because it gives the cation-to-anion ratio.

2. *Nonmetal with nonmetal: electron sharing and covalent bonding* (Figure 9.2B). When two atoms differ little, or not at all, in their tendencies to lose or gain electrons, we observe *electron sharing* and **covalent bonding,** which occurs most commonly between nonmetal atoms. Each atom holds onto its own electrons tightly (high IE) and attracts other electrons (highly negative EA). The nucleus of each atom attracts the valence electrons of the other, which draws the atoms together. The shared electron pair is typically *localized* between the two atoms, linking them in a covalent bond of a particular length and strength. In most cases, separate molecules result when atoms bond covalently. Note that the chemical formula of a covalent compound is the *molecular formula* because it gives the actual numbers of atoms in each molecule.

**Figure 9.2** Three models of chemical bonding.

**A  Ionic bonding**

**B  Covalent bonding**

**C  Metallic bonding**

3. *Metal with metal: electron pooling and metallic bonding* (Figure 9.2C). Metal atoms are relatively large, and their few outer electrons are well shielded by filled inner levels (core electrons). Thus, they lose outer electrons easily (low IE) and do not gain them readily (slightly negative or positive EA). These properties lead metal atoms to share their valence electrons, but not by covalent bonding. In the simplest model of **metallic bonding,** the enormous number of atoms in a sample of a metal *pool* their valence electrons into a "sea" of electrons that "flows" between and around each metal-ion core (nucleus plus inner electrons), thereby attracting them together. Unlike the localized electrons in covalent bonding, electrons in metallic bonding are *delocalized,* moving freely throughout the entire piece of metal.

In the world of real substances, there are exceptions to these idealized models, so you can't always predict bond type from positions of the elements in the periodic table. As just one example, when the metal beryllium [Group 2A(2)] combines with the nonmetal chlorine [Group 7A(17)], there is more electron sharing than transferring—that is, the bonding is more covalent than ionic. Thus, just as we see gradations in atomic behavior within a group or period, we see gradations in type of bonding between atoms from different groups and periods (Figure 9.3).

**Figure 9.3** Gradations in bond type among Period 3 *(black type)* and Group 4A *(red type)* elements.

## Lewis Symbols and the Octet Rule

Before examining each of the models, let's learn a method for depicting the valence electrons of interacting atoms that predicts how they bond. In a **Lewis electron-dot symbol** (named for the American chemist G. N. Lewis), the element symbol represents the nucleus *and* inner electrons, and dots around the symbol represent the valence electrons (Figure 9.4). Note that the pattern of dots is the same for elements within a group.

**Figure 9.4** Lewis electron-dot symbols for elements in Periods 2 and 3.

We use these steps to write the Lewis symbol for any main-group element:

1. Note its A-group number (1A to 8A), which tells the number of valence electrons.
2. Place one dot at a time on each of the four sides (top, right, bottom, left) of the element symbol.
3. Keep adding dots, pairing them, until all are used up.

The specific placement of dots is not important; that is, in addition to the one shown in Figure 9.4, the Lewis symbol for nitrogen can *also* be written as

$$\cdot\ddot{N}\colon \quad \text{or} \quad \cdot\dot{\ddot{N}}\cdot \quad \text{or} \quad \colon\ddot{N}\cdot$$

The Lewis symbol provides information about an element's bonding behavior:

- For a *metal,* the *total* number of dots is the number of electrons an atom loses to form a cation.
- For a *nonmetal,* the number of *unpaired* dots equals either the number of electrons an atom *gains* to form an anion or the number it *shares* to form covalent bonds.

The Lewis symbol for carbon illustrates the last point. Rather than one pair of dots and two unpaired dots, as its electron configuration seems to call for ([He] $2s^2 2p^2$), carbon has four unpaired dots because it forms four bonds. Larger nonmetals can form as many bonds as the number of dots in their Lewis symbol (Chapter 10).

In his pioneering studies, Lewis generalized much of bonding behavior into the **octet rule:** *when atoms bond, they lose, gain, or share electrons to attain a filled outer level of eight electrons (or two,* for H and Li). The octet rule holds for nearly all of the compounds of Period 2 elements and a large number of others as well.

### ■ Summary of Section 9.1

- Nearly all naturally occurring substances consist of atoms or ions bonded to others. Chemical bonding allows atoms to lower their energy.
- Ionic bonding occurs when metal atoms transfer electrons to nonmetal atoms, and the resulting ions attract each other and form an ionic solid.
- Covalent bonding is most common between nonmetal atoms and usually results in individual molecules. Bonded atoms share one or more pairs of electrons that are localized between them.
- Metallic bonding occurs when many metal atoms pool their valence electrons into a delocalized electron "sea" that holds all the atoms in the sample together.
- The Lewis electron-dot symbol of a main-group atom shows valence electrons as dots surrounding the element symbol.
- The octet rule says that, when bonding, many atoms lose, gain, or share electrons to attain a filled outer level of eight (or two) electrons.

---

## 9.2 • THE IONIC BONDING MODEL

The central idea of the ionic bonding model is the *transfer of electrons from metal atoms to nonmetal atoms to form ions that attract each other into a solid compound.* In most cases, for the main groups, the ion that forms has a filled outer level of either two or eight electrons, the number in the nearest noble gas (octet rule).

The transfer of an electron from a lithium atom to a fluorine atom is depicted in three ways in Figure 9.5. In each, Li loses its single outer electron and is left with a filled $n = 1$ level (two $e^-$), while F gains a single electron to fill its $n = 2$ level (eight $e^-$). In this case, each atom is one electron away from the configuration of its nearest noble gas, so the number of electrons lost by each Li equals the number gained by each F. Therefore, equal numbers of $Li^+$ and $F^-$ ions form, as the formula LiF indicates. That is, in ionic bonding, *the total number of electrons lost by the metal atom(s) equals the total number of electrons gained by the nonmetal atom(s).*

**Figure 9.5** Three ways to depict electron transfer in the formation of $Li^+$ and $F^-$. The electron being transferred is shown in red.

**Sample Problem 9.1** | **Depicting Ion Formation**

**Problem** Use partial orbital diagrams and Lewis symbols to depict the formation of $Na^+$ and $O^{2-}$ ions from the atoms, and give the formula of the compound formed.

**Plan** First we draw the orbital diagrams and Lewis symbols for Na and O atoms. To attain filled outer levels, Na loses one electron and O gains two. To make the number of electrons lost equal the number gained, two Na atoms are needed for each O atom.

**Solution**

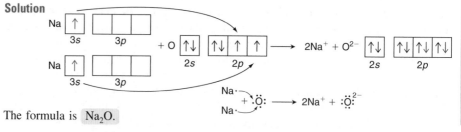

The formula is $Na_2O$.

**Follow-Up Problem 9.1** Use condensed electron configurations and Lewis symbols to depict the formation of $Mg^{2+}$ and $Cl^-$ ions from the atoms, and give the formula of the compound formed.

## Why Ionic Compounds Form: The Importance of Lattice Energy

You may be surprised to learn that energy is *absorbed* during electron transfer. So why does it occur? And, in view of this absorption of energy, why do ionic substances exist at all? As you'll see, the answer involves the enormous quantity of energy *released* after electron transfer, as the ions form a solid.

1. *The electron-transfer process.* Consider the electron-transfer process for the formation of lithium fluoride, which involves a gaseous Li atom losing an electron, and a gaseous F atom gaining it:

- The first ionization energy ($IE_1$) of Li is the energy absorbed when 1 mol of gaseous Li atoms loses 1 mol of valence electrons:

$$Li(g) \longrightarrow Li^+(g) + e^- \qquad IE_1 = 520 \text{ kJ}$$

- The first electron affinity ($EA_1$) of F is the energy released when 1 mol of gaseous F atoms gains 1 mol of electrons:

$$F(g) + e^- \longrightarrow F^-(g) \qquad EA_1 = -328 \text{ kJ}$$

- Taking the sum shows that electron transfer *by itself* requires energy:

$$Li(g) + F(g) \longrightarrow Li^+(g) + F^-(g) \qquad IE_1 + EA_1 = 192 \text{ kJ}$$

2. *Other steps that absorb energy.* The total energy needed prior to ion formation adds to the sum of $IE_1$ and $EA_1$: metallic lithium must be made into gaseous atoms (161 kJ/mol), and fluorine molecules must be broken into separate atoms (79.5 kJ/mol).

3. *Steps that release energy.* Despite these endothermic steps, the standard enthalpy of formation ($\Delta H_f^\circ$) of solid LiF is −617 kJ/mol; that is, 617 kJ is *released* when 1 mol of LiF($s$) forms from its elements. Formation of LiF is typical of reactions between active metals and nonmetals: ionic solids form readily (Figure 9.6).

If the overall reaction releases energy, there must be some step that is exothermic enough to outweigh the endothermic steps. This step involves the *strong attraction between pairs of oppositely charged ions.* When 1 mol of $Li^+(g)$ and 1 mol of $F^-(g)$ form 1 mol of gaseous LiF molecules, a large quantity of heat is released:

$$Li^+(g) + F^-(g) \longrightarrow LiF(g) \qquad \Delta H^\circ = -755 \text{ kJ}$$

But, as you know, under ordinary conditions, LiF does not exist as gaseous molecules: *even more energy is released when the separate gaseous ions coalesce into a crystalline solid* because each ion attracts *several* oppositely charged ions:

$$Li^+(g) + F^-(g) \longrightarrow LiF(s) \qquad \Delta H^\circ = -1050 \text{ kJ}$$

The negative of this enthalpy change is 1050 kJ, the lattice energy of LiF. The **lattice energy** ($\Delta H_{lattice}^\circ$) is the enthalpy change that accompanies the reverse of this equation—1 mol of ionic solid separating into gaseous ions.

### Determining Lattice Energy with a Born-Haber Cycle
The magnitude of the lattice energy is a measure of the strength of the ionic interactions and influences macroscopic properties, such as melting point, hardness, and solubility. Despite playing this crucial role in the formation of ionic compounds, lattice energy cannot be measured directly. One way to determine it applies Hess's law (see Section 6.5) in a **Born-Haber cycle,** a series of steps from elements to ionic solid for which all the enthalpies* are known except the lattice energy.

**A**

**B**

**Figure 9.6 The exothermic formation of sodium bromide. A,** Sodium (in beaker under mineral oil) and bromine. **B,** The reaction is rapid and vigorous.

---

*Strictly speaking, ionization energy (IE) and electron affinity (EA) are internal energy changes ($\Delta E$), not enthalpy changes ($\Delta H$), but in these steps, $\Delta H = \Delta E$ because $\Delta V = 0$ (see Section 6.2).

Let's go through a Born-Haber cycle for the formation of lithium fluoride to calculate $\Delta H_{\text{lattice}}^{\circ}$. Figure 9.7 shows two possible paths, a direct combination reaction ($\Delta H_{\text{f}}^{\circ}$; *black arrow*) and a multistep path (*orange arrows*) in which one step is the unknown $\Delta H_{\text{lattice}}^{\circ}$. Hess's law tells us both paths involve the same overall enthalpy change:

$$\Delta H_{\text{f}}^{\circ} \text{ of LiF}(s) = \text{sum of } \Delta H^{\circ} \text{ values for multistep path}$$

Hess's law lets us choose *hypothetical* steps whose enthalpy changes we can measure, even though *they are **not** the actual steps that occur when lithium reacts with fluorine*. We identify each $\Delta H^{\circ}$ by its step number in Figure 9.7:

*Step 1. From solid Li to Li atoms.* This step, called *atomization,* has the enthalpy change $\Delta H_{\text{atom}}^{\circ}$. It involves breaking metallic bonds, so it absorbs energy:

$$\text{Li}(s) \longrightarrow \text{Li}(g) \qquad \Delta H_{\text{step 1}}^{\circ} = \Delta H_{\text{atom}}^{\circ} = 161 \text{ kJ}$$

*Step 2. From $F_2$ molecules to F atoms.* This step involves breaking a covalent bond, so it absorbs energy; as we discuss later, this is the *bond energy* (BE) of $F_2$. Since we need 1 mol of F atoms to make 1 mol of LiF, we start with $\frac{1}{2}$ mol of $F_2$:

$$\tfrac{1}{2}\text{F}_2(g) \longrightarrow \text{F}(g) \qquad \Delta H_{\text{step 2}}^{\circ} = \tfrac{1}{2}(\text{BE of F}_2) = \tfrac{1}{2}(159 \text{ kJ}) = 79.5 \text{ kJ}$$

*Step 3. From Li to $Li^+$.* Removing the $2s$ electron from Li absorbs energy:

$$\text{Li}(g) \longrightarrow \text{Li}^+(g) + \text{e}^- \qquad \Delta H_{\text{step 3}}^{\circ} = \text{IE}_1 = 520 \text{ kJ}$$

*Step 4. From F to $F^-$.* Adding an electron to F releases energy:

$$\text{F}(g) + \text{e}^- \longrightarrow \text{F}^-(g) \qquad \Delta H_{\text{step 4}}^{\circ} = \text{EA}_1 = -328 \text{ kJ}$$

*Step 5. From gaseous ions to ionic solid.* Forming solid LiF from gaseous $\text{Li}^+$ and $\text{F}^-$ releases a lot of energy. The enthalpy change for this step is unknown but is, by definition, the negative of the lattice energy:

$$\text{Li}^+(g) + \text{F}^-(g) \longrightarrow \text{LiF}(s) \qquad \Delta H_{\text{step 5}}^{\circ} = -\Delta H_{\text{lattice}}^{\circ} \text{ of LiF} = ?$$

The enthalpy change of the combination reaction (*black arrow*) is

$$\text{Li}(s) + \tfrac{1}{2}\text{F}_2(g) \longrightarrow \text{LiF}(s) \qquad \Delta H_{\text{overall}}^{\circ} = \Delta H_{\text{f}}^{\circ} = -617 \text{ kJ}$$

**Figure 9.7** The Born-Haber cycle for lithium fluoride. The formation of LiF(s) from its elements can happen in one combination reaction *(black arrow)* or in five steps *(orange arrows)*. The unknown enthalpy change is $\Delta H_{\text{step 5}}^{\circ}$ ($-\Delta H_{\text{lattice}}^{\circ}$ of LiF).

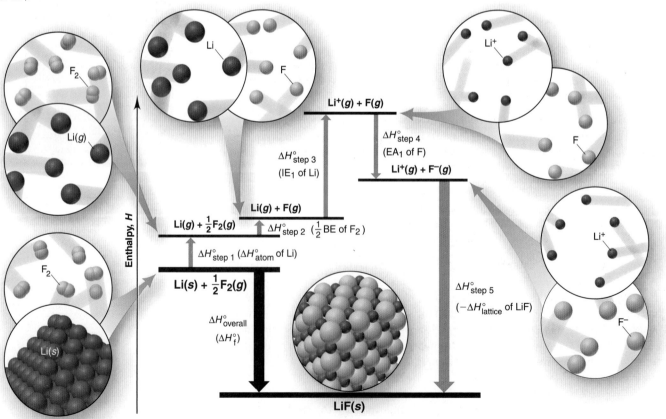

We set $\Delta H_f^\circ$ equal to the sum of the $\Delta H^\circ$ values for the steps and solve for $\Delta H_{lattice}^\circ$:

$$\Delta H_f^\circ = \Delta H_{step\ 1}^\circ + \Delta H_{step\ 2}^\circ + \Delta H_{step\ 3}^\circ + \Delta H_{step\ 4}^\circ + (-\Delta H_{lattice}^\circ \text{ of LiF})$$

Solving for $-\Delta H_{lattice}^\circ$ of LiF gives

$$\begin{aligned}
-\Delta H_{lattice}^\circ \text{ of LiF} &= \Delta H_f^\circ - (\Delta H_{step\ 1}^\circ + \Delta H_{step\ 2}^\circ + \Delta H_{step\ 3}^\circ + \Delta H_{step\ 4}^\circ) \\
&= -617 \text{ kJ} - [161 \text{ kJ} + 79.5 \text{ kJ} + 520 \text{ kJ} + (-328 \text{ kJ})] \\
&= -1050 \text{ kJ}
\end{aligned}$$

And changing the sign gives,

$$\Delta H_{lattice}^\circ \text{ of LiF} = -(-1050 \text{ kJ}) = 1050 \text{ kJ}$$

Note that *the lattice energy is, by far, the largest component of the multistep process.* (Problems 9.30 and 9.31 are among several that focus on Born-Haber cycles.)

The Born-Haber cycle shows that the energy *required* for elements to form ions is *supplied* by the attraction among the ions in the solid. And the "take-home lesson" is that *ionic solids exist **only** because the lattice energy far exceeds the total energy needed to form the ions.*

## Periodic Trends in Lattice Energy

The lattice energy results from electrostatic interactions among ions, so its magnitude depends on ionic size, ionic charge, and ionic arrangement in the solid. Therefore, we expect to see periodic trends in lattice energy.

**Explaining the Trends with Coulomb's Law**  Recall from Chapter 2 that **Coulomb's law** states that the electrostatic energy between particles A and B is directly proportional to the product of their charges and inversely proportional to the distance between them:

$$\text{Electrostatic energy} \propto \frac{\text{charge A} \times \text{charge B}}{\text{distance}}$$

Lattice energy is directly proportional to electrostatic energy. In an ionic solid, cations and anions lie as close to each other as possible, so the distance between them is the sum of the ionic radii (see Figure 8.28, p. 320):

$$\text{Electrostatic energy} \propto \frac{\text{cation charge} \times \text{anion charge}}{\text{cation radius} + \text{anion radius}} \propto \Delta H_{lattice}^\circ \qquad \textbf{(9.1)}$$

This relationship helps us explain the effects of ionic size and charge on trends in lattice energy:

1. *Effect of ionic size.* As we move down a group, ionic radii increase, so the electrostatic energy between cations and anions decreases; thus, lattice energies should decrease as well. Figure 9.8 on the next page shows that, for the alkali-metal halides, lattice energy decreases down the group whether we hold the cation constant (LiF to LiI) or the anion constant (LiF to RbF).

2. *Effect of ionic charge.* Across a period, ionic charge changes. For example, lithium fluoride and magnesium oxide have cations and anions of about equal radii ($Li^+ = 76$ pm and $Mg^{2+} = 72$ pm; $F^- = 133$ pm and $O^{2-} = 140$ pm). The major difference is between singly charged $Li^+$ and $F^-$ ions and doubly charged $Mg^{2+}$ and $O^{2-}$ ions. The difference in the lattice energies of the two compounds is striking:

$$\Delta H_{lattice}^\circ \text{ of LiF} = 1050 \text{ kJ/mol} \qquad \text{and} \qquad \Delta H_{lattice}^\circ \text{ of MgO} = 3923 \text{ kJ/mol}$$

This nearly fourfold increase in $\Delta H_{lattice}^\circ$ reflects the fourfold increase in the product of the charges ($1 \times 1$ vs. $2 \times 2$) in the numerator of Equation 9.1.

**Why Does MgO Exist?**  We might ask how ionic solids, like MgO, with its doubly charged ions, could even form. After all, forming 1 mol of $Mg^{2+}$ involves the sum of the first *and* second ionization energies:

$$Mg(g) \longrightarrow Mg^{2+}(g) + 2e^- \qquad \Delta H^\circ = IE_1 + IE_2 = 738 \text{ kJ} + 1450 \text{ kJ} = 2188 \text{ kJ}$$

**Figure 9.8 Trends in lattice energy.** The lattice energies are shown for compounds formed from a given Group 1A(1) cation *(left side)* and one of the Group 7A(17) anions *(bottom)*. LiF (smallest ions) has the highest lattice energy, and RbI (largest ions) has the lowest.

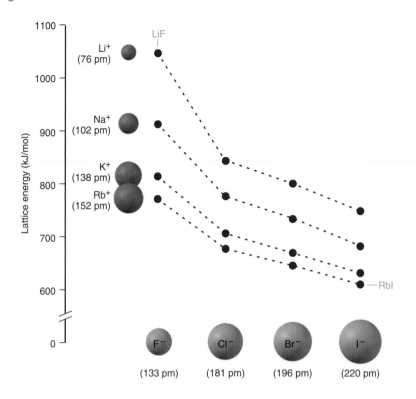

And, while forming 1 mol of $O^-$ ions is exothermic (first electron affinity, $EA_1$), adding a second mole of electrons (second electron affinity, $EA_2$) is endothermic because the electron is added to a negative ion. The overall formation of $O^{2-}$ ions is endothermic:

$$
\begin{array}{lll}
O(g) + e^- \longrightarrow O^-(g) & \Delta H^\circ = EA_1 & = -141 \text{ kJ} \\
O^-(g) + e^- \longrightarrow O^{2-}(g) & \Delta H^\circ = EA_2 & = \phantom{-}878 \text{ kJ} \\
\hline
O(g) + 2e^- \longrightarrow O^{2-}(g) & \Delta H^\circ = EA_1 + EA_2 = & \phantom{-}737 \text{ kJ}
\end{array}
$$

There are also the endothermic steps for converting $Mg(s)$ to $Mg(g)$ (148 kJ/mol) and breaking $\frac{1}{2}$ mol of $O_2$ molecules into O atoms (498 kJ/mol). Nevertheless, the 2+ and 2− ionic charges make the lattice energy so large ($\Delta H^\circ_{\text{lattice}}$ = 3923 kJ/mol) that solid MgO forms readily whenever Mg burns in air ($\Delta H^\circ_f$ = −601 kJ/mol).

## How the Model Explains the Properties of Ionic Compounds

The central role of any model is to explain the facts. With atomic-level views, we can see how the ionic bonding model accounts for the properties of ionic solids:

1. *Physical behavior.* As a typical ionic compound, a piece of rock salt (NaCl) is *hard* (does not dent), *rigid* (does not bend), and *brittle* (cracks without deforming). These properties arise from the strong attractive forces that hold the ions *in specific positions*. Moving them out of position requires overcoming these forces, so rock salt does not dent or bend. If enough force *is* applied, ions of like charge are brought next to each other, and repulsions between them crack the sample suddenly (Figure 9.9).

**Figure 9.9 Why ionic compounds crack.** **A,** Ionic compounds crack when struck with enough force. **B,** When a force moves like charges near each other, repulsions cause a crack.

**Solid ionic compound**     **Molten ionic compound**     **Ionic compound dissolved in water**

**Figure 9.10** Electrical conductance and ion mobility.

2. *Electrical conductivity.* Ionic compounds typically *do not* conduct electricity in the solid state but *do* conduct when melted or dissolved. According to the model, the solid consists of fixed ions, but when it melts or dissolves, the ions can move and carry a current (Figure 9.10).

3. *Thermal conductivity.* Large amounts of energy would be needed to free the ions from their positions and separate them. Thus, we would expect ionic compounds to have high melting points and much higher boiling points (Table 9.1). In fact, the interionic attraction is so strong that the vapor consists of **ion pairs,** gaseous ionic molecules, rather than individual ions (Figure 9.11). In their normal state, as you know, ionic compounds are solid arrays of ions, and *no separate molecules exist.*

| Table **9.1** Melting and Boiling Points of Some Ionic Compounds | | |
|---|---|---|
| **Compound** | **mp (°C)** | **bp (°C)** |
| CsBr | 636 | 1300 |
| NaI | 661 | 1304 |
| MgCl$_2$ | 714 | 1412 |
| KBr | 734 | 1435 |
| CaCl$_2$ | 782 | >1600 |
| NaCl | 801 | 1413 |
| LiF | 845 | 1676 |
| KF | 858 | 1505 |
| MgO | 2852 | 3600 |

## ▌ Summary of Section 9.2

- In ionic bonding, a metal transfers electrons to a nonmetal, and the resulting ions attract each other to form a solid.
- Main-group elements often attain a filled outer level (either eight electrons or two) by forming ions with the electron configuration of the nearest noble gas.
- Ion formation by itself *absorbs* energy, but more than enough energy is *released* when the ions form a solid. The lattice energy, the energy required to separate the solid into gaseous ions, is the reason ionic solids exist.
- The lattice energy is determined by applying Hess's law in a Born-Haber cycle.
- Lattice energies increase with higher ionic charge and decrease with larger ionic radius.
- According to the ionic bonding model, the strong electrostatic attractions that keep ions in position explain why ionic solids are hard, conduct a current only when melted or dissolved, and have high melting and boiling points.
- Ion pairs form when an ionic compound vaporizes.

**Figure 9.11** Ion pairs formed when an ionic compound vaporizes.

# 9.3 • THE COVALENT BONDING MODEL

Look through the *Handbook of Chemistry and Physics,* and you'll find that the number of covalent compounds dwarfs the number of ionic compounds. Molecules held together by covalent bonds range from tiny, diatomic hydrogen to biological and synthetic macromolecules with thousands of atoms. And covalent bonds occur in all polyatomic ions, too. Without doubt, *sharing electrons is the main way that atoms interact.*

## The Formation of a Covalent Bond

Why does hydrogen gas consist of $H_2$ molecules and not separate H atoms? Figure 9.12 plots the potential energy of a system of two isolated H atoms versus the distance between their nuclei (see also Figure 2.14, p. 60). Let's start at the right end of the curve and move along it as the atoms get closer:

- *At point 1,* the atoms are far apart, and each acts as though the other were not present.
- *At point 2,* the distance between the atoms has decreased enough for each nucleus to start attracting the other atom's electron, which lowers the potential energy. As the atoms get closer, these attractions increase, but so do repulsions between the nuclei and between the electrons.
- *At point 3* (bottom of the energy "well"), the maximum attraction is achieved in the face of the increasing repulsion, and the system has its minimum energy.
- *At point 4,* if it were reached, the atoms would be too close, and the rise in potential energy from increasing repulsions would push them apart toward point 3 again.

Thus, a **covalent bond** arises from the balance between the nuclei attracting the electrons and electrons and nuclei repelling each other. (We'll return to Figure 9.12 shortly.)

   *Formation of a covalent bond always results in greater electron density **between** the nuclei.* Figure 9.13 depicts this fact with a cross section of a space-filling model (A), an *electron density contour map* (B), and an *electron density relief map* (C).

**Figure 9.12 Covalent bond formation in H₂.** The energy difference between points 1 and 3 is the $H_2$ *bond energy* (432 kJ/mol): it is released when the bond forms and absorbed to break the bond. The internuclear distance at point 3 is the $H_2$ *bond length* (74 pm).

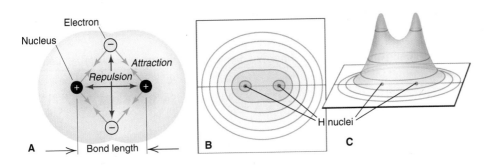

**Figure 9.13** Distribution of electron density in $H_2$. **A,** At some distance (bond length), attractions balance repulsions. Electron density *(blue shading)* is high around and between the nuclei. **B,** Electron density doubles with each concentric curve. **C,** The highest regions of electron density are shown as peaks.

## Bonding Pairs and Lone Pairs

To achieve a full outer (valence) level of electrons, *each atom in a covalent bond "counts" the shared electrons as belonging entirely to itself.* Thus, the two shared electrons in $H_2$ simultaneously fill the outer level of *both* H atoms, as clarified by the blue circles added below (which are *not* part of the Lewis structures). The **shared pair,** or **bonding pair,** is represented by a pair of dots or a line:

bonding pair (H : H)    or    H—H

An outer-level electron pair that is *not* involved in bonding is called a **lone pair,** or **unshared pair.** The bonding pair in HF fills the outer level of the H atom *and,* together with three lone pairs, fills the outer level of the F atom as well:

bonding pair (H : F :) lone pairs    or    H—F̈:

In $F_2$ the bonding pair and three lone pairs fill the outer level of *each* F atom:

(:F̈ : F̈:)    or    :F̈—F̈:

(This text generally shows bonding pairs as lines and lone pairs as dots.)

## Properties of a Covalent Bond: Order, Energy, and Length

A covalent bond has three important properties that are closely related to one another and to the compound's reactivity—bond order, bond energy, and bond length.

1. *Bond order.* The **bond order** is the number of electron pairs being shared by a given pair of atoms:

- A **single bond,** as shown above in $H_2$, HF, or $F_2$, is the most common bond and consists of one bonding pair of electrons. Thus, a *single bond has a bond order of 1.*
- Many molecules (and ions) contain *multiple bonds,* in which more than one pair is shared between two atoms. Multiple bonds usually involve C, O, and/or N atoms. A **double bond** consists of two bonding electron pairs, four electrons shared between two atoms, so *the bond order is 2.* Ethylene ($C_2H_4$) contains a carbon-carbon double bond and four carbon-hydrogen single bonds:

(H : C :: C : H with H's)   or   H₂C=CH₂ structure

*Each* carbon "counts" the four electrons in the double bond and the four in its two single bonds to hydrogens to attain an octet.

- A **triple bond** consists of three shared pairs: two atoms share six electrons, so *the bond order is 3.* The $N_2$ molecule has a triple bond, and each N atom also has a lone pair. Six shared and two unshared electrons give *each* N atom an octet:

(:N ::: N:)    or    :N≡N:

2. *Bond energy.* The strength of a covalent bond depends on the magnitude of the attraction between the nuclei and shared electrons. The **bond energy (BE)** (also called *bond enthalpy* or *bond strength*) is the energy needed to overcome this attraction and is defined as the standard enthalpy change for breaking the bond in 1 mol

### Table 9.2 Average Bond Energies (kJ/mol) and Bond Lengths (pm)

| Bond | Energy | Length | Bond | Energy | Length | Bond | Energy | Length | Bond | Energy | Length |
|------|--------|--------|------|--------|--------|------|--------|--------|------|--------|--------|
| **Single Bonds** | | | | | | | | | | | |
| H—H | 432 | 74 | N—H | 391 | 101 | Si—H | 323 | 148 | S—H | 347 | 134 |
| H—F | 565 | 92 | N—N | 160 | 146 | Si—Si | 226 | 234 | S—S | 266 | 204 |
| H—Cl | 427 | 127 | N—P | 209 | 177 | Si—O | 368 | 161 | S—F | 327 | 158 |
| H—Br | 363 | 141 | N—O | 201 | 144 | Si—S | 226 | 210 | S—Cl | 271 | 201 |
| H—I | 295 | 161 | N—F | 272 | 139 | Si—F | 565 | 156 | S—Br | 218 | 225 |
| | | | N—Cl | 200 | 191 | Si—Cl | 381 | 204 | S—I | ~170 | 234 |
| | | | N—Br | 243 | 214 | Si—Br | 310 | 216 | | | |
| C—H | 413 | 109 | N—I | 159 | 222 | Si—I | 234 | 240 | F—F | 159 | 143 |
| C—C | 347 | 154 | | | | | | | F—Cl | 193 | 166 |
| C—Si | 301 | 186 | O—H | 467 | 96 | P—H | 320 | 142 | F—Br | 212 | 178 |
| C—N | 305 | 147 | O—P | 351 | 160 | P—Si | 213 | 227 | F—I | 263 | 187 |
| C—O | 358 | 143 | O—O | 204 | 148 | P—P | 200 | 221 | Cl—Cl | 243 | 199 |
| C—P | 264 | 187 | O—S | 265 | 151 | P—F | 490 | 156 | Cl—Br | 215 | 214 |
| C—S | 259 | 181 | O—F | 190 | 142 | P—Cl | 331 | 204 | Cl—I | 208 | 243 |
| C—F | 453 | 133 | O—Cl | 203 | 164 | P—Br | 272 | 222 | Br—Br | 193 | 228 |
| C—Cl | 339 | 177 | O—Br | 234 | 172 | P—I | 184 | 246 | Br—I | 175 | 248 |
| C—Br | 276 | 194 | O—I | 234 | 194 | | | | I—I | 151 | 266 |
| C—I | 216 | 213 | | | | | | | | | |
| **Multiple Bonds** | | | | | | | | | | | |
| C=C | 614 | 134 | N=N | 418 | 122 | C≡C | 839 | 121 | N≡N | 945 | 110 |
| C=N | 615 | 127 | N=O | 607 | 120 | C≡N | 891 | 115 | N≡O | 631 | 106 |
| C=O | 745 | 123 | $O_2$ | 498 | 121 | C≡O | 1070 | 113 | | | |
| | (799 in $CO_2$) | | | | | | | | | | |

Internuclear distance (bond length) / Covalent radius

F₂ — 143 pm / 72 pm
Cl₂ — 199 pm / 100 pm
Br₂ — 228 pm / 114 pm
I₂ — 266 pm / 133 pm

**Figure 9.14** Bond length and covalent radius.

of gaseous molecules. Bond breakage is an *endothermic* process, so *bond energy is always positive:*

$$A—B(g) \longrightarrow A(g) + B(g) \qquad \Delta H°_{\text{bond breaking}} = BE_{A-B} \text{ (always > 0)}$$

The bond energy is the difference in energy between separated and bonded atoms (the potential energy difference between points 1 and 3, the energy "well" in Figure 9.12). *The same quantity of energy absorbed to break the bond is released when the bond forms.* Bond formation is an *exothermic* process, so *the sign of its enthalpy change is always negative:*

$$A(g) + B(g) \longrightarrow A—B(g) \qquad \Delta H°_{\text{bond forming}} = -BE_{A-B} \text{ (always < 0)}$$

Table 9.2 lists the energies of some common bonds. By definition,

- *Stronger bonds are lower in energy (have a deeper energy well).*
- *Weaker bonds are higher in energy (have a shallower energy well).*

The energy of a given bond varies slightly from molecule to molecule and even within the same molecule, so each value is an *average* bond energy.

3. *Bond length.* A covalent bond has a **bond length,** the distance between the nuclei of two bonded atoms. In Figure 9.12, bond length is the distance between the nuclei at the point of minimum energy (bottom of the well), and Table 9.2 shows the lengths of some covalent bonds. Like bond energies, these values are *average* bond lengths for a bond in different substances. Bond length is related to the sum of the radii of the bonded atoms. In fact, most atomic radii are calculated from measured bond lengths (see Figure 8.14C, p. 310). Bond lengths for a series of similar bonds, as in the halogens, increase with atomic size (Figure 9.14).

*The order, energy, and length of a covalent bond are interrelated.* Two nuclei are more strongly attracted to two shared pairs than to one, so double-bonded atoms are drawn closer together *and* are more difficult to pull apart than single-bonded atoms: *for a given pair of atoms, a higher bond order results in a shorter bond length and*

**Table 9.3 The Relation of Bond Order, Bond Length, and Bond Energy**

| Bond | Bond Order | Average Bond Length (pm) | Average Bond Energy (kJ/mol) |
|------|------------|--------------------------|------------------------------|
| C—O | 1 | 143 | 358 |
| C=O | 2 | 123 | 745 |
| C≡O | 3 | 113 | 1070 |
| C—C | 1 | 154 | 347 |
| C=C | 2 | 134 | 614 |
| C≡C | 3 | 121 | 839 |
| N—N | 1 | 146 | 160 |
| N=N | 2 | 122 | 418 |
| N≡N | 3 | 110 | 945 |

*a higher bond energy.* Thus, as Table 9.3 shows, for a given pair of atoms, *a shorter bond is a stronger bond.*

In some cases, we can see a relation among atomic size, bond length, and bond energy by varying one of the atoms in a single bond while holding the other constant:

- *Variation within a group.* The trend in carbon-halogen single bond lengths, C—I > C—Br > C—Cl, parallels the trend in atomic size, I > Br > Cl, and is opposite to the trend in bond energy, C—Cl > C—Br > C—I.
- *Variation within a period.* Looking again at single bonds involving carbon, the trend in bond lengths, C—N > C—O > C—F, is opposite to the trend in bond energy, C—F > C—O > C—N.

---

**Sample Problem 9.2**    **Comparing Bond Length and Bond Strength**

**Problem** Without referring to Table 9.2, rank the bonds in each set in order of *decreasing* bond length and *decreasing* bond strength:
**(a)** S—F, S—Br, S—Cl      **(b)** C=O, C—O, C≡O

**Plan (a)** S is singly bonded to three different halogen atoms, so the bond order is the same. Bond length increases and bond strength decreases as the halogen's atomic radius increases. **(b)** The same two atoms are bonded, but the bond orders differ. In this case, bond strength increases and bond length decreases as bond order increases.

**Solution (a)** Atomic size increases down a group, so F < Cl < Br.

Bond length: S—Br > S—Cl > S—F

Bond strength: S—F > S—Cl > S—Br

**(b)** By ranking the bond orders, C≡O > C=O > C—O, we obtain

Bond length: C—O > C=O > C≡O

Bond strength: C≡O > C=O > C—O

**Check** From Table 9.2, we see that the rankings are correct.

**Comment** Remember that for bonds involving pairs of different atoms, as in part (a), *the relationship between length and strength holds* only *for single bonds* and not in every case, so apply it carefully.

**Follow-Up Problem 9.2** Rank the bonds in each set in order of *increasing* bond length and *increasing* bond strength: **(a)** Si—F, Si—C, Si—O; **(b)** N=N, N—N, N≡N.

---

## How the Model Explains the Properties of Covalent Substances

The covalent bonding model proposes that electron sharing between pairs of atoms leads to *strong, localized bonds.* Most, but not all, covalent substances consist of individual molecules. These *molecular* covalent substances have very different *physical* properties than *network* covalent solids because different types of forces give rise to them.

**Figure 9.15** Strong forces within molecules and weak forces between them.

Strong covalent bonds **within** molecules do not break.

Gaseous phase

Liquid phase

Weak forces **between** molecules are overcome.

1. *Physical properties of molecular covalent substances.* At first glance, the model seems inconsistent with physical properties of covalent substances. Most are gases (such as methane and ammonia), liquids (such as benzene and water), or low-melting solids (such as sulfur and paraffin wax). If covalent bonds are so strong (~200 to 500 kJ/mol), why do covalent substances melt and boil at such low temperatures?

To answer this, we'll focus on two different forces: (1) *strong bonding forces* hold the atoms together within the molecule, and (2) *weak intermolecular forces* act between separate molecules in the sample. It is the weak forces *between* molecules that account for the physical properties of *molecular* covalent substances. For example, look what happens when pentane ($C_5H_{12}$) boils (Figure 9.15): weak forces *between* pentane molecules are overcome, not the strong C—C and C—H bonds *within* each pentane molecule.

2. *Physical properties of network covalent solids.* Some covalent substances do not consist of separate molecules. Rather, these *network covalent solids* are held together by covalent bonds *between atoms throughout the sample,* and their properties *do* reflect the strength of covalent bonds. Two examples are quartz and diamond (Figure 9.16). Quartz ($SiO_2$; *top*) has silicon-oxygen covalent bonds in three dimensions; no separate $SiO_2$ molecules exist. It is very hard and melts at 1550°C. Diamond (*bottom*) has covalent bonds connecting each carbon atom to four others. It is the hardest natural substance known and melts at around 3550°C. Thus, covalent bonds *are* strong, but most covalent substances consist of separate molecules with weak forces between them. (We discuss intermolecular forces in detail in Chapter 12.)

3. *Electrical conductivity.* An electric current is carried by either mobile electrons or mobile ions. Most covalent substances are poor electrical conductors, whether melted or dissolved, because their electrons are localized as either shared or unshared pairs, and no ions are present. The Tools of the Laboratory essay describes a tool used widely for studying the types of bonds in covalent substances.

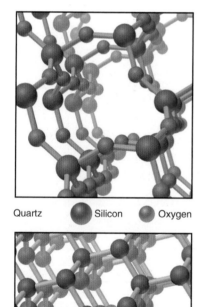

Quartz    ● Silicon    ● Oxygen

Diamond    ● Carbon

**Figure 9.16** Covalent bonds of network covalent solids: quartz and diamond.

## ▌ Summary of Section 9.3

- A shared, localized pair of valence electrons holds the nuclei of two atoms together in a covalent bond, filling each atom's outer level.
- Bond order is the number of shared pairs between two atoms. Bond energy is the energy absorbed to separate the atoms; the same quantity of energy is released when the bond forms. Bond length is the distance between their nuclei.
- For a given pair of atoms, bond order is directly related to bond energy and inversely related to bond length.
- Molecular covalent substances are soft and low melting because of the weak forces *between* the molecules, not the strong bonding forces *within* them. Network covalent solids are hard and high melting because covalent bonds join all the atoms in the sample.
- Most covalent substances have low electrical conductivity because their electrons are localized and ions are absent.
- Atoms in a covalent bond vibrate, and the energies of these vibrations are studied with IR spectroscopy.

**I**nfrared (IR) spectroscopy is an instrumental technique most often used to study covalently bonded molecules. The key components of an IR spectrometer are the same as those of other types of spectrometers (see Figure B7.3, p. 273). The source emits radiation of many wavelengths, but only those in the IR region are selected. The sample is typically a pure liquid or solid that absorbs varying amounts of certain IR wavelengths. An IR spectrum consists of peaks that indicate these various absorptions.

## Molecular Vibrations and IR Absorption

An IR spectrum indicates the types of bonds in a molecule based on their vibrations. All molecules undergo movement through space, rotation around several axes, and vibrations of bonds. Consider a sample of ethane gas. The $H_3C-CH_3$ molecules zoom throughout the container, but let's disregard motion through space and focus on other motions. The whole molecule rotates and its two $CH_3$ groups rotate about the $C-C$ bond. More important to IR spectroscopy, each pair of atoms is vibrating as though the bonds were springs. Figure B9.1 depicts the vibrations of diatomic and triatomic molecules; larger molecules vibrate in many more ways.

The energies of IR photons are in the range of these vibrational energies. *Each vibration has a frequency based on the type of motion, masses of the atoms, and strength of the bond.* The frequencies correspond to IR wavelengths between 2.5 and 25 μm. *The energy of these vibrations is quantized.* Just as an atom can absorb a photon whose energy equals the difference between *electron* energy levels, a molecule can absorb an IR photon whose energy equals the difference between *vibrational* energy levels.

## IR Radiation and Global Warming

Carbon dioxide, $O=C=O$, is a linear molecule that bends and stretches symmetrically and asymmetrically when it absorbs IR radiation (Problem B9.2). Sunlight is absorbed by Earth's surface and re-emitted as heat, much of which is IR radiation. Atmospheric $CO_2$ absorbs this radiation and re-emits it, thus warming the atmosphere (see Chemical Connections, pp. 249–251).

## Compound Identification

An IR spectrum can be used to identify a compound for three related reasons:

1. *Each kind of bond absorbs a specific range of wavelengths.* That is, a $C-C$ bond absorbs a different range than does a $C=C$ bond, a $C-H$ bond, a $C=O$ bond, and so forth.
2. *Different types of organic compounds have characteristic spectra.* The different groupings of atoms that define an alcohol, a carboxylic acid, an ether, and so forth (see Chapter 15) absorb differently.
3. *Each compound has a unique spectrum.* The IR spectrum acts like a fingerprint to identify the compound, because the quantity of each wavelength absorbed depends on the detailed molecular structure. For example, no other compound has the IR spectrum of acrylonitrile, a compound used to make plastics (Figure B9.2, *next page*).

*(continued)*

**DIATOMIC MOLECULE**

Stretch

**LINEAR TRIATOMIC MOLECULE**

Stretch symmetrical

Stretch asymmetrical

Bend

**NONLINEAR TRIATOMIC MOLECULE**

Stretch symmetrical

Stretch asymmetrical

Bend

**Figure B9.1** Vibrational motions in general diatomic and triatomic molecules.

**Figure B9.2** The infrared (IR) spectrum of acrylonitrile. In this typical IR spectrum, many absorption bands (peaks) of differing depths and sharpness appear. Most correspond to a particular type of vibration (stretch, bend, rock, wag, or twist). Some broad peaks (e.g., "combina-tion band") represent several overlapping vibrations. The bottom axis is given as wavenumber, the inverse of wavelength, and has units of $cm^{-1}$. (The scale expands to the right of 2000 $cm^{-1}$.)

Recall from Chapter 3 that constitutional (structural) isomers have the same molecular formula but different structures. We should see very different IR spectra for the isomers diethyl ether and 2-butanol because their molecular structures are so dissimilar (Figure B9.3). But, even the very similar 1,3-dimethylbenzene and 1,4-dimethylbenzene have different spectra (Figure B9.4).

## Problems

**B9.1** In Figure B9.2, the peak labeled "C=C stretch" occurs at a shorter wavelength (higher wavenumber) than that labeled "C—C stretch," as it does in the IR spectrum of any sub-stance with those bonds. Explain the relative positions of these peaks. In what relative position along the wavelength scale of Figure B9.2 would you expect to find a peak for a C≡C stretch? Explain.

**B9.2** The vibrations of a $CO_2$ molecule are symmetrical stretch, bend, and asymmetrical stretch (Figure B9.1), with frequencies of $4.02\times10^{13}$ $s^{-1}$, $2.00\times10^{13}$ $s^{-1}$, and $7.05\times10^{13}$ $s^{-1}$, respectively.
(a) What wavelengths correspond to these vibrations?
(b) Calculate the energy (in J) of each vibration. Which uses the least energy?

**Figure B9.3** The infrared spectra of 2-butanol (*green*) and diethyl ether (*red*).

**Figure B9.4** The infrared spectra of 1,3-dimethylbenzene (*green*) and 1,4-dimethylbenzene (*red*).

# 9.4 • BOND ENERGY AND CHEMICAL CHANGE

The relative strengths of the bonds in reactants and products determine whether heat is released or absorbed in a chemical reaction. In Chapter 20, you'll see that the change in bond energy is one of two factors determining whether the reaction occurs at all. In this section, we'll discuss the origin of the enthalpy of reaction ($\Delta H_{rxn}$), use bond energies to calculate it, and look at the energy available from fuels and foods.

## Changes in Bond Energy: Where Does $\Delta H^\circ_{rxn}$ Come From?

In Chapter 6, we discussed the heat involved in a chemical change but never asked a central question: where does the enthalpy of reaction ($\Delta H^\circ_{rxn}$) come from? For example, when 1 mol of $H_2$ and 1 mol of $F_2$ react to form 2 mol of HF at 1 atm and 298 K,

$$H_2(g) + F_2(g) \longrightarrow 2HF(g) + 546 \text{ kJ}$$

where does the 546 kJ come from? We find the answer by looking closely at the energies of the molecules involved. A system's total internal energy is composed of its kinetic energy and potential energy. Let's see how these change during the formation of HF:

- *Kinetic energy.* The most important contributions to the kinetic energy are the molecules' movements in space, rotations, and vibrations. However, since kinetic energy is proportional to temperature, which is constant at 298 K, it doesn't change during the reaction.
- *Potential energy.* The most important contributions to the potential energy are phase changes and changes in the attraction between vibrating atoms, between nucleus and electrons (and between electrons) in each atom, between protons and neutrons in each nucleus, and between nuclei and the shared electron pair in each bond. Of these, there are no phase changes, vibrational forces vary only slightly as the bonded atoms change, and forces within the atoms and nuclei don't change at all. The only significant change in potential energy comes from changes in the attraction between the nuclei and the shared electron pair—the bond energy.

Thus, our answer to "where does $\Delta H^\circ_{rxn}$ come from?" is that it doesn't really "come from" anywhere: *the heat released or absorbed during a chemical change is due to differences between reactant bond energies and product bond energies.*

## Using Bond Energies to Calculate $\Delta H^\circ_{rxn}$

Hess's law allows us to think of any reaction as a two-step process, whether or not it actually occurs that way:

1. *A quantity of heat is absorbed ($\Delta H^\circ > 0$) to break the reactant bonds and form separate atoms.*
2. *A different quantity of heat is then released ($\Delta H^\circ < 0$) when the atoms form product bonds.*

The sum (symbolized by $\Sigma$) of these enthalpy changes is the enthalpy of reaction, $\Delta H^\circ_{rxn}$:

$$\Delta H^\circ_{rxn} = \Sigma \Delta H^\circ_{\text{reactant bonds broken}} + \Sigma \Delta H^\circ_{\text{product bonds formed}} \qquad \text{(9.2)}$$

- In an exothermic reaction, the magnitude of $\Delta H^\circ_{\text{product bonds formed}}$ is *greater* than that of $\Delta H^\circ_{\text{reactant bonds broken}}$, so the sum, $\Delta H^\circ_{rxn}$, is *negative* (heat is released).
- In an endothermic reaction, the opposite situation is true, the magnitude of $\Delta H^\circ_{\text{product bonds formed}}$ is *smaller* than that of $\Delta H^\circ_{\text{reactant bonds broken}}$, so $\Delta H^\circ_{rxn}$ is *positive* (heat is absorbed).

An equivalent form of Equation 9.2 uses bond energies:

$$\Delta H^\circ_{rxn} = \Sigma BE_{\text{reactant bonds broken}} - \Sigma BE_{\text{product bonds formed}}$$

(We need the minus sign because all bond energies are positive.)

Typically, only certain bonds break and form during a reaction, but with Hess' law, the following is a simpler method of calculating $\Delta H^\circ_{rxn}$:

1. Break **all** the reactant bonds to obtain individual atoms.
2. Use the atoms to form **all** the product bonds.
3. Add the bond energies, with appropriate signs, to obtain the enthalpy of reaction.

(This method assumes reactants and products do not change physical state; additional heat is involved when phase changes occur. We address this topic in Chapter 12.)

Let's use the method to calculate $\Delta H^\circ_{rxn}$ for two reactions:

1. *Formation of HF.* When 1 mol of H—H bonds and 1 mol of F—F bonds absorb energy and break, the 2 mol of H atoms and 2 mol of F atoms form 2 mol of H—F bonds, which releases energy (Figure 9.17). We find the bond energy values in Table 9.2 (p. 340) and use a positive sign for bonds broken and a negative sign for bonds formed:

*Bonds broken:*

$$1 \times \text{H—H} = (1\ mol)(432\ kJ/mol) = 432\ kJ$$
$$\underline{1 \times \text{F—F} = (1\ mol)(159\ kJ/mol) = 159\ kJ}$$
$$\Sigma\Delta H^\circ_{\text{reactant bonds broken}} = 591\ kJ$$

*Bonds formed:*

$$2 \times \text{H—F} = (2\ mol)(-565\ kJ/mol) = \Sigma\Delta H^\circ_{\text{product bonds formed}} = -1130\ kJ$$

Applying Equation 9.2 gives

$$\Delta H^\circ_{rxn} = \Sigma\Delta H^\circ_{\text{reactant bonds broken}} + \Sigma\Delta H^\circ_{\text{product bonds formed}}$$
$$= 591\ kJ + (-1130\ kJ) = -539\ kJ$$

The small discrepancy between this bond energy value ($-539$ kJ) and the value from tabulated $\Delta H^\circ$ values ($-546$ kJ) is due to variations in experimental method.

2. *Combustion of $CH_4$.* In this more complicated reaction, all the bonds in $CH_4$ and $O_2$ break, and the atoms form all the bonds in $CO_2$ and $H_2O$ (Figure 9.18). Once again, we use Table 9.2 and appropriate signs for bonds broken and bonds formed:

*Bonds broken:*

$$4 \times \text{C—H} = (4\ mol)(413\ kJ/mol) = 1652\ kJ$$
$$\underline{2 \times \text{O}_2 = (2\ mol)(498\ kJ/mol) = \phantom{0}996\ kJ}$$
$$\Sigma\Delta H^\circ_{\text{reactant bonds broken}} = 2648\ kJ$$

*Bonds formed:*

$$2 \times \text{C}=\text{O} = (2\ mol)(-799\ kJ/mol) = -1598\ kJ$$
$$\underline{4 \times \text{O—H} = (4\ mol)(-467\ kJ/mol) = -1868\ kJ}$$
$$\Sigma\Delta H^\circ_{\text{product bonds formed}} = -3466\ kJ$$

Applying Equation 9.2 gives

$$\Delta H^\circ_{rxn} = \Sigma\Delta H^\circ_{\text{reactant bonds broken}} + \Sigma\Delta H^\circ_{\text{product bonds formed}}$$
$$= 2648\ kJ + (-3466\ kJ) = -818\ kJ$$

**Figure 9.17** Using bond energies to calculate $\Delta H^\circ_{rxn}$ for HF formation.

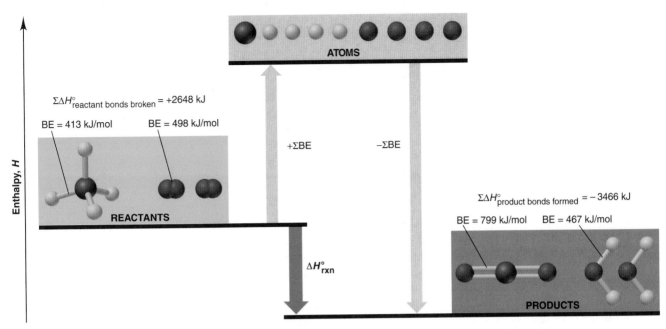

**Figure 9.18** Using bond energies to calculate $\Delta H^\circ_{rxn}$ for the combustion of methane.

In addition to variations in experimental method, there is a more basic reason for the discrepancy between the $\Delta H^\circ_{rxn}$ obtained from bond energies ($-818$ kJ) and the value obtained by calorimetry ($-802$ kJ; Section 6.3). A bond energy is an *average* value for a given bond over many compounds. The value *in a particular substance* is usually close, but not equal, to the average. For example, the C—H bond energy of 413 kJ/mol is the average for C—H bonds in many molecules. In fact, 415 kJ is actually required to break 1 mol of C—H bonds in methane, or 1660 kJ for 4 mol of these bonds, which gives a $\Delta H^\circ_{rxn}$ closer to the calorimetric value. Thus, it isn't surprising to find small discrepancies between $\Delta H^\circ_{rxn}$ values obtained in different ways.

---

**Sample Problem 9.3** | **Using Bond Energies to Calculate $\Delta H^\circ_{rxn}$**

**Problem** Calculate $\Delta H^\circ_{rxn}$ for the chlorination of methane to form chloroform:

$$H{-}\underset{\displaystyle H}{\overset{\displaystyle H}{C}}{-}H \;+\; 3\,Cl{-}Cl \;\longrightarrow\; Cl{-}\underset{\displaystyle Cl}{\overset{\displaystyle H}{C}}{-}Cl \;+\; 3\,H{-}Cl$$

**Plan** *All* the reactant bonds break, and *all* the product bonds form. We find the bond energies in Table 9.2 and substitute the two sums, with correct signs, into Equation 9.2.

**Solution** Finding the standard enthalpy changes for bonds broken and for bonds formed: For bonds broken, the bond energy values are

$$
\begin{aligned}
4 \times \text{C—H} &= (4\ \text{mol})(413\ \text{kJ/mol}) = 1652\ \text{kJ}\\
3 \times \text{Cl—Cl} &= (3\ \text{mol})(243\ \text{kJ/mol}) = \underline{\ \ 729\ \text{kJ}}\\
&\qquad\qquad\qquad \Sigma\Delta H^\circ_{\text{bonds broken}} = 2381\ \text{kJ}
\end{aligned}
$$

For bonds formed, the values are

$$
\begin{aligned}
3 \times \text{C—Cl} &= (3\ \text{mol})(-339\ \text{kJ/mol}) = -1017\ \text{kJ}\\
1 \times \text{C—H} &= (1\ \text{mol})(-413\ \text{kJ/mol}) = \ \ -413\ \text{kJ}\\
3 \times \text{H—Cl} &= (3\ \text{mol})(-427\ \text{kJ/mol}) = \underline{-1281\ \text{kJ}}\\
&\qquad\qquad\qquad \Sigma\Delta H^\circ_{\text{bonds formed}} = -2711\ \text{kJ}
\end{aligned}
$$

Calculating $\Delta H^\circ_{rxn}$:

$$
\begin{aligned}
\Delta H^\circ_{rxn} &= \Sigma\Delta H^\circ_{\text{bonds broken}} + \Sigma\Delta H^\circ_{\text{bonds formed}}\\
&= 2381\ \text{kJ} + (-2711\ \text{kJ})\\
&= \boxed{-330\ \text{kJ}}
\end{aligned}
$$

**Check** The signs of the enthalpy changes are correct: $\Sigma\Delta H^\circ_{\text{bonds broken}} > 0$, and $\Sigma\Delta H^\circ_{\text{bonds formed}} < 0$. More energy is released than absorbed, so $\Delta H^\circ_{\text{rxn}}$ is negative:

$$\sim 2400 \text{ kJ} + [\sim(-2700 \text{ kJ})] = -300 \text{ kJ}$$

**Follow-Up Problem 9.3** One of the most important industrial reactions is the formation of ammonia from its elements:

$$\text{N} \equiv \text{N} + 3 \text{ H} - \text{H} \longrightarrow 2 \text{ H} - \overset{\displaystyle |}{\underset{\displaystyle \text{H}}{\text{N}}} - \text{H}$$

Use bond energies to calculate $\Delta H^\circ_{\text{rxn}}$.

## Bond Strengths and the Heat Released from Fuels and Foods

A *fuel* is a material that reacts with atmospheric oxygen to release energy *and* is available at a reasonable cost. The most common fuels for machines are hydrocarbons and coal, and the most common ones for organisms are fats and carbohydrates. All of these fuels are composed of large organic molecules with many C—C and C—H bonds and fewer C—O and O—H bonds. According to our two-step approach, when the fuel reacts with $O_2$, all of the bonds break, and the C, H, and O atoms form C=O and O—H bonds in the products ($CO_2$ and $H_2O$). Because their combustion is exothermic, the total of the bond energies in the products is *greater* than the total in the reactants. *Weaker bonds (less stable, more reactive) are easier to break than stronger bonds (more stable, less reactive) because they are already higher in energy.* Therefore, the bonds in $CO_2$ and $H_2O$ are stronger (lower energy, more stable) than those in gasoline (or cooking oil) and $O_2$ (weaker, higher energy, less stable).

   *Fuels with more weak bonds yield more energy than fuels with fewer weak bonds.* When a hydrocarbon burns, C—C and C—H bonds break; when an alcohol burns, C—O and O—H bonds break as well. Table 9.2 (p. 340) shows that the sum for C—C and C—H bonds (760 kJ/mol) is less than the sum for C—O and O—H bonds (825 kJ/mol). Therefore, it takes more energy to break the bonds of a fuel with a lot of C—O and O—H bonds. Thus, in general, *a fuel with fewer bonds to O releases more energy* (Figure 9.19).

   Both fats and carbohydrates serve as high-energy foods and consist of chains or rings of C atoms attached to H atoms, with some C—O, C=O, and O—H bonds *(shown in red below):*

**Figure 9.19** Relative bond strength and energy from fuels.

| Table **9.4** Enthalpies of Reaction for Combustion of Some Foods | |
|---|---|
| **Substance** | $\Delta H_{\text{rxn}}$ (kJ/g) |
| **Fats** | |
| Vegetable oil | −37.0 |
| Margarine | −30.1 |
| Butter | −30.0 |
| **Carbohydrates** | |
| Table sugar | |
| (sucrose) | −16.2 |
| Brown rice | −14.9 |
| Maple syrup | −10.4 |

Triolein, a fat

Sucrose, a carbohydrate

Carbohydrates have fewer chains of C atoms and bonds to H and more bonds to O. Fats "contain more Calories" per gram than carbohydrates because fats have fewer bonds to O (Table 9.4).

## ▌ Summary of Section 9.4

* The only component of internal energy that changes significantly during a reaction is the bond energies of reactants and products, and this change appears as the enthalpy of reaction, $\Delta H^\circ_{\text{rxn}}$.
* A reaction involves breaking reactant bonds and forming product bonds. Applying Hess's law, we use tabulated bond energies to calculate $\Delta H^\circ_{\text{rxn}}$.
* Bonds in fuels are weaker (less stable, higher energy) than bonds in the combustion products. Fuels with more weak bonds release more energy than fuels with fewer.

# 9.5 • BETWEEN THE EXTREMES: ELECTRONEGATIVITY AND BOND POLARITY

Scientific models are idealized descriptions of reality. The ionic and covalent bonding models portray compounds as formed by *either* complete electron transfer *or* complete electron sharing. But, in real substances, most atoms are joined by *polar covalent bonds*—partly ionic and partly covalent (Figure 9.20). In this section, we explore the "in-between" nature of these bonds and its importance in the properties of substances.

## Electronegativity

**Electronegativity (EN)** is the relative ability of a bonded atom to attract shared electrons.* We might expect the H—F bond energy to be the average of an H—H bond (432 kJ/mol) and an F—F bond (159 kJ/mol), or 296 kJ/mol. But, the actual HF bond energy is 565 kJ/mol, or 269 kJ/mol *higher!* To explain this difference, the American chemist Linus Pauling reasoned this way: If F attracted the shared electron pair more strongly than H, that is, if F were more *electronegative* than H, the electrons would spend more time closer to F, and this unequal sharing would make the F end of the bond partially negative and the H end partially positive. The electrostatic attraction between these partial charged bond "poles" would *increase* the energy required to break the bond. From studies with many other compounds, Pauling derived a scale of *relative EN values* based on fluorine having the highest EN value, 4.0 (Figure 9.21).

---

*Electronegativity refers to a *bonded* atom attracting a shared pair; electron affinity refers to a gaseous atom gaining an electron to form an anion. Elements with a high EN also have a highly negative EA.

**Figure 9.20 Bonding between the models.** Pure ionic bonding (*top*) and pure covalent bonding (*bottom*) are far less common than polar covalent bonding (*middle*).

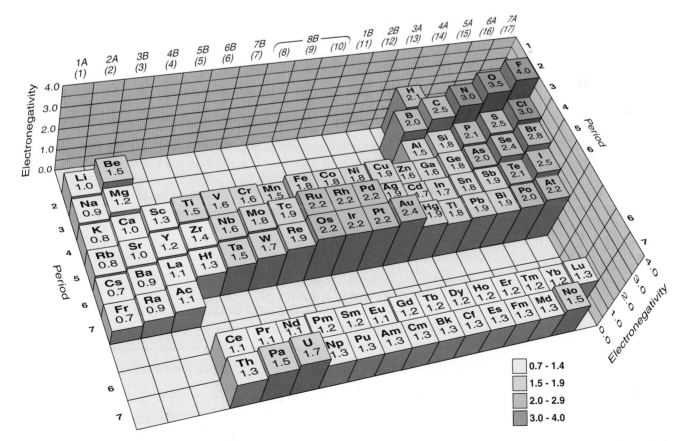

**Figure 9.21 The Pauling electronegativity (EN) scale.** The height of each post is proportional to the EN, which is shown on top. The key has several EN cutoffs. In the main groups, EN *increases* across and *decreases* down. The transition and inner transition elements show little change in EN. Here hydrogen is placed near elements with similar EN values.

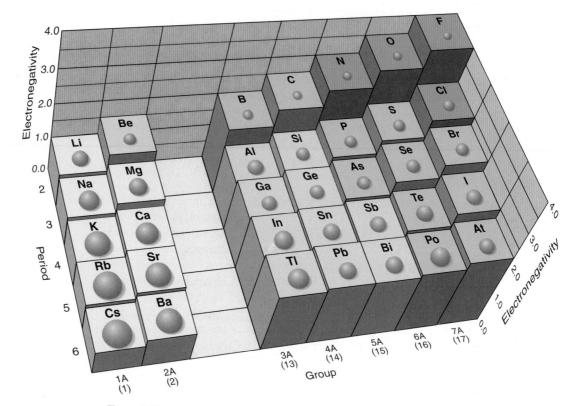

**Figure 9.22** Electronegativity and atomic size.

**Trends in Electronegativity** In general, *electronegativity is inversely related to atomic size* because the nucleus of a smaller atom is closer to the shared pair than the nucleus of a larger atom, so it attracts the electrons more strongly (Figure 9.22):

- *Down a main group,* electronegativity (height of post) decreases as size (hemisphere on top of post) increases.
- *Across a period of main-group elements,* electronegativity increases.
- Nonmetals are *more* electronegative than metals.

The most electronegative element is fluorine, with oxygen a close second. Thus, except when it bonds with fluorine, oxygen always pulls bonding electrons toward itself. The least electronegative element (also referred to as the most *electropositive*) is francium, in the lower left corner of the periodic table, but it is radioactive and extremely rare, so for all practical purposes, cesium is the most electropositive.*

**Electronegativity and Oxidation Number** An important use of electronegativity is in determining an atom's oxidation number (O.N.; see Section 4.5):

1. The more electronegative atom in a bond is assigned *all* the *shared* electrons; the less electronegative atom is assigned *none.*
2. Each atom in a bond is assigned *all* of its *unshared* electrons.
3. The oxidation number is given by

$$\text{O.N.} = \text{no. of valence e}^- - (\text{no. of shared e}^- + \text{no. of unshared e}^-)$$

In HCl, for example, Cl is more electronegative than H. Cl has 7 valence electrons and is assigned 8 (2 shared + 6 unshared), so its O.N. is $7 - 8 = -1$. The H atom has 1 valence electron and is assigned none, so its O.N. is $1 - 0 = +1$.

---

*In 1934, the American physicist Robert S. Mulliken developed electronegativity values based on atomic properties: $EN = (IE - EA)/2$. By this approach as well, fluorine, with a high ionization energy (IE) and a large negative electron affinity (EA), has a high EN; and cesium, with a low IE and a small EA, has a low EN.

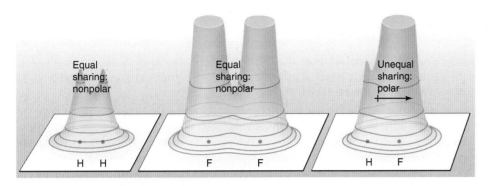

**Figure 9.23** Electron density distributions in $H_2$, $F_2$, and HF. In HF, the electron density shifts from H to F. (The electron density peak for F has been cut off to limit the figure height.)

## Bond Polarity and Partial Ionic Character

Whenever atoms of different electronegativities form a bond, such as H (2.1) and F (4.0) in HF, the bonding pair is shared *unequally*. This unequal distribution of electron density results in a **polar covalent bond.** It is depicted by a polar arrow ($\longmapsto$) pointing toward the partially negative pole or by $\delta+$ and $\delta-$ symbols (see Figure 4.1):

$$\overset{\longmapsto}{H-\ddot{\underset{..}{F}}:} \quad \text{or} \quad \overset{\delta+ \;\; \delta-}{H-\ddot{\underset{..}{F}}:}$$

In the H—H and F—F bonds, where the atoms are identical, the bonding pair is shared *equally,* and a **nonpolar covalent bond** results. In Figure 9.23, relief maps show the distribution of electron density in $H_2$, $F_2$, and HF.

**The Importance of Electronegativity Difference ($\Delta$EN)** The **electronegativity difference ($\Delta$EN),** the difference between the EN values of the bonded atoms, is directly related to a bond's polarity. It ranges from 0.0 in a diatomic element, such as $H_2$, $O_2$, or $Cl_2$, all the way up to 3.3, the difference between the most electronegative atom, F (4.0), and the most electropositive, Cs (0.7), in the ionic compound CsF.

Another parameter closely related to $\Delta$EN is the **partial ionic character** of a bond: *a greater $\Delta$EN results in larger partial charges and higher partial ionic character.* Consider three Cl-containing gaseous molecules: $\Delta$EN for LiCl($g$) is $3.0 - 1.0 = 2.0$; for HCl($g$), it is $3.0 - 2.1 = 0.9$; and for $Cl_2(g)$, it is $3.0 - 3.0 = 0.0$. Thus, the bond in LiCl has more ionic character than the one in HCl, which has more than the one in $Cl_2$.

Here are two approaches that quantify ionic character. Both use arbitrary cutoffs, which is not really consistent with the actual gradation in bonding:

1. *$\Delta$EN range.* This approach divides bonds into mostly ionic, polar covalent, mostly covalent, and nonpolar covalent based on a range of $\Delta$EN values (Figure 9.24).

2. *Percent ionic character.* This approach is based on the behavior of a diatomic molecule in an electric field. A plot of *percent ionic character* vs. $\Delta$EN for several gaseous molecules shows that, as expected, *percent ionic character generally increases with $\Delta$EN* (Figure 9.25A). A value of 50% divides ionic from covalent bonds. Note that a substance like $Cl_2(g)$ has 0% ionic character, but none has 100% ionic character: *electron sharing occurs to some extent in every bond,* even in an alkali halide (Figure 9.25B).

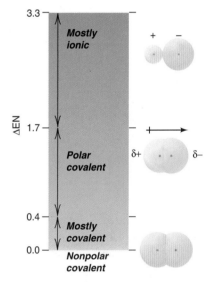

**Figure 9.24** $\Delta$EN ranges for classifying the partial ionic character of bonds.

**Figure 9.25** Percent ionic character as a function of $\Delta$EN. **A,** $\Delta$EN correlates with ionic character. **B,** Even in highly ionic LiF ($\Delta$EN = 3.0), the relief map shows some electron sharing between the ions.

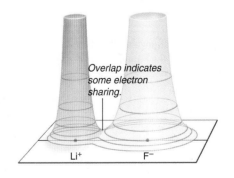

**A**          **B**

## Sample Problem 9.4 Determining Bond Polarity from EN Values

**Problem** (a) Use a polar arrow to indicate the polarity of each bond: N—H, F—N, I—Cl.
(b) Rank the following bonds in order of *increasing* polarity and *decreasing* percent ionic character: H—N, H—O, H—C.

**Plan** (a) We use Figure 9.21 to find the EN values for the atoms and point the polar arrow toward the negative end. (b) To rank the bond polarity, we determine ΔEN: the higher the value, the greater the polarity. Percent ionic character is also directly related to ΔEN (and bond polarity); it decreases in the opposite order that polarity increases.

**Solution** (a) The EN of N = 3.0 and the EN of H = 2.1, so $\overleftarrow{N—H}$
The EN of F = 4.0 and the EN of N = 3.0, so $\overleftarrow{F—N}$

The EN of I = 2.5 and the EN of Cl = 3.0, so $\overrightarrow{I—Cl}$

(b) The ΔEN values are 0.9 for H—N, 1.4 for H—O, and 0.4 for H—C.
The order of *increasing* bond polarity is  H—C < H—N < H—O.
The order of *decreasing* percent ionic character is  H—O > H—N > H—C.

**Check** In (b), we can check the order of bond polarity using periodic trends. Each bond involves H and a Period 2 atom. Since size decreases and EN increases across a period, the polarity is greatest for the bond to O (farthest to the right in Period 2).

**Comment** In Chapter 10, you'll see that the bond polarity contributes to the overall polarity of the molecule, which is a major factor determining behavior.

**Follow-Up Problem 9.4** Arrange each set of bonds in order of increasing polarity, and indicate bond polarity with δ+ and δ− symbols:
(a) Cl—F, Br—Cl, Cl—Cl          (b) Si—Cl, P—Cl, S—Cl, Si—Si

## The Gradation in Bonding Across a Period

A metal and a nonmetal—elements from the left and right sides of the periodic table—have a relatively large ΔEN and typically form an ionic compound. Two nonmetals—both from the right side of the table—have a small ΔEN and form a covalent compound. When we combine chlorine with each of the other Period 3 elements, starting with sodium, we observe a steady decrease in ΔEN and a gradation in bond type from ionic through polar covalent to nonpolar covalent.

Figure 9.26 shows an electron density relief map of a bond in each of the common Period 3 chlorides; note the steady increase in the height of electron density *between* the peaks—the bonding region—which indicates an *increase in electron sharing*. Figure 9.27 shows samples of common Period 3 chlorides—NaCl, $MgCl_2$, $AlCl_3$, $SiCl_4$, $PCl_3$, and $SCl_2$, as well as $Cl_2$—along with the change in ΔEN and two physical properties:

- NaCl. Sodium chloride is a white (colorless) crystalline solid with a ΔEN of 2.1, a high melting point, and high electrical conductivity when molten—ionic by any criterion. However, just as for LiF (Figure 9.25B), a small but significant region of electron sharing appears in the relief map.
- $MgCl_2$. With a ΔEN of 1.8, magnesium chloride is still ionic, but it has a lower melting point and lower conductivity, as well as slightly more electron sharing.

**Figure 9.26** Electron density distributions in bonds of the Period 3 chlorides. Note the steady increase in electron sharing from left to right.

Shared e⁻ density
(bonding region) increases ⟶

Na    Cl    Mg    Cl    Al    Cl

**Figure 9.27** Properties of the Period 3 chlorides. As ΔEN decreases, melting point and electrical conductivity decrease because the bond type changes from ionic to polar covalent to nonpolar covalent.

- AlCl₃. Rather than being a three-dimensional lattice of $Al^{3+}$ and $Cl^-$ ions, aluminum chloride, with a ΔEN value of 1.5, consists of layers of highly polar Al—Cl bonds. Weak forces between layers result in a much lower melting point, and the low conductivity implies few free ions. And, electron density between the nuclei is higher.

- SiCl₄, PCl₃, SCl₂, and Cl₂. The trend toward more covalent bonding continues through the remaining substances. Each occurs as separate molecules, which have no conductivity and such weak forces *between* them that melting points are below 0°C. In Cl₂, the bond is nonpolar (ΔEN = 0.0). The relief maps show the increasing height of the electron density in the bonding region.

Thus, *as ΔEN decreases, the bond becomes more covalent,* and the character of the substance changes from ionic solid to covalent gas.

## ■ Summary of Section 9.5

- Electronegativity is the ability of a bonded atom to attract shared electrons, which generates opposite partial charges at the ends of the bond and contributes to the bond energy.
- Electronegativity increases across a period and decreases down a group, the reverse of the trends in atomic size.
- The larger the ΔEN for two bonded atoms, the more polar the bond is and the greater its ionic character.
- For Period 3 chlorides, there is a gradation in bond type from ionic to polar covalent to nonpolar covalent.

# 9.6 • AN INTRODUCTION TO METALLIC BONDING

In this section, you'll see how a simple, qualitative model for metallic bonding accounts for the properties of metals; a more detailed model is presented in Chapter 12.

## The Electron-Sea Model

Metals can transfer electrons to nonmetals and form ionic solids, such as NaCl. And experiments with metals in the gas phase show that two metal atoms can even share their valence electrons to form gaseous, diatomic molecules, such as $Na_2$. But what holds the atoms together in a chunk of Na metal? The **electron-sea model** of metallic bonding proposes that all the metal atoms in the sample contribute their valence electrons to form a delocalized electron "sea" throughout the piece, with the metal ions (nuclei and core electrons) lying in an orderly array (see Figure 9.2C). *All the atoms in the sample share the electrons,* and the piece is held together by the mutual attraction of the metal cations for the mobile, valence electrons. Thus, bonding in metals is fundamentally different than the other two types:

- *In contrast to ionic bonding,* the metal ions are not held in place as rigidly.
- *In contrast to covalent bonding,* no particular pair of metal atoms is bonded through a localized electron pair.
- *Instead of forming compounds,* two or more metals typically form **alloys,** solid mixtures of variable composition. Alloys appear in car and airplane bodies, bridges, coins, jewelry, dental fillings, and many other familiar objects.

## How the Model Explains the Properties of Metals

The physical properties of metals vary over a wide range. Two features of the electron-sea model that account for these properties are (1) the *regularity,* but not rigidity, of the metal-ion array and (2) the *number* and *mobility* of the valence electrons.

1. *Melting and boiling points.* Nearly all metals are solids with moderate to high melting points and much higher boiling points (Table 9.5). These properties are related to the energy of the metallic bonding. Melting points are only moderately high because the cations can move without breaking the attraction to the surrounding electrons. Boiling points are very high because each cation and its valence electron(s) must break away from the others. Gallium provides a striking example: it can melt in your hand (mp 29.8°C) but doesn't boil until over 2400°C.

Periodic trends are consistent with the strength of the bonding:

- *Down a group,* melting points decrease because the larger metal ions have a weaker attraction to the electron sea.
- *Across a period,* melting points increase. Alkaline earth metals [Group 2A(2)] have higher melting points than alkali metals [Group 1A(1)] because their 2+ cations have stronger attractions to twice as many valence electrons (Figure 9.28).

**Table 9.5 Melting and Boiling Points of Some Metals**

| Element | mp (°C) | bp (°C) |
|---|---|---|
| Lithium (Li) | 180 | 1347 |
| Tin (Sn) | 232 | 2623 |
| Aluminum (Al) | 660 | 2467 |
| Barium (Ba) | 727 | 1850 |
| Silver (Ag) | 961 | 2155 |
| Copper (Cu) | 1083 | 2570 |
| Uranium (U) | 1130 | 3930 |

**Figure 9.28** Melting points of Group 1A(1) and Group 2A(2) metals.

2. *Mechanical properties.* When a piece of metal is deformed by a hammer, the metal ions do not repel each other, but rather slide past each other through the electron sea and end up in new positions; thus metals dent and bend, as shown in Figure 9.29. Compare this behavior with the interionic repulsions that occur when an ionic solid is struck (see Figure 9.9, p. 336).

**Figure 9.29** Why metals dent and bend rather than crack.

How thin is gold leaf?

All the Group 1B(11) metals—copper, silver, and gold—are soft enough to be machined into sheets (malleable) and wires (ductile), but gold is in a class by itself. One gram of gold, about the size of a small ball-bearing, can be drawn into a wire 20 μm thick and 165 m long or hammered into a 1.0-m² sheet that is 230 atoms (about 70 nm) thick *(see photo)*!

3. *Electrical conductivity.* Unlike ionic and covalent substances, metals are good conductors of electricity in both the solid and liquid states because of their mobile electrons. When a piece of metal wire is attached to a battery, electrons flow from one terminal into the wire, replacing the electrons that flow from the wire into the other terminal. Foreign atoms disrupt the array of metal atoms and reduce conductivity. Copper used in electrical wiring is over 99.99% pure because traces of other atoms drastically restrict electron flow.

4. *Thermal conductivity.* Mobile electrons also make metals good conductors of heat. Place your hand on a piece of metal and a piece of wood that are both at room temperature. The metal feels colder because it conducts heat away from your hand much faster than the wood. The mobile, delocalized electrons in the metal disperse the heat from your hand more quickly than the localized electron pairs in the covalent bonds of wood.

## ■ Summary of Section 9.6

- According to the electron-sea model, the valence electrons of the metal atoms in a sample are highly delocalized and attract all the metal cations, holding them together.

- Metals have only moderately high melting points because the metal ions remain attracted to the electron sea even if their relative positions change.

- Boiling involves complete separation of individual cations with their valence electrons from all the others, so metals have very high boiling points.

- Metals can be deformed because the electron sea prevents repulsions among the cations.

- Metals conduct electricity and heat because their electrons are mobile.

# CHAPTER REVIEW GUIDE

## Understand These Concepts

1. How differences in atomic properties lead to differences in bond type; the basic distinctions among the three types of bonding (§9.1)
2. The essential features of ionic bonding: electron transfer to form ions, and their electrostatic attraction to form a solid (§9.2)
3. How lattice energy is ultimately responsible for the formation of ionic compounds (§9.2)
4. How ionic compound formation is conceptualized as occurring in hypothetical steps (a Born-Haber cycle) to calculate the lattice energy (§9.2)
5. How Coulomb's law explains the periodic trends in lattice energy (§9.2)
6. Why ionic compounds are brittle and high melting and conduct electricity only when molten or dissolved in water (§9.2)
7. How nonmetal atoms form a covalent bond (§9.3)
8. How bonding and lone electron pairs fill the outer (valence) level of each atom in a molecule (§9.3)
9. The interrelationships among bond order, bond length, and bond energy (§9.3)
10. How the distinction between bonding and nonbonding forces explains the properties of covalent molecules and network covalent solids (§9.3)
11. How changes in bond strength account for the enthalpy of reaction (§9.4)

12. How a reaction can be divided conceptually into bond-breaking and bond-forming steps (§9.4)
13. The periodic trends in electronegativity and the inverse relationship of EN values to atomic sizes (§9.5)
14. How bond polarity arises from differences in the electronegativities of bonded atoms; the direction of bond polarity (§9.5)
15. The change in partial ionic character with $\Delta$EN and the change from ionic to polar covalent to nonpolar covalent bonding across a period (§9.5)
16. The role of delocalized electrons in metallic bonding (§9.6)
17. How the electron-sea model explains why metals bend, have very high boiling points, and conduct electricity in solid or molten form (§9.6)

## Master These Skills

1. Using Lewis electron-dot symbols to depict main-group atoms (§9.1)
2. Depicting the formation of ions with electron configurations, orbital diagrams, and Lewis symbols, and writing the formula of the ionic compound (SP 9.1)
3. Calculating lattice energy from the enthalpies of the steps to ionic compound formation (§9.2)
4. Ranking similar covalent bonds according to their length and strength (SP 9.2)
5. Using bond energies to calculate $\Delta H^{\circ}_{rxn}$ (SP 9.3)
6. Determining bond polarity from EN values (SP 9.4)

**Section 9.1**
ionic bonding (330)
covalent bonding (330)
metallic bonding (331)
Lewis electron-dot symbol (331)
octet rule (331)

**Section 9.2**
lattice energy ($\Delta H^{\circ}_{lattice}$) (333)

Born-Haber cycle (333)
Coulomb's law (335)
ion pair (337)

**Section 9.3**
covalent bond (338)
bonding (shared) pair (339)
lone (unshared) pair (339)
bond order (339)
single bond (339)

double bond (339)
triple bond (339)
bond energy (BE) (339)
bond length (340)
infrared (IR) spectroscopy (343)

**Section 9.5**
electronegativity (EN) (349)
polar covalent bond (351)

nonpolar covalent bond (351)
electronegativity difference ($\Delta$EN) (351)
partial ionic character (351)

**Section 9.6**
electron-sea model (354)
alloy (354)

**9.1** Relating the energy of attraction to the lattice energy (335):

$$\text{Electrostatic energy} \propto \frac{\text{cation charge} \times \text{anion charge}}{\text{cation radius} + \text{anion radius}} \propto \Delta H^{\circ}_{lattice}$$

**9.2** Calculating enthalpy of reaction from bond enthalpies or bond energies (345):

$$\Delta H^{\circ}_{rxn} = \Sigma \Delta H^{\circ}_{\text{reactant bonds broken}} + \Sigma \Delta H^{\circ}_{\text{product bonds formed}}$$

or

$$\Delta H^{\circ}_{rxn} = \Sigma BE_{\text{reactant bonds broken}} - \Sigma BE_{\text{product bonds formed}}$$

## Brief Solutions to Follow-Up Problems

**9.1** Mg ([Ne] $3s^2$) + 2Cl ([Ne] $3s^2 3p^5$) $\longrightarrow$

$$Mg^{2+} \text{ ([Ne])} + 2Cl^- \text{ ([Ne] } 3s^2 3p^6)$$

$\cdot Mg \cdot + \overset{\cdot\cdot}{\underset{\cdot\cdot}{:Cl:}} \longrightarrow Mg^{2+} + 2 :\overset{\cdot\cdot}{\underset{\cdot\cdot}{Cl}}:^-$ Formula: $MgCl_2$

**9.2** (a) Bond length: Si—F < Si—O < Si—C
Bond strength: Si—C < Si—O < Si—F
(b) Bond length: N≡N < N=N < N—N
Bond strength: N—N < N=N < N≡N

**9.3** N≡N + 3 H—H $\longrightarrow$ 2 H—N—H
with H below N

$\Sigma \Delta H°_{\text{bonds broken}}$ = 1 N≡N + 3 H—H
= 945 kJ + 1296 kJ = 2241 kJ
$\Sigma \Delta H°_{\text{bonds formed}}$ = 6 N—H = −2346 kJ
$\Delta H°_{\text{rxn}}$ = −105 kJ

**9.4** (a) Cl—Cl < $\overset{\delta+}{Br}$—$\overset{\delta-}{Cl}$ < $\overset{\delta+}{Cl}$—$\overset{\delta-}{F}$

(b) Si—Si < $\overset{\delta+}{S}$—$\overset{\delta-}{Cl}$ < $\overset{\delta+}{P}$—$\overset{\delta-}{Cl}$ < $\overset{\delta+}{Si}$—$\overset{\delta-}{Cl}$

# PROBLEMS

Problems with **colored** numbers are answered in Appendix E and worked in detail in the Student Solutions Manual. Problem sections match those in the text and provide the numbers of relevant sample problems. Most offer Concept Review Questions, Skill-Building Exercises (grouped in pairs covering the same concept), and Problems in Context. The Comprehensive Problems are based on material from any section or previous chapter.

## Atomic Properties and Chemical Bonds

### Concept Review Questions

**9.1** In general terms, how does each of the following atomic properties influence the metallic character of the main-group elements in a period?
(a) Ionization energy
(b) Atomic radius
(c) Number of outer electrons
(d) Effective nuclear charge

**9.2** Three solids are represented below. What is the predominant type of intramolecular bonding in each?

**9.3** What is the relationship between the tendency of a main-group element to form a monatomic ion and its position in the periodic table? In what part of the table are the main-group elements that typically form cations? Anions?

### Skill-Building Exercises (grouped in similar pairs)
**9.4** Which member of each pair is *more* metallic?
(a) Na or Cs      (b) Mg or Rb      (c) As or N

**9.5** Which member of each pair is *less* metallic?
(a) I or O      (b) Be or Ba      (c) Se or Ge

**9.6** State the type of bonding—ionic, covalent, or metallic—you would expect in each: (a) CsF(s); (b) $N_2(g)$; (c) Na(s).

**9.7** State the type of bonding—ionic, covalent, or metallic—you would expect in each: (a) $ICl_3(g)$; (b) $N_2O(g)$; (c) LiCl(s).

**9.8** State the type of bonding—ionic, covalent, or metallic—you would expect in each: (a) $O_3(g)$; (b) $MgCl_2(s)$; (c) $BrO_2(g)$.

**9.9** State the type of bonding—ionic, covalent, or metallic—you would expect in each: (a) Cr(s); (b) $H_2S(g)$; (c) CaO(s).

**9.10** Draw a Lewis electron-dot symbol for (a) Rb; (b) Si; (c) I.

**9.11** Draw a Lewis electron-dot symbol for (a) Ba; (b) Kr; (c) Br.

**9.12** Draw a Lewis electron-dot symbol for (a) Sr; (b) P; (c) S.

**9.13** Draw a Lewis electron-dot symbol for (a) As; (b) Se; (c) Ga.

**9.14** Give the group number and general electron configuration of an element with each electron-dot symbol: (a) ·Ẍ: (b) Ẋ·

**9.15** Give the group number and general electron configuration of an element with each electron-dot symbol: (a) ·Ẍ: (b) ·Ẋ·

## The Ionic Bonding Model
(Sample Problem 9.1)

### Concept Review Questions
**9.16** If energy is required to form monatomic ions from metals and nonmetals, why do ionic compounds exist?

**9.17** (a) In general, how does the lattice energy of an ionic compound depend on the charges and sizes of the ions? (b) Ion arrangements of three general salts are represented below. Rank them in order of increasing lattice energy.

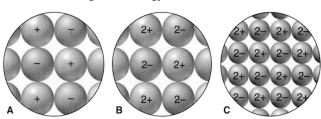

**9.18** When gaseous $Na^+$ and $Cl^-$ ions form gaseous NaCl ion pairs, 548 kJ/mol of energy is released. Why, then, does NaCl occur as a solid under ordinary conditions?

**9.19** To form $S^{2-}$ ions from gaseous sulfur atoms requires 214 kJ/mol, but these ions exist in solids such as $K_2S$. Explain.

**Skill-Building Exercises** (grouped in similar pairs)

**9.20** Use condensed electron configurations and Lewis electron-dot symbols to depict the ions formed from each of the following atoms, and predict the formula of their compound:
(a) Ba and Cl   (b) Sr and O   (c) Al and F   (d) Rb and O

**9.21** Use condensed electron configurations and Lewis electron-dot symbols to depict the ions formed from each of the following atoms, and predict the formula of their compound:
(a) Cs and S   (b) O and Ga   (c) N and Mg   (d) Br and Li

**9.22** For each ionic compound formula, identify the main group to which X belongs:  (a) $XF_2$; (b) MgX; (c) $X_2SO_4$.

**9.23** For each ionic compound formula, identify the main group to which X belongs:  (a) $X_3PO_4$; (b) $X_2(SO_4)_3$; (c) $X(NO_3)_2$.

**9.24** For each ionic compound formula, identify the main group to which X belongs:  (a) $X_2O_3$; (b) $XCO_3$; (c) $Na_2X$.

**9.25** For each ionic compound formula, identify the main group to which X belongs:  (a) $CaX_2$; (b) $Al_2X_3$; (c) $XPO_4$.

**9.26** For each pair, choose the compound with the higher lattice energy, and explain your choice: (a) BaS or CsCl; (b) LiCl or CsCl.

**9.27** For each pair, choose the compound with the higher lattice energy, and explain your choice: (a) CaO or CaS; (b) BaO or SrO.

**9.28** For each pair, choose the compound with the lower lattice energy, and explain your choice: (a) CaS or BaS; (b) NaF or MgO.

**9.29** For each pair, choose the compound with the lower lattice energy, and explain your choice: (a) NaF or NaCl; (b) $K_2O$ or $K_2S$.

**9.30** Use the following to calculate the $\Delta H^\circ_{\text{lattice}}$ of NaCl:

| | |
|---|---|
| $Na(s) \longrightarrow Na(g)$ | $\Delta H^\circ = \quad 109 \text{ kJ}$ |
| $Cl_2(g) \longrightarrow 2Cl(g)$ | $\Delta H^\circ = \quad 243 \text{ kJ}$ |
| $Na(g) \longrightarrow Na^+(g) + e^-$ | $\Delta H^\circ = \quad 496 \text{ kJ}$ |
| $Cl(g) + e^- \longrightarrow Cl^-(g)$ | $\Delta H^\circ = -349 \text{ kJ}$ |
| $Na(s) + \frac{1}{2}Cl_2(g) \longrightarrow NaCl(s)$ | $\Delta H^\circ = -411 \text{ kJ}$ |

Compared with the lattice energy of LiF (1050 kJ/mol), is the magnitude of the value for NaCl what you expected? Explain.

**9.31** Use the following to calculate the $\Delta H^\circ_{\text{lattice}}$ of $MgF_2$:

| | |
|---|---|
| $Mg(s) \longrightarrow Mg(g)$ | $\Delta H^\circ = \quad 148 \text{ kJ}$ |
| $F_2(g) \longrightarrow 2F(g)$ | $\Delta H^\circ = \quad 159 \text{ kJ}$ |
| $Mg(g) \longrightarrow Mg^+(g) + e^-$ | $\Delta H^\circ = \quad 738 \text{ kJ}$ |
| $Mg^+(g) \longrightarrow Mg^{2+}(g) + e^-$ | $\Delta H^\circ = 1450 \text{ kJ}$ |
| $F(g) + e^- \longrightarrow F^-(g)$ | $\Delta H^\circ = -328 \text{ kJ}$ |
| $Mg(s) + F_2(g) \longrightarrow MgF_2(s)$ | $\Delta H^\circ = -1123 \text{ kJ}$ |

Compared with the lattice energy of LiF (1050 kJ/mol) or the lattice energy you calculated for NaCl in Problem 9.30, does the relative magnitude of the value for $MgF_2$ surprise you? Explain.

**Problems in Context**

**9.32** Aluminum oxide ($Al_2O_3$) is a widely used industrial abrasive (emery, corundum), for which the specific application depends on the hardness of the crystal. What does this hardness imply about the magnitude of the lattice energy? Would you have predicted from the chemical formula that $Al_2O_3$ is hard? Explain.

**9.33** Born-Haber cycles were used to obtain the first reliable values for electron affinity by considering the EA value as the unknown and using a theoretically calculated value for the lattice energy. Use a Born-Haber cycle for KF and the following values to calculate a value for the electron affinity of fluorine:

| | |
|---|---|
| $K(s) \longrightarrow K(g)$ | $\Delta H^\circ = \quad 90 \text{ kJ}$ |
| $K(g) \longrightarrow K^+(g) + e^-$ | $\Delta H^\circ = \quad 419 \text{ kJ}$ |
| $F_2(g) \longrightarrow 2F(g)$ | $\Delta H^\circ = \quad 159 \text{ kJ}$ |
| $K(s) + \frac{1}{2}F_2(g) \longrightarrow KF(s)$ | $\Delta H^\circ = -569 \text{ kJ}$ |
| $K^+(g) + F^-(g) \longrightarrow KF(s)$ | $\Delta H^\circ = -821 \text{ kJ}$ |

**The Covalent Bonding Model**
(Sample Problem 9.2)

**Concept Review Questions**

**9.34** Describe the interactions that occur between individual chlorine atoms as they approach each other and form $Cl_2$. What combination of forces gives rise to the energy holding the atoms together and to the final internuclear distance?

**9.35** Define bond energy using the H—Cl bond as an example. When this bond breaks, is energy absorbed or released? Is the accompanying $\Delta H$ value positive or negative? How do the magnitude and sign of this $\Delta H$ value relate to the value that accompanies H—Cl bond formation?

**9.36** For single bonds between similar types of atoms, how does the strength of the bond relate to the sizes of the atoms? Explain.

**9.37** How does the energy of the bond between a given pair of atoms relate to the bond order? Why?

**9.38** When liquid benzene ($C_6H_6$) boils, does the gas consist of molecules, ions, or separate atoms? Explain.

**Skill-Building Exercises** (grouped in similar pairs)

**9.39** Using the periodic table only, arrange the members of each of the following sets in order of increasing bond *strength:*
(a) Br—Br, Cl—Cl, I—I   (b) S—H, S—Br, S—Cl
(c) C=N, C—N, C≡N

**9.40** Using the periodic table only, arrange the members of each of the following sets in order of increasing bond *length:*
(a) H—F, H—I, H—Cl   (b) C—S, C=O, C—O
(c) N—H, N—S, N—O

**Problem in Context**

**9.41** Formic acid (HCOOH; structural formula shown below) is secreted by certain species of ants when they bite.

$$\underset{\displaystyle H-\overset{\displaystyle \overset{\textstyle O}{\|}}{C}-O-H}{}$$

Rank the relative strengths of (a) the C—O and C=O bonds and (b) the H—C and H—O bonds. Explain these rankings.

**Bond Energy and Chemical Change**
(Sample Problem 9.3)

**Concept Review Questions**

**9.42** Write a solution Plan (without actual numbers, but including the bond energies you would use and how you would combine them algebraically) for calculating the total enthalpy change of the following reaction:

$$H_2(g) + O_2(g) \longrightarrow H_2O_2(g) \quad (H-O-O-H)$$

**9.43** The text points out that, for similar types of substances, one with weaker bonds is usually more reactive than one with stronger bonds. Why is this generally true?

**9.44** Why is there a discrepancy between a heat of reaction obtained from calorimetry and one obtained from bond energies?

**Skill-Building Exercises** (grouped in similar pairs)

**9.45** Which of the following gases would you expect to have the greater heat of reaction per mole for combustion? Why?

methane   or   formaldehyde

**9.46** Which of the following gases would you expect to have the greater heat of reaction per mole for combustion? Why?

ethanol   or   methanol

**9.47** Use bond energies to calculate the heat of reaction:

**9.48** Use bond energies to calculate the heat of reaction:

**Problems in Context**

**9.49** An important industrial route to extremely pure acetic acid is the reaction of methanol with carbon monoxide:

Use bond energies to calculate the enthalpy of reaction.

**9.50** Sports trainers treat sprains and soreness with ethyl bromide. It is manufactured by reacting ethylene with hydrogen bromide:

Use bond energies to find the enthalpy of reaction.

### Between the Extremes: Electronegativity and Bond Polarity
(Sample Problem 9.4)

**Concept Review Questions**

**9.51** Describe the vertical and horizontal trends in electronegativity (EN) among the main-group elements. According to Pauling's

scale, what are the two most electronegative elements? The two least electronegative elements?

**9.52** What is the general relationship between $IE_1$ and EN for the elements? Why?

**9.53** Is the H—O bond in water nonpolar covalent, polar covalent, or ionic? Define each term, and explain your choice.

**9.54** How does electronegativity differ from electron affinity?

**9.55** How is the partial ionic character of a bond in a diatomic molecule related to $\Delta$EN for the bonded atoms? Why?

**Skill-Building Exercises** (grouped in similar pairs)

**9.56** Using the periodic table only, arrange the elements in each set in order of *increasing* EN: (a) S, O, Si; (b) Mg, P, As.

**9.57** Using the periodic table only, arrange the elements in each set in order of *increasing* EN: (a) I, Br, N; (b) Ca, H, F.

**9.58** Using the periodic table only, arrange the elements in each set in order of *decreasing* EN: (a) N, P, Si; (b) Ca, Ga, As.

**9.59** Using the periodic table only, arrange the elements in each set in order of *decreasing* EN: (a) Br, Cl, P; (b) I, F, O.

**9.60** Use Figure 9.21, p. 349, to indicate the polarity of each bond with a *polar arrow:* (a) N—B; (b) N—O; (c) C—S; (d) S—O; (e) N—H; (f) Cl—O.

**9.61** Use Figure 9.21, p. 349, to indicate the polarity of each bond with *partial charges:* (a) Br—Cl; (b) F—Cl; (c) H—O; (d) Se—H; (e) As—H; (f) S—N.

**9.62** Which is the more polar bond in each of the following pairs from Problem 9.60: (a) or (b); (c) or (d); (e) or (f)?

**9.63** Which is the more polar bond in each of the following pairs from Problem 9.61: (a) or (b); (c) or (d); (e) or (f)?

**9.64** Are the bonds in each of the following substances ionic, non-polar covalent, or polar covalent? Arrange the substances with polar covalent bonds in order of increasing bond polarity:
(a) $S_8$ (b) RbCl (c) $PF_3$ (d) $SCl_2$ (e) $F_2$ (f) $SF_2$

**9.65** Are the bonds in each of the following substances ionic, non-polar covalent, or polar covalent? Arrange the substances with polar covalent bonds in order of increasing bond polarity:
(a) KCl (b) $P_4$ (c) $BF_3$ (d) $SO_2$ (e) $Br_2$ (f) $NO_2$

**9.66** Rank the members of each set of compounds in order of *increasing* ionic character of their bonds. Use *polar arrows* to indicate the bond polarity of each:
(a) HBr, HCl, HI   (b) $H_2O$, $CH_4$, HF   (c) $SCl_2$, $PCl_3$, $SiCl_4$

**9.67** Rank the members of each set of compounds in order of *decreasing* ionic character of their bonds. Use *partial charges* to indicate the bond polarity of each:
(a) $PCl_3$, $PBr_3$, $PF_3$   (b) $BF_3$, $NF_3$, $CF_4$   (c) $SeF_4$, $TeF_4$, $BrF_3$

**Problem in Context**

**9.68** The energy of the C—C bond is 347 kJ/mol, and that of the Cl—Cl bond is 243 kJ/mol. Which of the following values might you expect for the C—Cl bond energy? Explain.
(a) 590 kJ/mol (sum of the values given)
(b) 104 kJ/mol (difference of the values given)
(c) 295 kJ/mol (average of the values given)
(d) 339 kJ/mol (greater than the average of the values given)

## An Introduction to Metallic Bonding

### Concept Review Questions

**9.69** (a) List four physical characteristics of a solid metal.
(b) List two chemical characteristics of a metallic element.

**9.70** Briefly account for the following relative values:
(a) The melting points of Na and K are 89°C and 63°C, respectively.
(b) The melting points of Li and Be are 180°C and 1287°C, respectively.
(c) Li boils more than 1100°C higher than it melts.

**9.71** Magnesium metal is easily deformed by an applied force, whereas magnesium fluoride is shattered. Why do these two solids behave so differently?

## Comprehensive Problems

**9.72** Geologists have a rule of thumb: when molten rock cools and solidifies, crystals of compounds with the smallest lattice energies appear at the bottom of the mass. Suggest a reason for this.

**9.73** Acetylene gas (ethyne; $HC \equiv CH$) burns in an oxyacetylene torch to produce carbon dioxide and water vapor. The heat of reaction for the combustion of acetylene is 1259 kJ/mol. (a) Calculate the $C \equiv C$ bond energy, and compare your value with that in Table 9.2, p. 340. (b) When 500.0 g of acetylene burns, how many kilojoules of heat are given off? (c) How many grams of $CO_2$ form? (d) How many liters of $O_2$ at 298 K and 18.0 atm are consumed?

**9.74** Use Lewis electron-dot symbols to represent the formation of (a) $BrF_3$ from bromine and fluorine atoms; (b) $AlF_3$ from aluminum and fluorine atoms.

**9.75** Even though so much energy is required to form a metal cation with a 2+ charge, the alkaline earth metals form halides with general formula $MX_2$, rather than MX.
(a) Use the following data to calculate the $\Delta H_f^\circ$ of MgCl:

| | | |
|---|---|---|
| $Mg(s) \longrightarrow Mg(g)$ | $\Delta H^\circ =$ | 148 kJ |
| $Cl_2(g) \longrightarrow 2Cl(g)$ | $\Delta H^\circ =$ | 243 kJ |
| $Mg(g) \longrightarrow Mg^+(g) + e^-$ | $\Delta H^\circ =$ | 738 kJ |
| $Cl(g) + e^- \longrightarrow Cl^-(g)$ | $\Delta H^\circ =$ | −349 kJ |

$\Delta H_{lattice}^\circ$ of MgCl = 783.5 kJ/mol

(b) Is MgCl favored energetically relative to Mg and $Cl_2$? Explain.
(c) Use Hess's law to calculate $\Delta H^\circ$ for the conversion of MgCl to $MgCl_2$ and Mg ($\Delta H_f^\circ$ of $MgCl_2 = -641.6$ kJ/mol).
(d) Is MgCl favored energetically relative to $MgCl_2$? Explain.

**9.76** Gases react explosively if the heat released when the reaction begins is sufficient to cause more reaction, which leads to a rapid expansion of the gases. Use bond energies to calculate $\Delta H^\circ$ of the following reactions, and predict which occurs explosively:
(a) $H_2(g) + Cl_2(g) \longrightarrow 2HCl(g)$
(b) $H_2(g) + I_2(g) \longrightarrow 2HI(g)$
(c) $2H_2(g) + O_2(g) \longrightarrow 2H_2O(g)$

**9.77** By using photons of specific wavelengths, chemists can dissociate gaseous HI to produce H atoms with certain speeds. When HI dissociates, the H atoms move away rapidly, whereas the heavier I atoms move more slowly. (a) What is the longest wavelength (in nm) that can dissociate a molecule of HI? (b) If a photon of 254 nm is used, what is the excess energy (in J) over that needed

for dissociation? (c) If this excess energy is carried away by the H atom as kinetic energy, what is its speed (in m/s)?

**9.78** In developing the concept of electronegativity, Pauling used the term *excess bond energy* for the difference between the actual bond energy of X—Y and the average bond energies of X—X and Y—Y (see text discussion for the case of HF). Based on the values in Figure 9.21, p. 349, which of the following substances contains bonds with no excess bond energy?
(a) $PH_3$     (b) $CS_2$     (c) BrCl     (d) $BH_3$     (e) $Se_8$

**9.79** Use condensed electron configurations to predict the relative hardnesses and melting points of rubidium ($Z = 37$), vanadium ($Z = 23$), and cadmium ($Z = 48$).

**9.80** Without stratospheric ozone ($O_3$), harmful solar radiation would cause gene alterations. Ozone forms when the bond in $O_2$ breaks and each O atom reacts with another $O_2$ molecule. It is destroyed by reaction with Cl atoms formed when the C—Cl bond in synthetic chemicals breaks. Find the wavelengths of light that can break the C—Cl bond and the bond in $O_2$.

**9.81** "Inert" xenon actually forms many compounds, especially with highly electronegative fluorine. The $\Delta H_f^\circ$ values for xenon difluoride, tetrafluoride, and hexafluoride are −105, −284, and −402 kJ/mol, respectively. Find the average bond energy of the Xe—F bonds in each fluoride.

**9.82** The HF bond length is 92 pm, 16% shorter than the sum of the covalent radii of H (37 pm) and F (72 pm). Suggest a reason for this difference. Similar data show that the difference becomes smaller down the group, from HF to HI. Explain.

**9.83** There are two main types of covalent bond breakage. In homolytic breakage (as in Table 9.2, p. 340), each atom in the bond gets one of the shared electrons. In some cases, the electronegativity of adjacent atoms affects the bond energy. In heterolytic breakage, one atom gets both electrons and the other gets none; thus, a cation and an anion form.
(a) Why is the C—C bond in $H_3C$—$CF_3$ (423 kJ/mol) stronger than that in $H_3C$—$CH_3$ (376 kJ/mol)?
(b) Use bond energy and any other data to calculate the enthalpy of reaction for the heterolytic cleavage of $O_2$.

**9.84** Find the longest wavelengths of light that can cleave the bonds in elemental nitrogen, oxygen, and fluorine.

**9.85** The work function ($\phi$) of a metal is the minimum energy needed to remove an electron from its surface. (a) Is it easier to remove an electron from a gaseous silver atom or from the surface of solid silver ($\phi = 7.59 \times 10^{-19}$ J; IE = 731 kJ/mol)? (b) Explain the results in terms of the electron-sea model of metallic bonding.

**9.86** Lattice energies can also be calculated for covalent solids using a Born-Haber cycle, and the network solid silicon dioxide has one of the highest $\Delta H_{lattice}^\circ$ values. Silicon dioxide is found in pure crystalline form as transparent rock quartz. Much harder than glass, this material was once prized for making lenses for optical devices and expensive spectacles. Use Appendix B and the following data to calculate $\Delta H_{lattice}^\circ$ of $SiO_2$:

| | | |
|---|---|---|
| $Si(s) \longrightarrow Si(g)$ | $\Delta H^\circ =$ | 454 kJ |
| $Si(g) \longrightarrow Si^{4+}(g) + 4e^-$ | $\Delta H^\circ =$ | 9949 kJ |
| $O_2(g) \longrightarrow 2O(g)$ | $\Delta H^\circ =$ | 498 kJ |
| $O(g) + 2e^- \longrightarrow O^{2-}(g)$ | $\Delta H^\circ =$ | 737 kJ |

**9.87** The average C—H bond energy in $CH_4$ is 415 kJ/mol. Use Table 9.2 (p. 340) and the following to calculate the average C—H bond energy in ethane ($C_2H_6$; C—C bond), in ethene ($C_2H_4$; C=C bond), and in ethyne ($C_2H_2$; C≡C bond):

$$C_2H_6(g) + H_2(g) \longrightarrow 2CH_4(g) \qquad \Delta H^\circ_{rxn} = -65.07 \text{ kJ/mol}$$
$$C_2H_4(g) + 2H_2(g) \longrightarrow 2CH_4(g) \qquad \Delta H^\circ_{rxn} = -202.21 \text{ kJ/mol}$$
$$C_2H_2(g) + 3H_2(g) \longrightarrow 2CH_4(g) \qquad \Delta H^\circ_{rxn} = -376.74 \text{ kJ/mol}$$

**9.88** Carbon-carbon bonds form the "backbone" of nearly every organic and biological molecule. The average bond energy of the C—C bond is 347 kJ/mol. Calculate the frequency and wavelength of the least energetic photon that can break an average C—C bond. In what region of the electromagnetic spectrum is this radiation?

**9.89** In a future hydrogen-fuel economy, the cheapest source of $H_2$ will certainly be water. It takes 467 kJ to produce 1 mol of H atoms from water. What is the frequency, wavelength, and minimum energy of a photon that can free an H atom from water?

**9.90** Dimethyl ether ($CH_3OCH_3$) and ethanol ($CH_3CH_2OH$) are constitutional isomers (see Table 3.4, p. 103). (a) Use Table 9.2 (p. 340) to calculate $\Delta H^\circ_{rxn}$ for the formation of each compound as a gas from methane and oxygen; water vapor also forms. (b) State which reaction is more exothermic. (c) Calculate $\Delta H^\circ_{rxn}$ for the conversion of ethanol to dimethyl ether.

**9.91** Enthalpies of reaction calculated from bond energies and from enthalpies of formation are often, but not always, close to each other.
(a) Industrial ethanol ($CH_3CH_2OH$) is produced by a catalytic reaction of ethylene ($CH_2$=$CH_2$) with water at high pressures and temperatures. Calculate $\Delta H^\circ_{rxn}$ for this gas-phase hydration of ethylene to ethanol, using bond energies and then using enthalpies of formation.
(b) Ethylene glycol is produced by the catalytic oxidation of ethylene to ethylene oxide, which then reacts with water to form ethylene glycol:

$$CH_2\!-\!CH_2(l) + H_2O(l) \longrightarrow HOCH_2CH_2OH(l)$$

The $\Delta H^\circ_{rxn}$ for this hydrolysis step, based on enthalpies of formation, is −97 kJ/mol. Calculate $\Delta H^\circ_{rxn}$ for the hydrolysis using bond energies.
(c) Why are the two values relatively close for the hydration in part (a) but not close for the hydrolysis in part (b)?

# The Shapes of Molecules

## Concepts and skills to review before you study this chapter

- electron configurations of main-group elements (Section 8.2)
- electron-dot symbols (Section 9.1)
- octet rule (Section 9.1)
- bond order, bond length, and bond energy (Sections 9.3 and 9.4)
- polar covalent bonds and bond polarity (Section 9.5)

In the everyday world, the shapes of interacting objects often reflect their function—cup and saucer, mortar and pestle, or the matching shapes of hand and glove. The same is true in the molecular world. But, with all the symbols, lines, and dots you've been seeing, it's easy to forget that every molecule has a characteristic minute architecture. Each atom, bonding pair, and lone pair has its own position relative to the others, with definite angles and distances between them that are determined by the attractive and repulsive forces governing all matter. Molecular shape plays a crucial role in the interactions of reactants, the behavior of synthetic materials, and especially in the life-sustaining processes in cells.

**IN THIS CHAPTER . . .** We learn how to picture molecules by applying two approaches that explain their shapes, and we examine some effects of molecular shape on physical and biochemical behavior.
- We learn how to apply the octet rule to convert a molecular formula into a flat structural formula that shows atom attachments and electron-pair locations.
- We see how electron delocalization limits our ability to depict a molecule with a single structural formula and requires us to apply the concept of resonance.
- We introduce bond angle and apply a theory that converts two-dimensional formulas into three-dimensional shapes.
- We describe five basic classes of shapes that many molecules adopt, how multiple bonds and lone pairs affect them, and how to combine smaller molecular portions into the shapes of more complex molecules.
- We discuss the relation among bond polarity, shape, and molecular polarity and the effect of polarity on behavior.
- We describe a few examples of shape influencing biological function.

## 10.1 • DEPICTING MOLECULES AND IONS WITH LEWIS STRUCTURES

The first step toward visualizing a molecule is to convert its molecular formula to its **Lewis structure** (or **Lewis formula**\*), which shows electron-dot symbols for the atoms, the bonding pairs as lines, and the lone pairs that fill each atom's outer level (valence shell) as pairs of dots.

### Applying the Octet Rule to Write Lewis Structures

To write a Lewis structure, we decide on the relative placement of the atoms in the molecule or polyatomic ion and then distribute the total number of valence electrons as bonding and lone pairs. In many, but not all, cases, the octet rule (Section 9.1) guides us in distributing the electrons. We begin with species that "obey" the octet rule, in which each atom fills its outer level with eight electrons (or two for hydrogen).

---

\*A Lewis *structure* does **not** indicate the three-dimensional shape, so it may be more correct to call it a Lewis *formula*, but we follow convention and use the term *structure*.

**Figure 10.1** The steps in converting a molecular formula into a Lewis structure.

**Molecules with Single Bonds** Figure 10.1 lays out the steps for writing Lewis structures for species with only single bonds. Let's use nitrogen trifluoride, $NF_3$, to introduce the steps:

*Step 1. Place the atoms relative to each other.* For compounds with the general molecular formula $AB_n$, place the atom with the *lower group number* in the center because it needs more electrons to attain an octet; usually, this is also the atom with the *lower electronegativity*. In $NF_3$, the N (Group 5A; EN = 3.0) has five electrons and so needs three, whereas each F (Group 7A; EN = 4.0) has seven and needs only one; thus, N goes in the center with the three F atoms around it:

$$
\begin{array}{c}
F \\
N \\
F \quad \ \ F
\end{array}
$$

If the atoms have the same group number, as in $SO_3$, place the atom with the *higher period number* (also lower EN) in the center. H can form only one bond, so it is *never* a central atom.

*Step 2. Determine the total number of valence electrons.*
- For molecules, add up the valence electrons of the atoms. (Recall that the number of valence electrons equals the A-group number.) In $NF_3$, N has five valence electrons, and each F has seven:

$$[1 \times N(5e^-)] + [3 \times F(7e^-)] = 5e^- + 21e^- = 26 \text{ valence } e^-$$

- For polyatomic ions, *add* one $e^-$ for each negative charge, or *subtract* one $e^-$ for each positive charge.

*Step 3. Draw a single bond from each surrounding atom to the central atom, and subtract $2e^-$ from the total for each bond to find the number of $e^-$ remaining:*

$$
\begin{array}{c}
F \\
| \\
F-N-F
\end{array}
$$

$$3 \text{ N}-\text{F bonds} \times 2e^- = 6e^- \qquad \text{so} \qquad 26e^- - 6e^- = 20e^- \text{ remaining}$$

*Step 4. Distribute the remaining electrons in pairs so that each atom ends up with $8e^-$ (or $2e^-$ for H).* First, place lone pairs on the *surrounding (more electronegative) atoms* to give each an octet. If any electrons remain, place them around the central atom—each F gets 3 pairs ($3 \times 6e^- = 18e^-$) and the N gets 1 ($2e^-$), for a total of $20e^-$. Then check that each atom has $8e^-$:

$$
\begin{array}{c}
:\ddot{F}: \\
| \\
:\ddot{F}-\ddot{N}-\ddot{F}:
\end{array}
$$

This is the Lewis structure for $NF_3$. It is a neutral species, so the total number of electrons (bonds plus lone pairs) equals the sum of the valence electrons:

$$6e^- \text{ in three bonds} + 20e^- \text{ in ten lone pairs} = 26 \text{ valence } e^-$$

If we were writing a Lewis structure for a polyatomic ion, we would also take the charge into account, as described in step 2.

Since Lewis structures do not indicate shape, an equally correct depiction of $NF_3$ is

$$
\begin{array}{c}
:\ddot{F}: \\
| \\
:\ddot{F}-N-\ddot{F}:
\end{array}
$$

or any other that retains the *same connections among the atoms*—a central N atom connected by single bonds to each of three surrounding F atoms.

Using these four steps, you can write a Lewis structure for any singly bonded species with a central C, N, or O atom, as well as for some species with central atoms from higher periods. In nearly all their compounds,

- Hydrogen atoms form one bond.
- Carbon atoms form four bonds.
- Nitrogen atoms form three bonds.
- Oxygen atoms form two bonds.
- Surrounding halogens form one bond; fluorine is *always* a surrounding atom.

---

## Sample Problem 10.1  Writing Lewis Structures for Molecules with One Central Atom

**Problem** Write a Lewis structure for $CCl_2F_2$, one of the compounds responsible for the depletion of stratospheric ozone.

**Solution** *Step 1.* Place the atoms relative to each other. In $CCl_2F_2$, carbon has the lowest group number and EN, so it is the central atom (*see margin*). The halogen atoms surround it, but their specific positions are not important.

*Step 2.* Determine the total number of valence electrons (from A-group numbers): C is in Group 4A; F and Cl are in Group 7A. Therefore, we have

$$[1 \times C(4e^-)] + [2 \times F(7e^-)] + [2 \times Cl(7e^-)] = 32 \text{ valence } e^-$$

*Step 3.* Draw single bonds to the central atom (*see margin*) and subtract $2e^-$ for each bond:

$$4 \text{ bonds} \times 2e^- = 8e^- \quad \text{so} \quad 32e^- - 8e^- = 24e^- \text{ remaining}$$

*Step 4.* Distribute the remaining electrons in pairs, beginning with the surrounding atoms, so that each atom has an octet. Each surrounding halogen gets 3 pairs (*see margin*).

**Check** Always check that each atom has an octet. Bonding electrons belong to each atom in the bond. The total number in bonds ($8e^-$) and lone pairs ($24e^-$) equals 32 valence $e^-$. As expected, C has four bonds and the surrounding halogens have one each.

**Follow-Up Problem 10.1** Write a Lewis structure for **(a)** $H_2S$; **(b)** $OF_2$; **(c)** $SOCl_2$.

*Step 1:*
```
       Cl
    F  C  F
       Cl
```

*Step 3:*
```
       Cl
       |
    F—C—F
       |
       Cl
```

*Step 4:*
```
        ..
       :Cl:
        |
    ..  |  ..
   :F—C—F:
    ..  |  ..
       :Cl:
        ..
```

---

In molecules with two or more central atoms bonded to each other, it is usually clear which atoms are central and which surrounding.

---

## Sample Problem 10.2  Writing Lewis Structures for Molecules with More Than One Central Atom

**Problem** Write the Lewis structure for methanol (molecular formula $CH_4O$), an important industrial alcohol that can be used as a gasoline alternative in cars.

**Solution** *Step 1.* Place the atoms relative to each other. The H atoms can have only one bond, so C and O must be central and adjacent to each other. C has four bonds and O has two, so we arrange the H atoms accordingly (*see margin*).

*Step 2.* Find the sum of valence electrons (C is in Group 4A, O is in Group 6A):

$$[1 \times C(4e^-)] + [1 \times O(6e^-)] + [4 \times H(1e^-)] = 14e^-$$

*Step 3.* Add single bonds (*see margin*) and subtract $2e^-$ for each bond:

$$5 \text{ bonds} \times 2e^- = 10e^- \quad \text{so} \quad 14e^- - 10e^- = 4e^- \text{ remaining}$$

*Step 4.* Add the remaining electrons in pairs to fill each valence level. C already has an octet, and each H shares $2e^-$ with the C; so the remaining $4e^-$ form two lone pairs on O to give the Lewis structure for methanol (*see margin*).

**Check** Each H atom has $2e^-$, and C and O each have $8e^-$. The total number of valence electrons is $14e^-$, which equals $10e^-$ in bonds plus $4e^-$ in two lone pairs. Each H has one bond, C has four, and O has two.

**Follow-Up Problem 10.2** Write a Lewis structure for **(a)** hydroxylamine ($NH_3O$); **(b)** dimethyl ether ($C_2H_6O$; no O—H bonds).

*Step 1:*
```
       H
    H  C  O  H
       H
```

*Step 3:*
```
       H
       |
    H—C—O—H
       |
       H
```

*Step 4:*
```
       H
       |   ..
    H—C—O—H
       |
       H
```

**Molecules with Multiple Bonds** In most cases, if there are not enough electrons for the central atom(s) to attain an octet, a multiple bond is present, and we add the following step to the procedure for writing a Lewis structure:

*Step 5. Cases involving multiple bonds.* If a central atom does not end up with an octet, change a lone pair on a surrounding atom into another bonding pair to the central atom, thus forming a multiple bond.

---

**Sample Problem 10.3** — **Writing Lewis Structures for Molecules with Multiple Bonds**

**Problem** Write Lewis structures for the following:
**(a)** Ethylene ($C_2H_4$), the most important reactant in the manufacture of polymers
**(b)** Nitrogen ($N_2$), the most abundant atmospheric gas

**Plan** We show the structure resulting from steps 1 to 4: placing the atoms, counting the total valence electrons, making single bonds, and distributing the remaining valence electrons in pairs to attain octets. Then we continue with step 5, if needed.

**Solution (a)** For $C_2H_4$. After steps 1 to 4, we have

*Step 5.* Change a lone pair to a bonding pair. The right C has an octet, but the left C has only $6e^-$, so we change the lone pair to another bonding pair between the two C atoms:

**(b)** For $N_2$. After steps 1 to 4, we have :N̈—N̈:
*Step 5.* Neither N has an octet, so we change a lone pair to a bonding pair, :N̈=N:
In this case, moving one lone pair to make a double bond still does not give the right N an octet, so we move a lone pair from the left N to make a triple bond, :N≡N:

**Check (a)** Each C has four bonds and counts the $4e^-$ in the double bond as part of its own octet. The valence electron total is $12e^-$, all in six bonds. **(b)** Each N counts the $6e^-$ in the triple bond as part of its own octet. The valence electron total is $10e^-$, which equals the electrons in three bonds and two lone pairs.

**Follow-Up Problem 10.3** Write Lewis structures for **(a)** CO (the only common molecule in which C has three bonds); **(b)** HCN; **(c)** $CO_2$.

---

## Resonance: Delocalized Electron-Pair Bonding

We often find that, for a molecule or polyatomic ion with *double bonds next to single bonds,* we can write more than one Lewis structure. Which, if any, is correct?

**The Need for Resonance Structures** To understand this issue, consider ozone ($O_3$), an air pollutant at ground level but an absorber of harmful ultraviolet (UV) radiation in the stratosphere. Two Lewis structures (with lettered O atoms for clarity) are

In structure I, oxygen B has a double bond to oxygen A and a single bond to oxygen C. In structure II, the single and double bonds are reversed. You can rotate I to get II, so these are *not* different types of ozone molecules, but different Lewis structures for the *same* molecule.

In fact, *neither* Lewis structure depicts $O_3$ accurately, because the two oxygen-oxygen bonds in $O_3$ are actually identical in length and energy. The bonds in $O_3$ have properties between an O—O bond and an O=O bond, something like a "one-and-a-half" bond. The molecule is shown more correctly with two Lewis structures, called

**resonance structures** (or **resonance forms**), and a two-headed resonance arrow ($\longleftrightarrow$) between them. Resonance structures *have the same relative placement of atoms but different locations of bonding and lone electron pairs.* You can convert one resonance form to another by moving lone pairs to bonding positions, and vice versa:

Blue horse          Red donkey

|||

Purple mule

*Resonance structures are not real bonding depictions:* $O_3$ does *not* change back and forth quickly from structure I to structure II. The actual molecule is a **resonance hybrid,** an average of the resonance forms. ●

**Electron Delocalization** Our need for more than one Lewis structure to depict $O_3$ is due to **electron-pair delocalization.** In a single, double, or triple bond, each electron pair is *localized* between the bonded atoms. In a resonance hybrid, two of the electron pairs (one bonding and one lone pair) are *delocalized:* their density is "spread" over a few adjacent atoms. (This delocalization involves just a few $e^-$ pairs, so it is *much* less extensive than the electron delocalization in metals that we saw in Section 9.6.)

In $O_3$, the result is two identical bonds, each consisting of a single bond (the localized pair) and a *partial bond* (the contribution from one of the delocalized pairs). We draw the resonance hybrid with a curved dashed line to show the delocalized pairs:

resonance hybrid

Resonance is very common. For example, benzene ($C_6H_6$, *shown below*) has two important resonance forms in which alternating single and double bonds have different positions. The actual molecule is an average of the two forms with six C—C bonds and three electron pairs delocalized over all six C atoms. The delocalized pairs are often shown as a dashed circle (or simply a circle):

● **A Purple Mule, Not a Blue Horse and a Red Donkey** A mule is a genetic mix, a hybrid, of a horse and a donkey; it is not a horse one instant and a donkey the next. Similarly, the color purple is a mix of red and blue, not red one instant and blue the next. In the same sense, a resonance hybrid is one molecular species, not one resonance form this instant and another resonance form the next. The problem is that we cannot depict the actual species, the hybrid, accurately with a single Lewis structure.

resonance forms

or

resonance hybrid

**Fractional Bond Orders** Partial bonding, as in resonance hybrids, often leads to fractional bond orders. For $O_3$, we have

$$\text{Bond order} = \frac{3 \text{ electron pairs}}{2 \text{ bonded-atom pairs}} = 1\tfrac{1}{2}$$

The carbon-to-carbon bond order in benzene is 9 electron pairs/6 bonded-atom pairs, or $1\tfrac{1}{2}$ also. For the carbonate ion, $CO_3^{2-}$, three resonance structures can be drawn. Each has 4 electron pairs shared among 3 bonded-atom pairs, so the bond order is $\tfrac{4}{3}$, or $1\tfrac{1}{3}$. One of the three resonance structures for $CO_3^{2-}$ is

Note here (and in Sample Problem 10.4) that the Lewis structure of a polyatomic ion is written in *square brackets with the ion charge outside the brackets.*

## Sample Problem 10.4 Writing Resonance Structures

**Problem** Write resonance structures for the nitrate ion, $NO_3^-$, and find the bond order.

**Plan** We write a Lewis structure, remembering to add $1e^-$ to the total number of valence electrons because of the $1-$ ionic charge. Then we move lone and bonding pairs to write other resonance forms and connect them with the resonance arrow. The bond order is the number of shared electron pairs divided by the number of atom pairs.

**Solution** After steps 1 to 4, we have

*Step 5.* Since N has only $6e^-$, we change a lone pair on one of the O atoms to a bonding pair to form a double bond, which gives each atom an octet. All the O atoms are equivalent, however, so we can move a lone pair from any one of the three and obtain three resonance structures:

The bond order is

$$\frac{4 \text{ shared electron pairs}}{3 \text{ bonded-atom pairs}} = 1\tfrac{1}{3}$$

**Check** Each structure has the same relative placement of atoms, an octet around each atom, and $24e^-$ (the sum of the valence electron total and $1e^-$ from the ionic charge, distributed in four bonds and eight lone pairs).

**Comment** These three resonance forms contribute equally to the resonance hybrid because all of the surrounding atoms are identical. This is not always the case, as you'll see next.

**Follow-Up Problem 10.4** One of the three resonance structures for $CO_3^{2-}$ was shown just before Sample Problem 10.4. Draw the other two.

## Formal Charge: Selecting the More Important Resonance Structure

If one resonance form "looks" more like the resonance hybrid than the others, it "weights" the average in its favor. One way to select the more important resonance form is by determining each atom's **formal charge,** the charge it would have *if the bonding electrons were shared equally.* We'll examine this concept and then see how formal charge compares with oxidation number.

**Determining Formal Charge** An atom's formal charge is its total number of valence electrons minus *all* of its unshared valence electrons and *half* of its shared valence electrons. Thus,

> Formal charge of atom =
> no. of valence $e^-$ − (no. of unshared valence $e^-$ + $\frac{1}{2}$ no. of shared valence $e^-$) **(10.1)**

For example, in $O_3$, the formal charge of oxygen A in resonance form I is

6 valence $e^-$ − (4 unshared $e^-$ + $\frac{1}{2}$ of 4 shared $e^-$) = 6 − 4 − 2 = 0

The formal charges of all the atoms in the two $O_3$ resonance forms are

$O_A[6 − 4 − \tfrac{1}{2}(4)] = 0$
$O_B[6 − 2 − \tfrac{1}{2}(6)] = +1$
$O_C[6 − 6 − \tfrac{1}{2}(2)] = −1$

$O_A[6 − 6 − \tfrac{1}{2}(2)] = −1$
$O_B[6 − 2 − \tfrac{1}{2}(6)] = +1$
$O_C[6 − 4 − \tfrac{1}{2}(4)] = 0$

Forms I and II have the same formal charges but on different O atoms, so they contribute equally to the resonance hybrid. *Formal charges must sum to the actual charge on the species:* zero for a molecule or the ionic charge for an ion.

Note that, in I, instead of oxygen's usual two bonds, $O_B$ has three bonds and $O_C$ has one. Only when an atom has a zero formal charge does it have its usual number of bonds; the same holds for C in $CO_3^{2-}$, N in $NO_3^-$, and so forth.

**Choosing the More Important Resonance Form** Three criteria help us choose the more important resonance structure:

- Smaller formal charges (positive *or* negative) are preferable to larger ones.
- The *same* nonzero formal charges on adjacent atoms are not preferred.
- A more negative formal charge should reside on a more electronegative atom.

As in the case of $O_3$, the resonance forms for $CO_3^{2-}$, $NO_3^-$, and benzene all have identical atoms surrounding the central atom(s) and, thus, have identical formal charges and are equally important contributors to the resonance hybrid. But, let's apply these criteria to the cyanate ion, $NCO^-$, which has two *different* atoms around the central one. Three resonance forms with formal charges are

Formal charges:
Resonance forms:

Form I is *not* an important contributor to the hybrid because it has a larger formal charge on N and a positive formal charge on the more electronegative O. Forms II and III have the same magnitude of charges, but III has a $-1$ charge on O, the more electronegative atom. Therefore, II and III are more important than I, and III is more important than II.

**Formal Charge Versus Oxidation Number** Formal charge (used to examine resonance structures) is *not* the same as oxidation number (used to monitor redox reactions):

- For a *formal charge*, bonding electrons are *shared equally* by the atoms (as if the bonding were *nonpolar covalent*), so each atom has half of them:

$$\text{Formal charge} = \text{valence } e^- - (\text{lone pair } e^- + \tfrac{1}{2} \text{ bonding } e^-)$$

- For an *oxidation number*, bonding electrons are *transferred completely* to the more electronegative atom (as if the bonding were *pure ionic*):

$$\text{Oxidation number} = \text{valence } e^- - (\text{lone pair } e^- + \text{bonding } e^-)$$

For the three cyanate ion resonance structures,

Formal charges:
Oxidation numbers:

Notice that the oxidation numbers *do not* change from one resonance form to another (because the electronegativities *do not* change), but the formal charges *do* change (because the numbers of bonding and lone pairs *do* change).

## Lewis Structures for Exceptions to the Octet Rule

The octet rule applies to most molecules (and ions) with Period 2 central atoms, but not every one, and not to many with central atoms from Period 3 and higher. Three important exceptions occur in molecules with (1) electron-deficient atoms, (2) odd-electron atoms, and (3) atoms with expanded valence shells. In this discussion, you'll also see that formal charge has limitations for selecting the best resonance form.

**Molecules with Electron-Deficient Atoms** Gaseous molecules containing either beryllium or boron as the central atom are often **electron deficient:** they have *fewer* than eight electrons around the central atom. The Lewis structures, with formal charges, of gaseous beryllium chloride* and boron trifluoride are

---

*Even though beryllium is in Group 2A(2), most Be compounds have considerable covalent bonding. For example, molten $BeCl_2$ does not conduct electricity, indicating a lack of ions.

There are only four electrons around Be and six around B. Surrounding halogen atoms don't form multiple bonds to the central atoms to give them an octet, because the halogens are much more electronegative. Formal charges make the following structures unlikely:

(Some data for $BF_3$ show a shorter than expected B—F bond. Shorter bonds indicate double-bond character, so the structure with the B═F bond may be a minor contributor to a resonance hybrid.) Electron-deficient atoms often attain an octet by forming additional bonds in reactions. When $BF_3$ reacts with ammonia, for instance, a compound forms in which boron attains an octet:*

**Molecules with Odd-Electron Atoms** A few molecules contain a central atom with an odd number of valence electrons, so they cannot have all their electrons in pairs. Most have a central atom from an odd-numbered group, such as N [Group 5A(15)] or Cl [Group 7A(17)]. These are called **free radicals**, species that contain a lone (unpaired) electron, which makes them paramagnetic (Section 8.4) and extremely reactive. Free radicals are dangerous because they can bond to an H atom in a biomolecule and extract it, which forms a new free radical. This step repeats and can disrupt genes and membranes. Recent studies suggest that free radicals may be involved in cancer and even aging. Antioxidants like vitamin E interrupt free-radical proliferation.

Consider the free radical nitrogen dioxide, $NO_2$, a major contributor to urban smog, that is formed when the NO in auto exhaust is oxidized. $NO_2$ has several resonance forms. Two differ in terms of which O atom is doubly bonded, as in the case of ozone. Two others have the lone electron residing on the N or on an O, so the resonance hybrid has the lone electron delocalized over these two atoms:

Let's see if formal charge considerations help us decide where the electron resides most of the time. The form with it on the singly bonded O has zero formal charges (*right*), while the form with it on N (*left*) has some nonzero charges. Thus, based on formal charge, the form on the right is more important. But, chemical facts suggest otherwise. Free radicals often react with each other to pair their lone electrons. When two $NO_2$ molecules react, the lone electrons pair up to form the N—N bond in dinitrogen tetraoxide ($N_2O_4$) and each N attains an octet:

Thus, given the way $NO_2$ reacts, the lone electron may spend most of its time on N, making *that* form more important. Apparently, in this case, formal charge is not very useful for picking the most important resonance form; we'll see other cases below.

**Expanded Valence Shells** Many molecules (and ions) have more than eight valence electrons around the central atom. *An atom expands its valence shell to form more bonds, which releases energy.* The central atom must be large and have empty orbitals that can hold the additional pairs. Therefore, **expanded valence shells** occur only with *nonmetals from Period 3 or higher because they have d orbitals available.* Such a central atom may be bonded to more than four atoms, or to four or fewer.

---

*Reactions in which one species "donates" an electron pair to another to form a covalent bond are Lewis acid-base reactions, which we discuss fully in Chapter 18.

1. *Central atom bonded to more than four atoms.* Phosphorus pentachloride, $PCl_5$, is a fuming yellow-white solid used to manufacture lacquers and films. It forms when phosphorus trichloride, $PCl_3$, reacts with chlorine gas. The P in $PCl_3$ has an octet, but two more bonds to chlorine form and P expands its valence shell to 10 electrons in $PCl_5$. Note that when $PCl_5$ forms, *one* Cl—Cl bond breaks *(left side of the equation)*, and *two* P—Cl bonds form *(right side),* for a net increase of one bond:

Sulfur hexafluoride, $SF_6$, a dense and inert gas, is used as an electrical insulator. Analogously to $PCl_5$, it forms when sulfur tetrafluoride, $SF_4$, reacts with $F_2$. The S in $SF_4$ already has an expanded valence shell of 10 electrons, but two more bonds to F expand the valence shell further to 12 electrons:

2. *Central atoms bonded to four or fewer atoms.* By applying the concept of formal charge, we can draw Lewis structures with expanded valence shells of central atoms bonded to *four or fewer* atoms. The S in $SF_4$ is one example, and others follow:

- *Sulfuric acid.* Two resonance forms of $H_2SO_4$, with formal charges, are

Form I obeys the octet rule, but it has several nonzero formal charges. In form II, sulfur has 12 electrons (6 bonds) around it, but all zero formal charges. Thus, based on the formal charge rules alone, II contributes more than I to the resonance hybrid. More important than whether rules are followed, form II is consistent with observation. In gaseous $H_2SO_4$, the two sulfur-oxygen bonds *with* an H atom attached to the O are 157 pm long, whereas the two sulfur-oxygen bonds *without* an H atom are 142 pm long. This shorter bond indicates double-bond character, and other measurements indicate greater electron density in the bonds without the attached H.

- *Sulfate ion.* When sulfuric acid loses two $H^+$ ions, it forms the sulfate ion, $SO_4^{2-}$. Measurements indicate all the bonds in $SO_4^{2-}$ are 149 pm long, between the length of an S=O bond (~142 pm) and that of an S—O bond (~157 pm). Six of the seven resonance forms consistent with these data have an expanded valence shell and zero formal charges. Two of the six *(left)* and the one that obeys the octet rule *(right)* are

- *Two sulfur oxides.* Measurements show that the sulfur-oxygen bonds in $SO_2$ and $SO_3$ are all approximately 142 pm long, indicating S=O bonds. Lewis structures consistent with these data have zero formal charges *(two at left),* but others *(two at right)* obey the octet rule:

3. *Limitations of Lewis structures and formal charge.* Chemistry has been a central science for well over two centuries, yet controversies often arise over interpretation of

data, even in established areas like bonding and structure. We've seen that a single Lewis structure often cannot accurately depict a molecule, so we need several resonance forms to do so.

Formal charge rules have limitations, too. They were not useful in choosing the correct location for the lone electron in $NO_2$. And, quantum-mechanical calculations indicate that resonance forms with expanded valence shells that have zero formal charges look *less* like the actual species than forms that follow the octet rule but have higher formal charges. Shorter bonds arise, these findings suggest, not from double-bond character, but because the higher formal charges draw the bonded atoms closer. Such considerations favor the octet-rule forms for $H_2SO_4$, $SO_4^{2-}$, $SO_2$, and $SO_3$. Thus, formal charge may be a useful tool for selecting the most important resonance form, but it is far from perfect. Nevertheless, while keeping these contrary findings in mind, we will continue to draw structures based on formal charge rules because they provide a simple approach consistent with experimental data.

---

**Sample Problem 10.5** | **Writing Lewis Structures for Octet-Rule Exceptions**

**Problem** Write a Lewis structure and identify the octet-rule exception for **(a)** $SClF_5$; **(b)** $H_3PO_4$ (draw two resonance forms and select the more important); **(c)** $BFCl_2$.

**Plan** We write each Lewis structure and examine it for exceptions to the octet rule. **(a)** and **(b)** The central atoms are in Period 3, so they can have more than an octet. **(c)** The central atom is B, which can have fewer than an octet of electrons.

**Solution** **(a)** $SClF_5$ has an *expanded valence shell*. The Lewis structure is

**(b)** $H_3PO_4$ has two resonance forms. The structures, with formal charges, are

Structure I obeys the octet rule but has nonzero formal charges. Structure II has an expanded valence shell with zero formal charges. According to formal charge rules, structure II is the more important form.

**(c)** $BFCl_2$ is an *electron-deficient molecule;* B has only six electrons surrounding it:

**Comment** In (b), structure II is consistent with bond-length measurements, which show one shorter (152 pm) phosphorus-oxygen bond and three longer (157 pm) ones. Nevertheless, as for $H_2SO_4$, calculations show that structure I may be more important.

**Follow-Up Problem 10.5** Write a Lewis structure with minimal formal charges for **(a)** $POCl_3$; **(b)** $ClO_2$; **(c)** $XeF_4$.

---

## ◼ Summary of Section 10.1

- A stepwise process converts a molecular formula into a Lewis structure, a two-dimensional representation of a molecule (or ion) that shows the placement of atoms and distribution of valence electrons among bonding and lone pairs.
- When two or more Lewis structures can be drawn for the same relative placement of atoms, the actual structure is a hybrid of those resonance forms.

- Formal charges can be useful for choosing the more important contributor to the hybrid, but experimental data always determine the choice.
- Molecules with an electron-deficient atom (central Be or B) or an odd-electron atom (free radicals) have less than an octet around the central atom but often attain an octet in reactions.
- In a molecule (or ion) with a central atom from Period 3 or higher, that atom can have more than eight valence electrons because it is larger and has empty *d* orbitals for expanding its valence shell.

# 10.2 • VALENCE-SHELL ELECTRON-PAIR REPULSION (VSEPR) THEORY

Virtually every biochemical process hinges to a great extent on the shapes of interacting molecules. Every medicine you take, odor you smell, or flavor you taste depends on part or all of one molecule fitting together with another. Biologists have found that complex behaviors in many organisms, such as mating, defense, navigation, and feeding, often depend on one molecule's shape matching that of another. In this section, we discuss a model for predicting the shape of a molecule.

To obtain the molecular shape, chemists start with the Lewis structure and apply **valence-shell electron-pair repulsion (VSEPR) theory.** Its basic principle is that, *to minimize repulsions, each group of valence electrons around a central atom is located as far as possible from the others.* A "group" of electrons is any number that occupies a localized region around an atom: single bond, double bond, triple bond,* lone pair, or even lone electron. The **molecular shape** is the three-dimensional arrangement of nuclei joined by the bonding groups.

## Electron-Group Arrangements and Molecular Shapes

When two, three, four, five, or six objects attached to a central point maximize the space between them, five geometric patterns result, which Figure 10.2A shows with balloons. If the objects are valence-electron groups, repulsions maximize the space each occupies around the central atom, and we obtain the five *electron-group arrangements* seen in the great majority of molecules and polyatomic ions.

**Classifying Molecular Shapes** *The electron-group arrangement* is defined by the bonding *and* nonbonding electron groups, but the *molecular shape* is defined by the relative positions of the nuclei, which are connected by the bonding groups only. Figure 10.2B shows the molecular shapes that occur when *all* the surrounding electron groups are *bonding* groups. When some are *nonbonding* groups, no nucleus is attached so dif-

**Figure 10.2 Electron-group repulsions and molecular shapes. A,** Five geometric orientations arise when each balloon occupies as much space as possible. **B,** Mutually repelling bonding groups (*gray sticks*) attach a surrounding atom (*dark gray*) to the central atom (*red*). The name is the electron-group arrangement.

*The two electron pairs in a double bond (or the three pairs in a triple bond) occupy separate orbitals, so they remain near each other and act as one electron group (see Chapter 11).

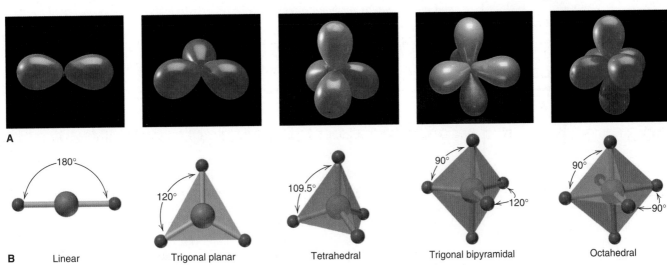

**A**

**B**   Linear          Trigonal planar          Tetrahedral          Trigonal bipyramidal          Octahedral

180°     120°     109.5°     90°  120°     90°  90°

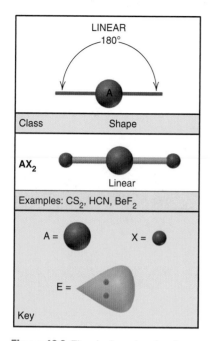

**Figure 10.3** The single molecular shape of the linear electron-group arrangement. The key (*bottom*) for A, X, and E also refers to Figures 10.4, 10.5, 10.7, and 10.8.

ferent molecular shapes occur. Thus, *the same electron-group arrangement can give rise to different molecular shapes:* some with all bonding groups (as in Figure 10.2B) and others with bonding and nonbonding groups. To classify molecular shapes, we assign each a specific $AX_mE_n$ designation, where *m* and *n* are integers, A is the central atom, X is a surrounding atom, and E is a nonbonding valence-electron group (usually a lone pair).

**The Importance of Bond Angle** The **bond angle** is the angle formed by the nuclei of two surrounding atoms with the nucleus of the central atom at the vertex. The angles shown for the shapes in Figure 10.2B are *ideal* bond angles determined by basic geometry alone. We observe them when all the bonding groups are the same and connected to the same type of atom. When this is not the case, the real bond angles deviate from the ideal angles:

| X real = ideal | Y real ≠ ideal | Z real ≠ ideal | :Ä: real ≠ ideal |

## The Molecular Shape with Two Electron Groups (Linear Arrangement)

Two electron groups attached to a central atom point in opposite directions. This **linear arrangement** of electron groups results in a molecule with a **linear shape** and a bond angle of 180°. Figure 10.3 shows the general form (*top*) and shape (*middle*) with VSEPR shape class ($AX_2$), and gives the formulas of some linear molecules.

Gaseous beryllium chloride ($BeCl_2$) is a linear molecule. Recall that gaseous Be compounds are electron deficient, with two electron pairs around the central Be:

$$:\ddot{C}l\overset{180°}{-}Be-\ddot{C}l:$$

In carbon dioxide, the central C atom forms two double bonds with the O atoms:

$$\ddot{O}\overset{180°}{=}C=\ddot{O}$$

Each double bond acts as one electron group and is 180° away from the other. The lone pairs on the O atoms of $CO_2$ or on the Cl atoms of $BeCl_2$ are *not* involved in the molecular shape: only electron groups around the *central* atom affect shape.

## Molecular Shapes with Three Electron Groups (Trigonal Planar Arrangement)

Three electron groups around a central atom point to the corners of an equilateral triangle, which gives the **trigonal planar arrangement** and an ideal bond angle of 120° (Figure 10.4). This arrangement has two molecular shapes—one with all bonding groups and the other with one lone pair. It allows us to see *the effects of lone pairs and double bonds on bond angles.*

1. *All bonding groups: trigonal planar shape ($AX_3$).* Boron trifluoride ($BF_3$), another electron-deficient molecule, is an example. It has six electrons around the central B atom in three single bonds to F atoms. The four nuclei lie in a plane, and each F—B—F angle is 120°:

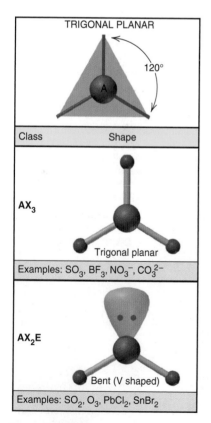

**Figure 10.4** The two molecular shapes of the trigonal planar electron-group arrangement.

The nitrate ion ($NO_3^-$) is one of several polyatomic ions with the trigonal planar shape. One of three resonance forms of the nitrate ion (Sample Problem 10.4) is

The resonance hybrid has three identical bonds of bond order $1\frac{1}{3}$, so the ideal bond angle is observed.

2. *One lone pair: bent or V shape (AX$_2$E).* Gaseous tin(II) chloride is a molecule with a **bent shape,** or **V shape,** with three electron groups in a trigonal plane and a lone pair at one of the triangle's corners. A lone pair often has a major effect on bond angle. Because it is held by only one nucleus, a lone pair is less confined than a bonding pair and so exerts stronger repulsions. In general, *a lone pair repels bonding pairs more than bonding pairs repel each other, so it decreases the angle between bonding pairs.* Note the 95° bond angle in SnCl$_2$, which is considerably less than the ideal 120°:

### Effect of Double Bonds on Bond Angle

When the surrounding atoms and electron groups are not identical, the bond angles may also be affected. Consider formaldehyde (CH$_2$O), whose uses include the manufacture of countertops and the production of methanol. Its trigonal planar shape is due to two types of surrounding atoms (O and H) and two types of electron groups (single and double bonds):

The actual H—C—H bond angle is less than the ideal 120° because *the greater electron density of a double bond repels electrons in single bonds more than the single bonds repel each other.*

## Molecular Shapes with Four Electron Groups (Tetrahedral Arrangement)

Shapes based on two or three electron groups lie in a plane, but four electron groups require three dimensions to maximize separation. Consider methane, whose Lewis structure (*below, left*) shows four bonds pointing to the corners of a square, which suggests 90° bond angles. But, *Lewis structures do **not** depict shape.* In three dimensions, the four electron groups lie at the corners of a *tetrahedron,* a polyhedron with four faces made of equilateral triangles, giving bond angles of 109.5° (Figure 10.5).

A *perspective drawing* for methane (*above, middle*) indicates depth by using solid and dashed wedges for bonds out of the plane of the page. The normal bond lines (*blue*) are in the plane of the page; the solid wedge (*green*) is the bond from the C atom in the plane of the page to the H above that plane; and the dashed wedge (*red*) is the bond from the C to the H below the plane of the page. The ball-and-stick model (*above, right*) shows the tetrahedral shape more clearly.

*All molecules or ions with four electron groups around a central atom adopt the* ***tetrahedral arrangement.*** There are three shapes with this arrangement:

1. *All bonding groups: tetrahedral shape (AX$_4$).* Methane has a tetrahedral shape, a very common geometry in organic molecules. In Sample Problem 10.1, we drew the Lewis structure for CCl$_2$F$_2$, without regard to relative placement of the four halogen atoms around the carbon atom. Because Lewis structures are flat, it may seem like you can write two different ones for CCl$_2$F$_2$, but they represent the same molecule, as a twist of the wrist reveals (Figure 10.6, *next page*).

**Figure 10.5** The three molecular shapes of the tetrahedral electron-group arrangement.

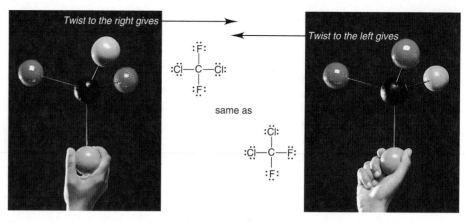

**Figure 10.6 Lewis structures do not indicate molecular shape.** In this model, Cl is green and F is yellow.

*2. One lone pair: trigonal pyramidal shape (AX$_3$E).* Ammonia (NH$_3$) is an example of a molecule with a **trigonal pyramidal shape,** a tetrahedron with one vertex "missing." Stronger repulsions by the lone pair make the H—N—H bond angle slightly less than the ideal 109.5°. The lone pair forces the N—H pairs closer to each other, and the bond angle is 107.3°. NF$_3$ (see page 364) also has a trigonal pyramidal shape.

Picturing shapes is a great way to visualize a reaction. For instance, when ammonia reacts with an acid, the lone pair on N forms a bond to the H$^+$ and yields the ammonium ion (NH$_4^+$), one of many tetrahedral polyatomic ions. As the lone pair becomes a bonding pair, the H—N—H angle expands from 107.3° to 109.5°:

*3. Two lone pairs: bent or V shape (AX$_2$E$_2$).* Water is the most important V-shaped molecule with the tetrahedral arrangement. [Note that, in the trigonal planar arrangement, the V shape has two bonding groups and *one* lone pair (AX$_2$E), and its ideal bond angle is 120°, not 109.5°.] Repulsions from two lone pairs are greater than from one, and the H—O—H bond angle is 104.5°, less than the H—N—H angle in NH$_3$:

Thus, for similar molecules within a given electron-group arrangement, electron-electron repulsions cause deviations from ideal bond angles in the following order:

Lone pair–lone pair > lone pair–bonding pair > bonding pair–bonding pair    **(10.2)**

## Molecular Shapes with Five Electron Groups (Trigonal Bipyramidal Arrangement)

All molecules with five or six electron groups have a central atom from Period 3 or higher because only those atoms have *d* orbitals available to expand the valence shell.

**Relative Positions of Electron Groups** Five mutually repelling electron groups form the **trigonal bipyramidal arrangement,** in which two trigonal pyramids share a common base (Figure 10.7). This is the only case in which *there are two different positions for electron groups and two ideal bond angles.* Three **equatorial groups** lie in a trigonal plane that includes the central atom, and two **axial groups** lie above and below this plane. Therefore, a 120° bond angle separates equatorial groups, and a 90° angle separates axial from equatorial groups. Two factors come into play:

- The greater the bond angle, the weaker the repulsions, so *equatorial-equatorial (120°) repulsions are weaker than axial-equatorial (90°) repulsions.*
- The stronger repulsions from lone pairs means that, when possible, *lone pairs occupy equatorial positions.*

**Shapes for the Trigonal Bipyramidal Arrangement** The tendency for lone pairs to occupy equatorial positions, and thus minimize stronger axial-equatorial repulsions, governs three of the four shapes for this arrangement.

1. *All bonding groups: trigonal bipyramidal shape ($AX_5$).* Phosphorus pentachloride ($PCl_5$) has a trigonal bipyramidal shape. With five identical surrounding atoms, the bond angles are ideal:

2. *One lone pair: seesaw shape ($AX_4E$).* Sulfur tetrafluoride ($SF_4$), a strong fluorinating agent, has the **seesaw shape;** in Figure 10.7, the "seesaw" is tipped on an end. This is the first example of *lone pairs occupying equatorial positions* to minimize repulsions. The lone pair repels all four bonding pairs, reducing the bond angles to 101.5° and 86.8°:

3. *Two lone pairs: T shape ($AX_3E_2$).* Bromine trifluoride ($BrF_3$), one of many compounds with fluorine bonded to a larger halogen, has a **T shape.** Since both lone pairs occupy equatorial positions, we see a greater decrease in the axial-equatorial bond angle, down to 86.2°:

4. *Three lone pairs: linear shape ($AX_2E_3$).* The triiodide ion ($I_3^-$), which forms when $I_2$ dissolves in aqueous $I^-$ solution, is linear. With three equatorial lone pairs and two axial bonding pairs, the three nuclei form a straight line and a 180° X—A—X bond angle:

**Figure 10.7** The four molecular shapes of the trigonal bipyramidal electron-group arrangement.

**Figure 10.8** The three molecular shapes of the octahedral electron-group arrangement.

# Molecular Shapes with Six Electron Groups (Octahedral Arrangement)

Six electron groups form the **octahedral arrangement.** An *octahedron* is a polyhedron with eight equilateral triangles for faces and six identical vertices (Figure 10.8). Each of the six groups points to a corner, which gives a 90° ideal bond angle.

1. *All bonding groups: octahedral shape ($AX_6$).* When seesaw-shaped $SF_4$ reacts with more $F_2$ (see pp. 371 and 377), the central S atom expands its valence shell further to form octahedral sulfur hexafluoride ($SF_6$):

2. *One lone pair: square pyramidal shape ($AX_5E$).* Iodine pentafluoride ($IF_5$) has a **square pyramidal shape.** Note that it makes no difference where one lone pair resides because all the bond angles are 90°. The lone pair reduces the bond angles to 81.9°:

3. *Two lone pairs: square planar shape ($AX_4E_2$).* Xenon tetrafluoride ($XeF_4$) has a **square planar shape.** To avoid stronger 90° lone pair–lone pair repulsions, two lone pairs lie *opposite* each other:

Figure 10.9 displays the shapes possible for elements in different periods, and Figure 10.10 summarizes the molecular shapes we've discussed.

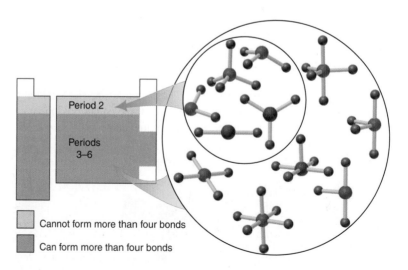

**Figure 10.9** Molecular shapes for central atoms in Period 2 and in higher periods.

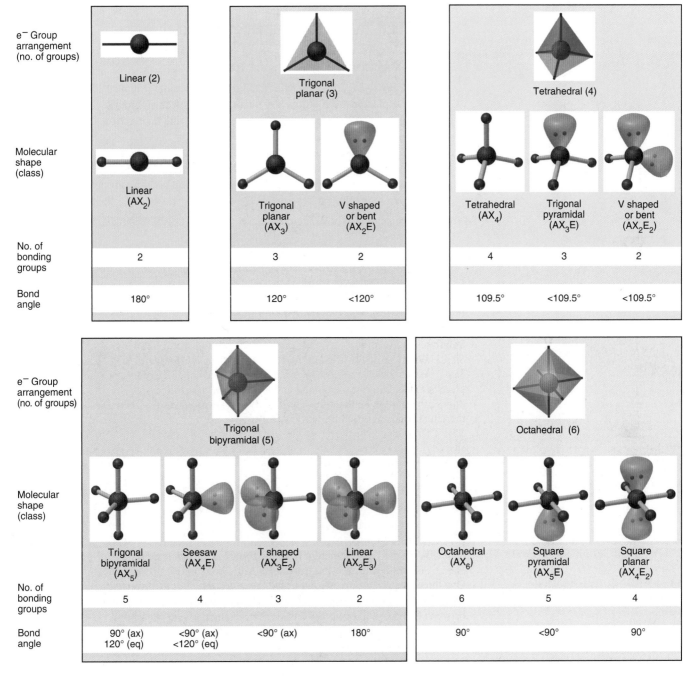

**Figure 10.10** A summary of common molecular shapes with two to six electron groups.

**Figure 10.11** The four steps in converting a molecular formula to a molecular shape.

## Using VSEPR Theory to Determine Molecular Shape

Let's apply a stepwise method for using VSEPR theory to determine a molecular shape from a molecular formula (Figure 10.11):

*Step 1. Write the Lewis structure* from the molecular formula (Figure 10.1, p. 364) to see the relative placement of atoms and the number of electron groups.

*Step 2. Assign an electron-group arrangement* by counting *all* electron groups (bonding plus nonbonding) around the central atom.

*Step 3. Predict the ideal bond angle* from the electron-group arrangement and *the effect of any deviation* caused by lone pairs or double bonds.

*Step 4. Draw and name the molecular shape* by counting bonding groups and nonbonding groups separately.

The next two sample problems apply these steps.

---

**Sample Problem 10.6**    **Examining Shapes with Two, Three, or Four Electron Groups**

**Problem** Draw the molecular shapes and predict the bond angles (relative to the ideal angles) of **(a)** $PF_3$ and **(b)** $COCl_2$.

**Solution** **(a)** For $PF_3$.
*Step 1.* Write the Lewis structure from the formula (*see below, left*).
*Step 2.* Assign the electron-group arrangement: Three bonding groups and one lone pair give four electron groups around P and the *tetrahedral arrangement*.
*Step 3.* Predict the bond angle: The ideal bond angle is 109.5°. There is one lone pair, so the actual bond angle will be less than 109.5°.
*Step 4.* Draw and name the molecular shape: With one lone pair, $PF_3$ has a trigonal pyramidal shape ($AX_3E$):

**(b)** For $COCl_2$.
*Step 1.* Write the Lewis structure from the formula (*see below, left*).
*Step 2.* Assign the electron-group arrangement: Two single bonds and one double bond give three electron groups around C and the *trigonal planar arrangement*.
*Step 3.* Predict the bond angles: The ideal bond angle is 120°, but the double bond between C and O will compress the Cl—C—Cl angle to less than 120°.
*Step 4.* Draw and name the molecular shape: With three electron groups and no lone pairs, $COCl_2$ has a trigonal planar shape ($AX_3$):

**Check** We compare the answers with the general information in Figure 10.10.

**Comment** Be sure the Lewis structure is correct because it determines the other steps.

**Follow-Up Problem 10.6** Draw the molecular shapes and predict the bond angles (relative to the ideal angles) of **(a)** $CS_2$; **(b)** $PbCl_2$; **(c)** $CBr_4$; **(d)** $SF_2$.

**Sample Problem 10.7** Examining Shapes with Five or Six Electron Groups

**Problem** Draw the molecular shapes and predict the bond angles (relative to the ideal angles) of **(a)** $SbF_5$ and **(b)** $BrF_5$.

**Plan** We proceed as in Sample Problem 10.6, being sure to minimize the number of axial-equatorial repulsions.

**Solution (a)** For $SbF_5$.

*Step 1.* Lewis structure (*see below, left*).

*Step 2.* Electron-group arrangement: With five electron groups, this is the *trigonal bipyramidal* arrangement.

*Step 3.* Bond angles: All the groups and surrounding atoms are identical, so the bond angles are ideal: 120° between equatorial groups and 90° between axial and equatorial groups.

*Step 4.* Molecular shape: Five electron groups and no lone pairs give the trigonal bipyramidal shape ($AX_5$):

**(b)** For $BrF_5$.

*Step 1.* Lewis structure (*see below, left*).

*Step 2.* Electron-group arrangement: Six electron groups give the *octahedral* arrangement.

*Step 3.* Bond angles: The lone pair will make all bond angles less than the ideal 90°.

*Step 4.* Molecular shape: With one lone pair, $BrF_5$ has the square pyramidal shape ($AX_5E$):

**Check** We compare our answers with Figure 10.10.

**Comment** We will also see the linear, tetrahedral, square planar, and octahedral shapes in an important group of substances, called *coordination compounds,* in Chapter 23.

**Follow-Up Problem 10.7** Draw the molecular shapes and predict the bond angles (relative to the ideal angles) of **(a)** $ICl_2^-$; **(b)** $ClF_3$; **(c)** $SOF_4$.

## Molecular Shapes with More Than One Central Atom

The shapes of molecules with more than one central atom are composites of the shapes around each of the atoms. Here are two examples:

1. Ethane ($CH_3CH_3$; molecular formula $C_2H_6$) is a component of natural gas. With four bonding groups and no lone pairs around the two central carbons, ethane is shaped like two overlapping tetrahedra (Figure 10.12A).

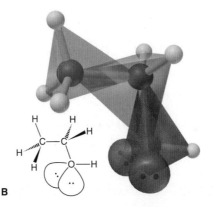

**Figure 10.12** The tetrahedral shapes around the central atoms and the overall shapes of ethane **(A)** and ethanol **(B)**.

2. Ethanol ($CH_3CH_2OH$; molecular formula $C_2H_6O$), the intoxicating substance in beer, wine, and whiskey, has three central atoms (Figure 10.12B). The $CH_3$— group is tetrahedrally shaped, and the —$CH_2$— group has four bonding groups around its central C atom, so it is also tetrahedrally shaped. The O atom has two bonding groups and two lone pairs around it, so the —OH group has a V shape ($AX_2E_2$).

---

**Sample Problem 10.8** Predicting Molecular Shapes with More Than One Central Atom

**Problem** Determine the shape around each central atom in acetone, $(CH_3)_2CO$.

**Plan** There are three central C atoms, two of which are in $CH_3$— groups. We determine the shape around one central atom at a time.

**Solution** *Step 1.* Lewis structure (*see below, left*).

*Step 2.* Electron-group arrangement: Each $CH_3$— group has four electron groups around its central C, so its electron-group arrangement is *tetrahedral*. The third C atom has three electron groups around it, so it has the *trigonal planar arrangement.*

*Step 3.* Bond angles: The H—C—H angle in $CH_3$— should be near the ideal 109.5°. The C=O double bond will compress the C—C—C angle to less than the ideal 120°.

*Step 4.* Shapes around central atoms: With four electron groups and no lone pairs, the shape around C in each $CH_3$— is tetrahedral ($AX_4$). With three electron groups and no lone pairs, the shape around the middle C is trigonal planar ($AX_3$):

**Follow-Up Problem 10.8** Determine the shape around each central atom and predict any deviations from ideal bond angles in the following: **(a)** $H_2SO_4$; **(b)** propyne ($C_3H_4$; there is one C≡C bond); **(c)** $S_2F_2$.

---

## ■ Summary of Section 10.2

- VSEPR theory proposes that each electron group (single bond, multiple bond, lone pair, or lone electron) around a central atom remains as far from the others as possible.
- Five electron-group arrangements are possible when two, three, four, five, or six electron groups surround a central atom. Each arrangement is associated with one or more molecular shapes, depending on the numbers of bonding and lone pairs.
- Ideal bond angles are based on the regular geometric arrangements. Deviations from them occur when surrounding atoms and/or electron groups are not identical.
- Lone pairs and double bonds exert stronger repulsions than single bonds.
- Shapes of larger molecules are composites of the shapes around each central atom.

---

# 10.3 • MOLECULAR SHAPE AND MOLECULAR POLARITY

Knowing the shape of its molecules is key to understanding the physical and chemical behavior of a substance. One of the most far-reaching effects of molecular shape is molecular polarity, which can influence melting and boiling points, solubility, reactivity, and even biological function.

Recall from Chapter 9 that a covalent bond is *polar* when the atoms have different electronegativities and, thus, share the electrons unequally. In diatomic molecules, such as HF, the only bond is polar, so the molecule is polar. In larger molecules, *both shape and bond polarity determine* **molecular polarity,** an imbalance of charge over the whole molecule or large portion of it. Polar molecules become oriented in an electric field, with their partially charged ends pointing toward the oppositely charged plates (Figure 10.13). **Dipole moment ($\mu$)** is a measure of molecular polarity, given in the unit *debye* (D)* derived from SI units of charge (coulomb, C) and length (m): $1 \text{ D} = 3.34 \times 10^{-30}$ C·m.

## Bond Polarity, Bond Angle, and Dipole Moment

The presence of polar bonds does not *always* result in a polar molecule; we must also consider shape and the atoms surrounding the central atom. Here are three cases:

1. *$CO_2$: polar bonds, nonpolar molecule.* In carbon dioxide, the electronegativity difference between C (EN = 2.5) and O (EN = 3.5) makes each C=O bond polar. But $CO_2$ is linear, so the bonds point 180° from each other. The two bond polarities are counterbalanced, and the molecule has *no net dipole moment* ($\mu = 0$ D). The electron density model shows regions of high negative charge (*red*) distributed equally on either side of the central region of high positive charge (*blue*):

2. *$H_2O$: polar bonds, polar molecule.* Water also has two polar bonds, but it *is* polar ($\mu = 1.85$ D). In each O—H bond, electron density is pulled from H (EN = 2.1) toward O (EN = 3.5). Bond polarities are *not* counterbalanced because the molecule is V shaped (also see Figure 4.1, p. 138). The bond polarities are partially reinforced, making the O end partially negative and the other end (the region between the H atoms) partially positive:

(The molecular polarity of water has some amazing effects, from determining the composition of the oceans to supporting life itself, as you'll see in Chapter 12.)

3. *Same shapes, different polarities.* When different molecules have the same shape, the identities of the surrounding atoms affect polarity. Carbon tetrachloride ($CCl_4$) and chloroform ($CHCl_3$) are tetrahedral molecules with very different polarities. In $CCl_4$, all the surrounding atoms are Cl atoms. Each C—Cl bond is polar ($\Delta$EN = 0.5), but the molecule is nonpolar ($\mu = 0$ D) because the bond polarities counterbalance each other. In $CHCl_3$, an H replaces one Cl, disrupting the balance and giving chloroform a significant dipole moment ($\mu = 1.01$ D):

**B Electric field off**

**C Electric field on**

**Figure 10.13 The orientation of polar molecules in an electric field.**
**A,** Space-filling (*left*) and electron-density models (*right*) of the polar HF molecule. **B,** With the external electric field off, HF molecules are oriented randomly. **C,** With the field on, the molecules, on average, become oriented.

---

*The unit is named for the Dutch-American scientist Peter Debye (1884–1966) who won the Nobel Prize in 1936 for contributions to the fields of molecular structure and solution behavior.

## Sample Problem 10.9 Predicting the Polarity of Molecules

**Problem** For each of the following, use the molecular shape and EN values and trends (Figure 9.20, p. 349) to predict the direction of bond and molecular polarity, if present:
**(a)** Ammonia, $NH_3$
**(b)** Boron trifluoride, $BF_3$
**(c)** Carbonyl sulfide, COS (atom sequence SCO)

**Plan** We draw and name the molecular shape and point a polar arrow toward the atom with higher EN in each bond. If the bond polarities balance one another, the molecule is nonpolar; if they reinforce each other, we show the direction of the molecular polarity.

**Solution** **(a)** For $NH_3$. The molecular shape is trigonal pyramidal. N (EN = 3.0) is more electronegative than H (EN = 2.1), so the bond polarities point toward N and partially reinforce each other; thus the molecular polarity points toward N:

molecular shape

bond polarities

molecular polarity

Therefore, ammonia is polar.
**(b)** For $BF_3$. The molecular shape is trigonal planar. F (EN = 4.0) is farther to the right in Period 2 than B (EN = 2.0), so it is more electronegative; thus, each bond polarity points toward F. However, the bond angle is 120°, so the three bond polarities balance each other, and $BF_3$ has no molecular polarity:

molecular shape

bond polarities

no molecular polarity

Therefore, boron trifluoride is nonpolar.
**(c)** For COS. The molecular shape is linear. With C and S having the same EN, the C=S bond is nonpolar, but the C=O bond is quite polar (ΔEN = 1.0), so there is a net molecular polarity toward the O:

$\ddot{S}=C=\ddot{O}$
molecular shape

bond polarity

molecular polarity

Therefore, carbonyl sulfide is polar.

**Check** The electron density models confirm our conclusions. Note that, in (b), the negative (*red*) regions surround the central B (*blue*) symmetrically.

## Follow-Up Problem 10.9 Show the bond polarities and molecular polarity, if any, for each of the following:
**(a)** Dichloromethane ($CH_2Cl_2$)
**(b)** Iodine oxide pentafluoride ($IOF_5$)
**(c)** Nitrogen tribromide ($NBr_3$).

## The Effect of Molecular Polarity on Behavior

Earlier we mentioned that molecular polarity influences physical behavior. Let's see how a molecular property like dipole moment affects a macroscopic property like boiling point. Consider the two dichloroethylenes shown below. They have the *same* molecular formula ($C_2H_2Cl_2$) but *different* physical and chemical properties; that is, they are constitutional isomers (Section 3.3). Both molecules are planar, with a trigonal planar shape around each C atom. The *trans* isomer is nonpolar ($\mu = 0$ D) because the polar C—Cl bonds balance each other. The *cis* isomer is polar ($\mu = 1.90$ D) because the bond polarities partially reinforce each other, with the molecular polarity pointing between the Cl atoms.

A liquid boils when it forms bubbles against the atmospheric pressure. To enter the bubble, the molecules in the liquid must overcome the weak attractive forces *between* them. Because of their polarity, the *cis* molecules attract each other more strongly than the *trans* molecules do. Since more energy is needed to overcome the stronger attractions, we expect the *cis* isomer to have a higher boiling point: *cis*-1,2-dichloroethylene boils 13°C higher than *trans*-1,2-dichloroethylene.

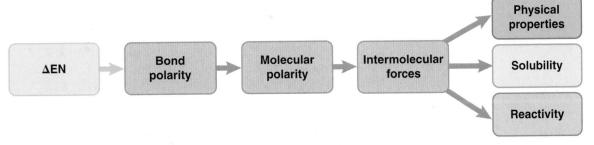

Figure 10.14 shows the chain of influences of atomic properties on the behavior of substances. We extend these relationships in Chapter 12, and the upcoming Chemical Connections essay discusses some biological effects of molecular shape and polarity.

**Figure 10.14** The influence of atomic properties on macroscopic behavior.

$$\Delta EN \rightarrow \boxed{\text{Bond polarity}} \rightarrow \boxed{\text{Molecular polarity}} \rightarrow \boxed{\text{Intermolecular forces}} \rightarrow \begin{cases} \boxed{\text{Physical properties}} \\ \boxed{\text{Solubility}} \\ \boxed{\text{Reactivity}} \end{cases}$$

## ▌ Summary of Section 10.3

- Bond polarity and molecular shape determine molecular polarity, which is measured as a dipole moment.
- A molecule with polar bonds is not necessarily a polar molecule. When bond polarities counterbalance each other, the molecule is nonpolar; when they reinforce each other, the molecule is polar.
- Molecular shape and polarity can affect physical properties, such as boiling point, and they play a central role in biological function.

# CHEMICAL CONNECTIONS | Molecular Shape, Biological Receptors, and the Sense of Smell

## TO SENSORY PHYSIOLOGY

A biological cell can be thought of as a membrane-bound sack filled with an aqueous fluid containing many molecules of various shapes. Many complex processes begin when a molecular "key" fits into a molecular "lock" with a complementary shape. Typically, the key is a small molecule circulating in cellular or other bodily fluid, and the lock, the *biological receptor,* is a large molecule often embedded in a membrane. The *receptor site* is a small region of the receptor with a shape that matches the molecular key. Thousands of molecules per second collide with the receptor site, but when one with the correct shape does, the receptor "grabs" it through intermolecular attractions, and the biological response begins.

### Molecular Shape and the Sense of Smell

Molecular shapes fitting together is crucial to the sense of smell (olfaction). To have an odor, a substance must be a gas or a volatile liquid or solid and must be at least slightly soluble in the aqueous film of the nasal passages. And the odorous molecule, or a portion of it, must fit into one of the receptor sites on nerve endings in this area. When this happens, nerve impulses travel to the brain, which interprets them as a specific odor.

Over half a century ago, a new theory proposed that molecular shape (and sometimes polarity), but *not* composition, determines odor. It stated that any molecule producing one of seven primary odors—camphor-like, musky, floral, minty, ethereal, pungent, and putrid—matches a receptor site of a particular shape. Figure B10.1 shows three of the seven sites holding a molecule with that odor.

Several predictions of the theory proved to be correct:

- If different substances fit a given receptor, they have the same odor. The four molecules in Figure B10.2 fit the camphor-like receptor and smell like moth repellent.
- If different parts of a molecule fit different receptors, it has a mixed odor. Portions of benzaldehyde fit the camphor-like, floral, and minty receptors, and it smells like almonds; other molecules with this odor fit the same three receptors.

But, other predictions were not confirmed. For example, an odor predicted from the shape was often not the odor smelled. The reason is that molecules may not have the same shape in solution at the receptor as they have in the gas phase.

Evidence from the 1990s suggests that the original model is far too simple. The 2004 Nobel Prize in medicine or physiology was given to Richard Axel and Linda B. Buck for showing that olfaction involves about 1000 different receptors and molecules fitting various combinations of them produce the over 10,000 odors humans smell.

Thus, although the process is much more complex than originally thought, the central idea that odor depends on molecular shape is valid and is being actively researched in the food, cosmetics, and insecticide industries.

### Biological Significance of Molecular Shape

*Countless other examples show that no chemical property is more crucial to living systems than molecular shape.* Here are just a few of the many biochemical processes controlled by one molecule fitting into a receptor site on another:

- Enzymes are proteins that bind cellular reactants and speed their reaction. An early step in energy metabolism involves glucose binding to the "active" site of the enzyme hexokinase (Figure B10.3).
- Nerve impulses are transmitted when small molecules released from one nerve fit into receptors on the next. Mind-altering drugs act by chemically disrupting the molecular fit at such nerve receptors in the brain.
- One type of immune response is triggered when a molecule on a bacterial surface binds to the receptors on "killer" cells in the bloodstream.
- Hormones regulate processes by fitting into and activating specific receptors on target tissues and organs.
- Genes function when certain nucleic acid molecules fit into specific regions of others.

Floral          Camphor-like          Ethereal

**Figure B10.1** Shapes of some olfactory receptor sites.

**Figure B10.2** Different molecules with the same odor.

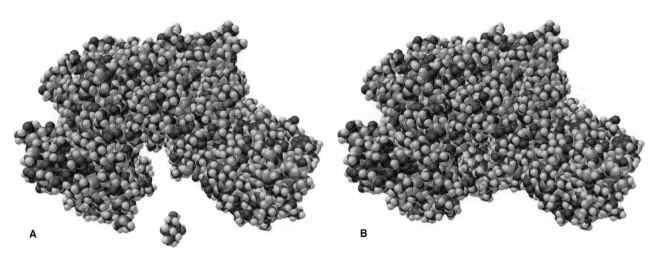

**Figure B10.3** Molecular shape and enzyme action. **A,** A small sugar molecule (*bottom*) is shown near a specific region of an enzyme molecule. **B,** When the sugar lands in that region, the reaction begins.

## Problems

**B10.1** As you'll learn in Chapter 11, groups joined by a single bond rotate freely around the bond, but those joined by double bonds don't. Peptide bonds make up a major portion of protein chains. Determine the molecular shape around the central C and N atoms in the two resonance forms of the peptide bond:

**B10.2** Lewis structures of mescaline, a hallucinogenic compound in peyote cactus, and dopamine, a neurotransmitter in the mammalian brain, are shown below. Suggest a reason for mescaline's ability to disrupt nerve impulses.

mescaline          dopamine

# CHAPTER REVIEW GUIDE

## Learning Objectives
Relevant section (§) and/or sample problem (SP) numbers appear in parentheses.

### Understand These Concepts

1. How Lewis structures depict the atoms, bonding pairs, and lone electron pairs in a molecule or polyatomic ion (§10.1)
2. How resonance and electron delocalization explain bond properties in many compounds with double bonds adjacent to single bonds (§10.1)
3. The meaning of formal charge and how it is used to select the most important resonance structure; the difference between formal charge and oxidation number (§10.1)
4. The octet rule and its three major exceptions—molecules with a central atom that has an electron deficiency, an odd number of electrons, or an expanded valence shell (§10.1)
5. How electron-group repulsions lead to molecular shapes (§10.2)
6. The five electron-group arrangements and their associated molecular shapes (§10.2)
7. Why double bonds and lone pairs cause deviations from ideal bond angles (§10.2)
8. How bond polarities and molecular shape combine to give a molecule polarity (§10.3)

### Master These Skills

1. Using a stepwise method for writing a Lewis structure from a molecular formula (SPs 10.1–10.3, 10.5)
2. Writing resonance structures for molecules and ions (SP 10.4)
3. Calculating the formal charge of any atom in a molecule or ion (SP 10.5)
4. Predicting molecular shapes from Lewis structures (SPs 10.6–10.8)
5. Using molecular shape and electronegativity values to predict the polarity of a molecule (SP 10.9)

## Key Terms
Page numbers appear in parentheses.

**Section 10.1**
Lewis structure (Lewis formula) (363)
resonance structure (resonance form) (367)
resonance hybrid (367)
electron-pair delocalization (367)
formal charge (368)
electron deficient (369)
free radical (370)
expanded valence shell (370)

**Section 10.2**
valence-shell electron-pair repulsion (VSEPR) theory (373)
molecular shape (373)
bond angle (374)
linear arrangement (374)
linear shape (374)
trigonal planar arrangement (374)
bent shape (V shape) (375)
tetrahedral arrangement (375)
trigonal pyramidal shape (376)
trigonal bipyramidal arrangement (376)
equatorial group (376)
axial group (377)
seesaw shape (377)
T shape (377)
octahedral arrangement (378)
square pyramidal shape (378)
square planar shape (378)

**Section 10.3**
molecular polarity (383)
dipole moment (μ) (383)

## Key Equations and Relationships
Page numbers appear in parentheses.

**10.1** Calculating the formal charge on an atom (368):

Formal charge of atom
= no. of valence $e^-$
    − (no. of unshared valence $e^-$ + $\frac{1}{2}$ no. of shared valence $e^-$)

**10.2** Ranking the effect of electron-pair repulsions on bond angle (376):
Lone pair–lone pair > lone pair–bonding pair > bonding pair–bonding pair

## Brief Solutions to Follow-Up Problems

**10.1** (a) H—S̈—H  (b) :Ö—Ö:  with :F̈: :F̈:  (c) :O:  S  :C̈l: :C̈l:

**10.2** (a) H—N̈—Ö—H with H  (b) H H | | H—C—Ö—C—H | | H H

**10.3** (a) :C≡O:  (b) H—C≡N:  (c) :Ö=C=Ö:

**10.4** [ :O: ‖ C :Ö: :Ö: ]²⁻ ↔ [ :O: | C :Ö: Ö: ]²⁻

**10.5** (a) :O: ‖ P :C̈l: | :C̈l: :C̈l:  (b) :Ö: Cl: :Ö: :Ö:  (c) :F̈: :F̈: Xe :F̈: :F̈:

**10.6** (a) S̈=C=S̈  Linear, 180°  (b) Pb  :C̈l: :C̈l:  V shaped, <120°

(c) :B̈r: :B̈r—C—B̈r: :B̈r:  Tetrahedral, 109.5°  (d) S  :F̈: :F̈:  V shaped, <109.5°

**10.7**
(a) [ :C̈l: I :C̈l: ]⁻  Linear, 180°

(b) :F̈: Cl—F̈: :F̈:  T shaped, <90°

(c) :F̈: :F̈: S=O :F̈:  Trigonal bipyramidal  $F_{eq}$—S—$F_{eq}$ angle <120°  $F_{ax}$—S—$F_{eq}$ angle <90°

**10.8** (a)  :O: S=O O H O H  S is tetrahedral; double bonds compress O—S—O angle to <109.5°. Shape around each O in an —OH is V shape; lone pairs compress H—O—S angle to <109.5°.

(b) H H—C—C≡C—H H  Shape around C in $CH_3$— is tetrahedral, with angles ~109.5°; other C atoms are linear, 180°.

(c) :F̈: S=S :F̈:  V shape around each S; F—S—S angle <109.5°.

**10.9**
(a) :C̈l: H—C—C̈l: H H

(b) :O: :F̈: I :F̈: :F̈: :F̈:

(c) N :B̈r: :B̈r: :B̈r:

---

## PROBLEMS

Problems with **colored** numbers are answered in Appendix E and worked in detail in the Student Solutions Manual. Problem sections match those in the text and provide the numbers of relevant sample problems. Most offer Concept Review Questions, Skill-Building Exercises (grouped in pairs covering the same concept), and Problems in Context. The Comprehensive Problems are based on material from any section or previous chapter.

### Depicting Molecules and Ions with Lewis Structures
(Sample Problems 10.1 to 10.5)

**Concept Review Questions**

**10.1** Which of these atoms *cannot* serve as a central atom in a Lewis structure: (a) O; (b) He; (c) F; (d) H; (e) P? Explain.

**10.2** When is a resonance hybrid needed to adequately depict the bonding in a molecule? Using $NO_2$ as an example, explain how a resonance hybrid is consistent with the actual bond length, bond strength, and bond order.

**10.3** In which of these bonding patterns does X obey the octet rule?

(a)  (b)  (c)  (d)  (e)  (f)  (g)  (h)

—Ẍ— | |  :Ẍ— |  Ẍ | |  ≡X:  —Ẍ=  —Ẍ=  Ẍ  :Ẍ:²⁻

**10.4** What is required for an atom to expand its valence shell? Which of the following atoms can expand its valence shell: F, S, H, Al, Se, Cl?

**Skill-Building Exercises** (grouped in similar pairs)

**10.5** Draw a Lewis structure for (a) $SiF_4$; (b) $SeCl_2$; (c) $COF_2$ (C is central).

**10.6** Draw a Lewis structure for (a) $PH_4^+$; (b) $C_2F_4$; (c) $SbH_3$.

**10.7** Draw a Lewis structure for (a) $PF_3$; (b) $H_2CO_3$ (both H atoms are attached to O atoms); (c) $CS_2$.

**10.8** Draw a Lewis structure for (a) $CH_4S$; (b) $S_2Cl_2$; (c) $CHCl_3$.

**10.9** Draw Lewis structures of all the important resonance forms of (a) $NO_2^+$; (b) $NO_2F$ (N is central).

**10.10** Draw Lewis structures of all the important resonance forms of (a) $HNO_3$ ($HONO_2$); (b) $HAsO_4^{2-}$ ($HOAsO_3^{2-}$).

**10.11** Draw Lewis structures of all the important resonance forms of (a) $N_3^-$; (b) $NO_2^-$.

**10.12** Draw Lewis structures of all the important resonance forms of (a) $HCO_2^-$ (H is attached to C); (b) $HBrO_4$ ($HOBrO_3$).

**10.13** Draw the Lewis structure with lowest formal charges, and determine the charge of each atom in (a) $IF_5$; (b) $AlH_4^-$.

**10.14** Draw the Lewis structure with lowest formal charges, and determine the charge of each atom in (a) OCS; (b) NO.

**10.15** Draw the Lewis structure with lowest formal charges, and determine the charge of each atom in (a) $CN^-$; (b) $ClO^-$.

**10.16** Draw the Lewis structure with lowest formal charges, and determine the charge of each atom in (a) $BF_4^-$; (b) ClNO.

**10.17** Draw a Lewis structure for a resonance form of each ion with the lowest possible formal charges, show the charges, and give oxidation numbers of the atoms: (a) $BrO_3^-$; (b) $SO_3^{2-}$.

**10.18** Draw a Lewis structure for a resonance form of each ion with the lowest possible formal charges, show the charges, and give oxidation numbers of the atoms: (a) $AsO_4^{3-}$; (b) $ClO_2^-$.

**10.19** These species do not obey the octet rule. Draw a Lewis structure for each, and state the type of octet-rule exception:
(a) $BH_3$      (b) $AsF_4^-$      (c) $SeCl_4$

**10.20** These species do not obey the octet rule. Draw a Lewis structure for each, and state the type of octet-rule exception:
(a) $PF_6^-$      (b) $ClO_3$      (c) $H_3PO_3$ (one P—H bond)

**10.21** These species do not obey the octet rule. Draw a Lewis structure for each, and state the type of octet-rule exception:
(a) $BrF_3$      (b) $ICl_2^-$      (c) $BeF_2$

**10.22** These species do not obey the octet rule. Draw a Lewis structure for each, and state the type of octet-rule exception:
(a) $O_3^-$      (b) $XeF_2$      (c) $SbF_4^-$

**Problems in Context**

**10.23** Molten beryllium chloride reacts with chloride ion from molten NaCl to form the $BeCl_4^{2-}$ ion, in which the Be atom attains an octet. Show the net ionic reaction with Lewis structures.

**10.24** Despite many attempts, the perbromate ion ($BrO_4^-$) was not prepared in the laboratory until about 1970. (In fact, articles were published explaining theoretically why it could never be prepared!) Draw a Lewis structure for $BrO_4^-$ in which all atoms have lowest formal charges.

**10.25** Cryolite ($Na_3AlF_6$) is an indispensable component in the electrochemical production of aluminum. Draw a Lewis structure for the $AlF_6^{3-}$ ion.

**10.26** Phosgene is a colorless, highly toxic gas that was employed against troops in World War I and it is used today as a key reactant in organic syntheses. From the following resonance structures, select the one with the lowest formal charges:

A         B         C

## Valence-Shell Electron-Pair Repulsion (VSEPR) Theory

(Sample Problems 10.6 to 10.8)

**Concept Review Questions**

**10.27** If you know the formula of a molecule or ion, what is the first step in predicting its shape?

**10.28** In what situation is the name of the molecular shape the same as the name of the electron-group arrangement?

**10.29** Which of the following numbers of electron groups can give rise to a bent (V-shaped) molecule: two, three, four, five, six? Draw an example for each case, showing the shape classification ($AX_mE_n$) and the ideal bond angle.

**10.30** Name all the molecular shapes that have a tetrahedral electron-group arrangement.

**10.31** Consider the following molecular shapes:

A        B        C        D

(a) Which has the most electron pairs (both shared and unshared) around the central atom?
(b) Which has the most unshared pairs around the central atom?
(c) Do any have only shared pairs around the central atom?

**10.32** Use wedge-bond perspective drawings (if necessary) to sketch the atom positions in a general molecule of formula (not shape class) $AX_n$ that has each of the following shapes:
(a) V shaped    (b) trigonal planar      (c) trigonal bipyramidal
(d) T shaped    (e) trigonal pyramidal    (f) square pyramidal

**10.33** What would you expect to be the electron-group arrangement around atom A in each of the following cases? For each arrangement, give the ideal bond angle and the direction of any expected deviation:

(a) X—A: (with X above and X below)   (b) X—A≡X   (c) X=A—X (with X above)   (d) X—Ä—X

(e) X=A=X   (f) :A (with X substituents)

**Skill-Building Exercises** (grouped in similar pairs)

**10.34** Determine the electron-group arrangement, molecular shape, and ideal bond angle(s) for each of the following:
(a) $O_3$      (b) $H_3O^+$    (c) $NF_3$

**10.35** Determine the electron-group arrangement, molecular shape, and ideal bond angle(s) for each of the following:
(a) $SO_4^{2-}$      (b) $NO_2^-$    (c) $PH_3$

**10.36** Determine the electron-group arrangement, molecular shape, and ideal bond angle(s) for each of the following:
(a) $CO_3^{2-}$      (b) $SO_2$      (c) $CF_4$

**10.37** Determine the electron-group arrangement, molecular shape, and ideal bond angle(s) for each of the following:
(a) $SO_3$      (b) $N_2O$ (N is central)      (c) $CH_2Cl_2$

**10.38** Name the shape and give the $AX_mE_n$ classification and ideal bond angle(s) for each of the following general molecules:

(a)          (b)          (c)

**10.39** Name the shape and give the $AX_mE_n$ classification and ideal bond angle(s) for each of the following general molecules:

(a)          (b)          (c)

**10.40** Determine the shape, ideal bond angle(s), and the direction of any deviation from those angles for each of the following:
(a) $ClO_2^-$    (b) $PF_5$    (c) $SeF_4$    (d) $KrF_2$

**10.41** Determine the shape, ideal bond angle(s), and the direction of any deviation from those angles for each of the following:
(a) $ClO_3^-$    (b) $IF_4^-$    (c) $SeOF_2$    (d) $TeF_5^-$

**10.42** Determine the shape around each central atom in each molecule, and explain any deviation from ideal bond angles:
(a) $CH_3OH$    (b) $N_2O_4$ $(O_2NNO_2)$

**10.43** Determine the shape around each central atom in each molecule, and explain any deviation from ideal bond angles:
(a) $H_3PO_4$ (no H—P bond)    (b) $CH_3$—O—$CH_2CH_3$

**10.44** Determine the shape around each central atom in each molecule, and explain any deviation from ideal bond angles:
(a) $CH_3COOH$                  (b) $H_2O_2$

**10.45** Determine the shape around each central atom in each molecule, and explain any deviation from ideal bond angles:
(a) $H_2SO_3$ (no H—S bond)    (b) $N_2O_3$ ($ONNO_2$)

**10.46** Arrange the following $AF_n$ species in order of *increasing* F—A—F bond angles: $BF_3$, $BeF_2$, $CF_4$, $NF_3$, $OF_2$.

**10.47** Arrange the following $ACl_n$ species in order of *decreasing* Cl—A—Cl bond angles: $SCl_2$, $OCl_2$, $PCl_3$, $SiCl_4$, $SiCl_6^{2-}$.

**10.48** State an ideal value for each of the bond angles in each molecule, and note where you expect deviations:

(a)          (b)          (c)

(a)
H
|
H—C=N—Ö—H

(b)
H   H
|   |
H—C—Ö—C—H
|   |
H   H

(c)
H
|
:O:
|
H—Ö—B—Ö—H

**10.49** State an ideal value for each of the bond angles in each molecule, and note where you expect deviations:

(a)          (b)          (c)

(a)
Ö=N—Ö—H
|
:O:

(b)
H
|
H—C—C=Ö
|
H   H

(c)
:O:
||
H—C—Ö—H

**Problems in Context**

**10.50** Because both tin and carbon are members of Group 4A(14), they form structurally similar compounds. However, tin exhibits a greater variety of structures because it forms several ionic species. Predict the shapes and ideal bond angles, including any deviations, for the following:
(a) $Sn(CH_3)_2$    (b) $SnCl_3^-$    (c) $Sn(CH_3)_4$
(d) $SnF_5^-$    (e) $SnF_6^{2-}$

**10.51** In the gas phase, phosphorus pentachloride exists as separate molecules. In the solid phase, however, the compound is composed of alternating $PCl_4^+$ and $PCl_6^-$ ions. What change(s) in molecular shape occur(s) as $PCl_5$ solidifies? How does the Cl—P—Cl angle change?

## Molecular Shape and Molecular Polarity
(Sample Problem 10.9)

**Concept Review Questions**

**10.52** For molecules of general formula $AX_n$ (where $n > 2$), how do you determine if a molecule is polar?

**10.53** How can a molecule with polar covalent bonds not be polar? Give an example.

**10.54** Explain in general why the shape of a biomolecule is important to its function.

**Skill-Building Exercises** (grouped in similar pairs)

**10.55** Consider the molecules $SCl_2$, $F_2$, $CS_2$, $CF_4$, and $BrCl$.
(a) Which has bonds that are the most polar?
(b) Which molecules have a dipole moment?

**10.56** Consider the molecules $BF_3$, $PF_3$, $BrF_3$, $SF_4$, and $SF_6$.
(a) Which has bonds that are the most polar?
(b) Which molecules have a dipole moment?

**10.57** Which molecule in each pair has the greater dipole moment? Give the reason for your choice.
(a) $SO_2$ or $SO_3$    (b) ICl or IF
(c) $SiF_4$ or $SF_4$    (d) $H_2O$ or $H_2S$

**10.58** Which molecule in each pair has the greater dipole moment? Give the reason for your choice.
(a) $ClO_2$ or $SO_2$    (b) HBr or HCl
(c) $BeCl_2$ or $SCl_2$    (d) $AsF_3$ or $AsF_5$

**Problems in Context**

**10.59** There are three different dichloroethylenes (molecular formula $C_2H_2Cl_2$), which we can designate X, Y, and Z. Compound X has no dipole moment, but compound Z does. Compounds X and Z each combine with hydrogen to give the same product:

$$C_2H_2Cl_2 \,(X \text{ or } Z) + H_2 \longrightarrow ClCH_2\text{—}CH_2Cl$$

What are the structures of X, Y, and Z? Would you expect compound Y to have a dipole moment?

**10.60** Dinitrogen difluoride, $N_2F_2$, is the only stable, simple inorganic molecule with an N=N bond. The compound occurs in *cis* and *trans* forms.
(a) Draw the molecular shapes of the two forms of $N_2F_2$.
(b) Predict the direction of the polarity, if any, of each form.

## Comprehensive Problems

**10.61** In addition to ammonia, nitrogen forms three other hydrides: hydrazine ($N_2H_4$), diazene ($N_2H_2$), and tetrazene ($N_4H_4$).

**(a)** Use Lewis structures to compare the strength, length, and order of the nitrogen-nitrogen bonds in hydrazine, diazene, and $N_2$.
**(b)** Tetrazene (atom sequence $H_2NNNNH_2$) decomposes above 0°C to hydrazine and nitrogen gas. Draw a Lewis structure for tetrazene, and calculate $\Delta H°_{rxn}$ for this decomposition.

**10.62** Draw a Lewis structure for each species: **(a)** $PF_5$; **(b)** $CCl_4$; **(c)** $H_3O^+$; **(d)** $ICl_3$; **(e)** $BeH_2$; **(f)** $PH_2^-$; **(g)** $GeBr_4$; **(h)** $CH_3^-$; **(i)** $BCl_3$; **(j)** $BrF_4^+$; **(k)** $XeO_3$; **(l)** $TeF_4$.

**10.63** Give the molecular shape of each species in Problem 10.62.

**10.64** Consider the following reaction of silicon tetrafluoride:

$$SiF_4 + F^- \longrightarrow SiF_5^-$$

**(a)** Which depiction below best illustrates the change in molecular shape around Si? **(b)** Give the name and $AX_mE_n$ designation of each shape in the depiction chosen in part (a).

**10.65** Both aluminum and iodine form chlorides, $Al_2Cl_6$ and $I_2Cl_6$, with "bridging" Cl atoms. The Lewis structures are

**(a)** What is the formal charge on each atom? **(b)** Which of these molecules has a planar shape? Explain.

**10.66** The VSEPR model was developed before any xenon compounds had been prepared. Thus, these compounds provided an excellent test of the model's predictive power. What would you have predicted for the shapes of $XeF_2$, $XeF_4$, and $XeF_6$?

**10.67** When $SO_3$ gains two electrons, $SO_3^{2-}$ forms. **(a)** Which depiction shown below best illustrates the change in molecular shape around S? **(b)** Does molecular polarity change during this reaction?

**10.68** The actual bond angle in $NO_2$ is 134.3°, and in $NO_2^-$ it is 115.4°, although the ideal bond angle is 120° in both. Explain.

**10.69** "Inert" xenon actually forms several compounds, especially with the highly electronegative elements oxygen and fluorine. The simple fluorides $XeF_2$, $XeF_4$, and $XeF_6$ are all formed by direct reaction of the elements. As you might expect from the size of the xenon atom, the Xe—F bond is not a strong one. Calculate the Xe—F bond energy in $XeF_6$, given that the enthalpy of formation is −402 kJ/mol.

**10.70** Propylene oxide is used to make many products, including plastics such as polyurethane. One method for synthesizing it involves oxidizing propene with hydrogen peroxide:

$$CH_3 — CH = CH_2 + H_2O_2 \longrightarrow CH_3 — CH — CH_2 + H_2O$$

**(a)** What is the molecular shape and ideal bond angle around each carbon atom in propylene oxide?
**(b)** Predict any deviation from the ideal for the actual C—C—C bond angles (assume the three atoms in the ring form an equilateral triangle).

**10.71** Chloral, $Cl_3C—CH=O$, reacts with water to form the sedative and hypnotic agent chloral hydrate, $Cl_3C—CH(OH)_2$. Draw Lewis structures for these substances, and describe the change in molecular shape, if any, that occurs around each of the carbon atoms during the reaction.

**10.72** Like several other bonds, carbon-oxygen bonds have lengths and strengths that depend on the bond order. Draw Lewis structures for the following species, and arrange them in order of increasing carbon-oxygen bond length and then by increasing carbon-oxygen bond strength: **(a)** CO; **(b)** $CO_3^{2-}$; **(c)** $H_2CO$; **(d)** $CH_4O$; **(e)** $HCO_3^-$ (H attached to O).

**10.73** In the 1980s, there was an international agreement to destroy all stockpiles of mustard gas, $ClCH_2CH_2SCH_2CH_2Cl$. When this substance contacts the moisture in eyes, nasal passages, and skin, the —OH groups of water replace the Cl atoms and create high local concentrations of hydrochloric acid, which cause severe blistering and tissue destruction. Write a balanced equation for this reaction, and calculate $\Delta H°_{rxn}$.

**10.74** The four bonds of carbon tetrachloride ($CCl_4$) are polar, but the molecule is nonpolar because the bond polarity is canceled by the symmetric tetrahedral shape. When other atoms substitute for some of the Cl atoms, the symmetry is broken and the molecule becomes polar. Use Figure 9.21 (p. 349) to rank the following molecules from the least polar to the most polar: $CH_2Br_2$, $CF_2Cl_2$, $CH_2F_2$, $CH_2Cl_2$, $CBr_4$, $CF_2Br_2$.

**10.75** Ethanol ($CH_3CH_2OH$) is being used as a gasoline additive or alternative in many parts of the world.
**(a)** Use bond energies to find $\Delta H°_{rxn}$ for the combustion of gaseous ethanol. (Assume $H_2O$ forms as a gas.)
**(b)** In its standard state at 25°C, ethanol is a liquid. Its vaporization requires 40.5 kJ/mol. Correct the value from part (a) to find the enthalpy of reaction for the combustion of liquid ethanol.
**(c)** How does the value from part (b) compare with the value you calculate from standard enthalpies of formation (Appendix B)?
**(d)** "Greener" methods produce ethanol from corn and other plant material, but the main industrial method involves hydrating ethylene from petroleum. Use Lewis structures and bond energies to calculate $\Delta H°_{rxn}$ for the formation of gaseous ethanol from ethylene gas with water vapor.

**10.76** In the following compounds, the C atoms form a single ring. Draw a Lewis structure for each compound, identify cases for which resonance exists, and determine the carbon-carbon bond order(s): **(a)** $C_3H_4$; **(b)** $C_3H_6$; **(c)** $C_4H_6$; **(d)** $C_4H_4$; **(e)** $C_6H_6$.

**10.77** An experiment requires 50.0 mL of 0.040 M NaOH for the titration of 1.00 mmol of acid. Mass analysis of the acid shows 2.24% hydrogen, 26.7% carbon, and 71.1% oxygen. Draw the Lewis structure of the acid.

**10.78** A gaseous compound has a composition by mass of 24.8% carbon, 2.08% hydrogen, and 73.1% chlorine. At STP, the gas has a density of 4.3 g/L. Draw a Lewis structure that fits these facts. Would another structure be equally satisfactory? Explain.

**10.79** Perchlorates are powerful oxidizing agents used in fireworks, flares, and the booster rockets of space shuttles. Lewis structures for the perchlorate ion ($ClO_4^-$) can be drawn with all single bonds or with one, two, or three double bonds. Draw each of these possible resonance forms, use formal charges to determine the most important, and calculate its average bond order.

**10.80** Methane burns in oxygen to form carbon dioxide and water vapor. Hydrogen sulfide burns in oxygen to form sulfur dioxide and water vapor. Use bond energies (Table 9.2, p. 340) to determine the enthalpy of each reaction per mole of $O_2$ (assume Lewis structures with zero formal charges; BE of S=O is 552 kJ/mol).

**10.81** Use Lewis structures to determine which *two* of the following are unstable: (a) $SF_2$; (b) $SF_3$; (c) $SF_4$; (d) $SF_5$; (e) $SF_6$.

**10.82** A major short-lived, neutral species in flames is OH. (a) What is unusual about the electronic structure of OH? (b) Use the standard enthalpy of formation of OH(g) (39.0 kJ/mol) and bond energies to calculate the O—H bond energy in OH(g). (c) From the average value for the O—H bond energy in Table 9.2 (p. 340) and your value for the O—H bond energy in OH(g), find the energy needed to break the first O—H bond in water.

**10.83** Pure $HN_3$ (atom sequence HNNN) is explosive. In aqueous solution, it is a weak acid that yields the azide ion, $N_3^-$. Draw resonance structures to explain why the nitrogen-nitrogen bond lengths are equal in $N_3^-$ but unequal in $HN_3$.

**10.84** Except for nitrogen, the elements of Group 5A(15) all form pentafluorides, and most form pentachlorides. The chlorine atoms of $PCl_5$ can be replaced with fluorine atoms one at a time to give, successively, $PCl_4F$, $PCl_3F_2$, ... , $PF_5$. (a) Given the sizes of F and Cl, would you expect the first two F substitutions to be at axial or equatorial positions? Explain. (b) Which of the five fluorine-containing molecules have no dipole moment?

**10.85** Dinitrogen monoxide ($N_2O$) supports combustion in a manner similar to oxygen, with the nitrogen atoms forming $N_2$. Draw three resonance structures for $N_2O$ (one N is central), and use formal charges to decide the relative importance of each. What correlation can you suggest between the most important structure and the observation that $N_2O$ supports combustion?

**10.86** Oxalic acid ($H_2C_2O_4$) is found in toxic concentrations in rhubarb leaves. The acid forms two ions, $HC_2O_4^-$ and $C_2O_4^{2-}$, by the sequential loss of $H^+$ ions. Draw Lewis structures for the three species, and comment on the relative lengths and strengths of their carbon-oxygen bonds. The connections among the atoms are shown below with single bonds only.

$$H-O \qquad O-H$$
$$C-C$$
$$O \qquad O$$

**10.87** The Murchison meteorite that landed in Australia in 1969 contained 92 different amino acids, including 21 found in Earth organisms. A skeleton structure (single bonds only) of one of these extraterrestrial amino acids is shown below.

$$H_3N-CH-C-O$$
$$| \qquad |$$
$$CH_2 \quad O$$
$$|$$
$$CH_3$$

Draw a Lewis structure, and identify any atoms having a nonzero formal charge.

**10.88** Hydrazine ($N_2H_4$) is used as a rocket fuel because it reacts very exothermically with oxygen to form nitrogen gas and water vapor. The heat released and the increase in number of moles of gas provide thrust. Calculate the enthalpy of reaction.

**10.89** A student isolates a product with the molecular shape shown at right (F is orange). (a) If the species is a neutral compound, can the black sphere represent selenium (Se)? (b) If the species is an anion, can the black sphere represent N? (c) If the black sphere represents Br, what is the charge of the species?

**10.90** When gaseous sulfur trioxide is dissolved in concentrated sulfuric acid, disulfuric acid forms:

$$SO_3(g) + H_2SO_4(l) \longrightarrow H_2S_2O_7(l)$$

Use bond energies (Table 9.2, p. 340) to determine $\Delta H°_{rxn}$. (The S atoms in $H_2S_2O_7$ are bonded through an O atom. Assume Lewis structures with zero formal charges; BE of S=O is 552 kJ/mol.)

**10.91** A molecule of formula $AY_3$ is found experimentally to be polar. Which molecular shapes are possible and which are impossible for $AY_3$?

**10.92** Consider the following molecular shapes:

**A**    **B**    **C**

(a) Match each shape with one of the following species: $XeF_3^+$, $SbBr_3$, $GaCl_3$.
(b) Which, if any, is polar?
(c) Which has the most valence electrons around the central atom?

**10.93** Hydrogen cyanide can be catalytically reduced with hydrogen to form methylamine. Use Lewis structures and bond energies to determine $\Delta H°_{rxn}$ for

$$HCN(g) + 2H_2(g) \longrightarrow CH_3NH_2(g)$$

**10.94** Ethylene, $C_2H_4$, and tetrafluoroethylene, $C_2F_4$, are used to make the polymers polyethylene and polytetrafluoroethylene (Teflon), respectively.
(a) Draw the Lewis structures for $C_2H_4$ and $C_2F_4$, and give the ideal H—C—H and F—C—F bond angles.
(b) The actual H—C—H and F—C—F bond angles are 117.4° and 112.4°, respectively. Explain these deviations.

**10.95** Using bond lengths in Table 9.2 (p. 340) and assuming ideal geometry, calculate each of the following distances:
(a) Between H atoms in $C_2H_2$
(b) Between F atoms in $SF_6$ (two answers)
(c) Between equatorial F atoms in $PF_5$

**10.96** Phosphorus pentachloride, a key industrial compound with annual world production of about $2 \times 10^7$ kg, is used to make other compounds. It reacts with sulfur dioxide to produce phosphorus oxychloride ($POCl_3$) and thionyl chloride ($SOCl_2$). Draw a Lewis structure, and name the molecular shape of each product.

# Theories of Covalent Bonding

## Concepts and skills to review before you study this chapter

- atomic orbital shapes (Section 7.4)
- exclusion principle (Section 8.1)
- Hund's rule (Section 8.2)
- Lewis structures (Section 10.1)

- resonance in covalent bonding (Section 10.1)
- molecular shapes (Section 10.2)
- molecular polarity (Section 10.3)

All scientific models have limitations because they are simplifications of reality. The VSEPR theory, covered in Chapter 10, accounts for molecular shapes, but it doesn't explain how they arise from interactions of atomic orbitals. After all, the orbitals described in Chapter 7 aren't oriented toward the corners of, say, an octahedron, like the ones shown at left for the sulfur in $SF_6$. Moreover, knowing the shape doesn't help us explain the magnetic and spectral properties of molecules; only an understanding of their orbitals and energy levels can.

The two theories presented in this chapter focus on different questions and complement each other. Don't be concerned if we need several models to explain a complex phenomenon like bonding. In every science, one model may account for some aspect of a topic better than another, and several are employed to explain a wider range of phenomena.

**IN THIS CHAPTER . . .** We introduce two theories of bonding in molecules based on the interactions of the orbitals of their atoms.
- We discuss valence bond (VB) theory, which rationalizes molecular shapes through interactions of atomic orbitals during bonding to form hybrid orbitals.
- We apply VB theory to sigma and pi bonds, the two types of covalent bonds.
- We see why parts of molecules don't rotate freely around multiple bonds, which has major effects on reactivity, physical properties, and biological behavior.
- We discuss molecular orbital (MO) theory, which explains molecular energy levels and properties through formation of orbitals that spread over the whole molecule.
- We apply MO theory to understand key properties of some diatomic and simple polyatomic molecules.

# 11.1 • VALENCE BOND (VB) THEORY AND ORBITAL HYBRIDIZATION

What *is* a covalent bond, and what characteristic gives it strength? And how can we explain *molecular* shapes based on the interactions of *atomic* orbitals? The most useful approach for answering these questions is based on quantum mechanics (Chapter 7) and called **valence bond (VB) theory.**

## The Central Themes of VB Theory

The basic principle of VB theory is that *a covalent bond forms when orbitals of two atoms overlap and a pair of electrons occupy the overlap region.* In the terminology of quantum mechanics, overlap of the two orbitals means their wave functions are *in phase* (constructive interference), so the amplitude between the nuclei increases (see Figure 7.5, p. 265). The central themes of VB theory derive from this principle:

1. *Opposing spins of the electron pair.* As the exclusion principle (Section 8.1) prescribes, the space formed by the overlapping orbitals *has a maximum capacity for two electrons that have opposite (paired) spins.* In the simplest case, a molecule of $H_2$ forms when the 1s orbitals of two H atoms overlap, and the electrons, with their spins paired, spend more time in the overlap region (up and down arrows in Figure 11.1).

**Figure 11.1** Orbital overlap and spin pairing in $H_2$.

**A Hydrogen fluoride, HF**

**B Fluorine, F₂**

**Figure 11.2** Orbital orientation and maximum overlap. (The $2p_x$ orbital is shown bonding; the other two 2p orbitals of F are omitted for clarity.)

2. *Maximum overlap of bonding orbitals.* Bond strength depends on the attraction between nuclei and shared electrons, so *the greater the orbital overlap, the stronger the bond.* Extent of overlap depends on orbital shape and direction. An *s* orbital is spherical, so its orientation is the same in any direction, but *p* and *d* orbitals have specified directions. Thus, a *p* or *d* orbital involved in a bond is oriented so as to maximize overlap. In HF, for example, the 1*s* orbital of H overlaps a half-filled 2*p* orbital of F *along its long axis* (Figure 11.2A). In F₂, the two half-filled 2*p* orbitals interact end to end, that is, *along the long axes* of the orbitals (Figure 11.2B).

3. *Hybridization of atomic orbitals.* To account for the bonding in diatomic molecules, we picture direct overlap of *s* and/or *p* orbitals of isolated atoms. But how can we account for the shape of a molecule like methane from the shapes and orientations of C and H atomic orbitals? A C atom ([He] $2s^22p^2$) has two valence electrons in the spherical 2*s* orbital and one each in two of the three mutually perpendicular 2*p* orbitals. If the half-filled *p* orbitals overlap the 1*s* orbitals of two H atoms, *two* C—H bonds would form with a 90° H—C—H bond angle. But methane has the formula CH₄, not CH₂, and its bond angle is 109.5°.

To explain such facts, Linus Pauling proposed that, during bonding, *the valence atomic orbitals in the isolated atoms become **different** when they are in the molecule.* Quantum-mechanical calculations show that if we mathematically "mix" certain combinations of orbitals, we form new ones whose spatial orientations *do* match the observed molecular shapes. The process of orbital mixing is called **hybridization,** and the new atomic orbitals are called **hybrid orbitals.**

4. *Features of hybrid orbitals.* Here are some central points about hybrid orbitals that arise during bonding:

- The *number* of hybrid orbitals formed *equals* the number of atomic orbitals mixed.
- The *type* of hybrid orbitals formed *varies* with the types of atomic orbitals mixed.
- The *shape* and *orientation* of a hybrid orbital *maximizes* overlap with the orbital of the other atom in the bond.

You can think of hybridization as a process in which atomic orbitals mix, hybrid orbitals form, they overlap other orbitals, and electrons enter the overlap region with opposing spins, thus forming stable bonds. In truth, hybridization is a concept to explain the results we calculate that predict the molecular shapes we observe.

## Types of Hybrid Orbitals

We postulate the type of hybrid orbitals in a molecule *after* we observe its shape. Note that the orientations of the five types of hybrid orbitals we discuss next correspond to the five electron-group arrangements in VSEPR theory.

***sp* Hybridization** When two electron groups surround the central atom, we observe a linear shape, which means the bonding orbitals must have a linear orientation.

1. *Orbitals mixed and orbitals formed.* VB theory proposes two *nonequivalent* orbitals of a central atom, one *s* and one *p*, mix and form two *equivalent* **sp hybrid orbitals** that are oriented 180° apart (Figure 11.3A). The shape of these hybrid orbitals, with one large and one small lobe, differs markedly from the shapes of the atomic orbitals. The orbital orientations increase electron density *in the bonding direction.*

2. *Overlap of orbitals from central and surrounding atoms: BeCl₂.* In beryllium chloride, the Be atom is *sp* hybridized. Figure 11.3B depicts the hybridization of Be in an orbital box diagram, and part C shows an orbital box diagram with shaded contours instead of arrows. Bond formation with Cl is shown in part D. The filled 2*s* and one of the three empty 2*p* orbitals of Be mix and form two half-filled *sp* orbitals. Two empty unhybridized 2*p* orbitals of Be lie perpendicular to each other and to the *sp* hybrids. The hybrid orbitals overlap the half-filled 3*p* orbital in each of two Cl atoms. The four electrons—two from Be and one from each Cl—appear as pairs with opposite spins in the two overlap regions. (The 3*p* and *sp* hybrid orbitals that are partially colored on the left become fully colored on the right, after the bonds form and each orbital is filled with two electrons.)

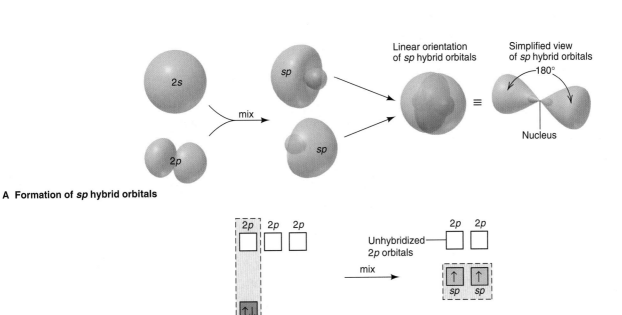

**A Formation of *sp* hybrid orbitals**

**B Orbital box diagram**

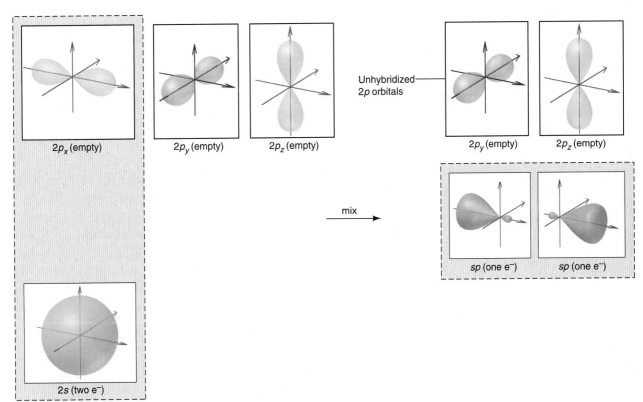

**C Box diagram with orbital contours**

**D Formation of BeCl₂**

**Figure 11.3** Formation and orientation of *sp* hybrid orbitals and the bonding in BeCl₂. **A,** One 2*s* and one 2*p* atomic orbital mix to form two *sp* hybrid orbitals. (The simplified hybrid orbitals at far right are used elsewhere, often even without the small lobe.) **B,** The orbital box diagram for hybridization of Be, drawn vertically. **C,** The orbital box diagram with orbital contours. **D,** Overlap of Be and Cl orbitals to form BeCl₂. (Only the Cl 3*p* orbital involved in bonding is shown.)

**$sp^2$ Hybridization** We use this type of hybridization to rationalize the two shapes possible for the trigonal planar electron-group arrangement.

1. *Orbitals mixed and orbitals formed.* Mixing one *s* and two *p* orbitals gives three **$sp^2$ hybrid orbitals** that point to the corners of an equilateral triangle, their axes 120° apart. (In hybrid orbitals, unlike in electron configurations, superscripts refer to the number of *atomic orbitals* of a given type, *not* the number of *electrons* in the orbital: thus, one *s* and two *p* orbitals give $s^1p^2$, or $sp^2$.) The third 2*p* orbital remains unhybridized.

2. *Overlap of orbitals from central and surrounding atoms: $BF_3$.* The central B atom in $BF_3$ is $sp^2$ hybridized, with the three $sp^2$ orbitals in a trigonal plane and the third 2*p* orbital unhybridized and perpendicular to this plane (Figure 11.4). Each half-filled $sp^2$ orbital overlaps the half-filled 2*p* orbital of an F atom, and the six valence electrons—three from B and one from each of the three F atoms—form three bonding pairs.

**Figure 11.4** The $sp^2$ hybrid orbitals in $BF_3$. **A,** The orbital box diagram shows the formation of three $sp^2$ hybrid orbitals. One 2*p* orbital is unhybridized and empty. **B,** Contour depiction of $BF_3$.

3. *Placement of lone pairs.* To account for other molecular shapes within a given electron-group arrangement, one or more hybrid orbitals contains a lone pair. In ozone ($O_3$), for example, the central O is $sp^2$ hybridized and a lone pair fills one of the three $sp^2$ orbitals.

**$sp^3$ Hybridization** The type of hybridization that accounts for the shape of methane applies to any species with a tetrahedral electron-group arrangement.

1. *Orbitals mixed and orbitals formed.* Mixing one *s* and three *p* orbitals gives four **$sp^3$ hybrid orbitals** that point to the corners of a tetrahedron.

2. *Overlap of orbitals from central and surrounding atoms: $CH_4$.* The C atom in methane is $sp^3$ hybridized. Its four valence electrons half-fill the four $sp^3$ hybrids, which overlap the half-filled 1*s* orbitals of four H atoms to form four C—H bonds (Figure 11.5).

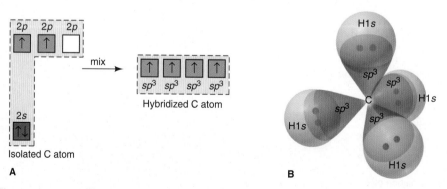

**Figure 11.5** The $sp^3$ hybrid orbitals in $CH_4$. **A,** The orbital box diagram shows formation of four $sp^3$ hybrids. **B,** Contour depiction of $CH_4$, with electron pairs shown as dots.

**Figure 11.6** The $sp^3$ hybrid orbitals in NH$_3$ and H$_2$O. **A,** The orbital box diagrams show $sp^3$ hybridization, with lone pairs filling one (NH$_3$) or two (H$_2$O) hybrid orbitals. **B,** Contour depictions.

3. *Placement of lone pairs.* The trigonal pyramidal shape of NH$_3$ arises when a lone pair fills any one of the four $sp^3$ orbitals of N, and the bent shape of H$_2$O arises when lone pairs fill any two of the $sp^3$ orbitals of O (Figure 11.6).

**$sp^3d$ Hybridization** Molecules with shapes due to the trigonal bipyramidal electron-group arrangement have central atoms from Period 3 or higher. VB theory proposes that $d$ orbitals, as well as $s$ and $p$ orbitals, are mixed to form hybrid orbitals.

1. *Orbitals mixed and orbitals formed.* Mixing one 3$s$, the three 3$p$, and one of the five 3$d$ orbitals gives five **$sp^3d$ hybrid orbitals,** which point to the corners of a trigonal bipyramid.

2. *Overlap of orbitals from central and surrounding atoms: PCl$_5$.* The P atom in PCl$_5$ is $sp^3d$ hybridized. Each hybrid orbital overlaps a 3$p$ orbital of a Cl atom, and ten valence electrons—five from P and one from each of the five Cl atoms—form five P—Cl bonds (Figure 11.7).

3. *Placement of lone pairs.* Seesaw, T-shaped, and linear molecules have lone pairs in, respectively, one, two, or three of the central atom's $sp^3d$ orbitals.

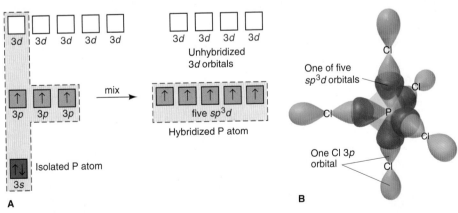

**Figure 11.7** The $sp^3d$ hybrid orbitals in PCl$_5$. **A,** The orbital box diagram shows the formation of five half-filled $sp^3d$ orbitals. Four 3$d$ orbitals are unhybridized and empty. **B,** Contour depiction of PCl$_5$. (For clarity, unhybridized 3$d$ orbitals, the other two Cl 3$p$ orbitals, and the five bonding P—Cl pairs are not shown.)

**Figure 11.8 The $sp^3d^2$ hybrid orbitals in $SF_6$. A,** The orbital box diagram shows formation of six half-filled $sp^3d^2$ orbitals; three $3d$ orbitals remain unhybridized and empty. **B,** Contour depiction of $SF_6$.

$sp^3d^2$ **Hybridization** The VB model proposes that molecules with shapes having the octahedral electron-group arrangement also use $d$ orbitals to form hybrids.

1. *Orbitals mixed and orbitals formed.* Mixing one $3s$, the three $3p$, and two $3d$ orbitals gives six $sp^3d^2$ **hybrid orbitals,** which point to the corners of an octahedron.

2. *Overlap of orbitals from central and surrounding atoms: $SF_6$.* The S atom in $SF_6$ is $sp^3d^2$ hybridized. Each half-filled hybrid orbital overlaps a half-filled $2p$ orbital of an F atom, and 12 valence electrons—six from S and one from each of the six F atoms—form six S—F bonds (Figure 11.8).

3. *Placement of lone pairs.* Square pyramidal and square planar molecules have lone pairs in one and two of the central atom's $sp^3d^2$ orbitals, respectively.

Table 11.1 summarizes the numbers and types of atomic orbitals that mix to form the five types of hybrid orbitals. Figure 11.9 shows three conceptual steps from a molecular formula to the hybrid orbitals in the molecule, and Sample Problem 11.1 focuses on the last step of that process.

| Table **11.1** Composition and Orientation of Hybrid Orbitals | | | | | |
|---|---|---|---|---|---|
| | **Linear** | **Trigonal Planar** | **Tetrahedral** | **Trigonal Bipyramidal** | **Octahedral** |
| **Atomic orbitals mixed** | one $s$<br>one $p$ | one $s$<br>two $p$ | one $s$<br>three $p$ | one $s$<br>three $p$<br>one $d$ | one $s$<br>three $p$<br>two $d$ |
| **Hybrid orbitals formed** | two $p$ | three $sp^2$ | four $sp^3$ | five $sp^3d$ | six $sp^3d^2$ |
| **Unhybridized orbitals remaining** | two $p$ | one $p$ | none | four $d$ | three $d$ |
| **Orientation** | | | | | |

**Figure 11.9** From molecular formula to hybrid orbitals. (See Figures 10.1, p. 364, and 10.10, p. 379.)

**Sample Problem 11.1    Postulating Hybrid Orbitals in a Molecule**

**Problem** Use partial orbital diagrams to describe how mixing the atomic orbitals of the central atom(s) leads to the hybrid orbitals in each of the following:
**(a)** Methanol, $CH_3OH$    **(b)** Sulfur tetrafluoride, $SF_4$

**Plan** Prior to the Solution steps below, we have used the molecular formula to draw the Lewis structure and determined the electron-group arrangement of each central atom. Then, starting from there, we use Table 11.1 to postulate the type of hybrid orbitals. We write the partial orbital diagram for each central atom before and after the orbitals are hybridized.

**Solution (a)** For $CH_3OH$. The electron-group arrangement is tetrahedral around both the C and the O atom, so each mixed one $2s$ and three $2p$ to become $sp^3$ hybridized. The C atom has four half-filled $sp^3$ orbitals:

The O atom has two half-filled $sp^3$ orbitals and two filled with lone pairs:

**(b)** For $SF_4$. The electron-group arrangement is trigonal bipyramidal, so the central S atom is $sp^3d$ hybridized, which means one $3s$, three $3p$, and one $3d$ orbital are mixed. One hybrid orbital is filled with a lone pair, and four are half-filled. Four unhybridized $3d$ orbitals remain empty:

**Follow-Up Problem 11.1** Use partial orbital diagrams to show how the atomic orbitals of the central atom mix to form hybrid orbitals in **(a)** beryllium fluoride, $BeF_2$; **(b)** silicon tetrachloride, $SiCl_4$; **(c)** xenon tetrafluoride, $XeF_4$.

**Limitations to the Concept of Hybridization** We rely on the VSEPR and VB theories to rationalize an observed molecular shape. In some cases, however, the theories may not be consistent with other findings.

   1. *Hybridization does not apply: large nonmetal hydrides.* Consider the Lewis structure and bond angle of $H_2S$:

Based on VSEPR theory, we would predict that, as in $H_2O$, the four electron groups around $H_2S$ point to the corners of a tetrahedron, and the two lone pairs compress the H—S—H bond angle below the ideal 109.5°. Based on VB theory, we would propose that the $3s$ and $3p$ orbitals of the S atom mix and form four $sp^3$ hybrids, two of which are filled with lone pairs, while the other two overlap $1s$ orbitals of two H atoms and are filled with bonding pairs.

But observation does *not* support these arguments. The bond angle of 92° is close to the 90° angle between *unhybridized p* orbitals. Similar angles occur in the hydrides of other large nonmetals of Groups 5A(15) and 6A(16). Why apply a theory if the facts don't warrant it? Real factors—bond length, atomic size, and electrostatic repulsions—influence shape. Larger atoms form longer bonds to H, which decreases repulsions; thus, overlap of *unhybridized* orbitals explains these shapes.

*2. d-Orbital hybridization is less important: rationalizing shapes with expanded valence shells.* Quantum-mechanical calculations show that *d*-orbitals have such high energies that they do not hybridize effectively with the *much* more stable *s* and *p* orbitals of a given *n* value. Thus, for example, some have proposed that $SF_6$ is most stable when the bonding orbitals of the central S use a combination of *sp*-hybrid orbitals and unhybridized $3p$-orbitals instead of $sp^3d^2$ hybrid orbitals. Others prefer explanations that involve molecular orbitals or even ionic structures. These topics are beyond the scope of this text, and while they are being actively debated, we will continue to use the traditional, though limited, approach of including *d*-orbital hybridization for molecules with expanded valence shells.

## Summary of Section 11.1

- VB theory explains that a covalent bond forms when two atomic orbitals overlap and two electrons with paired (opposite) spins spend more time in the overlapped regions.
- To explain molecular shape, the theory proposes that, during bonding, atomic orbitals mix to form hybrid orbitals with a different shape and direction. This process gives rise to greater overlap and, thus, stronger bonds.
- Based on the observed molecular shape (and the related electron-group arrangement), we postulate the type of hybrid orbital that accounts for the shape. In many cases, especially molecules with larger central atoms, the concept of hybridization has major limitations.

## 11.2 • MODES OF ORBITAL OVERLAP AND THE TYPES OF COVALENT BONDS

Orbitals can overlap by two *modes*—end to end or side to side—which gives rise to two types of covalent bonds—*sigma* and *pi*. We'll use VB theory to describe the two types here and, as you'll see, they are described by molecular orbital theory as well.

### Orbital Overlap in Single and Multiple Bonds

Ethane ($C_2H_6$), ethylene ($C_2H_4$), and acetylene ($C_2H_2$) have different shapes. Ethane is tetrahedral at both carbons with bond angles near the ideal 109.5°. Ethylene is trigonal planar at both carbons with bond angles near the ideal 120°. Acetylene is linear with bond angles of 180°:

ethane                    ethylene                    acetylene

In these molecules, two modes of orbital overlap result in two types of bonds.

### End-to-End Overlap and Sigma (σ) Bonding

Both C atoms of ethane are $sp^3$ hybridized (Figure 11.10). The C—C bond arises from overlap of the end of one $sp^3$ orbital with the end of the other. *End-to-end* overlap forms a **sigma (σ) bond,** which has its *highest electron density along the bond axis* and is shaped like an ellipse rotated

**Figure 11.10** The σ bonds in ethane ($C_2H_6$). **A,** Depiction using atomic contours. **B,** An electron density model shows very slightly positive (*blue*) and negative (*red*) regions. **C,** Wedge-bond perspective drawing.

about its long axis (like a football). *All single bonds are σ bonds*, including the six C—H bonds in ethane.

**Side-to-Side Overlap and Pi (π) Bonding** For this type of bonding, we'll examine ethylene and acetylene:

1. *In ethylene*, each C atom is $sp^2$ hybridized. The four valence electrons of C half-fill the three $sp^2$ orbitals *and* the unhybridized 2*p* orbital, which lies perpendicular to the $sp^2$ plane (Figure 11.11). Two $sp^2$ orbitals of each C form C—H σ bonds. The third $sp^2$ orbital forms a σ bond with the other C. With the σ-bonded C atoms near each other, their half-filled 2*p* orbitals overlap *side to side*, which forms a **pi (π) bond.** It has *two regions (lobes) of electron density*, one above and one below the σ-bond axis. *The two electrons in one π bond occupy both lobes. A double bond consists of one σ bond and one π bond*, which increases electron density between the nuclei (Figure 11.11D). The two electron pairs act as one electron group because each pair occupies a different orbital, which reduces repulsions.

**Figure 11.11** The σ and π bonds in ethylene ($C_2H_4$). **A,** The C—C σ bond and the four C—H σ bonds are shown with the unhybridized 2*p* orbitals. **B,** An accurate depiction of the 2*p* orbitals shows the side-to-side overlap; σ bonds are shown in ball-and-stick form. **C,** Two overlapping regions comprise *one* π bond, which is occupied by two electrons. **D,** With four electrons (one σ bond and one π bond) between the C atoms, electron density (*red*) is higher. **E,** Wedge-bond perspective drawing.

Two lobes of one π bond

2. *In acetylene*, each C atom is *sp* hybridized, and its four valence electrons half-fill the two *sp* hybrids *and* the two unhybridized 2*p* orbitals (Figure 11.12). Each C forms a C—H σ bond with one *sp* orbital and a C—C σ bond with the other. Side-to-side overlap of one pair of 2*p* orbitals gives one π bond, with electron density above and below the σ bond. Side-to-side overlap of the other pair of 2*p* orbitals gives another π bond, 90° away from the first, with electron density in front and back of the σ bond. The result is a *cylindrically symmetrical* H—C≡C—H molecule. Note the greater electron density between the C atoms created by the six bonding electrons. Any triple bond *consists of one σ and two π bonds*.

Two lobes of one π bond

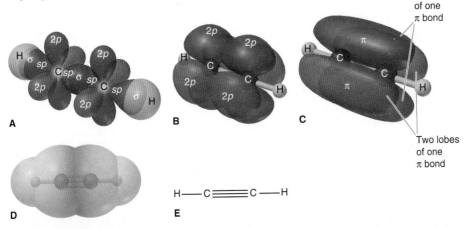

Two lobes of one π bond

**Figure 11.12** The σ bonds and π bonds in acetylene ($C_2H_2$). **A,** A contour depiction shows the C—C σ bond, the two C—H σ bonds, and two unhybridized 2*p* orbitals (one pair is in *red* for clarity). **B,** The 2*p* orbitals (accurate form) overlap side to side; σ bonds are shown by a ball-and-stick model. **C,** Overlapping regions of two π bonds, one black and the other red. **D,** The molecule has cylindrical symmetry. Six electrons (one σ bond and two π bonds) create even higher electron density (*red*) between the C atoms. **E,** Bond-line drawing.

**Mode of Overlap, Bond Strength, and Bond Order** Because orbitals overlap less side to side than end to end, a π bond is weaker than a σ bond; thus, for carbon-carbon bonds, a double bond is less than twice as strong as a single bond (Table 9.2, p. 340). Figure 11.13 shows electron density relief maps of the three types of carbon-carbon bonds; note the increasing electron density between the nuclei from single to double to triple bond.

**Figure 11.13** Electron density and bond order in ethane, ethylene, and acetylene.

Lone-pair repulsions, bond polarities, and other factors affect overlap between other pairs of atoms. Nevertheless, as a rough approximation, in terms of bond order (BO), a double bond (BO = 2) is about twice as strong as a single bond (BO = 1), and a triple bond (BO = 3) is about three times as strong.

---

**Sample Problem 11.2** | **Describing the Types of Bonds in Molecules**

**Problem** Describe the types of bonds and orbitals in acetone, $(CH_3)_2CO$.

**Plan** We use the shape around each central atom to postulate the hybrid orbitals used and use unhybridized orbitals to form the C=O bond.

**Solution** The shapes are tetrahedral around each C of the two $CH_3$ (methyl) groups and trigonal planar around the middle C (see Sample Problem 10.8, p. 382). Thus, the middle C has three $sp^2$ orbitals and one unhybridized $p$ orbital. Each of the two methyl C atoms has four $sp^3$ orbitals. Three of these form σ bonds with the $1s$ orbitals of H atoms; the fourth forms a σ bond with an $sp^2$ orbital of the middle C. Thus, two of the three $sp^2$ orbitals of the middle C form σ bonds to the other two C atoms.

The O atom is also $sp^2$ hybridized and has an unhybridized $p$ orbital that can form a π bond. Two of the O atom's $sp^2$ orbitals hold lone pairs, and the third forms a σ bond with the third $sp^2$ orbital of the middle C atom. The unhybridized, half-filled $2p$ orbitals of C and O form a π bond. The σ and π bonds constitute the C=O bond:

**Comment** Why would the O atom in acetone be hybridized? After all, it could use two perpendicular $p$ orbitals for the σ and π bonds with C and leave the other $p$ and the $s$ orbital to hold the two lone pairs. Instead, having each lone pair in an $sp^2$ orbital oriented away from the C=O bond lowers electron-electron repulsions.

**Follow-Up Problem 11.2** Describe the types of bonds and orbitals in **(a)** hydrogen cyanide, HCN, and **(b)** carbon dioxide, $CO_2$.

## Orbital Overlap and Molecular Rotation

The type of overlap—end-to-end or side-to-side—affects rotation around the bond:

- *Sigma bond.* A σ *bond allows free rotation* because the extent of overlap is not affected. If you could hold one $CH_3$ group of ethane, the other $CH_3$ could spin without affecting the overlap of the C—C σ bond (see Figure 11.10).
- *Pi bond.* A π *bond restricts rotation* because *p* orbitals must be parallel to each other to overlap most effectively. Holding one $CH_2$ group in ethylene and trying to spin the other decreases the side-to-side overlap and breaks the π bond. For this reason, distinct *cis* and *trans* structures exist for compounds such as 1,2-dichloroethylene (Section 10.3). As Figure 11.14 shows, the π bond allows two *different* arrangements of atoms around the C atoms, which has a major effect on molecular polarity (see p. 385). Rotation around a triple bond is not meaningful: each triple-bonded C atom is bonded to one other group in a linear arrangement, so there can be no difference in the relative positions of attached groups.

*cis*-1,2-Dichloroethylene

*trans*-1,2-Dichloroethylene

**Figure 11.14** Restricted rotation around a π bond. *Cis-* and *trans*-1,2-dichloroethylene are different molecules because the π bond restricts rotation.

## ▋ Summary of Section 11.2

- End-to-end overlap of atomic orbitals forms a σ bond, which allows free rotation of the bonded parts of the molecule.
- Side-to-side overlap forms a π bond, which restricts rotation.
- A multiple bond consists of a σ bond and either one π bond (double bond) or two (triple bond). Multiple bonds have greater electron density between the nuclei than single bonds do and, thus, higher bond energies.

# 11.3 • MOLECULAR ORBITAL (MO) THEORY AND ELECTRON DELOCALIZATION

Scientists choose the model that best answers a question: VSEPR for one about molecular shape and VB theory for one about orbital overlap. But neither adequately explains magnetic and spectral properties, and both understate the importance of electron delocalization. To deal with phenomena like these, which involve molecular energy levels, chemists choose **molecular orbital (MO) theory.** The MO model is a quantum-mechanical treatment for molecules similar to the one for atoms (Chapter 8): just as an atom has atomic orbitals (AOs) of given energies and shapes that are occupied by the atom's electrons, a molecule has **molecular orbitals (MOs)** of given energies and shapes that are occupied by the molecule's electrons.

There is a key distinction between VB and MO theories:

- VB theory pictures a molecule as a group of atoms bonded through *localized* overlapping of valence-shell atomic and/or hybrid orbitals occupied by electrons.
- MO theory pictures a molecule as a collection of nuclei with orbitals *delocalized* over the whole molecule and occupied by electrons.

Despite its usefulness, MO theory has a drawback in that MOs are more difficult to visualize than the shapes of VSEPR theory or the hybrid orbitals of VB theory.

## The Central Themes of MO Theory

Several key ideas of MO theory appear in its description of $H_2$ and other simple species: how MOs form, what their energies and shapes are, and how they fill with electrons.

**Formation of Molecular Orbitals** Just as we need approximations to solve the Schrödinger equation for any atom with more than one electron, we need an approximation to determine the MOs of even the simplest molecule, $H_2$. The approximation is

**A Amplitudes of wave functions added**

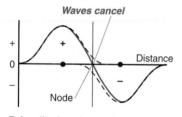

**B Amplitudes of wave functions subtracted**

**Figure 11.15** An analogy between light waves and atomic wave functions.

to mathematically *combine* (add or subtract) AOs (atomic wave functions) of nearby atoms to form MOs (molecular wave functions). Thus, when two H nuclei lie near each other, their AOs overlap and combine in two ways:

- *Adding the wave functions together.* This combination forms a **bonding MO,** which has *a region of high electron density between the nuclei.* Additive overlap is analogous to light waves reinforcing each other, which makes the amplitude higher and the light brighter. For electron waves, the overlap *increases* the probability that the electrons are between the nuclei (Figure 11.15A).
- *Subtracting the wave functions from each other.* This combination forms an **antibonding MO,** which has *a node, a region of zero electron density, between the nuclei* (Figure 11.15B). Subtractive overlap is analogous to light waves canceling each other, causing the light to disappear. With electron waves, the probability that the electrons lie between the nuclei *decreases* to zero.

The two possible combinations for hydrogen atoms $H_A$ and $H_B$ are

AO of $H_A$ + AO of $H_B$ = bonding MO of $H_2$ (more $e^-$ density between nuclei)

AO of $H_A$ − AO of $H_B$ = antibonding MO of $H_2$ (less $e^-$ density between nuclei)

Notice that *the number of AOs combined always equals the number of MOs formed:* two H atomic orbitals combine to form two $H_2$ molecular orbitals.

**Shape and Energy of $H_2$ Molecular Orbitals** Bonding and antibonding MOs have different shapes and energies. Figure 11.16 shows these orbitals for $H_2$:

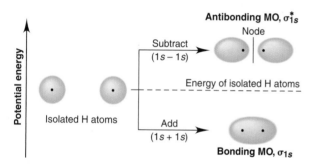

**Figure 11.16** Contours and energies of $H_2$ bonding and antibonding MOs.

- *Bonding MO.* A bonding MO is *lower in energy* than the AOs that form it. Because it is spread mostly *between* the nuclei, nuclear repulsions decrease while nucleus-electron attractions increase. Moreover, two electrons in this MO can delocalize their charges over a larger volume than in nearby, separate AOs, which lowers electron repulsions. Because of these electrostatic effects, when electrons occupy this orbital, the $H_2$ molecule is *more stable* than the separate H atoms.
- *Antibonding MO.* An antibonding MO is *higher in energy* than the AOs that form it. With most of its electron density *outside* the internuclear region, it has a node between the nuclei, and nuclear repulsions increase. Therefore, when electrons occupy this orbital, the $H_2$ molecule is *less stable* than the separate H atoms.

Both the bonding and antibonding MOs of $H_2$ are **sigma ($\sigma$) MOs** because they are cylindrically symmetrical about an imaginary line between the nuclei. The bonding MO is denoted by $\sigma_{1s}$; that is, a $\sigma$ MO derived from $1s$ AOs. Antibonding orbitals are denoted with a superscript star: the antibonding MO derived from $1s$ AOs is $\sigma_{1s}^*$ (spoken "sigma, one ess, star").

For AOs to interact enough to form MOs, they must be similar in *energy* and *orientation.* The $1s$ orbitals of two H atoms have identical energy and orientation, so they interact strongly. We'll revisit this requirement for molecules composed of many-electron atoms.

**Electrons in Molecular Orbitals** Several aspects of MO theory—filling of MOs, energy-level diagrams, electron configuration, and bond order—relate to earlier ideas:

1. *Filling MOs with electrons.* Electrons enter MOs just as they do AOs:
- MOs are filled in order of increasing energy (aufbau principle).
- An MO can hold a maximum of two electrons with opposite spins (exclusion principle).
- Orbitals of equal energy are half-filled, with spins parallel, before any of them are filled (Hund's rule).

2. *MO energy-level diagrams.* A **molecular orbital (MO) diagram** shows the relative energy and number of electrons in each MO, as well as the AOs from which they formed. In the MO diagram for $H_2$ (Figure 11.17), two electrons, one from the AO of each H, fill the $H_2$ bonding MO, while the antibonding MO remains empty.

$H_2$ bond order = $\frac{1}{2}(2 - 0) = 1$

**Figure 11.17** MO diagram for $H_2$.
The vertical placement of the boxes indicates relative energies. Orbital occupancy is shown with arrows and color (dark = full, pale = half-filled, none = empty).

3. *Electron configuration.* Just as we write an electron configuration for an atom, we can write one for a molecule. The symbol of each occupied MO is written in parentheses, with the number of electrons in it as a superscript outside: the electron configuration of $H_2$ is $(\sigma_{1s})^2$.

4. *Bond order.* In a Lewis structure, bond order is the number of electron pairs per atom-to-atom linkage. The **MO bond order** is the number of electrons in bonding MOs minus the number in antibonding MOs, divided by two:

$$\text{Bond order} = \tfrac{1}{2}[(\text{no. of } e^- \text{ in bonding MO}) - (\text{no. of } e^- \text{ in antibonding MO})] \qquad \textbf{(11.1)}$$

Here are three key points about MO bond order:

- Bond order > 0: the molecule is more stable than the separate atoms, so it *will* form. For $H_2$, the bond order is $\tfrac{1}{2}(2 - 0) = 1$.
- Bond order = 0: the molecule is as stable as the separate atoms, so it will *not* form (occurs when equal numbers of electrons occupy bonding and antibonding MOs).
- In general, the *higher* the bond order, the *stronger* the bond is.

**Do He$_2^+$ and He$_2$ Exist?** One of the early triumphs of MO theory was its ability to *predict* the existence of $He_2^+$, the helium molecule-ion, which consists of two He nuclei and three electrons. Let's use MO diagrams to see why $He_2^+$ exists but $He_2$ doesn't:

- In $He_2^+$, the $1s$ AOs form MOs (Figure 11.18A). The three electrons are distributed as a pair in the $\sigma_{1s}$ MO and a lone electron in the $\sigma_{1s}^*$ MO. The bond order is $\tfrac{1}{2}(2 - 1) = \tfrac{1}{2}$. Thus, $He_2^+$ has a relatively weak bond, but it should exist. Indeed, this species has been observed frequently when He atoms collide with $He^+$ ions. Its electron configuration is $(\sigma_{1s})^2(\sigma_{1s}^*)^1$.
- In $He_2$, with four electrons in the $\sigma_{1s}$ and $\sigma_{1s}^*$ MOs, both the bonding and antibonding orbitals are filled (Figure 11.18B). Stabilization from the electron pair in the bonding MO is canceled by destabilization from the electron pair in the antibonding MO. With a zero bond order $[\tfrac{1}{2}(2 - 2) = 0]$, we predict, and experiment has so far confirmed, that a covalent $He_2$ molecule does not exist.

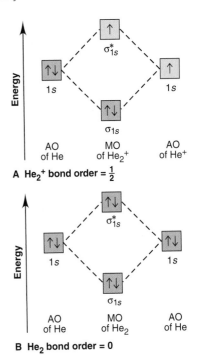

**A He$_2^+$ bond order = $\tfrac{1}{2}$**

**B He$_2$ bond order = 0**

**Figure 11.18** MO diagrams for $He_2^+$ and $He_2$.

---

**Sample Problem 11.3    Predicting Stability of Species Using MO Diagrams**

**Problem** Use MO diagrams to find bond orders and predict whether $H_2^+$ and $H_2^-$ exist. If either exists, write its electron configuration.

**Plan** Since the $1s$ AOs form the MOs, the MO diagrams are similar to the one for $H_2$. We find the number of electrons in each species and distribute them one at a time to the MOs in order of increasing energy. We obtain the bond order with Equation 11.1 and write the electron configuration as described in the text.

**Solution** For $H_2^+$. $H_2$ has two $e^-$, so $H_2^+$ has only one, which enters the bonding MO (*see diagram, below left*). The bond order is $\tfrac{1}{2}(1 - 0) = \tfrac{1}{2}$, so we predict that $H_2^+$ exists. The electron configuration is $(\sigma_{1s})^1$.

For $H_2^-$. $H_2$ has two $e^-$, so $H_2^-$ has three. We place two paired $e^-$ in the bonding MO and one unpaired $e^-$ in the antibonding MO (*see diagram, below right*). The bond order is $\tfrac{1}{2}(2 - 1) = \tfrac{1}{2}$, so we predict that $H_2^-$ exists. The electron configuration is $(\sigma_{1s})^2(\sigma_{1s}^*)^1$.

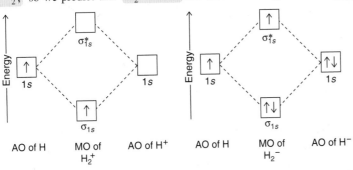

**Check** The number of electrons in the MOs equals the number of electrons in the AOs.

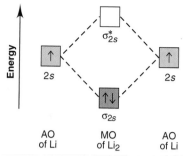

**A Li₂ bond order = 1**

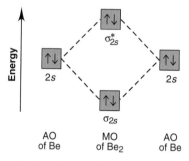

**B Be₂ bond order = 0**

**Figure 11.19** Bonding in s-block homonuclear diatomic molecules. Only outer (valence) AOs interact enough to form MOs.

**Comment** Both species have been detected spectroscopically, $H_2^+$ in the material around stars and $H_2^-$ in the laboratory.

**Follow-Up Problem 11.3** Use an MO diagram to find the bond order and predict whether two $H^-$ ions could form $H_2^{2-}$. If it does exist, write its electron configuration.

## Homonuclear Diatomic Molecules of Period 2 Elements

**Homonuclear diatomic molecules** are composed of two identical atoms. In addition to $H_2$ from Period 1, you're familiar with $N_2$, $O_2$, and $F_2$ from Period 2 as the elemental forms under standard conditions. Others in Period 2—$Li_2$, $Be_2$, $B_2$, $C_2$, and $Ne_2$—are observed, if at all, at high temperatures. We'll divide them into molecules from the $s$ block, Groups 1A(1) and 2A(2), and the $p$ block, Groups 3A(13) through 8A(18).

### Bonding in the s-Block Homonuclear Diatomic Molecules

Both Li and Be occur as metals under normal conditions, but MO theory can examine their stability as diatomic gases, dilithium ($Li_2$) and diberyllium ($Be_2$).

These atoms have electrons in inner ($1s$) and outer ($2s$) AOs, but we ignore the inner ones because, in general, *only outer (valence) AOs interact enough to form MOs*. Like those formed from $1s$ AOs, these $2s$ AOs form σ MOs, cylindrically symmetrical around the internuclear axis.

- In $Li_2$, the two valence electrons fill the bonding ($σ_{2s}$) MO, with opposing spins, leaving the antibonding ($σ_{2s}^*$) MO empty (Figure 11.19A). The bond order is $\frac{1}{2}(2 - 0) = 1$. In fact, $Li_2$ *has* been observed; the electron configuration is $(σ_{2s})^2$.
- In $Be_2$, the four valence electrons fill the $σ_{2s}$ and $σ_{2s}^*$ MOs (Figure 11.19B), giving an orbital occupancy similar to that in $He_2$. The bond order is $\frac{1}{2}(2 - 2) = 0$, and the ground state of $Be_2$ has never been observed.

### Shape and Energy of MOs from Atomic p-Orbital Combinations

As we move to boron, atomic $2p$ orbitals are occupied. Recall that $p$ orbitals can overlap by two modes, which correspond to two ways their wave functions combine (Figure 11.20):

- End-to-end combination gives a pair of σ MOs, the $σ_{2p}$ and $σ_{2p}^*$.
- Side-to-side combination gives a pair of **pi (π) MOs**, $π_{2p}$ and $π_{2p}^*$.

Despite the different shapes, MOs derived from $p$ orbitals are like those from $s$ orbitals. Bonding MOs have most of the electron density *between* the nuclei, and antibonding MOs have most *outside* the internuclear region, with a node between the nuclei.

**Figure 11.20** Shapes and energies of σ and π MOs from combinations of $2p$ atomic orbitals. **A,** The $p$ orbitals lying along the internuclear axis (designated $p_x$) overlap end to end and form $σ_{2p}$ and $σ_{2p}^*$ MOs. **B,** The $p$ orbitals perpendicular to the internuclear axis overlap side to side and form two π MOs. (The $p_y$ interactions, shown here, are the same as for the $p_z$, for a total of four π MOs.)

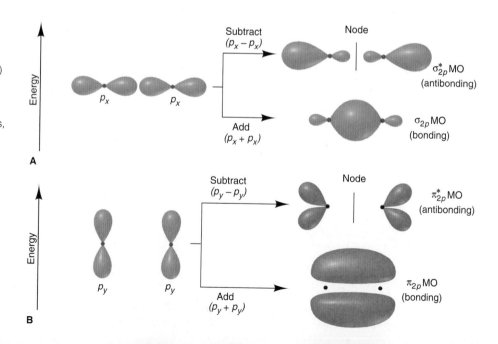

The order of energy levels for MOs, whether bonding or antibonding, is based on the order of AO energy levels *and* on the mode of the *p*-orbital overlap:

- MOs formed from 2*s* orbitals are *lower in energy* than MOs formed from 2*p* orbitals because 2*s* AOs are lower in energy than 2*p* AOs.
- Bonding MOs are *lower in energy* than antibonding MOs: $\sigma_{2p}$ is lower in energy than $\sigma_{2p}^*$ and $\pi_{2p}$ is lower than $\pi_{2p}^*$.
- Atomic *p* orbitals overlap more extensively end to end than side to side. Thus, the $\sigma_{2p}$ MO is usually lower in energy than the $\pi_{2p}$ MO. We also find that the destabilizing effect of the $\sigma_{2p}^*$ MO is greater than that of the $\pi_{2p}^*$ MO.

Thus, the energy order for MOs derived from 2*p* orbitals is typically

$$\sigma_{2p} < \pi_{2p} < \pi_{2p}^* < \sigma_{2p}^*$$

Each atom has three mutually perpendicular 2*p* orbitals. When the six *p* orbitals in two atoms combine, the two that interact end to end form one σ and one σ* MO, and the two pairs of orbitals that interact side to side form two π MOs and two π* MOs. Placing these orientations within the energy order gives the *expected* MO diagram for the *p*-block Period 2 homonuclear diatomic molecules (Figure 11.21A).

Recall that only AOs of similar energy interact enough to form MOs. This fact leads to two energy orders:

1. **Without *s* and *p* orbital mixing: $O_2$, $F_2$, and $Ne_2$.** The order in Figure 11.21A assumes that *s* and *p* AOs are so different in energy that they do not interact; we say the orbitals do not *mix*. Lying at the right of Period 2, O, F, and Ne are relatively small. Thus, as electrons start to pair up in the half-filled 2*p* orbitals, strong repulsions raise the energy of the 2*p* orbitals high enough above the 2*s* orbitals to prevent orbital mixing.

2. **With *s* and *p* orbital mixing: $B_2$, $C_2$, and $N_2$.** B, C, and N atoms are relatively large, with 2*p* AOs only half-filled, so repulsions are weaker. As a result, orbital energies are close enough for some mixing to occur between the 2*s* of one atom and the end-on 2*p* of the other. The effect is to *lower* the energy of the $\sigma_{2s}$ and $\sigma_{2s}^*$ MOs and *raise* the energy of the $\sigma_{2p}$ and $\sigma_{2p}^*$ MOs; the π MOs are not affected. The MO diagram for $B_2$, $C_2$, and $N_2$ reflects this mixing (Figure 11.21B). The only difference from the MO diagram for $O_2$, $F_2$, and $Ne_2$ is the *reverse in energy order* of the $\sigma_{2p}$ and $\pi_{2p}$ MOs.

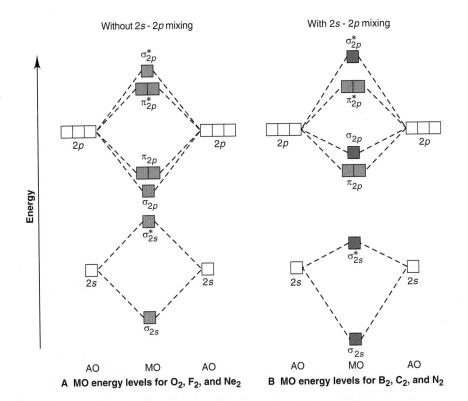

**Figure 11.21** Relative MO energy levels for Period 2 homonuclear diatomic molecules. (For clarity, the MOs affected by mixing are shown in *purple*.)

**A** MO energy levels for $O_2$, $F_2$, and $Ne_2$

**B** MO energy levels for $B_2$, $C_2$, and $N_2$

**Figure 11.22 MO occupancy and some properties of $B_2$ through $Ne_2$.** Energy order and occupancy of MOs are above bar graphs of bond energy and length, bond order, magnetic properties, and outer (valence) electron configuration.

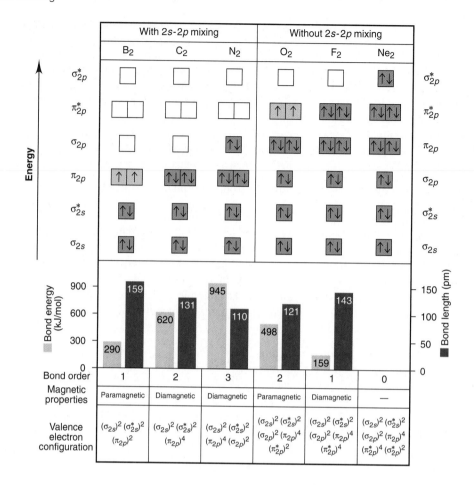

### Bonding in the *p*-Block Homonuclear Diatomic Molecules

Figure 11.22 shows the MOs, electron occupancy, and some properties of $B_2$ through $Ne_2$. Note that

1. *Higher* bond order correlates with *greater* bond energy and *shorter* bond length.

2. Orbital occupancy correlates with magnetic properties. Recall from Chapter 8 that if a substance has unpaired electrons, it is *paramagnetic,* and if all electrons are paired, the substance is *diamagnetic;* the same applies to molecules. Let's examine the MO occupancy and some properties of these molecules:

- $B_2$. The $B_2$ molecule has six outer electrons: four fill the $\sigma_{2s}$ and $\sigma_{2s}^*$ MOs. The remaining two electrons occupy the two $\pi_{2p}$ MOs, one in each orbital, in keeping with Hund's rule. With four electrons in bonding MOs and two in antibonding MOs, the bond order of $B_2$ is $\frac{1}{2}(4 - 2) = 1$. As expected from the two lone electrons, $B_2$ is paramagnetic.

- $C_2$. Two additional electrons in $C_2$ fill the two $\pi_{2p}$ MOs. With two more bonding electrons than $B_2$, the bond order of $C_2$ is 2 and the bond is stronger and shorter. But with all the electrons paired, $C_2$ is diamagnetic.

- $N_2$. Two more electrons in $N_2$ fill the $\sigma_{2p}$ MO, so the molecule is also diamagnetic. The bond order of 3 is consistent with the triple bond in the Lewis structure and with a stronger, shorter bond.

- $O_2$. With this molecule, we see the power of MO theory over VB theory and others based on electrons in localized orbitals. It is impossible to write one Lewis structure consistent with the fact that $O_2$ is double bonded and paramagnetic. We can write one with a double bond and paired electrons, and another with a single bond and two unpaired electrons:

$$\ddot{\text{O}}{=}\ddot{\text{O}} \quad or \quad :\dot{\text{O}}{-}\dot{\text{O}}:$$

MO theory resolves this paradox beautifully: with eight electrons in bonding MOs and four in antibonding MOs, the bond order is $\frac{1}{2}(8 - 4) = 2$, and it is paramagnetic because *one* electron occupies each of *two* $\pi_{2p}^*$ MOs with unpaired (parallel) spins. A thin stream of liquid $O_2$ will remain suspended between the poles of a powerful magnet (Figure 11.23). As expected, the bond is weaker and longer than the one in $N_2$.

- $F_2$. Two more electrons in $F_2$ fill the $\pi^*_{2p}$ orbitals, so it is diamagnetic. The bond has an order of 1 and is weaker and longer than the one in $O_2$. Note that this bond is shorter, yet about half as strong as the single bond in $B_2$. We might have expected it to be stronger because F is smaller than B. But 18 electrons in the smaller volume of $F_2$ cause greater repulsions than the 10 in $B_2$, so the $F_2$ bond is weaker.
- $Ne_2$. The final member of the Period 2 series doesn't exist for the same reason $He_2$ doesn't: all the MOs are filled, which gives a bond order of zero.

**Figure 11.23** The paramagnetic properties of $O_2$.

---

## Sample Problem 11.4 | Using MO Theory to Explain Bond Properties

**Problem** Explain the following data with diagrams showing the occupancy of MOs:

|                     | $N_2$ | $N_2^+$ | $O_2$ | $O_2^+$ |
|---------------------|-------|---------|-------|---------|
| Bond energy (kJ/mol) | 945   | 841     | 498   | 623     |
| Bond length (pm)     | 110   | 112     | 121   | 112     |

**Plan** The data show that removing an electron from each parent molecule has opposite effects: $N_2^+$ has a weaker, longer bond than $N_2$, but $O_2^+$ has a stronger, shorter bond than $O_2$. We determine the valence electrons in each species, draw the sequence of MO energy levels (showing orbital mixing in $N_2$ but not in $O_2$), and fill them with electrons. To explain the data, we calculate bond orders, which relate directly to bond energy and inversely to bond length.

**Solution** Determining the valence electrons:

N has 5 valence $e^-$, so $N_2$ has 10 and $N_2^+$ has 9

O has 6 valence $e^-$, so $O_2$ has 12 and $O_2^+$ has 11

Drawing and filling the MO diagrams:

| $N_2$ | | $N_2^+$ | $O_2$ | | $O_2^+$ |
|---|---|---|---|---|---|
| ☐ | $\sigma^*_{2p}$ | ☐ | ☐ | $\sigma^*_{2p}$ | ☐ |
| ☐ ☐ | $\pi^*_{2p}$ | ☐ ☐ | ↑ ↑ | $\pi^*_{2p}$ | ↑ ☐ |
| ↑↓ | $\sigma_{2p}$ | ↑ | ↑↓ ↑↓ | $\pi_{2p}$ | ↑↓ ↑↓ |
| ↑↓ ↑↓ | $\pi_{2p}$ | ↑↓ ↑↓ | ↑↓ | $\sigma_{2p}$ | ↑↓ |
| ↑↓ | $\sigma^*_{2s}$ | ↑↓ | ↑↓ | $\sigma^*_{2s}$ | ↑↓ |
| ↑↓ | $\sigma_{2s}$ | ↑↓ | ↑↓ | $\sigma_{2s}$ | ↑↓ |

Calculating bond orders:

$$\tfrac{1}{2}(8-2)=3 \qquad \tfrac{1}{2}(7-2)=2.5 \qquad \tfrac{1}{2}(8-4)=2 \qquad \tfrac{1}{2}(8-3)=2.5$$

Explaining the data:
1. When $N_2$ becomes $N_2^+$, a *bonding* electron is removed, so the bond order decreases. Thus, $N_2^+$ has a weaker, longer bond than $N_2$.
2. When $O_2$ becomes $O_2^+$, an *antibonding* electron is removed, so the bond order increases. Thus, $O_2^+$ has a stronger, shorter bond than $O_2$.

**Check** The answers make sense in terms of bond order, bond energy, and bond length. Check that the total number of bonding and antibonding electrons equals the number of valence electrons calculated.

## Follow-Up Problem 11.4 
Determine the bond orders for the following species: $F_2^{2-}$, $F_2^-$, $F_2$, $F_2^+$, $F_2^{2+}$. List the species in order of increasing bond energy and in order of increasing bond length.

## Two Heteronuclear Diatomic Molecules: HF and NO

*Heteronuclear* diatomic molecules have asymmetric MO diagrams because the AOs of the *different* atoms have unequal energies. Atoms with greater effective nuclear charge ($Z_{eff}$) pull their electrons closer, so they have more stable (lower energy) AOs (Section 8.1) and higher EN values (Section 9.5). Let's examine the bonding in HF and NO.

**Bonding in HF**   To form the MOs in HF, we decide which AOs will combine. The high $Z_{eff}$ of F holds its electrons so tightly that the 1$s$, 2$s$, and 2$p$ orbitals of F have lower energy than the 1$s$ of H. The half-filled F 2$p$ orbital interacts with the H 1$s$ through end-on overlap, which forms σ and σ* MOs. The two filled 2$p$ orbitals of F are called **nonbonding MOs.** Because they are not involved in bonding, they have the same energy as the isolated AOs (Figure 11.24A).

The bonding MO is closer in energy to the AOs of F, so the F 2$p$ orbital contributes more to the HF bond than the H 1$s$ does. In polar covalent molecules, *bonding MOs are closer in energy to the AOs of the more electronegative atom.* In effect, fluorine's greater electronegativity lowers the energy of the bonding MO and draws the bonding electrons closer.

**Bonding in NO**   Nitrogen monoxide (nitric oxide) is highly reactive because of its lone electron. Two possible Lewis structures for NO, with formal charges (Section 10.1), are

$$\overset{0\quad 0}{:\!N\!=\!\ddot{O}:} \quad \text{or} \quad \overset{-1\ +1}{:\!\ddot{N}\!=\!\ddot{O}:}$$
$$\textbf{I} \qquad\qquad \textbf{II}$$

Both structures show a double bond, but the *measured* bond energy suggests a bond order *higher* than 2. Moreover, it is not clear where the lone electron resides, although the lower formal charges for structure I suggest that it is on the N.

The MO diagram is asymmetric, with the AOs of the more electronegative O lower in energy (Figure 11.24B). When the 11 valence electrons fill the MOs of NO, the lone electron occupies one of the $\pi^*_{2p}$ orbitals. Eight bonding and three antibonding electrons give a bond order of $\frac{1}{2}(8 - 3) = 2.5$, more in keeping with the data than either Lewis structure. Bonding electrons lie in MOs closer in energy to the AOs of the O atom. The 2$p$ orbitals of N contribute more to the orbital that holds the lone electron, so it spends more time closer to N. (This diagram shows the energy order *with* 2$s$–2$p$ mixing, as in Figure 11.21, but the result is the same as the order without mixing.)

**Figure 11.24** The MO diagrams for HF and NO. **A,** In HF, the bonding MO is closer in energy to the 2$p$ orbital of F. (The 2$s$ AO of F is not shown.) **B,** In NO, the lone electron occupies an MO closer in energy to the 2$p$ of N.

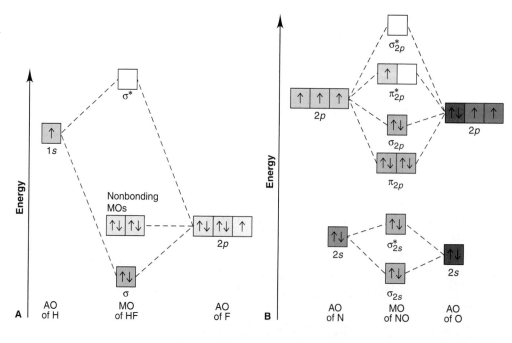

## Two Polyatomic Molecules: Benzene and Ozone

The orbital shapes and MO diagrams for polyatomic molecules are too complex for a detailed treatment here. But we'll briefly discuss how the model eliminates the need for resonance forms and helps explain the effects of the absorption of energy.

Recall that we cannot draw one Lewis structure for either benzene or ozone, so we draw separate forms of a resonance hybrid. The VB model also uses resonance because it relies on *localized* bonds. In contrast, MO theory pictures a structure of delocalized σ and π MOs. Figure 11.25 shows the lowest energy π-bonding MOs in benzene and ozone. The extended areas of electron density allow delocalization of one π-bonding electron pair over the entire molecule, thus eliminating the need for separate resonance forms:

- *In benzene*, the upper and lower hexagonal lobes of this MO lie above and below the σ plane of the six C nuclei.
- *In ozone*, the two lobes of this MO extend over and under the three O nuclei.

The full MO diagrams for these molecules help us rationalize how bonding electrons in $O_3$ become excited and occupy empty antibonding orbitals when the molecule absorbs UV radiation in the stratosphere, and why the UV spectrum of benzene has its characteristic absorption bands.

**Benzene, $C_6H_6$**

**Ozone, $O_3$**

**Figure 11.25** The lowest energy π-bonding MOs in benzene and ozone.

### ■ Summary of Section 11.3

- Molecular orbital (MO) theory treats a molecule as a collection of nuclei with MOs delocalized over the entire structure.
- Atomic orbitals of comparable energy can be added or subtracted to obtain bonding or antibonding MOs, respectively.
- Bonding MOs, whether σ or π, have most of the electron density between the nuclei and are lower in energy than the AOs; most of the electron density in antibonding MOs does not lie between the nuclei, so these MOs are higher in energy.
- MOs are filled in order of their energy with paired electrons having opposite spins.
- MO diagrams show energy levels and orbital occupancy. Diagrams for the Period 2 homonuclear diatomic molecules explain bond energy, bond length, and magnetic behavior.
- In heteronuclear diatomic molecules, the more electronegative atom contributes more to the bonding MOs.
- MO theory eliminates the need for resonance forms to depict larger molecules.

## CHAPTER REVIEW GUIDE

**Learning Objectives**    Relevant section (§) and/or sample problem (SP) numbers appear in parentheses.

### Understand These Concepts

1. The main ideas of valence bond theory—orbital overlap, opposing electron spins, and hybridization—as a means of rationalizing molecular shapes (§11.1)
2. How orbitals mix to form hybrid orbitals with different spatial orientations (§11.1)
3. The distinction between end-to-end and side-to-side overlap and the origin of sigma (σ) and pi (π) bonds in simple molecules (§11.2)
4. How these two modes of orbital overlap lead to single, double, and triple bonds (§11.2)
5. Why π bonding restricts rotation around double bonds (§11.2)
6. The distinction between the localized bonding of VB theory and the delocalized bonding of MO theory (§11.3)
7. How addition or subtraction of AOs forms bonding or antibonding MOs (§11.3)
8. The shapes of MOs formed from combinations of two *s* orbitals and combinations of two *p* orbitals (§11.3)
9. How MO bond order predicts the stability of molecular species (§11.3)
10. How MO theory explains the bonding and magnetic properties of homonuclear and heteronuclear diatomic molecules of Period 2 elements (§11.3)

### Master These Skills

1. Using molecular shape to postulate the hybrid orbitals used by a central atom (SP 11.1)
2. Describing the types of orbitals and bonds in a molecule (SP 11.2)
3. Drawing MO diagrams, writing electron configurations, and calculating bond orders of molecular species (SP 11.3)
4. Explaining bond and magnetic properties with MO theory (SP 11.4)

**Key Equations and Relationships** Page numbers appear in parentheses.

**11.1** Calculating the MO bond order (407): Bond order $= \frac{1}{2}[$(no. of e$^-$ in bonding MO) $-$ (no. of e$^-$ in antibonding MO)$]$

## Brief Solutions to Follow-Up Problems

**11.1** (a) Shape is linear, so Be is $sp$ hybridized.

Isolated Be atom          Hybridized Be atom

(b) Shape is tetrahedral, so Si is $sp^3$ hybridized.

Isolated Si atom          Hybridized Si atom

(c) Shape is square planar, so Xe is $sp^3d^2$ hybridized.

Isolated Xe atom          Hybridized Xe atom

**11.2** (a) H—C≡N:

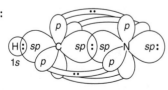

HCN is linear, so C is $sp$ hybridized. N is also $sp$ hybridized. One $sp$ of C overlaps the $1s$ of H to form a $\sigma$ bond. The other $sp$ of C overlaps one $sp$ of N to form a $\sigma$ bond. The other $sp$ of N holds a lone pair. Two unhybridized $p$ orbitals of N and two of C overlap to form two $\pi$ bonds.

(b) Ö=C=Ö

$CO_2$ is linear, so C is $sp$ hybridized. Both O atoms are $sp^2$ hybridized. Each $sp$ of C overlaps one $sp^2$ of an O to form two $\sigma$ bonds. Each of the two unhybridized $p$ orbitals of C forms a $\pi$ bond with the unhybridized $p$ of one of the two O atoms. Two $sp^2$ of each O hold lone pairs.

**11.3**

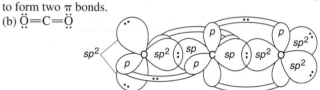

AO of H$^-$    MO of H$_2{}^{2-}$    AO of H$^-$

Does not exist: bond order $= \frac{1}{2}(2-2) = 0$.

**11.4** Bond orders: $F_2{}^{2-} = 0$; $F_2{}^- = \frac{1}{2}$; $F_2 = 1$; $F_2{}^+ = 1\frac{1}{2}$
  $F_2{}^{2+} = 2$
Bond energy: $F_2{}^{2-} < F_2{}^- < F_2 < F_2{}^+ < F_2{}^{2+}$
Bond length: $F_2{}^{2+} < F_2{}^+ < F_2 < F_2{}^-$; $F_2{}^{2-}$ does not exist

# PROBLEMS

Problems with **colored** numbers are answered in Appendix E and worked in detail in the Student Solutions Manual. Problem sections match those in the text and provide the numbers of relevant sample problems. Most offer Concept Review Questions, Skill-Building Exercises (grouped in pairs covering the same concept), and Problems in Context. The Comprehensive Problems are based on material from any section or previous chapter.

## Valence Bond (VB) Theory and Orbital Hybridization
(Sample Problem 11.1)

### Concept Review Questions

**11.1** What type of central-atom orbital hybridization corresponds to each electron-group arrangement: (a) trigonal planar; (b) octahedral; (c) linear; (d) tetrahedral; (e) trigonal bipyramidal?

**11.2** What is the orbital hybridization of a central atom that has one lone pair and bonds to: (a) two other atoms; (b) three other atoms; (c) four other atoms; (d) five other atoms?

**11.3** How do carbon and silicon differ with regard to the *types* of orbitals available for hybridization? Explain.

**11.4** How many hybrid orbitals form when four atomic orbitals of a central atom mix? Explain.

### Skill-Building Exercises (grouped in similar pairs)

**11.5** Give the number and type of hybrid orbital that forms when each set of atomic orbitals mixes:
(a) two $d$, one $s$, and three $p$      (b) three $p$ and one $s$

**11.6** Give the number and type of hybrid orbital that forms when each set of atomic orbitals mixes:
(a) one $p$ and one $s$      (b) three $p$, one $d$, and one $s$

**11.7** What is the hybridization of nitrogen in each of the following: (a) NO; (b) $NO_2$; (c) $NO_2^-$?

**11.8** What is the hybridization of carbon in each of the following: (a) $CO_3^{2-}$; (b) $C_2O_4^{2-}$; (c) $NCO^-$?

**11.9** What is the hybridization of chlorine in each of the following: (a) $ClO_2$; (b) $ClO_3^-$; (c) $ClO_4^-$?

**11.10** What is the hybridization of bromine in each of the following: (a) $BrF_3$; (b) $BrO_2^-$; (c) $BrF_5$?

**11.11** Which types of atomic orbitals of the central atom mix to form hybrid orbitals in (a) $SiClH_3$; (b) $CS_2$; (c) $SCl_3F$; (d) $NF_3$?

**11.12** Which types of atomic orbitals of the central atom mix to form hybrid orbitals in (a) $Cl_2O$; (b) $BrCl_3$; (c) $PF_5$; (d) $SO_3^{2-}$?

**11.13** Phosphine ($PH_3$) reacts with borane ($BH_3$) as follows:
$$PH_3 + BH_3 \longrightarrow H_3P-BH_3$$
(a) Which of the illustrations below depicts the change, if any, in the orbital hybridization of P during this reaction? (b) Which depicts the change, if any, in the orbital hybridization of B?

**11.14** The illustrations below depict differences in orbital hybridization of some tellurium (Te) fluorides. (a) Which depicts the difference, if any, between $TeF_6$ (*left*) and $TeF_5^-$ (*right*)? (b) Which depicts the difference, if any, between $TeF_4$ (*left*) and $TeF_6$ (*right*)?

**11.15** Use partial orbital diagrams to show how the atomic orbitals of the central atom lead to hybrid orbitals in (a) $GeCl_4$; (b) $BCl_3$; (c) $CH_3^+$.

**11.16** Use partial orbital diagrams to show how the atomic orbitals of the central atom lead to hybrid orbitals in (a) $BF_4^-$; (b) $PO_4^{3-}$; (c) $SO_3$.

**11.17** Use partial orbital diagrams to show how the atomic orbitals of the central atom lead to hybrid orbitals in (a) $SeCl_2$; (b) $H_3O^+$; (c) $IF_4^-$.

**11.18** Use partial orbital diagrams to show how the atomic orbitals of the central atom lead to hybrid orbitals in (a) $AsCl_3$; (b) $SnCl_2$; (c) $PF_6^-$.

### Problems in Context

**11.19** Methyl isocyanate, $CH_3-\ddot{N}=C=\ddot{O}:$, is an intermediate in the manufacture of many pesticides. In 1984 a leak from a manufacturing plant resulted in the death of more than 2000 people in Bhopal, India. What are the hybridizations of the N atom and the two C atoms in methyl isocyanate? Sketch the molecular shape.

## Modes of Orbital Overlap and the Types of Covalent Bonds
(Sample Problem 11.2)

### Concept Review Questions

**11.20** Are these statements true or false? Correct any false ones.
(a) Two σ bonds comprise a double bond.
(b) A triple bond consists of one π bond and two σ bonds.
(c) Bonds formed from atomic $s$ orbitals are always σ bonds.
(d) A π bond restricts rotation about the σ-bond axis.
(e) A π bond consists of two pairs of electrons.
(f) End-to-end overlap results in a bond with electron density above and below the bond axis.

### Skill-Building Exercises (grouped in similar pairs)

**11.21** Describe the hybrid orbitals used by the central atom and the type(s) of bonds formed in (a) $NO_3^-$; (b) $CS_2$; (c) $CH_2O$.

**11.22** Describe the hybrid orbitals used by the central atom and the type(s) of bonds formed in (a) $O_3$; (b) $I_3^-$; (c) $COCl_2$ (C is central).

**11.23** Describe the hybrid orbitals used by the central atom(s) and the type(s) of bonds formed in (a) FNO; (b) $C_2F_4$; (c) $(CN)_2$.

**11.24** Describe the hybrid orbitals used by the central atom(s) and the type(s) of bonds formed in (a) $BrF_3$; (b) $CH_3C≡CH$; (c) $SO_2$.

**Problem in Context**

**11.25** 2-Butene ($CH_3CH=CHCH_3$) is a starting material in the manufacture of lubricating oils and many other compounds. Draw two different structures for 2-butene, indicating the $\sigma$ and $\pi$ bonds in each.

## Molecular Orbital (MO) Theory and Electron Delocalization

(Sample Problems 11.3 and 11.4)

**Concept Review Questions**

**11.26** Two $p$ orbitals from one atom and two $p$ orbitals from another atom are combined to form molecular orbitals for the joined atoms. How many MOs will result from this combination? Explain.

**11.27** Certain atomic orbitals on two atoms were combined to form the following MOs. Name the atomic orbitals used and the MOs formed, and explain which MO has higher energy:

**11.28** How do the bonding and antibonding MOs formed from a given pair of AOs compare to each other with respect to (a) energy; (b) presence of nodes; (c) internuclear electron density?

**11.29** Antibonding MOs always have at least one node. Can a bonding MO have a node? If so, draw an example.

**Skill-Building Exercises** (grouped in similar pairs)

**11.30** How many electrons does it take to fill (a) a $\sigma$ bonding MO; (b) a $\pi$ antibonding MO; (c) the MOs formed from combination of the $1s$ orbitals of two atoms?

**11.31** How many electrons does it take to fill (a) the MOs formed from combination of the $2p$ orbitals of two atoms; (b) a $\sigma_{2p}^*$ MO; (c) the MOs formed from combination of the $2s$ orbitals of two atoms?

**11.32** The molecular orbitals depicted below are derived from $2p$ atomic orbitals in $F_2^+$. (a) Give the orbital designations. (b) Which is occupied by at least one electron in $F_2^+$? (c) Which is occupied by only one electron in $F_2^+$?

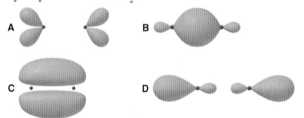

**11.33** The molecular orbitals depicted below are derived from $n = 2$ atomic orbitals. (a) Give the orbital designations. (b) Which is highest in energy? (c) Lowest in energy? (d) Rank the MOs in order of increasing energy for $B_2$.

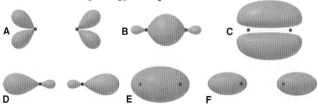

**11.34** Use MO diagrams and the bond orders you obtain from them to answer: (a) Is $Be_2^+$ stable? (b) Is $Be_2^+$ diamagnetic? (c) What is the outer (valence) electron configuration of $Be_2^+$?

**11.35** Use MO diagrams and the bond orders you obtain from them to answer: (a) Is $O_2^-$ stable? (b) Is $O_2^-$ paramagnetic? (c) What is the outer (valence) electron configuration of $O_2^-$?

**11.36** Use MO diagrams to place $C_2^-$, $C_2$, and $C_2^+$ in order of (a) increasing bond energy; (b) increasing bond length.

**11.37** Use MO diagrams to place $B_2^+$, $B_2$, and $B_2^-$ in order of (a) decreasing bond energy; (b) decreasing bond length.

## Comprehensive Problems

**11.38** Predict the shape, state the hybridization of the central atom, and give the ideal bond angle(s) and any expected deviations for:
(a) $BrO_3^-$ (b) $AsCl_4^-$ (c) $SeO_4^{2-}$ (d) $BiF_5^{2-}$
(e) $SbF_4^+$ (f) $AlF_6^{3-}$ (g) $IF_4^+$

**11.39** Butadiene (*right*) is a colorless gas used to make synthetic rubber and many other compounds. (a) How many $\sigma$ bonds and $\pi$ bonds does the molecule have? (b) Are *cis-trans* arrangements about the double bonds possible? Explain.

**11.40** Epinephrine (or adrenaline; *below*) is a naturally occurring hormone that is also manufactured commercially for use as a heart stimulant, a nasal decongestant, and a glaucoma treatment.

(a) What is the hybridization of each C, O, and N atom? (b) How many $\sigma$ bonds does the molecule have? (c) How many $\pi$ electrons are delocalized in the ring?

**11.41** Use partial orbital diagrams to show how the atomic orbitals of the central atom lead to the hybrid orbitals in:
(a) $IF_2^-$ (b) $ICl_3$ (c) $XeOF_4$ (d) $BHF_2$

**11.42** Isoniazid (*below*) is an antibacterial agent that is very useful against many common strains of tuberculosis. (a) How many $\sigma$ bonds are in the molecule? (b) What is the hybridization of each C and N atom?

**11.43** Hydrazine, $N_2H_4$, and carbon disulfide, $CS_2$, form a cyclic molecule (*below*). (a) Draw Lewis structures for $N_2H_4$ and $CS_2$. (b) How do electron-group arrangement, molecular shape, and hybridization of N change when $N_2H_4$ reacts to form the product? (c) How do electron-group arrangement, molecular shape, and hybridization of C change when $CS_2$ reacts to form the product?

**11.44** In each of the following equations, what hybridization change, if any, occurs for the underlined atom?
(a) $\underline{B}F_3 + NaF \longrightarrow Na^+BF_4^-$
(b) $\underline{P}Cl_3 + Cl_2 \longrightarrow PCl_5$
(c) $\underline{H}C{\equiv}CH + H_2 \longrightarrow H_2C=CH_2$
(d) $\underline{Si}F_4 + 2F^- \longrightarrow SiF_6^{2-}$
(e) $\underline{S}O_2 + \frac{1}{2}O_2 \rightarrow SO_3$

**11.45** The ionosphere lies about 100 km above Earth's surface. This layer consists mostly of NO, $O_2$, and $N_2$, and photoionization creates $NO^+$, $O_2^+$, and $N_2^+$. (a) Use MO theory to compare the bond orders of the molecules and ions. (b) Does the magnetic behavior of each species change when its ion forms?

**11.46** Glyphosate (*below*) is a common herbicide that is relatively harmless to animals but deadly to most plants. Describe the shape around and the hybridization of the P, N, and three numbered C atoms.

**11.47** Tryptophan is one of the amino acids found in proteins:

(a) What is the hybridization of each of the numbered C, N, and O atoms? (b) How many σ bonds are present in tryptophan? (c) Predict the bond angles at points a, b, and c.

**11.48** Some species with two oxygen atoms only are the oxygen molecule, $O_2$, the peroxide ion, $O_2^{2-}$, the superoxide ion, $O_2^-$, and the dioxygenyl ion, $O_2^+$. Draw an MO diagram for each, rank them in order of increasing bond length, and find the number of unpaired electrons in each.

**11.49** Molecular nitrogen, carbon monoxide, and cyanide ion are isoelectronic. (a) Draw an MO diagram for each. (b) CO and $CN^-$ are toxic. What property may explain why $N_2$ isn't?

**11.50** There is concern in health-related government agencies that the American diet contains too much meat, and numerous recommendations have been made urging people to consume more fruit and vegetables. One of the richest sources of vegetable protein is soy, available in many forms. Among these is soybean curd, or tofu, which is a staple of many Asian diets. Chemists have isolated an anticancer agent called *genistein* from tofu, which may explain the much lower incidence of cancer among people in the Far East. A valid Lewis structure for genistein is

(a) Is the hybridization of each C in the right-hand ring the same? Explain. (b) Is the hybridization of the O atom in the center ring the same as that of the O atoms in OH groups? Explain. (c) How many carbon-oxygen σ bonds are there? How many carbon-oxygen π bonds? (d) Do all the lone pairs on oxygens occupy the same type of hybrid orbital? Explain.

**11.51** An organic chemist synthesizes the molecule below:

(a) Which of the orientations of hybrid orbitals shown below are present in the molecule? (b) Are there any present that are not shown below? If so, what are they? (c) How many of each type of hybrid orbital are present?

**11.52** Simple proteins consist of amino acids linked together in a long chain; a small portion of such a chain is

Experiment shows that rotation about the C—N bond (indicated by the arrow) is somewhat restricted. Explain with resonance structures, and show the types of bonding involved.

**11.53** Sulfur forms oxides, oxoanions, and halides. What is the hybridization of the central S in $SO_2$, $SO_3$, $SO_3^{2-}$, $SCl_4$, $SCl_6$, and $S_2Cl_2$ (atom sequence Cl—S—S—Cl)?

**11.54** The compound 2,6-dimethylpyrazine (*below*) gives chocolate its odor and is used in flavorings. (a) Which atomic orbitals mix to form the hybrid orbitals of N? (b) In what type of hybrid orbital do the lone pairs of N reside? (c) Is C in $CH_3$ hybridized the same as any C in the ring? Explain.

**11.55** Acetylsalicylic acid (aspirin), the most widely used medicine in the world, has the Lewis structure shown below. (a) What is the hybridization of each C and each O atom? (b) How many localized π bonds are present? (c) How many C atoms have a trigonal planar shape around them? A tetrahedral shape?

**11.56** Linoleic acid is an essential fatty acid found in many vegetable oils, such as soy, peanut, and cottonseed. A key structural feature of the molecule is the *cis* orientation around its two double bonds, where $R_1$ and $R_2$ represent two different groups that form the rest of the molecule.

(a) How many different compounds are possible, changing only the *cis-trans* arrangements around these two double bonds?
(b) How many are possible for a similar compound with three double bonds?

# Intermolecular Forces: Liquids, Solids, and Phase Changes

## Concepts and skills to review before you study this chapter

- properties of gases, liquids, and solids (Section 5.1)
- kinetic-molecular theory of gases (Section 5.5)
- kinetic and potential energy (Section 6.1)
- enthalpy change, heat capacity, and Hess's law (Sections 6.2, 6.3, and 6.5)
- diffraction of light (Section 7.1)
- Coulomb's law (Section 9.2)
- chemical bonding models (Chapter 9)
- molecular polarity (Section 10.3)
- molecular orbital treatment of diatomic molecules (Section 11.3)

All the matter in and around you occurs in one or more of the three physical states—gas, liquid, or solid. Under different conditions, many substances can occur in any of the states. We're all familiar with the states of water: we inhale and exhale gaseous water; drink, excrete, and wash with liquid water; and shovel, slide on, or cool our drinks with solid water. And, given the right conditions, even other solids (gold jewelry, table salt), liquids (gasoline, antifreeze), and gases (air, $CO_2$ bubbles) can exist in one or both of the other states.

The three states were introduced in Chapter 1 and their properties were compared when we examined gases in Chapter 5. You saw there that the particles in gases are, on average, very far apart. Now, we examine liquids and solids, which are called *condensed* states because their *particles are very close together*.

**IN THIS CHAPTER . . .** We explore the interplay of forces that give rise to the three states of matter and their changes, with special attention to liquids and solids.

- We use kinetic-molecular theory to see how relative magnitudes of potential and kinetic energy account for the behavior of gases, liquids, and solids and how temperature is related to phase changes.
- We calculate the heat associated with warming or cooling a phase and with a phase change.
- We highlight the effects of temperature and pressure on phases and their changes with phase diagrams.
- We describe the types and relative strengths of the intermolecular forces that occur within pure substances.
- We see how intermolecular forces give rise to the properties of liquids.
- As a special case, we trace the unique and vital physical properties of water to the electron configurations of its atoms.
- We discuss the properties of solids, emphasizing the relationship between type of bonding and predominant intermolecular force, and we examine the methods used to study crystal structure.
- We introduce key features of several kinds of advanced materials—semiconductors, liquid crystals, ceramics, polymers, and nanostructures.

## 12.1 • AN OVERVIEW OF PHYSICAL STATES AND PHASE CHANGES

Each physical state is called a **phase,** a physically distinct, homogeneous part of system. The water in a closed container constitutes one phase; the water vapor above the liquid is a second phase; add some ice, and there are three.

In this section, you'll see that interactions between the potential energy and the kinetic energy of the particles give rise to the properties of each phase:

- The *potential energy* in the form of **intermolecular forces** (or, more generally, *interparticle forces*) tends to draw the molecules together. According to Coulomb's law, the electrostatic potential energy depends on the charges of the particles and the distances between them (Section 9.2).
- The *kinetic energy* associated with the random motion of the molecules tends to disperse them. It is related to their average speed and is proportional to the absolute temperature (Section 5.5).

These interactions also explain **phase changes,** changes in physical state from one phase to another—liquid to solid, solid to gas, and so forth.

### A Kinetic-Molecular View of the Three States
Imagine yourself among the particles in any of the three states of water. Look closely and you'll discover two types of electrostatic forces at work:

1. *Intra*molecular (bonding) forces exist *within* each molecule. The *chemical* behavior of the three states is identical because each consists of the same bent, polar H—O—H molecules held together by identical covalent bonding forces.
2. *Inter*molecular (nonbonding) forces exist *between* the molecules. The *physical* behavior of the states is different because the strengths of these forces differ from state to state.

Whether a substance occurs as a gas, liquid, or solid depends on the interplay of the potential and kinetic energy:

- *In a gas,* the potential energy (energy of attraction) is small relative to the kinetic energy (energy of motion); thus, on average, the particles are far apart. This large distance has several macroscopic consequences: a gas fills its container, is highly compressible, and flows easily through another gas (Table 12.1).
- *In a liquid,* attractions are stronger because the particles are touching, but they have enough kinetic energy to move randomly around each other. Thus, a liquid conforms to the shape of its container but has a surface, it resists an applied force and thus compresses very slightly, and it flows, but *much* more slowly than gases.
- *In a solid,* the attractions dominate the motion so much that the particles are fixed in position relative to one another, just jiggling in place. Thus, a solid has its own shape, compresses even less than liquids, and does not flow significantly.

The environment provides a perfect demonstration of these differences in ability to flow (*see photo*). Atmospheric gases mix so well that the lowest 80 km of air has a uniform composition. Much less mixing in the oceans allows the composition at various depths to support different species. And rocks intermingle so little that adjacent strata remain separated for millions of years.

How does ability to flow influence composition in nature?

| Table **12.1** A Macroscopic Comparison of Gases, Liquids, and Solids | | | |
| --- | --- | --- | --- |
| **State** | **Shape and Volume** | **Compressibility** | **Ability to Flow** |
| Gas | Conforms to shape and volume of container | High | High |
| Liquid | Conforms to shape of container; volume limited by surface | Very low | Moderate |
| Solid | Maintains its own shape and volume | Almost none | Almost none |

### Types of Phase Changes and Their Enthalpies
When we consider phase changes, understanding the effect of temperature is critical:

- As *temperature increases,* the average kinetic energy does too, so the faster moving particles overcome attractions more easily.
- As *temperature decreases,* particles slow, so attractions can pull them together.

Each phase change has a name and an associated enthalpy change:

1. *Gas to liquid, and vice versa.* As the temperature drops, the molecules in the gas phase come together and form a liquid in the process of **condensation;** the opposite process, changing from a liquid to a gas, is **vaporization.**

2. *Liquid to solid, and vice versa.* As the temperature drops further, the particles move slower and become fixed in position in the process of **freezing;** the opposite change is called **melting,** or **fusion.** In common speech, *freezing* implies low temperature because we think of water. But, molten metals, for example, freeze (solidify) at much higher temperatures and have medical, industrial, and artistic applications, such as gold dental crowns, steel auto bodies, and bronze statues.

3. *Gas to solid, and vice versa.* All three states of water are familiar because they are stable under ordinary conditions. Carbon dioxide, on the other hand, is familiar as a gas and a solid (dry ice), but liquid $CO_2$ occurs only at pressures of 5.1 atm or greater. At ordinary conditions, solid $CO_2$ changes directly to a gas, a process called **sublimation.** Freeze-dried foods are prepared by sublimation. The opposite process, changing from a gas directly into a solid, is called **deposition**—ice crystals form on a cold window from the deposition of water vapor (Figure 12.1A).

The accompanying enthalpy changes are either exothermic or endothermic:

- *Exothermic changes.* As the molecules of a gas attract each other into a liquid, and then become fixed in a solid, the system of particles *loses* energy, which is released as heat. Thus, *condensing, freezing, and depositing are exothermic changes.*
- *Endothermic changes.* Heat must be absorbed by the system to overcome the attractive forces that keep the particles fixed in place in a solid or near each other in a liquid. Thus, *melting, vaporizing, and subliming are endothermic changes.*

Sweating has a cooling effect because heat from your body vaporizes the water. To achieve this cooling, cats lick themselves and dogs pant (Figure 12.1B).

For a pure substance, each phase change is accompanied by a standard enthalpy change, given in units of *kilojoules per mole* (measured at 1 atm and the temperature of the change). For vaporization, it is the **heat** (or *enthalpy*) **of vaporization ($\Delta H^\circ_{vap}$),** and for fusion (melting), it is the **heat** (or *enthalpy*) **of fusion ($\Delta H^\circ_{fus}$).** In the case of water, we have

$$H_2O(l) \longrightarrow H_2O(g) \qquad \Delta H = \Delta H^\circ_{vap} = 40.7 \text{ kJ/mol (at } 100°C)$$
$$H_2O(s) \longrightarrow H_2O(l) \qquad \Delta H = \Delta H^\circ_{fus} = 6.02 \text{ kJ/mol (at } 0°C)$$

The reverse processes, condensing and freezing, have enthalpy changes of the *same magnitude but opposite sign:*

$$H_2O(g) \longrightarrow H_2O(l) \qquad \Delta H = -\Delta H^\circ_{vap} = -40.7 \text{ kJ/mol}$$
$$H_2O(l) \longrightarrow H_2O(s) \qquad \Delta H = -\Delta H^\circ_{fus} = -6.02 \text{ kJ/mol}$$

Water behaves typically in that it takes much less energy to melt the solid than to vaporize the liquid: $\Delta H^\circ_{fus} < \Delta H^\circ_{vap}$; that is, it takes less energy to reduce the intermolecular forces enough for the molecules to move out of their fixed positions (melt a solid) than to separate them completely (vaporize a liquid) (Figure 12.2).

**A Deposition**

**B Vaporization**

**Figure 12.1** Two familiar phase changes.

**Figure 12.2** Heats of vaporization and fusion for several common substances.

The **heat** (or *enthalpy*) **of sublimation ($\Delta H^\circ_{subl}$)** is the enthalpy change when 1 mol of a substance sublimes, and the negative of this value is the change when 1 mol of the substance deposits. Since sublimation can be considered a combination of melting and vaporizing, Hess's law (Section 6.5) says that the heat of sublimation equals the sum of the heats of fusion and vaporization:

$$\begin{array}{ll} \text{Solid} \longrightarrow \text{liquid} & \Delta H^\circ_{fus} \\ \underline{\text{Liquid} \longrightarrow \text{gas}} & \underline{\Delta H^\circ_{vap}} \\ \text{Solid} \longrightarrow \text{gas} & \Delta H^\circ_{subl} \end{array}$$

Figure 12.3 on the next page summarizes the phase changes and their enthalpy changes.

**Figure 12.3** Phase changes and their enthalpy changes. Fusion (or melting), vaporization, and sublimation are endothermic changes (positive $\Delta H°$), whereas freezing, condensation, and deposition are exothermic changes (negative $\Delta H°$).

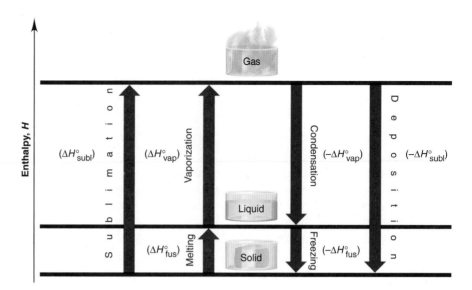

## Summary of Section 12.1

- Because of the relative magnitudes of intermolecular forces (potential energy) and average speed (kinetic energy), the particles in a gas are far apart and moving randomly, those in a liquid are in contact and moving relative to each other, and those in a solid are in contact and in fixed positions. These molecular-level differences account for macroscopic differences in shape, compressibility, and ability to flow.

- When a solid becomes a liquid (melting, or fusion), a liquid becomes a gas (vaporization), or a solid becomes a gas (sublimation), energy is absorbed to overcome intermolecular forces and increase the average distance between particles. As particles come closer together in the reverse changes (freezing, condensation, and deposition), energy is released. Each phase change is associated with a given enthalpy change under specified conditions.

# 12.2 • QUANTITATIVE ASPECTS OF PHASE CHANGES

Many phase changes occur around you every day, accompanied by the release or absorption of heat. When it rains, water vapor has condensed to a liquid, which changes back to a gas as puddles dry up. In the spring, solid water melts, and in winter, it freezes again. And the same phase changes take place whenever you make a pot of tea or a tray of ice cubes. In this section, we quantify the heat involved in a phase change and examine the equilibrium nature of the process.

## Heat Involved in Phase Changes

We apply a kinetic-molecular approach to phase changes with a **heating-cooling curve,** which shows the changes in temperature of a sample when heat is absorbed or released at a constant rate. Let's examine what happens when 2.50 mol of gaseous water in a closed container undergoes a change from 130°C to −40°C at a constant pressure of 1 atm. We'll divide this process into five heat-releasing (exothermic) stages (Figure 12.4):

*Stage 1. Gaseous water cools.* Water molecules zoom chaotically at a range of speeds, smashing into each other and the container walls. At the starting temperature, the most probable speed of the molecules, and thus their average kinetic energy ($E_k$), is high enough to overcome the potential energy ($E_p$) of attractions. As the temperature falls, the average $E_k$ decreases and attractions become more important. The change is

$$H_2O(g)\ [130°C] \longrightarrow H_2O(g)\ [100°C]$$

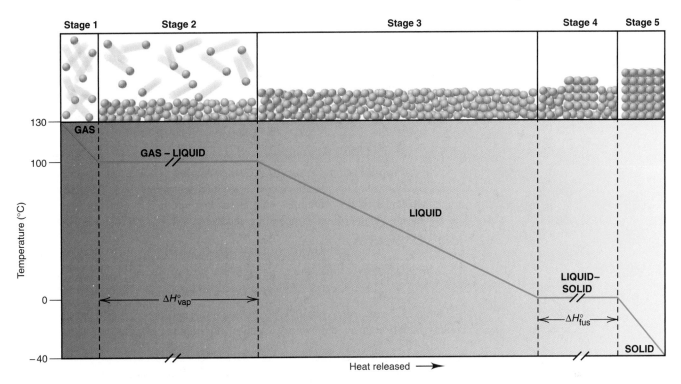

**Figure 12.4 A cooling curve for the conversion of gaseous water to ice.** A plot of temperature vs. heat released as gaseous water changes to ice is shown, with a molecular-level depiction for each stage. The slopes of the lines in stages 1, 3, and 5 reflect the molar heat capacities of the phases. Although not drawn to scale, the line in stage 2 is longer than the line in stage 4 because $\Delta H^{\circ}_{vap}$ of water is greater than $\Delta H^{\circ}_{fus}$. A plot of temperature vs. heat absorbed starting at $-40°C$ would have the same steps but in reverse order.

The heat ($q$) is the product of the amount (number of moles, $n$) of water, the molar heat capacity of *gaseous* water, $C_{water(g)}$, and the temperature change, $\Delta T$ ($T_{final} - T_{initial}$):

$$q = n \times C_{water(g)} \times \Delta T = (2.50 \text{ mol}) (33.1 \text{ J/mol·°C}) (100°C - 130°C)$$
$$= -2482 \text{ J} = -2.48 \text{ kJ}$$

The minus sign indicates that heat is released.*

*Stage 2. Gaseous water condenses.* At the condensation point, intermolecular attractions cause the slowest of the molecules to aggregate into microdroplets and then a bulk liquid. Note that, during the phase change,

- The temperature of the sample, and thus its average $E_k$, is constant. At the same temperature, molecules move farther between collisions in a gas than in a liquid, but their *average* speed is the same.
- Releasing heat from the sample decreases the average $E_p$ as the molecules approach each other.

Thus, at 100°C, gaseous and liquid water have the same average $E_k$, but the liquid has lower average $E_p$. The change is

$$H_2O(g) \, [100°C] \longrightarrow H_2O(l) \, [100°C]$$

The heat is the amount ($n$) times the negative of the heat of vaporization ($-\Delta H^{\circ}_{vap}$):

$$q = n(-\Delta H^{\circ}_{vap}) = (2.50 \text{ mol}) (-40.7 \text{ kJ/mol}) = -102 \text{ kJ}$$

This stage contributes the *greatest portion of the total heat released* because of the large decrease in $E_p$ as the molecules become so much closer in the liquid than they were in the gas.

---

*For purposes of canceling, the units for molar heat capacity, $C$, include °C, rather than K, but this doesn't affect the magnitude of $C$ because these two units represent the same temperature increment.

*Stage 3. Liquid water cools.* The molecules in the liquid state continue to lose heat, which appears as a decrease in temperature, that is, as a decrease in the most probable molecular speed and, thus, the average $E_k$. The temperature decreases as long as the sample remains liquid. The change is

$$H_2O(l)\,[100°C] \longrightarrow H_2O(l)\,[0°C]$$

The heat depends on amount ($n$), the molar heat capacity of *liquid* water, and $\Delta T$:

$$q = n \times C_{water(l)} \times \Delta T = (2.50\ \text{mol})\,(75.4\ \text{J/mol·°C})\,(0°C - 100°C)$$
$$= -18{,}850\ \text{J} = -18.8\ \text{kJ}$$

*Stage 4. Liquid water freezes.* At 0°C, the sample loses $E_p$ as increasing intermolecular attractions cause the molecules to align themselves into the crystalline structure of ice. Molecular motion continues only as random jiggling about fixed positions. As we saw during condensation, temperature and average $E_k$ are constant during freezing. The change is

$$H_2O(l)\,[0°C] \longrightarrow H_2O(s)\,[0°C]$$

The heat is equal to $n$ times the negative of the heat of fusion ($-\Delta H^°_{fus}$):

$$q = n(-\Delta H^°_{fus}) = (2.50\ \text{mol})\,(-6.02\ \text{kJ/mol}) = -15.0\ \text{kJ}$$

*Stage 5. Solid water cools.* With motion restricted to jiggling in place, further cooling merely reduces the average speed of this jiggling. The change is

$$H_2O(s)\,[0°C] \longrightarrow H_2O(s)\,[-40°C]$$

The heat depends on $n$, the molar heat capacity of *solid* water, and $\Delta T$:

$$q = n \times C_{water(s)} \times \Delta T = (2.50\ \text{mol})\,(37.6\ \text{J/mol·°C})\,(-40°C - 0°C)$$
$$= -3760\ \text{J} = -3.76\ \text{kJ}$$

According to Hess's law, the total heat released is the sum of the heats released for the individual stages. The sum of $q$ for stages 1 to 5 is $-142$ kJ. Two key points stand out for this or any similar process, whether exothermic or endothermic:

- *Within a phase,* heat flow is accompanied by *a change in temperature,* which is associated with a change in average $E_k$, as *the most probable speed of the molecules changes.* The heat released or absorbed depends on the amount of substance, the molar heat capacity *for that phase,* and the change in temperature.
- *During a phase change,* heat flow occurs at a *constant temperature,* which is associated with a change in average $E_p$, as *the average distance between molecules changes.* Both phases are present and (as you'll see below) are in equilibrium during the change. The heat released or absorbed depends on the amount of substance and the enthalpy change for that phase change.

Let's work a molecular-scene sample problem to make sure these ideas are clear.

---

**Sample Problem 12.1** | **Finding the Heat of a Phase Change Depicted by Molecular Scenes**

**Problem** The scenes below represent a phase change of water. Select data from the previous discussion to find the heat (in kJ) released or absorbed when 24.3 g of $H_2O$ undergoes this change.

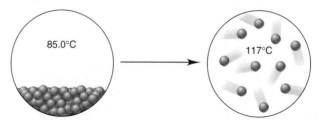

**Plan** From the molecular scenes, data in the text, and the given mass (24.3 g) of water, we have to find the heat that accompanies this change. The scenes show a disorderly, condensed phase at 85.0°C changing to separate molecules at 117°C. Thus, the phase change they depict is vaporization, an endothermic process. The text data are given per mole, so we first convert the mass (g) of water to amount (mol). There are three stages: (1) heating the liquid from 85.0°C to 100.°C, (2) converting liquid water at 100.°C to gaseous water at 100.°C, and (3) heating the gas from 100.°C to 117°C (*see margin*). We add the values of $q$ for these stages to obtain the total heat.

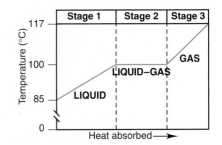

**Solution** Converting from mass (g) of $H_2O$ to amount (mol):

$$\text{Amount (mol) of } H_2O = 24.3 \text{ g } H_2O \times \frac{1 \text{ mol}}{18.02 \text{ g } H_2O} = 1.35 \text{ mol}$$

Finding the flow accompanying stage 1, $H_2O(l)\,[85.0°C] \longrightarrow H_2O(l)\,[100.°C]$:

$$q = n \times C_{\text{water}(l)} \times \Delta T = (1.35 \text{ mol})\,(75.4 \text{ J/mol·°C})\,(100.°C - 85.0°C)$$
$$= 1527 \text{ J} = 1.53 \text{ kJ}$$

Finding the heat accompanying stage 2, $H_2O(l)\,[100.°C] \longrightarrow H_2O(g)\,[100.°C]$:

$$q = n(\Delta H°_{\text{vap}}) = (1.35 \text{ mol})\,(40.7 \text{ kJ/mol}) = 54.9 \text{ kJ}$$

Finding the heat accompanying stage 3, $H_2O(g)\,[100.°C] \longrightarrow H_2O(g)\,[117°C]$:

$$q = n \times C_{\text{water}(g)} \times \Delta T = (1.35 \text{ mol})\,(33.1 \text{ J/mol·°C})\,(117°C - 100.°C)$$
$$= 759.6 \text{ J} = 0.760 \text{ kJ}$$

Adding the three heats together to find the total heat of the process:

$$\text{Total heat (kJ)} = 1.53 \text{ kJ} + 54.9 \text{ kJ} + 0.760 \text{ kJ} = \boxed{57.2 \text{ kJ}}$$

**Check** The heat should have a positive value because it is absorbed. Be sure to round to check each value of $q$; for example, in stage 1, 1.33 mol $\times$ 75 J/mol·°C $\times$ 15°C = 1500 J. Note that the phase change itself (stage 2) requires the most energy and, thus, dominates the final answer. The $\Delta H°_{\text{vap}}$ units include kJ, whereas the molar heat capacity units include J, which is a thousandth as large.

**Follow-Up Problem 12.1** The scenes below represent a phase change of water. Select data from the text discussion to find the heat (in kJ) released or absorbed when 2.25 mol of $H_2O$ undergoes this change.

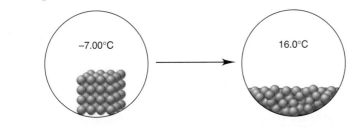

## The Equilibrium Nature of Phase Changes

In everyday experience, phase changes take place in *open* containers—the outdoors, a pot on a stove, the freezer compartment of a refrigerator—so they are not reversible. But, in a *closed* container, *phase changes **are** reversible and reach equilibrium,* just as chemical changes do. In this discussion, we examine the three phase equilibria.

**Liquid-Gas Equilibria** Vaporization and condensation are familar events. Let's see how these processes differ in open and closed systems of a liquid in a flask:

1. *Open system: nonequilibrium process.* Picture an *open* flask containing a pure liquid at constant temperature. Within their range of speeds, some molecules at the surface have a high enough $E_k$ to overcome attractions and vaporize. Nearby molecules fill the gap, and with heat supplied by the constant-temperature surroundings, the process continues until the entire liquid phase is gone.

2. *Closed system: equilibrium process.* Now picture a *closed* flask at constant temperature and assume a vacuum exists above a liquid (Figure 12.5A, *next page*). Two processes take place: Some molecules at the surface have a high enough $E_k$ to *vaporize*. After a short time, molecules in the vapor collide with the surface, and the slower ones are attracted strongly enough to *condense*.

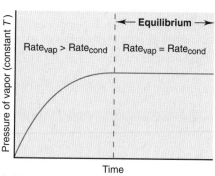

**A** Molecules in the liquid vaporize.
**B** Molecules vaporize and condense at the same rate.
**C** Plot of pressure vs. time.

**Figure 12.5** Liquid-gas equilibrium. **A,** Molecules leave the surface at a constant rate and the pressure rises. **B,** At equilibrium, the same number of molecules leave and enter the liquid in a given time. **C,** Pressure increases until, at equilibrium, it is constant.

At first, these two processes occur at different rates. The number of molecules in a given surface area is constant, so the number of molecules leaving the surface per unit time—the rate of vaporization—is also constant, and the pressure increases. With time, the number of molecules colliding with and entering the surface—the rate of condensation—increases as the vapor becomes more populated, so the increase in pressure slows. Eventually, the rate of condensation equals the rate of vaporization; from this time onward, *the pressure is constant* (Figure 12.5B).

Macroscopically, the situation at this point seems static, but at the molecular level, molecules are entering and leaving the liquid at equal rates. The system has reached a state of *dynamic equilibrium:*

$$\text{liquid} \rightleftharpoons \text{gas}$$

The pressure exerted by the vapor at equilibrium is called the *equilibrium vapor pressure,* or just the **vapor pressure,** of the liquid at that temperature. Figure 12.5C depicts the entire process graphically. If we started with a larger flask, the number of molecules in the vapor would be greater at equilibrium. But, as long as the temperature is constant and some liquid is present, the vapor pressure will be the same.

3. *Disturbing a system at equilibrium.* Let's see what happens if we alter certain conditions, called "disturbing" the system:
- *Decrease in pressure.* Suppose we pump some vapor out of the flask, immediately lowering the pressure. (In a cylinder fitted with a piston, we lower the pressure by moving the piston outward, thus increasing the volume.) The rate of condensation temporarily falls below the rate of vaporization (the forward process is faster) because fewer molecules enter the liquid than leave it. The pressure rises until, after a short time, the condensation rate increases enough for equilibrium to be reached again.
- *Increase in pressure.* Suppose we pump more vapor in (or move the piston inward, thus decreasing the volume), thereby immediately raising the pressure. The rate of condensation temporarily exceeds the rate of vaporization because more molecules enter the liquid than leave it (the reverse process is faster). Soon, however, the condensation rate decreases until the pressure again reaches the equilibrium value.

This general behavior of a liquid and its vapor is seen in any system at equilibrium: *when a system at equilibrium is disturbed, it counteracts the disturbance until it re-establishes equilibrium.* We'll return to this key idea often in later chapters.

## The Effects of Temperature and Intermolecular Forces on Vapor Pressure

While the vapor pressure is not affected by the removal or addition of gas, it is affected by two other factors—a change in temperature and a change in the gas, that is, in the types of intermolecular forces:

1. *Effect of temperature.* Temperature has a major effect on vapor pressure because it changes the fraction of molecules moving fast enough to escape the liquid and, by the same token, the fraction moving slowly enough to be recaptured. In Figure 12.6, we see the familiar skewed bell-shaped curve of the distribution of molecular speeds (see also Figure 5.6, page 188). At the higher temperature, $T_2$, more molecules have

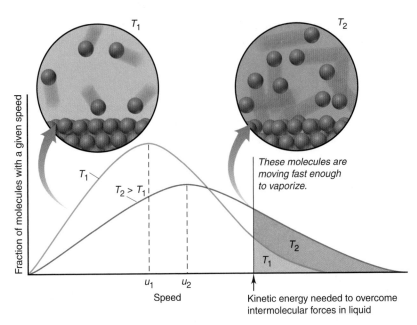

**Figure 12.6** The effect of temperature on the distribution of molecular speeds.

enough energy to leave the surface. Thus, in general, *the higher the temperature is, the higher the vapor pressure:*

$$\text{higher } T \implies \text{ higher } P$$

2. *Effect of intermolecular forces.* At a given $T$, all substances have the same average $E_k$. Therefore, molecules with weaker intermolecular forces are held less tightly at the surface and vaporize more easily. In general, *the weaker the intermolecular forces are, the higher the vapor pressure:*

$$\text{weaker forces} \implies \text{ higher } P$$

Figure 12.7 shows the vapor pressure of three liquids as a function of temperature:

- The effect of temperature is seen in the steeper rise as the temperature increases.
- The effect of intermolecular forces is seen in the values of the vapor pressure, the short, horizontal dashed lines intersecting the vertical (pressure) axis at a given temperature *(vertical dashed line at 20°C):* the intermolecular forces in diethyl ether (highest vapor pressure) are weaker than those in ethanol, which are weaker than those in water (lowest vapor pressure).

**Quantifying the Effect of Temperature** The nonlinear relationship between $P$ and $T$ is converted to a linear one with the **Clausius-Clapeyron equation:**

$$\ln P = \frac{-\Delta H_{vap}}{R}\left(\frac{1}{T}\right) + C$$
$$y \;=\;\quad m \quad\; x \;+\; b$$

where $\ln P$ is the natural logarithm of the vapor pressure, $\Delta H_{vap}$ is the heat of vaporization, $R$ is the universal gas constant (8.314 J/mol·K), $T$ is the absolute temperature, and $C$ is a constant (not related to heat capacity). The equation is often used to find the heat of vaporization. The equation for a straight line is shown under it in blue, with $y = \ln P$, $x = 1/T$, $m$ (the slope) $= -\Delta H_{vap}/R$, and $b$ (the $y$-axis intercept) $= C$. A plot of $\ln P$ vs. $1/T$ gives a straight line, as shown for diethyl ether and water in Figure 12.8.

A two-point version of the Clausius-Clapeyron equation allows us to calculate $\Delta H_{vap}$ if vapor pressures at two temperatures are known:

$$\ln \frac{P_2}{P_1} = \frac{-\Delta H_{vap}}{R}\left(\frac{1}{T_2} - \frac{1}{T_1}\right) \qquad \textbf{(12.1)}$$

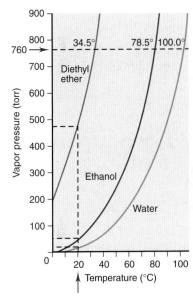

**Figure 12.7** Vapor pressure as a function of temperature and intermolecular forces.

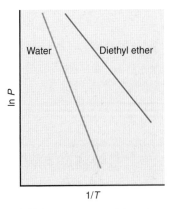

**Figure 12.8** Linear plots of the relationship between vapor pressure and temperature. The slope is steeper for water because its $\Delta H_{vap}$ is greater.

If $\Delta H_{vap}$ and $P_1$ at $T_1$ are known, we can also calculate the vapor pressure ($P_2$) at any other temperature ($T_2$) or the temperature at any other pressure.

---

**Sample Problem 12.2** | **Applying the Clausius-Clapeyron Equation**

**Problem** The vapor pressure of ethanol is 115 torr at 34.9°C. If $\Delta H_{vap}$ of ethanol is 40.5 kJ/mol, calculate the temperature (in °C) when the vapor pressure is 760 torr.

**Plan** We are given $\Delta H_{vap}$, $P_1$, $P_2$, and $T_1$ and substitute them into Equation 12.1 to solve for $T_2$. The value of $R$ here is 8.314 J/mol·K, so we must convert $T_1$ to K to obtain $T_2$, and then convert $T_2$ back to °C.

**Solution** Substituting the values into Equation 12.1 and solving for $T_2$:

$$\ln\frac{P_2}{P_1} = \frac{-\Delta H_{vap}}{R}\left(\frac{1}{T_2} - \frac{1}{T_1}\right)$$

$$T_1 = 34.9°C + 273.15 = 308.0 \text{ K}$$

$$\ln\frac{760 \text{ torr}}{115 \text{ torr}} = \left(-\frac{40.5\times10^3 \text{ J/mol}}{8.314 \text{ J/mol·K}}\right)\left(\frac{1}{T_2} - \frac{1}{308.0 \text{ K}}\right)$$

$$1.888 = (-4.87\times10^3)\left[\frac{1}{T_2} - (3.247\times10^{-3})\right]$$

$$T_2 = 350. \text{ K}$$

Converting $T_2$ from K to °C:

$$T_2 = 350. \text{ K} - 273.15 = \boxed{77°C}$$

**Check** Round off to check the math. The change is in the right direction: higher $P$ should occur at higher $T$. As we discuss next, a substance has a vapor pressure of 760 torr at its *normal boiling point*. Checking the *CRC Handbook of Chemistry and Physics* shows that the boiling point of ethanol is 78.5°C, very close to our answer.

**Follow-Up Problem 12.2** At 34.1°C, the vapor pressure of water is 40.1 torr. What is the vapor pressure at 85.5°C? The $\Delta H_{vap}$ of water is 40.7 kJ/mol.

---

**Vapor Pressure and Boiling Point** Let's discuss what is happening when a liquid boils and then see the effect of pressure on boiling point.

1. *How a liquid boils.* In an *open* container, the weight of the atmosphere bears down on a liquid surface. As the temperature rises, molecules move more quickly throughout the liquid. At some temperature, the average $E_k$ of the molecules in the liquid is great enough for them to form bubbles of vapor *in the interior,* and the liquid boils. At any lower temperature, the bubbles collapse as soon as they start to form because the external pressure is greater than the vapor pressure inside the bubbles. Thus, the **boiling point** *is the temperature at which the vapor pressure equals the external pressure,* which is usually that of the atmosphere. As in condensation and freezing, once boiling begins, the temperature of the liquid remains constant until all of the liquid is gone.

2. *Effect of pressure on boiling point.* The boiling point of a liquid varies with elevation. At high elevations, a lower atmospheric pressure is exerted on the liquid surface, so molecules in the interior need less kinetic energy to form bubbles. Thus, *the boiling point depends on the applied pressure.*

In mountainous regions, food takes *more* time to cook because the boiling point is lower and the boiling liquid is not as hot; for instance, in Boulder, Colorado (elevation 5430 ft, or 1655 m), water boils at 94°C. On the other hand, in a pressure cooker, food takes *less* time to cook because the boiling point is higher at the higher pressure. The *normal boiling point* is observed at standard atmospheric pressure (760 torr, or 101.3 kPa; *long, horizontal dashed line* in Figure 12.7).

**Solid-Liquid Equilibria** The particles in a crystal are continually jiggling about their fixed positions. As the temperature rises, the particles jiggle more rapidly, until some have enough kinetic energy to break free of their positions. At this point, melting begins. As more molecules enter the liquid (molten) phase, some collide with the solid and become fixed in position again. Because the phases remain in contact, a dynamic equilibrium is established when the melting rate equals the freezing rate. The temperature at which this occurs is called the **melting point.** The temperature remains fixed at the melting point until all the solid melts.

Because liquids and solids are nearly incompressible, pressure has little effect on the rates of melting and freezing: a plot of pressure vs. temperature for a solid-liquid phase change is typically a *nearly* vertical straight line.

**Solid-Gas Equilibria** Sublimation is not very familiar because solids have *much* lower vapor pressures than liquids. A substance sublimes rather than melts because the intermolecular attractions are not great enough to keep the molecules near each other when they leave the solid state. Some solids *do* have high enough vapor pressures to sublime at ordinary conditions, including dry ice (carbon dioxide), iodine (Figure 12.9), and moth repellants, all nonpolar molecules with weak intermolecular forces.

The plot of pressure vs. temperature for a solid-gas phase change reflects the large effect of temperature on vapor pressure; thus, it resembles the liquid-gas curve in rising steeply with higher temperatures.

**Figure 12.9** Iodine subliming. After the solid sublimes, $I_2$ vapor deposits on a cold surface (water-filled inner test tube).

## Phase Diagrams: Effect of Pressure and Temperature on Physical State

The **phase diagram** of a substance combines the liquid-gas, solid-liquid, and solid-gas curves and gives the conditions of temperature and pressure at which each phase is stable and where phase changes occur.

**The Phase Diagram for $CO_2$ and Most Substances** The diagram for $CO_2$, which is typical of most substances, has four general features (Figure 12.10):

1. *Regions of the diagram.* Each region presents the conditions of pressure and temperature for which the phase is stable. If another phase is placed under those conditions, it will change to the stable phase. In general, the solid is stable at low temperature and high pressure, the gas at high temperature and low pressure, and the liquid at intermediate conditions.

2. *Lines between regions.* The lines are the phase-transition curves discussed earlier. Any point along a line shows the pressure and temperature at which the phases are in equilibrium. The solid-liquid line has a slightly *positive* slope (slants to the *right* with increasing pressure) because, for most substances, the solid is more dense than the liquid: an increase in pressure converts the liquid to the solid. (Water is *the* major exception.)

3. *The triple point.* The three phase-transition curves meet at the **triple point,** at which all three phases are in equilibrium. As strange as it sounds, at the triple point in Figure 12.10, $CO_2$ is subliming and depositing, melting and freezing, and vaporizing and condensing simultaneously! Substances with several solid and/or liquid forms can have more than one triple point.

The $CO_2$ phase diagram shows why dry ice (solid $CO_2$) doesn't melt under ordinary conditions. The triple-point pressure is 5.1 atm, so liquid $CO_2$ doesn't occur at 1 atm because it is not stable. The horizontal dashed line at 1.0 atm crosses the solid-gas line, so when solid $CO_2$ is heated, it sublimes at $-78°C$ rather than melts. If our normal atmospheric pressure were 5.2 atm, liquid $CO_2$ *would* occur.

4. *The critical point.* Heat a liquid in a closed container and its density decreases. At the same time, more of the liquid vaporizes, so the density of the vapor increases. At the **critical point,** the two densities become equal and the phase boundary disappears. The temperature at

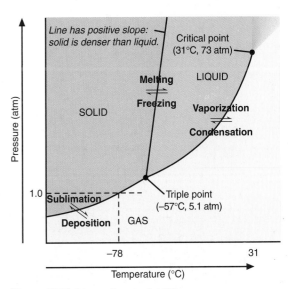

**Figure 12.10** Phase diagram for $CO_2$. (The slope of the solid-liquid line is exaggerated, and the axes are not linear in both this figure and Figure 12.11.)

the critical point is the *critical temperature* ($T_c$), and the pressure is the *critical pressure* ($P_c$). The average $E_k$ is so high at this point that the vapor cannot be condensed at any pressure. The two most common gases in air have critical temperatures far below room temperature: $O_2$ cannot be condensed above $-119°C$, and $N_2$ above $-147°C$.

Beyond the critical temperature, a *supercritical fluid* (SCF) exists rather than separate liquid and gaseous phases. An SCF expands and contracts like a gas and has unusual solvent properties. Supercritical $CO_2$ is used to extract caffeine from coffee beans, nicotine from tobacco, and fats from potato chips, and acts as a dry cleaning agent. Lower the pressure, and the SCF disperses as a harmless gas. Supercritical $H_2O$ dissolves nonpolar substances, even though liquid water cannot. Studies are under way to use supercritical $H_2O$ for removing nonpolar organic toxins, such as PCBs, from industrial waste.

**The Solid-Liquid Line for Water** The phase diagram for water differs from others in one major respect that reveals a key property. Unlike almost any other substance, the solid form is *less dense* than the liquid; that is, *water expands upon freezing*. Thus, the solid-liquid line has a *negative* slope (slants to the *left* with increasing pressure): an increase in pressure converts the solid to the liquid, and the higher the pressure, the lower the temperature at which water freezes (Figure 12.11). The vertical dashed line at $-1°C$ crosses the solid-liquid line, which means that ice melts with only an increase in pressure.

The triple point of water occurs at low pressure (0.006 atm). Therefore, when solid water is heated at 1.0 atm (*horizontal dashed line*), the solid-liquid line is crossed at 0°C, the normal melting point. Thus, ice melts rather than sublimes. The horizontal dashed line then crosses the liquid-gas curve at 100°C, the normal boiling point.

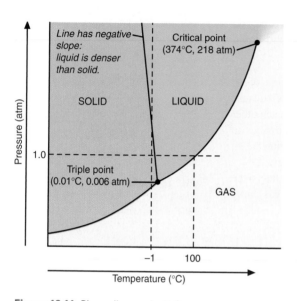

**Figure 12.11** Phase diagram for $H_2O$.

## Summary of Section 12.2

- A heating-cooling curve depicts the change in temperature when a substance absorbs or releases heat at a constant rate. Within a phase, temperature (and average $E_k$) changes. During a phase change, temperature (and average $E_k$) is constant, but $E_p$ changes. The total enthalpy change for the system is found using Hess's law.
- In a closed container, the liquid and gas phases of a substance reach equilibrium. The vapor pressure, the pressure of the gas at equilibrium, is related directly to temperature and inversely to the strength of the intermolecular forces.
- The Clausius-Clapeyron equation relates the vapor pressure to the temperature and is often used to find $\Delta H_{vap}$.
- A liquid in an open container boils when its vapor pressure equals the external pressure.
- Solid-liquid equilibrium occurs at the melting point. Some solids sublime because they have very weak intermolecular forces.
- The phase diagram of a substance shows the phase that is stable at any $P$ and $T$, the conditions at which phase changes occur, and the conditions at the critical point and the triple point. Water differs from most substances in that its solid phase is less dense than its liquid phase, so its solid-liquid line has a negative slope.

# 12.3 • TYPES OF INTERMOLECULAR FORCES

In Chapter 9, we saw that bonding (*intra*molecular) forces are due to the attraction between cations and anions (ionic bonding), nuclei and electron pairs (covalent bonding), or metal cations and delocalized electrons (metallic bonding). But the nature of the phases and their changes are due primarily to *inter*molecular (nonbonding) forces, which arise from the attraction between molecules with partial charges or between ions and molecules. Coulomb's law explains why the two types of forces differ in magnitude:

- *Bonding forces are relatively strong* because larger charges are closer together.
- *Intermolecular forces are relatively weak* because smaller charges are farther apart.

# How Close Can Molecules Approach Each Other?

To see the minimum distance *between* molecules, consider solid $Cl_2$. When we measure the distances between two Cl nuclei, we obtain two different values (Figure 12.12A):

- *Bond length and covalent radius.* The shorter distance, called the *bond length*, is between *two bonded Cl atoms in the same molecule*. One-half this distance is the *covalent radius*.
- *Van der Waals distance and radius.* The longer distance is between *two nonbonded Cl atoms in adjacent molecules*. It is called the *van der Waals (VDW) distance*. At this distance, intermolecular attractions balance electron-cloud repulsions; thus, the VDW distance is as close as one $Cl_2$ molecule can approach another. The **van der Waals radius** is one-half the closest distance between nuclei of identical *nonbonded* atoms. The VDW radius of an atom is *always larger than its covalent radius.* Like covalent radii, VDW radii decrease across a period and increase down a group (Figure 12.12B).

As we discuss intermolecular forces (also called *van der Waals forces*), consult Table 12.2, which compares them with bonding forces.

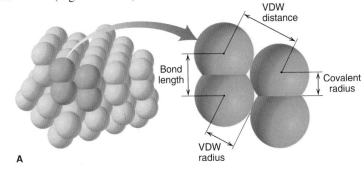

**Figure 12.12** Covalent and van der Waals radii and their periodic trends. **A,** The van der Waals (VDW) radius is one-half the distance between adjacent *nonbonded* atoms ($\frac{1}{2}$ × VDW distance). **B,** Like covalent radii (*blue quarter-circles and numbers*), VDW radii (*red quarter-circles and numbers*) increase down a group and decrease across a period.

## Table 12.2 Comparison of Bonding and Nonbonding (Intermolecular) Forces

| Force | Model | Basis of Attraction | Energy (kJ/mol) | Example |
|---|---|---|---|---|
| **Bonding** | | | | |
| Ionic | | Cation–anion | 400–4000 | NaCl |
| Covalent | | Nuclei–shared $e^-$ pair | 150–1100 | H—H |
| Metallic | | Cations–delocalized electrons | 75–1000 | Fe |
| **Nonbonding (Intermolecular)** | | | | |
| Ion-dipole | | Ion charge–dipole charge | 40–600 | $Na^+ \cdots O$ with H, H |
| H bond | $-A-H \cdots :B-$ | Polar bond to H–dipole charge (high EN of N, O, F) | 10–40 | $:\ddot{O}-H \cdots :\ddot{O}-H$ with H, H |
| Dipole-dipole | | Dipole charges | 5–25 | I—Cl $\cdots$ I—Cl |
| Ion–induced dipole | | Ion charge–polarizable $e^-$ cloud | 3–15 | $Fe^{2+} \cdots O_2$ |
| Dipole–induced dipole | | Dipole charge–polarizable $e^-$ cloud | 2–10 | H—Cl $\cdots$ Cl—Cl |
| Dispersion (London) | | Polarizable $e^-$ clouds | 0.05–40 | F—F $\cdots$ F—F |

**Figure 12.13 Polar molecules and dipole-dipole forces.** (Spaces between the molecules are exaggerated.)

## Ion-Dipole Forces

When an ion and a nearby polar molecule (dipole) attract each other, an **ion-dipole force** results. The most important example takes place when an ionic compound dissolves in water. The ions become separated because the attractions between the ions and the oppositely charged poles of the $H_2O$ molecules are stronger than the attractions between the ions themselves. Ion-dipole forces in solutions and their associated energy are discussed fully in Chapter 13.

## Dipole-Dipole Forces

In Figure 10.13 (p. 383), an external electric field orients gaseous polar molecules. The polar molecules in liquids and solids lie near each other, and their partial charges act as tiny electric fields and give rise to **dipole-dipole forces:** the positive pole of one molecule attracts the negative pole of another (Figure 12.13). The orientation is more orderly in a solid than in a liquid because the average kinetic energy is lower.

These forces depend on the magnitude of the molecular dipole moment. For compounds of similar molar mass, the greater the molecular dipole moment, the greater the dipole-dipole forces, so the more energy it takes to separate the molecules; thus the boiling point is higher. Methyl chloride, for instance, has a smaller dipole moment than acetaldehyde and boils at a lower temperature (Figure 12.14).

**Figure 12.14 Dipole moment and boiling point.** (Relative strength of the dipole moments is indicated by color intensities in the electron-density models.)

## The Hydrogen Bond

A special type of dipole-dipole force arises between molecules that have *an H atom bonded to a small, highly electronegative atom with lone electron pairs, specifically N, O, or F.* The H—N, H—O, and H—F bonds are very polar. When the partially positive H of one molecule is attracted to the partially negative lone pair on the N, O, or F of another molecule, a **hydrogen bond (H bond)** forms. Thus, the atom sequence of an H bond (dotted line) is —B:····H—A—, where A *and* B are N, O, or F. Three examples are

$$—\ddot{\underset{\cdot\cdot}{F}}:····H—\ddot{\underset{\cdot\cdot}{O}}— \qquad —\ddot{\underset{\cdot\cdot}{O}}:····H—\ddot{N}— \qquad —\ddot{N}:····H—\ddot{\underset{\cdot\cdot}{O}}:$$

The small sizes of N, O, and F are essential to H bonding for two reasons:

1. The atoms are so electronegative that their covalently bonded H is highly positive.
2. The lone pair on the N, O, or F of the other molecule can come close to the H.

**The Significance of Hydrogen Bonding** Hydrogen bonding has a profound impact in many systems. We'll examine one effect on physical properties and preview its importance in biological systems, which we address in Chapters 13 and 15.

Figure 12.15 shows the effect of H bonding on the boiling points of the binary hydrides of Groups 4A(14) through 7A(17). For reasons we'll discuss shortly, boiling points rise with molar mass, as the Group 4A(14) hydrides show. However, the first member in each of the other groups—$NH_3$, $H_2O$, and HF—deviates enormously from this expected trend. Within samples of these substances, the molecules form strong H bonds, so it takes more energy for the molecules to separate and enter the gas phase. For example, on the basis of molar mass alone, we would expect water to boil about 200°C lower than it actually does (*red dashed line*). (In Section 12.5 we'll discuss the effects that H bonds in water have in nature.)

The significance of hydrogen bonding in biological systems cannot be emphasized too strongly. In Chapter 13, you'll see that it is a key feature in the structure and function of the biological macromolecules—proteins and nucleic acids. It is also responsible for the action of many *enzymes*, the proteins that speed metabolic reactions.

---

**Sample Problem 12.3**    **Drawing Hydrogen Bonds Between Molecules of a Substance**

**Problem** Which of the following substances exhibits H bonding? For any that do, show the H bonds between two of its molecules.

(a) $C_2H_6$    (b) $CH_3OH$    (c) $CH_3\overset{\displaystyle O}{\overset{\displaystyle \|}{C}}-NH_2$

**Plan** If the molecule does *not* contain N, O, or F, it cannot form H bonds. If it contains any of these atoms covalently bonded to H, we draw two molecules in the —B:⋯⋯H—A— pattern.

**Solution** (a) For $C_2H_6$. No N, O, or F, so no H bonds can form.
(b) For $CH_3OH$. The H covalently bonded to the O in one molecule forms an H bond to the lone pair on the O of an adjacent molecule:

```
        H
        |
    H—C—H            H
        |             |
    H—Ö:⋯⋯H—Ö—C—H
                      |
                      H
```

(c) For $CH_3\overset{\displaystyle O}{\overset{\|}{C}}—NH_2$. Two of these molecules can form one H bond between an H bonded to N and the O, or they can form two such H bonds:

A third possibility (not shown) could be between an H attached to N in one molecule and the lone pair of N in another molecule.

**Check** The —B:····H—A— sequence (with A and B either N, O, or F) is present.

**Comment** Note that H covalently bonded to C *does not form H bonds* because carbon is not electronegative enough to make the C—H bond sufficiently polar.

**Follow-Up Problem 12.3** Which of these substances exhibits H bonding? Draw the H bond(s) between two molecules of the substance where appropriate.

(a) $CH_3\overset{\displaystyle O}{\overset{\|}{C}}—OH$  (b) $CH_3CH_2OH$  (c) $CH_3\overset{\displaystyle O}{\overset{\|}{C}}CH_3$

## Polarizability and Induced Dipole Forces

Even though electrons are attracted to nuclei and localized in bonding and lone pairs, we often picture them as "clouds" of negative charge because they are in constant motion. A nearby electric field can *induce* a distortion in the cloud, pulling electron density toward a positive pole of a field or pushing it away from a negative one:

- *For a nonpolar molecule,* the distortion induces a temporary dipole moment.
- *For a polar molecule,* it enhances the dipole moment already present.

In addition to charged plates connected to a battery, the source of the electric field can be the charge of an ion or the partial charges of a polar molecule.

How easily an electron cloud can be distorted is called its **polarizability.** Smaller atoms (or ions) are less polarizable than larger ones because their electrons are closer to the nucleus and therefore held more tightly. Thus, we observe several trends:

- Polarizability *increases down a group* because atomic size increases and larger electron clouds are easier to distort.
- Polarizability *decreases across a period* because increasing $Z_{eff}$ makes the atoms smaller and holds the electrons more tightly.
- Cations are *less* polarizable than their parent atoms because they are smaller; anions are *more* polarizable because they are larger.

Ion–induced dipole and dipole–induced dipole forces are the two types of charge-induced dipole forces; they are most important in solution, so we'll focus on them in Chapter 13. Nevertheless, *polarizability affects all intermolecular forces.*

## Dispersion (London) Forces

So far, we've discussed forces that depend on the existing charge of an ion or a polar molecule. But what forces cause nonpolar substances like octane, chlorine, and argon to condense and solidify? As you'll see, polarizability plays the central role in the most universal intermolecular force.

*The intermolecular force responsible for the condensed states of nonpolar substances is the* **dispersion force** (or **London force,** named for Fritz London, the physicist who explained its quantum-mechanical basis). Dispersion forces *are present between all particles (atoms, ions, and molecules) because they are caused by the motion of electrons in atoms.* Let's examine key aspects of this force:

1. *Source.* Picture one atom in a sample of, say, argon gas. Over time, its 18 electrons are distributed uniformly, so the atom is nonpolar. But at any instant, there may be more electrons on one side of the nucleus than the other, which gives the atom an *instantaneous dipole.* When a pair of argon atoms is far apart, they don't influence each other, but when close together, *the instantaneous dipole in one atom induces a dipole in its neighbor,* and they attract each other. This process spreads to other atoms and throughout the sample. At low temperatures, these attractions keep the atoms together (Figure 12.16). Thus, dispersion forces are *instantaneous dipole–induced dipole forces.*

2. *Prevalence.* While they are the *only* force existing between nonpolar particles, *dispersion forces contribute to the energy of attraction in all substances* because they exist between *all* particles. In fact, except for the forces between small, highly polar molecules or between molecules forming H bonds, the *dispersion force is the dominant intermolecular force.* Calculations show, for example, that 85% of the attraction between HCl molecules is due to dispersion forces and only 15% to dipole-dipole forces. Even for water, 75% of the attraction comes from H bonds and 25% from dispersion forces.

3. *Relative strength.* The relative strength of dispersion forces depends on the polarizability of the particles, so they are weak for small particles, like $H_2$ and He, but stronger for larger particles, like $I_2$ and Xe. *Polarizability depends on the number of electrons, which correlates closely with molar mass* because heavier particles are either larger atoms or molecules with more atoms and, thus, more electrons. For this reason, as molar mass increases down the Group 4A(14) hydrides (see Figure 12.15), or down the halogens or the noble gases, dispersion forces increase and so do boiling points (Figure 12.17).

4. *Effect of molecular shape.* For a pair of nonpolar substances with the same molar mass, a molecular shape that has more area over which electron clouds can be distorted allows stronger attractions. For example, the two five-carbon alkanes, *n*-pentane and neopentane (2,2-dimethylpropane) are structural isomers—same molecular formula ($C_5H_{12}$) but different properties. *n*-Pentane is more cylindrical and neopentane more spherical (Figure 12.18). Thus, two *n*-pentane molecules make more contact than do two neopentane molecules, so dispersion forces act at more points, and *n*-pentane has a higher boiling point.

Figure 12.19 on the next page shows how to determine the intermolecular forces in a sample.

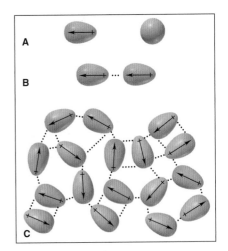

**Figure 12.16 Dispersion forces among nonpolar particles. A,** When atoms are far apart, an instantaneous dipole in one atom (*left*) doesn't influence another. **B,** When atoms are close together, the instantaneous dipole in one atom induces a dipole in the other. **C,** The process occurs through the sample.

**Figure 12.17** Molar mass and trends in boiling point.

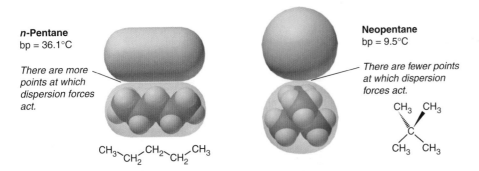

*n*-Pentane
bp = 36.1°C

There are more points at which dispersion forces act.

$CH_3-CH_2-CH_2-CH_2-CH_3$

Neopentane
bp = 9.5°C

There are fewer points at which dispersion forces act.

**Figure 12.18** Molecular shape, intermolecular contact, and boiling point.

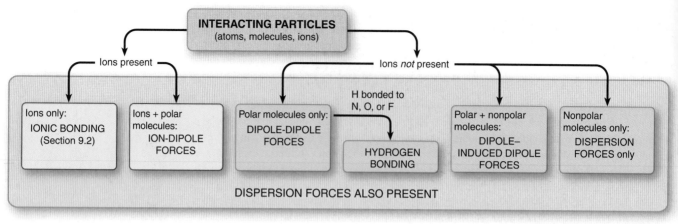

**Figure 12.19** Determining the intermolecular forces in a sample.

## Sample Problem 12.4 | Predicting the Types of Intermolecular Forces

**Problem** For each substance, identify the key bonding and/or intermolecular force(s), and predict which one of the pair has the higher boiling point:
**(a)** $MgCl_2$ or $PCl_3$
**(b)** $CH_3NH_2$ or $CH_3F$
**(c)** $CH_3OH$ or $CH_3CH_2OH$
**(d)** Hexane ($CH_3CH_2CH_2CH_2CH_2CH_3$) or 2,2-dimethylbutane $\left( \begin{array}{c} CH_3 \\ | \\ CH_3CCH_2CH_3 \\ | \\ CH_3 \end{array} \right)$

**Plan** We examine the formulas and structures for key differences between members of the pair: Are ions present? Are molecules polar or nonpolar? Is N, O, or F bonded to H? Do the molecules have different masses or shapes?
To rank boiling points, we consult Figure 12.19 and Table 12.2. Remember that
• Bonding forces are stronger than intermolecular forces.
• Hydrogen bonding is a strong type of dipole-dipole force.
• Dispersion forces are decisive when the difference is molar mass or molecular shape.

**Solution (a)** $MgCl_2$ consists of $Mg^{2+}$ and $Cl^-$ ions held together by ionic bonding forces; $PCl_3$ consists of polar molecules, so intermolecular dipole-dipole forces are present. The forces in $MgCl_2$ are stronger, so it should have a higher boiling point.
**(b)** $CH_3NH_2$ and $CH_3F$ both consist of polar molecules of about the same molar mass. $CH_3NH_2$ has N—H bonds, so it can form H bonds (*see margin*). $CH_3F$ contains a C—F bond but no H—F bond, so dipole-dipole forces occur but not H bonds. Therefore, $CH_3NH_2$ should have the higher boiling point.
**(c)** $CH_3OH$ and $CH_3CH_2OH$ molecules both contain an O—H bond, so they can form H bonds (*see margin*). $CH_3CH_2OH$ has an additional —$CH_2$— group and thus a larger molar mass, which correlates with stronger dispersion forces; therefore, it should have a higher boiling point.
**(d)** Hexane and 2,2-dimethylbutane are nonpolar molecules of the same molar mass but different molecular shapes (*see margin*). Cylindrical hexane molecules make more intermolecular contact than more compact 2,2-dimethylbutane molecules do, so hexane should have stronger dispersion forces and a higher boiling point.

**Check** The actual boiling points show that our predictions are correct:
**(a)** $MgCl_2$ (1412°C) and $PCl_3$ (76°C)
**(b)** $CH_3NH_2$ (−6.3°C) and $CH_3F$ (−78.4°C)
**(c)** $CH_3OH$ (64.7°C) and $CH_3CH_2OH$ (78.5°C)
**(d)** Hexane (69°C) and 2,2-dimethylbutane (49.7°C)

**Comment** Dispersion forces are *always* present, but in parts (a) and (b), they are much less significant than the other forces that occur.

## Follow-Up Problem 12.4
In each pair, identify the intermolecular forces present for each substance, and predict which substance has the higher boiling point:
**(a)** $CH_3Br$ or $CH_3F$    **(b)** $CH_3CH_2CH_2OH$ or $CH_3CH_2OCH_3$    **(c)** $C_2H_6$ or $C_3H_8$

**(b)**

**(c)**

2,2-Dimethylbutane

Hexane

# ■ Summary of Section 12.3

- The van der Waals radius determines the shortest distance over which intermolecular forces operate; it is always larger than the covalent radius.
- Intermolecular forces are much weaker than bonding (intramolecular) forces.
- Ion-dipole forces occur between ions and polar molecules.
- Dipole-dipole forces occur between oppositely charged poles on polar molecules.
- Hydrogen bonding, a special type of dipole-dipole force, occurs when H bonded to N, O, or F is attracted to the lone pair of N, O, or F in another molecule.
- Electron clouds can be distorted (polarized) in an electric field.
- Ion– and dipole–induced dipole forces arise between a charge and the dipole it induces in another molecule.
- Dispersion (London) forces are instantaneous dipole–induced dipole forces that occur among all particles and increase with number of electrons (molar mass). Molecular shape determines the extent of contact between molecules and can be a factor in the strength of dispersion forces.

# 12.4 • PROPERTIES OF THE LIQUID STATE

Of the three states, only liquids combine the ability to flow with the effects of strong intermolecular forces. We understand this state least at the molecular level. Because of the *random* arrangement of the particles in a gas, any region of the sample is virtually identical to any other. And, different regions of a crystalline solid are identical because of the *orderly* arrangement of the particles (Section 12.6). Liquids, however, have regions that are orderly one moment and random the next. Despite this complexity, many macroscopic properties, such as surface tension, capillarity, and viscosity are well understood.

## Surface Tension

Intermolecular forces have different effects on a molecule at the surface compared with one in the interior (Figure 12.20):

- An interior molecule is attracted by others on all sides.
- A surface molecule is only attracted by others below and to the sides, so it experiences a *net attraction downward.*

Therefore, to increase attractions and become more stable, a surface molecule tends to move into the interior. For this reason, *a liquid surface has the fewest molecules and, thus, the smallest area possible.* In effect, the surface behaves like a "taut skin" covering the interior.

The only way to increase the surface area is for molecules to move up by breaking attractions in the interior, which requires energy. The **surface tension** is the energy required to increase the surface area and has units of $J/m^2$ (Table 12.3). In general, *the stronger the forces are between particles, the more energy it takes to increase the surface area, so the greater the surface tension.* Water has a high surface tension because its molecules form multiple H bonds. *Surfactants* (*surf*ace-*act*ive agents), such as soaps, petroleum recovery agents, and fat emulsifiers, decrease the surface tension of water by congregating at the surface and disrupting the H bonds.

**Figure 12.20** The molecular basis of surface tension.

| Table **12.3** Surface Tension and Forces Between Particles | | | |
|---|---|---|---|
| **Substance** | **Formula** | **Surface Tension ($J/m^2$) at 20°C** | **Major Force(s)** |
| Diethyl ether | $CH_3CH_2OCH_2CH_3$ | $1.7 \times 10^{-2}$ | Dipole-dipole; dispersion |
| Ethanol | $CH_3CH_2OH$ | $2.3 \times 10^{-2}$ | H bonding |
| Butanol | $CH_3CH_2CH_2CH_2OH$ | $2.5 \times 10^{-2}$ | H bonding; dispersion |
| Water | $H_2O$ | $7.3 \times 10^{-2}$ | H bonding |
| Mercury | $Hg$ | $48 \times 10^{-2}$ | Metallic bonding |

A water strider's widespread legs don't exert enough pressure to exceed the surface tension.

Surface tension is the cause of many familiar phenomena. Bubbles are round because this shape minimizes the surface area around the gas, and surface tension is the reason some insects can walk on water (*see photo*).

## Capillarity

The rising of a liquid against the pull of gravity through a narrow space, such as a thin tube, is called *capillary action,* or **capillarity.** Capillarity results from a competition between the intermolecular forces within the liquid (cohesive forces) and those between the liquid and the tube walls (adhesive forces). Let's look at the difference between the capillarities of water and mercury in glass:

1. *Water in glass.* When you place a narrow glass tube in water, why does the liquid rise up the tube and form a concave meniscus? Glass is mostly silicon dioxide ($SiO_2$), so water molecules form adhesive H bonding forces with the O atoms of the glass. As a result, a thin film of water creeps up the wall. At the same time, cohesive H bonding forces between water molecules, which give rise to surface tension, make the surface taut. These adhesive and cohesive forces combine to raise the water level and produce the concave meniscus (Figure 12.21A). The liquid rises until gravity pulling down is balanced by adhesive forces pulling up.

2. *Mercury in glass.* When you place a glass tube in a dish of mercury, why does the liquid drop below the level in the dish and form a convex meniscus? The cohesive forces among the mercury atoms are metallic bonds, so they are *much* stronger than the mostly dispersion adhesive forces between mercury and glass. As a result, the liquid pulls away from the walls. At the same time, the surface atoms are being pulled toward the interior by mercury's high surface tension, so the level drops. These combined forces produce the concave meniscus seen in a laboratory barometer (Figure 12.21B).

Capillarity plays a key role in many everyday events. The adhesive (dipole–induced dipole) forces between water and a nonpolar surface are much weaker than the cohesive (H-bond) forces within water. As a result, water pulls away from a nonpolar surface and forms beaded droplets, as on a freshly waxed car or on the waxy coating of a leaf after a rainfall. Even more familiar, after a shower, capillary action draws water away from your body through the closely spaced fibers in the cotton towel, which is made of cellulose molecules, so the water molecules also form H bonds with the —OH groups of cellulose.

**Figure 12.21** Capillary action and the shape of the water or mercury meniscus in glass. **A,** Water displays a concave meniscus. **B,** Mercury displays a convex meniscus.

# Viscosity

**Viscosity** is the resistance of a fluid to flow, and it results from intermolecular attractions that impede the movement of molecules around and past each other. Both gases and liquids flow, but liquid viscosities are *much* higher because there are many more points for intermolecular forces to act due to the much shorter distances. Let's examine two factors—temperature and molecular shape—that influence viscosity:

- *Effect of temperature. Viscosity decreases with heating* (Table 12.4). Faster moving molecules overcome intermolecular forces more easily, so the resistance to flow decreases. Next time you heat cooking oil, watch the oil flow more easily and spread out in the pan as it warms.
- *Effect of molecular shape.* Small, spherical molecules make little contact and pour easily, like buckshot from a bowl. Long molecules make more contact and become entangled and pour slowly, like cooked spaghetti from a bowl. Thus, given the same types of intermolecular forces, liquids consisting of longer molecules have higher viscosities.

To protect engine parts during long drives, motor oils contain *polymeric viscosity improvers.* As the oil warms, these additive molecules change from compact spheres to long strands that become tangled with the long hydrocarbon molecules of the oil. Greater dispersion forces increase the viscosity to compensate for the oil thinning due to heating.

| Table **12.4** Viscosity of Water at Several Temperatures | |
|---|---|
| Temperature (°C) | Viscosity (N·s/m²)* |
| 20 | $1.00 \times 10^{-3}$ |
| 40 | $0.65 \times 10^{-3}$ |
| 60 | $0.47 \times 10^{-3}$ |
| 80 | $0.35 \times 10^{-3}$ |

*The units of viscosity are newton-seconds per square meter.

## Summary of Section 12.4

- Surface tension is a measure of the energy required to increase a liquid's surface area. Greater intermolecular forces within a liquid create higher surface tension.
- Capillarity, the rising of a liquid through a narrow space, occurs when the forces between a liquid and a surface (adhesive) are greater than those within the liquid (cohesive).
- Viscosity, the resistance to flow, depends on molecular shape and decreases with temperature. Stronger intermolecular forces create higher viscosity.

# 12.5 • THE UNIQUENESS OF WATER

Water is absolutely amazing stuff, with some of the most unusual properties of any substance, but it is so familiar we take it for granted. Like any substance, its properties arise inevitably from those of its atoms. Each O and H atom attains a filled outer level by sharing electrons in single bonds. With two bonding pairs and two lone pairs around O and a large electronegativity difference in each O—H bond, the $H_2O$ molecule is bent and highly polar. This arrangement is crucial because it allows each molecule to engage in four H bonds with its neighbors (Figure 12.22). From these basic atomic and molecular facts emerges unique and remarkable macroscopic behavior.

**Figure 12.22 H-bonding ability of water.** One $H_2O$ molecule can form four H bonds to other molecules, resulting in a tetrahedral arrangement.

## Solvent Properties of Water

The *great solvent power* of water results from its polarity and H-bonding ability:

- It dissolves ionic compounds through ion-dipole forces that separate the ions from the solid and keep them in solution (see Figure 4.2, p. 138).
- It dissolves polar nonionic substances, such as ethanol ($CH_3CH_2OH$) and glucose ($C_6H_{12}O_6$), by H bonding.
- It dissolves nonpolar atmospheric gases to a limited extent through dipole–induced dipole and dispersion forces.

Water is the environmental and biological solvent, forming the complex solutions we know as oceans, lakes, and cytoplasm. Aquatic animals could not survive without dissolved $O_2$, nor could aquatic plants without dissolved $CO_2$. Tiny marine animals form coral reefs made of carbonates from dissolved $CO_2$ and $HCO_3^-$. Life began in a "primordial soup," an aqueous mixture of simple molecules from which emerged larger molecules capable of self-sustaining reactions. From a chemical point of view, all organisms, from bacteria to humans, are highly organized systems of membranes enclosing and compartmentalizing complex aqueous solutions.

## Thermal Properties of Water

When a substance is heated, some of the added energy increases average molecular speed, some increases molecular vibration and rotation, and some is used to overcome intermolecular forces.

1. *Specific heat capacity.* Because water has so many strong H bonds, its *specific heat capacity* is higher than any common liquid. With oceans covering 70% of Earth's surface, daytime energy from the Sun causes relatively small changes in temperature, allowing life to survive. On the waterless, airless Moon, temperatures range from 100°C to −150°C during a complete lunar day. Even in Earth's deserts, day-night temperature differences of 40°C are common.

2. *Heat of vaporization.* Numerous strong H bonds give water a very *high heat of vaporization.* Two examples show why this is crucial. The average adult has 40 kg of body water and generates about 10,000 kJ of heat a day from metabolism. If this heat were used to increase the average $E_k$ of water molecules in the body, the rise in body temperaure of tens of degrees would mean immediate death. Instead, the heat is converted to $E_p$ as it breaks H bonds and evaporates sweat, resulting in a stable body temperature and minimal loss of body fluid. On a planetary scale, the Sun's energy vaporizes ocean water in warm latitudes, and the potential energy is released as heat to warm cooler regions when the vapor condenses to rain. This global-scale cycling of water powers many weather patterns.

## Surface Properties of Water

Hydrogen bonding is also responsible for water's *high surface tension* and *high capillarity.* Except for some molten metals and salts, water has the highest surface tension of any liquid. It keeps plant debris resting on a pond surface, providing shelter and nutrients for fish and insects. High capillarity means water rises through the tiny spaces between soil particles, so plant roots can absorb deep groundwater during dry periods.

## The Unusual Density of Solid Water

In the solid state, the tetrahedral pattern of H bonding (see Figure 12.22) leads to the hexagonal, *open structure* of ice (Figure 12.23A), and the symmetrical beauty of snowflakes (Figure 12.23B) reflects this hexagonal organization. The large spaces within ice make *the solid less dense than the liquid* and explain the negative slope of the solid-liquid line in the phase diagram for water (see Figure 12.11, p. 430). As pressure is applied, some H bonds break, so the ordered crystal structure is disrupted, and the ice liquefies. When ice melts at 0°C, the loosened molecules pack much more closely, filling spaces in the collapsing solid structure. As a result, liquid water is most dense (1.000 g/mL) at around 4°C (3.98°C). With more heating, the density decreases through normal thermal expansion. This behavior has major effects in nature:

- *Surface ice of lakes.* When the surface of a lake freezes in winter, the ice floats. If the solid were denser than the liquid, as is true for nearly every other substance, the surface water would freeze and sink until the entire lake was solid. Aquatic life would not survive from year to year.
- *Nutrient turnover.* As lake water becomes colder in early winter, it becomes more dense *before* it freezes. Similarly, in spring, less dense ice thaws to form more dense water *before* the water expands. During both of these seasonal density changes, the top layer of water reaches maximum density first and sinks. The next layer of water rises because it is slightly less dense, reaches 4°C, and likewise sinks. This alternation of sinking and rising distributes nutrients and dissolved oxygen.
- *Soil formation.* When rain fills crevices in rocks and freezes, an outward force is applied that is relieved when the ice melts. In time, this repeated freeze-thaw stress cracks the rock. Over eons, this effect helps produce sand and soil.

**A**

**B**

**Figure 12.23** The hexagonal structure of ice. **A,** The open, hexagonal molecular structure of ice. **B,** The beauty of six-pointed snowflakes reflects this hexagonal structure.

**Figure 12.24** The unique macroscopic behavior of water that emerges from its atomic and molecular properties.

The far-reaching consequences of the properties of water illustrate chemistry's central theme: the macroscopic world we know is the cumulative outcome of the atomic world we seek to know (Figure 12.24).

## ▌ Summary of Section 12.5

- The atomic properties of H and O result in water's bent molecular shape, polarity, and H-bonding ability.
- These properties give water the ability to dissolve many ionic and polar compounds.
- Water's high specific heat capacity and heat of vaporization give Earth and its organisms a narrow temperature range.
- The high surface tension and capillarity are essential to plants and animals.
- Because water expands on freezing, lake life survives in winter, nutrients mix from seasonal density changes, and soil forms through freeze-thaw stress on rocks.

# 12.6 • THE SOLID STATE: STRUCTURE, PROPERTIES, AND BONDING

Stroll through a museum's mineral collection, and you'll be struck by the variety and beauty of crystalline solids. In this section, we discuss the structural features of these and other solids and the intermolecular forces that create them. We also consider the main bonding model that explains many properties of solids.

## Structural Features of Solids

We can divide solids into two broad categories:

- **Crystalline solids** have well defined shapes because their particles—atoms, molecules, or ions—occur in an orderly arrangement (Figure 12.25, *next page*).
- **Amorphous solids** have poorly defined shapes because their particles lack an orderly arrangement throughout the sample.

**Figure 12.25** The beauty of crystalline solids. **A,** Wulfanite. **B,** Barite (*left*) on calcite (*right*). **C,** Beryl (emerald). **D,** Quartz (amethyst).

**A Portion of 3-D lattice**

**B 2-D analogy for unit cell and lattice**

**Figure 12.26** The crystal lattice and the unit cell. **A,** A small portion of a lattice is shown as points connected by lines, with a unit cell (*colored*). **B,** A checkerboard analogy for a lattice.

**The Crystal Lattice and the Unit Cell** The particles in a crystal are packed tightly in an orderly, three-dimensional array. As the simplest case, consider the particles as *identical* spherical atoms, and imagine a point at the center of each. The collection of points forms a regular pattern called the crystal **lattice.** The lattice consists of *all points with identical surroundings;* that is, there is no way to tell if you moved from one lattice point to another.

Figure 12.26A shows a portion of a lattice and the **unit cell,** the *smallest* portion that gives the crystal if it is repeated in all directions. A two-dimensional analogy for a unit cell and the resulting crystal lattice appears in a checkerboard (Figure 12.26B), a section of tiled floor, a strip of wallpaper, or any other pattern that is constructed from a repeating unit.

There are 7 crystal systems and 14 types of unit cells that occur in nature, but we will be concerned primarily with the *cubic system.* The solid states of a majority of metallic elements, some covalent compounds, and many ionic compounds occur as cubic lattices. A key parameter of any lattice is the **coordination number**, the number of *nearest* neighbors of a particle. There are three types of cubic unit cells within the cubic system:

1. In the **simple cubic unit cell** (Figure 12.27A), the centers of eight identical particles define the corners of a cube (shown in the expanded view, *top row*). The particles touch along the cube edges (see the space-filling view, *second row*), but they do not touch diagonally along the cube faces or through its center. An expanded portion of the crystal (*third row*) shows that the coordination number of each particle is 6: four in its own layer, one in the layer above, and one in the layer below.
2. In the **body-centered cubic unit cell** (Figure 12.27B), identical particles lie at each corner *and* in the center of the cube. Those at the corners do not touch each other, but they all touch the one in the center. Each particle is surrounded by eight nearest neighbors, four above and four below, so the coordination number is 8.
3. In the **face-centered cubic unit cell** (Figure 12.27C), identical particles lie at each corner *and* in the center of each face but not in the center of the cube. Particles at the corners touch those in the faces but not each other. The coordination number is 12.

How many particles make up a unit cell? For particles of the same size, *the higher the coordination number is, the greater the number of particles in a given volume.* Since one unit cell touches another, with no gaps, a particle at a corner or face is *shared* by adjacent cells. In the cubic unit cells, the particle at each corner is part of eight adjacent cells (Figure 12.27, *third row*), so one-eighth of each particle belongs to each cell (*bottom row*). There are eight corners in a cube, so

- A simple cubic unit cell contains $8 \times \frac{1}{8}$ particle = 1 particle.
- A body-centered cubic unit cell contains $8 \times \frac{1}{8}$ particle = 1 particle plus 1 particle in the center, for a total of 2 particles.
- A face-centered cubic unit cell contains $8 \times \frac{1}{8}$ particle = 1 particle plus one-half particle in each of the six faces, or $6 \times \frac{1}{2}$ particle = 3 particles, for a total of 4 particles.

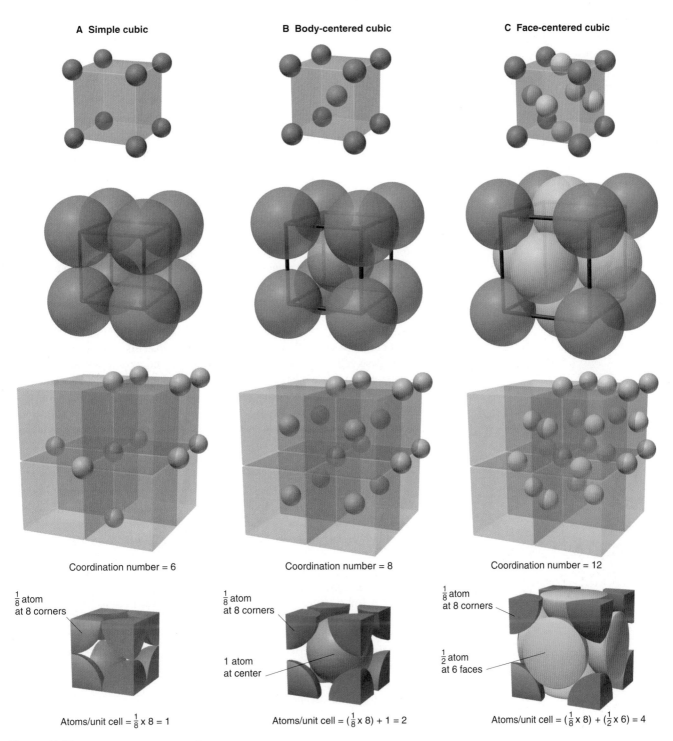

**A  Simple cubic**

**B  Body-centered cubic**

**C  Face-centered cubic**

Coordination number = 6

Coordination number = 8

Coordination number = 12

$\frac{1}{8}$ atom at 8 corners

Atoms/unit cell = $\frac{1}{8}$ × 8 = 1

$\frac{1}{8}$ atom at 8 corners

1 atom at center

Atoms/unit cell = ($\frac{1}{8}$ × 8) + 1 = 2

$\frac{1}{8}$ atom at 8 corners

$\frac{1}{2}$ atom at 6 faces

Atoms/unit cell = ($\frac{1}{8}$ × 8) + ($\frac{1}{2}$ × 6) = 4

**Figure 12.27 The three cubic unit cells. A,** Simple cubic unit cell. **B,** Body-centered cubic unit cell. **C,** Face-centered cubic unit cell. *Top row:* Cubic arrangements of atoms in expanded view. *Second row:* Space-filling view of these cubic arrangements. All atoms are identical but, for clarity, corner atoms are blue, body-centered atoms pink, and face-centered atoms yellow. *Third row:* A unit cell (*shaded blue*) in an expanded portion of the crystal. The number of nearest neighbors around one particle (*dark blue in center*) is the coordination number. *Bottom row:* The total numbers of atoms in the actual unit cell. The simple cubic has one atom, the body-centered has two, and the face-centered has four.

The efficient packing of fruit.

**Packing Efficiency and the Creation of Unit Cells** Unit cells result from the ways atoms pack together, which are similar to the ways that macroscopic spheres—marbles, golf balls, fruit—are packed (*see photo*). Let's pack *identical* spheres to create the three cubic unit cells and the hexagonal unit cell and determine the **packing efficiency,** the percentage of the total volume occupied by the spheres themselves:

1. *The simple cubic unit cell.* When we arrange the first layer of spheres in vertical and horizontal rows, large diamond-shaped spaces are formed (Figure 12.28A, *cutaway portion*). If we place the next layer of spheres *directly above* the first, we obtain an arrangement based on the *simple* cubic unit cell (Figure 12.28B). The spheres occupy only 52% of the unit-cell volume, so 48% is empty space between them. This is a very inefficient way to pack spheres, so neither fruit nor atoms are typically packed this way.

2. *The body-centered cubic unit cell.* Rather than placing the second layer (colored *green* for clarity) directly above the first, we use space more efficiently by placing it on the diamond-shaped spaces in the first layer (Figure 12.28C). Then we pack the third layer onto the diamond-shaped spaces in the second, which makes the first and third layers line up vertically. This arrangement is based on the *body-centered* cubic unit cell, and its packing efficiency is much higher at 68%. Several metallic elements, including chromium, iron, and all the Group 1A(1) elements, have a crystal structure based on this unit cell.

3. *The hexagonal and face-centered cubic unit cells.* Spheres are packed most efficiently in these cells. First, in the bottom layer (labeled *a, orange*), we shift every other row laterally so that the large diamond-shaped spaces become smaller triangular spaces. Then we place the second layer (labeled *b, green*) over these spaces (Figure 12.28D).

In layer *b*, notice that some spaces are orange because they lie above *spheres* in layer *a*, whereas other spaces are white because they lie above *spaces* in layer *a*. We can place the third layer in either of two ways, which gives rise to two different unit cells:

- *Hexagonal unit cell.* If we place the third layer of spheres (*orange*) over the orange spaces (look down and left to Figure 12.28E), they lie directly over the spheres in layer *a*. Every other layer is placed identically (an *abab. . .* layering pattern), and we obtain **hexagonal closest packing,** which is based on the *hexagonal* unit cell.
- *Face-centered unit cell.* If we place the third layer of spheres (*blue*) over the white spaces in layer *b* (look down and right to Figure 12.28F), the placement is different from layers *a* and *b* (an *abcabc. . .* pattern) and we obtain **cubic closest packing,** which is based on the *face-centered cubic* unit cell.

The packing efficiency of both hexagonal and cubic closest packing is 74%, and the coordination number of both is 12. Most metallic elements crystallize in one or the other of these arrangements. Magnesium, titanium, and zinc are some that adopt the hexagonal structure; nickel, copper, and lead adopt the cubic structure, as do many ionic compounds and other substances, such as $CO_2$, $CH_4$, and most noble gases.

In Sample Problem 12.5, we use density and our knowledge of unit cells to find an atomic radius.

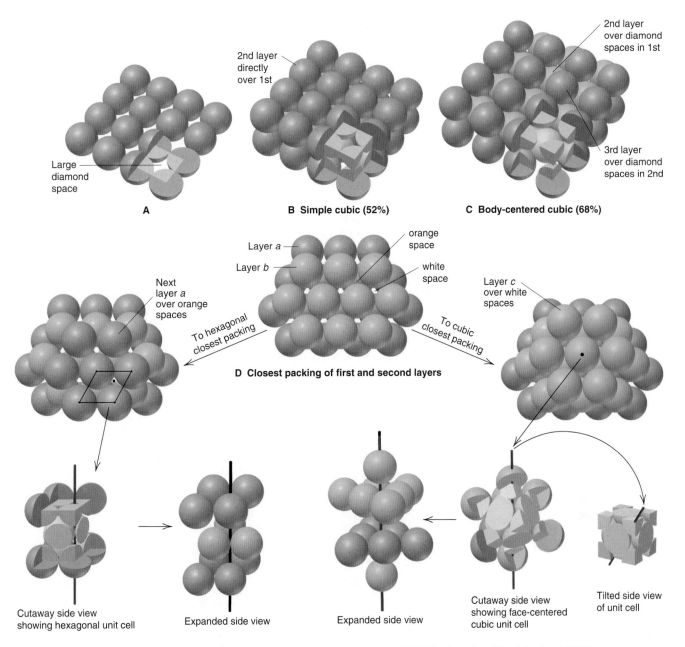

**Figure 12.28** Packing spheres to obtain three cubic and hexagonal unit cells. **A,** In the first layer, each sphere lies next to another horizontally and vertically; note the large diamond-shaped spaces (*see cutaway*). **B,** If the spheres in the next layer lie directly over those in the first, the packing is based on the simple cubic unit cell (*pale orange cube, lower right corner*). **C,** If the spheres in the next layer lie in the diamond-shaped spaces of the first layer, the packing is based on the *body-centered cubic* unit cell (*lower right corner*). **D,** The closest possible packing of the first layer (*layer a, orange*) is obtained by shifting every other row in part A to obtain smaller triangular spaces. The spheres of the second layer (*layer b, green*) are placed above these spaces; note the orange and white spaces that result. **E,** When the third layer (*next layer a, orange*) is placed over the orange spaces, we obtain an *abab*. . . pattern and the hexagonal unit cell. **F,** When the third layer (*layer c, blue*) covers the white spaces, we get an *abcabc*. . . pattern and the face-centered cubic unit cell.

## Sample Problem 12.5 — Determining Atomic Radius

**Problem** Barium is the largest nonradioactive alkaline earth metal. It has a body-centered cubic unit cell and a density of 3.62 g/cm$^3$. What is the atomic radius of barium? (Volume of a sphere: $V = \frac{4}{3}\pi r^3$.)

**Plan** An atom is spherical, so we can find its radius from its volume. If we multiply the reciprocal of density (volume/mass) by the molar mass (mass/mole), we find the volume/mole of Ba metal. The metal crystallizes in the body-centered cubic structure, so 68% of this volume is occupied by 1 mol of the Ba atoms themselves (see Figure 12.28C). Dividing by Avogadro's number gives the volume of one Ba atom, from which we find the radius.

**Solution** Combining steps to find the volume of 1 mol of Ba metal:

$$\text{Volume/mole of Ba metal} = \frac{1}{\text{density}} \times \mathcal{M} = \frac{1 \text{ cm}^3}{3.62 \text{ g Ba}} \times \frac{137.3 \text{ g Ba}}{1 \text{ mol Ba}} = 37.9 \text{ cm}^3/\text{mol Ba}$$

Finding the volume (cm$^3$) of 1 mol of Ba *atoms:*

$$\text{Volume/mole of Ba atoms} = \text{cm}^3/\text{mol Ba} \times \text{packing efficiency}$$
$$= 37.9 \text{ cm}^3/\text{mol Ba} \times 0.68 = 26 \text{ cm}^3/\text{mol Ba atoms}$$

Finding the volume of one Ba atom:

$$\text{Volume of Ba atom} = \frac{26 \text{ cm}^3}{1 \text{ mol Ba atoms}} \times \frac{1 \text{ mol Ba atoms}}{6.022 \times 10^{23} \text{ Ba atoms}} = 4.3 \times 10^{-23} \text{ cm}^3/\text{Ba atom}$$

Finding the atomic radius of Ba from the volume of a sphere:

$$V \text{ of Ba atom} = \tfrac{4}{3}\pi r^3 \qquad \text{so} \qquad r^3 = \frac{3V}{4\pi}$$

Thus,

$$r = \sqrt[3]{\frac{3V}{4\pi}} = \sqrt[3]{\frac{3(4.3 \times 10^{-23} \text{ cm}^3)}{4 \times 3.14}} = 2.2 \times 10^{-8} \text{ cm}$$

**Check** The order of magnitude is correct for an atom ($\sim 10^{-8}$ cm $\approx 10^{-10}$ m). The actual value for barium is, in fact, $2.22 \times 10^{-8}$ cm (see Figure 8.9).

**Follow-Up Problem 12.5** Iron crystallizes in a body-centered cubic structure. The volume of one Fe atom is $8.38 \times 10^{-24}$ cm$^3$, and the density of Fe is 7.874 g/cm$^3$. Calculate an approximate value for Avogadro's number.

**Road Map**

| Density (g/cm$^3$) of Ba metal |
| :---: |

find reciprocal and multiply by $\mathcal{M}$ (g/mol)

| Volume (cm$^3$) per mole of Ba metal |
| :---: |

multiply by packing efficiency

| Volume (cm$^3$) per mole of Ba atoms |
| :---: |

divide by Avogadro's number

| Volume (cm$^3$) of Ba atom |
| :---: |

$V = \frac{4}{3}\pi r^3$

| Radius (cm) of Ba atom |
| :---: |

Our understanding of crystal structures comes from our ability to "see" them. Two techniques for doing this are described in Tools of the Laboratory.

The edge length of the unit cell is obtained from x-ray crystallography. We can then apply the Pythagorean theorem and some arithmetic to find atomic (or ionic) radii in the three cubic unit cells (Figure 12.29). Sample Problem 12.6 shows this approach.

**Figure 12.29** Edge length and atomic (ionic) radius in the three cubic unit cells.

**Simple cubic**

$A = 2r$

**Body-centered cubic**

$C^2 = A^2 + B^2 = 2A^2$
$D^2 = A^2 + C^2 = 3A^2$
$D = \sqrt{3}\,A = 4r$
$A = \dfrac{4r}{\sqrt{3}}$

**Face-centered cubic**

$C^2 = A^2 + B^2 = 2A^2$
$C = 4r$
$C^2 = 16r^2 = 2A^2$
$A = \sqrt{8}\,r$

Various tools exist for measuring atomic-scale dimensions, and two of the most powerful are **x-ray diffraction analysis** and **scanning tunneling microscopy.**

## X-Ray Diffraction Analysis

In Chapter 7, we saw how diffraction patterns of bright and dark regions appear when light passes through slits spaced as far apart as the wavelength (see Figure 7.5, p. 265). X-ray wavelengths are about the same size as the spaces between layers of spheres in a crystal, so we use the spaces as "slits" to diffract x-rays.

As one example, let's use this approach to measure the distance ($d$) between two adjacent layers of atoms in a simplified lattice (Figure B12.1). Two waves impinge on the crystal at an angle

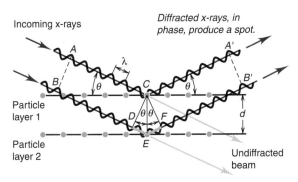

Figure B12.1 Diffraction of x-rays by crystal planes.

$\theta$ and are diffracted at that angle by the layers. When the first wave strikes the top layer and the second strikes the next layer, they are *in phase* (peaks aligned with peaks and troughs with troughs). If they are still in phase after being diffracted, they form a spot on a photographic plate. This will occur only if the additional distance traveled by the second wave ($DE + EF$ in the figure) is a whole number of wavelengths, $n\lambda$, where $n$ is a positive integer referred to as the *order* of the diffraction. From trigonometry, we find that

$$n\lambda = 2d \sin \theta$$

where $\theta$ is the angle of incoming light and $d$, the unknown, is the distance between layers. This is the *Bragg equation,* named for W. H. Bragg and his son W. L. Bragg, who shared the Nobel Prize in physics in 1915 for their work on crystal structure analysis.

Rotating the crystal changes $\theta$ and produces different sets of spots. Eventually, the complete diffraction pattern reveals distances and angles in the lattice (Figure B12.2). X-ray diffraction analysis is used in many studies, but its greatest recent impact is uncovering the structures of DNA and proteins.

## Scanning Tunneling Microscopy

This technique, invented by Gerd Binnig and Heinrich Rohrer, who won the Nobel Prize in physics in 1986, is used to observe surfaces. It is based on the idea that an electron has a small, but finite, probability of being so far from its nucleus that it can move ("tunnel") closer to another atom.

In practice, an extremely sharp tungsten-tipped probe, the source of the tunneling electrons, is placed very close (about

*(continued)*

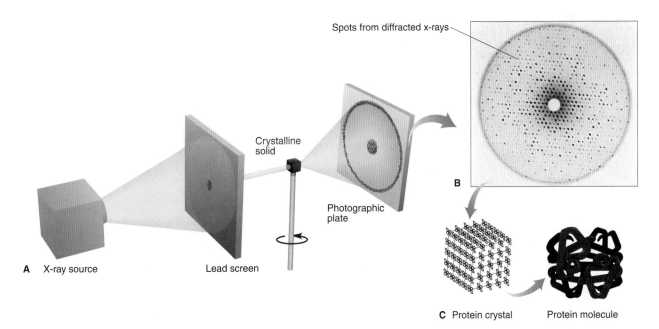

**Figure B12.2** Formation of an x-ray diffraction pattern of the protein hemoglobin. **A,** A sample of crystalline protein is rotated to obtain different angles of incoming and diffracted x-rays. **B,** The diffraction pattern is a complex series of spots. **C,** Computerized analysis provides a picture of the molecule.

0.5 nm) to the surface under study. A small applied electric potential increases the probability that the electrons will tunnel across this minute gap. The probe moves tiny distances up and down to maintain the constant current across the gap, thus following the surface at the atomic scale. This movement is monitored electronically, and after many scans, a three-dimensional map of the surface is obtained. The method has revealed images of atoms and molecules coated on surfaces and is being used to study the nature of defects and many other surface features (Figure B12.3).

**Figure B12.3** A scanning tunneling micrograph of cesium atoms (*red*) on gallium arsenide.

## Problems

**B12.1** X-rays of wavelength $\lambda = 0.709 \times 10^{-10}$ m undergo a first-order ($n = 1$) diffraction of $11.6°$ when aimed at crystalline nickel. What is the spacing between layers of Ni atoms?

**B12.2** A first-order ($n = 1$) diffraction of x-rays aimed at a crystal of NaCl occurs at $15.9°$.
(a) What is the wavelength (in pm) of the x-rays?
(b) At what angle would a second-order ($n = 2$) diffraction appear?

---

### Sample Problem 12.6 | Determining Atomic Radius from the Unit Cell

**Problem** Copper adopts cubic closest packing, and the edge length of the unit cell is 361.5 pm. What is the atomic radius of copper?

**Plan** Cubic closest packing has a face-centered cubic unit cell, and we know the edge length. With Figure 12.29 and $A = 361.5$ pm, we solve for $r$ (*see margin*).

$B$
$A = 361.5$ pm
$C$
$r = ?$

**Solution** Using the Pythagorean theorem to find $C$, the diagonal of the cell's face:

$$C = \sqrt{A^2 + B^2}$$

The unit cell is a cube, so $A = B$. Therefore,

$$C = \sqrt{2A^2} = \sqrt{2(361.5 \text{ pm})^2} = 511.2 \text{ pm}$$

Finding $r$: $C = 4r$. Therefore, $r = 511.2$ pm/4 = $\boxed{127.8 \text{ pm.}}$

**Check** Rounding and quickly checking the math gives

$$C = \sqrt{2(4 \times 10^2 \text{ pm})^2} = \sqrt{2(16 \times 10^4 \text{ pm}^2)}$$

or ~500–600 pm; thus, $r \approx 125$–150 pm.

The actual value for copper is 128 pm (see Figure 8.15, p. 311).

**Follow-Up Problem 12.6** Iron crystallizes in a body-centered cubic structure. If the atomic radius of Fe is 126 pm, find the edge length (in nm) of the unit cell.

# Types and Properties of Crystalline Solids

The five most important types of solids are defined by the type(s) of particle(s) in the crystal (Table 12.5). We'll highlight interparticle forces and physical properties.

**Atomic Solids** Individual atoms held together only by *dispersion forces* form an **atomic solid,** and the noble gases [Group 8A(18)] are the only substances that form such solids. The very weak forces among the atoms mean melting and boiling points and heats of vaporization and fusion are all very low, rising smoothly with increasing molar mass. Argon crystallizes in a cubic closest packed structure (Figure 12.30), as do the other noble gases.

**Figure 12.30** Cubic closest packing of frozen argon (face-centered cubic unit cell).

**Molecular Solids** In the many thousands of **molecular solids,** individual molecules occupy the lattice points. Various combinations of dipole-dipole, dispersion, and H-bonding forces account for a wide range of physical properties. Dispersion forces in nonpolar substances lead to melting points that generally increase with molar mass (Table 12.5). Among polar molecules, dipole-dipole forces and, where possible, H bonding occur. Most molecular solids have much higher melting points than atomic solids (noble gases) but much lower melting points than other types of solids. Methane crystallizes in a face-centered cubic structure with the center of each carbon as the lattice point (Figure 12.31).

**Figure 12.31** Cubic closest packing (face-centered unit cell) of frozen $CH_4$.

**Ionic Solids** To maximize attractions in a binary **ionic solid,** cations are surrounded by as many anions as possible, and vice versa, with *the smaller of the ions (usually the cation) lying in the spaces (holes) formed by the packing of the larger (usually the anion).* The unit cell is the smallest portion that maintains the composition; that is, *the unit cell has the same cation/anion ratio as the empirical formula.*

## Table **12.5** Characteristics of the Major Types of Crystalline Solids

| Type | Particle(s) | Interparticle Forces | Physical Properties | Examples [mp, °C] |
|------|-------------|----------------------|---------------------|-------------------|
| Atomic | Atoms | Dispersion | Soft, very low mp, poor thermal and electrical conductors | Group 8A(18) (Ne [−249] to Rn [−71]) |
| Molecular | Molecules | Dispersion, dipole-dipole, H bonds | Fairly soft, low to moderate mp, poor thermal and electrical conductors | *Nonpolar\** $O_2$ [−219], $C_4H_{10}$ [−138] $Cl_2$ [−101], $C_6H_{14}$ [−95], $P_4$ [44.1] *Polar* $SO_2$ [−73], $CHCl_3$ [−64], $HNO_3$ [−42], $H_2O$ [0.0], $CH_3COOH$ [17] |
| Ionic | Positive and negative ions | Ion-ion attraction | Hard and brittle, high mp, good thermal and electrical conductors when molten | NaCl [801] $CaF_2$ [1423] MgO [2852] |
| Metallic | Atoms | Metallic bond | Soft to hard, low to very high mp, excellent thermal and electrical conductors, malleable and ductile | Na [97.8] Zn [420] Fe [1535] |
| Network covalent | Atoms | Covalent bond | Very hard, very high mp, usually poor thermal and electrical conductors | $SiO_2$ (quartz) [1610] C (diamond) [~4000] |

*\*Nonpolar molecular solids are arranged in order of increasing molar mass. Note the correlation with increasing melting point (mp).*

As a result of cation-anion contact, the interparticle forces (ionic bonds) are *much* stronger than the van der Waals forces in atomic or molecular solids. The properties of ionic solids are a direct consequence of the *fixed ion positions* and *very strong attractive forces,* which create a high lattice energy. Thus, ionic solids typically have high melting points and low electrical conductivities. When a large quantity of heat is supplied and the ions gain enough kinetic energy to break free of their positions, the solid melts and the mobile ions conduct a current. Ionic compounds are hard because only a strong external force can change the relative positions of the huge number of ions attracting one another. If enough force *is* applied to move them, ions of like charge are brought near each other, and their repulsions crack the crystal (see Figure 9.8, p. 336).

Ionic solids often adopt cubic closest packed crystal structures. We'll describe two examples with a 1/1 ratio of ions and then two with a 2/1 (or 1/2) ratio:

1. The *sodium chloride structure* is found in many ionic compounds, including most alkali [Group 1A(1)] halides and hydrides, alkaline earth [Group 2A(2)] oxides and sulfides, and several transition-metal oxides and sulfides. To visualize this structure, imagine $Cl^-$ anions and $Na^+$ cations in separate face-centered cubic arrays. Now picture the two arrays penetrating each other, the smaller $Na^+$ ions ending up in the holes between the larger $Cl^-$ ions (Figure 12.32A). Thus, each $Na^+$ is surrounded by six $Cl^-$, and vice versa (coordination number = 6). Figure 12.32B is a space-filling depiction of the unit cell: four $Cl^-$ $[(8 \times \frac{1}{8}) + (6 \times \frac{1}{2}) = 4\ Cl^-]$ and four $Na^+$ $[(12 \times \frac{1}{4}) + 1$ in the center $= 4\ Na^+]$, give a 1/1 ion ratio.

**Figure 12.32** The sodium chloride structure. **A,** Expanded view. **B,** Space-filling model of the NaCl unit cell.

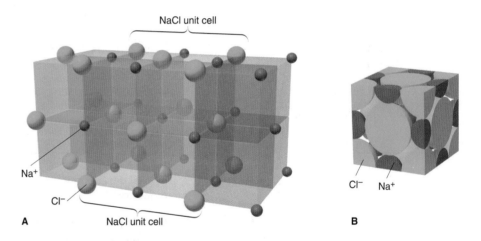

2. The *zinc blende (ZnS) structure* can be pictured as two face-centered cubic arrays, one of $Zn^{2+}$ ions (*gray*) and the other of $S^{2-}$ ions (*yellow*), penetrating each other such that each ion is tetrahedrally surrounded by four of the other ions (coordination number = 4) (Figure 12.33). There are four $[(8 \times \frac{1}{8}) + (6 \times \frac{1}{2}) = 4]\ S^{2-}$ ions and four $Zn^{2+}$ ions for a 1/1 ion ratio. Many other compounds, including AgI, CdS, and the copper(I) halides, adopt the zinc blende structure.

**Figure 12.33** The zinc blende structure. **A,** Expanded view (with bonds shown for clarity). **B,** The unit cell is expanded a bit to show interior ions.

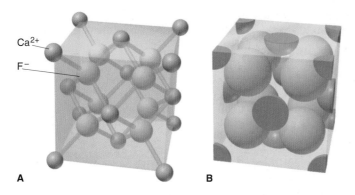

**Figure 12.34** The fluorite structure. **A,** Expanded view (with bonds shown for clarity). **B,** The unit cell is expanded a bit to show interior ions.

3. The *fluorite (CaF₂) structure* is common among salts with a 1/2 cation/anion ratio that have relatively large cations and small anions, such as $SrF_2$ and $BaCl_2$. In $CaF_2$, the unit cell is a face-centered cubic array of $Ca^{2+}$ ions with $F^-$ ions occupying *all* eight available holes (Figure 12.34). This results in a $Ca^{2+}/F^-$ ratio of 4/8, or 1/2.

4. The *antifluorite structure* is common in compounds with a 2/1 cation/anion ratio and a relatively large anion (such as $K_2S$). The ion arrangement is the opposite of that in the fluorite structure: the cations occupy all eight holes formed by the cubic closest packing of the anions.

**Metallic Solids** Most metallic elements crystallize in one of the two closest packed structures (Figure 12.35). In contrast to the weak dispersion forces in atomic solids, powerful metallic bonding forces hold atoms together in **metallic solids.** The properties of metals—high electrical and thermal conductivity, luster, and malleability—result from their delocalized electrons (Section 9.6). Melting points and hardnesses are related to the packing efficiency and number of valence electrons. For example, Group 2A metals are harder and melt higher than Group 1A metals (see Figure 9.27, pp. 352–353), because the 2A metals have twice as many delocalized valence electrons.

**Network Covalent Solids** Strong covalent bonds link the atoms together in a **network covalent solid;** thus, separate particles are not present. These substances adopt a variety of crystal structures depending on the details of their bonding.

As a consequence of strong bonding, all network covalent solids have extremely high melting and boiling points, but their conductivity and hardness vary. Two examples with the same composition but strikingly different properties are the two common crystalline forms of elemental carbon, graphite and diamond:

- *Graphite* occurs as stacked flat sheets of hexagonal carbon rings with a strong σ-bond framework and delocalized π bonds, reminiscent of benzene; the arrangement looks like chicken wire or honeycomb. Whereas the π-bonding electrons of benzene are delocalized over one ring, those of graphite are delocalized over the entire sheet. Thus, graphite conducts electricity well—it is a common electrode material—but only in the plane of the sheets. The sheets interact via dispersion forces, and impurities, such as $O_2$, between the sheets allow them to slide past each other, which explains why graphite is soft and used as a lubricant.
- *Diamond* adopts a face-centered cubic unit cell, with each C tetrahedrally bonded to four others in an endless array. Throughout the crystal, strong single bonds make diamond the hardest natural substance known. Like most network covalent solids, diamond does not conduct electricity because the bonding electrons are localized.

These properties are compared in Table 12.6 on the next page.

The most important network covalent solids are the *silicates,* which consist of extended arrays of covalently bonded silicon and oxygen atoms. Quartz ($SiO_2$) is a common example. We'll discuss silicates, which form the structure of clays, rocks, and many minerals, when we consider the chemistry of silicon in Chapter 14.

**Figure 12.35** Crystal structures of metals. **A,** Copper adopts cubic closest packing. **B,** Magnesium adopts hexagonal closest packing.

**Table 12.6 Comparison of the Properties of Diamond and Graphite**

| Property | Graphite | | Diamond | |
|---|---|---|---|---|
| Density (g/cm³) | 2.27 | | 3.51 | |
| Hardness | <1 (very soft) | | 10 (hardest) | |
| Melting point (K) | 4100 | | 4100 | |
| Color | Shiny black | | Colorless transparent | |
| Electrical conductivity | High (along sheet) | | None | |
| $\Delta H^\circ_{rxn}$ for combustion (kJ/mol) | −393.5 | | −395.4 | |
| $\Delta H^\circ_f$ (kJ/mol) | 0 (standard state) | | 1.90 | |

**Figure 12.36** Crystalline and amorphous silicon dioxide. **A,** Cristobalite, a crystalline form of silica (SiO₂), shows cubic closest packing. **B,** Quartz glass is amorphous with a generally disordered structure.

## Amorphous Solids

Amorphous solids are noncrystalline. Many have small, somewhat ordered regions interspersed among large disordered regions. Charcoal, rubber, and glass are examples.

The process that forms quartz glass is typical of many amorphous solids. Crystalline quartz ($SiO_2$), which adopts cubic closest packing, is melted and the viscous liquid is cooled rapidly to prevent it from recrystallizing. The chains of Si and O atoms cannot orient themselves quickly enough, so they solidify in a distorted jumble containing gaps and misaligned rows (Figure 12.36). The absence of regularity confers some properties of a liquid; in fact, glasses are sometimes referred to as *supercooled liquids*.

## Bonding in Solids: Molecular Orbital Band Theory

Chapter 9 introduced a qualitative model of metallic bonding, with metal ions submerged in a "sea" of mobile, delocalized valence electrons. Molecular orbital (MO) theory offers a more quantitative, and therefore more useful, model called **band theory.** We'll focus on bonding in metals and the conductivity of metals, metalloids, and nonmetals.

**Formation of Valence and Conduction Bands** Recall from Section 11.3 that when two atoms form a diatomic molecule, their atomic orbitals (AOs) combine to form an equal number of molecular orbitals (MOs). Figure 12.37 shows the formation of MOs in lithium. To form Li₂, each Li atom has four valence orbitals (one 2s and three

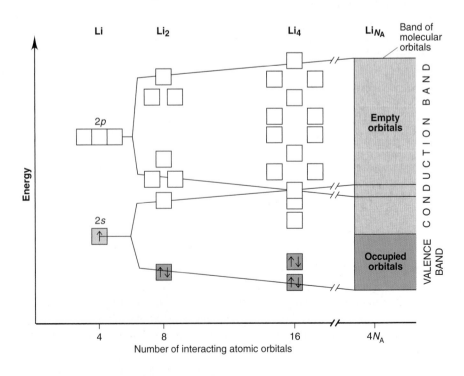

**Figure 12.37** The band of molecular orbitals in lithium metal.

2p) that combine to form eight MOs, four bonding and four antibonding. The order of MOs shows 2s-2p mixing (Figure 11.21B, p. 409). Two more Li atoms form $Li_4$, a slightly larger aggregate, with 16 delocalized MOs. As more Li atoms join the cluster, more MOs are created, and their energy levels lie closer and closer together. Extending this process to 7 g (1 mol) of lithium results in $6 \times 10^{23}$ Li atoms ($Li_{N_A}$) combining to form an extremely large number (4 × Avogadro's number) of delocalized MOs. *The energies of the MOs are so close that they form a continuum, or band, of MOs.*

The lower energy MOs are occupied by the $2s^1$ valence electrons and make up the **valence band.** The empty MOs that are higher in energy make up the **conduction band.** In Li metal, the valence band is derived from the 2s AOs, and the conduction band is derived from 2s and mostly 2p AOs. In $Li_2$, two valence electrons fill the lowest energy bonding MO and leave the antibonding MO empty. In Li metal, 1 mol of valence electrons fills the valence band and leaves the conduction band empty.

**How Band Theory Explains Metallic Properties** The key to understanding the properties of metals is that *the valence and conduction bands are contiguous,* that is, the highest level of one touches the lowest of the other. This means that, given an infinitesimal quantity of energy, electrons jump from the filled valence band to the unfilled conduction band: the electrons are completely delocalized.

- *Electrical conductivity.* Metals conduct so well because an applied field easily excites the highest energy valence electrons into empty conduction orbitals, allowing them to move through the sample.
- *Luster.* With so many closely spaced levels available, electrons absorb and release photons of many frequencies as they move between the valence and conduction bands.
- *Malleability.* Under an applied force, layers of positive metal ions move past each other, always protected from mutual repulsions by the delocalized electrons.
- *Thermal conductivity.* When a metal wire is heated, the highest energy electrons are excited and their extra energy is transferred as kinetic energy along the wire's length.

**Conductivity of Solids and the Size of the Energy Gap** Like metal atoms, large numbers of nonmetal and metalloid atoms can form bands of MOs. Band theory explains differences in electrical conductivity and the effect of temperature among these three classes of substances in terms of the presence of an energy gap between their valence and conduction bands (Figure 12.38):

1. *Conductors (metals).* The valence and conduction bands of a **conductor** have *no energy gap* between them, so electrons flow when a tiny electrical potential difference is applied. When the temperature is raised, greater random motion of the atoms hinders electron movement: conductivity *decreases* when a metal is heated.
2. *Semiconductors (metalloids).* In a **semiconductor,** a *small energy gap* exists between the valence and conduction bands. Thermally excited electrons can cross the gap, allowing a small current to flow: in contrast to a conductor, conductivity *increases* when a semiconductor is heated.
3. *Insulators (nonmetals).* In an **insulator,** a *large energy gap* exists between the bands: no current is observed even when the substance is heated.

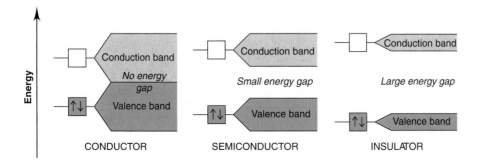

**Figure 12.38** Electrical conductivity in a conductor, semiconductor, and insulator.

Another type of electrical conductivity, called **superconductivity,** has been the focus of intensive research for the past few decades. When metals conduct at ordinary temperatures, moving electrons collide with vibrating atoms; the reduction in their flow appears as resistive heating and represents a loss of energy.

For many years, to conduct with no energy loss—to superconduct—required minimizing atom movement by cooling with liquid helium (bp = 4 K; price ≈ $11/L). Then, in 1986, certain ionic oxides that superconduct near the boiling point of liquid nitrogen (bp = 77 K; price = $0.20/L) were prepared. Like metal conductors, oxide superconductors, such as $YBa_2Cu_3O_7$, have no gap between bands. In 1989, oxides with Bi and Tl instead of Y and Ba were synthesized and found to superconduct at 125 K; and in 1993, an oxide with Hg, Ba, and Ca, in addition to Cu and O, superconducted at 133 K. Such materials could transmit electricity with no loss of energy, allowing power plants to be located far from cities. They could be part of ultrasmall microchips for ultrafast computers, electromagnets to levitate superfast trains, and inexpensive medical diagnostic equipment with superb image clarity. However, the oxides are brittle and not easy to machine, and when warmed, the superconductivity may disappear and not return on cooling. Addressing these and related problems will involve chemists, physicists, and engineers for many years.

## ▌ Summary of Section 12.6

- Particles in crystalline solids lie at points that form a structure of repeating unit cells.
- The three types of unit cells of the cubic system are simple, body-centered, and face-centered. The highest packing efficiency occurs with cubic (face-centered) and hexagonal closest packing.
- Bond angles and distances in a crystal are determined with x-ray diffraction analysis and scanning tunneling microscopy. These data are used to determine atomic radii.
- Atomic [Group 8A(18)] solids adopt cubic closest packing, with atoms held together by weak dispersion forces.
- Molecular solids have molecules at the lattice points and often adopt cubic closest packing. Combinations of intermolecular forces (dispersion, dipole-dipole, and H bonding) result in physical properties that vary greatly.
- Ionic solids crystallize with one ion filling holes in the cubic closest packed array of the other. High melting points, hardness, and low conductivity arise from strong ionic attractions.
- Most metals have a closest packed structure. Their physical properties result from the high packing efficiency and the presence of delocalized electrons.
- Atoms of network covalent solids are covalently bonded throughout the sample, so these substances have very high melting and boiling points.
- Amorphous solids have little regularity in their structure.
- Band theory proposes that atomic orbitals of many atoms combine to form a continuum, or band, of molecular orbitals. Metals are electrical conductors because electrons move freely from the filled (valence) band to the empty (conduction) band. Insulators have a large energy gap between the two portions, and semiconductors have a small gap, which can be bridged by heating.

## 12.7 • ADVANCED MATERIALS

In the last few decades, the exciting field of materials science has grown from solid-state chemistry, physics, and engineering. Objects that were once considered futuristic fantasies are becoming realities: powerful, ultrafast computers smaller than this book; cars powered by sunlight and made of nonmetallic parts stronger than steel and lighter than aluminum; ultrasmall machines constructed by manipulating individual atoms and molecules. In this section, we briefly discuss some of these remarkable materials.

# Electronic Materials

The ideal of a perfectly ordered crystal is attainable only if the crystal is grown very slowly under carefully controlled conditions. When crystals form more rapidly, **crystal defects** inevitably form. Planes of particles are misaligned, particles are out of place or missing entirely, and foreign particles replace those that belong in the lattice. Although defects usually weaken a substance, they can be introduced intentionally to improve materials, giving them increased strength, hardness, or conductivity. Centuries of metal-working exemplify the traditional importance of defects, which is the basis of modern electronic materials.

**Introducing Defects in Welding and Alloying** In the process of *welding* two metals together, *vacancies* form near the surface when atoms vaporize, and then these vacancies move deeper as atoms from lower rows rise to fill the gaps. Welding causes the two types of metal atoms to intermingle and fill each other's vacancies. Metal *alloying* introduces several kinds of crystal defects, as when some atoms of a second metal occupy lattice sites of the first. Often, the alloy is harder than the pure metal; an example is brass, an alloy of copper with zinc. One reason the welded metals are stronger and the alloy is harder is that the second metal contributes additional valence electrons for metallic bonding.

**Doped Semiconductors** By controlling the number of valence electrons through the creation of specific types of crystal defects, chemists and engineers can greatly increase the conductivity of a semiconductor. Pure silicon [Si; Group 4A(14)], conducts poorly at room temperature because an energy gap separates its filled valence band from its conduction band (Figure 12.39A). Its conductivity can be greatly enhanced by **doping,** adding small amounts of other elements to increase or decrease the number of valence electrons in the bands:

- *n-Type semiconductor: increasing the number of valence electrons.* When Si is doped with phosphorus [or another Group 5A(15) element], P atoms occupy some of the lattice sites. Since P has one more valence electron than Si, this additional electron must enter an empty orbital in the conduction band, thus bridging the energy gap and increasing conductivity. Such doping creates an *n-type semiconductor,* so called because extra *n*egative charges (electrons) are present (Figure 12.39B).
- *p-Type semiconductor: decreasing the number of valence electrons.* When Si is doped with gallium [or another Group 3A(13) element], Ga atoms occupy some sites (Figure 12.39C). Since Ga has one fewer valence electron than Si, some of the orbitals in the valence band are empty, which creates a positive site. Si electrons can migrate to these empty orbitals, thereby increasing conductivity. Such doping creates a *p-type semiconductor,* so called because the empty orbitals act as *p*ositive holes.

**A  Pure silicon crystal**    **B  n-Type doping with phosphorus**    **C  p-Type doping with gallium**

**Figure 12.39** Crystal structures and band representations of doped semiconductors. **A,** Pure silicon has an energy gap between its valence and conduction bands, which keeps conductivity low at room temperature. **B,** Doping silicon with phosphorus (*purple*) adds additional valence electrons. **C,** Doping silicon with gallium (*orange*) removes electrons from the valence band and introduces positive holes.

**A** Flow of electrons and holes creates a current.    **B** No current.

**Figure 12.40 The p-n junction.** Placing a p-type semiconductor adjacent to an n-type creates a p-n junction.

In contact with each other, an n-type and a p-type semiconductor form a *p-n junction.* When the negative terminal of a battery is connected to the n-type portion and the positive terminal to the p-type portion, electrons (*yellow, negative spheres*) flow freely in the n-to-p direction, which has the simultaneous effect of moving holes (*white, positive spheres*) in the p-to-n direction (Figure 12.40A). No current flows if the terminals are reversed (Figure 12.40B). Such unidirectional current flow makes a p-n junction act as a *rectifier,* a device that converts alternating current into direct current. A p-n junction in a modern integrated circuit can be made smaller than a square 10 μm on a side.

A modern computer chip the size of a nickel may incorporate millions of p-n junctions in the form of *transistors.* One of the most common types, an n-p-n transistor, is made by sandwiching a p-type portion between two n-type portions to form adjacent p-n junctions. The current flowing through one junction controls the current flowing through the other and results in an amplified signal.

One of the more common types of *solar cell* is, in essence, a p-n junction with an n-type surface exposed to a light source. Light provides the energy to free electrons from the n-type region and accelerate them through an external circuit into the p-type region, thus producing a current.

## Liquid Crystals

Incorporated in the membrane of every cell in your body and in the display of every electronic device are **liquid crystals.** These materials flow like liquids but, like crystalline solids, pack at the molecular level with a high degree of order.

**Ordering of the Particles** Let's examine how particles are ordered in the three physical states and how this affects their properties. Both gases and liquids are *isotropic*—their physical properties are the same in every direction within the phase. For example, the viscosity of a gas or a liquid is the same regardless of direction. Glasses and other amorphous solids are also isotropic because they have no regular lattice structure.

In contrast, crystalline solids have a high degree of order among their particles. The properties of a crystal *do* depend on direction, so a crystal is *anisotropic.* The facets in a cut diamond, for instance, arise because the crystal cracks in one direction more easily than in another. Liquid crystals are anisotropic in several physical properties, including electrical and optical properties, which differ with direction through the phase.

**Molecular Characteristics** Liquid crystal phases consist of individual molecules with two characteristics: (1) a long, cylindrical shape and (2) a structure that fosters intermolecular attractions but inhibits perfect crystalline packing. Molecules that form liquid crystal phases have rodlike shapes and certain groups—in the cases shown in Figure 12.41, flat, benzene-like ring systems—that keep the molecules extended. Many of these molecules also have polarity associated with the long molecular axis. A strong electric field can orient these polar molecules like compass needles in a magnetic field.

The viscosity of a liquid crystal phase is lowest in the direction parallel to the long axis. Like moistened microscope slides, it is easier for the molecules to slide along each other (because the total attractive force remains the same), than it is for

**Figure 12.41** **Structures of two typical molecules that form liquid crystal phases.** Note the long, extended shapes and the regions of high (*red*) and low (*blue*) electron density.

them to pull apart from each other sideways. As a result, the molecules tend to align while the phase flows.

**Controlling Conditions to Form Phases** Liquid crystal phases can arise in two general ways, and, sometimes, either way can occur in the same substance:

1. *Thermotropic phases* develop as a result of a change in temperature. As a crystalline solid is heated, the molecules leave their lattice sites, but the intermolecular interactions are still strong enough to keep the molecules aligned with each other along their long axes. Like any other phase, the liquid crystal phase has sharp transition temperatures, but they occur over a relatively small temperature range. Further heating provides enough kinetic energy for the molecules to become disordered, as in a normal liquid. The typical range for liquid crystal phases of pure substances is from <1°C to as much as 10°C, but mixing phases of two or more substances can greatly extend this range. For this reason, the liquid crystal phases used within display devices, as well as those within cell membranes, consist of mixtures of molecules.

2. *Lyotropic phases* occur in solution as the result of changes in concentration, but the conditions for forming such a phase vary for different substances. For example, when purified, some biomolecules that exist in cell membranes form lyotropic phases in water at the temperature that occurs within the organism. At the other extreme, Kevlar, a fiber used in bulletproof vests and high-performance sports equipment, forms a lyotropic phase in concentrated $H_2SO_4$ solution.

In some cases, a substance that forms a given liquid crystal phase under one set of conditions forms other phases under different conditions. Thus, a given thermotropic liquid crystal substance can pass from disordered liquid through a series of distinct liquid crystal phases to an ordered crystal through a decrease in temperature. A lyotropic substance can undergo similar changes through an increase in concentration.

**Types of Order in Liquid Crystal Phases** Molecules that form liquid crystal phases can exhibit various types of order. Three common types are nematic, cholesteric, and smectic:

1. In a *nematic phase,* the molecules lie in the same direction but their ends are not aligned, much like a school of fish swimming in synchrony (Figure 12.42A, *next page*). The nematic phase is the least ordered type of liquid crystal phases.

**A Nematic**  **B Cholesteric**  **C Smectic**

**Figure 12.42** The three common types of ordering in liquid crystal phases.

**A**

**B**

**Figure 12.43** Liquid crystal–type phases in biological systems. **A,** Nematic arrays of tobacco mosaic virus particles within the fluid of a tobacco leaf. **B,** The smectic-like arrangement of actin and myosin protein filaments in voluntary muscle cells.

2. In a *cholesteric phase,* which is somewhat more ordered, the molecules lie in layers that each exhibit nematic-type ordering. Rather than lying in parallel fashion, however, each layer is rotated by a fixed angle with respect to the next layer to give a helical (corkscrew) arrangement. A cholesteric phase is often called a *twisted nematic phase* (Figure 12.42B).

3. In a *smectic phase,* which is the most ordered, the molecules lie parallel to each other, *with* their ends aligned, in layers that are stacked directly over each other (Figure 12.42C). The long molecular axis has a well-defined angle (shown in the figure as 90°) with respect to the plane of the layer. The molecules in Figure 12.41 form nematic or smectic phases. Liquid crystal–type phases appear in many biological systems (Figure 12.43).

**Applications of Liquid Crystals** The ability to control the orientation of the molecules in a liquid crystal allows us to produce materials with high strength or unique optical properties:

1. *High-strength applications* involve the use of extremely long molecules called *polymers.* While in a thermotropic liquid crystal phase and during their flow through the processing equipment, these molecules become highly aligned, like the fibers in wood. Cooling solidifies them into fibers, rods, and sheets that can be shaped into materials with superior mechanical properties. Sporting equipment, supersonic aircraft parts, and the sails used in the America's Cup races are fabricated from these polymeric materials. (We discuss the structure and physical behavior of polymers later in this section and their synthesis in Chapter 15.)

2. *Optical applications* include the liquid crystal displays (LCDs) used in countless devices, such as watches, calculators, cell phones, and computers. All depend on *changes in molecular orientation in an electric field.* Figure 12.44 shows a small portion of a wristwatch LCD. Layers of nematic phases are sandwiched between thin glass plates that incorporate transparent electrodes. The long molecular axis lies parallel to the plane of the plates. The distance between plates (6–8 μm) allows the molecular axis within each succeeding layer to twist just enough for the molecular orientation at the bottom plate to be 90° from that at the top plate. Above and below this "sandwich" are thin polarizing filters that allow light waves oriented in only one direction to pass through. The filters are placed in a "crossed" arrangement, so that light passing through the top filter must twist 90° to pass through the bottom filter. This whole grouping of filters, plates, and liquid crystal phase lies on a mirror.

A current generated by the watch battery controls the orientation of the molecules. With the current on in one region of the display, the molecules become oriented *toward* the field, and thus block the light from passing through to the bottom filter, so that region appears dark. With the current off in another region, light passes through the molecules and bottom filter to the mirror and back again, so that region appears bright.

Cholesteric liquid crystals are used in applications that involve color changes with temperature. The twisted molecular orientation "unwinds" with heating, and the extent of the unwinding determines the color. Liquid crystal thermometers include a mixture of substances to widen their range of temperatures. Newer uses include "mapping" the area of a tumor, detecting faulty connections in electronic circuit boards, and nondestructive testing of materials under stress.

## Ceramic Materials

First developed by Stone Age people, **ceramics** are nonmetallic, nonpolymeric solids hardened by high temperature. Clay ceramics consist of silicate microcrystals suspended in a glassy cementing medium. In "firing" a ceramic pot, for example, a kiln heats the object made of an aluminosilicate clay, such as kaolinite, to 1500°C and the clay loses water:

$$Si_2Al_2O_5(OH)_4(s) \longrightarrow Si_2Al_2O_7(s) + 2H_2O(g)$$

During the heating process, the structure rearranges to an extended network of Si-centered and Al-centered tetrahedra of O atoms (Section 14.6).

Bricks, porcelain, glazes, and other clay ceramics are hard and resistant to heat and chemicals. Today's high-tech ceramics have these characteristics in addition to superior electrical and magnetic properties (Table 12.7). As just one example, consider the unusual electrical behavior of certain zinc oxide (ZnO) composites. Ordinarily a semiconductor, ZnO can be doped so that it becomes a conductor. Imbedding particles of the doped oxide into an insulating ceramic produces a variable resistor: at low voltage, the material conducts poorly, but at high voltage, it conducts well. The changeover voltage can be "preset" by controlling the size of the ZnO particles and the thickness of the insulating medium.

**Preparing Modern Ceramics** Among the important modern ceramics are silicon carbide (SiC) and nitride ($Si_3N_4$), boron nitride (BN), and the superconducting oxides. They are prepared by standard chemical methods that involve driving off a volatile component during the reaction:

1. *SiC ceramics* are made from compounds used in silicone polymer manufacture (we'll discuss these polymers in Section 14.6):

$$n(CH_3)_2SiCl_2(l) + 2nNa(s) \longrightarrow 2nNaCl(s) + [(CH_3)_2Si]_n(s)$$

This product is heated to 800°C to form the ceramic:

$$[(CH_3)_2Si]_n \longrightarrow nCH_4(g) + nH_2(g) + nSiC(s)$$

Silicon carbide can also be prepared by the direct reaction of silicon and graphite under vacuum:

$$Si(s) + C(graphite) \xrightarrow{\sim 1500°C} SiC(s)$$

### Table 12.7 Some Uses of Modern Ceramics and Ceramic Mixtures

| Ceramic | Applications |
|---|---|
| $SiC$, $Si_3N_4$, $TiB_2$, $Al_2O_3$ | Whiskers (fibers) to strengthen Al and other ceramics |
| $Si_3N_4$ | Car engine parts; turbine rotors for "turbo" cars; electronic sensor units |
| $Si_3N_4$, $BN$, $Al_2O_3$ | Support or layering materials (as insulators) in electronic microchips |
| $SiC$, $Si_3N_4$, $TiB_2$, $ZrO_2$, $Al_2O_3$, $BN$ | Cutting tools, edge sharpeners (as coatings and whole devices), scissors, surgical tools, industrial "diamond" |
| $BN$, $SiC$ | Armor-plating reinforcement fibers (as in Kevlar composites) |
| $ZrO_2$, $Al_2O_3$ | Surgical implants (hip and knee joints) |

Polarizer
Top plate
LC layer
Bottom plate
Polarizer
Mirror

**Current on:** molecules align, light blocked, dark region

**Current off:** molecules not aligned, light passes, bright region

**Figure 12.44 A liquid crystal display (LCD).** A close-up of the "2" on a wristwatch LCD reveals two polarizers sandwiching two glass plates, which sandwich a liquid crystal (LC) layer, all lying on a mirror. When light waves enter the first polarizer, waves oriented in one direction emerge to enter the LC layer. Enlarging a dark region (*top blow-up*) shows the LC molecules aligned, keeping light waves from passing through; thus, the viewer sees no light. Enlarging a bright region (*bottom blow-up*) shows the LC molecules rotating the plane of the light waves, which can then pass through and reach the viewer.

The nitride is also prepared by reaction of the elements:

$$3Si(s) + 2N_2(g) \xrightarrow{>1300°C} Si_3N_4(s)$$

2. *BN ceramics* are produced through the reaction of boron trichloride or boric acid with ammonia:

$$B(OH)_3(s) + 3NH_3(g) \longrightarrow B(NH_2)_3(s) + 3H_2O(g)$$

Heat drives off some of the bound nitrogen as $NH_3$ to yield the ceramic:

$$B(NH_2)_3(s) \xrightarrow{\Delta} 2NH_3(g) + BN(s)$$

3. One type of *superconducting oxide* is made by heating a mixture of barium carbonate with copper and yttrium oxides, followed by further heating in the presence of $O_2$:

$$4BaCO_3(s) + 6CuO(s) + Y_2O_3(s) \xrightarrow{\Delta} 2YBa_2Cu_3O_{6.5}(s) + 4CO_2(g)$$

$$YBa_2Cu_3O_{6.5}(s) + \tfrac{1}{4}O_2(g) \xrightarrow{\Delta} YBa_2Cu_3O_7(s)$$

**Ceramic Structures and Uses** Structures of several ceramic materials are shown in Figure 12.45.

1. *Silicon carbide* has a diamond-like structure. Network covalent bonding gives this material great strength. It is made into thin fibers, called *whiskers,* to reinforce other ceramics and prevent cracking in a composite structure, much like steel rods reinforcing concrete.

2. *Silicon nitride* is virtually inert chemically, retains its strength and wear resistance for extended periods above 1000°C, is dense and hard, and acts as an electrical insulator. Many automakers are testing it in high-efficiency car and truck engines because of its low weight, tolerance of high operating temperature, and little need for lubrication.

3. *BN ceramics* exist in two structures, analogous to the common crystalline forms of carbon. In the graphite-like form, BN has extraordinary properties as an electrical insulator. At high temperature and very high pressure (1800°C and $8.5 \times 10^4$ atm), it converts to a diamond-like structure, which is extremely hard and durable. Both forms are virtually invisible to radar.

4. *Superconducting oxides* often contain copper in an unusual oxidation state. In $YBa_2Cu_3O_7$, for instance, assuming oxidation states of +3 for Y, +2 for Ba, and −2 for O, the three Cu atoms have a total oxidation state of +7. This is allocated as $Cu(II)_2Cu(III)$, with one Cu in the unusual +3 state. X-ray diffraction analysis indicates that a distortion in the structure makes four of the oxide ions unusually close to the $Y^{3+}$ ion, which aligns the Cu ions into chains within the crystal. It is suspected that a specific half-filled $3d$ orbital in Cu oriented toward a neighboring $O^{2-}$ ion may be associated with superconductivity.

**A  $YBa_2Cu_3O_7$**

**B  Silicon carbide**

**C  Cubic BN (borazon)**

**Figure 12.45** Expanded view of the atom arrangements in some modern ceramic materials.

Because of brittleness, it is difficult to fashion these ceramics into wires, but methods for making films and ribbons have been developed. The brittleness arises from the strength of the ionic-covalent bonding and the resulting inability to deform. Under stress, a microfine defect widens until the material cracks. One new method forms defect-free superconducting oxide ceramics using controlled packing and heat-treating of extremely small, uniform oxide particles coated with organic polymers. Another method is aimed at arresting a widening crack. The ceramics are embedded with zirconia ($ZrO_2$), whose crystal structure expands up to 5% under mechanical stress. When an advancing crack reaches them, the zirconia particles pinch it shut. A third method prepares the material of precisely grown crystals of $Al_2O_3$ and $GdAlO_3$, which become entangled during the solidification process. The resulting material bends without cracking above 1800 K.

## Polymeric Materials

A **polymer** (Greek, "many parts") is an extremely large molecule, or **macromolecule,** consisting of a covalently linked chain of smaller molecules, called **monomers** (Greek, "one part"). The monomer is the *repeat unit* of the polymer, and a polymer may have hundreds to hundreds of thousands of repeat units. Many types of monomers give polymers the complete repertoire of intermolecular forces.

- *Synthetic* polymers are created in the laboratory.
- *Natural* polymers (or *biopolymers*) are created within organisms.

In this section, we examine the physical nature of synthetic polymers and explore the role of intermolecular forces in their properties and uses. In Chapter 15, we'll examine the types of monomers, the preparation of synthetic polymers, and the monomers, structures, and functions of some biopolymers.

**Dimensions of a Polymer Chain** Polymers differ from smaller molecules in terms of molar mass, chain length, shape, and size. We'll discuss these, using polyethylene, by far the most common synthetic polymer, as an example.

1. *Polymer mass.* The molar mass of a polymer chain ($\mathcal{M}_{polymer}$, in g/mol, often referred to as the *molecular weight*) depends on the molar mass of the repeat unit ($\mathcal{M}_{repeat}$) and the **degree of polymerization ($n$),** the number of repeat units in the chain:

$$\mathcal{M}_{polymer} = \mathcal{M}_{repeat} \times n$$

For example, the molar mass of the ethylene repeat unit ($-CH_2-CH_2-$) is 28 g/mol. If an individual polyethylene chain in a plastic grocery bag has a degree of polymerization of 7100, the molar mass of that chain is

$$\mathcal{M}_{polymer} = \mathcal{M}_{repeat} \times n = (28 \text{ g/mol}) (7.1 \times 10^3) = 2.0 \times 10^5 \text{ g/mol}$$

Table 12.8 shows some other examples.

| Table 12.8 Molar Masses of Some Common Polymers | | | |
|---|---|---|---|
| **Name** | $\mathcal{M}_{polymer}$ **(g/mol)** | **$n$** | **Uses** |
| Acrylates | $2 \times 10^5$ | $2 \times 10^3$ | Rugs, carpets |
| Polyamide (nylons) | $1.5 \times 10^4$ | $1.2 \times 10^2$ | Tires, fishing line |
| Polycarbonate | $1 \times 10^5$ | $4 \times 10^2$ | Compact discs |
| Polyethylene | $3 \times 10^5$ | $1 \times 10^4$ | Grocery bags |
| Polyethylene (ultrahigh molecular weight) | $5 \times 10^6$ | $2 \times 10^5$ | Hip joints |
| Poly(ethylene terephthalate) | $2 \times 10^4$ | $1 \times 10^2$ | Soda bottles |
| Polystyrene | $3 \times 10^5$ | $3 \times 10^3$ | Packing, coffee cups |
| Poly(vinyl chloride) | $1 \times 10^5$ | $1.5 \times 10^3$ | Plumbing |

However, even though the monomer repeat unit in any given chain has the same molar mass, the degree of polymerization often varies considerably from chain to chain. Thus, *a sample of a synthetic polymer has a distribution of chain lengths and molar masses*. Polymer chemists use various definitions of the *average* molar mass, and a common one is the *number-average molar mass*, $\mathcal{M}_n$:

$$\mathcal{M}_n = \frac{\text{total mass of all chains}}{\text{number of moles of chains}}$$

If the number-average molar mass of the polyethylene in grocery bags is, say, $1.6 \times 10^5$ g/mol, the chains may vary in molar mass from about $7.0 \times 10^4$ to $3.0 \times 10^5$ g/mol.

2. *Polymer chain length.* The long axis of a polymer chain is called its *backbone*. The length of an *extended* backbone is simply the number of repeat units (degree of polymerization, *n*) times the length of each repeat unit ($l_0$). For instance, the length of an ethylene repeat unit is about 250 pm, so the extended length of our particular grocery-bag polyethylene chain is

Length of extended chain $= n \times l_0 = (7.1 \times 10^3)(2.5 \times 10^2 \text{ pm}) = 1.8 \times 10^6 \text{ pm}$

Comparing this length with the thickness of the chain, which is about 40 pm, shows the threadlike nature of the extended chain (length about 50,000 times width).

3. *Coiled shape and size.* A polymer molecule, however, whether pure or in solution, doesn't exist as an extended chain. In principle, the shape of the molecule arises from free rotation around all the single bonds. Thus, as each repeat unit rotates randomly, the chain continuously changes direction, turning back on itself many times and eventually arriving at the **random coil** shape that most polymers adopt (Figure 12.46). In reality, rotation is not completely free because intermolecular forces between chain portions, between different chains, and/or between chain and solvent have significant effects on the actual shape of a polymer chain.

**Figure 12.46 The random-coil shape of a polymer chain.** Note the random coiling of the chain's carbon atoms (*black*). Sections of several nearby chains (*red, green,* and *yellow*) are entangled with this chain, kept near one another by dispersion forces. In reality, entangling chains fill any gaps shown here.

The size of the coiled chain is expressed by its **radius of gyration, $R_g$,** the average distance from the center of mass of the molecule to the outer edge of the coil (Figure 12.46). Even though $R_g$ is reported as a single value for a given polymer, it represents an average value for many chains. The mathematical expression for the radius of gyration includes the length of each repeat unit and the degree of polymerization:*

$$R_g = \sqrt{\frac{nl_0^2}{6}}$$

As expected, the radius of gyration increases with the degree of polymerization, and thus with the molar mass as well. Light-scattering measurements correlate with these calculated results, so for many polymers the radius of gyration can be determined experimentally.

For our grocery-bag polyethylene chain, we have

$$R_g = \sqrt{\frac{nl_0^2}{6}} = \sqrt{\frac{(7.1 \times 10^3)(2.5 \times 10^2 \text{ pm})^2}{6}} = 8.6 \times 10^3 \text{ pm}$$

Doubling the radius gives a diameter of $1.7 \times 10^4$ pm for the coiled chain, less than one-hundredth the length of the extended chain!

**Polymer Crystallinity**  A sample of a given polymer is not just a disorderly jumble of chains. If the molecular structure allows neighboring chains to pack together and if the chemical groups lead to favorable dipole-dipole, H-bonding, and/or dispersion forces, portions of the chains can align regularly and exhibit crystallinity.

However, the crystallinity of a polymer is very different from the crystal structures we discussed earlier. In those structures, the orderly array extends over many atoms or molecules, and the unit cell includes at least one atom or molecule. In contrast, the orderly regions of a polymer rarely involve even one whole molecule (Figure 12.47). At best, a polymer is *semicrystalline*, because parts of the molecule align with parts of neighboring molecules (or with other parts of the same chain), while most of the chain remains as a random coil.

---

*The mathematical derivation of $R_g$ is beyond the scope of this text, but it is analogous to the two-dimensional "walk of the drunken sailor." With each step, the sailor stumbles in random directions and, given enough time, ends up very close to the starting position. The radius of gyration quantifies how far the end of the polymer chain (the sailor) has gone from the origin.

*Crystalline regions from different chains can interact.*

*A polyethylene chain may have several crystalline regions.*

**Figure 12.47  The semicrystallinity of a polymer chain.**  Several crystalline regions (*darker color*) have randomly coiled regions between them. Crystalline regions from nearby chains (*red* and *yellow*) align with those in the main chain.

**Viscosity of Pure and Dissolved Polymers** Some of the most important uses of polymers arise from their ability to change the viscosity of a solvent in which they are dissolved and to undergo temperature-dependent changes in their own viscosity.

1. *Dissolved polymers.* When an appreciable amount of polymer (about 5–15 mass %) dissolves, the viscosity of the solution is much higher than that of the pure solvent. In fact, polymers are added to increase the viscosity of many common materials, such as motor oil, paint, and salad dressing. As the random coil of a polymer moves through a solution, solvent molecules are attracted to it through intermolecular forces (Figure 12.48). Thus, as the solution flows, the polymer coil drags along solvent molecules that are interacting with other solvent molecules and other coils, and flow is reduced. Increasing the polymer concentration increases the viscosity because coils are more likely to become entangled.

Viscosity is a property of a particular polymer-solvent pair at a given temperature. The size (radius of gyration) of a random coil in solution increases with molar mass, and so does the viscosity. To improve polymer manufacture, chemists have developed equations to predict the viscosity of polymers of different molar masses in a variety of solvents (see Problem 12.142).

2. *Pure polymers.* Intermolecular forces also play a major role in the flow of a pure polymer sample. At temperatures high enough to melt them, many polymers exist as viscous liquids, flowing more like honey than water. The forces between the chains, as well as the entangling of chains, hinder the flow. As the temperature decreases, the intermolecular attractions exert a greater effect, and the eventual result is a rigid solid. If the chains don't crystallize, the resulting material is called a *polymer glass.* The transition from a liquid to a glass occurs over a narrow temperature range (10–20°C) for a given polymer; temperature at the midpoint of the range is

**Figure 12.48 The viscosity of a polymer in aqueous solution.** A section of a poly(ethylene oxide) chain *(left panel)* forms H bonds between the lone pairs of the chain's O atoms and the H atoms of water molecules. A polymer chain *(blue and red coiled rod, center panel)* forms many H bonds with water molecules that allow the chain to interact with other chains. As the concentration of polymer increases *(three right panels),* the viscosity of the solution increases.

called the *glass transition temperature, $T_g$*. Like window glass, many polymer glasses are transparent, such as polystyrene in drinking cups and polycarbonate in eyeglass lenses.

**Plasticity of Polymers**  The flow-related properties of polymers give rise to their familiar **plastic** mechanical behavior. The word "plastic" refers to a material that, when deformed, retains its new shape; in contrast, when an "elastic" object is deformed, it returns to its original shape. Many polymers can be deformed (stretched, bent, twisted) when warm and retain their deformed shape when cooled. In this way, they are made into milk bottles, car parts, and countless other everyday objects.

**Molecular Architecture of Polymers**  A polymer's architecture—its overall spatial layout and molecular structure—is crucial to its properties. In addition to linear chains, more complex architectures arise through branching and crosslinking:

1. **Branches** are smaller chains appended to a polymer backbone. As the number of branches increases, the chains cannot pack as well, so the degree of crystallinity decreases and the polymer is less rigid. A small amount of branching occurs as a side reaction in the preparation of high-density polyethylene (HDPE). It is still largely linear and rigid enough for use in milk containers. In contrast, much more branching is intentionally induced to prepare low-density polyethylene (LDPE). The chains cannot pack well, so crystallinity is low. This polymer is used in flexible, transparent food storage bags.

*Dendrimers* are prepared from monomers with three or more attachment points, so each monomer forms branches. In essence, then, dendrimers have no backbone and consist only of branches. A dendrimer has a constantly increasing number of branches and an incredibly large number of end groups at its outer edge. Chemists use dendrimers to bind one polymer to another to create films and fibers and to deliver drugs in medical applications.

2. **Crosslinks** can be thought of as branches that link one chain to another. The extent of crosslinking leads to remarkable differences in properties. A small degree of crosslinking often yields a *thermoplastic* polymer, one that still flows at high temperatures. But, as the extent of crosslinking increases, a thermoplastic polymer is transformed into a *thermoset* polymer, one that can no longer flow because it has become a single network. Below their glass transition temperatures, some thermosets are extremely rigid and strong, making them ideal as matrix materials in high-strength composites (*see photo*).

Above their glass transition temperatures, many thermosets become **elastomers,** polymers that can be stretched and immediately spring back to their initial shapes when released, like a trampoline or a rubber band. When you stretch a rubber band, individual polymer chains flow for only a short distance before the connectivity of the network returns them to their original positions. Table 12.9 lists some elastomers.

Bicycle helmet containing a thermoset polymer.

| **Table 12.9 Some Common Elastomers** | | |
|---|---|---|
| **Name** | **$T_g$ (°C)** | **Uses** |
| Poly(dimethyl siloxane) | −123 | Breast implants |
| Polybutadiene | −106 | Rubber bands |
| Polyisoprene | −65 | Surgical gloves |
| Polychloroprene (neoprene) | −43 | Footwear; medical tubing |

**Impact of Monomer Sequence**  Differences in monomer sequences influence polymer properties as well. A *homopolymer* consists of one type of monomer (A—A—A—A—A— ⋯), whereas a **copolymer** consists of two or more types. The simplest copolymer is called an *AB block copolymer* because a chain (block) of monomer A and a chain of monomer B are linked at one point:

$$\cdots —A—A—A—A—A—B—B—B—B—B— \cdots$$

If the intermolecular forces between the A and B portions of the chain are weaker than those between different regions within each portion, the A and B portions form their own random coils. This ability makes AB block copolymers ideal *adhesives* for joining two polymer surfaces covalently. An ABA block copolymer has A chains linked at each end of a B chain:

$$\cdots -A-A-A-B-(B)_n-B-A-A-A- \cdots$$

Some of these block copolymers act as *thermoplastic elastomers,* materials shaped at high temperature that become elastomers at room temperature; many are used in the modern footwear industry.

Silicone polymers are described briefly in Chapter 14, and organic reactions that form polymer chains from monomers are examined in Chapter 15.

## Nanotechnology: Designing Materials Atom by Atom

**Nanotechnology** is the science and engineering of nanoscale systems, whose sizes range from 1 to 100 nm. (Recall that 1 nm is $10^{-9}$ m—about one-billionth the width of your dorm-room desk or one-millionth the width of your pen tip. A nanometer is to a meter as a marble is to Earth!) Nanotechnology joins scientists from physics, materials science, chemistry, biology, environmental science, medicine, and many branches of engineering.

Nanoscale materials behave neither like atoms, which are smaller ($1\times10^1$ nm), nor like crystals, which are at least $1\times10^5$ nm. The different behavior is due to a surface area that is similar to their interior volume—for example, a 5-nm particle has about half of its atoms on its surface. Cut a piece of ordinary aluminum foil into pieces just large enough to see with a light microscope and they still behave like the original piece. But, if you could cut the original piece into 20–30-nm pieces, they would explode. Indeed, aluminum nanoparticles are used in fireworks and propellants.

As so often happens in science, a technological advance allows a new field to blossom. Nanotechnologists can use the scanning tunneling microscope (see Tools of the Laboratory, pp. 447–448) and the similar scanning probe and atomic force microscopes to examine the chemical and physical properties of nanostructures and build them up, in many cases, atom by atom.

Two features of nanoscale engineering occur routinely in nature:

1. *Self-assembly* is the ability of smaller, simpler parts to organize themselves into a larger, more complex whole. On the molecular scale, self-assembly refers to atoms or small molecules aggregating through intermolecular forces. Oppositely charged regions on two such particles make contact to form a larger particle, which in turn aggregates with another to form a still larger one.
2. *Controlled orientation* is the positioning of two molecules near each other long enough for intermolecular forces to result in a change, often a bond breaking or forming. All enzymes function this way.

Because this new field changes many times faster than a textbook does, we can only provide a glimpse of a few exciting research directions in nanotechnology.

**Nanoscale Optical Materials** *Quantum dots* are nanoparticles of semiconducting materials, such as gallium arsenide (GaAs) or gallium selenide (GaSe), that are smaller than 10 nm. Rather than having a band of energy levels, the dot has discrete energy levels, much like a single atom. As in atoms, the energy levels can be studied with spectroscopy; unlike atoms, quantum dots can be modified chemically. When high-energy (short-wavelength) UV light irradiates a suspension of quantum dots, they become excited and emit radiation of lower energy (longer wavelength). Most importantly, the emitted wavelengths depend on the size of the dots: the larger the particles, the longer the wavelength emitted. Thus, the color of the emitted light can be "tuned" by varying the dimensions of the nanoparticles (Figure 12.49). One use for quantum dots is the imaging of specific cells. The dot is encapsulated in a coating

2.3 ———————→ 5.5
Size (nm)

**Figure 12.49 The colors of quantum dots.** The smaller the dots, the shorter the emitted wavelengths.

and then bonded to a particular protein used by a target organ. The cells in the target incorporate the protein, along with its attached quantum dot, and the location of the protein is viewed spectroscopically.

**Nanostructured Materials** *Nanostructuring*, the construction of bulk materials from nanoscale building blocks, increases strength, ductility, plasticity, and many other properties. The resulting *nanocomposites* behave as liquid magnets, ductile cements, conducting elastomers, and many other unique materials.

One example mimics a familiar natural material. Bones are natural nanocomposites of hydroxyapatite (a type of calcium phosphate) and other minerals. Synthetic nanocrystalline hydroxyapatite has been made with weight-bearing properties identical to bone that provides a framework for natural bone tissue to grow into and heal a fracture. Another material, called a *ferrofluid,* consists of magnetic nanoparticles (usually magnetite, $Fe_3O_4$) dispersed in a viscous fluid. When placed in a magnetic field, the particles align to conform to the shape of the field (Figure 12.50). Ferrofluids find uses in automobile shock absorbers, magnetic plastics, audio speakers, computer hard drives, high-vacuum valves, and many other devices.

**Figure 12.50 The magnetic behavior of a ferrofluid.** Nanoparticles of magnetite ($Fe_3O_4$) dispersed in a viscous fluid are suspended between the poles of a magnet.

**High-Surface-Area Materials** Carbon nanotubes have remarkable mechanical and electrical properties. But, a possible future application involves storing $H_2$ gas for hydrogen-powered vehicles. Currently, $H_2$ is stored in metal cylinders at high pressures (>70 atm). Porous solids, such as carbon nanotubes, can store the same amount of gas at much lower pressures because they have surface areas of 4500 m²/g—about four football fields per gram of material! Thus, a medium-sized container of nanotubes could store a large amount of $H_2$ fuel under conditions safe enough for a family car.

Other high-surface-area materials being developed are porous membranes for water purification or batteries and multilayer films that incorporate photosynthetic molecules for high-efficiency solar cells. A very exciting development is the molecule-specific biosensor, which can detect as little as $10^{-14}$ mol of DNA using color changes in gold nanoparticles. Such biosensors could circulate freely in the bloodstream to measure levels of specific disease-related molecules, deliver drugs to individual cells, and even alter individual genes.

**Nanomachines** In nature, the virus is a marvel of nanoscale engineering, designed for delivering genetic material to infect a host cell. For example, the T4 virus latches onto a bacterial cell with its tail fibers, bores through the bacterial membrane with its end plate, and then injects the payload of DNA, packaged in its head, into the bacterium. These complex functions are performed by a biological "machine" measuring $60 \times 200$ nm. Researchers are exploring ways for viruses to deliver medicinal agents to specific cells. In other feats of nanoscale engineering, researchers have created nanovalves, nanopropellers, and even a nanocar, complete with a chassis, axles, and buckyball wheels, that is only 4 nm wide and is "driven" on a gold surface under the direction of an atomic force microscope (Figure 12.51).

**Figure 12.51 Driving a nanocar.**

## ◼ Summary of Section 12.7

- Doping increases the conductivity of semiconductors and is essential to modern electronic materials. Doping silicon with Group 5A(15) atoms introduces negative sites (n-type semiconductor) by adding valence electrons to the conduction band, whereas doping with Group 3A(13) atoms adds positive holes (p-type semiconductor) by emptying some orbitals in the valence band. Placing these two types of semiconductors in contact with one another forms a p-n junction. Sandwiching a p-type portion between two n-type portions forms a transistor.

- Liquid crystal phases flow like liquids but have molecules ordered like crystalline solids. Typically, the molecules have rodlike shapes, and their intermolecular forces keep them aligned. Thermotropic phases are prepared by heating the solid; lyotropic phases form when the solvent concentration is varied. The nematic, cholesteric, and smectic phases of liquid crystals differ in their molecular order. Liquid crystal applications depend on controlling the orientation of the molecules.

- Ceramics are very resistant to heat and chemicals. Most are network covalent solids formed at high temperature from simple reactants. They add lightweight strength to other materials.

- Polymers are extremely large molecules that adopt the shape of a random coil, as a result of intermolecular forces. A polymer sample has an average molar mass because it consists of chains with a range of lengths. The high viscosity of a polymer arises from attractions between chains or, in the case of a dissolved polymer, between chains and solvent. By varying the degrees of branching, crosslinking, and ordering (crystallinity), chemists tailor polymers with specific properties.

- Nanoscale materials can be made through construction processes involving self-assembly and controlled orientation of molecules.

# CHAPTER REVIEW GUIDE

## Learning Objectives    Relevant section (§) and/or sample problem (SP) numbers appear in parentheses.

### Understand These Concepts

1. How the interplay between kinetic and potential energy underlies the properties of the three states of matter and their phase changes (§12.1)
2. The processes involved, both within a phase and during a phase change, when heat is added or removed from a pure substance (§12.2)
3. The meaning of vapor pressure and how phase changes are dynamic equilibrium processes (§12.2)
4. How temperature and intermolecular forces influence vapor pressure (§12.2)
5. The relation between vapor pressure and boiling point (§12.2)
6. How a phase diagram shows the phases of a substance at differing conditions of pressure and temperature (§12.2)
7. The distinction between bonding and intermolecular forces on the basis of Coulomb's law and the meaning of the van der Waals radius of an atom (§12.3)
8. The types and relative strengths of intermolecular forces acting in a substance (dipole-dipole, H-bonding, dispersion), the impact of H bonding on physical properties, and the meaning of polarizability (§12.3)
9. The meanings of surface tension, capillarity, and viscosity and how intermolecular forces influence their magnitudes (§12.4)
10. How the important macroscopic properties of water arise from atomic and molecular properties (§12.5)
11. The meaning of *crystal lattice* and the characteristics of the three types of cubic unit cells (§12.6)
12. How packing of spheres gives rise to the hexagonal and cubic unit cells (§12.6)
13. Types of crystalline solids and how their intermolecular forces give rise to their properties (§12.6)
14. How band theory accounts for the properties of metals and the relative conductivities of metals, nonmetals, and metalloids (§12.6)
15. The structures, properties, and functions of modern materials (doped semiconductors, liquid crystals, ceramics, polymers, and nanostructures) (§12.7)

### Master These Skills

1. Calculating the overall enthalpy change when heat is gained or lost by a pure substance (§12.2 and SP 12.1)
2. Using the Clausius-Clapeyron equation to examine the relationship between vapor pressure and temperature (SP 12.2)
3. Using a phase diagram to predict the physical state and/or phase change of a substance (§12.2)
4. Determining whether a substance can form H bonds and drawing the H-bonded structures (SP 12.3)
5. Predicting the types and relative strength of the bonding and intermolecular forces acting within a substance from its structure (SP 12.4)
6. Finding the number of particles in a unit cell (§12.6)
7. Calculating atomic radius from the crystal structure of an element (SP 12.5, 12.6)

## Key Terms
Page numbers appear in parentheses.

**Section 12.1**
phase (419)
intermolecular forces (419)
phase change (420)
condensation (420)
vaporization (420)
freezing (420)
melting (fusion) (420)
sublimation (421)
deposition (421)
heat of vaporization ($\Delta H^{\circ}_{vap}$)
  (421)
heat of fusion ($\Delta H^{\circ}_{fus}$) (421)
heat of sublimation ($\Delta H^{\circ}_{subl}$)
  (421)

**Section 12.2**
heating-cooling curve (422)
vapor pressure (426)
Clausius-Clapeyron equation
  (427)
boiling point (428)
melting point (429)

phase diagram (429)
triple point (429)
critical point (429)

**Section 12.3**
van der Waals radius (431)
ion-dipole force (432)
dipole-dipole force (432)
hydrogen bond (H bond)
  (432)
polarizability (434)
dispersion (London) force
  (435)

**Section 12.4**
surface tension (437)
capillarity (438)
viscosity (439)

**Section 12.6**
crystalline solid (441)
amorphous solid (441)
lattice (442)
unit cell (442)
coordination number (442)

simple cubic unit cell (442)
body-centered cubic unit cell
  (442)
face-centered cubic unit cell
  (442)
packing efficiency (444)
hexagonal closest packing
  (444)
cubic closest packing (444)
x-ray diffraction analysis
  (447)
scanning tunneling
  microscopy (447)
atomic solid (449)
molecular solid (449)
ionic solid (449)
metallic solid (451)
network covalent solid (451)
band theory (452)
valence band (453)
conduction band (453)
conductor (453)

semiconductor (453)
insulator (453)
superconductivity (454)

**Section 12.7**
crystal defect (455)
doping (455)
liquid crystal (456)
ceramic (459)
polymer (461)
macromolecule (461)
monomer (461)
degree of polymerization ($n$)
  (461)
random coil (462)
radius of gyration ($R_g$) (463)
plastic (465)
branch (465)
crosslink (465)
elastomer (465)
copolymer (465)
nanotechnology (466)

## Key Equations and Relationships
Page number appears in parentheses.

**12.1** Using the vapor pressure at one temperature to find the vapor pressure at another temperature (two-point form of the Clausius-Clapeyron equation) (427):

$$\ln \frac{P_2}{P_1} = \frac{-\Delta H_{vap}}{R}\left(\frac{1}{T_2} - \frac{1}{T_1}\right)$$

## Brief Solutions to Follow-Up Problems

**12.1** The scenes represent solid water at $-7.00°C$ melting to liquid water at $16.0°C$, so there are three stages.
Stage 1, $H_2O(s)\ [-7.00°C] \longrightarrow H_2O(s)\ [0.00°C]$:
$q = n \times C_{water(s)} \times \Delta T = (2.25\ mol)\ (37.6\ J/mol·°C)\ (7.00°C)$
  $= 592\ J = 0.592\ kJ$
Stage 2, $H_2O(s)\ [0.00°C] \longrightarrow H_2O(l)\ [0.00°C]$:
$q = n(\Delta H^{\circ}_{fus}) = (2.25\ mol)\ (6.02\ kJ/mol) = 13.5\ kJ$
Stage 3, $H_2O(l)\ [0.00°C] \longrightarrow H_2O(l)\ [16.0°C]$:
$q = n \times C_{water(l)} \times \Delta T = (2.25\ mol)\ (75.4\ J/mol·°C)\ (16.0°C)$
  $= 2714\ J = 2.71\ kJ$
Total heat (kJ) $= 0.592\ kJ + 13.5\ kJ + 2.71\ kJ = 16.8\ kJ$

**12.2** $\ln \dfrac{P_2}{P_1} = \left(\dfrac{-40.7 \times 10^3\ J/mol}{8.314\ J/mol·K}\right)$
$\times \left(\dfrac{1}{273.15 + 85.5\ K} - \dfrac{1}{273.15 + 34.1\ K}\right)$
  $= (-4.90 \times 10^3\ K)\ (-4.6 \times 10^{-4}\ K^{-1}) = 2.28$
$\dfrac{P_2}{P_1} = 9.8$; thus, $P_2 = 40.1\ torr \times 9.8 = 3.9 \times 10^2\ torr$

**12.3** (a)

H–C–C–O:⋯⋯H–Ö ... C–C–H   (b) H–C–C–Ö:
                Ö–H⋯⋯:O

(c) No H bonding

H–C–C–Ö–H

**12.4** (a) Dipole-dipole, dispersion; $CH_3Br$
(b) H bonds, dipole-dipole, dispersion; $CH_3CH_2CH_2OH$
(c) Dispersion; $C_3H_8$

**12.5** Avogadro's no. $= \dfrac{1\ cm^3}{7.874\ g\ Fe} \times \dfrac{55.85\ g\ Fe}{1\ mol\ Fe} \times 0.68$
$\times \dfrac{1\ Fe\ atom}{8.38 \times 10^{-24}\ cm^3}$
  $= 5.8 \times 10^{23}\ Fe\ atoms/mol\ Fe$

**12.6** From Figure 12.29B,
$A = \dfrac{4r}{\sqrt{3}} = \dfrac{4(126\ pm)}{\sqrt{3}} = 291\ pm$

$r = 126\ pm$

$\leftarrow A = ? \rightarrow$

# PROBLEMS

Problems with **colored** numbers are in Appendix E and worked in detail in the Student Solutions Manual. Problem sections match those in the text and provide the numbers of relevant sample problems. Most offer Concept Review Questions, Skill-Building Exercises (grouped in pairs covering the same concept), and Problems in Context. The Comprehensive Problems are based on material from any section or previous chapter.

## Overview of Physical States and Phase Changes

### Concept Review Questions

**12.1** How does the energy of attraction between particles compare with their energy of motion in a gas and in a solid? As part of your answer, identify two macroscopic properties that differ between a gas and a solid.

**12.2** (a) Why are gases more easily compressed than liquids? (b) Why do liquids have a greater ability to flow than solids?

**12.3** What type of forces, intramolecular or intermolecular: (a) Prevent ice cubes from adopting the shape of their container? (b) Are overcome when ice melts? (c) Are overcome when liquid water is vaporized? (d) Are overcome when gaseous water is converted to hydrogen gas and oxygen gas?

**12.4** (a) Why is the heat of fusion ($\Delta H_{fus}$) of a substance smaller than its heat of vaporization ($\Delta H_{vap}$)? (b) Why is the heat of sublimation ($\Delta H_{subl}$) of a substance greater than its $\Delta H_{vap}$? (c) At a given temperature and pressure, how does the magnitude of the heat of vaporization of a substance compare with that of its heat of condensation?

### Skill-Building Exercises (grouped in similar pairs)

**12.5** Which forces are intramolecular and which intermolecular? (a) Those preventing oil from evaporating at room temperature (b) Those preventing butter from melting in a refrigerator (c) Those allowing silver to tarnish (d) Those preventing $O_2$ in air from forming O atoms

**12.6** Which forces are intramolecular and which intermolecular? (a) Those allowing fog to form on a cool, humid evening (b) Those allowing water to form when $H_2$ is sparked (c) Those allowing liquid benzene to crystallize when cooled (d) Those responsible for the low boiling point of hexane

**12.7** Name the phase change in each of these events: (a) Dew appears on a lawn in the morning. (b) Icicles change into liquid water. (c) Wet clothes dry on a summer day.

**12.8** Name the phase change in each of these events: (a) A diamond film forms on a surface from gaseous carbon atoms in a vacuum. (b) Mothballs in a bureau drawer disappear over time. (c) Molten iron from a blast furnace is cast into ingots ("pigs").

### Problems in Context

**12.9** Liquid propane, a widely used fuel, is produced by compressing gaseous propane. During the process, approximately 15 kJ of energy is released for each mole of gas liquefied. Where does this energy come from?

**12.10** Many heat-sensitive and oxygen-sensitive solids, such as camphor, are purified by warming under vacuum. The solid vaporizes directly, and the vapor crystallizes on a cool surface. What phase changes are involved in this method?

## Quantitative Aspects of Phase Changes
(Sample Problems 12.1 and 12.2)

### Concept Review Questions

**12.11** Describe the changes (if any) in potential energy and in kinetic energy among the molecules when gaseous $PCl_3$ condenses to a liquid at a fixed temperature.

**12.12** When benzene is at its melting point, two processes occur simultaneously and balance each other. Describe these processes on the macroscopic and molecular levels.

**12.13** Liquid hexane (bp = 69°C) is placed in a closed container at room temperature. At first, the pressure of the vapor phase increases, but after a short time, it stops changing. Why?

**12.14** Explain the effect of strong intermolecular forces on each of these parameters: (a) critical temperature; (b) boiling point; (c) vapor pressure; (d) heat of vaporization.

**12.15** Match each numbered point in the phase diagram for compound Q with the correct molecular depiction below:

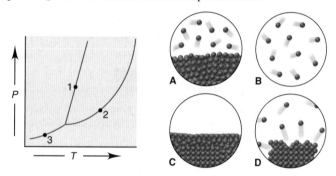

**12.16** A liquid is in equilibrium with its vapor in a closed vessel at a fixed temperature. The vessel is connected by a stopcock to an evacuated vessel. When the stopcock is opened, will the final pressure of the vapor be different from the initial value if (a) some liquid remains; (b) all the liquid is first removed? Explain.

**12.17** The phase diagram for substance A has a solid-liquid line with a positive slope, and that for substance B has a solid-liquid line with a negative slope. What macroscopic property can distinguish A from B?

**12.18** Why does water vapor at 100°C cause a more severe burn than liquid water at 100°C?

### Skill-Building Exercises (grouped in similar pairs)

**12.19** From the data below, calculate the total heat (in J) needed to convert 22.00 g of ice at −6.00°C to liquid water at 0.500°C:

| mp at 1 atm: | 0.0°C | $\Delta H_{fus}^{\circ}$: | 6.02 kJ/mol |
|---|---|---|---|
| $c_{liquid}$: | 4.21 J/g·°C | $c_{solid}$: | 2.09 J/g·°C |

**12.20** From the data below, calculate the total heat (in J) needed to convert 0.333 mol of gaseous ethanol at 300°C and 1 atm to liquid ethanol at 25.0°C and 1 atm:

| bp at 1 atm: | 78.5°C | $\Delta H_{vap}^{\circ}$: | 40.5 kJ/mol |
|---|---|---|---|
| $c_{gas}$: | 1.43 J/g·°C | $c_{liquid}$: | 2.45 J/g·°C |

**12.21** A liquid has a $\Delta H_{vap}^{\circ}$ of 35.5 kJ/mol and a boiling point of 122°C at 1.00 atm. What is its vapor pressure at 113°C?

**12.22** Diethyl ether has a $\Delta H_{vap}^{\circ}$ of 29.1 kJ/mol and a vapor pressure of 0.703 atm at 25.0°C. What is its vapor pressure at 95.0°C?

**12.23** What is the $\Delta H°_{vap}$ of a liquid that has a vapor pressure of 621 torr at 85.2°C and a boiling point of 95.6°C at 1 atm?

**12.24** Methane ($CH_4$) has a boiling point of −164°C at 1 atm and a vapor pressure of 42.8 atm at −100°C. What is the heat of vaporization of $CH_4$?

**12.25** Use these data to draw a qualitative phase diagram for ethylene ($C_2H_4$). Is $C_2H_4(s)$ more or less dense than $C_2H_4(l)$?
bp at 1 atm:       −103.7°C
mp at 1 atm:       −169.16°C
Critical point:       9.9°C and 50.5 atm
Triple point:       −169.17°C and 1.20×10⁻³ atm

**12.26** Use these data to draw a qualitative phase diagram for $H_2$. Does $H_2$ sublime at 0.05 atm? Explain.
mp at 1 atm:                13.96 K
bp at 1 atm:                20.39 K
Triple point:                13.95 K and 0.07 atm
Critical point:                33.2 K and 13.0 atm
Vapor pressure of solid at 10 K:       0.001 atm

### Problems in Context

**12.27** Sulfur dioxide is produced in enormous amounts for sulfuric acid production. It melts at −73°C and boils at −10.°C. Its $\Delta H°_{fus}$ is 8.619 kJ/mol and its $\Delta H°_{vap}$ is 25.73 kJ/mol. The specific heat capacities of the liquid and gas are 0.995 J/g·K and 0.622 J/g·K, respectively. How much heat is required to convert 2.500 kg of solid $SO_2$ at the melting point to a gas at 60.°C?

**12.28** Butane is a common fuel used in cigarette lighters and camping stoves. Normally supplied in metal containers under pressure, the fuel exists as a mixture of liquid and gas, so high temperatures may cause the container to explode. At 25.0°C, the vapor pressure of butane is 2.3 atm. What is the pressure in the container at 135°C ($\Delta H°_{vap}$ = 24.3 kJ/mol)?

**12.29** Use Figure 12.10, p. 429, to answer the following:
(a) Carbon dioxide is sold in steel cylinders under pressures of approximately 20 atm. Is there liquid $CO_2$ in the cylinder at room temperature (~20°C)? At 40°C? At −40°C? At −120°C?
(b) Carbon dioxide is also sold as solid chunks, called *dry ice*, in insulated containers. If the chunks are warmed by leaving them in an open container at room temperature, will they melt?
(c) If a container is nearly filled with dry ice and then sealed and warmed to room temperature, will the dry ice melt?
(d) If dry ice is compressed at a temperature below its triple point, will it melt?

### Types of Intermolecular Forces
(Sample Problems 12.3 and 12.4)

#### Concept Review Questions

**12.30** Why are covalent bonds typically much stronger than intermolecular forces?

**12.31** (a) Name the type of force depicted in each scene below.
(b) Rank the forces in order of increasing strength.

**12.32** Oxygen and selenium are members of Group 6A(16). Water forms H bonds, but $H_2Se$ does not. Explain.

**12.33** In solid $I_2$, is the distance between the two I nuclei of one $I_2$ molecule longer or shorter than the distance between two I nuclei of adjacent $I_2$ molecules? Explain.

**12.34** Polar molecules exhibit dipole-dipole forces. Do they also exhibit dispersion forces? Explain.

**12.35** Distinguish between *polarizability* and *polarity*. How does each influence intermolecular forces?

**12.36** How can one nonpolar molecule induce a dipole in a nearby nonpolar molecule?

**Skill-Building Exercises** (grouped in similar pairs)

**12.37** What is the strongest interparticle force in each substance?
(a) $CH_3OH$      (b) $CCl_4$       (c) $Cl_2$

**12.38** What is the strongest interparticle force in each substance?
(a) $H_3PO_4$      (b) $SO_2$       (c) $MgCl_2$

**12.39** What is the strongest interparticle force in each substance?
(a) $CH_3Cl$      (b) $CH_3CH_3$       (c) $NH_3$

**12.40** What is the strongest interparticle force in each substance?
(a) Kr      (b) BrF       (c) $H_2SO_4$

**12.41** Which member of each pair of compounds forms intermolecular H bonds? Draw the H-bonded structures in each case:
(a) CH$_3$CHCH$_3$ or $CH_3SCH_3$       (b) HF or HBr
      |
      OH

**12.42** Which member of each pair of compounds forms intermolecular H bonds? Draw the H-bonded structures in each case:
(a) $(CH_3)_2NH$ or $(CH_3)_3N$      (b) $HOCH_2CH_2OH$ or $FCH_2CH_2F$

**12.43** Which forces oppose vaporization of each substance?
(a) Hexane      (b) Water       (c) $SiCl_4$

**12.44** Which forces oppose vaporization of each substance?
(a) $Br_2$      (b) $SbH_3$       (c) $CH_3NH_2$

**12.45** Which has the greater polarizability? Explain.
(a) $Br^-$ or $I^-$  (b) $CH_2$=$CH_2$ or $CH_3$—$CH_3$  (c) $H_2O$ or $H_2Se$

**12.46** Which has the greater polarizability? Explain.
(a) $Ca^{2+}$ or Ca  (b) $CH_3CH_3$ or $CH_3CH_2CH_3$  (c) $CCl_4$ or $CF_4$

**12.47** Which member in each pair of liquids has the *higher* vapor pressure at a given temperature? Explain.
(a) $C_2H_6$ or $C_4H_{10}$  (b) $CH_3CH_2OH$ or $CH_3CH_2F$
(c) $NH_3$ or $PH_3$

**12.48** Which member in each pair of liquids has the *lower* vapor pressure at a given temperature? Explain.
(a) $HOCH_2CH_2OH$ or $CH_3CH_2CH_2OH$
(b) $CH_3COOH$ or $(CH_3)_2C$=$O$       (c) HF or HCl

**12.49** Which substance has the *lower* boiling point? Explain.
(a) LiCl or HCl    (b) $NH_3$ or $PH_3$    (c) Xe or $I_2$

**12.50** Which substance has the *higher* boiling point? Explain.
(a) $CH_3CH_2OH$ or $CH_3CH_2CH_3$       (b) NO or $N_2$
(c) $H_2S$ or $H_2Te$

**12.51** Which substance has the *lower* boiling point? Explain.
(a) $CH_3CH_2CH_2CH_3$ or CH$_2$—CH$_2$       (b) NaBr or $PBr_3$
                                                                               |            |
                                                                              CH$_2$—CH$_2$
(c) $H_2O$ or HBr

**12.52** Which substance has the *higher* boiling point? Explain.
(a) $CH_3OH$ or $CH_3CH_3$    (b) FNO or ClNO

(c)

$$\underset{H}{\overset{F}{\diagdown}}C=C\underset{H}{\overset{F}{\diagup}} \quad or \quad \underset{F}{\overset{H}{\diagdown}}C=C\underset{H}{\overset{F}{\diagup}}$$

### Problems in Context

**12.53** For pairs of molecules in the gas phase, average H-bond dissociation energies are 17 kJ/mol for $NH_3$, 22 kJ/mol for $H_2O$, and 29 kJ/mol for HF. Explain this increase in H-bond strength.

**12.54** Dispersion forces are the only intermolecular forces present in motor oil, yet it has a high boiling point. Explain.

**12.55** Why does the antifreeze ingredient ethylene glycol ($HOCH_2CH_2OH$; $M = 62.07$ g/mol) have a boiling point of 197.6°C, whereas propanol ($CH_3CH_2CH_2OH$; $M = 60.09$ g/mol), a compound with a similar molar mass, has a boiling point of only 97.4°C?

### Properties of the Liquid State
#### Concept Review Questions

**12.56** Before the phenomenon of surface tension was understood, physicists described the surface of water as being covered with a "skin." What causes this skinlike phenomenon?

**12.57** Small, equal-sized drops of oil, water, and mercury lie on a waxed floor. How does each liquid behave? Explain.

**12.58** Why does an aqueous solution of ethanol ($CH_3CH_2OH$) have a lower surface tension than water?

**12.59** Why are units of energy per area ($J/m^2$) used for surface tension values?

**12.60** Does the *strength* of the intermolecular forces in a liquid change as the liquid is heated? Explain. Why does liquid viscosity decrease with rising temperature?

#### Skill-Building Exercises (grouped in similar pairs)

**12.61** Rank the following in order of *increasing* surface tension at a given temperature, and explain your ranking:
(a) $CH_3CH_2CH_2OH$    (b) $HOCH_2CH(OH)CH_2OH$
(c) $HOCH_2CH_2OH$

**12.62** Rank the following in order of *decreasing* surface tension at a given temperature, and explain your ranking:
(a) $CH_3OH$    (b) $CH_3CH_3$    (c) $H_2C=O$

**12.63** Rank the compounds in Problem 12.61 in order of *decreasing* viscosity at a given temperature; explain your ranking.

**12.64** Rank the compounds in Problem 12.62 in order of *increasing* viscosity at a given temperature; explain your ranking.

### Problems in Context

**12.65** Soil vapor extraction (SVE) is used to remove volatile organic pollutants, such as chlorinated solvents, from soil at hazardous waste sites. Vent wells are drilled, and a vacuum pump is applied to the subsurface. (a) How does this remove pollutants? (b) Why does heating combined with SVE speed the process?

**12.66** Use Figure 12.2, p. 421 to answer the following: (a) Does it take more heat to melt 12.0 g of $CH_4$ or 12.0 g of Hg? (b) Does it take more heat to vaporize 12.0 g of $CH_4$ or 12.0 g of Hg? (c) What is the principal intermolecular force in each sample?

**12.67** Pentanol ($C_5H_{11}OH$; $M = 88.15$ g/mol) has nearly the same molar mass as hexane ($C_6H_{14}$; $M = 86.17$ g/mol) but is more than 12 times as viscous at 20°C. Explain.

### The Uniqueness of Water
#### Concept Review Questions

**12.68** For what types of substances is water a good solvent? For what types is it a poor solvent? Explain.

**12.69** A water molecule can engage in as many as four H bonds. Explain.

**12.70** Warm-blooded animals have a narrow range of body temperature because their bodies have a high water content. Explain.

**12.71** What property of water keeps plant debris on the surface of lakes and ponds? What is the ecological significance of this?

**12.72** A drooping plant can be made upright by watering the ground around it. Explain.

**12.73** Describe the molecular basis of the property of water responsible for the presence of ice on the surface of a frozen lake.

**12.74** Describe in molecular terms what occurs when ice melts.

### The Solid State: Structure, Properties, and Bonding
(Sample Problems 12.5 and 12.6)
#### Concept Review Questions

**12.75** What is the difference between an amorphous solid and a crystalline solid on the macroscopic and molecular levels? Give an example of each.

**12.76** How are a solid's unit cell and crystal structure related?

**12.77** For structures consisting of identical atoms, how many atoms are contained in the simple, body-centered, and face-centered cubic unit cells? Explain how you obtained the values.

**12.78** An element has a crystal structure in which the width of the cubic unit cell equals the diameter of an atom. What type of unit cell does it have?

**12.79** What specific difference in the positioning of spheres gives a crystal structure based on the face-centered cubic unit cell less empty space than one based on the body-centered cubic unit cell?

**12.80** Both solid Kr and solid Cu consist of individual atoms. Why do their physical properties differ so much?

**12.81** What is the energy gap in band theory? Compare its size in superconductors, conductors, semiconductors, and insulators.

**12.82** Predict the effect (if any) of an increase in temperature on the electrical conductivity of (a) a conductor; (b) a semiconductor; (c) an insulator.

**12.83** Besides the type of unit cell, what information is needed to find the density of a solid consisting of identical atoms?

#### Skill-Building Exercises (grouped in similar pairs)

**12.84** What type of crystal lattice does each metal form? (The number of atoms per unit cell is given in parentheses.)
(a) Ni (4)    (b) Cr (2)    (c) Ca (4)

**12.85** What is the number of atoms per unit cell for each metal?
(a) Polonium, Po    (b) Manganese, Mn    (c) Silver, Ag

**12.86** When cadmium oxide reacts to form cadmium selenide, a change in unit cell occurs, as depicted below:

(a) What is the change in unit cell?
(b) Does the coordination number of cadmium change? Explain.

**12.87** As molten iron cools to 1674 K, it adopts one type of cubic unit cell; then, as the temperature drops below 1181 K, it changes to another, as depicted below:

(a) What is the change in unit cell?
(b) Which crystal structure has the greater packing efficiency?

**12.88** Of the five major types of crystalline solid, which does each of the following form, and why: (a) Ni; (b) $F_2$; (c) $CH_3OH$; (d) Sn; (e) Si; (f) Xe?

**12.89** Of the five major types of crystalline solid, which does each of the following form, and why: (a) SiC; (b) $Na_2SO_4$; (c) $SF_6$; (d) cholesterol ($C_{27}H_{45}OH$); (e) KCl; (f) BN?

**12.90** Zinc oxide adopts the zinc blende crystal structure (Figure P12.90). How many $Zn^{2+}$ ions are in the ZnO unit cell?

**12.91** Calcium sulfide adopts the sodium chloride crystal structure (Figure P12.91). How many $S^{2-}$ ions are in the CaS unit cell?

**Figure P12.90**

**Figure P12.91**

**12.92** Zinc selenide (ZnSe) crystallizes in the zinc blende structure (see Figure P12.90) and has a density of 5.42 g/cm³.
(a) How many Zn and Se ions are in each unit cell?
(b) What is the mass of a unit cell?
(c) What is the volume of a unit cell?
(d) What is the edge length of a unit cell?

**12.93** An element crystallizes in a face-centered cubic lattice and has a density of 1.45 g/cm³. The edge of its unit cell is $4.52 \times 10^{-8}$ cm.
(a) How many atoms are in each unit cell?
(b) What is the volume of a unit cell?
(c) What is the mass of a unit cell?
(d) Calculate an approximate atomic mass for the element.

**12.94** Classify each of the following as a conductor, insulator, or semiconductor: (a) phosphorus; (b) mercury; (c) germanium.

**12.95** Classify each of the following as a conductor, insulator, or semiconductor: (a) carbon (graphite); (b) sulfur; (c) platinum.

**12.96** Predict the effect (if any) of an increase in temperature on the electrical conductivity of (a) antimony; (b) tellurium; (c) bismuth.

**12.97** Predict the effect (if any) of a decrease in temperature on the electrical conductivity of (a) silicon; (b) lead; (c) germanium.

### Problems in Context

**12.98** Polonium, the Period 6 member of Group 6A(16), is a rare radioactive metal that is the only element with a crystal structure based on the simple cubic unit cell. If its density is 9.142 g/cm³, calculate an approximate atomic radius for polonium.

**12.99** The coinage metals—copper, silver, and gold—crystallize in a cubic closest packed structure. Use the density of copper (8.95 g/cm³) and its molar mass (63.55 g/mol) to calculate an approximate atomic radius for copper.

**12.100** One of the most important enzymes in the world—nitrogenase, the plant protein that catalyzes nitrogen fixation—contains active clusters of iron, sulfur, and molybdenum atoms. Crystalline molybdenum (Mo) has a body-centered cubic unit cell ($d$ of Mo = 10.28 g/cm³). (a) Determine the edge length of the unit cell. (b) Calculate the atomic radius of Mo.

**12.101** Tantalum (Ta; $d$ = 16.634 g/cm³ and $\mathcal{M}$ = 180.9479 g/mol) has a body-centered cubic structure with a unit-cell edge length of 3.3058 Å. Use these data to calculate Avogadro's number.

### Advanced Materials

#### Concept Review Questions

**12.102** When tin is added to copper, the resulting alloy (bronze) is much harder than copper. Explain.

**12.103** In the process of doping a semiconductor, certain impurities are added to increase its electrical conductivity. Explain this process for an n-type and a p-type semiconductor.

**12.104** State two molecular characteristics of substances that typically form liquid crystals. How is each related to function?

**12.105** Distinguish between isotropic and anisotropic substances. To which category do liquid crystals belong?

**12.106** How are the properties of high-tech ceramics the same as those of traditional clay ceramics, and how are they different? Refer to specific substances in your answer.

**12.107** Why is the average molar mass of a polymer sample different from the molar mass of an individual chain?

**12.108** How does the random coil shape relate to the radius of gyration of a polymer chain?

**12.109** What factor(s) influence the viscosity of a polymer solution? What factor(s) influence the viscosity of a molten polymer? What is a polymer glass?

**12.110** Use an example to show how branching and crosslinking can affect the physical behavior of a polymer.

#### Skill-Building Exercises (grouped in similar pairs)

**12.111** Silicon and germanium are both semiconducting elements from Group 4A(14) that can be doped to improve their conductivity. Would each of the following form an n-type or a p-type semiconductor: (a) Ge doped with P; (b) Si doped with In?

**12.112** Would each of the following form an n-type or a p-type semiconductor: (a) Ge doped with As; (b) Si doped with B?

**12.113** The repeat unit in a polystyrene coffee cup has the formula $C_6H_5CHCH_2$. If the molar mass of the polymer is $3.5 \times 10^5$ g/mol, what is the degree of polymerization?

**12.114** The monomer of poly(vinyl chloride) has the formula $C_2H_3Cl$. If there are 1565 repeat units in a single chain of the polymer, what is the molecular mass (in amu) of that chain?

**12.115** The polypropylene (repeat unit $CH_3CHCH_2$) in a plastic toy has a molar mass of $2.8 \times 10^5$ g/mol and a repeat unit length of 0.252 pm. Calculate the radius of gyration.

**12.116** The polymer that is used to make 2-L soda bottles [poly(ethylene terephthalate)] has a repeat unit with molecular formula $C_{10}H_8O_4$ and length 1.075 nm. Calculate the radius of gyration of a chain with molar mass of $2.30 \times 10^4$ g/mol.

## Comprehensive Problems

**12.117** A 0.75-L bottle is cleaned, dried, and closed in a room where the air is 22°C and 44% relative humidity (that is, the water vapor in the air is 0.44 of the equilibrium vapor pressure at 22°C). The bottle is then brought outside and stored at 0.0°C.
(a) What mass of liquid water condenses inside the bottle?
(b) Would liquid water condense at 10°C? (See Table 5.2, p. 200.)

**12.118** In an experiment, 5.00 L of $N_2$ is saturated with water vapor at 22°C and then compressed to half its volume at constant $T$.
(a) What is the partial pressure of $H_2O$ in the compressed gas mixture? (b) What mass of water vapor condenses to liquid?

**12.119** Barium is the largest nonradioactive alkaline earth metal. It has a body-centered cubic unit cell and a density of 3.62 g/cm³. What is the atomic radius of barium? (Volume of a sphere: $V = \frac{4}{3}\pi r^3$.)

**12.120** Two important characteristics used to evaluate the risk of fire or explosion are a compound's *lower flammable limit* (LFL) and *flash point*. The LFL is the minimum percentage by volume in air that is ignitable. Below that, the mixture is too "lean" to burn. The flash point is the temperature at which the air over a confined liquid becomes ignitable. *n*-Hexane boils at 68.7°C at 1 atm. At 20.0°C, its vapor pressure is 121 mmHg. The LFL of *n*-hexane is 1.1%. Calculate the flash point of *n*-hexane.

**12.121** Bismuth is used to calibrate instruments employed in high-pressure studies because it has several well-characterized crystalline phases. Its phase diagram (*right*) shows the liquid phase and five solid phases that are stable above 1 katm (1000 atm) and up to 300°C.
(a) Which solid phases are stable at 25°C? (b) Which phase is stable at 50 katm and 175°C? (c) As the pressure is reduced from 100 to 1 katm at 200°C, what phase transitions does bismuth undergo? (d) What phases are present at each of the triple points?

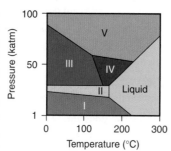

**12.122** In making computer chips, a 4.00-kg cylindrical ingot of ultrapure n-type doped silicon that is 5.20 inches in diameter is sliced into wafers $1.12 \times 10^{-4}$ m thick.
(a) Assuming no waste, how many wafers can be made?
(b) What is the mass of a wafer ($d$ of Si = 2.34 g/cm³; $V$ of a cylinder = $\pi r^2 h$)?
(c) A key step in making p-n junctions for the chip is chemical removal of the oxide layer on the wafer through treatment with gaseous HF. Write a balanced equation for this reaction.
(d) If 0.750% of the Si atoms are removed during the treatment in part (c), how many moles of HF are required per wafer, assuming 100% reaction yield?

**12.123** Methyl salicylate, $C_8H_8O_3$, the odorous constituent of oil of wintergreen, has a vapor pressure of 1.00 torr at 54.3°C and 10.0 torr at 95.3°C. (a) What is its vapor pressure at 25°C? (b) What is the minimum number of liters of air that must pass over a sample of the compound at 25°C to vaporize 1.0 mg of it?

**12.124** Mercury (Hg) vapor is toxic and readily absorbed from the lungs. At 20.°C, mercury ($\Delta H_{vap} = 59.1$ kJ/mol) has a vapor pressure of $1.20 \times 10^{-3}$ torr, which is high enough to be hazardous. To reduce the danger to workers in processing plants, Hg is cooled to lower its vapor pressure. At what temperature would the vapor pressure of Hg be at the safer level of $5.0 \times 10^{-5}$ torr?

**12.125** Polytetrafluoroethylene (Teflon) has a repeat unit with the formula $F_2C-CF_2$. A sample of the polymer consists of fractions with the following distribution of chains:

| Fraction | Average no. of repeat units | Amount (mol) of polymer |
|---|---|---|
| 1 | 273 | 0.10 |
| 2 | 330 | 0.40 |
| 3 | 368 | 1.00 |
| 4 | 483 | 0.70 |
| 5 | 525 | 0.30 |
| 6 | 575 | 0.10 |

(a) Determine the molar mass of each fraction.
(b) Determine the number-average molar mass of the sample.
(c) Another type of average molar mass of a polymer sample is called the *weight-average molar mass*, $\mathcal{M}_w$:

$$\mathcal{M}_w = \frac{\Sigma\,(\mathcal{M}\text{ of fraction} \times \text{mass of fraction})}{\text{total mass of all fractions}}$$

Calculate the weight-average molar mass of the above sample.

**12.126** A greenhouse contains 256 m³ of air at a temperature of 26°C, and a humidifier in it vaporizes 4.20 L of water. (a) What is the pressure of water vapor in the greenhouse, assuming that none escapes and that the air was originally completely dry ($d$ of $H_2O$ = 1.00 g/mL)? (b) What total volume of liquid water would have to be vaporized to saturate the air (i.e., achieve 100% relative humidity)? (See Table 5.2, p. 200.)

**12.127** Like most transition metals, tantalum (Ta) exhibits several oxidation states. Give the formula of each tantalum compound whose unit cell is depicted below:

**12.128** KF has the same type of crystal structure as NaCl. The unit cell of KF has an edge length of 5.39 Å. Find the density of KF.

**12.129** Furfural, which is prepared from corncobs, is an important solvent in synthetic rubber manufacturing, and it is reduced to furfuryl alcohol, which is used to make polymer resins. Furfural can also be oxidized to 2-furoic acid.

furfuryl alcohol       furfural       2-furoic acid

(a) Which of these compounds can form H bonds? Draw structures in each case.

(b) The molecules of some substances can form an "internal" H bond, that is, an H bond *within* a molecule. This takes the form of a polygon with atoms as corners and bonds as sides and an H bond as one of the sides. Which of these molecules is (are) likely to form a stable internal H bond? Draw the structure. (*Hint:* Structures with 5 or 6 atoms as corners are most stable.)

**12.130** On a humid day in New Orleans, the temperature is 22.0°C, and the partial pressure of water vapor in the air is 31.0 torr. The 9000-ton air-conditioning system in the Louisiana Superdome maintains an inside air temperature of 22.0°C also, but a partial pressure of water vapor of 10.0 torr. The volume of air in the dome is $2.4 \times 10^6$ m³, and the total pressure is 1.0 atm both inside and outside the dome. (a) What mass of water (in metric tons) must be removed every time the inside air is completely replaced with outside air? (*Hint:* How many moles of gas are in the dome? How many moles of water vapor? How many moles of dry air? How many moles of outside air must be added to the air in the dome to simulate the composition of outside air?) (b) Find the heat released when this mass of water condenses.

**12.131** The boiling point of amphetamine, $C_9H_{13}N$, is 201°C at 760 torr and 83°C at 13 torr. What is the concentration (in g/m³) of amphetamine when it is in contact with 20.°C air?

**12.132** Diamond has a face-centered cubic unit cell, with four more C atoms in tetrahedral holes within the cell. Densities of diamonds vary from 3.01 g/cm³ to 3.52 g/cm³ because C atoms are missing from some holes. (a) Calculate the unit-cell edge length of the densest diamond. (b) Assuming the cell dimensions are fixed, how many C atoms are in the unit cell of the diamond with the lowest density?

**12.133** Is it possible for a salt of formula $AB_3$ to have a face-centered cubic unit cell of anions with cations in all the eight available holes? Explain.

**12.134** The density of solid gallium at its melting point is 5.9 g/cm³, whereas that of liquid gallium is 6.1 g/cm³. Is the temperature at the triple point higher or lower than the normal melting point? Is the slope of the solid-liquid line for gallium positive or negative?

**12.135** A 4.7-L sealed bottle containing 0.33 g of liquid ethanol, $C_2H_6O$, is placed in a refrigerator and reaches equilibrium with its vapor at −11°C. (a) What mass of ethanol is present in the vapor? (b) When the container is removed and warmed to room temperature, 20.°C, will all the ethanol vaporize? (c) How much liquid ethanol would be present at 0.0°C? The vapor pressure of ethanol is 10. torr at −2.3°C and 40. torr at 19°C.

**12.136** Substance A has the following properties.

| | | | |
|---|---|---|---|
| mp at 1 atm: | −20.°C | bp at 1 atm: | 85°C |
| $\Delta H_{fus}$: | 180. J/g | $\Delta H_{vap}$: | 500. J/g |
| $c_{solid}$: | 1.0 J/g·°C | $c_{liquid}$: | 2.5 J/g·°C |
| $c_{gas}$: | 0.5 J/g·°C | | |

At 1 atm, a 25-g sample of A is heated from −40.°C to 100.°C at a constant rate of 450. J/min. (a) How many minutes does it take to heat the sample to its melting point? (b) How many minutes does it take to melt the sample? (c) Perform any other necessary calculations, and draw a curve of temperature vs. time for the entire heating process.

**12.137** An aerospace manufacturer is building a prototype experimental aircraft that cannot be detected by radar. Boron nitride is chosen for incorporation into the body parts, and the boric acid/ammonia method is used to prepare the ceramic material. Given 85.5% and 86.8% yields for the two reaction steps, how much boron nitride can be prepared from 1.00 metric ton of boric acid and 12.5 m³ of ammonia at 275 K and $3.07 \times 10^3$ kPa? Assume that ammonia does not behave ideally under these conditions and is recycled completely in the reaction process.

**12.138** The ball-and-stick models below represent three compounds with the same molecular formula, $C_4H_8O_2$:

(a) Which compound(s) can form intermolecular H bonds?
(b) Which has the highest viscosity?

**12.139** The $\Delta H_f^\circ$ of gaseous dimethyl ether $(CH_3OCH_3)$ is −185.4 kJ/mol; the vapor pressure is 1.00 atm at −23.7°C and 0.526 atm at −37.8°C. (a) Calculate $\Delta H_{vap}^\circ$ of dimethyl ether. (b) Calculate $\Delta H_f^\circ$ of liquid dimethyl ether.

**12.140** The crystal structure of sodium is based on the body-centered cubic unit cell. What is the mass of one unit cell of Na?

**12.141** The *intrinsic viscosity* of a solute in a solvent, $[\eta]_{solvent}$, is the portion of the total viscosity due to the solute and is related to solute shape. In polymer science, it relates as well to intermolecular interactions between solvent and polymer: higher $[\eta]_{solvent}$ means stronger interaction. The $[\eta]_{solvent}$ values of polymers in solution are given by the Mark-Houwink equation, $[\eta]_{solvent} = K\mathcal{M}^a$, where $\mathcal{M}$ is the molar mass of the polymer, and $K$ and $a$ are constants specific to the polymer and solvent. Use the data below for 25°C to answer the following questions:

| Polymer | Solvent | $K$ (mL/g) | $a$ |
|---|---|---|---|
| Polystyrene | Benzene | $9.5 \times 10^{-3}$ | 0.74 |
| | Cyclohexane | $8.1 \times 10^{-2}$ | 0.50 |
| Polyisobutylene | Benzene | $8.3 \times 10^{-2}$ | 0.50 |
| | Cyclohexane | $2.6 \times 10^{-1}$ | 0.70 |

(a) A polystyrene sample has a molar mass of 104,160 g/mol. Calculate the intrinsic viscosity in benzene and in cyclohexane. Which solvent has stronger interactions with the polymer?
(b) A different polystyrene sample has a molar mass of 52,000 g/mol. Calculate its $[\eta]_{benzene}$. Given a polymer standard of known $\mathcal{M}$, how could you use its measured $[\eta]$ in a given solvent to determine the molar mass of any sample of that polymer?
(c) Compare $[\eta]$ of a polyisobutylene sample [repeat unit $(CH_3)_2CCH_2$] with a molar mass of 104,160 g/mol with that of the polystyrene in part (a). What does this suggest about the solvent-polymer interactions of the two samples?

**12.142** One way of purifying gaseous $H_2$ is to pass it under high pressure through the holes of a metal's crystal structure. Palladium, which adopts a cubic closest packed structure, absorbs more $H_2$ than any other element and is one of the metals used for this purpose. How the metal and $H_2$ interact is unclear, but it is estimated that the density of absorbed $H_2$ approaches that of liquid hydrogen (70.8 g/L). What volume (in L) of gaseous $H_2$ (at STP) can be packed into the spaces of 1 dm³ of palladium metal?

# The Properties of Mixtures: Solutions and Colloids

## Concepts and skills to review before you study this chapter

- separation of mixtures (Section 2.9)
- calculations involving mass percent (Section 3.1) and molarity (Section 3.5)
- electrolytes; water as solvent (Sections 4.1 and 12.5)
- mole fraction and Dalton's law (Section 5.4)
- intermolecular forces and polarizability (Section 12.3)
- monomers and polymers (Section 12.7)
- vapor pressure of liquids (Section 12.2)

Virtually all the gases, liquids, and solids in the real world are *mixtures*—two or more substances mixed together physically, not combined chemically. Synthetic mixtures, such as glass and soap, usually contain only a dozen or so components, but natural mixtures, such as seawater and soil, often contain over 50. Living mixtures, such as trees and students, are the most complex—even a simple bacterial cell (*photo*) contains well over 5000 different compounds (Table 13.1).

Recall from Chapter 2 that a mixture has two defining characteristics: *its composition is variable,* and *it retains some properties of its components.* We focus here on two common types of mixtures—solutions and colloids—whose main differences relate to particle size and number of phases:

- A *solution* is a *homogeneous* mixture; thus, it exists as one phase. In a solution, the particles are individual atoms, ions, or small molecules.
- A *colloid* is a type of *heterogeneous* mixture. A heterogeneous mixture has two or more phases. They may be visibly distinct, like pebbles in concrete, or not, like the much smaller particles in the colloids smoke and milk. In a colloid, the particles are typically macromolecules or aggregations of small molecules that are dispersed so finely they don't settle out.

**Table 13.1 Approximate Composition of a Bacterium**

| Substance | Mass % of Cell | Number of Types | Number of Molecules |
|---|---|---|---|
| Water | ~70 | 1 | $5\times10^{10}$ |
| Ions | 1 | 20 | ? |
| Sugars* | 3 | 200 | $3\times10^{8}$ |
| Amino acids* | 0.4 | 100 | $5\times10^{7}$ |
| Lipids* | 2 | 50 | $3\times10^{7}$ |
| Nucleotides* | 0.4 | 200 | $1\times10^{7}$ |
| Other small molecules | 0.2 | ~200 | ? |
| Macromolecules (proteins, nucleic acids, polysaccharides) | 23 | ~5000 | $6\times10^{6}$ |

*Includes precursors and metabolites.

**IN THIS CHAPTER . . .** We focus on how intermolecular forces and other energy considerations affect a solute dissolving in a solvent, how we calculate concentrations, and how solutions differ from pure substances. We also briefly consider the behavior and applications of colloids.
- We survey intermolecular forces between solute and solvent and find that substances with similar types of forces form a solution.
- We see how the dual polarity of organic molecules gives rise to these same intermolecular forces, which determine the structures and functions of soaps, antibiotics, biological macromolecules, and cell membranes.
- We use a stepwise cycle to see why a substance dissolves and examine the roles of the heat of solution and the dispersal of matter. To understand the latter factor, we introduce the concept of entropy.
- We examine the equilibrium nature of solubility and see how temperature and pressure affect it.
- We define various solution concentration units and see how to interconvert them mathematically.
- We see why the physical properties of solutions are different from those of pure substances and how we apply those differences.
- We investigate colloids and apply solution and colloid chemistry to the purification of water.

## 13.1 • TYPES OF SOLUTIONS: INTERMOLECULAR FORCES AND SOLUBILITY

A **solute** dissolves in a **solvent** to form a solution. In general, *the solvent is the most abundant component,* but in some cases, the substances are **miscible**—soluble in each other in any proportion—so the terms "solute" and "solvent" lose their meaning. *The physical state of the solvent usually determines the physical state of the solution.* Solutions can be gaseous, liquid, or solid, but we focus mostly on liquid solutions because they are by far the most important.

The **solubility (S)** of a solute is the maximum amount that dissolves in a fixed quantity of a given solvent at a given temperature, where an excess of the solute is present. Different solutes have different solubilities:

- Sodium chloride (NaCl), $S = 39.12$ g/100. mL water at 100.°C.
- Silver chloride (AgCl), $S = 0.0021$ g/100. mL water at 100.°C.

Solubility is a *quantitative* term, but *dilute* and *concentrated* are qualitative, referring to the *relative* amounts of dissolved solute; the NaCl solution above is concentrated, and the AgCl solution is dilute.

A given solute may dissolve in one solvent and not another. The explanation lies in the relative strengths of the intermolecular forces within both solute and solvent and between them. The useful rule-of-thumb **"like dissolves like"** says that *substances with similar types of intermolecular forces dissolve in each other.* Thus, by knowing the forces, we can often predict whether a solute will dissolve in a solvent.

### Intermolecular Forces in Solution

All the intermolecular forces we discussed for pure substances also occur in solutions (Figure 13.1; also see Section 12.3):

1. *Ion-dipole forces* are the principal force involved when an ionic compound dissolves in water. Two events occur simultaneously:
   - *Forces compete.* When a salt is added to water, an ion and the oppositely charged pole of a water molecule attract each other. These attractions compete with and overcome attractions between the ions, and the crystal structure breaks down.
   - *Hydration shells form.* As an ion separates, water molecules cluster around it in **hydration shells.** The number of water molecules in the closest shell depends on the ion's size: four fit tetrahedrally around small ions like $Li^+$, while the larger $Na^+$ and $F^-$ have six water molecules surrounding them octahedrally (Figure 13.2). In the innermost shell, normal H bonding is disrupted to form the ion-dipole forces. But these water molecules are H bonded to others in the next shell, and those are H bonded to others still farther away.
2. *Hydrogen bonding* is the principal force in solutions of polar, O- and N-containing organic and biological compounds, such as alcohols, amines, and amino acids.
3. *Dipole-dipole forces,* in the absence of H bonding, allow polar molecules like propanal ($CH_3CH_2CHO$) to dissolve in polar solvents like dichloromethane ($CH_2Cl_2$).
4. **Ion–induced dipole forces,** one type of *charge-induced dipole force,* rely on polarizability. They arise when an ion's charge distorts the electron cloud of a nearby nonpolar molecule. This type of force initiates the binding of the $Fe^{2+}$ ion in hemoglobin to an $O_2$ molecule entering a red blood cell.
5. **Dipole–induced dipole forces,** also based on polarizability, arise when a polar molecule distorts the electron cloud of a nonpolar molecule. They are weaker than ion–induced dipole forces because the charge of each pole is less than an ion's (Coulomb's law). The solubility in water of atmospheric $O_2$, $N_2$, and noble gases, while limited, is due in part to these forces. Paint thinners and grease solvents also use them.
6. *Dispersion forces* contribute to the solubility of all solutes in all solvents, but they are the *principal* intermolecular force in solutions of nonpolar substances, such as those in petroleum or gasoline.

The same forces keep biological macromolecules in their active shapes (Section 13.2).

**Ion-dipole** (40–600)

**H bond** (10–40)
Methanol ($CH_3OH$) — $H_2O$

**Dipole-dipole** (5–25)
Ethanal ($CH_3CHO$) — Chloroform ($CHCl_3$)

**Ion–induced dipole** (3–15)
$Cl^-$ — Hexane ($C_6H_{14}$)

**Dipole–induced dipole** (2–10)
$H_2O$ — Xenon

**Dispersion** (0.05–40)
Octane ($C_8H_{18}$) — $C_6H_{14}$

**Figure 13.1 Types of intermolecular forces in solutions.** Forces are listed in order of decreasing strength (values are in kJ/mol), with an example of each.

**Figure 13.2** Hydration shells around an Na$^+$ ion.  Ion-dipole forces orient water molecules around an ion. In the innermost shell here, six water molecules surround the cation octahedrally.

## Liquid Solutions and the Role of Molecular Polarity

From cytoplasm to tree sap, gasoline to cleaning fluid, iced tea to urine, liquid solutions are very familiar. Water is the most prominent solvent, but there are many other liquid solvents, with polarities from very polar to nonpolar.

**Applying the Like-Dissolves-Like Rule**  The like-dissolves-like rule says that when the forces *within* the solute are *similar* to those *within* the solvent, the forces *replace* each other and a solution forms. Thus,

- *Salts are soluble in water* because the strong ion-dipole attractions between ion and water are so similar to the strong attractions between the ions and the strong H bonds between water molecules that they *can* replace each other.
- *Salts are insoluble in hexane ($C_6H_{14}$)* because the weak ion–induced dipole forces between ion and nonpolar hexane *cannot* replace attractions between the ions.
- *Oil is insoluble in water* because the weak dipole–induced dipole forces between oil and water molecules cannot replace the strong H bonds within water molecules and the extensive dispersion forces within the oil.
- *Oil is soluble in hexane* because dispersion forces in one readily replace dispersion forces in the other.

**Dual Polarity and Effects on Solubility**  To examine these ideas further, let's compare the solubilities of a series of alcohols in water and hexane, solvents with very different intermolecular forces. Alcohols are organic compounds that have a dual polarity, a polar hydroxyl (—OH) group bonded to a nonpolar hydrocarbon group:

- The —OH portion interacts through strong H bonds with water and through weak dipole–induced dipole forces with hexane.
- The hydrocarbon portion interacts through many dispersion forces with hexane and through weak dipole–induced dipole forces with water.

The general formula for an alcohol is $CH_3(CH_2)_nOH$, and we'll look at straight-chain examples with one to six carbons ($n = 0$ to $5$):

1. *Solubility in water is high for smaller alcohols.* From the models in Table 13.2 *(next page)*, we see that the —OH group is a relatively large portion of the alcohols with one to three carbons ($n = 0$ to $2$). These molecules interact with each other through H bonding, just as water molecules do. When they mix with water, H bonding in solute and in solvent is replaced by H bonding *between* solute and solvent (Figure 13.3, *next page*). As a result, these smaller alcohols are miscible with water.

| Table **13.2** Solubility* of a Series of Alcohols in Water and in Hexane | | | |
|---|---|---|---|
| **Alcohol** | **Model** | **Solubility in Water** | **Solubility in Hexane** |
| $CH_3OH$ (methanol) | | $\infty$ | 1.2 |
| $CH_3CH_2OH$ (ethanol) | | $\infty$ | $\infty$ |
| $CH_3(CH_2)_2OH$ (1-propanol) | | $\infty$ | $\infty$ |
| $CH_3(CH_2)_3OH$ (1-butanol) | | 1.1 | $\infty$ |
| $CH_3(CH_2)_4OH$ (1-pentanol) | | 0.30 | $\infty$ |
| $CH_3(CH_2)_5OH$ (1-hexanol) | | 0.058 | $\infty$ |

*Expressed in mol alcohol/1000 g solvent at 20°C.

2. *Solubility in water is low for larger alcohols.* Solubility decreases dramatically for alcohols larger than three carbons ($n > 2$); in fact, those with chains longer than six carbons are insoluble in water. For larger alcohols to dissolve, the nonpolar chains have to move among the water molecules, replacing weak attractions with water for strong H bonds between water molecules. While the —OH portion of such an alcohol forms H bonds to water, these cannot make up for all the other H bonds between water molecules that have to break to make room for the hydrocarbon portion.

Table 13.2 shows that the opposite trend occurs with hexane:

1. *Solubility in hexane is low for smaller alcohols.* For alcohols in hexane, in addition to dispersion forces, weak dipole–induced dipole forces exist between the —OH of methanol ($CH_3OH$) and hexane. These cannot replace the strong H bonding between $CH_3OH$ molecules, so solubility is low.

2. *Solubility in hexane is high for larger alcohols.* In any larger alcohol ($n > 0$), dispersion forces between the hydrocarbon portion and hexane *can* replace dispersion forces between hexane molecules. With only weak forces within the solvent to be replaced, even ethanol, with a two-carbon chain, has enough dispersion forces between it and hexane to be miscible.

**Figure 13.3** Like dissolves like: solubility of methanol in water. H bonds in water and in methanol replace one another when the two substances form a solution.

**Water**          **Methanol**          **A solution of water and methanol**

Many organic molecules have polar and nonpolar portions, which determine their solubility. For example, carboxylic acids and amines behave like alcohols: methanoic acid (HCOOH, formic acid) and methanamine ($CH_3NH_2$) are miscible with water and slightly soluble in hexane, whereas hexanoic acid [$CH_3(CH_2)_4COOH$] and 1-hexanamine [$CH_3(CH_2)_5NH_2$] are slightly soluble in water and very soluble in hexane.

## Sample Problem 13.1 | Predicting Relative Solubilities

**Problem** Predict which solvent will dissolve more of the given solute:
**(a)** Sodium chloride in methanol ($CH_3OH$) or in 1-propanol ($CH_3CH_2CH_2OH$)
**(b)** Ethylene glycol ($HOCH_2CH_2OH$) in hexane ($CH_3CH_2CH_2CH_2CH_2CH_3$) or in water
**(c)** Diethyl ether ($CH_3CH_2OCH_2CH_3$) in water or in ethanol ($CH_3CH_2OH$)

**Plan** We examine the formulas of solute and solvent to determine the forces in and between solute and solvent. A solute is more soluble in a solvent whose intermolecular forces are similar to, and therefore can replace, its own.

**Solution** **(a)** Methanol. NaCl is ionic, so it dissolves through ion-dipole forces. Both methanol and 1-propanol have a polar —OH group, but the hydrocarbon portion of each alcohol interacts only weakly with the ions and 1-propanol has a longer hydrocarbon portion than methanol.
**(b)** Water. Ethylene glycol molecules have two —OH groups, so they interact with each other through H bonding. H bonds formed with $H_2O$ can replace these H bonds between solute molecules better than dipole–induced dipole forces with hexane can.
**(c)** Ethanol. Diethyl ether molecules interact through dipole-dipole and dispersion forces. They can form H bonds to $H_2O$ or to ethanol. But ethanol can also interact with the ether effectively through dispersion forces because it has a hydrocarbon chain.

**Follow-Up Problem 13.1** Which solute is more soluble in the given solvent:
**(a)** 1-butanol ($CH_3CH_2CH_2CH_2OH$) or 1,4-butanediol ($HOCH_2CH_2CH_2CH_2OH$) in water; **(b)** chloroform ($CHCl_3$) or carbon tetrachloride ($CCl_4$) in water?

**Gas-Liquid Solutions** A substance with very weak intermolecular attractions has a low boiling point and is a gas under ordinary conditions. Likewise, it is not very soluble in water because solute-solvent forces are weak. Thus, for nonpolar or slightly polar gases, boiling point generally correlates with solubility in water (Table 13.3).

The small amount of a nonpolar gas that *does* dissolve may be vital. At 25°C and 1 atm, the solubility of $O_2$ is only 3.2 mL/100. mL of water, but aquatic animal life requires it. At times, the solubility of a nonpolar gas may *seem* high because it is also *reacting* with solvent. Oxygen seems more soluble in blood than in water because it bonds to hemoglobin in red blood cells. Carbon dioxide, which is essential for aquatic plants and coral-reef growth, seems very soluble in water (~81 mL of $CO_2$/100. mL of $H_2O$ at 25°C and 1 atm) because it is dissolving *and* reacting:

$$CO_2(g) + H_2O(l) \longrightarrow H^+(aq) + HCO_3^-(aq)$$

| Table 13.3 Correlation Between Boiling Point and Solubility in Water | | |
|---|---|---|
| **Gas** | **Solubility ($M$)*** | **bp (K)** |
| He | $4.2 \times 10^{-4}$ | 4.2 |
| Ne | $6.6 \times 10^{-4}$ | 27.1 |
| $N_2$ | $10.4 \times 10^{-4}$ | 77.4 |
| CO | $15.6 \times 10^{-4}$ | 81.6 |
| $O_2$ | $21.8 \times 10^{-4}$ | 90.2 |
| NO | $32.7 \times 10^{-4}$ | 121.4 |

*At 273 K and 1 atm.

## Gas Solutions and Solid Solutions

Gas solutions and solid solutions also have vital importance and numerous applications.

**Gas-Gas Solutions** *All gases are miscible with each other.* Air is the classic example of a gaseous solution, consisting of about 18 gases in widely differing proportions. Anesthetic gas proportions are finely adjusted to the needs of the patient and the length of the surgical procedure. The proportions of many industrial gas mixtures, such as $CO/H_2$ in syngas production or $N_2/H_2$ in ammonia production, are controlled to optimize product yield under varying conditions of temperature and pressure.

**Gas-Solid Solutions** *When a gas dissolves in a solid, it occupies the spaces between the closely packed particles.* Hydrogen gas can be purified by passing an impure sample through palladium. Only $H_2$ molecules are small enough to fit between the

Pd atoms, where they form Pd—H bonds. The H atoms move from one Pd atom to another and emerge from the metal as $H_2$ molecules (see Figure 14.2, p. 525).

The ability of gases to dissolve in a solid also has disadvantages. The electrical conductivity of copper is greatly reduced by the presence of $O_2$, which dissolves into the crystal structure and reacts to form copper(I) oxide. High-conductivity copper is prepared by melting and recasting the metal in an $O_2$-free atmosphere.

**Solid-Solid Solutions** Solids diffuse so little that their mixtures are usually heterogeneous. Some solid-solid solutions can be formed by melting the solids and then mixing them and allowing them to freeze. Many **alloys,** mixtures of elements that have a metallic character, are solid-solid solutions (although several have microscopic heterogeneous regions). In a *substitutional alloy* like brass (Figure 13.4A), atoms of zinc replace atoms of the main element, copper, at some sites in the cubic-closest packing array. In an *interstitial alloy* like carbon steel (Figure 13.4B), atoms of carbon (a nonmetal is typical in this type of alloy) fill some of the spaces (*interstices*) between atoms of the main element, iron, in the body-centered array.

Waxes are also solid-solid solutions. Most are amorphous solids with some small regions of crystalline regularity. A natural *wax* is defined as a solid of biological origin that is insoluble in water and soluble in nonpolar solvents. Beeswax, which bees secrete to build their combs, is a homogeneous mixture of fatty acids, long-chain carboxylic acids, and hydrocarbons in which some of the molecules contain chains more than 40 carbon atoms long. Carnauba wax, from a South American palm, is a mixture of compounds, each consisting of a fatty acid bound to a long-chain alcohol. It is hard but forms a thick gel in nonpolar solvents, so it is perfect for waxing cars.

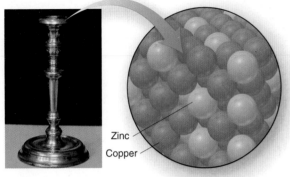

**A  Brass, a substitutional alloy**

**B  Carbon steel, an interstitial alloy**

**Figure 13.4** The arrangement of atoms in two types of alloys.

## ▊ Summary of Section 13.1

- A solution is a homogeneous mixture of a solute dissolved in a solvent through the action of intermolecular forces.
- Ion-dipole, ion–induced dipole, and dipole–induced dipole forces occur in solutions, in addition to all the intermolecular forces that also occur in pure substances.
- If similar intermolecular forces occur in solute and solvent, they replace each other when the substances mix and a solution is likely to form ("like dissolves like").
- When ionic compounds dissolve in water, the ions become surrounded by hydration shells of H-bonded water molecules.
- Solubility of organic molecules in various solvents depends on the relative sizes of their polar and nonpolar portions.
- The solubility of nonpolar gases in water is low because of weak intermolecular forces. Gases are miscible with one another and dissolve in solids by fitting into spaces in the crystal structure.
- Solid-solid solutions include alloys and waxes, and some are formed by mixing molten components.

# 13.2 • INTERMOLECULAR FORCES AND BIOLOGICAL MACROMOLECULES

The three-dimensional shapes of proteins, nucleic acids, and cell membranes and the functions of soaps and antibiotics depend on intermolecular forces and are explained by two ideas:

- Polar and ionic groups attract water, but nonpolar groups do not.
- Just as separate molecules attract each other, so do distant groups on the same molecule.

# The Structures of Proteins

**Proteins** are unbranched polymers formed from about 20 different monomers called **amino acids.** They range in size from about 50 amino acids ($\mathcal{M} \approx 5{\times}10^3$ g/mol) to several thousand ($\mathcal{M} \approx 5{\times}10^5$ g/mol). Proteins with a few types of amino acids in repeating patterns have extended helical or sheetlike shapes and give structure to hair, skin, and so forth. Proteins with many types of amino acids have complex, globular shapes and function as antibodies, enzymes and so forth. Let's see how intermolecular forces among amino acids influence the shapes of globular proteins.

**The Polarity of Amino-Acid Side Chains** In the cell, a free amino acid has four groups bonded to its α-carbon (Figure 13.5): charged carboxyl (—COO⁻) and amine (—NH₃⁺) groups, an H atom, and a *side chain,* which ranges from an H atom to a two-ringed $C_9H_8N$ group. Amino acids can be classified by the polarity or charge of their side chains: nonpolar, polar, and ionic. A few examples are

one of 20 different side chains

α-carbon

**Figure 13.5** The charged form of an amino acid under physiological conditions.

| NONPOLAR | POLAR | | IONIC | |
|---|---|---|---|---|

Leucine  Serine  Cysteine  Lysine  Glutamic acid

In a protein, the carboxyl group of one amino acid is linked covalently to the amine group of the next by a *peptide* bond. (We discuss amino acid structures and peptide bond formation in Chapter 15.) Thus, as Figure 13.6 shows, the *backbone* of a protein is a polypeptide chain: an *α-carbon connected through a peptide bond (orange screen) to the next α-carbon,* and so forth. The various side chains (*gray screens*) dangle off the α-carbons on alternate sides of the chain.

Glutamic acid
Carbon  Nitrogen  Oxygen  Hydrogen
Serine
Glycine
Lysine
Peptide bond

**Figure 13.6** A portion of a polypeptide chain. Three peptide bonds (*orange screens*) join four amino acids in this chain portion.

**Intermolecular Forces and Protein Shape** The same forces that act between separate molecules are responsible for a protein's shape, because *distant groups on the protein chain end up near each other as the chain bends.* Figure 13.7 depicts the forces within the protein and between the protein and the aqueous medium of the cell. In general order of importance, they are

- Covalent peptide bonds create the backbone (polypeptide chain).
- Helical and sheetlike segments arise from *H bonds between the C═O of one peptide bond and the N—H of another.*
- Polar and ionic side chains protrude into the surrounding cell fluid, interacting with water through ion-dipole forces and H bonds.
- Nonpolar side chains interact through dispersion forces within the nonaqueous protein interior.
- The —SH ends of two cysteine side chains form a covalent —S—S— bond, a *disulfide bridge,* between distant parts of the chain that fixes a bend.
- Oppositely charged ends of ionic side chains, —COO⁻ and —NH₃⁺ groups, that lie near each other form an electrostatic *salt link* (or *ion pair*) that creates bend in the protein chain.
- Other H bonds between side chains keep distant chain portions near each other.

Thus, *soluble proteins have polar-ionic exteriors and nonpolar interiors.* As we emphasize in Chapter 15, *the amino acid sequence of a protein determines its shape, which determines its function.*

**Figure 13.7 The forces that maintain protein structure.** Covalent, ionic, and intermolecular forces act between parts of a protein and between the protein and surrounding $H_2O$ molecules to determine the protein's shape. (Water molecules and some amino-acid side chains are shown as ball-and-stick models within space-filling contours.)

## Dual Polarity in Soaps, Membranes, and Antibiotics

Dual polarity, which we discussed in regard to the solubility of alcohols, also helps explain how soaps, cell membranes, and antibiotics function.

**Action of Soaps**  A **soap** is the salt formed when a strong base (metal hydroxide) reacts with a *fatty acid,* a carboxylic acid with a long hydrocarbon chain. A typical soap molecule is made up of a nonpolar "tail" 15–19 carbons long and a polar-ionic "head" consisting of a —COO⁻ group and the cation of the strong base. The cation greatly influences a soap's properties. Lithium soaps are hard and high melting and used in car lubricants. Potassium soaps are low melting and used in liquid form. Softer, more water-soluble sodium soaps, including sodium stearate, $CH_3(CH_2)_{16}COONa$, are components of common bar soaps:

Sodium stearate, $C_{17}H_{35}COONa$

When grease on your hands or clothes is immersed in soapy water, the soap molecule's nonpolar tails interact with the nonpolar grease molecules through dispersion forces, while the polar-ionic heads attract water molecules through ion-dipole forces and H bonds. Tiny aggregates of grease molecules, embedded with soap molecules whose polar-ionic heads stick into the water, are flushed away by added water (Figure 13.8).

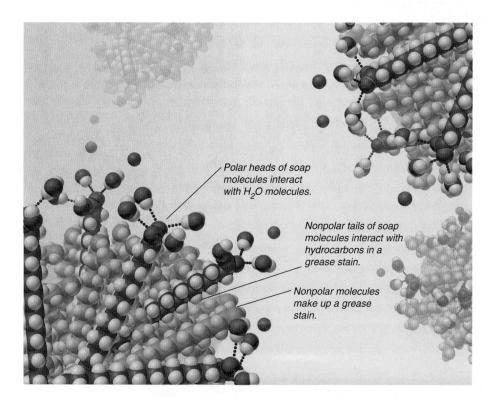

*Polar heads of soap molecules interact with H₂O molecules.*

*Nonpolar tails of soap molecules interact with hydrocarbons in a grease stain.*

*Nonpolar molecules make up a grease stain.*

**Figure 13.8** The cleaning ability of a soap depends on the dual polarity of its molecules.

**Lipid Bilayers and the Structure of the Cell Membrane**  The most abundant molecules in cell membranes are *phospholipids*. Like soaps, they have a dual polarity—a nonpolar tail consists of two fatty acid chains, and an organophosphate group is the polar-ionic head (Figure 13.9). Remarkably, phospholipids self-assemble in water into a sheetlike double layer called a **lipid bilayer,** with the tails of the two layers touching and the heads in the water. In the laboratory, bilayers form spherical vesicles that trap water inside. These structures are favored energetically because of their intermolecular forces:

- Ion-dipole forces occur between polar heads and water inside and outside.
- Dispersion forces occur between nonpolar tails within the bilayer interior.
- Minimal contact exists between nonpolar tails and water.

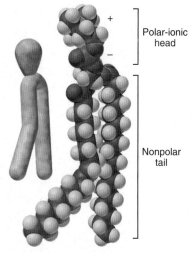

Polar-ionic head

Nonpolar tail

**Figure 13.9**  A membrane phospholipid. Lecithin (phosphatidylcholine), a phospholipid, is shown as a space-filling model and as a simplified purple-and-gray shape.

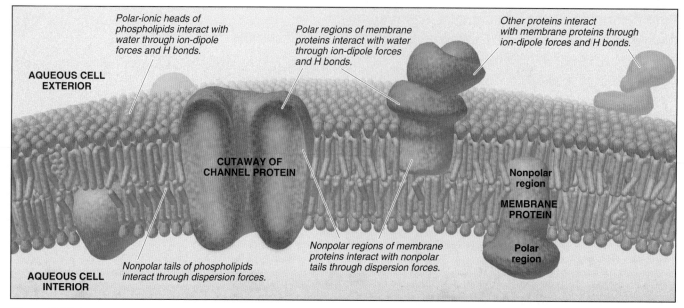

AQUEOUS CELL
EXTERIOR

Polar-ionic heads of
phospholipids interact with
water through ion-dipole
forces and H bonds.

Polar regions of membrane
proteins interact with water
through ion-dipole forces
and H bonds.

Other proteins interact
with membrane proteins through
ion-dipole forces and H bonds.

CUTAWAY OF
CHANNEL PROTEIN

Nonpolar
region

MEMBRANE
PROTEIN

Polar
region

Nonpolar regions of membrane
proteins interact with nonpolar
tails through dispersion forces.

Nonpolar tails of phospholipids
interact through dispersion forces.

AQUEOUS CELL
INTERIOR

**Figure 13.10** Intermolecular forces and
cell membrane structure.

A typical animal cell membrane consists of a phospholipid bilayer with proteins partially embedded in it (Figure 13.10). Membrane proteins, which play countless essential roles, differ fundamentally from soluble proteins in terms of their dual polarity:

• Soluble proteins have polar exteriors and nonpolar interiors. They form ion-dipole and H-bonding forces between water and *polar groups on the exterior* and dispersion forces between *nonpolar groups in the interior* (see Figure 13.7).

• Membrane proteins have exteriors that are partially polar and partially nonpolar. They have polar groups on the *exterior portion that juts into the aqueous surroundings* and nonpolar groups on *the exterior portion embedded in the membrane*. The nonpolar groups thus can form dispersion forces with the phospholipid tails of the bilayer. Channel proteins also have polar groups lining the aqueous channel.

**Action of Antibiotics** A key function of the membrane is to balance internal and external ion concentrations: $Na^+$ is excluded from the cell, and $K^+$ is kept inside. Gramicidin A and similar antibiotics act by forming channels in the bacterial membrane through which ions flow (Figure 13.11). Two helical gramicidin A molecules, their nonpolar groups outside and polar groups inside, lie end to end to form a channel through the membrane. The nonpolar outside stabilizes the molecule in the membrane through dispersion forces, and the polar inside passes the ions along using ion-dipole forces, like a "bucket brigade." Over $10^7$ ions pass in and out through each of these channels per second, and the microorganism soon dies.

**Figure 13.11** The mode of action of the
antibiotic gramicidin A. The $K^+$ ions are
shown leaving the cell. At the same time
(not shown), $Na^+$ ions enter the cell.

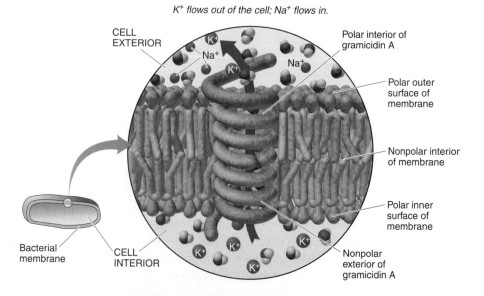

$K^+$ flows out of the cell; $Na^+$ flows in.

CELL
EXTERIOR

Polar interior of
gramicidin A

Polar outer
surface of
membrane

Nonpolar interior
of membrane

Polar inner
surface of
membrane

Nonpolar
exterior of
gramicidin A

Bacterial
membrane

CELL
INTERIOR

## The Structure of DNA

The chemical information that guides the design and construction, and therefore the function, of all proteins is contained in **nucleic acids,** unbranched polymers made up of monomers called **mononucleotides.** Each mononucleotide consists of an N-containing base, a sugar, and a phosphate group (Figure 13.12). In DNA (*deoxyribonucleic acid*), the sugar is *2-deoxyribose,* in which —H substitutes for —OH on the second C atom of the five-C sugar ribose.

The repeating pattern of the DNA chain is *sugar linked to phosphate linked to sugar linked to phosphate,* and so on. Attached to each sugar is one of four N-containing bases, flat ring structures that dangle off the polynucleotide chain, similar to the way amino-acid side chains dangle off the polypeptide chain.

**Intermolecular Forces and the Double Helix** DNA exists as two chains wrapped around each other in a **double helix** stabilized by intermolecular forces (Figure 13.13):

- *On the more polar exterior,* negatively charged sugar-phosphate groups interact with the aqueous surroundings via ion-dipole forces and H bonds.
- *In the less polar interior,* flat, N-containing bases stack above each other and interact by dispersion forces.
- *Bases form specific interchain H bonds;* that is, each base in one chain is always H bonded with its complementary base in the other chain. Thus, *the base sequence of one chain is the H-bonded complement of the base sequence of the other.*

A DNA molecule contains millions of H bonds linking bases in these prescribed pairs. The *total* energy of the H bonds keeps the chains together, but each H bond is weak enough (around 5% of a typical covalent single bond) that a few at a time can break as the chains separate during crucial cellular processes. (In Chapter 15, we'll see how H-bonded base pairs are essential for protein synthesis and DNA replication.)

**Figure 13.12** A short portion of the polynucleotide chain of DNA.

**Figure 13.13** The double helix of DNA. A segment of DNA (*left*) has its polar-ionic sugar-phosphate portion (*pink*) facing the water and the nonpolar bases (*gray*) stacking in the interior. The expanded portion (*right*) shows an H-bonded pair of the bases guanine and cytosine.

## ▌ Summary of Section 13.2

- In soluble proteins, polar and ionic amino-acid side chains on the exterior interact with surrounding water, and nonpolar side chains in the interior interact with each other.
- With polar-ionic heads *and* nonpolar tails, a soap dissolves grease *and* interacts with water.
- Like soaps, phospholipids also have dual polarity. They assemble into a water-impermeable lipid bilayer. In a cell membrane, the embedded portion of membrane proteins has exterior nonpolar side chains that face the nonpolar tails in the lipid bilayer. Some antibiotics form channels with nonpolar exteriors and polar interiors that shuttle ions through the cell membrane.
- DNA forms a double helix with a sugar-phosphate, polar-ionic exterior. In the interior, N-containing bases H bond in specific pairs and stack through dispersion forces.

# 13.3 • WHY SUBSTANCES DISSOLVE: UNDERSTANDING THE SOLUTION PROCESS

The qualitative *macroscopic* rule "like dissolves like" is based on *molecular* interactions between solute and solvent. To see *why* like dissolves like, we'll break down the solution process conceptually into steps and examine them quantitatively.

## Heat of Solution: Solution Cycles

Before a solution forms, solute particles are attracting each other, as are solvent particles. For one to dissolve in the other, three steps must take place, each accompanied by an enthalpy change:

*Step 1. Solute particles separate from each other.* This step involves overcoming intermolecular attractions, so it is *endothermic:*

$$\text{Solute (aggregated)} + heat \longrightarrow \text{solute (separated)} \qquad \Delta H_{\text{solute}} > 0$$

*Step 2. Solvent particles separate from each other.* This step also involves overcoming attractions, so it is *endothermic,* too:

$$\text{Solvent (aggregated)} + heat \longrightarrow \text{solvent (separated)} \qquad \Delta H_{\text{solvent}} > 0$$

*Step 3. Solute and solvent particles mix and form a solution.* The different particles attract each other and come together, so this step is *exothermic:*

$$\text{Solute (separated)} + \text{solvent (separated)} \longrightarrow \text{solution} + heat \qquad \Delta H_{\text{mix}} < 0$$

The overall process is called a *thermochemical solution cycle,* and in yet another application of Hess's law, we combine the three individual enthalpy changes to find the **heat of solution ($\Delta H_{\text{soln}}$),** the total enthalpy change that occurs when solute and solvent form a solution:

$$\Delta H_{\text{soln}} = \Delta H_{\text{solute}} + \Delta H_{\text{solvent}} + \Delta H_{\text{mix}} \qquad \textbf{(13.1)}$$

Overall solution formation is exothermic or endothermic, and $\Delta H_{\text{soln}}$ is either positive or negative, depending on the relative sizes of the individual $\Delta H$ values:

- *Exothermic process:* $\Delta H_{\text{soln}} < 0$. If the sum of the endothermic terms ($\Delta H_{\text{solute}} + \Delta H_{\text{solvent}}$) is *smaller* than the exothermic term ($\Delta H_{\text{mix}}$), the process is exothermic and $\Delta H_{\text{soln}}$ is negative (Figure 13.14A).
- *Endothermic process:* $\Delta H_{\text{soln}} > 0$. If the sum of the endothermic terms is *larger* than the exothermic term, the process is endothermic and $\Delta H_{\text{soln}}$ is positive (Figure 13.14B). If $\Delta H_{\text{soln}}$ is highly positive, the solute may not dissolve significantly in that solvent.

**A  Exothermic solution process**

**B  Endothermic solution process**

**Figure 13.14** Enthalpy components of the heat of solution. **A,** $\Delta H_{\text{mix}}$ is larger than the sum of $\Delta H_{\text{solute}}$ and $\Delta H_{\text{solvent}}$, so $\Delta H_{\text{soln}}$ is negative.   **B,** $\Delta H_{\text{mix}}$ is smaller than the sum of $\Delta H_{\text{solute}}$ and $\Delta H_{\text{solvent}}$, so $\Delta H_{\text{soln}}$ is positive.

# Heat of Hydration: Ionic Solids in Water

The $\Delta H_{solvent}$ and $\Delta H_{mix}$ components of the solution cycle are difficult to measure individually. Combined, they equal the enthalpy change for **solvation,** the process of surrounding a solute particle with solvent particles:

$$\Delta H_{solvation} = \Delta H_{solvent} + \Delta H_{mix}$$

Solvation in water is called **hydration.** Thus, enthalpy changes for separating the water molecules ($\Delta H_{solvent}$) and mixing the separated solute with them ($\Delta H_{mix}$) are combined into the **heat of hydration ($\Delta H_{hydr}$).** In water, Equation 13.1 becomes

$$\Delta H_{soln} = \Delta H_{solute} + \Delta H_{hydr}$$

The heat of hydration is a key factor in dissolving an ionic solid. Breaking H bonds in water is more than compensated for by forming the stronger ion-dipole forces, so hydration of an ion is *always* exothermic. The $\Delta H_{hydr}$ of an ion is defined as the enthalpy change for the hydration of 1 mol of separated (gaseous) ions:

$$M^+(g) \text{ [or } X^-(g)] \xrightarrow{H_2O} M^+(aq) \text{ [or } X^-(aq)] \qquad \Delta H_{hydr\ of\ the\ ion} \text{ (always } <0)$$

**Importance of Charge Density** Heats of hydration exhibit trends based on the ion's **charge density,** the ratio of its charge to its volume. In general, the higher the charge density, the more negative $\Delta H_{hydr}$ is. Coulomb's law explains why: the higher the charge of an ion and the smaller its radius, the closer it gets to the oppositely charged pole of an $H_2O$ (see Figure 2.12, p. 57), and the stronger the attraction. Thus,

- A 2+ ion attracts $H_2O$ molecules more strongly than a 1+ ion of similar size.
- A small 1+ ion attracts $H_2O$ molecules more strongly than a large 1+ ion.

Periodic trends in $\Delta H_{hydr}$ values are based on trends in charge density (Table 13.4):

- *Down a group,* the charge stays the same and the size increases; thus, the charge densities decrease, as do the $\Delta H_{hydr}$ values.
- *Across a period,* say, from Group 1A(1) to Group 2A(2), the 2A ion has a smaller radius *and* a higher charge, so its charge density and $\Delta H_{hydr}$ are greater.

**Components of Aqueous Heats of Solution** To separate an ionic solute, MX, into gaseous ions ($\Delta H_{solute}$) requires a lot of energy; recall from Chapter 9 that this is the lattice energy, and it is highly positive:

$$MX(s) \longrightarrow M^+(g) + X^-(g) \qquad \Delta H_{solute} \text{ (always } >0) = \Delta H_{lattice}$$

Thus, for ionic compounds in water, the heat of solution is the lattice energy (always positive) plus the combined heats of hydration of the ions (always negative):

$$\Delta H_{soln} = \Delta H_{lattice} + \Delta H_{hydr\ of\ the\ ions} \tag{13.2}$$

Once again, the sizes of the individual terms determine the sign of $\Delta H_{soln}$.

Figure 13.15 (*next page*) shows enthalpy diagrams for three ionic solutes dissolving in water:

- *NaCl.* Sodium chloride has a small positive $\Delta H_{soln}$ (3.9 kJ/mol) because its lattice energy is only slightly greater than the combined ionic heats of hydration: if you dissolve NaCl in water in a flask, you don't feel any temperature change.
- *NaOH.* Sodium hydroxide has a large negative $\Delta H_{soln}$ (−44.5 kJ/mol) because its lattice energy is much *smaller* than the combined ionic heats of hydration: if you dissolve NaOH in water, the flask feels hot.
- *NH₄NO₃.* Ammonium nitrate has a large positive $\Delta H_{soln}$ (25.7 kJ/mol) because its lattice energy is much *larger* than the combined ionic heats of hydration: if you dissolve $NH_4NO_3$ in water, the flask feels cold.

Hot and cold packs consist of a thick outer pouch of water and a thin inner pouch of a salt. A squeeze breaks the inner pouch, and the salt dissolves. Most hot packs use anhydrous $CaCl_2$ ($\Delta H_{soln} = -82.8$ kJ/mol), and cold packs use $NH_4NO_3$ ($\Delta H_{soln} = 25.7$ kJ/mol). A cold pack can keep the solution at 0°C for about half an hour. In Japan, some soup is sold in double-walled cans with a salt in a packet immersed in water between the walls. Open the can and the packet breaks, the salt dissolves, and the soup quickly warms to about 90°C.

| Table **13.4** Trends in Ionic Heats of Hydration | | |
|---|---|---|
| Ion | Ionic Radius (pm) | $\Delta H_{hydr}$ (kJ/mol) |
| **Group 1A(1)** | | |
| $Na^+$ | 102 | −410 |
| $K^+$ | 138 | −336 |
| $Rb^+$ | 152 | −315 |
| $Cs^+$ | 167 | −282 |
| **Group 2A(2)** | | |
| $Mg^{2+}$ | 72 | −1903 |
| $Ca^{2+}$ | 100 | −1591 |
| $Sr^{2+}$ | 118 | −1424 |
| $Ba^{2+}$ | 135 | −1317 |
| **Group 7A(17)** | | |
| $F^-$ | 133 | −431 |
| $Cl^-$ | 181 | −313 |
| $Br^-$ | 196 | −284 |
| $I^-$ | 220 | −247 |

**A NaCl.** $\Delta H_{lattice}$ is slightly larger than $\Delta H_{hydr}$: $\Delta H_{soln}$ is small and positive.

**Figure 13.15** Enthalpy diagrams for three ionic compounds dissolving in water.

**B NaOH.** $\Delta H_{hydr}$ dominates: $\Delta H_{soln}$ is large and negative.

**C NH₄NO₃.** $\Delta H_{lattice}$ dominates: $\Delta H_{soln}$ is large and positive.

## The Solution Process and the Change in Entropy

The heat of solution ($\Delta H_{soln}$) is one of two factors that determine whether a solute dissolves. The other factor is the natural tendency of a system of particles to spread out and the system's kinetic energy to become more dispersed or distributed. A thermodynamic variable called **entropy (S)** is directly related to the number of ways a system can disperse its energy, which is closely related to the freedom of motion of the particles.

Let's see what it means for a system to "distribute its energy." We'll first compare the three physical states and then compare solute and solvent with solution.

**Entropy and the Three Physical States** The states of matter differ significantly in their entropy.
- In a solid, the particles are fixed in their positions with little freedom of motion. In a liquid, they can move around each other and so have greater freedom of motion. And in a gas, the particles have little restriction and much more freedom of motion.
- The more freedom of motion the particles have, the more ways they can distribute their kinetic energy; thus, a liquid has higher entropy than a solid, and a gas has higher entropy than a liquid:

$$S_{gas} > S_{liquid} > S_{solid}$$

- We can also look at the *change* in entropy ($\Delta S$) of a phase change. Thus, for example, the change in entropy when a liquid vaporizes ($\Delta S_{vap} = S_{gas} - S_{liquid}$) is positive ($\Delta S_{vap} > 0$), the change in entropy when a liquid freezes (fusion) ($\Delta S_{fus} = S_{solid} - S_{liquid}$) is negative ($\Delta S_{fus} < 0$), and so forth.

**Entropy and the Formation of Solutions** The formation of solutions also involves a change in entropy. *A solution usually has higher entropy than the pure solute and pure solvent* because the number of ways to distribute the energy is related to the number of interactions between different molecules. There are far more interactions possible when solute and solvent are mixed than when they are pure; thus,

$$S_{soln} > (S_{solute} + S_{solvent}) \qquad \text{or} \qquad \Delta S_{soln} > 0$$

You know from everyday experience that solutions form naturally, but pure solutes and solvents don't: you've seen sugar dissolve in water, but you've never seen a sugar solution separate into pure sugar and water. In Chapter 20, we'll see that energy is needed to reverse the natural tendency of systems to distribute their energy—to get "mixed up." Water treatment plants, oil refineries, steel mills, and many other industrial facilities expend a lot of energy to separate mixtures into pure components.

**Figure 13.16** Enthalpy diagrams for dissolving (A) NaCl and (B) octane in hexane.

**A NaCl.** $\Delta H_{mix}$ is **much** smaller than $\Delta H_{solute}$: $\Delta H_{soln}$ is so much larger than the entropy increase due to mixing that NaCl does **not** dissolve.

**B Octane.** $\Delta H_{soln}$ is very small, but the entropy increase due to mixing is large, so octane dissolves.

**Enthalpy vs. Entropy Changes in Solution Formation** Solution formation involves the interplay of two factors: systems change toward a state of *lower enthalpy* and *higher entropy,* so the relative sizes of $\Delta H_{soln}$ and $\Delta S_{soln}$ determine whether a solution forms. Let's consider three solute-solvent pairs to see which factor dominates:

1. *NaCl in hexane.* Given their very different intermolecular forces, we predict that sodium chloride does *not* dissolve in hexane ($C_6H_{14}$) (Figure 13.16A). Separating the solvent is easy because the dispersion forces are weak ($\Delta H_{solvent} \geq 0$), but separating the solute requires supplying the very large $\Delta H_{lattice}$ ($\Delta H_{solute} \gg 0$). Mixing releases little heat because ion–induced dipole forces between $Na^+$ (or $Cl^-$) and hexane are weak ($\Delta H_{mix} \leq 0$). Because the sum of the endothermic terms is *much* larger than the exothermic term, $\Delta H_{soln} \gg 0$. *A solution does not form because the entropy increase from mixing solute and solvent would be much smaller than the enthalpy increase required to separate the solute:* $\Delta S_{mix} \ll \Delta H_{solute}$.

2. *Octane in hexane.* We predict that octane ($C_8H_{18}$) is soluble in hexane because both are held together by dispersion forces of similar strength; in fact, they are miscible. That is, both $\Delta H_{solute}$ and $\Delta H_{solvent}$ are around zero. The similar forces mean that $\Delta H_{mix}$ is around zero also. And a lot of heat is not released; in fact, $\Delta H_{soln}$ is around zero (Figure 13.16B). So why does a solution form so readily? *With no enthalpy change driving the process, octane dissolves in hexane because the entropy increases greatly when the pure substances mix:* $\Delta S_{mix} \gg \Delta H_{soln}$.

3. *$NH_4NO_3$ in water.* A large enough increase in entropy can sometimes cause a solution to form even when the enthalpy increase is large ($\Delta H_{soln} \gg 0$). As we saw in Figure 13.15C, when ammonium nitrate ($NH_4NO_3$) dissolves in water, the process is highly endothermic; that is, $\Delta H_{lattice} \gg \Delta H_{hydr\ of\ the\ ions}$. Nevertheless, *the increase in entropy that occurs when the crystal breaks down and the ions mix with water molecules is greater than the increase in enthalpy:* $\Delta S_{soln} > \Delta H_{soln}$.

In Chapter 20, we'll return in depth to the relation between enthalpy and entropy to understand physical and chemical systems.

## Summary of Section 13.3

- In a thermochemical solution cycle, the heat of solution is the sum of the endothermic separations of solute and of solvent and the exothermic mixing of their particles.
- In water, the combination of solvent separation and mixing with solute particles is hydration. For ions, heats of hydration depend on the ion's charge density but are always negative because ion-dipole forces are strong.
- Systems naturally increase their entropy (distribute their energy in more ways). A gas has higher entropy than a liquid, which has higher entropy than a solid, and a solution has higher entropy than the pure solute and solvent.
- Relative sizes of the enthalpy and entropy changes determine solution formation. A substance with a positive $\Delta H_{soln}$ dissolves *only* if $\Delta S_{soln}$ is larger than $\Delta H_{soln}$.

**Figure 13.17 Equilibrium in a saturated solution.** At some temperature, the number of solute particles dissolving (*white arrows*) per unit time equals the number recrystallizing (*black arrows*).

# 13.4 • SOLUBILITY AS AN EQUILIBRIUM PROCESS

When an excess amount of solid is added to a solvent, particles leave the crystal, are surrounded by solvent, and move away. Some dissolved solute particles collide with undissolved solute and recrystallize, but, as long as the rate of dissolving is greater than the rate of recrystallizing, the concentration rises. At a given temperature, when solid is dissolving at the same rate as dissolved particles are recrystallizing, the concentration remains constant and *undissolved solute is in equilibrium with dissolved solute:*

$$\text{Solute (undissolved)} \rightleftharpoons \text{solute (dissolved)}$$

Figure 13.17 shows an ionic solid in equilibrium with dissolved cations and anions.

Three terms express the extent of this solution process:

- A **saturated solution** is at equilibrium and contains the maximum amount of dissolved solute at a given temperature in the presence of undissolved solute. Therefore, if you filter off the solution and add more solute, it doesn't dissolve.
- An **unsaturated solution** contains *less* than the equilibrium concentration of dissolved solute; add more solute, and more dissolves until the solution is saturated.
- A **supersaturated solution** contains *more* than the equilibrium concentration and is unstable relative to the saturated solution; add a "seed" crystal of solute or tap the container, and the excess solute crystallizes immediately, leaving a saturated solution (Figure 13.18). You can often prepare a supersaturated solution if the solute is more soluble at higher temperature. While heating, dissolve more than the amount required for saturation at some lower temperature, and then slowly cool the solution. If the excess solute remains dissolved, the solution is supersaturated.

## Effect of Temperature on Solubility

You know that more sugar dissolves in hot tea than in iced tea; in fact, temperature affects the solubility of most substances. Let's examine the effects of temperature on the solubility of solids and gases.

**Temperature and the Solubility of Solids in Water** Like sugar, *most solids are more soluble at higher temperatures* (Figure 13.19). Note that cerium sulfate is one of several exceptions, mostly other sulfates. Some salts have higher solubility up to a certain temperature and then lower solubility at still higher temperatures.

A

B

C

**Figure 13.18 Sodium acetate crystallizing from a supersaturated solution.** When a seed crystal of sodium acetate is added to a supersaturated solution of it **(A)**, solute begins to crystallize **(B)** and continues until the remaining solution is saturated **(C)**.

**Figure 13.19** Relation between solubility and temperature for several ionic compounds.

Unfortunately, the effect of temperature on solubility is a complex phenomenon, and the sign of $\Delta H_{soln}$ does not reflect that complexity. Tabulated $\Delta H_{soln}$ values give the enthalpy change for making a solution at the standard state of 1 $M$; but in order to understand the effect of temperature, we need to know the sign of the enthalpy change very close to the point of saturation, which may differ from the sign of the tabulated value. For example, tables give a negative $\Delta H_{soln}$ for NaOH and a positive one for $NH_4NO_3$, yet both compounds are more soluble at higher temperatures. The point is that, although the effect of temperature reflects the equilibrium nature of solubility, no single measure can predict the effect for a given solute.

**Temperature and the Solubility of Gases in Water** The effect of temperature on *gas* solubility is much more predictable. When a solid dissolves in a liquid, the solute particles must separate, so $\Delta H_{solute} > 0$. In contrast, gas particles are already separated, so $\Delta H_{solute} \approx 0$. Because hydration is exothermic ($\Delta H_{hydr} < 0$), the sum of these two terms is negative. Thus, $\Delta H_{soln} < 0$ for all gases in water:

$$\text{Solute}(g) + \text{water}(l) \rightleftharpoons \text{saturated solution}(aq) + \text{heat}$$

Thus, *gas solubility in water* **decreases** *with rising temperature (addition of heat).* Gases have weak intermolecular forces with water. When the temperature rises, the average kinetic energy increases, allowing the gas particles to easily overcome these forces and re-enter the gas phase.

This behavior leads to *thermal pollution.* Many electric power plants use large amounts of water from a nearby river or lake for cooling, and the warmed water is returned to the source. The metabolic rates of fish and other aquatic animals increase in this warmer water, increasing their need for $O_2$. But the concentration of dissolved $O_2$ is lower in warm water, so they become "oxygen deprived." Also, the less dense warm water floats and prevents $O_2$ from reaching the cooler water below. Thus, even creatures at deeper levels become oxygen deprived. Farther from the plant, the water temperature and $O_2$ solubility return to normal. To mitigate the problem, cooling towers lower the temperature of the water before it exits the plant (Figure 13.20); nuclear power plants use a similar approach (Section 24.7).

**Figure 13.20** Preventing thermal pollution with cooling towers.

## Effect of Pressure on Solubility

*Pressure has little effect on the solubility of liquids and solids* because they are almost incompressible. But it has a *major* effect on the solubility of gases. Consider a piston-cylinder assembly with a gas above a saturated aqueous solution of the gas (Figure 13.21A). At equilibrium, at a given pressure, the same number of gas molecules enter and leave the solution per unit time:

$$\text{Gas} + \text{solvent} \rightleftharpoons \text{saturated solution}$$

Push down on the piston, and you disturb the equilibrium: gas volume decreases, so gas pressure (and concentration) increases, and gas particles collide with the liquid surface more often. Thus, more particles enter than leave the solution per unit time (Figure 13.21B). More gas dissolves to reduce this disturbance (a shift to the right in the preceding equation) until the system re-establishes equilibrium (Figure 13.21C).

The relation between gas pressure and solubility has many familiar applications. In a closed can of cola, dissolved $CO_2$ is in equilibrium with 4 atm of $CO_2$ in the small

**Figure 13.21** The effect of pressure on gas solubility.

What happens to gases dissolved in the blood of a scuba diver?

volume above the solution. Open the can and the dissolved $CO_2$ bubbles out of solution until the drink goes "flat" because it reaches equilibrium with $CO_2$ in air ($P_{CO_2}$ = $3 \times 10^{-4}$ atm). In a different situation (*see photo*), scuba divers who breathe compressed air have a high concentration of $N_2$ dissolved in their blood. If they ascend too quickly, they may suffer decompression sickness (the "bends"), in which lower external pressure allows the dissolved $N_2$ to form bubbles in the blood that block capillaries.

**Henry's law** expresses the quantitative relationship between gas pressure and solubility: *the solubility of a gas ($S_{gas}$) is directly proportional to the partial pressure of the gas ($P_{gas}$) above the solution:*

$$S_{gas} = k_H \times P_{gas} \qquad (13.3)$$

where $k_H$ is the *Henry's law constant* and is specific for a given gas-solvent combination at a given temperature. With $S_{gas}$ in mol/L and $P_{gas}$ in atm, the units of $k_H$ are mol/L·atm.

---

**Sample Problem 13.2**     **Using Henry's Law to Calculate Gas Solubility**

**Problem** The partial pressure of carbon dioxide gas inside a bottle of cola is 4 atm at 25°C. What is the solubility of $CO_2$? The Henry's law constant for $CO_2$ in water is $3.3 \times 10^{-2}$ mol/L·atm at 25°C.

**Plan** We know $P_{CO_2}$ (4 atm) and the value of $k_H$ ($3.3 \times 10^{-2}$ mol/L·atm), so we substitute them into Equation 13.3 to find $S_{CO_2}$.

**Solution** $S_{CO_2} = k_H \times P_{CO_2} = (3.3 \times 10^{-2} \text{ mol/L·atm})(4 \text{ atm}) = \boxed{0.1 \text{ mol/L}}$

**Check** The units are correct. We rounded to one significant figure because there is one in the pressure value. A 0.5-L bottle of cola has about 0.2 g of dissolved $CO_2$.

**Follow-Up Problem 13.2** If air contains 78% $N_2$ by volume, what is the solubility of $N_2$ in water at 25°C and 1 atm ($k_H$ for $N_2$ in $H_2O$ at 25°C = $7 \times 10^{-4}$ mol/L·atm)?

---

## ■ Summary of Section 13.4

- A solution that contains the maximum amount of dissolved solute in the presence of excess undissolved solute is saturated. A saturated solution is in equilibrium with excess solute, because solute particles are entering and leaving the solution at the same rate.
- Most solids are more soluble at higher temperatures.
- All gases have a negative $\Delta H_{soln}$ in water, so heating lowers gas solubility in water.
- Henry's law says that the solubility of a gas is directly proportional to its partial pressure above the solution.

---

## 13.5 • CONCENTRATION TERMS

Concentration is the *proportion* of a substance in a mixture, so it is an *intensive* property (like density and temperature), one that does not depend on the quantity of mixture: 1.0 L or 1.0 mL of 0.1 *M* NaCl have the same concentration. Concentration is a ratio of quantities (Table 13.5), most often solute to *solution,* but sometimes solute to *solvent.* Both parts of the ratio can be given in units of mass, volume, or amount (mol), and chemists express concentration by several terms, including molarity, molality, and various expressions of "parts of solute per part by solution."

### Molarity and Molality

Two very common concentration terms are molarity and molality:

1. Molarity (*M*) is the *number of moles of solute dissolved in 1 L of solution:*

$$\text{Molarity } (M) = \frac{\text{amount (mol) of solute}}{\text{volume (L) of solution}} \qquad (13.4)$$

| Table **13.5** Concentration Definitions | |
|---|---|
| **Concentration Term** | **Ratio** |
| Molarity ($M$) | $\dfrac{\text{amount (mol) of solute}}{\text{volume (L) of solution}}$ |
| Molality ($m$) | $\dfrac{\text{amount (mol) of solute}}{\text{mass (kg) of solvent}}$ |
| Parts by mass | $\dfrac{\text{mass of solute}}{\text{mass of solution}}$ |
| Parts by volume | $\dfrac{\text{volume of solute}}{\text{volume of solution}}$ |
| Mole fraction ($X$) | $\dfrac{\text{amount (mol) of solute}}{\text{amount (mol) of solute + amount (mol) of solvent}}$ |

In Chapter 3, we used molarity to convert liters of solution into amount of dissolved solute. Molarity has two drawbacks that affect its use in precise work:
- *Effect of temperature.* A liquid expands when heated, so a unit volume of hot solution contains less solute than one of cold solution; thus, the molarity is different.
- *Effect of mixing.* Because of solute-solvent interactions that are difficult to predict, *volumes may not be additive:* adding 500. mL of one solution to 500. mL of another may not give 1000. mL of final solution.

   2. **Molality ($m$)** does not contain volume in its ratio; it is *the number of moles of solute dissolved in 1000 g (1 kg) of solvent:*

$$\text{Molality } (m) = \frac{\text{amount (mol) of solute}}{\text{mass (kg) of solvent}} \qquad (13.5)$$

Note that molality includes the quantity of *solvent,* not solution. Molality has two advantages over molarity for precise work:
- *Effect of temperature.* Molal solutions are based on *masses* of components, not *volume.* And since mass does not change with temperature, neither does molality.
- *Effect of mixing.* Unlike volumes, masses *are* additive: adding 500. g of one solution to 500. g of another *does* give 1000. g of final solution.

For these reasons, molality is the preferred term when temperature, and hence density, may change, as in a study of physical properties. Note that, in the case of water, 1 L has a mass of 1 kg, so *molality and molarity are nearly the same for dilute aqueous solutions.*

## Sample Problem 13.3    Calculating Molality

**Problem** What is the molality of a solution prepared by dissolving 32.0 g of $CaCl_2$ in 271 g of water?

**Plan** To use Equation 13.5, we convert mass of $CaCl_2$ (32.0 g) to amount (mol) with the molar mass (g/mol) and then divide by the mass of water (271 g), being sure to convert from grams to kilograms (see the road map).

**Solution** Converting from grams of solute to moles:

$$\text{Amount (mol) of } CaCl_2 = 32.0 \text{ g } CaCl_2 \times \frac{1 \text{ mol } CaCl_2}{110.98 \text{ g } CaCl_2} = 0.288 \text{ mol } CaCl_2$$

Finding molality:

$$\text{Molality} = \frac{\text{mol solute}}{\text{kg solvent}} = \frac{0.288 \text{ mol } CaCl_2}{271 \text{ g} \times \dfrac{1 \text{ kg}}{10^3 \text{ g}}} = \boxed{1.06 \, m \, CaCl_2}$$

**Road Map**

Mass (g) of $CaCl_2$

divide by $\mathcal{M}$ (g/mol)

Amount (mol) of $CaCl_2$

divide by kg of water

Molality ($m$) of $CaCl_2$ solution

**Check** The answer seems reasonable: the given amount (mol) of $CaCl_2$ and mass (kg) of $H_2O$ are about the same, so their ratio is about 1.

**Follow-Up Problem 13.3** How many grams of glucose ($C_6H_{12}O_6$) must be dissolved in 563 g of ethanol ($C_2H_5OH$) to prepare a $2.40 \times 10^{-2}$ *m* solution?

## Parts of Solute by Parts of Solution

Several concentration terms relate the number of solute (or solvent) parts to a number of *solution* parts. Both can be expressed in units of mass, volume, or amount (mol).

**Parts by Mass** The most common of these terms is **mass percent, % (w/w),** which you encountered in Chapter 3. The word *percent* means "per hundred," so mass percent means mass of solute dissolved in 100. parts by mass of solution:

$$\text{Mass percent} = \frac{\text{mass of solute}}{\text{mass of solute} + \text{mass of solvent}} \times 100$$
$$= \frac{\text{mass of solute}}{\text{mass of solution}} \times 100 \qquad (13.6)$$

Mass percent values appear on jars of solid chemicals to indicate impurities.

Two very similar terms are parts per million (ppm) by mass and parts per billion (ppb) by mass, or grams of solute per million or per billion grams of solution: in Equation 13.6, you multiply by $10^6$ or by $10^9$, respectively, instead of by 100. Environmental toxicologists use these units to measure pollutants. For example, TCDD (*t*etra*c*hloro*d*ibenzo*d*ioxin) (*see margin*), a byproduct of paper bleaching, is unsafe at soil levels above 1 ppb. From normal contact with air, water, and soil, North Americans have an average of 0.01 ppb TCDD in their tissues.

Is this deadly toxin in your body?

**Parts by Volume** The most common parts-by-volume term is **volume percent, % (v/v),** the volume of solute in 100. volumes of solution:

$$\text{Volume percent} = \frac{\text{volume of solute}}{\text{volume of solution}} \times 100 \qquad (13.7)$$

For example, rubbing alcohol is an aqueous solution of isopropanol (a three-carbon alcohol) that contains 70 volumes of alcohol in 100. volumes of solution, or 70% (v/v).

Parts by volume is often used to express tiny concentrations of liquids or gases. Minor atmospheric components occur in parts per million by volume (ppmv). For example, about 0.05 ppmv of the toxic gas carbon monoxide (CO) is in clean air, 1000 times as much (50 ppmv of CO) in air over urban traffic, and 10,000 times as much (500 ppmv of CO) in cigarette smoke. *Pheromones* are compounds secreted by members of a species to signal food, danger, sexual readiness, and so forth. Many organisms, including dogs and monkeys, release pheromones, and researchers suspect that humans do as well. Some insect pheromones, such as the sexual attractant of the gypsy moth, are active at a few hundred molecules per milliliter of air, 100 parts per quadrillion by volume.

A concentration term often used in health-related facilities for aqueous solutions is % (w/v), a ratio of solute *weight* (actually mass) to solution *volume*. Thus, a 1.5% (w/v) NaCl solution contains 1.5 g of NaCl per 100. mL of *solution*.

**Mole Fraction** The **mole fraction (*X*)** of a solute is the ratio of number of moles of solute to the total number of moles (solute plus solvent), that is, parts by mole:

$$\text{Mole fraction } (X) = \frac{\text{amount (mol) of solute}}{\text{amount (mol) of solute} + \text{amount (mol) of solvent}} \qquad (13.8)$$

Put another way, the mole fraction gives the proportion of solute (or solvent) particles in solution. The *mole percent* is the mole fraction expressed as a percentage:

$$\text{Mole percent (mol \%)} = \text{mole fraction} \times 100$$

## Sample Problem 13.4 — Expressing Concentrations in Parts by Mass, Parts by Volume, and Mole Fraction

**Problem** (a) Find the concentration of calcium ion (in ppm) in a 3.50-g pill that contains 40.5 mg of $Ca^{2+}$.
(b) The label on a 0.750-L bottle of Italian chianti indicates "11.5% alcohol by volume." How many liters of alcohol does the wine contain?
(c) A sample of rubbing alcohol contains 142 g of isopropyl alcohol ($C_3H_7OH$) and 58.0 g of water. What are the mole fractions of alcohol and water?

**Plan** (a) We know the mass of $Ca^{2+}$ (40.5 mg) and the mass of the pill (3.50 g). We convert the mass of $Ca^{2+}$ from mg to g, find the mass ratio of $Ca^{2+}$ to pill, and multiply by $10^6$ to obtain ppm. (b) We know the volume % (11.5%, or 11.5 parts by volume of alcohol to 100. parts of chianti) and the total volume (0.750 L), so we use Equation 13.7 to find liters of alcohol. (c) We know the mass and formula of each component, so we convert masses to amounts (mol) and apply Equation 13.8 to find the mole fractions.

**Solution** (a) Finding parts per million by mass of $Ca^{2+}$. Combining the steps, we have

$$\text{ppm } Ca^{2+} = \frac{\text{mass of } Ca^{2+}}{\text{mass of pill}} \times 10^6 = \frac{40.5 \text{ mg } Ca^{2+} \times \frac{1 \text{ g}}{10^3 \text{ mg}}}{3.50 \text{ g}} \times 10^6$$

$$= 1.16 \times 10^4 \text{ ppm } Ca^{2+}$$

(b) Finding volume (L) of alcohol:

$$\text{Volume (L) of alcohol} = 0.750 \text{ L chianti} \times \frac{11.5 \text{ L alcohol}}{100. \text{ L chianti}}$$

$$= 0.0862 \text{ L}$$

(c) Finding mole fractions. Converting from mass (g) to amount (mol):

$$\text{Amount (mol) of } C_3H_7OH = 142 \text{ g } C_3H_7OH \times \frac{1 \text{ mol } C_3H_7OH}{60.09 \text{ g } C_3H_7OH} = 2.36 \text{ mol } C_3H_7OH$$

$$\text{Amount (mol) of } H_2O = 58.0 \text{ g } H_2O \times \frac{1 \text{ mol } H_2O}{18.02 \text{ g } H_2O} = 3.22 \text{ mol } H_2O$$

Calculating mole fractions:

$$X_{C_3H_7OH} = \frac{\text{moles of } C_3H_7OH}{\text{total moles}} = \frac{2.36 \text{ mol}}{2.36 \text{ mol} + 3.22 \text{ mol}} = 0.423$$

$$X_{H_2O} = \frac{\text{moles of } H_2O}{\text{total moles}} = \frac{3.22 \text{ mol}}{2.36 \text{ mol} + 3.22 \text{ mol}} = 0.577$$

**Check** (a) The mass ratio is about 0.04 g/4 g $= 10^{-2}$, and $10^{-2} \times 10^6 = 10^4$ ppm, so it seems correct. (b) The volume % is a bit more than 10%, so the volume of alcohol should be a bit more than 75 mL (0.075 L). (c) Always check that the *mole fractions add up to 1:* 0.423 + 0.577 = 1.000.

**Follow-Up Problem 13.4** An alcohol solution contains 35.0 g of 1-propanol ($C_3H_7OH$) and 150. g of ethanol ($C_2H_5OH$). Calculate the mass percent and the mole fraction of each alcohol.

## Interconverting Concentration Terms

All the terms we just discussed represent different ways of expressing concentration, so they are interconvertible. Keep these points in mind:

• To convert a term based on amount to one based on mass, you need the molar mass. These conversions are similar to the mass-mole conversions you've done earlier.
• To convert a term based on mass to one based on volume, you need the solution *density*. Given the mass of solution, the density (mass/volume) gives the volume, or vice versa.
• Molality includes quantity of *solvent;* the other terms include quantity of *solution.*

### Sample Problem 13.5    Interconverting Concentration Terms

**Problem** Hydrogen peroxide is a powerful oxidizing agent; it is used in concentrated solution in rocket fuel, but in dilute solution in hair bleach. An aqueous solution of $H_2O_2$ is 30.0% by mass and has a density of 1.11 g/mL. Calculate the **(a)** molality, **(b)** mole fraction of $H_2O_2$, and **(c)** molarity.

**Plan** We know the mass % (30.0) and the density (1.11 g/mL). **(a)** For molality, we need the amount (mol) of solute and the mass (kg) of *solvent*. If we assume 100.0 g of solution, the mass % equals the grams of $H_2O_2$, which we subtract to obtain the grams of solvent. To find molality, we convert grams of $H_2O_2$ to moles and divide by mass of solvent (converting g to kg). **(b)** To find the mole fraction, we use the moles of $H_2O_2$ [from part (a)] and convert the grams of $H_2O$ to moles. Then we divide the moles of $H_2O_2$ by the total moles. **(c)** To find molarity, we assume 100.0 g of solution and use the solution density to find the volume. Then we divide the moles of $H_2O_2$ [from part (a)] by *solution* volume (in L).

**Solution** **(a)** From mass % to molality. Finding mass of solvent (assuming 100.0 g of solution):

$$\text{Mass (g) of } H_2O = 100.0 \text{ g solution} - 30.0 \text{ g } H_2O_2 = 70.0 \text{ g } H_2O$$

Converting from grams of $H_2O_2$ to moles:

$$\text{Amount (mol) of } H_2O_2 = 30.0 \text{ g } H_2O_2 \times \frac{1 \text{ mol } H_2O_2}{34.02 \text{ g } H_2O_2} = 0.882 \text{ mol } H_2O_2$$

Calculating molality:

$$\text{Molality of } H_2O_2 = \frac{0.882 \text{ mol } H_2O_2}{70.0 \text{ g} \times \dfrac{1 \text{ kg}}{10^3 \text{ g}}} = \boxed{12.6 \ m \ H_2O_2}$$

**(b)** From mass % to mole fraction:

$$\text{Amount (mol) of } H_2O_2 = 0.882 \text{ mol } H_2O_2 \left[\text{from part (a)}\right]$$

$$\text{Amount (mol) of } H_2O = 70.0 \text{ g } H_2O \times \frac{1 \text{ mol } H_2O}{18.02 \text{ g } H_2O} = 3.88 \text{ mol } H_2O$$

$$X_{H_2O_2} = \frac{0.882 \text{ mol}}{0.882 \text{ mol} + 3.88 \text{ mol}} = \boxed{0.185}$$

**(c)** From mass % and density to molarity. Converting from solution mass to volume:

$$\text{Volume (mL) of solution} = 100.0 \text{ g} \times \frac{1 \text{ mL}}{1.11 \text{ g}} = 90.1 \text{ mL}$$

Calculating molarity:

$$\text{Molarity} = \frac{\text{mol } H_2O_2}{\text{L soln}} = \frac{0.882 \text{ mol } H_2O_2}{90.1 \text{ mL} \times \dfrac{1 \text{ L soln}}{10^3 \text{ mL}}} = \boxed{9.79 \ M \ H_2O_2}$$

**Check** Rounding shows the answers to be reasonable: **(a)** The ratio of ~0.9 mol/0.07 kg is greater than 10. **(b)** ~0.9 mol $H_2O_2$/(1 mol + 4 mol) ≈ 0.2. **(c)** The ratio of moles to liters (0.9/0.09) is around 10.

**Follow-Up Problem 13.5** Concentrated hydrochloric acid is 11.8 $M$ HCl and has a density of 1.190 g/mL. Calculate the mass %, molality, and mole fraction of HCl.

## ▌Summary of Section 13.5

- The concentration of a solution is independent of the quantity of solution and can be expressed as molarity (mol solute/L solution), molality (mol solute/kg solvent), parts by mass (mass solute/mass solution), parts by volume (volume solute/volume solution), or mole fraction [mol solute/(mol solute + mol solvent)] (Table 13.5).
- Molality is based on mass, so it is independent of temperature; the mole fraction gives the proportion of dissolved particles.
- If, in addition to the quantities of solute and solution, the solution density is known, the various ways of expressing concentration are interconvertible.

# 13.6 • COLLIGATIVE PROPERTIES OF SOLUTIONS

The presence of solute gives a solution different physical properties than the pure solvent. But, in the case of four important properties, it is the *number* of solute particles, *not* their chemical identity, that makes the difference. These **colligative properties** (*colligative* means "collective") are vapor pressure lowering, boiling point elevation, freezing point depression, and osmotic pressure. Most of the effects are small, but they have many applications, including some vital to organisms.

We predict the magnitude of a colligative property from the solute formula, which shows the number of particles in solution and is closely related to our classification of solutes (Chapter 4) by their ability to conduct an electric current (Figure 13.22):

1. *Electrolytes.* An aqueous solution of an **electrolyte** conducts because the solute separates into ions as it dissolves.
   - *Strong electrolytes*—soluble salts, strong acids, and strong bases—dissociate completely, so their solutions conduct well.
   - *Weak electrolytes*—weak acids and weak bases—dissociate very little, so their solutions conduct poorly.

2. *Nonelectrolytes.* Compounds such as sugar and alcohol do not dissociate into ions at all. They are **nonelectrolytes** because their solutions do not conduct a current.

   Thus we can predict that

- *For nonelectrolytes,* 1 mol of compound yields 1 mol of particles in solution. For example, 0.35 *M* glucose contains 0.35 mol of solute particles per liter.
- *For strong electrolytes,* 1 mol of compound yields the amount (mol) of ions in the formula unit: 0.4 *M* $Na_2SO_4$ has 0.8 mol of $Na^+$ ions and 0.4 mol of $SO_4^{2-}$ ions, or 1.2 mol of particles, per liter (see Sample Problem 4.1, p. 138).
- *For weak electrolytes,* the calculation is complicated because the solution reaches equilibrium; we examine these systems in Chapters 18 and 19.

In this section, we discuss colligative properties of three types of solute—nonvolatile nonelectrolytes, volatile nonelectrolytes, and strong electrolytes.

## Nonvolatile Nonelectrolyte Solutions

We start with solutions of *nonvolatile nonelectrolytes,* because they provide the clearest examples of the colligative properties. These solutes do not dissociate and have negligible vapor pressure at the boiling point of the solvent; sucrose (table sugar) dissolved in water is an example.

**Vapor Pressure Lowering** *The vapor pressure of a nonvolatile nonelectrolyte solution is always lower than the vapor pressure of the pure solvent.* The difference in vapor pressures is the **vapor pressure lowering ($\Delta P$).**

1. *Why the vapor pressure of a solution is lower.* We can explain this lowering in terms of maintaining equilibrium or increasing entropy (Figure 13.23, *next page*):
- *Maintaining equilibrium.* In pure solvent, the opposing rates of vaporization (molecules leaving the liquid) and of condensation (molecules entering the liquid) are equal at equilibrium. In a solution, some solute molecules are on the surface, so the number of solvent molecules on the surface is lower; therefore, fewer vaporize per unit time. To maintain equilibrium, fewer gas molecules must enter the liquid, which happens if the vapor pressure is lower.
- *Increasing entropy.* A solvent vaporizes because the gaseous state has higher entropy than the liquid. But, with dissolved particles present, the solution already has higher entropy, so the solvent has less tendency to vaporize.

**A  Strong electrolyte**

**B  Weak electrolyte**

**C  Nonelectrolyte**

**Figure 13.22 Conductivity of three types of electrolyte solutions. A,** For strong electrolytes, the number of particles equals the number of ions in a formula unit. **B,** Weak electrolytes form few ions. **C,** For nonelectrolytes, the number of particles equals the number of molecules.

**Figure 13.23 Effect of solute on the vapor pressure of solution. A,** Equilibrium between a liquid and its vapor occurs when equal numbers of molecules vaporize and condense in a given time. **B,** Solute molecules decrease the number of solvent molecules at the surface *and* increase the entropy, so equilibrium occurs at a lower vapor pressure.

*Equilibrium is reached with a given number of particles in the vapor.*

*Equilibrium is reached with fewer particles in the vapor.*

Solvent molecules

Nonvolatile solute molecules

**A Pure solvent**

**B Solvent and dissolved solute**

2. *Quantifying vapor pressure lowering.* **Raoult's law** says that the vapor pressure of solvent above a solution ($P_{solvent}$) equals the mole fraction of solvent ($X_{solvent}$) times the vapor pressure of the pure solvent ($P^{\circ}_{solvent}$):

$$P_{solvent} = X_{solvent} \times P^{\circ}_{solvent} \tag{13.9}$$

Since $X_{solvent}$ is less than 1 in a solution, $P_{solvent}$ is less than $P^{\circ}_{solvent}$. An **ideal solution** is one that follows Raoult's law at any concentration. However, just as real gases deviate from ideality, so do real solutions. In practice, Raoult's law works reasonably well for *dilute* solutions and becomes exact at infinite dilution.

Let's see how the *amount* of dissolved solute affects $\Delta P$. The solution consists of solvent and solute, so the sum of their mole fractions equals 1:

$$X_{solvent} + X_{solute} = 1; \quad \text{thus,} \quad X_{solvent} = 1 - X_{solute}$$

From Raoult's law, we have

$$P_{solvent} = X_{solvent} \times P^{\circ}_{solvent} = (1 - X_{solute}) \times P^{\circ}_{solvent}$$

Multiplying through on the right side gives

$$P_{solvent} = P^{\circ}_{solvent} - (X_{solute} \times P^{\circ}_{solvent})$$

Rearranging and introducing $\Delta P$ gives

$$P^{\circ}_{solvent} - P_{solvent} = \Delta P = X_{solute} \times P^{\circ}_{solvent} \tag{13.10}$$

Thus, $\Delta P$ equals the mole fraction of solute times the vapor pressure of the pure solvent—a relationship applied in the next sample problem.

**Road Map**

Volume (mL) of glycerol (or $H_2O$)

↓ multiply by density (g/mL)

Mass (g) of glycerol (or $H_2O$)

↓ divide by $\mathcal{M}$ (g/mol)

Amount (mol) of glycerol (or $H_2O$)

↓ divide by total number of moles

Mole fraction ($X$) of glycerol

↓ multiply by $P^{\circ}_{H_2O}$

Vapor pressure lowering ($\Delta P$)

**Sample Problem 13.6 Using Raoult's Law to Find $\Delta P$**

**Problem** Find the vapor pressure lowering, $\Delta P$, when 10.0 mL of glycerol ($C_3H_8O_3$) is added to 500. mL of water at 50.°C. At this temperature, the vapor pressure of pure water is 92.5 torr and its density is 0.988 g/mL. The density of glycerol is 1.26 g/mL.

**Plan** To calculate $\Delta P$, we use Equation 13.10. We are given the vapor pressure of pure water ($P^{\circ}_{H_2O} = 92.5$ torr), so we just need the mole fraction of glycerol, $X_{glycerol}$. We convert the given volume of glycerol (10.0 mL) to mass using the given density (1.26 g/L), find the molar mass from the formula, and convert mass (g) to amount (mol). The same procedure gives amount of $H_2O$. From these amounts, we find $X_{glycerol}$ and $\Delta P$.

**Solution** Calculating the amount (mol) of glycerol and of water:

$$\text{Amount (mol) of glycerol} = 10.0 \text{ mL glycerol} \times \frac{1.26 \text{ g glycerol}}{1 \text{ mL glycerol}} \times \frac{1 \text{ mol glycerol}}{92.09 \text{ g glycerol}}$$

$$= 0.137 \text{ mol glycerol}$$

$$\text{Amount (mol) of } H_2O = 500. \text{ mL } H_2O \times \frac{0.988 \text{ g } H_2O}{1 \text{ mL } H_2O} \times \frac{1 \text{ mol } H_2O}{18.02 \text{ g } H_2O} = 27.4 \text{ mol } H_2O$$

Calculating the mole fraction of glycerol:

$$X_{glycerol} = \frac{0.137 \text{ mol}}{0.137 \text{ mol} + 27.4 \text{ mol}} = 0.00498$$

Finding the vapor pressure lowering:

$$\Delta P = X_{glycerol} \times P^{\circ}_{H_2O} = 0.00498 \times 92.5 \text{ torr} = \boxed{0.461 \text{ torr}}$$

**Check** The amount of each component seems correct: for glycerol, ~10 mL ×
1.25 g/mL ÷ 100 g/mol = 0.125 mol; for $H_2O$, ~500 mL × 1 g/mL ÷ 20 g/mol =
25 mol. The small $\Delta P$ is reasonable because the mole fraction of solute is small.

**Comment** **1.** The calculation assumes that glycerol is nonvolatile. At 1 atm, glycerol
boils at 290.0°C, so the vapor pressure of glycerol at 50°C is negligible. **2.** To introduce
the calculation, we assume the solution is close to ideal and Raoult's law holds.

**Follow-Up Problem 13.6** Calculate the vapor pressure lowering of a solution of
2.00 g of aspirin ($\mathcal{M}$ = 180.15 g/mol) in 50.0 g of methanol ($CH_3OH$) at 21.2°C.
Pure methanol has a vapor pressure of 101 torr at this temperature.

## Boiling Point Elevation
*A solution boils at a higher temperature than the pure
solvent.* This colligative property results from the previous vapor pressure lowering:

1. *Why a solution boils at a higher T.* Recall
that the boiling point, $T_b$, of a liquid is the temperature at which its vapor pressure equals the external
pressure, $P_{ext}$. But, the vapor pressure of a solution
is always lower than that of the pure solvent. Therefore, it is lower than $P_{ext}$ at $T_b$ of the solvent, so
the solution doesn't boil. Thus, the **boiling point
elevation** ($\Delta T_b$) results because a higher temperature is needed to raise the solution's vapor pressure
to equal $P_{ext}$.

We superimpose a phase diagram for the solu-
tion on one for the solvent to see $\Delta T_b$ (Figure 13.24):
the gas-liquid line for the solution lies *below* the line
for the solvent at any *T* and to the right of it at any
*P*, and the line crosses 1 atm ($P_{ext}$, or $P_{atm}$) at a
higher *T*.

2. *Quantifying boiling point elevation.* Like
vapor pressure lowering, boiling point elevation is
proportional to the concentration of solute:

$$\Delta T_b \propto m \qquad \text{or} \qquad \Delta T_b = K_b m \qquad (13.11)$$

where *m* is the solution molality and $K_b$ is the *molal boiling point elevation constant.*
Since $\Delta T_b > 0$, we subtract the lower solvent $T_b$ from the higher solution $T_b$:

$$\Delta T_b = T_{b(solution)} - T_{b(solvent)}$$

Molality is used because it relates to mole fraction and, thus, to particles of solute,
and it is not affected by temperature.

The constant $K_b$ has units of degrees Celsius per molal unit (°C/*m*) and is specific
for a given solvent (Table 13.6). The $K_b$ for water is 0.512°C/*m*, so $\Delta T_b$ for aqueous

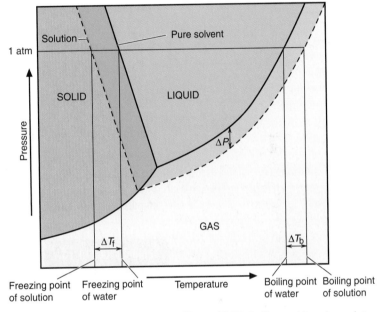

**Figure 13.24** **Boiling and freezing points
of solvent and solution.** Phase diagrams
of an aqueous solution (*dashed lines*)
and of pure water (*solid lines*) show
that, by lowering the vapor pressure
($\Delta P$), a solute elevates the boiling point
($\Delta T_b$) and depresses the freezing point
($\Delta T_f$). (The slope of the solid-liquid line is
exaggerated.)

| Table **13.6** Molal Boiling Point Elevation and Freezing Point Depression Constants of Several Solvents | | | | |
|---|---|---|---|---|
| **Solvent** | **Boiling Point (°C)*** | $K_b$ **(°C/*m*)** | **Melting Point (°C)** | $K_f$ **(°C/*m*)** |
| Acetic acid | 117.9 | 3.07 | 16.6 | 3.90 |
| Benzene | 80.1 | 2.53 | 5.5 | 4.90 |
| Carbon disulfide | 46.2 | 2.34 | −111.5 | 3.83 |
| Carbon tetrachloride | 76.5 | 5.03 | −23 | 30. |
| Chloroform | 61.7 | 3.63 | −63.5 | 4.70 |
| Diethyl ether | 34.5 | 2.02 | −116.2 | 1.79 |
| Ethanol | 78.5 | 1.22 | −117.3 | 1.99 |
| Water | 100.0 | 0.512 | 0.0 | 1.86 |

*At 1 atm.

solutions is quite small. For example, if you dissolve 1.00 mol of glucose (180. g; 1.00 mol of particles) or 0.500 mol of NaCl (29.2 g; also 1.00 mol of particles) in 1.00 kg of water at 1 atm, the solutions will boil at 100.512°C instead of 100.000°C.

**Freezing Point Depression** *A solution freezes at a lower temperature than the pure solvent,* and this colligative property also results from vapor pressure lowering:

1. *Why a solution freezes at a lower T.* Only solvent vaporizes from solution, so solute molecules are left behind. Similarly, *only solvent freezes,* again leaving solute molecules behind. The freezing point of a solution is the temperature at which its vapor pressure equals that of the pure solvent, that is, when solid solvent and liquid solution are in equilibrium. The **freezing point depression ($\Delta T_f$)** occurs because the vapor pressure of the solution is always lower than that of the solvent, so the solution freezes at a lower temperature; that is, only at a lower temperature will solvent particles leave and enter the solid at the same rate. In Figure 13.24, the solid-liquid line for the solution is to the left of the pure solvent line at 1 atm, or any pressure.

2. *Quantifying freezing point depression.* Like $\Delta T_b$, the freezing point depression is proportional to the molal concentration of solute:

$$\Delta T_f \propto m \quad \text{or} \quad \Delta T_f = K_f m \qquad \text{(13.12)}$$

where $K_f$ is the *molal freezing point depression constant,* which also has units of °C/*m* (see Table 13.6). Also, like $\Delta T_b$, $\Delta T_f > 0$, but in this case, we subtract the lower solution $T_f$ from the higher solvent $T_f$:

$$\Delta T_f = T_{f(solvent)} - T_{f(solution)}$$

Here, too, the effect in aqueous solution is small because $K_f$ for water is just 1.86°C/*m*. Thus, at 1 atm, 1 *m* glucose, 0.5 *m* NaCl, and 0.33 *m* K$_2$SO$_4$, all solutions with 1 mol of particles per kilogram of water, freeze at $-1.86$°C instead of at 0.00°C.

---

## Sample Problem 13.7    Determining Boiling and Freezing Points of a Solution

**Problem** You add 1.00 kg of ethylene glycol ($C_2H_6O_2$) antifreeze to 4450 g of water in your car's radiator. What are the boiling and freezing points of the solution?

**Plan** To find the boiling and freezing points, we need $\Delta T_b$ and $\Delta T_f$. We first find the molality by converting mass of solute (1.00 kg) to amount (mol) and dividing by mass of solvent (4450 g, converted to kg). Then we calculate $\Delta T_b$ and $\Delta T_f$ from Equations 13.11 and 13.12 (using constants from Table 13.6). We add $\Delta T_b$ to the solvent boiling point and subtract $\Delta T_f$ from its freezing point. The road map shows the steps.

**Road Map**

**Solution** Calculating the molality:

$$\text{Amount (mol) of } C_2H_6O_2 = 1.00 \text{ kg } C_2H_6O_2 \times \frac{10^3 \text{ g}}{1 \text{ kg}} \times \frac{1 \text{ mol } C_2H_6O_2}{62.07 \text{ g } C_2H_6O_2}$$

$$= 16.1 \text{ mol } C_2H_6O_2$$

$$\text{Molality} = \frac{\text{mol solute}}{\text{kg solvent}} = \frac{16.1 \text{ mol } C_2H_6O_2}{4450 \text{ g } H_2O \times \frac{1 \text{ kg}}{10^3 \text{ g}}} = 3.62 \text{ m } C_2H_6O_2$$

Finding the boiling point elevation and $T_{b(solution)}$, with $K_b = 0.512$°C/*m*:

$$\Delta T_b = \frac{0.512°C}{m} \times 3.62 \text{ m} = 1.85°C$$

$$T_{b(solution)} = T_{b(solvent)} + \Delta T_b = 100.00°C + 1.85°C = \boxed{101.85°C}$$

Finding the freezing point depression and $T_{f(solution)}$, with $K_f = 1.86$°C/*m*:

$$\Delta T_f = \frac{1.86°C}{m} \times 3.62 \text{ m} = 6.73°C$$

$$T_{f(solution)} = T_{f(solvent)} - \Delta T_f = 0.00°C - 6.73°C = \boxed{-6.73°C}$$

**Check** The changes in boiling and freezing points should be in the same proportion as the constants used. That is, $\Delta T_b / \Delta T_f$ should equal $K_b / K_f$: 1.85/6.73 = 0.275 = 0.512/1.86.

**Comment** These answers are approximate because the concentration far exceeds that of a *dilute* solution, for which Raoult's law is most accurate.

**Follow-Up Problem 13.7** What is the lowest molality of ethylene glycol solution that will protect your car's coolant from freezing at 0.00°F? (Assume the solution is ideal.)

**Osmotic Pressure** This colligative property occurs when solutions of higher and lower concentrations are separated by a **semipermeable membrane,** one that allows solvent, but *not* solute, to pass through. The phenomenon is called **osmosis:** a net flow of solvent into the more concentrated solution causes a pressure difference known as *osmotic pressure.* Many organisms regulate internal concentrations by osmosis.

1. *Why osmotic pressure arises.* Consider a simple apparatus in which a semipermeable membrane lies at the curve of a U tube and separates an aqueous sugar solution from pure water. Water molecules pass in *either* direction, but the larger sugar molecules do not. Because sugar molecules are on the solution side of the membrane, fewer water molecules touch that side, so fewer leave the solution than enter it in a given time (Figure 13.25A). The *net flow of water into the solution* increases its volume and thus decreases its concentration.

As the height of the solution rises and the height of the water falls, a pressure difference forms that resists more water entering and pushes some water back through the membrane. When water is being pushed out of the solution at the same rate it is entering, the system is at equilibrium (Figure 13.25B). The pressure difference at this point is the **osmotic pressure (Π),** which is the same as the pressure that must be applied to *prevent* net movement of water from solvent to solution (or from lower to higher concentration, Figure 13.25C).

2. *Quantifying osmotic pressure.* The osmotic pressure is proportional to the number of solute particles in a given solution *volume,* that is, to the molarity (*M*):

$$\Pi \propto \frac{n_{solute}}{V_{soln}} \quad \text{or} \quad \Pi \propto M$$

The proportionality constant is *R* times the absolute temperature *T*. Thus,

$$\Pi = \frac{n_{solute}}{V_{soln}} RT = MRT \qquad \textbf{(13.13)}$$

Osmotic pressure is ...

... the pressure that must be applied to prevent increased volume.

**Figure 13.25 The development of osmotic pressure. A,** In a given time, more solvent enters the solution through the membrane than leaves. **B,** At equilibrium, solvent flow is equalized. **C,** The *osmotic pressure* (Π) *prevents* the volume change.

Pure solvent

Solution

Net movement of solvent

Semipermeable membrane

Solute molecules

Solvent molecules

**A  Rate into solution >
    rate out of solution**

**B  Rate in = rate out due to
    difference in heights**

**C  Rate in = rate out due to
    applied (osmotic) pressure**

The similarity of Equation 13.13 to the ideal gas law ($P = nRT/V$) is not surprising, because both relate the pressure of a system to its concentration and temperature.

**The Underlying Theme of Colligative Properties** A common theme runs through our explanations of the four colligative properties of nonvolatile solutes. Each property arises because solute particles cannot move between two phases:

- They cannot enter the gas phase, which leads to *vapor pressure lowering* and *boiling point elevation*.
- They cannot enter the solid phase, which leads to *freezing point depression*.
- They cannot cross a semipermeable membrane, which leads to *osmotic pressure*.

In each situation, the presence of solute decreases the mole fraction of solvent, which lowers the number of solvent particles leaving the solution per unit time. This lowering requires a new balance in numbers of particles moving between two phases per unit time, and this new balance results in the measured colligative property.

## Using Colligative Properties to Find Solute Molar Mass

Each colligative property is proportional to solute concentration. Thus, by measuring the property—lower freezing point, higher boiling point, and so forth—we determine the amount (mol) of solute particles and, given the mass of solute, the molar mass.

In principle, any of the colligative properties can be used but, of the four, osmotic pressure creates the largest changes and, thus, the most precise measurements. Polymer chemists and biochemists estimate molar masses as great as $10^5$ g/mol by measuring osmotic pressure. Because only a tiny fraction of a mole of a macromolecular solute dissolves, the change in the other colligative properties would be too small.

---

**Sample Problem 13.8** | **Determining Molar Mass from Osmotic Pressure**

**Problem** Biochemists have discovered more than 400 mutant varieties of hemoglobin, the blood protein that carries $O_2$. A physician dissolves 21.5 mg of one variety in water to make 1.50 mL of solution at 5.0°C. She measures an osmotic pressure of 3.61 torr. What is the molar mass of the protein?

**Plan** We know the osmotic pressure ($\Pi = 3.61$ torr), $R$, and $T$ (5.0°C). We convert $\Pi$ from torr to atm, and $T$ from °C to K, and then use Equation 13.13 to solve for molarity ($M$). Then we calculate the amount (mol) of hemoglobin from the known volume (1.50 mL) and use the known mass (21.5 mg) to find $\mathcal{M}$.

**Solution** Combining unit conversion steps and solving for molarity:

$$M = \frac{\Pi}{RT} = \frac{\dfrac{3.61 \text{ torr}}{760 \text{ torr}/1 \text{ atm}}}{\left(0.0821 \dfrac{\text{atm·L}}{\text{mol·K}}\right)(273.15 \text{ K} + 5.0)} = 2.08\times10^{-4} \ M$$

Finding amount (mol) of solute (after changing mL to L):

$$\text{Amount (mol) of solute} = M \times V = \frac{2.08\times10^{-4} \text{ mol}}{1 \text{ L soln}} \times 0.00150 \ L \text{ soln} = 3.12\times10^{-7} \text{ mol}$$

Calculating molar mass of hemoglobin (after changing mg to g):

$$\mathcal{M} = \frac{0.0215 \text{ g}}{3.12\times10^{-7} \text{ mol}} = 6.89\times10^4 \text{ g/mol}$$

**Check** The small osmotic pressure implies a very low molarity. Hemoglobin is a biopolymer, so we expect a small number of moles [$(\sim2\times10^{-4}$ mol/L)$(1.5\times10^{-3}$ L$) = 3\times10^{-7}$ mol] and a high $\mathcal{M}$ ($\sim21\times10^{-3}$ g/$3\times10^{-7}$ mol $= 7\times10^4$ g/mol). Mammalian hemoglobin has a molar mass of 64,500 g/mol.

**Follow-Up Problem 13.8** At 37°C, 0.30 $M$ sucrose has about the same osmotic pressure as blood. What is the osmotic pressure of blood?

---

**Road Map**

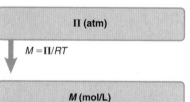

$\boxed{\Pi \text{ (atm)}}$

$M = \Pi/RT$ ↓

$\boxed{M \text{ (mol/L)}}$

multiply by volume (L) of solution ↓

$\boxed{\textbf{Amount (mol) of solute}}$

divide *into* mass (g) of solute ↓

$\boxed{\mathcal{M} \text{ (g/mol)}}$

# Volatile Nonelectrolyte Solutions

What is the effect on vapor pressure when the solute *is* volatile, that is, when the vapor consists of solute *and* solvent molecules? From Raoult's law (Equation 13.9),

$$P_{solvent} = X_{solvent} \times P°_{solvent} \quad \text{and} \quad P_{solute} = X_{solute} \times P°_{solute}$$

where $X_{solvent}$ and $X_{solute}$ are the mole fractions in the *liquid* phase. According to Dalton's law (p. 99), the total vapor pressure is the sum of the partial vapor pressures:

$$P_{total} = P_{solvent} + P_{solute} = (X_{solvent} \times P°_{solvent}) + (X_{solute} \times P°_{solute})$$

Thus, just as a nonvolatile solute lowers the vapor pressure of the solvent by making the solvent's mole fraction less than 1, *the presence of each volatile component lowers the vapor pressure of the other* by making each mole fraction less than 1.

Let's examine this idea with a solution of benzene ($C_6H_6$) and toluene ($C_7H_8$), which are miscible, in which the mole fractions in the liquid are equal: $X_{ben} = X_{tol} = 0.500$. At 25°C, the vapor pressures of the pure substances are 95.1 torr for benzene ($P°_{ben}$) and 28.4 torr for toluene ($P°_{tol}$). Note that benzene is *more volatile* than toluene. We find the partial pressures from Raoult's law:

$$P_{ben} = X_{ben} \times P°_{ben} = 0.500 \times 95.1 \text{ torr} = 47.6 \text{ torr}$$
$$P_{tol} = X_{tol} \times P°_{tol} = 0.500 \times 28.4 \text{ torr} = 14.2 \text{ torr}$$

Thus, the presence of benzene in the liquid lowers the vapor pressure of toluene, and vice versa.

Now let's calculate the mole fraction of each substance *in the vapor* by applying Dalton's law. Recall from Section 5.4 that $X_A = P_A/P_{total}$. Therefore, for benzene and toluene in the vapor,

$$X_{ben} = \frac{P_{ben}}{P_{total}} = \frac{47.6 \text{ torr}}{47.6 \text{ torr} + 14.2 \text{ torr}} = 0.770$$

$$X_{tol} = \frac{P_{tol}}{P_{total}} = \frac{14.2 \text{ torr}}{47.6 \text{ torr} + 14.2 \text{ torr}} = 0.230$$

The key point is that *the vapor has a higher mole fraction of the **more** volatile component.* Through a single vaporization-condensation step, a 50/50 *liquid* ratio of benzene-to-toluene created a 77/23 *vapor* ratio. Condense this vapor into a separate container, and the new *liquid* would have this 77/23 composition, and the new *vapor* above it would be enriched still further in the more volatile benzene.

In the laboratory method of **fractional distillation,** a solution of two or more volatile components is attached to a *fractionating column* packed with glass beads (or ceramic chunks) and connected to a condenser and collection flask. As the solution is heated and the vapor mixture meets the beads, numerous vaporization-condensation steps enrich the mixture until the vapor leaving the column, and thus the liquid finally collected, consists only of the most volatile component (see Figure 13.28).

# Strong Electrolyte Solutions

For colligative properties of strong electrolyte solutions, the solute formula tells us the number of particles. For instance, the boiling point elevation ($\Delta T_b$) of 0.050 *m* NaCl should be $2 \times \Delta T_b$ of 0.050 *m* glucose ($C_6H_{12}O_6$), because NaCl dissociates into two particles per formula unit. Thus, we use a multiplying factor called the *van't Hoff factor (i),* named after the Dutch chemist Jacobus van't Hoff (1852–1911):

$$i = \frac{\text{measured value for electrolyte solution}}{\text{expected value for nonelectrolyte solution}}$$

To calculate colligative properties for strong electrolyte solutions, we include *i*:

| | |
|---|---|
| For vapor pressure lowering: | $\Delta P = i(X_{solute} \times P°_{solvent})$ |
| For boiling point elevation: | $\Delta T_b = i(K_b m)$ |
| For freezing point depression: | $\Delta T_f = i(K_f m)$ |
| For osmotic pressure: | $\Pi = i(MRT)$ |

**Figure 13.26** Nonideal behavior of strong electrolyte solutions. Van't Hoff factors (*i*) for 0.050 *m* solutions show the largest deviation for salts with multiply-charged ions. Glucose (a nonelectrolyte) behaves as expected.

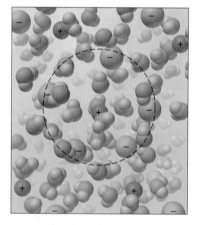

**Figure 13.27** An ionic atmosphere model for nonideal behavior of electrolyte solutions.

**Nonideal Solutions and Ionic Atmospheres** *If* strong electrolyte solutions behaved ideally, the factor *i* would be the amount (mol) of particles in solution divided by the amount (mol) of dissolved solute; that is, *i* would be 2 for KBr, 3 for $Mg(NO_3)_2$, and so forth. However, *most strong electrolyte solutions are* ***not*** *ideal,* and the measured value of *i* is typically *lower* than the value expected from the formula. For example, for the boiling point elevation of 0.050 *m* NaCl, the expected value is 2.0, but, from experiment, we have

$$i = \frac{\Delta T_b \text{ of } 0.050 \ m \text{ NaCl}}{\Delta T_b \text{ of } 0.050 \ m \text{ glucose}} = \frac{0.049°C}{0.026°C} = 1.9$$

It seems as though the ions are not behaving independently, even though other evidence indicates that soluble salts dissociate completely. One clue to understanding the results is that multiply-charged ions cause a larger deviation (Figure 13.26).

To explain this nonideal behavior, we picture positive ions clustered, on average, near negative ions, and vice versa, to form an **ionic atmosphere** of net opposite charge (Figure 13.27). In effect, each type of ion acts "tied up," so its actual concentration seems *lower*. The *effective* concentration is the *stoichiometric* concentration, which is based on the formula multiplied by *i*. The greater the charge, the stronger the attractions, which explains the larger deviation for salts with multiply-charged ions.

**Comparing Real Solutions and Real Gases** At ordinary conditions and concentrations, particles are *much* closer together in liquids than in gases. And, as a result, nonideal behavior is much more common, and the deviations much larger. Nevertheless, the two systems have similarities:

- Gases display nearly ideal behavior at low pressures because the distances between particles are large. Similarly, the van't Hoff factor (*i*) approaches the ideal value as the solution becomes more dilute, that is, as the distance between ions increases.
- Attractions between particles cause deviations from the expected pressure in gases and from the expected size of a colligative property in ionic solutions.
- For both real gases and real solutions, we use empirically determined numbers (van der Waals constants or van't Hoff factors) to transform theories (the ideal gas law or Raoult's law) into more useful relations.

---

**Sample Problem 13.9** | **Depicting Strong Electrolyte Solutions**

**Problem** A 0.952-g sample of magnesium chloride dissolves in 100. g of water in a flask.

**(a)** Which scene depicts the solution best?
**(b)** What is the amount (mol) represented by each green sphere?
**(c)** Assuming the solution is ideal, what is its freezing point (at 1 atm)?

**Plan** **(a)** We find the numbers of cations and anions per formula unit from the name and compare it with the three scenes. **(b)** We convert the given mass to amount (mol), use the answer from part (a) to find moles of chloride ions (*green spheres*), and divide by the number of green spheres to get moles/sphere. **(c)** We find the molality (*m*) from amount (mol) of solute divided by the given mass of water (changed to kg). We multiply $K_f$ for water (Table 13.6) by *m* to get $\Delta T_f$, and then subtract that from 0.000°C to get the solution freezing point.

**Solution** **(a)** The formula is $MgCl_2$; only scene A has 1 $Mg^{2+}$ for every 2 $Cl^-$.

**(b)** Amount (mol) of $MgCl_2 = \dfrac{0.952 \text{ g } MgCl_2}{95.21 \text{ g/mol } MgCl_2} = 0.0100 \text{ mol } MgCl_2$

Therefore,    Amount (mol) of $Cl^- = 0.0100$ mol $MgCl_2 \times \dfrac{2\ Cl^-}{1\ MgCl_2} = 0.0200$ mol $Cl^-$

$$\text{Moles/sphere} = \frac{0.0200\ \text{mol}\ Cl^-}{8\ \text{spheres}} = 2.50 \times 10^{-3}\ \text{mol/sphere}$$

**(c)**    $\text{Molality}\ (m) = \dfrac{\text{mol of solute}}{\text{kg of solvent}} = \dfrac{0.0100\ \text{mol}\ MgCl_2}{100.\ \text{g} \times \dfrac{1\ \text{kg}}{1000\ \text{g}}} = 0.100\ m\ MgCl_2$

Assuming an ideal solution, $i = 3$ for $MgCl_2$ (3 ions per formula unit), so we have

$$\Delta T_f = i(K_f m) = 3(1.86°C/m \times 0.100\ m) = 0.558°C$$

and $$T_f = 0.000°C - 0.558°C = -0.558°C$$

**Check** Let's quickly check the $\Delta T_f$ in part (c): We have 0.01 mol dissolved in 0.1 kg, or 0.1 $m$. Then, rounding $K_f$, we have about $3(2°C/m \times 0.1\ m) = 0.6°C$.

**Follow-Up Problem 13.9** The $MgCl_2$ solution in the sample problem has a density of 1.006 g/mL at 20.0°C. **(a)** What is the osmotic pressure of the solution? **(b)** A U tube, with semipermeable membrane, is filled with the solution in the left arm and a glucose solution of equal molarity in the right. After time, which scene depicts the U tube best?

MgCl₂          Glucose

**A**          **B**          **C**

# Applications of Colligative Properties

Two colligative properties in particular, freezing point depression and osmotic pressure, have key applications that involve all three types of solutes we've discussed, nonvolatile and volatile nonelectrolytes and strong electrolytes.

**Uses of Freezing Point Depression** Applications of this property appear in everyday life, nature, and industry:

- *Plane de-icer and car antifreeze.* The main ingredient in plane de-icer and car antifreeze, ethylene glycol ($C_2H_6O_2$), lowers the freezing point of water in winter and raises its boiling point in summer. Due to extensive H bonding, ethylene glycol is miscible with water and nonvolatile at 100°C.

Ethylene glycol

- *Biological antifreeze.* Structurally similar to ethylene glycol and also miscible with water, glycerol ($C_3H_8O_3$) is produced by some fish and insects, including the common housefly, to lower the freezing point of their blood and thus allow them to survive winters.

Glycerol

- *De-icing sidewalks and roads.* NaCl, or a mixture of it with $CaCl_2$, is used to melt ice on roads. A small amount dissolves in the ice by lowering its freezing point and melting it. More salt dissolves, more ice melts, and so forth. An advantage of $CaCl_2$ is that it has a highly negative $\Delta H_{soln}$, so heat is released when it dissolves, which melts more ice.

- *Refining petroleum and silicon.* Countless vaporization-condensation steps within a 30-m fractionating tower separate the hundreds of volatile compounds in crude oil into a few "fractions" based on boiling point range (Figure 13.28). Impure silicon is refined by continuous melting and refreezing into a sample pure enough for use in computer chips (Chapter 22).

Gasoline vapors

Condenser

Gas

Gasoline
38°C

Kerosene
150°C

Heating oil
260°C

Lubricating oil
315°C – 370°C

Crude oil
vapors from
heater

Steam

Residue
(asphalt, tar)

**Figure 13.28** Fractional distillation in petroleum refining.

**Figure 13.29 Osmotic pressure and cell shape.** Isotonic (*top*), hypotonic (*middle*), and hypertonic (*bottom*) solutions influence the shape of a red blood cell.

**Uses of Osmotic Pressure** Of the four colligative properties, this one has the most applications vital to organisms.

- *Tonicity and cell shape.* The term *tonicity* refers to the tone, or firmness, of a cell. Placing the cell in an *isotonic* solution, one that has the same concentration of particles as the cell fluid, maintains the cell's normal shape because water enters and leaves the cell at the same rate (Figure 13.29, *top*). A *hypotonic* solution has a lower concentration of particles, so water enters the cell faster than it leaves, causing the cell to burst (*middle*). In contrast, a *hypertonic* solution has a higher concentration, so the cell shrinks because water leaves faster than it enters (*bottom*). To maintain cell shape, contact-lens rinse is isotonic saline (0.15 *M* NaCl), as are solutions used to deliver nutrients or drugs intravenously.

- *Absorption of water by trees.* Tree sap is a more concentrated solution than surrounding groundwater, so water passes through root membranes into the tree, creating an osmotic pressure that can exceed 20 atm in the tallest trees.

- *Regulation of water volume in the body.* Of the four major biological cations—$Na^+$, $K^+$, $Mg^{2+}$, and $Ca^{2+}$—sodium ion has the primary role of regulating water volume. It accounts for over 90 mol % of cations *outside* a cell: high $Na^+$ draws water out of the cell and low $Na^+$ leaves more inside. And the primary role of the kidneys is to regulate $Na^+$ concentration.

- *Food preservation.* Before refrigeration, salt was valued as a preservative. Packed onto food, salt causes microbes on the surface to shrivel as they lose water. In fact, it was so highly prized for this purpose that Roman soldiers were paid in salt, from which comes the word *salary*.

## ▌ Summary of Section 13.6

- Colligative properties arise from the number, not type, of dissolved solute particles.
- Compared to pure solvent, a solution has lower vapor pressure (Raoult's law), elevated boiling point, and depressed freezing point, and it gives rise to osmotic pressure.
- Colligative properties are used to determine solute molar mass; osmotic pressure gives the most precise measurements.
- When solute *and* solvent are volatile, each lowers the vapor pressure of the other, with the vapor pressure of the more volatile component greater. When the vapor is condensed, the new solution is richer in that component than the original solution.
- Calculating colligative properties of electrolyte solutions requires a factor (*i*) that adjusts for the number of ions per formula unit. These solutions exhibit nonideal behavior because charge attractions effectively reduce the concentration of ions.

## 13.7 • THE STRUCTURE AND PROPERTIES OF COLLOIDS

Particle size plays a defining role in three types of mixtures:

- *Suspensions.* Stir a handful of fine sand into a glass of water, and the particles are suspended at first but gradually settle to the bottom. Sand in water is a **suspension,** a *heterogeneous* mixture containing particles large enough (>1000 nm) to be visibly distinct from the surrounding fluid.

- *Solutions.* In contrast, stirring sugar into water forms a solution, a *homogeneous* mixture in which the particles are invisible, individual sugar molecules (around 1 nm) distributed evenly throughout the surrounding fluid.

- *Colloids.* Between these extremes is a large group of mixtures called *colloidal dispersions,* or **colloids,** in which a dispersed (solute-like) substance is distributed throughout a dispersing (solvent-like) substance. The particles are larger than simple molecules but too small to settle out.

In this section, we examine the classification and key features of colloids.

1. *Particle size and surface area.* Colloidal particles range in diameter from 1 to 1000 nm ($10^{-9}$ to $10^{-6}$ m). It may be a single macromolecule (natural or synthetic) or an aggregate of many atoms, ions, or molecules. As a result of the small particle size, a

colloid has a *very large total surface area*. A cube with 1-cm sides has a total surface area of 6 cm$^2$. If it's divided equally into 10$^{12}$ cubes, the cubes are the size of large colloidal particles and have a total surface area of 60,000 cm$^2$, or 6 m$^2$. The enormous surface area of a colloid attracts other particles through various intermolecular forces.

2. *Classification of colloids.* Colloids are commonly classified by the physical state of the dispersed and dispersing substances (Table 13.7). Many familiar commercial products and natural objects are colloids. Whipped cream and shaving cream are *foams,* a gas dispersed in a liquid. Styrofoam is a *solid foam,* a gas dispersed in a solid. Most biological fluids are aqueous *sols,* solids dispersed in water: proteins and nucleic acids are the colloidal-size particles dispersed in an aqueous fluid of ions and small molecules within a cell. Soaps and detergents work by forming an *emulsion,* a liquid dispersed in another liquid. Other emulsions are mayonnaise and hand cream. Bile salts convert fats to an emulsion in the watery fluid of the small intestine.

**Table 13.7  Types of Colloids**

| Colloid Type | Dispersed Substance | Dispersing Medium | Example(s) |
|---|---|---|---|
| Aerosol | Liquid | Gas | Fog |
| Aerosol | Solid | Gas | Smoke |
| Foam | Gas | Liquid | Whipped cream |
| Solid foam | Gas | Solid | Marshmallow |
| Emulsion | Liquid | Liquid | Milk |
| Solid emulsion | Liquid | Solid | Butter |
| Sol | Solid | Liquid | Paint, cell fluid |
| Solid sol | Solid | Solid | Opal |

3. *Tyndall effect and Brownian motion.* Light passing through a colloid is scattered randomly because the dispersed particles have sizes similar to wavelengths of visible light (400 to 750 nm). The scattered light beam appears broader than one passing through a solution, an example of the **Tyndall effect** (Figure 13.30). Dust scatters sunlight shining through it, as does mist pierced by headlights.

Under low magnification, colloidal particles exhibit *Brownian motion,* an erratic change of speed and direction. Brownian motion results from collisions with molecules of the dispersing medium, and Einstein's explanation of it in 1905 led many to accept the molecular nature of matter.

4. *Stabilizing and destabilizing colloids.* Why don't colloidal particles aggregate and settle out? Colloidal particles dispersed in water have charged surfaces that stabilize the colloid through ion-dipole forces. Molecules with dual polarities, like lipids and soaps, form spherical *micelles,* with the charged heads on the exterior and hydrocarbon tails in the interior (Section 13.2). Aqueous proteins mimic this arrangement, with charged amino acid groups facing the water and nonpolar groups buried within the molecule. Oily particles can be dispersed in water by adding ions, which are adsorbed onto their surfaces. Repulsions between the ions on the oil and partial charges on water molecules prevent the particles from aggregating.

Despite these forces, various methods that coagulate the particles destabilize the colloid. Heating makes the particles collide more often and with enough force to coalesce and settle out. Addition of an electrolyte solution containing oppositely charged ions neutralizes the surface charges, so the particles coagulate and settle. In smokestack gases from a coal-burning power plant, ions become adsorbed onto uncharged colloidal particles, which are then attracted to the charged plates of a device called a *Cotrell precipitator* installed in the stack. At the mouths of rivers, where salt concentrations increase near an ocean or sea, colloidal clay particles coalesce into muddy deltas, like those of the Mississippi and the Nile (Figure 13.31). Thus, the city of New Orleans and the ancient Egyptian empire were made possible by such large-scale colloid chemistry.

The upcoming Chemical Connections essay applies solution and colloid chemistry to the purification of water for residential and industrial use.

A

B

**Figure 13.30** Light scattering and the Tyndall effect. **A,** The narrow, barely visible light beam that passes through a solution (*left*), is scattered and broadened by passing through a colloid (*right*). **B,** Sunlight is scattered by dust in air.

**Figure 13.31** The Nile delta (reddish-brown area).

M ost water destined for human use comes from lakes, rivers, reservoirs, or groundwater. Present in this essential resource may be soluble toxic organic compounds and high concentrations of $NO_3^-$ and $Fe^{3+}$, colloidal clay and microbes, and suspended debris. Let's see how water is treated to remove these dissolved, dispersed, and suspended particles.

## Water Treatment Plants

Treating water involves several steps (Figure B13.1):

*Step 1. Screening and settling.* As water enters the facility, screens remove debris, and settling removes particles such as sand.

*Step 2. Coagulating.* This step and the next two remove colloids. These particles have negative surfaces that repel each other. Added aluminum sulfate [cake alum; $Al_2(SO_4)_3$] or iron(III) chloride ($FeCl_3$), which supply $Al^{3+}$ or $Fe^{3+}$ that neutralize the charges, coagulates the particles through intermolecular forces.

*Step 3. Flocculating and sedimenting.* Mixing water and flocculating agents in large basins causes a fluffy *floc* to form. Added cationic polymers form long-chain bridges between floc particles, which grow bigger and heavier and flow into other basins, where they form a sediment and are removed. Some plants use *dissolved air flotation* (DAF) instead: bubbles forced through the water attach to the floc, and the floating mass is skimmed.

*Step 4. Filtering.* Various filters remove remaining particles. In *slow sand filters,* the water passes through sand and/or gravel of increasing particle size. In *rapid sand filters,* the sand is backwashed with water, and the colloidal mass is removed. Membrane filters (*not shown*) with pore sizes of 0.1–10 μm are thin tubes bundled together inside a vessel. The water is forced into these tubes, and the colloid-free filtrate is collected from a large central tube. Filtration is very effective at removing microorganisms resistant to disinfecting.

*Step 5. Disinfecting.* Water sources often contain harmful microorganisms that are killed by one of three agents:
- Chlorine, as aqueous bleach ($ClO^-$) or $Cl_2$, is most common, but carcinogenic chlorinated organic compounds can form.
- UV light emitted by high-intensity fluorescent tubes disinfects by disrupting microorganisms' DNA.
- Ozone ($O_3$) gas is a powerful oxidizing agent.

Sodium fluoride (NaF) to prevent tooth decay and phosphate salts to prevent leaching of lead from pipes may then be added.

*Step 6 (not shown). Adsorbing onto granular activated carbon (GAC).* Petroleum and other organic contaminants are removed by adsorption. GAC is a highly porous agent formed by "activating" wood, coal, or coconut shells with steam: 1 kg of GAC has a surface area of 275 acres!

## Water Softening via Ion Exchange

Water with large amounts of 2+ ions, such as $Ca^{2+}$ and $Mg^{2+}$, is called **hard water.** Combined with fatty-acid anions in soap, these cations form solid deposits on clothes, washing machines, and sinks:

$$Ca^{2+}(aq) + 2C_{17}H_{35}COONa(aq) \longrightarrow$$
soap

$$(C_{17}H_{35}COO)_2Ca(s) + 2Na^+(aq)$$
insoluble deposit

When a large amount of $HCO_3^-$ is present, the cations form *scale,* a carbonate deposit in boilers and hot-water pipes that interferes with the transfer of heat:

$$Ca^{2+}(aq) + 2HCO_3^-(aq) \longrightarrow CaCO_3(s) + CO_2(g) + H_2O(l)$$

**Figure B13.1** The typical steps in municipal water treatment.

**Figure B13.2** Ion exchange to remove hard-water cations.

Removing hard-water cations, called **water softening,** is done by exchanging $Na^+$ ions for $Ca^{2+}$ and $Mg^{2+}$ ions. A domestic **ion exchange** system contains an insoluble polymer *resin* with bonded anionic groups, such as $-SO_3^-$ or $-COO^-$, and $Na^+$ ions for charge balance (Figure B13.2). The hard-water cations displace the $Na^+$ ions and bind to the anionic groups. When the resin sites are occupied, the resin is regenerated with concentrated $Na^+$ solution that exchanges $Na^+$ ions for bound $Ca^{2+}$ and $Mg^{2+}$.

## Membrane Processes and Reverse Osmosis

Membranes with $0.0001-0.01$ $\mu m$ pores can remove unwanted ions from water. Recall that solutions of different concentrations separated by a semipermeable membrane create osmotic pressure. In **reverse osmosis,** a pressure *greater* than the osmotic pressure is *applied* to the more concentrated solution to force water back through the membrane and filter out ions. In homes, toxic *heavy-metal ions,* such as $Pb^{2+}$, $Cd^{2+}$, and $Hg^{2+}$, are removed this way. On a large scale, reverse osmosis is used for **desalination,** which can convert seawater (40,000 ppm of ions) to drinking water (400 ppm) (Figure B13.3).

## Wastewater Treatment

**Wastewater,** used domestic or industrial water, is treated in several ways before being returned to a natural source:

- In *primary* treatment, the water enters a settling basin to remove particles.
- In *biological* treatment, bacteria metabolize organic compounds and are then removed by settling.
- In *advanced* treatment, a process is tailored to remove a specific pollutant. For example, ammonia, which causes excessive growth of plants and algae, is removed in two steps:
  1. *Nitrification.* Certain bacteria oxidize ammonia (electron donor) with $O_2$ (electron acceptor) to form nitrate ion:

$$NH_4^+ + 2O_2 \longrightarrow NO_3^- + 2H^+ + H_2O$$

  2. *Denitrification.* Other bacteria oxidize an added compound like methanol ($CH_3OH$) using the $NO_3^-$:

$$5CH_3OH + 6NO_3^- \longrightarrow 3N_2 + 5CO_2 + 7H_2O + 6OH^-$$

Thus, the process converts $NH_3$ in wastewater to $N_2$, which is released to the atmosphere.

### Problems

**B13.1** Briefly answer each of the following:
(a) Why is cake alum $[Al_2(SO_4)_3]$ added during water purification?
(b) Why is water that contains large amounts of $Ca^{2+}$ and $Mg^{2+}$ difficult to use for cleaning?
(c) What is the meaning of "reverse" in reverse osmosis?
(d) Why might a water treatment plant use ozone as a disinfectant instead of chlorine?
(e) How does passing a saturated NaCl solution through a "spent" ion-exchange resin regenerate the resin?

**B13.2** Wastewater discharged into a stream by a sugar refinery contains 3.55 g of sucrose ($C_{12}H_{22}O_{11}$) per liter. A government-sponsored study is testing the feasibility of removing the sugar by reverse osmosis. What pressure must be applied to the apparatus at 20.°C to produce pure water?

**Figure B13.3** Reverse osmosis to remove ions. **A,** Part of a reverse-osmosis permeator. **B,** Each permeator contains a bundle of hollow fibers of semipermeable membrane. **C,** Pumping seawater at high pressure removes ions and purer water enters the fibers and is collected.

## ■ Summary of Section 13.7

- Particles in a colloid are smaller than those in a suspension and larger than those in a solution.
- Colloids are classified by the physical states of the dispersed and dispersing substances and involve many combinations of gas, liquid, and/or solid.
- Colloids have extremely large surface areas, scatter incoming light (Tyndall effect), and exhibit random (Brownian) motion.
- Colloidal particles in water are stabilized by charged surfaces that keep them dispersed, but they can be coagulated by heating or by the addition of ions.
- Solution behavior and colloid chemistry are applied to water treatment and purification.

# CHAPTER REVIEW GUIDE

## Learning Objectives   Relevant section (§) and/or sample problem (SP) numbers appear in parentheses.

### Understand These Concepts

1. The quantitative meaning of solubility (§13.1)
2. The major types of intermolecular forces in solution and their relative strengths (§13.1)
3. How the like-dissolves-like rule depends on intermolecular forces (§13.1)
4. Why gases have relatively low solubilities in water (§13.1)
5. General characteristics of solutions formed by various combinations of gases, liquids, and solids (§13.1)
6. How intermolecular forces stabilize the structures of proteins, the cell membrane, and DNA (§13.2)
7. The enthalpy components of a solution cycle and their effect on $\Delta H_{soln}$ (§13.3)
8. The dependence of $\Delta H_{hydr}$ on ionic charge density and the factors that determine whether ionic solution processes are exothermic or endothermic (§13.3)
9. The meaning of entropy and how the balance between the change in enthalpy and the change in entropy governs the solution process (§13.3)
10. The distinctions among saturated, unsaturated, and supersaturated solutions, and the equilibrium nature of a saturated solution (§13.4)
11. The relation between temperature and the solubility of solids (§13.4)
12. Why the solubility of gases in water decreases with a rise in temperature (§13.4)
13. The effect of gas pressure on solubility and its quantitative expression as Henry's law (§13.4)
14. The meaning of molarity, molality, mole fraction, and parts by mass or by volume of a solution, and how to convert among them (§13.5)
15. The distinction between electrolytes and nonelectrolytes in solution (§13.6)
16. The four colligative properties and their dependence on number of dissolved particles (§13.6)
17. Ideal solutions and the importance of Raoult's law (§13.6)
18. How the phase diagram of a solution differs from that of the pure solvent (§13.6)
19. Why the vapor over a solution of volatile nonelectrolyte is richer in the more volatile component (§13.6)
20. Why electrolyte solutions are not ideal and the meanings of the van't Hoff factor and ionic atmosphere (§13.6)
21. How particle size distinguishes suspensions, colloids, and solutions (§13.7)
22. How colloidal behavior is demonstrated by the Tyndall effect and Brownian motion (§13.7)

### Master These Skills

1. Predicting relative solubilities from intermolecular forces (SP 13.1)
2. Using Henry's law to calculate the solubility of a gas (SP 13.2)
3. Expressing concentration in terms of molality, parts by mass, parts by volume, and mole fraction (SPs 13.3, 13.4)
4. Interconverting among the various terms for expressing concentration (SP 13.5)
5. Using Raoult's law to calculate the vapor pressure lowering of a solution (SP 13.6)
6. Determining boiling point elevation and freezing point depression of a solution (SP 13.7)
7. Using a colligative property to calculate the molar mass of a solute (SP 13.8)
8. Calculating the composition of vapor over a solution of volatile nonelectrolyte (§13.6)
9. Calculating the van't Hoff factor $i$ from the magnitude of a colligative property (§13.6)
10. Using a solution depiction to determine colligative properties (SP 13.9)

## Key Terms   Page numbers appear in parentheses.

**Section 13.1**
solute (478)
solvent (478)
miscible (478)
solubility (S) (478)
like-dissolves-like rule (478)
hydration shell (478)
ion–induced dipole force (478)
dipole–induced dipole force (478)
alloy (482)

**Section 13.2**
protein (483)
amino acid (483)
soap (485)
lipid bilayer (485)
nucleic acid (487)

mononucleotide (487)
double helix (487)

**Section 13.3**
heat of solution ($\Delta H_{\text{soln}}$) (488)
solvation (489)
hydration (489)
heat of hydration ($\Delta H_{\text{hydr}}$) (489)
charge density (489)
entropy (S) (490)

**Section 13.4**
saturated solution (492)
unsaturated solution (492)
supersaturated solution (492)
Henry's law (494)

**Section 13.5**
molality (m) (495)
mass percent [% (w/w)] (496)
volume percent [% (v/v)] (496)
mole fraction (X) (496)

**Section 13.6**
colligative property (499)
electrolyte (499)
nonelectrolyte (499)
vapor pressure lowering ($\Delta P$) (499)
Raoult's law (500)
ideal solution (500)
boiling point elevation ($\Delta T_{\text{b}}$) (501)
freezing point depression ($\Delta T_{\text{f}}$) (502)

semipermeable membrane (503)
osmosis (503)
osmotic pressure ($\Pi$) (503)
fractional distillation (505)
ionic atmosphere (506)

**Section 13.7**
suspension (508)
colloid (508)
Tyndall effect (509)
hard water (510)
water softening (511)
ion exchange (511)
reverse osmosis (511)
desalination (511)
wastewater (511)

## Key Equations and Relationships   Page numbers appear in parentheses.

**13.1** Dividing the general heat of solution into component enthalpies (488):

$$\Delta H_{\text{soln}} = \Delta H_{\text{solute}} + \Delta H_{\text{solvent}} + \Delta H_{\text{mix}}$$

**13.2** Dividing the heat of solution of an ionic compound in water into component enthalpies (489):

$$\Delta H_{\text{soln}} = \Delta H_{\text{lattice}} + \Delta H_{\text{hydr of the ions}}$$

**13.3** Relating gas solubility to its partial pressure (Henry's law) (494):

$$S_{\text{gas}} = k_{\text{H}} \times P_{\text{gas}}$$

**13.4** Defining concentration in terms of molarity (494):

$$\text{Molarity } (M) = \frac{\text{amount (mol) of solute}}{\text{volume (L) of solution}}$$

**13.5** Defining concentration in terms of molality (495):

$$\text{Molality } (m) = \frac{\text{amount (mol) of solute}}{\text{mass (kg) of solvent}}$$

**13.6** Defining concentration in terms of mass percent (496):

$$\text{Mass percent } [\% \text{ (w/w)}] = \frac{\text{mass of solute}}{\text{mass of solution}} \times 100$$

**13.7** Defining concentration in terms of volume percent (496):

$$\text{Volume percent } [\% \text{ (v/v)}] = \frac{\text{volume of solute}}{\text{volume of solution}} \times 100$$

**13.8** Defining concentration in terms of mole fraction (496):

Mole fraction (X)

$$= \frac{\text{amount (mol) of solute}}{\text{amount (mol) of solute} + \text{amount (mol) of solvent}}$$

**13.9** Expressing the relationship between the vapor pressure of solvent above a solution and its mole fraction in the solution (Raoult's law) (500):

$$P_{\text{solvent}} = X_{\text{solvent}} \times P^{\circ}_{\text{solvent}}$$

**13.10** Calculating the vapor pressure lowering due to solute (500):

$$\Delta P = X_{\text{solute}} \times P^{\circ}_{\text{solvent}}$$

**13.11** Calculating the boiling point elevation of a solution (501):

$$\Delta T_{\text{b}} = K_{\text{b}} m$$

**13.12** Calculating the freezing point depression of a solution (502):

$$\Delta T_{\text{f}} = K_{\text{f}} m$$

**13.13** Calculating the osmotic pressure of a solution (503):

$$\Pi = \frac{n_{\text{solute}}}{V_{\text{soln}}} RT = MRT$$

## Brief Solutions to Follow-Up Problems

**13.1** (a) 1,4-Butanediol is more soluble in water because it can form more H bonds.
(b) Chloroform is more soluble in water because of dipole-dipole forces.

**13.2** $S_{N_2} = (7 \times 10^{-4} \text{ mol/L·atm})(0.78 \text{ atm})$
$= 5 \times 10^{-4} \text{ mol/L}$

**13.3** Mass (g) of glucose

$= 563 \text{ g ethanol} \times \dfrac{1 \text{ kg}}{10^3 \text{ g}} \times \dfrac{2.40 \times 10^{-2} \text{ mol glucose}}{1 \text{ kg ethanol}}$

$\times \dfrac{180.16 \text{ g glucose}}{1 \text{ mol glucose}}$

$= 2.43 \text{ g glucose}$

**13.4** Mass % $C_3H_7OH = \dfrac{35.0 \text{ g}}{35.0 \text{ g} + 150. \text{ g}} \times 100$

$= 18.9 \text{ mass \%}$

Mass % $C_2H_5OH = 100.0 - 18.9$

$= 81.1 \text{ mass \%}$

$X_{C_3H_7OH} = \dfrac{35.0 \text{ g } C_3H_7OH \times \dfrac{1 \text{ mol } C_3H_7OH}{60.09 \text{ g } C_3H_7OH}}{\left(35.0 \text{ g } C_3H_7OH \times \dfrac{1 \text{ mol } C_3H_7OH}{60.09 \text{ g } C_3H_7OH}\right) + \left(150. \text{ g } C_2H_5OH \times \dfrac{1 \text{ mol } C_2H_5OH}{46.07 \text{ g } C_2H_5OH}\right)} = 0.152$

$X_{C_2H_5OH} = 1.000 - 0.152 = 0.848$

**13.5** Mass % HCl $= \dfrac{\text{mass of HCl}}{\text{mass of soln}} \times 100$

$= \dfrac{\dfrac{11.8 \text{ mol HCl}}{1 \text{ L soln}} \times \dfrac{36.46 \text{ g HCl}}{1 \text{ mol HCl}}}{\dfrac{1.190 \text{ g}}{1 \text{ mL soln}} \times \dfrac{10^3 \text{ mL}}{1 \text{ L}}} \times 100$

$= 36.2 \text{ mass \% HCl}$

Mass (kg) of soln $= 1 \text{ L soln} \times \dfrac{1.190 \times 10^{-3} \text{ kg soln}}{1 \times 10^{-3} \text{ L soln}}$

$= 1.190 \text{ kg soln}$

Mass (kg) of HCl $= 11.8 \text{ mol HCl} \times \dfrac{36.46 \text{ g HCl}}{1 \text{ mol HCl}} \times \dfrac{1 \text{ kg}}{10^3 \text{ g}}$

$= 0.430 \text{ kg HCl}$

Molality of HCl $= \dfrac{\text{mol HCl}}{\text{kg water}} = \dfrac{\text{mol HCl}}{\text{kg soln} - \text{kg HCl}}$

$= \dfrac{11.8 \text{ mol HCl}}{0.760 \text{ kg } H_2O} = 15.5 \text{ m HCl}$

$X_{HCl} = \dfrac{\text{mol HCl}}{\text{mol HCl} + \text{mol } H_2O}$

$= \dfrac{11.8 \text{ mol}}{11.8 \text{ mol} + \left(760 \text{ g } H_2O \times \dfrac{1 \text{ mol}}{18.02 \text{ g } H_2O}\right)} = 0.219$

**13.6** $\Delta P = X_{\text{aspirin}} \times P^{\circ}_{\text{methanol}}$

$= \dfrac{\dfrac{2.00 \text{ g}}{180.15 \text{ g/mol}}}{\dfrac{2.00 \text{ g}}{180.15 \text{ g/mol}} + \dfrac{50.0 \text{ g}}{32.04 \text{ g/mol}}} \times 101 \text{ torr}$

$= 0.713 \text{ torr}$

**13.7** Molality of $C_2H_6O_2 = \dfrac{(32°F - 0.00°F)\left(\dfrac{5°C}{9°F}\right)}{1.86°C/m} = 9.56 \text{ m}$

**13.8** $\Pi = MRT = (0.30 \text{ mol/L})\left(0.0821 \dfrac{\text{atm·L}}{\text{mol·K}}\right)(37°C + 273.15)$

$= 7.6 \text{ atm}$

**13.9** (a) Mass of 0.100 m solution

$= 1 \text{ kg water} + 0.100 \text{ mol } MgCl_2$
$= 1000 \text{ g} + 9.52 \text{ g} = 1009.52 \text{ g}$

Volume of solution $= 1009.52 \text{ g} \times \dfrac{1 \text{ mL}}{1.006 \text{ g}} = 1003 \text{ mL}$

Molarity $= \dfrac{9.52 \text{ g } MgCl_2}{1003 \text{ mL soln}} \times \dfrac{1 \text{ mol}}{95.21 \text{ g } MgCl_2} \times \dfrac{10^3 \text{ mL}}{1 \text{ L}}$

$= 9.97 \times 10^{-2} \text{ M}$

Osmotic pressure ($\Pi$)

$= i(MRT)$

$= 3(9.97 \times 10^{-2} \text{ mol/L})\left(0.0821 \dfrac{\text{atm·L}}{\text{mol·K}}\right)(293 \text{ K})$

$= 7.19 \text{ atm}$

(b) Scene C

# PROBLEMS

Problems with **colored** numbers are answered in Appendix E and worked in detail in the Student Solutions Manual. Problem sections match those in the text and provide the numbers of relevant sample problems. Most offer Concept Review Questions, Skill-Building Exercises (grouped in pairs covering the same concept), and Problems in Context. The Comprehensive Problems are based on material from any section or previous chapter.

## Types of Solutions: Intermolecular Forces and Solubility
(Sample Problem 13.1)

**Concept Review Questions**

**13.1** Describe how properties of seawater illustrate the two characteristics that define mixtures.

**13.2** What types of intermolecular forces give rise to hydration shells in an aqueous solution of sodium chloride?

**13.3** Acetic acid is miscible with water. Would you expect carboxylic acids with general formula $CH_3(CH_2)_nCOOH$ to become more or less water soluble as $n$ increases? Explain.

**13.4** Which would you expect to be more effective as a soap, sodium acetate or sodium stearate? Explain.

**13.5** Hexane and methanol are miscible as gases but only slightly soluble in each other as liquids. Explain.

**13.6** Hydrogen chloride (HCl) gas is much more soluble than propane gas ($C_3H_8$) in water, even though HCl has a lower boiling point. Explain.

**Skill-Building Exercises** (grouped in similar pairs)

**13.7** Which gives the more concentrated solution, (a) $KNO_3$ in $H_2O$ or (b) $KNO_3$ in carbon tetrachloride ($CCl_4$)? Explain.

**13.8** Which gives the more concentrated solution, stearic acid [$CH_3(CH_2)_{16}COOH$] in (a) $H_2O$ or (b) $CCl_4$? Explain.

**13.9** What is the strongest type of intermolecular force between solute and solvent in each solution?

(a) CsCl(s) in $H_2O(l)$
(b) $CH_3CCH_3(l)$ in $H_2O(l)$ (with O double bonded)
(c) $CH_3OH(l)$ in $CCl_4(l)$

**13.10** What is the strongest type of intermolecular force between solute and solvent in each solution?
(a) Cu(s) in Ag(s)
(b) $CH_3Cl(g)$ in $CH_3OCH_3(g)$
(c) $CH_3CH_3(g)$ in $CH_3CH_2CH_2NH_2(l)$

**13.11** What is the strongest type of intermolecular force between solute and solvent in each solution?
(a) $CH_3OCH_3(g)$ in $H_2O(l)$
(b) Ne(g) in $H_2O(l)$
(c) $N_2(g)$ in $C_4H_{10}(g)$

**13.12** What is the strongest type of intermolecular force between solute and solvent in each solution?
(a) $C_6H_{14}(l)$ in $C_8H_{18}(l)$
(b) $H_2C{=}O(g)$ in $CH_3OH(l)$
(c) $Br_2(l)$ in $CCl_4(l)$

**13.13** Which member of each pair is more soluble in diethyl ether? Why?

(a) NaCl(s) or HCl(g)
(b) $H_2O(l)$ or $CH_3CH(l)$ (with O double bonded)
(c) $MgBr_2(s)$ or $CH_3CH_2MgBr(s)$

**13.14** Which member of each pair is more soluble in water? Why?
(a) $CH_3CH_2OCH_2CH_3(l)$ or $CH_3CH_2OCH_3(g)$
(b) $CH_2Cl_2(l)$ or $CCl_4(l)$
(c)

cyclohexane    tetrahydropyran

## Problems in Context

**13.15** The dictionary defines *homogeneous* as "uniform in composition throughout." River water is a mixture of dissolved compounds, such as calcium bicarbonate, and suspended soil particles. Is river water homogeneous? Explain.

**13.16** Gluconic acid is a derivative of glucose used in cleaners and in the dairy and brewing industries. Caproic acid is a carboxylic acid used in the flavoring industry. Although both are six-carbon acids (*see structures below*), gluconic acid is soluble in water and nearly insoluble in hexane, whereas caproic acid has the opposite solubility behavior. Explain.

$$CH_2{-}CH{-}CH{-}CH{-}CH{-}COOH$$
(with OH groups) gluconic acid

$$CH_3{-}CH_2{-}CH_2{-}CH_2{-}CH_2{-}COOH$$
caproic acid

## Intermolecular Forces and Biological Macromolecules

**Concept Review Questions**

**13.17** Name three intermolecular forces that stabilize the shape of a soluble, globular protein, and explain how they act.

**13.18** Name three intermolecular forces that stabilize the structure of DNA, and explain how they act.

**13.19** How can relatively weak H bonds hold the double helix together yet allow DNA to function?

**13.20** Is the sodium salt of propanoic acid as effective a soap as sodium stearate? Explain.

**13.21** What intermolecular forces stabilize a lipid bilayer?

**13.22** In what way do proteins embedded in a membrane differ structurally from soluble proteins?

**13.23** Histones are proteins that control gene function by attaching through salt links to exterior regions of DNA. Name an amino acid whose side chain is often found on the exterior of histones.

## Why Substances Dissolve: Understanding the Solution Process

**Concept Review Questions**

**13.24** What is the relationship between solvation and hydration?

**13.25** For a general solvent, which enthalpy terms in the thermochemical solution cycle are combined to obtain $\Delta H_{solvation}$?

**13.26** (a) What is the charge density of an ion, and what two properties of an ion affect it?
(b) Arrange the following in order of increasing charge density:

(c) How do the two properties in part (a) affect the ionic heat of hydration, $\Delta H_{hydr}$?

**13.27** For $\Delta H_{soln}$ to be very small, what quantities must be nearly equal in magnitude? Will their signs be the same or opposite?

**13.28** Water is added to a flask containing solid $NH_4Cl$. As the salt dissolves, the solution becomes colder.
(a) Is the dissolving of $NH_4Cl$ exothermic or endothermic?
(b) Is the magnitude of $\Delta H_{lattice}$ of $NH_4Cl$ larger or smaller than the combined $\Delta H_{hydr}$ of the ions? Explain.
(c) Given the answer to (a), why does $NH_4Cl$ dissolve in water?

**13.29** An ionic compound has a highly negative $\Delta H_{soln}$ in water. Would you expect it to be very soluble or nearly insoluble in water? Explain in terms of enthalpy and entropy changes.

**Skill-Building Exercises** (grouped in similar pairs)

**13.30** Sketch an enthalpy diagram for the process of dissolving $KCl(s)$ in $H_2O$ (endothermic).

**13.31** Sketch an enthalpy diagram for the process of dissolving $NaI(s)$ in $H_2O$ (exothermic).

**13.32** Which ion in each pair has greater charge density? Explain.
(a) $Na^+$ or $Cs^+$      (b) $Sr^{2+}$ or $Rb^+$       (c) $Na^+$ or $Cl^-$
(d) $O^{2-}$ or $F^-$      (e) $OH^-$ or $SH^-$       (f) $Mg^{2+}$ or $Ba^{2+}$
(g) $Mg^{2+}$ or $Na^+$   (h) $NO_3^-$ or $CO_3^{2-}$

**13.33** Which ion has the lower ratio of charge to volume? Explain.
(a) $Br^-$ or $I^-$       (b) $Sc^{3+}$ or $Ca^{2+}$     (c) $Br^-$ or $K^+$
(d) $S^{2-}$ or $Cl^-$    (e) $Sc^{3+}$ or $Al^{3+}$     (f) $SO_4^{2-}$ or $ClO_4^-$
(g) $Fe^{3+}$ or $Fe^{2+}$ (h) $Ca^{2+}$ or $K^+$

**13.34** Which has the *larger* $\Delta H_{hydr}$ in each pair of Problem 13.32?

**13.35** Which has the *smaller* $\Delta H_{hydr}$ in each pair of Problem 13.33?

**13.36** (a) Use the following data to calculate the combined heat of hydration for the ions in potassium bromate ($KBrO_3$):
$$\Delta H_{lattice} = 745 \text{ kJ/mol} \qquad \Delta H_{soln} = 41.1 \text{ kJ/mol}$$
(b) Which ion contributes more to the answer to part (a)? Why?

**13.37** (a) Use the following data to calculate the combined heat of hydration for the ions in sodium acetate ($NaC_2H_3O_2$):
$$\Delta H_{lattice} = 763 \text{ kJ/mol} \qquad \Delta H_{soln} = 17.3 \text{ kJ/mol}$$
(b) Which ion contributes more to the answer to part (a)? Why?

**13.38** State whether the entropy of the system increases or decreases in each of the following processes:
(a) Gasoline burns in a car engine.
(b) Gold is extracted and purified from its ore.
(c) Ethanol ($CH_3CH_2OH$) dissolves in 1-propanol ($CH_3CH_2CH_2OH$).

**13.39** State whether the entropy of the system increases or decreases in each of the following processes:
(a) Pure gases are mixed to prepare an anesthetic.
(b) Electronic-grade silicon is prepared from sand.
(c) Dry ice (solid $CO_2$) sublimes.

**Problems in Context**

**13.40** Besides its use in making black-and-white film, silver nitrate ($AgNO_3$) is used similarly in forensic science. The NaCl left behind in the sweat of a fingerprint is treated with $AgNO_3$ solution to form AgCl. This precipitate is developed to show the black-and-white fingerprint pattern. Given $\Delta H_{lattice}$ of $AgNO_3 = 822$ kJ/mol and $\Delta H_{hydr} = -799$ kJ/mol, calculate its $\Delta H_{soln}$.

## Solubility as an Equilibrium Process
(Sample Problem 13.2)

**Concept Review Questions**

**13.41** You are given a bottle of solid X and three aqueous solutions of X—one saturated, one unsaturated, and one supersaturated. How would you determine which solution is which?

**13.42** Potassium permanganate ($KMnO_4$) has a solubility of 6.4 g/100 g of $H_2O$ at 20°C and a curve of solubility vs. temperature that slopes upward to the right. How would you prepare a supersaturated solution of $KMnO_4$?

**13.43** Why does the solubility of any gas in water decrease with rising temperature?

**Skill-Building Exercises** (grouped in similar pairs)

**13.44** For a saturated aqueous solution of each of the following at 20°C and 1 atm, will the solubility increase, decrease, or stay the same when the indicated change occurs?
(a) $O_2(g)$, increase $P$       (b) $N_2(g)$, increase $V$

**13.45** For a saturated aqueous solution of each of the following at 20°C and 1 atm, will the solubility increase, decrease, or stay the same when the indicated change occurs?
(a) $He(g)$, decrease $T$       (b) $RbI(s)$, increase $P$

**13.46** The Henry's law constant ($k_H$) for $O_2$ in water at 20°C is $1.28 \times 10^{-3}$ mol/L·atm. (a) How many grams of $O_2$ will dissolve in 2.50 L of $H_2O$ that is in contact with pure $O_2$ at 1.00 atm? (b) How many grams of $O_2$ will dissolve in 2.50 L of $H_2O$ that is in contact with air, where the partial pressure of $O_2$ is 0.209 atm?

**13.47** Argon makes up 0.93% by volume of air. Calculate its solubility (mol/L) in water at 20°C and 1.0 atm. The Henry's law constant for Ar under these conditions is $1.5 \times 10^{-3}$ mol/L·atm.

**Problems in Context**

**13.48** Caffeine is about 10 times as soluble in hot water as in cold water. A chemist puts a hot-water extract of caffeine into an ice bath, and some caffeine crystallizes. Is the remaining solution saturated, unsaturated, or supersaturated?

**13.49** The partial pressure of $CO_2$ gas above the liquid in a bottle of champagne at 20°C is 5.5 atm. What is the solubility of $CO_2$ in champagne? Assume Henry's law constant is the same for champagne as for water: at 20°C, $k_H = 3.7 \times 10^{-2}$ mol/L·atm.

**13.50** Respiratory problems are treated with devices that deliver air with a higher partial pressure of $O_2$ than normal air. Why?

## Concentration Terms
(Sample Problems 13.3 to 13.5)

**Concept Review Questions**

**13.51** Explain the difference between molarity and molality. Under what circumstances would molality be a more accurate measure of the concentration of a prepared solution than molarity? Why?

**13.52** Which way of expressing concentration includes (a) volume of solution; (b) mass of solution; (c) mass of solvent?

**13.53** A solute has a solubility in water of 21 g/kg solvent. Is this value the same as 21 g/kg solution? Explain.

**13.54** You want to convert among molarity, molality, and mole fraction of a solution. You know the masses of solute and solvent and the volume of solution. Is this enough information to carry out all the conversions? Explain.

**13.55** When a solution is heated, which ways of expressing concentration change in value? Which remain unchanged? Explain.

**Skill-Building Exercises** (grouped in similar pairs)

**13.56** Calculate the molarity of each aqueous solution:
(a) 32.3 g of table sugar ($C_{12}H_{22}O_{11}$) in 100. mL of solution
(b) 5.80 g of $LiNO_3$ in 505 mL of solution

**13.57** Calculate the molarity of each aqueous solution:
(a) 0.82 g of ethanol ($C_2H_5OH$) in 10.5 mL of solution
(b) 1.27 g of gaseous $NH_3$ in 33.5 mL of solution

**13.58** Calculate the molarity of each aqueous solution:
(a) 78.0 mL of 0.240 $M$ NaOH diluted to 0.250 L with water
(b) 38.5 mL of 1.2 $M$ $HNO_3$ diluted to 0.130 L with water

**13.59** Calculate the molarity of each aqueous solution:
(a) 25.5 mL of 6.25 $M$ HCl diluted to 0.500 L with water
(b) 8.25 mL of $2.00\times10^{-2}$ $M$ KI diluted to 12.0 mL with water

**13.60** How would you prepare the following aqueous solutions?
(a) 365 mL of $8.55\times10^{-2}$ $M$ $KH_2PO_4$ from solid $KH_2PO_4$
(b) 465 mL of 0.335 $M$ NaOH from 1.25 $M$ NaOH

**13.61** How would you prepare the following aqueous solutions?
(a) 2.5 L of 0.65 $M$ NaCl from solid NaCl
(b) 15.5 L of 0.3 $M$ urea [$(NH_2)_2C{=}O$] from 2.1 $M$ urea

**13.62** How would you prepare the following aqueous solutions?
(a) 1.40 L of 0.288 $M$ KBr from solid KBr
(b) 255 mL of 0.0856 $M$ $LiNO_3$ from 0.264 $M$ $LiNO_3$

**13.63** How would you prepare the following aqueous solutions?
(a) 57.5 mL of $1.53\times10^{-3}$ $M$ $Cr(NO_3)_3$ from solid $Cr(NO_3)_3$
(b) $5.8\times10^3$ $m^3$ of 1.45 $M$ $NH_4NO_3$ from 2.50 $M$ $NH_4NO_3$

**13.64** Calculate the molality of the following:
(a) A solution containing 85.4 g of glycine ($NH_2CH_2COOH$) dissolved in 1.270 kg of $H_2O$
(b) A solution containing 8.59 g of glycerol ($C_3H_8O_3$) in 77.0 g of ethanol ($C_2H_5OH$)

**13.65** Calculate the molality of the following:
(a) A solution containing 174 g of HCl in 757 g of $H_2O$
(b) A solution containing 16.5 g of naphthalene ($C_{10}H_8$) in 53.3 g of benzene ($C_6H_6$)

**13.66** What is the molality of a solution consisting of 44.0 mL of benzene ($C_6H_6$; $d = 0.877$ g/mL) in 167 mL of hexane ($C_6H_{14}$; $d = 0.660$ g/mL)?

**13.67** What is the molality of a solution consisting of 2.66 mL of carbon tetrachloride ($CCl_4$; $d = 1.59$ g/mL) in 76.5 mL of methylene chloride ($CH_2Cl_2$; $d = 1.33$ g/mL)?

**13.68** How would you prepare the following aqueous solutions?
(a) $3.10\times10^2$ g of 0.125 $m$ ethylene glycol ($C_2H_6O_2$) from ethylene glycol and water
(b) 1.20 kg of 2.20 mass % $HNO_3$ from 52.0 mass % $HNO_3$

**13.69** How would you prepare the following aqueous solutions?
(a) 1.50 kg of 0.0355 $m$ ethanol ($C_2H_5OH$) from ethanol and water
(b) 445 g of 13.0 mass % HCl from 34.1 mass % HCl

**13.70** A solution contains 0.35 mol of isopropanol ($C_3H_7OH$) dissolved in 0.85 mol of water. (a) What is the mole fraction of isopropanol? (b) The mass percent? (c) The molality?

**13.71** A solution contains 0.100 mol of NaCl dissolved in 8.60 mol of water. (a) What is the mole fraction of NaCl? (b) The mass percent? (c) The molality?

**13.72** What mass of cesium bromide must be added to 0.500 L of water ($d = 1.00$ g/mL) to produce a 0.400 $m$ solution? What are the mole fraction and the mass percent of CsBr?

**13.73** What are the mole fraction and the mass percent of a solution made by dissolving 0.30 g of KI in 0.400 L of water ($d = 1.00$ g/mL)?

**13.74** Calculate the molality, molarity, and mole fraction of $NH_3$ in an 8.00 mass % aqueous solution ($d = 0.9651$ g/mL).

**13.75** Calculate the molality, molarity, and mole fraction of $FeCl_3$ in a 28.8 mass % aqueous solution ($d = 1.280$ g/mL).

**Problems in Context**

**13.76** Wastewater from a cement factory contains 0.25 g of $Ca^{2+}$ ion and 0.056 g of $Mg^{2+}$ ion per 100.0 L of solution. The solution density is 1.001 g/mL. Calculate the $Ca^{2+}$ and $Mg^{2+}$ concentrations in ppm (by mass).

**13.77** An automobile antifreeze mixture is made by mixing equal volumes of ethylene glycol ($d = 1.114$ g/mL; $M = 62.07$ g/mol) and water ($d = 1.00$ g/mL) at 20°C. The density of the mixture is 1.070 g/mL. Express the concentration of ethylene glycol as:
(a) Volume percent     (b) Mass percent     (c) Molarity
(d) Molality            (e) Mole fraction

## Colligative Properties of Solutions
(Sample Problems 13.6 to 13.9)

**Concept Review Questions**

**13.78** The chemical formula of a solute does *not* affect the extent of the solution's colligative properties. What characteristic of a solute *does* affect these properties? Name a physical property of a solution that *is* affected by the chemical formula of the solute.

**13.79** What is a nonvolatile nonelectrolyte? Why is this type of solute the simplest case for examining colligative properties?

**13.80** In what sense is a strong electrolyte "strong"? What property of the substance makes it a strong electrolyte?

**13.81** Express Raoult's law in words. Is Raoult's law valid for a solution of a volatile solute? Explain.

**13.82** What are the most important differences between the phase diagram of a pure solvent and the phase diagram of a solution of that solvent?

**13.83** Is the composition of the vapor at the top of a fractionating column different from the composition at the bottom? Explain.

**13.84** Is the boiling point of 0.01 $m$ KF($aq$) higher or lower than that of 0.01 $m$ glucose($aq$)? Explain.

**13.85** Which aqueous solution has a boiling point closer to its predicted value, 0.050 $m$ NaF or 0.50 $m$ KCl? Explain.

**13.86** Which aqueous solution has a freezing point closer to its predicted value, 0.01 $m$ NaBr or 0.01 $m$ $MgCl_2$? Explain.

**13.87** The freezing point depression constants of the solvents cyclohexane and naphthalene are 20.1°C/$m$ and 6.94°C/$m$, respectively. Which solvent would give a more accurate result if you are using freezing point depression to determine the molar mass of a substance that is soluble in either one? Why?

**Skill-Building Exercises** (grouped in similar pairs)

**13.88** Classify the following substances as strong electrolytes, weak electrolytes, or nonelectrolytes:
(a) Hydrogen chloride (HCl)     (b) Potassium nitrate ($KNO_3$)
(c) Glucose ($C_6H_{12}O_6$)     (d) Ammonia ($NH_3$)

**13.89** Classify the following substances as strong electrolytes, weak electrolytes, or nonelectrolytes:
(a) Sodium permanganate ($NaMnO_4$)
(b) Acetic acid ($CH_3COOH$)
(c) Methanol ($CH_3OH$)
(d) Calcium acetate [$Ca(C_2H_3O_2)_2$]

**13.90** How many moles of solute particles are present in 1 L of each of the following aqueous solutions?
(a) 0.3 $M$ KBr          (b) 0.065 $M$ $HNO_3$
(c) $10^{-4}$ $M$ $KHSO_4$    (d) 0.06 $M$ ethanol ($C_2H_5OH$)

**13.91** How many moles of solute particles are present in 1 mL of each of the following aqueous solutions?
(a) 0.02 $M$ $CuSO_4$          (b) 0.004 $M$ $Ba(OH)_2$
(c) 0.08 $M$ pyridine ($C_5H_5N$)    (d) 0.05 $M$ $(NH_4)_2CO_3$

**13.92** Which solution has the lower freezing point?
(a) 11.0 g of $CH_3OH$ in 100. g of $H_2O$ *or*
22.0 g of $CH_3CH_2OH$ in 200. g of $H_2O$
(b) 20.0 g of $H_2O$ in 1.00 kg of $CH_3OH$ *or*
20.0 g of $CH_3CH_2OH$ in 1.00 kg of $CH_3OH$

**13.93** Which solution has the higher boiling point?
(a) 38.0 g of $C_3H_8O_3$ in 250. g of ethanol *or*
38.0 g of $C_2H_6O_2$ in 250. g of ethanol
(b) 15 g of $C_2H_6O_2$ in 0.50 kg of $H_2O$ *or*
15 g of NaCl in 0.50 kg of $H_2O$

**13.94** Rank the following aqueous solutions in order of increasing (a) osmotic pressure; (b) boiling point; (c) freezing point; (d) vapor pressure at 50°C:
(I) 0.100 $m$ $NaNO_3$
(II) 0.100 $m$ glucose
(III) 0.100 $m$ $CaCl_2$

**13.95** Rank the following aqueous solutions in order of decreasing (a) osmotic pressure; (b) boiling point; (c) freezing point; (d) vapor pressure at 298 K:
(I) 0.04 $m$ urea [$(NH_2)_2C{=}O$]
(II) 0.01 $m$ $AgNO_3$
(III) 0.03 $m$ $CuSO_4$

**13.96** Calculate the vapor pressure of a solution of 34.0 g of glycerol ($C_3H_8O_3$) in 500.0 g of water at 25°C. The vapor pressure of water at 25°C is 23.76 torr. (Assume ideal behavior.)

**13.97** Calculate the vapor pressure of a solution of 0.39 mol of cholesterol in 5.4 mol of toluene at 32°C. Pure toluene has a vapor pressure of 41 torr at 32°C. (Assume ideal behavior.)

**13.98** What is the freezing point of 0.251 $m$ urea in water?

**13.99** What is the boiling point of 0.200 $m$ lactose in water?

**13.100** The boiling point of ethanol ($C_2H_5OH$) is 78.5°C. What is the boiling point of a solution of 6.4 g of vanillin ($\mathcal{M}$ = 152.14 g/mol) in 50.0 g of ethanol ($K_b$ of ethanol = 1.22°C/$m$)?

**13.101** The freezing point of benzene is 5.5°C. What is the freezing point of a solution of 5.00 g of naphthalene ($C_{10}H_8$) in 444 g of benzene ($K_f$ of benzene = 4.90°C/$m$)?

**13.102** What is the minimum mass of ethylene glycol ($C_2H_6O_2$) that must be dissolved in 14.5 kg of water to prevent the solution from freezing at −12.0°F? (Assume ideal behavior.)

**13.103** What is the minimum mass of glycerol ($C_3H_8O_3$) that must be dissolved in 11.0 mg of water to prevent the solution from freezing at −15°C? (Assume ideal behavior.)

**13.104** Calculate the molality and van't Hoff factor ($i$) for the following aqueous solutions:
(a) 1.00 mass % NaCl, freezing point = −0.593°C
(b) 0.500 mass % $CH_3COOH$, freezing point = −0.159°C

**13.105** Calculate the molality and van't Hoff factor ($i$) for the following aqueous solutions:
(a) 0.500 mass % KCl, freezing point = −0.234°C
(b) 1.00 mass % $H_2SO_4$, freezing point = −0.423°C

### Problems in Context

**13.106** In a study designed to prepare new gasoline-resistant coatings, a polymer chemist dissolves 6.053 g of poly(vinyl alcohol) in enough water to make 100.0 mL of solution. At 25°C, the osmotic pressure of this solution is 0.272 atm. What is the molar mass of the polymer sample?

**13.107** The U.S. Food and Drug Administration lists dichloromethane ($CH_2Cl_2$) and carbon tetrachloride ($CCl_4$) among the many cancer-causing chlorinated organic compounds. What are the partial pressures of these substances in the vapor above a solution of 1.60 mol of $CH_2Cl_2$ and 1.10 mol of $CCl_4$ at 23.5°C? The vapor pressures of pure $CH_2Cl_2$ and $CCl_4$ at 23.5°C are 352 torr and 118 torr, respectively. (Assume ideal behavior.)

## The Structure and Properties of Colloids
### Concept Review Questions

**13.108** Is the fluid inside a bacterial cell considered a solution, a colloid, or both? Explain.

**13.109** What type of colloid is each of the following?
(a) Milk      (b) Fog       (c) Shaving cream

**13.110** What is Brownian motion, and what causes it?

**13.111** In a movie theater, you can see the beam of projected light. What phenomenon does this exemplify? Why does it occur?

**13.112** Why don't soap micelles coagulate and form large globules? Is soap more effective in freshwater or in seawater? Why?

### Comprehensive Problems

**13.113** The three aqueous ionic solutions below have total volumes of 25. mL for A, 50. mL for B, and 100. mL for C. If each sphere represents 0.010 mol of ions, calculate: (a) the total molarity of ions for each solution; (b) the highest molarity of solute; (c) the lowest molality of solute (assuming the solution densities are equal); (d) the highest osmotic pressure (assuming ideal behavior).

**13.114** An aqueous solution is 10.% glucose by mass ($d$ = 1.039 g/mL at 20°C). Calculate its freezing point, boiling point at 1 atm, and osmotic pressure.

**13.115** Because zinc has nearly the same atomic radius as copper ($d$ = 8.95 g/cm³), zinc atoms substitute for some copper atoms in the many types of brass. Calculate the density of the brass with (a) 10.0 atom % Zn and (b) 38.0 atom % Zn.

**13.116** Gold occurs in seawater at an average concentration of $1.1{\times}10^{-2}$ ppb. How many liters of seawater must be processed to recover 1 troy ounce of gold, assuming 81.5% efficiency (*d* of sea-water = 1.025 g/mL; 1 troy ounce = 31.1 g)?

**13.117** Use atomic properties to explain why xenon is 11 times as soluble as helium in water at 0°C on a mole basis.

**13.118** Which of the following best represents a molecular-scale view of an ionic compound in aqueous solution? Explain.

**A**     **B**     **C**

**13.119** Four 0.50 *m* aqueous solutions are depicted below. Assume the solutions behave ideally: (a) Which has the highest boiling point? (b) Which has the lowest freezing point? (c) Can you determine which one has the highest osmotic pressure? Explain.

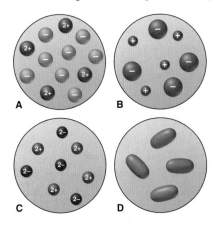

**A**     **B**

**C**     **D**

**13.120** Thermal pollution from industrial wastewater causes the temperature of river or lake water to increase, which can affect fish survival as the concentration of dissolved $O_2$ decreases. Use the following data to find the molarity of $O_2$ at each temperature (assume the solution density is the same as water):

| Temperature (°C) | Solubility of $O_2$ (mg/kg $H_2O$) | Density of $H_2O$ (g/mL) |
|---|---|---|
| 0.0 | 14.5 | 0.99987 |
| 20.0 | 9.07 | 0.99823 |
| 40.0 | 6.44 | 0.99224 |

**13.121** Pyridine (*right*) is an essential portion of many biologically active compounds, such as nicotine and vitamin $B_6$. Like ammonia, it has a nitrogen with a lone pair, which makes it act as a weak base. Because it is miscible in a wide range of solvents, from water to benzene, pyridine is one of the most important bases and solvents in organic syntheses. Account for its solubility behavior in terms of intermolecular forces.

**13.122** A chemist is studying small organic compounds for their potential use as an antifreeze. When 0.243 g of a compound is dissolved in 25.0 mL of water, the freezing point of the solution is −0.201°C. (a) Calculate the molar mass of the compound (*d* of water = 1.00 g/mL). (b) Analysis shows that the compound is 53.31 mass % C and 11.18 mass % H, the remainder being O. Calculate the empirical and molecular formulas of the compound. (c) Draw a Lewis structure for a compound with this formula that forms H bonds and another for one that does not.

**13.123** Air in a smoky bar contains $4.0 \times 10^{-6}$ mol/L of CO. What mass of CO is inhaled by a bartender who respires at a rate of 11 L/min during an 8.0-h shift?

**13.124** Is 50% by mass of methanol dissolved in ethanol different from 50% by mass of ethanol dissolved in methanol? Explain.

**13.125** Three gaseous mixtures of $N_2$ (blue), $Cl_2$ (green), and Ne (purple) are depicted below. (a) Which has the smallest mole fraction of $N_2$? (b) Which have the same mole fraction of Ne? (c) Rank all three in order of increasing mole fraction of $Cl_2$.

**A**     **B**     **C**

**13.126** A water treatment plant needs to attain a fluoride concentration of $4.50 \times 10^{-5}$ *M*. (a) What mass of NaF must be added to a 5000.-L blending tank of water? (b) What mass per day of fluoride is ingested by a person who drinks 2.0 L of this water?

**13.127** Four U tubes each have distilled water in the right arm, a solution in the left arm, and a semipermeable membrane between arms. (a) If the solute is KCl, which solution is most concentrated? (b) If each solute is different but all the solutions have the same molarity, which contains the smallest number of dissolved ions?

**A**     **B**     **C**     **D**

**13.128** β-Pinene ($C_{10}H_{16}$) and α-terpineol ($C_{10}H_{18}O$) are used in cosmetics to provide a "fresh pine" scent. At 367 K, the pure substances have vapor pressures of 100.3 torr and 9.8 torr, respectively. What is the composition of the vapor (in terms of mole fractions) above a solution containing equal masses of these compounds at 367 K? (Assume ideal behavior.)

**13.129** A solution of 1.50 g of solute dissolved in 25.0 mL of $H_2O$ at 25°C has a boiling point of 100.45°C. (a) What is the molar mass of the solute if it is a nonvolatile nonelectrolyte and the solution behaves ideally (*d* of $H_2O$ at 25°C = 0.997 g/mL)? (b) Conductivity measurements show the solute to be ionic of general formula $AB_2$ or $A_2B$. What is the molar mass if the solution behaves ideally? (c) Analysis indicates an empirical formula of $CaN_2O_6$. Explain the difference between the actual formula mass and that calculated from the boiling point elevation. (d) Find the van't Hoff factor (*i*) for this solution.

**13.130** A pharmaceutical preparation made with ethanol ($C_2H_5OH$) is contaminated with methanol ($CH_3OH$). A sample of vapor above the liquid mixture contains a 97/1 mass ratio of $C_2H_5OH$ to $CH_3OH$. What is the mass ratio of these alcohols in the liquid? At the temperature of the liquid, the vapor pressures of $C_2H_5OH$ and $CH_3OH$ are 60.5 torr and 126.0 torr, respectively.

**13.131** Water treatment plants commonly use chlorination to destroy bacteria. A byproduct is chloroform ($CHCl_3$), a suspected carcinogen, produced when HOCl, formed by reaction of $Cl_2$ and water, reacts with dissolved organic matter. The United States, Canada, and the World Health Organization have set a limit of 100. ppb of

CHCl$_3$ in drinking water. Convert this concentration into molarity, molality, mole fraction, and mass percent.

**13.132** A saturated Na$_2$CO$_3$ solution is prepared, and a small excess of solid is present (white pile in beaker). A seed crystal of Na$_2^{14}$CO$_3$, ($^{14}$C is a radioactive isotope of $^{12}$C) is added (small red piece), and the radioactivity is measured over time. (a) Would you expect radioactivity in the solution? Explain. (b) Would you expect radioactivity in all the solid or just in the seed crystal? Explain.

Saturated Na$_2$CO$_3$ soln

**13.133** A biochemical engineer isolates a bacterial gene fragment and dissolves a 10.0-mg sample in enough water to make 30.0 mL of solution. The osmotic pressure of the solution is 0.340 torr at 25°C. (a) What is the molar mass of the gene fragment? (b) If the solution density is 0.997 g/mL, how large is the freezing point depression for this solution ($K_f$ of water = 1.86°C/$m$)?

**13.134** A river is contaminated with 0.65 mg/L of dichloroethylene (C$_2$H$_2$Cl$_2$). What is the concentration (in ng/L) of dichloroethylene at 21°C in the air breathed by a person swimming in the river ($k_H$ for C$_2$H$_2$Cl$_2$ in water is 0.033 mol/L·atm)?

**13.135** At an air-water interface, fatty acids such as oleic acid lie in a one-molecule-thick layer (*monolayer*), with the heads in the water and the tails perpendicular in the air. When 2.50 mg of oleic acid is placed on a water surface, it forms a circular monolayer 38.6 cm in diameter. Find the surface area (in cm$^2$) occupied by one molecule (ℳ of oleic acid = 283 g/mol).

**13.136** A simple device used for estimating the concentration of total dissolved solids in an aqueous solution works by measuring the electrical conductivity of the solution. The method assumes that equal concentrations of different solids give approximately the same conductivity, and that the conductivity is proportional to concentration. The table below gives some actual electrical conductivities (in arbitrary units) for solutions of selected solids at the indicated concentrations (in ppm by mass):

| Sample | Conductivity | | |
| --- | --- | --- | --- |
| | 0 ppm | 5.00×10$^3$ ppm | 10.00×10$^3$ ppm |
| CaCl$_2$ | 0.0 | 8.0 | 16.0 |
| K$_2$CO$_3$ | 0.0 | 7.0 | 14.0 |
| Na$_2$SO$_4$ | 0.0 | 6.0 | 11.0 |
| Seawater (dil) | 0.0 | 8.0 | 15.0 |
| Sucrose (C$_{12}$H$_{22}$O$_{11}$) | 0.0 | 0.0 | 0.0 |
| Urea [(NH$_2$)$_2$C=O] | 0.0 | 0.0 | 0.0 |

(a) How reliable are these measurements for estimating concentrations of dissolved solids? (b) For what types of substances might this method have a large error? Why? (c) Based on this method, an aqueous CaCl$_2$ solution has a conductivity of 14.0 units. Calculate its mole fraction and molality.

**13.137** Two beakers are placed in a closed container (*left*). One beaker contains water, the other a concentrated aqueous sugar solution. With time, the solution volume increases and the water volume decreases (*right*). Explain on the molecular level.

**13.138** The release of volatile organic compounds into the atmosphere is regulated to limit ozone formation. In a laboratory simulation, 5% of the ethanol in a liquid detergent is released. Thus, a "down-the-drain" factor of 0.05 is used to estimate ethanol emissions from the detergent. The $k_H$ values for ethanol and 2-butoxyethanol (C$_4$H$_9$OCH$_2$CH$_2$OH) are 5×10$^{-6}$ atm·m$^3$/mol and 1.6×10$^{-6}$ atm·m$^3$/mol, respectively. (a) Estimate a "down-the-drain" factor for 2-butoxyethanol in the detergent. (b) What is the $k_H$ for ethanol in units of L·atm/mol? (c) Is this value consistent with a value given as 0.64 Pa·m$^3$/mol?

**13.139** Although other solvents are available, dichloromethane (CH$_2$Cl$_2$) is still often used to "decaffeinate" drinks because the solubility of caffeine in CH$_2$Cl$_2$ is 8.35 times that in water. (a) A 100.0-mL sample of cola containing 10.0 mg of caffeine is extracted with 60.0 mL of CH$_2$Cl$_2$. What mass of caffeine remains in the aqueous phase? (b) A second identical cola sample is extracted with two successive 30.0-mL portions of CH$_2$Cl$_2$. What mass of caffeine remains in the aqueous phase after each extraction? (c) Which approach extracts more caffeine?

**13.140** How do you prepare 250. g of 0.150 $m$ aqueous NaHCO$_3$?

**13.141** Tartaric acid occurs in crystalline residues found in wine vats. It is used in baking powders and as an additive in foods. It contains 32.3% by mass carbon and 3.97% by mass hydrogen; the balance is oxygen. When 0.981 g of tartaric acid is dissolved in 11.23 g of water, the solution freezes at −1.26°C. Find the empirical and molecular formulas of tartaric acid.

**13.142** Methanol (CH$_3$OH) and ethanol (C$_2$H$_5$OH) are miscible because the major intermolecular force for each is hydrogen bonding. In some methanol-ethanol solutions, the mole fraction of methanol is higher, but the mass percent of ethanol is higher. What is the range of mole fraction of methanol for these solutions?

**13.143** A solution of 5.0 g of benzoic acid (C$_6$H$_5$COOH) in 100.0 g of carbon tetrachloride has a boiling point of 77.5°C. (a) Calculate the molar mass of benzoic acid in the solution. (b) Suggest a reason for the difference between the molar mass based on the formula and that found in part (a).

**13.144** Derive a general equation that expresses the relationship between the molarity and the molality of a solution. Why are the numerical values of these two terms approximately equal for very dilute aqueous solutions?

**13.145** A florist prepares a solution of nitrogen-phosphorus fertilizer by dissolving 5.66 g of NH$_4$NO$_3$ and 4.42 g of (NH$_4$)$_3$PO$_4$ in enough water to make 20.0 L of solution. What are the molarities of NH$_4^+$ and of PO$_4^{3-}$ in the solution?

**13.146** Suppose coal-fired power plants used water in scrubbers to remove SO$_2$ from smokestack gases (see Chemical Connections, p. 249). (a) If the partial pressure of SO$_2$ in the stack gases is 2.0×10$^{-3}$ atm, what is the solubility of SO$_2$ in the scrubber liquid ($k_H$ for SO$_2$ in water is 1.23 mol/L·atm at 200.°C)? (b) From your answer to part (a), why are basic solutions, such as limewater slurries [Ca(OH)$_2$], used in scrubbers?

**13.147** Urea is a white crystalline solid used as a fertilizer, in the pharmaceutical industry, and in the manufacture of certain polymer resins. Analysis of urea reveals that, by mass, it is 20.1% carbon, 6.7% hydrogen, 46.5% nitrogen and the balance oxygen. (a) Find the empirical formula of urea. (b) A 5.0 g/L solution of urea in water has an osmotic pressure of 2.04 atm, measured at 25°C. What is the molar mass and molecular formula of urea?

**13.148** The total concentration of dissolved particles in blood is 0.30 $M$. An intravenous (IV) solution must be isotonic with blood, which means it must have the same concentration.
(a) To relieve dehydration, a patient is given 100. mL/h of IV glucose ($C_6H_{12}O_6$) for 2.5 h. What mass (g) of glucose did she receive? (b) If isotonic saline (NaCl) is used, what is the molarity of the solution? (c) If the patient is given 150. mL/h of IV saline for 1.5 h, how many grams of NaCl did she receive?

**13.149** Deviations from Raoult's law lead to the formation of *azeotropes,* constant boiling mixtures that cannot be separated by distillation, making industrial separations difficult. For components A and B, there is a positive deviation if the A-B attraction is less than A-A and B-B attractions (A and B reject each other), and a negative deviation if the A-B attraction is greater than A-A and B-B attractions. If the A-B attraction is nearly equal to the A-A and B-B attractions, the solution obeys Raoult's law. Explain whether the behavior of each pair will be nearly ideal, have a positive deviation, or a negative deviation:
(a) Benzene ($C_6H_6$) and methanol
(b) Water and ethyl acetate
(c) Hexane and heptane
(d) Methanol and water
(e) Water and hydrochloric acid

**13.150** Acrylic acid ($CH_2$=CHCOOH) is a monomer used to make superabsorbent polymers and various compounds for paint and adhesive production. At 1 atm, it boils at 141.5°C but is prone to polymerization. Its vapor pressure at 25°C is 4.1 mbar. What pressure (in mmHg) is needed to distill the pure acid at 65°C?

**13.151** To effectively stop polymerization, certain inhibitors require the presence of a small amount of $O_2$. At equilibrium with 1 atm of air, the concentration of $O_2$ dissolved in the monomer acrylic acid ($CH_2$=CHCOOH) is $1.64\times10^{-3}$ $M$. (a) What is the $k_H$ (mol/L·atm) for $O_2$ in acrylic acid? (b) If 0.005 atm of $O_2$ is sufficient to stop polymerization, what is the molarity of $O_2$? (c) What is the mole fraction? (d) What is the concentration in ppm? (Pure acrylic acid is 14.6 $M$; $P_{O_2}$ in air is 0.2095 atm.)

**13.152** Volatile organic solvents have been implicated in adverse health effects in industrial workers. Greener methods are phasing these solvents out. Rank the solvents in Table 13.6 (p. 501) in terms of increasing volatility.

**13.153** At ordinary temperatures, water is a poor solvent for organic substances. But at high pressure and above 200°C, water develops many properties of organic solvents. Find the minimum pressure needed to maintain water as a liquid at 200.°C ($\Delta H_{vap}$ = 40.7 kJ/mol at 100°C and 1.00 atm; assume it remains constant with temperature).

**13.154** In ice-cream making, the ingredients are kept below 0.0°C in an ice-salt bath. (a) Assuming that NaCl dissolves completely and forms an ideal solution, what mass of it is needed to lower the melting point of 5.5 kg of ice to −5.0°C? (b) Given the same assumptions as in part (a), what mass of $CaCl_2$ is needed?

**13.155** Perfluorocarbons (PFCs), hydrocarbons with all H atoms replaced by F atoms, have very weak cohesive forces. One unusual application has a live mouse submerged in $O_2$-saturated PFCs.
(a) At 298 K, perfluorohexane ($C_6F_{14}$, $\mathcal{M}$ = 338 g/mol, $d$ = 1.674 g/mL) in equilibrium with 101,325 Pa of $O_2$ has a mole fraction of $O_2$ of $4.28\times10^{-3}$. What is the $k_H$ in mol/L·atm?
(b) According to one source, the $k_H$ for $O_2$ in water at 25°C is 756.7 L·atm/mol. What is the solubility of $O_2$ in water at 25°C in

ppm? (c) Rank the $k_H$ values in descending order for $O_2$ in water, ethanol, $C_6F_{14}$, and $C_6H_{14}$. Explain your ranking.

**13.156** The solubility of $N_2$ in blood is a serious problem for divers breathing compressed air (78% $N_2$ by volume) at depths greater than 50 ft.
(a) What is the molarity of $N_2$ in blood at 1.00 atm?
(b) What is the molarity of $N_2$ in blood at a depth of 50. ft?
(c) Find the volume (in mL) of $N_2$, measured at 25°C and 1.00 atm, released per liter of blood when a diver at a depth of 50. ft rises to the surface ($k_H$ for $N_2$ in water at 25°C is $7.0\times10^{-4}$ mol/L·atm and at 37°C is $6.2\times10^{-4}$ mol/L·atm; assume $d$ of water is 1.00 g/mL).

**13.157** Figure 12.11 (p. 430) shows the phase changes of pure water. Consider how the diagram would change if air were present at 1 atm and dissolved in the water. (a) Would the three phases of water still attain equilibrium at some temperature? Explain. (b) In principle, would that temperature be higher, lower, or the same as the triple point for pure water? Explain. (c) Would ice sublime at a few degrees below the freezing point under this pressure? Explain. (d) Would the liquid have the same vapor pressure as that shown in Figure 12.9B at 100°C? At 120°C?

**13.158** KNO$_3$, KClO$_3$, KCl, and NaCl are recrystallized as follows:
*Step 1.* A saturated aqueous solution of the compound is prepared at 50°C.
*Step 2.* The mixture is filtered to remove undissolved compound.
*Step 3.* The filtrate is cooled to 0°C.
*Step 4.* The crystals that form are filtered, dried, and weighed.
(a) Which compound has the highest percent recovery and which the lowest (see Figure 13.19, p. 492)?
(b) Starting with 100. g of each compound, how many grams of each can be recovered?

**13.159** Eighty proof whiskey is 40% ethanol ($C_2H_5OH$) by volume. A man has 7.0 L of blood and drinks 28 mL of the whiskey, of which 22% of the ethanol goes into his blood.
(a) What concentration (in g/mL) of ethanol is in his blood ($d$ of ethanol = 0.789 g/mL)?
(b) What volume (in mL) of whiskey would raise his blood alcohol level to $8.0\times10^{-4}$ g/mL, the level at which a person is considered intoxicated?

**13.160** Soft drinks are canned under 4 atm of $CO_2$ and release $CO_2$ when opened.
(a) How many moles of $CO_2$ are dissolved in a 355-mL can of soda before it is opened?
(b) After it has gone flat?
(c) What volume (in L) would the released $CO_2$ occupy at 1.00 atm and 25°C ($k_H$ for $CO_2$ at 25°C is $3.3\times10^{-2}$ mol/L·atm; $P_{CO_2}$ in air is $3\times10^{-4}$ atm)?

**13.161** Gaseous $O_2$ in equilibrium with $O_2$ dissolved in water at 283 K is depicted at right. (a) Which scene below represents the system at 298 K? (b) Which scene represents the system when the pressure of $O_2$ is increased by half?

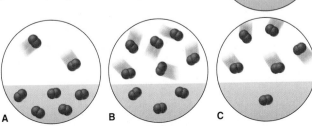

A          B          C

# Periodic Patterns in the Main-Group Elements

Scarlet king snake

Coral snake

# Concepts and skills to review before you study this chapter

- redox behavior and oxidation states (Section 4.5)
- electron configurations (Section 8.2)
- trends in atomic size, ionization energy, metallic behavior, and electronegativity (Sections 8.3, 8.4, and 9.5)
- trends in element properties and type of bonding (Sections 8.4 and 9.5)
- models of ionic, covalent, and metallic bonding (Sections 9.2, 9.3, 9.6, and 12.6)

- resonance and formal charge (Section 10.1)
- molecular shape and polarity (Sections 10.2 and 10.3)
- orbital hybridization and modes of orbital overlap (Sections 11.1 and 11.2)
- phase changes and phase diagrams, intermolecular forces, and crystalline solids (Sections 12.2, 12.3, and 12.6)

# 14

Recurring patterns appear throughout nature, helping us make sense of the diversity in the world around us. For example, knowing that the highly venomous coral snake has a red/yellow/black/yellow/red banding pattern would be very helpful should we come across one in the woods! This recurring pattern distinguishes the coral snake from the nonvenomous scarlet king snake, which has a red/black/yellow/black/red banding pattern. As you'll see in the upcoming discussions, patterns also help us make sense of the behavior of the elements in terms of the atomic, chemical, and physical properties we have been studying.

**IN THIS CHAPTER . . .** We apply general ideas of bonding, structure, and reactivity (from Chapters 7–12) to the main-group elements and see how their behavior correlates with their position in the periodic table.
- We begin with hydrogen, the simplest element, considering its position in the periodic table and examining the three types of hydrides.
- We then survey Period 2 and the general changes in chemical and physical properties from left to right across the periodic table.
- In each of the remaining eight sections, we deal with one of the eight families of main-group elements, exploring vertical trends in physical and chemical properties in each group and focusing on some especially important elements—boron, carbon, silicon, nitrogen, phosphorus, oxygen, sulfur, and the halogens.

## 14.1 • HYDROGEN, THE SIMPLEST ATOM

A hydrogen atom consists of a nucleus with a single positive charge, surrounded by a single electron. Despite this simple structure, or perhaps because of it, hydrogen may be the most important element of all. In the Sun, hydrogen (H) nuclei combine to form helium (He) nuclei in a process that provides nearly all Earth's energy. About 90% of all the atoms in the universe are H atoms, making it the most abundant element by far. On Earth, only tiny amounts of the free, diatomic element occur naturally, but hydrogen is abundant in combination with oxygen in water. Because of its simple structure and low molar mass, nonpolar gaseous $H_2$ is colorless and odorless, and its extremely weak dispersion forces result in very low melting ($-259°C$) and boiling points ($-253°C$).

### Where Does Hydrogen Fit in the Periodic Table?

Hydrogen has no perfectly suitable position in the periodic table (Figure 14.1). Depending on the property, hydrogen may fit better in Group 1A(1), 4A(14), or 7A(17):

- *Like the Group 1A(1) elements*, hydrogen has an outer electron configuration of $ns^1$, a single valence electron, and a common +1 oxidation state. However, unlike the alkali metals, hydrogen *shares* its electron with nonmetals rather than transferring it to them. Moreover, hydrogen has a much higher ionization energy (IE = 1311 kJ/mol) and electronegativity (EN = 2.1) than the alkali metals. By comparison, lithium has

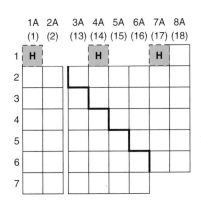

**Figure 14.1** Where does hydrogen belong?

an ionization energy of only 520 kJ/mol and an electronegativity of 1.0, the highest of the alkali metals.

- *Like the Group 4A(14) elements,* hydrogen has a half-filled valence level (but with only one electron) and similar ionization energy, electron affinity, electronegativity, and bond energies.
- *Like the Group 7A(17) elements,* hydrogen occurs as diatomic molecules and fills its outer (valence) level either by electron sharing or by gaining one electron from a metal to form an anion (hydride, $H^-$) with a $1-$ charge. However, while the monatomic halide ions ($X^-$) are common and stable, the $H^-$ ion is rare and reactive. Moreover, hydrogen has a lower electronegativity (EN = 2.1) than any of the halogens (ENs range from 2.2 to 4.0) and lacks their three valence electron pairs.

Hydrogen's unique behavior is attributable to its tiny size. Hydrogen has a high IE because its electron is very close to the nucleus, with no inner electrons to shield it from the positive charge. It has a low EN (for a nonmetal) because it has only one proton to attract bonding electrons. In this chapter, hydrogen will appear in either Group 1A(1) or 7A(17) depending on the property being considered.

## Highlights of Hydrogen Chemistry

In Chapters 12 and 13, we discussed hydrogen bonding and its impact on physical properties (melting and boiling points, heats of fusion and vaporization, and specific heat capacities) and solubilities. You learned that H bonding plays a critical part in stabilizing Earth's climate as well as your body temperature, and you glimpsed its role in the functional structures of biomolecules. In Chapter 6 (see Chemical Connections, p. 251) we considered the possible future use of hydrogen as a fuel, and in Chapter 22 we'll see how hydrogen is produced industrially and how it is used to recover some metals from their ores. Hydrogen is very reactive, combining with nearly every element, so we focus here on the three types of hydrides.

**Ionic (Saltlike) Hydrides** With very reactive metals, such as those in Group 1A(1) and the larger members of Group 2A(2) (Ca, Sr, and Ba), hydrogen forms *saltlike hydrides*—white, crystalline solids composed of the metal cation and the hydride ion:

$$2Li(s) + H_2(g) \longrightarrow 2LiH(s)$$
$$Ca(s) + H_2(g) \longrightarrow CaH_2(s)$$

In water, $H^-$ is a strong base that pulls $H^+$ from surrounding $H_2O$ molecules to form $H_2$ and $OH^-$:

$$NaH(s) + H_2O(l) \longrightarrow Na^+(aq) + OH^-(aq) + H_2(g)$$

The hydride ion is also a powerful reducing agent; for example, it reduces Ti(IV) to the free metal:

$$TiCl_4(l) + 4LiH(s) \longrightarrow Ti(s) + 4LiCl(s) + 2H_2(g)$$

**Covalent (Molecular) Hydrides** Hydrogen reacts with nonmetals to form many *covalent hydrides,* such as $CH_4$, $PH_3$, $H_2S$, and HCl. Most are gases consisting of small molecules, but many hydrides of boron and carbon are liquids or solids that consist of much larger molecules. In most covalent hydrides, hydrogen has an oxidation number of $+1$ because the other nonmetal has a higher electronegativity.

Conditions for preparing the covalent hydrides depend on the reactivity of the other nonmetal. For example, with stable, triple-bonded $N_2$, hydrogen reacts at high temperatures (~400°C) and pressures (~250 atm), and the reaction needs a catalyst to proceed at any practical speed:

$$N_2(g) + 3H_2(g) \xrightarrow{\text{catalyst}} 2NH_3(g) \quad \Delta H^\circ_{rxn} = -91.8 \text{ kJ}$$

Industrial facilities throughout the world use this reaction to produce millions of tons of ammonia each year for fertilizers, explosives, and synthetic fibers. On the other hand, hydrogen combines rapidly with reactive, single-bonded $F_2$, even at extremely low temperatures ($-196°C$):

$$F_2(g) + H_2(g) \longrightarrow 2HF(g) \quad \Delta H°_{rxn} = -546 \text{ kJ}$$

**Metallic (Interstitial) Hydrides** Many transition elements form *metallic (interstitial) hydrides,* in which $H_2$ molecules (and H atoms) occupy the holes in the metal's crystal structure (Figure 14.2). Thus, such hydrides are *not* compounds but gas-solid solutions. Also, unlike ionic and covalent hydrides, interstitial hydrides, such as $TiH_{1.7}$, typically lack a single, stoichiometric formula because the metal can incorporate variable amounts of hydrogen, depending on the pressure and temperature of the gas. It was thought that metallic hydrides might serve as "storage containers" for hydrogen fuel in cars. Unfortunately, the metals that store the most hydrogen are expensive and heavy and release hydrogen only at very high temperatures.

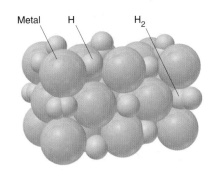

**Figure 14.2** A metallic (interstitial) hydride.

# 14.2 • TRENDS ACROSS THE PERIODIC TABLE: THE PERIOD 2 ELEMENTS

Table 14.1 on pages 526 and 527 presents the trends in atomic properties of the Period 2 elements, lithium through neon, and the physical and chemical properties that emerge from them. In general, these trends apply to the other periods as well. Note the following points:

- Electrons fill the one *ns* and the three *np* orbitals according to Pauli's exclusion principle and Hund's rule.
- As a result of increasing nuclear charge and the addition of electrons to orbitals of the same energy level (same *n* value), atomic size generally decreases, whereas first ionization energy and electronegativity generally increase (see the bar graphs on p. 527).
- Metallic character decreases with increasing nuclear charge as period members change from metals to metalloids to nonmetals.
- Reactivity is highest at the left and right ends of the period, except for the inert noble gas, because Li and F are only one electron away from attaining a filled outer level.
- Bonding between atoms of an element changes from metallic, to covalent in networks, to covalent in individual molecules, to none (noble gases exist as separate atoms). As expected, physical properties, such as melting point, change abruptly at the network/molecule boundary, which occurs in Period 2 between carbon (solid) and nitrogen (gas).
- Bonding between each element and an active nonmetal changes from ionic, to polar covalent, to covalent. Bonding between each element and an active metal changes from metallic to polar covalent to ionic.
- The acid-base behavior of the common element oxide in water changes from basic to amphoteric to acidic as the bond between the element and oxygen changes from ionic to covalent.
- Reducing strength decreases through the metals, and oxidizing strength increases through the nonmetals. In Period 2, common oxidation numbers (O.N.s) equal the A-group number for Li and Be and the A-group number minus eight for O and F. Boron has several O.N.s, Ne has none, and C and N show all possible O.N.s for their groups.

**The Anomalous Behavior of Period 2 Members** One point that is not shown in Table 14.1 is the *anomalous (unrepresentative) behavior of the Period 2 elements within their groups.* This behavior arises from the relatively *small size* and *small number of orbitals* in the outer energy level of these elements.

## Table 14.1 Trends in Atomic, Physical, and Chemical Properties of the Period 2 Elements

| Group:<br>Element/At. No.: | 1A(1)<br>Lithium (Li) $Z = 3$ | 2A(2)<br>Beryllium (Be) $Z = 4$ | 3A(13)<br>Boron (B) $Z = 5$ | 4A(14)<br>Carbon (C) $Z = 6$ |
|---|---|---|---|---|
| **Atomic Properties** | | | | |
| **Condensed electron configuration; partial orbital diagram** | [He] $2s^1$ <br><br> 2s    2p | [He] $2s^2$ <br><br> 2s    2p | [He] $2s^2 2p^1$ <br><br> 2s    2p | [He] $2s^2 2p^2$ <br><br> 2s    2p |
| **Physical Properties** | | | | |
| **Appearance** | | | | |
| **Metallic character** | Metal | Metal | Metalloid | Nonmetal |
| **Hardness** | Soft | Hard | Very hard | Graphite: soft<br>Diamond: extremely hard |
| **Melting point/ boiling point** | Low mp for a metal | High mp | Extremely high mp | Extremely high mp |
| **Chemical Properties** | | | | |
| **General reactivity** | Reactive | Low reactivity at room temperature | Low reactivity at room temperature | Low reactivity at room temperature; graphite more reactive |
| **Bonding among atoms of element** | Metallic | Metallic | Network covalent | Network covalent |
| **Bonding with nonmetals** | Ionic | Polar covalent | Polar covalent | Covalent ($\pi$ bonds common) |
| **Bonding with metals** | Metallic | Metallic | Polar covalent | Polar covalent |
| **Acid-base behavior of common oxide** | Strongly basic | Amphoteric | Very weakly acidic | Very weakly acidic |
| **Redox behavior (O.N.)** | Strong reducing agent $(+1)$ | Moderately strong reducing agent $(+2)$ | Complex hydrides good reducing agents $(+3, -3)$ | Every oxidation state from $+4$ to $-4$ |
| **Relevance/Uses of Element and Compounds** | | | | |
| | Li soaps for auto grease; thermonuclear bombs; high-voltage, low-weight batteries; treatment of bipolar disorders ($Li_2CO_3$) | Rocket nose cones; alloys for springs and gears; nuclear reactor parts; x-ray tubes | Cleaning agent (borax); eyewash, antiseptic (boric acid); armor ($B_4C$); borosilicate glass; plant nutrient | Graphite: lubricant, structural fiber<br>Diamond: jewelry, cutting tools, protective films<br>Limestone ($CaCO_3$)<br>Organic compounds: drugs, fuels, textiles, biomolecules, etc. |

| 5A(15)<br>Nitrogen (N) $Z = 7$ | 6A(16)<br>Oxygen (O) $Z = 8$ | 7A(17)<br>Fluorine (F) $Z = 9$ | 8A(18)<br>Neon (Ne) $Z = 10$ |
|---|---|---|---|
| [He] $2s^2 2p^3$ | [He] $2s^2 2p^4$ | [He] $2s^2 2p^5$ | [He] $2s^2 2p^6$ |
| Nonmetal | Nonmetal | Nonmetal | Nonmetal |
| — | — | — | — |
| Very low mp and bp | Very low mp and bp | Very low mp and bp | Extremely low mp and bp |
| Inactive at room temperature | Very reactive | Extremely reactive | Chemically inert |
| Covalent $N_2$ molecules | Covalent $O_2$ (or $O_3$) molecules | Covalent $F_2$ molecules | None; separate atoms |
| Covalent ($\pi$ bonds common) | Covalent ($\pi$ bonds common) | Covalent | None |
| Ionic/polar covalent; anions with active metals | Ionic | Ionic | None |
| Strongly acidic ($NO_2$) | — | Acidic | None |
| Every oxidation state from +5 to −3 | $O_2$ (and $O_3$) very strong oxidizing agents (−2) | Strongest oxidizing agent (−1) | None |
| Component of proteins, nucleic acids; ammonia for fertilizers, explosives; oxides involved in manufacturing and air pollution (smog, acid rain) | Component of biological macromolecules; final oxidizer in residential, industrial, and biological energy production | Manufacture of coatings (Teflon); glass etching (HF); refrigerants involved in ozone depletion (CFCs); dental protection (NaF, $SnF_2$) | Electrified gas in advertising signs |

No sample available

**Atomic radius (pm)**

Li 152, Be 112, B 85, C 77, N 75, O 73, F 72, Ne 71

1A (1)  2A (2)  3A (13)  4A (14)  5A (15)  6A (16)  7A (17)  8A (18)

**First ionization energy (kJ/mol)**

Li 520, Be 899, B 800, C 1086, N 1402, O 1314, F 1681, Ne 2080

1A (1)  2A (2)  3A (13)  4A (14)  5A (15)  6A (16)  7A (17)  8A (18)

**Electronegativity**

Li 1.0, Be 1.5, B 2.0, C 2.5, N 3.0, O 3.5, F 4.0

1A (1)  2A (2)  3A (13)  4A (14)  5A (15)  6A (16)  7A (17)  8A (18)

1. *Anomalous properties of lithium.* In Group 1A(1), Li is the only member that forms a simple oxide and nitride, $Li_2O$ and $Li_3N$, on reaction with $O_2$ and $N_2$ in air and the only member that forms molecular compounds with organic halides:

$$2Li(s) + CH_3CH_2Cl(g) \longrightarrow CH_3CH_2Li(s) + LiCl(s)$$

Because of its small size, $Li^+$ has a relatively high charge density. Therefore, it can deform nearby electron clouds to a much greater extent than the other 1A ions can, which increases orbital overlap and gives many lithium salts significant covalent character. Thus, LiCl, LiBr, and LiI are much more soluble in polar organic solvents, such as ethanol and acetone, than are the halides of Na and K, because the lithium halide bond polarity interacts with these solvents through dipole-dipole forces. The small, highly positive $Li^+$ makes dissociation of Li salts into ions more difficult in water; thus, the fluoride, carbonate, hydroxide, and phosphate of Li are much less soluble in water than those of Na and K.

2. *Anomalous properties of beryllium.* In Group 2A(2), beryllium displays especially anomalous behavior. Because of the extremely high charge density of $Be^{2+}$, the discrete ion does not exist, and *all Be compounds exhibit covalent bonding.* With only two valence electrons, Be does not attain an octet in its simple gaseous compounds (Section 10.1). When it bonds to an electron-rich atom, however, this electron deficiency is overcome as the gas condenses. Consider beryllium chloride ($BeCl_2$). At temperatures greater than 900°C, it consists of linear molecules in which two *sp* hybrid orbitals hold four electrons around the central Be (Figure 14.3A). As it cools, the molecules bond together, solidifying in long chains with each Cl bridging two Be atoms. Each Be is $sp^3$ hybridized to finally attain an octet (Figure 14.3B).

3. *Anomalous properties of other Period 2 elements.* In Group 3A(13), boron is the only member to form a complex family of compounds with metals and covalent compounds with hydrogen (boranes). Carbon, in Group 4A(14), shows extremely unusual behavior: it bonds to itself (and a small number of other elements) so extensively and diversely that it gives rise to countless organic compounds. In Group 5A(15), triple-bonded, unreactive, gaseous nitrogen is dramatically different from its reactive, solid family members. Oxygen, the only gas in Group 6A(16), is much more reactive than sulfur and the other members. In Group 7A(17), fluorine is so electronegative that it reacts violently with water, and it is the only member that forms a weak hydrohalic acid, HF.

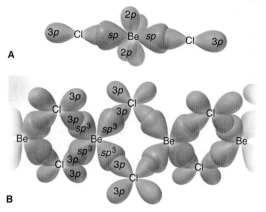

**Figure 14.3** Overcoming electron deficiency in beryllium chloride.

# 14.3 • GROUP 1A(1): THE ALKALI METALS

The first group of elements in the periodic table is named for the alkaline (basic) nature of their oxides and for the basic solutions the elements form in water. Group 1A(1) provides the best example of regular trends with no significant exceptions. All the elements in the group—lithium (Li), sodium (Na), potassium (K), rubidium (Rb), cesium (Cs), and rare, radioactive francium (Fr)*—are very reactive metals. The Family Portrait of Group 1A(1) is the first in a series that provides an overview of each of the main groups, summarizing key atomic, physical, and chemical properties.

## Why Are the Alkali Metals Soft, Low Melting, and Lightweight?

Alkali metals have some properties that are unique for metals:

- They are unusually soft and can be easily cut with a knife. Na has the consistency of cold butter and K can be squeezed like clay.

---

*Francium is so rare (estimates indicate only 15 g of the element in the top kilometer of Earth's crust) that its properties are largely unknown. Therefore, we will mention it only occasionally in the discussion.

# Group 1A(1): The Alkali Metals | Family Portrait

## KEY ATOMIC PROPERTIES, PHYSICAL PROPERTIES, AND REACTIONS

**KEY**
Atomic No.
**Symbol**
Atomic mass
Valence e⁻ configuration
(Common oxidation states)

| 3 | Li | 6.941 | $2s^1$ | (+1) |

| 11 | Na | 22.99 | $3s^1$ | (+1) |

| 19 | K | 39.10 | $4s^1$ | (+1) |

| 37 | Rb | 85.47 | $5s^1$ | (+1) |

| 55 | Cs | 132.9 | $6s^1$ | (+1) |

| 87 | Fr | (223) | $7s^1$ | (+1) |

No sample available

$ns^1$

**GROUP 1A(1)**

| | Atomic radius (pm) | Ionic radius (pm) |
|---|---|---|
| Li | 152 | Li⁺ 76 |
| Na | 186 | Na⁺ 102 |
| K | 227 | K⁺ 138 |
| Rb | 248 | Rb⁺ 152 |
| Cs | 265 | Cs⁺ 167 |
| Fr | (~270) | Fr⁺ 180 |

## Atomic Properties

Group electron configuration is $ns^1$. All members have the +1 oxidation state and form an E⁺ ion. Atoms have the largest size and lowest IE and EN in their periods. Down the group, atomic and ionic size increase, while IE and EN decrease.

Electronegativity
| | EN | IE₁ |
|---|---|---|
| Li | 1.0 | 520 |
| Na | 0.9 | 496 |
| K | 0.8 | 419 |
| Rb | 0.8 | 403 |
| Cs | 0.7 | 376 |
| Fr | 0.7 | ~375 |

First ionization energy (kJ/mol)

## Physical Properties

Metallic bonding is relatively weak because there is only one valence electron. Therefore, these metals are soft with relatively low melting and boiling points. These values decrease down the group because larger atom cores attract delocalized electrons less strongly. Large atomic size and low atomic mass result in low density; thus, density generally increases down the group because mass increases more than size.

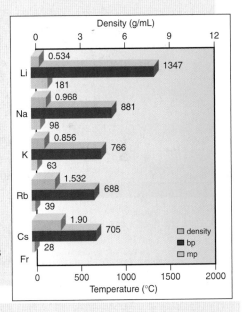

Density (g/mL)
| | density | bp | mp |
|---|---|---|---|
| Li | 0.534 | 1347 | 181 |
| Na | 0.968 | 881 | 98 |
| K | 0.856 | 766 | 63 |
| Rb | 1.532 | 688 | 39 |
| Cs | 1.90 | 705 | 28 |
| Fr | | | |

Temperature (°C)

## Reactions

**1.** The alkali metals reduce H in $H_2O$ from the +1 to the 0 oxidation state (E represents any element in the group):

$$2E(s) + 2H_2O(l) \longrightarrow 2E^+(aq) + 2OH^-(aq) + H_2(g)$$

The reaction becomes more vigorous down the group.

**2.** The alkali metals reduce oxygen, but the product depends on the metal. Li forms the oxide, $Li_2O$; Na forms the peroxide (O.N. of O = −1), $Na_2O_2$; K, Rb, and Cs form the superoxide (O.N. of O = −½), $EO_2$:

$$4Li(s) + O_2(g) \longrightarrow 2Li_2O(s)$$
$$2Na(s) + O_2(g) \longrightarrow Na_2O_2(s)$$
$$K(s) + O_2(g) \longrightarrow KO_2(s)$$

In emergency breathing units, $KO_2$ reacts with $H_2O$ and $CO_2$ in exhaled air to release $O_2$ (Section 22.4).

**3.** The alkali metals reduce hydrogen to form ionic (saltlike) hydrides:

$$2E(s) + H_2(g) \longrightarrow 2EH(s)$$

NaH is an industrial base and reducing agent that is used to prepare other reducing agents, such as $NaBH_4$.

**4.** The alkali metals reduce halogens to form ionic halides:

$$2E(s) + X_2 \longrightarrow 2EX(s) \qquad (X = F, Cl, Br, I)$$

Lithium floating in oil floating on water.

- Alkali metals have lower melting and boiling points than any other group of metals. Li is the only alkali metal that has a melting point above 100°C, and Cs melts only a few degrees above room temperature.
- They have lower densities than most metals. Li floats on lightweight household oil (*see photo*).

The unusual physical behavior of the alkali metals can be traced to their atomic size, the largest in their respective periods, and to the $ns^1$ valence electron configuration. Because the single valence electron is relatively far from the nucleus, there is only a weak attraction between the delocalized electrons and the metal-ion cores in the crystal structure. This weak metallic bonding means that the alkali metal crystal structure can be easily deformed or broken down, which results in a soft consistency and low melting point. The low densities of the alkali metals result from their having the lowest molar masses and largest atomic radii (and, thus, volumes) in their periods.

## Why Are the Alkali Metals So Reactive?

The alkali metals are extremely reactive elements. They are *powerful reducing agents,* always occurring in nature as 1+ cations rather than as free metals. (As we discuss in Section 22.4, highly endothermic reduction processes are required to prepare the free metals industrially from their molten salts.) Some examples of their reactivity follow:

- The alkali metals (E)* reduce halogens to form ionic solids in highly exothermic reactions:

$$2E(s) + X_2 \longrightarrow 2EX(s) \qquad (X = F, Cl, Br, I)$$

- They reduce hydrogen in water, reacting vigorously (Rb and Cs explosively) to form $H_2$ and a metal hydroxide solution (*see photo*):

$$2E(s) + 2H_2O(l) \longrightarrow 2E^+(aq) + 2OH^-(aq) + H_2(g)$$

- They reduce molecular hydrogen to form ionic hydrides:

$$2E(s) + H_2(g) \longrightarrow 2EH(s)$$

Potassium reacting with water.

- They reduce $O_2$ in air, and thus tarnish rapidly. Because of this reactivity, Na and K are usually kept under mineral oil (an unreactive liquid) in the laboratory, and Rb and Cs are handled with gloves under an inert argon atmosphere.

The $ns^1$ configuration, which is the basis for their physical properties, is also the reason why alkali metals form salts so readily. Properties based on the $ns^1$ configuration are involved in each of the following steps, which take place in the reaction between an alkali metal and a nonmetal:

1. *The solid metal separates into gaseous atoms.* Consistent with the alkali metals' low melting and boiling points, their weak metallic bonding leads to *low values for $\Delta H_{atom}$* (the heat needed to convert the solid into individual gaseous atoms), which decrease down the group:

$$E(s) \longrightarrow E(g) \qquad \Delta H_{atom} \text{ (Li > Na > K > Rb > Cs)}$$

2. *The metal atom becomes a cation after transferring its outer electron to the nonmetal.* Alkali metals have *low ionization energies* (the lowest in their periods) and form *cations with small radii* since a great decrease in size occurs when the outer electron is lost: the volume of the $Li^+$ ion is less than 13% of the volume of the Li atom! Thus, Group 1A(1) ions are small spheres with considerable charge density.

3. *The resulting cations and anions attract each other to form an ionic solid.* Group 1A(1) salts have *high lattice energies* because the small cations lie close to the anions. Thus, the endothermic atomization and ionization steps are easily outweighed by the highly exothermic formation of the solid. For a given anion, the trend in lattice energy is the inverse of the trend in cation size: *as the cation becomes larger, the lattice energy becomes smaller.* This steady decrease in lattice energy within the Group 1A(1) and 2A(2) chlorides is shown in Figure 14.4.

| LiCl | 853 | BeCl$_2$ | 3020 |
| NaCl | 786 | MgCl$_2$ | 2526 |
| KCl | 715 | CaCl$_2$ | 2258 |
| RbCl | 689 | SrCl$_2$ | 2156 |
| CsCl | 659 | BaCl$_2$ | 2056 | 1A(1) |
| FrCl | 632 | RaCl$_2$ | 2004 | 2A(2) |

0     1000     2000     3000
Lattice energy (kJ/mol)

**Figure 14.4** Lattice energies of the Group 1A(1) and 2A(2) chlorides.

*Throughout the chapter, we use E to represent any element in a group.

Despite the strong ionic attractions in the solid, *nearly all Group 1A(1) salts are water soluble.* The attraction between the ions and water molecules creates a highly exothermic heat of hydration ($\Delta H_{hydr}$), and a large increase in entropy occurs when ions in the organized crystal become dispersed and hydrated in solution; together, these factors outweigh the high lattice energy.

The magnitude of the hydration energy *decreases* as ionic size increases:

$$E^+(g) \longrightarrow E^+(aq) \quad \Delta H = -\Delta H_{hydr} \, (Li^+ > Na^+ > K^+ > Rb^+ > Cs^+)$$

Interestingly, the *smaller* ions attract water molecules strongly enough to form larger *hydrated ions.* This size trend has a major effect on the function of nerves, kidneys, and cell membranes because the *sizes* of $Na^+(aq)$ and $K^+(aq)$, the most common cations in cell fluids, influence their movement in and out of cells.

# 14.4 • GROUP 2A(2): THE ALKALINE EARTH METALS

The Group 2A(2) elements are called *alkaline earth metals* because their oxides give basic (alkaline) solutions and melt at such high temperatures that they remained as solids ("earths") in the alchemists' fires. The group is a fascinating collection of elements: rare beryllium (Be), common magnesium (Mg) and calcium (Ca), less familiar strontium (Sr) and barium (Ba), and radioactive radium (Ra). The Group 2A(2) Family Portrait *(next page)* presents an overview of these elements.

## How Do the Physical Properties of the Alkaline Earth and Alkali Metals Compare?

In general terms, the elements in Groups 1A(1) and 2A(2) behave as close cousins. Whatever differences occur between the groups are those of degree, not kind, and are due to the change in outer electron configuration: $ns^2$ vs. $ns^1$. Two electrons are available from each 2A atom for metallic bonding, and the nucleus contains one additional positive charge. These factors strengthen the attraction between delocalized electrons and atom cores. Consequently, melting and boiling points are much higher for 2A metals than for the corresponding 1A metals; in fact, the 2A elements melt at around the same temperatures as the 1A elements boil! Compared to transition metals such as iron and chromium, the alkaline earths are soft and lightweight, but their stronger metallic bonding and smaller atomic sizes make them harder and denser than the alkali metals.

## How Do the Chemical Properties of the Alkaline Earth and Alkali Metals Compare?

Group 2A(2) elements have smaller atomic radii and higher ionization energies than Group 1A(1) elements. This is due to the fact that the second valence electron in an alkaline earth metal lies in the same sublevel as the first and thus it is not shielded from the additional nuclear charge very well, so $Z_{eff}$ is greater. This greater attraction of the nucleus for the valence electrons makes those electrons more difficult to remove. Despite the higher IEs, *all the alkaline earths (except Be) form ionic compounds* as 2+ cations. Beryllium behaves differently because so much energy is needed to remove two electrons from this tiny atom that it never forms discrete $Be^{2+}$ ions, and its bonds are polar covalent.

Like the alkali metals, the alkaline earth metals are *strong reducing agents:*

- Each one reduces $O_2$ in air to form the oxide (Ba also forms the peroxide, $BaO_2$).
- Except for Be and Mg, which form adherent oxide coatings, the alkaline earths reduce $H_2O$ at room temperature to form $H_2$.
- Except for Be, the alkaline earths reduce the halogens, $N_2$, and $H_2$ to form ionic compounds.

The Group 2A oxides are strongly basic (except for amphoteric BeO) and react with acidic oxides to form salts, such as sulfites and carbonates; for example,

$$SrO(s) + CO_2(g) \longrightarrow SrCO_3(s)$$

## KEY ATOMIC PROPERTIES, PHYSICAL PROPERTIES, AND REACTIONS

| KEY | |
|---|---|
| | Atomic No. |
| | **Symbol** |
| | Atomic mass |
| | Valence e⁻ configuration |
| | (Common oxidation states) |

4
**Be**
9.012
$2s^2$
(+2)

12
**Mg**
24.30
$3s^2$
(+2)

20
**Ca**
40.08
$4s^2$
(+2)

38
**Sr**
87.62
$5s^2$
(+2)

56
**Ba**
137.3
$6s^2$
(+2)

88
**Ra**
(226)
$7s^2$
(+2)

No sample available

**GROUP 2A(2)**

| Atomic radius (pm) | Ionic radius (pm) |
|---|---|
| Be 112 | |
| Mg 160 | Mg²⁺ 72 |
| Ca 197 | Ca²⁺ 100 |
| Sr 215 | Sr²⁺ 118 |
| Ba 222 | Ba²⁺ 135 |
| Ra (~220) | Ra²⁺ 148 |

### Atomic Properties

Group electron configuration is $ns^2$ (filled $ns$ sublevel). All members have the +2 oxidation state and, except for Be, form compounds with an $E^{2+}$ ion. Atomic and ionic sizes increase down the group but are smaller than for the corresponding 1A(1) elements. IE and EN decrease down the group but are higher than for the corresponding 1A(1) elements.

### Physical Properties

Metallic bonding involves two valence electrons. These metals are still relatively soft but are much harder than the 1A(1) metals. Melting and boiling points generally decrease, and densities generally increase down the group. These values are much higher than for 1A(1) elements, and the trend is not as regular.

### Reactions

**1.** The metals reduce $O_2$ to form the oxides:
$$2E(s) + O_2(g) \longrightarrow 2EO(s)$$
Ba also forms the peroxide, $BaO_2$.

**2.** The larger metals reduce water to form hydrogen gas:
$$E(s) + 2H_2O(l) \longrightarrow E^{2+}(aq) + 2OH^-(aq) + H_2(g)$$
$$(E = Ca, Sr, Ba)$$
Be and Mg form an oxide coating that allows only slight reaction.

**3.** The metals reduce halogens to form ionic halides:
$$E(s) + X_2 \longrightarrow EX_2(s) \quad [X = F \text{ (not with Be)}, Cl, Br, I]$$

**4.** Most of the elements reduce hydrogen to form ionic hydrides:
$$E(s) + H_2(g) \longrightarrow EH_2(s) \quad (E = \text{all except Be})$$

**5.** The elements reduce nitrogen to form ionic nitrides:
$$3E(s) + N_2(g) \longrightarrow E_3N_2(s)$$

**6.** Except for amphoteric BeO, the element oxides are basic:
$$EO(s) + H_2O(l) \longrightarrow E^{2+}(aq) + 2OH^-(aq)$$
$Ca(OH)_2$ is a component of cement and mortar.

**7.** All carbonates undergo thermal decomposition to the oxide:
$$ECO_3(s) \xrightarrow{\Delta} EO(s) + CO_2(g)$$
This reaction is used to produce CaO (lime) in huge amounts from naturally occurring limestone.

Natural carbonates, such as limestone and marble, are major structural materials and the commercial sources for most 2A compounds. Calcium carbonate is heated to obtain calcium oxide (lime); this important industrial compound has essential roles in steelmaking, water treatment, and smokestack scrubbing and is used to make glass, whiten paper, and neutralize acidic soil.

The alkaline earth metals are reactive because the high lattice energies of their compounds more than compensate for the large total IE required for forming 2+ cations (Section 9.2). Group 2A salts have much higher lattice energies than Group 1A salts (see Figure 14.4) because the 2A cations are smaller and doubly charged, resulting in much higher charge densities, which lead to lower solubility of 2A salts in water. Although higher charge density increases heat of hydration, it increases lattice energy even more. In fact, most 2A fluorides, carbonates, phosphates, and sulfates have very low solubility, unlike the corresponding 1A compounds. Nevertheless, the ion-dipole attractions between 2+ ions and water molecules are so strong that many slightly soluble 2A salts crystallize as hydrates; two examples are Epsom salt, $MgSO_4 \cdot 7H_2O$, used as a soak for inflammations, and gypsum, $CaSO_4 \cdot 2H_2O$, used as the bonding material between the paper sheets in wallboard and as the cement in surgical casts.

## Diagonal Relationships: Lithium and Magnesium

One of the clearest ways in which atomic properties influence chemical behavior appears in the **diagonal relationships,** similarities between a Period 2 element and one diagonally down and to the right in Period 3 (Figure 14.5).

The first of three such relationships occurs between Li and Mg, which have similar atomic and ionic sizes. Note that *one period down increases atomic (or ionic) size and one group to the right decreases it.* Thus, Li has a radius of 152 pm and Mg has a radius of 160 pm; the $Li^+$ radius is 76 pm and that of $Mg^{2+}$ is 72 pm. From similar atomic properties emerge similar chemical properties. Both elements form nitrides with $N_2$, hydroxides and carbonates that decompose easily with heat, organic compounds with a polar covalent metal-carbon bond, and salts with similar solubilities. We'll discuss the diagonal relationships between Be and Al and between B and Si in upcoming sections.

**Figure 14.5** Three diagonal relationships in the periodic table.

---

# 14.5 • GROUP 3A(13): THE BORON FAMILY

The third family of main-group elements contains both familiar and unusual members, which engage in some exotic bonding and have strange physical properties. Boron (B) heads the family, but, as you'll see, its properties are not representative. Metallic aluminum (Al) has properties that are more typical of the group, but its great abundance and importance contrast with the rareness of gallium (Ga), indium (In), thallium (Tl), and, of course, the recently synthesized element 113. The atomic, physical, and chemical properties of these elements are summarized in the Group 3A(13) Family Portrait *(next page).*

## How Do Transition Elements Influence Group 3A(13) Properties?

Group 3A(13) is the first of the *p* block. If you look at the main groups only, the elements of this group seem to be just one group away from those of Group 2A(2). In Period 4 and higher, however, a large gap separates the two groups (see Figure 8.11, p. 306). The gap holds 10 transition elements (*d* block) each in Periods 4 to 7 and an additional 14 inner transition elements (*f* block) in Periods 6 and 7. Recall from Section 8.1 that *d* and *f* electrons penetrate very little, and so spend very little time near the nucleus. Thus, the heavier 3A members—Ga, In, and Tl (and presumably element 113)—have nuclei with many more protons, but their outer (*s* and *p*)

# Group 3A(13): The Boron Family

## KEY ATOMIC PROPERTIES, PHYSICAL PROPERTIES, AND REACTIONS

| KEY | Atomic No.<br>**Symbol**<br>Atomic mass<br>Valence e⁻ configuration<br>(Common oxidation states) |
| --- | --- |

**5**
**B**
10.81
$2s^2 2p^1$
(+3)

**13**
**Al**
26.98
$3s^2 3p^1$
(+3)

**31**
**Ga**
69.72
$4s^2 4p^1$
(+3, +1)

**49**
**In**
114.8
$5s^2 5p^1$
(+3, +1)

**81**
**Tl**
204.4
$6s^2 6p^1$
(+1)

**113**
Observed in experiments at Dubna, Russia, in 2003
(284)
$7s^2 7p^1$

$ns^2 np^1$

**GROUP 3A(13)**

| Atomic radius (pm) | Ionic radius (pm) |
| --- | --- |
| B 85 | |
| Al 143 | $Al^{3+}$ 54 |
| Ga 135 | $Ga^{3+}$ 62 |
| In 167 | $In^{3+}$ 80 |
| Tl 170 | $Tl^+$ 150 |

## Atomic Properties

Group electron configuration is $ns^2 np^1$. All except Tl commonly display the +3 oxidation state. The +1 state becomes more common down the group. Atomic size is smaller and EN is higher than for 2A(2) elements; IE is lower, however, because it is easier to remove an electron from the higher energy $p$ sublevel. Atomic size, IE, and EN do not change as expected down the group because there are intervening transition and inner transition elements.

## Physical Properties

Bonding changes from network covalent in B to metallic in the rest of the group. Thus, B has a much higher melting point than the others, but there is no overall trend. Boiling points decrease down the group. Densities increase down the group.

## Reactions

1. The elements react sluggishly, if at all, with water:

$$2Ga(s) + 6H_2O(hot) \longrightarrow 2Ga^{3+}(aq) + 6OH^-(aq) + 3H_2(g)$$
$$2Tl(s) + 2H_2O(steam) \longrightarrow 2Tl^+(aq) + 2OH^-(aq) + H_2(g)$$

Al becomes covered with a layer of $Al_2O_3$ that prevents further reaction.

2. When strongly heated in pure $O_2$, all members form oxides:

$$4E(s) + 3O_2(g) \xrightarrow{\Delta} 2E_2O_3(s) \qquad (E = B, Al, Ga, In)$$
$$4Tl(s) + O_2(g) \xrightarrow{\Delta} 2Tl_2O(s)$$

Oxide acidity decreases down the group: $B_2O_3$ (weakly acidic) > $Al_2O_3$ > $Ga_2O_3$ > $In_2O_3$ > $Tl_2O$ (strongly basic), and the +1 oxide is more basic than the +3 oxide.

3. All members reduce halogens ($X_2$):

$$2E(s) + 3X_2 \longrightarrow 2EX_3 \qquad (E = B, Al, Ga, In)$$
$$2Tl(s) + X_2 \longrightarrow 2TlX(s)$$

The $BX_3$ compounds are volatile and covalent. Trihalides of Al, Ga, and In are (mostly) ionic solids.

electrons are only partially shielded from the much higher positive charge; as a result, these elements have greater $Z_{eff}$ values than the two lighter members of the group. This stronger nuclear attraction affects many properties of the heavier 3A elements. For example, Ga, In, and Tl have smaller atomic radii and larger ionization energies and electronegativities than expected. The deviations for Ga and In reflect the *d*-block *contraction in size* and can be explained by limited shielding by the *d* electrons of the 10 additional protons of the first transition series. Similarly, the deviations for Tl reflect the *f*-block (lanthanide) contraction and can be explained by limited shielding by the *f* electrons of the 14 additional protons of the first inner transition series.

Physical properties are influenced by the type of bonding in the element. Boron is a network covalent metalloid—black, hard, and very high melting. The other group members are metals—shiny and relatively soft and low melting. Aluminum's low density and three valence electrons make it an exceptional conductor: for a given mass, aluminum conducts a current twice as effectively as copper. Gallium has the largest liquid temperature range of any element: it melts at skin temperature (*see photo,* p. 534) but does not boil until 2403°C. Its metallic bonding is too weak to keep the Ga atoms fixed when the solid is warmed, but strong enough to keep them from escaping the molten metal until it is very hot. An important use of gallium is in the production of gallium arsenide (GaAs) semiconductors. Since GaAs chips create a current when they absorb light and emit light when a current is supplied, they are used in light-powered calculators, wrist watches, and solar panels.

## What New Features Appear in the Chemical Properties of Group 3A(13)?

Looking down Group 3A(13), we see a wide range of chemical behavior. Boron, the anomalous member from Period 2, is the first metalloid we've encountered so far and the only one in the group. It is much less reactive at room temperature than the other members and forms covalent bonds exclusively. Although aluminum acts like a metal physically, its halides exist in the gas phase as covalent *dimers*—molecules formed by joining two identical smaller molecules (Figure 14.6)—and its oxide is amphoteric rather than basic. Most of the other 3A compounds are ionic, but they have more covalent character than similar 2A compounds. Because the 3A cations are smaller and more highly charged than the 2A cations, they polarize an anion's electron cloud more effectively.

The redox behavior of the elements in this group provides a chance to note three general principles that appear in Groups 3A(13) to 6A(16):

1. *Presence of multiple oxidation states.* Many of the larger elements in these groups also have an important oxidation state *two lower than the A-group number.* The lower state occurs when the atoms lose their *np* electrons only, not their two *ns* electrons. This fact is often called the *inert-pair effect* (Section 8.4).

2. *Increasing prominence of the lower oxidation state.* When a group exhibits more than one oxidation state, *the lower state becomes more prominent going down the group.* In Group 3A(13), for instance, all members exhibit the +3 state, but the +1 state first appears with some compounds of gallium and becomes the only important state of thallium.

3. *Relative basicity of oxides.* In general, *oxides of the element in the lower oxidation state are more basic than oxides in the higher oxidation state.* A good example in Group 3A(13) is that $In_2O$ is more basic than $In_2O_3$. In general, when an element has more than one oxidation state, *it acts more like a metal in its lower state,* and this, too, is related to ionic charge density. In this example, the lower charge of $In^+$ does not polarize the $O^{2-}$ ion as much as the higher charge of $In^{3+}$ does. Thus, in compounds of general formula $E_2O$, the E-to-O bonding is more ionic than it is in $E_2O_3$ compounds, so the $O^{2-}$ ion is more available to act as a base.

**Figure 14.6** The dimeric structure of gaseous aluminum chloride.

## Highlights of Boron Chemistry

Like the other Period 2 elements, the chemical behavior of boron is strikingly different from that of the other members of its group. As was pointed out earlier, *all boron compounds are covalent,* and unlike the other Group 3A(13) members, boron forms network covalent compounds or large molecules with metals, H, O, N, and C. The unifying feature of many boron compounds is the element's *electron deficiency,* but boron adopts two strategies to fill its outer level: accepting a bonding pair from an electron-rich atom and forming bridge bonds with an electron-poor atom.

**Accepting a Bonding Pair from an Electron-Rich Atom** In gaseous boron trihalides ($BX_3$), the B atom is electron deficient, with only six electrons around it (Section 10.1). To attain an octet, the B atom accepts a lone pair of electrons from an electron-rich atom (*blue*) and forms a covalent bond:

$$BF_3(g) + :NH_3(g) \longrightarrow F_3B—NH_3(g)$$

(Such reactions, in which one reactant accepts an electron pair from another to form a covalent bond, are very widespread in inorganic, organic, and biochemical processes. They are known as *Lewis acid-base reactions,* and we'll discuss them in Chapters 18 and 23 and see examples of them throughout the second half of the text.)

Similarly, B has only six electrons in boric acid, $B(OH)_3$ (sometimes written as $H_3BO_3$). In water, the acid itself does not release a proton. Rather, it accepts an electron pair from the O in $H_2O$, forming a fourth bond and releasing an $H^+$ ion:

$$B(OH)_3(s) + H_2O(l) \rightleftharpoons B(OH)_4^-(aq) + H^+(aq)$$

Boron's outer shell is filled in the wide variety of borate salts, such as the mineral borax (sodium borate), $Na_2[B_4O_5(OH)_4] \cdot 8H_2O$, used for decades as a household cleaning agent. Strong heating of boric acid (or borate salts) drives off water molecules and gives molten boron oxide:

$$2B(OH)_3(s) \xrightarrow{\Delta} B_2O_3(l) + 3H_2O(g)$$

When mixed with silica ($SiO_2$), the molten oxide forms borosilicate glass. Its high transparency and small change in size when heated or cooled make borosilicate glass useful in cookware and in the glassware used in the lab (*see photo*).

Labware made of borosilicate glass.

**Forming Bridge Bonds with an Electron-Poor Atom** In elemental boron and its many hydrides (boranes), there is no electron-rich atom to supply boron with electrons. In these substances, boron attains an octet through some unusual bonding. In diborane ($B_2H_6$) and many larger boranes, for example, two types of B—H bonds exist. The first type is a normal electron-pair bond. The valence bond picture in Figure 14.7 shows an $sp^3$ orbital of B overlapping a $1s$ orbital of H in each of the four terminal B—H bonds, using two of the three electrons in the valence level of each B atom.

The other type of bond is a hydride **bridge bond** (or three-center, two-electron bond), in which *each B—H—B grouping is held together by only two electrons.* Two $sp^3$ orbitals, one from *each* B, overlap an H $1s$ orbital between them. Two electrons move through this extended bonding orbital—one from one of the B atoms and the other from the H atom—and join the two B atoms via the H atom bridge. Notice

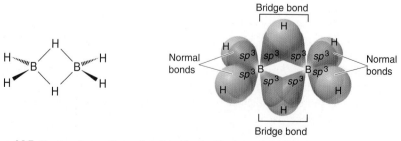

**Figure 14.7** The two types of covalent bonding in diborane.

that *each B atom is surrounded by eight electrons:* four from the two normal B—H bonds and four from the two B—H—B bridge bonds with a tetrahedral arrangement around each B atom. In many boranes and in elemental boron (Figure 14.8), one B atom bridges two others in a three-center, two-electron B—B—B bond.

## Diagonal Relationships: Beryllium and Aluminum

Beryllium in Group 2A(2) and aluminum in Group 3A(13) are another pair of diagonally related elements. Both form oxoanions in strong base: beryllate, $Be(OH)_4^{2-}$, and aluminate, $Al(OH)_4^-$. Both have bridge bonds in their hydrides and chlorides. Both form oxide coatings impervious to reaction with water (which explains aluminum's great use as a structural metal), and both oxides are amphoteric, extremely hard, and high melting. Although the atomic and ionic sizes of these elements differ, the small, highly charged $Be^{2+}$ and $Al^{3+}$ ions polarize nearby electron clouds strongly. Therefore, some Al compounds and all Be compounds have significant covalent character.

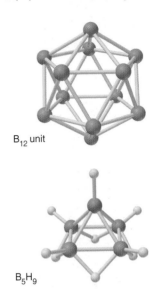

B$_{12}$ unit

B$_5$H$_9$

**Figure 14.8** The boron icosahedron and one of the boranes.

# 14.6 • GROUP 4A(14): THE CARBON FAMILY

The whole range of elemental behavior occurs within Group 4A(14): nonmetallic carbon (C) leads off, followed by the metalloids silicon (Si) and germanium (Ge), with metallic tin (Sn) and lead (Pb) next, and recently synthesized element 114 at the bottom of the group. Information about the compounds of C and of Si fills libraries: organic chemistry, most polymer chemistry, and biochemistry are based on carbon, whereas geochemistry and some extremely important polymer and electronic technologies are based on silicon. The Group 4A(14) Family Portrait *(next page)* summarizes atomic, physical, and chemical properties.

## How Does the Bonding in an Element Affect Physical Properties?

The elements of Group 4A(14) and their neighbors in Groups 3A(13) and 5A(15) illustrate how physical properties, such as melting point and heat of fusion ($\Delta H_{fus}$), depend on the type of bonding in an element (Table 14.2). Within Group 4A, the large decrease in melting point between the network covalent solids C and Si is due to longer, weaker bonds in the Si structure; the large decrease between Ge and Sn is due to the change from covalent network to metallic bonding. Similarly, considering horizontal trends, the large increases in melting point and $\Delta H_{fus}$ across a period between Al and Si and between Ga and Ge reflect the change from metallic to covalent network bonding. Note the abrupt rises in the values for these properties from metallic Al, Ga, and Sn to the network covalent metalloids Si, Ge, and Sb, and note the abrupt drops from the covalent networks of C and Si to the individual molecules of N and P in Group 5A.

**Table 14.2  Bond Type and the Melting Process in Groups 3A(13) to 5A(15)**

| Period | Group 3A(13) | | | | Group 4A(14) | | | | Group 5A(15) | | | |
|---|---|---|---|---|---|---|---|---|---|---|---|---|
| | Element | Bond Type | Melting Point (°C) | $\Delta H_{fus}$ (kJ/mol) | Element | Bond Type | Melting Point (°C) | $\Delta H_{fus}$ (kJ/mol) | Element | Bond Type | Melting Point (°C) | $\Delta H_{fus}$ (kJ/mol) |
| 2 | B | Covalent network | 2180 | 23.6 | C | Covalent network | 4100 | Very high | N | Covalent molecule | −210 | 0.7 |
| 3 | Al | Metallic | 660 | 10.5 | Si | Covalent network | 1420 | 50.6 | P | Covalent molecule | 44.1 | 2.5 |
| 4 | Ga | Metallic | 30 | 5.6 | Ge | Covalent network | 945 | 36.8 | As | Covalent network | 816 | 27.7 |
| 5 | In | Metallic | 157 | 3.3 | Sn | Metallic | 232 | 7.1 | Sb | Covalent network | 631 | 20.0 |
| 6 | Tl | Metallic | 304 | 4.3 | Pb | Metallic | 327 | 4.8 | Bi | Metallic | 271 | 10.5 |

**Key:**
- Metallic
- Covalent network
- Covalent molecule
- Metal
- Metalloid
- Nonmetal

# Family Portrait — Group 4A(14): The Carbon Family

## KEY ATOMIC PROPERTIES, PHYSICAL PROPERTIES, AND REACTIONS

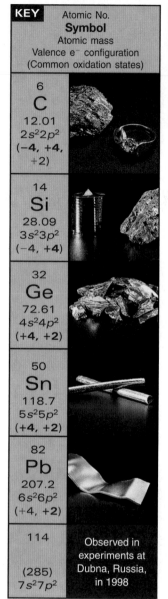

**KEY**

Atomic No.
**Symbol**
Atomic mass
Valence e⁻ configuration
(Common oxidation states)

| | |
|---|---|
| 6 **C** 12.01 $2s^2 2p^2$ (−4, +4, +2) | |
| 14 **Si** 28.09 $3s^2 3p^2$ (−4, +4) | |
| 32 **Ge** 72.61 $4s^2 4p^2$ (+4, +2) | |
| 50 **Sn** 118.7 $5s^2 5p^2$ (+4, +2) | |
| 82 **Pb** 207.2 $6s^2 6p^2$ (+4, +2) | |
| 114 (285) $7s^2 7p^2$ | Observed in experiments at Dubna, Russia, in 1998 |

$ns^2 np^2$

**GROUP 4A(14)**

| Atomic radius (pm) | Ionic radius (pm) |
|---|---|
| C 77 | |
| Si 118 | |
| Ge 122 | |
| Sn 140 | Sn²⁺ 118 |
| Pb 146 | Pb²⁺ 119 |

## Atomic Properties

Group electron configuration is $ns^2 np^2$. Down the group, the number of oxidation states decreases, and the lower (+2) state becomes more common. Down the group, size increases. Because transition and inner transition elements intervene, IE and EN do not decrease smoothly.

Electronegativity / First ionization energy (kJ/mol)

| Element | EN | IE₁ |
|---|---|---|
| C | 2.5 | 1086 |
| Si | 1.8 | 786 |
| Ge | 1.8 | 761 |
| Sn | 1.8 | 708 |
| Pb | 1.9 | 715 |

## Physical Properties

Trends in properties, such as decreasing hardness and melting point, are due to changes in types of bonding within the solid: covalent network in C, Si, and Ge; metallic in Sn and Pb *(see text)*. Down the group, density increases because of several factors, including differences in crystal packing.

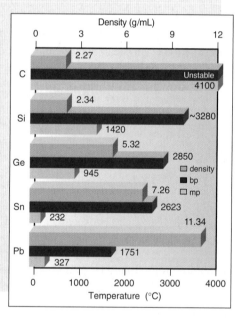

Density (g/mL) / Temperature (°C)

| Element | density | bp | mp |
|---|---|---|---|
| C | 2.27 | Unstable | 4100 |
| Si | 2.34 | ~3280 | 1420 |
| Ge | 5.32 | 2850 | 945 |
| Sn | 7.26 | 2623 | 232 |
| Pb | 11.34 | 1751 | 327 |

## Reactions

**1.** The elements are oxidized by halogens:

$$E(s) + 2X_2 \longrightarrow EX_4 \quad (E = C, Si, Ge)$$

The +2 halides are more stable for tin and lead, $SnX_2$ and $PbX_2$.

**2.** The elements are oxidized by $O_2$:

$$E(s) + O_2(g) \longrightarrow EO_2 \quad (E = C, Si, Ge, Sn)$$

Pb forms the +2 oxide, PbO. Oxides become more basic down the group. The reaction of $CO_2$ and $H_2O$ provides the weak acidity of natural unpolluted waters:

$$CO_2(g) + H_2O(l) \rightleftharpoons [H_2CO_3(aq)]$$
$$\rightleftharpoons H^+(aq) + HCO_3^-(aq)$$

**3.** Hydrocarbons react with $O_2$ to form $CO_2$ and $H_2O$. The reaction for methane is adapted to yield heat or electricity:

$$CH_4(g) + 2O_2(g) \longrightarrow CO_2(g) + 2H_2O(g)$$

**4.** Silica is reduced to form elemental silicon:

$$SiO_2(s) + 2C(s) \longrightarrow Si(s) + 2CO(g)$$

This crude silicon is made ultrapure through zone refining for use in the manufacture of computer chips.

**Allotropism: Different Forms of an Element** Striking variations in physical properties often appear among **allotropes,** different crystalline or molecular forms of a substance. One allotrope is usually more stable than another at a particular pressure and temperature. Group 4A(14) provides the first important examples of allotropism, in the forms of carbon and tin.

1. *Allotropes of carbon.* It is difficult to imagine two substances made entirely of the same atom that are more different than graphite and diamond. Graphite is a black electrical conductor that is soft and "greasy," whereas diamond is a colorless electrical insulator that is extremely hard. Graphite is the standard state of carbon, the more stable form at ordinary temperature and pressure, conditions indicated by the red dot in the phase diagram in Figure 14.9. Fortunately for jewelry owners, diamond changes to graphite at a negligible rate under normal conditions.

In the mid-1980s, a newly discovered allotrope of carbon began generating great interest. Mass spectrometric analysis of soot had shown evidence for a soccer ball–shaped molecule of formula $C_{60}$ (Figure 14.10A). More recently, the molecule has also been found in geological samples formed by meteorite impacts, even the one that occurred around the time the dinosaurs became extinct. The molecule has been dubbed *buckminsterfullerene* (informally called a "buckyball") after the architect-engineer R. Buckminster Fuller, who designed structures with similar shapes. Excitement rose in 1990, when scientists learned how to prepare multigram quantities of $C_{60}$ (Figure 14.10A, *photo*) and related fullerenes, enough to study macroscopic behavior and possible applications. Since then, metal atoms have been incorporated into the structure and many different atoms and groups (fluorine, hydroxyl groups, sugars, etc.) have been attached, resulting in compounds with a range of useful properties.

In 1991, scientists passed an electric discharge through graphite rods surrounded by helium and sealed in a container and obtained extremely thin (~1 nm in diameter) graphite-like tubes with fullerene ends (Figure 14.10B; the model shows concentric nanotubes, colored differently for clarity, without the usual fullerene ends). These *nanotubes* are rigid and, on a mass basis, much stronger than steel along their long axis. They also conduct electricity along this axis because of the delocalized electrons. With potential applications in nanoscale electronics, energy storage, catalysis, polymers, and medicine, fullerene and nanotube chemistry is an active area in materials research. (The 2010 Nobel Prize in physics was awarded for research into a new form of carbon called *graphene*. It has remarkable conductivity and strength, yet exists as extended sheets only one atom thick.)

2. *Allotropes of tin.* Tin has two allotropes. White β-tin is stable at room temperature and above, whereas gray α-tin is the more stable form below 13°C (56°F). When white tin is kept for long periods at a low temperature, some converts to microcrystals of gray tin. The random formation and growth of these regions of gray tin, which has a different crystal structure, weaken the metal and make it crumble. In the unheated cathedrals of medieval northern Europe, tin pipes of magnificent organs were sometimes destroyed by the "tin disease" caused by this allotropic transition.

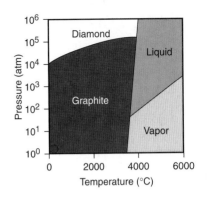

**Figure 14.9** Phase diagram of carbon.

**Figure 14.10** Crystalline buckminsterfullerene and a buckyball (A) and nanotubes (B).

## How Does the Type of Bonding Change in Group 4A(14) Compounds?

The Group 4A(14) elements display a wide range of chemical behavior, from the covalent compounds of carbon to the ionic compounds of lead. Carbon's intermediate EN of 2.5 ensures that it virtually always forms covalent bonds, but the larger members of the group form bonds with increasing ionic character. With nonmetals, Si and Ge form strong polar covalent bonds, such as the Si—O bond, which is one of the strongest of any Period 3 element (BE = 368 kJ/mol) and is responsible for the physical and chemical stability of Earth's solid surface, as we discuss later in this section. Although individual Sn or Pb ions rarely exist, the bonding of either element with a nonmetal has considerable ionic character.

The pattern of elements having more than one oxidation state observed in Group 3A(13) also appears here. Thus, compounds with Si in the +4 state are much more stable than those with Si in the +2 state, whereas compounds with Pb in the +2 state are more stable than those with Pb in the +4 state. These elements behave more like metals in the lower oxidation state. For example, $SnCl_2$ and $PbCl_2$ are white, relatively high-melting, water-soluble crystals—typical properties of a salt (Figure 14.11)—whereas $SnCl_4$ is a volatile, benzene-soluble liquid, and $PbCl_4$ is a thermally unstable oil. Similarly, SnO and PbO are more basic than $SnO_2$ and $PbO_2$: because the +2 metals are less able to polarize the $O^{2-}$ ion, the E-to-O bonding is more ionic.

**Figure 14.11** Salt-like +2 chlorides and oily +4 chlorides show greater metallic character of tin and lead in the lower oxidation state.

## Highlights of Carbon Chemistry

Like the other Period 2 elements, carbon is an anomaly in its group; indeed, it may be an anomaly in the entire periodic table. Carbon forms bonds with the smaller Group 1A(1) and 2A(2) metals, many transition metals, the halogens, and many other metalloids and nonmetals. It also exhibits every oxidation state possible for its group, from +4 in $CO_2$ and halides like $CCl_4$ through −4 in $CH_4$.

**Organic Compounds** Two major properties of carbon give rise to the enormous field of organic chemistry.

- Carbon has the ability to bond to itself—a process known as *catenation*. As a result of its small size and its capacity for four bonds, carbon can form chains, branches, and rings that lead to myriad structures. Add a lot of H, some O and N, a bit of S, P, halogens, and a few metals, and you have the whole organic world! Figure 14.12 shows three of the several million organic compounds known.
- Carbon has the ability to form multiple bonds. Multiple bonds are common in carbon structures because the C—C bond is short enough for side-to-side overlap of two half-filled $2p$ orbitals to form π bonds. (In Chapter 15, we discuss in detail how the atomic properties of carbon give rise to the diverse structures and reactivities of organic compounds.)

Because the other 4A members are larger, E—E bonds become longer and weaker, so catenation and multiple bonding are much less important down the group.

**Acrylonitrile**          **PCB**          **Lysine**

**Figure 14.12** Three of the several million known organic compounds of carbon. Acrylonitrile, a precursor of acrylic fibers. A typical PCB (one of the polychlorinated biphenyls). Lysine, one of about 20 amino acids that occur in proteins.

**Inorganic Compounds** In contrast to its organic compounds, carbon's inorganic compounds are simple.

1. *Carbonates.* Metal carbonates are the main mineral form. Marble, limestone, chalk, coral, and several other types are found in enormous deposits throughout the world. Many of these compounds are remnants of fossilized marine organisms. Carbonates are used in several common antacids because they react with the HCl in stomach acid:

$$CaCO_3(s) + 2HCl(aq) \longrightarrow CaCl_2(aq) + CO_2(g) + H_2O(l)$$

Identical net ionic reactions with sulfuric and nitric acids protect lakes bounded by limestone deposits from the harmful effects of acid rain.

2. *Oxides.* Unlike the other 4A members, which form only solid network-covalent or ionic oxides, carbon forms two common gaseous oxides, $CO_2$ and $CO$.

- Carbon dioxide is essential to all life: it is the primary source of carbon in plants through photosynthesis—and animals eat the plants. Its aqueous solution is the cause of mild acidity in natural waters. However, its atmospheric buildup from deforestation and excessive use of fossil fuels is severely affecting the global climate.
- Carbon monoxide forms when carbon or its compounds burn in an inadequate supply of $O_2$:

$$2C(s) + O_2(g) \longrightarrow 2CO(g)$$

Carbon monoxide is a key component of syngas fuels (see Chemical Connections, p. 249) and is widely used in the production of methanol, formaldehyde, and other major industrial compounds. CO binds strongly to many transition metals. When inhaled in cigarette smoke or polluted air, it enters the blood and binds strongly to the Fe(II) in hemoglobin, preventing the normal binding of $O_2$, and to other iron-containing proteins. The cyanide ion ($CN^-$) is *isoelectronic* with CO:

$$[:C\equiv N:]^- \quad \text{same electronic structure as} \quad :C\equiv O:$$

Cyanide binds to many of the same iron-containing proteins and is also toxic.

3. *Halides.* Carbon halides have major uses as solvents and in structural plastics. The chlorofluorocarbons (CFCs, or Freons) have short, strong carbon-halogen bonds that make them both useful and harmful (Figure 14.13). Chemically and thermally stable, nontoxic, and nonflammable, they are excellent cleaners for electronic parts, coolants in refrigerators and air conditioners, and propellants in aerosol cans. However, their bond strengths also mean that CFCs decompose *very* slowly near Earth's surface. In the stratosphere, they are bombarded by ultraviolet (UV) radiation, which breaks the otherwise stable C—Cl bonds, releasing free Cl atoms that initiate ozone-destroying reactions (Chapter 16). Legal production of CFCs has ended in the United States, but international production and smuggling are widespread.

**Figure 14.13** Freon-12 ($CCl_2F_2$), a chlorofluorocarbon.

$SiO_4^{4-}$

**Silicate ion in zircon**

$Si_2O_7^{6-}$

**Silicate ion in hemimorphite**

$Si_6O_{18}^{12-}$

**Silicate ion in beryl**

**Figure 14.14** Structures of the silicate anions in some minerals.

## Highlights of Silicon Chemistry

To a great extent, the chemistry of silicon is the chemistry of the *silicon-oxygen bond*. Just as carbon forms unending C—C chains, the —Si—O— grouping repeats itself endlessly in a wide variety of **silicates,** the most important minerals on the planet, and in **silicones,** synthetic polymers that have many applications:

1. *Silicate minerals.* From common sand and clay to semiprecious amethyst and carnelian, silicate minerals are the dominant form of matter in the nonliving world. Oxygen, the most abundant element on Earth, and silicon, the next most abundant, compose these minerals and account for four of every five atoms on the surface of the planet!

The silicate building unit is the *orthosilicate grouping,* —SiO$_4$—, a tetrahedral arrangement of four oxygens around a central silicon. Several well-known minerals contain $SiO_4^{4-}$ ions or small groups of them linked together. The gemstone zircon ($ZrSiO_4$) contains one unit; hemimorphite [$Zn_4(OH)_2Si_2O_7 \cdot H_2O$] contains two units linked through an oxygen corner; and beryl ($Be_3Al_2Si_6O_{18}$), the major source of beryllium, contains six units joined into a cyclic ion (Figure 14.14). In extended structures, one of the O atoms links the next Si—O group to form chains, a second one forms crosslinks to neighboring chains to form sheets, and the third forms more crosslinks to create three-dimensional frameworks. Chains of silicate groups compose the asbestos minerals, sheets give rise to talc and mica, and frameworks occur in feldspar and quartz (Figure 14.15).

**Figure 14.15** Quartz is a three-dimensional framework silicate.

2. *Silicone polymers.* Unlike the naturally occurring silicates, silicone polymers are manufactured substances, consisting of alternating Si and O atoms with two organic groups also bonded to each Si atom in a very long Si—O chain, as in *poly(dimethyl siloxane):*

$$\cdots \text{O}-\underset{\underset{\text{CH}_3}{|}}{\overset{\overset{\text{CH}_3}{|}}{\text{Si}}}-\text{O}-\underset{\underset{\text{CH}_3}{|}}{\overset{\overset{\text{CH}_3}{|}}{\text{Si}}}-\text{O}-\underset{\underset{\text{CH}_3}{|}}{\overset{\overset{\text{CH}_3}{|}}{\text{Si}}}-\text{O}-\underset{\underset{\text{CH}_3}{|}}{\overset{\overset{\text{CH}_3}{|}}{\text{Si}}}-\text{O}-\underset{\underset{\text{CH}_3}{|}}{\overset{\overset{\text{CH}_3}{|}}{\text{Si}}}-\text{O}\cdots$$

Silicones have properties of both plastics and minerals. The organic groups give them the flexibility and weak intermolecular forces between chains that are characteristic of a plastic, while the O—Si—O backbone confers the thermal stability and nonflammability of a mineral. Structures similar to those of the silicates can be created by adding various reactants to form silicone chains, sheets, and frameworks. Chains are oily liquids used as lubricants and as components of car polish and makeup. Sheets are components of gaskets, space suits, and contact lenses. Frameworks find uses as laminates on circuit boards, in nonstick cookware, and in artificial skin and bone.

## Diagonal Relationships: Boron and Silicon

The final diagonal relationship that we consider occurs between the metalloids boron and silicon, which are both semiconductors (Section 12.6). Both B and Si and their mineral oxoanions—borates and silicates—occur in extended covalent networks. Both boric acid [$B(OH)_3$] and silicic acid [$Si(OH)_4$] are weakly acidic solids that occur as layers held together by widespread H bonding. Their hydrides—the compact boranes and the extended silanes—are both flammable, low-melting compounds that act as reducing agents.

# 14.7 • GROUP 5A(15): THE NITROGEN FAMILY

The first two elements of Group 5A(15), gaseous nonmetallic nitrogen (N) and solid nonmetallic phosphorus (P), play major roles in both nature and industry. Below these nonmetals are two metalloids, arsenic (As) and antimony (Sb), followed by the metal bismuth (Bi), and the recently synthesized element 115. The Group 5A(15) Family Portrait *(next page)* provides an overview.

## What Accounts for the Wide Range of Physical Behavior in Group 5A(15)?

Group 5A(15) displays the widest range of physical behavior we've seen so far because of large changes in bonding and intermolecular forces:

- *Nitrogen* occurs as a gas consisting of $N_2$ molecules with such weak intermolecular forces that the element *boils* more than 200°C below room temperature.
- *Phosphorus* exists most commonly as tetrahedral $P_4$ molecules in the solid phase. Because P is heavier and more polarizable than N, it has stronger dispersion forces and melts about 25°C above room temperature.
- *Arsenic* consists of extended, puckered sheets in which each As atom is covalently bonded to three others and has nonbonding interactions with three nearest neighbors in adjacent sheets, giving As the highest melting point in the group.
- *Antimony* has a similar covalent network, also resulting in a high melting point.
- *Bismuth* has metallic bonding and thus a lower melting point than As and Sb.

**Two Allotropes of Phosphorus** Phosphorus has several allotropes, which have very different properties. Two major ones are white and red phosphorus.

- *White phosphorus* consists of individual tetrahedral molecules (Figure 14.16A, p. 545), making it a low melting whitish, waxy solid that is soluble in nonpolar solvents. Each P atom uses its half-filled $3p$ orbitals to bond to the other three; with a small 60° bond angle and thus, weak P—P bonds, it is highly reactive (Figure 14.16B).

# Group 5A(15): The Nitrogen Family

## KEY ATOMIC PROPERTIES, PHYSICAL PROPERTIES, AND REACTIONS

**KEY**
Atomic No.
**Symbol**
Atomic mass
Valence e⁻ configuration
(Common oxidation states)

| | |
|---|---|
| 7 **N** 14.01 $2s^2 2p^3$ (**−3, +5,** +4, +3, +2, +1) | |
| 15 **P** 30.97 $3s^2 3p^3$ (**−3, +5,** +3) | |
| 33 **As** 74.92 $4s^2 4p^3$ (**−3, +5,** +3) | |
| 51 **Sb** 121.8 $5s^2 5p^3$ (**−3, +5,** +3) | |
| 83 **Bi** 209.0 $6s^2 6p^3$ (+3) | |
| 115 (288) $7s^2 7p^3$ | Observed in experiments at Dubna, Russia, in 2003 |

$ns^2np^3$

**GROUP 5A(15)**

| Atomic radius (pm) | | Ionic radius (pm) |
|---|---|---|
| N 75 | | N³⁻ 146 |
| P 110 | | P³⁻ 212 |
| As 120 | | |
| Sb 140 | | |
| Bi 150 | | Bi³⁺ 103 |

## Atomic Properties

Group electron configuration is $ns^2np^3$. The $np$ sublevel is half-filled, with each $p$ orbital containing one electron (parallel spin). The number of oxidation states decreases down the group, and the lower (+3) state becomes more common. Atomic properties follow generally expected trends. The large (~50%) increase in size from N to P correlates with the much lower IE and EN of P.

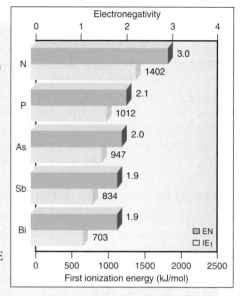

## Physical Properties

Physical properties reflect the change from individual molecules (N, P) to network covalent solid (As, Sb) to metal (Bi). Thus, melting points increase and then decrease. Large atomic size and low atomic mass result in low density. Because mass increases more than size down the group, the density of the elements as solids increases. The dramatic increase in density from P to As is due to the intervening transition elements.

## Reactions

**1.** Nitrogen is "fixed" industrially in the Haber process:

$$N_2(g) + 3H_2(g) \rightleftharpoons 2NH_3(g)$$

Further reactions convert $NH_3$ to $NO$, $NO_2$, and $HNO_3$ *(see text)*. Hydrides of some other group members are formed from reaction in water (or with $H_3O^+$) of a metal phosphide, arsenide, and so forth:

$$Ca_3P_2(s) + 6H_2O(l) \longrightarrow 2PH_3(g) + 3Ca(OH)_2(aq)$$

**2.** Halides are formed by direct combination of the elements:

$$2E(s) + 3X_2 \longrightarrow 2EX_3 \quad \text{(E = all except N)}$$
$$EX_3 + X_2 \longrightarrow EX_5 \quad \text{(E = all except N and Bi with X = F and Cl, but no } BiCl_5; E = P \text{ for } X = Br)$$

**3.** Oxoacids are formed from the halides in a reaction with water that is common to many nonmetal halides:

$$EX_3 + 3H_2O(l) \longrightarrow H_3EO_3(aq) + 3HX(aq) \quad \text{(E = all except N)}$$
$$EX_5 + 4H_2O(l) \longrightarrow H_3EO_4(aq) + 5HX(aq) \quad \text{(E = all except N and Bi)}$$

Note that the oxidation number of E does *not* change.

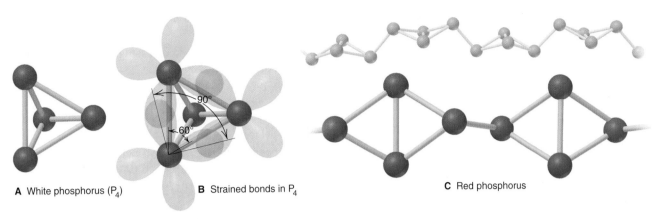

**A** White phosphorus ($P_4$)    **B** Strained bonds in $P_4$    **C** Red phosphorus

**Figure 14.16** Two allotropes of phosphorus.

- *Red phosphorus* is formed by heating the white form in the absence of air. One of the P—P bonds in each tetrahedron breaks, and those $3p$ orbitals overlap with others to form chains of $P_4$ units (Figure 14.16C). The chains make the red allotrope much less reactive, high melting, and insoluble.

## What Patterns Appear in the Chemical Behavior of Group 5A(15)?

The same general pattern of chemical behavior that we discussed for Group 4A(14) appears again in this group, reflected in the change from nonmetallic N to metallic Bi. The overwhelming majority of Group 5A(15) compounds have *covalent bonds*. Whereas N can form no more than four bonds, the next three members can expand their valence shells by using empty *d* orbitals.

1. *Formation of ions.* For a 5A element to form an ion with a noble gas electron configuration, it must *gain* three electrons, the last two in endothermic steps. Nevertheless, the enormous lattice energy released when such highly charged anions attract cations drives their formation. However, the 3− anion of N occurs only in compounds with active metals, such as $Li_3N$ and $Mg_3N_2$ (and that of P may occur in $Na_3P$). Metallic Bi forms mostly covalent compounds but exists as a cation in a few compounds, such as $BiF_3$ and $Bi(NO_3)_3 \cdot 5H_2O$, through *loss* of its three valence *p* electrons.

2. *Oxidation states and oxides.* As in Groups 3A and 4A, fewer oxidation states occur down the group, with the lower state becoming more prominent: N exhibits every state possible for a 5A element, from +5 to −3; only the +5 and +3 states are common for P, As, and Sb; and +3 is the only common state of Bi. The oxides change from acidic to amphoteric to basic, reflecting the increase in the metallic character of the elements. In addition, the lower oxide of an element is more basic than the higher oxide, reflecting the greater ionic character of the E-to-O bonding in the lower oxide.

3. *Formation of hydrides.* All the Group 5A(15) elements form gaseous hydrides of formula $EH_3$. Except for $NH_3$, these are extremely reactive and poisonous and are synthesized by reaction of a metal phosphide, arsenide, and so forth, which acts as a strong base in water or aqueous acid. For example,

$$Ca_3As_2(s) + 6H_2O(l) \longrightarrow 2AsH_3(g) + 3Ca(OH)_2(aq)$$

Ammonia is made industrially by direct combination of the elements at high pressure and moderately high temperature:

$$N_2(g) + 3H_2(g) \rightleftharpoons 2NH_3(g)$$

Nitrogen forms a second hydride, hydrazine, $N_2H_4$. Like $NH_3$, hydrazine is a weak base; it is used to make antituberculin drugs, plant growth regulators, and fungicides.

Molecular properties of the Group 5A(15) hydrides reveal some interesting bonding and structural patterns:

- Despite its much lower molar mass, $NH_3$ melts and boils at higher temperatures than the other 5A hydrides as a result of H *bonding*.
- Bond angles decrease from 107.3° for $NH_3$ to around 90° for the other hydrides, which suggests that the larger atoms use unhybridized $p$ orbitals.
- E—H bond lengths increase down the group, so bond strength and thermal stability decrease: $AsH_3$ decomposes at 250°C, $SbH_3$ at 20°C, and $BiH_3$ at −45°C.

We'll see these features—H bonding for the smallest member, change in bond angles, change in bond energies—in the hydrides of Group 6A(16) as well.

4. *Types and properties of halides.* The Group 5A(15) elements all form trihalides ($EX_3$). All except nitrogen form pentafluorides ($EF_5$), but only a few other pentahalides ($PCl_5$, $PBr_5$, $AsCl_5$, and $SbCl_5$) are known. Nitrogen cannot form pentahalides because it cannot expand its valence shell. Most trihalides are prepared by direct combination:

$$P_4(s) + 6Cl_2(g) \longrightarrow 4PCl_3(l)$$

The pentahalides form with excess halogen:

$$PCl_3(l) + Cl_2(g) \longrightarrow PCl_5(s)$$

As with the hydrides, the thermal stability of the halides decreases as the E—X bond becomes longer. Among the nitrogen halides, for example, $NF_3$ is a stable, rather unreactive gas. $NCl_3$ is explosive and reacts rapidly with water. (The chemist who first prepared it lost three fingers and an eye!) $NBr_3$ can only be made below −87°C. $NI_3$ has never been prepared, but an ammoniated product ($NI_3 \cdot NH_3$) explodes at the slightest touch.

5. *Reaction of halides in water.* In a reaction pattern *typical of many nonmetal halides*, each 5A halide reacts with water to yield the hydrogen halide and the oxoacid, in which E has the *same* O.N. as in the original halide. For example, $PX_5$ (O.N. of P = +5) produces phosphoric acid (O.N. of P = +5) and HX:

$$PCl_5(s) + 4H_2O(l) \longrightarrow H_3PO_4(l) + 5HCl(g)$$

## Highlights of Nitrogen Chemistry

Surely the most striking highlight of nitrogen chemistry is the inertness of $N_2$ itself. Nearly four-fifths of the atmosphere consists of $N_2$, and the other fifth is nearly all $O_2$, a very strong oxidizing agent. Nevertheless, the searing temperature of lightning is required for significant amounts of atmospheric nitrogen oxides to form. Although $N_2$ is inert at moderate temperatures, it reacts at high temperatures with $H_2$, Li, Group 2A(2) members, B, Al, C, Si, Ge, $O_2$, and many transition elements. In fact, nearly every element in the periodic table forms bonds to N. Here we focus on the oxides and the oxoacids and their salts.

**Nitrogen Oxides** Nitrogen is remarkable for having six stable oxides, each with a *positive* enthalpy of formation because of the great strength of the N≡N bond (BE = 945 kJ/mol). Their structures and some properties are shown in Table 14.3. Unlike the hydrides and halides of nitrogen, the oxides are planar. Nitrogen displays all its positive oxidation states in these compounds, and in $N_2O$ and $N_2O_3$, the two N atoms have different states. Let's highlight the three most important:

1. *Dinitrogen monoxide* ($N_2O$; also called *dinitrogen oxide* or *nitrous oxide*) is the dental anesthetic "laughing gas" and the propellant in canned whipped cream. It is a linear molecule with an electronic structure best described by three resonance forms (note formal charges):

$$\overset{0 \quad +1 \quad -1}{:N\equiv N-\ddot{O}:} \longleftrightarrow \overset{-1 \quad +1 \quad 0}{:\ddot{N}=N=\ddot{O}:} \longleftrightarrow \overset{-2 \quad +1 \quad +1}{:\ddot{N}-N\equiv O:}$$

most important                    least important

2. *Nitrogen monoxide* (NO; also called *nitrogen oxide* or *nitric oxide*) is an odd-electron molecule with biochemical functions ranging from neurotransmission to control of blood flow. In Section 11.3, we used MO theory to explain its bonding. The

## Table **14.3** Structures and Properties of the Nitrogen Oxides

| Formula | Name | Space-filling Model | Lewis Structure | Oxidation State of N | $\Delta H_f^\circ$(kJ/mol) at 298 K | Comment |
|---------|------|---------------------|-----------------|----------------------|-------------------------------------|---------|
| $N_2O$ | Dinitrogen monoxide (dinitrogen oxide; nitrous oxide) | | $:N\equiv N-\ddot{O}:$ | +1 (0, +2) | 82.0 | Colorless gas; used as dental anesthetic ("laughing gas") and aerosol propellant |
| NO | Nitrogen monoxide (nitrogen oxide; nitric oxide) | | $:\dot{N}=\ddot{O}:$ | +2 | 90.3 | Colorless, paramagnetic gas; biochemical messenger; air pollutant |
| $N_2O_3$ | Dinitrogen trioxide | | | +3 (+2, +4) | 83.7 | Reddish brown gas (reversibly dissociates to NO and $NO_2$) |
| $NO_2$ | Nitrogen dioxide | | | +4 | 33.2 | Orange-brown, paramagnetic gas formed during $HNO_3$ manufacture; poisonous air pollutant |
| $N_2O_4$ | Dinitrogen tetraoxide | | | +4 | 9.16 | Colorless to yellow liquid (reversibly dissociates to $NO_2$) |
| $N_2O_5$ | Dinitrogen pentaoxide | | | +5 | 11.3 | Colorless, volatile solid consisting of $NO_2^+$ and $NO_3^-$; gas consists of $N_2O_5$ molecules |

commercial preparation of NO through the oxidation of ammonia occurs as a first step in the production of nitric acid:

$$4NH_3(g) + 5O_2(g) \longrightarrow 4NO(g) + 6H_2O(g)$$

Nitrogen monoxide is also produced whenever air is heated to high temperatures, as in a car engine or a lightning storm:

$$N_2(g) + O_2(g) \xrightarrow{\text{high } T} 2NO(g)$$

Heating converts NO to two other oxides:

$$3NO(g) \xrightarrow{\Delta} N_2O(g) + NO_2(g)$$

This type of redox reaction is called a **disproportionation.** It occurs when a substance *acts as both the oxidizing and reducing agents in a reaction.* In the process, an atom with an intermediate oxidation state in the reactant occurs in both lower and higher states in the products: the oxidation state of N in NO (+2) is intermediate between that in $N_2O$ (+1) and that in $NO_2$ (+4).

3. *Nitrogen dioxide* ($NO_2$), a brown poisonous gas, forms to a small extent when NO reacts with additional oxygen:

$$2NO(g) + O_2(g) \rightleftharpoons 2NO_2(g)$$

Like NO, $NO_2$ is also an odd-electron molecule with the electron more localized on the N atom. Thus, $NO_2$ dimerizes reversibly to *dinitrogen tetraoxide:*

$$O_2N\cdot(g) + \cdot NO_2(g) \rightleftharpoons O_2N-NO_2(g) \quad \text{(or } N_2O_4\text{)}$$

Thunderstorms form NO and $NO_2$ and carry them down to the soil, where they act as natural fertilizers. In urban traffic, however, their formation leads to *photochemical smog (see photo)* in a series of reactions also involving sunlight, ozone ($O_3$), unburned gasoline, and various other species.

Photochemical smog over Los Angeles, California.

**Nitrogen Oxoacids and Oxoanions** There are two common oxoacids of nitrogen (Figure 14.17):

1. *Nitric acid* ($HNO_3$) is produced in the *Ostwald process;* we have already seen the first two steps—the oxidations of $NH_3$ to NO and of NO to $NO_2$. The final step is a disproportionation (p. 547), as the oxidation numbers show:

$$3\overset{+4}{N}O_2(g) + H_2O(l) \longrightarrow 2H\overset{+5}{N}O_3(aq) + \overset{+2}{N}O(g)$$

The NO is recycled to make more $NO_2$.

In nitric acid, as in all oxoacids, *the acidic H is attached to one of the O atoms.* When the proton is lost, the trigonal planar nitrate ion is formed (Figure 14.17A). In the laboratory, nitric acid is used as a strong oxidizing acid. The products of its reactions with metals vary with the metal's reactivity and the acid's concentration. In the following examples, notice from the net ionic equations that *the $NO_3^-$ ion is the oxidizing agent.* Nitrate ion that is not reduced is a spectator ion and does not appear in the net ionic equations.

- With an active metal, such as Al, and dilute acid, N is reduced from the +5 state all the way to the −3 state in the ammonium ion, $NH_4^+$:

$$8Al(s) + 30HNO_3(aq; 1\ M) \longrightarrow 8Al(NO_3)_3(aq) + 3NH_4NO_3(aq) + 9H_2O(l)$$
$$8Al(s) + 30H^+(aq) + 3NO_3^-(aq) \longrightarrow 8Al^{3+}(aq) + 3NH_4^+(aq) + 9H_2O(l)$$

- With a less reactive metal, such as Cu, and more concentrated acid, N is reduced to the +2 state in NO:

$$3Cu(s) + 8HNO_3(aq; 3\ \text{to}\ 6\ M) \longrightarrow 3Cu(NO_3)_2(aq) + 4H_2O(l) + 2NO(g)$$
$$3Cu(s) + 8H^+(aq) + 2NO_3^-(aq) \longrightarrow 3Cu^{2+}(aq) + 4H_2O(l) + 2NO(g)$$

- With still more concentrated acid, N is reduced only to the +4 state in $NO_2$ (p. 6):

$$Cu(s) + 4HNO_3(aq; 12\ M) \longrightarrow Cu(NO_3)_2(aq) + 2H_2O(l) + 2NO_2(g)$$
$$Cu(s) + 4H^+(aq) + 2NO_3^-(aq) \longrightarrow Cu^{2+}(aq) + 2H_2O(l) + 2NO_2(g)$$

Nitrates form when $HNO_3$ reacts with metals or with their hydroxides, oxides, or carbonates. *All nitrates are soluble in water.*

2. *Nitrous acid* ($HNO_2$), a much weaker acid than $HNO_3$, forms when metal nitrites are treated with a strong acid:

$$NaNO_2(aq) + HCl(aq) \longrightarrow HNO_2(aq) + NaCl(aq)$$

This acid forms the planar nitrite ion (Figure 14.17B) in which nitrogen's lone pair reduces the ideal 120° bond angle to 115°. These two acids reveal a *general pattern in relative acid strength among oxoacids: the more O atoms bonded to the central nonmetal, the stronger the acid.* The O atoms pull electron density from the N atom, which in turn pulls electron density from the O of the O—H bond, facilitating the release of the $H^+$ ion to $H_2O$. The O atoms also act to stabilize the resulting oxoanion by delocalizing its negative charge. The same pattern occurs in the oxoacids of sulfur and the halogens; we'll discuss the pattern quantitatively in Chapter 18.

**Figure 14.17** The structures of nitric and nitrous acids and their oxoanions.

Nitric acid (HNO$_3$)

$-H^+$

120°

Nitrate ion (NO$_3^-$)

**A**

Nitrous acid (HNO$_2$)

$-H^+$

115°

Nitrite ion (NO$_2^-$)

**B**

## Highlights of Phosphorus Chemistry

Like nitrogen, phosphorus forms important oxides (although not as many) and oxoacids. Here we focus on these compounds as well as on some other important phosphorus compounds.

**Phosphorus Oxides** Phosphorus forms two important oxides.

1. *Tetraphosphorus hexaoxide* ($P_4O_6$) has P in its +3 oxidation state. It forms when white $P_4$ reacts with limited oxygen:

$$P_4(s) + 3O_2(g) \longrightarrow P_4O_6(s)$$

$P_4O_6$ has the same tetrahedral orientation of the P atoms in $P_4$, with an O atom between each pair of P atoms (Figure 14.18A).

2. *Tetraphosphorus decaoxide* ($P_4O_{10}$) has P in the +5 oxidation state. Commonly known as "phosphorus pentoxide" from the empirical formula ($P_2O_5$), it forms when $P_4$ burns in excess $O_2$:

$$P_4(s) + 5O_2(g) \longrightarrow P_4O_{10}(s)$$

Its structure can be viewed as that of $P_4O_6$ with another O atom bonded to each of the four corner P atoms (Figure 14.18B). $P_4O_{10}$ is a powerful drying agent.

**A** $P_4O_6$

**B** $P_4O_{10}$

**Figure 14.18** Important oxides of phosphorus.

**Phosphorus Oxoacids and Oxoanions** The two common phosphorus oxoacids are phosphorous acid (note the change in spelling) and phosphoric acid.

1. *Phosphorous acid* ($H_3PO_3$) is formed when $P_4O_6$ reacts with water:

$$P_4O_6(s) + 6H_2O(l) \longrightarrow 4H_3PO_3(l)$$

The formula $H_3PO_3$ is misleading because the acid has only two acidic H atoms; the third is bonded to the central P and does not dissociate. Phosphorous acid is a weak acid in water but reacts completely in two steps with excess strong base:

Salts of phosphorous acid contain the phosphite ion, $HPO_3^{2-}$.

2. *Phosphoric acid* ($H_3PO_4$), one of the "top-10" most important compounds in chemical manufacturing, is formed in a vigorous exothermic reaction of $P_4O_{10}$ with water:

$$P_4O_{10}(s) + 6H_2O(l) \longrightarrow 4H_3PO_4(l)$$

The presence of many H bonds makes pure $H_3PO_4$ syrupy, more than 75 times as viscous as water. The laboratory-grade concentrated acid is an 85% by mass aqueous solution. $H_3PO_4$ is a weak triprotic acid; in water, it loses one proton in the following equilibrium reaction:

$$H_3PO_4(l) + H_2O(l) \rightleftharpoons H_2PO_4^-(aq) + H_3O^+(aq)$$

In excess strong base, however, the three protons dissociate completely in three steps to give the three phosphate oxoanions:

dihydrogen phosphate ion

hydrogen phosphate ion

phosphate ion

Phosphoric acid has a central role in fertilizer production and is also used as an additive in soft drinks to give a touch of tartness. The various phosphate salts also have numerous essential applications. $Na_3PO_4$ is a paint stripper and grease remover. $K_3PO_4$ is used to stabilize latex for synthetic rubber, and $K_2HPO_4$ is a radiator corrosion inhibitor. Ammonium phosphates are used as fertilizers and as flame retardants on curtains, and calcium phosphates are used in baking powders and toothpastes, as mineral supplements in livestock feed, and as fertilizers.

**Figure 14.19** The diphosphate ion and polyphosphates.

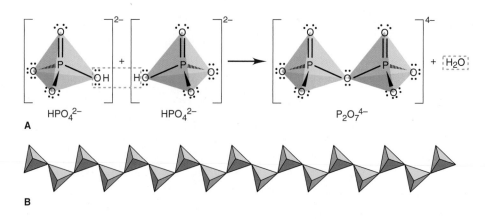

**A**

**B**

**Polyphosphates** Hydrogen phosphates lose water when heated as they form P—O—P linkages in the formation of compounds called *polyphosphates*. This type of reaction, in which an $H_2O$ molecule is lost for every pair of groups that join, is called a **dehydration-condensation;** it occurs frequently in the formation of polyoxoanion chains and other polymeric structures, both synthetic and natural. For example, sodium diphosphate, $Na_4P_2O_7$, is prepared by heating sodium hydrogen phosphate:

$$2Na_2HPO_4(s) \xrightarrow{\Delta} Na_4P_2O_7(s) + H_2O(g)$$

The diphosphate ion, $P_2O_7^{4-}$, the smallest of the polyphosphates, consists of two $PO_4$ units linked through a common oxygen corner (Figure 14.19A). Its reaction with water, the reverse of the previous reaction, generates heat:

$$P_2O_7^{4-}(aq) + H_2O(l) \longrightarrow 2HPO_4^-(aq) + heat$$

A similar process is put to vital use by organisms, when a third $PO_4$ unit linked to diphosphate creates the triphosphate grouping, part of the all-important high-energy biomolecule adenosine triphosphate (ATP). In Chapters 20 and 21, we discuss the central role of ATP in biological energy production. Extended polyphosphate chains consist of many tetrahedral $PO_4$ units (Figure 14.19B) and are structurally similar to silicate chains.

**Phosphorus Compounds with Sulfur and Nitrogen** Phosphorus forms many sulfides and nitrides. $P_4S_3$ is used in "strike anywhere" match heads, and $P_4S_{10}$ is used in the manufacture of organophosphorus pesticides, such as malathion. Compounds of phosphorus and nitrogen called *polyphosphazenes* have properties similar to those of silicones. The $—(R_2)P{=}N—$ unit is isoelectronic with the silicone unit, $—(R_2)Si—N—$. Sheets, films, fibers, and foams of polyphosphazene are water repellent, flame resistant, solvent resistant, and flexible at low temperatures—perfect for the gaskets and O-rings in spacecraft and polar vehicles.

# 14.8 • GROUP 6A(16): THE OXYGEN FAMILY

The first two members of this family—gaseous nonmetallic oxygen (O) and solid nonmetallic sulfur (S)—are among the most important elements in industry, the environment, and living things. Two metalloids, selenium (Se) and tellurium (Te), appear below them, followed by the lone metal—radioactive polonium (Po)—and recently synthesized element 116. The Group 6A(16) Family Portrait displays the features of these elements.

## How Do the Oxygen and Nitrogen Families Compare Physically?

Group 6A(16) resembles Group 5A(15) in many respects, so let's look at some common themes. The pattern of physical properties we saw in Group 5A appears again in this group.

# Group 6A(16): The Oxygen Family

## Family Portrait

# KEY ATOMIC PROPERTIES, PHYSICAL PROPERTIES, AND REACTIONS

KEY
Atomic No.
**Symbol**
Atomic mass
Valence e⁻ configuration
(Common oxidation states)

| 8 |
| O |
| 16.00 |
| $2s^2 2p^4$ |
| (−1, −2) |

| 16 |
| S |
| 32.07 |
| $3s^2 3p^4$ |
| (−2, +6, +4, +2) |

| 34 |
| Se |
| 78.96 |
| $4s^2 4p^4$ |
| (−2, +6, +4, +2) |

| 52 |
| Te |
| 127.6 |
| $5s^2 5p^4$ |
| (−2, +6, +4, +2) |

| 84 |
| Po |
| (209) |
| $6s^2 6p^4$ |
| (+4, +2) |

| 116 |
| (292) |
| $7s^2 7p^4$ |
| Observed in experiments at Dubna, Russia, in 2004 |

$ns^2np^4$

**GROUP 6A(16)**

| Atomic radius (pm) | Ionic radius (pm) |
|---|---|
| O 73 | O²⁻ 140 |
| S 103 | S²⁻ 184 |
| Se 119 | Se²⁻ 198 |
| Te 142 | |
| Po 168 | Po⁴⁺ 94 |

## Atomic Properties

Group electron configuration is $ns^2np^4$. As in Groups 3A(13) and 5A(15), a lower (+4) oxidation state becomes more common down the group. Down the group, atomic and ionic sizes increase, and IE and EN decrease.

## Physical Properties

Melting points increase through Te, which has covalent bonding, and then decrease for Po, which has metallic bonding. Densities of the elements as solids increase steadily.

## Reactions

**1.** Halides are formed by direct combination:

$$E(s) + X_2(g) \longrightarrow \text{various halides}$$
$$(E = S, Se, Te; X = F, Cl)$$

**2.** The other elements in the group are oxidized by $O_2$:

$$E(s) + O_2(g) \longrightarrow EO_2 \quad (E = S, Se, Te, Po)$$

$SO_2$ is oxidized further, and the product is used in the final step of $H_2SO_4$ manufacture *(see text):*

$$2SO_2(g) + O_2(g) \longrightarrow 2SO_3(g)$$

**3.** The thiosulfate ion is formed when an alkali metal sulfite reacts with sulfur, as in the preparation of "hypo," photographers' developing solution:

$$S_8(s) + 8Na_2SO_3(s) \longrightarrow 8Na_2S_2O_3(aq)$$

- *Oxygen,* like nitrogen, occurs as a low-boiling diatomic gas.
- *Sulfur,* like phosphorus, occurs as a polyatomic molecular solid.
- *Selenium,* like arsenic, commonly occurs as a gray metalloid.
- *Tellurium,* like antimony, is slightly more metallic than the preceding group member but still displays network covalent bonding.
- *Polonium,* like bismuth, has a metallic crystal structure.

As in Group 5A, electrical conductivities increase steadily down Group 6A as bonding changes from nonmetal molecules (insulators) to metalloid networks (semiconductors) to a metallic solid (conductor).

**Allotropism in the Oxygen Family** Allotropism is more common in Group 6A(16) than in Group 5A(15).

1. *Oxygen.* Oxygen has two allotropes: life-giving dioxygen ($O_2$), and poisonous triatomic ozone ($O_3$). Oxygen gas is colorless, odorless, paramagnetic, and thermally stable. In contrast, ozone gas is bluish, has a pungent odor, is diamagnetic, and decomposes in heat and especially in ultraviolet (UV) light:

$$2O_3(g) \xrightarrow{\text{UV}} 3O_2(g)$$

This ability to absorb high-energy photons makes stratospheric ozone vital to life. A thinning of the ozone layer, observed above the North Pole and especially the South Pole, means that more UV light is reaching Earth's surface, with potentially hazardous effects. (We'll discuss the chemical causes of ozone depletion in Chapter 16.)

2. *Sulfur.* Sulfur is the allotrope "champion" of the periodic table, with more than 10 forms. The S atom's ability to bond to other S atoms (catenate) creates rings and chains, many with S—S bond lengths that range from 180 pm to 260 pm and bond angles from 90° to 180°. At room temperature, the sulfur molecule is a crown-shaped ring of eight atoms, called *cyclo-$S_8$* (Figure 14.20). The most stable allotrope is orthorhombic α-$S_8$, which consists of cyclo-$S_8$; all other S allotropes eventually revert to this one.

**Figure 14.20** The cyclo-$S_8$ molecule. **A,** Top view of a space-filling model. **B,** Side view of a ball-and-stick model; note the crownlike shape.

3. *Selenium.* Selenium also has several allotropes, some consisting of crown-shaped $Se_8$ molecules. Gray Se is composed of layers of helical chains. When molten glass, cadmium sulfide, and gray Se are mixed and heated in the absence of air, a ruby-red glass forms, which you may still see when you stop at a traffic light. The ability of gray Se to conduct an electric current when illuminated is used by the photocopying industry. A film of amorphous Se is deposited on an aluminum drum and electrostatically charged. Exposure to a document produces an "image" of low and high positive charges corresponding to the document's bright and dark areas. Negatively charged black, dry ink (toner) particles are attracted to the regions of high charge more than to those of low charge. This pattern of black particles is transferred electrostatically to paper, and the particles are fused to the paper's surface by heat or solvent. Excess toner is removed from the Se film, the charges are "erased" by exposure to light, and the film is ready for the next page.

## How Do the Oxygen and Nitrogen Families Compare Chemically?

Changes in chemical behavior in Group 6A(16) are also similar to those in Group 5A(15). Even though O and S occur as anions much more often than do N and P, like N and P, they bond covalently with almost every other nonmetal. Covalent bonds appear in the compounds of Se and Te (as in those of As and Sb), whereas Po behaves like a metal (as does Bi) in some of its saltlike compounds. In contrast to nitrogen, oxygen has few common oxidation states, but the earlier pattern returns with the other Group 6A members: the $+6$, $+4$, and $-2$ states occur most often, with the lower positive ($+4$) state becoming more common in Te and Po [as the lower positive ($+3$) state does in Sb and Bi].

The range in atomic properties is wider in this group than in Group 5A(15) because of oxygen's high EN (3.5) and great oxidizing strength, second only to that of fluorine. But the other members of Group 6A behave very little like oxygen: they are much less electronegative, form anions much less often ($S^{2-}$ occurs with active metals), and their hydrides exhibit no H bonding.

**Types and Properties of Hydrides** Oxygen forms two hydrides, water and hydrogen peroxide ($H_2O_2$). Both have relatively high boiling points and viscosities due to hydrogen bonding. In peroxides, O is in the $-1$ oxidation state, midway between that in $O_2$ (zero) and that in oxides ($-2$); thus, $H_2O_2$ readily disproportionates:

$$H_2O_2(l) \longrightarrow H_2O(l) + \tfrac{1}{2}O_2(g)$$

Aside from its familiar use as a hair bleach and topical disinfectant, much more $H_2O_2$ is used to bleach paper pulp, textiles, straw, and leather, and in sewage treatment to oxidize bacteria.

The other 6A elements form foul-smelling, poisonous, gaseous hydrides ($H_2E$) on treatment with acid of the metal sulfide, selenide, and so forth. For example,

$$FeSe(s) + 2HCl(aq) \longrightarrow H_2Se(g) + FeCl_2(aq)$$

Hydrogen sulfide also forms naturally in swamps from the breakdown of organic matter. It is as toxic as HCN, and even worse, it anesthetizes your olfactory nerves, so that as its concentration increases, you smell it less! The other hydrides are about 100 times *more* toxic.

In their bonding and thermal stability, these Group 6A hydrides have several features in common with those of Group 5A:

- Only water and $H_2O_2$ can form H bonds, so they melt and boil much higher than the other $H_2E$ compounds (see Figure 12.15, p. 433).
- Bond angles drop from the nearly tetrahedral value for $H_2O$ (104.5°) to around 90° for the larger 6A hydrides, suggesting that the central atom uses unhybridized $p$ orbitals.
- E—H bond length increases (bond energy decreases) down the group. Thus, $H_2Te$ decomposes above 0°C, and $H_2Po$ can be made only in extreme cold because thermal energy from the radioactive Po decomposes it. Another result of longer (weaker) bonds is that the 6A hydrides are acids in water, and their acidity increases from $H_2S$ to $H_2Po$.

**Types and Properties of Halides** Except for O, the Group 6A elements form a wide range of halides, whose structure and reactivity patterns depend on the *sizes of the central atom and the surrounding halogens:*

- Sulfur forms many fluorides, a few chlorides, one bromide, but no stable iodides.
- As the central atom becomes larger, the halides become more stable. Thus, tetrachlorides and tetrabromides of Se, Te, and Po are known, as are tetraiodides of Te and Po. Hexafluorides are known only for S, Se, and Te.

The inverse relationship between bond length and bond strength that we've seen previously does not account for this pattern. Rather, it is based on the effect of electron repulsions due to crowding of lone pairs and halogen (X) atoms around the central Group 6A atom. With S, the larger X atoms would be too crowded, which explains why sulfur iodides do not occur. With increasing size of E, and therefore increasing length of E—X bonds, however, lone pairs and X atoms do not crowd each other as much, so a greater number of stable halides form.

## Highlights of Oxygen Chemistry: Range of Oxide Properties

Oxygen is the most abundant element on Earth's surface, occurring both as the free element and in innumerable oxides, silicates, carbonates, and phosphates, as well as in water. Virtually all free $O_2$ has a biological origin, having been formed for billions of years by photosynthetic algae and multicellular plants in an overall equation that looks deceptively simple:

$$n H_2O(l) + n CO_2(g) \xrightarrow{\text{light}} n O_2(g) + (CH_2O)_n \text{ (carbohydrates)}$$

The reverse process occurs during combustion and respiration. Through these $O_2$-forming and $O_2$-utilizing processes, the $1.5 \times 10^9 \text{ km}^3$ of water on Earth is, on average, used and remade every 2 million years!

Every element (except He, Ne, and Ar) forms at least one oxide, many by direct combination. A broad spectrum of properties characterizes these compounds. Some oxides are gases that condense at very low temperatures, such as CO (bp = $-192°C$); others are solids that melt at extremely high temperatures, such as BeO (mp = $2530°C$). Oxides cover the full range of conductivity: insulators (MgO), semiconductors (NiO), conductors ($ReO_3$), and superconductors ($YBa_2Cu_3O_7$). They may be thermally stable (CaO) or unstable (HgO), as well as chemically reactive ($Li_2O$) or inert ($Fe_2O_3$).

Given this vast range of behavior, another useful way to classify element oxides is by their acid-base properties. The oxides of Group 6A(16) exhibit expected trends in acidity, with $SO_3$ the most acidic and $PoO_2$ the most basic.

## Highlights of Sulfur Chemistry

Like phosphorus, sulfur forms two common oxides and two oxoacids, one of which is essential to a wide variety of industries. There are also several important metal sulfides.

**Sulfur Oxides** Sulfur forms two important oxides.

1. *Sulfur dioxide* ($SO_2$) has S in its +4 oxidation state. It is a colorless, choking gas that forms when S, $H_2S$, or a metal sulfide burns in air:

$$2H_2S(g) + 3O_2(g) \longrightarrow 2H_2O(g) + 2SO_2(g)$$
$$4FeS_2(s) + 11O_2(g) \longrightarrow 2Fe_2O_3(s) + 8SO_2(g)$$

2. *Sulfur trioxide* ($SO_3$), which has S in the +6 oxidation state, is produced when sulfur dioxide reacts in oxygen. A catalyst (Chapter 16) must be used to speed up this very slow reaction. En route to the production of sulfuric acid, a vanadium(V) oxide catalyst is used:

$$SO_2(g) + \tfrac{1}{2}O_2(g) \xrightarrow{V_2O_5/K_2O \text{ catalyst}} SO_3(g)$$

**Sulfur Oxoacids** Sulfur forms two important oxoacids.

1. *Sulfurous acid* ($H_2SO_3$), formed when sulfur dioxide dissolves in water, exists in equilibrium with hydrated $SO_2$ rather than as stable $H_2SO_3$ molecules:

$$SO_2(aq) + H_2O(l) \rightleftharpoons [H_2SO_3(aq)] \rightleftharpoons H^+(aq) + HSO_3^-(aq)$$

Sulfurous acid is weak and has two acidic protons, forming the hydrogen sulfite (bisulfite, $HSO_3^-$) and sulfite ($SO_3^{2-}$) ions with strong base. Because the S in $SO_3^{2-}$ is in the +4 state and is easily oxidized to the +6 state, sulfites are good reducing agents and are used to preserve foods and wine by eliminating undesirable products of air oxidation.

2. *Sulfuric acid* ($H_2SO_4$) is produced when $SO_2$ is oxidized catalytically to $SO_3$, which is then absorbed into concentrated $H_2SO_4$ and treated with additional $H_2O$:

$$SO_3 \text{ (in concentrated } H_2SO_4) + H_2O(l) \longrightarrow H_2SO_4(l)$$

With more than 40 million tons produced each year in the United States alone, $H_2SO_4$ ranks first among all industrial chemicals; it is vital to fertilizer production, metal, pigment, and textile processing, and soap and detergent manufacturing. (The production of $H_2SO_4$ will be discussed in detail in Chapter 22.)

**Figure 14.21** The dehydration of sugar by sulfuric acid.

Concentrated laboratory-grade sulfuric acid is a viscous, colorless liquid that is 98% $H_2SO_4$ by mass. Like other strong acids, $H_2SO_4$ dissociates completely in water, forming the hydrogen sulfate (or bisulfate) ion, a much weaker acid:

hydrogen sulfate ion            sulfate ion

Most common hydrogen sulfates and sulfates are water soluble, but those of Group 2A(2) members (except $MgSO_4$), $Ag^+$, and $Pb^{2+}$ are not.

Concentrated sulfuric acid is an excellent dehydrating agent. Its loosely held proton transfers to water in a highly exothermic formation of hydronium ($H_3O^+$) ions. This process can occur even when the reacting substance contains no free water. For example, $H_2SO_4$ dehydrates wood, natural fibers, and many other organic substances, such as table sugar $(CH_2O)_n$, by removing the components of water from the molecular structure, leaving behind a carbonaceous mass (Figure 14.21).

Sulfuric acid is one of the components of acid rain. Enormous amounts of $SO_2$ are emitted by coal-burning power plants, petroleum refineries, and metal-ore smelters (*see photo*). In contact with rain, the $SO_2$ and its oxidation product $SO_3$ form $H_2SO_3$ and $H_2SO_4$ in the atmosphere, which then fall in rain, snow, and dust on animals, plants, buildings, and lakes (see Chemical Connections, pp. 793–794).

**Metal Sulfides** Many metals combine directly with S to form *metal sulfides*. Sulfide ores are mined for the extraction of many metals, including copper, zinc, lead, and silver. Aside from the sulfides of Groups 1A(1) and 2A(2), most metal sulfides do not have discrete $S^{2-}$ ions. Several transition metals, such as chromium, iron, and nickel, form covalent, alloy-like, nonstoichiometric compounds with S, such as $Cr_{0.88}S$ or $Fe_{0.86}S$. Some important minerals contain $S_2^{2-}$ ions; an example is iron pyrite, or "fool's gold" ($FeS_2$). We discuss the metallurgy of ores in Chapter 22.

Industrial sources produce the sulfur oxides that lead to acid rain.

# 14.9 • GROUP 7A(17): THE HALOGENS

The last elements of great reactivity are found in Group 7A(17). The halogens begin with fluorine (F), the strongest electron "grabber" of all. Chlorine (Cl, by far the most important industrially), bromine (Br), and iodine (I) also form compounds with most elements, and even rare, radioactive astatine (At) is thought to be reactive. The key features of Group 7A(17) are presented in the Family Portrait (*next page*).

## What Accounts for the Regular Changes in the Halogens' Physical Properties?

Like the alkali metals at the other end of the periodic table, the halogens display regular trends in their physical properties. However, whereas melting and boiling points and heats of fusion and vaporization *decrease* down Group 1A(1), these properties *increase* down Group 7A(17). The reason for these opposite trends is the different type of bonding in the elements. The alkali metals consist of atoms held together by metallic bonding, which

## KEY ATOMIC PROPERTIES, PHYSICAL PROPERTIES, AND REACTIONS

**KEY**
Atomic No.
**Symbol**
Atomic mass
Valence e⁻ configuration
(Common oxidation states)

| 9 |
| --- |
| **F** |
| 19.00 |
| $2s^22p^5$ |
| $(-1)$ |

Photograph not available

| 17 |
| --- |
| **Cl** |
| 35.45 |
| $3s^23p^5$ |
| $(-1, +7,$ |
| $+5, +3,$ |
| $+1)$ |

| 35 |
| --- |
| **Br** |
| 79.90 |
| $4s^24p^5$ |
| $(-1, +7,$ |
| $+5, +3,$ |
| $+1)$ |

| 53 |
| --- |
| **I** |
| 126.9 |
| $5s^25p^5$ |
| $(-1, +7,$ |
| $+5, +3,$ |
| $+1)$ |

| 85 |
| --- |
| **At** |
| (210) |
| $6s^26p^5$ |
| $(-1)$ |

Extremely rare, no sample available

$ns^2np^5$

**GROUP 7A(17)**

| Atomic radius (pm) | | Ionic radius (pm) |
| --- | --- | --- |
| F 72 | | F⁻ 133 |
| Cl 100 | | Cl⁻ 181 |
| Br 114 | | Br⁻ 196 |
| I 133 | | I⁻ 220 |
| At (140) | | no data |

### Atomic Properties

Group electron configuration is $ns^2np^5$; elements lack one electron to complete their outer level. The $-1$ oxidation state is the most common for all members. Except for F, the halogens exhibit all odd-numbered states ($+7$ through $-1$). Down the group, atomic and ionic sizes increase steadily, as IE and EN decrease.

### Physical Properties

Down the group, melting and boiling points increase smoothly as a result of stronger dispersion forces between larger molecules. The densities of the elements as liquids (at the given $T$) increase steadily with molar mass.

**Electronegativity**

| | |
| --- | --- |
| F | 4.0 — 1681 |
| Cl | 3.0 — 1256 |
| Br | 2.8 — 1143 |
| I | 2.5 — 1009 |
| At | 2.2 — (926) |

☐ EN
☐ IE₁

First ionization energy (kJ/mol)

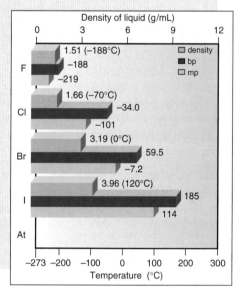

**Density of liquid (g/mL)**

☐ density
■ bp
☐ mp

| | |
| --- | --- |
| F | 1.51 (−188°C); −188; −219 |
| Cl | 1.66 (−70°C); −34.0; −101 |
| Br | 3.19 (0°C); 59.5; −7.2 |
| I | 3.96 (120°C); 185; 114 |
| At | |

Temperature (°C)

### Reactions

**1.** The halogens ($X_2$) oxidize many metals and nonmetals. The reaction with hydrogen, although not used commercially for HX production (except for high-purity HCl), is characteristic of these strong oxidizing agents:

$$X_2 + H_2(g) \longrightarrow 2HX(g)$$

**2.** The halogens undergo disproportionation in water:

$$X_2 + H_2O(l) \rightleftharpoons HX(aq) + HXO(aq)$$
$$(X = Cl, Br, I)$$

In aqueous base, the reaction goes to completion to form hypohalites *(see text)* and, at higher temperatures, halates, for example:

$$3Cl_2(g) + 6OH^-(aq) \xrightarrow{\Delta} ClO_3^-(aq) + 5Cl^-(aq) + 3H_2O(l)$$

*decreases* in strength as the atoms become larger. The halogens, on the other hand, exist as diatomic molecules that interact through dispersion forces, which *increase* in strength as the atoms become larger and more easily polarized. Thus, $F_2$ is a very pale yellow gas, $Cl_2$ a yellow-green gas, $Br_2$ a brown-orange liquid, and $I_2$ a purple-black solid.

## Why Are the Halogens So Reactive?

The Group 7A(17) elements react with most metals and nonmetals to form many ionic and covalent compounds: metal and nonmetal halides, halogen oxides, and oxoacids. The main reason for halogen reactivity is the same as for alkali metal reactivity—an electron configuration one electron away from that of a noble gas. Whereas a 1A metal atom must lose one electron to attain a filled outer level, *a 7A nonmetal atom must gain one electron to fill its outer level*. It accomplishes this filling in either of two ways:

1. Gaining an electron from a metal atom, thus forming a negative ion as the metal forms a positive one.
2. Sharing an electron pair with a nonmetal atom, thus forming a covalent bond.

**Electronegativity and Bond Properties** The halogens display the largest range in electronegativity of any group, but all are electronegative enough to behave as nonmetals. Down the group, reactivity reflects the decrease in electronegativity: $F_2$ is the most reactive and $I_2$ the least. The exceptional reactivity of elemental $F_2$ is also related to the weakness of the F—F bond. Although bond energy generally decreases as atomic size increases down the group (Figure 14.22), $F_2$ deviates from this trend. The short F—F bond is weaker than expected because lone pairs on each small F atom repel those on the other. As a result of these factors, $F_2$ reacts with every element (except He, Ne, and Ar), in many cases, explosively.

**Figure 14.22** Bond energies and bond lengths of the halogens.

**Redox Behavior** The halogens act as *oxidizing agents* in the majority of their reactions, and halogens higher in the group can oxidize halide ions lower down:

$$F_2(g) + 2X^-(aq) \longrightarrow 2F^-(aq) + X_2(aq) \quad (X = Cl, Br, I)$$

Thus, the oxidizing ability of $X_2$ increases *up* the group: the higher the EN, the more strongly each X atom pulls electrons away. Similarly, the reducing ability of $X^-$ increases *down* the group: the larger the ion, the more easily it gives up its electron (Figure 14.23A). Aqueous $Cl_2$ added to a solution of $I^-$ (Figure 14.23B, *top layer*) oxidizes the $I^-$ to $I_2$, which dissolves in the $CCl_4$ solvent (*bottom layer*) to give a purple solution.

**Figure 14.23** The relative oxidizing ability of the halogens.

$Cl_2(aq) + 2I^-(aq) \longrightarrow 2Cl^-(aq) + I_2$ (in $CCl_4$)

The halogens undergo some important aqueous redox chemistry. Fluorine is such a powerful oxidizing agent that it reacts vigorously with water, oxidizing the O to produce $O_2$, some $O_3$, and HFO (hypofluorous acid). The other halogens undergo disproportionations (note the oxidation numbers):

$$\overset{0}{X_2} + H_2O(l) \rightleftharpoons \overset{-1}{H}X(aq) + \overset{+1}{H}XO(aq) \qquad (X = Cl, Br, I)$$

At equilibrium, very little product is present unless excess $OH^-$ ion is added, which reacts with the HX and HXO and drives the reaction to completion:

$$X_2 + 2OH^-(aq) \longrightarrow X^-(aq) + XO^-(aq) + H_2O(l)$$

When X is Cl, the product mixture acts as a bleach: household bleach is a dilute solution of sodium hypochlorite (NaClO). Heating causes $XO^-$ to disproportionate further, creating oxoanions with X in a higher oxidation state:

$$\overset{+1}{3XO^-}(aq) \overset{\Delta}{\longrightarrow} \overset{-1}{2X^-}(aq) + \overset{+5}{X}O_3^-(aq)$$

## Highlights of Halogen Chemistry

In this section, we examine the compounds the halogens form with hydrogen and with each other, as well as their oxides, oxoanions, and oxoacids.

### The Hydrogen Halides

The halogens form gaseous hydrogen halides (HX) through direct combination with $H_2$ or through the action of a concentrated acid on the metal halide (a nonoxidizing acid is used for HBr and HI):

$$CaF_2(s) + H_2SO_4(l) \longrightarrow CaSO_4(s) + 2HF(g)$$

$$3NaBr(s) + H_3PO_4(l) \longrightarrow Na_3PO_4(s) + 3HBr(g)$$

Commercially, most HCl is formed as a byproduct in the chlorination of hydrocarbons for plastics production:

$$CH_2{=}CH_2(g) + Cl_2(g) \longrightarrow ClCH_2CH_2Cl(l) \overset{500°C}{\longrightarrow} CH_2{=}CHCl(g) + HCl(g)$$
vinyl chloride

In this case, the vinyl chloride reacts in a separate process to form poly(vinyl chloride), or PVC, a polymer used extensively in plumbing and other piping needs.

In water, gaseous HX molecules form a *hydrohalic acid*. Only HF, with its relatively short, strong bond, forms a weak acid:

$$HF(g) + H_2O(l) \rightleftharpoons H_3O^+(aq) + F^-(aq)$$

HF has many uses, including the synthesis of cryolite ($Na_3AlF_6$) for aluminum production (Chapter 22), of fluorocarbons for refrigeration, and of NaF for water fluoridation. HF is also used in nuclear fuel processing and for glass etching.

The other hydrohalic acids dissociate completely to form the stoichiometric amount of $H_3O^+$ ions:

$$HBr(g) + H_2O(l) \longrightarrow H_3O^+(aq) + Br^-(aq)$$

(We saw reactions similar to these in Chapter 4. They involve *transfer* of a proton from acid to $H_2O$ and are classified as *Brønsted-Lowry acid-base reactions*. In Chapter 18, we discuss them thoroughly and examine the relation between bond length and acidity of the larger HX molecules.)

HCl, a common laboratory reagent, is used in the "pickling" of steel to remove adhering oxides and in the production of syrups, rayon, and plastic. HCl(*aq*) occurs naturally in the stomach fluids of mammals.

### Interhalogen Compounds: The "Halogen Halides"

Halogens react exothermically with one another to form many **interhalogen compounds.** The simplest are diatomic molecules, such as ClF or BrCl. Every binary combination of the four common halogens is known. The more electronegative halogen is in the $-1$ oxidation state, and the less electronegative is in the $+1$ state. Interhalogens of general formula

$XY_n$ ($n$ = 3, 5, 7) form through a variety of reactions, including direct reaction of the elements. In every case, the central atom has the lower *electronegativity* and a positive oxidation state.

Some interhalogens are used commercially as powerful *fluorinating agents,* which react with metals, nonmetals, and oxides—even wood and asbestos:

$$Sn(s) + ClF_3(l) \longrightarrow SnF_2(s) + ClF(g)$$
$$P_4(s) + 5ClF_3(l) \longrightarrow 4PF_3(g) + 3ClF(g) + Cl_2(g)$$
$$2B_2O_3(s) + 4BrF_3(l) \longrightarrow 4BF_3(g) + 2Br_2(l) + 3O_2(g)$$

Their reactions with water are nearly explosive and yield HF and the *oxoacid with the central halogen in the same oxidation state,* for example:

$$3H_2O(l) + \overset{+5}{Br}F_5(l) \longrightarrow 5HF(g) + H\overset{+5}{Br}O_3(aq)$$

**The Oddness and Evenness of Oxidation States** *Almost all stable molecules have paired electrons,* either as bonding or lone pairs. Therefore, *when bonds form or break, two electrons are involved, so the oxidation state changes by 2.* For this reason, odd-numbered groups exhibit odd-numbered oxidation states and even-numbered groups exhibit even-numbered states.

1. *Odd-numbered oxidation states.* Consider the interhalogens. Four general formulas are XY, $XY_3$, $XY_5$, and $XY_7$; examples are shown in Figure 14.24. With Y in the −1 state, X must be in the +1, +3, +5, and +7 state, respectively. The −1 state arises when Y fills its valence level; the +7 state arises when the central halogen (X) is completely oxidized, that is, when all seven valence electrons have shifted away from it to the more electronegative Y atoms around it.

Let's examine the iodine fluorides to see why the oxidation states jump by two units. When $I_2$ reacts with $F_2$, IF forms (note the oxidation number of I):

$$I_2 + F_2 \longrightarrow 2\overset{+1}{I}F$$

In $IF_3$, I uses *two* more valence electrons to form *two* more bonds:

$$\overset{+1}{I}F + F_2 \longrightarrow \overset{+3}{I}F_3$$

Otherwise, an unstable lone-electron species containing two fluorines would form. With more fluorine, another jump of two units occurs and the pentafluoride forms:

$$\overset{+3}{I}F_3 + F_2 \longrightarrow \overset{+5}{I}F_5$$

With still more fluorine, the heptafluoride forms:

$$\overset{+5}{I}F_5 + F_2 \longrightarrow \overset{+7}{I}F_7$$

2. *Even-numbered oxidation states.* An element in an even-numbered group, such as sulfur in Group 6A(16), shows the same tendency to have paired electrons in its compounds. Elemental sulfur (oxidation number, O.N. = 0) gains or shares two electrons to complete its shell (O.N. = −2). It uses two electrons to react with fluorine, for example, to form $SF_2$ (O.N. = +2), two more electrons for $SF_4$ (O.N. = +4), and two more for $SF_6$ (O.N. = +6).

| Linear, XY | T-shaped, $XY_3$ | Square pyramidal, $XY_5$ | Pentagonal bipyramidal, $XY_7$ |

**Figure 14.24** Molecular shapes of the main types of interhalogen compounds.

Thus, an element with one even state typically has all even states, and an element with one odd state typically has all odd states. To reiterate the main point, *successive oxidation states differ by two units because stable molecules have electrons in pairs around their atoms.*

**Halogen Oxides, Oxoacids, and Oxoanions** The Group 7A(17) elements form many oxides that are *powerful oxidizing agents and acids in water.* Dichlorine monoxide ($Cl_2O$) and especially chlorine dioxide ($ClO_2$) are used to bleach paper (Figure 14.25). $ClO_2$ is unstable to heat and shock, so it is prepared on site, and more than 100,000 tons are used annually:

$$2NaClO_3(s) + SO_2(g) + H_2SO_4(aq) \longrightarrow 2ClO_2(g) + 2NaHSO_4(aq)$$

The dioxide has an unpaired electron and Cl in the unusual +4 oxidation state.

**Figure 14.25 Chlorine oxides.** Structures show each central Cl atom with its lowest formal charge.

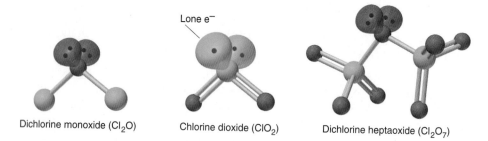

Lone e⁻

Dichlorine monoxide ($Cl_2O$)   Chlorine dioxide ($ClO_2$)   Dichlorine heptaoxide ($Cl_2O_7$)

Chlorine is in its highest (+7) oxidation state in dichlorine heptaoxide, $Cl_2O_7$, which is a symmetrical molecule formed when two $HClO_4$ ($HO-ClO_3$) molecules undergo a dehydration-condensation reaction:

$$O_3Cl-O\boxed{H + HO}-ClO_3 \longrightarrow O_3Cl-O-ClO_3(l) + H_2O(l)$$

The halogen oxoacids and oxoanions are produced by reaction of the halogens and their oxides with water. Most of the oxoacids are stable only in solution. Table 14.4 shows ball-and-stick models of the acids in which each atom has its lowest formal charge; note the formulas, which emphasize that H is bonded to O. The hypohalites ($XO^-$), halites ($XO_2^-$), and halates ($XO_3^-$) are oxidizing agents formed by aqueous disproportionation reactions [see the Group 7A(17) Family Portrait,

## Table 14.4 The Known Halogen Oxoacids*

| Central Atom | Hypohalous Acid (HOX) | Halous Acid (HOXO) | Halic Acid (HOXO₂) | Perhalic Acid (HOXO₃) |
|---|---|---|---|---|
| Fluorine | HOF | — | — | — |
| Chlorine | HOCl | HOClO | HOClO₂ | HOClO₃ |
| Bromine | HOBr | (HOBrO)? | HOBrO₂ | HOBrO₃ |
| Iodine | HOI | — | HOIO₂ | HOIO₃, (HO)₅IO |
| Oxoanion | Hypohalite | Halite | Halate | Perhalate |

*Lone pairs are shown only on the halogen atom, and each atom has its lowest formal charge.

reaction 2]. You may have heated solid alkali chlorates in the laboratory to form small amounts of $O_2$:

$$2MClO_3(s) \xrightarrow{\Delta} 2MCl(s) + 3O_2(g)$$

Potassium chlorate is the oxidizer in "safety" matches.

Several perhalates ($XO_4^-$) are also strong oxidizing agents. Thousands of tons of perchlorates are made each year for use in explosives and fireworks. Ammonium perchlorate, prepared from sodium perchlorate, is the oxidizing agent for the aluminum powder in the solid-fuel booster rockets of space shuttles; each launch uses more than 700 tons of $NH_4ClO_4$:

$$10Al(s) + 6NH_4ClO_4(s) \longrightarrow 4Al_2O_3(s) + 12H_2O(g) + 3N_2(g) + 2AlCl_3(g)$$

The relative strengths of the halogen oxoacids depend on two factors:

1. *Electronegativity of the halogen.* Among oxoacids with the halogen in the same oxidation state, such as the halic acids, $HXO_3$ (or $HOXO_2$), acid strength decreases as the halogen's EN decreases:

$$HOClO_2 > HOBrO_2 > HOIO_2$$

The more electronegative the halogen, the more electron density it removes from the O—H bond, and the more easily the proton is lost.

2. *Oxidation state of the halogen.* Among oxoacids of a given halogen, such as chlorine, acid strength decreases as the oxidation state of the halogen decreases:

$$HOClO_3 > HOClO_2 > HOClO > HOCl$$

The higher the oxidation state (number of attached O atoms) of the halogen, the more electron density it pulls from the O—H bond. We consider these trends quantitatively in Chapter 18.

# 14.10 • GROUP 8A(18): THE NOBLE GASES

The last main group consists of individual atoms too "noble" to interact much with others. The Group 8A(18) elements display regular trends in physical properties and very low, if any, reactivity. The group consists of the following elements: helium (He), the second most abundant element in the universe; neon (Ne); argon (Ar); krypton (Kr) and xenon (Xe), the only members for which compounds have been well studied; and finally, radioactive radon (Rn). The noble gases make up about 1% by volume of the atmosphere, primarily due to the abundance of Ar. The Group 8A(18) Family Portrait *(next page)* presents an overview of these elements.

## Physical Properties of the Noble Gases

Lying at the far right side of the periodic table, the Group 8A(18) elements consist of individual atoms with filled outer levels and the smallest radii in their periods: even Li, the smallest alkali metal (152 pm), is bigger than Rn, the largest noble gas (140 pm). These elements come as close to behaving as ideal gases as any other substances. Only at very low temperatures do they condense and solidify. In fact, He is the only substance that does *not* solidify by a reduction in temperature alone; it requires an increase in pressure as well. Helium has the lowest melting point known ($-272.2°C$ at 25 atm), only one degree above 0 K ($-273.15°C$), and it boils only about three degrees higher. Weak dispersion forces hold these elements in condensed states, with melting and boiling points that increase, as expected, with molar mass.

## How Can Noble Gases Form Compounds?

Ever since their discovery in the late 19th century, these elements had been considered, and even formerly named, the "inert" gases. Atomic theory and, more important, all experiments had supported this idea. Then, in 1962, all this changed when the first

# KEY ATOMIC AND PHYSICAL PROPERTIES

| KEY | Atomic No. |
|---|---|
| | **Symbol** |
| | Atomic mass |
| | Valence e⁻ configuration |
| | (Common oxidation states) |

| 2 | |
|---|---|
| **He** | |
| 4.003 | |
| $1s^2$ | |
| (none) | |

| 10 | |
|---|---|
| **Ne** | |
| 20.18 | |
| $2s^2 2p^6$ | |
| (none) | |

| 18 | |
|---|---|
| **Ar** | |
| 39.95 | |
| $3s^2 3p^6$ | |
| (none) | |

| 36 | |
|---|---|
| **Kr** | |
| 83.80 | |
| $4s^2 4p^6$ | |
| (+2) | |

| 54 | |
|---|---|
| **Xe** | |
| 131.3 | |
| $5s^2 5p^6$ | |
| (+8, +6, +4, +2) | |

| 86 | Mass |
|---|---|
| **Rn** | spectral |
| (222) | peak |
| $6s^2 6p^6$ | |
| (+2) | |

$ns^2np^6$

**GROUP 8A(18)**

Atomic radius (pm)

He 31

Ne 71

Ar 98

Kr 112

Xe 131

Rn (140)

## Atomic Properties

Group electron configuration is $1s^2$ for He and $ns^2np^6$ for the others. The valence shell is filled. Only Kr, Xe, and Rn are known to form compounds. The more reactive Xe exhibits all even oxidation states (+2 to +8). This group contains the smallest atoms with the highest IEs in their periods. Down the group, atomic size increases and IE decreases steadily. (EN values are given only for Kr and Xe.)

## Physical Properties

Melting and boiling points of these gaseous elements are extremely low but increase down the group because of stronger dispersion forces. Note the extremely small liquid ranges. Densities (at STP) increase steadily, as expected.

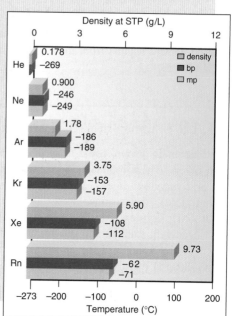

noble gas compound was prepared. How, with filled outer levels and extremely high ionization energies, *can* noble gases react?

The discovery of noble gas reactivity is a classic example of clear thinking in the face of an unexpected event. At the time, a young inorganic chemist named Neil Bartlett was studying platinum fluorides, known to be strong oxidizing agents. When he accidentally exposed $PtF_6$ to air, its deep-red color lightened slightly, and analysis showed that the $PtF_6$ had oxidized $O_2$ to form the ionic compound $[O_2]^+[PtF_6]^-$. Knowing that the ionization energy of the oxygen molecule ($O_2 \longrightarrow O_2^+ + e^-$; IE = 1175 kJ/mol) is very close to $IE_1$ of xenon (1170 kJ/mol), Bartlett reasoned that $PtF_6$ might be able to oxidize xenon. Shortly thereafter, he prepared $XePtF_6$, an orange-yellow solid. Within a few months, the white crystalline $XeF_2$ and $XeF_4$ (Figure 14.26) were also prepared. In addition to its +2 and +4 oxidation states, Xe has the +6 state in several compounds, such as $XeF_6$, and the +8 state in the unstable oxide, $XeO_4$. A few compounds of Kr and Rn have also been made.

**Figure 14.26** Crystals of xenon tetra-fluoride ($XeF_4$).

# CHAPTER REVIEW GUIDE

## Learning Objectives    Relevant section (§) numbers appear in parentheses.

### Understand These Concepts

*Note: Many characteristic reactions appear in the "Important Reactions" section of each group's Family Portrait.*

1. How hydrogen is similar to, yet different from, alkali metals and halogens; the differences between ionic, covalent, and metallic hydrides (§14.1)
2. Key horizontal trends in atomic properties, types of bonding, oxide acid-base properties, and redox behavior as the elements change from metals to nonmetals (§14.2)
3. How small atomic size and limited number of valence orbitals account for the anomalous behavior of the Period 2 member of each group (§14.2)
4. How the $ns^1$ configuration accounts for the physical and chemical properties of the alkali metals (§14.3)
5. How the $ns^2$ configuration accounts for the key differences between Groups 1A(1) and 2A(2) (§14.4)
6. The basis of the three important diagonal relationships (Li/Mg, Be/Al, B/Si) (§14.4–14.6)
7. How the presence of inner $(n - 1)d$ electrons affects properties in Group 3A(13) (§14.5)
8. Patterns among larger members of Groups 3A(13) to 6A(16): two common oxidation states (inert-pair effect), lower state more important down the group, and more basic lower oxide (§14.5–14.8)
9. How boron attains an octet of electrons (§14.5)
10. The effect of bonding on the physical behavior of Groups 4A(14) to 6A(16) (§14.6–14.8)
11. Allotropism in carbon, phosphorus, and sulfur (§14.6–14.8)
12. How atomic properties lead to catenation and multiple bonds in organic compounds (§14.6)
13. Structures and properties of the silicates and silicones (§14.6)
14. Patterns of behavior among hydrides and halides of Groups 5A(15) and 6A(16) (§14.7, 14.8)
15. The meaning of disproportionation (§14.7)
16. Structure and chemistry of the nitrogen oxides and oxoacids (§14.7)
17. Structure and chemistry of the phosphorus oxides and oxoacids (§14.7)
18. Dehydration-condensation reactions and polyphosphate structures (§14.7)
19. Structure and chemistry of the sulfur oxides and oxoacids (§14.8)
20. How the $ns^2np^5$ configuration accounts for halogen reactivity with metals (§14.9)
21. Why the oxidation states of an element change by two units (§14.9)
22. Structure and chemistry of the halogen oxides and oxoacids (§14.9)
23. How the $ns^2np^6$ configuration accounts for the relative inertness of the noble gases (§14.10)

## Key Terms    Page numbers appear in parentheses.

**Section 14.4**
diagonal relationship (533)

**Section 14.5**
bridge bond (536)

**Section 14.6**
allotrope (539)
silicate (542)
silicone (542)

**Section 14.7**
disproportionation reaction (547)
dehydration-condensation reaction (550)

**Section 14.9**
interhalogen compound (558)

# PROBLEMS

Problems with **colored** numbers are answered in Appendix E and worked in detail in the Student Solutions Manual. Problem sections match those in the text and provide the numbers of relevant sample problems. Most offer Concept Review Questions, Skill-Building Exercises (grouped in pairs covering the same concept), and Problems in Context. The Comprehensive Problems are based on material from any section or previous chapter.

## Hydrogen, the Simplest Atom

### Concept Review Questions

**14.1** Hydrogen has only one proton, but its $IE_1$ is much greater than that of lithium, which has three protons. Explain.

**14.2** Sketch a periodic table, and label the areas containing elements that give rise to the three types of hydrides.

### Skill-Building Exercises (grouped in similar pairs)

**14.3** Draw Lewis structures for the following compounds, and predict which member of each pair will form hydrogen bonds:
(a) $NF_3$ or $NH_3$      (b) $CH_3OCH_3$ or $CH_3CH_2OH$

**14.4** Draw Lewis structures for the following compounds, and predict which member of each pair will form hydrogen bonds:
(a) $NH_3$ or $AsH_3$      (b) $CH_4$ or $H_2O$

**14.5** Complete and balance the following equations:
(a) An active metal reacting with acid,
$$Al(s) + HCl(aq) \longrightarrow$$
(b) A saltlike (alkali metal) hydride reacting with water,
$$LiH(s) + H_2O(l) \longrightarrow$$

**14.6** Complete and balance the following equations:
(a) A saltlike (alkaline earth metal) hydride reacting with water,
$$CaH_2(s) + H_2O(l) \longrightarrow$$
(b) Reduction of a metal halide by hydrogen to form a metal,
$$PdCl_2(aq) + H_2(g) \longrightarrow$$

### Problems in Context

**14.7** Compounds such as $NaBH_4$, $Al(BH_4)_3$, and $LiAlH_4$ are complex hydrides used as reducing agents in many syntheses.
(a) Give the oxidation state of each element in these compounds.
(b) Write a Lewis structure for the polyatomic anion in $NaBH_4$, and predict its shape.

**14.8** Unlike the $F^-$ ion, which has an ionic radius close to 133 pm in all alkali metal fluorides, the ionic radius of $H^-$ varies from 137 pm in LiH to 152 pm in CsH. Suggest an explanation for the large variability in the size of $H^-$ but not $F^-$.

## Trends Across the Periodic Table: The Period 2 Elements

### Concept Review Questions

**14.9** How does the maximum oxidation number vary across a period in the main groups? Is the pattern in Period 2 different?

**14.10** What correlation, if any, exists for the Period 2 elements between group number and the number of covalent bonds the element typically forms? How is the correlation different for elements in Periods 3 to 6?

**14.11** Each of the chemically active Period 2 elements forms stable compounds in which it has bonds to fluorine.
(a) What are the names and formulas of these compounds?
(b) Does $\Delta EN$ increase or decrease left to right across the period?

(c) Does percent ionic character increase or decrease left to right?
(d) Draw Lewis structures for these compounds.

**14.12** Period 6 is unusual in several ways.
(a) It is the longest period in the table. How many elements belong to Period 6? How many metals?
(b) It contains no metalloids. Where is the metal/nonmetal boundary in Period 6?

**14.13** An element forms an oxide, $E_2O_3$, and a fluoride, $EF_3$.
(a) Of which two groups might E be a member?
(b) How does the group to which E belongs affect the properties of the oxide and the fluoride?

**14.14** Fluorine lies between oxygen and neon in Period 2. Whereas atomic sizes and ionization energies of these three elements change smoothly, their electronegativities display a dramatic change. What is this change, and how do their electron configurations explain it?

## Group 1A(1): The Alkali Metals

### Concept Review Questions

**14.15** Lithium salts are often much less soluble in water than the corresponding salts of other alkali metals. For example, at 18°C, the concentration of a saturated LiF solution is $1.0 \times 10^{-2}$ M, whereas that of a saturated KF solution is 1.6 M. How would you explain this behavior?

**14.16** The alkali metals play virtually the same general chemical role in all their reactions. (a) What is this role? (b) How is it based on atomic properties? (c) Using sodium, write two balanced equations that illustrate this role.

**14.17** How do atomic properties account for the low densities of the Group 1A(1) elements?

### Skill-Building Exercises (grouped in similar pairs)

**14.18** Each of the following properties shows a regular trend in Group 1A(1). Predict whether each increases or decreases *down* the group: (a) density; (b) ionic size; (c) E—E bond energy; (d) $IE_1$; (e) magnitude of $\Delta H_{hydr}$ of $E^+$ ion.

**14.19** Each of the following properties shows a regular trend in Group 1A(1). Predict whether each increases or decreases *up* the group: (a) melting point; (b) E—E bond length; (c) hardness; (d) molar volume; (e) lattice energy of EBr.

**14.20** Write a balanced equation for the formation from its elements of sodium peroxide, an industrial bleach.

**14.21** Write a balanced equation for the formation of rubidium bromide through a reaction of a strong acid and a strong base.

### Problems in Context

**14.22** Although the alkali metal halides can be prepared directly from the elements, the far less expensive industrial route is treatment of the carbonate or hydroxide with aqueous hydrohalic acid (HX) followed by recrystallization. Balance the reaction between potassium carbonate and aqueous hydroiodic acid.

**14.23** Lithium forms several useful organolithium compounds. Calculate the mass percent of Li in the following:
(a) Lithium stearate ($C_{17}H_{35}COOLi$), a water-resistant grease used in cars because it does not harden at cold temperatures
(b) Butyllithium ($LiC_4H_9$), a reagent in organic syntheses

## Group 2A(2): The Alkaline Earth Metals

### Concept Review Questions

**14.24** How do Groups 1A(1) and 2A(2) compare with respect to reaction of the metals with water?

**14.25** Alkaline earth metals are involved in two key diagonal relationships in the periodic table. (a) Give the two pairs of elements in these diagonal relationships. (b) For each pair, cite two similarities that demonstrate the relationship. (c) Why are the members of each pair so similar in behavior?

**14.26** The melting points of alkaline earth metals are many times higher than those of the alkali metals. Explain this difference on the basis of atomic properties. Name three other physical properties for which Group 2A(2) metals have higher values than the corresponding 1A(1) metals.

### Skill-Building Exercises (grouped in similar pairs)

**14.27** Write a balanced equation for each reaction:
(a) "Slaking" of lime (treatment with water)
(b) Combustion of calcium in air

**14.28** Write a balanced equation for each reaction:
(a) Thermal decomposition of witherite (barium carbonate)
(b) Neutralization of stomach acid (HCl) by milk of magnesia (magnesium hydroxide)

### Problems in Context

**14.29** Lime (CaO) is one of the most abundantly produced chemicals in the world. Write balanced equations for these reactions:
(a) The preparation of lime from natural sources
(b) The use of slaked lime to remove $SO_2$ from flue gases
(c) The reaction of lime with arsenic acid ($H_3AsO_4$) to manufacture the insecticide calcium arsenate
(d) The regeneration of NaOH in the paper industry by reaction of lime with aqueous sodium carbonate

**14.30** In some reactions, Be behaves like a typical alkaline earth metal; in others, it does not. Complete and balance the following:
(a) $BeO(s) + H_2O(l) \longrightarrow$
(b) $BeCl_2(l) + Cl^-(l; \text{from molten NaCl}) \longrightarrow$
In which reaction does Be behave like the other Group 2A(2) members?

## Group 3A(13): The Boron Family

### Concept Review Questions

**14.31** How do the transition metals in Period 4 affect the pattern of ionization energies in Group 3A(13)? How does this pattern compare with that in Group 3B(3)?

**14.32** How do the acidities of aqueous solutions of $Tl_2O$ and $Tl_2O_3$ compare with each other? Explain.

**14.33** Despite the expected decrease in atomic size, there is an unexpected drop in the first ionization energy between Groups 2A(2) and 3A(13) in Periods 2 through 4. Explain this pattern in terms of electron configurations and orbital energies.

**14.34** Many compounds of Group 3A(13) elements have chemical behavior that reflects an electron deficiency.
(a) What is the meaning of *electron deficiency?*
(b) Give two reactions that illustrate this behavior.

**14.35** Boron's chemistry is not typical of its group.
(a) Cite three ways in which boron and its compounds differ significantly from the other 3A(13) members and their compounds.
(b) What is the reason for these differences?

### Skill-Building Exercises (grouped in similar pairs)

**14.36** Rank the following oxides in order of increasing aqueous *acidity:* $Ga_2O_3$, $Al_2O_3$, $In_2O_3$.

**14.37** Rank the following hydroxides in order of increasing aqueous *basicity:* $Al(OH)_3$, $B(OH)_3$, $In(OH)_3$.

**14.38** Thallium forms the compound $TlI_3$. What is the apparent oxidation state of Tl in this compound? Given that the anion is $I_3^-$, what is the actual oxidation state of Tl? Draw the shape of the anion, giving its VSEPR class and bond angles. Propose a reason why the compound does not exist as $(Tl^{3+})(I^-)_3$.

**14.39** Very stable dihalides of the Group 3A(13) metals are known. What is the apparent oxidation state of Ga in $GaCl_2$? Given that $GaCl_2$ consists of a $Ga^+$ cation and a $GaCl_4^-$ anion, what are the actual oxidation states of Ga? Draw the shape of the anion, giving its VSEPR class and bond angles.

### Problems in Context

**14.40** Give the name and symbol or formula of a Group 3A(13) element or compound that fits each description or use:
(a) Component of heat-resistant (Pyrex-type) glass
(b) Largest temperature range for liquid state of an element
(c) Elemental substance with three-center, two-electron bonds
(d) Metal protected from oxidation by adherent oxide coat
(e) Toxic metal that lies between two other toxic metals

**14.41** Indium (In) reacts with HCl to form a diamagnetic solid with the formula $InCl_2$. (a) Write condensed electron configurations for In, $In^+$, $In^{2+}$, and $In^{3+}$. (b) Which of these species is (are) diamagnetic and which paramagnetic? (c) What is the apparent oxidation state of In in $InCl_2$? (d) Given your answers to parts (b) and (c), explain how $InCl_2$ can be diamagnetic.

**14.42** Use VSEPR theory to draw structures, with ideal bond angles, for boric acid and the anion it forms when it reacts with water.

**14.43** Boron nitride (BN) has a structure similar to graphite, but is a white insulator rather than a black conductor. It is synthesized by heating diboron trioxide with ammonia at about 1000°C.
(a) Write a balanced equation for the formation of BN; water also forms.
(b) Calculate $\Delta H^\circ_{rxn}$ for the production of BN ($\Delta H^\circ_f$ of BN is $-254$ kJ/mol).
(c) Boron is obtained from the mineral borax, $Na_2B_4O_7 \cdot 10H_2O$. How much borax is needed to produce 1.0 kg of BN, assuming 72% yield?

## Group 4A(14): The Carbon Family

### Concept Review Questions

**14.44** How does the basicity of $SnO_2$ in water compare with that of $CO_2$? Explain.

**14.45** Nearly every compound of silicon has the element in the +4 oxidation state. In contrast, most compounds of lead have the element in the +2 state.
(a) What general observation do these facts illustrate?
(b) Explain in terms of atomic and molecular properties.
(c) Give an analogous example from Group 3A(13).

**14.46** The sum of $IE_1$ through $IE_4$ for Group 4A(14) elements shows a decrease from C to Si, a slight increase from Si to Ge, a decrease from Ge to Sn, and an increase from Sn to Pb.
(a) What is the expected trend for IEs down a group?
(b) Suggest a reason for the deviations in Group 4A(14).
(c) Which group might show even greater deviations?

**14.47** Give explanations for the large drops in melting point from C to Si and from Ge to Sn.

**14.48** What is an allotrope? Name two Group 4A(14) elements that exhibit allotropism, and identify two of their allotropes.

**14.49** Even though EN values vary relatively little down Group 4A(14), the elements change from nonmetal to metal. Explain.

**14.50** How do atomic properties account for the enormous number of carbon compounds? Why don't other Group 4A(14) elements behave similarly?

**Skill-Building Exercises** (grouped in similar pairs)

**14.51** Draw a Lewis structure for each species:
(a) The cyclic silicate ion $Si_4O_{12}^{8-}$
(b) A cyclic hydrocarbon with formula $C_4H_8$

**14.52** Draw a Lewis structure for each species:
(a) The cyclic silicate ion $Si_6O_{18}^{12-}$
(b) A cyclic hydrocarbon with formula $C_6H_{12}$

**Problems in Context**

**14.53** Zeolite A, $Na_{12}[(AlO_2)_{12}(SiO_2)_{12}]\cdot27H_2O$, is used to soften water by replacing $Ca^{2+}$ and $Mg^{2+}$ with $Na^+$. Hard water from a certain source is $4.5\times10^{-3}$ $M$ $Ca^{2+}$ and $9.2\times10^{-4}$ $M$ $Mg^{2+}$, and a pipe delivers 25,000 L of this hard water per day. What mass (in kg) of zeolite A is needed to soften a week's supply of the water? (Assume zeolite A loses its capacity to exchange ions when 85 mol % of its $Na^+$ has been lost.)

**14.54** Give the name and symbol or formula of a Group 4A(14) element or compound that fits each description or use:
(a) Hardest known natural substance
(b) Medicinal antacid
(c) Atmospheric gas implicated in the greenhouse effect
(d) Gas that binds to Fe(II) in blood
(e) Element used in the manufacture of computer chips

**14.55** One similarity between B and Si is the explosive combustion of their hydrides in air. Write balanced equations for the combustion of $B_2H_6$ and of $Si_4H_{10}$.

## Group 5A(15): The Nitrogen Family

**Concept Review Questions**

**14.56** Which Group 5A(15) elements form trihalides? Pentahalides? Explain.

**14.57** As you move down Group 5A(15), the melting points of the elements increase and then decrease. Explain.

**14.58** (a) What is the range of oxidation states shown by the elements of Group 5A(15) as you move down the group? (b) How does this range illustrate the general rule for the range of oxidation states in groups on the right side of the periodic table?

**14.59** Bismuth(V) compounds are such powerful oxidizing agents that they have not been prepared in pure form. How is this fact consistent with the location of Bi in the periodic table?

**14.60** Rank the following oxides in order of increasing acidity in water: $Sb_2O_3$, $Bi_2O_3$, $P_4O_{10}$, $Sb_2O_5$.

**Skill-Building Exercises** (grouped in similar pairs)

**14.61** Assuming acid strength relates directly to electronegativity of the central atom, rank $H_3PO_4$, $HNO_3$, and $H_3AsO_4$ in order of *increasing* acid strength.

**14.62** Assuming acid strength relates directly to number of O atoms bonded to the central atom, rank $H_2N_2O_2$ [or $(HON)_2$];

$HNO_3$ (or $HONO_2$); and $HNO_2$ (or $HONO$) in order of *decreasing* acid strength.

**14.63** Complete and balance the following:
(a) $As(s) + \text{excess } O_2(g) \longrightarrow$
(b) $Bi(s) + \text{excess } F_2(g) \longrightarrow$
(c) $Ca_3As_2(s) + H_2O(l) \longrightarrow$

**14.64** Complete and balance the following:
(a) $\text{Excess } Sb(s) + Br_2(l) \longrightarrow$
(b) $HNO_3(aq) + MgCO_3(s) \longrightarrow$
(c) $K_2HPO_4(s) \xrightarrow{\Delta}$

**14.65** Complete and balance the following:
(a) $N_2(g) + Al(s) \xrightarrow{\Delta}$       (b) $PF_5(g) + H_2O(l) \longrightarrow$

**14.66** Complete and balance the following:
(a) $AsCl_3(l) + H_2O(l) \longrightarrow$       (b) $Sb_2O_3(s) + NaOH(aq) \longrightarrow$

**14.67** Based on the relative sizes of F and Cl, predict the structure of $PF_2Cl_3$.

**14.68** Use the VSEPR model to predict the structure of the cyclic ion $P_3O_9^{3-}$.

**Problems in Context**

**14.69** The pentafluorides of the larger members of Group 5A(15) have been prepared, but N can have only eight electrons. A claim has been made that, at low temperatures, a compound with the empirical formula $NF_5$ forms. Draw a possible Lewis structure for this compound. (*Hint:* $NF_5$ is ionic.)

**14.70** Give the name and symbol or formula of a Group 5A(15) element or compound that fits each description or use:
(a) Hydride that exhibits hydrogen bonding
(b) Compound used in "strike-anywhere" match heads
(c) Oxide used as a laboratory drying agent
(d) Odd-electron molecule (two examples)
(e) Compound used as an additive in soft drinks

**14.71** In addition to those in Table 14.3, other less stable nitrogen oxides exist. Draw a Lewis structure for each of the following:
(a) $N_2O_2$, a dimer of nitrogen monoxide with an N—N bond
(b) $N_2O_2$, a dimer of nitrogen monoxide with no N—N bond
(c) $N_2O_3$ with no N—N bond
(d) $NO^+$ and $NO_3^-$, products of the ionization of liquid $N_2O_4$

**14.72** Nitrous oxide ($N_2O$), the "laughing gas" used as an anesthetic by dentists, is made by thermal decomposition of solid $NH_4NO_3$. Write a balanced equation for this reaction. What are the oxidation states of N in $NH_4NO_3$ and in $N_2O$?

**14.73** Write balanced equations for the thermal decomposition of potassium nitrate ($O_2$ is also formed in both cases): (a) at low temperature to the nitrite; (b) at high temperature to the metal oxide and nitrogen.

## Group 6A(16): The Oxygen Family

**Concept Review Questions**

**14.74** Rank the following in order of increasing electrical conductivity, and explain your ranking: Po, S, Se.

**14.75** The oxygen and nitrogen families have some obvious similarities and differences.
(a) State two general physical similarities between Group 5A(15) and 6A(16) elements.
(b) State two general chemical similarities between Group 5A(15) and 6A(16) elements.
(c) State two chemical similarities between P and S.

(d) State two physical similarities between N and O.
(e) State two chemical differences between N and O.

**14.76** A molecular property of the Group 6A(16) hydrides changes abruptly down the group. This change has been explained in terms of a change in orbital hybridization.
(a) Between what periods does the change occur?
(b) What is the change in the molecular property?
(c) What is the change in hybridization?
(d) What other group displays a similar change?

**Skill-Building Exercises** (grouped in similar pairs)

**14.77** Complete and balance the following:
(a) $NaHSO_4(aq) + NaOH(aq) \longrightarrow$
(b) $S_8(s) + excess\ F_2(g) \longrightarrow$
(c) $FeS(s) + HCl(aq) \longrightarrow$
(d) $Te(s) + I_2(s) \longrightarrow$

**14.78** Complete and balance the following:
(a) $H_2S(g) + O_2(g) \longrightarrow$
(b) $SO_3(g) + H_2O(l) \longrightarrow$
(c) $SF_4(g) + H_2O(l) \longrightarrow$
(d) $Al_2Se_3(s) + H_2O(l) \longrightarrow$

**14.79** Is each oxide basic, acidic, or amphoteric in water: (a) $SeO_2$; (b) $N_2O_3$; (c) $K_2O$; (d) BeO; (e) BaO?

**14.80** Is each oxide basic, acidic, or amphoteric in water: (a) MgO; (b) $N_2O_5$; (c) CaO; (d) $CO_2$; (e) $TeO_2$?

**14.81** Rank the following hydrides in order of *increasing* acid strength: $H_2S$, $H_2O$, $H_2Te$.

**14.82** Rank the following species in order of *decreasing* acid strength: $H_2SO_4$, $H_2SO_3$, $HSO_3^-$.

**Problems in Context**

**14.83** Describe the physical changes observed when solid sulfur is heated from room temperature to 440°C and then poured quickly into cold water. Explain the molecular changes responsible for the macroscopic changes.

**14.84** Give the name and symbol or formula of a Group 6A(16) element or compound that fits each description or use:
(a) Unstable allotrope of oxygen
(b) Oxide having sulfur with the same O.N. as in sulfuric acid
(c) Air pollutant produced by burning sulfur-containing coal
(d) Powerful dehydrating agent
(e) Compound used in solution in the photographic process

**14.85** Give the oxidation state of sulfur in (a) $S_8$; (b) $SF_4$; (c) $SF_6$; (d) $H_2S$; (e) $FeS_2$; (f) $H_2SO_4$; (g) $Na_2S_2O_3 \cdot 5H_2O$.

**14.86** Disulfur decafluoride is intermediate in reactivity between $SF_4$ and $SF_6$. It disproportionates at 150°C to these monosulfur fluorides. Write a balanced equation for this reaction, and give the oxidation state of S in each compound.

## Group 7A(17): The Halogens

**Concept Review Questions**

**14.87** (a) Give the physical state and color of each halogen at STP.
(b) Explain the change in physical state down Group 7A(17) in terms of molecular properties.

**14.88** (a) What are the common oxidation states of the halogens?
(b) Give an explanation based on electron configuration for the range and values of the oxidation states of chlorine.
(c) Why is fluorine an exception to the pattern of oxidation states found for the other group members?

**14.89** How many electrons does a halogen atom need to complete its octet? Give examples of the ways a Cl atom can do so.

**14.90** Select the stronger bond in each pair:
(a) Cl—Cl or Br—Br       (b) Br—Br or I—I
(c) F—F or Cl—Cl. Why doesn't the F—F bond strength follow the group trend?

**14.91** In addition to interhalogen compounds, many interhalogen ions exist. Would you expect interhalogen ions with a 1+ or a 1− charge to have an even or odd number of atoms? Explain.

**14.92** (a) A halogen ($X_2$) disproportionates in base in several steps to $X^-$ and $XO_3^-$. Write the overall equation for the disproportionation of $Br_2$ to $Br^-$ and $BrO_3^-$.
(b) Write a balanced equation for the reaction of $ClF_5$ with aqueous base (see the reaction of $BrF_5$ shown on p. 559).

**Skill-Building Exercises** (grouped in similar pairs)

**14.93** Complete and balance the following equations. If no reaction occurs, write NR:
(a) $Rb(s) + Br_2(l) \longrightarrow$       (b) $I_2(s) + H_2O(l) \longrightarrow$
(c) $Br_2(l) + I^-(aq) \longrightarrow$       (d) $CaF_2(s) + H_2SO_4(l) \longrightarrow$

**14.94** Complete and balance the following equations. If no reaction occurs, write NR:
(a) $H_3PO_4(l) + NaI(s) \longrightarrow$       (b) $Cl_2(g) + I^-(aq) \longrightarrow$
(c) $Br_2(l) + Cl^-(aq) \longrightarrow$       (d) $ClF(g) + F_2(g) \longrightarrow$

**14.95** Rank the following acids in order of *increasing* acid strength: $HClO$, $HClO_2$, $HBrO$, $HIO$.

**14.96** Rank the following acids in order of *decreasing* acid strength: $HBrO_3$, $HBrO_4$, $HIO_3$, $HClO_4$.

**Problems in Context**

**14.97** Give the name and symbol or formula of a Group 7A(17) element or compound that fits each description or use:
(a) Used in etching glass
(b) Compound used in household bleach
(c) Weakest hydrohalic acid
(d) Element that is a liquid at room temperature
(e) Organic chloride used to make PVC.

**14.98** An industrial chemist treats solid NaCl with concentrated $H_2SO_4$ and obtains gaseous HCl and $NaHSO_4$. When she substitutes solid NaI for NaCl, gaseous $H_2S$, solid $I_2$, and $S_8$ are obtained but no HI. (a) What type of reaction did the $H_2SO_4$ undergo with NaI? (b) Why does NaI, but not NaCl, cause this type of reaction? (c) To produce HI(g) by the reaction of NaI with an acid, how does the acid have to differ from sulfuric acid?

**14.99** Rank the halogens $Cl_2$, $Br_2$, and $I_2$ in order of increasing oxidizing strength based on their products with metallic Re: $ReCl_6$, $ReBr_5$, $ReI_4$. Explain your ranking.

## Group 8A(18): The Noble Gases

**14.100** Which noble gas is the most abundant in the universe? In Earth's atmosphere?

**14.101** What oxidation states does Xe show in its compounds?

**14.102** Why do the noble gases have such low boiling points?

**14.103** Explain why Xe, and to a limited extent Kr, form compounds, whereas He, Ne, and Ar do not.

**14.104** (a) Why do stable xenon fluorides have an even number of F atoms? (b) Why do the ionic species $XeF_3^+$ and $XeF_7^-$ have odd numbers of F atoms? (c) Predict the shape of $XeF_3^+$.

## Comprehensive Problems

**14.105** Xenon tetrafluoride reacts with antimony pentafluoride to form the ionic complex $[XeF_3]^+[SbF_6]^-$. (a) Which depiction shows the molecular shapes of the reactants and product? (b) How, if at all, does the hybridization of xenon change in the reaction?

**14.106** Given the following information,

$$H^+(g) + H_2O(g) \longrightarrow H_3O^+(g) \qquad \Delta H = -720 \text{ kJ}$$
$$H^+(g) + H_2O(l) \longrightarrow H_3O^+(aq) \qquad \Delta H = -1090 \text{ kJ}$$
$$H_2O(l) \longrightarrow H_2O(g) \qquad \Delta H = 40.7 \text{ kJ}$$

calculate the heat of solution of the hydronium ion:

$$H_3O^+(g) \xrightarrow{\text{H}_2\text{O}} H_3O^+(aq)$$

**14.107** The electronic transition in Na from $3p^1$ to $3s^1$ gives rise to a bright yellow-orange emission at 589.2 nm. What is the energy of this transition?

**14.108** Unlike other Group 2A(2) metals, beryllium reacts like aluminum and zinc with concentrated aqueous base to release hydrogen gas and form oxoanions of formula $M(OH)_4^{n-}$. Write equations for the reactions of these three metals with NaOH.

**14.109** The interhalogen IF undergoes the reaction depicted below (I is purple and F is green):

(a) Write the balanced equation. (b) Name the interhalogen product. (c) What type of reaction is shown? (d) If each molecule of IF represents $2.50 \times 10^{-3}$ mol, what mass of each product forms?

**14.110** The main reason alkali metal dihalides ($MX_2$) do *not* form is the high $IE_2$ of the metal. (a) Why is $IE_2$ so high for alkali metals? (b) The $IE_2$ for Cs is 2255 kJ/mol, low enough for $CsF_2$ to form exothermically ($\Delta H_f^\circ = -125$ kJ/mol). This compound cannot be synthesized, however, because CsF forms with a much greater release of heat ($\Delta H_f^\circ = -530$ kJ/mol). Thus, the breakdown of $CsF_2$ to CsF happens readily. Write the equation for this breakdown, and calculate the enthalpy of reaction per mole of CsF.

**14.111** Semiconductors made from elements in Groups 3A(13) and 5A(15) are typically prepared by direct reaction of the elements at high temperature. An engineer treats 32.5 g of molten gallium with 20.4 L of white phosphorus vapor at 515 K and 195 kPa. If purification losses are 7.2% by mass, how many grams of gallium phosphide will be prepared?

**14.112** Two substances with empirical formula HNO are hyponitrous acid ($M = 62.04$ g/mol) and nitroxyl ($M = 31.02$ g/mol).
(a) What is the molecular formula of each species?
(b) For each species, draw the Lewis structure having the lowest formal charges. (*Hint:* Hyponitrous acid has an N=N bond.)
(c) Predict the shape around the N atoms of each species.
(d) When hyponitrous acid loses two protons, it forms the hyponitrite ion. Draw *cis* and *trans* forms of this ion.

**14.113** The species CO, $CN^-$, and $C_2^{2-}$ are isoelectronic.
(a) Draw their Lewis structures.
(b) Draw their MO diagrams (assume $2s$-$2p$ mixing, as in $N_2$), and give the bond order and electron configuration for each.

**14.114** The Ostwald process is a series of three reactions used for the industrial production of nitric acid from ammonia.
(a) Write a series of balanced equations for the Ostwald process.
(b) If NO is *not* recycled, how many moles of $NH_3$ are consumed per mole of $HNO_3$ produced?
(c) In a typical industrial unit, the process is very efficient, with a 96% yield for the first step. Assuming 100% yields for the subsequent steps, what volume of concentrated aqueous nitric acid (60.% by mass; $d = 1.37$ g/mL) can be prepared for each cubic meter of a gas mixture that is 90.% air and 10.% $NH_3$ by volume at the industrial conditions of 5.0 atm and 850.°C?

**14.115** All common plant fertilizers contain nitrogen compounds. Determine the mass % of N in (a) ammonia; (b) ammonium nitrate; (c) ammonium hydrogen phosphate.

**14.116** Producer gas is a fuel formed by passing air over red-hot coke (amorphous carbon). What mass of a producer gas that consists of 25% CO, 5.0% $CO_2$, and 70.% $N_2$ by mass can be formed from 1.75 metric tons of coke, assuming an 87% yield?

**14.117** Gaseous $F_2$ reacts with water to form HF and $O_2$. In NaOH solution, $F_2$ forms $F^-$, water, and oxygen difluoride ($OF_2$), a highly toxic gas and powerful oxidizing agent. The $OF_2$ reacts with excess $OH^-$, forming $O_2$, water, and $F^-$. (a) For each reaction, write a balanced equation, give the oxidation state of O in all compounds, and identify the oxidizing and reducing agents. (b) Draw a Lewis structure for $OF_2$, and predict its shape.

**14.118** What is a disproportionation reaction, and which of the following fit the description?
(a) $I_2(s) + KI(aq) \longrightarrow KI_3(aq)$
(b) $2ClO_2(g) + H_2O(l) \longrightarrow HClO_3(aq) + HClO_2(aq)$
(c) $Cl_2(g) + 2NaOH(aq) \longrightarrow$
$$NaCl(aq) + NaClO(aq) + H_2O(l)$$
(d) $NH_4NO_2(s) \longrightarrow N_2(g) + 2H_2O(g)$
(e) $3MnO_4^{2-}(aq) + 2H_2O(l) \longrightarrow$
$$2MnO_4^-(aq) + MnO_2(s) + 4OH^-(aq)$$
(f) $3AuCl(s) \longrightarrow AuCl_3(s) + 2Au(s)$

**14.119** Explain the following observations:
(a) In reactions with $Cl_2$, phosphorus forms $PCl_5$ in addition to the expected $PCl_3$, but nitrogen forms only $NCl_3$.
(b) Carbon tetrachloride is unreactive toward water, but silicon tetrachloride reacts rapidly and completely. (To give what?)

(c) The sulfur-oxygen bond in $SO_4^{2-}$ is shorter than expected for an S—O single bond.
(d) Chlorine forms $ClF_3$ and $ClF_5$, but $ClF_4$ is unknown.

**14.120** Which group(s) of the periodic table is (are) described by each of the following general statements?
(a) The elements form compounds of VSEPR class $AX_3E$.
(b) The free elements are strong oxidizing agents and form monatomic ions and oxoanions.
(c) The atoms form compounds by combining with two other atoms that donate one electron each.
(d) The free elements are strong reducing agents, show only one nonzero oxidation state, and form mainly ionic compounds.
(e) The elements can form stable compounds with only three bonds, but as a central atom, they can accept a pair of electrons from a fourth atom without expanding their valence shell.
(f) Only larger members of the group are chemically active.

**14.121** Diiodine pentaoxide ($I_2O_5$) was discovered by Joseph Gay-Lussac in 1813, but its structure was unknown until 1970! Like $Cl_2O_7$, it can be prepared by the dehydration-condensation of the corresponding oxoacid.
(a) Name the precursor oxoacid, write a reaction for formation of the oxide, and draw a likely Lewis structure.
(b) Data show that the bonds to the terminal O are shorter than the bonds to the bridging O. Why?
(c) $I_2O_5$ is one of the few chemicals that can oxidize CO rapidly and completely; elemental iodine forms in the process. Write a balanced equation for this reaction.

**14.122** Bromine monofluoride (BrF) disproportionates to bromine gas and bromine tri- and pentafluorides. Use the following to find $\Delta H_{rxn}^{\circ}$ for the decomposition of BrF to its elements:

$$3BrF(g) \longrightarrow Br_2(g) + BrF_3(l) \quad \Delta H_{rxn} = -125.3 \text{ kJ}$$
$$5BrF(g) \longrightarrow 2Br_2(g) + BrF_5(l) \quad \Delta H_{rxn} = -166.1 \text{ kJ}$$
$$BrF_3(l) + F_2(g) \longrightarrow BrF_5(l) \quad \Delta H_{rxn} = -158.0 \text{ kJ}$$

**14.123** White phosphorus is prepared by heating phosphate rock [principally $Ca_3(PO_4)_2$] with sand and coke:

$$Ca_3(PO_4)_2(s) + SiO_2(s) + C(s) \longrightarrow$$
$$CaSiO_3(s) + CO(g) + P_4(g) \text{ [unbalanced]}$$

How many kilograms of phosphate rock are needed to produce 315 mol of $P_4$, assuming that the conversion is 90.% efficient?

**14.124** Element E forms an oxide of general structure A and a chloride of general structure B, shown at right. For the anion $EF_5^-$, what is (a) the molecular shape; (b) the hybridization of E; (c) the O.N. of E?

**14.125** From its formula, one might expect CO to be quite polar, but its dipole moment is actually low (0.11 D). (a) Draw the Lewis structure for CO. (b) Calculate the formal charges. (c) Based on your answers to parts (a) and (b), explain why the dipole moment is so low.

**14.126** When an alkaline earth carbonate is heated, it releases $CO_2$, leaving the metal oxide. The temperature at which each Group 2A(2) carbonate yields a $CO_2$ partial pressure of 1 atm is

| Carbonate | Temperature (°C) |
|---|---|
| $MgCO_3$ | 542 |
| $CaCO_3$ | 882 |
| $SrCO_3$ | 1155 |
| $BaCO_3$ | 1360 |

(a) Suggest a reason for this trend. (b) Mixtures of $CaCO_3$ and MgO are used to absorb dissolved silicates from boiler water. How would you prepare a mixture of $CaCO_3$ and MgO from dolomite, which contains $CaCO_3$ and $MgCO_3$?

**14.127** The bond angles in the nitrite ion, nitrogen dioxide, and the nitronium ion ($NO_2^+$) are 115°, 134°, and 180°, respectively. Explain these values using Lewis structures and VSEPR theory.

**14.128** A common method for producing a gaseous hydride is to treat a salt containing the anion of the volatile hydride with a strong acid.
(a) Write an equation for each of the following examples: (1) the production of HF from $CaF_2$; (2) the production of HCl from NaCl; (3) the production of $H_2S$ from FeS.
(b) In some cases, even a weak acid such as water will suffice if the anion of the salt has a sufficiently strong attraction for protons. An example is the production of $PH_3$ from $Ca_3P_2$ and water. Write the equation for this reaction.
(c) By analogy, predict the products and write the equation for the reaction of $Al_4C_3$ with water.

**14.129** Chlorine trifluoride was formerly used in the production of uranium hexafluoride for the U.S. nuclear industry:

$$U(s) + 3ClF_3(l) \longrightarrow UF_6(l) + 3ClF(g)$$

How many grams of $UF_6$ can form from 1.00 metric ton of uranium ore that is 1.55% by mass uranium and 12.75 L of chlorine trifluoride ($d = 1.88$ g/mL)?

**14.130** Chlorine is used to make bleach solutions containing 5.25% NaClO (by mass). Assuming 100% yield in the reaction producing NaClO from $Cl_2$, how many liters of $Cl_2(g)$ at STP will be needed to make 1000. L of bleach solution ($d = 1.07$ g/mL)?

**14.131** The triatomic molecular ion $H_3^+$ was first detected and characterized by J. J. Thomson using mass spectrometry. Use the bond energy of $H_2$ (432 kJ/mol) and the proton affinity of $H_2$ ($H_2 + H^+ \longrightarrow H_3^+$; $\Delta H = -337$ kJ/mol) to calculate the enthalpy of reaction for $H + H + H^+ \longrightarrow H_3^+$.

**14.132** An atomic hydrogen torch is used for cutting and welding thick sheets of metal. When $H_2$ passes through an electric arc, the molecules decompose into atoms, which react with $O_2$. Temperatures over 5000°C are reached, which can melt all metals. Write equations for the breakdown of $H_2$ to H atoms and for the subsequent overall reaction of the H atoms with oxygen. Use Appendix B to find the standard heat of each reaction per mole of product.

**14.133** Which of the following oxygen ions are paramagnetic: $O^+$, $O^-$, $O^{2-}$, $O^{2+}$?

**14.134** Copper(II) hydrogen arsenite ($CuHAsO_3$) is a green pigment once used in wallpaper. In damp conditions, mold metabolizes this compound to trimethylarsine [$(CH_3)_3As$], a highly toxic gas. (a) Calculate the mass percent of As in each compound. (b) How much $CuHAsO_3$ must react to reach a toxic level in a room that measures 12.35 m × 7.52 m × 2.98 m (arsenic is toxic at 0.50 mg/m³)?

**14.135** Hydrogen peroxide can act as either an oxidizing agent or a reducing agent. (a) When $H_2O_2$ is treated with aqueous KI, $I_2$ forms. In which role is $H_2O_2$ acting? What is the oxygen-containing product formed? (b) When $H_2O_2$ is treated with aqueous $KMnO_4$, the purple color of $MnO_4^-$ disappears and a gas forms. In which role is $H_2O_2$ acting? What is the oxygen-containing product formed?

# Organic Compounds and the Atomic Properties of Carbon

## Concepts and skills to review before you study this chapter

- naming straight-chain alkanes (Section 2.8)
- constitutional isomerism (Section 3.2)
- ΔEN and bond polarity (Section 9.5)
- resonance structures (Section 10.1)
- VSEPR theory (Section 10.2)
- orbital hybridization (Section 11.1)

- σ and π bonding (Section 11.2)
- intermolecular forces and synthetic and biological macromolecules (Sections 12.3, 12.7, and 13.2)
- properties of the Period 2 elements (Section 14.2)
- properties of the Group 4A(14) elements (Section 14.6)

Organic compounds occur throughout every living thing and in countless products—like jelly beans in a plastic container! Jelly beans are composed of sugars, gelatin, and starch—all organic compounds. And the plastic container is a combination of polymeric organic compounds. In fact, except for a few inorganic salts and ever-present water, nearly everything you put into or on your body—jelly beans, medicine, cosmetics, and clothing—consists of organic compounds. Organic fuels warm our homes, cook our meals, and power our vehicles. Major industries are devoted to producing organic compounds, including plastics, pharmaceuticals, and insecticides.

What *is* an organic compound? The dictionary definition is "a compound of carbon," but that definition is too general because it includes carbonates, cyanides, carbides, cyanates, and other carbon-containing ionic compounds that most chemists classify as inorganic. Here is a more specific definition: all **organic compounds** contain carbon, nearly always bonded to other carbons and hydrogen, and often to other elements.

In the early 19th century, organic compounds were usually obtained from living things, so they were thought to possess a spiritual "vital force" that made them impossible to synthesize and fundamentally different from inorganic compounds. Today, we know that *the same chemical principles govern organic and inorganic systems* because the behavior of a compound arises from the properties of its elements.

**IN THIS CHAPTER . . .** We apply the text's central theme to the enormous field of organic chemistry to see how the structures and reactivities of organic molecules emerge naturally from the properties of their component atoms.

- We begin by reviewing the atomic properties of carbon and seeing how they lead to the complex structures and reactivity of organic molecules.
- We then focus on writing and naming hydrocarbons as a prelude to naming other types of organic compounds.
- We classify the main types of organic reactions in terms of bond order and apply them to the functional groups that characterize families of organic compounds.
- We examine the giant organic molecules of commerce and life—synthetic and natural polymers.

## 15.1 • THE SPECIAL NATURE OF CARBON AND THE CHARACTERISTICS OF ORGANIC MOLECULES

Although there is nothing mystical about organic molecules, their indispensable role in biology and industry leads us to ask if carbon has some extraordinary attributes that give it a special chemical "personality." Of course, each element has its own specific properties, and carbon is no more unique than sodium, hafnium, or any other element. But the atomic properties of carbon do give it bonding capabilities beyond those of any other element, which in turn lead to the two obvious characteristics of organic molecules—structural complexity and chemical diversity.

## The Structural Complexity of Organic Molecules

Most organic molecules have more complex structures than most inorganic molecules. A quick review of carbon's atomic properties and bonding behavior shows why.

### Electron Configuration, Electronegativity, and Covalent Bonding

Carbon forms covalent bonds in all its elemental forms and compounds, sharing electrons to attain a filled outer (valence) level. Carbon's formation of covalent bonds, rather than ionic bonds, is the result of its electron configuration and its electronegativity value:

- Carbon's ground-state electron configuration of [He] $2s^2 2p^2$—four electrons more than He and four fewer than Ne—means that the formation of carbon ions is energetically impossible under ordinary conditions. The loss of four electrons to form the $C^{4+}$ cation requires energy equal to the sum of $IE_1$ through $IE_4$; the gain of four electrons to form the $C^{4-}$ anion requires the sum of $EA_1$ through $EA_4$, the last three steps of which are endothermic.
- Lying at the center of Period 2, carbon has an electronegativity (EN = 2.5) that is midway between that of the most metallic element (Li, EN = 1.0) and the most nonmetallic element (F, EN = 4.0) of Period 2 (Figure 15.1).

**Figure 15.1** The position of carbon in the periodic table.

### Bond Properties, Catenation, and Molecular Shape

The *number* and *strength* of carbon's bonds lead to its property of **catenation,** the ability to bond to itself, which in turn allows it to form a multitude of chemically and thermally stable chain, ring, and branched compounds. Carbon's small size and ability to form hybrid orbitals and multiple bonds increase the number of different molecules by affecting molecular shape:

- Through the process of orbital hybridization (Section 11.1), carbon forms four bonds in virtually all its compounds, and they point in as many as four different directions.
- The small size of carbon allows close approach to another atom and thus greater orbital overlap, so carbon forms relatively short, strong bonds.
- The C—C bond is short enough to allow side-to-side overlap of half-filled, unhybridized *p* orbitals and the formation of multiple bonds, which restrict rotation of attached groups (see Figure 11.14, p. 405).

### Molecular Stability

Although silicon and several other elements also catenate, none can form chains as stable as those of carbon. Atomic and bonding properties confer three crucial differences between C and Si chains that explain why C chains are so stable and, therefore, so common:

- *Atomic size and bond strength.* As atomic size increases down Group 4A(14), bonds between identical atoms become longer and weaker. Thus, a C—C bond (347 kJ/mol) is much stronger than an Si—Si bond (226 kJ/mol).
- *Relative enthalpies of reaction.* A C—C bond (347 kJ/mol), a C—O bond (358 kJ/mol), and a C—Cl bond (339 kJ/mol) have nearly the same energy, so relatively little heat is released when a C chain reacts and one bond replaces the other. In contrast, an Si—O bond (368 kJ/mol) or an Si—Cl bond (381 kJ/mol) is much stronger than an Si—Si bond (226 kJ/mol), so a large quantity of heat is released when an Si chain reacts.
- *Orbitals available for reaction.* Unlike C, Si has low-energy *d* orbitals that can be attacked (occupied) by the lone pairs of incoming reactants. For example, ethane ($CH_3$—$CH_3$) is stable in water and does not react in air unless sparked, whereas disilane ($SiH_3$—$SiH_3$) breaks down in water and ignites spontaneously in air.

## The Chemical Diversity of Organic Molecules

In addition to their complex geometries, organic compounds are noted for their sheer number and diverse chemical behavior. Several million organic compounds are known, and thousands more are discovered or synthesized each year. This incredible diversity is also founded on atomic and bonding behavior and is due to three inter-related factors, discussed below.

**Bonding to Heteroatoms** Many organic compounds contain **heteroatoms,** atoms other than C or H. The most common heteroatoms are N and O, but S, P, and the halogens often occur, and organic compounds with other elements are known as well. Figure 15.2 shows that 23 different molecular structures are possible from various arrangements of four C atoms singly bonded to each other, just one O atom (either singly or doubly bonded), and the necessary number of H atoms.

**Electron Density and Reactivity** Most reactions start—that is, a new bond begins to form—*when a region of high electron density on one molecule meets a region of low electron density on another.* These regions may be due to the presence of a multiple bond or to the properties of carbon-heteroatom bonds. Consider the reactivities of four bonds commonly found in organic molecules:

- *The C—C bond.* When C is singly bonded to another C, as occurs in portions of nearly every organic molecule, the EN values are equal and the bond is nonpolar. Therefore, in general, *C—C bonds are unreactive.*
- *The C—H bond.* This bond, which also occurs in nearly every organic molecule, is short (109 pm) and very nearly nonpolar, with EN values of H (2.1) and C (2.5). Thus, *C—H bonds are largely unreactive.*
- *The C—O bond.* This bond, which occurs in many types of organic molecules, is highly polar ($\Delta EN = 1.0$), with the O end of the bond electron rich and the C end electron poor. As a result of this imbalance in electron density, *the C—O bond is reactive,* and, given appropriate conditions, a reaction will occur there.
- *Bonds to other heteroatoms.* Even when a carbon-heteroatom bond has a small $\Delta EN$, such as that for C—Br ($\Delta EN = 0.3$), or none at all, as for C—S ($\Delta EN = 0$), the heteroatoms are generally large, so their bonds to carbon are long, weak, and thus *reactive.*

**Importance of Functional Groups** One of the most important ideas in organic chemistry is that of the **functional group,** a specific combination of bonded atoms that reacts in a *characteristic* way, no matter what molecule it occurs in. In nearly every case, *the reaction of an organic compound takes place at the functional group.* As you'll see, we often substitute a general symbol for the remainder of the organic molecule because it usually stays the same while the functional group reacts. Functional groups include carbon-carbon multiple bonds and several combinations of carbon-heteroatom bonds, and each has its own pattern of reactivity. A particular bond may be a functional group itself or *part* of one or more functional groups. For example, the C—O bond occurs in four functional groups. We will discuss the reactivity of three of these groups in this chapter:

alcohol group        carboxylic acid group        ester group

**Figure 15.2** Heteroatoms and different bonding arrangements lead to great chemical diversity.

## ■ Summary of Section 15.1

- Carbon's small size, intermediate electronegativity, four valence electrons, and ability to form multiple bonds result in the structural complexity of organic compounds.
- These factors lead to carbon's ability to catenate, which creates chains, branches, and rings of C atoms. Small size and absence of *d* orbitals in its valence level lead to strong, chemically resistant bonds that point in as many as four directions from each C.
- Carbon's ability to bond to many other elements, including O and N, creating polar bonds and resulting in greater reactivity, leads to the chemical diversity of organic compounds.
- Most organic compounds contain functional groups, specific groupings of bonded atoms that react in characteristic ways.

## 15.2 • THE STRUCTURES AND CLASSES OF HYDROCARBONS

A fanciful, anatomical analogy can be made between an organic molecule and an animal. The carbon-carbon bonds form the skeleton: the longest continual chain is the backbone, and any branches are the limbs. Covering the skeleton is a skin of hydrogen atoms, with functional groups protruding at specific locations, like chemical fingers ready to grab an incoming reactant. In this section, we "dissect" one group of compounds down to their skeletons and see how to name and draw them.

**Hydrocarbons,** the simplest type of organic compound, are a large group of substances containing only H and C atoms. Some common fuels, such as natural gas and gasoline, are hydrocarbon mixtures. Some hydrocarbons, such as ethylene, acetylene, and benzene, are important *feedstocks,* precursor reactants used to make other compounds.

### Carbon Skeletons and Hydrogen Skins

Let's begin by examining the possible bonding arrangements of C atoms only (leaving off the H atoms for now) in simple skeletons without multiple bonds or rings. To distinguish different skeletons, focus on the *arrangement* of C atoms (that is, the successive linkages of one to another) and keep in mind that *groups joined by a single (sigma) bond are relatively free to rotate* (Section 11.2).

Structures with one, two, or three carbons can be arranged in only one way. Whether you draw three C atoms in a line or with a bend, the arrangement is the same. Four C atoms, however, have two possible arrangements—a four-C chain or a three-C chain with a one-C branch at the central C:

Even when we show the chains more realistically, with the bends due to the tetrahedral shape around the C atoms (as in the ball-and-stick models above), the situation is the same. Notice that if the branch is added to either end of the three-C chain, it is simply a bend in a four-C chain, *not* a different arrangement. Similarly, if the branch points down instead of up, it represents the same arrangement because groups joined by a single bond rotate.

As the total number of C atoms increases, the number of different arrangements increases as well. Five C atoms have 3 possible arrangements (Figure 15.3A); 6 C atoms can be arranged in 5 ways, 7 C atoms in 9 ways, 10 C atoms in 75 ways, and

**Figure 15.3** Some five-carbon skeletons.

20 C atoms in more than 300,000 ways! If we include multiple bonds and rings, the number of arrangements increases further. For example, including one C=C bond in the five-C skeletons creates 5 more arrangements (Figure 15.3B), and including one ring creates 5 more (Figure 15.3C).

When determining the number of different skeletons for a given number of C atoms, remember that

- Each C atom can form a *maximum* of four single bonds, or two single and one double bond, or one single and one triple bond.
- The *arrangement* of C atoms determines the skeleton, so a straight chain and a bent chain represent the same skeleton.
- Groups joined by a single bond can *rotate,* so a branch pointing down is the same as one pointing up. (Recall that a double bond restricts rotation.)

If we put a hydrogen "skin" on a carbon skeleton, we obtain a hydrocarbon. Figure 15.4 shows that a skeleton has the correct number of H atoms when each C has four bonds. Sample Problem 15.1 provides practice drawing hydrocarbons.

**Figure 15.4** Adding the H-atom skin to the C-atom skeleton.

A C atom single-bonded to one other atom gets three H atoms.

A C atom single-bonded to two other atoms gets two H atoms.

A C atom single-bonded to three other atoms gets one H atom.

A C atom single-bonded to four other atoms is already fully bonded (no H atoms).

A double-bonded C atom is treated as if it were bonded to two other atoms.

A double- and single-bonded C atom or a triple-bonded C atom is treated as if it were bonded to three other atoms.

---

**Sample Problem 15.1** | **Drawing Hydrocarbons**

**Problem** Draw structures that have different atom arrangements for hydrocarbons with:
**(a)** Six C atoms, no multiple bonds, and no rings
**(b)** Four C atoms, one double bond, and no rings
**(c)** Four C atoms, no multiple bonds, and one ring

**Plan** In each case, we draw the longest carbon chain first and then work down to smaller chains with branches at different points along them. The process typically involves trial and error. Then, we add H atoms to give each C a total of four bonds.

**Solution** **(a)** Compounds with six C atoms:

**(b)** Compounds with four C atoms and one double bond:

4-C chains:

$$H{-}\overset{\overset{\displaystyle H}{|}}{\underset{\underset{\displaystyle H}{|}}{C}}{-}\overset{\overset{\displaystyle H}{|}}{C}{=}\overset{\overset{\displaystyle H}{|}}{C}{-}\overset{\overset{\displaystyle H}{|}}{\underset{\underset{\displaystyle H}{|}}{C}}{-}H \qquad H{-}\overset{\overset{\displaystyle H}{|}}{\underset{\underset{\displaystyle H}{|}}{C}}{-}\overset{\overset{\displaystyle H}{|}}{\underset{\underset{\displaystyle H}{|}}{C}}{-}\overset{\overset{\displaystyle H}{|}}{C}{=}\overset{\overset{\displaystyle H}{|}}{C}{-}H$$

3-C chain:

$$H{-}\overset{\overset{\displaystyle H}{|}}{\underset{\underset{\underset{\underset{\displaystyle H}{|}}{\underset{\displaystyle H{-}C{-}H}{|}}}{|}}{C}}{-}\overset{\overset{\displaystyle H}{|}}{C}{=}\overset{\overset{\displaystyle H}{|}}{C}{-}H$$

**(c)** Compounds with four C atoms and one ring:

4-C ring:

$$\begin{array}{cc} \overset{\displaystyle H}{|} & \overset{\displaystyle H}{|} \\ H{-}C{-} & C{-}H \\ | & | \\ H{-}C{-} & C{-}H \\ \underset{\displaystyle H}{|} & \underset{\displaystyle H}{|} \end{array}$$

3-C ring:

$$H{-}\overset{\overset{\displaystyle H}{|}}{\underset{\underset{\displaystyle H}{|}}{C}}{-}\overset{\overset{\overset{\displaystyle C}{/ \backslash}}{}}{\underset{\underset{\displaystyle H}{|}}{C}}{-}\overset{\overset{\displaystyle H}{|}}{\underset{\underset{\displaystyle H}{|}}{C}}{-}H$$

**Check** Be sure each skeleton has the correct number of C atoms, multiple bonds, and/or rings, and no arrangements are repeated or omitted; remember a double bond counts as two bonds.

**Comment** Avoid some *common mistakes:*

In (a): $C{-}\overset{\overset{\displaystyle }{|}}{\underset{\underset{\displaystyle C}{|}}{C}}{-}C{-}C{-}C$ is the same skeleton as $C{-}C{-}C{-}\overset{\overset{\displaystyle C}{|}}{C}{-}C$

$C{-}\overset{\overset{\displaystyle }{|}}{\underset{\underset{\displaystyle C}{|}}{C}}{-}\overset{\overset{\displaystyle C}{|}}{C}{-}C$ is the same skeleton as $C{-}\overset{\overset{\displaystyle C}{|}}{C}{-}\overset{\overset{\displaystyle C}{|}}{C}{-}C$

In (b): $C{-}C{-}C{=}C$ is the same skeleton as $C{=}C{-}C{-}C$

The double bond restricts rotation, so, in addition to the *cis* form shown in part (b), another possibility is the *trans* form:

$$H{-}\overset{\overset{\displaystyle H}{|}}{\underset{\underset{\displaystyle H}{|}}{C}}{-}\overset{\overset{\displaystyle H}{|}}{C}{=}\overset{\overset{\displaystyle H}{|}}{C}{-}\overset{\overset{\displaystyle H}{|}}{C}{-}H$$

(We discuss *cis* and *trans* forms fully later in this section.)

Also, avoid drawing too many bonds to one C, as here:

$$H{-}\overset{\overset{\displaystyle H}{|}}{\underset{\underset{\underset{\underset{\displaystyle H}{|}}{\underset{\displaystyle H{-}C{-}H}{|}}}{|}}{C}}{-}\overset{\overset{\displaystyle H}{|}}{C}{=}\overset{\overset{\overset{\displaystyle H}{|}}{\underbrace{\quad}_{\text{5 bonds}}}}{C}{-}H$$

In (c): there are too many bonds to one C in

$$H{-}\overset{\overset{\displaystyle H}{|}}{\underset{\underset{\displaystyle H}{|}}{C}}{-}\overset{\overset{\overset{\displaystyle C}{/ \backslash}}{}}{\underset{\underset{\displaystyle H}{|}}{C}}{-}\overset{\overset{\displaystyle H\text{—5 bonds}}{}}{\underset{\underset{\displaystyle H}{|}}{C}}{-}H$$

**Follow-Up Problem 15.1** Draw all hydrocarbons that have different atom arrangements with: **(a)** Seven C atoms, no multiple bonds, and no rings (nine arrangements) **(b)** Five C atoms, one triple bond, and no rings (three arrangements)

---

Hydrocarbons can be classified into four main groups. In the remainder of this section, we discuss naming, as well as some structural features and physical properties of each group. Later, we'll discuss the chemical behavior of the hydrocarbons.

## Alkanes: Hydrocarbons with Only Single Bonds

A hydrocarbon that contains only single bonds is an **alkane** (general formula $C_nH_{2n+2}$, where $n$ is a positive integer). For example, if $n = 5$, the formula is $C_5H_{[(2\times5)+2]}$, or $C_5H_{12}$. The alkanes comprise a **homologous series,** one in which each member differs from the next by a $-CH_2-$ (methylene) group. In an alkane, each C is $sp^3$ hybridized. Because each C is bonded to the *maximum number of other atoms* (C or H), alkanes are referred to as **saturated hydrocarbons.**

**Naming Alkanes** You learned the straight-chain alkanes in Section 2.8. Here we discuss general rules for naming any alkane and, by extension, other organic compounds as well. The key point is that *each chain, branch, or ring has a name based on the **number** of C atoms.* The name of a compound has three portions:

PREFIX + **ROOT** + SUFFIX

- *Root:* The root tells the number of C atoms in the longest *continuous* chain in the molecule. The roots for the ten smallest alkanes are shown in Table 15.1. As you can see, there are special roots for compounds with chains of one to four C atoms; roots of longer chains are based on Greek numbers.
- *Suffix:* The suffix tells the *type of organic compound* that is being named; that is, it identifies the key functional group the molecule possesses. The suffix is placed *after* the root.
- *Prefix:* Each prefix identifies a *group attached to the main chain* and the number of the carbon to which it is attached. Prefixes identifying hydrocarbon branches are the same as root names (Table 15.1) but have *-yl* as their ending. Each prefix is placed *before* the root.

For example, in the name 2-methylbutane, *2-methyl-* is the prefix (a one-carbon branch is attached to C-2 of the main chain), *-but-* is the root (the main chain has four C atoms), and *-ane* is the suffix (the compound is an alkane).

To obtain the systematic name of a compound,

1. Name the longest chain (root).
2. Add the compound type (suffix).
3. Name any branches (prefix).

Table 15.2 presents the rules for naming any organic compound and applies them to an alkane component of gasoline. Other organic compounds are named with a variety of other prefixes and suffixes (see Table 15.5, p. 592). In addition to these *systematic* names, some *common* names are still in use.

**Depicting Alkanes with Formulas and Models** Chemists have several ways to depict organic compounds. Expanded, condensed, and carbon-skeleton formulas are easy to draw; ball-and-stick and space-filling models show the actual shapes.

**Table 15.1 Numerical Roots for Carbon Chains and Branches**

| Roots | Number of C Atoms |
|---|---|
| meth- | 1 |
| eth- | 2 |
| prop- | 3 |
| but- | 4 |
| pent- | 5 |
| hex- | 6 |
| hept- | 7 |
| oct- | 8 |
| non- | 9 |
| dec- | 10 |

**Table 15.2 Rules for Naming an Organic Compound**

1. Naming the longest chain (root)
   - (a) Find the longest *continuous* chain of C atoms.
   - (b) Select the root that corresponds to the number of C atoms in this chain.

$$CH_3 - CH - CH - CH_2 - CH_2 - CH_3$$
with $CH_3$ above the second carbon and $CH_2 - CH_3$ below the third carbon

6 carbons $\Longrightarrow$ hex-

2. Naming the compound type (suffix)
   - (a) For alkanes, add the suffix *-ane* to the chain root. (Other suffixes appear in Table 15.5 with their functional group and compound type.)
   - (b) If the chain forms a ring, the name is preceded by *cyclo-*.

hex- + -ane $\Longrightarrow$ hexane

3. Naming the branches (prefixes) (If the compound has no branches, the name consists of the root and suffix.)
   - (a) Each branch name consists of a subroot (number of C atoms) and the ending *-yl* to signify that it is not part of the main chain.
   - (b) Branch names precede the chain name. When two or more branches are present, their names appear in *alphabetical* order.
   - (c) To specify where the branch occurs along the chain, number the main-chain C atoms consecutively, starting at the end *closer* to a branch, to achieve the *lowest* numbers for the branches. Precede each branch name with the number of the main-chain C to which that branch is attached.

$CH_3$ methyl
$$CH_3 - CH - CH - CH_2 - CH_2 - CH_3$$
$CH_2 - CH_3$ ethyl
ethylmethylhexane

$CH_3$
$$\overset{1}{CH_3} - \overset{2}{CH} - \overset{3}{CH} - \overset{4}{CH_2} - \overset{5}{CH_2} - \overset{6}{CH_3}$$
$CH_2 - CH_3$
3-ethyl-2-methylhexane

**Expanded formula**     **Condensed formula**     **Carbon-skeleton formula**     **Ball-and-stick model**     **Space-filling model**

**Figure 15.5** Ways of depicting the alkane 3-ethyl-2-methylhexane.

The *expanded formula* shows each atom and bond. One type of *condensed formula* groups each C atom with its H atoms. *Carbon-skeleton formulas* show only carbon-carbon bonds and appear as zig-zag lines, often with branches. *Each end or bend of a zig-zag line or branch represents a C atom attached to the number of H atoms that gives it a total of four bonds:*

propane     $CH_3$—$CH_2$—$CH_3$          2,3-dimethylbutane     $CH_3$—$CH$—$CH$—$CH_3$

Figure 15.5 shows these formulas (and models) of the compound named in Table 15.2.

**Cyclic Hydrocarbons** A **cyclic hydrocarbon** contains one or more rings in its structure. When a straight-chain alkane ($C_nH_{2n+2}$) forms a ring, two H atoms are lost as the C—C bond forms to join the two ends of the chain. Thus, *cycloalkanes* have the general formula $C_nH_{2n}$. Cyclic hydrocarbons are often drawn with carbon-skeleton formulas (Figure 15.6, *top row*). Except for three-carbon rings, *cycloalkanes are nonplanar*, as the models show. This structural feature arises from the tetrahedral shape around each C atom and the need to minimize electron repulsions between adjacent H atoms. As a result, orbital overlap of adjacent C atoms is maximized. The most stable form of cyclohexane is called the *chair conformation* (Figure 15.6D).

**Figure 15.6** Depicting cycloalkanes.

**A Cyclopropane**     **B Cyclobutane**     **C Cyclopentane**     **D Cyclohexane**

# Constitutional Isomerism and the Physical Properties of Alkanes

Recall from Section 3.2 that two or more compounds with the same molecular formula but different properties are called **isomers.** Those with *different arrangements of bonded atoms* are **constitutional** (or **structural**) **isomers;** alkanes with the same number of C atoms but different skeletons are examples. The smallest alkane to exhibit constitutional isomerism has four C atoms: two different compounds have the formula $C_4H_{10}$ (Table 15.3). The unbranched one is butane (common name, *n*-butane; *n*- stands for "normal," or having a straight chain), and the other is 2-methylpropane (common name, *iso*butane). Similarly, three compounds have the formula $C_5H_{12}$. The unbranched isomer is pentane (common name, *n*-pentane); the one with a methyl group at C-2 of a four-C chain is 2-methylbutane (common name, *iso*pentane). The third isomer has two methyl branches on C-2 of a three-C chain, so its name is 2,2-dimethylpropane (common name, *neo*pentane).

**Dispersion Forces and Boiling Points** Because alkanes are nearly nonpolar, we expect their physical properties to be determined by dispersion forces, and the boiling points in Table 15.3 bear this out. The four-C alkanes boil lower than the five-C compounds. Moreover, within each group of isomers, the more spherical member (isobutane or neopentane) boils lower than the more elongated one (*n*-butane or *n*-pentane). As you saw in Chapter 12, this trend occurs because a spherical shape leads to less intermolecular contact, and thus lower total dispersion forces, than does an elongated shape.

A particularly clear example of the effect of dispersion forces on physical properties occurs among the unbranched alkanes (*n*-alkanes). Among these compounds, boiling points increase steadily with chain length: the longer the chain,

**Table 15.3  The Constitutional Isomers of $C_4H_{10}$ and $C_5H_{12}$**

| Systematic Name (Common Name) | Expanded Formula | Condensed and Skeleton Formulas | Space-Filling Model | Density (g/mL) | Boiling Point (°C) |
|---|---|---|---|---|---|
| Butane (*n*-butane) | | $CH_3-CH_2-CH_2-CH_3$ | | 0.579 | −0.5 |
| 2-Methylpropane (isobutane) | | $CH_3-CH-CH_3$ <br> $\quad\quad\;\; CH_3$ | | 0.549 | −11.6 |
| Pentane (*n*-pentane) | | $CH_3-CH_2-CH_2-CH_2-CH_3$ | | 0.626 | 36.1 |
| 2-Methylbutane (isopentane) | | $CH_3-CH-CH_2-CH_3$ <br> $\quad\quad\;\; CH_3$ | | 0.620 | 27.8 |
| 2,2-Dimethylpropane (neopentane) | | $\quad\quad\; CH_3$ <br> $CH_3-C-CH_3$ <br> $\quad\quad\; CH_3$ | | 0.614 | 9.5 |

| | | |
|---|---|---|
| methane ($CH_4$; $\mathcal{M}$ = 16.04) | $CH_4$ | −164 |
| ethane ($C_2H_6$; $\mathcal{M}$ = 30.07) | $CH_3CH_3$ | −89 |
| propane ($C_3H_8$; $\mathcal{M}$ = 44.09) | $CH_3CH_2CH_3$ | −42 |
| butane ($C_4H_{10}$; $\mathcal{M}$ = 58.12) | $CH_3CH_2CH_2CH_3$ | −0.5 |
| pentane ($C_5H_{12}$; $\mathcal{M}$ = 72.15) | $CH_3CH_2CH_2CH_2CH_3$ | 36 |
| hexane ($C_6H_{14}$; $\mathcal{M}$ = 86.17) | $CH_3CH_2CH_2CH_2CH_2CH_3$ | 69 |
| heptane ($C_7H_{16}$; $\mathcal{M}$ = 100.20) | $CH_3CH_2CH_2CH_2CH_2CH_2CH_3$ | 98 |
| octane ($C_8H_{18}$; $\mathcal{M}$ = 114.22) | $CH_3CH_2CH_2CH_2CH_2CH_2CH_2CH_3$ | 126 |
| nonane ($C_9H_{20}$; $\mathcal{M}$ = 128.25) | $CH_3CH_2CH_2CH_2CH_2CH_2CH_2CH_2CH_3$ | 151 |
| decane ($C_{10}H_{22}$; $\mathcal{M}$ = 142.28) | $CH_3CH_2CH_2CH_2CH_2CH_2CH_2CH_2CH_2CH_3$ | 174 |

Temperature (°C)

**Figure 15.7** Formulas, molar masses (in g/mol), structures, and boiling points (at 1 atm pressure) of the first 10 unbranched alkanes.

the greater the intermolecular contact, the stronger the dispersion forces, and the higher the boiling point (Figure 15.7). Pentane (five C atoms) is the smallest *n*-alkane that exists as a liquid at room temperature. The solubility of alkanes, and of all hydrocarbons, is easy to predict from the like-dissolves-like rule (Section 13.1). Alkanes are miscible in each other and in other nonpolar solvents, such as benzene, but are nearly insoluble in water. The solubility of pentane in water, for example, is only 0.36 g/L at room temperature.

## Chiral Molecules and Optical Isomerism

Another type of isomerism exhibited by some alkanes and many other organic (as well as some inorganic) compounds is called *stereoisomerism*. **Stereoisomers** are molecules with the same arrangement of atoms *but different orientations of groups in space. Optical isomerism* is one type of stereoisomerism: *when two objects are mirror images of each other and cannot be superimposed, they are* **optical isomers,** also called *enantiomers.* To use a familiar example, your right hand is an optical isomer of your left. Look at your right hand in a mirror: the *image* is identical to your left hand (Figure 15.8). No matter how you twist your arms around, however, your hands cannot lie on top of each other with your palms facing in the same direction and be superimposed. They are not superimposable because each is *asymmetric:* there is no plane of symmetry that divides your hand into two identical parts.

**Figure 15.8** An analogy for optical isomers.

**Asymmetry and Chirality** An asymmetric molecule is called **chiral** (Greek *cheir,* "hand"). Typically, an organic molecule *is chiral if it contains a carbon atom that is bonded to four **different** groups.* This C atom is called a *chiral center,* or an asymmetric carbon. In 3-methylhexane, for example, C-3 is a chiral center, because it is bonded to four different groups: $H—$, $CH_3—$, $CH_3—CH_2—$, and $CH_3—CH_2—CH_2—$ (Figure 15.9A). Like your two hands, the two forms are mirror images and cannot be superimposed on each other: when two of the groups are superimposed, the other two are opposite each other. Thus, the two forms are optical isomers. The central C atom in the amino acid alanine is also a chiral center (Figure 15.9B).

**Figure 15.9** Two chiral molecules.

**A  Optical isomers of 3-methylhexane**

**B  Optical isomers of alanine**

**Properties of Optical Isomers** Unlike constitutional isomers, which have different physical properties such as boiling point, optical isomers are identical in all but two respects:

1. In their physical properties, *optical isomers differ only in the direction that each isomer rotates the plane of polarized light.* A **polarimeter** is used to measure the angle that the plane is rotated (Figure 15.10). A beam of light consists of waves that oscillate in all planes. A polarizing filter blocks all waves except those in one plane, so the light emerging through the filter is *plane-polarized.* An optical isomer is **optically active** because it rotates the plane of this polarized light. (Liquid crystal displays incorporate polarizing filters and optically active compounds; see Figure 12.44, p. 459.) The *dextrorotatory* isomer (designated *d* or +) rotates the plane of light clockwise; the *levorotatory* isomer (designated *l* or −) is the mirror image of the *d* isomer and rotates the plane counterclockwise. An equimolar mixture of the two isomers (called a *racemic mixture*) does not rotate the plane of light because the dextrorotation cancels the levorotation. The *specific rotation* is a characteristic, measurable property of an optical isomer at a certain temperature, concentration, and wavelength of light.

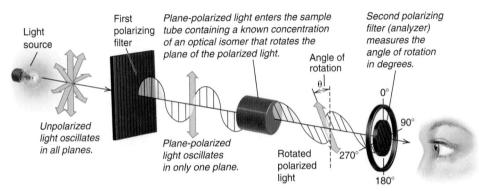

**Figure 15.10** The rotation of plane-polarized light by an optically active substance.

2. In their chemical properties, *optical isomers differ only in a chiral (asymmetric) chemical environment,* one that distinguishes "right-handed" from "left-handed" molecules. As an analogy, your right hand fits well in your right glove but not in your left glove. Typically, one isomer of an optically active reactant is added to a mixture of optical isomers of another compound. The products of the reaction have different properties and can be separated.

**The Role of Optical Isomerism in Organisms and Medicines** Optical isomerism plays a vital role in living cells. Nearly all carbohydrates and amino acids are optically active, but only one of the isomers is biologically usable. For example, *d*-glucose is metabolized for energy, but *l*-glucose is not, and is excreted unused. Similarly, *l*-alanine is incorporated naturally into proteins, but *d*-alanine is not. An organism can utilize only one of a pair of optical isomers because of its enzymes (Section 16.7). Enzymes are proteins that speed virtually every reaction in a living cell by binding to the reactants; an enzyme distinguishes one optical isomer from another because its binding site is chiral (asymmetric) (Figure 15.11). The shape of one optical isomer fits at the binding site, but the mirror image shape of the other isomer does not fit, so it cannot bind.

**Figure 15.11** The binding site of an enzyme.

Many drugs are chiral molecules. One optical isomer has certain biological activity, and the other has either a different type of activity or none at all. Naproxen (*see margin*), a pain reliever and anti-inflammatory agent, is an example: one isomer is active as an anti-arthritic agent, and the other is a potent liver toxin that must be removed from the mixture during synthesis. The notorious drug thalidomide is another example: one optical isomer is active against depression, whereas the other causes fetal mutations and deaths. Tragically, this drug was sold in the 1950s as the racemic mixture and caused limb malformations in many newborns whose mothers had it prescribed to relieve "morning sickness" during pregnancy.

Naproxen

## Alkenes: Hydrocarbons with Double Bonds

A hydrocarbon that contains at least one C=C bond is called an **alkene.** With two H atoms removed to make the double bond, alkenes have the general formula $C_nH_{2n}$. The double-bonded C atoms are $sp^2$ hybridized. Because their carbon atoms are bonded to fewer than the maximum of four atoms each, alkenes are considered **unsaturated hydrocarbons.**

Alkene names differ from those of alkanes in two respects:

1. The main chain (root) *must* contain both C atoms of the double bond, even if it is not the longest chain. The chain is numbered from the end *closer* to the C=C bond, and the position of the bond is indicated by the number of the *first* C atom in it.
2. The suffix for alkenes is *-ene.*

For example, there are three four-C alkenes ($C_4H_8$), two unbranched and one branched (see Sample Problem 15.1b). The branched isomer is 2-methylpropene; the unbranched isomer with the C=C bond between C-1 and C-2 is 1-butene; the unbranched isomer with the C=C bond between C-2 and C-3 is 2-butene. As you'll see next, there are two isomers of 2-butene, but they are of a different sort (discussed briefly in Sections 10.3 and 11.2).

**The C=C Bond and Geometric (*cis-trans*) Isomerism** There are two major structural differences between alkanes and alkenes.

- Alkanes have a *tetrahedral* geometry (bond angles of ~109.5°) around each C atom, whereas the double-bonded C atoms in alkenes are *trigonal planar* (~120°).
- The C—C bond *allows* rotation of bonded groups, so the atoms in an alkane continually change their relative positions; in contrast, the π bond of the alkene C=C bond *restricts* rotation, so the relative positions of the atoms attached to the double bond are fixed.

This rotational restriction leads to another type of stereoisomerism. **Geometric isomers** (also called *cis-trans* **isomers**) have different orientations of groups around a double bond (or similar structural feature). Table 15.4 shows the two geometric isomers of 2-butene (also see Comment, Sample Problem 15.1). One isomer, *cis*-2-butene, has the $CH_3$ groups on the *same* side of the C=C bond, whereas the other isomer, *trans*-2-butene, has them on *opposite* sides of the C=C bond. In general, the *cis* isomer has the *larger portions of the main chain* (in this case, two $CH_3$ groups) *on the same side* of the double bond, and the *trans* isomer has them on opposite sides. For a molecule to have geometric isomers, *each C atom in the C=C bond must be bonded to two different groups.*

Like structural isomers, geometric isomers have different physical properties. Note in Table 15.4 that the two 2-butenes differ in molecular shape *and* physical properties. The *cis* isomer has a bend in the chain that the *trans* isomer lacks. In Chapters 10 and 12, you saw how such a difference affects molecular polarity and physical properties, which arise from differing strengths of intermolecular attractions.

| Table **15.4** The Geometric Isomers of 2-Butene | | | | |
|---|---|---|---|---|
| Systematic Name | Condensed and Skeleton Formulas | Space-Filling Model | Density (g/mL) | Boiling Point (°C) |
| *cis*-2-Butene | | | 0.621 | 3.7 |
| trans-2-Butene | | | 0.604 | 0.9 |

**Geometric Isomers and the Chemistry of Vision** The difference in properties between geometric isomers has profound effects in biological systems. For example, the first step in the sequence of events that allows us to see relies on the different shapes of a pair of geometric isomers. *Retinal,* a 20-C compound consisting of a 15-C chain with five 1-C branches and 5 C=C bonds, is part of the molecule responsible for receiving light energy that is converted to electrical signals that are transmitted to the brain. There are two biologically occurring isomers of retinal, which have very different shapes. The all-*trans* isomer has a *trans* orientation around all five double bonds and is elongated. The 11-*cis* isomer has a *cis* orientation around the C=C bond between C-11 and C-12, which results in a bend in the structure at that double bond.

Certain cells of the retina are densely packed with *rhodopsin,* a large protein covalently bonded to 11-*cis* retinal. The initial chemical event in vision occurs when rhodopsin absorbs a photon of visible light. The energy range of visible photons (165–293 kJ/mol) encompasses the energy needed to break a C=C π bond (about 250 kJ/mol). Within a few millionths of a second after rhodopsin absorbs a photon, the 11-*cis* π bond of retinal breaks, the intact σ bond between C-11 and C-12 rotates, and the π bond re-forms to produce all-*trans* retinal (Figure 15.12).

**Figure 15.12** The initial chemical event in vision and the change in the shape of retinal.

11-*cis* retinal

all-*trans* retinal

The rapid and significant change in shape of retinal causes the attached protein to change its shape as well, triggering a flow of ions into the retina's cells and initiating electrical impulses, which the optic nerve conducts to the brain. Meanwhile, the free all-*trans* retinal diffuses away from the protein and is changed back to the *cis* form, which then binds to the protein portion again. Because of the speed and efficiency with which light causes such a large structural change in retinal, natural selection has made it the photon absorber in organisms as different as purple bacteria, mollusks, insects, and vertebrates.

## Alkynes: Hydrocarbons with Triple Bonds

Hydrocarbons that contain at least one C≡C bond are called **alkynes.** Their general formula is $C_nH_{2n-2}$ because they have two H atoms fewer than alkenes with the same number of carbons. Because a carbon involved in a C≡C bond can bond to only one other atom, the geometry around each C atom is linear (180°): each C is *sp* hybridized. Alkynes are named in the same way as alkenes, except that the suffix is -*yne*. Because of their localized π electrons, C=C and C≡C bonds are electron rich and act as functional groups. Thus, alkenes and alkynes are much more reactive than alkanes, as we'll discuss in Section 15.4.

**Sample Problem 15.2** | **Naming Alkanes, Alkenes, and Alkynes**

**Problem** Give the systematic name for each of the following, indicate the chiral center in part (d), and draw two geometric isomers for part (e):

**(a)**

$$CH_3-\underset{\underset{CH_3}{|}}{\overset{\overset{CH_3}{|}}{C}}-CH_2-CH_3$$

**(b)**

$$CH_3-CH_2-\underset{\underset{\underset{CH_3}{|}}{CH_2}}{\overset{\overset{CH_3}{|}}{CH}}-CH-CH_3$$

**(c)**

**(d)**

$$CH_3-CH_2-\underset{}{\overset{\overset{CH_3}{|}}{CH}}-CH=CH_2$$

**(e)**

$$CH_3-CH_2-CH=\underset{\underset{CH_3}{|}}{\overset{\overset{CH_3}{|}}{C}}-CH-CH_3$$

**Plan** For (a) to (c), we refer to Table 15.2, p. 577. We first name the longest chain (*root-*) and add the suffix *-ane* because there are only single bonds. Then we find the *lowest* branch numbers by counting C atoms from the end *closer* to a branch. Finally, we name each branch (*root-* + *-yl*) and put the names alphabetically before the root name. For (d) and (e), the longest chain that *includes* the multiple bond is numbered from the end closer to it. For (d), the chiral center is the C atom bonded to four different groups. In (e), the *cis* isomer has larger groups on the same side of the double bond, and the *trans* isomer has them on opposite sides.

**Solution**

**(a)**

**2,2-dimethylbutane**

When a type of branch appears more than once, we group the branch numbers and indicate the number of branches with a prefix, as in 2,2-*di*methyl.

**(b)**

**3,4-dimethylhexane**

In this case, we can number the chain from either end because the branches are the same and are attached to the two central C atoms.

**(c)**

**1-ethyl-2-methylcyclopentane**

We number the ring C atoms so that a branch is attached to C-1.

**(d)**

**3-methyl-1-pentene**

**(e)**

*cis*-2,3-dimethyl-3-hexene

*trans*-2,3-dimethyl-3-hexene

**Check** A good check (and excellent practice) is to reverse the process by drawing structures for the names to see if you come up with the structures given in the problem.

**Comment 1.** In (b), C-3 and C-4 are chiral centers, as are C-1 and C-2 in (c). However, in (b) the molecule is not chiral: it has a plane of symmetry between C-3 and C-4, so each half of the molecule rotates light in opposite directions. **2.** Avoid these common mistakes: In (b), 2-ethyl-3-methylpentane is wrong: the longest chain is *hexane*. In (c), 1-methyl-2-ethylcyclopentane is wrong: the branch names should appear *alphabetically*.

**Follow-Up Problem 15.2** Draw condensed formulas for the following compounds: **(a)** 3-ethyl-3-methyloctane; **(b)** 1-ethyl-3-propylcyclohexane (also draw a carbon-skeleton formula for this compound); **(c)** 3,3-diethyl-1-hexyne; **(d)** *trans*-3-methyl-3-heptene.

## Aromatic Hydrocarbons: Cyclic Molecules with Delocalized π Electrons

Unlike the cycloalkanes, **aromatic hydrocarbons** are planar molecules, usually with one or more rings of six C atoms, and are often drawn with alternating single and double bonds. As you learned for benzene (Section 10.1), however, all the ring bonds are identical, with values of length and strength *between* those of a C—C and a C=C

*Resonance forms have alternating single and double bonds.*

*Resonance hybrid shows the delocalized electrons as either an unbroken or a dashed circle.*

or

**A**

σ-bond plane

delocalized π cloud

**B**

**Figure 15.13** Representations of benzene.

bond. To indicate this, benzene is also shown as a resonance hybrid, with a circle (or dashed circle) representing the delocalized character of the π electrons (Figure 15.13A). An orbital picture shows the two lobes of the delocalized π cloud above and below the hexagonal plane of the σ-bonded C atoms (Figure 15.13B).

The systematic naming of simple aromatic compounds is quite straightforward. Usually, benzene is the parent compound, and attached groups, or *substituents,* are named as prefixes. However, many common names are still in use. For example, benzene with one methyl group attached is systematically named *methylbenzene* but is better known by its common name, *toluene.* With only one substituent present in toluene, we do not number the ring C atoms; when two or more groups are attached, however, we number in such a way that one of the groups is attached to ring C-1:

methylbenzene
(toluene)
bp = 110.6°C

1,2-dimethylbenzene
(*o*-xylene)
bp = 144.4°C

1,3-dimethylbenzene
(*m*-xylene)
bp = 139.1°C

1,4-dimethylbenzene
(*p*-xylene)
bp = 138.3°C

In common names, the positions of two groups are indicated by *o-* (ortho) for groups on adjacent ring C atoms, *m-* (meta) for groups separated by one ring C atom, and *p-* (para) for groups on opposite ring C atoms. The dimethylbenzenes (commonly known as *xylenes*) are important solvents and feedstocks for polyester fibers and dyes. Benzene and many other aromatic hydrocabons have been shown to have carcinogenic (cancer-causing) activity.

The number of isomers increases with more than two attached groups. For example, there are six isomers for a compound with one methyl and three nitro (—$NO_2$) groups attached to a benzene ring; the explosive TNT, shown below, is one of the isomers:

$O_2N$     $NO_2$

$NO_2$

2,4,6-trinitromethylbenzene
(trinitrotoluene, TNT)

One of the most important methods for determining the structures of organic molecules is discussed in the upcoming Tools of the Laboratory essay.

In addition to mass spectrometry (Chapter 2) and infrared (IR) spectroscopy (Chapter 9), one of the most useful tools for analyzing organic and biochemical structures is **nuclear magnetic resonance (NMR) spectroscopy,** which measures the molecular environments of certain nuclei in a molecule.

Like electrons, several types of nuclei such as $^{13}C$, $^{19}F$, $^{31}P$, and $^{1}H$ can spin in either of two directions, each of which creates a tiny magnetic field. In this discussion, we focus primarily on $^{1}H$-NMR spectroscopy, which examines the proton, $^{1}H$, the nucleus of the most common isotope of hydrogen. Generally oriented randomly, the magnetic fields of all the protons in a sample of compound, when placed in a strong external magnetic field ($B_0$), become aligned either with the external field (parallel) or against it (antiparallel). Most nuclei adopt the parallel orientation, which is slightly lower in energy. The energy difference ($\Delta E$) between the two energy states (spin states) lies in the radio-frequency (rf) region of the electromagnetic spectrum (Figure B15.1).

When a proton in the lower energy (parallel) spin state absorbs a photon in the radio-frequency region with an energy equal to $\Delta E$, the proton "flips," in a process called *resonance,* to the higher energy (antiparallel) spin state. The system then re-emits that energy, which is detected by the rf receiver of the $^{1}H$-NMR spectrometer. The $\Delta E$ between the two states depends on the *actual* magnetic field felt by each proton, which is affected by the tiny magnetic fields of the *electrons* of atoms adjacent to that proton. Thus, the $\Delta E$ required for resonance of each proton depends on the specific molecular environment of the proton—the C atoms, electronegative atoms, multiple bonds, and aromatic rings around it. The protons in different molecular environments produce different peaks in the $^{1}H$-NMR spectrum.

An $^{1}H$-NMR spectrum, which is unique for each compound, is a series of peaks that represents the resonance of each proton as a function of the changing magnetic field. The *chemical shift* of the protons in a given environment is where a peak appears. The chemical shifts are shown relative to that of an added standard, tetramethylsilane [$(CH_3)_4Si$, or TMS]. TMS has 12 protons bonded to four C atoms that are bonded to one Si atom in a tetrahedral arrangement, so all 12 protons are in identical environments and produce only one peak.

Figure B15.2 shows the $^{1}H$-NMR spectrum of acetone. The six protons of acetone have identical environments: all six are bonded to two C atoms that are each bonded to the C atom in a C=O bond. So one peak is produced, but at a different position from the TMS peak. The spectrum of dimethoxymethane in Figure B15.3 shows *two* peaks in addition to the TMS peak since there are protons in two different environments. The taller peak is due to the six $CH_3$ protons, and the shorter peak is due to the two $CH_2$ protons. The area under each peak (given here in units of chart-paper spaces) is proportional to *the number of protons in a given environment.* Note that the area ratio is $20.3/6.8 \approx 3/1$, the same as the ratio of six $CH_3$ protons to two $CH_2$ protons. Thus by analyzing the chemical shifts and peak areas, the chemist learns the type and number of hydrogen atoms in the compound.

**Figure B15.1** The basis of proton spin resonance.

**Figure B15.2** The $^{1}H$-NMR spectrum of acetone.

**Figure B15.3** The $^{1}H$-NMR spectrum of dimethoxymethane.

NMR has many applications in biochemistry and medicine. Applying the principle to imaging of organs and other body parts is known as computer-aided magnetic resonance imaging, or MRI. For example, an MRI scan of the head (Figure B15.4) can reveal a brain tumor by mapping levels of metabolic activity in different regions of the brain.

**Figure B15.4** An MRI scan showing a brain tumor.

## Problems

**B15.1** How many peaks appear in the NMR spectrum of each isomer of $C_4H_{10}$ and of $C_5H_{12}$ shown in Table 15.3 (p. 579)?

**B15.2** Radio-frequency radiation is used in NMR since $\Delta E$, the energy difference between the two spin states of the proton, is very small. Calculate the $\Delta E$ (in J/mol) that corresponds to a frequency of 200. MHz.

**B15.3** Consider three isomers of $C_4H_8Br_2$:

$$\underset{\textbf{A}}{\overset{\displaystyle\overset{Br}{|}}{H_2C}-CH_2-CH_2-\overset{\displaystyle\overset{Br}{|}}{CH_2}} \qquad \underset{\textbf{B}}{H_3C-\overset{\displaystyle\overset{CH_3}{|}}{\underset{\displaystyle\underset{Br}{|}}{C}}-\overset{\displaystyle\overset{Br}{|}}{CH_2}} \qquad \underset{\textbf{C}}{\overset{\displaystyle\overset{Br}{|}}{H_2C}-\overset{\displaystyle\overset{CH_3}{|}}{\underset{\displaystyle\underset{H}{|}}{C}}-\overset{\displaystyle\overset{Br}{|}}{CH_2}}$$

Which of these isomers is characterized by a $^1$H-NMR spectrum that consists of two peaks with a 3/1 ratio?

## Variations on a Theme: Catenated Inorganic Hydrides

In brief discussions called Variations on a Theme found throughout this chapter, we examine similarities between organic and inorganic compounds. From this perspective, you'll see that the behavior of carbon is remarkable, but not unique, in the chemistry of the elements.

Although no other element has as many different hydrides as carbon, catenated hydrides occur for several other elements, and many ring, chain, and cage structures are known.

- *Boranes.* One such group of inorganic compounds is the boron hydrides, or boranes (Section 14.5). Although their varied shapes rival those of the hydrocarbons, the weakness of their unusual bridge bonds renders most of them thermally and chemically unstable.

- *Silanes.* An obvious structural similarity exists between alkanes and the silicon hydrides, or silanes. Silanes even have an analogous general formula $(Si_nH_{2n+2})$. Branched silanes are known, but no cyclic or unsaturated (containing an Si=Si bond) compounds had been prepared until very recently. Unlike alkanes, silanes are unstable thermally and ignite spontaneously in air.

- *Polysulfanes.* Sulfur's ability to catenate is second only to carbon's, and many chains and rings occur among its allotropes (Section 14.8). A number of sulfur hydrides, or polysulfanes, are known. However, these molecules are unbranched chains with H atoms only at the ends ($H-S_n-H$). Like the silanes, the polysulfanes are oxidized easily and decompose readily, yielding sulfur's only stable hydride, $H_2S$, and its most stable allotrope, cyclo-$S_8$.

## ■ Summary of Section 15.2

- Hydrocarbons contain only C and H atoms, so their physical properties depend on the strength of their dispersion forces.
- Names of organic compounds have a root for the longest chain, a prefix for any attached group, and a suffix for the type of compound.
- Alkanes ($C_nH_{2n+2}$) have only single bonds. Cycloalkanes ($C_nH_{2n}$) have ring structures that are typically nonplanar. Alkenes ($C_nH_{2n}$) have at least one C=C bond. Alkynes ($C_nH_{2n-2}$) have at least one C≡C bond. Aromatic hydrocarbons have at least one planar ring with delocalized $\pi$ electrons.
- Isomers are compounds with the same molecular formula but different properties.
- Constitutional (structural) isomers have different atom arrangements.
- Stereoisomers (optical and geometric) have the same arrangement of atoms, but their atoms are oriented differently in space. Optical isomers cannot be superimposed on each other because they are asymmetric, with four different groups bonded to the C that is the chiral center. They have identical physical and chemical properties except in their rotation of plane-polarized light and their reaction with chiral reactants. Geometric (*cis-trans*) isomers have groups oriented differently around a C=C bond, which restricts rotation.
- Light converts a *cis* isomer of retinal to the all-*trans* form, which initiates the process of vision.
- $^1$H-NMR spectroscopy indicates the relative numbers of H atoms in the various environments within an organic molecule.
- Boron, silicon, and sulfur also form catenated hydrides, but these are unstable.

---

# 15.3 • SOME IMPORTANT CLASSES OF ORGANIC REACTIONS

In Chapter 4, we classified chemical reactions based on the chemical process involved (precipitation, acid-base, or redox) and then briefly included a classification based on the number of reactants and products (combination, decomposition, or displacement). We take a similar approach here with organic reactions, but in reverse order.

From here on, we use an uppercase R with a single bond, R—, to signify a general organic group attached to one of the atoms shown; you can usually picture R— as an **alkyl group,** a saturated hydrocarbon group with one bond available to link to another atom. Thus, R—CH$_2$—Br has an alkyl group attached to a CH$_2$ group bonded to a Br atom; R—CH=CH$_2$ is an alkene with an alkyl group attached to one of the carbons in the double bond; and so forth. (Often, when more than one R group is present, we write R, R′, R″, and so forth, to indicate that these groups may be different.)

## Types of Organic Reactions

Three important organic reaction types are *addition, elimination,* and *substitution* reactions, which can be identified by comparing the *number of bonds to C* in reactants and products.

**Addition Reactions** An **addition reaction** occurs when an unsaturated reactant becomes a saturated product:

$$R{-}CH{=}CH{-}R \ + \ X{-}Y \longrightarrow R{-}\overset{\displaystyle X}{\underset{\displaystyle |}{C}}H{-}\overset{\displaystyle Y}{\underset{\displaystyle |}{C}}H{-}R$$

Note the C atoms are bonded to *more* atoms in the product than in the reactant.

The C=C and C≡C bonds and the C=O bond commonly undergo addition reactions. In each case, the $\pi$ bond breaks, leaving the $\sigma$ bond intact. In the product, the two C atoms (or C and O) form two additional $\sigma$ bonds. Let's examine the standard enthalpy of reaction ($\Delta H^{\circ}_{rxn}$) for a typical addition reaction to see why these reactions occur. Consider the reaction between ethene (common name, ethylene) and HCl:

$$CH_2{=}CH_2 \quad + \quad H{-}Cl \quad \longrightarrow \quad H{-}CH_2{-}CH_2{-}Cl$$

| Reactants (bonds broken) | Product (bonds formed) |
|---|---|
| 1 C=C = 614 kJ | 1 C—C = −347 kJ |
| 4 C—H = 1652 kJ | 5 C—H = −2065 kJ |
| 1 H—Cl = 427 kJ | 1 C—Cl = −339 kJ |
| Total = 2693 kJ | Total = −2751 kJ |

$$\Delta H^{\circ}_{rxn} = \Sigma\Delta H^{\circ}_{\text{bonds broken}} + \Sigma\Delta H^{\circ}_{\text{bonds formed}} = 2693 \text{ kJ} + (-2751 \text{ kJ}) = -58 \text{ kJ}$$

The reaction is exothermic. By looking at the *net* change in bonds, we see that the driving force for many additions is the formation of two σ bonds (in this case, C—H and C—Cl) from one σ bond (in this case, H—Cl) and one relatively weak π bond. An addition reaction is the basis of a color test for the presence of C=C bonds (Figure 15.14).

**Figure 15.14  A color test for C=C bonds. A,** $Br_2$ (in pipet) reacts with a compound that has a C=C bond (in beaker), and its orange-brown color disappears:

$$\underset{}{\overset{}{{>}C{=}C{<}}} + Br_2 \longrightarrow -\overset{Br}{\underset{}{\overset{|}{C}}}-\overset{}{\underset{Br}{\overset{|}{C}}}-$$

**B,** This compound has no C=C bond, so the $Br_2$ does not react.

**Elimination Reactions  Elimination reactions** are the opposite of addition reactions. They occur when a saturated reactant becomes an unsaturated product:

$$R{-}\overset{Y}{\underset{}{\overset{|}{C}H}}{-}\overset{X}{\underset{}{\overset{|}{C}H_2}} \longrightarrow R{-}CH{=}CH_2 + X{-}Y$$

Note that the C atoms are bonded to *fewer* atoms in the product than in the reactant. A pair of halogen atoms, an H atom and a halogen atom, or an H atom and an —OH group are typically eliminated, but C atoms are not. Thus, the driving force for many elimination reactions is the formation of a small, stable molecule, such as HCl($g$) or $H_2O$, which increases the entropy of the system (Section 13.3):

$$CH_3{-}\overset{OH}{\underset{}{\overset{|}{C}H}}{-}\overset{H}{\underset{}{\overset{|}{C}H_2}} \xrightarrow{H_2SO_4} CH_3{-}CH{=}CH_2 \quad + \quad H{-}OH$$

$$\xrightarrow{H_2SO_4}$$

**Substitution Reactions  A substitution reaction** occurs when an atom (or group) from an added reagent substitutes for one attached to a carbon in the organic reactant:

$$R{-}\overset{}{\underset{}{\overset{|}{C}}}{-}X + {:}Y \longrightarrow R{-}\overset{}{\underset{}{\overset{|}{C}}}{-}Y + {:}X$$

Note that the C atom is bonded to the *same number* of atoms in the product as in the reactant. The C atom may be saturated or unsaturated, and X and Y can be many different atoms, but generally *not* C. The main flavor ingredient in banana oil, for instance, forms through a substitution reaction; note that the O substitutes for the Cl:

$$CH_3{-}\overset{O}{\overset{\|}{C}}{-}Cl \ + \ HO{-}CH_2{-}CH_2{-}\overset{CH_3}{\underset{}{\overset{|}{C}H}}{-}CH_3 \longrightarrow CH_3{-}\overset{O}{\overset{\|}{C}}{-}O{-}CH_2{-}CH_2{-}\overset{CH_3}{\underset{}{\overset{|}{C}H}}{-}CH_3 \ + \ H{-}Cl$$

**Sample Problem 15.3** **Recognizing the Type of Organic Reaction**

**Problem** State whether each reaction is an addition, elimination, or substitution:

(a) $CH_3-CH_2-CH_2-Br \longrightarrow CH_3-CH=CH_2 + HBr$

(b) $+ H_2 \longrightarrow$

(c) $CH_3\overset{\overset{\displaystyle O}{\|}}{C}-Br + CH_3CH_2OH \longrightarrow CH_3\overset{\overset{\displaystyle O}{\|}}{C}-OCH_2CH_3 + HBr$

**Plan** We determine the type of reaction by looking for any change in the number of atoms bonded to C:

• More atoms bonded to C is an *addition*.
• Fewer atoms bonded to C is an *elimination*.
• Same number of atoms bonded to C is a *substitution*.

**Solution** (a) Elimination: two bonds in the reactant, C—H and C—Br, are absent in the product, so fewer atoms are bonded to C.

(b) Addition: two more C—H bonds have formed in the product, so more atoms are bonded to C.

(c) Substitution: the reactant C—Br bond becomes a C—O bond in the product, so the same number of atoms are bonded to C.

**Follow-Up Problem 15.3** Write a balanced equation for each of the following:

(a) An addition reaction between 2-butene and $Cl_2$
(b) A substitution reaction between $CH_3-CH_2-CH_2-Br$ and $OH^-$
(c) The elimination of $H_2O$ from $(CH_3)_3C-OH$

## The Redox Process in Organic Reactions

An important process in many organic reactions is *oxidation-reduction*. Even though a redox reaction always involves both an oxidation and a reduction, organic chemists typically *focus on the organic reactant only*. Instead of monitoring the change in oxidation numbers of the various C atoms in a redox reaction, chemists usually note the movement of electron density around a C atom by counting the number of bonds to more electronegative atoms (usually O) or to less electronegative atoms (usually H). A more electronegative atom takes some electron density from the C, whereas a less electronegative atom gives some electron density to the C. Therefore,

• When a C atom in the organic reactant forms more bonds to O or fewer bonds to H, thus losing some electron density, the reactant is oxidized, and the reaction is called an *oxidation*.
• When a C atom in the organic reactant forms fewer bonds to O or more bonds to H, thus gaining some electron density, the reactant is reduced, and the reaction is called a *reduction*.

The most dramatic redox reactions are combustion reactions. All organic compounds contain C and H atoms and burn in excess $O_2$ to form $CO_2$ and $H_2O$. For ethane, the reaction is

$$2CH_3-CH_3 + 7O_2 \longrightarrow 4CO_2 + 6H_2O$$

Obviously, when ethane is converted to $CO_2$ and $H_2O$, each of its C atoms has more bonds to O and fewer bonds to H. Thus, ethane is oxidized, and this reaction is referred to as an *oxidation,* even though $O_2$ is reduced as well.

Most oxidations do not involve a breakup of the entire molecule, however. When 2-propanol reacts with potassium dichromate in acidic solution (a common oxidizing agent in organic reactions), it forms 2-propanone (acetone):

$$CH_3-\underset{\underset{\displaystyle \text{OH}}{|}}{CH}-CH_3 \xrightarrow[H_2SO_4]{K_2Cr_2O_7} CH_3-\overset{\overset{\displaystyle O}{\|}}{C}-CH_3$$

$$\text{2-propanol} \qquad\qquad\qquad \text{2-propanone}$$

Note that C-2 has one fewer bond to H and one more bond to O in 2-propanone than it does in 2-propanol. Thus, 2-propanol is oxidized, so this is an *oxidation*. Don't forget, however, that the dichromate ion is reduced at the same time:

$$Cr_2O_7^{2-} + 14H^+ + 6e^- \longrightarrow 2Cr^{3+} + 7H_2O$$

The addition reaction between $H_2$ and an alkene is also a *reduction:*

$$CH_2{=}CH_2 + H_2 \xrightarrow{\text{Pd}} CH_3{-}CH_3$$

Note that each C has more bonds to H in ethane than it has in ethene, so the ethene is reduced. The $H_2$ is oxidized in the process, and the palladium shown over the arrow acts as a catalyst to speed up the reaction (Section 16.7).

## ▌Summary of Section 15.3

- In an addition reaction, a $\pi$ bond breaks, and the two C atoms (or one C and one O) are bonded to more atoms in the product.
- In an elimination reaction, a $\pi$ bond forms, with the two C atoms bonded to fewer atoms in the product.
- In a substitution reaction, one atom bonded to C is replaced by another, but the total number of atoms bonded to the C does not change.
- In an organic redox reaction, the organic reactant is oxidized if at least one of its C atoms forms more bonds to O atoms (or fewer bonds to H atoms), and it is reduced if a C atom forms more bonds to H (or fewer bonds to O).

# 15.4 • PROPERTIES AND REACTIVITIES OF COMMON FUNCTIONAL GROUPS

The central organizing principle of organic chemistry is the *functional group. The distribution of electron density in a functional group is a major factor in the reactivity of the compound.* The electron density can be high, as in the C=C and C≡C bonds, or it can be low at one end of a bond and high at the other, as in the C—Cl and C—O bonds. Such electron-rich or polar bonds enhance the oppositely charged pole in the other reactant. As a result, the reactants attract each other and begin a sequence of bond-forming and bond-breaking steps that lead to a product. Thus, *the intermolecular forces that affect physical properties and solubility also affect reactivity.* Table 15.5 (next page) lists some of the important functional groups in organic compounds.

When we classify functional groups by bond order (single, double, and so forth), they tend to follow certain patterns of reactivity:

- Functional groups with only single bonds undergo elimination or substitution.
- Functional groups with double or triple bonds undergo addition.
- Functional groups with both single and double bonds undergo substitution.

We will learn how to name compounds that contain each functional group, examine some of their common properties, and summarize their common reactions.

## Functional Groups with Only Single Bonds

The most common functional groups with only single bonds are alcohols, haloalkanes, and amines.

**Alcohols** The **alcohol** functional group consists of a carbon bonded to an —OH group, $-\overset{\displaystyle |}{\underset{\displaystyle |}{C}}-\overset{..}{\underset{..}{O}}-H$, and the general formula of an alcohol is R—OH. Alcohols are named by dropping the final *-e* from the parent hydrocarbon name and adding the suffix *-ol*. Thus, the two-carbon alcohol is ethanol (ethan- + -ol). The common name is the hydrocarbon *root-* + *-yl*, followed by "alcohol"; thus, the common name of ethanol is ethyl alcohol. (This substance, obtained from fermented grain, has been consumed by

## Table 15.5 Important Functional Groups in Organic Compounds

| Functional Group | Compound Type | Prefix or Suffix of Name | Example | | Systematic Name (Common Name) |
|---|---|---|---|---|---|
| | | | **Lewis Structure** | **Ball-and-Stick Model** | |
| C=C | alkene | -ene | | | ethene (ethylene) |
| —C≡C— | alkyne | -yne | H—C≡C—H | | ethyne (acetylene) |
| —C—Ö—H | alcohol | -ol | | | methanol (methyl alcohol) |
| —C—Ẍ: (X = halogen) | haloalkane | halo- | | | chloromethane (methyl chloride) |
| —C—N— | amine | -amine | | | ethanamine (ethylamine) |
| —C—H (:O:) | aldehyde | -al | | | ethanal (acetaldehyde) |
| —C—C—C— (:O:) | ketone | -one | | | 2-propanone (acetone) |
| —C—Ö—H (:O:) | carboxylic acid | -oic acid | | | ethanoic acid (acetic acid) |
| —C—Ö—C— (:O:) | ester | -oate | | | methyl ethanoate (methyl acetate) |
| —C—N— (:O:) | amide | -amide | | | ethanamide (acetamide) |
| —C≡N: | nitrile | -nitrile | | | ethanenitrile (acetonitrile, methyl cyanide |

people as an intoxicant in beverages since ancient times; today, it is recognized as the most abused drug in the world.) Alcohols are common organic reactants, and the functional group occurs in many biomolecules, including carbohydrates, sterols, and some amino acids. Figure 15.15 shows the names, structures, and uses of some important compounds that contain the alcohol group.

The physical properties of the smaller alcohols are similar to those of water. They have high melting and boiling points as a result of hydrogen bonding, and they dissolve polar molecules and some salts.

Alcohols undergo elimination and substitution reactions.

- The elimination of H and OH, called *dehydration,* requires acid and forms an alkene:

**Methanol (methyl alcohol)**
Byproduct in coal gasification; de-icing agent; gasoline substitute; precursor of organic compounds

$$\text{cyclohexanol} \xrightarrow{\text{H}^+} \text{cyclohexene} + \text{H}_2\text{O}$$

The elimination of two H atoms is an *oxidation* and requires an inorganic oxidizing agent, such as potassium dichromate ($K_2Cr_2O_7$) in aqueous $H_2SO_4$. The product has a C=O group:

$$\text{CH}_3-\text{CH}_2-\overset{\text{OH}}{\underset{\text{}}{\text{CH}}}-\text{CH}_3 \xrightarrow[\text{H}_2\text{SO}_4]{\text{K}_2\text{Cr}_2\text{O}_7} \text{CH}_3-\text{CH}_2-\overset{\text{O}}{\overset{\|}{\text{C}}}-\text{CH}_3$$

2-butanol          2-butanone

**1,2-Ethanediol (ethylene glycol)**
Main component of auto antifreeze

Alcohols with an OH group at the end of the chain (R—CH$_2$—OH) can be oxidized further to acids. (This is *not* an elimination.) Wine turns sour, for example, when the ethanol in contact with air is oxidized to acetic acid:

$$\text{CH}_3-\overset{\text{OH}}{\underset{\text{}}{\text{CH}_2}} \xrightarrow[-\text{H}_2\text{O}]{\frac{1}{2}\text{O}_2} \text{CH}_3-\overset{\text{O}}{\overset{\|}{\text{CH}}} \xrightarrow{\frac{1}{2}\text{O}_2} \text{CH}_3-\overset{\text{O}}{\overset{\|}{\text{C}}}-\text{OH}$$

**Serine**
Amino acid found in most proteins

- Substitution yields products with other single-bonded functional groups. Reactions of hydrohalic acids with many alcohols give haloalkanes:

$$\text{R}_2\text{CH}-\text{OH} + \text{HBr} \longrightarrow \text{R}_2\text{CH}-\text{Br} + \text{HOH}$$

As you'll see below, *the C atom undergoing the change in a substitution is bonded to a more electronegative element,* which makes it partially positive and, thus, a target for a negatively charged or electron-rich group of an incoming reactant.

**Cholesterol**
Major sterol in animals; essential for cell membranes; precursor of steroid hormones

**Figure 15.15** Some molecules with the alcohol functional group.

**Haloalkanes** A *halogen* atom (X) bonded to a carbon gives the **haloalkane** functional

group, $-\overset{|}{\underset{|}{\text{C}}}-\overset{..}{\underset{..}{\text{X}}}:$ , and compounds with the general formula R—X. Haloalkanes

(common name, **alkyl halides**) are named by identifying the halogen with a prefix on the hydrocarbon name and numbering the C atom to which the halogen is attached, as in bromomethane, 2-chloropropane, or 1,3-diiodohexane.

Like alcohols, haloalkanes undergo substitution and elimination reactions.

- Just as many alcohols undergo substitution to form alkyl halides when treated with halide ions in acid, many halides undergo substitution to form alcohols in base. For example, OH⁻ attacks the positive C end of the C—X bond and displaces X⁻:

$$\text{CH}_3-\text{CH}_2-\text{CH}_2-\text{CH}_2-\text{Br} + \text{OH}^- \longrightarrow \text{CH}_3-\text{CH}_2-\text{CH}_2-\text{CH}_2-\text{OH} + \text{Br}^-$$

1-bromobutane                    1-butanol

Substitutions by groups such as —CN, —SH, —OR, and —NH$_2$ allow chemists to convert alkyl halides to a host of other families of compounds.

• Just as addition of HX *to* an alkene produces haloalkanes, elimination of HX *from* a haloalkane by reaction with a strong base, such as potassium ethoxide, produces an alkene:

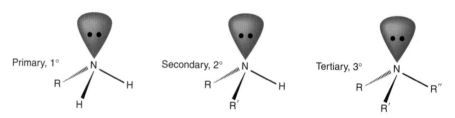

2-chloro-2-methylpropane     potassium ethoxide        2-methylpropene

Haloalkanes have many important uses, but some, like the chlorofluorocarbons, cause serious environmental problems (Chemical Connections, pp. 664–665). Also, some halogenated aromatic hydrocarbons (*aryl* halides) are carcinogenic in mammals, have severe neurological effects in humans, and, to make matters worse, are very stable and accumulate in the environment. For example, the polychlorinated biphenyls (PCBs) (Figure 15.16), used as insulating fluids in electrical transformers, have accumulated for decades in rivers and lakes and have been incorporated into the food chain. PCBs in natural waters pose health risks and present an enormous cleanup problem.

**Figure 15.16** A tetrachlorobiphenyl, one of 209 polychlorinated biphenyls (PCBs).

**Amines** The **amine** functional group is $-\overset{\displaystyle |}{\underset{\displaystyle |}{C}}-\overset{\displaystyle |}{\underset{\displaystyle |}{\ddot{N}}}-$ . Chemists classify amines as derivatives of ammonia, with R groups in place of one or more of the H atoms in $NH_3$. *Primary* (1°) amines are $RNH_2$, *secondary* (2°) amines are $R_2NH$, and *tertiary* (3°) amines are $R_3N$. Like ammonia, amines have trigonal pyramidal shapes and a lone pair of electrons on a partially negative N atom, which is the key to amine reactivity (Figure 15.17).

**Figure 15.17** General structures of amines.

Primary, 1°        Secondary, 2°        Tertiary, 3°

Systematic names drop the final *-e* of the alkane and add the suffix *-amine,* as in ethanamine. However, there is still wide usage of common names, in which the suffix *-amine* follows the name of the alkyl group; thus, methylamine has one methyl group attached to N, diethylamine has two ethyl groups attached, and so forth. Figure 15.18 shows that the amine functional group occurs in many biomolecules.

Primary and secondary amines can form H bonds, so they have higher melting and boiling points than hydrocarbons and alkyl halides of similar molar mass. For example, dimethylamine ($\mathcal{M}$ = 45.09 g/mol) boils 45°C higher than ethyl fluoride

**Figure 15.18** Some biomolecules with the amine functional group.

**Lysine (primary amine)**
Amino acid found in most proteins

**Adenine (primary amine)**
Component of nucleic acids

**Epinephrine (adrenaline; secondary amine)**
Neurotransmitter in brain; hormone released during stress

**Cocaine (tertiary amine)**
Brain stimulant; widely abused drug

($\mathcal{M} = 48.06$ g/mol). Trimethylamine has a greater molar mass than dimethylamine, but it melts more than 20°C *lower* because trimethylamine molecules do not have an H atom attached to the N for H bonding.

Amines of low molar mass are fishy smelling, water soluble, and weakly basic because of the lone pair on N. The reaction with water proceeds only slightly to the right to reach equilibrium:

$$CH_3-\ddot{N}H_2 + H_2O \rightleftharpoons CH_3-\overset{+}{N}H_3 + OH^-$$

The lone pair is also the reason amines undergo substitution reactions: the lone pair attacks the partially positive C in alkyl halides to displace $X^-$ and form a larger amine:

$$2\ CH_3-CH_2-\ddot{N}H_2\ +\ CH_3-CH_2-Cl\ \longrightarrow\ CH_3-CH_2-\ddot{N}H\ +\ CH_3-CH_2-\overset{+}{N}H_3Cl^-$$
$$\underset{CH_3-CH_2}{|}$$

| ethylamine | chloroethane | diethylamine | ethylammonium chloride |

(Two molecules of ethylamine are needed: one attacks the chloroethane, and the other binds the released $H^+$ to prevent it from remaining on the diethylamine product.)

---

### Sample Problem 15.4    Predicting the Reactions of Alcohols, Alkyl Halides, and Amines

**Problem** Determine the reaction type and predict the product(s) for each reaction:

(a) $CH_3-CH_2-CH_2-I\ +\ NaOH\ \longrightarrow$

(b) $CH_3-CH_2-Br\ +\ 2\ CH_3-CH_2-CH_2-NH_2\ \longrightarrow$

(c) $CH_3-\underset{\underset{OH}{|}}{CH}-CH_3\ \xrightarrow[H_2SO_4]{Cr_2O_7^{2-}}$

**Plan** We first determine the functional group(s) of the reactant(s) and then examine any inorganic reagent(s) to decide on the reaction type, keeping in mind that, in general, these functional groups undergo substitution or elimination. In (a), the reactant is an alkyl halide, so the $OH^-$ of the inorganic reagent substitutes for $I^-$. In (b), the reactants are an amine and an alkyl halide, so the N of the amine substitutes for the Br. In (c), the reactant is an alcohol, the inorganic reagents form a strong oxidizing agent, and the alcohol group undergoes elimination to form a C=O.

**Solution** (a) Substitution: The products are $CH_3-CH_2-CH_2-OH\ +\ NaI$

(b) Substitution: The products are $CH_3-CH_2-CH_2-\underset{\underset{CH_2-CH_3}{|}}{NH}\ +\ CH_3-CH_2-CH_2-\overset{+}{N}H_3Br^-$

(c) Elimination: (oxidation): The product is $CH_3-\underset{\underset{O}{\|}}{C}-CH_3$

**Check** The only changes should be at the functional group.

### Follow-Up Problem 15.4    Fill in the blank in each reaction. (*Hint:* Examine any inorganic compounds and the organic product to determine the organic reactant.)

(a) _____ $+\ CH_3-ONa\ \longrightarrow\ CH_3-CH=\underset{\underset{CH_3}{\overset{CH_3}{|}}}{C}-CH_3\ +\ NaCl\ +\ CH_3-OH$

(b) _____ $\xrightarrow[H_2SO_4]{Cr_2O_7^{2-}}\ CH_3-CH_2-\underset{\overset{\|}{O}}{C}-OH$

---

### Variations on a Theme: Inorganic Compounds with Single Bonds to O, X, and N    The —OH group occurs frequently in inorganic compounds. All oxoacids contain at least one —OH, usually bonded to a relatively electronegative nonmetal atom, which in most cases is bonded to other O atoms. Oxoacids are acidic in water because these additional O atoms pull electron density from the central nonmetal, which pulls electron density from the O—H bond, releasing an $H^+$ ion and stabilizing

the oxoanion through resonance. Alcohols are *not* acidic in water because they lack the additional O atoms and the electronegative nonmetal.

Halides of nearly every nonmetal are known, and many undergo substitution reactions in base. As in the case of an alkyl halide, the process involves an attack on the partially positive central atom by OH⁻:

Thus, alkyl halides undergo the same general reaction as other nonmetal halides, such as $BCl_3$, $SiF_4$, and $PCl_5$.

The bonds between nitrogen and larger nonmetals, such as Si, P, and S, have significant double-bond character, which affects structure and reactivity. For example, $(SiH_3)_3N$, trisilylamine, the Si analog of trimethylamine, is trigonal planar, rather than trigonal pyramidal, because of the formation of a double bond between N and Si. Because the lone pair on N is delocalized in this π bond, trisilylamine is not basic.

## Functional Groups with Double Bonds

The most important functional groups with double bonds are the C=C group of alkenes and the C=O group of aldehydes and ketones. Both appear in many organic and biological molecules. *Their most common reaction type is addition.*

**Alkenes** The C=C bond is the essential portion of the *alkene* functional group, 

$\diagdown$C=C$\diagdown$ . Although they undergo elimination to alkynes, *alkenes typically undergo addition.* The electron-rich double bond is readily attracted to the partially positive H atoms of hydronium ions and hydrohalic acids, yielding alcohols and alkyl halides, respectively:

**Figure 15.19** The stability of benzene.

## Comparing the Reactivities of Alkenes and Aromatic Compounds

The *localized* unsaturation of alkenes is very different from the *delocalized* unsaturation of aromatic compounds. That is, despite the way we depict its resonance forms, benzene does *not* have double bonds. Thus, benzene does not decolorize $Br_2$.

In general, aromatic rings are much *less* reactive than alkenes because of their delocalized π electrons. For example, let's compare the enthalpies of reaction for the addition of $H_2$. Hydrogenation of cyclohexene, with one C=C bond, has a $\Delta H^\circ_{rxn}$ of $-120$ kJ/mol. Then, for the imaginary molecule "cyclohexatriene," that is, the structure with three C=C bonds, the hypothetical $\Delta H^\circ_{rxn}$ for hydrogenation would be three times as much, or $-360$ kJ/mol. Hydrogenation of benzene has a $\Delta H^\circ_{rxn}$ of $-208$ kJ/mol. Thus, the $\Delta H^\circ_{rxn}$ for hydrogenation of benzene is 152 kJ/mol *less* than that for "cyclohexatriene." This energy difference is attributed to the aromatic resonance stabilization of benzene (Figure 15.19).

This extra energy needed to break up the delocalized π system means *addition* reactions with benzene occur rarely. But, benzene does undergo many *substitution* reactions in which the delocalization is retained when an H atom attached to a ring C is replaced by another group:

## Aldehydes and Ketones

**Aldehydes and Ketones** The C=O bond, or **carbonyl group,** is one of the most chemically versatile.

- In the **aldehyde** functional group, the carbonyl C is bonded to H (and often to another C), so it occurs *at the end of a chain*, $R-\overset{\overset{H}{|}}{C}=\ddot{O}$. Aldehyde names drop the final -*e* from the alkane name and add -*al;* thus, the three-C aldehyde is propanal.
- In the **ketone** functional group, the carbonyl C is bonded to two other C atoms, $-\overset{|}{\underset{|}{C}}-\overset{:\ddot{O}:}{\overset{||}{C}}-\overset{|}{\underset{|}{C}}-$, so it occurs *within the chain*. Ketones, $R-\overset{\overset{O}{||}}{C}-R'$, are named by numbering the carbonyl C, dropping the final -*e* from the alkane name, and adding -*one*. For example, the unbranched, five-C ketone with the carbonyl C as C-2 in the chain is named 2-pentanone. Figure 15.20 shows some common carbonyl compounds.

Aldehydes and ketones are formed by the oxidation of alcohols:

$$CH_3-CH_2-OH \xrightarrow{\text{oxidation}} CH_3-\overset{\overset{O}{||}}{C}-H$$

ethanol → ethanal (common name, acetaldehyde)

 3-pentanol $\xrightarrow{\text{oxidation}}$  3-pentanone (common name, diethylketone)

Conversely, as a result of their unsaturation, carbonyl compounds can undergo *addition* and be reduced to alcohols:

cyclobutanone $\xrightarrow{\text{reduction}}$ cyclobutanol

**Figure 15.20** Some common aldehydes and ketones.

**Methanal (formaldehyde)**
Used to make resins in plywood, dishware, counter-tops; biological preservative

**Ethanal (acetaldehyde)**
Narcotic product of ethanol metabolism; used to make perfumes, flavors, plastics, other chemicals

**Benzaldehyde**
Artificial almond flavoring

**2-Propanone (acetone)**
Solvent for fat, rubber, plastic, varnish, lacquer; chemical feedstock

**2-Butanone (methyl ethyl ketone)**
Important solvent

**A** Electron density model

**B** Charged resonance form

**Figure 15.21** The polar carbonyl group.

Like the C=C bond, the C=O bond is *electron rich;* unlike the C=C bond, it is *highly polar* ($\Delta EN = 1.0$). Figure 15.21 emphasizes this polarity with an orbital contour model (Figure 15.21A) and a charged resonance form (Figure 15.21B).

As a result of the bond polarity, addition often occurs with an electron-rich group bonding to the carbonyl C and an electron-poor group bonding to the carbonyl O. **Organometallic compounds,** which have a metal atom (usually Li or Mg) attached to an R group through a polar covalent bond, take part in this type of reaction. In a two-step sequence, they convert carbonyl compounds to alcohols with *different carbon skeletons:*

$$R-\overset{\delta+}{CH}=\overset{\delta-}{O} + \overset{\delta-}{R'}-\overset{\delta+}{Li} \xrightarrow{H_2O} R-\overset{\overset{\displaystyle OH}{|}}{CH}-R' + LiOH$$

In the following example, the electron-rich C bonded to Li in ethyllithium, $CH_3CH_2-Li$, attacks the electron-poor carbonyl C of 2-propanone, adding its ethyl group; at the same time, the Li adds to the carbonyl O. Treating the mixture with water forms the C—OH group in the product, 2-methyl-2-butanol:

Note that the product skeleton combines the two reactant skeletons. The field of *organic synthesis* often employs organometallic compounds to create new compounds with different skeletons.

---

**Sample Problem 15.5** **Predicting the Steps in a Reaction Sequence**

**Problem** Fill in the blanks in the following reaction sequence:

$$CH_3-CH_2-\overset{\overset{\displaystyle Br}{|}}{CH}-CH_3 \xrightarrow{OH^-} \underline{\qquad} \xrightarrow[H_2SO_4]{Cr_2O_7{}^{2-}} \underline{\qquad} \xrightarrow{CH_3-Li} \xrightarrow{H_2O} \underline{\qquad}$$

**Plan** For each step, we examine the functional group of the reactant and the reagent above the yield arrow to decide on the most likely product.

**Solution** The sequence starts with an alkyl halide reacting with $OH^-$. Substitution gives an alcohol. Oxidation of this alcohol with acidic dichromate gives a ketone. Finally, a two-step reaction of a ketone with $CH_3-Li$ and then water forms an alcohol with a carbon skeleton that has the $CH_3-$ group attached to the carbonyl C:

$$CH_3-CH_2-\overset{\overset{\displaystyle Br}{|}}{CH}-CH_3 \xrightarrow{OH^-} CH_3-CH_2-\overset{\overset{\displaystyle OH}{|}}{CH}-CH_3 \xrightarrow[H_2SO_4]{Cr_2O_7{}^{2-}} CH_3-CH_2-\overset{\overset{\displaystyle O}{||}}{C}-CH_3 \xrightarrow{CH_3-Li} \xrightarrow{H_2O} CH_3-CH_2-\overset{\overset{\displaystyle OH}{|}}{\underset{\underset{\displaystyle CH_3}{|}}{C}}-CH_3$$

2-bromobutane      2-butanol      2-butanone      2-methyl-2-butanol

**Check** In this case, make sure that the first two reactions alter the functional group only and that the final steps change the C skeleton.

**Follow-Up Problem 15.5** Choose reactants to obtain the following products:

**(a)** $\underline{\qquad} \xrightarrow[H_2SO_4]{Cr_2O_7{}^{2-}}$ 

**(b)**

$\underline{\qquad} \xrightarrow{CH_3-CH_2-Li} \xrightarrow{H_2O}$

**Variations on a Theme: Inorganic Compounds with Double Bonds** Homonuclear (same kind of atom) double bonds are rare for atoms other than C. However, we've seen many double bonds between O and other nonmetals, for example, in the oxides of S, N, and the halogens. Like carbonyl compounds, these substances undergo addition reactions. For example, the partially negative O of water attacks the partially positive S of $SO_3$ to form sulfuric acid:

S bonded to 3 atoms          S bonded to 4 atoms

## Functional Groups with Both Single and Double Bonds

A family of three functional groups contains C double bonded to O (a carbonyl group) *and* single bonded to O or N. The parent of the family is the **carboxylic acid** group, —C—ÖH, also called the *carboxyl group* and written —COOH. *The most important reaction type of this family is substitution from one member to another.* Substitution for the —OH by the —OR of an alcohol gives the **ester** group, —C—Ö—R; substitution by the —N̈— of an amine gives the **amide** group, —C—N̈—.

**Methanoic acid (formic acid)**
An irritating component
of ant and bee stings

**Carboxylic Acids** Carboxylic acids, R—C—OH, are named by dropping the *-e* from the alkane name and adding *-oic acid;* however, many common names are used. For example, the four-C acid is butanoic acid (the carboxyl C is counted when choosing the root); its common name is butyric acid. Figure 15.22 shows some important carboxylic acids. The carboxyl C already has three bonds, so it forms only one other. In formic acid (methanoic acid), the carboxyl C is bonded to an H, but in all other carboxylic acids it is bonded to a chain or ring.

Carboxylic acids are weak acids in water:

$$CH_3{-}\overset{O}{\underset{}{C}}{-}OH(l) + H_2O(l) \rightleftharpoons CH_3{-}\overset{O}{\underset{}{C}}{-}O^-(aq) + H_3O^+(aq)$$

ethanoic acid
(acetic acid)

**Butanoic acid (butyric acid)**
Odor of rancid butter;
suspected component of
monkey sex attractant

At equilibrium in a solution of typical concentration, more than 99% of the acid molecules are undissociated at any given moment. In strong base, however, a carboxylic acid reacts completely to form a salt and water:

$$CH_3{-}\overset{O}{\underset{}{C}}{-}OH(l) + NaOH(aq) \longrightarrow CH_3{-}\overset{O}{\underset{}{C}}{-}O^-(aq) + Na^+(aq) + H_2O(l)$$

**Benzoic acid**
Calorimetric standard;
used in preserving food,
dyeing fabric, curing tobacco

The anion of the salt is the *carboxylate ion,* named by dropping *-oic acid* and adding *-oate;* the sodium salt of butanoic acid, for instance, is sodium butanoate.

Carboxylic acids with long hydrocarbon chains are **fatty acids,** an essential group of compounds found in all cells. Animal fatty acids have saturated chains, whereas many fatty acids from plants are unsaturated, usually with the C=C bonds in the *cis* configuration. The double bonds make them much easier to metabolize. Nearly all fatty acid skeletons have an even number of C atoms—16 and 18 carbons are very common—because cells use two-carbon units in synthesizing them. Fatty acid salts, usually with a cation from Group 1A(1) or 2A(2), are soaps (Section 13.2).

**Octadecanoic acid (stearic acid)**
Found in animal fats; used in
making candles and soaps

**Figure 15.22** Some molecules with the carboxylic acid functional group.

Substitution of carboxylic acids and other members of this family occurs through a two-step sequence: *addition plus elimination equals substitution.* Addition to the trigonal planar C atom gives an unstable tetrahedral intermediate, which immediately undergoes elimination to revert to a trigonal planar product (in this case, X is OH):

$$R-\overset{\overset{\textstyle O}{\|}}{C}-X \ + \ Z-Y \ \underset{}{\overset{\text{addition}}{\rightleftharpoons}} \ \left[ R\cdots\overset{\overset{\textstyle O-Z}{|}}{\underset{Y}{C}}-X \right] \ \underset{}{\overset{\text{elimination}}{\rightleftharpoons}} \ R-\overset{\overset{\textstyle O}{\|}}{C}-Y \ + \ Z-X$$

Strong heating of a carboxylic acid forms an **acid anhydride** through a type of substitution called a *dehydration-condensation reaction* (Section 14.7), in which two molecules condense into one with loss of water:

$$R-\overset{\overset{\textstyle O}{\|}}{C}\boxed{-OH \ + \ H}O-\overset{\overset{\textstyle O}{\|}}{C}-R \ \overset{\Delta}{\longrightarrow} \ R-\overset{\overset{\textstyle O}{\|}}{C}-O-\overset{\overset{\textstyle O}{\|}}{C}-R \ + \ HOH$$

**Esters** The ester group, $-\overset{\overset{\textstyle O}{\|}}{C}-O-R$, is formed from an alcohol and a carboxylic acid. The first part of an ester name designates the alcohol portion and the second the acid portion (named in the same way as the carboxylate ion). For example, the ester formed between ethanol and ethanoic acid is ethyl ethanoate (common name, ethyl acetate), a solvent for nail polish and model glue.

The ester group occurs commonly in **lipids,** a large group of fatty biological substances. Most dietary fats are *triglycerides,* esters that are composed of three fatty acids linked to the alcohol 1,2,3-trihydroxypropane (common name, glycerol) and that function as energy stores. Some important lipids are shown in Figure 15.23; lecithin is one of several phospholipids that make up the lipid bilayer in all cell membranes (Section 13.2).

Esters, like acid anhydrides, form through a dehydration-condensation reaction; in this case, it is called an *esterification*:

$$R-\overset{\overset{\textstyle O}{\|}}{C}\boxed{-OH \ + \ H}-O-R' \ \overset{H^+}{\rightleftharpoons} \ R-\overset{\overset{\textstyle O}{\|}}{C}-O-R' \ + \ HOH$$

Note that the esterification reaction is reversible. The opposite of dehydration-condensation is **hydrolysis,** in which the O atom of water is attracted to the partially positive C atom of the ester, cleaving (lysing) the ester molecule into two parts. One part bonds to water's —OH, and the other part to water's other H. In the process of soap manufacture, or *saponification* (Latin *sapon,* "soap"), begun in ancient times, the ester bonds in animal or vegetable fats are hydrolyzed with a strong base:

$$
\begin{array}{l}
R-\overset{\overset{\textstyle O}{\|}}{C}-O-CH_2 \\
R'-\overset{\overset{\textstyle O}{\|}}{C}-O-CH \\
R''-\overset{\overset{\textstyle O}{\|}}{C}-O-CH_2
\end{array}
\ + \ 3NaOH \ \overset{\Delta}{\longrightarrow} \ 
\begin{array}{l}
R-\overset{\overset{\textstyle O}{\|}}{C}-O^-\,Na^+ \\
R'-\overset{\overset{\textstyle O}{\|}}{C}-O^-\,Na^+ \\
R''-\overset{\overset{\textstyle O}{\|}}{C}-O^-\,Na^+
\end{array}
\ + \ 
\begin{array}{l}
HO-CH_2 \\
HO-CH \\
HO-CH_2
\end{array}
$$

a triglyceride          3 soaps          glycerol

While carboxylic acids have pungent, vinegary, and cheesy odors, esters have pleasant odors. For example, ethyl butanoate has the scent of pineapple, and pentyl-pentanoate has the aroma of apples (*see photo*). Naturally occurring and synthetic esters are used to add fruity, floral, and herbal odors to foods, cosmetics, household deodorizers, and medicines.

Carboxylic acids and esters have some familiar and distinctive odors.

**Cetyl palmitate** The most common lipid in whale blubber

**Lecithin** Phospholipid found in all cell membranes

**Tristearin** Typical dietary fat used as an energy store in animals

**Figure 15.23** Some lipid molecules with the ester functional group.

**Amides** The product of a substitution between an amine (or $NH_3$) and an ester is an amide with the functional group $-\overset{\overset{\displaystyle O}{\|}}{C}-\overset{\displaystyle |}{N}-$. The partially negative N of the amine is attracted to the partially positive C of the ester, an alcohol (ROH) is lost, and an amide forms:

$$CH_3-\overset{\overset{\displaystyle O}{\|}}{C}-O-CH_3 \;+\; H\overset{\overset{\displaystyle \cdot\cdot}{N}}{\underset{H}{|}}-CH_2-CH_3 \;\longrightarrow\; CH_3-\overset{\overset{\displaystyle O}{\|}}{C}-\overset{\overset{\displaystyle H}{|}}{N}-CH_2-CH_3 \;+\; CH_3-OH$$

| methyl ethanoate (methyl acetate) | ethanamine (ethylamine) | N-ethylethanamide (N-ethylacetamide) | methanol |

Amides are named by denoting the amine portion with *N-* and replacing *-oic acid* from the parent carboxylic acid with *-amide*. In the amide produced in the preceding reaction, the ethyl group comes from the amine, and the acid portion comes from ethanoic acid (acetic acid). Some amides are shown in Figure 15.24. The most important example of the amide group is the *peptide bond* (discussed in Sections 13.2 and 15.6), which links amino acids in a protein.

An amide is hydrolyzed in hot water (or base) to a carboxylic acid and an amine. Thus, even though amides are not normally formed in the following way, they can be viewed as the result of a reversible dehydration-condensation:

$$R-\overset{\overset{\displaystyle O}{\|}}{C}\boxed{-OH \;+\; H}-\overset{\overset{\displaystyle H}{|}}{N}-R' \;\rightleftharpoons\; R-\overset{\overset{\displaystyle O}{\|}}{C}-\overset{\overset{\displaystyle H}{|}}{N}-R' \;+\; HOH$$

Compounds in the carboxylic acid family also undergo reduction to form other functional groups. For example, certain inorganic *reducing agents* convert acids or esters to alcohols and convert amides to amines:

$$R-\overset{\overset{\displaystyle O}{\|}}{C}-OH \;(or\; R-\overset{\overset{\displaystyle O}{\|}}{C}-O-R') \;\xrightarrow{\text{reduction}}\; R-CH_2-OH \;+\; HOH \;(or\; R'-OH)$$

$$R-\overset{\overset{\displaystyle O}{\|}}{C}-NH-R' \;\xrightarrow{\text{reduction}}\; R-CH_2-NH-R' \;+\; H_2O$$

**Figure 15.24** Some molecules with the amide functional group.

**Acetaminophen**
Active ingredient in nonaspirin pain relievers; used to make dyes and photographic chemicals

**N,N-Dimethylmethanamide (dimethylformamide)**
Major organic solvent; used in production of synthetic fibers

**Lysergic acid diethylamide (LSD-25)** A potent hallucinogen

## Sample Problem 15.6 — Predicting Reactions of the Carboxylic Acid Family

**Problem** Predict the product(s) of the following reactions:

(a) $CH_3-CH_2-CH_2-\overset{O}{\underset{\|}{C}}-OH$ + $CH_3-\overset{OH}{\underset{|}{CH}}-CH_3 \overset{H^+}{\rightleftharpoons}$

(b) $CH_3-\overset{CH_3}{\underset{|}{CH}}-CH_2-CH_2-\overset{O}{\underset{\|}{C}}-NH-CH_2-CH_3 \xrightarrow[H_2O]{NaOH}$

**Plan** We discussed substitution reactions (including addition-elimination and dehydration-condensation) and hydrolysis. **(a)** A carboxylic acid and an alcohol react, so the reaction must be a substitution to form an ester and water. **(b)** An amide reacts with $OH^-$, so it is hydrolyzed to an amine and a sodium carboxylate.

**Solution** **(a)** Formation of an ester:

$$CH_3-CH_2-CH_2-\overset{O}{\underset{\|}{C}}-O-\overset{CH_3}{\underset{|}{CH}}-CH_3 + H_2O$$

**(b)** Basic hydrolysis of an amide:

$$CH_3-\overset{CH_3}{\underset{|}{CH}}-CH_2-CH_2-\overset{O}{\underset{\|}{C}}-O^- + Na^+ + H_2N-CH_2-CH_3$$

**Check** Note that in part (b), the carboxylate ion forms, rather than the acid, because the aqueous NaOH that is present reacts with the carboxylic acid.

**Follow-Up Problem 15.6** Fill in the blanks in the following reactions:

(a) ____ + $CH_3-OH \overset{H^+}{\rightleftharpoons}$ ⟨benzene ring⟩$-CH_2-\overset{O}{\underset{\|}{C}}-O-CH_3 + H_2O$

(b) ____ + ____ $\longrightarrow$ $CH_3-CH_2-CH_2-\overset{O}{\underset{\|}{C}}-NH-CH_2-CH_3 + CH_3-OH$

| Acid | | Anhydride | |
|---|---|---|---|

$2\ R-\overset{:O:}{\underset{}{\overset{\|}{C}}}-\overset{..}{O}H \xrightarrow{-H_2O} R-\overset{:O:}{\underset{}{\overset{\|}{C}}}-\overset{..}{O}-\overset{:O:}{\underset{}{\overset{\|}{C}}}-R$

$2\ HO-\overset{:O:}{\underset{:OH}{\overset{\|}{P}}}-\overset{..}{O}H \xrightarrow{-H_2O} HO-\overset{:O:}{\underset{:OH}{\overset{\|}{P}}}-\overset{..}{O}-\overset{:O:}{\underset{:OH}{\overset{\|}{P}}}-\overset{..}{O}H$

$2\ HO-\overset{:O:}{\underset{:O:}{\overset{\|}{S}}}-\overset{..}{O}H \xrightarrow{-H_2O} HO-\overset{:O:}{\underset{:O:}{\overset{\|}{S}}}-\overset{..}{O}-\overset{:O:}{\underset{:O:}{\overset{\|}{S}}}-\overset{..}{O}H$

**Figure 15.25** The formation of carboxylic, phosphoric, and sulfuric acid anhydrides.

## Variations on a Theme: Oxoacids, Esters, and Amides of Other Nonmetals

A nonmetal that has both double and single bonds to oxygens occurs in most inorganic oxoacids, such as phosphoric, sulfuric, and chlorous acids. Those with additional O atoms are stronger acids than carboxylic acids.

Diphosphoric and disulfuric acids are acid anhydrides formed by dehydration-condensation reactions, like the one that yields a carboxylic acid anhydride (Figure 15.25). Inorganic oxoacids form esters and amides that are part of many biological molecules. We already saw that certain lipids are phosphate esters (see Figure 15.23). The first compound formed when glucose is digested is a phosphate ester (Figure 15.26A); a similar phosphate ester is a major structural feature of nucleic acids, as we'll see shortly. Amides of organic sulfur-containing oxoacids, called *sulfonamides,*

**A Glucose-6-phosphate**

**B Sulfanilamide**

**Figure 15.26** A phosphate ester and a sulfonamide.

are potent antibiotics; the simplest of these is depicted in Figure 15.26B. More than 10,000 different sulfonamides have been synthesized.

## Functional Groups with Triple Bonds

Alkynes and nitriles are the only two important functional groups with triple bonds.

**Alkynes** Alkynes, with an electron-rich —C≡C— group, undergo addition (by H$_2$O, H$_2$, HX, X$_2$, and so forth) to form double-bonded or saturated compounds:

$$CH_3—C≡CH \xrightarrow{H_2} CH_3—CH=CH_2 \xrightarrow{H_2} CH_3—CH_2—CH_3$$

propyne              propene              propane

**Nitriles** Nitriles (R—C≡N) contain the **nitrile** group (—C≡N:) and are made by substituting a CN$^-$ (cyanide) ion for X$^-$ in a reaction with an alkyl halide:

$$CH_3—CH_2—Cl + NaCN \longrightarrow CH_3—CH_2—C≡N + NaCl$$

This reaction is useful because it *increases the chain by one C atom*. Nitriles are versatile because once they are formed, they can be reduced to amines or hydrolyzed to carboxylic acids:

$$CH_3—CH_2—CH_2—NH_2 \xleftarrow{reduction} CH_3—CH_2—C≡N \xrightarrow[hydrolysis]{H_3O^+, H_2O} CH_3—CH_2—\overset{O}{\underset{||}{C}}—OH + NH_4^+$$

**Variations on a Theme: Inorganic Compounds with Triple Bonds** Triple bonds are as scarce in the inorganic world as in the organic world. Carbon monoxide (:C≡O:), elemental nitrogen (:N≡N:), and the cyanide ion ([:C≡N:]$^-$) are the only common examples.

You've seen quite a few functional groups by this time, and it is especially important that you can recognize them in a complex organic molecule. Sample Problem 15.7 provides some practice.

---

**Sample Problem 15.7**  **Recognizing Functional Groups**

**Problem** Circle and name the functional groups in the following molecules:

**(a)**  **(b)**  **(c)**

**Plan** We use Table 15.5 (p. 592) to identify the various functional groups.

**Solution**

**(a)** carboxylic acid, ester
**(b)** alcohol, 2° amine
**(c)** ketone, haloalkane, alkene

**Follow-Up Problem 15.7**  Circle and name the functional groups:

**(a)**  **(b)**

## ■ Summary of Section 15.4

- Organic reactions are initiated when regions of high and low electron density in reactant molecules attract each other.
- Functional groups containing only single bonds—alcohols, amines, and alkyl halides—take part in substitution and elimination reactions.
- Functional groups with double or triple bonds—alkenes, aldehydes, ketones, alkynes, and nitriles—generally take part in addition reactions.
- Aromatic compounds typically undergo substitution, rather than addition, because delocalization of the $\pi$ electrons stabilizes the ring.
- Functional groups with both double and single bonds—carboxylic acids, esters, and amides—generally take part in substitution reactions.
- Many reactions change one functional group to another, but some, including reactions with organometallic compounds and with the cyanide ion, change the carbon skeleton.

# 15.5 • THE MONOMER-POLYMER THEME I: SYNTHETIC MACROMOLECULES

In Chapter 12, you saw that polymers are extremely large molecules that consist of many monomeric repeat units. In that chapter, we focused on the mass, shape, and physical properties of polymers. Now we'll see how polymers are named and discuss the two types of organic reactions that link monomers covalently into a chain. To name a polymer, just add the prefix *poly-* to the monomer name, as in *polyethylene* or *polystyrene*. When the monomer has a two-word name, parentheses are used, as in *poly(vinyl chloride)*.

The two major types of reaction processes that form synthetic polymers lend their names to the resulting classes of polymer—addition and condensation.

## Addition Polymers

**Addition polymers** form when monomers undergo an addition reaction with one another. These substances are also called *chain-reaction* (or *chain-growth*) *polymers* because as each monomer adds to the chain, it forms a new reactive site to continue the process. The monomers of most addition polymers have the $\overset{\diagdown}{C}=\overset{\diagup}{C}$ grouping.

As you can see from Table 15.6, the essential chemical differences between an acrylic sweater, a plastic grocery bag, and a bowling ball are due to the different groups that are attached to the double-bonded C atoms of the monomer.

The *free-radical polymerization* of ethene (ethylene, $CH_2=CH_2$) to polyethylene is a simple example of the addition process (Figure 15.27). The monomer reacts to form a *free radical*, a species with an unpaired electron, which seeks an electron from another monomer to form a covalent bond:

*Step 1.* The process begins when an *initiator,* usually a peroxide, generates a free radical.

*Step 2.* The free radical attacks the $\pi$ bond of an ethylene molecule, forming a $\sigma$ bond with one of the $p$ electrons and leaving the other unpaired, the new free radical.

*Step 3.* This new free radical then attacks the $\pi$ bond of another ethylene molecule, joining it to the chain end, and the backbone of the polymer grows. As each ethylene adds, it leaves an unpaired electron on the growing end to find an electron "mate" and make the chain one repeat unit longer.

*Step 4.* This process stops when two free radicals form a covalent bond or when a very stable free radical is formed by addition of an *inhibitor* molecule.

Recent progress in controlling the high reactivity of free-radical species promises an even wider range of polymers. In one method, polymerization is initiated by the formation of a cation (or anion) instead of a free radical. The cationic (or anionic)

**Figure 15.27** Steps in the free-radical polymerization of ethylene.

## Table 15.6  Some Major Addition Polymers

| Monomer | Polymer | Applications |
|---|---|---|
| | polyethylene | Plastic bags; bottles; toys |
| | polytetrafluoroethylene | Cooking utensils (e.g., Teflon) |
| | polypropylene | Carpeting (indoor-outdoor); bottles |
| | poly(vinyl chloride) | Plastic wrap; garden hose; indoor plumbing |
| | polystyrene | Insulation; furniture; packing materials |
| | polyacrylonitrile | Yarns (e.g., Orlon, Acrilan), fabrics, and wigs |
| | poly(vinyl acetate) | Adhesives; paints; textile coatings; computer disks |
| | poly(vinylidene chloride) | Food wrap (e.g., Saran) |
| | poly(methyl methacrylate) | Glass substitute (e.g., Lucite, Plexiglas); bowling balls; paint |

reactive end of the chain attacks the $\pi$ bond of another monomer to form a new cationic (or anionic) end, and the process continues.

The most important polymerization reactions take place under relatively mild conditions through the use of catalysts that incorporate transition metals. In 1963, Karl Ziegler and Giulio Natta received the Nobel Prize in chemistry for developing *Ziegler-Natta catalysts,* which employ an organoaluminum compound, such as $Al(C_2H_5)_3$, and the tetrachloride of titanium or vanadium. Today, chemists use organometallic catalysts that are *stereoselective* to create polymers whose repeat units have groups spatially oriented in particular ways. Through the use of these catalysts, polyethylene chains with molar masses of $10^4$ to $10^5$ g/mol are made by varying conditions and reagents.

Similar methods are used to make polypropylenes, $+CH_2-CH+_n$, that have

$$\underset{\displaystyle CH_3}{|}$$

all the $CH_3$ groups of the repeat units oriented either on one side of the chain or on alternating sides. The different orientations lead to different packing efficiencies of the chains and, thus, different degrees of crystallinity, which lead to differences in such physical properties as density, rigidity, and elasticity (Section 12.7).

## Condensation Polymers

The monomers of **condensation polymers** must have *two functional groups;* we can designate such a monomer as A—R—B (where A and B may or may not be the same, and **R** is the rest of the molecule). Most commonly, the monomers link when an A group on one undergoes a *dehydration-condensation reaction* with a B group on another:

$$\tfrac{1}{2}n\text{H—A—R—B—OH} + \tfrac{1}{2}n\text{H—A—R—B—OH} \xrightarrow{-(n-1)\text{HOH}} \text{H}\underset{n}{\underbrace{\text{[A—R—B]}}}\text{OH}$$

Many condensation polymers are *copolymers,* those consisting of two or more different repeat units (Section 12.7). Two major types are polyamides and polyesters.

1. *Polyamides.* Condensation of carboxylic acid and amine monomers forms *polyamides (nylons).* One of the most common is *nylon-66,* manufactured by mixing equimolar amounts of a six-C diamine (1,6-diaminohexane) and a six-C diacid (1,6-hexanedioic acid). The basic amine reacts with the acid to form a "nylon salt." Heating drives off water and forms the amide bonds:

$$n\text{HO—}\overset{\text{O}}{\overset{\|}{\text{C}}}\text{—(CH}_2)_4\text{—}\overset{\text{O}}{\overset{\|}{\text{C}}}\text{—OH} + n\text{H}_2\text{N—(CH}_2)_6\text{—NH}_2 \xrightarrow[-(2n-1)\text{H}_2\text{O}]{\Delta} \text{HO}\left[\overset{\text{O}}{\overset{\|}{\text{C}}}\text{—(CH}_2)_4\text{—}\overset{\text{O}}{\overset{\|}{\text{C}}}\text{—NH—(CH}_2)_6\text{—NH}\right]_n\text{H}$$

In the laboratory, this nylon is made without heating by using a more reactive acid component (Figure 15.28). Covalent bonds within the chains give nylons great strength, and H bonds between chains give them great flexibility (see Table 2.8, p. 69). About half of all nylons are made to reinforce automobile tires; the others are used for rugs, clothing, fishing line, and so forth.

2. *Polyesters.* Condensation of carboxylic acid and alcohol monomers form *polyesters.* Dacron, a popular polyester fiber, is woven from polymer strands formed when equimolar amounts of 1,4-benzenedicarboxylic acid and 1,2-ethanediol react. Blending these polyester fibers with various amounts of cotton gives fabrics that are durable, easily dyed, and crease resistant. Extremely thin Mylar films, used for recording tape and food packaging, are also made from this polymer.

**Variations on a Theme: Inorganic Polymers** You already know that some synthetic polymers have inorganic backbones. In Chapter 14, we discussed the silicones, polymers with the repeat unit —(R$_2$)Si—O—. Depending on the chain crosslinks and the R groups, silicones range from oily liquids to elastic sheets to rigid solids and have applications that include artificial limbs and spacesuits. Polyphosphazenes exist as flexible chains even at low temperatures and have the repeat unit —(R$_2$)P=N—.

**Figure 15.28** The formation of nylon-66. In the laboratory, the six-C diacid chloride, which is more reactive than the diacid, is used as one monomer; the polyamide forms between the two liquid phases.

## ▌ Summary of Section 15.5

- Polymers are extremely large molecules that are made of repeat units called monomers.
- Addition polymers are formed from unsaturated monomers that commonly link through free-radical reactions.
- Most condensation polymers are formed by linking monomers that each have two functional groups through a dehydration-condensation reaction.
- Reaction conditions, catalysts, and monomers can be varied to produce polymers with different properties.

## 15.6 • THE MONOMER-POLYMER THEME II: BIOLOGICAL MACROMOLECULES

The monomer-polymer theme was being played out in nature eons before humans employed it to such great advantage. Biological macromolecules are condensation polymers created by nature's reaction chemistry and improved through evolution.

These remarkable molecules are the best demonstration of the versatility of carbon and its handful of atomic partners.

*Natural polymers,* such as polysaccharides, proteins, and nucleic acids, are the "stuff of life." Some have structures that make wood strong, hair curly, fingernails hard, and wool flexible. Others speed up the myriad reactions that occur in every cell or defend the body against infection. Still others possess the genetic information organisms need to forge other biomolecules. Remarkable as these giant molecules are, the functional groups of their monomers and the reactions that link them are identical to those of other, smaller organic molecules. Moreover, as you saw in Section 13.2, the same intermolecular forces that dissolve smaller molecules stabilize these giant molecules in the aqueous medium of the cell.

## Sugars and Polysaccharides

In essence, the same chemical change occurs when you burn a piece of wood or eat a piece of bread. Wood and bread are mixtures of *carbohydrates,* substances that provide energy through oxidation.

**Monomer Structure and Linkage** Glucose and other simple sugars, from the three-C *trioses* to the seven-C *heptoses,* are called **monosaccharides** and consist of carbon chains with attached hydroxyl and carbonyl groups. In addition to their roles as individual molecules engaged in energy metabolism, they serve as the monomer units of **polysaccharides.** Most natural polysaccharides are formed from five- and six-C units. In aqueous solution, *an alcohol group and the aldehyde (or ketone) group of the same monosaccharide react with each other to form a cyclic molecule with either a five- or six-membered ring.* For example, a molecule of glucose undergoes an internal addition reaction between the aldehyde group of C-1 and the alcohol group of C-5 (Figure 15.29A).

When two monosaccharides undergo a dehydration-condensation reaction, a **disaccharide** forms. For example, sucrose (table sugar) is a disaccharide of glucose (linked at C-1) and fructose (linked at C-2) (Figure 15.29B); lactose (milk sugar) is a disaccharide of glucose (C-1) and galactose (C-4); and maltose, used in brewing and as a sweetener, is a disaccharide of two glucose units (C-1 to C-4).

**Figure 15.29** The structure of glucose in aqueous solution and the formation of a disaccharide.

Lobster shells contain a polysaccharide called *chitin*.

**Types of Polysaccharides**  A polysaccharide consists of *many* monosaccharide units linked together. The three major natural polysaccharides—cellulose, starch, and glycogen—consist entirely of glucose units, but they differ in the ring positions of the links, in the orientation of certain bonds, and in the extent of crosslinking. Some other polysaccharides contain nitrogen in their attached groups. One of these nitrogen-containing polysaccharides is chitin (pronounced "KY-tin"), the main component of the tough, brittle, external skeletons of insects and crustaceans (*see photo*).

1. *Cellulose* is the most abundant organic chemical on Earth. More than 50% of the carbon in plants occurs in the cellulose of stems and leaves; wood is largely cellulose, and cotton is more than 90% cellulose. Cellulose consists of long chains of glucose. The great strength of wood is due largely to the countless H bonds between cellulose chains. The monomers are linked in a particular way from C-1 in one unit to C-4 in the next. Humans lack the enzymes to break this link, so we cannot digest cellulose (unfortunately!); however, microorganisms in the digestive tracts of some animals, such as cows, sheep, and termites, can.

2. *Starch* is a mixture of polysaccharides of glucose and serves as an *energy store* in plants. When a plant needs energy, some starch is broken down by hydrolysis of the bonds between units, and the released glucose is oxidized through a multistep metabolic pathway. Starch occurs in plant cells as insoluble granules of amylose, a helical molecule of several thousand glucose units, and amylopectin, a highly branched, bush-like molecule of up to a million glucose units. Most of the glucose units are linked by C-1 to C-4 bonds, as in cellulose, but a different orientation around the chiral C-1 allows our digestive enzymes to break starch down into monomers. A C-6 to C-1 crosslink joins chains every 24 to 30 units.

3. *Glycogen* functions as the energy storage molecule in animals. It occurs in liver and muscle cells as large, insoluble granules consisting of glycogen molecules made from 1000 to more than 500,000 glucose units. In glycogen, these units are linked by C-1 to C-4 bonds, as in starch, but the molecule is more highly crosslinked than starch, with C-6 to C-1 crosslinks every 8 to 12 units.

## Amino Acids and Proteins

As you saw in Section 15.5, synthetic polyamides (such as nylon-66) are formed from two monomers, one with a carboxyl group at each end and the other with an amine group at each end. **Proteins,** the polyamides of nature, are unbranched polymers formed from monomers called **amino acids.** As noted in Section 13.2, *each amino acid molecule has both a carboxyl group and an amine group.*

**Monomer Structure and Linkage**  An amino acid has both its carboxyl group and its amine group attached to the α-*carbon,* the second C atom in the chain. Proteins are made up of about 20 different types of amino acids, each with its own particular R group, ranging from an H atom to a polycyclic N-containing aromatic structure (Figure 15.30). The R groups play a major role in the shape and function of the protein.

In the aqueous cell fluid, the $NH_2$ and COOH groups of amino acids are charged because the carboxyl groups each transfer an $H^+$ ion to $H_2O$ to form $H_3O^+$. These $H_3O^+$ ions transfer the $H^+$ to the amine groups. The overall process can be viewed as an intramolecular acid-base reaction:

An H atom is the third group bonded to the α-carbon, and the fourth is the R group (also called the *side chain*).

**Figure 15.30 The common amino acids.** The R groups are screened gray, and the α-carbons (*boldface*), with carboxyl and amino groups, are screened yellow. Here the amino acids are shown with the charges they have under physiological conditions.

Each amino acid is linked to the next through a *peptide (amide) bond* formed by a dehydration-condensation reaction in which the carboxyl group of one monomer reacts with the amine group of the next.

peptide bond

Therefore, as noted in Section 13.2, the polypeptide chain—the backbone of the protein—has a repeating structure that consists of an α-*carbon bonded to an amide group bonded to the next* α-*carbon bonded to the next amide group,* and so forth (see Figure 13.6, p. 483). The various R groups dangle from the α-carbons on alternate sides of the chain.

**The Hierarchy of Protein Structure** *Each type of protein has its own amino acid composition,* specific numbers and proportions of the various amino acids. However, it is not the composition that defines the protein's role in the cell; rather, *the sequence of*

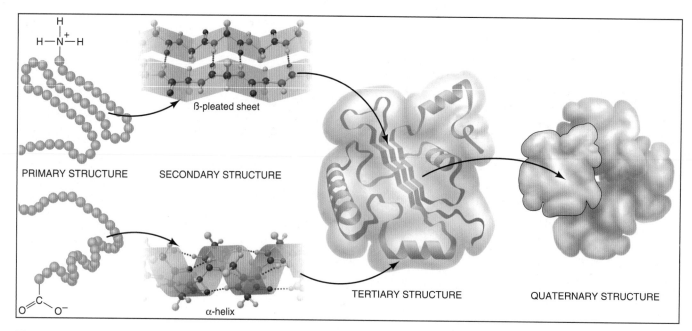

PRIMARY STRUCTURE    SECONDARY STRUCTURE    TERTIARY STRUCTURE    QUATERNARY STRUCTURE

β-pleated sheet

α-helix

**Figure 15.31** The structural hierarchy of proteins.

*amino acids determines the protein's shape and function.* Proteins range from about 50 to several thousand amino acids, yet from a purely mathematical point of view, even a small protein of 100 amino acids has a virtually limitless number of possible sequences of the 20 types of amino acids ($20^{100} \approx 10^{130}$). In fact, though, only a tiny fraction of these possibilities occur in actual proteins. For example, even in an organism as complex as a human being, there are only about $10^5$ different types of protein.

*A protein folds into its native shape as it is being synthesized in the cell.* Some shapes are simple—long helical tubes or undulating sheets. Others are far more complex—baskets, Y shapes, spheroid blobs, and countless other globular forms. Biochemists define a hierarchy for the overall structure of a protein (Figure 15.31):

1. *Primary (1°) structure,* the most basic level, refers to the sequence of covalently bonded amino acids in the polypeptide chain.
2. *Secondary (2°) structure* refers to sections of the chain that, as a result of H bonding between nearby peptide groupings, adopt shapes called α-helices and β-pleated sheets.
3. *Tertiary (3°) structure* refers to the three-dimensional folding of the whole polypeptide chain. Research shows that in many proteins, certain folding patterns form characteristic regions that play a role in the protein's function—binding a hormone, attaching to a membrane, forming a membrane channel, and so forth.
4. *Quaternary (4°) structure,* the most complex level, occurs in proteins made up of several polypeptide chains (subunits) and refers to the way the chains assemble into the overall multi-subunit protein. Hemoglobin, for example, consists of four subunits arranged as in Figure 15.31.

Note that *only the 1° structure involves covalent bonds; the 2°, 3°, and 4° structures rely primarily on intermolecular forces,* as discussed in Section 13.2.

**The Relation Between Structure and Function** Two broad classes of proteins differ in the complexity of their amino acid compositions and sequences and, therefore, in their structure and function:

1. *Fibrous proteins* have relatively simple amino acid compositions and correspondingly simple structures. They are key components of hair, wool, skin, and connective tissue—materials that require strength and flexibility. Like synthetic polymers, these proteins have a small number of different amino acids in a repeating sequence.

- *Collagen,* the most common animal protein, makes up as much as 40% of human body weight. More than 30% of its amino acids are glycine (G) and another 20% are proline (P). It is formed of three chains, each an extended helix, that wind tightly around each other. The peptide C=O groups in one chain form H bonds to the peptide N—H groups in another. The result is a long, triple-helical cable with the sequence —G—X—P—G—X—P— and so on (where X is another amino acid), as shown in Figure 15.32A. As the main protein component of tendons, skin, and blood-vessel walls, collagen has a high tensile strength; in fact, a 1-mm thick strand can support a 10-kg weight!

- In *silk fibroin,* secreted by the silk moth caterpillar, more than 85% of the amino acids are glycine, alanine, and serine (Figure 15.32B). Fibroin chain segments bend back and forth, running alongside each other, and form interchain H bonds to create a *pleated sheet.* Stacks of sheets interact through dispersion forces, which make fibroin strong and flexible but not very extendable—perfect for a silkworm's cocoon.

2. *Globular proteins* have much more complex compositions, often containing all 20 amino acids in varying proportions. As the name implies, globular proteins are typically more rounded and compact, with a wide variety of shapes and a correspondingly wide range of functions: defenders against bacterial invasion, messengers that trigger cell actions, catalysts of chemical change, membrane gatekeepers that maintain cellular concentrations, and many others.

The locations of particular amino-acid R groups are crucial to the protein's function. For example, in catalytic proteins, a few R groups form a crevice that closely matches the shape of reactant molecules. These groups typically hold the reactants through intermolecular forces and speed their reaction to products by bringing them together and twisting and stretching their bonds (Section 16.7). Experiment has established that a slight change in one of these critical R groups decreases the catalytic function dramatically. This fact supports the essential idea that *the protein's amino acid sequence determines its structure, which in turn determines its function:*

SEQUENCE $\Longrightarrow$ STRUCTURE $\Longrightarrow$ FUNCTION

Next, we'll see how the amino acid sequence of every protein in every organism is prescribed by the genetic information that is held within the organism's nucleic acids.

## Nucleotides and Nucleic Acids

An organism's nucleic acids construct its proteins. And, given that the proteins determine how the organism looks and behaves, no job could be more essential.

**Monomer Structure and Linkage** **Nucleic acids** are unbranched polymers that consist of linked monomer units called **mononucleotides,** which consist of an N-containing base, a sugar, and a phosphate group. The two types of nucleic acid, *ribonucleic acid* (RNA) and *deoxyribonucleic acid* (DNA), differ most obviously in the sugar portions of their mononucleotides. RNA contains *ribose,* a five-C sugar, and DNA contains *deoxyribose,* in which —H substitutes for —OH on the 2′ position of ribose. (Carbon atoms in the sugar portion are given numbers with a prime to distinguish them from carbon atoms in the base.)

Ribose in RNA

Deoxyribose in RNA

Attached to the sugar molecule at the 1′ carbon is one of four N-containing bases, either a pyrimidine (six-membered ring) or a purine (six- and five-membered rings sharing a side). The pyrimidines are cytosine (C), thymine (T), and uracil (U);

- Glycine
- X
- Proline

**A  Collagen**

Glycine

**B  Silk fibroin**    Alanine (or serine)

**Figure 15.32** The shapes of fibrous proteins.

**Figure 15.33** Nucleic acid precursors and their linkage.

Nucleoside triphosphate of ribonucleic acid (RNA)

Nucleoside triphosphate of deoxyribonucleic acid (DNA)

**A**

Portion of DNA polynucleotide chain

**B**

thymine occurs only in DNA and uracil occurs only in RNA. The purines are guanine (G) and adenine (A).

Cytosine (C)
DNA, RNA

Thymine (T)
DNA

Uracil (U)
RNA

Guanine (G)
DNA, RNA

Adenine (A)
DNA, RNA

A phosphate group is attached to the 5′ carbon of the sugar. The cellular precursors that form a nucleic acid are *nucleoside triphosphates* (Figure 15.33A). Dehydration-condensation reactions between them release inorganic diphosphate $(H_2P_2O_7^{2-})$ and create a phosphodiester bond between the phosphate group on the 5′ carbon of one sugar and the —OH group on the 3′ carbon of a second sugar to form a polynucleotide chain. Therefore, *the repeating pattern of the nucleic acid backbone is sugar-phosphate-sugar-phosphate,* and so on (Figure 15.33B), with the bases dangling off the chain, much as R groups dangle off the polypeptide chain of a protein.

**The Central Importance of Base Pairing** In the nucleus of the cell, DNA exists as two chains wrapped around each other in a **double helix** (Figure 15.34). The polar sugar-phosphate backbone of each DNA chain faces the watery outside and the *nonpolar bases on each chain form H bonds to each other* in the DNA core, which holds

**Figure 15.34** The double helix of DNA and a section showing base pairs.

the two chains together. A double helical DNA molecule may contain many millions of H-bonded bases in specified pairs. Two features of these **base pairs** are crucial to the structure and function of DNA:

- A pyrimidine and a purine are always paired, which gives the double helix a constant diameter.
- Each base is always paired with the same partner: A with T and G with C. Thus, *the base sequence on one chain is the complement of the sequence on the other.* For example, the sequence A—C—T on one chain is *always* paired with T—G—A on the other: A with T, C with G, and T with A.

Each DNA molecule is folded into a tangled mass that forms one of the cell's *chromosomes.* The DNA molecule is amazingly long and thin: if the largest human chromosome were stretched out, it would be 4 cm (more than 1.5 in) long; in the cell nucleus, however, it is wound into a structure only 5 nm in diameter—8 million times shorter! Segments of the DNA chains are the *genes* that contain the chemical information for synthesizing the organism's proteins.

**Protein Synthesis** *The information content of a gene resides in its base sequence.* In the **genetic code,** each base acts as a "letter," each three-base sequence as a "word," and *each word codes for a specific amino acid.* For example, the sequence C—A—C codes for the amino acid histidine, A—A—G codes for lysine, and so on. Through a complex series of interactions, greatly simplified in the overview in Figure 15.35 *(next page),* one amino acid at a time is positioned and linked to the next to gradually synthesize a protein. To fully appreciate this aspect of the chemical basis of biology, keep in mind that *this amazingly complex process occurs largely through H bonding between base pairs.*

There are two main steps in protein synthesis, transcription and translation. DNA occurs in the cell nucleus, but the genetic message is decoded outside the nucleus in

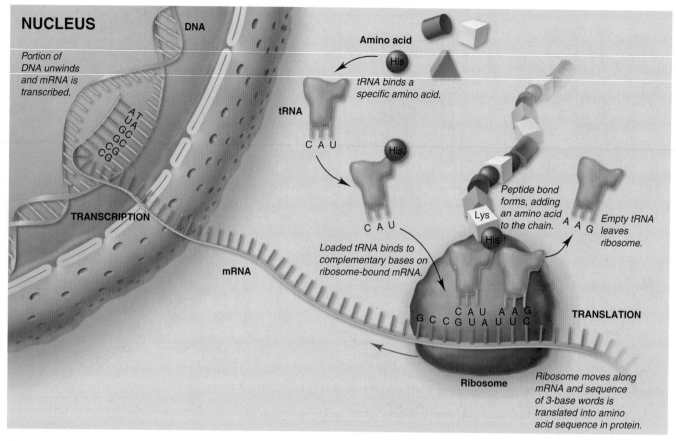

**NUCLEUS**

DNA

*Portion of DNA unwinds and mRNA is transcribed.*

Amino acid

His

*tRNA binds a specific amino acid.*

tRNA

C A U

His

**TRANSCRIPTION**

C A U

*Loaded tRNA binds to complementary bases on ribosome-bound mRNA.*

mRNA

Peptide bond forms, adding an amino acid to the chain.

Lys

His

A A G

*Empty tRNA leaves ribosome.*

C A U  A A G
G C C G U A U U C

**TRANSLATION**

**Ribosome**

*Ribosome moves along mRNA and sequence of 3-base words is translated into amino acid sequence in protein.*

**Figure 15.35** Key stages in protein synthesis.

the cytoplasm of the cell. Therefore, the information must be sent from the DNA to the synthesis site. RNA serves this messenger role.

**Transcription** is the process of producing a *messenger RNA* (mRNA) copy of the DNA information:

1. A portion of the DNA is temporarily unwound, and one chain segment acts as a template for the formation of a complementary chain of mRNA made by linking individual mononucleoside triphosphates.
2. The DNA code words are transcribed into RNA code words through base pairing. Cytosine (C) and guanine (G) are complementary bases. Adenine (A) is the complementary base for thymine (T) in DNA, and for uracil (U) in RNA.
3. The DNA rewinds, and mRNA moves out of the nucleus through pores in its membrane.

**Translation** is the process that uses the mRNA produced through transcription to synthesize the protein:

1. The mRNA binds, again through base pairing, to an RNA-rich particle in the cell called a *ribosome*, which moves along the mRNA strand.
2. *Transfer RNA* (tRNA) is used to bring amino acid molecules to the mRNA bound to the ribosome. The tRNA molecule has two key portions on opposite ends. On one end is a three-base sequence that is *the complement of a word on the mRNA*. On the opposite end is a *covalent binding site for the amino acid* that is coded by that word. So tRNA is used to "shuttle" the correct amino acid to the correct position on the mRNA.
3. The ribosome moves along the bound mRNA, one three-letter word at a time, while the tRNA molecules H-bond to the mRNA to position their amino acids near one another.
4. When a tRNA molecule attaches to the mRNA at the ribosome, it releases its amino acid, and an enzyme (not shown) catalyzes formation of a peptide bond to the growing chain of amino acids in the protein. Once empty of its amino acid, the tRNA molecule leaves the site.

In essence, then, protein synthesis involves *transcribing* the DNA three-base words into an RNA message of three-base words, and then *translating* the word, via three-base RNA carriers, into the sequence of linked amino acids that make up a protein:

DNA BASE SEQUENCE ⇒ RNA BASE SEQUENCE ⇒ PROTEIN AMINO ACID SEQUENCE

**DNA Replication**   Another complex series of interactions leads to *DNA replication,* the process in which DNA copies itself. When a cell divides, its chromosomes are replicated, or reproduced, ensuring that the new cells have the same number and types of genes. In this process (Figure 15.36):

- A small portion of the double helix is "unzipped," so each DNA chain can act as a template for a new chain.
- The bases in each DNA chain are H-bonded with the complementary bases of free mononucleoside triphosphate units.
- The new units are linked through phosphodiester bonds into a new chain in a process catalyzed by an enzyme called *DNA polymerase.*
- Gradually, each of the unzipped chains forms the complementary half of a double helix, which results in *two* double helices.

Because each base always pairs with its complement, the original double helix is copied and the genetic makeup of the cell preserved. (Base pairing is central to methods for learning the sequence of nucleotides in genes, and for analyzing evidence in criminal investigations, as the upcoming Chemical Connections essay shows.)

**Figure 15.36** Key stages in DNA replication.

## ▌ Summary of Section 15.6

- The three types of natural polymers—polysaccharides, proteins, and nucleic acids— are formed by dehydration-condensation reactions.
- Polysaccharides are formed from cyclic monosaccharides, such as glucose. Cellulose, starch, and glycogen have structural or energy-storage roles.
- Proteins are polyamides formed from as many as 20 different types of amino acids. Fibrous proteins have extended shapes and play structural roles. Globular proteins have compact shapes and play metabolic, immunologic, and hormonal roles. The amino acid sequence of a protein determines its shape and function.
- Nucleic acids (DNA and RNA) are polynucleotides consisting of four different mononucleotides. The base sequence of the DNA chain determines the sequence of amino acids in an organism's proteins. Hydrogen bonding between specific base pairs is the key to protein synthesis and DNA replication.
- DNA sequencing is used to determine the identity and order of nucleotides in a fragment of a DNA chain; DNA fingerprinting is used to identify a person from the unique pattern of repeating base sequences in his or her DNA.

Thanks to *DNA sequencing,* the process of determining the identity and order of DNA bases, we now know the sequence of the 3 billion nucleotide base pairs in the DNA of the entire human genome! Sequencing has become indispensable to molecular biology and biochemical genetics.

Just as indispensable to forensic science is *DNA fingerprinting* (or *DNA profiling*), a different process that employs similar methods. Since the discovery that portions of an individual's DNA are as unique as fingerprints, this technique has been applied in countless situations, such as identifying the remains of victims of the September 11, 2001 terrorist attacks.

## DNA Sequencing

A given chromosome in the nucleus may have 100 million nucleotide bases, but the sequencing process can only deal with DNA fragments about 2000 bases long. Therefore, the chromosome is first broken into pieces by enzymes that cleave at specific sites. Then, to obtain enough sample for analysis, the DNA is replicated through a variety of "amplification" methods, which make many copies of the individual DNA "target" fragments.

The most popular sequencing method is the *Sanger chain-termination method,* which uses chemically altered bases to stop the growth of a complementary DNA chain at specific locations. As you've learned, the chain consists of linked 2′-deoxyribonucleoside monophosphate units (dNMP, where N represents A, T, G, or C). The link is a phosphodiester bond from the 3′-OH of one unit to the 5′-OH of the next. The free monomers used to construct the chain are 2′-deoxyribonucleoside triphosphates (dNTP) (Figure B15.5A). The Sanger method uses a modified monomer, called a *di*deoxyribonucleoside triphosphate (ddNTP), in which the 3′-OH group is also missing from the ribose unit (Figure B15.5B). As soon as the ddNTP is incorporated into the growing chain, polymerization stops because there is no —OH group on the 3′ position to form a phosphodiester bond to the next dNTP unit.

The procedure is shown in Figure B15.6. After several preparation steps, the sample to be sequenced consists of single-stranded

**Figure B15.5** Nucleoside triphosphate monomers.

**Figure B15.6** Steps in the Sanger method of DNA sequencing.

DNA target fragments, each of which is attached to one strand of a double-stranded segment of DNA (Figure B15.6A). This sample is divided into four tubes, and to each tube is added a mixture of DNA polymerase, large amounts of all four dNTP's, and a small amount of one of the four ddNTP's. Thus, tube 1 contains polymerase, dATP, dGTP, dCTP, and dTTP, and, say, ddATP; tube 2 contains the same mixture, except ddGTP instead of ddATP; and so forth. After the polymerization reaction is complete, each tube contains the original target fragments paired to complementary chains of varying length (Figure B15.6B). The chain lengths vary because in tube 1, each complementary chain ends in ddA (designated **A** in the figure); in tube 2, each ends in ddG (G); in tube 3, each ends in ddC (C); and in tube 4, each ends in ddT (**T**).

Each double-stranded product is divided into single strands, and then the complementary chains are separated by means of *high-resolution polyacrylamide-gel electrophoresis*. This technique applies an electric field to separate charged species through differences in their rate of migration through pores in a gel: the smaller the species, the faster it moves. Polynucleotide fragments are commonly separated by electrophoresis because they have charged phosphate groups. High-resolution gels have pores that vary so slightly in size that they can separate fragments differing by only a single nucleotide.

In this step, each sample is applied to its own "lane" on a gel. After electrophoresis, the gel is scanned to locate the chains, which appear in bands. Because all four ddNTP's were used, all possible chain fragments are formed, so the sequence of the original DNA fragment can be determined (Figure B15.6C).

An automated approach begins with each ddNTP tagged with a different fluorescent dye that emits light of a distinct color. The entire mixture of complementary chains is introduced onto the gel and separated. The gel is scanned by a laser, which activates the dyes. The fluorescent intensity versus distance along the chain is detected and plotted by a computer (Figure B15.6D).

## DNA Fingerprinting

Modern techniques of DNA fingerprinting require less than 1 ng of DNA. Thus, in addition to blood and semen, licked stamps and envelopes, chewed gum, and clothing containing dead skin cells can also be sources of DNA.

Currently, the most successful and widely used DNA profiling procedure is called *short tandem repeat (STR) analysis*. STRs are specific areas on a chromosome that contain short (3–7 bases) sequences that repeat themselves within the DNA molecule. There are hundreds of different types of STRs, but each person has a unique number and assortment of types. Therefore, the more STRs that are characterized, the more discriminating the analysis.

Once the STRs have been amplified, they are separated by electrophoresis, and an analyst determines the number of base repeats within each STR. In Figure B15.7, stained gels containing the STRs of DNA in blood samples from several suspects are compared with those from the blood found at a crime scene. Suspect 3 has a pattern of STRs identical to that in the crime scene sample.

**Figure B15.7** STR analysis of DNA in the blood of seven suspects and that in blood found at a crime scene.

---

## Problems

**B15.4** If you were analyzing a DNA fragment with the base sequence TACAGGTTCAGT, how many complementary chain pieces would you obtain in the tube containing ddATP? In the tube containing ddCTP?

**B15.5** A DNA fragment is sequenced and the following complementary chain pieces are obtained from the four tubes:

1. The ddATP tube contains ATG and ATATG.
2. The ddTTP tube contains TG and TATG.
3. The ddCTP tube contains CATATG.
4. The ddGPT tube contains G.

What is the sequence of bases in the DNA fragment? Draw a sketch of the electrophoresis gel for this fragment similar to the one shown in Figure B15.6C.

# CHAPTER REVIEW GUIDE

## Learning Objectives
Relevant section (§) and/or sample problem (SP) numbers appear in parentheses.

### Understand These Concepts

1. How carbon's atomic properties give rise to its ability to form four strong covalent bonds, multiple bonds, and chains, which results in the great structural diversity of organic compounds (§15.1)
2. How carbon's atomic properties give rise to its ability to bond to various heteroatoms, which creates regions of charge imbalance that result in functional groups (§15.1)
3. Structures and names of alkanes, alkenes, and alkynes (§15.2)
4. The distinctions among constitutional, optical, and geometric isomers (§15.2)
5. The importance of optical isomerism in organisms (§15.2)
6. The effect of restricted rotation around a $\pi$ bond on the structures and properties of alkenes (§15.2)
7. The nature of organic addition, elimination, and substitution reactions (§15.3)
8. The properties and reaction types of the various functional groups (§15.4):
   • Substitution and elimination for alcohols, alkyl halides, and amines
   • Addition for alkenes, alkynes, and aldehydes and ketones
   • Substitution for the carboxylic acid family (acids, esters, and amides)
9. Why delocalization of electrons causes aromatic rings to have lower reactivity than alkenes (§15.4)
10. The polarity of the carbonyl bond and the importance of organometallic compounds in addition reactions of carbonyl compounds (§15.4)
11. How addition plus elimination lead to substitution in the reactions of the carboxylic acid family (§15.4)
12. How addition and condensation polymers form (§15.5)
13. The three types of biopolymers and their monomers (§15.6)

14. How amino acid sequence determines protein shape, which determines function (§15.6)
15. How complementary base pairing controls the processes of protein synthesis and DNA replication (§15.6)
16. How DNA base sequence determines RNA base sequence, which determines amino acid sequence (§15.6)

### Master These Skills

1. Drawing hydrocarbon structures given the number(s) of C atoms, multiple bonds, and rings (SP 15.1)
2. Naming hydrocarbons and drawing expanded, condensed, and carbon skeleton formulas (§15.2 and SP 15.2)
3. Drawing geometric isomers and identifying chiral centers of molecules (SP 15.2)
4. Recognizing the type of organic reaction from the structures of reactants and products (SP 15.3)
5. Recognizing an organic reaction as an oxidation or reduction from the structures of reactants and products (§15.3)
6. Determining reactants and products in reactions of alcohols, alkyl halides, and amines (SP 15.4 and Follow-Up)
7. Determining the products in a stepwise reaction sequence (SP 15.5)
8. Determining the reactants in reactions involving aldehydes and ketones (Follow-Up Problem 15.5)
9. Determining reactants and products in reactions of the carboxylic acid family (SP 15.6 and Follow-Up)
10. Recognizing and naming the functional groups in organic molecules (SP 15.7)
11. Drawing an abbreviated synthetic polymer structure based on monomer structures (§15.5)
12. Drawing small peptides from amino acid structures (§15.6)
13. Using the base-paired sequence of one DNA strand to predict the sequence of the other (§15.6)

## Key Terms
Page numbers appear in parentheses.

**Introduction**
organic compounds (571)

**Section 15.1**
catenation (572)
heteroatom (573)
functional group (573)

**Section 15.2**
hydrocarbon (574)
alkane ($C_nH_{2n+2}$) (576)
homologous series (576)
saturated hydrocarbon (576)
cyclic hydrocarbon (578)
isomers (579)
constitutional (structural) isomers (579)
stereoisomers (580)
optical isomers (580)

chiral molecule (580)
polarimeter (581)
optically active (581)
alkene ($C_nH_{2n}$) (582)
unsaturated hydrocarbon (582)
geometric (cis-trans) isomers (582)
alkyne ($C_nH_{2n-2}$) (583)
aromatic hydrocarbon (584)
nuclear magnetic resonance (NMR) spectroscopy (586)

**Section 15.3**
alkyl group (588)
addition reaction (588)
elimination reaction (589)
substitution reaction (589)

**Section 15.4**
alcohol (591)
haloalkane (alkyl halide) (593)
amine (594)
carbonyl group (597)
aldehyde (597)
ketone (597)
organometallic compound (598)
carboxylic acid (599)
ester (599)
amide (599)
fatty acid (599)
acid anhydride (600)
lipid (600)
hydrolysis (600)
nitrile (603)

**Section 15.5**
addition polymer (604)
condensation polymer (606)

**Section 15.6**
monosaccharide (607)
polysaccharide (607)
disaccharide (607)
protein (608)
amino acid (608)
nucleic acid (611)
mononucleotide (611)
double helix (612)
base pair (613)
genetic code (613)
transcription (614)
translation (614)

# Brief Solutions to Follow-Up Problems

**15.1** (a)

(b)

**15.2** (a) $CH_3-CH_2-CH_2-CH_2-CH_2-\underset{\underset{CH_3}{|}}{\overset{\overset{CH_2-CH_3}{|}}{C}}-CH_2-CH_3$

(b)

and

(c) $HC\equiv C-\underset{\underset{CH_2-CH_3}{|}}{\overset{\overset{CH_2-CH_3}{|}}{C}}-CH_2-CH_2-CH_3$

(d)

**15.3** (a) $CH_3-CH=CH-CH_3 + Cl_2 \longrightarrow$

$CH_3-\underset{\underset{Cl}{|}}{\overset{\overset{Cl}{|}}{CH}}-CH-CH_3$

(b) $CH_3-CH_2-CH_2-Br + OH^- \longrightarrow$

$CH_3-CH_2-CH_2-OH + Br^-$

(c)

**15.4** (a) $CH_3-\underset{\underset{Cl}{|}}{CH}-\underset{\overset{CH_3}{|}}{CH}-CH_3$ or $CH_3-CH_2-\underset{\underset{Cl}{|}}{\overset{\overset{CH_3}{|}}{C}}-CH_3$

(b) $CH_3-CH_2-CH_2-OH$

**15.5** (a)

(b)

**15.6** (a)

(b) $CH_3-CH_2-CH_2-\overset{\overset{O}{\|}}{C}-O-CH_3 + CH_3-CH_2-NH_2$

**15.7** (a)

alkene   aldehyde

(b)

amide   haloalkane

# PROBLEMS

Problems with **colored** numbers are answered in Appendix E and worked in detail in the Student Solutions Manual. Problem sections match those in the text and provide the numbers of relevant sample problems. Most offer Concept Review Questions, Skill-Building Exercises (grouped in pairs covering the same concept), and Problems in Context. The Comprehensive Problems are based on material from any section or previous chapter.

## The Special Nature of Carbon and the Characteristics of Organic Molecules

### Concept Review Questions

**15.1** Give the names and formulas of two carbon compounds that are organic and two that are inorganic.

**15.2** Explain each statement in terms of atomic properties:
(a) Carbon engages in covalent rather than ionic bonding.
(b) Carbon has four bonds in all its organic compounds.
(c) Carbon forms neither stable cations, like many metals, nor stable anions, like many nonmetals.
(d) Carbon bonds to itself more extensively than does any other element.
(e) Carbon forms stable multiple bonds.

**15.3** Carbon bonds to many elements other than itself.
(a) Name six elements that commonly bond to carbon in organic compounds.
(b) Which of these elements are heteroatoms?
(c) Which of these elements are more electronegative than carbon? Less electronegative?
(d) How does bonding of carbon to heteroatoms increase the number of organic compounds?

**15.4** Silicon lies just below carbon in Group 4A(14) and also forms four covalent bonds. Why aren't there as many silicon compounds as carbon compounds?

**15.5** What is the range of oxidation states for carbon? Name a compound in which carbon has its highest oxidation state and one in which it has its lowest.

**15.6** Which of these bonds to carbon would you expect to be relatively reactive: C—H, C—C, C—I, C=O, C—Li? Explain.

## The Structures and Classes of Hydrocarbons
(Sample Problems 15.1 and 15.2)

### Concept Review Questions

**15.7** (a) What structural feature is associated with each type of hydrocarbon: alkane, cycloalkane, alkene, and alkyne?
(b) Give the general formula for each type.
(c) Which hydrocarbons are considered saturated?

**15.8** Define each type of isomer: (a) constitutional; (b) geometric; (c) optical. Which types of isomers are stereoisomers?

**15.9** Among alkenes, alkynes, and aromatic hydrocarbons, only alkenes exhibit *cis-trans* isomerism. Why don't the others?

**15.10** Which objects are asymmetric (have no plane of symmetry): (a) a circular clock face; (b) a football; (c) a dime; (d) a brick; (e) a hammer; (f) a spring?

**15.11** Explain how a polarimeter works and what it measures.

**15.12** How does an aromatic hydrocarbon differ from a cycloalkane in terms of its bonding? How does this difference affect structure?

## Skill-Building Exercises (grouped in similar pairs)

**15.13** Draw all possible skeletons for a 7-C compound with
(a) A 6-C chain and 1 double bond
(b) A 5-C chain and 1 double bond
(c) A 5-C ring and no double bonds

**15.14** Draw all possible skeletons for a 6-C compound with
(a) A 5-C chain and 2 double bonds
(b) A 5-C chain and 1 triple bond
(c) A 4-C ring and no double bonds

**15.15** Add the correct number of hydrogens to each of the skeletons in Problem 15.13.

**15.16** Add the correct number of hydrogens to each of the skeletons in Problem 15.14.

**15.17** Draw correct structures, by making a single change, for any that are incorrect:

(a)   (b) $CH_3=CH-CH_2-CH_3$

(c)   (d)

**15.18** Draw correct structures, by making a single change, for any that are incorrect:

(a) $CH_3-CH=CH-CH_2-CH_3$   (b)

(c) $CH_3-C\equiv CH-CH_2-CH_3$   (d)

**15.19** Draw the structure or give the name of each compound:
(a) 2,3-dimethyloctane   (b) 1-ethyl-3-methylcyclohexane

(c)   (d)

**15.20** Draw the structure or give the name of each compound:

(a)   (b)

(c) 1,2-diethylcyclopentane   (d) 2,4,5-trimethylnonane

**15.21** Each of the following names is wrong. Draw structures based on them, and correct the names:
(a) 4-methylhexane          (b) 2-ethylpentane
(c) 2-methylcyclohexane     (d) 3,3-methyl-4-ethyloctane

**15.22** Each of the following names is wrong. Draw structures based on them, and correct the names:

(a) 3,3-dimethylbutane          (b) 1,1,1-trimethylheptane
(c) 1,4-diethylcyclopentane     (d) 1-propylcyclohexane

**15.23** Each of the following compounds can exhibit optical activity. Circle the chiral center(s) in each:

(a)

(b)

**15.24** Each of the following compounds can exhibit optical activity. Circle the chiral center(s) in each:

(a)

(b)

**15.25** Draw structures from the following names, and determine which compounds are optically active:
(a) 3-bromohexane          (b) 3-chloro-3-methylpentane
(c) 1,2-dibromo-2-methylbutane

**15.26** Draw structures from the following names, and determine which compounds are optically active:
(a) 1,3-dichloropentane     (b) 3-chloro-2,2,5-trimethylhexane
(c) 1-bromo-1-chlorobutane

**15.27** Which of the following structures exhibit geometric isomerism? Draw and name the two isomers in each case:

(a)   $CH_3-CH_2-CH=CH-CH_3$          (b)

(c)   $CH_3-C=CH-CH-CH_2-CH_3$
with $CH_3$ substituents

**15.28** Which of the following structures exhibit geometric isomerism? Draw and name the two isomers in each case:

(a) $CH_3-C-CH=CH-CH_3$ (with two $CH_3$)          (b)

(c) $Cl-CH_2-CH=C-CH_2-CH_2-CH_2-CH_3$ (with $CH_3$)

**15.29** Which compounds exhibit geometric isomerism? Draw and name the two isomers in each case:
(a) propene                (b) 3-hexene
(c) 1,1-dichloroethene     (d) 1,2-dichloroethene

**15.30** Which compounds exhibit geometric isomerism? Draw and name the two isomers in each case:
(a) 1-pentene              (b) 2-pentene
(c) 1-chloropropene        (d) 2-chloropropene

**15.31** Draw and name all the constitutional isomers of dichlorobenzene.

**15.32** Draw and name all the constitutional isomers of trimethylbenzene.

**Problems in Context**

**15.33** Butylated hydroxytoluene (BHT) is a common preservative added to cereals and other dry foods. Its systematic name is 1-hydroxy-2,6-di-*tert*-butyl-4-methylbenzene (where "*tert*-butyl" is 1,1-dimethylethyl). Draw the structure of BHT.

**15.34** There are two compounds with the name 2-methyl-3-hexene, but only one with the name 2-methyl-2-hexene. Explain with structures.

**15.35** Any tetrahedral atom with four different groups attached can be a chiral center. Which of these species is optically active?
(a) CHClBrF            (b) $NBrCl_2H^+$
(c) $PFClBrI^+$        (d) SeFClBrH

**15.36** Breaking the C=C π bond in the molecule retinal in the eye requires approximately 250 kJ/mol of energy. Find the longest wavelength (in nm) of visible light that has the energy to break the π bond.

## Some Important Classes of Organic Reactions
(Sample Problem 15.3)

**Concept Review Questions**

**15.37** In terms of numbers of reactant and product substances, which organic reaction type corresponds to (a) a combination reaction, (b) a decomposition reaction, (c) a displacement reaction?

**15.38** The same type of bond is broken in an addition reaction and formed in an elimination reaction. Name the type.

**15.39** Can a redox reaction also be an addition, elimination, or substitution reaction? Explain with examples.

**Skill-Building Exercises** (grouped in similar pairs)

**15.40** Determine the type of each of the following reactions:

(a) $CH_3-CH_2-CH(Br)-CH_3 \xrightarrow[\Delta]{NaOH}$
$CH_3-CH=CH-CH_3 + NaBr + H_2O$

(b) $CH_3-CH=CH-CH_2-CH_3 + H_2 \xrightarrow{Pt}$
$CH_3-CH_2-CH_2-CH_2-CH_3$

**15.41** Determine the type of each of the following reactions:

(a) $CH_3-CH(=O) + HCN \longrightarrow CH_3-CH(OH)-CN$

(b) $CH_3-C(=O)-O-CH_3 + CH_3-NH_2 \xrightarrow{H^+}$
$CH_3-C(=O)-NH-CH_3 + CH_3-OH$

**15.42** Write equations for the following: (a) an addition reaction between $H_2O$ and 3-hexene ($H^+$ is a catalyst); (b) an elimination reaction between 2-bromopropane and hot potassium ethoxide, $CH_3-CH_2-OK$ (KBr and ethanol are also products); (c) a light-induced substitution reaction between $Cl_2$ and ethane to form 1,1-dichloroethane.

**15.43** Write equations for the following: (a) a substitution reaction between 2-bromopropane and KI; (b) an addition reaction between cyclohexene and $Cl_2$; (c) an addition reaction between 2-propanone and $H_2$ (Ni metal is a catalyst).

**15.44** Based on the number of bonds and the nature of the bonded atoms, state whether each of the following changes is an oxidation or a reduction:

(a) $=CH_2$ becomes $—CH_2—OH$

(b) $=CH—$ becomes $—CH_2—$

(c) $\equiv C—$ becomes $—CH_2—$

**15.45** Based on the number of bonds and the nature of the bonded atoms, state whether each of the following changes is an oxidation or a reduction:

(a) $—\overset{|}{\underset{|}{C}}—OH$ becomes $—C=O$

(b) $—CH_2—OH$ becomes $=CH_2$

(c) $—\overset{O}{\overset{||}{C}}—\overset{|}{\underset{|}{C}}—$ becomes $—\overset{O}{\overset{||}{C}}—O—$

**15.46** Is the organic reactant oxidized, reduced, or neither in each of the following reactions?

(a) 2-hexene $\xrightarrow[\text{cold OH}]{\text{KMnO}_4}$ 2,3-dihydroxyhexane

(b) cyclohexane $\xrightarrow[\text{catalyst}]{\Delta}$ benzene + $3H_2$

**15.47** Is the organic reactant oxidized, reduced, or neither in each of the following reactions?

(a) 1-butyne + $H_2$ $\xrightarrow{\text{Pt}}$ 1-butene

(b) toluene $\xrightarrow[\text{H}_3\text{O}^+, \Delta]{\text{KMnO}_4}$ benzoic acid

### Problems in Context

**15.48** Phenylethylamine is a natural substance that is structurally similar to amphetamine. It is found in sources as diverse as almond oil and human urine, where it occurs at elevated concentrations as a result of stress and certain forms of schizophrenia. One method of synthesizing the compound for pharmacological and psychiatric studies involves two steps:

Classify each step as an addition, elimination, or substitution.

### Properties and Reactivities of Common Functional Groups
(Sample Problems 15.4 to 15.7)

### Concept Review Questions

**15.49** Compounds with nearly identical molar masses often have very different physical properties. Choose the compound with the higher value for each of the following properties, and explain your choice.
(a) Solubility in water: chloroethane or methylethylamine
(b) Melting point: diethyl ether or 1-butanol
(c) Boiling point: trimethylamine or propylamine

**15.50** Fill in each blank with a general formula for the type of compound formed:

**15.51** Of the three major types of organic reactions, which do *not* occur readily with benzene? Why?

**15.52** Why does the $C=O$ group react differently from the $C=C$ group? Show an example of the difference.

**15.53** Many substitution reactions are initiated by electrostatic attraction between reactants. Show where this attraction arises in the formation of an amide from an amine and an ester.

**15.54** Although both carboxylic acids and alcohols contain an $—OH$ group, one is acidic in water and the other is not. Explain.

**15.55** What reaction type is common to the formation of esters and acid anhydrides? What is the other product?

**15.56** Both alcohols and carboxylic acids undergo substitution, but the processes are very different. Explain.

### Skill-Building Exercises (grouped in similar pairs)

**15.57** Name the type of organic compound from each description of the functional group: (a) polar group that has only single bonds and does not include O or N; (b) group that is polar and has a triple bond; (c) group that has single and double bonds and is acidic in water; (d) group that has a double bond and must be at the end of a C chain.

**15.58** Name the type of organic compound from each description of the functional group: (a) N-containing group with single and double bonds; (b) group that is not polar and has a double bond; (c) polar group that has a double bond and cannot be at the end of a C chain; (d) group that has only single bonds and is basic in water.

**15.59** Circle and name the functional group(s) in each compound:

(a) $CH_3—CH=CH—CH_2—OH$  (b) $Cl—CH_2—\underset{}{\bigcirc}—\overset{O}{\overset{||}{C}}—OH$

(c)  (d) $N\equiv C—CH_2—\overset{}{\underset{\overset{||}{O}}{C}}—CH_3$

(e)

**15.60** Circle and name the functional group(s) in each compound:

(a)  (b) $I—CH_2—CH_2—C\equiv CH$

(c) $CH_2=CH—CH_2—\overset{O}{\overset{||}{C}}—O—CH_3$  (d) $CH_3—NH—\overset{O}{\overset{||}{C}}—\overset{O}{\overset{||}{C}}—O—CH_3$

(e) $CH_3—\overset{Br}{\underset{|}{CH}}—CH=CH—CH_2—NH—CH_3$

**15.61** Draw all alcohols with the formula $C_5H_{12}O$.

**15.62** Draw all aldehydes and ketones with the formula $C_5H_{10}O$.

**15.63** Draw all amines with the formula $C_4H_{11}N$.

**15.64** Draw all carboxylic acids with the formula $C_5H_{10}O_2$.

**15.65** Draw the product resulting from mild oxidation of (a) 2-butanol; (b) 2-methylpropanal; (c) cyclopentanol.

**15.66** Draw the alcohol you'd oxidize to produce (a) 2-methylpropanal; (b) 2-pentanone; (c) 3-methylbutanoic acid.

**15.67** Draw the organic product formed when the following compounds undergo a substitution reaction: (a) acetic acid and methylamine; (b) butanoic acid and 2-propanol; (c) formic acid and 2-methyl-1-propanol.

**15.68** Draw the organic product formed when the following compounds undergo a substitution reaction: (a) acetic acid and 1-hexanol; (b) propanoic acid and dimethylamine; (c) ethanoic acid and diethylamine.

**15.69** Draw condensed formulas for the carboxylic acid and alcohol that form the following esters:

(a)

(b)

(c) $CH_3-CH_2-O-\overset{O}{\underset{||}{C}}-CH_2-CH_2-$

**15.70** Draw condensed formulas for the carboxylic acid and amine that form the following amides:

(a) $H_3C-$⟨⟩$-CH_2-\overset{O}{\underset{||}{C}}-NH_2$

(b)

(c) $H\overset{O}{\underset{||}{C}}-NH-$⟨⟩

**15.71** Fill in the expected organic substances:

(a) $CH_3-CH_2-Br \xrightarrow{OH^-}$ ____ $\xrightarrow[H^+]{CH_3-CH_2-\overset{O}{\underset{||}{C}}-OH}$ ____

(b) $CH_3-CH_2-\overset{Br}{\underset{|}{CH}}-CH_3 \xrightarrow{CN^-}$ ____ $\xrightarrow{H_3O^+,\ H_2O}$ ____

**15.72** Fill in the expected organic substances:

(a) $CH_3-CH_2-CH=CH_2 \xrightarrow{H^+,\ H_2O}$ ____ $\xrightarrow{Cr_2O_7^{2-},\ H^+}$ ____

(b) $CH_3-CH_2-\overset{O}{\underset{||}{C}}-CH_3 \xrightarrow{CH_3-CH_2-Li} \xrightarrow{H_2O}$ ____

**15.73** Supply the missing organic and/or inorganic substances:

(a) $CH_3-CH_2-OH +$ ___?___ $\xrightarrow{H_3O^+,\ H_2O}$
$CH_3-CH_2-O-\overset{O}{\underset{||}{C}}-CH_2-CH_3$

(b) $CH_3-\overset{O}{\underset{||}{C}}-O-CH_3 \xrightarrow{?} CH_3-CH_2-NH-\overset{O}{\underset{||}{C}}-CH_3$

**15.74** Supply the missing organic and/or inorganic substances:

(a) $CH_3-\overset{Cl}{\underset{|}{CH}}-CH_3 \xrightarrow{?} CH_3-CH=CH_2 \xrightarrow{?} CH_3-\overset{Br}{\underset{|}{CH}}-\overset{Br}{\underset{|}{CH_2}}$

(b)
$CH_3-CH_2-CH_2-OH \xrightarrow{?} CH_3-CH_2-\overset{O}{\underset{||}{C}}-OH +$ ___?___ $\xrightarrow{?}$
$CH_3-CH_2-\overset{O}{\underset{||}{C}}-O-CH_2-$⟨⟩

**Problems in Context**

**15.75** (a) Draw the four isomers of $C_5H_{12}O$ that can be oxidized to an aldehyde. (b) Draw the three isomers of $C_5H_{12}O$ that can be oxidized to a ketone. (c) Draw the isomers of $C_5H_{12}O$ that cannot be easily oxidized to an aldehyde or ketone. (d) Name any isomer that is an alcohol.

**15.76** Ethyl formate ($H\overset{O}{\underset{||}{C}}-O-CH_2-CH_3$) is added to foods to give them the flavor of rum. How would you synthesize ethyl formate from ethanol, methanol, and any inorganic reagents?

## The Monomer-Polymer Theme I: Synthetic Macromolecules

**Concept Review Questions**

**15.77** Name the reaction processes that lead to the two types of synthetic polymers.

**15.78** Which functional group occurs in the monomers of addition polymers? How are these polymers different from one another?

**15.79** What is a free radical? How is it involved in polymer formation?

**15.80** Which intermolecular force is primarily responsible for the different types of polyethylene? Explain.

**15.81** Which of the two types of synthetic polymer is more similar chemically to biopolymers? Explain.

**15.82** Which functional groups react to form nylons? Polyesters?

**Skill-Building Exercises** (grouped in similar pairs)

**15.83** Draw an abbreviated structure for the following polymers, with brackets around the repeat unit:

(a) Poly(vinyl chloride) (PVC) from

(b) Polypropylene from

**15.84** Draw an abbreviated structure for the following polymers, with brackets around the repeat unit:
(a) Teflon from　　(b) Polystyrene from

**Problems in Context**

**15.85** Polyethylene terephthalate (PET) is used to make synthetic fibers, such as Dacron, thin films, such as Mylar, and bottles for carbonated beverages.

PET

PET is produced from ethylene glycol and either of two monomers, depending on whether the reaction proceeds by dehydration-condensation or by displacement. Write equations for the two syntheses. (*Hint:* The displacement is reversed by adding methanol to PET at high *T* and *P*.)

**15.86** Write a balanced equation for the reaction of dihydroxydimethylsilane (*right*) to form the condensation polymer known as Silly Putty.

$$\text{HO-Si-OH}\quad\overset{\displaystyle CH_3}{\underset{\displaystyle CH_3}{|}}$$

## The Monomer-Polymer Theme II: Biological Macromolecules

### Concept Review Questions

**15.87** Which type of polymer is formed from each of the following monomers: (a) amino acids; (b) alkenes; (c) simple sugars; (d) mononucleotides?

**15.88** What is the key structural difference between fibrous and globular proteins? How is it related, in general, to the proteins' amino acid composition?

**15.89** Protein shape, function, and amino acid sequence are interrelated. Which determines which?

**15.90** What linkage joins the monomers in each strand of DNA?

**15.91** What is base pairing? How does it pertain to DNA structure?

**15.92** RNA base sequence, protein amino acid sequence, and DNA base sequence are interrelated. Which determines which in the process of protein synthesis?

### Skill-Building Exercises (grouped in similar pairs)

**15.93** Draw the R group of (a) alanine; (b) histidine; (c) methionine.

**15.94** Draw the R group of (a) glycine; (b) isoleucine; (c) tyrosine.

**15.95** Draw the structure of each of the following tripeptides:
(a) Aspartic acid-histidine-tryptophan
(b) Glycine-cysteine-tyrosine with the charges that exist in cell fluid

**15.96** Draw the structure of each of the following tripeptides:
(a) Lysine-phenylalanine-threonine
(b) Alanine-leucine-valine with the charges that exist in cell fluid

**15.97** Write the sequence of the complementary DNA strand that pairs with each of the following DNA base sequences:
(a) TTAGCC          (b) AGACAT

**15.98** Write the sequence of the complementary DNA strand that pairs with each of the following DNA base sequences:
(a) GGTTAC          (b) CCCGAA

**15.99** Write the base sequence of the DNA template from which this RNA sequence was derived: UGUUACGGA. How many amino acids are coded for in this sequence?

**15.100** Write the base sequence of the DNA template from which this RNA sequence was derived: GUAUCAAUGAACUUG. How many amino acids are coded for in this sequence?

### Problems in Context

**15.101** Protein shapes are maintained by a variety of forces that arise from interactions between the amino-acid R groups. Name the amino acid that possesses each R group and the force that could arise in each of the following interactions:
(a) $-CH_2-SH$ with $HS-CH_2-$

(b) $-(CH_2)_4-NH_3^+$ with $^-O-\overset{\displaystyle O}{\overset{\displaystyle \|}{C}}-CH_2-$

(c) $-CH_2-\overset{\displaystyle O}{\overset{\displaystyle \|}{C}}-NH_2$ with $HO-CH_2-$

(d) $-\overset{\displaystyle CH_3}{\overset{\displaystyle |}{CH}}-CH_3$ with $\langle\!\langle\bigcirc\rangle\!\rangle-CH_2-$

**15.102** Amino acids have an average molar mass of 100 g/mol. How many bases on a single strand of DNA are needed to code for a protein with a molar mass of $5\times10^5$ g/mol?

### Comprehensive Problems

**15.103** Ethers (general formula R—O—R′) have many important uses. Until recently, methyl *tert*-butyl ether (MTBE, *right*) was used as an octane booster and fuel additive for gasoline. It increases the oxygen content of the fuel, which reduces CO emissions. MTBE is synthesized by the catalyzed reaction of 2-methylpropene with methanol.

(a) Write a balanced equation for the synthesis of MTBE. (*Hint:* Alcohols add to alkenes similarly to the way water does.)
(b) If the government required that auto fuel mixtures contain 2.7% oxygen by mass to reduce CO emissions, how many grams of MTBE would have to be added to each 100. g of gasoline?
(c) How many liters of MTBE would be in each liter of fuel mixture? (The density of both gasoline and MTBE is 0.740 g/mL.)
(d) How many liters of air (21% $O_2$ by volume) are needed at 24°C and 1.00 atm to fully combust 1.00 L of MTBE?

**15.104** An alcohol is oxidized to a carboxylic acid, and 0.2003 g of the acid is titrated with 45.25 mL of 0.03811 *M* NaOH. (a) What is the molar mass of the acid? (b) What are the molar mass and molecular formula of the alcohol?

**15.105** Some of the most useful compounds for organic synthesis are Grignard reagents (general formula R—MgX, where X is a halogen), which are made by combining an alkyl halide, R—X, with Mg. They are used to change the carbon skeleton of a starting carbonyl compound in a reaction similar to that with R—Li:

$$R'-\overset{\displaystyle O}{\overset{\displaystyle \|}{C}}-R'' + R-MgBr \longrightarrow R'-\overset{\displaystyle OMgBr}{\underset{\displaystyle R}{\overset{\displaystyle |}{\underset{|}{C}}}}-R'' \xrightarrow{H_2O}$$

$$R'-\overset{\displaystyle OH}{\underset{\displaystyle R}{\overset{\displaystyle |}{\underset{|}{C}}}}-R'' + Mg(OH)Br$$

(a) What is the product, after a final step with water, of the reaction between ethanal and the Grignard reagent of bromobenzene? (b) What is the product, after a final step with water, of the reaction between 2-butanone and the Grignard reagent of 2-bromopropane? (c) There are often two (or more) combinations of Grignard reagent and carbonyl compound that will give the same product. Choose another pair of reactants to give the product in (a). (d) What carbonyl compound must react with a Grignard reagent to yield a product with the —OH group at the *end* of the carbon chain? (e) What Grignard reagent and carbonyl compound would you use to prepare 2-methyl-2-butanol?

**15.106** Starting with the given organic reactant and any necessary inorganic reagents, explain how you would perform each of the following syntheses:

(a) From $CH_3-CH_2-CH_2-OH$, make $CH_3-\overset{\displaystyle Br}{\overset{\displaystyle |}{CH}}-CH_2-Br$

(b) From $CH_3-CH_2-CH_2-OH$, make $CH_3-\overset{\overset{\displaystyle O}{\|}}{C}-O-CH_2-CH_3$

**15.107** Compound A, composed of C, H, and O, is heated in a 1.00-L flask to 160.°C until all of the A has vaporized and displaced the air. The flask is then cooled, and 2.48 g of A remains. When 0.500 g of A burns in $O_2$, 0.409 g of $H_2O$ and 1.00 g of $CO_2$ are produced. Compound A is not acidic, but it can be oxidized to compound B, which is weakly acidic: 1.000 g of B is neutralized with 33.9 mL of 0.5 M sodium hydroxide. When B is heated to 260°C, it gives off water and forms C, whose solution in $CDCl_3$ (where D is deuterium, $^2H$) has one peak in its $^1H$-NMR spectrum. (a) What are the structures of A, B, and C? (b) Compound A is a controlled substance because it is metabolized to the weakly acidic "date rape" drug GHB, $C_4H_8O_3$. What are the structure and name of GHB?

**15.108** Cadaverine (1,5-diaminopentane) and putrescine (1,4-diaminobutane) are two compounds that are formed by bacterial action and are responsible for the odor of rotting flesh. Draw their structures. Suggest a series of reactions to synthesize putrescine from 1,2-dibromoethane and any inorganic reagents.

**15.109** Pyrethrins, such as jasmolin II (*below*), are a group of natural compounds synthesized by flowers of the genus *Chrysanthemum* (known as pyrethrum flowers) to act as insecticides.
(a) Circle and name the functional groups in jasmolin II.
(b) What is the hybridization of the numbered carbons?
(c) Which, if any, of the numbered carbons are chiral centers?

**15.110** Compound A is branched and optically active and contains C, H, and O. (a) A 0.500-g sample burns in excess $O_2$ to yield 1.25 g of $CO_2$ and 0.613 g of $H_2O$. Determine the empirical formula. (b) When 0.225 g of compound A vaporizes at 755 torr and 97°C, the vapor occupies 78.0 mL. Determine the molecular formula. (c) Careful oxidation of the compound yields a ketone. Name and draw compound A, and circle the chiral center.

**15.111** Ibuprofen is one of the most common anti-inflammatory drugs. (a) Identify the functional group(s) and chiral center(s) in ibuprofen. (b) Write a four-step synthesis of a racemic mixture of ibuprofen from 4-isobutylbenzaldehyde, using inorganic reactants and one organometallic reactant (see Problem 15.105).

ibuprofen                4-isobutylbenzaldehyde

**15.112** Which features of retinal make it so useful as a photon absorber in the visual systems of organisms?

**15.113** The polypeptide chain in proteins does not exhibit free rotation because of the partial double-bond character of the peptide bond. Explain this fact with resonance structures.

**15.114** Other nonmetals form compounds that are structurally analogous to those of carbon, but these inorganic compounds are usually more reactive. Predict any missing products and write balanced equations for each reaction: (a) the decomposition and chlorination of diborane to boron trichloride; (b) the combustion of pentaborane ($B_5H_9$) in $O_2$; (c) the hydrolysis of trisilane ($Si_3H_8$) to silica ($SiO_2$) and $H_2$; (d) the complete halogenation of disilane with $Cl_2$; (e) the thermal decomposition of $H_2S_5$ to hydrogen sulfide and sulfur molecules; (f) the hydrolysis of $PCl_5$.

**15.115** In addition to their use in water treatment, ion-exchange resins are used to extract Au, Ag, and Pt ions from solution. One of the most common resins consists of a polymer with a benzene-containing backbone to which sulfonic acid groups ($-SO_3H$) are added. (a) What monomer can be used to prepare the polymer backbone? (b) This polymer typically contains 4–16% crosslinking. Draw the structure of the benzene-containing monomer used to crosslink the polymer.

**15.116** Complete hydrolysis of a 100.00-g sample of a peptide gave the following amounts of individual amino acids (molar masses, in g/mol, appear in parentheses):

3.00 g of glycine (75.07)        0.90 g of alanine (89.10)
3.70 g of valine (117.15)        6.90 g of proline (115.13)
7.30 g of serine (105.10)        86.00 g of arginine (174.21)

(a) Why does the total mass of amino acids exceed the mass of peptide? (b) What are the relative numbers of amino acids in the peptide? (c) What is the minimum molar mass of the peptide?

**15.117** 2-Butanone is reduced by hydride ion donors, such as sodium borohydride ($NaBH_4$), to the alcohol 2-butanol. Even though the alcohol has a chiral center, the product isolated from the redox reaction is not optically active. Explain.

**15.118** Wastewater from a cheese factory has the following composition: 8.0 g/L protein ($C_{16}H_{24}O_5N_4$); 12 g/L carbohydrate ($CH_2O$); and 2.0 g/L fat ($C_8H_{16}O$). What is the total organic carbon (TOC) of the wastewater in g of C/L?

**15.119** Structures A, B, and C show the three common forms of vitamin A. (a) Match each structure with the correct vitamin A compound: retinal (an aldehyde), retinol (an alcohol), and retinoic acid (a carboxylic acid). (b) Retinal, the molecule responsible for the chemistry of vision, can be converted to retinol or to retinoic acid. Identify each of these reactions as a reduction or an oxidation. (c) Structure D is that of beta-carotene, found in carrots. Suggest a reason for the importance of beta-carotene in the vision process.

# Kinetics: Rates and Mechanisms of Chemical Reactions

## Concepts and skills to review before you study this chapter

- influence of temperature on molecular speed and collision frequency (Section 5.5)

You are in a small, thermoregulatory minority. About 85% of animal species—all reptiles and most amphibians, insects, and fish—rely predominantly on heat from the environment to maintain the speeds of the reactions that keep them alive. Only mammals (like us) and birds generate enough heat within their bodies for these reactions to proceed at a life-sustaining pace. Temperature, as you'll see, has a critical effect on the speed, or rate, of a reaction.

Until now, we haven't focused quantitatively on factors affecting reactions, other than the amounts of reactants and products and their molecular nature. Yet, while a balanced equation is essential for calculating yields, it tells us nothing about three dynamic aspects of chemical change:

- How fast is the reaction proceeding?
- How far will the reaction proceed toward completion?
- Will the reaction proceed by releasing energy or by requiring it?

This chapter addresses the first of these questions and focuses on the field of *kinetics*. We'll address the other two questions in upcoming chapters. Answering all three is crucial to understanding modern technology, the environment, and the reactions in living things.

**IN THIS CHAPTER . . .** We examine the rate of a reaction, the factors that affect it, the theories that explain those effects, and the stepwise changes reactants undergo as they transform into products.
- We introduce some general ideas about reaction rates and overview three key factors that affect them—concentration, physical state, and temperature.
- We express rate through a rate law and determine its components.
- We see how concentrations change as a reaction proceeds and discuss the meaning of half-life.
- To understand the effects of concentration and temperature on rate, we examine two related theories of chemical kinetics.
- We discuss reaction mechanisms, noting the steps a reaction goes through and picturing the chemical species that exists as reactant bonds are breaking and product bonds are forming.
- We see how catalysts increase reaction rates, highlighting two vital examples—the reactions in a living cell and the depletion of stratospheric ozone.

# 16.1 • FOCUSING ON REACTION RATE

By definition, in a chemical reaction, reactants change into products. **Chemical kinetics,** the study of how fast that change occurs, focuses on the **reaction rate,** the change in the concentrations of reactants (or products) as a function of time. Different reactions have different rates: *in a faster reaction (higher rate), the reactant concentration decreases quickly, whereas in a slower reaction (lower rate), it decreases slowly* (Figure 16.1, *next page*). Under any given set of conditions, a rate is determined by the nature of the reactants. At room temperature, for example, hydrogen reacts explosively with fluorine but extremely slowly with nitrogen:

$$H_2(g) + F_2(g) \longrightarrow 2HF(g) \quad \text{[very fast]}$$
$$3H_2(g) + N_2(g) \longrightarrow 2NH_3(g) \quad \text{[very slow]}$$

Furthermore, any given reaction has a different rate under different conditions.

**Figure 16.1** A faster reaction (*top*) and a slower reaction (*bottom*). As time elapses, reactant *decreases* and product *increases*.

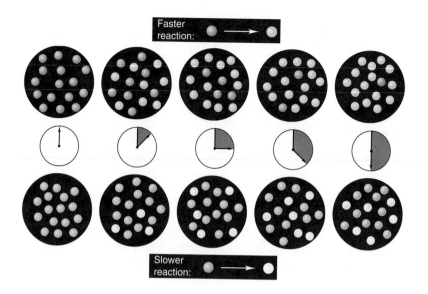

Chemical processes occur over a wide range of rates (Figure 16.2). Some—like a neutralization, a precipitation, or an explosion—may take a second or less. Processes that include many reactions—like the ripening of fruit—take days to months. Human aging continues for decades, and the formation of coal from dead plants takes hundreds of millions of years. Knowing the reaction rate can be essential: how quickly a medicine acts can make the difference between life and death, and how long a polymer takes to form can make the difference between profit and loss.

We can control four factors that affect rate: the concentrations of reactants, their physical state, the temperature of the reaction, and the use of a catalyst. We consider the first three here and the fourth in Section 16.7.

1. *Concentration: molecules must collide to react.* A major factor influencing reaction rate is reactant concentration. Consider the reaction between ozone and nitrogen monoxide (nitric oxide):

$$NO(g) + O_3(g) \longrightarrow NO_2(g) + O_2(g)$$

This reaction occurs in the stratosphere, where the oxide is released in the exhaust gases of supersonic aircraft, but it can be simulated in the lab. In a reaction vessel, the molecules zoom every which way, crashing into each other and the vessel walls, but a reaction can occur only when NO and $O_3$ molecules collide. The more molecules present, the more frequently they collide, and the more often they react. Thus, *reaction rate is proportional to the number of collisions, which depends on the concentration of reactants:*

$$\text{Rate} \propto \text{collision frequency} \propto \text{concentration}$$

2. *Physical state: molecules must mix to collide.* Collision frequency also depends on physical state, which determines how easily the reactants mix. When the reactants are in the same phase, as in an aqueous solution, random thermal motion brings them into contact, but gentle stirring mixes them further. When the reactants are in different phases, contact occurs only at the interface between the phases, so vigorous stirring or

**Figure 16.2** The wide range of reaction rates.

**Figure 16.3** The effect of surface area on reaction rate.

even grinding may be needed. Thus, *the more finely divided a solid or liquid reactant, the greater its surface area, the more contact it makes with the other reactant, and the faster the reaction occurs.* In Figure 16.3, a hot steel nail (*left*) placed in oxygen gas glows feebly, but the same mass of steel wool (*right*) bursts into flame. For the same reason, you start a campfire with twigs, not logs.

3. *Temperature: molecules must collide with enough energy.* Temperature usually has a major effect on the rate of a reaction. Two kitchen appliances employ this effect: a refrigerator slows down chemical processes that spoil food, whereas an oven speeds up other chemical processes that cook it. Temperature affects reaction rate by increasing the *frequency* and, more importantly, the *energy* of collisions:

- *Frequency of collisions.* Recall that molecules in a sample of gas have a range of speeds, with the most probable speed a function of the temperature (see Figure 5.14, p. 205). Thus, *at a higher temperature, collisions occur more frequently, and so more molecules react:*

$$\text{Rate} \propto \text{collision } \textbf{frequency} \propto \text{temperature}$$

A reaction can occur only if collision energy is high enough.

No reaction can occur if collision energy is too low.

**Figure 16.4** Sufficient collision energy is required for a reaction to occur.

- *Energy of collisions.* Even more important is that *temperature affects the kinetic energy* of the molecules. In the jumble of NO and $O_3$ molecules in the reaction vessel, most collisions have only enough energy for the molecules to bounce off each other. However, some collisions occur with sufficient energy for the molecules to react (Figure 16.4). *At a higher temperature, more sufficiently energetic collisions occur, and so more molecules react:*

$$\text{Rate} \propto \text{collision } \textbf{energy} \propto \text{temperature}$$

## ▌ Summary of Section 16.1

- Chemical kinetics focuses on reaction rate and the factors that affect it.
- Under a given set of conditions, each reaction has its own rate.
- Concentration affects rate by influencing the frequency of collisions between reactant molecules.
- Physical state affects rate by determining how well reactants can mix.
- Temperature affects rate by influencing the frequency and, more importantly, the energy of the collisions between reactant molecules.

## 16.2 • EXPRESSING THE REACTION RATE

In general terms, a *rate* is a change in some variable per unit of time. The most familiar examples relate to speed (*see photo*), the change in position of an object divided by the change in time. For instance, if we measure a runner's initial position, $x_1$, at time $t_1$, and final position, $x_2$, at time $t_2$, the average speed is

$$\text{Rate of motion (speed)} = \frac{\text{change in position}}{\text{change in time}} = \frac{x_2 - x_1}{t_2 - t_1} = \frac{\Delta x}{\Delta t}$$

For the rate of a *reaction*, we measure the changes in concentrations of reactants or products per unit time: *reactant concentrations decrease while product concentrations*

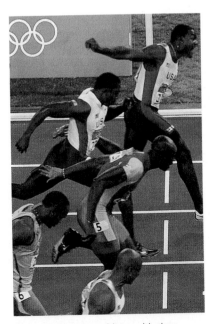

Runners change positions with time.

*increase.* For the general reaction A ⟶ B, we measure the initial reactant concentration ($A_1$) at $t_1$, allow the reaction to proceed, and then quickly measure the final reactant concentration ($A_2$) at $t_2$. The change in concentration divided by the change in time gives the rate:

$$\text{Rate} = -\frac{\text{change in concentration of A}}{\text{change in time}} = -\frac{\text{conc } A_2 - \text{conc } A_1}{t_2 - t_1} = -\frac{\Delta(\text{conc A})}{\Delta t}$$

The negative sign is important because, by convention, reaction rate is a *positive* number. But, since conc $A_2$ must be *lower* than conc $A_1$, the *change in concentration (final − initial) of reactant A is negative.* Therefore, we use the negative sign to convert the negative change in reactant concentration to a positive value for the rate. Suppose the concentration of A changes from 1.2 mol/L (conc $A_1$) to 0.75 mol/L (conc $A_2$) over a 125-s period. The rate is

$$\text{Rate} = -\frac{0.75 \text{ mol/L} - 1.2 \text{ mol/L}}{125 \text{ s} - 0 \text{ s}} = 3.6 \times 10^{-3} \text{ mol/L·s}$$

*Square brackets,* [ ], *indicate a concentration in moles per liter.* For example, [A] is the concentration of A in mol/L, and the rate expressed in terms of A is

$$\boxed{\text{Rate} = -\frac{\Delta[A]}{\Delta t}} \qquad (16.1)$$

The units for the rate are moles per liter per second (mol $L^{-1}$ $s^{-1}$, or mol/L·s), or any time unit convenient for the reaction (minutes, years, and so on).

If instead we measure the *product* concentrations to determine the rate, we find that conc $B_2$ is always *higher* than conc $B_1$. Thus, the *change* in product concentration, $\Delta[B]$, is *positive,* and the reaction rate for A ⟶ B expressed in terms of B is

$$\text{Rate} = +\frac{\Delta[B]}{\Delta t}$$

The plus sign is usually understood and not shown.

## Average, Instantaneous, and Initial Reaction Rates

In most cases, *the rate varies as a reaction proceeds.* Consider the reversible gas-phase reaction between ethylene and ozone, one of many reactions that may be involved in the formation of smog:

$$C_2H_4(g) + O_3(g) \rightleftharpoons C_2H_4O(g) + O_2(g)$$

The equation shows that for every molecule of $C_2H_4$ that reacts, a molecule of $O_3$ reacts; thus, $[O_3]$ and $[C_2H_4]$ decrease at the same rate:

$$\text{Rate} = -\frac{\Delta[C_2H_4]}{\Delta t} = -\frac{\Delta[O_3]}{\Delta t}$$

When we start with a known $[O_3]$ in a closed vessel at 30°C (303 K) and measure $[O_3]$ at 10.0-s intervals during the first minute after adding $C_2H_4$, we obtain the data in Table 16.1 and the plot of $[O_3]$ vs. $t$ in Figure 16.5 *(red curve).* Two key points are

- The data points in Figure 16.5 result in a curved line, which means that the rate is changing (a straight line would mean that the rate is constant).
- The rate *decreases* during the course of the reaction because we are plotting *reactant* concentration versus time: as $O_3$ molecules react, fewer are present to collide with $C_2H_4$ molecules, and the rate, the change in $[O_3]$ over time, therefore decreases.

Three types of reaction rates are shown in the figure:

1. *Average rate.* Over a given period of time, the **average rate** is the slope of the line joining two points along the curve. The rate over the entire 60.0 s is the total change in concentration divided by the total change in time (Figure 16.5, *line a*):

$$\text{Rate} = -\frac{\Delta[O_3]}{\Delta t} = -\frac{(1.10 \times 10^{-5} \text{ mol/L}) - (3.20 \times 10^{-5} \text{ mol/L})}{60.0 \text{ s} - 0.0 \text{ s}} = 3.50 \times 10^{-7} \text{ mol/L·s}$$

**Table 16.1 Concentration of $O_3$ at Various Times in Its Reaction with $C_2H_4$ at 303 K**

| Time (s) | Concentration of $O_3$ (mol/L) |
|---|---|
| 0.0 | $3.20 \times 10^{-5}$ |
| 10.0 | $2.42 \times 10^{-5}$ |
| 20.0 | $1.95 \times 10^{-5}$ |
| 30.0 | $1.63 \times 10^{-5}$ |
| 40.0 | $1.40 \times 10^{-5}$ |
| 50.0 | $1.23 \times 10^{-5}$ |
| 60.0 | $1.10 \times 10^{-5}$ |

This quantity, which is the slope of line **a** (that is, $\Delta[O_3]/\Delta t$), is the average rate over the entire period: during the first 60.0 s of the reaction, $[O_3]$ decreases an *average* of $3.50\times10^{-7}$ mol/L each second.

But, when you drive a car or ride a bike for a few miles, your speed over shorter distances may be lower or higher than your average speed. In the same sense, the decrease in $[O_3]$ over the whole time period does not show the rate over any shorter time period. This *change* in reaction rate is evident when we calculate the average rate over two shorter periods. For the first 10.0 s, between 0.0 s and 10.0 s, the average rate (Figure 16.5, *line b*) is

$$\text{Rate} = -\frac{\Delta[O_3]}{\Delta t} = -\frac{(2.42\times10^{-5}\text{ mol/L}) - (3.20\times10^{-5}\text{ mol/L})}{10.0\text{ s} - 0.0\text{ s}} = 7.80\times10^{-7}\text{ mol/L·s}$$

And, for the last 10.0 s, between 50.0 s and 60.0 s, the average rate (Figure 16.5, *line c*) is

$$\text{Rate} = -\frac{\Delta[O_3]}{\Delta t} = -\frac{(1.10\times10^{-5}\text{ mol/L}) - (1.23\times10^{-5}\text{ mol/L})}{60.0\text{ s} - 50.0\text{ s}} = 1.30\times10^{-7}\text{ mol/L·s}$$

The earlier rate is six times faster than the later rate.

2. *Instantaneous rate.* The shorter the time period we choose, the closer we come to the **instantaneous rate,** the rate at a particular instant during the reaction. *The slope of a line tangent to the curve at any point gives the instantaneous rate at that time.* For example, the rate at 35.0 s is $2.50\times10^{-7}$ mol/L·s, the slope of the line tangent to the curve through the point at $t = 35.0$ s (Figure 16.5, *line d* ). In general, we use the term *reaction rate* to mean *instantaneous* reaction rate.

3. *Initial rate.* The instantaneous rate at the moment the reactants are mixed (that is, at $t = 0$) is the **initial rate.** We use this rate to avoid a complication: as a reaction proceeds in the *forward* direction (reactants $\longrightarrow$ products), product increases, causing the *reverse* reaction (reactants $\longleftarrow$ products), to occur more quickly. To find the overall (net) rate, we would have to calculate the difference between the forward and reverse rates. But, for the initial rate, $t = 0$, so product concentrations are negligible, and so is the reverse rate. We find the initial rate from the slope of the line tangent to the curve at $t = 0$ s (Figure 16.5, *line e*). We typically use initial rates to find other kinetic parameters.

## Expressing Rate in Terms of Reactant and Product Concentrations

So far, for the reaction between $C_2H_4$ and $O_3$, we've expressed the rate in terms of $[O_3]$, which is *decreasing,* and the rate would be expressed the same way in terms of $[C_2H_4]$. However, the rate is exactly the opposite in terms of the product concentrations because they are *increasing.* From the balanced equation, we see that one molecule each of $C_2H_4O$ and of $O_2$ appear for every molecule of $C_2H_4$ and of $O_3$ that disappear. Thus, we can express the rate in terms of any of the four substances:

$$\text{Rate} = -\frac{\Delta[C_2H_4]}{\Delta t} = -\frac{\Delta[O_3]}{\Delta t} = \frac{\Delta[C_2H_4O]}{\Delta t} = \frac{\Delta[O_2]}{\Delta t}$$

Figure 16.6A plots the changes in concentrations of one reactant ($C_2H_4$) and one product ($O_2$) simultaneously. The curves have the same shape but are inverted relative to each other, because, *for this reaction,* product appears at the same rate that reactant disappears.

For many other reactions, though, reactants disappear and products appear at different rates. Consider the reaction between hydrogen and iodine to form hydrogen iodide:

$$H_2(g) + I_2(g) \longrightarrow 2HI(g)$$

From the balancing coefficients, we see that, for every molecule of $H_2$ that disappears, one molecule of $I_2$ disappears and *two* molecules of HI appear. In other words, the rate of $[H_2]$ decrease is the same as the rate of $[I_2]$ decrease, but both are only half the rate of $[HI]$ increase. Thus, in Figure 16.6B, the $[HI]$ curve rises twice as fast as the $[H_2]$ curve drops. If we refer the changes in $[I_2]$ and $[HI]$ to the change in $[H_2]$, we have

$$\text{Rate} = -\frac{\Delta[H_2]}{\Delta t} = -\frac{\Delta[I_2]}{\Delta t} = \frac{1}{2}\frac{\Delta[HI]}{\Delta t}$$

If, instead, we refer the changes in $[H_2]$ and $[I_2]$ to the change in $[HI]$, we obtain

$$\text{Rate} = \frac{\Delta[HI]}{\Delta t} = -2\frac{\Delta[H_2]}{\Delta t} = -2\frac{\Delta[I_2]}{\Delta t}$$

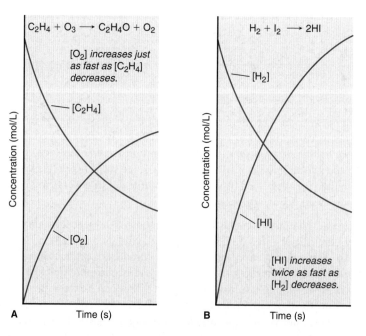

**Figure 16.6  Plots of [reactant] and [product] vs. time.  A,** $C_2H_4$ and $O_2$. **B,** $H_2$ and HI.

Note that this expression gives a rate that is double the previous one. Thus, *the expression for the rate of a reaction and its numerical value depend on which substance serves as the reference.*

We can summarize these results for any reaction,

$$aA + bB \longrightarrow cC + dD$$

where $a$, $b$, $c$, and $d$ are coefficients of the balanced equation, as follows:

$$\text{Rate} = -\frac{1}{a}\frac{\Delta[A]}{\Delta t} = -\frac{1}{b}\frac{\Delta[B]}{\Delta t} = \frac{1}{c}\frac{\Delta[C]}{\Delta t} = \frac{1}{d}\frac{\Delta[D]}{\Delta t} \qquad \text{(16.2)}$$

## Sample Problem 16.1 Expressing Rate in Terms of Changes in Concentration with Time

**Problem** Hydrogen gas has a nonpolluting combustion product (water vapor). It is used as a fuel aboard the space shuttle and in earthbound cars with prototype engines:

$$2H_2(g) + O_2(g) \longrightarrow 2H_2O(g)$$

**(a)** Express the rate in terms of changes in $[H_2]$, $[O_2]$, and $[H_2O]$ with time.
**(b)** When $[O_2]$ is decreasing at 0.23 mol/L·s, at what rate is $[H_2O]$ increasing?

**Plan (a)** Of the three substances in the equation, let's choose $O_2$ as the reference because its coefficient is 1. For every molecule of $O_2$ that disappears, two molecules of $H_2$ disappear. Thus, the rate of $[O_2]$ decrease is one-half the rate of $[H_2]$ decrease. By similar reasoning, the rate of $[O_2]$ decrease is one-half the rate of $[H_2O]$ increase. **(b)** Because $[O_2]$ is decreasing, the change in its concentration must be negative. We substitute the given rate as a negative value ($-0.23$ mol/L·s) into the expression and solve for $\Delta[H_2O]/\Delta t$.

**Solution (a)** Expressing the rate in terms of each component:

$$\text{Rate} = -\frac{\Delta[O_2]}{\Delta t} = -\frac{1}{2}\frac{\Delta[H_2]}{\Delta t} = \frac{1}{2}\frac{\Delta[H_2O]}{\Delta t}$$

**(b)** Calculating the rate of change of $[H_2O]$:

$$\frac{1}{2}\frac{\Delta[H_2O]}{\Delta t} = -\frac{\Delta[O_2]}{\Delta t} = -(-0.23 \text{ mol/L·s})$$

$$\frac{\Delta[H_2O]}{\Delta t} = 2(0.23 \text{ mol/L·s}) = \boxed{0.46 \text{ mol/L·s}}$$

**Check (a)** A good check is to use the rate expression to obtain the balanced equation: $[H_2]$ changes twice as fast as $[O_2]$, so two $H_2$ molecules react for each $O_2$. $[H_2O]$ changes twice as fast as $[O_2]$, so two $H_2O$ molecules form from each $O_2$. Thus, we get $2H_2 + O_2 \longrightarrow 2H_2O$. The values of $[H_2]$ and $[O_2]$ decrease, so they have minus signs; $[H_2O]$ increases, so it has a plus sign. Another check is to use Equation 16.2, with $A = H_2$, $a = 2$; $B = O_2$, $b = 1$; and $C = H_2O$, $c = 2$:

$$\text{Rate} = -\frac{1}{a}\frac{\Delta[A]}{\Delta t} = -\frac{1}{b}\frac{\Delta[B]}{\Delta t} = \frac{1}{c}\frac{\Delta[C]}{\Delta t}$$

or

$$\text{Rate} = -\frac{1}{2}\frac{\Delta[H_2]}{\Delta t} = -\frac{\Delta[O_2]}{\Delta t} = \frac{1}{2}\frac{\Delta[H_2O]}{\Delta t}$$

**(b)** Given the rate expression, it makes sense that the numerical value of the rate of $[H_2O]$ increase is twice that of $[O_2]$ decrease.

**Comment** Thinking through this type of problem at the molecular level is the best approach, but use Equation 16.2 to confirm your answer.

**Follow-Up Problem 16.1 (a)** Balance the following equation and express the rate in terms of the change in concentration with time for each substance:

$$NO(g) + O_2(g) \longrightarrow N_2O_3(g)$$

**(b)** How fast is $[O_2]$ decreasing when $[NO]$ is decreasing at a rate of $1.60 \times 10^{-4}$ mol/L·s?

■ **Summary of Section 16.2**

- The average reaction rate is the change in reactant (or product) concentration over a change in time, $\Delta t$. The rate slows as the reaction proceeds because reactants are used up.
- The instantaneous rate at time $t$ is the slope of the tangent to a curve that plots concentration vs. time.
- The initial rate, the instantaneous rate at $t = 0$, occurs when reactants have just been mixed and before any product accumulates.
- The expression for a reaction rate and its numerical value depend on which reaction component is being referenced.

# 16.3 • THE RATE LAW AND ITS COMPONENTS

The centerpiece of any kinetic study of a reaction is the **rate law** (or **rate equation**), which expresses the rate as a function of concentrations and temperature. The rate law is based on experiment, so any hypothesis about how the reaction occurs on the molecular level must conform to it.

In this discussion, we generally consider reactions for which the products do not appear in the rate law, so the rate depends only on *reactant* concentrations and temperature. For a general reaction occurring at a fixed temperature,

$$aA + bB + \cdots \longrightarrow cC + dD + \cdots$$

the rate law is

$$\text{Rate} = k[A]^m[B]^n \cdots \tag{16.3}$$

The term $k$ is a proportionality constant, called the **rate constant,** that is specific for a given reaction at a given temperature and does *not* change as the reaction proceeds. (As we'll see in Section 16.5, $k$ *does* change with temperature.) The exponents $m$ and $n$, called the **reaction orders,** define how the rate is affected by reactant concentration; we'll see how to determine them shortly. Two key points to remember are

- *The balancing coefficients a and b in the reaction equation are **not** necessarily related in any way to the reaction orders m and n.*
- *The components of the rate law—rate, reaction orders, and rate constant—**must** be found by experiment.*

In the remainder of this section, we'll find the components of the rate law by measuring concentrations to determine the *initial rate*, using initial rates to determine the *reaction orders,* and using these values to calculate the *rate constant*. With the rate law for a reaction, we can predict the rate for any initial concentrations.

## Some Laboratory Methods for Determining the Initial Rate

We determine an initial rate from a plot of concentration vs. time, so we need a quick, accurate method for measuring concentration. Let's briefly discuss three common approaches.

1. *Spectrometric methods* measure the concentration of a component that absorbs (or emits) characteristic wavelengths of light. For example, in the reaction of NO and $O_3$, only $NO_2$ has a color:

$$NO(g, \text{colorless}) + O_3(g, \text{colorless}) \longrightarrow O_2(g, \text{colorless}) + NO_2(g, \text{brown})$$

Known amounts of reactants are injected into a tube of known volume within a spectrometer (see Tools of the Laboratory, p. 273), which is set to measure the wavelength and intensity of the brown color. The rate of $NO_2$ formation is proportional to the increase in that intensity over time.

2. *Conductometric methods* rely on the change in electrical conductivity of the reaction solution when nonionic reactants form ionic products, or vice versa. Con-

sider the reaction between an organic halide, such as 2-bromo-2-methylpropane, and water:

$$(CH_3)_3C—Br(l) + H_2O(l) \longrightarrow (CH_3)_3C—OH(l) + H^+(aq) + Br^-(aq)$$

The HBr that forms is a strong acid, so it dissociates completely in the water. As time passes, more ions form, so the conductivity of the reaction mixture increases.

3. *Manometric methods* employ a manometer attached to a reaction vessel of fixed volume and temperature. The manometer measures the pressure over time of a reaction that involves a change in the number of moles of gas. Consider the reaction between zinc and acetic acid:

$$Zn(s) + 2CH_3COOH(aq) \longrightarrow Zn^{2+}(aq) + 2CH_3COO^-(aq) + H_2(g)$$

The rate is directly proportional to the increase in $H_2$ gas pressure.

## Determining Reaction Orders

With the initial rate in hand, we can determine reaction orders. Let's first discuss what reaction orders are and then see how to determine them by controlling reactant concentrations.

**Meaning and Terminology**   A reaction has an *individual* order "with respect to" or "in" each reactant, and an *overall* order, the sum of the individual orders.

Consider first the simplest case, a reaction with only one reactant, A:

$$A \longrightarrow products$$

- *First order.* If the rate doubles when [A] doubles, the rate depends on [A] raised to the first power, $[A]^1$ (the $^1$ is generally omitted). Thus, the reaction is *first order* in (or with respect to) A and *first order* overall:

$$Rate = k[A]^1 = k[A]$$

- *Second order.* If the rate quadruples when [A] doubles, the rate depends on [A] squared, $[A]^2$. In this case, the reaction is *second order* in A and *second order* overall:

$$Rate = k[A]^2$$

- *Zero order.* If the rate does not change when [A] doubles, the rate does *not* depend on [A], but we express this fact mathematically by saying that the rate depends on [A] raised to the zero power, $[A]^0$. The reaction is *zero order* in A and *zero order* overall:

$$Rate = k[A]^0 = k(1) = k$$

Figure 16.7 shows plots of [A] vs. time for first-, second-, and zero-order reactions. (In all cases, the value of $k$ was assumed to be the same.) Notice that

- The decrease in [A] doesn't change as time goes on for a zero-order reaction.
- The decrease slows down as time goes on for a first-order reaction.
- The decrease slows even more for a second-order reaction.

These results are reflected in Figure 16.8, which shows plots of rate vs. [A] for the same reaction orders. Notice that

- The plot is a horizontal line for the zero-order reaction because the rate doesn't change no matter what the value of [A].
- The plot is an upward-sloping *line* for the first-order reaction because the rate is directly proportional to [A].
- The plot is an upward-sloping *curve* for the second-order reaction because the rate increases exponentially with [A].

Let's look at some examples of observed rate laws and note the reaction orders. For the reaction between NO and hydrogen gas,

$$2NO(g) + 2H_2(g) \longrightarrow N_2(g) + 2H_2O(g)$$

the rate law is

$$Rate = k[NO]^2[H_2]$$

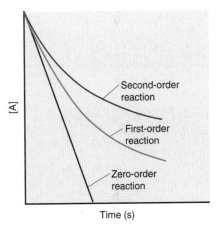

**Figure 16.7** Plots of reactant concentration, [A], vs. time for first-, second-, and zero-order reactions.

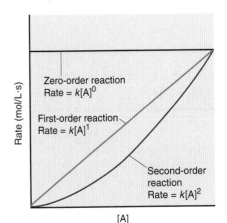

**Figure 16.8** Plots of rate vs. reactant concentration, [A], for first-, second-, and zero-order reactions.

This reaction is second order in NO. And, even though $H_2$ has a coefficient of 2 in the balanced equation, the reaction is first order in $H_2$. It is third order overall $(2 + 1 = 3)$.

For the reaction between nitrogen monoxide and ozone,

$$NO(g) + O_3(g) \longrightarrow NO_2(g) + O_2(g)$$

the rate law is

$$Rate = k[NO][O_3]$$

This reaction is first order with respect to NO and first order with respect to $O_3$, so it is second order overall $(1 + 1 = 2)$.

Finally, for the hydrolysis of 2-bromo-2-methylpropane,

$$(CH_3)_3C—Br(l) + H_2O(l) \longrightarrow (CH_3)_3C—OH(l) + H^+(aq) + Br^-(aq)$$

the rate law is

$$Rate = k[(CH_3)_3CBr]$$

This reaction is first order in 2-bromo-2-methylpropane and zero order with respect to $H_2O$, despite its coefficient of 1 in the balanced equation. If we want to note that water is a reactant, we can write

$$Rate = k[(CH_3)_3CBr][H_2O]^0$$

Overall, this is a first-order reaction $(1 + 0 = 1)$.

These examples reiterate an important point noted earlier: *reaction orders* ***cannot*** *be deduced from the balanced equation but* ***must*** *be determined from experimental data.*

Although usually positive integers or zero, reaction orders can also be fractional or negative. For the reaction

$$CHCl_3(g) + Cl_2(g) \longrightarrow CCl_4(g) + HCl(g)$$

a fractional order appears in the rate law:

$$Rate = k[CHCl_3][Cl_2]^{1/2}$$

This reaction order means that if, for example, $[Cl_2]$ increases by a factor of 4, the rate increases by a factor of 2, the square root of the change in $[Cl_2]$. The overall order of this reaction is $\frac{3}{2}$.

A negative reaction order means the rate *decreases* when the concentration of that component increases. Negative orders are often seen when the rate law includes products. For example, for the atmospheric reaction

$$2O_3(g) \rightleftharpoons 3O_2(g)$$

the rate law is

$$Rate = k[O_3]^2[O_2]^{-1} = k\frac{[O_3]^2}{[O_2]}$$

If $[O_2]$ doubles, the reaction proceeds half as fast. This reaction is second order in $O_3$ and negative first order in $O_2$, so it is first order overall $[2 + (-1) = 1]$.

---

**Sample Problem 16.2**  **Determining Reaction Orders from Rate Laws**

**Problem** For each of the following reactions, use the given rate law to determine the reaction order with respect to each reactant and the overall order:
(a) $2NO(g) + O_2(g) \longrightarrow 2NO_2(g)$; rate $= k[NO]^2[O_2]$
(b) $CH_3CHO(g) \longrightarrow CH_4(g) + CO(g)$; rate $= k[CH_3CHO]^{3/2}$
(c) $H_2O_2(aq) + 3I^-(aq) + 2H^+(aq) \longrightarrow I_3^-(aq) + 2H_2O(l)$; rate $= k[H_2O_2][I^-]$

**Plan** We inspect the exponents in the rate law, *not* the coefficients of the balanced equation, to find the individual orders, and then take their sum to find the overall reaction order.

**Solution** (a) The exponent of [NO] is 2, so the reaction is  second order with respect to  NO,  first order with respect to $O_2$,  and  third order overall.

(b) The reaction is  $\frac{3}{2}$ order in $CH_3CHO$  and  $\frac{3}{2}$ order overall.

(c) The reaction is  first order in $H_2O_2$, first order in $I^-$,  and  second order overall.  The reactant $H^+$ does not appear in the rate law, so the reaction is  zero order in $H^+$.

**Check** Be sure that each reactant has an order and that the sum of the individual orders gives the overall order.

**Follow-Up Problem 16.2** Experiment shows that the reaction

$$5Br^-(aq) + BrO_3^-(aq) + 6H^+(aq) \longrightarrow 3Br_2(l) + 3H_2O(l)$$

obeys this rate law: rate = $k[Br^-][BrO_3^-][H^+]^2$. What is the reaction order in each reactant and the overall reaction order?

**Determining Reaction Orders by Changing Reactant Concentrations** Now let's see how reaction orders are found *before* the rate law is known. Before looking at a real reaction, we'll go through the process for substances A and B in this reaction:

$$A + 2B \longrightarrow C + D$$

The rate law, expressed in general terms, is

$$Rate = k[A]^m[B]^n$$

To find the values of *m* and *n, we run a series of experiments in which one reactant concentration changes while the other is kept constant, and we measure the effect on the initial rate in each case.* Table 16.2 shows the results.

**Table 16.2   Initial Rates for the Reaction Between A and B**

| Experiment | Initial Rate (mol/L·s) | Initial [A] (mol/L) | Initial [B] (mol/L) |
|---|---|---|---|
| 1 | $1.75 \times 10^{-3}$ | $2.50 \times 10^{-2}$ | $3.00 \times 10^{-2}$ |
| 2 | $3.50 \times 10^{-3}$ | $5.00 \times 10^{-2}$ | $3.00 \times 10^{-2}$ |
| 3 | $3.50 \times 10^{-3}$ | $2.50 \times 10^{-2}$ | $6.00 \times 10^{-2}$ |
| 4 | $7.00 \times 10^{-3}$ | $5.00 \times 10^{-2}$ | $6.00 \times 10^{-2}$ |

1. *Finding m, the order with respect to A.* By comparing experiments 1 and 2, in which [A] doubles and [B] is constant, we can obtain *m*. First, we take the ratio of the general rate laws for thse two experiments:

$$\frac{Rate\ 2}{Rate\ 1} = \frac{k[A]_2^m[B]_2^n}{k[A]_1^m[B]_1^n}$$

where $[A]_2$ is the concentration of A in experiment 2, $[B]_1$ is the concentration of B in experiment 1, and so forth. Because *k* is a constant and [B] does not change between these two experiments, those quantities cancel:

$$\frac{Rate\ 2}{Rate\ 1} = \frac{k[A]_2^m[B]_2^n}{k[A]_1^m[B]_1^n} = \frac{[A]_2^m}{[A]_1^m} = \left(\frac{[A]_2}{[A]_1}\right)^m$$

Substituting the values from Table 16.2, we have

$$\frac{3.50 \times 10^{-3}\ mol/L \cdot s}{1.75 \times 10^{-3}\ mol/L \cdot s} = \left(\frac{5.00 \times 10^{-2}\ mol/L}{2.50 \times 10^{-2}\ mol/L}\right)^m$$

Dividing, we obtain

$$2.00 = (2.00)^m, \quad \text{so } m = 1$$

Thus, the reaction is first order in A, because when [A] doubles, the rate doubles.

2. *Finding n, the order with respect to B.* To find *n*, we compare experiments 3 and 1 in which [A] is held constant and [B] doubles:

$$\frac{Rate\ 3}{Rate\ 1} = \frac{k[A]_3^m\,[B]_3^n}{k[A]_1^m\,[B]_1^n}$$

As before, *k* is a constant, and in this pair of experiments, [A] does not change, so those quantities cancel, and we have

$$\frac{Rate\ 3}{Rate\ 1} = \frac{k[A]_3^m[B]_3^n}{k[A]_1^m[B]_1^n} = \frac{[B]_3^n}{[B]_1^n} = \left(\frac{[B]_3}{[B]_1}\right)^n$$

The actual values give

$$\frac{3.50\times10^{-3}\ \text{mol/L·s}}{1.75\times10^{-3}\ \text{mol/L·s}} = \left(\frac{6.00\times10^{-2}\ \text{mol/L}}{3.00\times10^{-2}\ \text{mol/L}}\right)^{n}$$

Dividing, we obtain

$$2.00 = (2.00)^{n}, \quad \text{so } n = 1$$

Thus, the reaction is also first order in B because when [B] doubles, the rate doubles. We can check this conclusion from experiment 4: when *both* [A] and [B] double, the rate should quadruple, and it does. Thus, the rate law, with *m* and *n* equal to 1, is

$$\text{Rate} = k[A][B]$$

Note, especially, that while the order with respect to B is 1, the coefficient of B in the balanced equation is 2. Thus, as we said earlier, *reaction orders must be determined from experiment.*

Next, let's go through this process for a real reaction, the one between oxygen and nitrogen monoxide, a key step in the formation of acid rain and in the industrial production of nitric acid:

$$O_2(g) + 2NO(g) \longrightarrow 2NO_2(g)$$

The general rate law is

$$\text{Rate} = k[O_2]^{m}[NO]^{n}$$

Table 16.3 shows experiments that change one reactant concentration while keeping the other constant. If we compare experiments 1 and 2, we see the effect of doubling $[O_2]$ on the rate. First, we take the ratio of their rate laws:

$$\frac{\text{Rate 2}}{\text{Rate 1}} = \frac{k[O_2]_2^{m}[NO]_2^{n}}{k[O_2]_1^{m}[NO]_1^{n}}$$

As before, the constant quantities—*k* and [NO]—cancel:

$$\frac{\text{Rate 2}}{\text{Rate 1}} = \frac{k[O_2]_2^{m}\cancel{[NO]_2^{n}}}{k[O_2]_1^{m}\cancel{[NO]_1^{n}}} = \frac{[O_2]_2^{m}}{[O_2]_1^{m}} = \left(\frac{[O_2]_2}{[O_2]_1}\right)^{m}$$

**Table 16.3  Initial Rates for the Reaction Between $O_2$ and NO**

| Experiment | Initial Rate (mol/L·s) | Initial Reactant Concentrations (mol/L) | |
|---|---|---|---|
| | | **[$O_2$]** | **[NO]** |
| 1 | $3.21\times10^{-3}$ | $1.10\times10^{-2}$ | $1.30\times10^{-2}$ |
| 2 | $6.40\times10^{-3}$ | $2.20\times10^{-2}$ | $1.30\times10^{-2}$ |
| 3 | $12.8\times10^{-3}$ | $1.10\times10^{-2}$ | $2.60\times10^{-2}$ |
| 4 | $9.60\times10^{-3}$ | $3.30\times10^{-2}$ | $1.30\times10^{-2}$ |
| 5 | $28.8\times10^{-3}$ | $1.10\times10^{-2}$ | $3.90\times10^{-2}$ |

Substituting the values from Table 16.3, we obtain

$$\frac{6.40\times10^{-3}\ \text{mol/L·s}}{3.21\times10^{-3}\ \text{mol/L·s}} = \left(\frac{2.20\times10^{-2}\ \text{mol/L}}{1.10\times10^{-2}\ \text{mol/L}}\right)^{m}$$

Dividing, we obtain

$$1.99 = (2.00)^{m}$$

Rounding to one significant figure gives

$$2 = 2^{m}, \quad \text{so } m = 1$$

Sometimes, the exponent is not as easy to find by inspection as it is here. In those cases, we solve for *m* with an equation of the form $a = b^{m}$:

$$m = \frac{\log a}{\log b} = \frac{\log 1.99}{\log 2.00} = 0.993$$

which rounds to 1. Thus, the reaction is first order in $O_2$: when $[O_2]$ doubles, the rate doubles.

To find the order with respect to NO, we compare experiments 3 and 1, in which $[O_2]$ is held constant and $[NO]$ is doubled:

$$\frac{\text{Rate 3}}{\text{Rate 1}} = \frac{k[O_2]_3^m[NO]_3^n}{k[O_2]_1^m[NO]_1^n}$$

Canceling the constant $k$ and unchanging $[O_2]$, we have

$$\frac{\text{Rate 3}}{\text{Rate 1}} = \left(\frac{[NO]_3}{[NO]_1}\right)^n$$

The actual values give

$$\frac{12.8\times10^{-3}\ \text{mol/L·s}}{3.21\times10^{-3}\ \text{mol/L·s}} = \left(\frac{2.60\times10^{-2}\ \text{mol/L}}{1.30\times10^{-2}\ \text{mol/L}}\right)^n$$

Dividing, we obtain

$$3.99 = (2.00)^n$$

Solving for $n$:

$$n = \frac{\log 3.99}{\log 2.00} = 2.00 \quad (\text{or } 2)$$

The reaction is second order in NO: when $[NO]$ doubles, the rate quadruples. Thus, the actual rate law is

$$\text{Rate} = k[O_2][NO]^2$$

In this case, the reaction orders happen to be the same as the equation coefficients; nevertheless, they must *always* be determined by experiment.

The next two sample problems offer practice with this approach; the first is based on data and the second on molecular scenes.

## Sample Problem 16.3   Determining Reaction Orders from Rate Data

**Problem** Many gaseous reactions occur in car engines and exhaust systems. One of these is

$$NO_2(g) + CO(g) \longrightarrow NO(g) + CO_2(g) \qquad \text{rate} = k[NO_2]^m[CO]^n$$

Use the following data to determine the individual and overall reaction orders:

| Experiment | Initial Rate (mol/L·s) | Initial [NO₂] (mol/L) | Initial [CO] (mol/L) |
|---|---|---|---|
| 1 | 0.0050 | 0.10 | 0.10 |
| 2 | 0.080 | 0.40 | 0.10 |
| 3 | 0.0050 | 0.10 | 0.20 |

**Plan** We need to solve the general rate law for $m$ and for $n$ and then add those orders to get the overall order. To solve for each exponent, we proceed as in the text, taking the ratio of the rate laws for two experiments in which only the reactant in question changes.

**Solution** Calculating $m$ in $[NO_2]^m$: We take the ratio of the rate laws for experiments 1 and 2, in which $[NO_2]$ varies but $[CO]$ is constant:

$$\frac{\text{Rate 2}}{\text{Rate 1}} = \frac{k[NO_2]_2^m[CO]_2^n}{k[NO_2]_1^m[CO]_1^n} = \left(\frac{[NO_2]_2}{[NO_2]_1}\right)^m \quad \text{or} \quad \frac{0.080\ \text{mol/L·s}}{0.0050\ \text{mol/L·s}} = \left(\frac{0.40\ \text{mol/L}}{0.10\ \text{mol/L}}\right)^m$$

This gives $16 = (4.0)^m$, so we have $m = \log 16/\log 4.0 = 2.0$. The reaction is  second  order in NO₂.

Calculating $n$ in $[CO]^n$: We take the ratio of the rate laws for experiments 1 and 3, in which $[CO]$ varies but $[NO_2]$ is constant:

$$\frac{\text{Rate 3}}{\text{Rate 1}} = \frac{k[NO_2]_3^2[CO]_3^n}{k[NO_2]_1^2[CO]_1^n} = \left(\frac{[CO]_3}{[CO]_1}\right)^n \quad \text{or} \quad \frac{0.0050\ \text{mol/L·s}}{0.0050\ \text{mol/L·s}} = \left(\frac{0.20\ \text{mol/L}}{0.10\ \text{mol/L}}\right)^n$$

We have $1.0 = (2.0)^n$, so $n = 0$. The rate does not change when $[CO]$ varies, so the reaction is  zero order in CO.

Therefore, the rate law is

$$\text{Rate} = k[NO_2]^2[CO]^0 = k[NO_2]^2(1) = k[NO_2]^2$$

The reaction is  second order overall.

**Check** A good check is to reason through the orders. If $m = 1$, quadrupling $[NO_2]$ would quadruple the rate; but the rate *more* than quadruples, so $m > 1$. If $m = 2$, quadrupling $[NO_2]$ would increase the rate by a factor of 16 ($4^2$). The ratio of rates is $0.080/0.005 = 16$, so $m = 2$. In contrast, increasing $[CO]$ has no effect on the rate, which can happen only if $[CO]^n = 1$, so $n = 0$.

**Follow-Up Problem 16.3** Find the rate law and the individual and overall reaction orders for the reaction $H_2 + I_2 \longrightarrow 2HI$ using the following data at 450°C:

| Experiment | Initial Rate (mol/L·s) | Initial [H₂] (mol/L) | Initial [I₂] (mol/L) |
|---|---|---|---|
| 1 | $1.9\times10^{-23}$ | 0.0113 | 0.0011 |
| 2 | $1.1\times10^{-22}$ | 0.0220 | 0.0033 |
| 3 | $9.3\times10^{-23}$ | 0.0550 | 0.0011 |
| 4 | $1.9\times10^{-22}$ | 0.0220 | 0.0056 |

---

**Sample Problem 16.4** **Determining Reaction Orders from Molecular Scenes**

**Problem** At a particular temperature and volume, two gases, A (*red*) and B (*blue*), react. The following molecular scenes represent starting mixtures for four experiments:

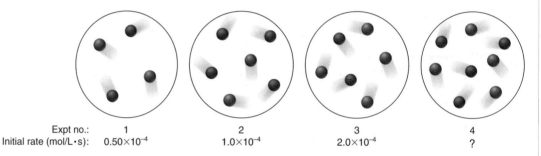

| Expt no.: | 1 | 2 | 3 | 4 |
|---|---|---|---|---|
| Initial rate (mol/L·s): | $0.50\times10^{-4}$ | $1.0\times10^{-4}$ | $2.0\times10^{-4}$ | ? |

**(a)** What is the reaction order with respect to A? With respect to B? The overall order?
**(b)** Write the rate law for the reaction.
**(c)** Predict the initial rate of Expt 4.

**Plan** **(a)** As before, we find the individual reaction orders by seeing how a change in each reactant changes the rate. In this case, however, instead of using concentration data, we count numbers of particles. The sum of the individual orders is the overall order. **(b)** To write the rate law, we use the orders from part (a) as exponents in the general rate law. **(c)** Using the results from Expts 1 through 3 and the rate law from part (b), we find the unknown initial rate of Expt 4.

**Solution** **(a)** Finding the individual and overall orders. For reactant A (*red*): Expts 1 and 2 show that when the number of particles of A doubles (from 2 to 4), with the number of particles of B constant (at 2), the rate doubles (from $0.5\times10^{-4}$ mol/L·s to $1.0\times10^{-4}$ mol/L·s). Thus, the order with respect to A is 1. For reactant B (*blue*): Expts 1 and 3 show that when the number of particles of B doubles (from 2 to 4), with the number of particles of A constant (at 2), the rate quadruples (from $0.5\times10^{-4}$ mol/L·s to $2.0\times10^{-4}$ mol/L·s). Thus, the order with respect to B is 2. The overall order is $1 + 2 = 3$.
**(b)** Writing the rate law: The general rate law is rate $= k[A]^m[B]^n$, so we have

$$\text{Rate} = k[A][B]^2$$

**(c)** Finding the initial rate of Expt 4: There are several possibilities, but let's compare Expts 3 and 4, in which the number of particles of A doubles (from 2 to 4) and the number of particles of B doesn't change. Since the rate law shows that the reaction is first order in A, the initial rate in Expt 4 should be double the initial rate in Expt 3, or $4.0\times10^{-4}$ mol/L·s.

**Check** A good check is to compare other pairs of experiments. **(a)** Comparing Expts 2 and 3 shows that the number of B doubles, which causes the rate to quadruple, and the number of A decreases by half, which causes the rate to halve; so the overall rate change should double (from $1.0 \times 10^{-4}$ mol/L·s to $2.0 \times 10^{-4}$ mol/L·s), which it does. **(c)** Comparing Expts 2 and 4, in which the number of A is constant and the number of B doubles, the rate should quadruple, which means the initial rate of Expt 4 would be $4.0 \times 10^{-4}$ mol/L·s, as we found.

**Follow-Up Problem 16.4** The scenes below show three experiments at a given temperature and volume involving reactants X (*black*) and Y (*green*):

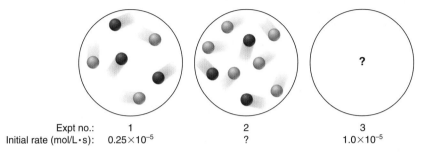

| Expt no.: | 1 | 2 | 3 |
|---|---|---|---|
| Initial rate (mol/L·s): | $0.25 \times 10^{-5}$ | ? | $1.0 \times 10^{-5}$ |

If the rate law for the reaction is rate $= k[X]^2$: **(a)** What is the initial rate of Expt 2? **(b)** Draw a scene for Expt 3 that involves a single change of the scene for Expt 1.

## Determining the Rate Constant

Let's find the rate constant for the reaction of $O_2$ and NO. With the rate, reactant concentrations, and reaction orders known, the sole remaining unknown in the rate law is the rate constant, $k$. We can use data from any of the experiments in Table 16.3 to solve for $k$. From experiment 1, for instance, we have

$$\text{Rate} = k[O_2]_1[NO]_1^2$$

$$k = \frac{\text{rate } 1}{[O_2]_1[NO]_1^2} = \frac{3.21 \times 10^{-3} \text{ mol/L·s}}{(1.10 \times 10^{-2} \text{ mol/L})(1.30 \times 10^{-2} \text{ mol/L})^2}$$

$$= \frac{3.21 \times 10^{-3} \text{ mol/L·s}}{1.86 \times 10^{-6} \text{ mol}^3/\text{L}^3} = 1.73 \times 10^3 \text{ L}^2/\text{mol}^2\text{·s}$$

Always check that the values of $k$ for a series of experiments are constant within experimental error. To three significant figures, the average value of $k$ for the five experiments in Table 16.3 is $1.72 \times 10^3$ L$^2$/mol$^2$·s.

With concentrations in mol/L and the reaction rate in units of mol/L·time, the units for $k$ depend on the order of the reaction and, of course, the time unit. For this reaction, the units for $k$, L$^2$/mol$^2$·s, are required to give a rate with units of mol/L·s:

$$\frac{\text{mol}}{\text{L·s}} = \frac{\text{L}^2}{\text{mol}^2\text{·s}} \times \frac{\text{mol}}{\text{L}} \times \left(\frac{\text{mol}}{\text{L}}\right)^2$$

The rate constant will *always* have these units for an overall third-order reaction with the time unit in seconds. Table 16.4 shows the units of $k$ for common integer overall orders, but you can always determine the units mathematically.

Figure 16.9 summarizes the steps for studying the kinetics of a reaction.

**Table 16.4 Units of the Rate Constant $k$ for Several Overall Reaction Orders**

| Overall Reaction Order | Units of $k$ ($t$ in seconds) |
|---|---|
| 0 | mol/L·s (or mol L$^{-1}$ s$^{-1}$) |
| 1 | 1/s (or s$^{-1}$) |
| 2 | L/mol·s (or L mol$^{-1}$ s$^{-1}$) |
| 3 | L$^2$/mol$^2$·s (or L$^2$ mol$^{-2}$ s$^{-1}$) |

General formula:

$$\text{Units of } k = \frac{\left(\dfrac{\text{L}}{\text{mol}}\right)^{\text{order}-1}}{\text{unit of } t}$$

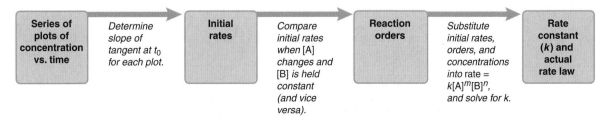

**Figure 16.9** Information sequence to determine the kinetic parameters of a reaction.

## ■ Summary of Section 16.3

● An experimentally determined rate law shows how the rate of a reaction depends on concentration. Considering only initial rates (that is, no products), the expression for a general rate law is rate = $k[A]^m[B]^n \cdots$. This reaction is $m$th order with respect to A and $n$th order with respect to B; the overall reaction order is $m + n$.

● With an accurate method for obtaining initial rates, reaction orders are determined experimentally by varying the concentration of one reactant at a time to see its effect on the rate.

● By substituting the known rate, concentrations, and reaction orders into the rate law, we solve for the rate constant, $k$.

# 16.4 • INTEGRATED RATE LAWS: CONCENTRATION CHANGES OVER TIME

The rate laws we've developed so far tell us the rate or concentration at a given instant, allowing us to answer questions such as "How fast is the reaction proceeding at the moment $y$ moles per liter of A are mixed with $z$ moles per liter of B?" and "What is [B], when [A] is $x$ moles per liter?" By employing different forms of the rate laws, called **integrated rate laws**, we can include time as a variable and answer questions such as "How long will it take to use up $x$ moles per liter of A?" and "What is [A] after $y$ minutes of reaction?"

## Integrated Rate Laws for First-, Second-, and Zero-Order Reactions

As we've seen, for a *general first-order reaction,* the rate is the negative of the change in [A] divided by the change in time:

$$\text{Rate} = -\frac{\Delta[A]}{\Delta t}$$

It can also be expressed in terms of the rate law:

$$\text{Rate} = k[A]$$

Setting these two expressions equal to each other gives

$$-\frac{\Delta[A]}{\Delta t} = k[A] \qquad \text{or} \qquad -\frac{\Delta[A]}{[A]} = k\Delta t$$

Through the methods of calculus, we integrate over time to obtain the integrated rate law for a first-order reaction:

$$\ln \frac{[A]_0}{[A]_t} = kt \qquad \text{(first-order reaction; rate} = k[A]\text{)} \qquad \textbf{(16.4)}$$

where ln is the natural logarithm, $[A]_0$ is the concentration of A at $t = 0$, and $[A]_t$ is the concentration of A at any time $t$.

For a *general second-order reaction* involving two reactants, A and B, the expression including time is complex. In the simpler case, the rate law contains only reactant A. Setting the two rate expressions equal to each other gives

$$\text{Rate} = -\frac{\Delta[A]}{\Delta t} = k[A]^2 \qquad \text{or} \qquad -\frac{\Delta[A]}{[A]^2} = k\Delta t$$

Integrating over time gives the integrated rate law for a second-order reaction involving one reactant:

$$\frac{1}{[A]_t} - \frac{1}{[A]_0} = kt \qquad \text{(second-order reaction; rate} = k[A]^2\text{)} \qquad \textbf{(16.5)}$$

For a *general zero-order reaction*, setting the two rate expressions equal to each other gives

$$\text{Rate} = -\frac{\Delta[A]}{\Delta t} = k[A]^0 = k \qquad \text{or} \qquad -\Delta[A] = k\Delta t$$

Integrating over time gives the integrated rate law for a zero-order reaction:

$$[A]_t - [A]_0 = -kt \qquad (\text{zero-order reaction; rate} = k[A]^0 = k) \qquad (16.6)$$

Sample Problem 16.5 shows one way integrated rate laws are applied.

---

**Sample Problem 16.5** **Determining the Reactant Concentration after a Given Time**

**Problem** At 1000°C, cyclobutane ($C_4H_8$) decomposes in a first-order reaction, with the very high rate constant of 87 $s^{-1}$, to two molecules of ethylene ($C_2H_4$).
**(a)** The initial $C_4H_8$ concentration is 2.00 $M$. What is the concentration after 0.010 s?
**(b)** What fraction of $C_4H_8$ has decomposed in this time?

**Plan (a)** We must find the concentration of cyclobutane at time $t$, $[C_4H_8]_t$. The problem tells us this is a first-order reaction, so we use the integrated first-order rate law:

$$\ln \frac{[C_4H_8]_0}{[C_4H_8]_t} = kt$$

We know $k$ (87 $s^{-1}$), $t$ (0.010 s), and $[C_4H_8]_0$ (2.00 $M$), so we can solve for $[C_4H_8]_t$.
**(b)** The fraction decomposed is the concentration that has decomposed divided by the initial concentration:

$$\text{Fraction decomposed} = \frac{[C_4H_8]_0 - [C_4H_8]_t}{[C_4H_8]_0}$$

**Solution (a)** Substituting the data into the integrated rate law:

$$\ln \frac{2.00 \text{ mol/L}}{[C_4H_8]_t} = (87 \text{ s}^{-1})(0.010 \text{ s}) = 0.87$$

Taking the antilog of both sides:

$$\frac{2.00 \text{ mol/L}}{[C_4H_8]_t} = e^{0.87} = 2.4$$

Solving for $[C_4H_8]_t$:

$$[C_4H_8]_t = \frac{2.00 \text{ mol/L}}{2.4} = \boxed{0.83 \text{ mol/L}}$$

**(b)** Finding the fraction that has decomposed after 0.010 s:

$$\frac{[C_4H_8]_0 - [C_4H_8]_t}{[C_4H_8]_0} = \frac{2.00 \text{ mol/L} - 0.83 \text{ mol/L}}{2.00 \text{ mol/L}} = \boxed{0.58}$$

**Check** The concentration remaining after 0.010 s (0.83 mol/L) is less than the starting concentration (2.00 mol/L), which makes sense. Raising $e$ to an exponent slightly less than 1 should give a number (2.4) slightly less than the value of $e$ (2.718). Moreover, the final result makes sense: a high rate constant indicates a fast reaction, so it's not surprising that so much decomposes in such a short time.

**Follow-Up Problem 16.5** At 25°C, hydrogen iodide breaks down very slowly to hydrogen and iodine: rate = $k[HI]^2$. The rate constant at 25°C is $2.4 \times 10^{-21}$ L/mol·s. If 0.0100 mol of HI($g$) is placed in a 1.0-L container, how long will it take for the concentration of HI to reach 0.00900 mol/L (10.0% reacted)?

## Determining Reaction Orders from an Integrated Rate Law

In Sample Problem 16.3, we found the reaction orders using rate data. If rate data are not available, we rearrange the integrated rate law into an equation for a straight line, $y = mx + b$, where $m$ is the slope and $b$ is the $y$-axis intercept. We then use a graphical method to find the order:

- For a *first-order reaction,* we have

$$\ln \frac{[A]_0}{[A]_t} = kt$$

From Appendix A, we know that $\ln \frac{a}{b} = \ln a - \ln b$, so we have

$$\ln [A]_0 - \ln [A]_t = kt$$

Rearranging gives

$$\underset{y \quad = \quad mx \quad + \quad b}{\ln [A]_t = -kt + \ln [A]_0}$$

Therefore, a plot of $\ln [A]_t$ vs. $t$ gives a straight line with slope $= -k$ and $y$ intercept $= \ln [A]_0$ (Figure 16.10A).

- For a *second-order reaction* with one reactant, we have

$$\frac{1}{[A]_t} - \frac{1}{[A]_0} = kt$$

Rearranging gives

$$\underset{y \quad = \quad mx + \quad b}{\frac{1}{[A]_t} = kt + \frac{1}{[A]_0}}$$

In this case, a plot of $1/[A]_t$ vs. $t$ gives a straight line with slope $= k$ and $y$ intercept $= 1/[A]_0$ (Figure 16.10B).

- For a *zero-order reaction,* we have

$$[A]_t - [A]_0 = -kt$$

Rearranging gives

$$\underset{y \quad = \quad mx + \quad b}{[A]_t = -kt + [A]_0}$$

A plot of $[A]_t$ vs. $t$ gives a straight line with slope $= -k$ and $y$ intercept $= [A]_0$ (Figure 16.10C).

Some trial-and-error graphical plotting is required to find the reaction order from the concentration and time data:

- If you obtain a straight line when you plot $\ln$ [reactant] vs. $t$, the reaction is *first order* with respect to that reactant.
- If you obtain a straight line when you plot $1/$[reactant] vs. $t$, the reaction is *second order* with respect to that reactant.
- If you obtain a straight line when you plot [reactant] vs. $t$, the reaction is *zero order* with respect to that reactant.

Figure 16.11 shows how to use this approach to determine the order for the decomposition of $N_2O_5$. When we plot the data from each column in the table versus time, we find that the plot of $\ln [N_2O_5]$ vs. $t$ *is* linear (part B), while the plots of $[N_2O_5]$ vs. $t$ (part A) and of $1/[N_2O_5]$ vs. $t$ (part C) are *not;* therefore, the decomposition is first order in $N_2O_5$.

### Reaction Half-Life

The **half-life** $(t_{1/2})$ of a reaction is the time it takes for the reactant concentration to reach *half its initial value.* A half-life has time units appropriate for the reaction and

**A First-order reaction**

**B Second-order reaction**

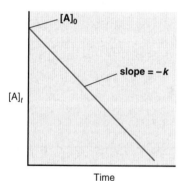

**C Zero-order reaction**

**Figure 16.10** Graphical method for finding the reaction order from the integrated rate law.

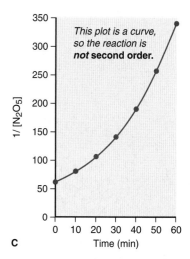

**Figure 16.11** Graphical determination of the reaction order for the decomposition of $N_2O_5$. The time and concentration data in the table are used to obtain the three plots, A, B, and C.

| Time (min) | $[N_2O_5]$ | $\ln [N_2O_5]$ | $1/[N_2O_5]$ |
|---|---|---|---|
| 0 | 0.0165 | −4.104 | 60.6 |
| 10 | 0.0124 | −4.390 | 80.6 |
| 20 | 0.0093 | −4.68 | $1.1 \times 10^2$ |
| 30 | 0.0071 | −4.95 | $1.4 \times 10^2$ |
| 40 | 0.0053 | −5.24 | $1.9 \times 10^2$ |
| 50 | 0.0039 | −5.55 | $2.6 \times 10^2$ |
| 60 | 0.0029 | −5.84 | $3.4 \times 10^2$ |

is characteristic of the reaction at a given temperature. For example, at 45°C, the half-life for the decomposition of $N_2O_5$, which we know is first order, is 24.0 min. Therefore, if we start with, say, 0.0600 mol/L of $N_2O_5$ at 45°C, 0.0300 mol/L will have reacted after 24 min (one half-life), and 0.0300 mol/L will remain; after 48 min (two half-lives), 0.0150 mol/L will remain; after 72 min (three half-lives), 0.0075 mol/L will remain, and so forth (Figure 16.12). The mathematical expression for the half-life depends on the overall order of the reaction.

**First-Order Reactions** We can derive an expression for the half-life of a first-order reaction from the integrated rate law, which is

$$\ln \frac{[A]_0}{[A]_t} = kt$$

By definition, after one half-life, $t = t_{1/2}$, and $[A]_t = \frac{1}{2}[A]_0$. Substituting and canceling $[A]_0$ gives

$$\ln \frac{[A]_0}{\frac{1}{2}[A]_0} = kt_{1/2} \qquad \text{or} \qquad \ln 2 = kt_{1/2}$$

**Figure 16.12** A plot of $[N_2O_5]$ vs. time for three reaction half-lives.

Then, solving for $t_{1/2}$, we have

$$t_{1/2} = \frac{\ln 2}{k} = \frac{0.693}{k} \qquad \text{(first-order process; rate} = k[A]) \qquad \textbf{(16.7)}$$

Because no concentration term appears, *for a first-order reaction, the time it takes to reach one-half the starting concentration is a constant and, thus, independent of reactant concentration.*

Decay of an unstable, radioactive nucleus is an example of a first-order process that does not involve a *chemical* change. For example, the half-life for the decay of uranium-235 is $7.1 \times 10^8$ yr. Thus, a sample of ore containing uranium-235 will have half the original mass of uranium-235 after $7.1 \times 10^8$ years: a sample containing 1 kg will contain 0.5 kg of uranium-235, a sample containing 1 mg will contain 0.5 mg, and so forth. (We discuss radioactive decay thoroughly in Chapter 24.)

The next two sample problems show some ways to use half-life in calculations: the first is based on molecular scenes.

---

**Sample Problem 16.6**   **Using Molecular Scenes to Find Quantities at Various Times**

**Problem** Substance A (*green*) decomposes to two other substances, B (*blue*) and C (*yellow*), in a first-order gaseous reaction. The molecular scenes below show a portion of the reaction mixture at two different times:

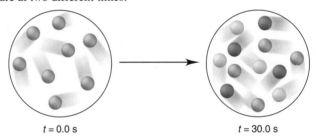

$t = 0.0$ s             $t = 30.0$ s

**(a)** Draw a similar molecular scene of the reaction mixture at $t = 60.0$ s.
**(b)** Find the rate constant of the reaction.
**(c)** If the total pressure ($P_{total}$) of the mixture is 5.00 atm at 90.0 s, what is the partial pressure of substance B ($P_B$)?

**Plan** We are shown molecular scenes of a reaction at two times with various numbers of reactant and product particles and have to predict quantities at two later times. **(a)** We count the number of A particles and see that A has decreased by half after 30.0 s; thus, the half-life is 30.0 s. The time $t = 60.0$ s represents two half-lives, so the number of A will decrease by half again, and each A forms one B and one C. **(b)** We substitute the value of the half-life in Equation 16.7 to find $k$. **(c)** First, we find the numbers of particles at $t = 90.0$ s, which represents three half-lives. To find $P_B$, we multiply the mole fraction of B, $X_B$, by $P_{total}$ (5.00 atm) (Chapter 5). To find $X_B$, we know that the number of particles is equivalent to the number of moles, so we divide the number of B particles by the total number of particles.

**Solution** **(a)** The number of A particles decreased from 8 to 4 in one half-life (30.0 s), so after two half-lives (60.0 s), the number would be 2 (1/2 of 4) A particles. Each A decomposes to 1 B and 1 C, so 6 (8 − 2) particles of A form 6 particles of B and 6 of C (*see margin*).
**(b)** Finding the rate constant, $k$:

$$t_{1/2} = \frac{0.693}{k} \qquad \text{so} \qquad k = \frac{0.693}{t_{1/2}} = \frac{0.693}{30.0 \text{ s}} = \boxed{2.31 \times 10^{-2} \text{ s}^{-1}}$$

**(c)** Finding the number of particles after 90.0 s: After a third half-life, there would be 1 A, 7 B, and 7 C particles.
Finding the mole fraction of B, $X_B$:

$$X_B = \frac{7}{1 + 7 + 7} = \frac{7}{15} = 0.467$$

Finding the partial pressure of B, $P_B$:

$$P_B = X_B \times P_{total} = 0.467 \times 5.00 \text{ atm} = \boxed{2.33 \text{ atm}}$$

**Check** For (b), rounding gives 0.7/30, which is a bit over 0.02, so the answer seems correct. For (c), $X_B$ is almost 0.5, so $P_B$ is a bit less than half of 5 atm, or <2.5 atm.

$t = 60.0$ s

**Follow-Up Problem 16.6** Substance X (*black*) changes to substance Y (*red*) in a first-order gaseous reaction. The scenes below represent the reaction mixture in cubic containers at two different times:

$t = 0.0$ min                    $t = 2.5$ min

(a) Draw a scene that represents the mixture at 5.0 min. (b) If each sphere represents 0.20 mol of particles and the volume of the cubic container is 0.50 L, what is the molarity of X at 10.0 min?

## Sample Problem 16.7 | Determining the Half-Life of a First-Order Reaction

**Problem** Cyclopropane is the smallest cyclic hydrocarbon. Because its 60° bond angles reduce orbital overlap, its bonds are weak. As a result, it is thermally unstable and rearranges to propene at 1000°C via the following first-order reaction:

$$\begin{matrix} & CH_2 & \\ & \diagup \, \backslash & \\ H_2C & \!\!\!\!\!-\!\!\!\!\! & CH_2(g) \end{matrix} \xrightarrow{\Delta} CH_3\!-\!CH\!=\!CH_2(g)$$

The rate constant is $9.2$ s$^{-1}$. (a) What is the half-life of the reaction? (b) How long does it take for the concentration of cyclopropane to reach one-quarter of the initial value?

**Plan** (a) The cyclopropane rearrangement is first order, so to find $t_{1/2}$ we use Equation 16.7 and substitute for $k$ ($9.2$ s$^{-1}$). (b) Each half-life decreases the concentration to one-half of its initial value, so two half-lives decrease it to one-quarter.

**Solution** (a) Solving for $t_{1/2}$:

$$t_{1/2} = \frac{\ln 2}{k} = \frac{0.693}{9.2 \text{ s}^{-1}} = \boxed{0.075 \text{ s}}$$

It takes 0.075 s for half the cyclopropane to form propene at this temperature.
(b) Finding the time to reach one-quarter of the initial concentration:

$$\text{Time} = 2(t_{1/2}) = 2(0.075 \text{ s}) = \boxed{0.15 \text{ s}}$$

**Check** For part (a), rounding gives $0.7/9$ s$^{-1}$ = 0.08 s, so the answer seems correct.

**Follow-Up Problem 16.7** Iodine-123 is used to study thyroid gland function. This radioactive isotope breaks down in a first-order process with a half-life of 13.1 h. What is the rate constant for the process?

**Second-Order Reactions** In contrast to the half-life of a first-order reaction, the half-life of a second-order reaction *does* depend on reactant concentration:

$$t_{1/2} = \frac{1}{k[A]_0} \qquad \text{(second-order process; rate} = k[A]^2)$$

Note that here *the half-life is **inversely** proportional to the initial reactant concentration*. This relationship means that a second-order reaction with a high initial reactant concentration has a *shorter* half-life, and one with a low initial reactant concentration has a *longer* half-life.

**Zero-Order Reactions** In contrast to the half-life of a second-order reaction, *the half-life of a zero-order reaction is **directly** proportional to the initial reactant concentration:*

$$t_{1/2} = \frac{[A]_0}{2k} \qquad \text{(zero-order process; rate} = k)$$

Thus, if a zero-order reaction begins with a high reactant concentration, it has a longer half-life than if it begins with a low reactant concentration.

**Table 16.5  An Overview of Zero-Order, First-Order, and Simple Second-Order Reactions**

| | Zero Order | First Order | Second Order |
|---|---|---|---|
| Rate law | rate $= k$ | rate $= k[A]$ | rate $= k[A]^2$ |
| Units for $k$ | mol/L·s | 1/s | L/mol·s |
| Half-life | $\dfrac{[A]_0}{2k}$ | $\dfrac{\ln 2}{k}$ | $\dfrac{1}{k[A]_0}$ |
| Integrated rate law in straight-line form | $[A]_t = -kt + [A]_0$ | $\ln [A]_t = -kt + \ln [A]_0$ | $1/[A]_t = kt + 1/[A]_0$ |
| Plot for straight line | $[A]_t$ vs. $t$ | $\ln [A]_t$ vs. $t$ | $1/[A]_t$ vs. $t$ |
| Slope, $y$ intercept | $-k, [A]_0$ | $-k, \ln [A]_0$ | $k, 1/[A]_0$ |

Table 16.5 summarizes the features of zero-, first-, and second-order reactions.

## Summary of Section 16.4

- Integrated rate laws are used to find either the time needed to reach a certain concentration of reactant or the concentration present after a given time.
- Rearrangements of the integrated rate laws that give equations in the form of a straight line allow us to determine reaction orders and rate constants graphically.
- The half-life is the time needed for the reactant concentration to reach half its initial value; for first-order reactions, the half-life is constant, that is, independent of concentration.

# 16.5 • THEORIES OF CHEMICAL KINETICS

As was pointed out at the beginning of the chapter, concentration and temperature have major effects on reaction rate. Chemists employ two models—*collision theory* and *transition state theory*—to explain these effects.

## Collision Theory: Basis of the Rate Law

The basic tenet of **collision theory** is that particles—atoms, molecules, or ions—must collide to react. But number of collisions can't be the only factor determining rate, or all reactions would be over in an instant. For example, at 1 atm and 20°C, the $N_2$ and $O_2$ molecules in 1 mL of air experience about $10^{27}$ collisions per second. If all that was needed for a reaction to occur was an $N_2$ molecule colliding with an $O_2$ molecule, our atmosphere would consist of almost all NO; in fact, only traces are present. Thus, this theory also relies on the concepts of collision energy and molecular structure to explain the effects of concentration and temperature on rate.

**Why Concentrations Are Multiplied in the Rate Law** Particles must collide to react, so the collision frequency, the number of collisions per unit time, provides an *upper limit* on how fast a reaction can take place. In its basic form, collision theory deals with one-step reactions, those in which two particles collide and form products: A + B ⟶ products. Suppose we have only two particles of A and two of B confined in a vessel. Figure 16.13 shows that four A-B collisions are possible. The laws of probability tell us that the number of collisions depends on the *product* of

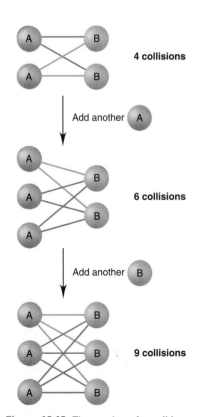

**4 collisions**

Add another (A)

**6 collisions**

Add another (B)

**9 collisions**

**Figure 16.13** The number of possible collisions is the product, not the sum, of reactant concentrations.

| Expt | [Ester] | [$H_2O$] | $T$ (K) | Rate (mol/L·s) | $k$ (L/mol·s) |
|------|---------|----------|---------|----------------|---------------|
| 1 | 0.100 | 0.200 | 288 | $1.04\times10^{-3}$ | 0.0521 |
| 2 | 0.100 | 0.200 | 298 | $2.02\times10^{-3}$ | 0.101 |
| 3 | 0.100 | 0.200 | 308 | $3.68\times10^{-3}$ | 0.184 |
| 4 | 0.100 | 0.200 | 318 | $6.64\times10^{-3}$ | 0.332 |

A

the numbers of reactant particles, not their sum. Thus, when we add another particle of A, six A-B collisions (3 × 2) are possible, not just five (3 + 2). Similarly, when we add another particle of B, nine A-B collisions (3 × 3) are possible, not just six (3 + 3). Thus, collision theory explains why we *multiply* the concentrations in the rate law to obtain the observed rate.

**The Effect of Temperature on the Rate Constant and the Rate** Temperature typically has a dramatic effect on reaction rate: for many reactions near room temperature, an increase of 10 K (10°C) doubles or triples the rate. Figure 16.14A shows kinetic data for an organic reaction—hydrolysis, or reaction with water, of the ester ethyl acetate. To understand the effect of temperature, we measure concentrations and times for the reaction run at different temperatures. Solving each rate expression for $k$ and plotting the results (Figure 16.14B), we find that $k$ *increases exponentially as $T$ increases.*

These results are consistent with findings obtained in 1889 by the Swedish chemist Svante Arrhenius. In its modern form, the **Arrhenius equation** is

$$k = Ae^{-E_a/RT} \tag{16.8}$$

where $k$ is the rate constant, $e$ is the base of natural logarithms, $T$ is the absolute temperature, and $R$ is the universal gas constant. (We'll focus on the term $E_a$ in the next subsection and the term $A$ a bit later.) Note the relationship between $k$ and $T$, especially that $T$ is in the denominator of a negative exponent. Thus, *as $T$ increases, the value of the negative exponent becomes smaller, which means $k$ becomes larger, so the rate increases:*

$$\text{Higher } T \implies \text{larger } k \implies \text{increased rate}$$

**The Central Importance of Activation Energy** The effect of temperature on $k$ is closely related to the **activation energy ($E_a$)** of a reaction, an energy *threshold* that the colliding molecules must exceed in order to react. As an analogy, in order to succeed at the high jump, an athlete must exert at least enough energy to get over the bar. Similarly, if reactant molecules collide with a certain minimum energy, they reach an *activated state,* from which they can change to products (Figure 16.15).

As you can see from Figure 16.15, a reversible reaction has two activation energies. The activation energy for the forward reaction, $E_{a(fwd)}$, is the energy difference between the activated state and the reactants; the activation energy for the reverse

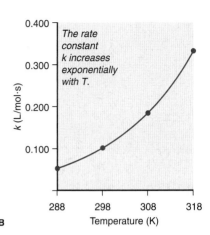

**Figure 16.14** Increase of the rate constant with temperature for the hydrolysis of an ester.

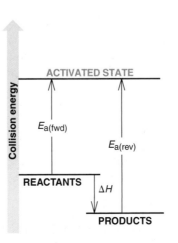

**Figure 16.15** Energy-level diagram for a reaction. Like a high jumper with enough energy to go over the bar, molecules must collide with enough energy, $E_a$, to reach an activated state. (This reaction is reversible and is exothermic in the forward direction.)

reaction, $E_{a(rev)}$, is the energy difference between the activated state and the products. The reaction represented in the diagram is exothermic ($\Delta H_{rxn} < 0$) in the forward direction. Thus, the products are at a lower energy than the reactants, and $E_{a(fwd)}$ is less than $E_{a(rev)}$. This difference equals the heat of reaction, $\Delta H_{rxn}$:

$$\Delta H_{rxn} = E_{a(fwd)} - E_{a(rev)} \tag{16.9}$$

**The Effect of Temperature on Collision Energy** A rise in temperature has two effects on moving particles: it causes a higher collision *frequency* and a higher collision *energy*. Let's see how each affects rate.

- *Collision frequency.* If particles move faster, they collide more often. Calculations show that a 10 K rise in temperature from, say, 288 K to 298 K, increases the average molecular speed by 2%, which would lead to, at most, a 4% increase in rate. Thus, higher collision frequency cannot possibly account for the doubling or tripling of rates observed with a 10 K rise. Indeed, the effect of temperature on collision *frequency* is only a minor factor.
- *Collision energy.* On the other hand, the effect of temperature on collision *energy* is a major factor. At a given temperature, the fraction $f$ of collisions with energy equal to or greater than $E_a$ is

$$f = e^{-E_a/RT}$$

where $e$ is the base of natural logarithms, $T$ is the absolute temperature, and $R$ is the universal gas constant. The right side of this expression appears in the Arrhenius equation (Equation 16.8), which shows that a rise in $T$ causes a larger $k$. We now see why—because *a rise in temperature enlarges the fraction of collisions with enough energy to exceed $E_a$* (Figure 16.16).

Table 16.6 shows that the magnitudes of *both $E_a$ and $T$ affect the size of this fraction* for the hydrolysis of the ester we discussed above. In the top portion, temperature is held constant, and the fraction of sufficiently energetic collisions shrinks several orders of magnitude with each 25-kJ/mol increase in $E_a$. (To extend the high jump analogy, as the height of the bar is raised, a smaller fraction of the athletes have enough energy to jump over it.) In the bottom portion, $E_a$ is held constant, and the fraction nearly doubles for each 10 K (10°C) rise in temperature.

Therefore, *the smaller the activation energy (or the higher the temperature), the larger the fraction of sufficiently energetic collisions, the larger the value of k, and the higher the reaction rate:*

Smaller $E_a$ (or higher $T$) $\Longrightarrow$ larger $f$ $\Longrightarrow$ larger $k$ $\Longrightarrow$ higher rate

**Calculating the Activation Energy** We can calculate $E_a$ from the Arrhenius equation by taking the natural logarithm of both sides of the equation, which recasts it into the form of an equation for a straight line:

$$k = Ae^{-E_a/RT}$$

$$\ln k = \ln A - \frac{E_a}{R}\left(\frac{1}{T}\right)$$

$$y = b + mx$$

| Table 16.6 The Effect of $E_a$ and $T$ on the Fraction ($f$) of Collisions with Sufficient Energy to Allow Reaction | |
|---|---|
| $E_a$ (kJ/mol) | $f$ (at $T = 298$ K) |
| 50 | $1.70\times10^{-9}$ |
| 75 | $7.03\times10^{-14}$ |
| 100 | $2.90\times10^{-18}$ |
| $T$ | $f$ (at $E_a = 50$ kJ/mol) |
| 25°C (298 K) | $1.70\times10^{-9}$ |
| 35°C (308 K) | $3.29\times10^{-9}$ |
| 45°C (318 K) | $6.12\times10^{-9}$ |

**Figure 16.16** The effect of temperature on the distribution of collision energies.

At $T_2$, with $T_2 > T_1$, a larger fraction of collisions have enough energy to exceed $E_a$.

A plot of $\ln k$ vs. $1/T$ gives a straight line whose slope is $-E_a/R$ and whose $y$ intercept is $\ln A$ (Figure 16.17). We know the constant $R$, so we can determine $E_a$ graphically from a series of $k$ values at different temperatures.

We can find $E_a$ in another way if we know the rate constants at two temperatures, $T_2$ and $T_1$:

$$\ln k_2 = \ln A - \frac{E_a}{R}\left(\frac{1}{T_2}\right) \qquad \ln k_1 = \ln A - \frac{E_a}{R}\left(\frac{1}{T_1}\right)$$

When we subtract $\ln k_1$ from $\ln k_2$, the term $\ln A$ drops out and the other terms can be rearranged to give

$$\ln \frac{k_2}{k_1} = -\frac{E_a}{R}\left(\frac{1}{T_2} - \frac{1}{T_1}\right) \qquad \text{(16.10)}$$

Then, we can solve for $E_a$, as in the next sample problem.

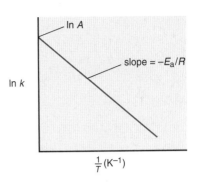

**Figure 16.17** Graphical determination of the activation energy.

---

## Sample Problem 16.8  Determining the Energy of Activation

**Problem** The decomposition of hydrogen iodide, $2HI(g) \longrightarrow H_2(g) + I_2(g)$, has rate constants of $9.51\times10^{-9}$ L/mol·s at 500. K and $1.10\times10^{-5}$ L/mol·s at 600. K. Find $E_a$.

**Plan** We are given the rate constants, $k_1$ and $k_2$, at two temperatures, $T_1$ and $T_2$, so we substitute into Equation 16.10 and solve for $E_a$.

**Solution** Rearranging Equation 16.10 to solve for $E_a$:

$$\ln \frac{k_2}{k_1} = -\frac{E_a}{R}\left(\frac{1}{T_2} - \frac{1}{T_1}\right)$$

$$E_a = -R\left(\ln \frac{k_2}{k_1}\right)\left(\frac{1}{T_2} - \frac{1}{T_1}\right)^{-1}$$

$$= -(8.314 \text{ J/mol·K})\left(\ln \frac{1.10\times10^{-5}\text{ L/mol·s}}{9.51\times10^{-9}\text{ L/mol·s}}\right)\left(\frac{1}{600.\text{ K}} - \frac{1}{500.\text{ K}}\right)^{-1}$$

$$= 1.76\times10^5 \text{ J/mol} = 1.76\times10^2 \text{ kJ/mol}$$

**Comment** Be sure to retain the same number of significant figures in $1/T$ as you have in $T$, or a significant error could be introduced. Round to the correct number of significant figures only at the final answer. On most pocket calculators, the expression $(1/T_2 - 1/T_1)$ is entered as follows: $(T_2)(1/x) - (T_1)(1/x) =$

**Follow-Up Problem 16.8** The reaction $2NOCl(g) \longrightarrow 2NO(g) + Cl_2(g)$ has an $E_a$ of $1.00\times10^2$ kJ/mol and a rate constant of 0.286 L/mol·s at 500. K. What is the rate constant at 490. K?

---

**The Effect of Molecular Structure on Rate** At ordinary temperatures, the enormous number of collisions per second between reactant particles is reduced by six or more orders of magnitude by counting only those with enough energy to react. And, even this tiny fraction of all collisions is typically much larger than the number of **effective collisions,** those that actually lead to product because *the atoms that become bonded in the product make contact.* Thus, to be effective, a collision must have enough energy *and* the appropriate *molecular orientation.*

In the Arrhenius equation, molecular orientation is contained in the term $A$:

$$k = Ae^{-E_a/RT}$$

This term is the **frequency factor,** the product of the collision frequency $Z$ and an *orientation probability factor, p,* which is specific for each reaction:

$$A = pZ$$

The factor $p$ is related to the structural complexity of the reactants. You can think of $p$ as the ratio of effectively oriented collisions to all possible collisions. Figure 16.18 shows a few of the collision orientations for the following reaction:

$$NO(g) + NO_3(g) \longrightarrow 2NO_2(g)$$

**Figure 16.18** The importance of molecular orientation to an effective collision. In the one effective orientation (*bottom*), contact occurs between the atoms that become bonded in the product.

Of the five orientations shown, only one has the effective orientation, with the N of NO making contact with an O of $NO_3$. Actually, the $p$ value for this reaction is 0.006: only 6 collisions in every 1000 (1 in 167) have the correct orientation.

*The more complex the molecular structure, the smaller the p value is.* Individual atoms are spherical, so reactions between them have $p$ values near 1: as long as reacting atoms collide with enough energy, the product forms. At the other extreme are biochemical reactions, in which two small molecules (or portions of larger molecules) react only when they collide with enough energy on a specific tiny region of a giant protein. The $p$ value for these reactions is often much less than $10^{-6}$, fewer than one in a million. The fact that countless such biochemical reactions are occurring in you right now attests to the astounding number of collisions per second!

## Transition State Theory: What the Activation Energy Is Used For

Collision theory explains the importance of effective collisions, and **transition state theory** focuses on the high-energy species that exists at the moment of an effective collision when reactants are becoming product.

**Visualizing the Transition State** As two molecules approach each other, repulsions between their electron clouds continually increase, so they slow down as some of their kinetic energy is converted to potential energy. If they collide, but the energy of the collision is *less* than the activation energy, the molecules bounce off each other.

However, in a tiny fraction of collisions in which the molecules are moving fast enough, *their kinetic energies push them together with enough force to overcome the repulsions and surpass the activation energy.* And, in an even tinier fraction of these sufficiently energetic collisions, the molecules are oriented effectively. In those cases, nuclei in one molecule attract electrons in the other, atomic orbitals overlap, electron densities shift, and some bonds lengthen and weaken while others shorten and strengthen. At some point during this smooth transformation, *a species with partial bonds exists* that is neither reactant nor product. This very unstable species, called the **transition state** (or **activated complex**) exists only at the instant of highest potential energy. Thus, *the activation energy of a reaction is used to reach the transition state.*

Transition states cannot be isolated, but the work of Ahmed H. Zewail, who received the 1999 Nobel Prize in chemistry, greatly expanded our knowledge of them. Using lasers pulsing at the time scale of bond vibrations ($10^{-15}$ s), he observed transition states forming and decomposing. A few, such as the one that forms as methyl bromide reacts with hydroxide ion, have been well studied:

$$BrCH_3 + OH^- \longrightarrow Br^- + CH_3OH$$

The electronegative bromine makes the carbon in $BrCH_3$ partially positive, and the carbon attracts the negatively charged oxygen in $OH^-$. As a C—O bond begins to form, the Br—C bond begins to weaken. In the transition state (Figure 16.19), C is surrounded by five atoms (trigonal bipyramidal; Section 10.2), which never occurs in its stable compounds. This high-energy species has three normal C—H bonds and two partial bonds, one from C to O and the other from Br to C.

Reaching the transition state does not guarantee that a reaction will proceed to products because *a transition state can change in either direction.* In this case, if the C—O bond continues to strengthen, products form; but, if the Br—C bond becomes stronger again, the transition state reverts to reactants.

**Depicting the Change with a Reaction Energy Diagram** A useful way to depict these events is with a **reaction energy diagram,** which plots how potential energy changes as the reaction proceeds from reactants to products (the *reaction progress*). The diagram shows the relative energy levels of reactants, products, and transition state, as well as the forward and reverse activation energies and the enthalpy of reaction.

The bottom of Figure 16.20 shows the diagram for the reaction of $BrCH_3$ and $OH^-$. This reaction is exothermic, so reactants are higher in energy than products, which means $E_{a(fwd)}$ is less than $E_{a(rev)}$. Above the diagram are molecular-scale views at various points during the reaction and corresponding structural formulas. At the top of

**Figure 16.19** The transition state of the reaction between $BrCH_3$ and $OH^-$. Note the partial (*dashed*) C—O and Br—C bonds and the trigonal bipyramidal shape.

the figure are electron density relief maps of the Br, C, and O atoms: note the gradual change in electron density from C overlapping Br (*left*) to C overlapping O (*right*).

Transition state theory proposes that *every reaction (or every step in an overall reaction) goes through its own transition state.* Figure 16.21 presents reaction energy diagrams for two gas-phase reactions. In each case, the structure of the transition state is predicted from the orientations of the reactant atoms that must become bonded in the product.

**Figure 16.20 Depicting the reaction between $BrCH_3$ and $OH^-$.** In order (*bottom to top*) are the reaction energy diagram with blow-up arrows at five points during the reaction, molecular-scale views, structural formulas, and electron density relief maps. Note the gradual, simultaneous C—O bond forming and Br—C bond breaking.

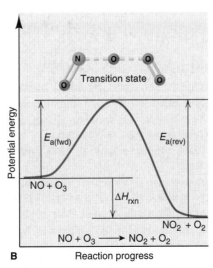

**Figure 16.21 Reaction energy diagrams and possible transition states for two reactions.**

**Sample Problem 16.9** Drawing Reaction Energy Diagrams and Transition States

**Problem** A key reaction in the upper atmosphere is

$$O_3(g) + O(g) \longrightarrow 2O_2(g)$$

The $E_{a(fwd)}$ is 19 kJ, and the $\Delta H_{rxn}$ for the reaction as written is $-392$ kJ. Draw a reaction energy diagram, predict a structure for the transition state, and calculate $E_{a(rev)}$.

**Plan** The reaction is highly exothermic ($\Delta H_{rxn} = -392$ kJ), so the products are much lower in energy than the reactants. The small $E_{a(fwd)}$ (19 kJ) means the energy of the reactants lies slightly below that of the transition state. We use Equation 16.9 to calculate $E_{a(rev)}$. To predict the transition state, we sketch the species and note that one of the bonds in $O_3$ weakens, and this partially bonded O begins forming a bond to the separate O atom.

**Solution** Solving for $E_{a(rev)}$:

$$\Delta H_{rxn} = E_{a(fwd)} - E_{a(rev)}$$

So,

$$E_{a(rev)} = E_{a(fwd)} - \Delta H_{rxn} = 19 \text{ kJ} - (-392 \text{ kJ}) = \boxed{411 \text{ kJ}}$$

The reaction energy diagram (not drawn to scale), with transition state, is

**Check** Rounding to find $E_{a(rev)}$ gives ~20 + 390 = 410.

**Follow-Up Problem 16.9** The following reaction energy diagram depicts another key atmospheric reaction. Label the axes, identify $E_{a(fwd)}$, $E_{a(rev)}$, and $\Delta H_{rxn}$, draw and label the transition state, and calculate $E_{a(rev)}$ for the reaction.

## ■ Summary of Section 16.5

- According to collision theory, reactant particles must collide to react, and the number of possible collisions is found by multiplying the number of reactant particles.
- As the Arrhenius equation shows, a rise in temperature increases the rate because it increases the rate constant.
- The activation energy, $E_a$, is the minimum energy needed for colliding particles to react.
- The relative $E_a$ values for the forward and reverse reactions depend on whether the overall reaction is exothermic or endothermic.
- At higher temperatures, more collisions have enough energy to exceed $E_a$.
- $E_a$ can be determined graphically from $k$ values obtained at different $T$ values.

- Molecules must collide with an effective orientation for them to react, so structural complexity decreases rate.
- Transition state theory focuses on the change of kinetic energy to potential energy as reactant particles collide and form an unstable transition state.
- Given a sufficiently energetic collision and an effective molecular orientation, the reactant species form the transition state, which either continues toward product(s) or reverts to reactant(s).
- A reaction energy diagram depicts the changing potential energy throughout a reaction's progress from reactants through transition states to products.

# 16.6 • REACTION MECHANISMS: THE STEPS FROM REACTANT TO PRODUCT

You can't understand how a car works by examining the body, wheels, and dashboard, or even the engine as a whole. You need to look inside the engine to see how its parts fit together and function. Similarly, by examining the overall balanced equation, we can't know how a reaction works. We must look "inside the reaction" to see how reactants change into products.

Most reactions occur through a **reaction mechanism,** a sequence of single reaction steps that sum to the overall equation. For example, a possible mechanism for the overall reaction

$$2A + B \longrightarrow E + F$$

might involve these three simpler steps:

(1) $A + B \longrightarrow C$
(2) $C + A \longrightarrow D$
(3) $\phantom{C +} D \longrightarrow E + F$

Adding the steps and canceling common substances gives the overall equation:

$$A + B + \cancel{C} + A + \cancel{D} \longrightarrow \cancel{C} + \cancel{D} + E + F \quad \text{or} \quad 2A + B \longrightarrow E + F$$

A mechanism is a hypothesis about how a reaction occurs; chemists *propose* a mechanism and then *test* to see that it fits with the observed rate law.

## Elementary Reactions and Molecularity

The individual steps that make up a reaction mechanism are called **elementary reactions** (or **elementary steps**). Each describes a *single molecular event*—one particle decomposing, two particles combining, and so forth.

An elementary step is characterized by its **molecularity,** the number of *reactant* particles in the step. Consider the mechanism for the breakdown of ozone in the stratosphere. The overall equation is

$$2O_3(g) \longrightarrow 3O_2(g)$$

A two-step mechanism has been proposed:

(1) $O_3(g) \longrightarrow O_2(g) + O(g)$
(2) $O_3(g) + O(g) \longrightarrow 2O_2(g)$

The first step is a **unimolecular reaction,** one that involves the decomposition or rearrangement of a single particle ($O_3$). The second step is a **bimolecular reaction,** one in which two particles ($O_3$ and $O$) react. Some *termolecular* elementary steps occur, but they are extremely rare because the probability of three particles colliding simultaneously with enough energy and an effective orientation is very small. Higher molecularities are not known. Therefore, in general, *we propose unimolecular and/or bimolecular reactions as reasonable steps in a mechanism.*

Because an elementary reaction occurs in one step, its rate law, unlike that for an overall reaction, *can* be deduced from the reaction stoichiometry: *reaction order equals molecularity.* Therefore, *only* for an elementary step, *we use the equation coefficients as the reaction orders in the rate law* (Table 16.7, *next page*).

**Table 16.7 Rate Laws for General Elementary Steps**

| Elementary Step | Molecularity | Rate Law |
|---|---|---|
| A $\longrightarrow$ product | Unimolecular | Rate = $k[A]$ |
| 2A $\longrightarrow$ product | Bimolecular | Rate = $k[A]^2$ |
| A + B $\longrightarrow$ product | Bimolecular | Rate = $k[A][B]$ |
| 2A + B $\longrightarrow$ product | Termolecular | Rate = $k[A]^2[B]$ |

---

**Sample Problem 16.10** | **Determining Molecularity and Rate Laws for Elementary Steps**

**Problem** The following elementary steps are proposed for a reaction mechanism:
(1) $\quad\quad NO_2Cl(g) \longrightarrow NO_2(g) + Cl(g)$
(2) $NO_2Cl(g) + Cl(g) \longrightarrow NO_2(g) + Cl_2(g)$
**(a)** Write the overall balanced equation.
**(b)** Determine the molecularity of each step.
**(c)** Write the rate law for each step.

**Plan** We find the overall equation from the sum of the elementary steps. The molecularity of each step equals the total number of *reactant* particles. We write the rate law for each step using the molecularities as reaction orders.

**Solution (a)** Writing the overall balanced equation:

$$NO_2Cl(g) \longrightarrow NO_2(g) + Cl(g)$$
$$NO_2Cl(g) + Cl(g) \longrightarrow NO_2(g) + Cl_2(g)$$

---

$$NO_2Cl(g) + NO_2Cl(g) + \cancel{Cl(g)} \longrightarrow NO_2(g) + \cancel{Cl(g)} + NO_2(g) + Cl_2(g)$$
$$2NO_2Cl(g) \longrightarrow 2NO_2(g) + Cl_2(g)$$

**(b)** Determining the molecularity of each step: The first step has one reactant, $NO_2Cl$, so it is unimolecular. The second step has two reactants, $NO_2Cl$ and $Cl$, so it is bimolecular.
**(c)** Writing rate laws for the elementary steps:
(1) Rate$_1$ = $k_1[NO_2Cl]$
(2) Rate$_2$ = $k_2[NO_2Cl][Cl]$

**Check** In part (a), be sure the equation is balanced; in part (c), be sure the substances in brackets are the *reactants* of each elementary step.

**Follow-Up Problem 16.10** These elementary steps are proposed for a mechanism:
(1) $\quad\quad\quad 2NO(g) \longrightarrow N_2O_2(g)$
(2) $\quad\quad\quad 2H_2(g) \longrightarrow 4H(g)$
(3) $N_2O_2(g) + H(g) \longrightarrow N_2O(g) + HO(g)$
(4) $\quad HO(g) + H(g) \longrightarrow H_2O(g)$
(5) $\quad H(g) + N_2O(g) \longrightarrow HO(g) + N_2(g)$
**(a)** Write the balanced equation for the overall reaction. **(b)** Determine the molecularity of each step. **(c)** Write the rate law for each step.

## The Rate-Determining Step of a Reaction Mechanism

All the elementary steps in a mechanism have their own rates. However, one step is usually *much* slower than the others. This step, called the **rate-determining step** (or **rate-limiting step**), limits how fast the overall reaction proceeds. Therefore, *the rate law of the rate-determining step becomes the rate law for the overall reaction.* ●
Consider the reaction between nitrogen dioxide and carbon monoxide:

$$NO_2(g) + CO(g) \longrightarrow NO(g) + CO_2(g)$$

If this reaction were an elementary step—that is, if the mechanism consisted of only one step—we could immediately write the overall rate law as

$$\text{Rate} = k[NO_2][CO]$$

● **A Rate-Determining Step for Traffic Flow** Imagine driving home on a wide street that goes over a toll bridge. Traffic flows smoothly until the road narrows at the approach to the toll booth. Past the bridge, traffic returns to normal, and you proceed a couple of miles further to your destination. Getting through the bottleneck to pay the toll takes longer than the rest of the trip combined and, therefore, determines the time for the whole trip.

But, as you saw in Sample Problem 16.3, experimental data show the rate law is

$$\text{Rate} = k[NO_2]^2$$

Thus, the overall reaction cannot be elementary.

A proposed two-step mechanism is

(1) $NO_2(g) + NO_2(g) \longrightarrow NO_3(g) + NO(g)$     [slow; rate determining]
(2) $NO_3(g) + CO(g) \longrightarrow NO_2(g) + CO_2(g)$     [fast]

In this mechanism, $NO_3$ functions as a **reaction intermediate,** a substance formed and used up during the reaction. Even though it does not appear in the overall balanced equation, a reaction intermediate is essential for the reaction to occur. Intermediates are less stable than the reactants and products, but unlike *much* less stable transition states, they have normal bonds and can sometimes be isolated.

Rate laws for the two elementary steps listed above are

(1) $\text{Rate}_1 = k_1[NO_2][NO_2] = k_1[NO_2]^2$

(2) $\text{Rate}_2 = k_2[NO_3][CO]$

Three key points to notice about this mechanism are

- If $k_1 = k$, the rate law for the rate-determining step (step 1) becomes identical to the observed rate law.
- Because the first step is slow, $[NO_3]$ is low. As soon as any $NO_3$ forms, it is consumed by the fast second step, so the reaction takes as long as the first step does.
- CO does not appear in the rate law (reaction order = 0) because it takes part in the mechanism *after* the rate-determining step.

## Correlating the Mechanism with the Rate Law

Coming up with a reasonable reaction mechanism is a classic demonstration of the scientific method. Using observations and data from rate experiments, we hypothesize the individual steps and then test our hypothesis with further evidence. If the evidence supports our mechanism, we can accept it; if not, we must propose a different one. We can never *prove* that a mechanism represents the *actual* chemical change, only that it is consistent with the data.

A valid mechanism must meet three criteria:

1. *The elementary steps must add up to the overall balanced equation.*
2. *The elementary steps must be reasonable.* They should generally involve one reactant particle (unimolecular) or two (bimolecular).
3. *The mechanism must correlate with the rate law,* not the other way around.

**Mechanisms with a Slow Initial Step** The reaction between $NO_2$ and CO that we considered earlier has a mechanism with a slow initial step; that is, the first step is rate-determining. The reaction between nitrogen dioxide and fluorine is another example:

$$2NO_2(g) + F_2(g) \longrightarrow 2NO_2F(g)$$

The experimental rate law is first order in $NO_2$ and in $F_2$,

$$\text{Rate} = k[NO_2][F_2]$$

and the accepted mechanism is

(1) $NO_2(g) + F_2(g) \longrightarrow NO_2F(g) + F(g)$     [slow; rate determining]
(2) $NO_2(g) + F(g) \longrightarrow NO_2F(g)$     [fast]

Note that the free fluorine atom is a reaction intermediate.

Let's see how this mechanism meets the three criteria.

1. The elementary reactions sum to the balanced equation:

$$NO_2(g) + NO_2(g) + F_2(g) + \cancel{F(g)} \longrightarrow NO_2F(g) + NO_2F(g) + \cancel{F(g)}$$

or

$$2NO_2(g) + F_2(g) \longrightarrow 2NO_2F(g)$$

2. Both steps are bimolecular and, thus, reasonable.
3. To determine whether the mechanism is consistent with the observed rate law, we first write the rate laws for the elementary steps:

(1) $Rate_1 = k_1[NO_2][F_2]$
(2) $Rate_2 = k_2[NO_2][F]$

Step 1 is the rate-determining step, and with $k_1 = k$, it is the same as the overall rate law, so the third criterion is met. Note that the second molecule of $NO_2$ is involved *after* the rate-determining step, so it does not appear in the overall rate law. Thus, as in the mechanism for the reaction of $NO_2$ and CO, *the overall rate law includes all the reactants involved in the rate-determining step.*

**Mechanisms with a Fast Initial Step** If the rate-limiting step in a mechanism is *not* the initial step, the product of the fast initial step builds up and starts reverting to reactant. With time, this *fast, reversible step reaches equilibrium,* as product changes to reactant as fast as it forms. As you'll see, this situation allows us to fit the mechanism to the overall rate law.

Consider once again the oxidation of nitrogen monoxide:

$$2NO(g) + O_2(g) \longrightarrow 2NO_2(g)$$

The observed rate law is

$$Rate = k[NO]^2[O_2]$$

and a proposed mechanism is

(1) $NO(g) + O_2(g) \rightleftharpoons NO_3(g)$     [fast, reversible]
(2) $NO_3(g) + NO(g) \longrightarrow 2NO_2(g)$     [slow; rate determining]

Let's go through the three criteria to see if this mechanism is valid. With cancellation of the reaction intermediate, $NO_3$, the sum of the steps gives the overall equation, so the first criterion is met:

$$NO(g) + O_2(g) + \cancel{NO_3(g)} + NO(g) \longrightarrow \cancel{NO_3(g)} + 2NO_2(g)$$

or $$2NO(g) + O_2(g) \longrightarrow 2NO_2(g)$$

Both steps are bimolecular, so the second criterion is met.

To see whether the third criterion—that the mechanism is consistent with the observed rate law—is met, we first write rate laws for the elementary steps:

(1) $Rate_{1(fwd)} = k_1[NO][O_2]$
    $Rate_{1(rev)} = k_{-1}[NO_3]$

where $k_{-1}$ is the rate constant and $NO_3$ is the reactant for the reverse reaction.

(2) $Rate_2 = k_2[NO_3][NO]$

Next, we show that the rate law for the rate-determining step (step 2) gives the overall rate law. As written, it does not, because it contains the intermediate $NO_3$, and *an overall rate law includes only reactants (and products).* We eliminate $[NO_3]$ from the rate law for step 2 by expressing it in terms of reactants, as follows. Step 1 reaches equilibrium when the forward and reverse rates are equal:

$$Rate_{1(fwd)} = Rate_{1(rev)} \quad \text{or} \quad k_1[NO][O_2] = k_{-1}[NO_3]$$

To express $[NO_3]$ in terms of reactants, we isolate it algebraically:

$$[NO_3] = \frac{k_1}{k_{-1}}[NO][O_2]$$

Then, substituting for $[NO_3]$ in the rate law for the slow step, step 2, we obtain

$$Rate_2 = k_2[NO_3][NO] = k_2\underbrace{\left(\frac{k_1}{k_{-1}}[NO][O_2]\right)}_{[NO_3]}[NO] = \frac{k_2k_1}{k_{-1}}[NO]^2[O_2]$$

With $k = \dfrac{k_2k_1}{k_{-1}}$, this rate law is identical to the overall rate law.

To summarize, we assess the validity of a mechanism with a fast initial step by

1. Writing rate laws for the fast step (both directions) and for the slow step.
2. Expressing [intermediate] in terms of [reactant] by setting the forward rate law of the reversible step equal to the reverse rate law, and solving for [intermediate].
3. Substituting the expression for [intermediate] into the rate law for the slow step to obtain the overall rate law.

Several end-of-chapter problems, including Problems 16.72 and 16.73, provide additional examples of this approach.

An important point to note is that, *for any mechanism, only reactants involved up to and including the slow (rate-determining) step appear in the overall rate law.*

### Depicting a Multistep Mechanism with a Reaction Energy Diagram

Figure 16.22 shows reaction energy diagrams for two reactions, each of which has a two-step mechanism. The reaction of $NO_2$ and $F_2$ (part A) starts with a slow step, and the reaction of NO and $O_2$ (part B) starts with a fast step. Both overall reactions are exothermic, so the product is lower in energy than the reactants. Note these key points:

- *Each step in the mechanism has its own peak with the transition state at the top.*
- The intermediates (F in part A and $NO_3$ in part B) are reactive, unstable species, so they are higher in energy than the reactants or product.
- The slow (rate-determining) step (step 1 in A and step 2 in B) has a *larger* $E_a$ than the other step.

**Figure 16.22** Reaction energy diagrams for the two-step reaction of (**A**) $NO_2$ and $F_2$ and of (**B**) NO and $O_2$.

A

B

### ■ Summary of Section 16.6

- The mechanisms of most common reactions consist of two or more elementary steps, each of which shows a single molecular event.
- The molecularity of an elementary step equals the number of reactant particles and is the same as the total reaction order of the step. Only unimolecular and bimolecular steps are reasonable.
- The rate-determining (slowest) step in a mechanism determines how fast the overall reaction occurs, and its rate law is equivalent to the overall rate law.
- Reaction intermediates are species that form in one step and react in a later one.

- For a mechanism to be valid, (1) the elementary steps must add up to the overall balanced equation, (2) the steps must be reasonable, and (3) the mechanism must correlate with the rate law.
- If a mechanism begins with a slow step, only those reactants involved in the slow step appear in the overall rate law.
- If a mechanism begins with a fast step, the product of the fast step accumulates as an intermediate, and the step reaches equilibrium. To show that the mechanism is valid, we express [intermediate] in terms of [reactant].
- Only reactants involved in steps up to and including the slow (rate-determining) step appear in the overall rate law.
- Each step in a mechanism has its own transition state, which appears at the top of a peak in the reaction-energy diagram. A slower step has a higher peak (larger $E_a$).

# 16.7 • CATALYSIS: SPEEDING UP A REACTION

Increasing the rate of a reaction has countless applications, in both engineering and biology. Higher temperature can speed up a reaction, but energy for industrial processes is costly and many organic and biological substances are heat sensitive. More commonly, by far, a reaction is accelerated by a **catalyst**, a substance that increases the rate *without* being consumed. Thus, only a small, nonstoichiometric amount of the catalyst is required to speed the reaction. Despite this, catalysts are employed in so many processes that several million tons are produced annually in the United States alone. Nature is the master designer and user of catalysts: every organism relies on protein catalysts, known as *enzymes,* to speed up life-sustaining reactions, and even the simplest bacterium employs thousands of them.

## The Basis of Catalytic Action

Each catalyst has its own specific way of functioning, but in general, *a catalyst causes a lower activation energy, which in turn makes the rate constant larger and, thus, the reaction rate higher:*

$$\text{Catalyst} \implies \text{lower } E_a \implies \text{larger } k \implies \text{higher rate}$$

Consider a general *uncatalyzed* reaction that proceeds by a one-step mechanism involving a bimolecular collision between the reactants A and B (Figure 16.23). The activation energy is relatively large, so the rate is relatively low:

$$A + B \longrightarrow \text{product} \qquad [\text{larger } E_a \implies \text{lower rate}]$$

In the *catalyzed* reaction, reactant A interacts with the catalyst in one step to form the intermediate C, and then C reacts with B in a second step to form product and regenerate the catalyst:

(1) A + catalyst $\longrightarrow$ C        [smaller $E_a \implies$ higher rate]
(2) C + B        $\longrightarrow$ product + catalyst    [smaller $E_a \implies$ higher rate]

Three points to note in Figure 16.23 are

- A catalyst speeds up the forward *and* reverse reactions. Thus, a reaction has the *same yield* with or without a catalyst, but the product forms *faster.*
- A catalyst causes a *lower total activation energy* by providing a *different mechanism* for the reaction. The total of the activation energies for both steps of the catalyzed pathway $[E_{a1(\text{fwd})} + E_{a2(\text{fwd})}]$ is less than the forward activation energy of the uncatalyzed pathway.
- The catalyst is *not* consumed, but rather used and then regenerated.

## Homogeneous Catalysis

Chemists classify catalysts based on whether or not they act in the same phase as the reactants and products. A **homogeneous catalyst** exists in solution with the reaction mixture, so it must be a gas, liquid, or soluble solid.

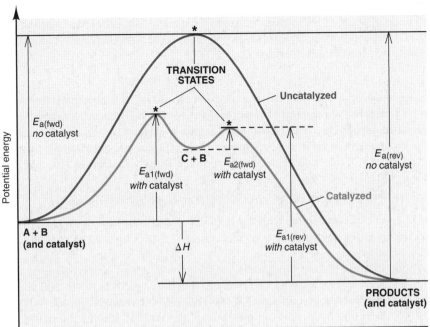

**Figure 16.23 Reaction energy diagram for a catalyzed (*green*) and an uncatalyzed (*red*) process.** A catalyst speeds a reaction by providing a different, lower energy pathway (*green*). (Only the first step of the catalyzed reverse reaction is labeled.)

A thoroughly studied example of homogeneous catalysis in the gas phase was formerly used in sulfuric acid manufacture. The key step, the oxidation of sulfur dioxide to sulfur trioxide, occurs so slowly that it is not economical:

$$SO_2(g) + \tfrac{1}{2}O_2(g) \longrightarrow SO_3(g)$$

In the presence of nitrogen monoxide, however, the reaction speeds up dramatically:

$$NO(g) + \tfrac{1}{2}O_2(g) \longrightarrow NO_2(g)$$
$$NO_2(g) + SO_2(g) \longrightarrow NO(g) + SO_3(g)$$

Note that NO and $NO_2$ cancel to give the overall reaction. Also, note that $NO_2$ acts as an intermediate (formed and then consumed) and NO as a catalyst (used and then regenerated).

Another well-studied example of homogeneous catalysis involves the decomposition of hydrogen peroxide in aqueous solution:

$$2H_2O_2(aq) \longrightarrow 2H_2O(l) + O_2(g)$$

Commercial $H_2O_2$ decomposes in light and in the presence of the small amounts of ions dissolved from glass, but it is quite stable in dark plastic containers. Many other substances speed its decomposition, including bromide ion, $Br^-$ (Figure 16.24). The catalyzed process is thought to occur in two steps:

$$2Br^-(aq) + H_2O_2(aq) + 2H^+(aq) \longrightarrow Br_2(aq) + 2H_2O(l)$$
$$Br_2(aq) + H_2O_2(aq) \longrightarrow 2Br^-(aq) + 2H^+(aq) + O_2(g)$$

In this case, $Br_2$, $Br^-$, and $H^+$ cancel to give the overall balanced equation, $Br^-$ (in the presence of $H^+$) is the catalyst, and $Br_2$ is the intermediate.

## Heterogeneous Catalysis

A **heterogeneous catalyst** speeds up a reaction in a different phase. Most often solids interacting with gaseous or liquid reactants, these catalysts have enormous surface areas, sometimes as much as 500 m$^2$/g. Very early in the reaction, the rate depends on reactant concentration, but almost immediately, the reaction becomes zero order: the rate-determining step occurs on the catalyst's surface, so once the reactant covers it, adding more reactant cannot increase the rate further.

**A**

**B**

**Figure 16.24 The catalyzed decomposition of $H_2O_2$. A,** A small amount of NaBr is added to a solution of $H_2O_2$. **B,** Oxygen gas forms quickly as $Br^-$(*aq*) catalyzes the $H_2O_2$ decomposition; the intermediate $Br_2$ turns the solution orange.

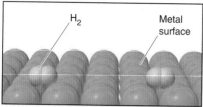

*$H_2$ adsorbs to metal surface.*

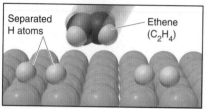

*Rate-limiting step is H—H bond breakage.*

*After $C_2H_4$ adsorbs, one C—H forms.*

*Another C—H bond forms; $C_2H_6$ leaves surface.*

**Figure 16.25** The metal-catalyzed hydrogenation of ethene.

A very important organic example of heterogeneous catalysis is **hydrogenation,** the addition of $H_2$ to C=C bonds to form C—C bonds. The petroleum, plastics, and food industries employ this process on an enormous scale. The simplest hydrogenation converts ethylene (ethene) to ethane:

$$H_2C=CH_2(g) + H_2(g) \longrightarrow H_3C-CH_3(g)$$

In the absence of a catalyst, the reaction is very slow. But, at high $H_2$ pressure (high $[H_2]$) and in the presence of finely divided Ni, Pd, or Pt metal, it is rapid even at ordinary temperatures. The Group 8B(10) metals catalyze by *chemically adsorbing the reactants onto their surface* (Figure 16.25). In the rate-determining step, the adsorbed $H_2$ splits into two H atoms that become weakly bonded to the catalyst's surface (catM):

$$H-H(g) + 2catM(s) \longrightarrow 2catM-H \text{ (H atoms bound to metal surface)}$$

Then, $C_2H_4$ adsorbs and reacts with the H atoms, one at a time, to form $C_2H_6$. Thus, the catalyst acts by lowering the activation energy of the slow step as part of a different mechanism.

A solid mixture of transition metals and their oxides forms a heterogeneous catalyst in your car's exhaust system. The catalytic converter speeds both the oxidation of toxic CO and unburned gasoline to $CO_2$ and $H_2O$ *and* the reduction of the pollutant NO to $N_2$. As in the hydrogenation mechanism, the catalyst adsorbs the molecules, which weakens and splits their bonds, thus allowing the atoms to form new bonds more quickly. The process is extremely efficient: for example, an NO molecule is split into catalyst-bound N and O atoms in less than $2 \times 10^{-12}$ s.

## Kinetics and Function of Biological Catalysts

Whereas most industrial chemical reactions occur under extreme conditions with high concentrations, thousands of complex reactions occur in every living cell in dilute solution at ordinary temperatures and pressures. Moreover, the rate of each reaction responds to the rates of other reactions, chemical signals from other cells, and environmental stress. In this marvelous chemical harmony, each rate is controlled by an **enzyme,** a protein catalyst whose function has been perfected through evolution.

Enzymes are globular proteins with complex shapes (Section 15.6) and molar masses ranging from about 15,000 to 1,000,000 g/mol. A small part of an enzyme's surface—like a hollow carved into a mountainside—is the **active site,** a region whose shape results from the amino acid side chains involved in catalyzing the reaction. Often far apart in the sequence of the polypeptide chain, these groups lie near each other because of the chain's three-dimensional folding. When the reactant molecules, called **substrates,** collide effectively with the active site, they become attached through *intermolecular forces,* and the chemical change begins.

**Characteristics of Enzyme Action** The catalytic behavior of enzymes has several common features:

1. *Catalytic activity.* An enzyme behaves like both types of catalyst. Enzymes are typically *much* larger than the substrate, and many enzymes are embedded within cell membranes. Thus, like a heterogeneous catalyst, an enzyme provides a surface on which one reactant is temporarily immobilized to wait until the other reactant lands nearby. But, like many homogeneous catalysts, the active site groups interact with the substrate(s) in multistep sequences in the presence of solvent and other species.

2. *Catalytic efficiency.* Enzymes are incredibly *efficient* in terms of the number of reactions catalyzed per unit time. For example, for the hydrolysis of urea,

$$(NH_2)_2C=O(aq) + 2H_2O(l) + H^+(aq) \longrightarrow 2NH_4^+(aq) + HCO_3^-(aq)$$

the rate constant is $3 \times 10^{-10}$ s$^{-1}$ for the uncatalyzed reaction in water at room temperature. Under the same conditions in the presence of the enzyme *urease* (pronounced "*yur*-ee-ase"), the rate constant is $3 \times 10^4$ s$^{-1}$, a $10^{14}$-fold increase. Enzymes typically increase rates by $10^8$ to $10^{20}$ times, values that industrial chemists who use catalysts can only dream of!

3. *Catalytic specificity.* As a result of the particular groups at the active site, enzymes are also highly *specific:* each enzyme generally catalyzes only one reaction. Urease catalyzes *only* the hydrolysis of urea, and no other enzyme does this.

**Models of Enzyme Action** Two models of enzyme action have been proposed. According to the earlier **lock-and-key model** (Figure 16.26A), when the "key" (substrate) fits the "lock" (active site), the chemical change begins. However, x-ray crystallographic and spectroscopic methods show that, in most cases, *the enzyme changes shape when the substrate lands at the active site.* Thus, according to the more current **induced-fit model** (Figure 16.26B), the substrate induces the active site to adopt a perfect fit. Rather than a rigid key in a lock, we picture a flexible hand in a glove; the "glove" (active site) does not attain its functional shape until the "hand" (substrate) moves into it.

**Kinetics of Enzyme Action** Kinetic studies of enzyme catalysis show that substrate (S) and enzyme (E) form an intermediate **enzyme-substrate complex (ES),** whose concentration determines the rate of formation of product (P). In other words, the rate of an enzyme-catalyzed reaction is proportional to the concentration of ES, that is, of reactant bound to catalyst. The steps common to virtually all enzyme-catalyzed reactions are

(1) $E + S \rightleftharpoons ES$      [fast, reversible]
(2)      $ES \longrightarrow E + P$      [slow; rate-determining]

Thus, rate $= k[ES]$. As in the heterogeneous catalysis of hydrogenation (Figure 16.25), [S] is much greater than [E], and once all the enzyme molecules are bound to substrate, [ES] is as high as possible. Then, increasing [S] has no effect on rate, and the process is zero order.

**Mechanisms of Enzyme Action** Enzymes employ a variety of reaction mechanisms. In some cases, the active-site groups bring specific atoms of the substrate close together. In others, the groups bound to the substrate move apart, stretching the bond to be broken. Many *hydrolases* have acidic groups that provide $H^+$ ions to speed bond cleavage. Two examples are lysozyme, an enzyme found in tears, which hydrolyzes a polysaccharide in bacterial cell walls to protect the eyes from infection, and chymotrypsin, an enzyme found in the small intestine, which hydrolyzes proteins during digestion.

No matter what their mode of action, *all enzymes catalyze by stabilizing the reaction's transition state.* For instance, in the lysozyme-catalyzed reaction, the transition state is a portion of the polysaccharide whose bonds have been twisted and stretched by the active site groups until it fits the active site well. Stabilizing the transition state lowers the activation energy and thus increases the rate.

Like enzyme-catalyzed reactions, the process of stratospheric ozone depletion includes both homegeneous and heterogeneous catalysis—as you'll see in the following Chemical Connections essay.

**Figure 16.26** Two models of enzyme action.

**A Lock-and-key model:** *fixed shape of active site matches shape of substrate(s).*

**B Induced-fit model:** *active site changes shape to bind substrate(s) more effectively.*

The stratospheric ozone layer absorbs UV radiation with wavelengths between 280 and 320 nm that is emitted by the Sun. If it reaches Earth's suface, this radiation has enough energy to damage genes by breaking bonds in DNA. Thus, depletion of stratospheric ozone increases human health risks, particularly the risks of skin cancer and cataracts (clouding of the eye's lens). The radiation may also damage plant life, especially forms at the bottom of the food chain. Both homogeneous and heterogeneous catalysts play roles in the depletion of ozone.

Before 1976, stratospheric ozone concentration varied seasonally but remained nearly constant from year to year as a result of a series of atmospheric reactions:

$$O_2 \xrightarrow{UV} 2O \qquad \text{[dissociation of } O_2 \text{ by UV]}$$
$$O + O_2 \longrightarrow O_3 \qquad \text{[ozone formation]}$$
$$O_3 + O \longrightarrow 2O_2 \qquad \text{[ozone breakdown]}$$

Then, in 1985, British scientists reported that a severe reduction of ozone, an *ozone hole,* appeared in the stratosphere over the Antarctic when the Sun ended the long winter darkness. Subsequent research by Paul J. Crutzen, Mario J. Molina, and F. Sherwood Rowland, for which they received the Nobel Prize in chemistry, revealed that industrial chlorofluorocarbons (CFCs) were lowering $[O_3]$ in the stratosphere by catalyzing the breakdown reaction.

Widely used as aerosol propellants, foaming agents, and air-conditioning coolants, large quantities of CFCs were released for years. Unreactive in the troposphere, CFC molecules gradually reach the stratosphere, where UV radiation splits them:

$$CF_2Cl_2 \xrightarrow{UV} CF_2Cl\cdot + Cl\cdot$$

(The dots are lone electrons resulting from C—Cl bond cleavage.)

Like many species with a lone electron (free radicals), atomic Cl is very reactive. It reacts with stratospheric $O_3$ to produce the intermediate chlorine monoxide (ClO·), which then reacts with a free O atom to regenerate a Cl atom:

$$O_3 + Cl\cdot \longrightarrow ClO\cdot + O_2$$
$$ClO\cdot + O \longrightarrow Cl\cdot + O_2$$

*The sum of these steps is the ozone breakdown reaction:*

$$O_3 + \cancel{Cl\cdot} + \cancel{ClO\cdot} + O \longrightarrow \cancel{ClO\cdot} + O_2 + \cancel{Cl\cdot} + O_2$$
$$\text{or} \qquad O_3 + O \longrightarrow 2O_2$$

Studies finding high [ClO·] over Antarctica supported this mechanism. Figure B16.1 shows the ozone hole expanding over the years in which CFCs accumulated.

Figure B16.2 shows the reaction energy diagram for the process. Note that *Cl acts as a homogeneous catalyst:* it exists in the same phase as the reactants, lowers the total activation energy via a different mechanism, and is regenerated. Each Cl atom has a stratospheric half-life of about 2 years, during which it speeds the breakdown of about 100,000 ozone molecules.

Later studies showed that the ozone hole enlarges by heterogeneous catalysis. Stratospheric clouds provide a surface for reactions that convert inactive chlorine compounds, such as HCl and chlorine nitrate $(ClONO_2)$, to substances, such as $Cl_2$, that are cleaved by UV radiation to Cl atoms. Fine particles in the stratosphere act in the same way: dust from the 1991 eruption of Mt. Pinatubo reduced stratospheric ozone for 2 years. The Montreal Protocol of 1987 and later amendments curtailed CFC production and proposed substituting hydrocarbon propellants, such as isobutane, $(CH_3)_3CH$. Nevertheless, because of the long lifetimes of CFCs, complete recovery of the ozone layer may take another century! The good news is that tropospheric halogen levels have begun to fall.

**Figure B16.1** Satellite images of the increasing size of the Antarctic ozone hole (*purple*).

**Figure B16.2** Reaction energy diagram for breakdown of $O_3$ by Cl atoms. (Not drawn to scale.)

## Problems

**B16.1** The catalytic destruction of ozone occurs via a two-step mechanism, where X can be one of several species:

(1)  $X + O_3 \longrightarrow XO + O_2$   [slow]
(2)  $XO + O \longrightarrow X + O_2$    [fast]

(a) Write the overall reaction and the rate law for each step.

(b) X acts as _____, and XO acts as _____.

**B16.2** Aircraft in the stratosphere release NO, which catalyzes ozone breakdown by the mechanism shown in Problem B16.1.

(a) Write the mechanism.

(b) When $[O_3]$ is $5 \times 10^{12}$ molecules/cm³ and $[NO]$ is $1.0 \times 10^9$ molecules/cm³, what is the rate of $O_3$ depletion ($k$ for the rate-determining step is $6 \times 10^{-15}$ cm³/molecule·s)?

**B16.3** In the mechanism for $O_3$ breakdown in Problem B16.1:

(a) Which would you expect to have a higher value for the $p$ factor, step 1 with NO or step 1 with Cl? Explain.

(b) Draw a possible transition state for the step with Cl.

## Summary of Section 16.7

- A catalyst increases the rate of a reaction without being consumed. It accomplishes this by providing another mechanism with a lower activation energy.
- Homogeneous catalysts function in the same phase as the reactants. Heterogeneous catalysts act in a different phase from the reactants.
- The hydrogenation of carbon-carbon double bonds takes place on a solid metal catalyst, which speeds up the rate-determining step, the breakage of the $H_2$ bond.
- Enzymes are protein catalysts of high efficiency and specificity that act by stabilizing the transition state and, thus, lowering the activation energy.
- Chlorine atoms from CFC molecules speed the breakdown of stratospheric $O_3$ by a process that has aspects of both homogeneous and heterogeneous catalysis.

# CHAPTER REVIEW GUIDE

**Learning Objectives**  Relevant section (§) and/or sample problem (SP) numbers appear in parentheses.

### Understand These Concepts

1. How reaction rate depends on concentration, physical state, and temperature (§16.1)
2. The meaning of reaction rate in terms of changing concentrations over time (§16.2)
3. How the rate can be expressed in terms of reactant or product concentrations (§16.2)
4. The distinction between average and instantaneous rate and why the instantaneous rate changes during the reaction (§16.2)
5. The interpretation of reaction rate in terms of reactant and product concentrations (§16.2)
6. The experimental basis of the rate law and the information needed to determine it—initial rate data, reaction orders, and rate constant (§16.3)
7. The importance of reaction order in determining the rate (§16.3)
8. How reaction order is determined from initial rates at different concentrations (§16.3)

9. How integrated rate laws show the dependence of concentration on time (§16.4)
10. What reaction half-life means and why it is constant for a first-order reaction (§16.4)
11. Why concentrations are multiplied in the rate law (§16.5)
12. Activation energy and the effect of temperature on the rate constant (Arrhenius equation) (§16.5)
13. How temperature affects rate by influencing collision energy and, thus, the fraction of collisions with energy exceeding the activation energy (§16.5)
14. Why molecular orientation and complexity influence the number of effective collisions and the rate (§16.5)
15. The transition state as the momentary species between reactants and products whose formation requires the activation energy (§16.5)
16. How an elementary step represents a single molecular event and its molecularity equals the number of colliding particles (§16.6)

17. How a reaction mechanism consists of several elementary steps, with the slowest step determining the overall rate (§16.6)
18. The criteria for a valid reaction mechanism (§16.6)
19. How a catalyst speeds a reaction by lowering the activation energy (§16.7)
20. The distinction between homogeneous and heterogeneous catalysis (§16.7)

### Master These Skills

1. Calculating instantaneous rate from the slope of a tangent to a concentration vs. time plot (§16.2)
2. Expressing reaction rate in terms of changes in concentration over time (SP16.1)
3. Determining reaction orders from a known rate law (SP16.2)
4. Determining reaction orders from changes in initial rate with concentration (SPs 16.3, 16.4)

5. Calculating the rate constant and its units (§16.3)
6. Using an integrated rate law to find concentration at a given time or the time to reach a given concentration (SP 16.5)
7. Determining reaction order graphically with a rearranged integrated rate law (§16.4)
8. Determining the half-life of a reaction (SPs 16.6, 16.7)
9. Using a form of the Arrhenius equation to calculate the activation energy (SP 16.8)
10. Using reaction energy diagrams to depict the energy changes during a reaction (SP 16.9)
11. Predicting a transition state for a simple reaction (SP 16.9)
12. Determining the molecularity and rate law for an elementary step (SP 16.10)
13. Constructing a mechanism with either a slow or a fast initial step (§16.6)

## Key Terms

Page numbers appear in parentheses.

**Section 16.1**
chemical kinetics (627)
reaction rate (627)

**Section 16.2**
average rate (630)
instantaneous rate (631)
initial rate (631)

**Section 16.3**
rate law (rate equation) (634)
rate constant (634)
reaction orders (634)

**Section 16.4**
integrated rate law (642)
half-life ($t_{1/2}$) (644)

**Section 16.5**
collision theory (648)
Arrhenius equation (649)
activation energy ($E_a$) (649)
effective collision (651)
frequency factor (651)
transition state theory (652)
transition state (activated complex) (652)
reaction energy diagram (652)

**Section 16.6**
reaction mechanism (655)
elementary reaction (elementary step) (655)
molecularity (655)
unimolecular reaction (655)
bimolecular reaction (655)
rate-determining (rate-limiting) step (656)
reaction intermediate (657)

**Section 16.7**
catalyst (660)
homogeneous catalyst (660)
heterogeneous catalyst (661)
hydrogenation (662)
enzyme (662)
active site (662)
substrate (662)
lock-and-key model (663)
induced-fit model (663)
enzyme-substrate complex (ES) (663)

## Key Equations and Relationships

Page numbers appear in parentheses.

**16.1** Expressing reaction rate in terms of reactant A (630):

$$\text{Rate} = -\frac{\Delta[A]}{\Delta t}$$

**16.2** Expressing the rate of a general reaction (633):

$$\text{Rate} = -\frac{1}{a}\frac{\Delta[A]}{\Delta t} = -\frac{1}{b}\frac{\Delta[B]}{\Delta t} = \frac{1}{c}\frac{\Delta[C]}{\Delta t} = \frac{1}{d}\frac{\Delta[D]}{\Delta t}$$

**16.3** Writing a general rate law (in which products do not appear) (634):

$$\text{Rate} = k[A]^m[B]^n \cdots$$

**16.4** Calculating the time to reach a given [A] in a first-order reaction (rate = k[A]) (642):

$$\ln\frac{[A]_0}{[A]_t} = kt$$

**16.5** Calculating the time to reach a given [A] in a simple second-order reaction (rate = k[A]²) (642):

$$\frac{1}{[A]_t} - \frac{1}{[A]_0} = kt$$

**16.6** Calculating the time to reach a given [A] in a zero-order reaction (rate = k) (643):

$$[A]_t - [A]_0 = -kt$$

**16.7** Finding the half-life of a first-order process (646):

$$t_{1/2} = \frac{\ln 2}{k} = \frac{0.693}{k}$$

**16.8** Relating the rate constant to the temperature (Arrhenius equation) (649):

$$k = Ae^{-E_a/RT}$$

**16.9** Relating the heat of reaction to the forward and reverse activation energies (650):

$$\Delta H_{rxn} = E_{a(fwd)} - E_{a(rev)}$$

**16.10** Calculating the activation energy (rearranged form of Arrhenius equation) (651):

$$\ln\frac{k_2}{k_1} = -\frac{E_a}{R}\left(\frac{1}{T_2} - \frac{1}{T_1}\right)$$

## Brief Solutions to Follow-Up Problems

**16.1** (a) $4NO(g) + O_2(g) \longrightarrow 2N_2O_3(g)$;

$$\text{rate} = -\frac{\Delta[O_2]}{\Delta t} = -\frac{1}{4}\frac{\Delta[NO]}{\Delta t} = \frac{1}{2}\frac{\Delta[N_2O_3]}{\Delta t}$$

(b) $-\dfrac{\Delta[O_2]}{\Delta t} = -\dfrac{1}{4}\dfrac{\Delta[NO]}{\Delta t} = -\dfrac{1}{4}(-1.60\times10\ \text{mol/L·s})$

$$= 4.00\times10^{-5}\ \text{mol/L·s}$$

**16.2** First order in $Br^-$, first order in $BrO_3^-$, second order in $H^+$, fourth order overall

**16.3** Rate $= k[H_2]^m[I_2]^n$. From experiments 1 and 3, $m = 1$. From experiments 2 and 4, $n = 1$. Therefore, rate $= k[H_2][I_2]$; second order overall.

**16.4** (a) The rate law shows the reaction is zero order in Y, so the rate is not affected by doubling Y: rate of Expt 2 = $0.25\times10^{-5}$ mol/L·s
(b) The rate of Expt 3 is four times that of Expt 1, so [X] doubles.

**16.5** $1/[HI]_1 - 1/[HI]_0 = kt$
$111\ \text{L/mol} - 100.\ \text{L/mol} = (2.4\times10^{-21}\ \text{L/mol·s})(t)$
$t = 4.6\times10^{21}$ s (or $1.5\times10^{14}$ yr)

**16.6** (a)   (b) At 10.0 min (4 half-lives), there are 0.75 particles of X.

$$\text{Amount (mol)} = 0.75\ \text{particles} \times \frac{0.20\ \text{mol X}}{1\ \text{particle}} = 0.15\ \text{mol X}$$

$$M = \frac{0.15\ \text{mol X}}{0.50\ \text{L}} = 0.30\ M$$

**16.7** $t_{1/2} = (\ln 2)/k$; $k = 0.693/13.1$ h $= 5.29\times10^{-2}$ h$^{-1}$

**16.8** $\ln \dfrac{0.286\ \text{L/mol·s}}{k_1} = -\dfrac{1.00\times10^5\ \text{J/mol}}{8.314\ \text{J/mol·K}}$

$$\times\left(\frac{1}{500.\ \text{K}} - \frac{1}{490.\ \text{K}}\right) = 0.491$$

$$k_1 = 0.175\ \text{L/mol·s}$$

**16.9**
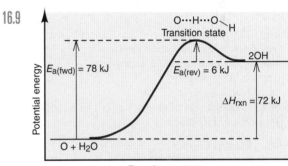

**16.10** (a) Balanced equation (after doubling step 4):
$2NO(g) + 2H_2(g) \longrightarrow N_2(g) + 2H_2O(g)$
(b) Step 2 is unimolecular. All others are bimolecular.
(c) Rate$_1 = k_1[NO]^2$; rate$_2 = k_2[H_2]$; rate$_3 = k_3[N_2O_2][H]$; rate$_4 = k_4[HO][H]$; rate$_5 = k_5[H][N_2O]$.

---

## PROBLEMS

Problems with **colored** numbers are answered in Appendix E and worked in detail in the Student Solutions Manual. Problem sections match those in the text and provide the numbers of relevant sample problems. Most offer Concept Review Questions, Skill-Building Exercises (grouped in pairs covering the same concept), and Problems in Context. The Comprehensive Problems are based on material from any section or previous chapter.

### Focusing on Reaction Rate

#### Concept Review Questions

**16.1** What variable of a chemical reaction is measured over time to obtain the reaction rate?

**16.2** How does an increase in pressure affect the rate of a gas-phase reaction? Explain.

**16.3** A reaction is carried out with water as the solvent. How does the addition of more water to the reaction vessel affect the rate of the reaction? Explain.

**16.4** A gas reacts with a solid that is present in large chunks. Then the reaction is run again with the solid pulverized. How does the increase in the surface area of the solid affect the rate of its reaction with the gas? Explain.

**16.5** How does an increase in temperature affect the rate of a reaction? Explain the two factors involved.

**16.6** In a kinetics experiment, a chemist places crystals of iodine in a closed reaction vessel, introduces a given quantity of $H_2$ gas, and obtains data to calculate the rate of HI formation. In a second experiment, she uses the same amounts of iodine and hydrogen, but first warms the flask to 130°C, a temperature above the sublimation point of iodine. In which of these experiments does the reaction proceed at a higher rate? Explain.

## Expressing the Reaction Rate
(Sample Problem 16.1)

### Concept Review Questions

**16.7** Define *reaction rate*. Assuming constant temperature and a closed reaction vessel, why does the rate change with time?

**16.8** (a) What is the difference between an average rate and an instantaneous rate? (b) What is the difference between an initial rate and an instantaneous rate?

**16.9** Give two reasons to measure initial rates in a kinetics study.

**16.10** For the reaction $A(g) \longrightarrow B(g)$, sketch two curves on the same set of axes that show
(a) The formation of product as a function of time
(b) The consumption of reactant as a function of time

**16.11** For the reaction $C(g) \longrightarrow D(g)$, [C] vs. time is plotted:

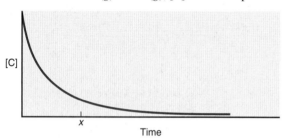

How do you determine each of the following?
(a) The average rate over the entire experiment
(b) The reaction rate at time $x$
(c) The initial reaction rate
(d) Would the values in parts (a), (b), and (c) be different if you plotted [D] vs. time? Explain.

### Skill-Building Exercises (grouped in similar pairs)

**16.12** The compound $AX_2$ decomposes according to the equation $2AX_2(g) \longrightarrow 2AX(g) + X_2(g)$. In one experiment, $[AX_2]$ was measured at various times and these data were obtained:

| Time (s) | $[AX_2]$ (mol/L) |
|---|---|
| 0.0 | 0.0500 |
| 2.0 | 0.0448 |
| 6.0 | 0.0300 |
| 8.0 | 0.0249 |
| 10.0 | 0.0209 |
| 20.0 | 0.0088 |

(a) Find the average rate over the entire experiment.
(b) Is the initial rate higher or lower than the rate in part (a)? Use graphical methods to estimate the initial rate.

**16.13** (a) Use the data from Problem 16.12 to calculate the average rate from 8.0 to 20.0 s.
(b) Is the rate at exactly 5.0 s higher or lower than the rate in part (a)? Use graphical methods to estimate the rate at 5.0 s.

**16.14** Express the rate of reaction in terms of the change in concentration of each of the reactants and products:
$$2A(g) \longrightarrow B(g) + C(g)$$
When [C] is increasing at 2 mol/L·s, how fast is [A] decreasing?

**16.15** Express the rate of reaction in terms of the change in concentration of each of the reactants and products:
$$D(g) \longrightarrow \tfrac{3}{2}E(g) + \tfrac{5}{2}F(g)$$
When [E] is increasing at 0.25 mol/L·s, how fast is [F] increasing?

**16.16** Express the rate of reaction in terms of the change in concentration of each of the reactants and products:
$$A(g) + 2B(g) \longrightarrow C(g)$$
When [B] is decreasing at 0.5 mol/L·s, how fast is [A] decreasing?

**16.17** Express the rate of reaction in terms of the change in concentration of each of the reactants and products:
$$2D(g) + 3E(g) + F(g) \longrightarrow 2G(g) + H(g)$$
When [D] is decreasing at 0.1 mol/L·s, how fast is [H] increasing?

**16.18** Reaction rate is expressed in terms of changes in concentration of reactants and products. Write a balanced equation for
$$\text{Rate} = -\frac{1}{2}\frac{\Delta[N_2O_5]}{\Delta t} = \frac{1}{4}\frac{\Delta[NO_2]}{\Delta t} = \frac{\Delta[O_2]}{\Delta t}$$

**16.19** Reaction rate is expressed in terms of changes in concentration of reactants and products. Write a balanced equation for
$$\text{Rate} = -\frac{\Delta[CH_4]}{\Delta t} = -\frac{1}{2}\frac{\Delta[O_2]}{\Delta t} = \frac{1}{2}\frac{\Delta[H_2O]}{\Delta t} = \frac{\Delta[CO_2]}{\Delta t}$$

### Problems in Context

**16.20** The decomposition of NOBr is studied manometrically because the number of moles of gas changes; it cannot be studied colorimetrically because both NOBr and $Br_2$ are reddish brown:
$$2NOBr(g) \longrightarrow 2NO(g) + Br_2(g)$$
Use the data below to answer the following:
(a) Determine the average rate over the entire experiment.
(b) Determine the average rate between 2.00 and 4.00 s.
(c) Use graphical methods to estimate the initial reaction rate.
(d) Use graphical methods to estimate the rate at 7.00 s.
(e) At what time does the instantaneous rate equal the average rate over the entire experiment?

| Time (s) | [NOBr] (mol/L) |
|---|---|
| 0.00 | 0.0100 |
| 2.00 | 0.0071 |
| 4.00 | 0.0055 |
| 6.00 | 0.0045 |
| 8.00 | 0.0038 |
| 10.00 | 0.0033 |

**16.21** The formation of ammonia is one of the most important processes in the chemical industry:
$$N_2(g) + 3H_2(g) \longrightarrow 2NH_3(g)$$
Express the rate in terms of changes in $[N_2]$, $[H_2]$, and $[NH_3]$.

**16.22** Although the depletion of stratospheric ozone threatens life on Earth today, its accumulation was one of the crucial processes that allowed life to develop in prehistoric times:
$$3O_2(g) \longrightarrow 2O_3(g)$$
(a) Express the reaction rate in terms of $[O_2]$ and $[O_3]$.
(b) At a given instant, the reaction rate in terms of $[O_2]$ is $2.17\times10^{-5}$ mol/L·s. What is it in terms of $[O_3]$?

## The Rate Law and Its Components
(Sample Problems 16.2 to 16.4)

### Concept Review Questions

**16.23** The rate law for the general reaction
$$aA + bB + \cdots \longrightarrow cC + dD + \cdots$$
is rate = $k[A]^m[B]^n \cdots$. (a) Explain the meaning of $k$. (b) Explain the meanings of $m$ and $n$. Does $m = a$ and $n = b$? Explain. (c) If

the reaction is first order in A and second order in B, and time is measured in minutes (min), what are the units for $k$?

**16.24** You are studying the reaction

$$A_2(g) + B_2(g) \longrightarrow 2AB(g)$$

to determine its rate law. Assuming that you have a valid experimental procedure for obtaining $[A_2]$ and $[B_2]$ at various times, explain how you determine (a) the initial rate, (b) the reaction orders, and (c) the rate constant.

**16.25** By what factor does the rate change in each of the following cases (assuming constant temperature)?
(a) A reaction is first order in reactant A, and [A] is doubled.
(b) A reaction is second order in reactant B, and [B] is halved.
(c) A reaction is second order in reactant C, and [C] is tripled.

**Skill-Building Exercises** (grouped in similar pairs)

**16.26** Give the individual reaction orders for all substances and the overall reaction order from the following rate law:

$$Rate = k[BrO_3^-][Br^-][H^+]^2$$

**16.27** Give the individual reaction orders for all substances and the overall reaction order from the following rate law:

$$Rate = k\frac{[O_3]^2}{[O_2]}$$

**16.28** By what factor does the rate in Problem 16.26 change if each of the following changes occurs: (a) $[BrO_3^-]$ is doubled; (b) $[Br^-]$ is halved; (c) $[H^+]$ is quadrupled?

**16.29** By what factor does the rate in Problem 16.27 change if each of the following changes occurs: (a) $[O_3]$ is doubled; (b) $[O_2]$ is doubled; (c) $[O_2]$ is halved?

**16.30** Give the individual reaction orders for all substances and the overall reaction order from this rate law:

$$Rate = k[NO_2]^2[Cl_2]$$

**16.31** Give the individual reaction orders for all substances and the overall reaction order from this rate law:

$$Rate = k\frac{[HNO_2]^4}{[NO]^2}$$

**16.32** By what factor does the rate in Problem 16.30 change if each of the following changes occurs: (a) $[NO_2]$ is tripled; (b) $[NO_2]$ and $[Cl_2]$ are doubled; (c) $[Cl_2]$ is halved?

**16.33** By what factor does the rate in Problem 16.31 change if each of the following changes occurs: (a) $[HNO_2]$ is doubled; (b) [NO] is doubled; (c) $[HNO_2]$ is halved?

**16.34** For the reaction

$$4A(g) + 3B(g) \longrightarrow 2C(g)$$

the following data were obtained at constant temperature:

| Experiment | Initial Rate (mol/L·min) | Initial [A] (mol/L) | Initial [B] (mol/L) |
|---|---|---|---|
| 1 | 5.00 | 0.100 | 0.100 |
| 2 | 45.0 | 0.300 | 0.100 |
| 3 | 10.0 | 0.100 | 0.200 |
| 4 | 90.0 | 0.300 | 0.200 |

(a) What is the order with respect to each reactant? (b) Write the rate law. (c) Calculate $k$ (using the data from Expt 1).

**16.35** For the reaction

$$A(g) + B(g) + C(g) \longrightarrow D(g)$$

the following data were obtained at constant temperature:

| Expt | Initial Rate (mol/L·s) | Initial [A] (mol/L) | Initial [B] (mol/L) | Initial [C] (mol/L) |
|---|---|---|---|---|
| 1 | $6.25\times10^{-3}$ | 0.0500 | 0.0500 | 0.0100 |
| 2 | $1.25\times10^{-2}$ | 0.1000 | 0.0500 | 0.0100 |
| 3 | $5.00\times10^{-2}$ | 0.1000 | 0.1000 | 0.0100 |
| 4 | $6.25\times10^{-3}$ | 0.0500 | 0.0500 | 0.0200 |

(a) What is the order with respect to each reactant? (b) Write the rate law. (c) Calculate $k$ (using the data from Expt 1).

**16.36** Without consulting Table 16.4, give the units of the rate constants for reactions with the following overall orders: (a) first order; (b) second order; (c) third order; (d) $\frac{5}{2}$ order.

**16.37** Give the overall reaction order that corresponds to a rate constant with each of the following units: (a) mol/L·s; (b) $yr^{-1}$; (c) $(mol/L)^{1/2}\cdot s^{-1}$; (d) $(mol/L)^{-5/2}\cdot min^{-1}$.

**Problems in Context**

**16.38** Phosgene is a toxic gas prepared by the reaction of carbon monoxide with chlorine:

$$CO(g) + Cl_2(g) \longrightarrow COCl_2(g)$$

These data were obtained in a kinetics study of its formation:

| Experiment | Initial Rate (mol/L·s) | Initial [CO] (mol/L) | Initial [Cl₂] (mol/L) |
|---|---|---|---|
| 1 | $1.29\times10^{-29}$ | 1.00 | 0.100 |
| 2 | $1.33\times10^{-30}$ | 0.100 | 0.100 |
| 3 | $1.30\times10^{-29}$ | 0.100 | 1.00 |
| 4 | $1.32\times10^{-31}$ | 0.100 | 0.0100 |

(a) Write the rate law for the formation of phosgene.
(b) Calculate the average value of the rate constant.

## Integrated Rate Laws: Concentration Changes over Time

(Sample Problems 16.5 to 16.7)

**Concept Review Questions**

**16.39** How are integrated rate laws used to determine reaction order? What is the order in reactant if a plot of
(a) The natural logarithm of [reactant] vs. time is linear?
(b) The inverse of [reactant] vs. time is linear?
(c) [Reactant] vs. time is linear?

**16.40** Define the *half-life* of a reaction. Explain on the molecular level why the half-life of a first-order reaction is constant.

**Skill-Building Exercises** (grouped in similar pairs)

**16.41** For the simple decomposition reaction

$$AB(g) \longrightarrow A(g) + B(g)$$

rate $= k[AB]^2$ and $k = 0.2$ L/mol·s. How long will it take for [AB] to reach one-third of its initial concentration of 1.50 $M$?

**16.42** For the reaction in Problem 16.41, what is [AB] after 10.0 s?

**16.43** In a first-order decomposition reaction, 50.0% of a compound decomposes in 10.5 min. (a) What is the rate constant of the reaction? (b) How long does it take for 75.0% of the compound to decompose?

**16.44** A decomposition reaction has a rate constant of 0.0012 yr$^{-1}$. (a) What is the half-life of the reaction? (b) How long does it take for [reactant] to reach 12.5% of its original value?

**Problems in Context**

**16.45** In a study of ammonia production, an industrial chemist discovers that the compound decomposes to its elements $N_2$ and $H_2$ in a first-order process. She collects the following data:

| Time (s) | 0 | 1.000 | 2.000 |
|---|---|---|---|
| [$NH_3$] (mol/L) | 4.000 | 3.986 | 3.974 |

(a) Use graphical methods to determine the rate constant.
(b) What is the half-life for ammonia decomposition?

## Theories of Chemical Kinetics

(Sample Problems 16.8 and 16.9)

**Concept Review Questions**

**16.46** What is the central idea of collision theory? How does this model explain the effect of concentration on reaction rate?

**16.47** Is collision frequency the only factor affecting rate? Explain.

**16.48** Arrhenius proposed that each reaction has an energy threshold that must be reached for the particles to react. The kinetic theory of gases proposes that the average kinetic energy of the particles is proportional to the absolute temperature. How do these concepts relate to the effect of temperature on rate?

**16.49** Use the exponential term in the Arrhenius equation to explain how temperature affects reaction rate.

**16.50** How is the activation energy determined from the Arrhenius equation?

**16.51** (a) Graph the relationship between $k$ (vertical axis) and $T$ (horizontal axis). (b) Graph the relationship between ln $k$ (vertical axis) and $1/T$ (horizontal axis). How is the activation energy determined from this graph?

**16.52** (a) For a reaction with a given $E_a$, how does an increase in $T$ affect the rate? (b) For a reaction at a given $T$, how does a decrease in $E_a$ affect the rate?

**16.53** In the reaction AB + CD $\rightleftharpoons$ EF, $4\times10^{-5}$ mol of AB molecules collide with $4\times10^{-5}$ mol of CD molecules. Will $4\times10^{-5}$ mol of EF form? Explain.

**16.54** Assuming the activation energies are equal, which of the following reactions will proceed at a higher rate at 50°C? Explain.

$$NH_3(g) + HCl(g) \longrightarrow NH_4Cl(s)$$
$$N(CH_3)_3(g) + HCl(g) \longrightarrow (CH_3)_3NHCl(s)$$

**Skill-Building Exercises** (grouped in similar pairs)

**16.55** For the reaction A($g$) + B($g$) $\longrightarrow$ AB($g$), how many unique collisions between A and B are possible if there are four particles of A and three particles of B present in the vessel?

**16.56** For the reaction A($g$) + B($g$) $\longrightarrow$ AB($g$), how many unique collisions between A and B are possible if 1.01 mol of A($g$) and 2.12 mol of B($g$) are present in the vessel?

**16.57** At 25°C, what is the fraction of collisions with energy equal to or greater than an activation energy of 100. kJ/mol?

**16.58** If the temperature in Problem 16.57 is increased to 50.°C, by what factor does the fraction of collisions with energy equal to or greater than the activation energy change?

**16.59** The rate constant of a reaction is $4.7\times10^{-3}$ s$^{-1}$ at 25°C, and the activation energy is 33.6 kJ/mol. What is $k$ at 75°C?

**16.60** The rate constant of a reaction is $4.50\times10^{-5}$ L/mol·s at 195°C and $3.20\times10^{-3}$ L/mol·s at 258°C. What is the activation energy of the reaction?

**16.61** For the reaction ABC + D $\rightleftharpoons$ AB + CD, $\Delta H^\circ_{rxn} = -55$ kJ/mol and $E_{a(fwd)} = 215$ kJ/mol. Assuming a one-step reaction, (a) draw a reaction energy diagram; (b) calculate $E_{a(rev)}$; and (c) sketch a possible transition state if ABC is V-shaped.

**16.62** For the reaction $A_2$ + $B_2$ $\longrightarrow$ 2AB, $E_{a(fwd)} = 125$ kJ/mol and $E_{a(rev)} = 85$ kJ/mol. Assuming the reaction occurs in one step, (a) draw a reaction energy diagram; (b) calculate $\Delta H^\circ_{rxn}$; and (c) sketch a possible transition state.

**Problems in Context**

**16.63** Understanding the high-temperature formation and breakdown of the nitrogen oxides is essential for controlling the pollutants generated from power plants and cars. The first-order breakdown of dinitrogen monoxide to its elements has rate constants of 0.76/s at 727°C and 0.87/s at 757°C. What is the activation energy of this reaction?

**16.64** Aqua regia, a mixture of HCl and $HNO_3$, has been used since alchemical times to dissolve many metals, including gold. Its orange color is due to the presence of nitrosyl chloride. Consider this one-step reaction for the formation of this compound:

$$NO(g) + Cl_2(g) \longrightarrow NOCl(g) + Cl(g) \qquad \Delta H^\circ = 83 \text{ kJ}$$

(a) Draw a reaction energy diagram, given $E_{a(fwd)}$ is 86 kJ/mol.
(b) Calculate $E_{a(rev)}$.
(c) Sketch a possible transition state for the reaction. (*Note:* The atom sequence of nitrosyl chloride is Cl—N—O.)

## Reaction Mechanisms: The Steps from Reactant to Product

(Sample Problem 16.10)

**Concept Review Questions**

**16.65** Is the rate of an overall reaction lower, higher, or equal to the average rate of the individual steps? Explain.

**16.66** Explain why the coefficients of an elementary step equal the reaction orders of its rate law but those of an overall reaction do not.

**16.67** Is it possible for more than one mechanism to be consistent with the rate law of a given reaction? Explain.

**16.68** What is the difference between a reaction intermediate and a transition state?

**16.69** Why is a bimolecular step more reasonable physically than a termolecular step?

**16.70** If a slow step precedes a fast step in a two-step mechanism, do the substances in the fast step appear in the rate law? Explain.

**16.71** If a fast step precedes a slow step in a two-step mechanism, how is the fast step affected? How is this effect used to determine the validity of the mechanism?

**Skill-Building Exercises** (grouped in similar pairs)

**16.72** The proposed mechanism for a reaction is
(1) A($g$) + B($g$) $\rightleftharpoons$ X($g$)      [fast]
(2) X($g$) + C($g$) $\longrightarrow$ Y($g$)      [slow]
(3) Y($g$) $\longrightarrow$ D($g$)      [fast]

(a) What is the overall equation?
(b) Identify the intermediate(s), if any.
(c) What are the molecularity and the rate law for each step?
(d) Is the mechanism consistent with the actual rate law: rate = $k[A][B][C]$?
(e) Is the following one-step mechanism equally valid: $A(g) + B(g) + C(g) \longrightarrow D(g)$?

**16.73** Consider the following mechanism:
(1) $ClO^-(aq) + H_2O(l) \rightleftharpoons HClO(aq) + OH^-(aq)$  [fast]
(2) $I^-(aq) + HClO(aq) \longrightarrow HIO(aq) + Cl^-(aq)$  [slow]
(3) $OH^-(aq) + HIO(aq) \longrightarrow H_2O(l) + IO^-(aq)$  [fast]
(a) What is the overall equation?
(b) Identify the intermediate(s), if any.
(c) What are the molecularity and the rate law for each step?
(d) Is the mechanism consistent with the actual rate law: rate = $k[ClO^-][I^-]$?

**Problems in Context**

**16.74** In a study of nitrosyl halides, a chemist proposes the following mechanism for the synthesis of nitrosyl bromide:

$$NO(g) + Br_2(g) \rightleftharpoons NOBr_2(g) \text{ [fast]}$$
$$NOBr_2(g) + NO(g) \longrightarrow 2NOBr(g) \text{ [slow]}$$

If the rate law is rate = $k[NO]^2[Br_2]$, is the proposed mechanism valid? If so, show that it satisfies the three criteria for validity.

**16.75** The rate law for $2NO(g) + O_2(g) \longrightarrow 2NO_2(g)$ is rate = $k[NO]^2[O_2]$. In addition to the mechanism in the text (p. 658), the following ones have been proposed:
I  $2NO(g) + O_2(g) \longrightarrow 2NO_2(g)$
II $2NO(g) \rightleftharpoons N_2O_2(g)$        [fast]
   $N_2O_2(g) + O_2(g) \longrightarrow 2NO_2(g)$        [slow]
III $2NO(g) \rightleftharpoons N_2(g) + O_2(g)$        [fast]
    $N_2(g) + 2O_2(g) \longrightarrow 2NO_2(g)$        [slow]
(a) Which of these mechanisms is consistent with the rate law?
(b) Which of these mechanisms is most reasonable? Why?

## Catalysis: Speeding Up a Reaction

### Concept Review Questions

**16.76** Consider the reaction $N_2O(g) \xrightarrow{Au} N_2(g) + \frac{1}{2}O_2(g)$.
(a) Does the gold catalyst (Au, above the arrow) act as a homogeneous or a heterogeneous catalyst?
(b) On the same set of axes, sketch the reaction energy diagrams for the catalyzed and the uncatalyzed reaction.

**16.77** Does a catalyst increase reaction rate by the same means as a rise in temperature does? Explain.

**16.78** In a classroom demonstration, hydrogen gas and oxygen gas are mixed in a balloon. The mixture is stable under normal conditions, but if a spark is applied to it or some powdered metal is added, the mixture explodes. (a) Is the spark acting as a catalyst? Explain. (b) Is the metal acting as a catalyst? Explain.

**16.79** A principle of green chemistry is that the energy needs of industrial processes should have minimal environmental impact. How can the use of catalysts lead to "greener" technologies?

**16.80** Enzymes are remarkably efficient catalysts that can increase reaction rates by as many as 20 orders of magnitude.
(a) How does an enzyme affect the transition state of a reaction, and how does this effect increase the reaction rate?

(b) What characteristics of enzymes give them this effectiveness as catalysts?

## Comprehensive Problems

**16.81** Experiments show that each of the following redox reactions is second order overall:
Reaction 1: $NO_2(g) + CO(g) \longrightarrow NO(g) + CO_2(g)$
Reaction 2: $NO(g) + O_3(g) \longrightarrow NO_2(g) + O_2(g)$
(a) When $[NO_2]$ in reaction 1 is doubled, the rate quadruples. Write the rate law for this reaction.
(b) When $[NO]$ in reaction 2 is doubled, the rate doubles. Write the rate law for this reaction.
(c) In each reaction, the initial concentrations of the reactants are equal. For each reaction, what is the ratio of the initial rate to the rate when the reaction is 50% complete?
(d) In reaction 1, the initial $[NO_2]$ is twice the initial $[CO]$. What is the ratio of the initial rate to the rate at 50% completion?
(e) In reaction 2, the initial $[NO]$ is twice the initial $[O_3]$. What is the ratio of the initial rate to the rate at 50% completion?

**16.82** Consider the following reaction energy diagram:

(a) How many elementary steps are in the reaction mechanism?
(b) Which step is rate limiting?
(c) Is the overall reaction exothermic or endothermic?

**16.83** Reactions between certain organic (alkyl) halides and water produce alcohols. Consider the overall reaction for t-butyl bromide (2-bromo-2-methylpropane):

$$(CH_3)_3CBr(aq) + H_2O(l) \longrightarrow$$
$$(CH_3)_3COH(aq) + H^+(aq) + Br^-(aq)$$

The experimental rate law is rate = $k[(CH_3)_3CBr]$. The accepted mechanism for the reaction is
(1) $(CH_3)_3C{-}Br(aq) \longrightarrow (CH_3)_3C^+(aq) + Br^-(aq)$  [slow]
(2) $(CH_3)_3C^+(aq) + H_2O(l) \longrightarrow (CH_3)_3C{-}OH_2^+(aq)$  [fast]
(3) $(CH_3)_3C{-}OH_2^+(aq) \longrightarrow H^+(aq) + (CH_3)_3C{-}OH(aq)$  [fast]
(a) Why doesn't $H_2O$ appear in the rate law?
(b) Write rate laws for the elementary steps.
(c) What reaction intermediates appear in the mechanism?
(d) Show that the mechanism is consistent with the experimental rate law.

**16.84** Archeologists can determine the age of an artifact made of wood or bone by measuring the amount of the radioactive isotope $^{14}C$ present in the object. The amount of isotope decreases in a first-order process. If 15.5% of the original amount of $^{14}C$ is present in a wooden tool at the time of analysis, what is the age of the tool? The half-life of $^{14}C$ is 5730 yr.

**16.85** A slightly bruised apple will rot extensively in about 4 days at room temperature (20°C). If it is kept in the refrigerator at 0°C, the same extent of rotting takes about 16 days. What is the activation energy for the rotting reaction?

**16.86** Benzoyl peroxide, the substance most widely used against acne, has a half-life of $9.8 \times 10^3$ days when refrigerated. How long will it take to lose 5% of its potency (95% remaining)?

**16.87** The rate law for the reaction

$$NO_2(g) + CO(g) \longrightarrow NO(g) + CO_2(g)$$

is rate = $k[NO_2]^2$; one possible mechanism is shown on p. 657.
(a) Draw a reaction energy diagram for that mechanism, given that $\Delta H^\circ_{overall} = -226$ kJ/mol.
(b) Consider the following alternative mechanism:
(1) $2NO_2(g) \longrightarrow N_2(g) + 2O_2(g)$     [slow]
(2) $2CO(g) + O_2(g) \longrightarrow 2CO_2(g)$     [fast]
(3) $N_2(g) + O_2(g) \longrightarrow 2NO(g)$     [fast]
Is the alternative mechanism consistent with the rate law? Is one mechanism more reasonable physically? Explain.

**16.88** Consider the following general reaction and data:

$$2A + 2B + C \longrightarrow D + 3E$$

| Expt | Initial Rate (mol/L·s) | Initial [A] (mol/L) | Initial [B] (mol/L) | Initial [C] (mol/L) |
|------|------------------------|---------------------|---------------------|---------------------|
| 1 | $6.0 \times 10^{-6}$ | 0.024 | 0.085 | 0.032 |
| 2 | $9.6 \times 10^{-5}$ | 0.096 | 0.085 | 0.032 |
| 3 | $1.5 \times 10^{-5}$ | 0.024 | 0.034 | 0.080 |
| 4 | $1.5 \times 10^{-6}$ | 0.012 | 0.170 | 0.032 |

(a) What is the reaction order with respect to each reactant?
(b) Calculate the rate constant.
(c) Write the rate law for this reaction.
(d) Express the rate in terms of changes in concentration with time for each of the components.

**16.89** In acidic solution, the breakdown of sucrose into glucose and fructose has this rate law: rate = $k[H^+][sucrose]$. The initial rate of sucrose breakdown is measured in a solution that is 0.01 $M$ $H^+$, 1.0 $M$ sucrose, 0.1 $M$ fructose, and 0.1 $M$ glucose. How does the rate change if
(a) [Sucrose] is changed to 2.5 $M$?
(b) [Sucrose], [fructose], and [glucose] are all changed to 0.5 $M$?
(c) $[H^+]$ is changed to 0.0001 $M$?
(d) [Sucrose] and $[H^+]$ are both changed to 0.1 $M$?

**16.90** The citric acid cycle is the central reaction sequence in human metabolism. One of the key steps is catalyzed by the enzyme isocitrate dehydrogenase and the oxidizing agent $NAD^+$. In yeast, the reaction is eleventh order:

Rate = $k[enzyme][isocitrate]^4[AMP]^2[NAD^+]^m[Mg^{2+}]^2$

What is the order with respect to $NAD^+$?

**16.91** The following molecular scenes represent starting mixtures I and II for the reaction of A (*black*) with B (*orange*):

I          II

Each sphere represents 0.010 mol, and the volume is 0.50 L. If the reaction is first order in A and first order in B and the initial rate for I is $8.3 \times 10^{-4}$ mol/L·min, what is the initial rate for II?

**16.92** Experiment shows that the rate of formation of carbon tetrachloride from chloroform,

$$CHCl_3(g) + Cl_2(g) \longrightarrow CCl_4(g) + HCl(g)$$

is first order in $CHCl_3$, $\frac{1}{2}$ order in $Cl_2$, and $\frac{3}{2}$ order overall. Show that the following mechanism is consistent with the rate law:
(1) $Cl_2(g) \rightleftharpoons 2Cl(g)$     [fast]
(2) $Cl(g) + CHCl_3(g) \longrightarrow HCl(g) + CCl_3(g)$     [slow]
(3) $CCl_3(g) + Cl(g) \longrightarrow CCl_4(g)$     [fast]

**16.93** A biochemist studying breakdown of the insecticide DDT finds that it decomposes by a first-order reaction with a half-life of 12 yr. How long does it take DDT in a soil sample to decompose from 275 ppbm to 10. ppbm (parts per billion by mass)?

**16.94** Insulin is a polypeptide hormone that is released into the blood from the pancreas and stimulates fat and muscle to take up glucose; the insulin is used up in a first-order process. In a certain patient, it has a half-life of 3.5 min. To maintain an adequate blood concentration of insulin, it must be replenished in a time interval equal to $1/k$. How long is the time interval for this patient?

**16.95** For the reaction $A(g) + B(g) \longrightarrow AB(g)$, the rate is 0.20 mol/L·s, when $[A]_0 = [B]_0 = 1.0$ mol/L. If the reaction is first order in B and second order in A, what is the rate when $[A]_0 = 2.0$ mol/L and $[B]_0 = 3.0$ mol/L?

**16.96** The acid-catalyzed hydrolysis of sucrose occurs by the following overall reaction, whose kinetic data are given below:

$$C_{12}H_{22}O_{11}(s) + H_2O(l) \longrightarrow C_6H_{12}O_6(aq) + C_6H_{12}O_6(aq)$$

sucrose                    glucose              fructose

| [Sucrose] (mol/L) | Time (h) |
|-------------------|----------|
| 0.501 | 0.00 |
| 0.451 | 0.50 |
| 0.404 | 1.00 |
| 0.363 | 1.50 |
| 0.267 | 3.00 |

(a) Determine the rate constant and the half-life of the reaction.
(b) How long does it take to hydrolyze 75% of the sucrose?
(c) Other studies have shown that this reaction is actually second order overall but appears to follow first-order kinetics. (Such a reaction is called a *pseudo–first-order reaction.*) Suggest a reason for this apparent first-order behavior.

**16.97** At body temperature (37°C), the rate constant of an enzyme-catalyzed decomposition is $2.3 \times 10^{14}$ times that of the uncatalyzed reaction. If the frequency factor, $A$, is the same for both processes, by how much does the enzyme lower the $E_a$?

**16.98** Is each of these statements true? If not, explain why.
(a) At a given $T$, all molecules have the same kinetic energy.
(b) Halving the $P$ of a gaseous reaction doubles the rate.
(c) A higher activation energy gives a lower reaction rate.
(d) A temperature rise of 10°C doubles the rate of any reaction.
(e) If reactant molecules collide with greater energy than the activation energy, they change into product molecules.
(f) The activation energy of a reaction depends on temperature.
(g) The rate of a reaction increases as the reaction proceeds.
(h) Activation energy depends on collision frequency.
(i) A catalyst increases the rate by increasing collision frequency.
(j) Exothermic reactions are faster than endothermic reactions.
(k) Temperature has no effect on the frequency factor ($A$).
(l) The activation energy of a reaction is lowered by a catalyst.

(m) For most reactions, $\Delta H_{rxn}$ is lowered by a catalyst.

(n) The orientation probability factor ($p$) is near 1 for reactions between single atoms.

(o) The initial rate of a reaction is its maximum rate.

(p) A bimolecular reaction is generally twice as fast as a unimolecular reaction.

(q) The molecularity of an elementary reaction is proportional to the molecular complexity of the reactant(s).

**16.99** For the decomposition of gaseous dinitrogen pentaoxide, $2N_2O_5(g) \longrightarrow 4NO_2(g) + O_2(g)$, the rate constant is $k = 2.8 \times 10^{-3}$ s$^{-1}$ at 60°C. The initial concentration of $N_2O_5$ is 1.58 mol/L. (a) What is $[N_2O_5]$ after 5.00 min? (b) What fraction of the $N_2O_5$ has decomposed after 5.00 min?

**16.100** Even when a mechanism is consistent with the rate law, later work may show it to be incorrect. For example, the reaction between hydrogen and iodine has this rate law: rate = $k[H_2][I_2]$. The long-accepted mechanism had a single bimolecular step; that is, the overall reaction was thought to be elementary:

$$H_2(g) + I_2(g) \longrightarrow 2HI(g)$$

In the 1960s, however, spectroscopic evidence showed the presence of free I atoms during the reaction. Kineticists have since proposed a three-step mechanism:

(1) $I_2(g) \rightleftharpoons 2I(g)$        [fast]

(2) $H_2(g) + I(g) \rightleftharpoons H_2I(g)$      [fast]

(3) $H_2I(g) + I(g) \longrightarrow 2HI(g)$    [slow]

Show that this mechanism is consistent with the rate law.

**16.101** Suggest an experimental method for measuring the change in concentration with time for each of the following reactions:

(a) $CH_3CH_2Br(l) + H_2O(l) \longrightarrow CH_3CH_2OH(l) + HBr(aq)$

(b) $2NO(g) + Cl_2(g) \longrightarrow 2NOCl(g)$

**16.102** An atmospheric chemist fills a container with gaseous $N_2O_5$ to a pressure of 125 kPa, and the gas decomposes to $NO_2$ and $O_2$. What is the partial pressure of $NO_2$, $P_{NO_2}$ (in kPa), when the total pressure is 178 kPa?

**16.103** Many drugs decompose in blood by a first-order process.

(a) Two tablets of aspirin supply 0.60 g of the active compound. After 30 min, this compound reaches a maximum concentration of 2 mg/100 mL of blood. If the half-life for its breakdown is 90 min, what is its concentration (in mg/100 mL) 2.5 h after it reaches its maximum concentration?

(b) For the decomposition of an antibiotic in a person with a normal temperature (98.6°F), $k = 3.1 \times 10^{-5}$ s$^{-1}$; for a person with a fever (temperature of 101.9°F), $k = 3.9 \times 10^{-5}$ s$^{-1}$. If the person with the fever must take another pill when $\frac{2}{3}$ of the first pill has decomposed, how many hours should she wait to take a second pill? A third pill? (Assume the pill is effective immediately.)

(c) Calculate $E_a$ for decomposition of the antibiotic in part (b).

**16.104** While developing a catalytic process to make ethylene glycol from synthesis gas (CO + H$_2$), a chemical engineer finds the rate is fourth order with respect to gas pressure. The uncertainty in the pressure reading is 5%. When the catalyst is modified, the rate increases by 10%. If you were the company patent attorney, would you file for a patent on this catalyst modification? Explain.

**16.105** Iodide ion reacts with chloromethane to displace chloride ion in a common organic substitution reaction:

$$I^- + CH_3Cl \longrightarrow CH_3I + Cl^-$$

(a) Draw a wedge-bond structure of chloroform and indicate the most effective direction of I$^-$ attack.

(b) The analogous reaction with 2-chlorobutane [Figure P16.105(b)] results in a major change in specific rotation as measured by polarimetry. Explain, showing a wedge-bond structure of the product.

(c) Under different conditions, 2-chlorobutane loses Cl$^-$ in a rate-determining step to form a planar intermediate [Figure P16.105(c)]. This cationic species reacts with HI and then loses H$^+$ to form a product that exhibits no optical activity. Explain, showing a wedge-bond structure.

**Figure P16.105(b)**       **Figure P16.105(c)**

**16.106** Assume water boils at 100.0°C in Houston (near sea level), and at 90.0°C in Cripple Creek, Colorado (near 9500 ft). If it takes 4.8 min to cook an egg in Cripple Creek and 4.5 min in Houston, what is $E_a$ for this process?

**16.107** Sulfonation of benzene has the following mechanism:

(1) $2H_2SO_4 \longrightarrow H_3O^+ + HSO_4^- + SO_3$      [fast]

(2) $SO_3 + C_6H_6 \longrightarrow H(C_6H_5^+)SO_3^-$          [slow]

(3) $H(C_6H_5^+)SO_3^- + HSO_4^- \longrightarrow C_6H_5SO_3^- + H_2SO_4$   [fast]

(4) $C_6H_5SO_3^- + H_3O^+ \longrightarrow C_6H_5SO_3H + H_2O$     [fast]

(a) Write an overall equation for the reaction. (b) Write the overall rate law in terms of the initial rate of the reaction.

**16.108** In the lower troposphere, ozone is one of the components of photochemical smog. It is generated in air when nitrogen dioxide, formed by the oxidation of nitrogen monoxide from car exhaust, reacts by the following mechanism:

(1) $NO_2(g) \xrightarrow[hv]{k_1} NO(g) + O(g)$

(2) $O(g) + O_2(g) \xrightarrow{k_2} O_3(g)$

Assuming the rate of formation of atomic oxygen in step 1 equals the rate of its consumption in step 2, use the data below to calculate (a) the concentration of atomic oxygen [O]; (b) the rate of ozone formation.

$k_1 = 6.0 \times 10^{-3}$ s$^{-1}$      $[NO_2] = 4.0 \times 10^{-9}$ M

$k_2 = 1.0 \times 10^6$ L/mol·s    $[O_2] = 1.0 \times 10^{-2}$ M

**16.109** Chlorine is commonly used to disinfect drinking water, and inactivation of pathogens by chlorine follows first-order kinetics. The following data show *E. coli* inactivation:

| Contact Time (min) | Percent (%) Inactivation |
|---|---|
| 0.00 | 0.0 |
| 0.50 | 68.3 |
| 1.00 | 90.0 |
| 1.50 | 96.8 |
| 2.00 | 99.0 |
| 2.50 | 99.7 |
| 3.00 | 99.9 |

(a) Determine the first-order inactivation constant, $k$. [*Hint*: % inactivation = $100 \times (1 - [A]/[A]_0)$.]

(b) How much contact time is required for 95% inactivation?

**16.110** The reaction and rate law for the gas-phase decomposition of dinitrogen pentaoxide are

$$2N_2O_5(g) \longrightarrow 4NO_2(g) + O_2(g) \qquad \text{rate} = k[N_2O_5]$$

Which of the following can be considered valid mechanisms for the reaction?

I   One-step collision

II  $2N_2O_5(g) \longrightarrow 2NO_3(g) + 2NO_2(g)$ [slow]
    $2NO_3(g) \longrightarrow 2NO_2(g) + 2O(g)$ [fast]
    $2O(g) \longrightarrow O_2(g)$ [fast]

III $N_2O_5(g) \rightleftharpoons NO_3(g) + NO_2(g)$ [fast]
    $NO_2(g) + N_2O_5(g) \longrightarrow 3NO_2(g) + O(g)$ [slow]
    $NO_3(g) + O(g) \longrightarrow NO_2(g) + O_2(g)$ [fast]

IV  $2N_2O_5(g) \rightleftharpoons 2NO_2(g) + N_2O_3(g) + 3O(g)$ [fast]
    $N_2O_3(g) + O(g) \longrightarrow 2NO_2(g)$ [slow]
    $2O(g) \longrightarrow O_2(g)$ [fast]

V   $2N_2O_5(g) \longrightarrow N_4O_{10}(g)$ [slow]
    $N_4O_{10}(g) \longrightarrow 4NO_2(g) + O_2(g)$ [fast]

**16.111** Nitrification is a biological process for removing $NH_3$ from wastewater as $NH_4^+$:

$$NH_4^+ + 2O_2 \longrightarrow NO_3^- + 2H^+ + H_2O$$

The first-order rate constant is given as

$$k_1 = 0.47e^{0.095\,(T\,=\,15°C)}$$

where $k_1$ is in day$^{-1}$ and $T$ is in °C.
(a) If the initial concentration of $NH_3$ is 3.0 mol/m$^3$, how long will it take to reduce the concentration to 0.35 mol/m$^3$ in the spring ($T = 20°C$)?
(b) In the winter ($T = 10°C$)?
(c) Using your answer to part (a), what is the rate of $O_2$ consumption?

**16.112** Carbon disulfide, a poisonous, flammable liquid, is an excellent solvent for phosphorus, sulfur, and some other nonmetals. A kinetic study of its gaseous decomposition reveals these data:

| Experiment | Initial Rate (mol/L·s) | Initial [CS$_2$] (mol/L) |
|---|---|---|
| 1 | $2.7 \times 10^{-7}$ | 0.100 |
| 2 | $2.2 \times 10^{-7}$ | 0.080 |
| 3 | $1.5 \times 10^{-7}$ | 0.055 |
| 4 | $1.2 \times 10^{-7}$ | 0.044 |

(a) Write the rate law for the decomposition of $CS_2$.
(b) Calculate the average value of the rate constant.

**16.113** Like any catalyst, palladium, platinum, and nickel catalyze both directions of a reaction: addition of hydrogen to (hydrogenation) and its elimination from (dehydrogenation) carbon double bonds.
(a) Which variable determines whether an alkene will be hydrogenated or dehydrogenated?
(b) Which reaction requires a higher temperature?
(c) How can all-*trans* fats arise during hydrogenation of fats that contain some *cis-* double bonds?

**16.114** In a *clock reaction,* a dramatic color change occurs at a time determined by concentration and temperature. Consider the iodine clock reaction, whose overall equation is

$$2I^-(aq) + S_2O_8^{2-}(aq) \longrightarrow I_2(aq) + 2SO_4^{2-}(aq)$$

As $I_2$ forms, it is immediately consumed by its reaction with a fixed amount of added $S_2O_3^{2-}$:

$$I_2(aq) + 2S_2O_3^{2-}(aq) \longrightarrow 2I^-(aq) + S_4O_6^{2-}(aq)$$

Once the $S_2O_3^{2-}$ is consumed, the excess $I_2$ forms a blue-black product with starch present in solution:

$$I_2 + \text{starch} \longrightarrow \text{starch·}I_2 \text{ (blue-black)}$$

The rate of the reaction is also influenced by the total concentration of ions, so KCl and $(NH_4)_2SO_4$ are added to maintain a constant value. Use the data below, obtained at 23°C, to determine:
(a) The average rate for each trial
(b) The order with respect to each reactant
(c) The rate constant
(d) The rate law for the overall reaction

| | Expt 1 | Expt 2 | Expt 3 |
|---|---|---|---|
| 0.200 *M* KI (mL) | 10.0 | 20.0 | 20.0 |
| 0.100 *M* Na$_2$S$_2$O$_8$ (mL) | 20.0 | 20.0 | 10.0 |
| 0.0050 *M* Na$_2$S$_2$O$_3$ (mL) | 10.0 | 10.0 | 10.0 |
| 0.200 *M* KCl (mL) | 10.0 | 0.0 | 0.0 |
| 0.100 *M* (NH$_4$)$_2$SO$_4$ (mL) | 0.0 | 0.0 | 10.0 |
| Time to color (s) | 29.0 | 14.5 | 14.5 |

**16.115** Heat transfer to and from a reaction flask is often a critical factor in controlling reaction rate. The heat transferred ($q$) depends on a heat transfer coefficient ($h$) for the flask material, the temperature difference ($\Delta T$) across the flask wall, and the commonly "wetted" area ($A$) of the flask and bath, $q = hA\Delta T$. When an exothermic reaction is run at a given $T$, there is a bath temperature at which the reaction can no longer be controlled, and the reaction "runs away" suddenly. A similar problem is often seen when a reaction is "scaled up" from, say, a half-filled small flask to a half-filled large flask. Explain these behaviors.

**16.116** The molecular scenes below represent the first-order reaction in which cyclopropane (*red*) is converted to propene (*green*):

$t = 0$ min          $t = 20$ min          $t = 60$ min

Determine (a) the half-life and (b) the rate constant.

**16.117** The growth of *Pseudomonas* bacteria is modeled as a first-order process with $k = 0.035$ min$^{-1}$ at 37°C. The initial *Pseudomonas* population density is $1.0 \times 10^3$ cells/L. (a) What is the population density after 2 h? (b) What is the time required for the population to go from $1.0 \times 10^3$ to $2.0 \times 10^3$ cells/L?

**16.118** Consider the following organic reaction, in which one halogen replaces another in an alkyl halide:

$$CH_3CH_2Br + KI \longrightarrow CH_3CH_2I + KBr$$

In acetone, this particular reaction goes to completion because KI is soluble in acetone but KBr is not. In the mechanism, I$^-$ approaches the carbon *opposite* to the Br (see Figure 16.20, with I$^-$ instead of OH$^-$). After Br$^-$ has been replaced by I$^-$ and precipitates as KBr, other I$^-$ ions react with the ethyl iodide by the same mechanism.

(a) If we designate the carbon bonded to the halogen as C-1, what is the shape around C-1 and the hybridization of C-1 in ethyl iodide?
(b) In the transition state, one of the two lobes of the unhybridized $2p$ orbital of C-1 overlaps a $p$ orbital of I, while the other lobe overlaps a $p$ orbital of Br. What is the shape around C-1 and the hybridization of C-1 in the transition state?
(c) The deuterated reactant, $CH_3CHDBr$ (where D is deuterium, $^2H$), has two optical isomers because C-1 is chiral. If the reaction is run with one of the isomers, the ethyl iodide is *not* optically active. Explain.

**16.119** Another radioisotope of iodine, $^{131}I$, is also used to study thyroid function (see Follow-Up Problem 16.7). A patient is given a sample that is $1.7\times10^{-4}\,M\,^{131}I$. If the half-life is 8.04 days, what fraction of the radioactivity remains after 30. days?

**16.120** The effect of substrate concentration on the first-order growth rate of a microbial population follows the Monod equation:

$$\mu = \frac{\mu_{max}\,S}{K_s + S}$$

where $\mu$ is the first-order growth rate ($s^{-1}$), $\mu_{max}$ is the maximum growth rate ($s^{-1}$), $S$ is the substrate concentration ($kg/m^3$), and $K_s$ is the value of $S$ that gives one-half the maximum growth rate ($kg/m^3$). For $\mu_{max} = 1.5\times10^{-4}\,s^{-1}$ and $K_s = 0.03\,kg/m^3$:
(a) Plot $\mu$ vs. $S$ for $S$ between 0.0 and 1.0 $kg/m^3$.
(b) The initial population density is $5.0\times10^3$ cells/$m^3$. What is the density after 1.0 h, if the initial $S$ is 0.30 $kg/m^3$?
(c) What is it if the initial $S$ is 0.70 $kg/m^3$?

**16.121** The scenes depict four initial reaction mixtures for the reaction of A (*blue*) and B (*yellow*), with and without a solid present (*gray cubes*). The initial rate, $-\Delta[A]/\Delta t$ (in mol/L·s), is shown, with each sphere representing 0.010 mol and the container volume at 0.50 L.

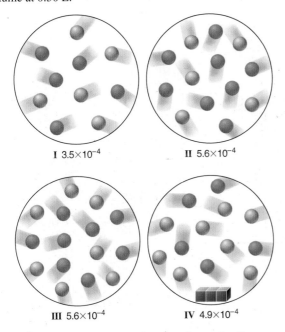

I 3.5×10⁻⁴               II 5.6×10⁻⁴

III 5.6×10⁻⁴             IV 4.9×10⁻⁴

(a) What is the rate law in the absence of a catalyst?
(b) What is the overall reaction order?

(c) Find the rate constant.
(d) Do the gray cubes have a catalytic effect? Explain.

**16.122** The mathematics of the first-order rate law can be applied to any situation in which a quantity decreases by a constant fraction per unit of time (or unit of any other variable).
(a) As light moves through a solution, its intensity decreases per unit distance traveled in the solution. Show that

$$\ln\left(\frac{\text{intensity of light leaving the solution}}{\text{intensity of light entering the solution}}\right)$$
$$= -\text{fraction of light removed per unit of length}$$
$$\times \text{distance traveled in solution}$$

(b) The value of your savings declines under conditions of constant inflation. Show that

$$\ln\left(\frac{\text{value remaining}}{\text{initial value}}\right)$$
$$= -\text{fraction lost per unit of time} \times \text{savings time interval}$$

**16.123** Figure 16.25 (p. 662) shows key steps in the metal-catalyzed (M) hydrogenation of ethylene:

$$C_2H_4(g) + H_2(g) \xrightarrow{\ M\ } C_2H_6(g)$$

Use the following symbols to write a mechanism that gives the overall equation:

| | |
|---|---|
| $H_2$(ads) | adsorbed hydrogen molecules |
| M—H | hydrogen atoms bonded to metal atoms |
| $C_2H_4$(ads) | adsorbed ethylene molecules |
| $C_2H_5$(ads) | adsorbed ethyl radicals |

**16.124** Human liver enzymes catalyze the degradation of ingested toxins. By what factor is the rate of a detoxification changed if an enzyme lowers the $E_a$ by 5 kJ/mol at 37°C?

**16.125** Acetone is one of the most important solvents in organic chemistry, used to dissolve everything from fats and waxes to airplane glue and nail polish. At high temperatures, it decomposes in a first-order process to methane and ketene ($CH_2$=C=O). At 600°C, the rate constant is $8.7\times10^{-3}\,s^{-1}$.
(a) What is the half-life of the reaction?
(b) How long does it take for 40.% of a sample of acetone to decompose?
(c) How long does it take for 90.% of a sample of acetone to decompose?

**16.126** A (*green*), B (*blue*), and C (*red*) are structural isomers. The molecular filmstrip depicts them undergoing a chemical change as time proceeds.

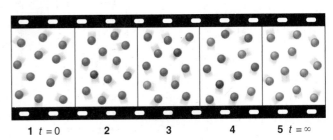

1 $t = 0$      2      3      4      5 $t = \infty$

(a) Write a mechanism for the reaction.
(b) What role does C play?

# Equilibrium: The Extent of Chemical Reactions

# 17

## Concepts and skills to review before you study this chapter

- reversibility of reactions (Section 4.7)
- equilibrium vapor pressure (Section 12.2)
- equilibrium nature of a saturated solution (Section 13.4)
- dependence of rate on concentration (Sections 16.2 and 16.5)
- rate laws for elementary reactions (Section 16.6)
- function of a catalyst (Section 16.7)

Just as reactions vary greatly in their speed, they also vary greatly in their extent. Indeed, kinetics and equilibrium apply to different aspects of a reaction:

- Kinetics applies to the *speed* (or rate) of a reaction, the concentration of reactant that disappears (or of product that appears) per unit time.
- Equilibrium applies to the *extent* of a reaction, the concentrations of reactant and product present after an unlimited time, that is, when no further change occurs.

As you'll see, at equilibrium, no further *net* change occurs because the forward and reverse reactions reach a *balance*. Like balls being juggled (*photo opposite*) or traffic going back and forth across a bridge or people going up and down an escalator, the change in one direction is balanced by the change in the other. A fast reaction may go almost completely, just partially, or only slightly toward products before this balance is reached. Consider acid dissociation in water. In 1 *M* HCl, virtually all the hydrogen chloride molecules are dissociated into ions, whereas fewer than 1% of the acetic acid molecules are dissociated in 1 *M* $CH_3COOH$. Yet both reactions take less than a second. Similarly, some slow reactions yield a large amount of product, whereas others yield very little. After a few years, a steel water-storage tank will rust, and it will do so completely given enough time. But, no matter how long you wait, the water inside the tank will not decompose to hydrogen and oxygen.

Knowing the extent of a given reaction is crucial. How much product— medicine, polymer, fuel—can you obtain from a particular reaction mixture? How can you adjust conditions to obtain more? If a reaction is slow but has a good yield, will a catalyst speed it up enough to make it useful?

**IN THIS CHAPTER . . .** We consider the principles of equilibrium in systems of gases and pure liquids and solids.
- We examine the equilibrium state at the macroscopic and molecular levels and see that equilibrium occurs when the forward and reverse reaction rates are equal.
- We contrast the reaction quotient, *Q*, which changes as the reaction proceeds, with the equilibrium constant, *K*, which applies to the reaction at equilibrium.
- We express the equilibrium condition in terms of concentrations or pressures and see how the two expressions are related.
- We develop a systematic approach to solving a variety of equilibrium problems.
- We compare values of *Q* and *K* to determine the direction in which a system must proceed to reach equilibrium.
- We introduce Le Châtelier's principle, which explains how a change in conditions—concentration, pressure, temperature, or catalyst—affects the equilibrium state, and we apply this principle to a major industrial process.
- We explore how equilibrium concepts operate in metabolic pathways.

## 17.1 • THE EQUILIBRIUM STATE AND THE EQUILIBRIUM CONSTANT

Experimental results from countless reactions have shown that, *given sufficient time, the concentrations of reactants and products no longer change*. This apparent cessation of chemical change occurs because *all reactions are reversible and reach a state of equilibrium*. Let's examine a chemical system at the macroscopic and molecular

**Figure 17.1 Reaching equilibrium on the macroscopic and molecular levels.**
**A,** The reaction mixture consists mostly of colorless $N_2O_4$. **B,** As $N_2O_4$ decomposes to $NO_2$, the mixture becomes pale brown. **C,** At equilibrium, the color and the concentrations of $NO_2$ and $N_2O_4$ no longer change. **D,** The reaction continues in both directions at equal rates, so the concentrations (and color) remain constant.

levels to see how equilibrium arises and then consider some quantitative aspects of the process:

1. *A macroscopic view of equilibrium.* The system we'll consider is the reversible gaseous reaction between colorless dinitrogen tetraoxide and brown nitrogen dioxide:

$$N_2O_4(g; \text{colorless}) \rightleftharpoons 2NO_2(g; \text{brown})$$

As soon as we introduce some liquid $N_2O_4$ (bp = 21°C) into a sealed container kept at 200°C, it vaporizes, and the gas begins to turn pale brown. As time passes, the brown darkens, until, after more time, the color stops changing. The first three photos in Figure 17.1 show the color change, and the last photo shows no further change.

2. *A molecular view of equilibrium.* On the molecular level, as shown in the blow-up circles of Figure 17.1, a dynamic scene unfolds. The $N_2O_4$ molecules fly wildly throughout the container, a few splitting into two $NO_2$ molecules. As time passes, more $N_2O_4$ molecules decompose and the concentration of $NO_2$ rises. As the number of $N_2O_4$ molecules decreases, $N_2O_4$ decomposition slows down. At the same time, as the number of $NO_2$ molecules increases, more collide, and formation of $N_2O_4$ speeds up. Eventually, the system reaches equilibrium: $N_2O_4$ molecules are decomposing into $NO_2$ molecules just as fast as $NO_2$ molecules are forming $N_2O_4$.

Thus, at equilibrium, *reactant and product concentrations are constant because a change in one direction is balanced by a change in the other as the forward and reverse rates become equal:*

$$\text{At equilibrium: rate}_{\text{fwd}} = \text{rate}_{\text{rev}} \qquad \textbf{(17.1)}$$

3. *A quantitiative view of equilibrium: a constant ratio of constants.* Let's see how reactant and product concentrations affect this process. At a particular temperature, when the system reaches equilibrium, we have

$$\text{rate}_{\text{fwd}} = \text{rate}_{\text{rev}}$$

In this reaction system, both forward and reverse reactions are elementary steps (Section 16.6), so we can write their rate laws directly from the balanced equation:

$$k_{\text{fwd}}[N_2O_4]_{\text{eq}} = k_{\text{rev}}[NO_2]^2_{\text{eq}}$$

where $k_{\text{fwd}}$ and $k_{\text{rev}}$ are the forward and reverse rate constants, respectively, and the subscript "eq" refers to concentrations at equilibrium. By rearranging, we set the ratio of the rate constants equal to the ratio of the concentration terms:

$$\frac{k_{\text{fwd}}}{k_{\text{rev}}} = \frac{[NO_2]^2_{\text{eq}}}{[N_2O_4]_{\text{eq}}}$$

The ratio of constants creates a new constant called the **equilibrium constant ($K$):**

$$K = \frac{k_{fwd}}{k_{rev}} = \frac{[NO_2]^2_{eq}}{[N_2O_4]_{eq}} \qquad (17.2)$$

Thus, *K is a number equal to a particular ratio of equilibrium concentrations of product(s) and reactant(s) at a particular temperature.*

4. *K as a measure of reaction extent.* The *magnitude* of $K$ is an indication of *how far a reaction proceeds toward product at a given temperature.* Different reactions, even at the same temperature, have a wide range of concentrations at equilibrium—from almost all reactant to almost all product—and so, they have a wide range of equilibrium constants. Here are three examples of different magnitudes of $K$:

- *Small K* (Figure 17.2A). If a reaction yields little product before reaching equilibrium, it has a small $K$; if $K$ is very small, we may say there is "no reaction." For example, there is "no reaction" between nitrogen and oxygen at 1000 K:*

$$N_2(g) + O_2(g) \rightleftharpoons 2NO(g) \qquad K = 1 \times 10^{-30}$$

- *Large K* (Figure 17.2B). Conversely, if a reaction reaches equilibrium with little reactant remaining, it has a large $K$; if $K$ is very large, we say the reaction "goes to completion." The oxidation of carbon monoxide "goes to completion" at 1000 K:

$$2CO(g) + O_2(g) \rightleftharpoons 2CO_2(g) \qquad K = 2.2 \times 10^{22}$$

- *Intermediate K* (Figure 17.2C). When significant amounts of both reactant and product are present at equilibrium, $K$ has an intermediate value, as when bromine monochloride breaks down to its elements at 1000 K:

$$2BrCl(g) \rightleftharpoons Br_2(g) + Cl_2(g) \qquad K = 5$$

## ▌Summary of Section 17.1

- Kinetics and equilibrium are distinct aspects of a reaction system, and the rate and extent of a reaction are not necessarily related.
- When the forward and reverse reactions occur at the same rate, concentrations no longer change and the system has reached equilibrium.
- The equilibrium constant ($K$) is a number based on a particular ratio of product and reactant concentrations: $K$ is small if a high concentration of reactant(s) is present at equilibrium, and it is large if a high concentration of product(s) is present at equilibrium.

---

*To distinguish the equilibrium constant from the temperature unit, the kelvin, the equilibrium constant is represented by a capital italic $K$, whereas the kelvin is a capital roman K. Also, since the kelvin is a unit, it always follows a number.

  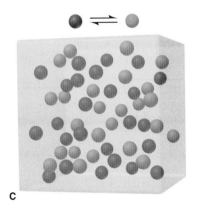

A                          B                          C

**Figure 17.2 The range of equilibrium constants. A,** For this reaction, $K = 1/49 = 0.020$. **B,** For this reaction, $K = 49/1 = 49$. **C,** For this reaction, $K = 25/25 = 1.0$.

# 17.2 • THE REACTION QUOTIENT AND THE EQUILIBRIUM CONSTANT

We have introduced the equilibrium constant in terms of a ratio of rate constants, but the original research on chemical equilibrium was developed many years before the principles of kinetics. In 1864, two Norwegian chemists, Cato Guldberg and Peter Waage, observed that *at a given temperature, a chemical system reaches a state in which a particular ratio of reactant and product concentrations has a constant value.* This is a statement of the **law of chemical equilibrium,** or the **law of mass action.**

## Changing Value of the Reaction Quotient

The particular ratio of concentration terms that we write for a given reaction is called the **reaction quotient** (*Q,* also known as the *mass-action expression*). For the reversible breakdown of $N_2O_4$ to $NO_2$, the reaction quotient is

$$N_2O_4(g) \rightleftharpoons 2NO_2(g) \quad Q = \frac{[NO_2]^2}{[N_2O_4]}$$

As the reaction proceeds toward equilibrium, the concentrations of reactants and products change continually, and so does their ratio, the value of $Q$: at a given temperature, at the beginning of the reaction, the concentrations have initial values, and $Q$ has an initial value; a moment later, the concentrations have slightly different values, and so does $Q$; after another moment, the concentrations and the value of $Q$ change further. These changes continue, *until the system reaches equilibrium.* At that point, reactant and product concentrations have their equilibrium values and no longer change. Thus, the value of $Q$ no longer changes and equals $K$ at that temperature:

$$\text{At equilibrium: } Q = K \tag{17.3}$$

In formulating the law of mass action, Guldberg and Waage found that, *for a particular system and temperature, the same equilibrium state is attained regardless of starting concentrations.* For example, for the $N_2O_4$-$NO_2$ system at 200°C, the data from four experiments appear in Table 17.1. Two essential points stand out:

- The ratio of *initial* concentrations *(fourth column)* varies widely but always gives the same ratio of *equilibrium* concentrations *(rightmost column).*
- The *individual* equilibrium concentrations are different in each case, but the *ratio* of these equilibrium concentrations is constant.

Thus, monitoring $Q$ tells whether the system has reached equilibrium or, if it hasn't, how far away it is and in which direction it is changing.

The curves in Figure 17.3 show experiment 1 in Table 17.1. Note that $[N_2O_4]$ and $[NO_2]$ change smoothly during the course of the reaction (as indicated by the changing brown color at the top), and so does the value of $Q$. Once the system reaches equilibrium (constant brown color), the concentrations no longer change and $Q$ equals $K$. In other words, for any given chemical system, $K$ *is a special value of $Q$ that occurs when the reactant and product concentrations have their equilibrium values.*

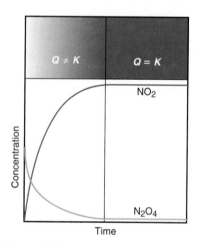

**Figure 17.3** The change in *Q* during the $N_2O_4$-$NO_2$ reaction. Based on data from Experiment 1 in Table 17.1.

| Table **17.1** Initial and Equilibrium Concentration Ratios for the $N_2O_4$-$NO_2$ System at 200°C (473 K) | | | | | | |
|---|---|---|---|---|---|---|
| | **Initial** | | | **Equilibrium** | | |
| **Expt** | **$[N_2O_4]$** | **$[NO_2]$** | **$Q$, $[NO_2]^2/[N_2O_4]$** | **$[N_2O_4]_{eq}$** | **$[NO_2]_{eq}$** | **$K$, $[NO_2]^2_{eq}/[N_2O_4]_{eq}$** |
| 1 | 0.1000 | 0.0000 | 0.0000 | 0.00357 | 0.193 | 10.4 |
| 2 | 0.0000 | 0.1000 | ∞ | 0.000924 | 0.0982 | 10.4 |
| 3 | 0.0500 | 0.0500 | 0.0500 | 0.00204 | 0.146 | 10.4 |
| 4 | 0.0750 | 0.0250 | 0.00833 | 0.00275 | 0.170 | 10.5 |

## Writing the Reaction Quotient in Its Various Forms

The reaction quotient *must* be written directly from the balanced equation. In contrast, as discussed in Chapter 16, the rate law for an overall reaction *cannot* be written from the balanced equation, but must be determined from rate data.

**Constructing the Reaction Quotient**  The most common form of the reaction quotient shows reactant and product terms as molar concentrations, which are designated by square brackets, [ ]. Thus, from now on, we designate the *reaction quotient based on concentrations* as $Q_c$. (We also designate the *equilibrium constant based on concentrations* as $K_c$.) For the general equation

$$aA + bB \rightleftharpoons cC + dD$$

where *a*, *b*, *c*, and *d* are the stoichiometric coefficients, the reaction quotient is

$$Q_c = \frac{[C]^c[D]^d}{[A]^a[B]^b} \qquad (17.4)$$

Thus, *Q is a ratio of product concentration terms multiplied together and divided by reactant concentration terms multiplied together, with each term raised to the power of its balancing coefficient.*

Two steps are needed to construct a reaction quotient for any chemical system:

1. *Start with the balanced equation.* For example, for the formation of ammonia from its elements, the balanced equation (with colored coefficients for reference) is

$$N_2(g) + 3H_2(g) \rightleftharpoons 2NH_3(g)$$

2. *Arrange the terms and exponents.* Place the product terms in the numerator and the reactant terms in the denominator, multiplied by each other, and raise each term to the power of its balancing coefficient (colored as in the balanced equation):

$$Q_c = \frac{[NH_3]^2}{[N_2][H_2]^3}$$

---

**Sample Problem 17.1**  **Writing the Reaction Quotient from the Balanced Equation**

**Problem**  Write the reaction quotient, $Q_c$, for each of the following reactions:
**(a)** The decomposition of dinitrogen pentaoxide, $N_2O_5(g) \rightleftharpoons NO_2(g) + O_2(g)$
**(b)** The combustion of propane, $C_3H_8(g) + O_2(g) \rightleftharpoons CO_2(g) + H_2O(g)$

**Plan**  We balance the equations and then construct the reaction quotient (Equation 17.4).

**Solution  (a)** $2N_2O_5(g) \rightleftharpoons 4NO_2(g) + O_2(g)$

$$Q_c = \frac{[NO_2]^4[O_2]}{[N_2O_5]^2}$$

**(b)** $C_3H_8(g) + 5O_2(g) \rightleftharpoons 3CO_2(g) + 4H_2O(g)$

$$Q_c = \frac{[CO_2]^3[H_2O]^4}{[C_3H_8][O_2]^5}$$

**Check**  Be sure that the exponents in $Q_c$ are the same as the balancing coefficients. A good check is to reverse the process and see if you obtain the balanced equation: change the numerator to products, the denominator to reactants, and the exponents to coefficients.

**Follow-Up Problem 17.1**  Write the reaction quotient, $Q_c$, for each of the following reactions:
**(a)** The first step in nitric acid production, $NH_3(g) + O_2(g) \rightleftharpoons NO(g) + H_2O(g)$
**(b)** The disproportionation of nitric oxide, $NO(g) \rightleftharpoons N_2O(g) + NO_2(g)$

**Why $Q$ and $K$ Are Unitless** In this text (and most others), *the values of $Q$ and $K$ are unitless numbers.* The reason is that each term in $Q$ represents the *ratio* of the quantity of the substance (molar concentration or pressure) to its thermodynamic standard-state quantity. Recall from Section 6.6 that the standard states are 1 $M$ for a substance in solution, 1 atm for a gas, and the pure substance for a liquid or solid. Thus, a concentration of 1.20 $M$ becomes

$$\frac{1.20\ M\ \text{(measured quantity)}}{1\ M\ \text{(standard-state quantity)}} = 1.20$$

Similarly, a pressure of 0.53 atm becomes $\dfrac{0.53\ \text{atm}}{1\ \text{atm}} = 0.53$. Since the quantity terms are unitless, their ratio, which gives the value of $Q$ (or $K$), is also unitless.

**Form of $Q$ for an Overall Reaction** We follow the same procedure for writing a reaction quotient whether an equation represents an individual reaction step or an overall multistep reaction. *If an overall reaction is the **sum** of two or more reactions, the overall reaction quotient (or equilibrium constant) is the **product** of the reaction quotients (or equilibrium constants) for the steps:*

$$Q_{\text{overall}} = Q_1 \times Q_2 \times Q_3 \times \cdots$$

and

$$K_{\text{overall}} = K_1 \times K_2 \times K_3 \times \cdots \qquad \text{(17.5)}$$

Sample Problem 17.2 demonstrates this point.

---

**Sample Problem 17.2** Writing the Reaction Quotient and Finding $K$ for an Overall Reaction

**Problem** Nitrogen dioxide is a toxic pollutant that contributes to photochemical smog. One way it forms is through the following sequence:

(1) $N_2(g) + O_2(g) \rightleftharpoons 2NO(g)$      $K_{c1} = 4.3 \times 10^{-25}$

(2) $2NO(g) + O_2(g) \rightleftharpoons 2NO_2(g)$      $K_{c2} = 6.4 \times 10^9$

**(a)** Show that the overall $Q_c$ for this reaction sequence is the same as the product of the $Q_c$'s for the individual reactions.
**(b)** Given that both reactions occur at the same temperature, find $K_c$ for the overall reaction.

**Plan** **(a)** We first write the overall reaction by adding the individual reactions and then write the overall $Q_c$. Next, we write the $Q_c$ for each step. We *add* the steps and *multiply* their $Q_c$'s, canceling common terms, to obtain the overall $Q_c$. **(b)** We know the individual $K_c$'s ($4.3 \times 10^{-25}$ and $6.4 \times 10^9$), so we multiply them to find $K_{c\text{(overall)}}$.

**Solution** **(a)** Writing the overall reaction and its reaction quotient:

$$\begin{array}{rl} (1) & N_2(g) + O_2(g) \rightleftharpoons \cancel{2NO(g)} \\ (2) & \cancel{2NO(g)} + O_2(g) \rightleftharpoons 2NO_2(g) \\ \hline \text{Overall:} & N_2(g) + 2O_2(g) \rightleftharpoons 2NO_2(g) \end{array}$$

$$Q_{c\text{(overall)}} = \frac{[NO_2]^2}{[N_2][O_2]^2}$$

Writing the reaction quotients for the individual steps:

For step 1, $$Q_{c1} = \frac{[NO]^2}{[N_2][O_2]}$$

For step 2, $$Q_{c2} = \frac{[NO_2]^2}{[NO]^2[O_2]}$$

Multiplying the individual reaction quotients and canceling:

$$Q_{c1} \times Q_{c2} = \frac{[\cancel{NO}]^2}{[N_2][O_2]} \times \frac{[NO_2]^2}{[\cancel{NO}]^2[O_2]} = \frac{[NO_2]^2}{[N_2][O_2]^2} = Q_{c\text{(overall)}}$$

**(b)** Calculating the overall $K_c$:

$$K_{c(overall)} = K_{c1} \times K_{c2} = (4.3 \times 10^{-25})(6.4 \times 10^9) = 2.8 \times 10^{-15}$$

**Check** Round off and check the calculation in part (b):

$$K_c \approx (4 \times 10^{-25})(6 \times 10^9) = 24 \times 10^{-16} = 2.4 \times 10^{-15}$$

**Follow-Up Problem 17.2** The following sequence of steps has been proposed for the overall reaction between $H_2$ and $Br_2$ to form HBr:

(1) $Br_2(g) \rightleftharpoons 2Br(g)$
(2) $Br(g) + H_2(g) \rightleftharpoons HBr(g) + H(g)$
(3) $H(g) + Br(g) \rightleftharpoons HBr(g)$

Write the overall balanced equation and show that the overall $Q_c$ is the product of the $Q_c$'s for the individual steps.

**Form of Q for a Forward and a Reverse Reaction** The form of the reaction quotient depends on the *direction* in which the balanced equation is written. Consider, for example, the oxidation of sulfur dioxide to sulfur trioxide. This reaction is a key step in acid rain formation and sulfuric acid production. The balanced equation is

$$2SO_2(g) + O_2(g) \rightleftharpoons 2SO_3(g)$$

The reaction quotient for this equation *as written* is

$$Q_{c(fwd)} = \frac{[SO_3]^2}{[SO_2]^2[O_2]}$$

If we had written the reverse reaction, the decomposition of sulfur trioxide,

$$2SO_3(g) \rightleftharpoons 2SO_2(g) + O_2(g)$$

the reaction quotient would be the *reciprocal* of $Q_{c(fwd)}$:

$$Q_{c(rev)} = \frac{[SO_2]^2[O_2]}{[SO_3]^2} = \frac{1}{Q_{c(fwd)}}$$

Thus, *a reaction quotient (or equilibrium constant) for a forward reaction is the **reciprocal** of the reaction quotient (or equilibrium constant) for the reverse reaction:*

$$Q_{c(fwd)} = \frac{1}{Q_{c(rev)}} \quad \text{and} \quad K_{c(fwd)} = \frac{1}{K_{c(rev)}} \qquad (17.6)$$

The $K_c$ values for the forward and reverse reactions shown above at 1000 K are

$$K_{c(fwd)} = 261 \quad \text{and} \quad K_{c(rev)} = \frac{1}{K_{c(fwd)}} = \frac{1}{261} = 3.83 \times 10^{-3}$$

These values make sense: if the forward reaction goes far to the right (high $K_c$), the reverse reaction does not (low $K_c$).

**Form of Q for a Reaction with Coefficients Multiplied by a Common Factor**
Multiplying all the coefficients of the equation by some factor also changes the form of $Q$. For example, multiplying all the coefficients in the equation for the formation of $SO_3$ by $\frac{1}{2}$ gives

$$SO_2(g) + \tfrac{1}{2}O_2(g) \rightleftharpoons SO_3(g)$$

For this equation, the reaction quotient is

$$Q'_{c(fwd)} = \frac{[SO_3]}{[SO_2][O_2]^{1/2}}$$

Notice that $Q_c$ for the halved equation equals $Q_c$ for the original equation raised to the $\frac{1}{2}$ power:

$$Q'_{c(fwd)} = Q_{c(fwd)}^{1/2} = \left( \frac{[SO_3]^2}{[SO_2]^2[O_2]} \right)^{1/2} = \frac{[SO_3]}{[SO_2][O_2]^{1/2}}$$

Once again, the same property holds for the equilibrium constants. Relating the halved reaction to the original, we have

$$K'_{c(fwd)} = K^{1/2}_{c(fwd)} = (261)^{1/2} = 16.2$$

It may seem that we have changed the extent of the reaction, as indicated by a different $K$, just by changing the coefficients of the equation, but that can't be true. *A particular $K$ has meaning only in relation to a particular equation.* If $K_{c(fwd)}$ and $K'_{c(fwd)}$ relate to different equations, we cannot compare them directly.

In general, *if all the coefficients of the balanced equation are multiplied by some factor, that factor becomes the exponent for relating the reaction quotients and the equilibrium constants.* For a multiplying factor $n$, which we can write as

$$n(aA + bB \rightleftharpoons cC + dD)$$

the reaction quotient and equilibrium constant are

$$Q' = Q^n = \left(\frac{[C]^c[D]^d}{[A]^a[B]^b}\right)^n \quad \text{and} \quad K' = K^n \quad \text{(17.7)}$$

---

**Sample Problem 17.3** | **Finding the Equilibrium Constant for an Equation Multiplied by a Common Factor**

**Problem** For the ammonia-formation reaction, the reference (ref) equation is

$$N_2(g) + 3H_2(g) \rightleftharpoons 2NH_3(g)$$

$K_c$ is $2.4\times10^{-3}$ at 1000 K. What are the values of $K_c$ for the following balanced equations?

**(a)** $\frac{1}{3}N_2(g) + H_2(g) \rightleftharpoons \frac{2}{3}NH_3(g)$      **(b)** $NH_3(g) \rightleftharpoons \frac{1}{2}N_2(g) + \frac{3}{2}H_2(g)$

**Plan** We compare each equation with the reference equation to see how the direction and coefficients have changed.

**Solution** The reaction quotient for the reference equation is $Q_{c(ref)} = \dfrac{[NH_3]^2}{[N_2][H_2]^3}$.

**(a)** This equation is the reference equation multiplied by $\frac{1}{3}$, so $K_c$ equals $K_{c(ref)}$ $(2.4\times10^{-3})$ raised to the $\frac{1}{3}$ power.

$$Q_c = Q^{1/3}_{c(ref)} = \left(\frac{[NH_3]^2}{[N_2][H_2]^3}\right)^{1/3} = \frac{[NH_3]^{2/3}}{[N_2]^{1/3}[H_2]}$$

Thus,

$$K_c = K^{1/3}_{c(ref)} = (2.4\times10^{-3})^{1/3} = \boxed{0.13}$$

**(b)** This equation is one-half the *reverse* of the reference equation, so $K_c$ is the reciprocal of $K_{c(ref)}$ raised to the $\frac{1}{2}$ power.

$$Q_c = \left(\frac{1}{Q_{c(ref)}}\right)^{1/2} = \left(\frac{1}{\dfrac{[NH_3]^2}{[N_2][H_2]^3}}\right)^{1/2} = \frac{[N_2]^{1/2}[H_2]^{3/2}}{[NH_3]}$$

Thus,

$$K_c = \left(\frac{1}{K_{c(ref)}}\right)^{1/2} = \left(\frac{1}{2.4\times10^{-3}}\right)^{1/2} = \boxed{20.}$$

**Check** A good check is to work the math backwards. **(a)** $(0.13)^3 = 2.2\times10^{-3}$, within rounding of $2.4\times10^{-3}$. The reaction goes in the same direction, so there should be mostly reactants, as $K_c < 1$ indicates. **(b)** $1/(20.)^2 = 2.5\times10^{-3}$, again within rounding. At equilibrium, the reverse reaction should yield mostly products, as $K_c > 1$ indicates.

**Follow-Up Problem 17.3** At 1200 K, the reaction of hydrogen and chlorine to form hydrogen chloride is

$$H_2(g) + Cl_2(g) \rightleftharpoons 2HCl(g) \quad K_c = 7.6\times10^8$$

Calculate $K_c$ for the following reactions:

**(a)** $\frac{1}{2}H_2(g) + \frac{1}{2}Cl_2(g) \rightleftharpoons HCl(g)$      **(b)** $\frac{4}{3}HCl(g) \rightleftharpoons \frac{2}{3}H_2(g) + \frac{2}{3}Cl_2(g)$

**Figure 17.4** The reaction quotient for a heterogeneous system depends only on concentrations that change.

$T = 650°C$

Same $[CO_2]$

Same $K$

CaO

CaCO$_3$

CaO

CaCO$_3$

**Form of Q for a Reaction Involving Pure Liquids or Solids** Until now, we've looked at reactions involving only gases. These are *homogeneous* equilibria, systems in which all the components are in the same phase. When the components are in different phases, the system reaches *heterogeneous* equilibrium.

Consider the decomposition of limestone to lime and carbon dioxide:

$$CaCO_3(s) \rightleftharpoons CaO(s) + CO_2(g)$$

Based on the rules for writing the reaction quotient, we have

$$Q_c = \frac{[CaO][CO_2]}{[CaCO_3]}$$

However, like its density, at a given temperature, a pure solid always has the same "concentration" that is, the same number of moles per liter of solid. Therefore, the concentration of a pure solid is constant, as is the concentration of a pure liquid.

Because we are concerned with concentrations that *change* as they approach equilibrium, *we eliminate the terms for pure liquids and solids from the reaction quotient.* To do this, we multiply both sides of the above equation by $[CaCO_3]$ and divide both sides by $[CaO]$ and get a new reaction quotient, $Q'_c$:

$$Q'_c = Q_c \frac{[CaCO_3]}{[CaO]} = [CO_2]$$

Thus, only the $CO_2$ concentration changes. As long as some CaO and CaCO$_3$ are present, the reaction quotient equals the $CO_2$ concentration (Figure 17.4).

Table 17.2 summarizes the ways of writing $Q$ and calculating $K$.

| Table **17.2** Ways of Expressing $Q$ and Calculating $K$ | | |
|---|---|---|
| **Form of Chemical Equations** | **Form of $Q$** | **Value of $K$** |
| Reference reaction: $A \rightleftharpoons B$ | $Q_{(ref)} = \dfrac{[B]}{[A]}$ | $K_{(ref)} = \dfrac{[B]_{eq}}{[A]_{eq}}$ |
| Reference reaction: $B \rightleftharpoons A$ | $Q = \dfrac{1}{Q_{(ref)}} = \dfrac{[A]}{[B]}$ | $K = \dfrac{1}{K_{(ref)}}$ |
| Reaction as sum of two steps: <br> (1) $A \rightleftharpoons C$ | $Q_1 = \dfrac{[C]}{[A]}; Q_2 = \dfrac{[B]}{[C]}$ | |
| (2) $C \rightleftharpoons B$ | $Q_{overall} = Q_1 \times Q_2 = Q_{(ref)}$ | $K_{overall} = K_1 \times K_2$ |
| | $= \dfrac{[\cancel{C}]}{[A]} \times \dfrac{[B]}{[\cancel{C}]} = \dfrac{[B]}{[A]}$ | $= K_{(ref)}$ |
| Coefficients multiplied by $n$ | $Q = Q_{(ref)}^n$ | $K = K_{(ref)}^n$ |
| Reaction with pure solid or liquid component, such as $A(s)$ | $Q = Q_{(ref)}[A] = [B]$ | $K = K_{(ref)}[A] = [B]$ |

## ■ Summary of Section 17.2

- The reaction quotient based on concentration, $Q_c$, is a particular ratio of product to reactant concentrations. The value of $Q_c$ changes as the reaction proceeds. When the system reaches equilibrium at a particular temperature, $Q_c = K_c$.
- If a reaction is the sum of two or more steps, the overall $Q$ (or $K$) is the product of the individual $Q$'s (or $K$'s).
- The *form* of $Q$ is based on the balanced equation exactly as written, so it changes if the equation is reversed or multiplied by some factor, and $K$ changes accordingly.
- The concentrations of pure liquids or solids do not appear in $Q$ because they are constant.
- Three criteria define a system at equilibrium:
  1. Reactant and product concentrations are constant over time.
  2. The opposing reaction rates are equal: $rate_{fwd} = rate_{rev}$.
  3. The reaction quotient equals the equilibrium constant: $Q = K$.

## 17.3 • EXPRESSING EQUILIBRIA WITH PRESSURE TERMS: RELATION BETWEEN $K_c$ AND $K_p$

It is easier to measure gas pressure than concentration, so when a reaction involves gases, we often express the reaction quotient in terms of partial pressures instead of concentrations. As long as the gases behave nearly ideally during the experiment, the ideal gas law (Section 5.3) allows us to relate pressure ($P$) to concentration ($n/V$):

$$PV = nRT, \quad \text{so} \quad P = \frac{n}{V}RT \quad \text{or} \quad \frac{P}{RT} = \frac{n}{V}$$

Thus, at constant $T$, *pressure is directly proportional to molar concentration.* For example, in the reaction between gaseous NO and $O_2$,

$$2NO(g) + O_2(g) \rightleftharpoons 2NO_2(g)$$

the *reaction quotient based on pressures, $Q_p$,* is

$$Q_p = \frac{P_{NO_2}^2}{P_{NO}^2 \times P_{O_2}}$$

The equilibrium constant obtained when all components are present at their equilibrium partial pressures is designated $K_p$, the *equilibrium constant based on pressures.* In many cases, $K_p$ has a value different from $K_c$. But if you know one, the *change in amount (mol) of gas, $\Delta n_{gas}$,* from the balanced equation allows you to calculate the other. Let's see how this conversion works for the oxidation of NO:

$$2NO(g) + O_2(g) \rightleftharpoons 2NO_2(g)$$

As the balanced equation shows,

$$3 \text{ mol } (2 \text{ mol} + 1 \text{ mol}) \text{ gaseous reactants} \rightleftharpoons 2 \text{ mol gaseous products}$$

With $\Delta$ meaning final *minus* initial (products *minus* reactants), we have

$$\Delta n_{gas} = \text{moles of gaseous product} - \text{moles of gaseous reactant} = 2 - 3 = -1$$

Keep this value of $\Delta n_{gas}$ in mind because it appears in the conversion that follows. The reaction quotient based on concentrations is

$$Q_c = \frac{[NO_2]^2}{[NO]^2[O_2]}$$

Rearranging the ideal gas law to $n/V = P/RT$, we write the terms in square brackets as $n/V$ and convert them to partial pressures, $P$; then we collect the $RT$ terms and cancel:

$$Q_c = \frac{\dfrac{n_{NO_2}^2}{V^2}}{\dfrac{n_{NO}^2}{V^2} \times \dfrac{n_{O_2}}{V}} = \frac{\dfrac{P_{NO_2}^2}{(RT)^2}}{\dfrac{P_{NO}^2}{(RT)^2} \times \dfrac{P_{O_2}}{RT}} = \frac{P_{NO_2}^2}{P_{NO}^2 \times P_{O_2}} \times \frac{\dfrac{1}{(RT)^2}}{\dfrac{1}{(RT)^2} \times \dfrac{1}{RT}}$$

$$= \frac{P_{NO_2}^2}{P_{NO}^2 \times P_{O_2}} \times RT$$

Note that the far right side of the previous expression is $Q_p$ multiplied by $RT$. Thus,

$$Q_c = Q_p(RT)$$

Also, at equilibrium, $K_c = K_p(RT)$; thus,

$$K_p = \frac{K_c}{RT} \qquad \text{or} \qquad K_c(RT)^{-1}$$

Note especially that *the exponent of the RT term equals the change in the amount (mol) of gas* $(\Delta n_{gas})$ *from the balanced equation,* $-1$. Thus, in general, we have

$$K_p = K_c(RT)^{\Delta n_{gas}} \qquad (17.8)$$

Based on Equation 17.8, *if the amount (mol) of gas does not change in the reaction,* $\Delta n_{gas} = 0$, so the $RT$ term drops out (i.e., equals 1), and $K_p = K_c$. (In calculations, be sure the units for $R$ are consistent with units for pressure.)

---

## Sample Problem 17.4 | Converting Between $K_c$ and $K_p$

**Problem** A chemical engineer injects limestone ($CaCO_3$) into the hot flue gas of a coal-burning power plant to form lime (CaO), which scrubs $SO_2$ from the gas and forms gypsum ($CaSO_4 \cdot 2H_2O$). Find $K_c$ for the following reaction:

$$CaCO_3(s) \rightleftharpoons CaO(s) + CO_2(g) \qquad K_p = 2.1 \times 10^{-4} \text{ (at 1000. K)}$$

**Plan** We know $K_p$ ($2.1 \times 10^{-4}$), so to convert between $K_p$ and $K_c$, we must first determine $\Delta n_{gas}$ from the balanced equation. Then we rearrange Equation 17.8. (If we assume that pressure is measured in atmospheres, $R = 0.0821$ atm·L/mol·K.)

**Solution** Determining $\Delta n_{gas}$: There is 1 mol of gaseous product and no gaseous reactant, so $\Delta n_{gas} = 1 - 0 = 1$.

Rearranging Equation 17.8 and calculating $K_c$:

$$K_p = K_c(RT)^1$$

so

$$K_c = K_p(RT)^{-1} = (2.1 \times 10^{-4})(0.0821 \times 1000.)^{-1}$$
$$= 2.6 \times 10^{-6}$$

**Check** Rounding gives

$$(2 \times 10^{-4})(0.1 \times 10^3)^{-1} = (2 \times 10^{-4})(10^{-2})$$
$$= 2 \times 10^{-6}.$$

**Follow-Up Problem 17.4** Calculate $K_p$ for the following reaction:

$$PCl_3(g) + Cl_2(g) \rightleftharpoons PCl_5(g) \qquad K_c = 1.67 \text{ (at 500. K)}$$

---

## Summary of Section 17.3

- For a gaseous reaction, the reaction quotient and the equilibrium constant can be expressed in terms of partial pressures ($Q_p$ and $K_p$).
- If you know $K_p$, you can find $K_c$, and vice versa: $K_p = K_c(RT)^{\Delta n_{gas}}$.

---

# 17.4 • COMPARING Q AND K TO DETERMINE REACTION DIRECTION

Suppose you have a mixture of reactants and products and you know $K$ at the temperature of the reaction. By comparing the value of $Q$ with $K$, you can tell whether the reaction has reached equilibrium or, if not, in which direction it is progressing. With product terms in the numerator of $Q$ and reactant terms in the denominator, *more product makes Q larger, and more reactant makes Q smaller.*

**Figure 17.5 Reaction direction and the relative sizes of *Q* and *K*.** When $Q_c$ is smaller or larger than $K_c$, the reaction continues until $Q_c = K_c$. Note that $K_c$ remains the same throughout.

Reactants ⟶ Products　　Equilibrium: no net change　　Reactants ⟵ Products

There are three possibilities for the relative sizes of *Q* and *K* (Figure 17.5):

- *Q* < *K*. If *Q* is smaller than *K*, the denominator (reactants) is large relative to the numerator (products). For *Q* to equal *K*, the reactants must decrease and the products increase. The reaction will progress to the right, toward products:

$$\text{If } Q < K, \text{ reactants} \longrightarrow \text{products}$$

- *Q* > *K*. If *Q* is larger than *K*, the numerator (products) will decrease and the denominator (reactants) will increase. The reaction will progress to the left, toward reactants:

$$\text{If } Q > K, \text{ reactants} \longleftarrow \text{products}$$

- *Q* = *K*. This situation occurs when the reactant and product terms equal their equilibrium values. No further net change takes place:

$$\text{If } Q = K, \text{ reactants} \rightleftharpoons \text{products}$$

Sample Problem 17.5 relies on molecular scenes to determine reaction direction, and Sample Problem 17.6 relies on concentration data.

---

**Sample Problem 17.5** **Using Molecular Scenes to Determine Reaction Direction**

**Problem** For the reaction $A(g) \rightleftharpoons B(g)$, the equilibrium mixture at 175°C is [A] = $2.8 \times 10^{-4}$ *M* and [B] = $1.2 \times 10^{-4}$ *M*. The molecular scenes below represent mixtures at various times during runs 1–4 of this reaction (A is *red*; B is *blue*). Does the reaction progress to the right or left or not at all for each mixture to reach equilibrium?

**Plan** We must compare $Q_c$ with $K_c$ to determine the reaction direction, so we first use the given equilibrium concentrations to find $K_c$. Then we count spheres and calculate $Q_c$ for each mixture. If $Q_c < K_c$, the reaction progresses to the right (reactants to products); if $Q_c > K_c$, it progresses to the left (products to reactants); and if $Q_c = K_c$, there is no further net change.

**Solution** Writing the reaction quotient and using the data to find $K_c$:

$$Q_c = \frac{[B]}{[A]} = \frac{1.2 \times 10^{-4}}{2.8 \times 10^{-4}} = 0.43 = K_c$$

Counting red (A) and blue (B) spheres to calculate $Q_c$ for each mixture:

1. $Q_c = 8/2 = 4.0$　　2. $Q_c = 3/7 = 0.43$　　3. $Q_c = 4/6 = 0.67$　　4. $Q_c = 2/8 = 0.25$

Comparing $Q_c$ with $K_c$ to determine reaction direction:

1. $Q_c > K_c$: left　　2. $Q_c = K_c$: no net change　　3. $Q_c > K_c$: left　　4. $Q_c < K_c$: right

**Check** Making an error in the calculation for $K_c$ would lead to incorrect conclusions throughout, so check that step: the exponents are the same, and 1.2/2.8 is a bit less than 0.5, as is the calculated $K_c$. You can check the final answers by inspection; for example, for the number of B (8) in mixture 1 to equal the number at equilibrium (3), more B must change to A, so the reaction must proceed to the left.

**Follow-Up Problem 17.5** At 338 K, the reaction $X(g) \rightleftharpoons Y(g)$ has a $K_c$ of 1.4. The scenes below represent different mixtures at 338 K, with X orange and Y green. In which direction does the reaction proceed (if at all) for each mixture to reach equilibrium?

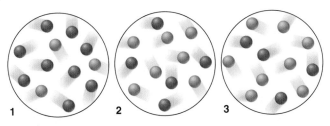

**Sample Problem 17.6** | **Using Concentrations to Determine Reaction Direction**

**Problem** For the reaction $N_2O_4(g) \rightleftharpoons 2NO_2(g)$, $K_c = 0.21$ at 100°C. At a point during the reaction, $[N_2O_4] = 0.12\ M$ and $[NO_2] = 0.55\ M$. Is the reaction at equilibrium? If not, in which direction is it progressing?

**Plan** We write $Q_c$, find its value by substituting the given concentrations, and compare its value with the given $K_c$.

**Solution** Writing the reaction quotient and solving for $Q_c$:

$$Q_c = \frac{[NO_2]^2}{[N_2O_4]} = \frac{0.55^2}{0.12} = 2.5$$

With $Q_c > K_c$, the reaction is not at equilibrium and will proceed to the left until $Q_c = K_c$.

**Check** With $[NO_2] > [N_2O_4]$, we expect to obtain a value for $Q_c$ that is greater than 0.21. If $Q_c > K_c$, the numerator will decrease and the denominator will increase until $Q_c = K_c$; that is, this reaction will proceed toward reactants.

**Follow-Up Problem 17.6** Chloromethane forms by the reaction

$$CH_4(g) + Cl_2(g) \rightleftharpoons CH_3Cl(g) + HCl(g)$$

At 1500 K, $K_p = 1.6 \times 10^4$. In the reaction mixture, $P_{CH_4} = 0.13$ atm, $P_{Cl_2} = 0.035$ atm, $P_{CH_3Cl} = 0.24$ atm, and $P_{HCl} = 0.47$ atm. Is $CH_3Cl$ or $CH_4$ forming?

### ■ Summary of Section 17.4

- We compare the values of $Q$ and $K$ to determine the direction in which a reaction will proceed toward equilibrium.
  - If $Q_c < K_c$, more product forms.
  - If $Q_c > K_c$, more reactant forms.
  - If $Q_c = K_c$, there is no net change.

# 17.5 • HOW TO SOLVE EQUILIBRIUM PROBLEMS

Many kinds of equilibrium problems arise in the real world—and on chemistry exams—but we can group most of them into two types:

1. We know the equilibrium quantities and solve for $K$.
2. We know $K$ and the initial quantities and solve for the equilibrium quantities.

## Using Quantities to Find the Equilibrium Constant

There are two common variations on this type of problem: one involves substituting quantities to solve for $K$, and the other requires first finding some of the quantities.

**Substituting Equilibrium Quantities into Q to Find K**   In this type of problem, we use given equilibrium quantities to calculate $K$. Suppose, for example, that equal amounts of gaseous hydrogen and iodine are injected into a 1.50-L flask at a fixed temperature. In time, the following equilibrium is attained:

$$H_2(g) + I_2(g) \rightleftharpoons 2HI(g)$$

At equilibrium, the flask contains 1.80 mol of $H_2$, 1.80 mol of $I_2$, and 0.520 mol of HI. We calculate $K_c$ by finding the concentrations from the amounts and flask volume and substituting into the reaction quotient from the balanced equation:

$$Q_c = \frac{[HI]^2}{[H_2][I_2]}$$

We divide each amount (mol) by the volume (L) to find each concentration (mol/L):

$$[H_2] = \frac{1.80 \text{ mol}}{1.50 \text{ L}} = 1.20 \ M$$

Similarly, $[I_2] = 1.20 \ M$, and $[HI] = 0.347 \ M$.

Substituting these values into the expression for $Q_c$ gives $K_c$:

$$K_c = \frac{(0.347)^2}{(1.20)(1.20)} = 8.36 \times 10^{-2}$$

## Using a Reaction Table to Find Equilibrium Quantities and K

When some quantities are not given, we determine them from the reaction stoichiometry and then find $K$. In the following example, note the use of the *reaction table*.

In a study of carbon oxidation, an evacuated vessel containing a small amount of powdered graphite is heated to 1080 K. Gaseous $CO_2$ is added to a pressure of 0.458 atm, and CO forms. At equilibrium, the total pressure is 0.757 atm. Calculate $K_p$.

As always, we start by writing the balanced equation and the reaction quotient:

$$CO_2(g) + C(\text{graphite}) \rightleftharpoons 2CO(g)$$

The data are given in atmospheres and we must find $K_p$, so we write the expression for $Q_p$; note that it does *not* include a term for the solid, C(graphite):

$$Q_p = \frac{P_{CO}^2}{P_{CO_2}}$$

We are given the initial $P_{CO_2}$ and the $P_{total}$ at equilibrium. To find $K_p$, we must find the equilibrium pressures of $CO_2$ and CO and then substitute them into $Q_p$.

Let's think through what happened in the vessel. An unknown portion of the $CO_2$ reacted with graphite to form an unknown amount of CO. We already know the *relative* amounts of $CO_2$ and CO from the balanced equation: for each mole of $CO_2$ that reacts, 2 mol of CO forms, which means that when $x$ atm of $CO_2$ reacts, $2x$ atm of CO forms:

$$x \text{ atm } CO_2 \longrightarrow 2x \text{ atm CO}$$

The pressure of $CO_2$ at equilibrium, $P_{CO_2(eq)}$, is the initial pressure, $P_{CO_2(init)}$, *minus* $x$, the $CO_2$ that reacts (the change in $P_{CO_2}$ due to the reaction):

$$P_{CO_2(init)} - x = P_{CO_2(eq)} = 0.458 - x$$

Similarly, the pressure of CO at equilibrium, $P_{CO(eq)}$, is the initial pressure, $P_{CO(init)}$, *plus* $2x$, the CO that forms (the change in $P_{CO}$ due to the reaction). $P_{CO(init)}$ is zero, so

$$P_{CO(init)} + 2x = 0 + 2x = 2x = P_{CO(eq)}$$

We'll summarize this information in a reaction table, similar to those in Chapter 3, but the "Final" quantities are those at equilibrium. The table shows the balanced equation and

- the *initial* quantities (concentrations or pressures) of reactants and products
- the *changes* in these quantities during the reaction
- the *equilibrium* quantities

| Pressure (atm) | $CO_2(g)$ | + | C(graphite) | $\rightleftharpoons$ | $2CO(g)$ |
|---|---|---|---|---|---|
| Initial | 0.458 | | — | | 0 |
| Change | $-x$ | | — | | $+2x$ |
| Equilibrium | $0.458 - x$ | | — | | $2x$ |

We treat each column like a list of numbers to add together: *the initial quantity plus the change in that quantity gives the equilibrium quantity*. Note that we *only* include substances whose concentrations change; thus, the column for C(graphite) is blank.

To solve for $K_p$, we substitute equilibrium values into $Q_p$, so we first have to find $x$. To do this, we use the other piece of data given, $P_{total(eq)}$. According to Dalton's law of partial pressures and using the equilibrium quantities from the reaction table,

$$P_{total(eq)} = 0.757 \text{ atm} = P_{CO_2(eq)} + P_{CO(eq)} = (0.458 \text{ atm} - x) + 2x$$

Thus,     $0.757 \text{ atm} = 0.458 \text{ atm} + x$     and     $x = 0.299 \text{ atm}$

With $x$ known, we determine the equilibrium partial pressures:

$$P_{CO_2(eq)} = 0.458 \text{ atm} - x = 0.458 \text{ atm} - 0.299 \text{ atm} = 0.159 \text{ atm}$$
$$P_{CO(eq)} = 2x = 2(0.299 \text{ atm}) = 0.598 \text{ atm}$$

Then we substitute them into $Q_p$ to find $K_p$:

$$Q_p = \frac{P^2_{CO(eq)}}{P_{CO_2(eq)}} = \frac{0.598^2}{0.159} = 2.25 = K_p$$

(From now on, the subscripts "init" and "eq" appear only when it is not clear whether a quantity is an initial or equilibrium value.)

---

## Sample Problem 17.7    Calculating $K_c$ from Concentration Data

**Problem** In order to study hydrogen halide decomposition, a researcher fills an evacuated 2.00-L flask with 0.200 mol of HI gas and allows the reaction to proceed at 453°C:

$$2HI(g) \rightleftharpoons H_2(g) + I_2(g)$$

At equilibrium, [HI] = 0.078 $M$. Calculate $K_c$.

**Plan** To calculate $K_c$, we need the equilibrium concentrations. We can find the initial [HI] from the amount (0.200 mol) and the flask volume (2.00 L), and we are given [HI] at equilibrium (0.078 $M$). From the balanced equation, when $2x$ mol of HI reacts, $x$ mol of $H_2$ and $x$ mol of $I_2$ form. We set up a reaction table, use the known [HI] at equilibrium to solve for $x$ (the change in [$H_2$] or [$I_2$]), and substitute the concentrations into $Q_c$.

**Solution** Calculating initial [HI]:

$$[HI] = \frac{0.200 \text{ mol}}{2.00 \text{ L}} = 0.100 \text{ } M$$

Setting up the reaction table, with $x$ = [$H_2$] or [$I_2$] that forms and $2x$ = [HI] that reacts:

| Concentration (M) | $2HI(g)$ | $\rightleftharpoons$ | $H_2(g)$ | + | $I_2(g)$ |
|---|---|---|---|---|---|
| Initial | 0.100 | | 0 | | 0 |
| Change | $-2x$ | | $+x$ | | $+x$ |
| Equilibrium | $0.100 - 2x$ | | $x$ | | $x$ |

Solving for $x$, using the known [HI] at equilibrium:

$$[HI] = 0.100 \text{ } M - 2x = 0.078 \text{ } M \qquad \text{so} \qquad x = 0.011 \text{ } M$$

Therefore, the equilibrium concentrations are

$$[H_2] = [I_2] = 0.011 \text{ } M \qquad \text{and we are given} \qquad [HI] = 0.078 \text{ } M$$

Substituting into the reaction quotient:

$$Q_c = \frac{[H_2][I_2]}{[HI]^2}$$

Thus,     $$K_c = \frac{(0.011)(0.011)}{0.078^2} = \boxed{0.020}$$

**Check** Rounding gives ~$0.01^2/0.08^2 = 0.02$. Because the initial [HI] of 0.100 $M$ fell slightly at equilibrium to 0.078 $M$, relatively little product formed; so we expect $K_c < 1$.

**Follow-Up Problem 17.7** The atmospheric oxidation of nitrogen monoxide, $2NO(g) + O_2(g) \rightleftharpoons 2NO_2(g)$, was studied at 184°C with initial pressures of 1.000 atm of NO and 1.000 atm of $O_2$. At equilibrium, $P_{O_2} = 0.506$ atm. Calculate $K_p$.

## Using the Equilibrium Constant to Find Quantities

The type of problem that involves finding equilibrium quantities also has several variations. Sample Problem 17.8 is one variation, in which we know $K$ and some of the equilibrium concentrations and must find another equilibrium concentration.

**Sample Problem 17.8** Determining Equilibrium Concentrations from $K_c$

**Problem** In a study of the conversion of methane to other fuels, a chemical engineer mixes gaseous $CH_4$ and $H_2O$ in a 0.32-L flask at 1200 K. At equilibrium, the flask contains 0.26 mol of CO, 0.091 mol of $H_2$, and 0.041 mol of $CH_4$. What is [$H_2O$] at equilibrium? $K_c = 0.26$ for this process at 1200 K.

**Plan** First, we write the balanced equation and the reaction quotient. We calculate the equilibrium concentrations from the given numbers of moles and the flask volume (0.32 L). Substituting these into $Q_c$ and setting it equal to the given $K_c$ (0.26), we solve for the unknown equilibrium concentration, [$H_2O$].

**Solution** Writing the balanced equation and reaction quotient:

$$CH_4(g) + H_2O(g) \rightleftharpoons CO(g) + 3H_2(g) \qquad Q_c = \frac{[CO][H_2]^3}{[CH_4][H_2O]}$$

Determining the equilibrium concentrations:

$$[CH_4] = \frac{0.041 \text{ mol}}{0.32 \text{ L}} = 0.13 \, M$$

Similarly, [CO] = 0.81 $M$ and [$H_2$] = 0.28 $M$.
Calculating [$H_2O$] at equilibrium: Since $Q_c = K_c$, rearranging gives

$$[H_2O] = \frac{[CO][H_2]^3}{[CH_4]K_c} = \frac{(0.81)(0.28)^3}{(0.13)(0.26)} = \boxed{0.53 \, M}$$

**Check** Always check by substituting the concentrations into $Q_c$ to confirm that the result is equal to $K_c$:

$$Q_c = \frac{[CO][H_2]^3}{[CH_4][H_2O]} = \frac{(0.81)(0.28)^3}{(0.13)(0.53)} = 0.26 = K_c$$

**Follow-Up Problem 17.8** Nitrogen monoxide decomposes by the following equation: $2NO(g) \rightleftharpoons N_2(g) + O_2(g)$; $K_c = 2.3 \times 10^{30}$ at 298 K. In the atmosphere, $P_{O_2} = 0.209$ atm and $P_{N_2} = 0.781$ atm. What is the equilibrium partial pressure of NO in the air we breathe? (*Hint:* You need $K_p$ to find the partial pressure.)

In a somewhat more involved variation, we know $K$ and *initial* quantities and must find *equilibrium* quantities, for which we use a reaction table. Sample Problem 17.9 focuses on this approach.

**Sample Problem 17.9** Determining Equilibrium Concentrations from Initial Concentrations and $K_c$

**Problem** Fuel engineers use the extent of the change from CO and $H_2O$ to $CO_2$ and $H_2$ to regulate the proportions of synthetic fuel mixtures. If 0.250 mol of CO and 0.250 mol of $H_2O$ gases are placed in a 125-mL flask at 900 K, what is the composition of the equilibrium mixture? At this temperature, $K_c$ is 1.56.

**Plan** We have to find the "composition" of the equilibrium mixture, in other words, the equilibrium concentrations. As always, we write the balanced equation and use it to write the reaction quotient. We find the initial [CO] and [H$_2$O] from the amounts (0.250 mol of each) and volume (0.125 L), use the balanced equation to define $x$ and set up a reaction table, substitute into $Q_c$, and solve for $x$, from which we calculate the concentrations.

**Solution** Writing the balanced equation and reaction quotient:

$$CO(g) + H_2O(g) \rightleftharpoons CO_2(g) + H_2(g) \qquad Q_c = \frac{[CO_2][H_2]}{[CO][H_2O]}$$

Calculating initial reactant concentrations:

$$[CO] = [H_2O] = \frac{0.250 \text{ mol}}{0.125 \text{ L}} = 2.00 \ M$$

Setting up the reaction table, with $x = $ [CO] and [H$_2$O] that react:

| Concentration (*M*) | CO(*g*) | + | H$_2$O(*g*) | $\rightleftharpoons$ | CO$_2$(*g*) | + | H$_2$(*g*) |
|---|---|---|---|---|---|---|---|
| Initial | 2.00 | | 2.00 | | 0 | | 0 |
| Change | $-x$ | | $-x$ | | $+x$ | | $+x$ |
| Equilibrium | $2.00 - x$ | | $2.00 - x$ | | $x$ | | $x$ |

Substituting into the reaction quotient and solving for $x$:

$$Q_c = \frac{[CO_2][H_2]}{[CO][H_2O]} = \frac{(x)(x)}{(2.00 - x)(2.00 - x)} = \frac{x^2}{(2.00 - x)^2}$$

At equilibrium, we have

$$Q_c = K_c = 1.56 = \frac{x^2}{(2.00 - x)^2}$$

We can apply the following math shortcut in this case *but not in general:* Because the right side of the equation is a perfect square, we take the square root of both sides:

$$\sqrt{1.56} = \frac{x}{2.00 - x} = \pm 1.25$$

A positive number (1.56) has a positive *and* a negative root, but in this case, only the positive root has any chemical meaning, so we ignore the negative root:*

$$1.25 = \frac{x}{2.00 - x} \qquad \text{or} \qquad 2.50 - 1.25x = x$$

So $\qquad\qquad 2.50 = 2.25x \qquad$ therefore $\qquad x = 1.11 \ M$

Calculating equilibrium concentrations:

$$[CO] = [H_2O] = 2.00 \ M - x = 2.00 \ M - 1.11 \ M = \boxed{0.89 \ M}$$
$$[CO_2] = [H_2] = x = \boxed{1.11 \ M}$$

**Check** Given the intermediate size of $K_c$ (1.56), it makes sense that the changes in concentration are moderate. It's a good idea to check that the sign of $x$ in the reaction table is correct—only reactants were initially present, so $x$ has a negative sign for reactants and a positive sign for products. Also check that the equilibrium concentrations give the known $K_c$: $\dfrac{(1.11)(1.11)}{(0.89)(0.89)} = 1.56$.

**Follow-Up Problem 17.9** The decomposition of HI at low temperature was studied by injecting 2.50 mol of HI into a 10.32-L vessel at 25°C. What is [H$_2$] at equilibrium for the reaction $2HI(g) \rightleftharpoons H_2(g) + I_2(g)$; $K_c = 1.26 \times 10^{-3}$?

---

*The negative root gives $-1.25 = \dfrac{x}{2.00 - x}$, or $-2.50 + 1.25x = x$.

So $\qquad\qquad -2.50 = 0.25x \quad$ and $\quad x = 10. \ M$
This value has no chemical meaning because we started with 2.00 *M* as the concentration of each reactant, so it is impossible for $x$ to be 10. *M*. Moreover, the square root of an equilibrium constant is another equilibrium constant, which cannot have a negative value.

**Using the Quadratic Formula to Find the Unknown** The shortcut we used to simplify the math in Sample Problem 17.9 is a special case that occurred because we started with equal concentrations of the reactants, but typically, we start with different concentrations of reactants. Suppose, for example, we start with 2.00 $M$ CO and 1.00 $M$ $H_2O$. Now, the reaction table becomes

| Concentration ($M$) | $CO(g)$ $+$ | $H_2O(g)$ $\rightleftharpoons$ | $CO_2(g)$ $+$ | $H_2(g)$ |
|---|---|---|---|---|
| Initial | 2.00 | 1.00 | 0 | 0 |
| Change | $-x$ | $-x$ | $+x$ | $+x$ |
| Equilibrium | $2.00 - x$ | $1.00 - x$ | $x$ | $x$ |

Substituting these values into $Q_c$, we obtain

$$Q_c = \frac{[CO_2][H_2]}{[CO][H_2O]} = \frac{(x)(x)}{(2.00 - x)(1.00 - x)} = \frac{x^2}{x^2 - 3.00x + 2.00}$$

At equilibrium, we have

$$1.56 = \frac{x^2}{x^2 - 3.00x + 2.00}$$

To solve for $x$ in this case, we rearrange the previous expression into the form of a *quadratic equation:*

$$a\,x^2 + b\,x + c = 0$$
$$0.56x^2 - 4.68x + 3.12 = 0$$

where $a = 0.56$, $b = -4.68$, and $c = 3.12$. Then we find $x$ with the quadratic formula (Appendix A):

$$x = \frac{-b \pm \sqrt{b^2 - 4ac}}{2a}$$

The $\pm$ sign means that we obtain two possible values for $x$:

$$x = \frac{4.68 \pm \sqrt{(-4.68)^2 - 4(0.56)(3.12)}}{2(0.56)}$$

$$x = 7.6\,M \quad \text{and} \quad x = 0.73\,M$$

But only one of the values makes sense chemically. In this case, the positive root gives the larger value and negative concentrations at equilibrium (for example, $2.00\,M -$ $7.6\,M = -5.6\,M$), which have no meaning. Therefore, $x = 0.73\,M$, and we have

$$[CO] = 2.00\,M - x = 2.00\,M - 0.73\,M = 1.27\,M$$
$$[H_2O] = 1.00\,M - x = 0.27\,M$$
$$[CO_2] = [H_2] = x = 0.73\,M$$

Checking to see if these values give the known $K_c$, we have

$$K_c = \frac{(0.73)(0.73)}{(1.27)(0.27)} = 1.6 \text{ (within rounding of 1.56)}$$

**A Simplifying Assumption for Finding the Unknown** In many cases, we can use chemical "common sense" to make an assumption that simplifies the math by avoiding the need to use the quadratic formula to find $x$. In general, *if a reaction has a relatively small K and a relatively large initial reactant concentration, the concentration change (x) can often be neglected.* This assumption does not mean that $x = 0$, because then there would be no reaction. It means that if a reaction starts with a high [reactant]$_{init}$ and proceeds very little to reach equilibrium (small $K$), the reactant concentration at equilibrium, [reactant]$_{eq}$, will be nearly the same as [reactant]$_{init}$.

Here's an everyday analogy for this assumption. On a bathroom scale, you weigh 158 lb. Take off your wristwatch, and you still weigh 158 lb. Within the accuracy of the scale, the weight of the watch is so small compared with your body weight that it can be neglected:

Initial body weight − weight of watch = final body weight ≈ initial body weight

Thus, let's say the initial concentration of A is 0.500 $M$ and, because of a small $K_c$, the concentration of A that reacts is 0.002 $M$. We can then assume that

$$0.500 \ M - 0.002 \ M = 0.498 \ M \approx 0.500 \ M$$

that is,

$$[A]_{init} - [A]_{reacting} = [A]_{eq} \approx [A]_{init} \qquad \text{(17.9)}$$

To justify the assumption that $x$ is negligible, we make sure the error introduced is not significant. One common criterion for "significant" is the 5% rule: *if the assumption results in a change that is less than 5% of the initial concentration, the error is not significant, and the assumption is justified.* Let's see how making this assumption simplifies the math and if it is justified in the cases of two different [reactant]$_{init}$ values.

---

**Sample Problem 17.10** | **Making a Simplifying Assumption to Calculate Equilibrium Concentrations**

**Problem** Phosgene is a potent chemical warfare agent that is now outlawed by international agreement. It decomposes by the reaction

$$COCl_2(g) \rightleftharpoons CO(g) + Cl_2(g) \qquad K_c = 8.3 \times 10^{-4} \ \text{(at 360°C)}$$

Calculate [CO], [Cl$_2$], and [COCl$_2$] when each of the following amounts of phosgene decomposes and reaches equilibrium in a 10.0-L flask:
**(a)** 5.00 mol of COCl$_2$      **(b)** 0.100 mol of COCl$_2$

**Plan** We know from the balanced equation that when $x$ mol of COCl$_2$ decomposes, $x$ mol of CO and $x$ mol of Cl$_2$ form. We use the volume (10.0 L) to convert amount (5.00 mol or 0.100 mol) to molar concentration, define $x$ and set up the reaction table, and substitute the values into $Q_c$. Before using the quadratic formula, we assume that $x$ is negligibly small. After solving for $x$, we check the assumption and find the equilibrium concentrations. If the assumption is not justified, we use the quadratic formula to find $x$.

**Solution** **(a)** For 5.00 mol of COCl$_2$. Writing the reaction quotient:

$$Q_c = \frac{[CO][Cl_2]}{[COCl_2]}$$

Calculating the initial reactant concentration, [COCl$_2$]$_{init}$:

$$[COCl_2]_{init} = \frac{5.00 \ \text{mol}}{10.0 \ \text{L}} = 0.500 \ M$$

Setting up the reaction table, with $x$ equal to [COCl$_2$]$_{reacting}$:

| Concentration (*M*) | COCl$_2$(g) $\rightleftharpoons$ | CO(g) + | Cl$_2$(g) |
|---|---|---|---|
| Initial | 0.500 | 0 | 0 |
| Change | $-x$ | $+x$ | $+x$ |
| Equilibrium | $0.500 - x$ | $x$ | $x$ |

If we use the equilibrium values in $Q_c$ with the given $K_c$, we obtain

$$Q_c = \frac{[CO][Cl_2]}{[COCl_2]} = \frac{x^2}{0.500 - x} = K_c = 8.3 \times 10^{-4}$$

Because $K_c$ is small, the reaction does not proceed very far to the right, so let's assume that $x$ ([COCl$_2$]$_{reacting}$) can be neglected. In other words, we assume that the equilibrium concentration is nearly the same as the initial concentration, 0.500 $M$:

$$[COCl_2]_{init} - [COCl_2]_{reacting} \approx [COCl_2]_{eq}$$

$$0.500 \ M - x \approx 0.500 \ M$$

Using this assumption, we substitute and solve for $x$:

$$K_c = 8.3 \times 10^{-4} \approx \frac{x^2}{0.500}$$

$$x^2 \approx (8.3 \times 10^{-4})(0.500) \qquad \text{so} \qquad x \approx 2.0 \times 10^{-2}$$

Checking the assumption by seeing if the error is $<5\%$:

$$\frac{[\text{Change}]}{[\text{Initial}]} \times 100 = \frac{2.0\times10^{-2}}{0.500} \times 100 = 4\% \ (<5\%, \text{ so the assumption is justified})$$

Solving for the equilibrium concentrations:

$$[CO] = [Cl_2] = x = \boxed{2.0\times10^{-2} \, M}$$
$$[COCl_2] = 0.500 \, M - x = \boxed{0.480 \, M}$$

**(b)** For 0.100 mol of $COCl_2$. The calculation in this case is the same as the calculation in part (a), except that $[COCl_2]_{init} = 0.100 \, \text{mol}/10.0 \, L = 0.0100 \, M$. Thus, at equilibrium,

$$Q_c = \frac{[CO][Cl_2]}{[COCl_2]} = \frac{x^2}{0.0100 - x} \quad = K_c = 8.3\times10^{-4}$$

Making the assumption that $0.0100 \, M - x \approx 0.0100 \, M$ and solving for $x$:

$$K_c = 8.3\times10^{-4} \approx \frac{x^2}{0.0100} \qquad x \approx 2.9\times10^{-3}$$

Checking the assumption:

$$\frac{2.9\times10^{-3}}{0.0100} \times 100 = 29\% \qquad (>5\%, \text{ so the assumption is } not \text{ justified})$$

We must solve the quadratic equation:

$$x^2 + (8.3\times10^{-4})x - (8.3\times10^{-6}) = 0$$

The only meaningful value of $x$ is $2.5\times10^{-3}$.
Solving for the equilibrium concentrations:

$$[CO] = [Cl_2] = \boxed{2.5\times10^{-3} \, M}$$
$$[COCl_2] = 1.00\times10^{-2} \, M - x = \boxed{7.5\times10^{-3} \, M}$$

**Check** Once again, use the calculated values to be sure you obtain the given $K_c$.

**Comment** The main point is that the simplifying assumption was justified at the high $[COCl_2]_{init}$ but *not* at the low $[COCl_2]_{init}$.

## Follow-Up Problem 17.10
In a study of the effect of temperature on halogen decomposition, 0.50 mol of $I_2$ was heated in a 2.5-L vessel, and the following reaction occurred: $I_2(g) \rightleftharpoons 2I(g)$.
**(a)** Calculate $[I_2]$ and $[I]$ at equilibrium at 600 K; $K_c = 2.94\times10^{-10}$.
**(b)** Calculate $[I_2]$ and $[I]$ at equilibrium at 2000 K; $K_c = 0.209$.

**Predicting When the Assumption Will Be Justified** To summarize, we assume that $x$ ($[A]_{reacting}$) can be neglected if $K_c$ is relatively small and/or $[A]_{init}$ is relatively large. The same holds for $K_p$ and $P_{A(init)}$. But *how* small or large must these variables be? Here's a benchmark for deciding when to make the assumption:

- If $\dfrac{[A]_{init}}{K_c} > 400$, the assumption is justified: neglecting $x$ introduces an error $< 5\%$.

- If $\dfrac{[A]_{init}}{K_c} < 400$, the assumption is *not* justified; neglecting $x$ introduces an error $> 5\%$, so we solve a quadratic equation to find $x$.

For example, using the values from Sample Problem 17.10, we have

Part (a): For $[A]_{init} = 0.500 \, M$, $\dfrac{0.500}{8.3\times10^{-4}} = 6.0\times10^2$, which is greater than 400.

Part (b): For $[A]_{init} = 0.0100 \, M$, $\dfrac{0.0100}{8.3\times10^{-4}} = 12$, which is less than 400.

We will make a similar assumption in many problems in Chapters 18 and 19.

## Problems Involving Mixtures of Reactants and Products

In the problems so far, the reaction *had* to go toward products because it started with only reactants. And therefore, in the reaction tables, we knew that the unknown change in reactant concentration had a negative sign ($-x$) and the change in product concentration had a positive sign ($+x$). If, however, we start with a *mixture* of reactants and products, the reaction direction is not obvious. In those cases, we apply the idea from Section 17.4 and first *compare the values of Q and K to find the direction the reaction is proceeding to reach equilibrium.* (To focus on this idea, Sample Problem 17.11 uses concentrations that avoid the need for the quadratic formula.)

---

**Sample Problem 17.11**  **Predicting Reaction Direction and Calculating Equilibrium Concentrations**

**Problem** The research and development unit of a chemical company is studying the reaction of $CH_4$ and $H_2S$, two components of natural gas:

$$CH_4(g) + 2H_2S(g) \rightleftharpoons CS_2(g) + 4H_2(g)$$

In one experiment, 1.00 mol of $CH_4$, 1.00 mol of $CS_2$, 2.00 mol of $H_2S$, and 2.00 mol of $H_2$ are mixed in a 250.-mL vessel at 960°C. At this temperature, $K_c = 0.036$.
**(a)** In which direction will the reaction proceed to reach equilibrium?
**(b)** If $[CH_4] = 5.56\ M$ at equilibrium, what are the equilibrium concentrations of the other substances?

**Plan** **(a)** To find the direction, we convert the given initial amounts and volume (0.250 L) to concentrations, calculate $Q_c$, and compare it with $K_c$. **(b)** Based on this information, we determine the sign of each concentration change for the reaction table and then use the known $[CH_4]$ at equilibrium (5.56 $M$) to determine $x$ and the other equilibrium concentrations.

**Solution** **(a)** Calculating the initial concentrations:

$$[CH_4] = \frac{1.00\ \text{mol}}{0.250\ \text{L}} = 4.00\ M$$

Similarly, $[H_2S] = 8.00\ M$, $[CS_2] = 4.00\ M$, and $[H_2] = 8.00\ M$.
Calculating the value of $Q_c$:

$$Q_c = \frac{[CS_2][H_2]^4}{[CH_4][H_2S]^2} = \frac{(4.00)(8.00)^4}{(4.00)(8.00)^2} = 64.0$$

Comparing $Q_c$ and $K_c$: $Q_c > K_c$ (64.0 > 0.036), so the reaction proceeds to the left. Therefore, concentrations of reactants increase and those of products decrease.
**(b)** Setting up a reaction table, with $x = [CS_2]$ that reacts, which equals $[CH_4]$ that forms:

| Concentration ($M$) | $CH_4(g)$ | $+$ | $2H_2S(g)$ | $\rightleftharpoons$ | $CS_2(g)$ | $+$ | $4H_2(g)$ |
|---|---|---|---|---|---|---|---|
| Intial | 4.00 | | 8.00 | | 4.00 | | 8.00 |
| Change | $+x$ | | $+2x$ | | $-x$ | | $-4x$ |
| Equilibrium | $4.00 + x$ | | $8.00 + 2x$ | | $4.00 - x$ | | $8.00 - 4x$ |

Solving for $x$: At equilibrium,

$$[CH_4] = 5.56\ M = 4.00\ M + x \qquad \text{so} \qquad x = 1.56\ M$$

Thus,  $[H_2S] = 8.00\ M + 2x = 8.00\ M + 2(1.56\ M) = 11.12\ M$
$[CS_2] = 4.00\ M - x = 2.44\ M$
$[H_2] = 8.00\ M - 4x = 1.76\ M$

**Check** The comparison of $Q_c$ and $K_c$ showed the reaction proceeding to the left. The given data from part (b) confirm this because $[CH_4]$ increases from 4.00 $M$ to 5.56 $M$ during the reaction. Check that the concentrations give the known $K_c$:

$$\frac{(2.44)(1.76)^4}{(5.56)(11.12)^2} = 0.0341, \text{ which is close to } 0.036$$

**Follow-Up Problem 17.11**  An inorganic chemist studying the reactions of phosphorus halides mixes 0.1050 mol of $PCl_5$ with 0.0450 mol of $Cl_2$ and 0.0450 mol of $PCl_3$ in a 0.5000-L flask at 250°C: $PCl_5(g) \rightleftharpoons PCl_3(g) + Cl_2(g)$; $K_c = 4.2 \times 10^{-2}$.
**(a)** In which direction will the reaction proceed?
**(b)** If $[PCl_5] = 0.2065\ M$ at equilibrium, what are the equilibrium concentrations of the other components?

Figure 17.6 groups the steps for solving equilibrium problems in which you know $K$ and some initial quantities and must find the equilibrium quantities.

## ■ Summary of Section 17.5

- In equilibrium problems, we typically use quantities (concentrations or pressures) of reactants and products to find $K$, or we use $K$ to find quantities.
- Reaction tables summarize the initial quantities, their changes during the reaction, and the equilibrium quantities. To simplify calculations, we assume that if $K$ is small and the initial quantity of reactant is large, the unknown change in reactant ($x$) can be neglected. If this assumption is not justified (that is, if the error is greater than 5%), we use the quadratic formula to find $x$.
- For reactions that start with a mixture of reactants and products, we first determine reaction direction by comparing $Q$ and $K$ to decide on the sign of $x$.

---

# 17.6 • REACTION CONDITIONS AND EQUILIBRIUM: LE CHÂTELIER'S PRINCIPLE

Change conditions so that a system is no longer at equilibrium and it has the remarkable ability to adjust itself and reattain equilibrium. This phenomenon is described by **Le Châtelier's principle:** when a chemical system at equilibrium is disturbed, it reattains equilibrium by undergoing a net reaction that reduces the effect of the disturbance.

Two phrases in this statement need further explanation:

1. How is a system "disturbed"? At equilibrium, $Q$ equals $K$. The system is disturbed when a change in conditions forces it temporarily out of equilibrium ($Q \neq K$). Three common disturbances are a change in concentration, a change in pressure (caused by a change in volume), or a change in temperature. We'll discuss each below.

2. What does a "net reaction" mean? This phrase refers to a shift in the *equilibrium position* to the right or left. The *equilibrium position* is defined by the specific equilibrium concentrations (or pressures). A shift to the right is a net reaction from reactant to product until equilibrium is reattained; a shift to the left is a net reaction from product to reactant. Thus, *concentrations (or pressures) change in a way that reduces the effect of the change in conditions, and the system attains a new equilibrium position.*

For the remainder of this section, we'll examine a system at equilibrium to see how it responds to changes in concentration, pressure (volume), or temperature; then, we'll see what happens when we add a catalyst. As our example, we use the gaseous reaction between phosphorus trichloride and chlorine to produce phosphorus pentachloride:

$$PCl_3(g) + Cl_2(g) \rightleftharpoons PCl_5(g)$$

Le Châtelier's principle holds for many systems at equilibrium in both the natural and social sciences—the effects of disease or drought on populations of predators and prey on the African plain (*see margin*), a change in the cost of petroleum based on a balance of supply and demand, even the formation of certain elements in the core of a star.

## The Effect of a Change in Concentration

When a system at equilibrium is disturbed by a change in concentration of one of the components, it reacts in the direction that reduces the change:

- If the concentration of A increases, the system reacts to consume some of it.
- If the concentration of B decreases, the system reacts to produce some of it.

Only components that appear in $Q$ can have an effect, so changes in the amounts of pure liquids and solids cannot.

### A Qualitative View of a Concentration Change

At 523 K, the $PCl_3$-$Cl_2$-$PCl_5$ system reaches equilibrium when

$$PCl_3(g) + Cl_2(g) \rightleftharpoons PCl_5(g) \qquad Q_c = \frac{[PCl_5]}{[PCl_3][Cl_2]} = 24.0 = K_c$$

---

### SOLVING EQUILIBRIUM PROBLEMS

**PRELIMINARY SETTING UP**

1. Write the balanced equation.
2. Write the reaction quotient, $Q$.
3. Convert all amounts into the correct units ($M$ or atm).

**WORKING ON THE REACTION TABLE**

4. When reaction direction is not known, compare $Q$ with $K$.
5. Construct a reaction table.

> ✓ Check the sign of $x$, the change in the concentration (or pressure).

**SOLVING FOR $x$ AND EQUILIBRIUM QUANTITIES**

6. Substitute the quantities into $Q$.
7. To simplify the math, assume that $x$ is negligible:
   ($[A]_{init} - x = [A]_{eq} \approx [A]_{init}$)
8. Solve for $x$.

> ✓ Check that assumption is justified (<5% error). If not, solve quadratic equation for $x$.

9. Find the equilibrium quantities.

> ✓ Check to see that calculated values give the known $K$.

**Figure 17.6** Steps in solving equilibrium problems.

Does Le Châtelier's principle apply to other systems?

Starting with $Q_c$ equal to $K_c$, let's think through some changes in concentration:

1. *Adding a reactant.* What happens if we disturb the system by adding some $Cl_2$ gas? To reduce the disturbance, the system will consume some of the added $Cl_2$ by shifting toward product. With regard to the reaction quotient, when the $[Cl_2]$ term increases, the value of $Q_c$ decreases; thus, $Q_c \neq K_c$. As some of the added $Cl_2$ reacts with some of the $PCl_3$ to form more $PCl_5$, the denominator becomes smaller again and the numerator larger, until eventually $Q_c = K_c$ again. Notice the changes in the new equilibrium concentrations: $[Cl_2]$ and $[PCl_5]$ are higher than in the original equilibrium position, and $[PCl_3]$ is lower. Nevertheless, the ratio of values gives the same $K_c$. Thus, *the equilibrium position shifts to the right when a component on the left is added:*

$$PCl_3 + Cl_2(\text{added}) \longrightarrow PCl_5$$

2. *Removing a reactant.* What happens if we disturb the system by removing some $PCl_3$? To reduce this disturbance, the system will replace the $PCl_3$ by consuming some $PCl_5$ and proceeding toward reactants. With regard to $Q_c$, when the $[PCl_3]$ term decreases, $Q_c$ increases, so $Q_c \neq K_c$. As some $PCl_5$ decomposes to $PCl_3$ and $Cl_2$, the numerator decreases and the denominator increases until $Q_c = K_c$ again. Once again, the new and old equilibrium concentrations are different, but the value of $K_c$ is not. Thus, *the equilibrium position shifts to the left when a component on the left is removed:*

$$PCl_3(\text{removed}) + Cl_2 \longleftarrow PCl_5$$

3. *Adding or removing a product.* The same points we just made for a reactant hold for a product. If we add $PCl_5$, the equilibrium position shifts to the left; if we remove some $PCl_5$, the equilibrium position shifts to the right.

In other words, no matter how the disturbance in concentration comes about, *the system reacts to consume some of the added substance or produce some of the removed substance* to make $Q_c = K_c$ again (Figure 17.7):

- The equilibrium position shifts to the *right* if a reactant is added or a product is removed: [reactant] increases or [product] decreases.
- The equilibrium position shifts to the *left* if a reactant is removed or a product is added: [reactant] decreases or [product] increases.

### A Quantitative View of a Concentration Change

As you saw, the system "reduces the effect of the disturbance." But the effect is not completely eliminated, as we can see from a quantitative comparison of original and new equilibrium positions.

Consider what happens when we add $Cl_2$ to a system whose original equilibrium position was established with $[PCl_3] = 0.200\ M$, $[Cl_2] = 0.125\ M$, and $[PCl_5] = 0.600\ M$. That is,

$$Q_c = \frac{[PCl_5]}{[PCl_3][Cl_2]} = \frac{0.600}{(0.200)(0.125)} = 24.0 = K_c$$

Now we add enough $Cl_2$ to increase its concentration by $0.075\ M$ to a new $[Cl_2]_{\text{init}}$ of $0.200\ M$. The reaction proceeds, and the system comes to a new equilibrium position. From Le Châtelier's principle, we predict that adding more reactant will shift the equilibrium position to the right. Experimental measurement shows that the new $[PCl_5]_{\text{eq}}$ is $0.637\ M$.

ANY OF THESE CHANGES CAUSES A SHIFT TO THE **RIGHT**.

increase    increase              decrease

$$PCl_3 + Cl_2 \rightleftharpoons PCl_5$$

decrease decrease              increase

ANY OF THESE CHANGES CAUSES A SHIFT TO THE **LEFT**.

**Figure 17.7** The effect of a change in concentration on a system at equilibrium.

| Table 17.3 The Effect of Added $Cl_2$ on the $PCl_3$-$Cl_2$-$PCl_5$ System | | | |
|---|---|---|---|
| **Concentration ($M$)** | $PCl_3(g)$ + | $Cl_2(g)$ $\rightleftharpoons$ | $PCl_5(g)$ |
| Original equilibrium | 0.200 | 0.125 | 0.600 |
| Disturbance | | +0.075 | |
| New initial | 0.200 | 0.200 | 0.600 |
| Change | $-x$ | $-x$ | $+x$ |
| New equilibrium | $0.200 - x$ | $0.200 - x$ | $0.600 + x$ |
| | | | $(0.637)*$ |

*Experimentally determined value.

Table 17.3 shows a reaction table of the entire process: the original equilibrium position, the disturbance, the (new) initial concentrations, the direction of $x$ (the change needed to reattain equilibrium), and the new equilibrium position. Figure 17.8 depicts the process.

Let's determine the new equilibrium concentrations. From Table 17.3,

$$[PCl_5] = 0.600\ M + x = 0.637\ M \qquad \text{so} \qquad x = 0.037\ M$$

Thus, $\qquad [PCl_3] = [Cl_2] = 0.200\ M - x = 0.200\ M - 0.037\ M = 0.163\ M$

Therefore, at equilibrium,

$$K_{c(original)} = \frac{0.600}{(0.200)(0.125)} = 24.0$$

$$K_{c(new)} = \frac{0.637}{(0.163)(0.163)} = 24.0$$

There are several key points to notice about the new equilibrium concentrations:

- As we predicted, $[PCl_5]$ (0.637 $M$) is higher than the original concentration (0.600 $M$).
- $[Cl_2]$ (0.163 $M$) is higher than the *original* equilibrium concentration (0.125 $M$), but lower than the new initial concentration (0.200 $M$); thus, the disturbance is *reduced but not eliminated*.
- $[PCl_3]$ (0.163 $M$), the other reactant, is lower than the original equilibrium concentration (0.200 $M$) because some reacted with the added $Cl_2$.
- Most importantly, although the position of equilibrium shifted to the right, *at a given temperature, $K_c$ does **not** change with a change in concentration.*

**Figure 17.8 The effect of added $Cl_2$ on the $PCl_3$-$Cl_2$-$PCl_5$ system.** The original equilibrium concentrations are shown at left *(gray region)*. When $Cl_2$ *(yellow curve)* is added, its concentration increases instantly *(vertical part of yellow curve)* and then falls gradually as it reacts with $PCl_3$ to form more $PCl_5$. Soon, equilibrium is re-established at new concentrations *(blue region)* but with the same $K$.

---

**Sample Problem 17.12 Predicting the Effect of a Change in Concentration on the Equilibrium Position**

**Problem** To improve air quality and obtain a useful product, chemists often remove sulfur from coal and natural gas by treating the contaminant hydrogen sulfide with $O_2$:

$$2H_2S(g) + O_2(g) \rightleftharpoons 2S(s) + 2H_2O(g)$$

What happens to
(a) $[H_2O]$ if $O_2$ is added?       (b) $[H_2S]$ if $O_2$ is added?
(c) $[O_2]$ if $H_2S$ is removed?       (d) $[H_2S]$ if sulfur is added?

**Plan** We write the reaction quotient to see how $Q_c$ is affected by each disturbance, relative to $K_c$. This effect tells us the direction in which the reaction proceeds for the system to reattain equilibrium and how each concentration changes.

**Solution** Writing the reaction quotient: $Q_c = \dfrac{[H_2O]^2}{[H_2S]^2[O_2]}$

(a) When $O_2$ is added, the denominator of $Q_c$ increases, so $Q_c < K_c$. The reaction proceeds to the right until $Q_c = K_c$ again, so $[H_2O]$ increases.

(b) As in part (a), when $O_2$ is added, $Q_c < K_c$. Some $H_2S$ reacts with the added $O_2$ as the reaction proceeds to the right, so $[H_2S]$ decreases.

**(c)** When $H_2S$ is removed, the denominator of $Q_c$ decreases, so $Q_c > K_c$. As the reaction proceeds to the left to re-form $H_2S$, more $O_2$ forms as well, so $[O_2]$ increases.

**(d)** The concentration of solid S is unchanged as long as some is present, so it does not appear in the reaction quotient. Adding more S has no effect, so $[H_2S]$ is unchanged (but see Comment 2 below).

**Check** Apply Le Châtelier's principle to see that the reaction proceeds in the direction that lowers the increased concentration or raises the decreased concentration.

**Comment 1.** As you know, sulfur exists most commonly as $S_8$. How would this change in formula affect the answers? The balanced equation and $Q_c$ would be

$$8H_2S(g) + 4O_2(g) \rightleftharpoons S_8(s) + 8H_2O(g) \qquad Q_c = \frac{[H_2O]^8}{[H_2S]^8[O_2]^4}$$

The value of $K_c$ is different for this equation, but the changes described in the problem have the same effects. Thus, shifts in equilibrium position predicted by Le Châtelier's principle are not affected by a change in the balancing coefficients.
**2.** In (d), you saw that adding a solid has no effect on the concentrations of other components: because *the **concentration** of the solid cannot change,* it does not appear in $Q$. But *the **amount** of solid can change.* Adding $H_2S$ shifts the reaction to the right, so more S forms.

**Follow-Up Problem 17.12** In a study of glass etching, a chemist examines the reaction between sand ($SiO_2$) and hydrogen fluoride at 150°C:

$$SiO_2(s) + 4HF(g) \rightleftharpoons SiF_4(g) + 2H_2O(g)$$

Predict the effect on $[SiF_4]$ when **(a)** $H_2O(g)$ is removed; **(b)** some liquid water is added; **(c)** HF is removed; **(d)** some sand is removed.

## The Effect of a Change in Pressure (Volume)

Changes in pressure can have a large effect on equilibrium systems containing gaseous components. (A change in pressure has a negligible effect on liquids and solids because they are nearly incompressible.) Pressure changes can occur in three ways:

- *Changing the concentration of a gaseous component.* We just considered the effect of changing the concentration of a component, and that reasoning applies here.
- *Adding an inert gas (one that does not take part in the reaction).* As long as the volume of the system is constant, adding an inert gas has no effect on the equilibrium position because *all concentrations, and thus partial pressures, remain the same.* Moreover, the inert gas does not appear in $Q$, so it cannot have an effect.
- *Changing the volume of the reaction vessel.* This change can cause a large shift in equilibrium position, but only for reactions in which the number of moles of gas, $n_{gas}$, changes.

Let's consider the two possible situations for the third way: changing the volume of the reaction vessel.

1. *Reactions in which $n_{gas}$ changes.* Suppose the $PCl_3$-$Cl_2$-$PCl_5$ system is in a cylinder-piston assembly. We press down on the piston to halve the volume, so the gas pressure doubles. To reduce this disturbance, the system responds by *reducing the number of gas molecules.* And the only way to do that is through a net reaction toward the side with *fewer moles of gas,* in this case, toward product:

$$PCl_3(g) + Cl_2(g) \longrightarrow PCl_5(g)$$

2 mol gas $\longrightarrow$ 1 mol gas

Recall that $Q_c = \dfrac{[PCl_5]}{[PCl_3][Cl_2]}$. When the volume is halved, the concentrations double, but the denominator of $Q_c$ is the product of two concentrations, so it quadruples while the numerator only doubles. Thus, $Q_c$ becomes less than $K_c$. As a result, the system forms more $PCl_5$ and a new equilibrium position is reached.

**Figure 17.9** The effect of a change in pressure (volume) on a system at equilibrium. The system of gases (*center*) is at equilibrium. For the reaction

$$\bullet + \circ \rightleftharpoons \bullet$$

an increase in pressure (*right*) decreases the volume, so the equilibrium shifts to form *fewer* molecules. A decrease in pressure (*left*) increases the volume, so the equilibrium shifts to form *more* molecules.

Thus, for a system that consists of gases at equilibrium, in which the amount (mol) of gas, $n_{gas}$, changes during the reaction (Figure 17.9):

- If the volume becomes smaller (pressure is higher), the reaction shifts so that the total number of gas molecules decreases.
- If the volume becomes larger (pressure is lower), the reaction shifts so that the total number of gas molecules increases.

2. *Reactions in which* $n_{gas}$ *does **not** change.* For the formation of hydrogen iodide from its elements, we have the same amount (mol) of gas on both sides:

$$H_2(g) + I_2(g) \rightleftharpoons 2HI(g)$$

$$2 \text{ mol gas} \longrightarrow 2 \text{ mol gas}$$

Therefore, $Q_c$ has the same number of terms in the numerator and denominator:

$$Q_c = \frac{[HI]^2}{[H_2][I_2]} = \frac{[HI][HI]}{[H_2][I_2]}$$

Because a change in volume has the same effect on the numerator and denominator, *there is **no** effect on the equilibrium position.*

In terms of the equilibrium constant, *a change in volume is, in effect, a change in concentration:* a decrease in volume raises the concentration, and vice versa. Therefore, like other changes in concentration, *a change in pressure due to a change in volume does **not** alter* $K_c$.

---

**Sample Problem 17.13**    **Predicting the Effect of a Change in Volume (Pressure) on the Equilibrium Position**

**Problem** How would you change the volume of each of the following reactions to *increase* the yield of the products?
**(a)** $CaCO_3(s) \rightleftharpoons CaO(s) + CO_2(g)$
**(b)** $S(s) + 3F_2(g) \rightleftharpoons SF_6(g)$
**(c)** $Cl_2(g) + I_2(g) \rightleftharpoons 2ICl(g)$

**Plan** Whenever gases are present, a change in volume causes a change in concentration. For reactions in which the number of moles of gas changes, if the volume decreases (pressure increases), the equilibrium position shifts to lower the pressure by reducing the number of moles of gas. A volume increase (pressure decrease) has the opposite effect.

**Solution** **(a)** The only gas is the product $CO_2$. To make the system produce more molecules of gas, that is, more $CO_2$, we increase the volume (decrease the pressure).
**(b)** With 3 mol of gas on the left and only 1 mol on the right, we decrease the volume (increase the pressure) to form fewer molecules of gas and, thus, more $SF_6$.
**(c)** The number of moles of gas is the same on both sides of the equation, so a change in volume (pressure) will have no effect on the yield of ICl.

**Check** Let's predict the relative values of $Q_c$ and $K_c$.
(a) $Q_c = [CO_2]$, so increasing the volume will make $Q_c < K_c$, and the system will yield more $CO_2$.
(b) $Q_c = [SF_6]/[F_2]^3$. Lowering the volume increases $[F_2]$ and $[SF_6]$ proportionately, but $Q_c$ decreases because of the exponent 3 in the denominator. To make $Q_c = K_c$ again, $[SF_6]$ must increase.
(c) $Q_c = [ICl]^2/[Cl_2][I_2]$. A change in volume (pressure) affects the numerator (2 mol) and denominator (2 mol) equally, so it will have no effect.

**Follow-Up Problem 17.13**   Would you increase or decrease the pressure (via a volume change) of each of the following reaction mixtures to *decrease* the yield of products?
(a) $2SO_2(g) + O_2(g) \rightleftharpoons 2SO_3(g)$
(b) $4NH_3(g) + 5O_2(g) \rightleftharpoons 4NO(g) + 6H_2O(g)$
(c) $CaC_2O_4(s) \rightleftharpoons CaCO_3(s) + CO(g)$

## The Effect of a Change in Temperature

Of the three types of disturbances that may occur—a change in concentration, pressure, or temperature—*only temperature changes alter K*. To see why, let's focus on the sign of $\Delta H^\circ_{rxn}$:

$$PCl_3(g) + Cl_2(g) \rightleftharpoons PCl_5(g) \qquad \Delta H^\circ_{rxn} = -111 \text{ kJ}$$

The forward reaction is exothermic (releases heat; $\Delta H^\circ_{rxn} < 0$), so the reverse reaction is endothermic (absorbs heat; $\Delta H^\circ_{rxn} > 0$):

$$PCl_3(g) + Cl_2(g) \longrightarrow PCl_5(g) + \textbf{\textit{heat}} \text{ (exothermic)}$$
$$PCl_3(g) + Cl_2(g) \longleftarrow PCl_5(g) + \textbf{\textit{heat}} \text{ (endothermic)}$$

If we consider *heat as a component of the equilibrium system,* a rise in temperature occurs when heat is "added" to the system and a drop in temperature occurs when heat is "removed" from the system. As with a change in any other component, the system shifts to reduce the effect of the change. Therefore, *a temperature increase (adding heat) favors the endothermic (heat-absorbing) direction, and a temperature decrease (removing heat) favors the exothermic (heat-releasing) direction.*

If we start with the system at equilibrium, $Q_c$ equals $K_c$. Increase the temperature, and the system absorbs the added heat by decomposing some $PCl_5$ to $PCl_3$ and $Cl_2$. The denominator of $Q_c$ becomes larger and the numerator smaller, so the system reaches a new equilibrium position at a smaller ratio of concentration terms, that is, a lower $K_c$. Similarly, if the temperature drops, the system releases more heat by forming more $PCl_5$ from some $PCl_3$ and $Cl_2$. The numerator of $Q_c$ becomes larger, the denominator smaller, and the new equilibrium position has a higher $K_c$. Thus,

- *A temperature rise will increase $K_c$ for a system with a positive $\Delta H^\circ_{rxn}$.*
- *A temperature rise will decrease $K_c$ for a system with a negative $\Delta H^\circ_{rxn}$.*

Let's review these ideas with a sample problem.

**Sample Problem 17.14**   **Predicting the Effect of a Change in Temperature on the Equilibrium Position**

**Problem** How does an *increase* in temperature affect the equilibrium concentration of the underlined substance and $K$ for each of the following reactions?
(a) $CaO(s) + H_2O(l) \rightleftharpoons \underline{Ca(OH)_2}(aq) \qquad \Delta H^\circ = -82 \text{ kJ}$
(b) $CaCO_3(s) \rightleftharpoons CaO(s) + \underline{CO_2}(g) \qquad \Delta H^\circ = 178 \text{ kJ}$
(c) $\underline{SO_2}(g) \rightleftharpoons S(s) + O_2(g) \qquad \Delta H^\circ = 297 \text{ kJ}$

**Plan** We write each equation to show heat as a reactant or product. The temperature increases when we add heat, so the system shifts to absorb the heat; that is, the endothermic reaction occurs. Thus, $K$ will increase if the forward reaction is endothermic and decrease if it is exothermic.

**Solution** **(a)** $CaO(s) + H_2O(l) \rightleftharpoons Ca(OH)_2(aq) + \textbf{\textit{heat}}$
Adding heat shifts the system to the left:  [$[Ca(OH)_2]$ and $K$ will decrease.]
**(b)** $CaCO_3(s) + \textbf{\textit{heat}} \rightleftharpoons CaO(s) + CO_2(g)$
Adding heat shifts the system to the right:  [$[CO_2]$ and $K$ will increase.]
**(c)** $SO_2(g) + \textbf{\textit{heat}} \rightleftharpoons S(s) + O_2(g)$
Adding heat shifts the system to the right:  [$[SO_2]$ will decrease and $K$ will increase.]

**Check** Check your answers by reasoning through a *decrease* in temperature: heat is removed and the exothermic direction is favored. All the answers should be opposite.

**Comment** Note that in (a) these ideas hold for solutions as well.

**Follow–Up Problem 17.14** How does a *decrease* in temperature affect the partial pressure of the underlined substance and the value of $K$ for each of the following reactions?
**(a)** $C(graphite) + \underline{2H_2(g)} \rightleftharpoons CH_4(g)$     $\Delta H° = -75$ kJ
**(b)** $\underline{N_2(g)} + O_2(g) \rightleftharpoons 2NO(g)$     $\Delta H° = 181$ kJ
**(c)** $P_4(s) + 10Cl_2(g) \rightleftharpoons \underline{4PCl_5(g)}$     $\Delta H° = -1528$ kJ

**The van't Hoff Equation: The Effect of *T* on *K*** The *van't Hoff equation* shows quantitatively how the equilibrium constant is affected by changes in temperature:

$$\ln \frac{K_2}{K_1} = -\frac{\Delta H°_{rxn}}{R} \left( \frac{1}{T_2} - \frac{1}{T_1} \right) \tag{17.10}$$

where $K_1$ is the equilibrium constant at $T_1$, $K_2$ is the equilibrium constant at $T_2$, and $R$ is the universal gas constant (8.314 J/mol·K). If we know $\Delta H°_{rxn}$ and $K$ at one temperature, the van't Hoff equation allows us to find $K$ at any other temperature (or to find $\Delta H°_{rxn}$, given the two $K$'s at two $T$'s).

Equation 17.10 confirms the qualitative prediction from Le Châtelier's principle: for a temperature rise, we have

$$T_2 > T_1 \quad\text{and}\quad 1/T_2 < 1/T_1$$

so

$$1/T_2 - 1/T_1 < 0$$

Therefore,

- For an endothermic reaction ($\Delta H°_{rxn} > 0$), the $-(\Delta H°_{rxn}/R)$ term is $<0$. With $1/T_2 - 1/T_1 < 0$, the right side of the equation is $>0$. Thus, $\ln (K_2/K_1) > 0$, so $K_2 > K_1$.
- For an exothermic reaction ($\Delta H°_{rxn} < 0$), the $-(\Delta H°_{rxn}/R)$ term is $>0$. With $1/T_2 - 1/T_1 < 0$, the right side of the equation is $<0$. Thus, $\ln (K_2/K_1) < 0$, so $K_2 < K_1$.

Here's a typical problem that requires the van't Hoff equation. Many coal gasification processes begin with the formation of syngas from carbon and steam:

$$C(s) + H_2O(g) \rightleftharpoons CO(g) + H_2(g) \qquad \Delta H°_{rxn} = 131 \text{ kJ/mol}$$

An engineer knows that $K_p$ is only $9.36 \times 10^{-17}$ at 25°C and therefore wants to find a temperature that allows a much higher yield. Calculate $K_p$ at 700.°C.

$$\ln \frac{K_2}{K_1} = -\frac{\Delta H°_{rxn}}{R} \left( \frac{1}{T_2} - \frac{1}{T_1} \right)$$

The temperatures must be in kelvins, and the units of $\Delta H°$ and $R$ must be made consistent:

$$\ln \left( \frac{K_{p2}}{9.36 \times 10^{-17}} \right) = -\frac{131 \times 10^3 \text{ J/mol}}{8.314 \text{ J/mol·K}} \left( \frac{1}{973 \text{ K}} - \frac{1}{298 \text{ K}} \right)$$

$$\frac{K_{p2}}{9.36 \times 10^{-17}} = 8.51 \times 10^{15}$$

$$K_{p2} = 0.797 \quad \text{(a much higher yield)}$$

(For further practice with the van't Hoff equation, see Problems 17.73 and 17.74.)

# The Lack of Effect of a Catalyst

Let's briefly consider what effect, if any, adding a catalyst would have on the system. Recall from Chapter 16 that a catalyst speeds up a reaction by lowering the activation energy, thereby increasing the forward *and* reverse rates to the same extent. Thus, *a catalyst shortens the time it takes to reach equilibrium but has **no** effect on the equilibrium position.* That is, if we add a catalyst to a mixture of $PCl_3$ and $Cl_2$ at 523 K, the system attains the *same* equilibrium concentrations of $PCl_3$, $Cl_2$, and $PCl_5$ *more quickly* than it does without the catalyst. Figure 17.10 shows an engine in an imaginary world where catalysts speed a reaction in only one direction. As you'll see in a moment, however, catalysts play key roles in optimizing reaction systems.

Table 17.4 summarizes the effects of changing conditions. Many changes alter the equilibrium *position*, but only temperature changes alter the equilibrium *constant*. Sample Problem 17.15 shows how to visualize equilibrium at the molecular level.

**Figure 17.10 Catalyzed perpetual motion?** This imaginary engine has a piston attached to a flywheel, whose rocker arm holds a catalyst that speeds $PCl_5$ breakdown but not formation. With the catalyst in the cylinder, $PCl_5$ breaks down faster than it forms, so the total gas pressure increases and the piston moves out. With the catalyst out of the cylinder, the old equilibrium returns, gas pressure lowers, and the piston moves in. If a catalyst *could* change the rate in only one direction, this machine would supply power with no input of external energy!

| Table **17.4** Effects of Various Disturbances on a System at Equilibrium | | |
|---|---|---|
| **Disturbance** | **Effect on Equilibrium Position** | **Effect on Value of $K$** |
| Concentration | | |
|   Increase [reactant] | Toward formation of product | None |
|   Decrease [reactant] | Toward formation of reactant | None |
|   Increase [product] | Toward formation of reactant | None |
|   Decrease [product] | Toward formation of product | None |
| Pressure | | |
|   Increase $P$ (decrease $V$) | Toward formation of fewer moles of gas | None |
|   Decrease $P$ (increase $V$) | Toward formation of more moles of gas | None |
|   Increase $P$ (add inert gas, no change in $V$) | None; concentrations unchanged | None |
| Temperature | | |
|   Increase $T$ | Toward absorption of heat | Increases if $\Delta H^\circ_{rxn} > 0$ <br> Decreases if $\Delta H^\circ_{rxn} < 0$ |
|   Decrease $T$ | Toward release of heat | Increases if $\Delta H^\circ_{rxn} < 0$ <br> Decreases if $\Delta H^\circ_{rxn} > 0$ |
| Catalyst added | None; forward and reverse rates increase equally; equilibrium attained sooner | None |

## Sample Problem 17.15 | Determining Equilibrium Parameters from Molecular Scenes

**Problem** For the reaction,

$$X(g) + Y_2(g) \rightleftharpoons XY(g) + Y(g) \qquad \Delta H > 0$$

the following molecular scenes depict different reaction mixtures (X is *green*, Y is *purple*):

1    2    3

**(a)** If $K = 2$ at the temperature of the reaction, which scene represents the mixture at equilibrium?
**(b)** Will the reaction mixtures in the other two scenes proceed toward reactants or toward products to reach equilibrium?
**(c)** For the mixture at equilibrium, how will a rise in temperature affect $[Y_2]$?

**Plan** (a) We are given the balanced equation and $K$ and must choose the scene that represents the mixture at equilibrium. We write $Q$, and for each scene, count particles and find the value of $Q$. Whichever scene gives a $Q$ equal to $K$ (2) represents the mixture at equilibrium. (b) For each of the other two reaction mixtures, we compare the value of $Q$ with 2. If $Q > K$, the numerator (product side) is too high, so the reaction proceeds toward reactants; if $Q < K$, the reaction proceeds toward products.
(c) We are given that $\Delta H > 0$, so we must see whether a rise in $T$ increases or decreases $[Y_2]$, one of the reactants.

**Solution** (a) For the reaction, we have $Q = \dfrac{[XY][Y]}{[X][Y_2]}$. Thus,

$$\text{scene 1: } Q = \frac{5 \times 3}{1 \times 1} = 15 \qquad \text{scene 2: } Q = \frac{4 \times 2}{2 \times 2} = 2 \qquad \text{scene 3: } Q = \frac{3 \times 1}{3 \times 3} = \frac{1}{3}$$

For scene 2, $Q = K$, so  scene 2 represents the mixture at equilibrium.
(b) For scene 1, $Q$ (15) $> K$ (2), so  the reaction proceeds toward reactants.
For scene 3, $Q$ ($\frac{1}{3}$) $< K$ (2), so  the reaction proceeds toward products.
(c) The reaction is endothermic, so heat acts as a reactant:

$$X(g) + Y_2(g) + heat \rightleftharpoons XY(g) + Y(g)$$

Therefore, adding heat to the left shifts the reaction to the right, so  $[Y_2]$ decreases.

**Check** (a) Remember that quantities in the numerator (or denominator) of $Q$ are multiplied, not added. For example, the denominator for scene 1 is $1 \times 1 = 1$, not $1 + 1 = 2$.
(c) A good check is to imagine that $\Delta H < 0$ and see if you get the opposite result:

$$X(g) + Y_2(g) \rightleftharpoons XY(g) + Y(g) + heat$$

If $\Delta H < 0$, adding heat would shift the reaction to the left and increase $[Y_2]$.

**Follow-Up Problem 17.15** For the reaction $C_2(g) + D_2(g) \rightleftharpoons 2CD(g)$; $\Delta H < 0$, these molecular scenes depict different reaction mixtures (C is *red*, D is *blue*):

1    2    3

At equilibrium

(a) Calculate the value of $K_p$. (b) In which direction will the reaction proceed for the mixtures *not* at equilibrium? (c) For the mixture at equilibrium, what effect will a rise in $T$ have on the total amount (mol) of gas (increase, decrease, no effect)? Explain.

## Applying Le Châtelier's Principle to the Synthesis of Ammonia

Le Châtelier's principle has countless applications in natural systems and in the chemical industry. As a case study, we'll look at the synthesis of ammonia, which, on a mole basis, is produced industrially in greater amount than any other compound. Then, a Chemical Connections essay applies the principle to metabolism.

Even though four of every five molecules in the atmosphere are $N_2$, the supply of *usable* nitrogen is limited because the strong triple bond in $N_2$ lowers its reactivity. Thus, the N atom is very difficult to "fix," that is, to combine with other atoms into useful compounds. Natural nitrogen fixation occurs through the fine-tuned activity of enzymes found in bacteria that live on plant roots, or through the brute force of lightning. But, nearly 13% of nitrogen fixation is done industrially via the **Haber process:**

$$N_2(g) + 3H_2(g) \rightleftharpoons 2NH_3(g) \qquad \Delta H^{\circ}_{rxn} = -91.8 \text{ kJ}$$

Developed by the German chemist Fritz Haber in 1913 and first used in a plant making 12,000 tons of ammonia a year, the process now yields over 110 million tons a year. Over 80% of this is used as fertilizer, with most of the remainder used to make explosives and nylons and other polymers, and smaller amounts going into production of refrigerants, rubber stabilizers, household cleaners, and pharmaceuticals.

**Optimizing Reaction Conditions: Yield vs. Rate** The Haber process applies equilibrium *and* kinetics principles to achieve a compromise that makes the process economical. From the balanced equation, we see three ways to maximize $NH_3$ yield:

1. *Decrease [$NH_3$].* Removing $NH_3$ as it forms will make the system shift toward producing more to reattain equilibrium.
2. *Decrease volume (increase pressure).* Because 4 mol of gas reacts to form 2 mol of gas, decreasing the volume will shift the system toward making fewer moles of gas.
3. *Decrease temperature.* Because the formation of $NH_3$ is exothermic, decreasing the temperature (removing heat) will shift the equilibrium position toward product, thereby increasing $K_c$ (Table 17.5).

Therefore, the conditions for maximizing the yield of product are continual removal of $NH_3$, high pressure, and low temperature. Figure 17.11 shows the percent yield of $NH_3$ at various combinations of pressure and temperature. Note the almost complete conversion (98.3%) to product at 1000 atm and 473 K (200.°C).

Although the *yield* is favored at this relatively low temperature, the *rate* of formation is so slow that the process is uneconomical. In practice, a compromise optimizes yield *and* rate. High pressure and continuous removal are used to increase yield, but the temperature is raised to a moderate level and *a catalyst is used to increase the rate.* Achieving the same rate without a catalyst would require much higher temperatures and, thus, result in a much lower yield.

**Table 17.5** Effect of Temperature on $K_c$ for Ammonia Synthesis

| $T$(K) | $K_c$ |
|---|---|
| 200. | $7.17 \times 10^{15}$ |
| 300. | $2.69 \times 10^{8}$ |
| 400. | $3.94 \times 10^{4}$ |
| 500. | $1.72 \times 10^{2}$ |
| 600. | $4.53 \times 10^{0}$ |
| 700. | $2.96 \times 10^{-1}$ |
| 800. | $3.96 \times 10^{-2}$ |

**Figure 17.11** Percent yield of ammonia vs. temperature at five different pressures. At very high *P* and low *T (top left)*, the yield is high, but the rate is low. Industrial conditions *(circle)* are between 200 and 300 atm at about 400°C.

**The Industrial Process** Stages in the industrial production of $NH_3$ are shown in Figure 17.12. To extend equipment life and minimize cost, modern plants operate at about 200 to 300 atm and around 673 K (400.°C). The stoichiometric ratio of reactant gases ($N_2/H_2 = 1/3$ by volume) is injected into the heated, pressurized reaction chamber. Some of the needed heat is supplied by $\Delta H^{\circ}_{rxn}$. The gases flow over catalyst beds that consist of 5-mm to 10-mm chunks of iron crystals embedded in a fused mixture of MgO, $Al_2O_3$, and $SiO_2$. The emerging equilibrium mixture contains about 35% $NH_3$ and is cooled by refrigeration until the $NH_3$ (b.p. −33.4°C) condenses; it is then removed and stored. Because $N_2$ and $H_2$ have much lower boiling points, they are recycled as gases by pumping them back into the reaction chamber.

**Figure 17.12** Key stages in the Haber process for synthesizing ammonia.

From the simplest bacterium to the most specialized neuron, every cell performs thousands of reactions that allow it to grow and reproduce, feed and excrete, move and communicate. Taken together, these myriad feats of breakdown, synthesis, and energy flow constitute the cell's *metabolism* and are organized into reaction sequences called **metabolic pathways.**

**Continual Shift Toward Product** In principle, each step in a metabolic pathway is a reversible reaction catalyzed by a specific enzyme (Section 16.7). However, equilibrium is never reached in a pathway, because the product of each reaction becomes the reactant of the next. Consider the five-step pathway by which the amino acid threonine is converted into the amino acid isoleucine (Figure B17.1). Threonine, supplied from a different region of the cell, forms ketobutyrate through the catalytic action of enzyme 1. The equilibrium position of reaction 1 shifts to the right because the product, ketobutyrate, is the reactant in reaction 2. Similarly, reaction 2 shifts to the right as its product, acetohydroxybutyrate, is used up in reaction 3. In this way, each subsequent reaction shifts the previous reaction to the right. The final product, isoleucine, is removed to make proteins elsewhere in the cell. Thus, the entire pathway operates in one direction.

**Creation of a Steady State** This continuous shift in equilibrium position has two consequences for metabolic pathways:

1. *Each step proceeds with nearly 100% yield:* Virtually every molecule of threonine that enters this region of the cell eventually changes to ketobutyrate, every molecule of ketobutyrate to the next product, and so on.
2. *Reactant and product concentrations remain nearly constant,* because they reach a *steady state*.
   - In an equilibrium system, equal rates in *opposing* directions create constant concentrations of reactants and products.
   - In a steady-state system, the rates of reactions in *one* direction—into, through, and out of the system—create constant concentrations of intermediates.

Ketobutyrate, for example, is formed in reaction 1 as fast as it is consumed in reaction 2, so its concentration is constant. (A steady-state amount of water results if you fill a sink and then adjust the flow of faucet and drain so that water enters as fast as it leaves.)

**Regulation by Feedback Inhibition** Recall from Chapter 16 that substrate concentrations are *much* higher than enzyme concentrations. If the active sites on all the enzyme molecules were always occupied, all cellular reactions would occur at their maximum rates. This might be ideal for an industrial process,

*Substrate can bind to active site when inhibitor is absent, so catalysis occurs.*

*Active site is deformed when inhibitor is present, so substrate cannot bind and no catalysis occurs.*

**A** Portion of enzyme — Inhibitor binding site

**B** Portion of enzyme — Inhibitor bound to site

**Figure B17.2** Effect of inhibitor binding on shape of active site. **A,** If the inhibitor site is not occupied, the enzyme catalyzes the reaction. **B,** If the inhibitor site is occupied, the enzyme does not function.

but an organism needs to control amounts carefully. To regulate product formation, certain key steps are catalyzed by *regulatory enzymes,* which contain an *inhibitor site* in addition to an active site: when the inhibitor site is occupied, the shape of the active site is deformed and the reaction is not catalyzed (Figure B17.2).

In the simplest case of metabolic regulation (Figure B17.1), *the final product of a pathway is the inhibitor, and the regulatory enzyme catalyzes the first step.* Suppose, for instance, that a cell is temporarily making less protein, so isoleucine is not being removed as quickly. As its concentration rises, isoleucine lands on the inhibitor site of threonine dehydratase, the first enzyme in the pathway, thereby inhibiting its own production. This process is called *end-product feedback inhibition.* More complex pathways have more elaborate regulatory schemes.

---

**Problem**

**B17.1** Many metabolites are products in branched pathways. In the one below, letters are compounds, and numbers are enzymes:

One method of control of these pathways occurs through inhibition of the first enzyme specific for a branch. (a) Which enzyme is inhibited by F? (b) Which enzyme is inhibited by I? (c) What is the disadvantage if F inhibited enzyme 1? (d) What would be the disadvantage if F inhibited enzyme 6?

Enzyme 1 — Threonine Dehydratase | Enzyme 2 | Enzyme 3 | Enzyme 4 | Enzyme 5

THREONINE ⇌ Ketobutyrate ⇌ Acetohydroxy-butyrate ⇌ Dihydroxy-methylvalerate ⇌ Ketomethyl-valerate ⇌ ISOLEUCINE

INHIBITION

**Figure B17.1** The biosynthesis of isoleucine from threonine. Isoleucine is synthesized from threonine in a sequence of five enzyme-catalyzed reactions. Once enough isoleucine is present, its concentra-tion builds up and inhibits threonine dehydratase, the first enzyme in the pathway.

# Summary of Section 17.6

- If a system at equilibrium is disturbed, it undergoes a net reaction that reduces the disturbance and returns the system to equilibrium.
- Changes in concentration cause a net reaction to consume the added component or to produce the removed component.
- For a reaction that involves a change in amount (mol) of gas, an increase in pressure (decrease in volume) causes a net reaction toward fewer moles of gas, and a decrease in pressure causes the opposite change.
- Although the equilibrium position changes as a result of a concentration or volume change, $K$ does not.
- A temperature change affects $K$: higher $T$ increases $K$ for an endothermic reaction (positive $\Delta H^\circ_{rxn}$) and decreases $K$ for an exothermic reaction (negative $\Delta H^\circ_{rxn}$).
- A catalyst causes the system to reach equilibrium more quickly by speeding forward and reverse reactions equally, but it does not affect the equilibrium position.
- Ammonia is produced in a process favored by high pressure, low temperature, and continual removal of product. To make the process economical, intermediate temperature and pressure and a catalyst are used.
- A metabolic pathway is a cellular reaction sequence with each step shifted completely toward product. Its overall yield is controlled by a feedback system that inhibits the activity of certain key enzymes.

# CHAPTER REVIEW GUIDE

**Learning Objectives**   Relevant section (§) and/or sample problem (SP) numbers appear in parentheses.

## Understand These Concepts

1. The distinction between the speed (rate) and the extent of a reaction (Introduction)
2. Why a system attains dynamic equilibrium when forward and reverse reaction rates are equal (§17.1)
3. The equilibrium constant as a number that is equal to a particular ratio of rate constants and of concentration terms (§17.1)
4. How the magnitude of $K$ is related to the extent of the reaction (§17.1)
5. Why the same equilibrium state is reached no matter what the starting concentrations of the reacting system (§17.2)
6. How the reaction quotient ($Q$) changes continuously until the system reaches equilibrium, at which point $Q = K$ (§17.2)
7. Why the form of $Q$ is based exactly on the balanced equation *as written* (§17.2)
8. How the *sum* of reaction steps gives the overall reaction, and the *product* of $Q$'s (or $K$'s) gives the overall $Q$ (or $K$) (§17.2)
9. Why pure solids and liquids do not appear in $Q$ (§17.2)
10. How the interconversion of $K_c$ and $K_p$ is based on the ideal gas law and $\Delta n_{gas}$ (§17.3)
11. How the reaction direction depends on the relative values of $Q$ and $K$ (§17.4)
12. How a reaction table is used to find an unknown quantity (concentration or pressure) (§17.5)
13. How assuming that the change in [reactant] is relatively small simplifies finding equilibrium quantities (§17.5)
14. How Le Châtelier's principle explains the effects of a change in concentration, pressure (volume), or temperature on a system at equilibrium and on $K$ (§17.6)

15. Why a change in temperature *does* affect $K$ (§17.6)
16. Why the addition of a catalyst does *not* affect $K$ (§17.6)
17. How adjusting reaction conditions and using a catalyst optimizes the synthesis of ammonia (§17.6).

## Master These Skills

1. Writing a reaction quotient ($Q$) from a balanced equation (SP 17.1)
2. Writing $Q$ and calculating $K$ for a reaction consisting of more than one step (SP 17.2)
3. Writing $Q$ and finding $K$ for an equation multiplied by a common factor (SP 17.3)
4. Writing $Q$ for heterogeneous equilibria (§17.2)
5. Converting between $K_c$ and $K_p$ (SP 17.4)
6. Comparing $Q$ and $K$ to determine reaction direction (SPs 17.5, 17.6)
7. Substituting quantities (concentrations or pressures) into $Q$ to find $K$ (§17.5)
8. Using a reaction table to determine quantities and find $K$ (SP 17.7)
9. Finding one equilibrium quantity from other equilibrium quantities and $K$ (SP 17.8)
10. Finding an equilibrium quantity from initial quantities and $K$ (SP 17.9)
11. Solving a quadratic equation for an unknown equilibrium quantity (§17.5)
12. Assuming that the change in [reactant] is relatively small to find equilibrium quantities and checking the assumption (SP 17.10)
13. Comparing the values of $Q$ and $K$ to find reaction direction and $x$, the unknown change in a quantity (SP 17.11)

Learning Objectives    *continued*

14. Using the relative values of $Q$ and $K$ to predict the effect of a change in concentration on the equilibrium position and on $K$ (SP 17.12)
15. Using Le Châtelier's principle and $\Delta n_{gas}$ to predict the effect of a change in pressure (volume) on the equilibrium position (SP 17.13)

16. Using Le Châtelier's principle and $\Delta H°$ to predict the effect of a change in temperature on the equilibrium position and on $K$ (SP 17.14)
17. Using the van't Hoff equation to calculate $K$ at one temperature given $K$ at another temperature (§17.6)
18. Using molecular scenes to find equilibrium parameters (SP 17.15)

## Key Terms    Page numbers appear in parentheses.

### Section 17.1
equilibrium constant ($K$) (679)

### Section 17.2
law of chemical equilibrium (law of mass action) (680)
reaction quotient ($Q$) (680)

### Section 17.6
Le Châtelier's principle (698)
Haber process (706)
metabolic pathway (708)

## Key Equations and Relationships    Page numbers appear in parentheses.

**17.1** Defining equilibrium in terms of reaction rates (678):

At equilibrium: $\text{rate}_{fwd} = \text{rate}_{rev}$

**17.2** Defining the equilibrium constant for the reaction $A \rightleftharpoons 2B$ (679):

$$K = \frac{k_{fwd}}{k_{rev}} = \frac{[B]_{eq}^2}{[A]_{eq}}$$

**17.3** Defining the equilibrium constant in terms of the reaction quotient (680):

At equilibrium: $Q = K$

**17.4** Expressing $Q_c$ for the reaction $aA + bB \rightleftharpoons cC + dD$ (681):

$$Q_c = \frac{[C]^c[D]^d}{[A]^a[B]^b}$$

**17.5** Finding the overall $K$ for a reaction sequence (682):

$$K_{overall} = K_1 \times K_2 \times K_3 \times \cdots$$

**17.6** Finding $K$ of a reaction from $K$ of the reverse reaction (683):

$$K_{fwd} = \frac{1}{K_{rev}}$$

**17.7** Finding $K$ of a reaction multiplied by a factor $n$ (684):

$$Q' = Q^n = \left(\frac{[C]^c[D]^d}{[A]^a[B]^b}\right)^n \qquad K' = K^n$$

**17.8** Relating $K$ based on pressures to $K$ based on concentrations (687):

$$K_p = K_c(RT)^{\Delta n_{gas}}$$

**17.9** Assuming that ignoring the concentration that reacts introduces no significant error (695):

$$[A]_{init} - [A]_{reacting} = [A]_{eq} \approx [A]_{init}$$

**17.10** Finding $K$ at one temperature given $K$ at another (van't Hoff equation) (704):

$$\ln\frac{K_2}{K_1} = -\frac{\Delta H°_{rxn}}{R}\left(\frac{1}{T_2} - \frac{1}{T_1}\right)$$

## Brief Solutions to Follow-Up Problems

**17.1** (a) $Q_c = \dfrac{[NO]^4[H_2O]^6}{[NH_3]^4[O_2]^5}$    (b) $Q_c = \dfrac{[N_2O][NO_2]}{[NO]^3}$

**17.2** $H_2(g) + Br_2(g) \rightleftharpoons 2HBr(g)$;

$$Q_{c(overall)} = \frac{[HBr]^2}{[H_2][Br_2]}$$

$$Q_{c(overall)} = Q_{c1} \times Q_{c2} \times Q_{c3}$$

$$= \frac{[Br]^2}{[Br_2]} \times \frac{[HBr][H]}{[Br][H_2]} \times \frac{[HBr]}{[H][Br]} = \frac{[HBr]^2}{[H_2][Br_2]}$$

**17.3** (a) $K_c = K_{c(ref)}^{1/2} = 2.8 \times 10^4$

(b) $K_c = \left(\dfrac{1}{K_{c(ref)}}\right)^{2/3} = 1.2 \times 10^{-6}$

**17.4** $K_p = K_c(RT)^{-1} = 1.67\left(0.0821\,\dfrac{atm \cdot L}{mol \cdot K} \times 500.\,K\right)^{-1}$

$$= 4.07 \times 10^{-2}$$

**17.5** $K_c = \dfrac{[Y]}{[X]} = 1.4$

1. $Q = 0.33$, right    2. $Q = 1.4$, no net change    3. $Q = 2.0$, left

**17.6** $Q_p = \dfrac{(P_{CH_3Cl})(P_{HCl})}{(P_{CH_4})(P_{Cl_2})} = \dfrac{(0.24)(0.47)}{(0.13)(0.035)} = 25$;

$Q_p < K_p$, so $CH_3Cl$ is forming.

**17.7** From the reaction table for $2NO + O_2 \rightleftharpoons 2NO_2$,

$P_{O_2} = 1.000$ atm $- x = 0.506$ atm    $x = 0.494$ atm

Also, $P_{NO} = 0.012$ atm and $P_{NO_2} = 0.988$ atm, so

$$K_p = \frac{0.988^2}{0.012^2(0.506)} = 1.3 \times 10^4$$

**17.8** Since $\Delta n_{gas} = 0$, $K_p = K_c = 2.3 \times 10^{30} = \dfrac{(0.781)(0.209)}{P_{NO}^2}$

Thus,        $P_{NO} = 2.7 \times 10^{-16}$ atm

**17.9** From the reaction table, $[H_2] = [I_2] = x$; $[HI] = 0.242 - 2x$.

Thus, $K_c = 1.26 \times 10^{-3} = \dfrac{x^2}{(0.242 - 2x)^2}$

Taking the square root of both sides, ignoring the negative root, and solving gives $x = [H_2] = 8.02 \times 10^{-3}\ M$.

**17.10** (a) Based on the reaction table, and assuming that $0.20\ M - x \approx 0.20\ M$,

$$K_c = 2.94 \times 10^{-10} \approx \frac{4x^2}{0.20} \qquad x \approx 3.8 \times 10^{-6}$$

Error $= 1.9 \times 10^{-3}\%$, so assumption is justified; therefore, at equilibrium, $[I_2] = 0.20\ M$ and $[I] = 7.6 \times 10^{-6}\ M$.
(b) Based on the same reaction table and assumption, $x \approx 0.10$; error is 50%, so assumption is *not* justified. Solve equation:

$$4x^2 + 0.209x - 0.042 = 0 \qquad x = 0.080\ M$$

Therefore, at equilibrium, $[I_2] = 0.12\ M$ and $[I] = 0.16\ M$.

**17.11** (a) $Q_c = \dfrac{(0.0900)(0.0900)}{0.2100} = 3.86 \times 10^{-2}$

$Q_c < K_c$, so reaction proceeds to the right.

(b) From the reaction table,

$$[PCl_5] = 0.2100\ M - x = 0.2065\ M \qquad \text{so} \qquad x = 0.0035\ M$$

Thus, $[Cl_2] = [PCl_3] = 0.0900\ M + x = 0.0935\ M$.

**17.12** (a) $[SiF_4]$ increases; (b) decreases; (c) decreases; (d) no effect.

**17.13** (a) Decrease $P$; (b) increase $P$; (c) increase $P$.

**17.14** (a) $P_{H_2}$ will decrease; $K$ will increase; (b) $P_{N_2}$ will increase; $K$ will decrease; (c) $P_{PCl_5}$ will increase; $K$ will increase.

**17.15** (a) Since $P = \dfrac{n}{V}RT$ and, in this case, $V$, $R$, and $T$ cancel,

$$K_p = \frac{n^2_{CD}}{n_{C_2} \times n_{D_2}} = \frac{16}{(2)(2)} = 4$$

(b) Scene 2, to the left; scene 3, to the right. (c) There are 2 mol of gas on each side of the balanced equation, so increasing $T$ has no effect on total moles of gas.

## PROBLEMS

Problems with **colored** numbers are answered in Appendix E and worked in detail in the Student Solutions Manual. Problem sections match those in the text and provide the numbers of relevant sample problems. Most offer Concept Review Questions, Skill-Building Exercises (grouped in pairs covering the same concept), and Problems in Context. The Comprehensive Problems are based on material from any section or previous chapter.

### The Equilibrium State and the Equilibrium Constant

**Concept Review Questions**

**17.1** A change in reaction conditions increases the rate of a certain forward reaction more than that of the reverse reaction. What is the effect on the equilibrium constant and on the concentrations of reactants and products at equilibrium?

**17.2** When a chemical company employs a new reaction to manufacture a product, the chemists consider its rate (kinetics) and yield (equilibrium). How do each of these affect the usefulness of a manufacturing process?

**17.3** If there is no change in concentrations, why is the equilibrium state considered dynamic?

**17.4** Is $K$ very large or very small for a reaction that goes essentially to completion? Explain.

**17.5** White phosphorus, $P_4$, is produced by the reduction of phosphate rock, $Ca_3(PO_4)_2$. If exposed to oxygen, the waxy, white solid smokes, bursts into flames, and releases a large quantity of heat:

$$P_4(g) + 5O_2(g) \rightleftharpoons P_4O_{10}(s) + heat$$

Does this reaction have a large or small equilibrium constant? Explain.

### The Reaction Quotient and the Equilibrium Constant

(Sample Problems 17.1 to 17.3)

**Concept Review Questions**

**17.6** For a given reaction at a given temperature, the value of $K$ is constant. Is the value of $Q$ also constant? Explain.

**17.7** In a study of the thermal decomposition of lithium peroxide,

$$2Li_2O_2(s) \rightleftharpoons 2Li_2O(s) + O_2(g)$$

a chemist finds that, as long as some $Li_2O_2$ is present at the end of the experiment, the amount of $O_2$ obtained in a given container at a given $T$ is the same. Explain.

**17.8** In a study of the formation of HI from its elements,

$$H_2(g) + I_2(g) \rightleftharpoons 2HI(g)$$

equal amounts of $H_2$ and $I_2$ were placed in a container, which was then sealed and heated.
(a) On one set of axes, sketch concentration vs. time curves for $H_2$ and HI, and explain how $Q$ changes as a function of time.
(b) Is the value of $Q$ different if $[I_2]$ is plotted instead of $[H_2]$?

**17.9** Explain the difference between a heterogeneous and a homogeneous equilibrium. Give an example of each.

**17.10** Does $Q$ for the formation of 1 mol of NO from its elements differ from $Q$ for the decomposition of 1 mol of NO to its elements? Explain and give the relationship between the two $Q$'s.

**17.11** Does $Q$ for the formation of 1 mol of $NH_3$ from $H_2$ and $N_2$ differ from $Q$ for the formation of $NH_3$ from $H_2$ and 1 mol of $N_2$? Explain and give the relationship between the two $Q$'s.

**Skill-Building Exercises** (grouped in similar pairs)

**17.12** Balance each reaction and write its reaction quotient, $Q_c$:
(a) $NO(g) + O_2(g) \rightleftharpoons N_2O_3(g)$
(b) $SF_6(g) + SO_3(g) \rightleftharpoons SO_2F_2(g)$
(c) $SClF_5(g) + H_2(g) \rightleftharpoons S_2F_{10}(g) + HCl(g)$

**17.13** Balance each reaction and write its reaction quotient, $Q_c$:
(a) $C_2H_6(g) + O_2(g) \rightleftharpoons CO_2(g) + H_2O(g)$
(b) $CH_4(g) + F_2(g) \rightleftharpoons CF_4(g) + HF(g)$
(c) $SO_3(g) \rightleftharpoons SO_2(g) + O_2(g)$

**17.14** Balance each reaction and write its reaction quotient, $Q_c$:
(a) $NO_2Cl(g) \rightleftharpoons NO_2(g) + Cl_2(g)$
(b) $POCl_3(g) \rightleftharpoons PCl_3(g) + O_2(g)$
(c) $NH_3(g) + O_2(g) \rightleftharpoons N_2(g) + H_2O(g)$

**17.15** Balance each reaction and write its reaction quotient, $Q_c$:
(a) $O_2(g) \rightleftharpoons O_3(g)$
(b) $NO(g) + O_3(g) \rightleftharpoons NO_2(g) + O_2(g)$
(c) $N_2O(g) + H_2(g) \rightleftharpoons NH_3(g) + H_2O(g)$

**17.16** At a particular temperature, $K_c = 1.6 \times 10^{-2}$ for
$$2H_2S(g) \rightleftharpoons 2H_2(g) + S_2(g)$$
Calculate $K_c$ for each of the following reactions:
(a) $\frac{1}{2}S_2(g) + H_2(g) \rightleftharpoons H_2S(g)$
(b) $5H_2S(g) \rightleftharpoons 5H_2(g) + \frac{5}{2}S_2(g)$

**17.17** At a particular temperature, $K_c = 6.5 \times 10^2$ for
$$2NO(g) + 2H_2(g) \rightleftharpoons N_2(g) + 2H_2O(g)$$
Calculate $K_c$ for each of the following reactions:
(a) $NO(g) + H_2(g) \rightleftharpoons \frac{1}{2}N_2(g) + H_2O(g)$
(b) $2N_2(g) + 4H_2O(g) \rightleftharpoons 4NO(g) + 4H_2(g)$

**17.18** Balance each of the following examples of heterogeneous equilibria and write each reaction quotient, $Q_c$:
(a) $Na_2O_2(s) + CO_2(g) \rightleftharpoons Na_2CO_3(s) + O_2(g)$
(b) $H_2O(l) \rightleftharpoons H_2O(g)$
(c) $NH_4Cl(s) \rightleftharpoons NH_3(g) + HCl(g)$

**17.19** Balance each of the following examples of heterogeneous equilibria and write each reaction quotient, $Q_c$:
(a) $H_2O(l) + SO_3(g) \rightleftharpoons H_2SO_4(aq)$
(b) $KNO_3(s) \rightleftharpoons KNO_2(s) + O_2(g)$
(c) $S_8(s) + F_2(g) \rightleftharpoons SF_6(g)$

**17.20** Balance each of the following examples of heterogeneous equilibria and write each reaction quotient, $Q_c$:
(a) $NaHCO_3(s) \rightleftharpoons Na_2CO_3(s) + CO_2(g) + H_2O(g)$
(b) $SnO_2(s) + H_2(g) \rightleftharpoons Sn(s) + H_2O(g)$
(c) $H_2SO_4(l) + SO_3(g) \rightleftharpoons H_2S_2O_7(l)$

**17.21** Balance each of the following examples of heterogeneous equilibria and write each reaction quotient, $Q_c$:
(a) $Al(s) + NaOH(aq) + H_2O(l) \rightleftharpoons Na[Al(OH)_4](aq) + H_2(g)$
(b) $CO_2(s) \rightleftharpoons CO_2(g)$
(c) $N_2O_5(s) \rightleftharpoons NO_2(g) + O_2(g)$

**Problems in Context**

**17.22** Write $Q_c$ for each of the following:
(a) Hydrogen chloride gas reacts with oxygen gas to produce chlorine gas and water vapor.
(b) Solid diarsenic trioxide reacts with fluorine gas to produce liquid arsenic pentafluoride and oxygen gas.
(c) Gaseous sulfur tetrafluoride reacts with liquid water to produce gaseous sulfur dioxide and hydrogen fluoride gas.

(d) Solid molybdenum(VI) oxide reacts with gaseous xenon difluoride to form liquid molybdenum(VI) fluoride, xenon gas, and oxygen gas.

**17.23** The interhalogen $ClF_3$ is prepared in a two-step fluorination of chlorine gas:
$$Cl_2(g) + F_2(g) \rightleftharpoons ClF(g)$$
$$ClF(g) + F_2(g) \rightleftharpoons ClF_3(g)$$
(a) Balance each step and write the overall equation.
(b) Show that the overall $Q_c$ equals the product of the $Q_c$'s for the individual steps.

**Expressing Equilibria with Pressure Terms: Relation Between $K_c$ and $K_p$**
(Sample Problem 17.4)

**Concept Review Questions**

**17.24** Guldberg and Waage proposed the definition of the equilibrium constant as a certain ratio of *concentrations*. What relationship allows us to use a particular ratio of *partial pressures* (for a gaseous reaction) to express an equilibrium constant? Explain.

**17.25** When are $K_c$ and $K_p$ equal, and when are they not?

**17.26** A certain reaction at equilibrium has more moles of gaseous products than of gaseous reactants.
(a) Is $K_c$ larger or smaller than $K_p$?
(b) Write a statement about the relative sizes of $K_c$ and $K_p$ for any gaseous equilibrium.

**Skill-Building Exercises** (grouped in similar pairs)

**17.27** Determine $\Delta n_{gas}$ for each of the following reactions:
(a) $2KClO_3(s) \rightleftharpoons 2KCl(s) + 3O_2(g)$
(b) $2PbO(s) + O_2(g) \rightleftharpoons 2PbO_2(s)$
(c) $I_2(s) + 3XeF_2(s) \rightleftharpoons 2IF_3(s) + 3Xe(g)$

**17.28** Determine $\Delta n_{gas}$ for each of the following reactions:
(a) $MgCO_3(s) \rightleftharpoons MgO(s) + CO_2(g)$
(b) $2H_2(g) + O_2(g) \rightleftharpoons 2H_2O(l)$
(c) $HNO_3(l) + ClF(g) \rightleftharpoons ClONO_2(g) + HF(g)$

**17.29** Calculate $K_c$ for each of the following equilibria:
(a) $CO(g) + Cl_2(g) \rightleftharpoons COCl_2(g)$; $K_p = 3.9 \times 10^{-2}$ at 1000. K
(b) $S_2(g) + C(s) \rightleftharpoons CS_2(g)$; $K_p = 28.5$ at 500. K

**17.30** Calculate $K_c$ for each of the following equilibria:
(a) $H_2(g) + I_2(g) \rightleftharpoons 2HI(g)$; $K_p = 49$ at 730. K
(b) $2SO_2(g) + O_2(g) \rightleftharpoons 2SO_3(g)$; $K_p = 2.5 \times 10^{10}$ at 500. K

**17.31** Calculate $K_p$ for each of the following equilibria:
(a) $N_2O_4(g) \rightleftharpoons 2NO_2(g)$; $K_c = 6.1 \times 10^{-3}$ at 298 K
(b) $N_2(g) + 3H_2(g) \rightleftharpoons 2NH_3(g)$; $K_c = 2.4 \times 10^{-3}$ at 1000. K

**17.32** Calculate $K_p$ for each of the following equilibria:
(a) $H_2(g) + CO_2(g) \rightleftharpoons H_2O(g) + CO(g)$; $K_c = 0.77$ at 1020. K
(b) $3O_2(g) \rightleftharpoons 2O_3(g)$; $K_c = 1.8 \times 10^{-56}$ at 570. K

**Comparing $Q$ and $K$ to Determine Reaction Direction**
(Sample Problems 17.5 and 17.6)

**Concept Review Questions**

**17.33** When the numerical value of $Q$ is less than $K$, in which direction does the reaction proceed to reach equilibrium? Explain.

**17.34** The following molecular scenes depict the aqueous reaction $2D \rightleftharpoons E$, with D *red* and E *blue*. Each sphere represents 0.0100 mol, but the volume is 1.00 L in scene A, whereas in scenes B and C, it is 0.500 L.

A        B        C

(a) If the reaction in scene A is at equilibrium, calculate $K_c$.
(b) Are the reactions in scenes B and C at equilibrium? Which, if either, is not, and in which direction will it proceed?

### Skill-Building Exercises (grouped in similar pairs)

**17.35** At 425°C, $K_p = 4.18 \times 10^{-9}$ for the reaction
$$2HBr(g) \rightleftharpoons H_2(g) + Br_2(g)$$
In one experiment, 0.20 atm of $HBr(g)$, 0.010 atm of $H_2(g)$, and 0.010 atm of $Br_2(g)$ are introduced into a container. Is the reaction at equilibrium? If not, in which direction will it proceed?

**17.36** At 100°C, $K_p = 60.6$ for the reaction
$$2NOBr(g) \rightleftharpoons 2NO(g) + Br_2(g)$$
In a given experiment, 0.10 atm of each component is placed in a container. Is the system at equilibrium? If not, in which direction will the reaction proceed?

### Problems in Context

**17.37** The water-gas shift reaction plays a central role in the chemical methods for obtaining cleaner fuels from coal:
$$CO(g) + H_2O(g) \rightleftharpoons CO_2(g) + H_2(g)$$
At a given temperature, $K_p = 2.7$. If 0.13 mol of CO, 0.56 mol of $H_2O$, 0.62 mol of $CO_2$, and 0.43 mol of $H_2$ are put in a 2.0-L flask, in which direction does the reaction proceed?

### How to Solve Equilibrium Problems
(Sample Problems 17.7 to 17.11)

### Concept Review Questions

**17.38** In the 1980s, CFC-11 was one of the most heavily produced chlorofluorocarbons. The last step in its formation is
$$CCl_4(g) + HF(g) \rightleftharpoons CFCl_3(g) + HCl(g)$$
If you start the reaction with equal concentrations of $CCl_4$ and HF, you obtain equal concentrations of $CFCl_3$ and HCl at equilibrium. Are the final concentrations of $CFCl_3$ and HCl equal if you start with unequal concentrations of $CCl_4$ and HF? Explain.

**17.39** For a problem involving the catalyzed reaction of methane and steam, the following reaction table was prepared:

| Pressure (atm) | $CH_4(g)$ | + | $2H_2O(g)$ | $\rightleftharpoons$ | $CO_2(g)$ | + | $4H_2(g)$ |
|---|---|---|---|---|---|---|---|
| Initial | 0.30 | | 0.40 | | 0 | | 0 |
| Change | $-x$ | | $-2x$ | | $+x$ | | $+4x$ |
| Equilibrium | $0.30 - x$ | | $0.40 - 2x$ | | $x$ | | $4x$ |

Explain the entries in the "Change" and "Equilibrium" rows.

**17.40** (a) What is the basis of the approximation that avoids using the quadratic formula to find an equilibrium concentration?
(b) When should this approximation *not* be made?

### Skill-Building Exercises (grouped in similar pairs)

**17.41** In an experiment to study the formation of HI(g),
$$H_2(g) + I_2(g) \rightleftharpoons 2HI(g)$$

$H_2(g)$ and $I_2(g)$ were placed in a sealed container at a certain temperature. At equilibrium, $[H_2] = 6.50 \times 10^{-5} \, M$, $[I_2] = 1.06 \times 10^{-3} \, M$, and $[HI] = 1.87 \times 10^{-3} \, M$. Calculate $K_c$ for the reaction at this temperature.

**17.42** Gaseous ammonia was introduced into a sealed container and heated to a certain temperature:
$$2NH_3(g) \rightleftharpoons N_2(g) + 3H_2(g)$$
At equilibrium, $[NH_3] = 0.0225 \, M$, $[N_2] = 0.114 \, M$, and $[H_2] = 0.342 \, M$. Calculate $K_c$ for the reaction at this temperature.

**17.43** Gaseous $PCl_5$ decomposes according to the reaction
$$PCl_5(g) \rightleftharpoons PCl_3(g) + Cl_2(g)$$
In one experiment, 0.15 mol of $PCl_5(g)$ was introduced into a 2.0-L container. Construct the reaction table for this process.

**17.44** Hydrogen fluoride, HF, can be made from the reaction
$$H_2(g) + F_2(g) \rightleftharpoons 2HF(g)$$
In one experiment, 0.10 mol of $H_2(g)$ and 0.050 mol of $F_2(g)$ are added to a 0.50-L flask. Write a reaction table for this process.

**17.45** For the following reaction, $K_p = 6.5 \times 10^4$ at 308 K:
$$2NO(g) + Cl_2(g) \rightleftharpoons 2NOCl(g)$$
At equilibrium, $P_{NO} = 0.35$ atm and $P_{Cl_2} = 0.10$ atm. What is the equilibrium partial pressure of $NOCl(g)$?

**17.46** For the following reaction, $K_p = 0.262$ at 1000°C:
$$C(s) + 2H_2(g) \rightleftharpoons CH_4(g)$$
At equilibrium, $P_{H_2}$ is 1.22 atm. What is the equilibrium partial pressure of $CH_4(g)$?

**17.47** Ammonium hydrogen sulfide decomposes according to the following reaction, for which $K_p = 0.11$ at 250°C:
$$NH_4HS(s) \rightleftharpoons H_2S(g) + NH_3(g)$$
If 55.0 g of $NH_4HS(s)$ is placed in a sealed 5.0-L container, what is the partial pressure of $NH_3(g)$ at equilibrium?

**17.48** Hydrogen sulfide decomposes according to the following reaction, for which $K_c = 9.30 \times 10^{-8}$ at 700°C:
$$2H_2S(g) \rightleftharpoons 2H_2(g) + S_2(g)$$
If 0.45 mol of $H_2S$ is placed in a 3.0-L container, what is the equilibrium concentration of $H_2(g)$ at 700°C?

**17.49** Even at high $T$, the formation of NO is not favored:
$$N_2(g) + O_2(g) \rightleftharpoons 2NO(g) \quad K_c = 4.10 \times 10^{-4} \text{ at } 2000°C$$
What is [NO] when a mixture of 0.20 mol of $N_2(g)$ and 0.15 mol of $O_2(g)$ reach equilibrium in a 1.0-L container at 2000°C?

**17.50** Nitrogen dioxide decomposes according to the reaction
$$2NO_2(g) \rightleftharpoons 2NO(g) + O_2(g)$$
where $K_p = 4.48 \times 10^{-13}$ at a certain temperature. If 0.75 atm of $NO_2$ is added to a container and allowed to come to equilibrium, what are the equilibrium partial pressures of $NO(g)$ and $O_2(g)$?

**17.51** Hydrogen iodide decomposes according to the reaction
$$2HI(g) \rightleftharpoons H_2(g) + I_2(g)$$
A sealed 1.50-L container initially holds 0.00623 mol of $H_2$, 0.00414 mol of $I_2$, and 0.0244 mol of HI at 703 K. When equilibrium is reached, the concentration of $H_2(g)$ is 0.00467 $M$. What are the concentrations of $HI(g)$ and $I_2(g)$?

**17.52** Compound A decomposes according to the equation
$$A(g) \rightleftharpoons 2B(g) + C(g)$$

A sealed 1.00-L container initially contains $1.75 \times 10^{-3}$ mol of A($g$), $1.25 \times 10^{-3}$ mol of B($g$), and $6.50 \times 10^{-4}$ mol of C($g$) at 100°C. At equilibrium, [A] is $2.15 \times 10^{-3}$ $M$. Find [B] and [C].

### Problems in Context

**17.53** In an analysis of interhalogen reactivity, 0.500 mol of ICl was placed in a 5.00-L flask, where it decomposed at a high $T$: $2ICl(g) \rightleftharpoons I_2(g) + Cl_2(g)$. Calculate the equilibrium concentrations of $I_2$, $Cl_2$, and ICl ($K_c = 0.110$ at this temperature).

**17.54** A toxicologist studying mustard gas, $S(CH_2CH_2Cl)_2$, a blistering agent, prepares a mixture of 0.675 $M$ $SCl_2$ and 0.973 $M$ $C_2H_4$ and allows it to react at room temperature (20.0°C):

$$SCl_2(g) + 2C_2H_4(g) \rightleftharpoons S(CH_2CH_2Cl)_2(g)$$

At equilibrium, $[S(CH_2CH_2Cl)_2] = 0.350$ $M$. Calculate $K_p$.

**17.55** The first step in $HNO_3$ production is the catalyzed oxidation of $NH_3$. Without a catalyst, a different reaction predominates:

$$4NH_3(g) + 3O_2(g) \rightleftharpoons 2N_2(g) + 6H_2O(g)$$

When 0.0150 mol of $NH_3(g)$ and 0.0150 mol of $O_2(g)$ are placed in a 1.00-L container at a certain temperature, the $N_2$ concentration at equilibrium is $1.96 \times 10^{-3}$ $M$. Calculate $K_c$.

**17.56** A key step in the extraction of iron from its ore is

$$FeO(s) + CO(g) \rightleftharpoons Fe(s) + CO_2(g) \quad K_p = 0.403 \text{ at } 1000°C$$

This step occurs in the 700°C to 1200°C zone within a blast furnace. What are the equilibrium partial pressures of CO($g$) and $CO_2(g)$ when 1.00 atm of CO($g$) and excess FeO($s$) react in a sealed container at 1000°C?

### Reaction Conditions and Equilibrium: Le Châtelier's Principle
(Sample Problems 17.12 to 17.15)

#### Concept Review Questions

**17.57** What does "disturbance" mean in Le Châtelier's principle?

**17.58** What is the difference between the equilibrium position and the equilibrium constant of a reaction? Which changes as a result of a change in reactant concentration?

**17.59** Scenes A, B, and C below depict the following reaction at three temperatures:

$$NH_4Cl(s) \rightleftharpoons NH_3(g) + HCl(g) \quad \Delta H°_{rxn} = 176 \text{ kJ}$$

A  B  C

(a) Which best represents the reaction mixture at the highest temperature? Explain. (b) Which best represents the reaction mixture at the lowest temperature? Explain.

**17.60** What is implied by the word "constant" in the term *equilibrium constant*? Give two reaction parameters that can be changed without changing the value of an equilibrium constant.

**17.61** Le Châtelier's principle is related ultimately to the rates of the forward and reverse steps in a reaction. Explain (a) why an increase in reactant concentration shifts the equilibrium position to the right but does not change $K$; (b) why a decrease in $V$ shifts the equilibrium position toward fewer moles of gas but does not

change $K$; (c) why a rise in $T$ shifts the equilibrium position of an exothermic reaction toward reactants and also changes $K$; and (d) why a rise in temperature of an endothermic reaction from $T_1$ to $T_2$ results in $K_2$ being larger than $K_1$.

**17.62** An equilibrium mixture of two solids and a gas, in the reaction $XY(s) \rightleftharpoons X(g) + Y(s)$, is depicted at right (X is *green* and Y is *black*). Does scene A, B, or C best represent the system at equilibrium after two formula units of Y($s$) is added? Explain.

A  B  C

#### Skill-Building Exercises (grouped in similar pairs)

**17.63** Consider this equilibrium system:

$$CO(g) + Fe_3O_4(s) \rightleftharpoons CO_2(g) + 3FeO(s)$$

How does the equilibrium position shift as a result of each of the following disturbances? (a) CO is added. (b) $CO_2$ is removed by adding solid NaOH. (c) Additional $Fe_3O_4(s)$ is added to the system. (d) Dry ice is added at constant temperature.

**17.64** Sodium bicarbonate undergoes thermal decomposition according to the reaction

$$2NaHCO_3(s) \rightleftharpoons Na_2CO_3(s) + CO_2(g) + H_2O(g)$$

How does the equilibrium position shift as a result of each of the following disturbances? (a) 0.20 atm of argon gas is added. (b) $NaHCO_3(s)$ is added. (c) $Mg(ClO_4)_2(s)$ is added as a drying agent to remove $H_2O$. (d) Dry ice is added at constant $T$.

**17.65** Predict the effect of *increasing* the container volume on the amounts of each reactant and product in the following reactions:
(a) $F_2(g) \rightleftharpoons 2F(g)$
(b) $2CH_4(g) \rightleftharpoons C_2H_2(g) + 3H_2(g)$

**17.66** Predict the effect of *increasing* the container volume on the amounts of each reactant and product in the following reactions:
(a) $CH_3OH(l) \rightleftharpoons CH_3OH(g)$
(b) $CH_4(g) + NH_3(g) \rightleftharpoons HCN(g) + 3H_2(g)$

**17.67** Predict the effect of *decreasing* the container volume on the amounts of each reactant and product in the following reactions:
(a) $H_2(g) + Cl_2(g) \rightleftharpoons 2HCl(g)$
(b) $2H_2(g) + O_2(g) \rightleftharpoons 2H_2O(l)$

**17.68** Predict the effect of *decreasing* the container volume on the amounts of each reactant and product in the following reactions:
(a) $C_3H_8(g) + 5O_2(g) \rightleftharpoons 3CO_2(g) + 4H_2O(l)$
(b) $4NH_3(g) + 3O_2(g) \rightleftharpoons 2N_2(g) + 6H_2O(g)$

**17.69** How would you adjust the *volume* of the container in order to maximize product yield in each of the following reactions?
(a) $Fe_3O_4(s) + 4H_2(g) \rightleftharpoons 3Fe(s) + 4H_2O(g)$
(b) $2C(s) + O_2(g) \rightleftharpoons 2CO(g)$

**17.70** How would you adjust the *volume* of the container in order to maximize product yield in each of the following reactions?
(a) $Na_2O_2(s) \rightleftharpoons 2Na(l) + O_2(g)$
(b) $C_2H_2(g) + 2H_2(g) \rightleftharpoons C_2H_6(g)$

**17.71** Predict the effect of *increasing* the temperature on the amounts of products in the following reactions:
(a) $CO(g) + 2H_2(g) \rightleftharpoons CH_3OH(g)$    $\Delta H^\circ_{rxn} = -90.7$ kJ
(b) $C(s) + H_2O(g) \rightleftharpoons CO(g) + H_2(g)$    $\Delta H^\circ_{rxn} = 131$ kJ
(c) $2NO_2(g) \rightleftharpoons 2NO(g) + O_2(g)$ (endothermic)
(d) $2C(s) + O_2(g) \rightleftharpoons 2CO(g)$ (exothermic)

**17.72** Predict the effect of *decreasing* the temperature on the amounts of reactants in the following reactions:
(a) $C_2H_2(g) + H_2O(g) \rightleftharpoons CH_3CHO(g)$    $\Delta H^\circ_{rxn} = -151$ kJ
(b) $CH_3CH_2OH(l) + O_2(g) \rightleftharpoons CH_3CO_2H(l) + H_2O(g)$
$\Delta H^\circ_{rxn} = -451$ kJ
(c) $2C_2H_4(g) + O_2(g) \rightleftharpoons 2CH_3CHO(g)$ (exothermic)
(d) $N_2O_4(g) \rightleftharpoons 2NO_2(g)$ (endothermic)

**17.73** The molecule $D_2$ (where D, deuterium, is $^2H$) undergoes a reaction with ordinary $H_2$ that leads to isotopic equilibrium:
$$D_2(g) + H_2(g) \rightleftharpoons 2DH(g)    K_p = 1.80 \text{ at } 298 \text{ K}$$
If $\Delta H^\circ_{rxn}$ is 0.32 kJ/mol DH, calculate $K_p$ at 500. K.

**17.74** The formation of methanol is important to the processing of new fuels. At 298 K, $K_p = 2.25 \times 10^4$ for the reaction
$$CO(g) + 2H_2(g) \rightleftharpoons CH_3OH(l)$$
If $\Delta H^\circ_{rxn} = -128$ kJ/mol $CH_3OH$, calculate $K_p$ at 0°C.

**Problems in Context**

**17.75** The minerals hematite ($Fe_2O_3$) and magnetite ($Fe_3O_4$) exist in equilibrium with atmospheric oxygen:
$$4Fe_3O_4(s) + O_2(g) \rightleftharpoons 6Fe_2O_3(s)   K_p = 2.5 \times 10^{87} \text{ at } 298 \text{ K}$$
(a) Determine $P_{O_2}$ at equilibrium. (b) Given that $P_{O_2}$ in air is 0.21 atm, in which direction will the reaction proceed to reach equilibrium? (c) Calculate $K_c$ at 298 K.

**17.76** The oxidation of $SO_2$ is the key step in $H_2SO_4$ production:
$$SO_2(g) + \tfrac{1}{2}O_2(g) \rightleftharpoons SO_3(g)    \Delta H^\circ_{rxn} = -99.2 \text{ kJ}$$
(a) What qualitative combination of $T$ and $P$ maximizes $SO_3$ yield?
(b) How does addition of $O_2$ affect $Q$? $K$?
(c) Why is catalysis used for this reaction?

**17.77** A mixture of 3.00 volumes of $H_2$ and 1.00 volume of $N_2$ reacts at 344°C to form ammonia. The equilibrium mixture at 110. atm contains 41.49% $NH_3$ by volume. Calculate $K_p$ for the reaction, assuming that the gases behave ideally.

**17.78** You are a member of a research team of chemists discussing plans for a plant to produce ammonia:
$$N_2(g) + 3H_2(g) \rightleftharpoons 2NH_3(g)$$
(a) The plant will operate at close to 700 K, at which $K_p$ is $1.00 \times 10^{-4}$, and employs the stoichiometric 1/3 ratio of $N_2/H_2$. At equilibrium, the partial pressure of $NH_3$ is 50. atm. Calculate the partial pressures of each reactant and $P_{total}$.
(b) One member of the team suggests the following: since the partial pressure of $H_2$ is cubed in the reaction quotient, the plant could produce the same amount of $NH_3$ if the reactants were in a 1/6 ratio of $N_2/H_2$ and could do so at a lower pressure, which would cut operating costs. Calculate the partial pressure of each reactant and $P_{total}$ under these conditions, assuming an unchanged partial pressure of 50. atm for $NH_3$. Is the suggestion valid?

**Comprehensive Problems**

**17.79** For the following equilibrium system, which of the changes will form more $CaCO_3$?
$$CO_2(g) + Ca(OH)_2(s) \rightleftharpoons CaCO_3(s) + H_2O(l)$$
$$\Delta H^\circ = -113 \text{ kJ}$$
(a) Decrease temperature at constant pressure (no phase change)

(b) Increase volume at constant temperature
(c) Increase partial pressure of $CO_2$
(d) Remove one-half of the initial $CaCO_3$

**17.80** The "filmstrip" represents five molecular scenes of a gaseous mixture as it reaches equilibrium over time:

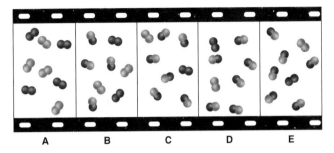

X is *purple* and Y is *orange*: $X_2(g) + Y_2(g) \rightleftharpoons 2XY(g)$.
(a) Write the reaction quotient, $Q$, for this reaction.
(b) If each particle represents 0.1 mol, find $Q$ for each scene.
(c) If $K > 1$, is time progressing to the right or to the left? Explain.
(d) Calculate $K$ at this temperature.
(e) If $\Delta H^\circ_{rxn} < 0$, which scene, if any, best represents the mixture at a higher temperature? Explain.
(f) Which scene, if any, best represents the mixture at a higher pressure (lower volume)? Explain.

**17.81** Ammonium carbamate ($NH_2COONH_4$) is a salt of carbamic acid that is found in the blood and urine of mammals. At 250.°C, $K_c = 1.58 \times 10^{-8}$ for the following equilibrium:
$$NH_2COONH_4(s) \rightleftharpoons 2NH_3(g) + CO_2(g)$$
If 7.80 g of $NH_2COONH_4$ is put into a 0.500-L evacuated container, what is the total pressure at equilibrium?

**17.82** Isolation of Group 8B(10) elements, used as industrial catalysts, involves a series of steps. For nickel, the sulfide ore is roasted in air: $Ni_3S_2(s) + O_2(g) \rightleftharpoons NiO(s) + SO_2(g)$. The metal oxide is reduced by the $H_2$ in water gas ($CO + H_2$) to impure Ni: $NiO(s) + H_2(g) \rightleftharpoons Ni(s) + H_2O(g)$. The CO in water gas then reacts with the metal in the Mond process to form gaseous nickel carbonyl, $Ni(s) + CO(g) \rightleftharpoons Ni(CO)_4(g)$, which is subsequently decomposed to the metal. (a) Balance each of the three steps, and obtain an overall balanced equation for the conversion of $Ni_3S_2$ to $Ni(CO)_4$. (b) Show that the overall $Q_c$ is the product of the $Q_c$'s for the individual reactions.

**17.83** Consider the formation of ammonia in two experiments.
(a) To a 1.00-L container at 727°C, 1.30 mol of $N_2$ and 1.65 mol of $H_2$ are added. At equilibrium, 0.100 mol of $NH_3$ is present. Calculate the equilibrium concentrations of $N_2$ and $H_2$, and find $K_c$ for the reaction: $2NH_3(g) \rightleftharpoons N_2(g) + 3H_2(g)$.
(b) In a different 1.00-L container at the same temperature, equilibrium is established with $8.34 \times 10^{-2}$ mol of $NH_3$, 1.50 mol of $N_2$, and 1.25 mol of $H_2$ present. Calculate $K_c$ for the reaction:
$$NH_3(g) \rightleftharpoons \tfrac{1}{2}N_2(g) + \tfrac{3}{2}H_2(g)$$
(c) What is the relationship between the $K_c$ values in parts (a) and (b)? Why aren't these values the same?

**17.84** An important industrial source of ethanol is the reaction, catalyzed by $H_3PO_4$, of steam with ethylene derived from oil:
$$C_2H_4(g) + H_2O(g) \rightleftharpoons C_2H_5OH(g)$$
$$\Delta H^\circ_{rxn} = -47.8 \text{ kJ}    K_c = 9 \times 10^3 \text{ at } 600. \text{ K}$$
(a) At equilibrium, $P_{C_2H_5OH} = 200.$ atm and $P_{H_2O} = 400.$ atm. Calculate $P_{C_2H_4}$. (b) Is the highest yield of ethanol obtained at high or low $P$? High or low $T$? (c) Calculate $K_c$ at 450. K. (d) In $NH_3$ manufacture, the yield is increased by condensing the $NH_3$ to a

liquid and removing it. Would condensing the $C_2H_5OH$ have the same effect in ethanol production? Explain.

**17.85** An industrial chemist introduces 2.0 atm of $H_2$ and 2.0 atm of $CO_2$ into a 1.00-L container at 25.0°C and then raises the temperature to 700.°C, at which $K_c = 0.534$:

$$H_2(g) + CO_2(g) \rightleftharpoons H_2O(g) + CO(g)$$

How many grams of $H_2$ are present at equilibrium?

**17.86** As an EPA scientist studying catalytic converters and urban smog, you want to find $K_c$ for the following reaction:

$$2NO_2(g) \rightleftharpoons N_2(g) + 2O_2(g) \qquad K_c = ?$$

Use the following data to find the unknown $K_c$:

$$\tfrac{1}{2}N_2(g) + \tfrac{1}{2}O_2(g) \rightleftharpoons NO(g) \qquad K_c = 4.8 \times 10^{-10}$$
$$2NO_2(g) \rightleftharpoons 2NO(g) + O_2(g) \qquad K_c = 1.1 \times 10^{-5}$$

**17.87** An engineer examining the oxidation of $SO_2$ in the manufacture of sulfuric acid determines that $K_c = 1.7 \times 10^8$ at 600. K:

$$2SO_2(g) + O_2(g) \rightleftharpoons 2SO_3(g)$$

(a) At equilibrium, $P_{SO_3} = 300.$ atm and $P_{O_2} = 100.$ atm. Calculate $P_{SO_2}$. (b) The engineer places a mixture of 0.0040 mol of $SO_2(g)$ and 0.0028 mol of $O_2(g)$ in a 1.0-L container and raises the temperature to 1000 K. At equilibrium, 0.0020 mol of $SO_3(g)$ is present. Calculate $K_c$ and $P_{SO_2}$ for this reaction at 1000. K.

**17.88** Phosgene ($COCl_2$) is a toxic substance that forms readily from carbon monoxide and chlorine at elevated temperatures:

$$CO(g) + Cl_2(g) \rightleftharpoons COCl_2(g)$$

If 0.350 mol of each reactant is placed in a 0.500-L flask at 600 K, what are the concentrations of all three substances at equilibrium ($K_c = 4.95$ at this temperature)?

**17.89** When 0.100 mol of $CaCO_3(s)$ and 0.100 mol of $CaO(s)$ are placed in an evacuated sealed 10.0-L container and heated to 385 K, $P_{CO_2} = 0.220$ atm after equilibrium is established:

$$CaCO_3(s) \rightleftharpoons CaO(s) + CO_2(g)$$

An additional 0.300 atm of $CO_2(g)$ is pumped in. What is the total mass (in g) of $CaCO_3$ after equilibrium is re-established?

**17.90** Use each of the following reaction quotients to write the balanced equation:

(a) $Q = \dfrac{[CO_2]^2[H_2O]^2}{[C_2H_4][O_2]^3}$ (b) $Q = \dfrac{[NH_3]^4[O_2]^7}{[NO_2]^4[H_2O]^6}$

**17.91** Hydrogenation of carbon-carbon $\pi$ bonds is important in the petroleum and food industries. The conversion of acetylene to ethylene is a simple example of the process:

$$C_2H_2(g) + H_2(g) \rightleftharpoons C_2H_4(g)$$

The calculated $K_c$ at 2000. K is $2.9 \times 10^8$. But the process is run at lower temperatures with the aid of a catalyst to prevent decomposition. Use $\Delta H°$ values to calculate $K_c$ at 300. K.

**17.92** For the reaction $M_2 + N_2 \rightleftharpoons 2MN$, scene A represents the mixture at equilibrium, with M *black* and N *orange*. If each molecule represents 0.10 mol and the volume is 1.0 L, how many moles of each substance will be present in scene B when that mixture reaches equilibrium?

A          B

**17.93** Highly toxic disulfur decafluoride decomposes by a free-radical process: $S_2F_{10}(g) \rightleftharpoons SF_4(g) + SF_6(g)$. In a study of the decomposition, $S_2F_{10}$ was placed in a 2.0-L flask and heated to 100°C; $[S_2F_{10}]$ was 0.50 M at equilibrium. More $S_2F_{10}$ was added, and when equilibrium was reattained, $[S_2F_{10}]$ was 2.5 M. How did $[SF_4]$ and $[SF_6]$ change from the original to the new equilibrium position after the addition of more $S_2F_{10}$?

**17.94** A study of the water-gas shift reaction (see Problem 17.37) was made in which equilibrium was reached with $[CO] = [H_2O] = [H_2] = 0.10$ M and $[CO_2] = 0.40$ M. After 0.60 mol of $H_2$ is added to the 2.0-L container and equilibrium is re-established, what are the new concentrations of all the components?

**17.95** A gaseous mixture of 10.0 volumes of $CO_2$, 1.00 volume of unreacted $O_2$, and 50.0 volumes of unreacted $N_2$ leaves an engine at 4.0 atm and 800. K. Assuming that the mixture reaches equilibrium, what are (a) the partial pressure and (b) the concentration (in picograms per liter, pg/L) of CO in this exhaust gas?

$$2CO_2(g) \rightleftharpoons 2CO(g) + O_2(g) \qquad K_p = 1.4 \times 10^{-28} \text{ at 800. K}$$

(The actual concentration of CO in exhaust gas is much higher because the gases do *not* reach equilibrium in the short transit time through the engine and exhaust system.)

**17.96** When ammonia is made industrially, the mixture of $N_2$, $H_2$, and $NH_3$ that emerges from the reaction chamber is far from equilibrium. Why does the plant supervisor use reaction conditions that produce less than the maximum yield of ammonia?

**17.97** The following reaction can be used to make $H_2$ for the synthesis of ammonia from the greenhouse gases carbon dioxide and methane:

$$CH_4(g) + CO_2(g) \rightleftharpoons 2CO(g) + 2H_2(g)$$

(a) What is the percent yield of $H_2$ when an equimolar mixture of $CH_4$ and $CO_2$ with a total pressure of 20.0 atm reaches equilibrium at 1200. K, at which $K_p = 3.548 \times 10^6$?
(b) What is the percent yield of $H_2$ for this system at 1300. K, at which $K_p = 2.626 \times 10^7$?
(c) Use the van't Hoff equation to find $\Delta H°_{rxn}$.

**17.98** The methane used to obtain $H_2$ for $NH_3$ manufacture is impure and usually contains other hydrocarbons, such as propane, $C_3H_8$. Imagine the reaction of propane occurring in two steps:

$$C_3H_8(g) + 3H_2O(g) \rightleftharpoons 3CO(g) + 7H_2(g)$$
$$K_p = 8.175 \times 10^{15} \text{ at 1200. K}$$
$$CO(g) + H_2O(g) \rightleftharpoons CO_2(g) + H_2(g)$$
$$K_p = 0.6944 \text{ at 1200. K}$$

(a) Write the overall equation for the reaction of propane and steam to produce carbon dioxide and hydrogen.
(b) Calculate $K_p$ for the overall process at 1200. K.
(c) When 1.00 volume of $C_3H_8$ and 4.00 volumes of $H_2O$, each at 1200. K and 5.0 atm, are mixed in a container, what is the final pressure? Assume the total volume remains constant, that the reaction is essentially complete, and that the gases behave ideally.
(d) What percentage of the $C_3H_8$ remains unreacted?

**17.99** Using $CH_4$ and steam as a source of $H_2$ for $NH_3$ synthesis requires high temperatures. Rather than burning $CH_4$ separately to heat the mixture, it is more efficient to inject some $O_2$ into the reaction mixture. All of the $H_2$ is thus released for the synthesis, and the heat of reaction for the combustion of $CH_4$ helps maintain the required temperature. Imagine the reaction occurring in two steps:

$$2CH_4(g) + O_2(g) \rightleftharpoons 2CO(g) + 4H_2(g)$$
$$K_p = 9.34 \times 10^{28} \text{ at 1000. K}$$

$$CO(g) + H_2O(g) \rightleftharpoons CO_2(g) + H_2(g)$$
$$K_p = 1.374 \text{ at } 1000. \text{ K}$$

(a) Write the overall equation for the reaction of methane, steam, and oxygen to form carbon dioxide and hydrogen.
(b) What is $K_p$ for the overall reaction?
(c) What is $K_c$ for the overall reaction?
(d) A mixture of 2.0 mol of $CH_4$, 1.0 mol of $O_2$, and 2.0 mol of steam with a total pressure of 30. atm reacts at 1000. K at constant volume. Assuming that the reaction is complete and the ideal gas law is a valid approximation, what is the final pressure?

**17.100** One mechanism for the synthesis of ammonia proposes that $N_2$ and $H_2$ molecules catalytically dissociate into atoms:

$$N_2(g) \rightleftharpoons 2N(g) \qquad \log K_p = -43.10$$
$$H_2(g) \rightleftharpoons 2H(g) \qquad \log K_p = -17.30$$

(a) Find the partial pressure of N in $N_2$ at 1000. K and 200. atm.
(b) Find the partial pressure of H in $H_2$ at 1000. K and 600. atm.
(c) How many N atoms and H atoms are present per liter?
(d) Based on these answers, which of the following is a more reasonable step to continue the mechanism after the catalytic dissociation? Explain.

$$N(g) + H(g) \longrightarrow NH(g)$$
$$N_2(g) + H(g) \longrightarrow NH(g) + N(g)$$

**17.101** The molecular scenes below depict the reaction $Y \rightleftharpoons 2Z$ at four different times, out of sequence, as it reaches equilibrium. Each sphere (Y is *red* and Z is *green*) represents 0.025 mol, and the volume is 0.40 L. (a) Which scene(s) represent(s) equilibrium? (b) List the scenes in the correct sequence. (c) Calculate $K_c$.

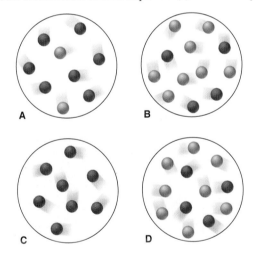

**17.102** For the equilibrium

$$H_2S(g) \rightleftharpoons 2H_2(g) + S_2(g) \qquad K_c = 9.0 \times 10^{-8} \text{ at } 700°C$$

the initial concentrations of the three gases are 0.300 $M$ $H_2S$, 0.300 $M$ $H_2$, and 0.150 $M$ $S_2$. Determine the equilibrium concentrations of the gases.

**17.103** The two most abundant atmospheric gases react to a tiny extent at 298 K in the presence of a catalyst:

$$N_2(g) + O_2(g) \rightleftharpoons 2NO(g) \qquad K_p = 4.35 \times 10^{-31}$$

(a) What are the equilibrium pressures of the three gases when the atmospheric partial pressures of $O_2$ (0.210 atm) and of $N_2$ (0.780 atm) are put into an evacuated 1.00-L flask at 298 K with the catalyst? (b) What is $P_{total}$ in the container? (c) Find $K_c$ at 298 K.

**17.104** The oxidation of nitrogen monoxide is favored at 457 K:

$$2NO(g) + O_2(g) \rightleftharpoons 2NO_2(g) \qquad K_p = 1.3 \times 10^4$$

(a) Calculate $K_c$ at 457 K. (b) Find $\Delta H_{rxn}°$ from standard heats of formation. (c) At what temperature does $K_c = 6.4 \times 10^9$?

**17.105** The kinetics and equilibrium of the decomposition of hydrogen iodide have been studied extensively:

$$2HI(g) \rightleftharpoons H_2(g) + I_2(g)$$

(a) At 298 K, $K_c = 1.26 \times 10^{-3}$ for this reaction. Calculate $K_p$.
(b) Calculate $K_c$ for the *formation* of HI at 298 K.
(c) Calculate $\Delta H_{rxn}°$ for HI decomposition from $\Delta H_f°$ values.
(d) At 729 K, $K_c = 2.0 \times 10^{-2}$ for HI decomposition. Calculate $\Delta H_{rxn}$ for this reaction from the van't Hoff equation.

**17.106** Isopentyl alcohol reacts with pure acetic acid to form isopentyl acetate, the essence of banana oil:

$$C_5H_{11}OH + CH_3COOH \rightleftharpoons CH_3COOC_5H_{11} + H_2O$$

A student adds a drying agent to remove $H_2O$ and thus increase the yield of banana oil. Is this approach reasonable? Explain.

**17.107** Isomers Q (*blue*) and R (*yellow*) interconvert. They are depicted in an equilibrium mixture in scene A. Scene B represents the mixture after addition of more Q. How many molecules of each isomer are present when the mixture in scene B attains equilibrium again?

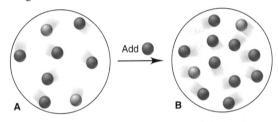

**17.108** Glauber's salt, $Na_2SO_4 \cdot 10H_2O$, was used by J. R. Glauber in the 17th century as a medicinal agent. At 25°C, $K_p = 4.08 \times 10^{-25}$ for the loss of waters of hydration from Glauber's salt:

$$Na_2SO_4 \cdot 10H_2O(s) \rightleftharpoons Na_2SO_4(s) + 10H_2O(g)$$

(a) What is the vapor pressure of water at 25°C in a closed container holding a sample of $Na_2SO_4 \cdot 10H_2O(s)$?
(b) How do the following changes affect the ratio (higher, lower, same) of hydrated form to anhydrous form for the system above?
(1) Add more $Na_2SO_4(s)$      (2) Reduce the container volume
(3) Add more water vapor       (4) Add $N_2$ gas

**17.109** In a study of synthetic fuels, 0.100 mol of CO and 0.100 mol of water vapor are added to a 20.00-L container at 900.°C, and they react to form $CO_2$ and $H_2$. At equilibrium, [CO] is $2.24 \times 10^{-3}$ $M$. (a) Calculate $K_c$ at this temperature. (b) Calculate $P_{total}$ in the flask at equilibrium. (c) How many moles of CO must be added to double this pressure? (d) After $P_{total}$ is doubled and the system reattains equilibrium, what is $[CO]_{eq}$?

**17.110** Synthetic diamonds are made under conditions of high temperature (2000 K) and high pressure ($10^{10}$ Pa; $10^5$ atm) in the presence of catalysts. Carbon's phase diagram is useful for finding the conditions for formation of natural and synthetic diamonds. Along the diamond-graphite line, the two allotropes are in equilibrium. (a) At point A, what is the sign of $\Delta H$ for the formation of diamond from graphite? Explain. (b) Which allotrope is denser? Explain.

# Acid-Base Equilibria

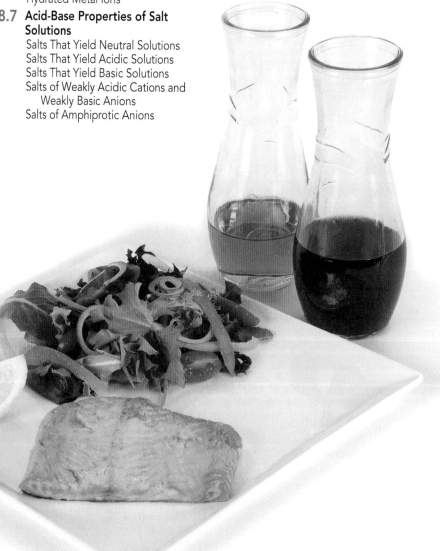

## Concepts and skills to review before you study this chapter

- role of water as solvent (Section 4.1)
- writing ionic equations (Section 4.2)
- acids, bases, and acid-base reactions (Section 4.4)

- proton transfer in acid-base reactions (Section 4.4)
- properties of an equilibrium constant (Section 17.2)
- solving equilibrium problems (Section 17.5)

Acids and bases played a central role in the alchemists' labs, and they remain indispensable, not only in modern academic and industrial research, but in many consumer products (Table 18.1), and even in a classic seafood dish.

The slice of lemon (citric acid) on the plate, and the vinegar (acetic acid) in the salad have a sour taste. In fact, sourness was a defining property since the 17th century: an acid was any substance that had a sour taste; reacted with active metals, such as aluminum and zinc, to produce hydrogen gas; and turned certain organic compounds specific colors. (We discuss *indicators* in this chapter and Chapter 19.) Similarly, a base (like the amines in fish) was any substance that had a bitter taste and slippery feel and turned the same organic compounds different colors. Moreover, it was known that *when acids and bases react, each cancels the properties of the other in a process called neutralization*. Although these early definitions described distinctive properties, they gave way to others based on molecular behavior. As science progresses, limited definitions are replaced by broader ones that explain more phenomena.

### Table 18.1 Some Common Acids and Bases and Their Household Uses

| Substance | Use |
|---|---|
| **Acids** | |
| Acetic acid, $CH_3COOH$ | Flavoring, preservative |
| Citric acid, $H_3C_6H_5O_7$ | Flavoring |
| Ascorbic acid, $H_2C_6H_6O_6$ | Vitamin C; nutritional supplement |
| Aluminum salts, $NaAl(SO_4)_2 \cdot 12H_2O$ | In baking powder, with sodium hydrogen carbonate |
| **Bases** | |
| Sodium hydroxide (lye), $NaOH$ | Oven and drain cleaners |
| Ammonia, $NH_3$ | Household cleaner |
| Sodium carbonate, $Na_2CO_3$ | Water softener, grease remover |
| Sodium hydrogen carbonate, $NaHCO_3$ | Fire extinguisher, rising agent in cake mixes (baking soda), mild antacid |
| Sodium phosphate, $Na_3PO_4$ | Cleaner for surfaces before painting or wallpapering |

**IN THIS CHAPTER . . .** We develop three definitions of acids and bases that explain an expanded range of reactions, and we apply equilibrium principles to understand acid-base behavior.

- We begin with the *Arrhenius* acid-base definition, which relies on formulas and behavior in water.
- We examine acid dissociation to see how acid variation in strength is expressed by a new equilibrium constant.
- We introduce the pH scale to measure the acidity of aqueous solutions.
- We discuss proton transfer in the *Brønsted-Lowry* acid-base definition, which expands the meaning of "base," along with the scope of acid-base reactions.
- We apply a systematic approach to solving acid-base equilibrium problems.
- We examine weak bases and their interdependence with weak acids.

- We examine the molecular structures of acids to rationalize their relative strengths.
- We determine the relative acidity of salts from the reactions of their cations and anions with water.
- We see that the designations "acid" and "base" depend on the substances' relative strengths *and* on the solvent.
- We discuss the *Lewis* acid-base definition, which greatly expands the meanings of "acid" and "acid-base reaction."

# 18.1 • ACIDS AND BASES IN WATER

Most laboratory work with acids and bases involves water, as do most environmental, biological, and industrial applications. Recall from our discussion in Chapter 4 that *water is* ***the*** *product in all reactions between strong acids and strong bases,* which the net ionic equation for any such reaction shows:

$$HX(aq) + MOH(aq) \longrightarrow MX(aq) + H_2O(l) \qquad \text{[molecular]}$$

And

$$H^+(aq) + OH^-(aq) \longrightarrow H_2O(l) \qquad \text{[net iconic]}$$

Furthermore, whenever an acid dissociates in water, solvent molecules participate in the reaction:

$$HA(g \text{ or } l) + H_2O(l) \longrightarrow A^-(aq) + H_3O^+(aq)$$

Water molecules surround the proton to form H-bonded species with the general formula $H(H_2O)_n^+$. The proton's charge density is so high that it attracts water especially strongly. The proton bonds covalently to one of the lone electron pairs of a water molecule's O atom to form a **hydronium ion, $H_3O^+$,** which forms H bonds to several other water molecules (see Figure 4.7, p. 147). To emphasize the active role of water and the proton-water interaction, the hydrated proton is usually shown in the text as $H_3O^+(aq)$ [although, for simplicity, we sometimes show it as $H^+(aq)$].

## Release of H⁺ or OH⁻ and the Arrhenius Acid-Base Definition

The earliest definition that highlighted the molecular nature of acids and bases is the **Arrhenius acid-base definition,** which classifies these substances in terms of their formulas and behavior *in water:*

- An *acid* is a substance with H in its formula that dissociates in water to yield $H_3O^+$.
- A *base* is a substance with OH in its formula that dissociates in water to yield $OH^-$.

Some typical Arrhenius acids are HCl, $HNO_3$, and HCN, and some typical bases are NaOH, KOH, and $Ba(OH)_2$. While Arrhenius bases contain discrete $OH^-$ ions in their structures, Arrhenius acids *never* contain discrete $H^+$ ions. Instead, they contain *covalently bonded H atoms that ionize when the molecule dissolves in water.*

When an acid and a base react, they undergo **neutralization.** The meaning of this term has changed, as we'll see, but in the Arrhenius sense, neutralization occurs when *the $H^+$ from the acid and the $OH^-$ from the base form $H_2O$.* A key point about neutralization that Arrhenius was able to explain is that no matter which strong acid and strong base react, and no matter which salt results, $\Delta H^{\circ}_{rxn}$ is $-55.9$ kJ per mole of water formed. Arrhenius suggested that the enthalpy change is always the same because the reaction is always the same—a hydrogen ion and a hydroxide ion form water:

$$H^+(aq) + OH^-(aq) \longrightarrow H_2O(l) \qquad \Delta H^{\circ}_{rxn} = -55.9 \text{ kJ}$$

The dissolved salt that is present, for example, NaCl in the reaction of sodium hydroxide with hydrochloric acid,

$$Na^+(aq) + OH^-(aq) + H^+(aq) + Cl^-(aq) \longrightarrow Na^+(aq) + Cl^-(aq) + H_2O(l)$$

exists as hydrated spectator ions and does not affect $\Delta H^{\circ}_{rxn}$.

Despite its importance at the time, limitations in the Arrhenius definition soon became apparent. Arrhenius and many others realized that even though some substances do *not* have discrete $OH^-$ ions, they still behave as bases. For example, $NH_3$ and $K_2CO_3$ also yield $OH^-$ in water. As you'll see shortly, broader acid-base definitions are required to include these species.

# Variation in Acid Strength: The Acid-Dissociation Constant ($K_a$)

Acids (and bases) are classified by their *strength*, the amount of $H_3O^+$ (or $OH^-$) produced per mole of substance dissolved, in other words, by the extent of their dissociation into ions (see Table 4.2, p. 146). Because acids and bases are electrolytes, their strength correlates with electrolyte strength: *strong electrolytes dissociate completely, and weak electrolytes dissociate slightly.*

1. *Strong acids dissociate **completely** into ions in water* (Figure 18.1A):

$$HA(g \text{ or } l) + H_2O(l) \longrightarrow H_3O^+(aq) + A^-(aq)$$

In a dilute solution of a strong acid, *HA molecules are no longer present:* $[H_3O^+] \approx [HA]_{init}$. In other words, $[HA]_{eq} \approx 0$, so the value of $K_c$ is extremely large:

$$Q_c = \frac{[H_3O^+][A^-]}{[HA][H_2O]} \qquad (\text{at equilibrium, } Q_c = K_c \gg 1)$$

Because the reaction is essentially complete, we usually don't express it as an equilibrium process. In dilute aqueous nitric acid, for example, there are virtually no undissociated nitric acid molecules:

$$HNO_3(l) + H_2O(l) \longrightarrow H_3O^+(aq) + NO_3^-(aq)$$

2. *Weak acids dissociate **slightly** into ions in water* (Figure 18.1B):

$$HA(aq) + H_2O(l) \rightleftharpoons H_3O^+(aq) + A^-(aq)$$

In a dilute solution of a weak acid, *the great majority of HA molecules are undissociated.* Thus, $[H_3O^+] \ll [HA]_{init}$, and $[HA]_{eq} \approx [HA]_{init}$, so $K_c$ is very small. Hydrocyanic acid is an example of a weak acid:

$$HCN(aq) + H_2O(l) \rightleftharpoons H_3O^+(aq) + CN^-(aq)$$

$$Q_c = \frac{[H_3O^+][CN^-]}{[HCN][H_2O]} \qquad (\text{at equilibrium, } Q_c = K_c \ll 1)$$

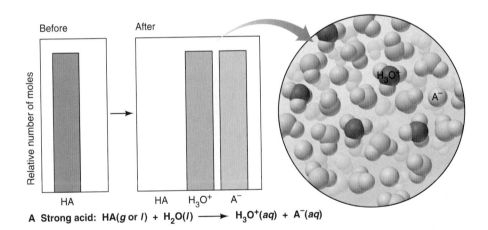

**A** Strong acid: $HA(g \text{ or } l) + H_2O(l) \longrightarrow H_3O^+(aq) + A^-(aq)$

**B** Weak acid: $HA(aq) + H_2O(l) \rightleftharpoons H_3O^+(aq) + A^-(aq)$

**Figure 18.1** **The extent of dissociation for strong acids and weak acids.** The bar graphs show the relative numbers of moles of species before (*left*) and after (*right*) acid dissociation. **A**, A strong acid dissociates completely; virtually no HA molecules are present. **B**, A weak acid dissociates very little, remaining mostly as intact HA molecules.

**Strong acid** **Weak acid**
**(1 _M_ HCl)** **(1 _M_ CH₃ COOH)**

**Figure 18.2** Reaction of zinc with a strong acid (*left*) and a weak acid (*right*).

(As in Chapter 17, brackets with no subscript mean molar concentration *at equilibrium*; that is, [X] means $[X]_{eq}$. In this chapter, we are dealing with systems *at equilibrium*, so instead of writing Q and stating that Q equals K at equilibrium, we'll express K directly as a collection of equilibrium concentration terms.)

The difference in $[H_3O^+]$ causes a much higher rate for the reaction of a strong acid with an active metal like zinc than for the same reaction of a weak acid (Figure 18.2):

$$Zn(s) + 2H_3O^+(aq) \longrightarrow Zn^{2+}(aq) + 2H_2O(l) + H_2(g)$$

In a strong acid, with its much higher $[H_3O^+]$, zinc reacts rapidly, forming bubbles of $H_2$ vigorously. In a weak acid, $[H_3O^+]$ is much lower, so zinc reacts slowly.

**The Meaning of $K_a$** We write a *specific* equilibrium constant for acid dissociation that only includes species whose concentrations change to any significant extent. The equilibrium expression for the dissociation of a general *weak acid*, HA, in water is

$$K_c = \frac{[H_3O^+][A^-]}{[HA][H_2O]}$$

The concentration of water $\left([H_2O] = \dfrac{1000\ g}{18.02\ g/mol} = 55.5\ M\right)$ is typically several orders of magnitude larger than [HA]. Therefore, $[H_2O]$ is essentially constant when HA dissociates. As you saw for pure liquids and solids (Section 17.2), we simplify the equilibrium expression by multiplying $K_c$ by $[H_2O]$ to define a new equilibrium constant, the **acid-dissociation constant** (or **acid-ionization constant**), $K_a$:

$$K_c[H_2O] = K_a = \frac{[H_3O^+][A^-]}{[HA]} \tag{18.1}$$

Like any equilibrium constant, $K_a$ is a number whose magnitude is temperature dependent and tells how far to the right the reaction has proceeded to reach equilibrium. Thus, *the stronger the acid, the higher $[H_3O^+]$ is at equilibrium, and the larger the $K_a$*:

$$\text{Stronger acid} \Longrightarrow \text{higher } [H_3O^+] \Longrightarrow \text{larger } K_a$$

**The Range of $K_a$ Values** Acid-dissociation constants of weak acids range over many orders of magnitude. Some benchmark $K_a$ values for typical weak acids give an idea of the fraction of HA molecules that dissociate into ions:

- For a weak acid with a relatively high $K_a$ ($\sim 10^{-2}$), a 1 *M* solution has ~10% of the HA molecules dissociated. The $K_a$ of chlorous acid ($HClO_2$) is $1.1 \times 10^{-2}$, and 1 *M* $HClO_2$ is 10.% dissociated.
- For a weak acid with a moderate $K_a$ ($\sim 10^{-5}$), a 1 *M* solution has ~0.3% of the HA molecules dissociated. The $K_a$ of acetic acid ($CH_3COOH$) is $1.8 \times 10^{-5}$, and 1 *M* $CH_3COOH$ is 0.42% dissociated.
- For a weak acid with a relatively low $K_a$ ($\sim 10^{-10}$), a 1 *M* solution has ~0.001% of the HA molecules dissociated. The $K_a$ of HCN is $6.2 \times 10^{-10}$, and 1 *M* HCN is 0.0025% dissociated.

Thus, for solutions of the same initial HA concentration, *the smaller the $K_a$, the lower the percent dissociation of HA*:

$$\text{Weaker acid} \Longrightarrow \text{lower \% dissociation of HA} \Longrightarrow \text{smaller } K_a$$

Table 18.2 lists $K_a$ values of some weak *monoprotic* acids, those with one ionizable proton. (A more extensive list is in Appendix C.) Note that the ionizable proton in organic acids is bound to the O in —COOH; H atoms bonded to C do *not* ionize.

**Table 18.2 $K_a$ Values for Some Monoprotic Acids at 25°C**

| Name (Formula) | Lewis Structure* | $K_a$ |
|---|---|---|
| Chlorous acid ($HClO_2$) | H—Ö—Cl̈=Ö | $1.1\times10^{-2}$ |
| Nitrous acid ($HNO_2$) | H—Ö—N̈=Ö | $7.1\times10^{-4}$ |
| Hydrofluoric acid (HF) | H—F̈: | $6.8\times10^{-4}$ |
| Formic acid (HCOOH) | H—C(:O:)—Ö—H | $1.8\times10^{-4}$ |
| Acetic acid ($CH_3COOH$) | H—C(H)(H)—C(:O:)—Ö—H | $1.8\times10^{-5}$ |
| Propanoic acid ($CH_3CH_2COOH$) | H—C(H)(H)—C(H)(H)—C(:O:)—Ö—H | $1.3\times10^{-5}$ |
| Hypochlorous acid (HClO) | H—Ö—Cl̈: | $2.9\times10^{-8}$ |
| Hydrocyanic acid (HCN) | H—C≡N: | $6.2\times10^{-10}$ |

ACID STRENGTH ↑

*Red type indicates the ionizable proton; all atoms have zero formal charge.

## Classifying the Relative Strengths of Acids and Bases

Using a table of $K_a$ values is the surest way to quantify strengths of weak acids, but you can classify acids and bases qualitatively as strong or weak from their formulas:

- *Strong acids.* Two types of strong acids, with examples *you should memorize*, are
  1. The hydrohalic acids HCl, HBr, and HI
  2. Oxoacids in which the number of O atoms exceeds the number of ionizable protons by two or more, such as $HNO_3$, $H_2SO_4$, and $HClO_4$; for example, in the case of $H_2SO_4$, 4 O's − 2 H's = 2

- *Weak acids.* There are many *more* weak acids than strong ones. Four types are
  1. The hydrohalic acid HF
  2. Acids in which H is not bonded to O or to a halogen, such as HCN and $H_2S$
  3. Oxoacids in which the number of O atoms equals or exceeds by one the number of ionizable protons, such as HClO, $HNO_2$, and $H_3PO_4$
  4. Carboxylic acids (general formula RCOOH, with the ionizable proton shown in red), such as $CH_3COOH$ and $C_6H_5COOH$

- *Strong bases.* Water-soluble compounds containing $O^{2-}$ or $OH^-$ ions are strong bases. The cations are usually those of the most active metals:
  1. $M_2O$ or MOH, where M = Group 1A(1) metal (Li, Na, K, Rb, Cs)
  2. MO or $M(OH)_2$, where M = Group 2A(2) metal (Ca, Sr, Ba)
     [MgO and $Mg(OH)_2$ are only slightly soluble in water, but the soluble portion dissociates completely.]

- *Weak bases.* Many compounds with an electron-rich nitrogen atom are weak bases (none is an Arrhenius base). The common structural feature is an N atom with a lone electron pair (shown in blue):
  1. Ammonia ($\ddot{N}H_3$)
  2. Amines (general formula $R\ddot{N}H_2$, $R_2\ddot{N}H$, or $R_3\ddot{N}$), such as $CH_3CH_2\ddot{N}H_2$, $(CH_3)_2\ddot{N}H$, and $(C_3H_7)_3\ddot{N}$

**Sample Problem 18.1** **Classifying Acid and Base Strength from the Chemical Formula**

**Problem** Classify each of the following compounds as a strong acid, weak acid, strong base, or weak base:
**(a)** KOH     **(b)** $(CH_3)_2CHCOOH$
**(c)** $H_2SeO_4$     **(d)** $(CH_3)_2CHNH_2$

**Plan** We examine the formula and classify each acid or base, using the text descriptions. Particular points to note for acids are the numbers of O atoms relative to ionizable H atoms and the presence of the —COOH group. For bases, note the nature of the cation or the presence of an N atom that has a lone pair.

**Solution (a)** Strong base: KOH is one of the Group 1A(1) hydroxides.
**(b)** Weak acid: $(CH_3)_2CHCOOH$ is a carboxylic acid, as indicated by the —COOH group.
**(c)** Strong acid: $H_2SeO_4$ is an oxoacid in which the number of O atoms exceeds the number of ionizable protons by two.
**(d)** Weak base: $(CH_3)_2CHNH_2$ has a lone pair on the N and is an amine.

**Follow-Up Problem 18.1** Which member of each pair is the stronger acid or base?
**(a)** HClO or HClO₃     **(b)** HCl or CH₃COOH     **(c)** NaOH or CH₃NH₂

## Summary of Section 18.1

- In aqueous solution, water binds the proton released from an acid to form a hydrated species represented by $H_3O^+(aq)$.
- By the Arrhenius definition, acids contain H and yield $H_3O^+$ in water, bases contain OH and yield $OH^-$ in water, and an acid-base reaction (neutralization) is the reaction of $H^+$ and $OH^-$ to form $H_2O$.
- Acid strength depends on $[H_3O^+]$ relative to [HA] in aqueous solution. Strong acids dissociate completely and weak acids slightly.
- The extent of dissociation is expressed by the acid-dissociation constant, $K_a$. Weak acids have $K_a$ values ranging from about $10^{-1}$ to $10^{-12}$.
- Many acids and bases can be classified as strong or weak based on their formulas.

# 18.2 • AUTOIONIZATION OF WATER AND THE pH SCALE

Before we discuss the next major acid-base definition, let's examine a crucial property of water that enables us to quantify $[H_3O^+]$: *water dissociates very slightly into ions* in an equilibrium process known as **autoionization** (or self-ionization):

Lone pair of O binds H⁺.

$H_2O(l)$          $H_2O(l)$          $H_3O^+(aq)$          $OH^-(aq)$

## The Equilibrium Nature of Autoionization: The Ion-Product Constant for Water ($K_w$)

Like any equilibrium process, the autoionization of water is described quantitatively by an equilibrium constant:

$$K_c = \frac{[H_3O^+][OH^-]}{[H_2O]^2}$$

Because the concentration of $H_2O$ (55.5 $M$) remains essentially constant, we multiply $K_c$ by $[H_2O]^2$ to obtain a new equilibrium constant, the **ion-product constant for water, $K_w$:**

$$K_c[H_2O]^2 = K_w = [H_3O^+][OH^-] = 1.0 \times 10^{-14} \text{ (at 25°C)} \qquad \text{(18.2)}$$

Notice that *one $H_3O^+$ ion and one $OH^-$ ion form for each $H_2O$ molecule that dissociates.* Therefore, in pure water, we find that

$$[H_3O^+] = [OH^-] = \sqrt{1.0 \times 10^{-14}} = 1.0 \times 10^{-7}\ M \text{ (at 25°C)}$$

Since pure water has a concentration of about 55.5 $M$, these equilibrium concentrations are attained when only 1 in 555 million water molecules dissociates reversibly into ions!

Autoionization of water affects aqueous acid-base chemistry in two major ways:

1. *A change in $[H_3O^+]$ causes an inverse change in $[OH^-]$, and vice versa:*

    Higher $[H_3O^+] \Longrightarrow$ lower $[OH^-]$     and     Higher $[OH^-] \Longrightarrow$ lower $[H_3O^+]$

Recall from Le Châtelier's principle (Section 17.6) that a change in concentration shifts the equilibrium position but does *not* change the equilibrium constant. Therefore, if some acid is added, $[H_3O^+]$ increases and $[OH^-]$ decreases as the ions react to form water; similarly, if some base is added, $[OH^-]$ increases and $[H_3O^+]$ decreases. In both cases, as long as the temperature is constant, the value of $K_w$ is constant.

2. *Both ions are present in all aqueous systems.* Thus, all acidic solutions contain a low $[OH^-]$, and all basic solutions contain a low $[H_3O^+]$. The equilibrium nature of autoionization allows us to define "acidic" and "basic" solutions in terms of relative magnitudes of $[H_3O^+]$ and $[OH^-]$:

    In an *acidic* solution,     $[H_3O^+] > [OH^-]$
    In a *neutral* solution,     $[H_3O^+] = [OH^-]$
    In a *basic* solution,      $[H_3O^+] < [OH^-]$

Figure 18.3 summarizes these relationships. Moreover, if you know the value of $K_w$ at a particular temperature and the concentration of one of the two ions, you can find the concentration of the other:

$$[H_3O^+] = \frac{K_w}{[OH^-]} \quad \text{or} \quad [OH^-] = \frac{K_w}{[H_3O^+]}$$

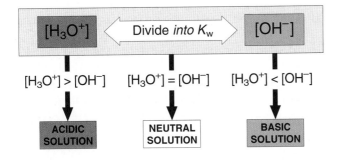

**Figure 18.3** The relationship between $[H_3O^+]$ and $[OH^-]$ and the relative acidity of solutions.

---

**Sample Problem 18.2**   **Calculating [H₃O⁺] or [OH⁻] in Aqueous Solution**

**Problem** A research chemist adds a measured amount of HCl gas to pure water at 25°C and obtains a solution with $[H_3O^+] = 3.0 \times 10^{-4}\ M$. Calculate $[OH^-]$. Is the solution neutral, acidic, or basic?

**Plan** We use the known value of $K_w$ at 25°C ($1.0 \times 10^{-14}$) and the given $[H_3O^+]$ ($3.0 \times 10^{-4}\ M$) to solve for $[OH^-]$. Then we compare $[H_3O^+]$ with $[OH^-]$ to determine whether the solution is acidic, basic, or neutral (see Figure 18.3).

**Solution** Calculating $[OH^-]$:

$$[OH^-] = \frac{K_w}{[H_3O^+]} = \frac{1.0 \times 10^{-14}}{3.0 \times 10^{-4}}$$

$$= 3.3 \times 10^{-11}\ M$$

Because $[H_3O^+] > [OH^-]$, the solution is acidic.

**Check** It makes sense that adding an acid to water results in an acidic solution. Also, since $[H_3O^+]$ is greater than $10^{-7}$ $M$, $[OH^-]$ must be less than $10^{-7}$ $M$ to give a constant $K_w$.

**Follow-Up Problem 18.2** Calculate $[H_3O^+]$ in a solution that has $[OH^-] = 6.7 \times 10^{-2}$ $M$ at 25°C. Is the solution neutral, acidic, or basic?

## Expressing the Hydronium Ion Concentration: The pH Scale

In aqueous solutions, $[H_3O^+]$ can vary from about 10 $M$ to $10^{-15}$ $M$. To handle numbers with negative exponents more conveniently in calculations, we convert them to positive numbers using a numerical system called a *p-scale*, the negative of the common (base-10) logarithm of the number. Applying this numerical system to $[H_3O^+]$ gives **pH**, the negative logarithm of $[H^+]$ (or $[H_3O^+]$):

$$pH = -\log [H_3O^+] \tag{18.3}$$

What is the pH of $10^{-12}$ $M$ $H_3O^+$ solution?

$$pH = -\log [H_3O^+] = -\log 10^{-12} = (-1)(-12) = 12$$

Similarly, a $10^{-3}$ $M$ $H_3O^+$ solution has a pH of 3, and a $5.4 \times 10^{-4}$ $M$ $H_3O^+$ solution has a pH of 3.27:

$$pH = -\log [H_3O^+] = (-1)(\log 5.4 + \log 10^{-4}) = 3.27$$

As with any measurement, the number of significant figures in a pH value reflects the precision with which the concentration is known. However, a pH value is a logarithm, so the number of significant figures in the concentration equals the number of digits *to the right of the decimal point in the pH value* (see Appendix A). In the preceding example, $5.4 \times 10^{-4}$ $M$ has two significant figures, so its negative logarithm, 3.27, has two digits to the right of the decimal point.

Note in particular that *the higher the pH, the lower the $[H_3O^+]$*. Therefore, *an acidic solution has a lower pH (higher $[H_3O^+]$) than a basic solution.* At 25°C in pure water, $[H_3O^+]$ is $1.0 \times 10^{-7}$ $M$, so

| | |
|---|---|
| pH of an acidic solution | $< 7.00$ |
| pH of a neutral solution | $= 7.00$ |
| pH of a basic solution | $> 7.00$ |

Figure 18.4 shows that the pH values of some familiar aqueous solutions fall within a range of 0 to 14.

Because the pH scale is logarithmic, a solution of pH 1.0 has an $[H_3O^+]$ that is 10 times higher than that of a pH 2.0 solution, 100 times higher than that of a pH 3.0 solution, and so forth. To find the $[H_3O^+]$ from the pH, you perform the opposite arithmetic process; that is, you find the negative antilog of pH:

$$[H_3O^+] = 10^{-pH}$$

A p-scale is used to express other quantities as well:

- Hydroxide ion concentration can be expressed as pOH:

$$pOH = -\log [OH^-]$$

  *Acidic solutions have a higher pOH (lower $[OH^-]$) than basic solutions.*
- Equilibrium constants can be expressed as p$K$:

$$pK = -\log K$$

*A low p$K$ corresponds to a high $K$.* A reaction that reaches equilibrium with mostly products present (proceeds far to the right) has a low p$K$ (high $K$), whereas one that has mostly reactants present at equilibrium has a high p$K$ (low $K$). Table 18.3 shows this relationship for aqueous equilibria of some weak acids.

**The Relations Among pH, pOH, and p$K_w$** Taking the negative log of both sides of the $K_w$ expression gives a very useful relationship among p$K_w$, pH, and pOH:

$$K_w = [H_3O^+][OH^-] = 1.0 \times 10^{-14} \text{ (at 25°C)}$$
$$-\log K_w = (-\log [H_3O^+]) + (-\log [OH^-]) = -\log (1.0 \times 10^{-14})$$

$$pK_w = pH + pOH = 14.00 \quad \text{(at 25°C)} \tag{18.4}$$

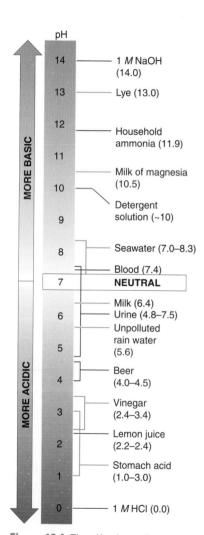

**Figure 18.4** The pH values of some familiar aqueous solutions.

**Table 18.3** The Relationship Between $K_a$ and $pK_a$

| Acid Name (Formula) | $K_a$ at 25°C | $pK_a$ |
|---|---|---|
| Hydrogen sulfate ion (HSO$_4^-$) | $1.0\times10^{-2}$ | 1.99 |
| Nitrous acid (HNO$_2$) | $7.1\times10^{-4}$ | 3.15 |
| Acetic acid (CH$_3$COOH) | $1.8\times10^{-5}$ | 4.75 |
| Hypobromous acid (HBrO) | $2.3\times10^{-9}$ | 8.64 |
| Phenol (C$_6$H$_5$OH) | $1.0\times10^{-10}$ | 10.00 |

Note these important points:

1. The sum of pH and pOH is $pK_w$ for any aqueous solution at any temperature, and $pK_w$ equals 14.00 at 25°C.
2. Because $K_w$ is constant, pH, pOH, [H$_3$O$^+$], and [OH$^-$] are interrelated:
   - [H$_3$O$^+$] and [OH$^-$] change in opposite directions.
   - pH and pOH also change in opposite directions.
   - At 25°C, the product of [H$_3$O$^+$] and [OH$^-$] is $1.0\times10^{-14}$, and the sum of pH and pOH is 14.00 (Figure 18.5).

| | [H$_3$O$^+$] | pH | [OH$^-$] | pOH |
|---|---|---|---|---|
| | $1.0 \times 10^{-15}$ | 15.00 | $1.0 \times 10^{1}$ | −1.00 |
| | $1.0 \times 10^{-14}$ | 14.00 | $1.0 \times 10^{0}$ | 0.00 |
| | $1.0 \times 10^{-13}$ | 13.00 | $1.0 \times 10^{-1}$ | 1.00 |
| BASIC | $1.0 \times 10^{-12}$ | 12.00 | $1.0 \times 10^{-2}$ | 2.00 |
| | $1.0 \times 10^{-11}$ | 11.00 | $1.0 \times 10^{-3}$ | 3.00 |
| | $1.0 \times 10^{-10}$ | 10.00 | $1.0 \times 10^{-4}$ | 4.00 |
| | $1.0 \times 10^{-9}$ | 9.00 | $1.0 \times 10^{-5}$ | 5.00 |
| | $1.0 \times 10^{-8}$ | 8.00 | $1.0 \times 10^{-6}$ | 6.00 |
| NEUTRAL | $1.0 \times 10^{-7}$ | 7.00 | $1.0 \times 10^{-7}$ | 7.00 |
| | $1.0 \times 10^{-6}$ | 6.00 | $1.0 \times 10^{-8}$ | 8.00 |
| | $1.0 \times 10^{-5}$ | 5.00 | $1.0 \times 10^{-9}$ | 9.00 |
| | $1.0 \times 10^{-4}$ | 4.00 | $1.0 \times 10^{-10}$ | 10.00 |
| | $1.0 \times 10^{-3}$ | 3.00 | $1.0 \times 10^{-11}$ | 11.00 |
| ACIDIC | $1.0 \times 10^{-2}$ | 2.00 | $1.0 \times 10^{-12}$ | 12.00 |
| | $1.0 \times 10^{-1}$ | 1.00 | $1.0 \times 10^{-13}$ | 13.00 |
| | $1.0 \times 10^{0}$ | 0.00 | $1.0 \times 10^{-14}$ | 14.00 |
| | $1.0 \times 10^{1}$ | −1.00 | $1.0 \times 10^{-15}$ | 15.00 |

MORE BASIC / MORE ACIDIC

**Figure 18.5** The relations among [H$_3$O$^+$], pH, [OH$^-$], and pOH.

## Sample Problem 18.3  Calculating [H$_3$O$^+$], pH, [OH$^-$], and pOH

**Problem** In an art restoration project, a conservator prepares copper-plate etching solutions by diluting concentrated HNO$_3$ to 2.0 $M$, 0.30 $M$, and 0.0063 $M$ HNO$_3$. Calculate [H$_3$O$^+$], pH, [OH$^-$], and pOH of the three solutions at 25°C.

**Plan** We know from its formula that HNO$_3$ is a strong acid, so it dissociates completely; thus, [H$_3$O$^+$] = [HNO$_3$]$_{init}$. We use the given concentrations and the value of $K_w$ at 25°C ($1.0\times10^{-14}$) to find [H$_3$O$^+$] and [OH$^-$] and then use them to calculate pH and pOH.

**Solution** Calculating the values for 2.0 $M$ HNO$_3$:

$$[H_3O^+] = \boxed{2.0\ M}$$

$$pH = -\log[H_3O^+] = -\log 2.0 = \boxed{-0.30}$$

$$[OH^-] = \frac{K_w}{[H_3O^+]} = \frac{1.0\times10^{-14}}{2.0} = \boxed{5.0\times10^{-15}\ M}$$

$$pOH = -\log(5.0\times10^{-15}) = \boxed{14.30}$$

Calculating the values for 0.30 $M$ HNO$_3$:

$$[H_3O^+] = \boxed{0.30\ M}$$

$$pH = -\log[H_3O^+] = -\log 0.30 = \boxed{0.52}$$

$$[OH^-] = \frac{K_w}{[H_3O^+]} = \frac{1.0\times10^{-14}}{0.30} = \boxed{3.3\times10^{-14}\ M}$$

$$pOH = -\log(3.3\times10^{-14}) = \boxed{13.48}$$

Calculating the values for 0.0063 $M$ HNO$_3$:

$$[H_3O^+] = \boxed{6.3\times10^{-3}\ M}$$

$$pH = -\log[H_3O^+] = -\log(6.3\times10^{-3}) = \boxed{2.20}$$

$$[OH^-] = \frac{K_w}{[H_3O^+]} = \frac{1.0\times10^{-14}}{6.3\times10^{-3}} = \boxed{1.6\times10^{-12}\ M}$$

$$pOH = -\log(1.6\times10^{-12}) = \boxed{11.80}$$

**Check** As the solution becomes more dilute, $[H_3O^+]$ decreases, so pH increases, as we expect. An $[H_3O^+] > 1.0\ M$, as in 2.0 $M$ HNO$_3$, gives a positive log, so it results in a negative pH. The arithmetic seems correct because pH + pOH = 14.00 in each case.

**Comment** On most calculators, finding the pH requires several keystrokes. For example, to find the pH of $6.3\times10^{-3}\ M$ HNO$_3$ solution, you enter: 6.3, EXP, 3, +/−, log, +/−.

**Follow-Up Problem 18.3** A solution of NaOH has a pH of 9.52. What is its pOH, $[H_3O^+]$, and $[OH^-]$ at 25°C?

**A**

**B**

**Figure 18.6** Methods for measuring the pH of an aqueous solution. **A,** pH paper. **B,** pH meter.

**Measuring pH** In the laboratory, pH values are usually obtained in two ways:

1. **Acid-base indicators** are organic molecules whose colors depend on the acidity of the solution in which they are dissolved. A pH can be estimated quickly with *pH paper,* a paper strip impregnated with one or a mixture of indicators. A drop of solution is placed on the strip, and the color is compared with a chart (Figure 18.6A).

2. A *pH meter* measures $[H_3O^+]$ by means of two electrodes immersed in the test solution. One electrode supplies a reference system; the other consists of a very thin glass membrane that separates a known internal $[H_3O^+]$ from the unknown external $[H_3O^+]$. The difference in $[H_3O^+]$ creates a voltage difference across the membrane, which is displayed in pH units (Figure 18.6B). We examine this device in Chapter 21.

## Summary of Section 18.2

- Pure water has a low conductivity because it autoionizes to a small extent in a process whose equilibrium constant is the ion-product constant for water, $K_w$ ($1.0\times10^{-14}$ at 25°C).
- $[H_3O^+]$ and $[OH^-]$ are inversely related: in acidic solution, $[H_3O^+]$ is greater than $[OH^-]$; the reverse is true in basic solution; and the two are equal in neutral solution.
- To express small values of $[H_3O^+]$, we use the pH scale (pH = $-\log[H_3O^+]$). Similarly, pOH = $-\log[OH^-]$, and p$K$ = $-\log K$.
- A high pH represents a low $[H_3O^+]$. In acidic solutions, pH < 7.00; in basic solutions, pH > 7.00; and in neutral solutions, pH = 7.00. The sum of pH and pOH equals p$K_w$ (14.00 at 25°C).
- A pH is typically measured with either an acid-base indicator or a pH meter.

## 18.3 • PROTON TRANSFER AND THE BRØNSTED-LOWRY ACID-BASE DEFINITION

Earlier we noted one limitation of the Arrhenius definition: many substances that yield OH$^-$ ions in water do not contain OH in their formulas. Examples include ammonia, the amines, and many salts of weak acids, such as NaF. Another limitation is that water had to be the solvent for acid-base reactions. In the early 20$^{th}$ century, J. N. Brønsted and T. M. Lowry suggested definitions that remove these limitations. (We introduced some of these ideas in Section 4.4.)

According to the **Brønsted-Lowry acid-base definition,**

- *An acid is a **proton donor,** any species that donates an H$^+$ion.* An acid must contain H in its formula; HNO$_3$ and H$_2$PO$_4^-$ are two of many examples. All Arrhenius acids are Brønsted-Lowry acids.
- *A base is a **proton acceptor,** any species that accepts an H$^+$ion.* A base must contain a lone pair of electrons to bind H$^+$; a few examples are NH$_3$, CO$_3^{2-}$, and F$^-$, as well as OH$^-$ itself. Brønsted-Lowry bases are not Arrhenius bases, but all Arrhenius bases contain the Brønsted-Lowry base OH$^-$.

From this perspective, an acid-base reaction occurs when *one species donates a proton and another species simultaneously accepts it: an acid-base reaction is thus a proton-transfer process.* Acid-base reactions can occur between gases, in nonaqueous solutions, and in heterogeneous mixtures, as well as in aqueous solutions.

According to this definition, an acid-base reaction occurs even when an acid (or a base) just dissolves in water, because water acts as the proton acceptor (or donor):

1. *Acid donates a proton to water* (Figure 18.7A). When HCl dissolves in water, an H$^+$ ion (a proton) is transferred from HCl to H$_2$O, where it becomes attached to a lone pair of electrons on the O atom, forming H$_3$O$^+$. Thus, HCl (the acid) has *donated* the H$^+$, and H$_2$O (the base) has *accepted* it:

$$\text{HCl}(g) + \text{H}_2\ddot{\text{O}}(l) \longrightarrow \text{Cl}^-(aq) + \text{H}_3\ddot{\text{O}}^+(aq)$$

2. *Base accepts a proton from water* (Figure 18.7B). When ammonia dissolves in water, an H$^+$ from H$_2$O is transferred to the lone pair of N, forming NH$_4^+$, and the H$_2$O becomes an OH$^-$ ion:

$$\ddot{\text{N}}\text{H}_3(aq) + \text{H}_2\text{O}(l) \rightleftharpoons \text{NH}_4^+(aq) + \text{OH}^-(aq)$$

In this case, H$_2$O (the acid) has *donated* the H$^+$, and NH$_3$ (the base) has *accepted* it.

Note that H$_2$O is *amphiprotic:* it acts as a base (accepts an H$^+$) in one case and as an acid (donates an H$^+$) in the other. Many other species are amphiprotic as well.

**Figure 18.7** Dissolving of an acid or base in water as a Brønsted-Lowry acid-base reaction. **A,** The acid HCl dissolving in the base water. **B,** The base NH$_3$ dissolving in the acid water.

## Conjugate Acid-Base Pairs

The Brønsted-Lowry definition provides a new way to look at these reactions because it focuses on the reactants *and* the products as acids and bases. For example, let's examine the reaction between hydrogen sulfide and ammonia:

$$\text{H}_2\text{S} + \text{NH}_3 \rightleftharpoons \text{HS}^- + \text{NH}_4^+$$

In the forward reaction, H$_2$S acts as an acid by donating an H$^+$ to NH$_3$, which acts as a base by accepting it. In the reverse reaction, the ammonium ion, NH$_4^+$, acts as an acid by donating an H$^+$ to the hydrogen sulfide ion, HS$^-$, which acts as a base. Notice that the acid, H$_2$S, becomes a base, HS$^-$, and the base, NH$_3$, becomes an acid, NH$_4^+$.

In Brønsted-Lowry terminology, H$_2$S and HS$^-$ are a **conjugate acid-base pair:** HS$^-$ is the conjugate base of the acid H$_2$S. Similarly, NH$_3$ and NH$_4^+$ are a conjugate acid-base pair: $NH_4^+$ is the conjugate acid of the base $NH_3$. *Every acid has a conjugate base, and every base has a conjugate acid.* For any conjugate acid-base pair,

• The conjugate base has one *fewer* H and one *more* minus charge than the acid.
• The conjugate acid has one *more* H and one *fewer* minus charge than the base.

A Brønsted-Lowry acid-base reaction occurs when *an acid and a base react to form their conjugate base and conjugate acid, respectively:*

$$acid_1 + base_2 \rightleftharpoons base_1 + acid_2$$

Table 18.4 shows some Brønsted-Lowry acid-base reactions. Note these points:

• Each reaction has an acid and a base as reactants *and* as products, comprising two conjugate acid-base pairs.
• Acids and bases can be neutral, cationic, or anionic.
• The same species can be an acid or a base (amphiprotic), depending on the other species reacting. Water behaves this way in reactions 1 and 4, and $HPO_4^{2-}$ does so in reactions 4 and 6.

### Table 18.4 The Conjugate Pairs in Some Acid-Base Reactions

| | Acid | + | Base | $\rightleftharpoons$ | Base | + | Acid |
|---|---|---|---|---|---|---|---|
| Reaction 1 | HF | + | $H_2O$ | | $F^-$ | + | $H_3O^+$ |
| Reaction 2 | HCOOH | + | $CN^-$ | | $HCOO^-$ | + | HCN |
| Reaction 3 | $NH_4^+$ | + | $CO_3^{2-}$ | | $NH_3$ | + | $HCO_3^-$ |
| Reaction 4 | $H_2PO_4^-$ | + | $OH^-$ | | $HPO_4^{2-}$ | + | $H_2O$ |
| Reaction 5 | $H_2SO_4$ | + | $N_2H_5^+$ | | $HSO_4^-$ | + | $N_2H_6^{2+}$ |
| Reaction 6 | $HPO_4^{2-}$ | + | $SO_3^{2-}$ | | $PO_4^{3-}$ | + | $HSO_3^-$ |

### Sample Problem 18.4 Identifying Conjugate Acid-Base Pairs

**Problem** The following reactions are important environmental processes. Identify the conjugate acid-base pairs.
**(a)** $H_2PO_4^-(aq) + CO_3^{2-}(aq) \rightleftharpoons HCO_3^-(aq) + HPO_4^{2-}(aq)$
**(b)** $H_2O(l) + SO_3^{2-}(aq) \rightleftharpoons OH^-(aq) + HSO_3^-(aq)$

**Plan** To find the conjugate pairs, we find the species that donated an $H^+$ (acid) and the species that accepted it (base). The acid (or base) on the left becomes its conjugate base (or conjugate acid) on the right. Remember, the conjugate acid has one more H and one fewer minus charge than its conjugate base.

**Solution (a)** $H_2PO_4^-$ has one more $H^+$ than $HPO_4^{2-}$; $CO_3^{2-}$ has one fewer $H^+$ than $HCO_3^-$. Therefore, $H_2PO_4^-$ and $HCO_3^-$ are the acids, and $HPO_4^{2-}$ and $CO_3^{2-}$ are the bases. The conjugate acid-base pairs are $H_2PO_4^-/HPO_4^{2-}$ and $HCO_3^-/CO_3^{2-}$.
**(b)** $H_2O$ has one more $H^+$ than $OH^-$; $SO_3^{2-}$ has one fewer $H^+$ than $HSO_3^-$. The acids are $H_2O$ and $HSO_3^-$; the bases are $OH^-$ and $SO_3^{2-}$. The conjugate acid-base pairs are $H_2O/OH^-$ and $HSO_3^-/SO_3^{2-}$.

**Follow-Up Problem 18.4** Identify the conjugate acid-base pairs:
**(a)** $CH_3COOH(aq) + H_2O(l) \rightleftharpoons CH_3COO^-(aq) + H_3O^+(aq)$
**(b)** $H_2O(l) + F^-(aq) \rightleftharpoons OH^-(aq) + HF(aq)$

## Relative Acid-Base Strength and the Net Direction of Reaction

The *net* direction of an acid-base reaction depends on relative acid and base strengths: *A reaction proceeds to the greater extent in the direction in which a stronger acid and stronger base form a weaker acid and weaker base.*

**Competition for the Proton** The net direction of the reaction of $H_2S$ and $NH_3$ is to the right ($K_c > 1$) because $H_2S$ is a stronger acid than $NH_4^+$, the other acid present, and $NH_3$ is a stronger base than $HS^-$, the other base:

$$H_2S \ + \ NH_3 \ \rightleftharpoons \ HS^- \ + \ NH_4^+$$
stronger acid + stronger base $\longrightarrow$ weaker base + weaker acid

You might think of the process as *a competition for the proton between the two bases*, $NH_3$ and $HS^-$, in which $NH_3$ wins.

The extent of acid (HA) dissociation in water depends on a competition for the proton between the two bases, $A^-$ and $H_2O$. Strong and weak acids give different results:

1. *Strong acids.* When the strong acid $HNO_3$ dissolves, it completely transfers an $H^+$ to the base, $H_2O$, forming the conjugate base $NO_3^-$ and the conjugate acid $H_3O^+$:

$$HNO_3 \ + \ H_2O \ \rightleftharpoons \ NO_3^- \ + \ H_3O^+$$
stronger acid + stronger base $\longrightarrow$ weaker base + weaker acid

Even though we show an equilibrium arrow here, the net direction is so far to the right that $K_c \gg 1$ and the reaction is essentially complete. $HNO_3$ is a stronger acid than $H_3O^+$, and $H_2O$ is a stronger base than $NO_3^-$. Thus, with a strong HA, $H_2O$ wins the competition for the proton because $A^-$ is a *much* weaker base. In fact, *the only acidic species that remains in strong-acid solutions is $H_3O^+$*.

2. *Weak acids.* On the other hand, with weak acids such as HF, the $A^-$ ($F^-$) wins the competition because it is a stronger base than $H_2O$ ($K_c < 1$):

$$HF \ + \ H_2O \ \rightleftharpoons \ F^- \ + \ H_3O^+$$
weaker acid + weaker base $\longleftarrow$ stronger base + stronger acid

**Ranking Conjugate Pairs** Based on evidence from many such reactions, we can rank conjugate pairs in terms of the ability of the acid to transfer its proton (Figure 18.8). Note

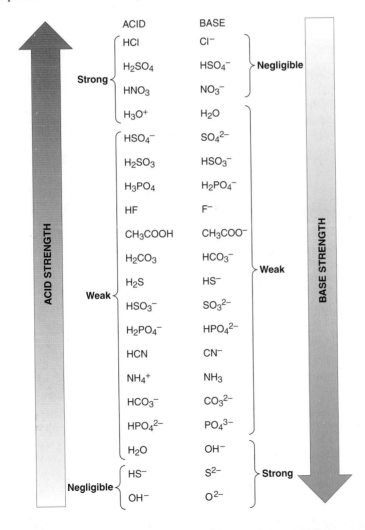

**Figure 18.8 Strengths of conjugate acid-base pairs.** The stronger the acid is, the weaker its conjugate base. The strongest acid is at top left and the strongest base at bottom right. When an acid reacts with a base farther down the list, the reaction proceeds to the right ($K_c > 1$).

that *a weaker acid has a stronger conjugate base:* the acid can't give up its proton very readily because its conjugate base is holding it too strongly.

We use Figure 18.8 to predict the net direction of a reaction between any two pairs, that is, whether the equilibrium position lies to the right ($K_c > 1$) or to the left ($K_c < 1$). *A reaction proceeds to the right if an acid reacts with a base lower on the list.* Here are two sample problems that demonstrate this key idea.

---

### Sample Problem 18.5    Predicting the Net Direction of an Acid-Base Reaction

**Problem** Predict the net direction and whether $K_c$ is greater or less than 1 for each of the following reactions (assume equal initial concentrations of all species):
(a) $H_2PO_4^-(aq) + NH_3(aq) \rightleftharpoons NH_4^+(aq) + HPO_4^{2-}(aq)$
(b) $H_2O(l) + HS^-(aq) \rightleftharpoons OH^-(aq) + H_2S(aq)$

**Plan** We identify the conjugate acid-base pairs and consult Figure 18.8 to see which acid and base are stronger. The reaction proceeds in the direction that the stronger acid and base form the weaker acid and base. If the reaction *as written* proceeds to the right, then [products] is higher than [reactants], so $K_c > 1$.

**Solution** (a) The conjugate pairs are $H_2PO_4^-/HPO_4^{2-}$ and $NH_4^+/NH_3$. Since $H_2PO_4^-$ is higher on the list of acids, it is stronger than $NH_4^+$; since $NH_3$ is lower on the list of bases, it is stronger than $HPO_4^{2-}$. Therefore,

$$H_2PO_4^-(aq) + \quad NH_3(aq) \quad \rightleftharpoons \quad HPO_4^{2-}(aq) + NH_4^+(aq)$$
stronger acid  +  stronger base  $\longrightarrow$  weaker base  +  weaker acid

The net direction is to the right, so $K_c > 1$.

(b) The conjugate pairs are $H_2O/OH^-$ and $H_2S/HS^-$. Since $H_2S$ is higher on the list of acids, and $OH^-$ is lower on the list of bases, we have

$$H_2O(l) \quad + \quad HS^-(aq) \rightleftharpoons \quad OH^-(aq) \quad + \quad H_2S(aq)$$
weaker acid  +  weaker base  $\longleftarrow$  stronger base  +  stronger acid

The net direction is to the left, so $K_c < 1$.

**Follow-Up Problem 18.5** Use balanced equations that show the net direction of the reaction to explain each of the following observations:
(a) You smell ammonia when $NH_3$ dissolves in water.
(b) The odor goes away when you add an excess of HCl to the solution in part (a).
(c) The odor returns when you add an excess of NaOH to the solution in part (b).

---

### Sample Problem 18.6    Using Molecular Scenes to Predict the Net Direction of an Acid-Base Reaction

**Problem** Given that 0.10 *M* HX (*blue and green*) has a pH of 2.88, and 0.10 *M* HY (*blue and orange*) has a pH of 3.52, which scene best represents the final mixture after equimolar solutions of HX and $Y^-$ are mixed?

1          2          3

**Plan** A stronger acid and base yield a weaker acid and base, so we have to determine the relative acid strengths of HX and HY in order to choose the correct molecular scene. The concentrations of the acid solutions are equal, so we can pick the stronger acid directly from the pH values of the two acid solutions. Because the stronger acid reacts to a greater extent, fewer molecules of it will be in the scene than molecules of the weaker acid.

**Solution** The HX solution has a lower pH (2.88) than the HY solution (3.52), so we know right away that HX is the stronger acid and $Y^-$ is the stronger base. Therefore, the reaction of HX and $Y^-$ has a $K_c > 1$, which means the equilibrium mixture will have more HY than HX. Scene 1 has equal numbers of HX and HY, which would occur if the acids were of equal strength, and scene 2 shows fewer HY than HX, which would occur if HY were stronger. Therefore, only  scene 3 is consistent with the relative acid strengths.

**Follow-Up Problem 18.6**  The scene below represents the equilibrium mixture after 0.10 *M* solutions of HA *(blue and red)* and $B^-$ *(black)* react: Does their reaction have a $K_c$ greater or less than 1? Which acid is stronger, HA or HB?

# Summary of Section 18.3

- The Brønsted-Lowry acid-base definition does not require that bases contain OH in their formula or that acid-base reactions occur in aqueous solution.
- An acid is a species that donates a proton and a base is one that accepts it, so an acid-base reaction is a proton-transfer process.
- When an acid donates a proton, it becomes the conjugate base; when a base accepts a proton, it becomes the conjugate acid. In an acid-base reaction, acids and bases form their conjugates. A stronger acid has a weaker conjugate base, and vice versa.
- An acid-base reaction proceeds to the greater extent in the direction in which a stronger acid and base form a weaker base and acid.

# 18.4 • SOLVING PROBLEMS INVOLVING WEAK-ACID EQUILIBRIA

Just as you saw in Chapter 17 for equilibrium problems in general, there are two general types of equilibrium problems involving weak acids and their conjugate bases:

1. Given equilibrium concentrations, find $K_a$.
2. Given $K_a$ and some concentrations, find other equilibrium concentrations.

For all of these problems, we'll apply the same problem-solving approach, notation system, and assumptions:

- *The problem-solving approach.* Start with what is given in the problem and move toward what you want to find. Make a habit of applying the following steps:
  1. Write the balanced equation and $K_a$ expression; these tell you what to find.
  2. Define *x* as the unknown change in concentration that occurs during the reaction. Frequently, $x = [HA]_{dissoc}$, the concentration of HA that dissociates, which, through the use of certain assumptions, also equals $[H_3O^+]$ and $[A^-]$ at equilibrium.
  3. Construct a reaction table (for most problems) that incorporates *x*.
  4. Make assumptions (usually that *x* is very small relative to the initial concentration; see below) that simplify the calculations.
  5. Substitute the values into the $K_a$ expression, and solve for *x*.
  6. Check that the assumptions are justified with the 5% test first used in Sample Problem 17.10, pp. 695–696. If they are not justified, use the quadratic formula to find *x*.

- *The notation system.* As always, molar concentration is indicated with brackets. A subscript refers to where the species comes from or when it occurs in the reaction process. For example, $[H_3O^+]_{\text{from HA}}$ is the molar concentration of $H_3O^+$ that comes from the dissociation of HA; $[HA]_{\text{init}}$ is the initial molar concentration of HA, that is, before dissociation; $[HA]_{\text{dissoc}}$ is the molar concentration of HA that dissociates; and so forth. A bracketed formula with *no* subscript represents the molar concentration of the species *at equilibrium.*

- *The assumptions.* We make two assumptions to simplify the arithmetic:
  1. $[H_3O^+]$ from the autoionization of water is negligible. It is so much smaller than the $[H_3O^+]$ from the dissociation of HA that we can neglect it in these problems:

$$[H_3O^+] = [H_3O^+]_{\text{from HA}} + [H_3O^+]_{\text{from H}_2\text{O}} \approx [H_3O^+]_{\text{from HA}}$$

   Note that each molecule of HA that dissociates forms one $H_3O^+$ and one $A^-$:

$$[HA]_{\text{dissoc}} = [H_3O^+] = [A^-]$$

  2. A weak acid has a small $K_a$. Therefore, it dissociates to such a small extent that we can neglect the change in its concentration to find its equilibrium concentration:

$$[HA] = [HA]_{\text{init}} - [HA]_{\text{dissoc}} \approx [HA]_{\text{init}}$$

## Finding $K_a$ Given Concentrations

This type of problem involves finding $K_a$ of a weak acid from the concentration of one of the species in solution, usually $[H_3O^+]$ from a given pH:

$$HA(aq) + H_2O(l) \rightleftharpoons H_3O^+(aq) + A^-(aq)$$

$$K_a = \frac{[H_3O^+][A^-]}{[HA]}$$

You prepare an aqueous solution of HA and measure its pH. Thus, you know $[HA]_{\text{init}}$, can calculate $[H_3O^+]$ from the pH, and then determine $[A^-]$ and $[HA]$ at equilibrium. You substitute these values into the $K_a$ expression and solve for $K_a$. Let's go through the approach in Sample Problem 18.7.

---

### Sample Problem 18.7 | Finding $K_a$ of a Weak Acid from the Solution pH

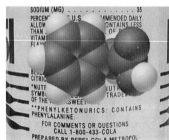

SODIUM (MG) .............. 35
PERCENT ... U.S. ... MENDED DAILY
ALLOW ... ONTAINS LESS
THAN ... OF
VITAM
FLA

**PHENYLKETONURICS: CONTAINS PHENYLALANINE.**
FOR COMMENTS OR QUESTIONS CALL 1-800-433-COLA
PREPARED BY PEPSI-COLA METROPOL·

Phenylalanine, one of the amino acids that make up aspartame, is metabolized to phenylacetic acid (model).

**Problem** Phenylacetic acid ($C_6H_5CH_2COOH$, simplified here to HPAc; *see model*) builds up in the blood of persons with phenylketonuria, an inherited disorder that, if untreated, causes mental retardation and death. A study of the acid shows that the pH of 0.12 *M* HPAc is 2.62. What is the $K_a$ of phenylacetic acid?

**Plan** We are given $[HPAc]_{\text{init}}$ (0.12 *M*) and the pH (2.62) and must find $K_a$. As always, we first write the equation for HPAc dissociation and the expression for $K_a$ to see which values we need. We assume $[H_3O^+]_{\text{from H}_2\text{O}}$ is negligible, so we can use the given pH to find $[H_3O^+]$, which equals $[PAc^-]$ and $[HPAc]_{\text{dissoc}}$. To find $[HPAc]$, we assume that, because it is a weak acid, very little dissociates, so $[HPAc]_{\text{init}} - [HPAc]_{\text{dissoc}} = [HPAc] \approx [HPAc]_{\text{init}}$. We make these assumptions, substitute the equilibrium values, solve for $K_a$, and then check the assumptions. Note that we *don't* need a reaction table here because the pH will give us $[HPAc]_{\text{dissoc}}$.

**Solution** Writing the dissociation equation and $K_a$ expression:

$$HPAc(aq) + H_2O(l) \rightleftharpoons H_3O^+(aq) + PAc^-(aq) \qquad K_a = \frac{[H_3O^+][PAc^-]}{[HPAc]}$$

Calculating $[H_3O^+]$:

$$[H_3O^+] = 10^{-\text{pH}} = 10^{-2.62} = 2.4 \times 10^{-3} \ M$$

Making the assumptions:
1. The calculated $[H_3O^+]$ ($2.4 \times 10^{-3}$ *M*) $>> [H_3O^+]_{\text{from H}_2\text{O}}$ ($1.0 \times 10^{-7}$ *M*), so we assume that $[H_3O^+] \approx [H_3O^+]_{\text{from HPAc}} = [PAc^-] = x$ (the change in $[HPAc]$, or $[HPAc]_{\text{dissoc}}$).
2. HPAc is a weak acid, so we assume that $[HPAc] = 0.12 \ M - x \approx 0.12 \ M$.

Solving for the equilibrium concentrations:

$$x \approx [H_3O^+] = [PAc^-] = 2.4\times10^{-3}\ M$$

$$[HPAc] = 0.12\ M - x = 0.12\ M - (2.4\times10^{-3}\ M) \approx 0.12\ M \text{ (to 2 sf)}$$

Substituting these values into $K_a$:

$$K_a = \frac{[H_3O^+][PAc^-]}{[HPAc]} \approx \frac{(2.4\times10^{-3})(2.4\times10^{-3})}{0.12} = \boxed{4.8\times10^{-5}}$$

Checking the assumptions by finding the percent error in concentration:

1. For $[H_3O^+]_{\text{from }H_2O}$: $\dfrac{1\times10^{-7}\ M}{2.4\times10^{-3}\ M} \times 100 = 4\times10^{-3}\%$ ($<5\%$; assumption is justified).

2. For $[HPAc]_{\text{dissoc}}$: $\dfrac{2.4\times10^{-3}\ M}{0.12\ M} \times 100 = 2.0\%$ ($<5\%$; assumption is justified).

**Check** The $[H_3O^+]$ makes sense: pH 2.62 should give $[H_3O^+]$ between $10^{-2}$ and $10^{-3}\ M$. The $K_a$ calculation also seems in the correct range: $(10^{-3})^2/10^{-1} = 10^{-5}$, and this value seems reasonable for a weak acid.

**Follow-Up Problem 18.7** The conjugate acid of ammonia is the weak acid $NH_4^+$. If a 0.2 $M$ $NH_4Cl$ solution has a pH of 5.0, what is the $K_a$ of $NH_4^+$?

## Finding Concentrations Given $K_a$

The second type of equilibrium problem gives some concentration data and $K_a$ and asks for the equilibrium concentration of some component. Such problems are very similar to those we solved in Chapter 17 in which a substance with a given initial concentration reacted to an unknown extent (see Sample Problems 17.9 to 17.11). We *will* use a reaction table in these problems to find the values, and, as we just found, $[H_3O^+]_{\text{from }H_2O}$ is so small relative to $[H_3O^+]_{\text{from }HA}$ that we will neglect it and enter the initial $[H_3O^+]$ in all reaction tables as zero.

---

**Sample Problem 18.8**   **Determining Concentration from $K_a$ and Initial [HA]**

**Problem** Propanoic acid ($CH_3CH_2COOH$, which we simplify as HPr) is a carboxylic acid whose salts are used to retard mold growth in foods. What is the $[H_3O^+]$ of 0.10 $M$ HPr ($K_a = 1.3\times10^{-5}$)?

**Plan** We know the initial concentration (0.10 $M$) and $K_a$ ($1.3\times10^{-5}$) of HPr, and we need to find $[H_3O^+]$. First, we write the balanced equation and the expression for $K_a$. We know $[HPr]_{\text{init}}$ but not $[HPr]$ (that is, the concentration at equilibrium). If we let $x = [HPr]_{\text{dissoc}}$, $x$ is also $[H_3O^+]_{\text{from }HPr}$ and $[Pr^-]$ because each HPr dissociates into one $H_3O^+$ and one $Pr^-$. With this information, we set up a reaction table. We assume that, because HPr has a small $K_a$, it dissociates very little. After solving for $x$, we check the assumption.

**Solution** Writing the balanced equation and expression for $K_a$:

$$HPr(aq) + H_2O(l) \rightleftharpoons H_3O^+(aq) + Pr^-(aq) \qquad K_a = \frac{[H_3O^+][Pr^-]}{[HPr]} = 1.3\times10^{-5}$$

Setting up a reaction table, with $x = [HPr]_{\text{dissoc}} = [Pr^-] = [H_3O^+]$:

| Concentration ($M$) | HPr($aq$) | + | H₂O($l$) | $\rightleftharpoons$ | H₃O⁺($aq$) | + | Pr⁻($aq$) |
|---|---|---|---|---|---|---|---|
| Initial | 0.10 | | — | | 0 | | 0 |
| Change | $-x$ | | — | | $+x$ | | $+x$ |
| Equilibrium | $0.10 - x$ | | — | | $x$ | | $x$ |

Making the assumption: $K_a$ is small, so $x$ is small compared with $[HPr]_{init}$; therefore, $[HPr]_{init} - x = [HPr] \approx [HPr]_{init}$, or $0.10\ M - x \approx 0.10\ M$. Substituting into the $K_a$ expression and solving for $x$:

$$K_a = \frac{[H_3O^+][Pr^-]}{[HPr]} = 1.3 \times 10^{-5} \approx \frac{(x)(x)}{0.10}$$

$$x \approx \sqrt{(0.10)(1.3 \times 10^{-5})} = \boxed{1.1 \times 10^{-3}\ M = [H_3O^+]}$$

Checking the assumption:

For $[HPr]_{dissoc}$: $\dfrac{1.1 \times 10^{-3}\ M}{0.10\ M} \times 100 = 1.1\%$ ($<5\%$; assumption is justified).

**Check** The $[H_3O^+]$ seems reasonable for a dilute solution of a weak acid with a moderate $K_a$. By reversing the calculation, we can check the math: $(1.1 \times 10^{-3})^2/0.10 = 1.2 \times 10^{-5}$, which is within rounding of the given $K_a$.

**Comment** In Chapter 17 we introduced a benchmark, aside from the 5% rule, to see if the assumption is justified (see the discussion following Sample Problem 17.10):

- If $\dfrac{[HA]_{init}}{K_a} > 400$, the assumption is justified: neglecting $x$ introduces an error $<5\%$.

- If $\dfrac{[HA]_{init}}{K_a} < 400$, the assumption is *not* justified; neglecting $x$ introduces an error $>5\%$, so we solve a quadratic equation to find $x$.

In this sample problem, we have $\dfrac{0.10}{1.3 \times 10^{-5}} = 7.7 \times 10^3$, which is greater than 400. The alternative situation occurs in the follow-up problem.

**Follow-Up Problem 18.8** Cyanic acid (HOCN) is an extremely acrid, unstable substance. What is the $[H_3O^+]$ of 0.10 $M$ HOCN ($K_a = 3.5 \times 10^{-4}$)?

## The Effect of Concentration on the Extent of Acid Dissociation

If we repeat the calculation in Sample Problem 18.8, but start with a lower [HPr], we observe a very interesting fact about the extent of dissociation of a weak acid. Suppose the initial concentration of HPr is one-tenth as much, 0.010 $M$ rather than 0.10 $M$. After filling in the reaction table and making the same assumptions, we find that

$$x = [H_3O^+] = [HPr]_{dissoc} = 3.6 \times 10^{-4}\ M$$

Now, let's compare the percentages of HPr molecules dissociated at the two different initial acid concentrations, using the relationship

$$\text{Percent HA dissociated} = \frac{[HA]_{dissoc}}{[HA]_{init}} \times 100 \qquad (18.5)$$

Case 1: $[HPr]_{init} = 0.10\ M$

$$\text{Percent HPr dissociated} = \frac{1.1 \times 10^{-3}\ M}{1.0 \times 10^{-1}\ M} \times 100 = 1.1\%$$

Case 2: $[HPr]_{init} = 0.010\ M$

$$\text{Percent HPr dissociated} = \frac{3.6 \times 10^{-4}\ M}{1.0 \times 10^{-2}\ M} \times 100 = 3.6\%$$

*As the initial acid concentration decreases, the percent dissociation of the acid increases.* Don't confuse the *concentration* of HA dissociated with the *percent* HA dissociated. The concentration, $[HA]_{dissoc}$, is lower in the diluted HA solution because the actual *number* of dissociated HA molecules is smaller. It is the *fraction* (or the *percent*) of dissociated HA molecules that increases with dilution.

This phenomenon is analogous to a change in container volume (pressure) for gases at equilibrium (Section 17.6). In the case of gases, an increase in volume shifts the equilibrium position to favor more moles of gas. In the case of HA dissociation, a lower HA concentration, which is the same as an increase in volume, shifts the equilibrium position to favor more moles of ions. Sample Problem 18.9 uses molecular scenes to highlight this idea. (Note that, in order to depict the scenes practically, the acid has a much higher percent dissociation than any real weak acid does.)

### Sample Problem 18.9 | Using Molecular Scenes to Determine the Extent of HA Dissociation

**Problem** A 0.15 *M* solution of HA *(blue and green)* is 33% dissociated. Which scene represents a sample of that solution after it is diluted with water?

1        2        3

**Plan** We are given the percent dissociation of the original HA solution (33%), and we know that the percent dissociation increases as the acid is diluted. Thus, we calculate the percent dissociation of each diluted sample and see which is greater than 33%. To determine percent dissociation, we apply Equation 18.5, with $HA_{dissoc}$ equal to the number of $H_3O^+$ (or $A^-$) and $HA_{init}$ equal to the number of HA *plus* the number of $H_3O^+$ (or $A^-$).

**Solution** Calculating the percent dissociation of each diluted solution with Equation 18.5:

Solution 1. Percent dissociated = 4/(5 + 4) × 100 = 44%
Solution 2. Percent dissociated = 2/(7 + 2) × 100 = 22%
Solution 3. Percent dissociated = 3/(6 + 3) × 100 = 33%

Therefore, scene 1 represents the diluted solution.

**Check** Let's confirm our choice by examining the other scenes: in scene 2, HA is *less* dissociated than originally, so that scene must represent a more concentrated HA solution; scene 3 represents another solution with the same percent dissociation as the original.

**Follow-Up Problem 18.9** The scene shown in the margin represents a sample of a weak acid HB *(blue and purple)* dissolved in water. Draw a scene that represents the same volume after the solution has been diluted with water.

## The Behavior of Polyprotic Acids

Acids with more than one ionizable proton are **polyprotic acids.** In solution, each dissociation step has a different $K_a$. For example, phosphoric acid is a triprotic acid (three ionizable protons), so it has three $K_a$ values:

$$H_3PO_4(aq) + H_2O(l) \rightleftharpoons H_2PO_4^-(aq) + H_3O^+(aq)$$

$$K_{a1} = \frac{[H_2PO_4^-][H_3O^+]}{[H_3PO_4]} = 7.2 \times 10^{-3}$$

$$H_2PO_4^-(aq) + H_2O(l) \rightleftharpoons HPO_4^{2-}(aq) + H_3O^+(aq)$$

$$K_{a2} = \frac{[HPO_4^{2-}][H_3O^+]}{[H_2PO_4^-]} = 6.3 \times 10^{-8}$$

$$HPO_4^{2-}(aq) + H_2O(l) \rightleftharpoons PO_4^{3-}(aq) + H_3O^+(aq)$$

$$K_{a3} = \frac{[PO_4^{3-}][H_3O^+]}{[HPO_4^{2-}]} = 4.2 \times 10^{-13}$$

The relative $K_a$ values show that $H_3PO_4$ is a much stronger acid than $H_2PO_4^-$, which is much stronger than $HPO_4^{2-}$.

**Table 18.5 Successive $K_a$ Values for Some Polyprotic Acids at 25°C**

| Name (Formula) | Lewis Structure* | $K_{a1}$ | $K_{a2}$ | $K_{a3}$ | |
|---|---|---|---|---|---|
| Oxalic acid ($H_2C_2O_4$) | H—Ö—C—C—Ö—H | $5.6\times10^{-2}$ | $5.4\times10^{-5}$ | | |
| Sulfurous acid ($H_2SO_3$) | H—Ö—S—Ö—H | $1.4\times10^{-2}$ | $6.5\times10^{-8}$ | | ACID STRENGTH |
| Phosphoric acid ($H_3PO_4$) | H—Ö—P—Ö—H | $7.2\times10^{-3}$ | $6.3\times10^{-8}$ | $4.2\times10^{-13}$ | |
| Arsenic acid ($H_3AsO_4$) | H—Ö—As—Ö—H | $6\times10^{-3}$ | $1.1\times10^{-7}$ | $3\times10^{-12}$ | |
| Carbonic acid ($H_2CO_3$) | H—Ö—C—Ö—H | $4.5\times10^{-7}$ | $4.7\times10^{-11}$ | | |
| Hydrosulfuric acid ($H_2S$) | H—S̈—H | $9\times10^{-8}$ | $1\times10^{-17}$ | | |

*Red type indicates the ionizable protons.

Table 18.5 lists some common polyprotic acids and their $K_a$ values. (More are listed in Appendix C.) Note that the general pattern seen for $H_3PO_4$ occurs for all polyprotic acids:

$$K_{a1} >> K_{a2} >> K_{a3}$$

This trend occurs because it is more difficult for an $H^+$ ion to leave a singly charged anion (such as $H_2PO_4^-$) than to leave a neutral molecule (such as $H_3PO_4$), and more difficult still for it to leave a doubly charged anion (such as $HPO_4^{2-}$). Successive $K_a$ values typically differ by several orders of magnitude. This fact simplifies calculations because *we usually neglect the $H_3O^+$ coming from the subsequent dissociations.*

---

**Sample Problem 18.10** **Calculating Equilibrium Concentrations for a Polyprotic Acid**

**Problem** Ascorbic acid ($H_2C_6H_6O_6$; $H_2Asc$ for this problem), known as vitamin C, is a diprotic acid ($K_{a1} = 1.0\times10^{-5}$ and $K_{a2} = 5\times10^{-12}$) found in citrus fruit. Calculate [$HAsc^-$], [$Asc^{2-}$], and the pH of 0.050 $M$ $H_2Asc$.

**Plan** We know the initial concentration (0.050 $M$) and both $K_a$'s for $H_2Asc$, and we have to calculate the equilibrium concentrations of all species and convert [$H_3O^+$] to pH. We first write the equations and $K_a$ expressions. Because $K_{a1} >> K_{a2}$, we can assume that the first dissociation produces almost all the $H_3O^+$: [$H_3O^+$]$_{\text{from } H_2Asc}$ >> [$H_3O^+$]$_{\text{from } HAsc^-}$. Also, because $K_{a1}$ is small, the amount of $H_2Asc$ that dissociates can be neglected. We set up a reaction table for the first dissociation, with $x$ equal to [$H_2Asc$]$_{\text{dissoc}}$, and then we solve for [$H_3O^+$] and [$HAsc^-$]. Because the second dissociation occurs to a much lesser extent, we can substitute values from the first dissociation directly to find [$Asc^{2-}$] from the second.

**Solution** Writing the equations and $K_a$ expressions:

$$H_2Asc(aq) + H_2O(l) \rightleftharpoons HAsc^-(aq) + H_3O^+(aq)$$

$$K_{a1} = \frac{[HAsc^-][H_3O^+]}{[H_2Asc]} = 1.0\times10^{-5}$$

$$HAsc^-(aq) + H_2O(l) \rightleftharpoons Asc^{2-}(aq) + H_3O^+(aq)$$

$$K_{a2} = \frac{[Asc^{2-}][H_3O^+]}{[HAsc^-]} = 5 \times 10^{-12}$$

Setting up a reaction table with $x = [H_2Asc]_{dissoc} = [HAsc^-] \approx [H_3O^+]$:

| Concentration ($M$) | $H_2Asc(aq)$ | + $H_2O(l)$ | $\rightleftharpoons$ | $H_3O^+(aq)$ | + $HAsc^-(aq)$ |
|---|---|---|---|---|---|
| Initial | 0.050 | — | | 0 | 0 |
| Change | $-x$ | — | | $+x$ | $+x$ |
| Equilibrium | $0.050 - x$ | — | | $x$ | $x$ |

Making the assumptions:
1. Because $K_{a2} \ll K_{a1}$, $[H_3O^+]_{from\ HAsc^-} \ll [H_3O^+]_{from\ H_2Asc}$. Therefore,

$$[H_3O^+]_{from\ H_2Asc} \approx [H_3O^+]$$

2. Because $K_{a1}$ is small, $[H_2Asc]_{init} - x = [H_2Asc] \approx [H_2Asc]_{init}$. Thus,

$$[H_2Asc] = 0.050\ M - x \approx 0.050\ M$$

Substituting into the expression for $K_{a1}$ and solving for $x$:

$$K_{a1} = \frac{[H_3O^+][HAsc^-]}{[H_2Asc]} = 1.0 \times 10^{-5} = \frac{x^2}{0.050 - x} \approx \frac{x^2}{0.050}$$

$$x = [HAsc^-] \approx [H_3O^+] \approx \boxed{7.1 \times 10^{-4}\ M}$$

$$pH = -\log[H_3O^+] = -\log(7.1 \times 10^{-4}) = \boxed{3.15}$$

Checking the assumptions:

1. $[H_3O^+]_{from\ HAsc^-} \ll [H_3O^+]_{from\ H_2Asc}$: For any second dissociation that does occur,

$$[H_3O^+]_{from\ HAsc^-} \approx \sqrt{[HAsc^-](K_{a2})} = \sqrt{(7.1 \times 10^{-4})(5 \times 10^{-12})} = 6 \times 10^{-8}\ M$$

This is even less than $[H_3O^+]_{from\ H_2O}$, so the assumption is justified.

2. $[H_2Asc]_{dissoc} \ll [H_2Asc]_{init}$: $\dfrac{7.1 \times 10^{-4}\ M}{0.050\ M} \times 100 = 1.4\%$ ($<5\%$; assumption is justified).

Also, note that

$$\frac{[H_2Asc]_{init}}{K_{a1}} = \frac{0.050}{1.0 \times 10^{-5}} = 5000 > 400$$

Using the equilibrium concentrations from the first dissociation to calculate $[Asc^{2-}]$:

$$K_{a2} = \frac{[H_3O^+][Asc^{2-}]}{[HAsc^-]} \quad \text{and} \quad [Asc^{2-}] = \frac{(K_{a2})[HAsc^-]}{[H_3O^+]}$$

$$[Asc^{2-}] = \frac{(5 \times 10^{-12})(7.1 \times 10^{-4})}{7.1 \times 10^{-4}} = \boxed{5 \times 10^{-12}\ M}$$

**Check** $K_{a1} \gg K_{a2}$, so it makes sense that $[HAsc^-] \gg [Asc^{2-}]$ because $Asc^{2-}$ is produced only in the second (much weaker) dissociation. Both $K_a$'s are small, so all concentrations except $[H_2Asc]$ should be much lower than the original 0.050 $M$.

**Follow-Up Problem 18.10** Oxalic acid ($HOOC-COOH$, or $H_2C_2O_4$) is the simplest diprotic carboxylic acid. Its commercial uses include bleaching straw and leather and removing rust and ink stains. Calculate the equilibrium values of $[H_2C_2O_4]$, $[HC_2O_4^-]$, and $[C_2O_4^{2-}]$, and find the pH of a 0.150 $M$ $H_2C_2O_4$ solution. Use $K_a$ values from Appendix C. (*Hint:* First check whether you need the quadratic equation to find $x$.)

■ **Summary of Section 18.4**

- Two common types of weak-acid equilibrium problems involve finding $K_a$ from a given concentration and finding a concentration from a given $K_a$.
- We simplify the arithmetic by assuming (1) that $[H_3O^+]_{\text{from } H_2O}$ is much smaller than $[H_3O^+]_{\text{from HA}}$ and can be neglected and (2) that weak acids dissociate so little that $[HA]_{\text{init}} \approx [HA]$ at equilibrium.
- The *fraction* of weak acid molecules that dissociates is greater in a more dilute solution, even though the total $[H_3O^+]$ is lower.
- Polyprotic acids have more than one ionizable proton, but we assume that the first dissociation provides virtually all the $H_3O^+$.

# 18.5 • WEAK BASES AND THEIR RELATION TO WEAK ACIDS

The Brønsted-Lowry concept expands the definition of a base to encompass a host of species that the Arrhenius definition excludes: *to accept a proton, a base needs only a lone electron pair.*

Let's examine the equilibrium system of a weak base (B) as it dissolves in water: B accepts a proton from $H_2O$, which acts as an acid, leaving behind an $OH^-$ ion:

$$B(aq) + H_2O(l) \rightleftharpoons BH^+(aq) + OH^-(aq)$$

This general reaction for a base in water is described by the equilibrium expression

$$K_c = \frac{[BH^+][OH^-]}{[B][H_2O]}$$

Based on our earlier reasoning, we incorporate $[H_2O]$ in the value of $K_c$ and obtain the **base-dissociation constant** (or **base-ionization constant**), $K_b$:

$$K_b = \frac{[BH^+][OH^-]}{[B]} \qquad \text{(18.6)}$$

Despite the name "base-dissociation constant," *no base dissociates in the process.*

As in the relation between $pK_a$ and $K_a$, we know that a lower $pK_b$ indicates a higher $K_b$, that is, a stronger base. In aqueous solution, the two large classes of weak bases are (1) the molecules ammonia and the amines and (2) the anions of weak acids.

## Molecules as Weak Bases: Ammonia and the Amines

Ammonia is the simplest N-containing compound that acts as a weak base in water:

$$NH_3(aq) + H_2O(l) \rightleftharpoons NH_4^+(aq) + OH^-(aq) \qquad K_b = 1.76 \times 10^{-5} \text{ (at 25°C)}$$

Despite labels on reagent bottles that read "ammonium hydroxide," an aqueous solution of ammonia consists largely of water and *unprotonated* $NH_3$ molecules, as its small $K_b$ indicates. In a 1.0 $M$ $NH_3$ solution, for example, $[OH^-] = [NH_4^+] = 4.2 \times 10^{-3}$ $M$, so about 99.6% of the $NH_3$ is not protonated. Table 18.6 shows the $K_b$ values for a few molecular bases. (A more extensive list appears in Appendix C.)

If one or more of the H atoms in ammonia is replaced by an organic group (designated as R), an *amine* results: $RNH_2$, $R_2NH$, or $R_3N$ (Section 15.4; see Figure 15.17). The key structural feature of these organic compounds, as in all Brønsted-Lowry bases, is *a lone pair of electrons that can bind the proton donated by the acid.* Figure 18.9 depicts this process for methylamine, the simplest amine.

**Figure 18.9** Abstraction of a proton from water by the base methylamine.

Lone pair of N binds $H^+$.

$CH_3NH_2$
Methylamine

$H_2O$

$CH_3NH_3^+$
Methylammonium ion

$OH^-$

**Table 18.6** $K_b$ Values for Some Molecular (Amine) Bases at 25°C

| Name (Formula) | Lewis Structure* | $K_b$ | |
|---|---|---|---|
| Diethylamine [$(CH_3CH_2)_2NH$] | H—C—C—N—C—C—H (with H atoms) | $8.6 \times 10^{-4}$ | **BASE STRENGTH** ↑ |
| Dimethylamine [$(CH_3)_2NH$] | H—C—N—C—H (with H atoms) | $5.9 \times 10^{-4}$ | |
| Methylamine ($CH_3NH_2$) | H—C—N—H (with H atoms) | $4.4 \times 10^{-4}$ | |
| Ammonia ($NH_3$) | H—N—H (with H) | $1.76 \times 10^{-5}$ | |
| Pyridine ($C_5H_5N$) | (ring) N: | $1.7 \times 10^{-9}$ | |
| Aniline ($C_6H_5NH_2$) | (ring) N—H (with H) | $4.0 \times 10^{-10}$ | |

*Blue type indicates the basic nitrogen and its lone pair.

To find the pH of a solution of a molecular weak base, we use an approach very similar to that for a weak acid: write the equilibrium expression, set up a reaction table to find [B]$_{reacting}$, make the usual assumptions, and then solve for [OH$^-$]. The only additional step is to convert [OH$^-$] to [H$_3$O$^+$] in order to calculate pH.

## Sample Problem 18.11   Determining pH from $K_b$ and Initial [B]

**Problem** Dimethylamine, $(CH_3)_2NH$ (*see margin*), a key intermediate in detergent manufacture, has a $K_b$ of $5.9 \times 10^{-4}$. What is the pH of 1.5 $M$ $(CH_3)_2NH$?

**Plan** We know the initial concentration (1.5 $M$) and $K_b$ ($5.9 \times 10^{-4}$) of $(CH_3)_2NH$ and have to find the pH. The amine reacts with water to form OH$^-$, so we have to find [OH$^-$] and then calculate [H$_3$O$^+$] and pH. We first write the balanced equation and $K_b$ expression. Because $K_b \gg K_w$, the [OH$^-$] from the autoionization of water is negligible, so we disregard it and assume that all the [OH$^-$] comes from the base reacting with water. Because $K_b$ is small, we assume that the amount of amine reacting, $[(CH_3)_2NH]_{reacting}$, can be neglected. We set up a reaction table, make the assumption, and solve for $x$. Then we check the assumption and convert [OH$^-$] to [H$_3$O$^+$] using $K_w$; finally, we calculate pH.

Dimethylamine

**Solution** Writing the balanced equation and $K_b$ expression:

$$(CH_3)_2NH(aq) + H_2O(l) \rightleftharpoons (CH_3)_2NH_2^+(aq) + OH^-(aq)$$

$$K_b = \frac{[(CH_3)_2NH_2^+][OH^-]}{[(CH_3)_2NH]}$$

Setting up the reaction table, with $x = [(CH_3)_2NH]_{reacting} = [(CH_3)_2NH_2^+] = [OH^-]$:

| Concentration (M) | $(CH_3)_2NH(aq)$ + | $H_2O(l)$ ⇌ | $(CH_3)_2NH_2^+(aq)$ + | $OH^-(aq)$ |
|---|---|---|---|---|
| Initial | 1.5 | — | 0 | 0 |
| Change | $-x$ | — | $+x$ | $+x$ |
| Equilibrium | $1.5 - x$ | — | $x$ | $x$ |

Making the assumption:

$K_b$ is small, so $[(CH_3)_2NH]_{init} - [(CH_3)_2NH]_{reacting} = [(CH_3)_2NH] \approx [(CH_3)_2NH]_{init}$; thus, $1.5\ M - x \approx 1.5\ M$.

Substituting into the $K_b$ expression and solving for $x$:

$$K_b = \frac{[(CH_3)_2NH_2^+][OH^-]}{[(CH_3)_2NH]} = 5.9 \times 10^{-4} \approx \frac{x^2}{1.5}$$

$$x = [OH^-] \approx 3.0 \times 10^{-2}\ M$$

Checking the assumption:

$$\frac{3.0 \times 10^{-2}\ M}{1.5\ M} \times 100 = 2.0\%\ (<5\%;\ \text{assumption is justified})$$

Note that the Comment in Sample Problem 18.8 applies in these cases as well:

$$\frac{[B]_{init}}{K_b} = \frac{1.5}{5.9 \times 10^{-4}} = 2.5 \times 10^3 > 400$$

Calculating pH:

$$[H_3O^+] = \frac{K_w}{[OH^-]} = \frac{1.0 \times 10^{-14}}{3.0 \times 10^{-2}} = 3.3 \times 10^{-13}\ M$$

$$pH = -\log(3.3 \times 10^{-13}) = \boxed{12.48}$$

**Check** The value of $x$ seems reasonable: $\sqrt{(\sim 6 \times 10^{-4})(1.5)} = \sqrt{9 \times 10^{-4}} = 3 \times 10^{-2}$. Because $(CH_3)_2NH$ is a weak base, the pH should be several pH units above 7.

Pyridine

**Follow-Up Problem 18.11** Pyridine ($C_5H_5N$, *see margin*) serves as a solvent *and* base in many organic syntheses. It has a p$K_b$ of 8.77. What is the pH of 0.10 $M$ pyridine?

## Anions of Weak Acids as Weak Bases

The other large group of Brønsted-Lowry bases consists of anions of weak acids:*

$$A^-(aq) + H_2O(l) \rightleftharpoons HA(aq) + OH^-(aq) \qquad K_b = \frac{[HA][OH^-]}{[A^-]}$$

For example, $F^-$, the anion of the weak acid HF, is a weak base:

$$F^-(aq) + H_2O(l) \rightleftharpoons HF(aq) + OH^-(aq) \qquad K_b = \frac{[HF][OH^-]}{[F^-]}$$

Why is a solution of HA acidic and a solution of $A^-$ basic? We'll find the answer from relative concentrations of species in 1 $M$ HF and in 1 $M$ NaF:

1. *The acidity of HA(aq).* HF is a weak acid, so the equilibrium position of the acid dissolving in water lies far to the left:

$$HF(aq) + H_2O(l) \overset{\longleftarrow}{\rightleftharpoons} H_3O^+(aq) + F^-(aq)$$

Water also contributes $H_3O^+$ and $OH^-$, but their concentrations are extremely small:

$$2H_2O(l) \overset{\longleftarrow}{\rightleftharpoons} H_3O^+(aq) + OH^-(aq)$$

Of all the species present—HF, $H_2O$, $H_3O^+$, $F^-$, and $OH^-$—the two that can influence the acidity of the solution are $H_3O^+$, predominantly from HF, and $OH^-$ from water. Thus, the HF solution is acidic because $[H_3O^+]_{\text{from HF}} >> [OH^-]_{\text{from } H_2O}$.

2. *The basicity of $A^-(aq)$.* Now, consider the species present in 1 $M$ NaF. The salt dissociates completely to yield 1 $M$ $Na^+$ and 1 $M$ $F^-$. The $Na^+$ behaves as a spectator ion, while some $F^-$ reacts as a weak base to produce small amounts of HF and $OH^-$:

$$F^-(aq) + H_2O(l) \overset{\longleftarrow}{\rightleftharpoons} HF(aq) + OH^-(aq)$$

---

*This equation and equilibrium expression are sometimes referred to as a *hydrolysis reaction* and a *hydrolysis constant*, $K_h$, because water is dissociated (hydrolyzed). Actually, except for the charge on the base, this process is the same as the proton-abstraction process by ammonia and amines. That is, $K_h$ is just another symbol for $K_b$, so we'll use $K_b$ throughout.

As before, water dissociation contributes minute amounts of $H_3O^+$ and $OH^-$. Thus, in addition to the $Na^+$ ion, the species present are the same as in the HF solution: HF, $H_2O$, $H_3O^+$, $F^-$, and $OH^-$. The two species that affect the acidity are $OH^-$, predominantly from $F^-$ reacting with water, and $H_3O^+$ from water. In this case, $[OH^-]_{from\ F^-} >> [H_3O^+]_{from\ H_2O}$, so the solution is basic.

To summarize,

- In an HA solution, $[HA] >> [A^-]$ and $[H_3O^+]_{from\ HA} >> [OH^-]_{from\ H_2O}$, so the solution is acidic.
- In an $A^-$ solution, $[A^-] >> [HA]$ and $[OH^-]_{from\ A^-} >> [H_3O^+]_{from\ H_2O}$, so the solution is basic.

## The Relation Between $K_a$ and $K_b$ of a Conjugate Acid-Base Pair

A key relationship exists between the $K_a$ of HA and the $K_b$ of $A^-$, which we can see by writing the two reactions as a reaction sequence and adding them:

$$\begin{aligned} \cancel{HA} + H_2O &\rightleftharpoons H_3O^+ + \cancel{A^-} \\ \cancel{A^-} + H_2O &\rightleftharpoons \cancel{HA} + OH^- \\ \hline 2H_2O &\rightleftharpoons H_3O^+ + OH^- \end{aligned}$$

*The sum of the two dissociation reactions is the autoionization of water.* Recall from Chapter 17 that, for a reaction that is the *sum* of two or more reactions, the overall equilibrium constant is the *product* of the individual equilibrium constants. Therefore, writing the equilibrium expressions for each reaction gives

$$\frac{[H_3O^+][\cancel{A^-}]}{[\cancel{HA}]} \times \frac{[\cancel{HA}][OH^-]}{[\cancel{A^-}]} = [H_3O^+][OH^-]$$

or
$$K_a \quad \times \quad K_b \quad = \quad K_w \tag{18.7}$$

This relationship allows us to find $K_a$ of the acid in a conjugate pair given $K_b$ of the base, and vice versa. Reference tables typically have $K_a$ and $K_b$ values for *molecular species only*. The $K_b$ for $F^-$ and the $K_a$ for $CH_3NH_3^+$, for example, do not appear in standard tables, but you can calculate them by looking up the value for the molecular conjugate species and relating it to $K_w$. To find the $K_b$ value for $F^-$, for instance, we look up the $K_a$ value for HF and apply Equation 18.7:

$$K_a \text{ of HF} = 6.8 \times 10^{-4} \text{ (from Appendix C)}$$

So, we have
$$K_a \text{ of HF} \times K_b \text{ of F}^- = K_w$$

or
$$K_b \text{ of F}^- = \frac{K_w}{K_a \text{ of HF}} = \frac{1.0 \times 10^{-14}}{6.8 \times 10^{-4}} = 1.5 \times 10^{-11}$$

---

**Sample Problem 18.12**    **Determining the pH of a Solution of A⁻**

**Problem** Sodium acetate ($CH_3COONa$, or NaAc for this problem) is used in textile dyeing. What is the pH of 0.25 $M$ NaAc at 25°C? $K_a$ of acetic acid (HAc) is $1.8 \times 10^{-5}$.

**Plan** We know the initial concentration of $Ac^-$ (0.25 $M$) and the $K_a$ of HAc ($1.8 \times 10^{-5}$), and we have to find the pH of the $Ac^-$ solution, which acts as a base in water. We write the base dissociation equation and $K_b$ expression. If we can find $[OH^-]$, we can use $K_w$ to find $[H_3O^+]$ and convert it to pH. To solve for $[OH^-]$, we need the $K_b$ of $Ac^-$, which we obtain from the $K_a$ of HAc by applying Equation 18.7. We set up a reaction table to find $[OH^-]$ and make the usual assumption that $K_b$ is small, so $[Ac^-]_{init} \approx [Ac^-]$.

**Solution** Writing the base dissociation equation and $K_b$ expression:

$$Ac^-(aq) + H_2O(l) \rightleftharpoons HAc(aq) + OH^-(aq) \qquad K_b = \frac{[HAc][OH^-]}{[Ac^-]}$$

Setting up the reaction table, with $x = [Ac^-]_{reacting} = [HAc] = [OH^-]$:

| Concentration ($M$) | Ac$^-$(aq) | + | H$_2$O(l) | ⇌ | HAc(aq) | + | OH$^-$(aq) |
|---|---|---|---|---|---|---|---|
| Initial | 0.25 | | — | | 0 | | 0 |
| Change | $-x$ | | — | | $+x$ | | $+x$ |
| Equilibrium | $0.25 - x$ | | — | | $x$ | | $x$ |

Solving for $K_b$ of Ac$^-$:

$$K_b = \frac{K_w}{K_a} = \frac{1.0 \times 10^{-14}}{1.8 \times 10^{-5}} = 5.6 \times 10^{-10}$$

Making the assumption: Because $K_b$ is small, $0.25\ M - x \approx 0.25\ M$.
Substituting into the expression for $K_b$ and solving for $x$:

$$K_b = \frac{[HAc][OH^-]}{[Ac^-]} = 5.6 \times 10^{-10} \approx \frac{x^2}{0.25} \qquad x = [OH^-] \approx 1.2 \times 10^{-5}\ M$$

Checking the assumption:

$$\frac{1.2 \times 10^{-5}\ M}{0.25\ M} \times 100 = 4.8 \times 10^{-3}\%\ (<5\%;\ \text{assumption is justified})$$

Also note that

$$\frac{0.25}{5.6 \times 10^{-10}} = 4.5 \times 10^8 > 400$$

Solving for pH:

$$[H_3O^+] = \frac{K_w}{[OH^-]} = \frac{1.0 \times 10^{-14}}{1.2 \times 10^{-5}} = 8.3 \times 10^{-10}\ M$$

$$pH = -\log(8.3 \times 10^{-10}) = \boxed{9.08}$$

**Check** The $K_b$ calculation seems reasonable: $\sim 10 \times 10^{-15}/2 \times 10^{-5} = 5 \times 10^{-10}$. Because Ac$^-$ is a weak base, $[OH^-] > [H_3O^+]$; thus, pH > 7, which makes sense.

**Follow-Up Problem 18.12** Sodium hypochlorite (NaClO) is the active ingredient in household laundry bleach. What is the pH of 0.20 $M$ NaClO?

## Summary of Section 18.5

- The extent to which a weak base accepts a proton from water to form OH$^-$ is expressed by a base-dissociation constant, $K_b$.
- Brønsted-Lowry bases include NH$_3$ and amines and the anions of weak acids. All produce basic solutions by accepting H$^+$ from water, which yields OH$^-$, thus making $[H_3O^+] < [OH^-]$.
- A solution of HA is acidic because [HA] >> [A$^-$], so $[H_3O^+] > [OH^-]$. A solution of A$^-$ is basic because [A$^-$] >> [HA], so $[OH^-] > [H_3O^+]$.
- By multiplying the expressions for $K_a$ of HA and $K_b$ of A$^-$, we obtain $K_w$. This relationship allows us to calculate either $K_a$ of BH$^+$ or $K_b$ of A$^-$.

# 18.6 • MOLECULAR PROPERTIES AND ACID STRENGTH

The strength of an acid depends on its ability to donate a proton, which depends in turn on the strength of the bond to the acidic proton. In this section, we apply trends in atomic and bond properties to determine the trends in acid strength of nonmetal hydrides and oxoacids and then discuss the acidity of hydrated metal ions.

## Acid Strength of Nonmetal Hydrides

Two factors determine how easily a proton is released from a nonmetal hydride:

- The electronegativity of the central nonmetal (E)
- The strength of the E—H bond

Figure 18.10 displays two periodic trends among the nonmetal hydrides:

1. *Across a period, acid strength increases.* The electronegativity of the nonmetal E determines the trend. From left to right, as E becomes more electronegative, it withdraws electron density from H, and the E—H bond becomes more polar. As a result, $H^+$ is pulled away more easily by an O atom of a water molecule. In aqueous solution, the hydrides of Groups 3A(13) to 5A(15) do not behave as acids, but an increase in acid strength is seen from Group 6A(16) to 7A(17).

2. *Down a group, acid strength increases.* E—H bond strength determines the trend. As E becomes larger, the E—H bond becomes longer and weaker, so $H^+$ comes off more easily.* For example, the hydrohalic acid strength increases down the group:

$$HF \ll HCl < HBr < HI$$

(This trend is not seen in aqueous solution, where HCl, HBr, and HI are all equally strong; we discuss how it *is* observed in Section 18.8.)

## Acid Strength of Oxoacids

*All oxoacids have the acidic H atom bonded to an O atom,* so bond length is not involved. Two other factors determine the acid strength of oxoacids (Section 14.8):

- The electronegativity of the central nonmetal (E)
- The number of O atoms around E (O.N. of E)

Figure 18.11 summarizes these trends:

1. *For oxoacids with the **same** number of O atoms, acid strength increases with the electronegativity of E.* Consider the hypohalous acids (HOE, where E is a halogen atom). The more electronegative E is, the more polar the O—H bond becomes and the more easily $H^+$ is lost (Figure 18.11A). Electronegativity decreases down a group, as does acid strength:

$K_a$ of HOCl $= 2.9 \times 10^{-8}$     $K_a$ of HOBr $= 2.3 \times 10^{-9}$     $K_a$ of HOI $= 2.3 \times 10^{-11}$

Similarly, in Group 6A(16), $H_2SO_4$ is stronger than $H_2SeO_4$; in Group 5A(15), $H_3PO_4$ is stronger than $H_3AsO_4$, and so forth.

**Figure 18.10** The effect of atomic and molecular properties on nonmetal hydride acidity.

**Figure 18.11** The relative strengths of oxoacids. **A,** Cl withdraws electron density (thickness of green arrow) from the O—H bond most effectively, making that bond most polar (relative size of δ symbols). **B,** Additional O atoms pull more electron density from the O—H bond.

2. *For oxoacids with **different** numbers of O atoms, acid strength increases with number of O atoms (or O.N. of central nonmetal).* The electronegative O atoms pull electron density away from E, which makes the O—H bond more polar. The more O atoms present, the greater the shift in electron density, and the more easily the $H^+$ ion comes off (Figure 18.11B). Therefore, the chlorine oxoacids ($HOClO_n$, with *n* from 0 to 3) increase in strength with the number of O atoms (and O.N. of Cl):

$K_a$ of HOCl $= 2.9 \times 10^{-8}$     $K_a$ of HOClO $= 1.12 \times 10^{-2}$     $K_a$ of HOClO$_2 \approx 1$     $K_a$ of HOClO$_3 > 10^7$

Similarly, $HNO_3$ is stronger than $HNO_2$, $H_2SO_4$ is stronger than $H_2SO_3$, and so forth.

*Actually, bond energy refers to bond breakage that forms an H atom, whereas acidity refers to bond breakage that forms an $H^+$ ion. Although these two types of bond breakage are not the same, the trends in bond energy and acid strength are opposite each other.

## Acidity of Hydrated Metal Ions

The aqueous solutions of certain metal ions are acidic because the *hydrated* metal ion transfers an $H^+$ ion to water. Consider a general metal nitrate, $M(NO_3)_n$, as it dissolves in water. The ions separate and the metal ion becomes bonded to some number of $H_2O$ molecules. This equation shows the hydration of the cation ($M^{n+}$) with $H_2O$ molecules and ($aq$); hydration of the anion ($NO_3^-$) is indicated by just ($aq$):

$$M(NO_3)_n(s) + xH_2O(l) \longrightarrow M(H_2O)_x^{n+}(aq) + nNO_3^-(aq)$$

If the metal ion, $M^{n+}$, is *small and highly charged*, its high charge density withdraws sufficient electron density from the O—H bonds of the bound water molecules for an $H^+$ to be released. Thus, the hydrated cation, $M(H_2O)_x^{n+}$, is a typical Brønsted-Lowry acid. The bound $H_2O$ that releases the $H^+$ becomes a bound $OH^-$ ion:

$$M(H_2O)_x^{n+}(aq) + H_2O(l) \rightleftharpoons M(H_2O)_{x-1}OH^{(n-1)+}(aq) + H_3O^+(aq)$$

Salts of most $M^{2+}$ and $M^{3+}$ ions yield acidic aqueous solutions. The $K_a$ values for some acidic hydrated metal ions appear in Appendix C.

Consider the small, highly charged $Al^{3+}$ ion. When an aluminum salt, such as $Al(NO_3)_3$, dissolves in water, the following steps occur:

$$Al(NO_3)_3(s) + 6H_2O(l) \longrightarrow Al(H_2O)_6^{3+}(aq) + 3NO_3^-(aq)$$
$$[\text{dissolution and hydration}]$$

$$Al(H_2O)_6^{3+}(aq) + H_2O(l) \rightleftharpoons Al(H_2O)_5OH^{2+}(aq) + H_3O^+(aq)$$
$$[\text{dissociation of weak acid}]$$

Note the formulas of the hydrated metal ions in the last step. When $H^+$ is released, the number of bound $H_2O$ molecules decreases by 1 (from 6 to 5) and the number of bound $OH^-$ ions increases by 1 (from 0 to 1), which reduces the ion's positive charge by 1 (from 3 to 2) (Figure 18.12). This pattern of changes in the formula of the hydrated metal ion before and after it loses a proton appears for any highly charged metal ion in water.

**Figure 18.12 The acidic behavior of the hydrated Al³⁺ ion.** The hydrated Al³⁺ ion is small and multiply charged and pulls electron density from the O—H bonds, so an H⁺ ion can be transferred to a nearby water molecule.

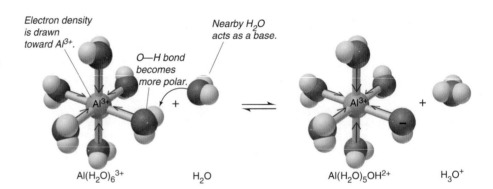

## ▌ Summary of Section 18.6

- For nonmetal hydrides, acid strength increases across a period, with the electronegativity of the nonmetal (E), and down a group, with the length of the E—H bond.
- For oxoacids with the same number of O atoms, acid strength increases with electronegativity of E; for oxoacids with the same E, acid strength increases with number of O atoms (or O.N. of E).
- Small, highly charged metal ions are acidic in water because they withdraw electron density from the O—H bonds of bound $H_2O$ molecules, releasing an $H^+$ ion to the solution.

# 18.7 • ACID-BASE PROPERTIES OF SALT SOLUTIONS

In many cases, when a salt dissolves, one or both of its ions may react with water and affect the pH of the solution. You've seen that cations of weak bases (such as $NH_4^+$) are acidic, anions of weak acids (such as $CN^-$) are basic, and small, highly charged metal cations (such as $Al^{3+}$) are acidic. In addition, certain ions (such as $H_2PO_4^-$ and $HCO_3^-$) can act as an acid or a base. In this section, we classify the acid-base behavior of the various types of salt solutions.

## Salts That Yield Neutral Solutions

*A salt consisting of the anion of a strong acid and the cation of a strong base yields a neutral solution because the ions do not react with water.* When a strong acid such as $HNO_3$ dissolves, the reaction goes essentially to completion because *the anion of a strong acid is a much weaker base than water.* The anion is hydrated, but *it does not react with water:*

$$HNO_3(l) + H_2O(l) \longrightarrow NO_3^-(aq) + H_3O^+(aq) \qquad \text{[dissolution and hydration]}$$

Similarly, a strong base, such as NaOH, dissolves completely. The cation, in this case $Na^+$, is hydrated, but *it is not small and charged enough to react with water:*

$$NaOH(s) \xrightarrow{H_2O} Na^+(aq) + OH^-(aq) \qquad \text{[dissolution and hydration]}$$

The anions of strong acids are the halide ions (except $F^-$) and ions of strong oxoacids, such as $NO_3^-$ and $ClO_4^-$. The cations of strong bases are Group 1A(1) and $Ca^{2+}$, $Sr^{2+}$, and $Ba^{2+}$ Group 2A(2). *Salts containing only these ions yield neutral solutions.*

## Salts That Yield Acidic Solutions

There are two types of these salts:

1. *A salt consisting of the cation of a weak base and the anion of a strong acid yields an acidic solution because the cation acts as a weak acid,* and the anion does not react. For example, $NH_4Cl$ yields an acidic solution because $NH_4^+$, the cation of the weak base $NH_3$, is a weak acid; $Cl^-$, the anion of the strong HCl, does not react:

$$NH_4Cl(s) \xrightarrow{H_2O} NH_4^+(aq) + Cl^-(aq) \qquad \text{[dissolution and hydration]}$$
$$NH_4^+(aq) + H_2O(l) \rightleftharpoons NH_3(aq) + H_3O^+(aq) \qquad \text{[dissociation of weak acid]}$$

2. *A salt consisting of a small, highly charged metal cation and the anion of a strong acid yields an acidic solution because the cation acts as a weak acid,* and the anion does not react. For example, $Fe(NO_3)_3$ yields an acidic solution because the hydrated $Fe^{3+}$ ion is a weak acid; $NO_3^-$, the anion of the strong $HNO_3$, does not react:

$$Fe(NO_3)_3(s) + 6H_2O(l) \xrightarrow{H_2O} Fe(H_2O)_6^{3+}(aq) + 3NO_3^-(aq) \quad \text{[dissolution and hydration]}$$
$$Fe(H_2O)_6^{3+}(aq) + H_2O(l) \rightleftharpoons Fe(H_2O)_5OH^{2+}(aq) + H_3O^+(aq)$$
$$\text{[dissociation of weak acid]}$$

## Salts That Yield Basic Solutions

*A salt consisting of the anion of a weak acid and the cation of a strong base yields a basic solution because the anion acts as a weak base,* and the cation does not react. Sodium acetate, for example, yields a basic solution because the $CH_3COO^-$ ion, the anion of the weak acid $CH_3COOH$, acts as a weak base; $Na^+$, the cation of the strong base NaOH, does not react:

$$CH_3COONa(s) \xrightarrow{H_2O} Na^+(aq) + CH_3COO^-(aq) \qquad \text{[dissolution and hydration]}$$
$$CH_3COO^-(aq) + H_2O(l) \rightleftharpoons CH_3COOH(aq) + OH^-(aq) \qquad \text{[reaction of weak base]}$$

**Sample Problem 18.13** | **Predicting Relative Acidity of Salt Solutions from Reactions of the Ions with Water**

**Problem** Predict whether aqueous solutions of the following salts are acidic, basic, or neutral, and write an equation for the reaction of any ion with water:
**(a)** Potassium perchlorate, $KClO_4$     **(b)** Sodium benzoate, $C_6H_5COONa$
**(c)** Chromium(III) nitrate, $Cr(NO_3)_3$

**Plan** The formula shows the cation and anion. Depending on an ion's ability to react with water, the solution will be neutral (strong-acid anion and strong-base cation), acidic (weak-base cation or highly charged metal cation with strong-acid anion), or basic (weak-acid anion and strong-base cation).

**Solution** **(a)** Neutral. The ions are $K^+$ and $ClO_4^-$. The $K^+$ is from the strong base KOH, and the $ClO_4^-$ is from the strong acid $HClO_4$. Neither ion reacts with water.
**(b)** Basic. The ions are $Na^+$ and $C_6H_5COO^-$. The $Na^+$ is the cation of the strong base NaOH, so it does not react with water. The benzoate ion, $C_6H_5COO^-$, is the anion of the weak acid benzoic acid, so it reacts with water to produce $OH^-$ ion:

$$C_6H_5COO^-(aq) + H_2O(l) \rightleftharpoons C_6H_5COOH(aq) + OH^-(aq)$$

**(c)** Acidic. The ions are $Cr^{3+}$ and $NO_3^-$. The $NO_3^-$ is the anion of the strong acid $HNO_3$, so it does not react with water. $Cr^{3+}$ is a small and highly charged, so the hydrated ion, $Cr(H_2O)_6^{3+}$, reacts with water to produce $H_3O^+$:

$$Cr(H_2O)_6^{3+}(aq) + H_2O(l) \rightleftharpoons Cr(H_2O)_5OH^{2+}(aq) + H_3O^+(aq)$$

**Follow-Up Problem 18.13**  Write equations to predict whether solutions of the following salts are acidic, basic, or neutral: **(a)** $KClO_2$; **(b)** $CH_3NH_3NO_3$; **(c)** CsI.

## Salts of Weakly Acidic Cations and Weakly Basic Anions

If a salt consists of a cation that is a weak acid *and* an anion that is a weak base, the overall acidity of the solution depends on the relative acid strength ($K_a$) or base strength ($K_b$) of the separated ions. Consider a solution of ammonium cyanide, $NH_4CN$, and the reactions that occur between the separated ions and water. Ammonium ion is the conjugate acid of a weak base, so it is a weak acid:

$$NH_4^+(aq) + H_2O(l) \rightleftharpoons NH_3(aq) + H_3O^+(aq)$$

Cyanide ion is the anion of a weak acid, so it is a weak base:

$$CN^-(aq) + H_2O(l) \rightleftharpoons HCN(aq) + OH^-(aq)$$

The reaction that goes farther to the right determines the pH of the solution, so we compare the $K_a$ of $NH_4^+$ with the $K_b$ of $CN^-$. Only molecular compounds are listed in $K_a$ and $K_b$ tables, so we calculate these values for the ions with Equation 18.7:

$$K_a \text{ of } NH_4^+ = \frac{K_w}{K_b \text{ of } NH_3} = \frac{1.0 \times 10^{-14}}{1.76 \times 10^{-5}} = 5.7 \times 10^{-10}$$

$$K_b \text{ of } CN^- = \frac{K_w}{K_a \text{ of } HCN} = \frac{1.0 \times 10^{-14}}{6.2 \times 10^{-10}} = 1.6 \times 10^{-5}$$

Because $K_b$ of $CN^- > K_a$ of $NH_4^+$, we know that $CN^-$ is a stronger base than $NH_4^+$ is an acid. Thus, $NH_4CN$ solution is basic.

## Salts of Amphiprotic Anions

The only salts left to consider are those in which the the cation comes from a strong base and the anion comes from a polyprotic acid with one or more ionizable protons still attached. These anions are amphiprotic—they can act as an acid and release a proton *to* water or as a base and abstract a proton *from* water. As in the previous case, to determine the overall acidity of their solutions, we compare the magnitudes of $K_a$ and $K_b$, but here, we compare both the $K_a$ and $K_b$ of the same species, the anion.

For example, $Na_2HPO_4$ consists of $Na^+$, the cation of a strong base, which does not react with water, and $HPO_4^{2-}$, the second anion of the weak polyprotic acid $H_3PO_4$. In water, the salt undergoes three steps:

1.        $Na_2HPO_4(s) \xrightarrow{H_2O} 2Na^+(aq) + HPO_4^{2-}(aq)$        [dissolution and hydration]

2.   $HPO_4^{2-}(aq) + H_2O(l) \rightleftharpoons PO_4^{3-}(aq) + H_3O^+(aq)$        [acting as a weak acid]

3.   $HPO_4^{2-}(aq) + H_2O(l) \rightleftharpoons H_2PO_4^-(aq) + OH^-(aq)$        [acting as a weak base]

We must decide whether step 2 or step 3 goes farther to the right. Appendix C lists the $K_a$ of $HPO_4^{2-}$ as $4.2\times10^{-13}$, but the $K_b$ of $HPO_4^{2-}$ is not given, so we find it with Equation 18.7:

$$K_b \text{ of } HPO_4^{2-} = \frac{K_w}{K_a \text{ of } H_2PO_4^-} \quad \text{or} \quad \frac{1.0\times10^{-14}}{6.3\times10^{-8}} = 1.6\times10^{-7}$$

Because $K_b$ ($1.6\times10^{-7}$) > $K_a$ ($4.2\times10^{-13}$), $HPO_4^{2-}$ is stronger as a base than as an acid, so a solution of $Na_2HPO_4$ is basic.

Table 18.7 displays the acid-base behavior of the various types of salts in water.

## Table 18.7  The Acid-Base Behavior of Salts in Water

| Relative Acidity: Examples | pH | Nature of Ions | Ion That Reacts with Water: Examples |
|---|---|---|---|
| Neutral: NaCl, KBr, $Ba(NO_3)_2$ | 7.0 | Cation of strong base Anion of strong acid | None |
| Acidic: $NH_4Cl$, $NH_4NO_3$, $CH_3NH_3Br$ | <7.0 | Cation of weak base Anion of strong acid | Cation: $NH_4^+ + H_2O \rightleftharpoons NH_3 + H_3O^+$ |
| Acidic: $Al(NO_3)_3$, $CrBr_3$, $FeCl_3$ | <7.0 | Small, highly charged cation Anion of strong acid | Cation: $Al(H_2O)_6^{3+} + H_2O \rightleftharpoons Al(H_2O)_5OH^{2+} + H_3O^+$ |
| Acidic/Basic: $NH_4ClO_2$, $NH_4CN$, $Pb(CH_3COO)_2$ | <7.0 if $K_{a(cation)} > K_{b(anion)}$ >7.0 if $K_{b(anion)} > K_{a(cation)}$ | Cation of weak base (or small, highly charged cation) Anion of weak acid | Cation *and* anion: $CH_3NH_3^+ + H_2O \rightleftharpoons CH_3NH_2 + H_3O^+$ $F^- + H_2O \rightleftharpoons HF + OH^-$ |
| Acidic/Basic: $NaH_2PO_4$, $KHCO_3$, $NaHSO_3$ | <7.0 if $K_{a(anion)} > K_{b(anion)}$ >7.0 if $K_{b(anion)} > K_{a(anion)}$ | Cation of strong base Anion of polyprotic acid | Anion: $HSO_3^- + H_2O \rightleftharpoons SO_3^{2-} + H_3O^+$ $HSO_3^- + H_2O \rightleftharpoons H_2SO_3 + OH^-$ |

## Sample Problem 18.14  Predicting the Relative Acidity of a Salt Solution from $K_a$ and $K_b$ of the Ions

**Problem** Determine whether an aqueous solution of zinc formate, $Zn(HCOO)_2$, at 25°C is acidic, basic, or neutral.

**Plan** The formula consists of the small, highly charged, and therefore weakly acidic, $Zn^{2+}$ cation and the weakly basic $HCOO^-$ anion of the weak acid HCOOH. To determine the relative acidity of the solution, we write equations that show the reactions of the ions with water, and then find $K_a$ of $Zn^{2+}$ (from Appendix C) and calculate $K_b$ of $HCOO^-$ (from $K_a$ of HCOOH in Appendix C) to see which ion reacts with water to a greater extent.

**Solution** Writing the reactions with water:

$$Zn(H_2O)_6^{2+}(aq) + H_2O(l) \rightleftharpoons Zn(H_2O)_5OH^+(aq) + H_3O^+(aq)$$
$$HCOO^-(aq) + H_2O(l) \rightleftharpoons HCOOH(aq) + OH^-(aq)$$

Obtaining $K_a$ and $K_b$ of the ions: From Appendix C, the $K_a$ of $Zn(H_2O)_6^{2+}(aq)$ is $1\times10^{-9}$. We obtain $K_a$ of HCOOH and solve for $K_b$ of HCOO$^-$:

$$K_b \text{ of } HCOO^- = \frac{K_w}{K_a \text{ of } HCOOH} = \frac{1.0\times10^{-14}}{1.8\times10^{-4}} = 5.6\times10^{-11}$$

$K_a$ of $Zn(H_2O)_6^{2+} > K_b$ of HCOO$^-$, so the solution is acidic.

**Follow-Up Problem 18.14**  Determine whether solutions of the following salts are acidic, basic, or neutral at 25°C: **(a)** $Cu(CH_3COO)_2$; **(b)** $NH_4F$; **(c)** $KHSO_3$.

## ▪ Summary of Section 18.7

- Salts that yield a neutral solution consist of ions that do not react with water.
- Salts that yield an acidic solution contain an unreactive anion and a cation that releases a proton to water.
- Salts that yield a basic solution contain an unreactive cation and an anion that accepts a proton from water.
- If both cation and anion react with water, the ion that reacts to the greater extent (higher $K$) determines the acidity or basicity of the salt solution.
- If the anion is amphiprotic (from a polyprotic acid), the strength of the anion as an acid ($K_a$) or as a base ($K_b$) determines the acidity of the salt.

## 18.8 • GENERALIZING THE BRØNSTED-LOWRY CONCEPT: THE LEVELING EFFECT

In general, *an acid yields the cation and a base yields the anion of solvent autoionization.* For example, in $H_2O$, all Brønsted-Lowry acids yield $H_3O^+$ and all Brønsted-Lowry bases yield OH$^-$, which are the ions that form when water autoionizes.

This idea lets us examine a key question: Why are all strong acids and strong bases *equally* strong in water? The answer is that *in water, the strongest acid possible is $H_3O^+$ and the strongest base possible is OH$^-$:*

- *For strong acids.* The moment we put gaseous HCl in water, it reacts with the base $H_2O$ to form $H_3O^+$. The same holds for any strong acid because it dissociates *completely* to form $H_3O^+$. Thus, we are actually observing the acid strength of $H_3O^+$.
- *For strong bases.* A strong base, such as $Ba(OH)_2$, dissociates completely in water to yield OH$^-$. Even strong bases that do not contain hydroxide ions in the solid, such as $K_2O$, do so. The oxide ion, which is a stronger base than OH$^-$, immediately takes a proton from water to form OH$^-$:

$$O^{2-}(aq) + H_2O(l) \longrightarrow 2OH^-(aq)$$

Thus, water exerts a **leveling effect** on any strong acid or base by reacting with it to form the products of water's autoionization. Acting as a base, water levels the strength of all strong acids by making them appear equally strong, and acting as an acid, it levels the strength of all strong bases.

Therefore, to rank the relative strengths of strong acids, we must dissolve them in a solvent that is a *weaker* base than water, so it accepts their protons less readily. For example, the hydrohalic acids increase in strength as the halogen becomes larger, as a result of the longer, weaker H—X bond (see Figure 18.10). But, in water, HF is weak, and HCl, HBr, and HI appear equally strong because they dissociate completely. When we dissolve them in acetic acid, however, *the acetic acid acts as the base* and accepts a proton:

$$\begin{array}{cccc}
\text{acid} & \text{base} & \text{base} & \text{acid} \\
HCl(g) + CH_3COOH(l) & \rightleftharpoons & Cl^-(acet) + CH_3COOH_2^+(acet) \\
HBr(g) + CH_3COOH(l) & \rightleftharpoons & Br^-(acet) + CH_3COOH_2^+(acet) \\
HI(g) + CH_3COOH(l) & \rightleftharpoons & I^-(acet) + CH_3COOH_2^+(acet)
\end{array}$$

[The use of (*acet*) instead of (*aq*) indicates solvation by $CH_3COOH$.] Because acetic acid is a *weaker base* than water, the three acids donate their protons to *different* extents. Measurements show that HI protonates the solvent to a greater extent than HBr, and HBr does so more than HCl; that is, in pure acetic acid, $K_{HI} > K_{HBr} > K_{HCl}$. Similarly, the relative strengths of strong bases are determined in a solvent that is a weaker acid than $H_2O$, such as liquid $NH_3$.

## Summary of Section 18.8

- Strong acids (or strong bases) dissociate completely to yield $H_3O^+$ (or $OH^-$) in water; in effect, water equalizes (levels) their strengths.
- Strong acids show differences in strength when dissolved in a weaker base than water, such as acetic acid.

---

# 18.9 • ELECTRON-PAIR DONATION AND THE LEWIS ACID-BASE DEFINITION

The final acid-base concept we consider was developed by Gilbert N. Lewis, whose contribution to understanding valence electron pairs in bonding we discussed in Chapter 9. Whereas the Brønsted-Lowry concept focuses on the proton in defining a species as an acid or a base, the Lewis concept highlights the role of the *electron pair*. The **Lewis acid-base definition** holds that

- A *base* is any species that *donates* an electron pair to form a bond.
- An *acid* is any species that *accepts* an electron pair to form a bond.

The Lewis definition, like the Brønsted-Lowry definition, requires that a base have an electron pair to donate, so it does not expand the classes of bases. However, *it greatly expands the classes of acids*. Many species, such as $CO_2$ and $Cu^{2+}$, that do not contain H in their formula (and thus cannot be Brønsted-Lowry acids) are Lewis acids because they accept an electron pair in reactions. Thus, the proton itself is a Lewis acid because it accepts the electron pair donated by a base:

$$B\colon\!+ H^+ \rightleftharpoons B—H^+$$

Thus, *all Brønsted-Lowry acids donate $H^+$, a Lewis acid.*

The product of a Lewis acid-base reaction is an **adduct,** *a single species that contains a **new** covalent bond:*

$$A + \colon\!B \rightleftharpoons A—B \text{ (adduct)}$$

Thus, the Lewis concept radically broadens the idea of an acid-base reaction:

- To Arrhenius, it is the formation of $H_2O$ from $H^+$ and $OH^-$.
- To Brønsted and Lowry, it is $H^+$ transfer from a stronger acid to a stronger base to form a weaker base and weaker acid.
- To Lewis, it is *the donation and acceptance of an electron pair to form a covalent bond in an adduct.*

  By definition, then,

- *A Lewis base must have a lone pair of electrons to donate.*
- *A Lewis acid must have a vacant orbital* (or the ability to rearrange its bonds to form one) to accept a lone pair and form a new bond.

In this section, we discuss molecules and positive ions that act as Lewis acids.

## Molecules as Lewis Acids

Many molecules act as Lewis acids. In every case, the atom accepting the electron pair has low electron density due to either an electron deficiency or a polar multiple bond.

**Lewis Acids with Electron-Deficient Atoms** The most important of the *electron-deficient* Lewis acids are compounds of the Group 3A(13) elements boron and aluminum. Recall from Chapters 10 and 14 that these compounds have fewer than eight electrons around the central atom, so they react to complete that atom's octet. For example, boron trifluoride accepts an electron pair from ammonia to form a covalent bond:

Aluminum chloride dissolves freely in relatively nonpolar diethyl ether when the ether's O atom donates an electron pair to Al to form a covalent bond:

This acidic behavior of boron and aluminum halides is often used in organic syntheses. For example, a methyl group is added to the benzene ring by the action of $CH_3Cl$ in the presence of $AlCl_3$. The Lewis acid $AlCl_3$ abstracts the Lewis base $Cl^-$ from $CH_3Cl$ to form an adduct that has a reactive $CH_3^+$ group, which then attacks the electron-rich benzene ring:

$$CH_3Cl + AlCl_3 \rightleftharpoons [CH_3]^+[Cl\!-\!AlCl_3]^-$$
$$\text{base} \qquad \text{acid} \qquad\qquad \text{adduct}$$

$$C_6H_6 + [CH_3]^+[Cl\!-\!AlCl_3]^- \rightleftharpoons C_6H_5CH_3 + AlCl_3 + HCl$$
$$\text{benzene} \qquad\qquad\qquad\qquad\qquad \text{toluene}$$

**Lewis Acids with Polar Multiple Bonds** Molecules with a polar double bond also function as Lewis acids. An electron pair on the Lewis base approaches the partially positive end of the double bond to form the new bond in the adduct, as the $\pi$ bond breaks. For example, consider the reaction of $SO_2$ in water. The electronegative O atoms in $SO_2$ make the central S partially positive. The O atom of water donates a lone pair to the S, thus forming an S—O bond and breaking one of the $\pi$ bonds. Then, a proton is transferred from water to the O that was part of the $\pi$ bond. The resulting adduct is sulfurous acid:

The analogous formation of a carbonate from a metal oxide and carbon dioxide occurs in a nonaqueous system. The $O^{2-}$ ion (shown coming from CaO) donates an electron pair to the partially positive C in $CO_2$, a $\pi$ bond breaks, and the $CO_3^{2-}$ ion (shown as part of $CaCO_3$) is the adduct:

## Metal Cations as Lewis Acids

In the Lewis sense, hydration of a metal ion is itself an acid-base reaction. As electron pairs on the O atoms of $H_2O$ molecules form covalent bonds, the hydrated cation is the adduct; thus, *a metal ion acts as a Lewis acid when it dissolves in water:*

Ammonia is a stronger Lewis base than water because, when it is added to the aqueous solution of the hydrated cation, it displaces $H_2O$, with $K >> 1$:

$$Ni(H_2O)_6^{2+}(aq) + 6NH_3(aq) \rightleftharpoons Ni(NH_3)_6^{2+}(aq) + 6H_2O(l)$$

hydrated adduct        base        ammoniated adduct

We discuss the equilibrium nature of these acid-base reactions in greater detail in Chapter 19, and we investigate the structures of these ions in Chapter 23.

Many biomolecules with central metal ions are Lewis adducts. Most often, O and N atoms of organic groups donate their lone pairs as the Lewis bases. Chlorophyll is a Lewis adduct of a central $Mg^{2+}$ and the four N atoms of a tetrapyrrole (porphin) ring system (Figure 18.13). Vitamin $B_{12}$ has a similar structure with a central $Co^{3+}$, and so does heme with a central $Fe^{2+}$. Several other metal ions, such as $Zn^{2+}$, $Mo^{2+}$, and $Cu^{2+}$, are bound at the active sites of enzymes and function as Lewis acids in the catalytic action.

---

### Sample Problem 18.15 | Identifying Lewis Acids and Bases

**Problem** Identify the Lewis acids and Lewis bases in the following reactions:
**(a)** $H^+ + OH^- \rightleftharpoons H_2O$  **(b)** $Cl^- + BCl_3 \rightleftharpoons BCl_4^-$  **(c)** $K^+ + 6H_2O \rightleftharpoons K(H_2O)_6^+$
**Plan** We examine the formulas to see which species accepts the electron pair (Lewis acid) and which donates it (Lewis base) in forming the adduct.

**Solution (a)** The $H^+$ ion accepts an electron pair from the $OH^-$ ion in forming a bond. $H^+$ is the acid and $OH^-$ is the base.
**(b)** The $Cl^-$ ion has four lone pairs and uses one to form a new bond to the central B. $BCl_3$ is the acid and $Cl^-$ is the base.
**(c)** The $K^+$ ion does not have any valence electrons to provide, so the bond is formed when electron pairs from O atoms of water enter empty orbitals on $K^+$. $K^+$ is the acid and $H_2O$ is the base.

**Check** The Lewis acids ($H^+$, $BCl_3$, and $K^+$) each have an unfilled valence shell that can accept an electron pair from the Lewis bases ($OH^-$, $Cl^-$, and $H_2O$).

**Follow-Up Problem 18.15** Identify the Lewis acids and Lewis bases:
**(a)** $OH^- + Al(OH)_3 \rightleftharpoons Al(OH)_4^-$     **(b)** $SO_3 + H_2O \rightleftharpoons H_2SO_4$
**(c)** $Co^{3+} + 6NH_3 \rightleftharpoons Co(NH_3)_6^{3+}$

---

## An Overview of Acid-Base Definitions

From a broader chemical perspective, the diversity of acid-base reactions takes on more unity. Chemists see a common theme in reactions as diverse as a standardized base being used to analyze an unknown fatty acid, baking soda being used in breadmaking, and even oxygen binding to hemoglobin in a blood cell. Let's see how the three acid-base definitions fit together.

1. The *Arrhenius definition,* which was the first attempt at describing acids and bases on the molecular level, is the most limited and narrow of the three. It applies only to species with an H atom or an OH group that is released as an ion when the species dissolves in water. Because relatively few species have these structural prerequisites, Arrhenius acid-base reactions are relatively few in number, and all occur in $H_2O$ and result in the formation of $H_2O$.

2. The *Brønsted-Lowry definition* sees acid-base reactions as proton-transfer processes that need not occur in water. A Brønsted-Lowry acid, like an Arrhenius acid, must have an H, but a Brønsted-Lowry base is any species with an electron pair available to accept a proton. This definition includes many more species as bases, including $OH^-$. It defines the acid-base reaction in terms of conjugate acid-base pairs, with an acid and a base on both sides of the reaction. The system reaches equilibrium based on the relative strengths of the acid, the base, and their conjugates.

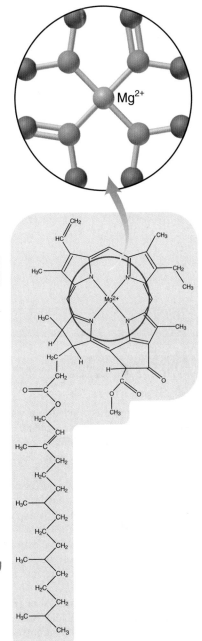

**Figure 18.13 The $Mg^{2+}$ ion as a Lewis acid in chlorophyll.** $Mg^{2+}$ accepts electron pairs from surrounding N atoms.

3. The *Lewis definition* has the widest scope and includes the other two. The defining event of a Lewis acid-base reaction is the donation and acceptance of an electron pair to form a new covalent bond in an adduct. Lewis bases still must have an electron pair to donate, but Lewis acids—the electron-pair acceptors—include many species not encompassed by the other definitions, including molecules with electron-deficient atoms or with polar double bonds, metal ions, and even $H^+$ itself.

## ■ Summary of Section 18.9

- The Lewis acid-base definition focuses on the donation or acceptance of an electron pair to form a new covalent bond in an adduct, the product of an acid-base reaction. Lewis bases donate the electron pair, and Lewis acids accept it.
- Thus, many species that do not contain H are Lewis acids. Molecules with polar double bonds act as Lewis acids, as do those with electron-deficient atoms.
- Metal ions act as Lewis acids when they dissolve in water, which acts as a Lewis base, to form the adduct, a hydrated cation.
- Many metal ions function as Lewis acids in biomolecules.

# CHAPTER REVIEW GUIDE

## Learning Objectives   Relevant section (§) and/or sample problem (SP) numbers appear in parentheses.

### Understand These Concepts

1. Why the proton is bonded to a water molecule, as $H_3O^+$, in all aqueous acid-base systems (§18.1)
2. The Arrhenius definitions of an acid and a base (§18.1)
3. Why all reactions of a strong acid and a strong base have the same $\Delta H_{rxn}^{\circ}$ (§18.1)
4. How the strength of an acid (or base) relates to the extent of its dissociation into ions in water (§18.1)
5. How relative acid strength is expressed by the acid-dissociation constant $K_a$ (§18.1)
6. Why water is a very weak electrolyte and how its autoionization is expressed by $K_w$ (§18.2)
7. Why $[H_3O^+]$ is inversely related to $[OH^-]$ in any aqueous solution (§18.2)
8. How the relative magnitudes of $[H_3O^+]$ and $[OH^-]$ define whether a solution is acidic, basic, or neutral (§18.2)
9. The Brønsted-Lowry definitions of an acid and a base and how an acid-base reaction can be viewed as a proton-transfer process (§18.3)
10. How water acts as a base (or as an acid) when an acid (or a base) dissolves in it (§18.3)
11. How a conjugate acid-base pair differs by one proton (§18.3)
12. How a Brønsted-Lowry acid-base reaction involves two conjugate acid-base pairs (§18.3)
13. Why a stronger acid and base react ($K_c > 1$) to form a weaker base and acid (§18.3)
14. How the percent dissociation of a weak acid increases as its concentration decreases (§18.4)
15. How a polyprotic acid dissociates in two or more steps and why only the first step supplies significant $[H_3O^+]$ (§18.4)
16. How weak bases in water accept a proton rather than dissociate; the meaning of $K_b$ and $pK_b$ (§18.5)
17. How ammonia, amines, and weak-acid anions act as weak bases in water (§18.5)

18. Why relative concentrations of HA and $A^-$ determine the acidity or basicity of their solution (§18.5)
19. The relationship of the $K_a$ and $K_b$ of a conjugate acid-base pair to $K_w$ (§18.5)
20. The effects of electronegativity, bond polarity, and bond strength on acid strength (§18.6)
21. Why aqueous solutions of small, highly charged metal ions are acidic (§18.6)
22. The various combinations of cations and anions that lead to acidic, basic, or neutral salt solutions (§18.7)
23. Why the strengths of strong acids are leveled in water but differentiated in a less basic solvent (§18.8)
24. The Lewis definitions of an acid and a base and how a Lewis acid-base reaction involves the donation and acceptance of an electron pair to form a covalent bond (§18.9)
25. How molecules with electron-deficient atoms, molecules with polar multiple bonds, and metal cations act as Lewis acids (§18.9)

### Master These Skills

1. Classifying strong and weak acids and bases from their formulas (SP 18.1)
2. Using $K_w$ to calculate $[H_3O^+]$ or $[OH^-]$ in an aqueous solution (SP 18.2)
3. Using p-scales to express $[H_3O^+]$, $[OH^-]$, and $K$ (§18.2)
4. Calculating $[H_3O^+]$, pH, $[OH^-]$, and pOH (SP 18.3)
5. Identifying conjugate acid-base pairs (SP 18.4)
6. Using relative acid strengths to predict the net direction of an acid-base reaction (SPs 18.5, 18.6)
7. Calculating $K_a$ of a weak acid from pH (SP 18.7)
8. Calculating $[H_3O^+]$ (and, thus, pH) from $K_a$ and $[HA]_{init}$ (SP 18.8)
9. Applying the quadratic equation to find a concentration (Follow-Up Problem 18.8)

10. Calculating the percent dissociation of a weak acid (§18.4 and SP 18.9)
11. Calculating $[H_3O^+]$ and other concentrations for a polyprotic acid (SP 18.10)
12. Calculating pH from $K_b$ and $[B]_{init}$ (SP 18.11)
13. Finding $K_b$ of $A^-$ from $K_a$ of HA and $K_w$ (§18.5 and SP 18.12)

14. Calculating pH from $K_b$ of $A^-$ and $[A^-]_{init}$ (SP 18.12)
15. Predicting relative acid strengths of nonmetal hydrides and oxoacids (§18.6)
16. Predicting the relative acidity of a salt solution from the nature of the cation and anion (SPs 18.13, 18.14)
17. Identifying Lewis acids and bases (SP 18.15)

## Key Terms    Page numbers appear in parentheses.

**Section 18.1**
hydronium ion, $H_3O^+$ (720)
Arrhenius acid-base definition (720)
neutralization (720)
acid-dissociation (acid-ionization) constant ($K_a$) (722)

**Section 18.2**
autoionization (724)
ion-product constant for water ($K_w$) (724)
pH (726)
acid-base indicator (728)

**Section 18.3**
Brønsted-Lowry acid-base definition (729)
proton donor (729)
proton acceptor (729)
conjugate acid-base pair (729)

**Section 18.4**
polyprotic acid (737)

**Section 18.5**
base-dissociation (base-ionization) constant ($K_b$) (740)

**Section 18.8**
leveling effect (750)

**Section 18.9**
Lewis acid-base definition (751)
adduct (751)

## Key Equations and Relationships    Page numbers appear in parentheses.

**18.1** Defining the acid-dissociation constant (722):

$$K_a = \frac{[H_3O^+][A^-]}{[HA]}$$

**18.2** Defining the ion-product constant for water (724):

$$K_w = [H_3O^+][OH^-] = 1.0 \times 10^{-14} \text{ (at 25°C)}$$

**18.3** Defining pH (726):

$$pH = -\log [H_3O^+]$$

**18.4** Relating $pK_w$ to pH and pOH (726):

$$pK_w = pH + pOH = 14.00 \text{ (at 25°C)}$$

**18.5** Finding the percent dissociation of HA (736):

$$\text{Percent HA dissociated} = \frac{[HA]_{dissoc}}{[HA]_{init}} \times 100$$

**18.6** Defining the base-dissociation constant (740):

$$K_b = \frac{[BH^+][OH^-]}{[B]}$$

**18.7** Expressing the relationship among $K_a$, $K_b$, and $K_w$ (743):

$$K_a \times K_b = K_w$$

## Brief Solutions to Follow-Up Problems

**18.1** (a) $HClO_3$; (b) HCl; (c) NaOH

**18.2** $[H_3O^+] = \dfrac{1.0 \times 10^{-14}}{6.7 \times 10^{-2}} = 1.5 \times 10^{-13}\ M$; basic

**18.3** $pOH = 14.00 - 9.52 = 4.48$
$[H_3O^+] = 10^{-9.52} = 3.0 \times 10^{-10}\ M$
$[OH^-] = \dfrac{1.0 \times 10^{-14}}{3.0 \times 10^{-10}} = 3.3 \times 10^{-5}\ M$

**18.4** (a) $CH_3COOH/CH_3COO^-$ and $H_3O^+/H_2O$
(b) $H_2O/OH^-$ and $HF/F^-$

**18.5** (a) $NH_3(g) + H_2O(l) \rightleftharpoons NH_4^+(aq) + OH^-(aq)$
(b) $NH_3(g) + H_3O^+(aq; \text{from HCl}) \longrightarrow NH_4^+(aq) + H_2O(l)$
(c) $NH_4^+(aq) + OH^-(aq; \text{from NaOH}) \longrightarrow NH_3(g) + H_2O(l)$

**18.6** There are more HB molecules than HA, so $K_c > 1$ and HA is the stronger acid.

**18.7** $NH_4^+(aq) + H_2O(l) \rightleftharpoons NH_3(aq) + H_3O^+(aq)$
$[H_3O^+] = 10^{-pH} = 10^{-5.0} = 1 \times 10^{-5}\ M = [NH_3]$
And, $[NH_4^+] = 0.2\ M - (1 \times 10^{-5}\ M) = 0.2\ M$

$$K_a = \frac{[NH_3][H_3O^+]}{[NH_4^+]} \approx \frac{(1 \times 10^{-5})^2}{0.2} = 5 \times 10^{-10}$$

**18.8** $K_a = \dfrac{[H_3O^+][OCN^-]}{[HOCN]} = \dfrac{(x)(x)}{0.10 - x} = 3.5 \times 10^{-4}$

Since $\dfrac{[HOCN]_{init}}{K_a} = \dfrac{0.10}{3.5 \times 10^{-4}} = 286 < 400$, you must solve a quadratic equation: $x^2 + (3.5 \times 10^{-4})x - (3.5 \times 10^{-5}) = 0$
$x = [H_3O^+] = 5.7 \times 10^{-3}\ M$

## Brief Solutions to Follow-Up Problems (continued)

**18.9** There is no single correct scene: any scene in which the total number of HB + $H_3O^+$ (or HB + B$^-$) is less than in the original solution, yet the number of HB dissociated is greater, would be correct, for example:

**18.10** $K_{a1} = \dfrac{[HC_2O_4^-][H_3O^+]}{[H_2C_2O_4]} = \dfrac{x^2}{0.150 - x} = 5.6\times10^{-2}$ Since $\dfrac{[H_2C_2O_4]_{init}}{K_{a1}} < 400$, you must solve a quadratic equation:

$x^2 + (5.6\times10^{-2})x - (8.4\times10^{-3}) = 0$

$x = [H_3O^+] = 0.068\ M;\ pH = 1.17$

$x = [HC_2O_4^-] = 0.068\ M;\ [H_2C_2O_4] = 0.150\ M - x = 0.082\ M$

$[C_2O_4^{2-}] = \dfrac{(K_{a2})[HC_2O_4^-]}{[H_3O^+]} = \dfrac{(5.4\times10^{-5})(0.068)}{0.068}$

$\qquad\quad = 5.4\times10^{-5}\ M$

**18.11** $K_b = \dfrac{[C_5H_5NH^+][OH^-]}{[C_5H_5N]} = 10^{-8.77} = 1.7\times10^{-9}$

Assuming $0.10\ M - x \approx 0.10\ M$, $K_b = 1.7\times10^{-9} \approx \dfrac{(x)(x)}{0.10}$;

$x = [OH^-] \approx 1.3\times10^{-5}\ M;\ [H_3O^+] = 7.7\times10^{-10}\ M;$
$pH = 9.11$

**18.12** $K_b$ of $ClO^- = \dfrac{K_w}{K_a\ \text{of HClO}} = \dfrac{1.0\times10^{-14}}{2.9\times10^{-8}} = 3.4\times10^{-7}$

Assuming $0.20\ M - x \approx 0.20\ M$,

$K_b = 3.4\times10^{27} = \dfrac{[HClO][OH^-]}{[ClO^-]} \approx \dfrac{x^2}{0.20}$;

$x = [OH^-] \approx 2.6\times10^{-4}\ M;\ [H_3O^+] = 3.8\times10^{-11}\ M;$
$pH = 10.42$

**18.13** (a) Basic:

$\qquad ClO_2^-(aq) + H_2O(l) \rightleftharpoons HClO(aq) + OH^-(aq)$

$K^+$ is from the strong base KOH.
(b) Acidic:

$\qquad CH_3NH_3^+(aq) + H_2O(l) \rightleftharpoons CH_3NH_2(aq) + H_3O^+(aq)$

$NO_3^-$ is from the strong acid $HNO_3$.
(c) Neutral: $Cs^+$ is from the strong base CsOH; $I^-$ is from the strong acid HI.

**18.14** (a) $K_a$ of $Cu(H_2O)_6^{2+} = 3\times10^{-8}$

$K_b$ of $CH_3COO^- = \dfrac{K_w}{K_a\ \text{of } CH_3COOH} = 5.6\times10^{-10}$

Since $K_a > K_b$, $Cu(CH_3COO)_2(aq)$ is acidic.

(b) $K_a$ of $NH_4^+ = \dfrac{K_w}{K_b\ \text{of } NH_3} = 5.7\times10^{-10}$

$K_b$ of $F^- = \dfrac{K_w}{K_a\ \text{of HF}} = 1.5\times10^{-11}$

Because $K_a > K_b$, $NH_4F(aq)$ is acidic.
(c) From Appendix C, $K_a$ of $HSO_3^- = 6.5\times10^{-8}$

$K_b$ of $HSO_3^- = \dfrac{K_w}{K_a\ \text{of } H_2SO_3} = 7.1\times10^{-13}$

Because $K_a > K_b$, $KHSO_3(aq)$ is acidic.

**18.15** (a) $OH^-$ is the Lewis base; $Al(OH)_3$ is the Lewis acid.
(b) $H_2O$ is the Lewis base; $SO_3$ is the Lewis acid.
(c) $NH_3$ is the Lewis base; $Co^{3+}$ is the Lewis acid.

## PROBLEMS

Problems with **colored** numbers are answered in Appendix E and worked in detail in the Student Solutions Manual. Problem sections match those in the text and provide the numbers of relevant sample problems. Most offer Concept Review Questions, Skill-Building Exercises (grouped in pairs covering the same concept), and Problems in Context. The Comprehensive Problems are based on material from any section or previous chapter.

*Note:* Unless stated otherwise, all problems refer to aqueous solutions at 298 K (25°C).

### Acids and Bases in Water
(Sample Problem 18.1)

#### Concept Review Questions

**18.1** What is the role of water in the Arrhenius acid-base definition?

**18.2** What do Arrhenius acids have in common? What do Arrhenius bases have in common? Explain neutralization in terms of the Arrhenius acid-base definition. What data led Arrhenius to propose this idea of neutralization?

**18.3** Why is the Arrhenius acid-base definition too limited? Give an example for which the Arrhenius definition does not apply.

**18.4** What do "strong" and "weak" mean for acids and bases? $K_a$ values of weak acids vary over more than 10 orders of magnitude. What do the acids have in common that makes them "weak"?

#### Skill-Building Exercises (grouped in similar pairs)
**18.5** Which of the following are Arrhenius acids?
(a) $H_2O$      (b) $Ca(OH)_2$      (c) $H_3PO_3$      (d) HI

**18.6** Which of the following are Arrhenius acids?
(a) $NaHSO_4$      (b) $CH_4$      (c) NaH      (d) $H_3N$

**18.7** Which of the following are Arrhenius bases?
(a) $H_3AsO_4$      (b) $Ba(OH)_2$      (c) HClO      (d) KOH

**18.8** Which of the following are Arrhenius bases?
(a) $CH_3COOH$      (b) HOH      (c) $CH_3OH$      (d) $H_2NNH_2$

**18.9** Write the $K_a$ expression for each of the following in water:
(a) HCN     (b) $HCO_3^-$     (c) HCOOH

**18.10** Write the $K_a$ expression for each of the following in water:
(a) $CH_3NH_3^+$     (b) HClO     (c) $H_2S$

**18.11** Write the $K_a$ expression for each of the following in water:
(a) $HNO_2$     (b) $CH_3COOH$     (c) $HBrO_2$

**18.12** Write the $K_a$ expression for each of the following in water:
(a) $H_2PO_4^-$     (b) $H_3PO_2$     (c) $HSO_4^-$

**18.13** Use Appendix C to rank the following in order of *increasing* acid strength: $HIO_3$, HI, $CH_3COOH$, HF.

**18.14** Use Appendix C to rank the following in order of *decreasing* acid strength: HClO, HCl, HCN, $HNO_2$.

**18.15** Classify each as a strong or weak acid or base:
(a) $H_3AsO_4$     (b) $Sr(OH)_2$     (c) HIO     (d) $HClO_4$

**18.16** Classify each as a strong or weak acid or base:
(a) $CH_3NH_2$     (b) $K_2O$     (c) HI     (d) HCOOH

**18.17** Classify each as a strong or weak acid or base:
(a) RbOH     (b) HBr     (c) $H_2Te$     (d) HClO

**18.18** Classify each as a strong or weak acid or base:
(a) $HOCH_2CH_2NH_2$     (b) $H_2SeO_4$     (c) $HS^-$     (d) $B(OH)_3$

## Autoionization of Water and the pH Scale
(Sample Problems 18.2 and 18.3)

### Concept Review Questions

**18.19** What is an autoionization reaction? Write equations for the autoionization reactions of $H_2O$ and of $H_2SO_4$.

**18.20** What is the difference between $K_c$ and $K_w$ for the autoionization of water?

**18.21** (a) What is the change in pH when $[OH^-]$ increases by a factor of 10? (b) What is the change in $[H_3O^+]$ when the pH decreases by 3 units?

**18.22** Which solution has the higher pH? Explain.
(a) A 0.1 $M$ solution of an acid with $K_a = 1 \times 10^{-4}$ or one with $K_a = 4 \times 10^{-5}$
(b) A 0.1 $M$ solution of an acid with $pK_a = 3.0$ or one with $pK_a = 3.5$
(c) A 0.1 $M$ solution or a 0.01 $M$ solution of a weak acid
(d) A 0.1 $M$ solution of a weak acid or a 0.1 $M$ solution of a strong acid
(e) A 0.1 $M$ solution of an acid or a 0.01 $M$ solution of a base
(f) A solution of pOH 6.0 or one of pOH 8.0

### Skill-Building Exercises (grouped in similar pairs)

**18.23** (a) What is the pH of 0.0111 $M$ NaOH? Is the solution neutral, acidic, or basic? (b) What is the pOH of $1.35 \times 10^{-3}$ $M$ HCl? Is the solution neutral, acidic, or basic?

**18.24** (a) What is the pH of 0.0333 $M$ $HNO_3$? Is the solution neutral, acidic, or basic? (b) What is the pOH of 0.0347 $M$ KOH? Is the solution neutral, acidic, or basic?

**18.25** (a) What is the pH of $6.14 \times 10^{-3}$ $M$ HI? Is the solution neutral, acidic, or basic? (b) What is the pOH of 2.55 $M$ $Ba(OH)_2$? Is the solution neutral, acidic, or basic?

**18.26** (a) What is the pH of $7.52 \times 10^{-4}$ $M$ CsOH? Is the solution neutral, acidic, or basic? (b) What is the pOH of $1.59 \times 10^{-3}$ $M$ $HClO_4$? Is the solution neutral, acidic, or basic?

**18.27** (a) What are $[H_3O^+]$, $[OH^-]$, and pOH in a solution with a pH of 9.85? (b) What are $[H_3O^+]$, $[OH^-]$, and pH in a solution with a pOH of 9.43?

**18.28** (a) What are $[H_3O^+]$, $[OH^-]$, and pOH in a solution with a pH of 3.47? (b) What are $[H_3O^+]$, $[OH^-]$, and pH in a solution with a pOH of 4.33?

**18.29** (a) What are $[H_3O^+]$, $[OH^-]$, and pOH in a solution with a pH of 4.77? (b) What are $[H_3O^+]$, $[OH^-]$, and pH in a solution with a pOH of 5.65?

**18.30** (a) What are $[H_3O^+]$, $[OH^-]$, and pOH in a solution with a pH of 8.97? (b) What are $[H_3O^+]$, $[OH^-]$, and pH in a solution with a pOH of 11.27?

**18.31** How many moles of $H_3O^+$ or $OH^-$ must you add per liter of HA solution to adjust its pH from 3.15 to 3.65? Assume a negligible volume change.

**18.32** How many moles of $H_3O^+$ or $OH^-$ must you add per liter of HA solution to adjust its pH from 9.33 to 9.07? Assume a negligible volume change.

**18.33** How many moles of $H_3O^+$ or $OH^-$ must you add to 5.6 L of HA solution to adjust its pH from 4.52 to 5.25? Assume a negligible volume change.

**18.34** How many moles of $H_3O^+$ or $OH^-$ must you add to 87.5 mL of HA solution to adjust its pH from 8.92 to 6.33? Assume a negligible volume change.

### Problems in Context

**18.35** The two molecular scenes below depict the relative concentrations of $H_3O^+$ *(purple)* in solutions of the same volume (with counter ions and solvent molecules omitted for clarity). If the pH in scene A is 4.8, what is the pH in scene B?

**A**                     **B**

**18.36** Like any equilibrium constant, $K_w$ changes with temperature. (a) Given that autoionization is endothermic, how does $K_w$ change with rising $T$? Explain with a reaction that includes heat as reactant or product. (b) In many medical applications, the value of $K_w$ at 37°C (body temperature) may be more appropriate than the value at 25°C, $1.0 \times 10^{-14}$. The pH of pure water at 37°C is 6.80. Calculate $K_w$, pOH, and $[OH^-]$ at this temperature.

## Proton Transfer and the Brønsted-Lowry Acid-Base Definition
(Sample Problems 18.4 to 18.6)

### Concept Review Questions

**18.37** How are the Arrhenius and Brønsted-Lowry acid-base definitions different? How are they similar? Name two Brønsted-Lowry bases that are not Arrhenius bases. Can you do the same for acids? Explain.

**18.38** What is a conjugate acid-base pair? What is the relationship between the two members of the pair?

**18.39** (a) A Brønsted-Lowry acid-base reaction proceeds in the net direction in which a stronger acid and stronger base form a weaker acid and weaker base. Explain.

(b) The molecular scene at right depicts an aqueous solution of two conjugate acid-base pairs: HA/A⁻ and HB/B⁻. The base in the first pair is represented by red spheres and the base in the second pair by green spheres; solvent molecules are omitted for clarity. Which is the stronger acid? Stronger base? Explain.

**18.40** What is an amphiprotic species? Name one and write balanced equations that show why it is amphiprotic.

**Skill-Building Exercises** (grouped in similar pairs)

**18.41** Write balanced equations and $K_a$ expressions for these Brønsted-Lowry acids in water:
(a) $H_3PO_4$  (b) $C_6H_5COOH$  (c) $HSO_4^-$

**18.42** Write balanced equations and $K_a$ expressions for these Brønsted-Lowry acids in water:
(a) HCOOH  (b) $HClO_3$  (c) $H_2AsO_4^-$

**18.43** Give the formula of the conjugate base:
(a) HCl  (b) $H_2CO_3$  (c) $H_2O$

**18.44** Give the formula of the conjugate base:
(a) $HPO_4^{2-}$  (b) $NH_4^+$  (c) $HS^-$

**18.45** Give the formula of the conjugate acid:
(a) $NH_3$  (b) $NH_2^-$  (c) nicotine, $C_{10}H_{14}N_2$

**18.46** Give the formula of the conjugate acid:
(a) $O^{2-}$  (b) $SO_4^{2-}$  (c) $H_2O$

**18.47** In each equation, label the acids, bases, and conjugate pairs:
(a) $HCl + H_2O \rightleftharpoons Cl^- + H_3O^+$
(b) $HClO_4 + H_2SO_4 \rightleftharpoons ClO_4^- + H_3SO_4^+$
(c) $HPO_4^{2-} + H_2SO_4 \rightleftharpoons H_2PO_4^- + HSO_4^-$

**18.48** In each equation, label the acids, bases, and conjugate pairs:
(a) $NH_3 + HNO_3 \rightleftharpoons NH_4^+ + NO_3^-$
(b) $O^{2-} + H_2O \rightleftharpoons OH^- + OH^-$
(c) $NH_4^+ + BrO_3^- \rightleftharpoons NH_3 + HBrO_3$

**18.49** In each equation, label the acids, bases, and conjugate pairs:
(a) $NH_3 + H_3PO_4 \rightleftharpoons NH_4^+ + H_2PO_4^-$
(b) $CH_3O^- + NH_3 \rightleftharpoons CH_3OH + NH_2^-$
(c) $HPO_4^{2-} + HSO_4^- \rightleftharpoons H_2PO_4^- + SO_4^{2-}$

**18.50** In each equation, label the acids, bases, and conjugate pairs:
(a) $NH_4^+ + CN^- \rightleftharpoons NH_3 + HCN$
(b) $H_2O + HS^- \rightleftharpoons OH^- + H_2S$
(c) $HSO_3^- + CH_3NH_2 \rightleftharpoons SO_3^{2-} + CH_3NH_3^+$

**18.51** Write balanced net ionic equations for the following reactions, and label the conjugate acid-base pairs:
(a) $NaOH(aq) + NaH_2PO_4(aq) \rightleftharpoons H_2O(l) + Na_2HPO_4(aq)$
(b) $KHSO_4(aq) + K_2CO_3(aq) \rightleftharpoons K_2SO_4(aq) + KHCO_3(aq)$

**18.52** Write balanced net ionic equations for the following reactions, and label the conjugate acid-base pairs:
(a) $HNO_3(aq) + Li_2CO_3(aq) \rightleftharpoons LiNO_3(aq) + LiHCO_3(aq)$
(b) $2NH_4Cl(aq) + Ba(OH)_2(aq) \rightleftharpoons$
$$2H_2O(l) + BaCl_2(aq) + 2NH_3(aq)$$

**18.53** The following aqueous species constitute two conjugate acid-base pairs. Use them to write one acid-base reaction with $K_c > 1$ and another with $K_c < 1$: $HS^-$, $Cl^-$, HCl, $H_2S$.

**18.54** The following aqueous species constitute two conjugate acid-base pairs. Use them to write one acid-base reaction with $K_c > 1$ and another with $K_c < 1$: $NO_3^-$, $F^-$, HF, $HNO_3$.

**18.55** Use Figure 18.8 (p. 745) to determine whether $K_c > 1$ for
(a) $HCl + NH_3 \rightleftharpoons NH_4^+ + Cl^-$
(b) $H_2SO_3 + NH_3 \rightleftharpoons HSO_3^- + NH_4^+$

**18.56** Use Figure 18.8 (p. 745) to determine whether $K_c > 1$ for
(a) $OH^- + HS^- \rightleftharpoons H_2O + S^{2-}$
(b) $HCN + HCO_3^- \rightleftharpoons H_2CO_3 + CN^-$

**18.57** Use Figure 18.8 (p. 745) to determine whether $K_c < 1$ for
(a) $NH_4^+ + HPO_4^{2-} \rightleftharpoons NH_3 + H_2PO_4^-$
(b) $HSO_3^- + HS^- \rightleftharpoons H_2SO_3 + S^{2-}$

**18.58** Use Figure 18.8 (p. 745) to determine whether $K_c < 1$ for
(a) $H_2PO_4^- + F^- \rightleftharpoons HPO_4^{2-} + HF$
(b) $CH_3COO^- + HSO_4^- \rightleftharpoons CH_3COOH + SO_4^{2-}$

## Solving Problems Involving Weak-Acid Equilibria
(Sample Problems 18.7 to 18.10)

**Concept Review Questions**

**18.59** In each of the following cases, is the concentration of acid before and after dissociation nearly the same or very different? Explain your reasoning: (a) a concentrated solution of a strong acid; (b) a concentrated solution of a weak acid; (c) a dilute solution of a weak acid; (d) a dilute solution of a strong acid.

**18.60** A sample of 0.0001 $M$ HCl has $[H_3O^+]$ close to that of a sample of 0.1 $M$ $CH_3COOH$. Are acetic acid and hydrochloric acid equally strong in these samples? Explain.

**18.61** In which of the following solutions will $[H_3O^+]$ be approximately equal to $[CH_3COO^-]$: (a) 0.1 $M$ $CH_3COOH$; (b) $1 \times 10^{-7}$ $M$ $CH_3COOH$; (c) a solution containing both 0.1 $M$ $CH_3COOH$ and 0.1 $M$ $CH_3COONa$? Explain.

**18.62** Why do successive $K_a$'s decrease for all polyprotic acids?

**Skill-Building Exercises** (grouped in similar pairs)

**18.63** A 0.15 $M$ solution of butanoic acid, $CH_3CH_2CH_2COOH$, contains $1.51 \times 10^{-3}$ $M$ $H_3O^+$. What is the $K_a$ of butanoic acid?

**18.64** A 0.035 $M$ solution of a weak acid (HA) has a pH of 4.88. What is the $K_a$ of the acid?

**18.65** Nitrous acid, $HNO_2$, has a $K_a$ of $7.1 \times 10^{-4}$. What are $[H_3O^+]$, $[NO_2^-]$, and $[OH^-]$ in 0.60 $M$ $HNO_2$?

**18.66** Hydrofluoric acid, HF, has a $K_a$ of $6.8 \times 10^{-4}$. What are $[H_3O^+]$, $[F^-]$, and $[OH^-]$ in 0.75 $M$ HF?

**18.67** Chloroacetic acid, $ClCH_2COOH$, has a $pK_a$ of 2.87. What are $[H_3O^+]$, pH, $[ClCH_2COO^-]$, and $[ClCH_2COOH]$ in 1.25 $M$ $ClCH_2COOH$?

**18.68** Hypochlorous acid, HClO, has a $pK_a$ of 7.54. What are $[H_3O^+]$, pH, $[ClO^-]$, and $[HClO]$ in 0.115 $M$ HClO?

**18.69** In a 0.20 $M$ solution, a weak acid is 3.0% dissociated.
(a) Calculate the $[H_3O^+]$, pH, $[OH^-]$, and pOH of the solution.
(b) Calculate $K_a$ of the acid.

**18.70** In a 0.735 $M$ solution, a weak acid is 12.5% dissociated.
(a) Calculate the $[H_3O^+]$, pH, $[OH^-]$, and pOH of the solution.
(b) Calculate $K_a$ of the acid.

**18.71** A 0.250-mol sample of HX is dissolved in enough $H_2O$ to form 655 mL of solution. If the pH of the solution is 3.54, what is the $K_a$ of HX?

**18.72** A $4.85 \times 10^{-3}$-mol sample of HY is dissolved in enough $H_2O$ to form 0.095 L of solution. If the pH of the solution is 2.68, what is the $K_a$ of HY?

**18.73** The weak acid HZ has a $K_a$ of $2.55 \times 10^{-4}$.
(a) Calculate the pH of 0.075 $M$ HZ.
(b) Calculate the pOH of 0.045 $M$ HZ.

**18.74** The weak acid HQ has a $pK_a$ of 4.89.
(a) Calculate the $[H_3O^+]$ of $3.5 \times 10^{-2}$ $M$ HQ.
(b) Calculate the $[OH^-]$ of 0.65 $M$ HQ.

**18.75** (a) Calculate the pH of 0.175 $M$ HY, if $K_a = 1.50 \times 10^{-4}$.
(b) Calculate the pOH of 0.175 $M$ HX, if $K_a = 2.00 \times 10^{-2}$.

**18.76** (a) Calculate the pH of 0.55 $M$ HCN, if $K_a = 6.2 \times 10^{-10}$.
(b) Calculate the pOH of 0.044 $M$ $HIO_3$, if $K_a = 0.16$.

**18.77** Use Appendix C to calculate the percent dissociation of 0.55 $M$ benzoic acid, $C_6H_5COOH$.

**18.78** Use Appendix C to calculate the percent dissociation of 0.050 $M$ $CH_3COOH$.

**18.79** Use Appendix C to calculate $[H_2S]$, $[HS^-]$, $[S^{2-}]$, $[H_3O^+]$, pH, $[OH^-]$, and pOH in a 0.10 $M$ solution of the diprotic acid hydrosulfuric acid.

**18.80** Use Appendix C to calculate $[H_2C_3H_2O_4]$, $[HC_3H_2O_4^-]$, $[C_3H_2O_4^{2-}]$, $[H_3O^+]$, pH, $[OH^-]$, and pOH in a 0.200 $M$ solution of the diprotic acid malonic acid.

**Problems in Context**

**18.81** Acetylsalicylic acid (aspirin), $HC_9H_7O_4$, is the most widely used pain reliever and fever reducer. Find the pH of 0.018 $M$ aqueous aspirin at body temperature ($K_a$ at 37°C $= 3.6 \times 10^{-4}$).

**18.82** Formic acid, HCOOH, the simplest carboxylic acid, is used in the textile and rubber industries and is secreted as a defense by many species of ants (family *Formicidae*). Calculate the percent dissociation of 0.75 $M$ HCOOH.

## Weak Bases and Their Relation to Weak Acids
(Sample Problems 18.11 and 18.12)

**Concept Review Questions**

**18.83** What is the key structural feature of all Brønsted-Lowry bases? How does this feature function in an acid-base reaction?

**18.84** Why are most anions basic in $H_2O$? Give formulas of four anions that are not basic.

**18.85** Except for the $Na^+$ spectator ion, aqueous solutions of $CH_3COOH$ and $CH_3COONa$ contain the same species. (a) What are the species (other than $H_2O$)? (b) Why is 0.1 $M$ $CH_3COOH$ acidic and 0.1 $M$ $CH_3COONa$ basic?

**Skill-Building Exercises** (grouped in similar pairs)

**18.86** Write balanced equations and $K_b$ expressions for these Brønsted-Lowry bases in water:
(a) Pyridine, $C_5H_5N$   (b) $CO_3^{2-}$

**18.87** Write balanced equations and $K_b$ expressions for these Brønsted-Lowry bases in water:
(a) Benzoate ion, $C_6H_5COO^-$   (b) $(CH_3)_3N$

**18.88** Write balanced equations and $K_b$ expressions for these Brønsted-Lowry bases in water:
(a) Hydroxylamine, $HO{-}NH_2$   (b) $HPO_4^{2-}$

**18.89** Write balanced equations and $K_b$ expressions for these Brønsted-Lowry bases in water:
(a) Guanidine, $(H_2N)_2C{=}NH$ (double-bonded N is most basic)
(b) Acetylide ion, $HC{\equiv}C^-$

**18.90** What is the pH of 0.070 $M$ dimethylamine?

**18.91** What is the pH of 0.12 $M$ diethylamine?

**18.92** What is the pH of 0.25 $M$ ethanolamine?

**18.93** What is the pH of 0.26 $M$ aniline?

**18.94** (a) What is the $K_b$ of the acetate ion?
(b) What is the $K_a$ of the anilinium ion, $C_6H_5NH_3^+$?

**18.95** (a) What is the $K_b$ of the benzoate ion, $C_6H_5COO^-$?
(b) What is the $K_a$ of the 2-hydroxyethylammonium ion, $HOCH_2CH_2NH_3^+$ ($pK_b$ of $HOCH_2CH_2NH_2 = 4.49$)?

**18.96** (a) What is the $pK_b$ of $ClO_2^-$?
(b) What is the $pK_a$ of the dimethylammonium ion, $(CH_3)_2NH_2^+$?

**18.97** (a) What is the $pK_b$ of $NO_2^-$?
(b) What is the $pK_a$ of the hydrazinium ion, $H_2N{-}NH_3^+$ ($K_b$ of hydrazine $= 8.5 \times 10^{-7}$)?

**18.98** (a) What is the pH of 0.150 $M$ KCN?
(b) What is the pH of 0.40 $M$ triethylammonium chloride, $(CH_3CH_2)_3NHCl$?

**18.99** (a) What is the pH of 0.100 $M$ sodium phenolate, $C_6H_5ONa$, the sodium salt of phenol?
(b) What is the pH of 0.15 $M$ methylammonium bromide, $CH_3NH_3Br$ ($K_b$ of $CH_3NH_2 = 4.4 \times 10^{-4}$)?

**18.100** (a) What is the pH of 0.65 $M$ potassium formate, HCOOK?
(b) What is the pH of 0.85 $M$ $NH_4Br$?

**18.101** (a) What is the pH of 0.75 $M$ NaF?
(b) What is the pH of 0.88 $M$ pyridinium chloride, $C_5H_5NHCl$?

**Problems in Context**

**18.102** Sodium hypochlorite solution, sold as chlorine bleach, is potentially dangerous because of the basicity of $ClO^-$, the active bleaching ingredient. What is $[OH^-]$ in an aqueous solution that is 6.5% NaClO by mass? What is the pH of the solution? (Assume $d$ of solution $= 1.0$ g/mL.)

**18.103** Codeine ($C_{18}H_{21}NO_3$) is a narcotic pain reliever that forms a salt with HCl. What is the pH of 0.050 $M$ codeine hydrochloride ($pK_b$ of codeine $= 5.80$)?

## Molecular Properties and Acid Strength

**Concept Review Questions**

**18.104** Across a period, how does the electronegativity of a nonmetal affect the acidity of its binary hydride?

**18.105** How does the atomic size of a nonmetal affect the acidity of its binary hydride?

**18.106** A strong acid has a weak bond to its acidic proton, whereas a weak acid has a strong bond to its acidic proton. Explain.

**18.107** Perchloric acid, $HClO_4$, is the strongest of the halogen oxoacids, and hypoiodous acid, HIO, is the weakest. What two factors govern this difference in acid strength?

**Skill-Building Exercises** (grouped in similar pairs)

**18.108** Choose the *stronger* acid in each of the following pairs:
(a) $H_2SeO_3$ or $H_2SeO_4$ (b) $H_3PO_4$ or $H_3AsO_4$ (c) $H_2S$ or $H_2Te$

**18.109** Choose the *weaker* acid in each of the following pairs:
(a) HBr or $H_2Se$ (b) $HClO_4$ or $H_2SO_4$ (c) $H_2SO_3$ or $H_2SO_4$

**18.110** Choose the *stronger* acid in each of the following pairs:
(a) $H_2Se$ or $H_3As$ (b) $B(OH)_3$ or $Al(OH)_3$ (c) $HBrO_2$ or HBrO

**18.111** Choose the *weaker* acid in each of the following pairs:
(a) HI or HBr (b) $H_3AsO_4$ or $H_2SeO_4$ (c) $HNO_3$ or $HNO_2$

**18.112** Use Appendix C to choose the solution with the *lower* pH:
(a) 0.5 $M$ $CuBr_2$ or 0.5 $M$ $AlBr_3$
(b) 0.3 $M$ $ZnCl_2$ or 0.3 $M$ $SnCl_2$

**18.113** Use Appendix C to choose the solution with the *lower* pH:
(a) 0.1 $M$ $FeCl_3$ or 0.1 $M$ $AlCl_3$
(b) 0.1 $M$ $BeCl_2$ or 0.1 $M$ $CaCl_2$

**18.114** Use Appendix C to choose the solution with the *higher* pH:
(a) 0.2 $M$ $Ni(NO_3)_2$ or 0.2 $M$ $Co(NO_3)_2$
(b) 0.35 $M$ $Al(NO_3)_3$ or 0.35 $M$ $Cr(NO_3)_3$

**18.115** Use Appendix C to choose the solution with the *higher* pH:
(a) 0.1 $M$ $NiCl_2$ or 0.1 $M$ NaCl
(b) 0.1 $M$ $Sn(NO_3)_2$ or 0.1 $M$ $Co(NO_3)_2$

## Acid-Base Properties of Salt Solutions
(Sample Problems 18.13 and 18.14)

**Concept Review Questions**

**18.116** What determines whether an aqueous solution of a salt will be acidic, basic, or neutral? Give an example of each type of salt.

**18.117** Why is aqueous NaF basic but aqueous NaCl neutral?

**18.118** The $NH_4^+$ ion forms acidic solutions, and the $CH_3COO^-$ ion forms basic solutions. However, a solution of ammonium acetate is almost neutral. Do all of the ammonium salts of weak acids form neutral solutions? Explain your answer.

**Skill-Building Exercises** (grouped in similar pairs)

**18.119** Explain with equations and calculations, when necessary, whether an aqueous solution of each of these salts is acidic, basic, or neutral: (a) KBr; (b) $NH_4I$; (c) KCN.

**18.120** Explain with equations and calculations, when necessary, whether an aqueous solution of each of these salts is acidic, basic, or neutral: (a) $Cr(NO_3)_3$; (b) NaHS; (c) $Zn(CH_3COO)_2$.

**18.121** Explain with equations and calculations, when necessary, whether an aqueous solution of each of these salts is acidic, basic, or neutral: (a) $Na_2CO_3$; (b) $CaCl_2$; (c) $Cu(NO_3)_2$.

**18.122** Explain with equations and calculations, when necessary, whether an aqueous solution of each of these salts is acidic, basic, or neutral: (a) $CH_3NH_3Cl$; (b) $KClO_4$; (c) $CoF_2$.

**18.123** Explain with equations and calculations, when necessary, whether an aqueous solution of each of these salts is acidic, basic, or neutral: (a) $SrBr_2$; (b) $Ba(CH_3COO)_2$; (c) $(CH_3)_2NH_2Br$.

**18.124** Explain with equations and calculations, when necessary, whether an aqueous solution of each of these salts is acidic, basic, or neutral: (a) $Fe(HCOO)_3$; (b) $KHCO_3$; (c) $K_2S$.

**18.125** Explain with equations and calculations, when necessary, whether an aqueous solution of each of these salts is acidic, basic, or neutral: (a) $(NH_4)_3PO_4$; (b) $Na_2SO_4$; (c) $LiClO$.

**18.126** Explain with equations and calculations, when necessary, whether an aqueous solution of each of these salts is acidic, basic, or neutral: (a) $Pb(CH_3COO)_2$; (b) $Cr(NO_2)_3$; (c) CsI.

**18.127** Rank the following salts in order of *increasing* pH of their 0.1 $M$ aqueous solutions:
(a) $KNO_3$, $K_2SO_3$, $K_2S$, $Fe(NO_3)_2$
(b) $NH_4NO_3$, $NaHSO_4$, $NaHCO_3$, $Na_2CO_3$

**18.128** Rank the following salts in order of *decreasing* pH of their 0.1 $M$ aqueous solutions:
(a) $FeCl_2$, $FeCl_3$, $MgCl_2$, $KClO_2$
(b) $NH_4Br$, $NaBrO_2$, NaBr, $NaClO_2$

## Generalizing the Brønsted-Lowry Concept: The Leveling Effect

**Concept Review Questions**

**18.129** Methoxide ion, $CH_3O^-$, and amide ion, $NH_2^-$, are very strong bases that are "leveled" by water. What does this mean? Write the reactions that occur in the leveling process. What species do the two leveled solutions have in common?

**18.130** Explain the differing extents of dissociation of $H_2SO_4$ in $CH_3COOH$, $H_2O$, and $NH_3$.

**18.131** In $H_2O$, HF is weak and the other hydrohalic acids are equally strong. In $NH_3$, however, all the hydrohalic acids are equally strong. Explain.

## Electron-Pair Donation and the Lewis Acid-Base Definition
(Sample Problem 18.15)

**Concept Review Questions**

**18.132** What feature must a molecule or ion have for it to act as a Lewis base? A Lewis acid? Explain the roles of these features.

**18.133** How do Lewis acids differ from Brønsted-Lowry acids? How are they similar? Do Lewis bases differ from Brønsted-Lowry bases? Explain.

**18.134** (a) Is a weak Brønsted-Lowry base necessarily a weak Lewis base? Explain with an example.
(b) Identify the Lewis bases in the following reaction:
$$Cu(H_2O)_4^{2+}(aq) + 4CN^-(aq) \rightleftharpoons Cu(CN)_4^{2-}(aq) + 4H_2O(l)$$
(c) Given that $K_c > 1$ for the reaction in part (b), which Lewis base is stronger?

**18.135** In which of the three acid-base concepts can water be a product of an acid-base reaction? In which is it the only product?

**18.136** (a) Give an example of a *substance* that is a base in two of the three acid-base definitions, but not in the third.
(b) Give an example of a *substance* that is an acid in one of the three acid-base definitions, but not in the other two.

**Skill-Building Exercises** (grouped in similar pairs)

**18.137** Which are Lewis acids and which are Lewis bases?
(a) $Cu^{2+}$ (b) $Cl^-$ (c) $SnCl_2$ (d) $OF_2$

**18.138** Which are Lewis acids and which are Lewis bases?
(a) $Na^+$ (b) $NH_3$ (c) $CN^-$ (d) $BF_3$

**18.139** Which are Lewis acids and which are Lewis bases?
(a) $BF_3$ (b) $S^{2-}$ (c) $SO_3^{2-}$ (d) $SO_3$

**18.140** Which are Lewis acids and which are Lewis bases?
(a) $Mg^{2+}$    (b) $OH^-$    (c) $SiF_4$    (d) $BeCl_2$

**18.141** Identify the Lewis acid and Lewis base in each equation:
(a) $Na^+ + 6H_2O \rightleftharpoons Na(H_2O)_6^+$
(b) $CO_2 + H_2O \rightleftharpoons H_2CO_3$
(c) $F^- + BF_3 \rightleftharpoons BF_4^-$

**18.142** Identify the Lewis acid and Lewis base in each equation:
(a) $Fe^{3+} + 2H_2O \rightleftharpoons FeOH^{2+} + H_3O^+$
(b) $H_2O + H^- \rightleftharpoons OH^- + H_2$
(c) $4CO + Ni \rightleftharpoons Ni(CO)_4$

**18.143** Classify the following as Arrhenius, Brønsted-Lowry, or Lewis acid-base reactions. A reaction may fit all, two, one, or none of the categories:
(a) $Ag^+ + 2NH_3 \rightleftharpoons Ag(NH_3)_2^+$
(b) $H_2SO_4 + NH_3 \rightleftharpoons HSO_4^- + NH_4^+$
(c) $2HCl \rightleftharpoons H_2 + Cl_2$
(d) $AlCl_3 + Cl^- \rightleftharpoons AlCl_4^-$

**18.144** Classify the following as Arrhenius, Brønsted-Lowry, or Lewis acid-base reactions. A reaction may fit all, two, one, or none of the categories:
(a) $Cu^{2+} + 4Cl^- \rightleftharpoons CuCl_4^{2-}$
(b) $Al(OH)_3 + 3HNO_3 \rightleftharpoons Al^{3+} + 3H_2O + 3NO_3^-$
(c) $N_2 + 3H_2 \rightleftharpoons 2NH_3$
(d) $CN^- + H_2O \rightleftharpoons HCN + OH^-$

## Comprehensive Problems

**18.145** Chloral ($Cl_3C-CH=O$) forms a monohydrate, chloral hydrate, the sleep-inducing depressant called "knockout drops" in old movies. (a) Write two possible structures for chloral hydrate, one involving hydrogen bonding and one that is a Lewis adduct. (b) What spectroscopic method could be used to identify the real structure? Explain.

**18.146** In humans, blood pH is maintained within a narrow range: *acidosis* occurs if the blood pH is below 7.35, and *alkalosis* occurs if the pH is above 7.45. Given that the $pK_w$ of blood is 13.63 at 37°C (body temperature), what is the normal range of $[H_3O^+]$ and of $[OH^-]$ in blood?

**18.147** The disinfectant phenol, $C_6H_5OH$, has a $pK_a$ of 10.0 in water, but 14.4 in methanol. (a) Why are the values different? (b) Is methanol a stronger or weaker base than water? (c) Write the dissociation reaction of phenol in methanol. (d) Write an expression for the autoionization constant of methanol.

**18.148** When carbon dioxide dissolves in water, it undergoes a multistep equilibrium process, with $K_{overall} = 4.5 \times 10^{-7}$, which is simplified to the following:

$$CO_2(g) + H_2O(l) \rightleftharpoons H_2CO_3(aq)$$
$$H_2CO_3(aq) + H_2O(l) \rightleftharpoons HCO_3^-(aq) + H_3O^+(aq)$$

(a) Classify each step as a Lewis or a Brønsted-Lowry reaction.
(b) What is the pH of nonpolluted rainwater in equilibrium with clean air ($P_{CO_2}$ in clean air = $3.2 \times 10^{-4}$ atm; Henry's law constant for $CO_2$ at 25°C is 0.033 mol/L·atm)?
(c) What is $[CO_3^{2-}]$ in rainwater ($K_a$ of $HCO_3^- = 4.7 \times 10^{-11}$)?
(d) If the partial pressure of $CO_2$ in clean air doubles in the next few decades, what will the pH of rainwater become?

**18.149** Seashells are mostly calcium carbonate, which reacts with $H_3O^+$ according to the equation

$$CaCO_3(s) + H_3O^+(aq) \rightleftharpoons Ca^{2+}(aq) + HCO_3^-(aq) + H_2O(l)$$

If $K_w$ increases at higher pressure, will seashells dissolve more rapidly near the surface of the ocean or at great depths? Explain.

**18.150** Many molecules with central atoms from Period 3 or higher take part in Lewis acid-base reactions in which the central atom expands its valence shell. $SnCl_4$ reacts with $(CH_3)_3N$ as follows:

(a) Identify the Lewis acid and the Lewis base in the reaction.
(b) Give the *nl* designation of the sublevel of the central atom in the acid before it accepts the lone pair.

**18.151** A chemist makes four successive ten-fold dilutions of $1.0 \times 10^{-5}$ *M* HCl. Calculate the pH of the original solution and of each diluted solution (through $1.0 \times 10^{-9}$ *M* HCl).

**18.152** Chlorobenzene, $C_6H_5Cl$, is a key intermediate in the manufacture of dyes and pesticides. It is made by the chlorination of benzene, catalyzed by $FeCl_3$, in this series of steps:
(1) $Cl_2 + FeCl_3 \rightleftharpoons FeCl_5$ (or $Cl^+FeCl_4^-$)
(2) $C_6H_6 + Cl^+FeCl_4^- \rightleftharpoons C_6H_6Cl^+ + FeCl_4^-$
(3) $C_6H_6Cl^+ \rightleftharpoons C_6H_5Cl + H^+$
(4) $H^+ + FeCl_4^- \rightleftharpoons HCl + FeCl_3$
(a) Which of the step(s) is (are) Lewis acid-base reactions?
(b) Identify the Lewis acids and bases in each of those steps.

**18.153** The beakers shown contain 0.300 L of aqueous solutions of a moderately weak acid HY. Each particle represents 0.010 mol; solvent molecules are omitted for clarity. (a) The reaction in beaker A is at equilibrium. Calculate $Q$ for B, C, and D to determine which, if any, is also at equilibrium. (b) For any not at equilibrium, in which direction does the reaction proceed? (c) Does dilution affect the extent of dissociation of a weak acid? Explain.

A          B          C          D

**18.154** The strength of an acid or base is related to its strength as an electrolyte. (a) Is the electrical conductivity of 0.1 *M* HCl higher, lower, or the same as that of 0.1 *M* $CH_3COOH$? Explain. (b) Is the electrical conductivity of $1 \times 10^{-7}$ *M* HCl higher, lower, or the same as that of $1 \times 10^{-7}$ *M* $CH_3COOH$? Explain.

**18.155** Esters, RCOOR′, are formed by the reaction of carboxylic acids, RCOOH, and alcohols, R′OH, where R and R′ are hydrocarbon groups. Many esters are responsible for the odors of fruit and, thus, have important uses in the food and cosmetics industries. The first two steps in the mechanism of ester formation are

(1) 
$$R-\overset{\overset{\displaystyle ..}{O}}{\underset{}{C}}-\ddot{O}H + H^+ \rightleftharpoons R-\overset{\overset{\displaystyle \ddot{O}H}{|}}{\underset{}{C}}-\overset{+}{\ddot{O}}H$$

(2) 
$$R-\overset{\overset{\displaystyle \ddot{O}H}{|}}{\underset{+}{C}}-\ddot{O}H + R'-\ddot{O}H \rightleftharpoons R-\overset{\overset{\displaystyle \ddot{O}H}{|}}{\underset{\underset{H}{\overset{|}{\underset{}{\overset{+}{O}-R'}}}}{C}}-\ddot{O}H$$

Identify the Lewis acids and Lewis bases in these two steps.

**18.156** Three beakers contain 100. mL of 0.10 $M$ HCl, HClO$_2$, and HClO, respectively. (a) Find the pH of each. (b) Describe quantitatively how to make the pH equal in the beakers through the addition of water only.

**18.157** Human urine has a normal pH of 6.2. If a person eliminates an average of 1250. mL of urine per day, how many H$^+$ ions are eliminated per week?

**18.158** Liquid ammonia autoionizes like water:

$$2NH_3(l) \longrightarrow NH_4^+(am) + NH_2^-(am)$$

where ($am$) represents solvation by NH$_3$.
(a) Write the ion-product constant expression, $K_{am}$.
(b) What are the strongest acid and base that can exist in NH$_3$($l$)?
(c) HNO$_3$ and HCOOH are leveled in NH$_3$($l$). Explain with equations.
(d) At the boiling point ($-33°C$), $K_{am} = 5.1 \times 10^{-27}$. Calculate [NH$_4^+$] at this temperature.
(e) Pure sulfuric acid also autoionizes. Write the ion-product constant expression, $K_{sulf}$, and find the concentration of the conjugate base at 20°C ($K_{sulf} = 2.7 \times 10^{-4}$ at 20°C).

**18.159** Thiamine hydrochloride (C$_{12}$H$_{18}$ON$_4$SCl$_2$) is a water-soluble form of thiamine (vitamin B$_1$; $K_a = 3.37 \times 10^{-7}$). How many grams of the hydrochloride must be dissolved in 10.00 mL of water to give a pH of 3.50?

**18.160** Tris(hydroxymethyl)aminomethane, known as TRIS or THAM, is a water-soluble base used to synthesize surfactants and pharmaceuticals, as an emulsifying agent in cosmetics, and in cleaning mixtures for textiles and leather. In biomedical research, solutions of TRIS are used to maintain nearly constant pH for the study of enzymes and other cellular components. Given that the pK$_b$ is 5.91, calculate the pH of 0.075 $M$ TRIS.

**18.161** When an Fe$^{3+}$ salt is dissolved in water, the solution becomes acidic due to formation of Fe(H$_2$O)$_5$OH$^{2+}$ and H$_3$O$^+$. The overall process involves both Lewis and Brønsted-Lowry acid-base reactions. Write the equations for the process.

**18.162** What is the pH of a vinegar with 5.0% (w/v) acetic acid in water?

**18.163** How would you differentiate between a strong and a weak monoprotic acid from the results of the following procedures? (a) Electrical conductivity of an equimolar solution of each acid is measured. (b) Equal molarities of each are tested with pH paper. (c) Zinc metal is added to solutions of equal concentration.

**18.164** The catalytic efficiency of an enzyme is called its *activity* and refers to the rate at which it catalyzes the reaction. Most enzymes have optimum activity over a relatively narrow pH range, which is related to the pH of the local cellular fluid. The pH profiles of three digestive enzymes are shown.

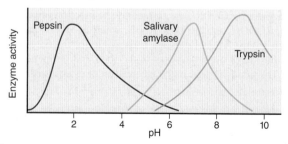

Salivary amylase begins digestion of starches in the mouth and has optimum activity at a pH of 6.8; pepsin begins protein digestion in the stomach and has optimum activity at a pH of 2.0; and

trypsin, released in pancreatic juices, continues protein digestion in the small intestine and has optimum activity at a pH of 9.5. Calculate [H$_3$O$^+$] in the local cellular fluid for each enzyme.

**18.165** Acetic acid has a $K_a$ of $1.8 \times 10^{-5}$, and ammonia has a $K_b$ of $1.8 \times 10^{-5}$. Find [H$_3$O$^+$], [OH$^-$], pH, and pOH for (a) 0.240 $M$ acetic acid and (b) 0.240 $M$ ammonia.

**18.166** The uses of sodium phosphate include clarifying crude sugar, manufacturing paper, removing boiler scale, and washing concrete. What is the pH of a solution containing 33 g of Na$_3$PO$_4$ per liter? What is [OH$^-$] of this solution?

**18.167** The Group 5A(15) hydrides react with boron trihalides in a reversible Lewis acid-base reaction. When 0.15 mol of PH$_3$BCl$_3$($s$) is introduced into a 3.0-L container at a certain temperature, $8.4 \times 10^{-3}$ mol of PH$_3$ is present at equilibrium: PH$_3$BCl$_3$($s$) $\rightleftharpoons$ PH$_3$($g$) + BCl$_3$($g$). (a) Find $K_c$ for the reaction at this temperature. (b) Draw a Lewis structure for the reactant.

**18.168** A 1.000 $m$ solution of chloroacetic acid (ClCH$_2$COOH) freezes at $-1.93°C$. Find the $K_a$ of chloroacetic acid. (Assume the molarities equal the molalities.)

**18.169** Sodium stearate (C$_{17}$H$_{35}$COONa) is a major component of bar soap. The $K_a$ of the stearic acid is $1.3 \times 10^{-5}$. What is the pH of 10.0 mL of a solution containing 0.42 g of sodium stearate?

**18.170** Calcium propionate [Ca(CH$_3$CH$_2$COO)$_2$; calcium propanoate] is a mold inhibitor used in food, tobacco, and pharmaceuticals. (a) Use balanced equations to show whether aqueous calcium propionate is acidic, basic, or neutral. (b) Use Appendix C to find the resulting pH when 8.75 g of Ca(CH$_3$CH$_2$COO)$_2$ dissolves in enough water to give 0.500 L of solution.

**18.171** A site in Pennsylvania receives a total annual deposition of 2.688 g/m$^2$ of sulfate from fertilizer and acid rain. The ratio by mass of ammonium sulfate/ammonium bisulfate/sulfuric acid is 3.0/5.5/1.0. (a) How much acid, expressed as kg of sulfuric acid, is deposited over an area of 10. km$^2$? (b) How many pounds of CaCO$_3$ are needed to neutralize this acid? (c) If 10. km$^2$ is the area of an unpolluted lake 3 m deep and there is no loss of acid, what pH would be attained in the year? (Assume constant volume.)

**18.172** (a) If $K_w = 1.139 \times 10^{-15}$ at 0°C and $5.474 \times 10^{-14}$ at 50°C, find [H$_3$O$^+$] and pH of water at 0°C and 50°C.
(b) The autoionization constant for heavy water (deuterium oxide, D$_2$O) is $3.64 \times 10^{-16}$ at 0°C and $7.89 \times 10^{-15}$ at 50°C. Find [D$_3$O$^+$] and pD of heavy water at 0°C and 50°C.
(c) Suggest a reason for these differences.

**18.173** HX ($\mathcal{M} = 150.$ g/mol) and HY ($\mathcal{M} = 50.0$ g/mol) are weak acids. A solution of 12.0 g/L of HX has the same pH as one containing 6.00 g/L of HY. Which is the stronger acid? Why?

**18.174** The beakers below depict the aqueous dissociations of weak acids HA (*blue and green*) and HB (*blue and yellow*); solvent molecules are omitted for clarity. If the HA solution is 0.50 L, and the HB solution is 0.25 L, and each particle represents 0.010 mol, find the $K_a$ of each acid. Which acid, if either, is stronger?

**18.175** In his acid-base studies, Arrhenius discovered an important fact involving reactions like the following:

$$KOH(aq) + HNO_3(aq) \longrightarrow ?$$
$$NaOH(aq) + HCl(aq) \longrightarrow ?$$

(a) Complete the reactions and use the data for the individual ions in Appendix B to calculate each $\Delta H^\circ_{rxn}$.
(b) Explain your results and use them to predict $\Delta H^\circ_{rxn}$ for

$$KOH(aq) + HCl(aq) \longrightarrow ?$$

**18.176** Putrescine [$NH_2(CH_2)_4NH_2$], found in rotting animal tissue, is now known to be in all cells and essential for normal and abnormal (cancerous) growth. It also plays a key role in the formation of GABA, a neurotransmitter. A 0.10 $M$ aqueous solution of putrescine has [$OH^-$] = $2.1\times10^{-3}$. What is the $K_b$?

**18.177** The molecular scene depicts the relative concentrations of $H_3O^+$ *(purple)* and $OH^-$ *(green)* in an aqueous solution at 25°C. (Counter ions and solvent molecules are omitted for clarity.) (a) Calculate the pH. (b) How many $H_3O^+$ ions would you have to draw for every $OH^-$ ion to depict a solution of pH 4?

**18.178** Polymers are not very soluble in water, but their solubility increases if they have charged groups. (a) Casein, a milk protein, contains many —$COO^-$ groups on its side chains. How does the solubility of casein vary with pH? (b) Histones are proteins essential to the function of DNA. They are weakly basic due to the presence of side chains with —$NH_2$ and =$NH$ groups. How does the solubility of a histone vary with pH?

**18.179** Hemoglobin (Hb) transports oxygen in the blood:

$$HbH^+(aq) + O_2(aq) + H_2O(l) \longrightarrow HbO_2(aq) + H_3O^+(aq)$$

In blood, [$H_3O^+$] is held nearly constant at $4\times10^{-8}$ $M$.
(a) How does the equilibrium position change in the lungs?
(b) How does it change in $O_2$-deficient cells?
(c) Excessive vomiting may lead to metabolic *alkalosis,* in which [$H_3O^+$] in blood *decreases.* How does this condition affect the ability of Hb to transport $O_2$?
(d) Diabetes mellitus may lead to metabolic *acidosis,* in which [$H_3O^+$] in blood *increases.* How does this condition affect the ability of Hb to transport $O_2$?

**18.180** Nitrogen is discharged from wastewater treatment facilities into rivers and streams, usually as $NH_3$ and $NH_4^+$:

$$NH_3(aq) + H_2O(l) \rightleftharpoons NH_4^+(aq) + OH^-(aq) \quad K_b = 1.76\times10^{-5}$$

One strategy for removing it is to raise the pH and "strip" the $NH_3$ from solution by bubbling air through the water. (a) At pH 7.00, what fraction of the total nitrogen in solution is $NH_3$, defined as [$NH_3$]/([$NH_3$] + [$NH_4^+$])? (b) What is the fraction at pH 10.00? (c) Explain the basis of ammonia stripping.

**18.181** A solution of propanoic acid ($CH_3CH_2COOH$), made by dissolving 7.500 g in sufficient water to make 100.0 mL, has a freezing point of $-1.890$°C.
(a) Calculate the molarity of the solution.

(b) Calculate the molarity of the propanoate ion. (Assume the molarity of the solution equals the molality.)
(c) Calculate the percent dissociation of propanoic acid.

**18.182** The antimalarial properties of quinine ($C_{20}H_{24}N_2O_2$) saved thousands of lives during construction of the Panama Canal. This substance is a classic example of the medicinal wealth of tropical forests. Both N atoms are basic, but the N (colored) of the 3° amine group is far more basic ($pK_b = 5.1$) than the N within the aromatic ring system ($pK_b = 9.7$). (a) A saturated solution of quinine in water is only $1.6\times10^{-3}$ $M$. What is the pH of this solution?

(b) Show that the aromatic N contributes negligibly to the pH of the solution.
(c) Because of its low solubility, quinine is given as the salt quinine hydrochloride ($C_{20}H_{24}N_2O_2\cdot HCl$), which is 120 times more soluble than quinine. What is the pH of 0.33 $M$ quinine hydrochloride?
(d) An antimalarial concentration in water is 1.5% quinine hydrochloride by mass ($d = 1.0$ g/mL). What is the pH?

**18.183** Drinking water is often disinfected with $Cl_2$, which hydrolyzes to form HClO, a weak acid but powerful disinfectant:

$$Cl_2(aq) + 2H_2O(l) \longrightarrow HClO(aq) + H_3O^+(aq) + Cl^-(aq)$$

The fraction of HClO in solution is defined as

$$\frac{[HClO]}{[HClO] + [ClO^-]}$$

(a) What is the fraction of HClO at pH 7.00 ($K_a$ of HClO = $2.9\times10^{-8}$)? (b) What is the fraction at pH 10.00?

**18.184** The following scenes represent three weak acids HA (where A = X, Y, or Z) dissolved in water ($H_2O$ is not shown):

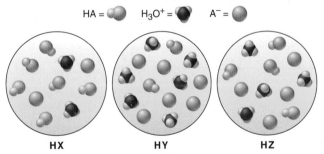

(a) Rank the acids in order of increasing $K_a$. (b) Rank the acids in order of increasing $pK_a$. (c) Rank the conjugate bases in order of increasing $pK_b$. (d) What is the percent dissociation of HX? (e) If equimolar amounts of the sodium salts of the acids (NaX, NaY, and NaZ) were dissolved in water, which solution would have the highest pOH? The lowest pH?

# Ionic Equilibria in Aqueous Systems

## Concepts and skills to review before you study this chapter

- solubility rules for ionic compounds (Section 4.3)
- effect of concentration on equilibrium position (Section 17.6)
- conjugate acid-base pairs (Section 18.3)
- calculations for weak-acid and weak-base equilibria (Sections 18.4 and 18.5)

- acid-base properties of salt solutions (Section 18.7)
- Lewis acids and bases (Section 18.9)

Expanding our view of the universal nature of equilibrium, we now examine aqueous ionic systems. The unique formations in limestone caves (*photo*) and the vast expanses of oceanic coral reefs arise from subtle shifts in carbonate solubility equilibria. Similar interactions prevent acidification of lakes. Organisms survive by maintaining cellular pH within narrow limits through complex carbonate and phosphate equilibria. In soils, equilibria involving clays control the availability of ionic nutrients for plants. In industrial settings, the same principles govern the softening of water and the purification of products by precipitation of unwanted ions. And they even explain how the weak acids in wine and vinegar influence the delicate taste of a fine sauce.

**IN THIS CHAPTER . . .** We define and quantify three aqueous ionic equilibrium systems—acid-base buffers, slightly soluble salts, and complex ions.

- We introduce the common-ion effect to explain how buffers work, and see why buffers are important and how to prepare them.
- We describe several types of acid-base titrations and the role of buffers in them.
- We see that slightly soluble salts have their own equilibrium constant and learn how a common ion and pH influence the solubility of these compounds.
- We use concepts of aqueous ionic equilibria to understand how a cave forms.
- We investigate how complex ions form and change from one type to another.

# 19.1 • EQUILIBRIA OF ACID-BASE BUFFERS

Why do some lakes become acidic when showered by acid rain, while others remain unaffected? How does blood maintain a constant pH in contact with countless cellular acid-base reactions? How can a chemist sustain a nearly constant $[H_3O^+]$ in reactions that consume or produce $H_3O^+$ or $OH^-$? The answer in each case depends on the action of a buffer, and in this section we discuss how buffers work and how to prepare them.

## What a Buffer Is and How It Works: The Common-Ion Effect

In everyday language, a buffer is something that lessens the impact of an external force. An **acid-base buffer** is a solution that *lessens the impact on pH from the addition of acid or base*. Add a small amount of $H_3O^+$ or $OH^-$ to an unbuffered solution, and the pH changes by several units, thus, $[H_3O^+]$ changes by *several orders of magnitude* (Figure 19.1).

**Figure 19.1** The effect of adding acid or base to an unbuffered solution. **A,** A 100-mL sample of dilute HCl is adjusted to pH 5.00 (*left*). **B,** Adding 1 mL of strong acid (*left*) or of strong base (*right*) changes the pH by several units.

**5.00**

**A** Unbuffered solution

**2.00** **12.00**

**B** After adding 1 mL of 1 *M* HCl    After adding 1 mL of 1 *M* NaOH

**Figure 19.2** **The effect of adding acid or base to a buffered solution.** **A,** A 100-mL sample of an acetate buffer, which was made by mixing 1 *M* CH₃COOH with 1 *M* CH₃COONa, is adjusted to pH 5.00. **B,** Add-ing 1 mL of strong acid (*left*) or of strong base (*right*) changes the pH negligibly.

The same addition of strong acid or strong base to a buffered solution causes only a minor change in pH (Figure 19.2). To withstand these additions, a buffer must have an acidic component that reacts with the added $OH^-$ *and* a basic component that reacts with the added $H_3O^+$. However, these components can't be any acid and base because they would neutralize each other. Most often, *the components of a buffer are a conjugate acid-base pair* (weak acid and conjugate base or weak base and conjugate acid). The buffer in Figure 19.2, for example, is a mixture of acetic acid ($CH_3COOH$) and acetate ion ($CH_3COO^-$).

**Presence of a Common Ion**  Buffers work through the **common-ion effect.** When you dissolve acetic acid in water, the acid dissociates slightly:

$$CH_3COOH(aq) + H_2O(l) \rightleftharpoons H_3O^+(aq) + CH_3COO^-(aq)$$

What happens if you now introduce acetate ion by adding the soluble salt sodium acetate? From Le Châtelier's principle (Section 17.6), we know that adding $CH_3COO^-$ ion will shift the equilibrium position to the left; thus, $[H_3O^+]$ decreases, in effect lowering the extent of acid dissociation:

$$CH_3COOH(aq) + H_2O(l) \overset{\longleftarrow}{\rightleftharpoons} H_3O^+(aq) + CH_3COO^-(aq; \text{added})$$

We get the same result when we add acetic acid to a sodium acetate solution instead of water. The acetate ion already present suppresses the acid from dissociating as much as it does in water, thus keeping the $[H_3O^+]$ lower. In either case, the effect is less acid dissociation. Acetate ion is called *the common ion* because it is "common" to both the acetic acid and sodium acetate solutions. *The common-ion effect occurs when a given ion is added to an equilibrium mixture that already contains that ion, and the position of equilibrium shifts away from forming it.*

Table 19.1 shows that the percent dissociation (and the $[H_3O^+]$) of an acetic acid solution decreases as the concentration of acetate ion (supplied by dissolving sodium acetate) increases. Thus, the *common ion, $A^-$, suppresses the dissociation of HA,* which makes the solution less acidic (higher pH).

| Table **19.1** The Effect of Added Acetate Ion on the Dissociation of Acetic Acid | | | | |
|---|---|---|---|---|
| **[CH₃COOH]ᵢₙᵢₜ** | **[CH₃COO⁻]ₐ𝒹𝒹ₑ𝒹** | **% Dissociation\*** | **H₃O⁺** | **pH** |
| 0.10 | 0.00 | 1.3 | $1.3 \times 10^{-3}$ | 2.89 |
| 0.10 | 0.050 | 0.036 | $3.6 \times 10^{-5}$ | 4.44 |
| 0.10 | 0.10 | 0.018 | $1.8 \times 10^{-5}$ | 4.74 |
| 0.10 | 0.15 | 0.012 | $1.2 \times 10^{-5}$ | 4.92 |

$$*\% \text{ Dissociation} = \frac{[CH_3COOH]_{\text{dissoc}}}{[CH_3COOH]_{\text{init}}} \times 100$$

**Relative Concentrations of Buffer Components** A buffer works because *large amounts of the acidic (HA) and basic (A⁻) components consume small amounts of added OH⁻ or H₃O⁺, respectively.* Consider what happens in a solution containing high $[CH_3COOH]$ and high $[CH_3COO^-]$ when we add small amounts of strong acid or base. The equilibrium expression for HA dissociation is

$$K_a = \frac{[CH_3COO^-][H_3O^+]}{[CH_3COOH]}$$

Solving for $[H_3O^+]$ gives

$$[H_3O^+] = K_a \times \frac{[CH_3COOH]}{[CH_3COO^-]}$$

Since $K_a$ is constant, *the $[H_3O^+]$ of the solution depends on the buffer-component concentration ratio,* $\frac{[CH_3COOH]}{[CH_3COO^-]}$:

- If the ratio $[HA]/[A^-]$ goes up, $[H_3O^+]$ goes up.
- If the ratio $[HA]/[A^-]$ goes down, $[H_3O^+]$ goes down.

Let's track this ratio as we add strong acid or strong base to a buffer in which $[HA] = [A^-]$ (Figure 19.3, *middle*):

1. *Strong acid.* When we add a small amount of strong acid, the $H_3O^+$ ions react with an *equal (stoichiometric) amount* of acetate ion from the buffer to form more acetic acid:

$$H_3O^+(aq; \text{added}) + CH_3COO^-(aq; \text{from buffer}) \longrightarrow CH_3COOH(aq) + H_2O(l)$$

As a result, $[CH_3COO^-]$ goes down by that small amount and $[CH_3COOH]$ goes up by that amount, which increases the buffer-component concentration ratio (Figure 19.3, *to the left*). The $[H_3O^+]$ increases *very* slightly.

2. *Strong base.* The addition of a small amount of strong base produces the opposite result. The $OH^-$ ions react with an *equal (stoichiometric) amount* of $CH_3COOH$ from the buffer to form that much more $CH_3COO^-$ (Figure 19.3, *to the right*):

$$CH_3COOH(aq; \text{from buffer}) + OH^-(aq; \text{added}) \longrightarrow CH_3COO^-(aq) + H_2O(l)$$

This time, the buffer-component concentration ratio decreases, which decreases $[H_3O^+]$ *very* slightly.

Thus, the buffer components consume *nearly all* the added $H_3O^+$ or $OH^-$. To reiterate, as long as the amount of added $H_3O^+$ or $OH^-$ is small compared with the

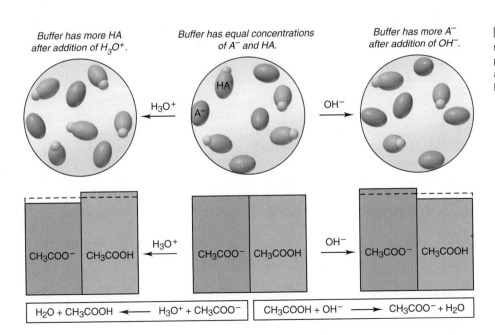

Buffer has more HA after addition of $H_3O^+$.

Buffer has equal concentrations of A⁻ and HA.

Buffer has more A⁻ after addition of $OH^-$.

**Figure 19.3 How a buffer works.** The relative concentrations of the buffer components, acetic acid (CH₃COOH, *red*) and acetate ion (CH₃COO⁻, *blue*) are indicated by the heights of the bars.

amounts of the buffer components, *the conversion of one component into the other produces a small change in the buffer-component concentration ratio and, consequently, a small change in [H₃O⁺] and in pH.* Sample Problem 19.1 demonstrates how small these pH changes typically are. Note that the latter two parts of the problem combine a stoichiometry portion, like the problems in Chapter 3, and a weak-acid dissociation portion, like those in Chapter 18.

---

**Sample Problem 19.1** Calculating the Effect of Added $H_3O^+$ or $OH^-$ on Buffer pH

**Problem** Calculate the pH:
**(a)** Of a buffer solution consisting of 0.50 *M* $CH_3COOH$ and 0.50 *M* $CH_3COONa$
**(b)** After adding 0.020 mol of solid NaOH to 1.0 L of the buffer solution in part (a)
**(c)** After adding 0.020 mol of HCl to 1.0 L of the buffer solution in part (a)
$K_a$ of $CH_3COOH = 1.8 \times 10^{-5}$. (Assume the additions cause negligible volume changes.)

**Plan** For each part, we know, or can find, $[CH_3COOH]_{init}$ and $[CH_3COO^-]_{init}$. We know the $K_a$ of $CH_3COOH$ ($1.8 \times 10^{-5}$) and need to find $[H_3O^+]$ at equilibrium and convert it to pH. **(a)** We use the given concentrations of buffer components (each 0.50 *M*) as the initial values. As in earlier problems, we assume that *x*, the $[CH_3COOH]$ that dissociates, which equals $[H_3O^+]$, is so small relative to $[CH_3COOH]_{init}$ that it can be neglected. We set up a reaction table, solve for *x*, and check the assumption. **(b)** and **(c)** We assume that the added $OH^-$ or $H_3O^+$ reacts completely with the buffer components to yield new $[CH_3COOH]_{init}$ and $[CH_3COO^-]_{init}$, and then the acid dissociates to an unknown extent. We set up two reaction tables. The first summarizes the stoichiometry of adding strong base (0.020 mol) or acid (0.020 mol). The second summarizes the dissociation of the new $[CH_3COOH]_{init}$, and we proceed as in part (a) to find the new $[H_3O^+]$.

**Solution** **(a)** The original pH: $[H_3O^+]$ in the original buffer. Setting up a reaction table with $x = [CH_3COOH]_{dissoc} = [H_3O^+]$ (as in Chapter 18, we assume that $[H_3O^+]$ from $H_2O$ is negligible and disregard it):

| Concentration (*M*) | $CH_3COOH(aq)$ | + $H_2O(l)$ | $\rightleftharpoons$ | $CH_3COO^-(aq)$ | + $H_3O^+(aq)$ |
|---|---|---|---|---|---|
| Initial | 0.50 | — | | 0.50 | 0 |
| Change | $-x$ | — | | $+x$ | $+x$ |
| Equilibrium | $0.50 - x$ | — | | $0.50 + x$ | $x$ |

Making the assumption and finding the equilibrium $[CH_3COOH]$ and $[CH_3COO^-]$: With $K_a$ small, *x* is small, so we assume

$$[CH_3COOH] = 0.50\ M - x \approx 0.50\ M \quad \text{and} \quad [CH_3COO^-] = 0.50\ M + x \approx 0.50\ M$$

Solving for *x* ($[H_3O^+]$ at equilibrium):

$$x = [H_3O^+] = K_a \times \frac{[CH_3COOH]}{[CH_3COO^-]} \approx (1.8 \times 10^{-5}) \times \frac{0.50}{0.50} = 1.8 \times 10^{-5}\ M$$

Checking the assumption:

$$\frac{1.8 \times 10^{-5}\ M}{0.50\ M} \times 100 = 3.6 \times 10^{-3}\% < 5\%$$

The assumption is justified, and we will use the same assumption in parts (b) and (c). Also, according to the other criterion (see Sample Problems 17.10 and 18.8),

$$\frac{[HA]_{init}}{K_a} = \frac{0.50}{1.8 \times 10^{-5}} = 2.8 \times 10^4 > 400$$

Calculating pH:

$$pH = -\log[H_3O^+] = -\log(1.8 \times 10^{-5}) = \boxed{4.74}$$

**(b)** The pH after adding base (0.020 mol of NaOH to 1.0 L of buffer). Finding $[OH^-]_{added}$:

$$[OH^-]_{added} = \frac{0.020\ \text{mol}\ OH^-}{1.0\ \text{L soln}} = 0.020\ M\ OH^-$$

Setting up a reaction table for the *stoichiometry* of adding $OH^-$ to $CH_3COOH$:

| Concentration (*M*) | $CH_3COOH(aq)$ | + $OH^-(aq)$ | $\longrightarrow$ | $CH_3COO^-(aq)$ | + $H_2O(l)$ |
|---|---|---|---|---|---|
| Initial | 0.50 | 0.020 | | 0.50 | — |
| Change | $-0.020$ | $-0.020$ | | $+0.020$ | — |
| Final | 0.48 | 0 | | 0.52 | — |

Setting up a reaction table for the *acid dissociation,* using these new initial concentrations. As in part (a), $x = [CH_3COOH]_{dissoc} = [H_3O^+]$:

| Concentration (M) | $CH_3COOH(aq)$ | $+ H_2O(l)$ | $\rightleftharpoons$ | $CH_3COO^-(aq)$ | $+ H_3O^+(aq)$ |
|---|---|---|---|---|---|
| Initial | 0.48 | — | | 0.52 | 0 |
| Change | $-x$ | — | | $+x$ | $+x$ |
| Equilibrium | $0.48 - x$ | — | | $0.52 + x$ | $x$ |

Making the assumption that $x$ is small, and solving for $x$:

$$[CH_3COOH] = 0.48\ M - x \approx 0.48\ M \quad \text{and} \quad [CH_3COO^-] = 0.52\ M + x \approx 0.52\ M$$

$$x = [H_3O^+] = K_a \times \frac{[CH_3COOH]}{[CH_3COO^-]} \approx (1.8 \times 10^{-5}) \times \frac{0.48}{0.52} = 1.7 \times 10^{-5}\ M$$

Calculating the pH:

$$pH = -\log[H_3O^+] = -\log(1.7 \times 10^{-5}) = \boxed{4.77}$$

The addition of strong base increased the concentration of the basic buffer component at the expense of the acidic buffer component. Note especially that the pH *increased only slightly,* from 4.74 to 4.77.

**(c)** The pH after adding acid (0.020 mol of HCl to 1.0 L of buffer). Finding $[H_3O^+]_{added}$:

$$[H_3O^+]_{added} = \frac{0.020\ \text{mol } H_3O^+}{1.0\ \text{L soln}} = 0.020\ M\ H_3O^+$$

Now we proceed as in part (b), by first setting up a reaction table for the *stoichiometry* of adding $H_3O^+$ to $CH_3COO^-$:

| Concentration (M) | $CH_3COO^-(aq)$ | $+ H_3O^+(aq)$ | $\longrightarrow$ | $CH_3COOH(aq)$ | $+ H_2O(l)$ |
|---|---|---|---|---|---|
| Initial | 0.50 | 0.020 | | 0.50 | — |
| Change | $-0.020$ | $-0.020$ | | $+0.020$ | — |
| Final | 0.48 | 0 | | 0.52 | — |

The reaction table for the *acid dissociation,* with $x = [CH_3COOH]_{dissoc} = [H_3O^+]$ is

| Concentration (M) | $CH_3COOH(aq)$ | $+ H_2O(l)$ | $\rightleftharpoons$ | $CH_3COO^-(aq)$ | $+ H_3O^+(aq)$ |
|---|---|---|---|---|---|
| Initial | 0.52 | — | | 0.48 | 0 |
| Change | $-x$ | — | | $+x$ | $+x$ |
| Equilibrium | $0.52 - x$ | — | | $0.48 + x$ | $x$ |

Making the assumption that $x$ is small, and solving for $x$:

$$[CH_3COOH] = 0.52\ M - x \approx 0.52\ M \quad \text{and} \quad [CH_3COO^-] = 0.48\ M + x \approx 0.48\ M$$

$$x = [H_3O^+] = K_a \times \frac{[CH_3COOH]}{[CH_3COO^-]} \approx (1.8 \times 10^{-5}) \times \frac{0.52}{0.48} = 2.0 \times 10^{-5}\ M$$

Calculating the pH:

$$pH = -\log[H_3O^+] = -\log(2.0 \times 10^{-5}) = \boxed{4.70}$$

The addition of strong acid increased the concentration of the acidic buffer component at the expense of the basic buffer component and *lowered* the pH only slightly, from 4.74 to 4.70.

**Check** The changes in $[CH_3COOH]$ and $[CH_3COO^-]$ occur in opposite directions in parts (b) and (c), which makes sense. The additions were of equal amounts, so the pH increase in (b) should equal the pH decrease in (c), within rounding.

**Comment** In part (a), we justified our assumption that $x$ can be neglected. Therefore, in parts (b) and (c), we could have used the "Final" values from the last line of the stoichiometry reaction tables directly for the ratio of buffer components; that would have allowed us to dispense with a reaction table for the acid dissociation. In subsequent problems in this chapter, we will follow this more straightforward approach.

**Follow-Up Problem 19.1** Calculate the pH of a buffer consisting of 0.50 $M$ HF and 0.45 $M$ $F^-$ **(a)** before and **(b)** after addition of 0.40 g of NaOH to 1.0 L of the buffer ($K_a$ of HF = $6.8 \times 10^{-4}$).

## The Henderson-Hasselbalch Equation

For any weak acid, HA, the dissociation equation and $K_a$ expression are

$$HA + H_2O \rightleftharpoons H_3O^+ + A^-$$

$$K_a = \frac{[H_3O^+][A^-]}{[HA]}$$

The key variable that determines $[H_3O^+]$ is the concentration *ratio* of acid species to base species, so, as before, rearranging to isolate $[H_3O^+]$ gives

$$[H_3O^+] = K_a \times \frac{[HA]}{[A^-]}$$

Taking the negative common (base 10) logarithm of both sides gives

$$-\log[H_3O^+] = -\log K_a - \log\left(\frac{[HA]}{[A^-]}\right)$$

from which definitions give   $pH = pK_a - \log\dfrac{[HA]}{[A^-]}$

Then, because of the nature of logarithms, when we invert the buffer-component concentration ratio, the sign of the logarithm changes, to give $pH = pK_a + \log\left(\dfrac{[A^-]}{[HA]}\right)$.

Generalizing the previous equation for any conjugate acid-base pair gives the **Henderson-Hasselbalch equation:**

$$pH = pK_a + \log\left(\frac{[\text{base}]}{[\text{acid}]}\right) \tag{19.1}$$

This relationship allows us to solve directly for pH instead of having to calculate $[H_3O^+]$ first. For instance, using the Henderson-Hasselbalch equation in part (b) of Sample Problem 19.1, the pH of the buffer after the addition of NaOH is

$$pH = pK_a + \log\left(\frac{[CH_3COO^-]}{[CH_3COOH]}\right) = 4.74 + \log\left(\frac{0.52}{0.48}\right) = 4.77$$

## Buffer Capacity and Buffer Range

Let's consider two key aspects of a buffer—its capacity and the closely related range.

**Buffer Capacity** **Buffer capacity** is a measure of the "strength" of the buffer, its ability to maintain the pH following addition of strong acid or base. Capacity depends ultimately on component concentrations, both the absolute and relative concentrations:

1. In terms of *absolute* concentrations, *the more concentrated the buffer components, the greater the capacity.* Thus, for a given amount of added $H_3O^+$ or $OH^-$, the pH of a higher capacity buffer changes less than the pH of a lower capacity buffer (Figure 19.4). Note that *buffer pH is independent of buffer capacity.* A buffer made of equal volumes of 1.0 $M$ $CH_3COOH$ and 1.0 $M$ $CH_3COO^-$ has the same pH (4.74) as a buffer made of equal volumes of 0.10 $M$ $CH_3COOH$ and 0.10 $M$ $CH_3COO^-$, but the more concentrated buffer has a greater capacity.

2. In terms of *relative* concentrations, *the closer the component concentrations are to each other, the greater the capacity.* As a buffer functions, the concentration of one component increases relative to the other. Because the concentration ratio determines the pH, the less the ratio changes, the less the pH changes. Let's compare the percent change in component concentration ratio for a buffer at two different initial ratios:

• Add 0.010 mol of $OH^-$ to 1.00 L of buffer with initial concentrations $[HA] = [A^-] = 1.000\ M$: $[A^-]$ becomes 1.010 $M$ and $[HA]$ becomes 0.990 $M$,

$$\frac{[A^-]_{init}}{[HA]_{init}} = \frac{1.000\ M}{1.000\ M} = 1.000 \qquad \frac{[A^-]_{final}}{[HA]_{final}} = \frac{1.010\ M}{0.990\ M} = 1.02$$

$$\text{Percent change} = \frac{1.02 - 1.000}{1.000} \times 100 = 2\%$$

*When strong base is added, the pH increases least for the most concentrated buffer.*

1.0 $M$

0.30 $M$

0.10 $M$

0.030 $M$

Concentration of buffer components

4.8   4.9   5.0   5.1

(initial pH = 4.74)

pH

**Figure 19.4** **The relation between buffer capacity and pH change.** The bars indicate the final pH values, after strong base was added, for four $CH_3COOH/CH_3COO^-$ buffers with the same initial pH (4.74) and different component concentrations.

- Add 0.010 mol of $OH^-$ to 1.00 L of buffer with initial concentrations [HA] = 0.250 $M$ and [$A^-$] = 1.750 $M$: [$A^-$] becomes 1.760 $M$ and [HA] becomes 0.240 $M$,

$$\frac{[A^-]_{init}}{[HA]_{init}} = \frac{1.750\ M}{0.250\ M} = 7.00 \qquad \frac{[A^-]_{final}}{[HA]_{final}} = \frac{1.760\ M}{0.240\ M} = 7.33$$

$$\text{Percent change} = \frac{7.33 - 7.00}{7.00} \times 100 = 4.7\%$$

Note that the change in the concentration ratio is more than twice as large when the initial component concentrations are different than when they are the same. Thus, *a buffer has the highest capacity when the component concentrations are equal.* In the Henderson-Hasselbalch equation, when [$A^-$] = [HA], their ratio is 1, the log term is 0, and so pH = $pK_a$:

$$pH = pK_a + \log\left(\frac{[A^-]}{[HA]}\right) = pK_a + \log 1 = pK_a + 0 = pK_a$$

Therefore, *a buffer whose pH is equal to or near the $pK_a$ of its acid component has the highest capacity* for a given concentration.

**Buffer Range** **Buffer range** is the pH range over which the buffer is effective and is also related to the *relative* buffer-component concentrations. The further the concentration ratio is from 1, the less effective the buffer (the lower the buffer capacity). In practice, if the [$A^-$]/[HA] ratio is greater than 10 or less than 0.1—that is, if one component concentration is more than 10 times the other—buffering action is poor. Since log 10 = +1 and log 0.1 = −1, *buffers have a usable range within ±1 pH unit of the $pK_a$ of the acid component:*

$$pH = pK_a + \log\left(\frac{10}{1}\right) = pK_a + 1 \qquad \text{and} \qquad pH = pK_a + \log\left(\frac{1}{10}\right) = pK_a - 1$$

---

**Sample Problem 19.2** **Using Molecular Scenes to Examine Buffers**

**Problem** The molecular scenes below represent samples of four HA/$A^-$ buffers. (HA is blue and green, $A^-$ is green, and other ions and water are not shown.)

1      2      3      4

**(a)** Which buffer has the highest pH?
**(b)** Which buffer has the greatest capacity?
**(c)** Should we add a small amount of concentrated strong acid or strong base to convert sample 1 to sample 2 (assuming no volume change)?

**Plan** The molecular scenes show varying numbers of weak acid molecules (HA) and the conjugate base ($A^-$). Because the volumes are equal, the scenes represent molarities as well as numbers. **(a)** As the pH rises, more HA loses its $H^+$ and becomes $A^-$, so the [$A^-$]/[HA] ratio will increase. We examine the scenes to see which has the highest ratio. **(b)** Buffer capacity depends on buffer-component concentration *and* ratio. We examine the scenes to see which has a high concentration and a ratio close to 1. **(c)** Adding strong acid converts some $A^-$ to HA, and adding strong base does the opposite. Comparing the [$A^-$]/[HA] ratios in samples 1 and 2 tells us which to add.

**Solution** **(a)** The [$A^-$]/[HA] ratios are as follows: For sample 1, [$A^-$]/[HA] = 3/3 = 1. Similarly, sample 2 = 0.5; sample 3 = 1; sample 4 = 2. Sample 4 has the highest pH because it has the highest [$A^-$]/[HA] ratio.
**(b)** Samples 1 and 3 have a [$A^-$]/[HA] ratio of 1, but sample 3 has the greater capacity because it has a higher concentration.
**(c)** Sample 2 has a lower [$A^-$]/[HA] ratio than sample 1, so we would add strong acid to sample 1 to convert some $A^-$ to HA.

**Follow-Up Problem 19.2** The molecular scene (*see margin*) shows a sample of an HB/B⁻ buffer. (HB is blue and yellow, B⁻ is yellow, and other ions and water are not shown.)
**(a)** Would you add a small amount of concentrated strong acid or strong base to increase the buffer capacity?
**(b)** Assuming no volume change, draw a scene that represents the buffer with the highest possible capacity after the addition in part (a).

## Preparing a Buffer

Even though chemical supply-houses offer buffers in a variety of pH values and concentrations, you may have to prepare a specific one, for example, in an environmental or biomedical application. Several steps are required to prepare a buffer:

1. *Choose the conjugate acid-base pair.* Deciding on the chemical composition is based to a large extent on the desired pH. Suppose that, for a biochemical experiment, you need a buffer whose pH is 3.90. Therefore, to maximize the capacity, the $pK_a$ of the acid component should be close to 3.90; or $K_a = 10^{-3.90} = 1.3 \times 10^{-4}$. A table of $K_a$ values (see Appendix C) shows that lactic acid ($pK_a = 3.86$), glycolic acid ($pK_a = 3.83$), and formic acid ($pK_a = 3.74$) are possibilities. To avoid substances that are common in biochemical systems, you choose formic acid, HCOOH, and formate ion, HCOO⁻, supplied by a soluble salt, such as sodium formate, HCOONa, as the basic component.

2. *Calculate the ratio of buffer component concentrations.* To find the ratio [A⁻]/[HA] that gives the desired pH, we have

$$pH = pK_a + \log\left(\frac{[A^-]}{[HA]}\right) \qquad \text{or} \qquad 3.90 = 3.74 + \log\left(\frac{[HCOO^-]}{[HCOOH]}\right)$$

$$\log\left(\frac{[HCOO^-]}{[HCOOH]}\right) = 0.16 \qquad \text{so} \qquad \left(\frac{[HCOO^-]}{[HCOOH]}\right) = 10^{0.16} = 1.4$$

Thus, for every 1.0 mol of HCOOH in a given volume of solution, you need 1.4 mol of HCOONa.

3. *Determine the buffer concentration.* For most laboratory-scale applications, concentrations of about 0.5 $M$ are suitable, but the decision is often based on availability of stock solutions. Suppose you have a large stock of 0.40 $M$ HCOOH and you need approximately 1.0 L of final buffer. First, you find the amount (mol) of sodium formate that will give the needed 1.4/1.0 ratio, and then convert to mass (g):

$$\text{Amount (mol) of HCOOH} = 1.0 \text{ L soln} \times \frac{0.40 \text{ mol HCOOH}}{1.0 \text{ L soln}} = 0.40 \text{ mol HCOOH}$$

$$\text{Amount (mol) of HCOONa} = 0.40 \text{ mol HCOOH} \times \frac{1.4 \text{ mol HCOONa}}{1.0 \text{ mol HCOOH}} = 0.56 \text{ mol HCOONa}$$

$$\text{Mass (g) of HCOONa} = 0.56 \text{ mol HCOONa} \times \frac{68.01 \text{ g HCOONa}}{1 \text{ mol HCOONa}} = 38 \text{ g HCOONa}$$

4. *Mix the solution and correct the pH.* You dissolve 38 g of sodium formate in the stock 0.40 $M$ HCOOH to a total volume of 1.0 L. Because of nonideal behavior (Section 13.6), the buffer may vary slightly from the desired pH, so you add strong acid or strong base dropwise, while monitoring the solution with a pH meter.

**Sample Problem 19.3** Preparing a Buffer

**Problem** An environmental chemist needs a carbonate buffer of pH 10.00 to study the effects of acid rain on limestone-rich soils. How many grams of $Na_2CO_3$ must she add to 1.5 L of 0.20 $M$ $NaHCO_3$ to make the buffer? $K_a$ of $HCO_3^-$ is $4.7 \times 10^{-11}$.

**Plan** The conjugate pair is $HCO_3^-$ (acid) and $CO_3^{2-}$ (base), and we know the buffer volume (1.5 L) and the concentration (0.20 $M$) of $HCO_3^-$, so we need the buffer-component concentration ratio that gives pH 10.00 and the mass of $Na_2CO_3$ to dissolve.

We convert pH to $[H_3O^+]$ and use the $K_a$ expression to solve for $[CO_3^{2-}]$. Multiplying by the volume of solution gives the amount (mol) of $CO_3^{2-}$ needed, which we convert to mass (g) of $Na_2CO_3$.

**Solution** Calculating $[H_3O^+]$: $[H_3O^+] = 10^{-pH} = 10^{-10.00} = 1.0\times10^{-10}\ M$
Solving for $[CO_3^{2-}]$ in the concentration ratio:

$$HCO_3^-(aq) + H_2O(l) \rightleftharpoons H_3O^+(aq) + CO_3^{2-}(aq) \qquad K_a = \frac{[H_3O^+][CO_3^{2-}]}{[HCO_3^-]}$$

So
$$[CO_3^{2-}] = \frac{K_a[HCO_3^-]}{[H_3O^+]} = \frac{(4.7\times10^{-11})(0.20)}{1.0\times10^{-10}} = 0.094\ M$$

Calculating the amount (mol) of $CO_3^{2-}$ needed for the given volume:

$$\text{Amount (mol) of } CO_3^{2-} = 1.5\ \text{L soln} \times \frac{0.094\ \text{mol } CO_3^{2-}}{1\ \text{L soln}} = 0.14\ \text{mol } CO_3^{2-}$$

Calculating the mass (g) of $Na_2CO_3$ needed:

$$\text{Mass (g) of } Na_2CO_3 = 0.14\ \text{mol } Na_2CO_3 \times \frac{105.99\ \text{g } Na_2CO_3}{1\ \text{mol } Na_2CO_3} = \boxed{15\ \text{g } Na_2CO_3}$$

The chemist should dissolve 15 g of $Na_2CO_3$ into about 1.3 L of 0.20 $M$ $NaHCO_3$ and add more 0.20 $M$ $NaHCO_3$ to make 1.5 L. Using a pH meter, she can then adjust the pH to 10.00 by dropwise addition of concentrated strong acid or base.

**Check** For a useful buffer range, the concentration of the acidic component, $[HCO_3^-]$, must be within a factor of 10 of the concentration of the basic component, $[CO_3^{2-}]$. And we have (1.5 L)(0.20 $M$ $HCO_3^-$), or 0.30 mol of $HCO_3^-$, and 0.14 mol of $CO_3^{2-}$; $0.30/0.14 = 2.1$. Make sure the relative amounts of components are reasonable: we want a pH below the $pK_a$ of $HCO_3^-$ (10.33), so we want more of the acidic than the basic species.

**Follow-Up Problem 19.3** How would you prepare a benzoic acid/benzoate buffer with pH = 4.25, starting with 5.0 L of 0.050 $M$ sodium benzoate ($C_6H_5COONa$) solution and adding the acidic component? $K_a$ of benzoic acid ($C_6H_5COOH$) is $6.3\times10^{-5}$.

Another way to prepare a buffer is to form one of the components by *partial neutralization* of the other. For example, you can prepare an $HCOOH/HCOO^-$ buffer by mixing aqueous solutions of HCOOH and NaOH. As $OH^-$ reacts with HCOOH, neutralization of some of the HCOOH produces the $HCOO^-$ needed:

HCOOH (HA total) + $OH^-$(amt added) $\longrightarrow$
    HCOOH (HA total − $OH^-$ amt added) + $HCOO^-$($OH^-$ amt added) + $H_2O$

This method is based on the same chemical process that occurs when a weak acid is titrated with a strong base, as you'll see in Section 19.2.

## ▌Summary of Section 19.1
- The pH of a buffered solution changes much less than the pH of an unbuffered solution when $H_3O^+$ or $OH^-$ is added.
- A buffer consists of a weak acid and its conjugate base (or a weak base and its conjugate acid). To be effective, the amounts of the components must be *much* greater than the amount of $H_3O^+$ or $OH^-$ added.
- The buffer-component concentration ratio determines the pH; the ratio and the pH are related by the Henderson-Hasselbalch equation.
- When $H_3O^+$ or $OH^-$ is added to a buffer, one component reacts to form the other; thus, $[H_3O^+]$ (and pH) changes only slightly.
- A concentrated (higher capacity) buffer undergoes smaller changes in pH than a dilute buffer. When the buffer pH equals the $pK_a$ of the acid component, the buffer has its highest capacity.
- A buffer has an effective pH range of $pK_a \pm 1$ pH unit.
- To prepare a buffer, choose the conjugate acid-base pair, calculate the ratio of components, determine the buffer concentration, and adjust the final solution to the desired pH.

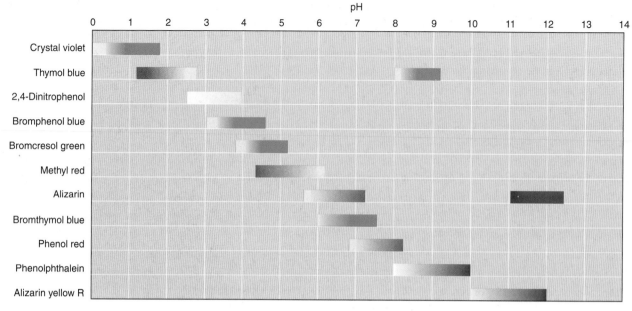

**Figure 19.5** Colors and approximate pH ranges of some common acid-base indicators.

## 19.2 • ACID-BASE TITRATION CURVES

In Chapter 4, we used titrations to quantify acid-base (and redox) reactions. In this section, we focus on the **acid-base titration curve,** a plot of pH vs. volume of titrant added. We discuss curves for strong acid–strong base, weak acid–strong base, weak base–strong acid, and polyprotic acid–strong base titrations. Running a titration is an exercise for the lab, but understanding the role of acid-base indicators and seeing how salt solutions (Section 18.7) and buffers are involved applies key principles of acid-base equilibria.

### Monitoring pH with Acid-Base Indicators

An *acid-base indicator* is a weak organic acid (denoted here as HIn) whose color differs from the color of its conjugate base (In⁻) and whose color change occurs over a specific, narrow pH range. Typically, one or both forms are intensely colored, so only a tiny amount of indicator is needed, far too little to affect the pH during the titration.

Figure 19.5 shows the color change(s) and pH range(s) of some acid-base indicators. To select an indicator, you must know the approximate pH of the titration end point, which means you know the ionic species present. Because the indicator is a weak acid, the [HIn]/[In⁻] ratio is governed by the [H₃O⁺] of the solution:

$$HIn(aq) + H_2O(l) \rightleftharpoons H_3O^+(aq) + In^-(aq) \qquad K_a \text{ of HIn} = \frac{[H_3O^+][In^-]}{[HIn]}$$

Therefore,
$$\frac{[HIn]}{[In^-]} = \frac{[H_3O^+]}{K_a}$$

An indicator's color reflects the concentration ratio:

- We see the HIn color if the [HIn]/[In⁻] ratio is 10/1 or greater.
- We see the In⁻ color if the [HIn]/[In⁻] ratio is 1/10 or less.
- Between these extremes, the two colors merge into an intermediate hue.

Thus, an indicator has a *color range* equal to a $10^2$-fold range in the [HIn]/[In] ratio: an *indicator changes color over a range of about 2 pH units.* For example, bromthymol blue has a pH range of about 6.0 to 7.6. As Figure 19.6 shows, it is yellow below that range (*left*), blue above it (*right*), and greenish in between (*center*).

**Figure 19.6** The color change of the indicator bromthymol blue.

## Strong Acid–Strong Base Titration Curves

Figure 19.7 shows a typical curve for the titration of a strong acid with a strong base, the data used to construct it, and molecular views of the key species in solution at various points during the titration.

**Features of the Curve**  There are three distinct regions of the titration curve, which correspond to three major changes in slope:

1. *The pH starts out low,* reflecting the high $[H_3O^+]$ of the strong acid, and increases slowly as acid is gradually neutralized by the added base.
2. *The pH rises 6 to 8 units very rapidly.* This steep increase begins when the amount (mol) of $OH^-$ added nearly equals the amount (mol) of $H_3O^+$ originally present in the acid. One or two more drops of base neutralize the remaining tiny excess of acid and introduce a tiny excess of base.
3. *The pH increases slowly* beyond the steep rise as more base is added.

Let's distinguish between the *equivalence point* and the *end point,* both of which occur on the steep portion of the curve:

- The **equivalence point** occurs when the *number of moles of added $OH^-$ equals the number of moles of $H_3O^+$ originally present. The solution consists of the anion of the strong acid and the cation of the strong base.* Recall from Chapter 18 that *these ions do not react with water, so the solution is neutral: pH = 7.00.*

| Volume of NaOH added (mL) | pH |
|---|---|
| 00.00 | 1.00 |
| 10.00 | 1.22 |
| 20.00 | 1.48 |
| 30.00 | 1.85 |
| 35.00 | 2.18 |
| 39.00 | 2.89 |
| 39.50 | 3.20 |
| 39.75 | 3.50 |
| 39.90 | 3.90 |
| 39.95 | 4.20 |
| 39.99 | 4.90 |
| 40.00 | 7.00 |
| 40.01 | 9.10 |
| 40.05 | 9.80 |
| 40.10 | 10.10 |
| 40.25 | 10.50 |
| 40.50 | 10.79 |
| 41.00 | 11.09 |
| 45.00 | 11.76 |
| 50.00 | 12.05 |
| 60.00 | 12.30 |
| 70.00 | 12.43 |
| 80.00 | 12.52 |

Titration of 40.00 mL of 0.1000 *M* HCl with 0.1000 *M* NaOH

pH = 7.00 at equivalence point

Total volume (mL)   40 + 0 = 40   40 + 20 = 60   40 + 40 = 80   40 + 60 = 100

**Figure 19.7**  **Curve for a strong acid–strong base titration.**  Data (*at left*) for the titration of 40.00 mL of 0.1000 *M* HCl with 0.1000 *M* NaOH. In the titration, pH increases gradually, then rapidly near and at the equivalence point, and then gradually again. In a strong acid–strong base titra- tion, pH = 7.00 at the equivalence point. Each molecular view shows the relative numbers of species, other than solvent, in a portion of the solution at one point during the titration. The circles increase in size in proportion to the increase in the solution's total volume.

• The **end point** occurs when the indicator, which we added before the titration, changes color. *We choose an indicator with a color change close to the pH of the equivalence point.* Figure 19.5 includes two indicators suitable for a strong acid–strong base titration. Methyl red changes from red at pH 4.2 to yellow at pH 6.3, and phenolphthalein changes from colorless at pH 8.3 to pink at pH 10.0. Neither change occurs *at* the equivalence point (pH 7.00), but both occur on the vertical portion of the curve. Therefore, when methyl red turns yellow or phenolphthalein pink, we are within a drop or two of the equivalence point. In practice, then, the *visible* end point signals the *invisible* equivalence point.

**Calculating the pH During This Titration** By knowing the chemical species present during the titration, we can calculate the pH at various points along the way:

1. *Initial solution of strong HA.* In Figure 19.7, 40.00 mL of 0.1000 *M* HCl is titrated with 0.1000 *M* NaOH. Because a strong acid is completely dissociated, [HCl] = [$H_3O^+$] = 0.1000 *M*. Therefore, the initial pH is*

$$pH = -\log[H_3O^+] = -\log(0.1000) = 1.00$$

2. *Before the equivalence point.* As we start adding base, some acid is neutralized and the volume of solution increases. To find the pH at various points up to the equivalence point, we find the *initial* amount (mol) of $H_3O^+$ and subtract the amount *reacted, which equals the amount (mol) of $OH^-$ added,* to find the amount (mol) of $H_3O^+$ remaining. Then, we use the *total* volume to calculate [$H_3O^+$] and convert to pH. For example, after adding 20.00 mL of 0.1000 *M* NaOH:

• *Find the amount (mol) of $H_3O^+$ remaining.*

Initial amount (mol) of $H_3O^+$ = 0.04000 L × 0.1000 *M* = 0.004000 mol $H_3O^+$
−Amount (mol) of $OH^-$ added = 0.02000 L × 0.1000 *M* = 0.002000 mol $OH^-$
_____
Amount (mol) of $H_3O^+$ remaining =                              0.002000 mol $H_3O^+$

• *Calculate [$H_3O^+$].* We divide by the *total volume* because one solution dilutes the ions in the other:

$$[H_3O^+] = \frac{\text{amount (mol) of } H_3O^+ \text{ remaining}}{\text{original volume of acid + volume of added base}}$$

$$= \frac{0.002000 \text{ mol } H_3O^+}{0.04000 \text{ L} + 0.02000 \text{ L}} = 0.03333 \, M \qquad pH = 1.48$$

Given the amount of $OH^-$ added, we are halfway to the equivalence point; but we are still on the initial slow rise of the curve, so the pH is still very low. Similar calculations give values up to the equivalence point.

3. *At the equivalence point.* After 40.00 mL of 0.1000 *M* NaOH (0.004000 mol of $OH^-$) has been added to the initial 0.004000 mol of $H_3O^+$, the equivalence point is reached. The solution contains $Na^+$ and $Cl^-$, neither of which reacts with water. Because of the autoionization of water, however,

$$[H_3O^+] = 1.0 \times 10^{-7} \, M \qquad pH = 7.00$$

4. *After the equivalence point.* From the equivalence point on, the pH calculation is based on the amount (mol) of *excess* $OH^-$ present. For example, after adding 50.00 mL of NaOH, we have

Total amount (mol) of $OH^-$ added = 0.05000 L × 0.1000 *M* = 0.005000 mol $OH^-$
−Amount (mol) of $H_3O^+$ consumed = 0.04000 L × 0.1000 *M* = 0.004000 mol $H_3O^+$
_____
Amount (mol) of excess $OH^-$ =                              0.001000 mol $OH^-$

$$[OH^-] = \frac{0.001000 \text{ mol } OH^-}{0.04000 \text{ L} + 0.05000 \text{ L}} = 0.01111 \, M \qquad pOH = 1.95$$

$$pH = pK_w - pOH = 14.00 - 1.95 = 12.05$$

---

*In acid-base titrations, volumes and concentrations are usually known to four significant figures, but pH is reported to no more than two digits to the right of the decimal point.

## Weak Acid–Strong Base Titration Curves

Figure 19.8 shows a curve for the titration of a weak acid with strong base: 40.00 mL of 0.1000 $M$ propanoic acid ($K_a = 1.3 \times 10^{-5}$) titrated with 0.1000 $M$ NaOH. (We abbreviate the acid, $CH_3CH_2COOH$, as HPr and the conjugate base, $CH_3CH_2COO^-$, as $Pr^-$.)

**Features of the Curve**  The dotted portion of the curve in Figure 19.8 corresponds to the bottom half of the strong acid–strong base curve (Figure 19.7). There are four key points to note for the weak acid curve, and the first three differ from the strong acid curve:

1. *The initial pH is higher.* Because the weak acid (HPr) dissociates slightly, much less $H_3O^+$ is present than with the strong acid.
2. *The curve rises gradually in the so-called buffer region before the steep rise to the equivalence point.* As HPr reacts with strong base, more $Pr^-$ forms, which creates an HPr/$Pr^-$ buffer. At the midpoint of the buffer region, half the initial HPr has reacted (that is, half of the $OH^-$ needed to reach the equivalence point has been added), so [HPr] = [$Pr^-$], or [$Pr^-$]/[HPr] = 1. Therefore, *the pH equals the $pK_a$*:

    Middle of buffer region: $pH = pK_a + \log\left(\dfrac{[Pr^-]}{[HPr]}\right) = pK_a + \log 1 = pK_a + 0 = pK_a$

    The pH observed at this point is used to estimate the $pK_a$ of an unknown acid.
3. *The pH at the equivalence point is above 7.00.* The solution contains the strong-base cation $Na^+$, which does not react with water, and the weak-acid anion $Pr^-$, which acts as a weak base to accept a proton from $H_2O$ and yield $OH^-$.
4. *The pH increases slowly* beyond the equivalence point as excess $OH^-$ is added.

The choice of indicator here is more limited than for a strong acid–strong base titration because the steep rise occurs over a smaller pH range. Phenolphthalein will work because it changes color within this range. But methyl red will not because its color change requires about 30 mL of titrant, rather than just a drop or two.

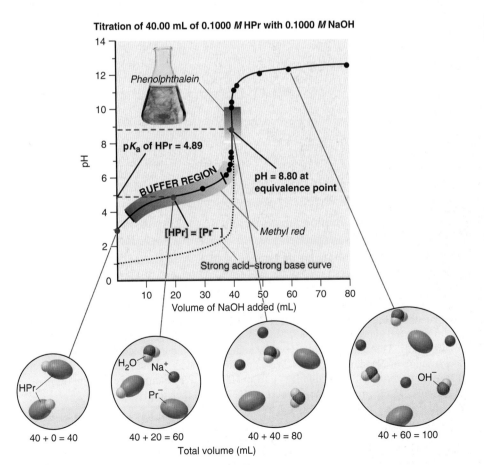

**Figure 19.8** Curve for a weak acid–strong base titration.

**Calculating the pH During This Titration** During the weak acid–strong base titration we must take into account the partial dissociation of the weak acid, the presence of the buffer, and the reaction of the conjugate base with water. Thus, each of four regions of the curve requires its own calculation to find $[H_3O^+]$:

1. *Initial HA solution.* Before base is added, a weak acid dissociates, so we find $[H_3O^+]$ as in Section 18.4: we set up a reaction table with $x = [HPr]_{dissoc}$, assume $[H_3O^+]$ (and $[Pr^-]$) $= [HPr]_{dissoc} << [HPr]_{init}$, and solve for $x$:

$$K_a = \frac{[H_3O^+][Pr^-]}{[HPr]} \approx \frac{x^2}{[HPr]_{init}} \qquad \text{therefore,} \qquad x = [H_3O^+] \approx \sqrt{K_a \times [HPr]_{init}}$$

2. *Solution of HA and added base.* As we add NaOH, HPr forms $Pr^-$. Thus, for much of the titration up to the equivalence point, we have an $HPr/Pr^-$ buffer. Therefore, we find $[H_3O^+]$ from

$$[H_3O^+] = K_a \times \frac{[HPr]}{[Pr^-]}$$

(Or, we can find pH directly with the Henderson-Hasselbalch equation.) Because *volumes cancel in the concentration ratio,* that is, $[HPr]/[Pr^-] =$ amount (mol) of $HPr$/amount (mol) of $Pr^-$, we don't need volumes or have to calculate concentrations.

3. *Equivalent amounts of HA and added base.* At the equivalence point, all of the HPr has reacted, so the solution contains $Pr^-$, which reacts with water to form $OH^-$:

$$Pr^-(aq) + H_2O(l) \rightleftharpoons HPr(aq) + OH^-(aq)$$

This explains why, in a weak acid–strong base titration, the pH $> 7.00$ at the equivalence point. To calculate $[H_3O^+]$ (see Section 18.5), we first find $K_b$ of $Pr^-$ from $K_a$ of HPr, set up a reaction table (assume $[Pr^-] >> [Pr^-]_{reacting}$), and solve for $[OH^-]$. Since we use a single concentration, $[Pr^-]$, to solve for $[OH^-]$, we *do* need the total volume. Then, we convert $[OH^-]$ to $[H_3O^+]$. These two steps are

(1) $[OH^-] \approx \sqrt{K_b \times [Pr^-]}$, where $K_b = \dfrac{K_w}{K_a}$ and $[Pr^-] = \dfrac{\text{amount (mol) of HPr}_{init}}{\text{total volume}}$

(2) $[H_3O^+] = \dfrac{K_w}{[OH^-]}$

Combining them into one step gives

$$[H_3O^+] \approx \frac{K_w}{\sqrt{K_b \times [Pr^-]}}$$

4. *Solution of excess base.* Beyond the equivalence point, as in the strong acid–strong base titration, we are adding excess $OH^-$:

$$[H_3O^+] = \frac{K_w}{[OH^-]} \qquad \text{where} \qquad [OH^-] = \frac{\text{amount (mol) of excess OH}^-}{\text{total volume}}$$

Sample Problem 19.4 shows the overall approach.

---

**Sample Problem 19.4** **Finding the pH During a Weak Acid–Strong Base Titration**

**Problem** Calculate the pH during the titration of 40.00 mL of 0.1000 *M* propanoic acid (HPr; $K_a = 1.3 \times 10^{-5}$) after each of the following additions of 0.1000 *M* NaOH:
**(a)** 0.00 mL          **(b)** 30.00 mL          **(c)** 40.00 mL          **(d)** 50.00 mL

**Plan** **(a)** 0.00 mL: No base has been added yet, so this is a weak-acid dissociation. We calculate the pH as we did in Section 18.4. **(b)** 30.00 mL: We find the amount (mol) of $Pr^-$ and of HPr, and substitute into the $K_a$ expression to solve for $[H_3O^+]$, and convert to pH. **(c)** 40.00 mL: The amount (mol) of NaOH added equals the initial amount (mol) of HPr, so a solution of $Na^+$ and $Pr^-$ exists. We calculate the pH as we did in Section 18.5, except that we need *total* volume to find $[Pr^-]$. **(d)** 50.00 mL: We calculate the amount (mol) of excess $OH^-$ in the total volume, convert to $[H_3O^+]$ and then to pH.

**Solution** **(a)** 0.00 mL of 0.1000 *M* NaOH added. Following the approach used in Sample Problem 18.8 and just described in the text, we obtain

$$[H_3O^+] \approx \sqrt{K_a \times [HPr]_{init}} = \sqrt{(1.3 \times 10^{-5})(0.1000)} = 1.1 \times 10^{-3} \, M \quad \text{so} \quad pH = \boxed{2.96}$$

**(b)** 30.00 mL of 0.1000 $M$ NaOH added. Calculating the ratio of moles of HPr to Pr$^-$:

$$\text{Initial amount (mol) of HPr} = 0.04000 \text{ L} \times 0.1000 \, M = 0.004000 \text{ mol HPr}$$
$$\text{Amount (mol) of NaOH added} = 0.03000 \text{ L} \times 0.1000 \, M = 0.003000 \text{ mol OH}^-$$

For every mole of NaOH, 1 mol of Pr$^-$ forms, so we have this stoichiometry reaction table:

| Amount (mol) | HPr($aq$) | + | OH$^-$($aq$) | $\longrightarrow$ | Pr$^+$($aq$) | + | H$_2$O($l$) |
|---|---|---|---|---|---|---|---|
| Initial | 0.004000 | | 0.003000 | | 0 | | — |
| Change | −0.003000 | | −0.003000 | | +0.003000 | | — |
| Final | 0.001000 | | 0 | | 0.003000 | | — |

The last line of the table gives the new initial amounts of HPr and Pr$^-$ that react to attain a new equilibrium. With $x$ very small, we assume that the [HPr]/[Pr$^-$] ratio at equilibrium is essentially equal to the ratio of these new initial amounts (see Comment in Sample Problem 19.1). Thus,

$$\frac{[\text{HPr}]}{[\text{Pr}^-]} = \frac{0.001000 \text{ mol}}{0.003000 \text{ mol}} = 0.3333$$

Solving for [H$_3$O$^+$]: $\quad [\text{H}_3\text{O}^+] = K_a \times \frac{[\text{HPr}]}{[\text{Pr}^-]} = (1.3 \times 10^{-5})(0.3333) = 4.3 \times 10^{-6} \, M$

$$\text{pH} = \boxed{5.37}$$

**(c)** 40.00 mL of 0.1000 $M$ NaOH added. Calculating [Pr$^-$] after all HPr has reacted:

$$[\text{Pr}^-] = \frac{0.004000 \text{ mol}}{0.04000 \text{ L} + 0.04000 \text{ L}} = 0.05000 \, M$$

Calculating $K_b$ using the given $K_a$ (see Sample Problem 18.2 for similar steps):

$$K_b = \frac{K_w}{K_a} = \frac{1.0 \times 10^{-14}}{1.3 \times 10^{-5}} = 7.7 \times 10^{-10}$$

Solving for [H$_3$O$^+$] as described above in the text for region 3 of the curve:

$$[\text{H}_3\text{O}^+] \approx \frac{K_w}{\sqrt{K_b \times [\text{Pr}^-]}} = \frac{1.0 \times 10^{-14}}{\sqrt{(7.7 \times 10^{-10})(0.05000)}} = 1.6 \times 10^{-9} \, M$$

$$\text{pH} = \boxed{8.80}$$

**(d)** 50.00 mL of 0.1000 $M$ NaOH added.

$$\text{Amount (mol) of excess OH}^- = (0.1000 \, M)(0.05000 \text{ L} - 0.04000 \text{ L}) = 0.001000 \text{ mol}$$

$$[\text{OH}^-] = \frac{\text{amount (mol) of excess OH}^-}{\text{total volume}} = \frac{0.001000 \text{ mol}}{0.09000 \text{ L}} = 0.01111 \, M$$

$$[\text{H}_3\text{O}^+] = \frac{K_w}{[\text{OH}^-]} = \frac{1.0 \times 10^{-14}}{0.01111} = 9.0 \times 10^{-13} \, M$$

$$\text{pH} = \boxed{12.05}$$

**Check** As expected, the pH increases through the four regions of the titration. Be sure to round off and check the arithmetic along the way.

**Follow-Up Problem 19.4** A chemist titrates 20.00 mL of 0.2000 $M$ HBrO ($K_a = 2.3 \times 10^{-9}$) with 0.1000 $M$ NaOH. What is the pH:
**(a)** Before any base is added?
**(b)** When [HBrO] = [BrO$^-$]?
**(c)** At the equivalence point?
**(d)** When the amount (mol) of OH$^-$ added is twice the amount of HBrO present initially?
**(e)** Sketch the titration curve; label the p$K_a$ and equivalence point.

## Weak Base–Strong Acid Titration Curves

The opposite of a weak acid–strong base titration is the titration of a weak base (NH$_3$) with a strong acid (HCl). This titration curve, shown in Figure 19.9 on the next page, has the *same shape as the weak acid–strong base curve, but it is inverted.*

**Figure 19.9** Curve for a weak base–strong acid titration.

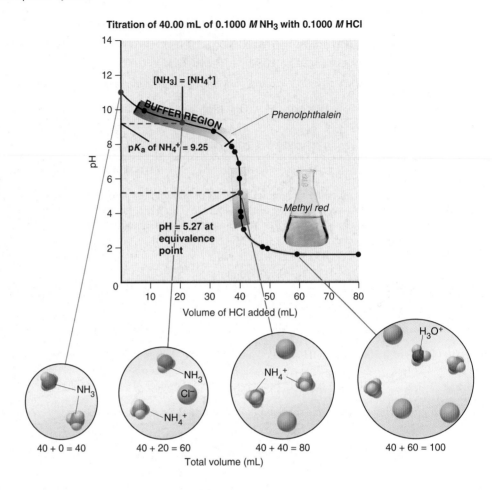

**Titration of 40.00 mL of 0.1000 $M$ NH$_3$ with 0.1000 $M$ HCl**

[NH$_3$] = [NH$_4^+$]

BUFFER REGION

Phenolphthalein

p$K_a$ of NH$_4^+$ = 9.25

Methyl red

pH = 5.27 at equivalence point

Volume of HCl added (mL)

H$_3$O$^+$

NH$_3$

NH$_3$

Cl$^-$

NH$_4^+$

NH$_4^+$

40 + 0 = 40     40 + 20 = 60     40 + 40 = 80     40 + 60 = 100

Total volume (mL)

Thus, we have the same features as the weak acid–strong base curve, but *the pH decreases* throughout the process:

1. *The initial weak-base solution has a pH well above 7.00* (see Sample Problem 18.11).
2. *The pH decreases gradually in the buffer region,* where significant amounts of NH$_3$ and its conjugate acid, NH$_4^+$, are present. At the midpoint of this region, *the pH equals the p$K_a$ of NH$_4^+$.*
3. *The curve drops steeply to the equivalence point.* All the NH$_3$ has reacted with added HCl, and the solution contains only NH$_4^+$ and Cl$^-$. Note that *the pH at the equivalence point is below 7.00* because Cl$^-$ does not react with water and NH$_4^+$ is acidic:

$$NH_4^+(aq) + H_2O(l) \rightleftharpoons NH_3(aq) + H_3O^+(aq)$$

4. *The pH decreases slowly* beyond the equivalence point as excess H$_3$O$^+$ is added.

For this titration, phenolphthalein changes color too slowly, but methyl red's change occurs on the steep portion of the curve and straddles the equivalence point, so it is the perfect choice.

## Titration Curves for Polyprotic Acids

Except for sulfuric acid, the common polyprotic acids are all weak. The successive $K_a$ values for a polyprotic acid differ by several orders of magnitude, as these values for sulfurous acid show:

$$H_2SO_3(aq) + H_2O(l) \rightleftharpoons HSO_3^-(aq) + H_3O^+(aq)$$
$$K_{a1} = 1.4 \times 10^{-2} \quad \text{and} \quad pK_{a1} = 1.85$$

$$HSO_3^-(aq) + H_2O(l) \rightleftharpoons SO_3^{2-}(aq) + H_3O^+(aq)$$
$$K_{a2} = 6.5 \times 10^{-8} \quad \text{and} \quad pK_{a2} = 7.19$$

Titration of 40.00 mL of 0.1000 *M* H₂SO₃ with 0.1000 *M* NaOH

**Figure 19.10** Curve for the titration of a weak polyprotic acid. Because the $K_a$ values are separated by several orders of magnitude, the titration curve looks like two weak acid–strong base curves joined.

In a titration of a diprotic acid such as $H_2SO_3$, two $OH^-$ ions are required to react with the two $H^+$ ions of each acid molecule. Figure 19.10 shows the titration curve for sulfurous acid with strong base. Because of the large difference in $K_a$ values, each mole of $H^+$ is titrated separately, so $H_2SO_3$ molecules lose one $H^+$ before any $HSO_3^-$ ions do:

$$H_2SO_3 \xrightarrow{\text{1 mol OH}^-} HSO_3^- \xrightarrow{\text{1 mol OH}^-} SO_3^{2-}$$

Several features of the curve are

- The same amount of base (0.004000 mol $OH^-$) is required per mole of $H^+$.
- There are two equivalence points and two buffer regions. The pH at the midpoint of each buffer region is equal to the $pK_a$ of that acidic species.
- The pH of the first equivalence point is below 7.00, because $HSO_3^-$ is a stronger acid than it is a base ($K_a$ of $HSO_3^- = 6.5 \times 10^{-8}$; $K_b$ of $HSO_3^- = 7.1 \times 10^{-13}$).

## Amino Acids as Biological Polyprotic Acids

Amino acids have the general formula $NH_2$—$CH(R)$—$COOH$, where R can be one of about 20 different groups (Sections 13.2 and 15.6). In essence, amino acids contain a weak base (—$NH_2$) and a weak acid (—$COOH$) on the same molecule. Both the amino and carboxylic acid groups are protonated at low pH: $^+NH_3$—$CH(R)$—$COOH$. Thus, in this form, the amino acid behaves like a polyprotic acid. For glycine, the simplest amino acid (R = H), the dissociation reactions and $pK_a$ values are

$$^+NH_3CH_2COOH(aq) + H_2O(l) \rightleftharpoons {}^+NH_3CH_2COO^-(aq) + H_3O^+(aq) \quad pK_{a1} = 2.35$$
$$^+NH_3CH_2COO^-(aq) + H_2O(l) \rightleftharpoons NH_2CH_2COO^-(aq) + H_3O^+(aq) \quad pK_{a2} = 9.78$$

These values show that the —$COOH$ group is *much* more acidic than the —$NH_3^+$ group. As we saw with $H_2SO_3$, the protons (*black circles*) are titrated separately, so all the —$COOH$ protons are removed before any —$NH_3^+$ protons are:

protonated (low pH) ——1 mol OH⁻→ zwitterion (neutral pH) ——1 mol OH⁻→ unprotonated (high pH)

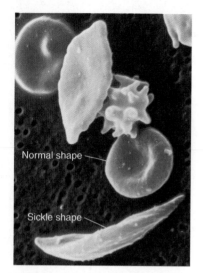

**Figure 19.11** Abnormal shape of red blood cells in sickle cell anemia.

Thus, at physiological pH (~7), which is between the two p$K_a$ values, *an amino acid exists as a zwitterion* (German *zwitter,* "double"), a species with opposite charges on the same molecule; for glycine it is $^+NH_3CH_2COO^-$.

Of the 20 different R groups of amino acids, several have *additional* —COO$^-$ or —NH$_3^+$ groups at pH 7 (see Figure 15.30, p. 609). When amino acids link to form a protein, their charged R groups give the protein its overall charge, which is often related to its function. A widely studied example of this relationship occurs in the hereditary disease sickle cell anemia. Normal red blood cells contain hemoglobin molecules that have two glutamic acid R groups (—CH$_2$CH$_2$COO$^-$) that each provide a negative charge at a critical region. Abnormal hemoglobin molecules in sickle cell anemia have two valine R groups (—CH$_3$), which are uncharged, at the same region. This change in just 2 of hemoglobin's 574 amino acids lowers charge repulsions between the hemoglobin molecules. As a result, they clump together in fiber-like structures, which leads to the sickle shape of the red blood cells (Figure 19.11). The misshapen cells block capillaries, and the painful course of sickle cell anemia usually ends in early death.

## ▌Summary of Section 19.2

- An acid-base (pH) indicator is a weak acid that has a differently colored conjugate base form and changes color over about 2 pH units.
- In a strong acid–strong base titration, the pH starts out low, rises slowly, then shoots up near the equivalence point (pH = 7).
- In a weak acid–strong base titration, the pH starts out higher, rises slowly in the buffer region (pH = p$K_a$ at the midpoint), and then rises quickly near the equivalence point (pH > 7).
- A weak base–strong acid titration curve has a shape that is the inverse of the weak acid–strong base case, with the pH decreasing to the equivalence point (pH < 7).
- Polyprotic acids have two or more acidic protons, each with its own $K_a$ value. Because the $K_a$'s differ by several orders of magnitude, each proton is titrated separately.
- Amino acids exist in charged forms that depend on the pH of the solution and determine the overall charge of a protein.

## 19.3 • EQUILIBRIA OF SLIGHTLY SOLUBLE IONIC COMPOUNDS

In this section, we explore an equilibirum system that involves the solubility of ionic compounds. Recall from Chapter 13 that most solutes, even those called "soluble," have a limited solubility in a particular solvent. In a saturated solution at a particular temperature, equilibrium exists between dissolved and undissolved solute. Slightly soluble ionic compounds, which we've been calling "insoluble," reach equilibrium with very little solute dissolved. In this introductory treatment, we will *assume* that, like a soluble ionic compound, the small amount of a slightly soluble ionic compound that does dissolve dissociates completely into ions.

### The Ion-Product Expression ($Q_{sp}$) and the Solubility-Product Constant ($K_{sp}$)

For a slightly soluble ionic compound, *equilibrium exists between solid solute and aqueous ions.* Thus, for example, for a saturated solution of lead(II) fluoride, we have

$$PbF_2(s) \rightleftharpoons Pb^{2+}(aq) + 2F^-(aq)$$

As for any equilibrium system, we can write a reaction quotient:

$$Q_c = \frac{[Pb^{2+}][F^-]^2}{[PbF_2]}$$

And, as in earlier cases, we multiply the constant concentration of the solid, [PbF$_2$], by $Q_c$. Doing so gives a relationship called the *ion-product expression, $Q_{sp}$*:

$$Q_{sp} = Q_c[PbF_2] = [Pb^{2+}][F^-]^2$$

When the solution is saturated, the numerical value of $Q_{sp}$ attains a constant value called the **solubility-product constant, $K_{sp}$.** The $K_{sp}$ for $PbF_2$ at 25°C, for example, is $3.6 \times 10^{-8}$. Like other equilibrium constants, $K_{sp}$ depends *only* on the temperature, not on the individual ion concentrations.

**Writing the Ion-Product Expression** The form of $Q_{sp}$ is identical to that of other reaction quotients: each concentration is raised to an exponent equal to the coefficient in the balanced equation, which in this case also *equals the subscript of each ion in the compound's formula.* At saturation, the concentration terms have their equilibrium values. Thus, in general, for a slightly soluble ionic compound, $M_pX_q$, composed of the ions $M^{n+}$ and $X^{z-}$, the ion-product expression at equilibrium is

$$Q_{sp} = [M^{n+}]^p[X^{z-}]^q = K_{sp} \qquad (19.2)$$

We'll write $Q_{sp}$ directly with the symbol $K_{sp}$.

**The Special Case of Metal Sulfides** The aqueous equilibria of metal sulfides have a special form of the ion-product expression. The sulfide ion, $S^{2-}$, is so basic that it reacts completely with water to form the hydrogen sulfide ion ($HS^-$) and $OH^-$:

$$S^{2-}(aq) + H_2O(l) \longrightarrow HS^-(aq) + OH^-(aq)$$

Although $S^{2-}$ is not stable in water, we can think of the dissolution process as the sum of two steps, with $S^{2-}$ formed in the first and consumed immediately in the second. Thus, for instance, for manganese(II) sulfide, we have

$$MnS(s) \rightleftharpoons Mn^{2+}(aq) + \cancel{S^{2-}(aq)}$$
$$\underline{\cancel{S^{2-}(aq)} + H_2O(l) \longrightarrow HS^-(aq) + OH^-(aq)}$$
$$MnS(s) + H_2O(l) \rightleftharpoons Mn^{2+}(aq) + HS^-(aq) + OH^-(aq)$$

Note that we have constant concentrations of water and the solid, so incorporating them into $Q_c$ gives the ion-product expression at equilibrium:

$$Q_c[MnS][H_2O] = K_{sp} = [Mn^{2+}][HS^-][OH^-]$$

## Sample Problem 19.5 Writing Ion-Product Expressions

**Problem** Write the ion-product expression at equilibrium for each compound:
**(a)** magnesium carbonate; **(b)** iron(II) hydroxide; **(c)** calcium phosphate; **(d)** silver sulfide.

**Plan** We write an equation for a saturated solution and then write the ion-product expression at equilibrium, $K_{sp}$ (Equation 19.2), noting the sulfide in part (d).

**Solution (a)** Magnesium carbonate:

$$MgCO_3(s) \rightleftharpoons Mg^{2+}(aq) + CO_3^{2-}(aq) \qquad K_{sp} = [Mg^{2+}][CO_3^{2-}]$$

**(b)** Iron(II) hydroxide:

$$Fe(OH)_2(s) \rightleftharpoons Fe^{2+}(aq) + 2OH^-(aq) \qquad K_{sp} = [Fe^{2+}][OH^-]^2$$

**(c)** Calcium phosphate:

$$Ca_3(PO_4)_2(s) \rightleftharpoons 3Ca^{2+}(aq) + 2PO_4^{3-}(aq) \qquad K_{sp} = [Ca^{2+}]^3[PO_4^{3-}]^2$$

**(d)** Silver sulfide:

$$Ag_2S(s) \rightleftharpoons 2Ag^+(aq) + \cancel{S^{2-}(aq)}$$
$$\underline{\cancel{S^{2-}(aq)} + H_2O(l) \longrightarrow HS^-(aq) + OH^-(aq)}$$
$$Ag_2S(s) + H_2O(l) \rightleftharpoons 2Ag^+(aq) + HS^-(aq) + OH^-(aq) \qquad K_{sp} = [Ag^+]^2[HS^-][OH^-]$$

**Check** Except for part (d), you can check by reversing the process to see if you obtain the formula of the compound from $K_{sp}$.

**Follow-Up Problem 19.5** Write the ion-product expression at equilibrium for each compound: **(a)** calcium sulfate; **(b)** chromium(III) carbonate; **(c)** magnesium hydroxide; **(d)** arsenic(III) sulfide.

## Calculations Involving the Solubility-Product Constant

In Chapters 17 and 18, we described two types of equilibrium problems. In one type, we use concentrations (or other quantities) to find $K$, and in the other, we use $K$ to find concentrations. Here we encounter the same two types.

**The Problem with Assuming Complete Dissociation** Before we focus on calculations, let's address a complication that affects accuracy and results in approximate answers. Our assumption that the small dissolved amount of these compounds dissociates completely into separate ions is an oversimplification. Many slightly soluble salts have polar covalent metal-nonmetal bonds, and partially dissociated or even undissociated species occur in solution. Here are two of many examples:

- With slightly soluble lead(II) chloride in water, the solution contains not only the separate $Pb^{2+}(aq)$ and $Cl^{-}(aq)$ ions we expect from complete dissociation, but also undissociated $PbCl_2(aq)$ molecules and $PbCl^{+}(aq)$ ions.
- In an aqueous solution of $CaSO_4$, undissociated ion pairs, $Ca^{2+}SO_4{}^{2-}(aq)$, are present.

These partly dissociated and undissociated species increase the *apparent* solubility of a slightly soluble salt above the value obtained by assuming complete dissociation. More advanced courses discuss these factors, but we simply mention them in the Comments of several sample problems. Thus, it is best to view the problem answers as first approximations.

**The Meaning of $K_{sp}$ and How to Determine It from Solubility Values** The $K_{sp}$ value indicates *how far the dissolution proceeds at equilibrium (saturation).* Table 19.2 presents a few $K_{sp}$ values; Appendix C lists many more. Note that all the values are low, but they range over many orders of magnitude. In Sample Problem 19.6, we find $K_{sp}$ from the solubility of a compound.

### Table 19.2 Solubility-Product Constants ($K_{sp}$) of Selected Ionic Compounds at 25°C

| Name, Formula | $K_{sp}$ |
|---|---|
| Aluminum hydroxide, $Al(OH)_3$ | $3 \times 10^{-34}$ |
| Cobalt(II) carbonate, $CoCO_3$ | $1.0 \times 10^{-10}$ |
| Iron(II) hydroxide, $Fe(OH)_2$ | $4.1 \times 10^{-15}$ |
| Lead(II) fluoride, $PbF_2$ | $3.6 \times 10^{-8}$ |
| Lead(II) sulfate, $PbSO_4$ | $1.6 \times 10^{-8}$ |
| Mercury(I) iodide, $Hg_2I_2$ | $4.7 \times 10^{-29}$ |
| Silver sulfide, $Ag_2S$ | $8 \times 10^{-48}$ |
| Zinc iodate, $Zn(IO_3)_2$ | $3.9 \times 10^{-6}$ |

---

### Sample Problem 19.6 Determining $K_{sp}$ from Solubility

**Problem** (a) Lead(II) sulfate ($PbSO_4$) is a key component in lead-acid car batteries. Its solubility in water at 25°C is $4.25 \times 10^{-3}$ g/100 mL solution. What is the $K_{sp}$ of $PbSO_4$?
(b) When lead(II) fluoride ($PbF_2$) is shaken with pure water at 25°C, the solubility is found to be 0.64 g/L. Calculate the $K_{sp}$ of $PbF_2$.

**Plan** We are given the solubilities in various units and must find $K_{sp}$. As always, we write a dissolution equation and the ion-product expression for each compound. This tells us the number of moles of each ion. We use the molar mass to convert the solubility of the compound from the given mass units to *molar solubility* (molarity), then use it to find the molarity of each ion, and substitute into the ion-product expression to calculate $K_{sp}$.

**Solution** (a) For $PbSO_4$. Writing the equation and ion-product ($K_{sp}$) expression:

$$PbSO_4(s) \rightleftharpoons Pb^{2+}(aq) + SO_4{}^{2-}(aq) \qquad K_{sp} = [Pb^{2+}][SO_4{}^{2-}]$$

Converting solubility to molar solubility:

$$\text{Molar solubility of } PbSO_4 = \frac{0.00425 \text{ g } PbSO_4}{100 \text{ mL soln}} \times \frac{1000 \text{ mL}}{1 \text{ L}} \times \frac{1 \text{ mol } PbSO_4}{303.3 \text{ g } PbSO_4}$$

$$= 1.40 \times 10^{-4} \, M \, PbSO_4$$

Determining molarities of the ions: Because 1 mol of $Pb^{2+}$ and 1 mol of $SO_4{}^{2-}$ form when 1 mol of $PbSO_4$ dissolves, $[Pb^{2+}] = [SO_4{}^{2-}] = 1.40 \times 10^{-4} \, M$.
Substituting these values into the ion-product expression to calculate $K_{sp}$:

$$K_{sp} = [Pb^{2+}][SO_4{}^{2-}] = (1.40 \times 10^{-4})^2 = \boxed{1.96 \times 10^{-8}}$$

(b) For $PbF_2$. Writing the equation and $K_{sp}$ expression:

$$PbF_2(s) \rightleftharpoons Pb^{2+}(aq) + 2F^{-}(aq) \qquad K_{sp} = [Pb^{2+}][F^{-}]^2$$

Converting solubility to molar solubility:

$$\text{Molar solubility of PbF}_2 = \frac{0.64 \text{ g PbF}_2}{1 \text{ L soln}} \times \frac{1 \text{ mol PbF}_2}{245.2 \text{ g PbF}_2} = 2.6 \times 10^{-3} \text{ M PbF}_2$$

Determining molarities of the ions: Since 1 mol of $Pb^{2+}$ and 2 mol of $F^-$ form when 1 mol of $PbF_2$ dissolves, we have

$$[Pb^{2+}] = 2.6 \times 10^{-3} \text{ M} \quad \text{and} \quad [F^-] = 2(2.6 \times 10^{-3} \text{ M}) = 5.2 \times 10^{-3} \text{ M}$$

Substituting these values into the ion-product expression to calculate $K_{sp}$:

$$K_{sp} = [Pb^{2+}][F^-]^2 = (2.6 \times 10^{-3})(5.2 \times 10^{-3})^2 = \boxed{7.0 \times 10^{-8}}$$

**Check** The low solubilities are consistent with $K_{sp}$ values being small. **(a)** The molar solubility seems about right: $\sim \dfrac{4 \times 10^{-2} \text{ g/L}}{3 \times 10^2 \text{ g/mol}} \approx 1.3 \times 10^{-4} \text{ M}$. Squaring this number gives $1.7 \times 10^{-8}$, close to the calculated $K_{sp}$. **(b)** Let's check the math in the final step as follows: $\sim(3 \times 10^{-3})(5 \times 10^{-3})^2 = 7.5 \times 10^{-8}$, close to the calculated $K_{sp}$.

**Comment** **1.** In part (b), the formula $PbF_2$ means that $[F^-]$ is twice $[Pb^{2+}]$. Then we follow the ion-product expression exactly and square this value of $[F^-]$.
**2.** The tabulated $K_{sp}$ values for these compounds (Table 19.2) are lower than our calculated values. For $PbF_2$, for instance, the tabulated value is $3.6 \times 10^{-8}$, but we calculated $7.0 \times 10^{-8}$ from solubility data. The discrepancy arises because we assumed that $PbF_2$ in solution dissociates completely to $Pb^{2+}$ and $F^-$. Here is an example of the complication pointed out earlier. Actually, about a third of the $PbF_2$ dissolves as $PbF^+(aq)$ and a small amount dissolves as undissociated $PbF_2(aq)$. The solubility given in the problem statement (0.64 g/L) is determined experimentally and includes these other species, which we did *not* include in our calculation.

**Follow-Up Problem 19.6** When fluorite ($CaF_2$; *see photo*) is pulverized and shaken in water at 18°C, 10.0 mL of solution contains $1.5 \times 10^{-4}$ g of solute. Find the $K_{sp}$ of $CaF_2$ at 18°C.

Fluorite.

## Determining Solubility from $K_{sp}$

The reverse of Sample Problem 19.6 involves finding the solubility of a compound based on its formula and $K_{sp}$ value. We'll use an approach similar to the one we used for weak acids in Sample Problem 18.8: we define the unknown amount dissolved—the molar solubility—as $S$, include ion concentrations in terms of this unknown in a reaction table, and solve for $S$.

---

**Sample Problem 19.7**  **Determining Solubility from $K_{sp}$**

**Problem** Calcium hydroxide (slaked lime) is a major component of mortar, plaster, and cement, and solutions of $Ca(OH)_2$ are used in industry as a strong, inexpensive base. Calculate the molar solubility of $Ca(OH)_2$ in water if $K_{sp}$ is $6.5 \times 10^{-6}$.

**Plan** We write the dissolution equation and the ion-product expression. We know $K_{sp}$ ($6.5 \times 10^{-6}$), so to find molar solubility ($S$), we set up a reaction table that expresses $[Ca^{2+}]$ and $[OH^-]$ in terms of $S$, substitute into the ion-product expression, and solve for $S$.

**Solution** Writing the equation and ion-product expression:

$$Ca(OH)_2(s) \rightleftharpoons Ca^{2+}(aq) + 2OH^-(aq) \qquad K_{sp} = [Ca^{2+}][OH^-]^2 = 6.5 \times 10^{-6}$$

Setting up a reaction table, with $S =$ molar solubility:

| Concentration (*M*) | Ca(OH)₂(s) | ⇌ | Ca²⁺(aq) | + | 2OH⁻(aq) |
|---|---|---|---|---|---|
| Initial | — | | 0 | | 0 |
| Change | — | | +S | | +2S |
| Equilibrium | — | | S | | 2S |

Substituting into the ion-product expression and solving for $S$:

$$K_{sp} = [Ca^{2+}][OH^-]^2 = (S)(2S)^2 = (S)(4S^2) = 4S^3 = 6.5 \times 10^{-6}$$

$$S = \sqrt[3]{\frac{6.5 \times 10^{-6}}{4}} = \boxed{1.2 \times 10^{-2} \, M}$$

**Check** We expect a low solubility from a slightly soluble salt. If we reverse the calculation, we should obtain the given $K_{sp}$: $4(1.2 \times 10^{-2})^3 = 6.9 \times 10^{-6}$, close to $6.5 \times 10^{-6}$.

**Comment 1.** Note that we did not double and *then* square $[OH^-]$. $2S$ *is* the $[OH^-]$, so we just squared it, as the ion-product expression required.

**2.** Once again, we assumed that the solid dissociates completely. Actually, the solubility is increased to about $2.0 \times 10^{-2} \, M$ by the presence of $CaOH^+(aq)$ formed in the reaction $Ca(OH)_2(s) \rightleftharpoons CaOH^+(aq) + OH^-(aq)$. Our calculated answer is only approximate because we did not take this other species into account.

**Follow-Up Problem 19.7** Milk of magnesia, a suspension of $Mg(OH)_2$ in water, relieves indigestion by neutralizing stomach acid. What is the molar solubility of $Mg(OH)_2$ ($K_{sp} = 6.3 \times 10^{-10}$) in water?

**Using $K_{sp}$ Values to Compare Solubilities** As long as we compare compounds with the *same total number of ions* in their formulas, $K_{sp}$ values indicate *relative* solubility: *the higher the $K_{sp}$, the greater the solubility* (Table 19.3). Note that for compounds that form three ions, the relationship holds whether the cation/anion ratio is 1/2 or 2/1, because the mathematical expression containing $S$ is the same ($4S^3$) in the calculation (see Sample Problem 19.7).

| Table 19.3 Relationship Between $K_{sp}$ and Solubility at 25°C | | | | |
|---|---|---|---|---|
| **No. of Ions** | **Formula** | **Cation/Anion** | **$K_{sp}$** | **Solubility ($M$)** |
| 2 | $MgCO_3$ | 1/1 | $3.5 \times 10^{-8}$ | $1.9 \times 10^{-4}$ |
| 2 | $PbSO_4$ | 1/1 | $1.6 \times 10^{-8}$ | $1.3 \times 10^{-4}$ |
| 2 | $BaCrO_4$ | 1/1 | $2.1 \times 10^{-10}$ | $1.4 \times 10^{-5}$ |
| 3 | $Ca(OH)_2$ | 1/2 | $6.5 \times 10^{-6}$ | $1.2 \times 10^{-2}$ |
| 3 | $BaF_2$ | 1/2 | $1.5 \times 10^{-6}$ | $7.2 \times 10^{-3}$ |
| 3 | $CaF_2$ | 1/2 | $3.2 \times 10^{-11}$ | $2.0 \times 10^{-4}$ |
| 3 | $Ag_2CrO_4$ | 2/1 | $2.6 \times 10^{-12}$ | $8.7 \times 10^{-5}$ |

## Effect of a Common Ion on Solubility

From Le Châtelier's principle, we know that *adding a common ion decreases the solubility of a slightly soluble ionic compound.* Consider a saturated solution of lead(II) chromate:

$$PbCrO_4(s) \rightleftharpoons Pb^{2+}(aq) + CrO_4^{2-}(aq) \qquad K_{sp} = [Pb^{2+}][CrO_4^{2-}] = 2.3 \times 10^{-13}$$

At a given temperature, $K_{sp}$ depends on the product of the ion concentrations. If the concentration of either ion goes up, the other goes down to maintain $K_{sp}$. Suppose we add $Na_2CrO_4$, a soluble salt, to the saturated $PbCrO_4$ solution. The concentration of the common ion, $CrO_4^{2-}$, increases, and some of it combines with $Pb^{2+}$ ion to form more solid $PbCrO_4$ (Figure 19.12). That is, the equilibrium position shifts to the left:

$$PbCrO_4(s) \rightleftharpoons Pb^{2+}(aq) + CrO_4^{2-}(aq; \text{ added})$$

As a result of the addition, $[Pb^{2+}]$ is lower. And, since $[Pb^{2+}]$ defines the solubility of $PbCrO_4$, in effect, the solubility of $PbCrO_4$ has decreased. Note that we would get the same result if $Na_2CrO_4$ solution were the solvent; that is, $PbCrO_4$ is more soluble in water than in aqueous $Na_2CrO_4$.

**A**

**B**

| $PbCrO_4(s) \rightleftharpoons Pb^{2+}(aq) + CrO_4^{2-}(aq)$ | $PbCrO_4(s) \rightleftharpoons Pb^{2+}(aq) + CrO_4^{2-}(aq;\ added)$ |

**Figure 19.12** The effect of a common ion on solubility. **A,** Lead(II) chromate, a slightly soluble salt, forms a saturated solution. **B,** When $Na_2CrO_4$ solution is added, the amount of $PbCrO_4(s)$ increases.

---

**Sample Problem 19.8** **Calculating the Effect of a Common Ion on Solubility**

**Problem** In Sample Problem 19.7, we calculated the solubility of $Ca(OH)_2$ in water. What is its solubility in $0.10\ M\ Ca(NO_3)_2$? $K_{sp}$ of $Ca(OH)_2$ is $6.5\times10^{-6}$.

**Plan** Addition of $Ca^{2+}$, the common ion, should lower the solubility. We write the equation and ion-product expression and set up a reaction table, with $[Ca^{2+}]_{init}$ reflecting the $0.10\ M\ Ca(NO_3)_2$ and $S$ equal to $[Ca^{2+}]_{from\ Ca(OH)_2}$. To simplify the math, we assume that, because $K_{sp}$ is low, $S$ is so small relative to $[Ca^{2+}]_{init}$ that it can be neglected. Then we solve for $S$ and check the assumption.

**Solution** Writing the equation and ion-product expression:

$$Ca(OH)_2(s) \rightleftharpoons Ca^{2+}(aq) + 2OH^-(aq) \qquad K_{sp} = [Ca^{2+}][OH^-]^2 = 6.5\times10^{-6}$$

Setting up the reaction table, with $S = [Ca^{2+}]_{from\ Ca(OH)_2}$:

| Concentration (*M*) | $Ca(OH)_2(s)$ | $\rightleftharpoons$ | $Ca^{2+}(aq)$ | $+$ | $2OH^-(aq)$ |
|---|---|---|---|---|---|
| Initial | — | | 0.10 | | 0 |
| Change | — | | $+S$ | | $+2S$ |
| Equilibrium | — | | $0.10 + S$ | | $2S$ |

Making the assumption: $K_{sp}$ is small, so $S \ll 0.10\ M$; thus, $0.10\ M + S \approx 0.10\ M$. Substituting into the ion-product expression and solving for $S$:

$$K_{sp} = [Ca^{2+}][OH^-]^2 = 6.5\times10^{-6} \approx (0.10)(2S)^2$$

Therefore,    $4S^2 \approx \dfrac{6.5\times10^{-6}}{0.10}$    so    $S \approx \sqrt{\dfrac{6.5\times10^{-5}}{4}} = \boxed{4.0\times10^{-3}\ M}$

Checking the assumption:    $\dfrac{4.0\times10^{-3}\ M}{0.10\ M} \times 100 = 4.0\% < 5\%$

**Check** In Sample Problem 19.7, the solubility of $Ca(OH)_2$ was $0.012\ M$; here it is $0.0040\ M$, one-third as much. As expected, the solubility *decreased* in the presence of added $Ca^{2+}$, the common ion.

**Follow-Up Problem 19.8** To improve the x-ray image used to diagnose intestinal disorders, a patient drinks an aqueous suspension of $BaSO_4$ before the procedure because $Ba^{2+}$ is opaque to x-rays (*photo*). However, $Ba^{2+}$ is also toxic; thus, $[Ba^{2+}]$ is lowered by adding dilute $Na_2SO_4$. What is the solubility of $BaSO_4$ ($K_{sp} = 1.1\times10^{-10}$) in **(a)** water and **(b)** $0.10\ M\ Na_2SO_4$?

$BaSO_4$ imaging of a large intestine.

## Effect of pH on Solubility

If a slightly soluble ionic compound contains the anion of a weak acid, *addition of $H_3O^+$ (from a strong acid) increases its solubility.* Once again, Le Châtelier's principle explains why. Consider a saturated solution of calcium carbonate:

$$CaCO_3(s) \rightleftharpoons Ca^{2+}(aq) + CO_3^{2-}(aq)$$

Adding strong acid introduces $H_3O^+$, which reacts with the anion of a weak acid, $CO_3^{2-}$, to form the anion of another weak acid, $HCO_3^-$:

$$CO_3^{2-}(aq) + H_3O^+(aq) \longrightarrow HCO_3^-(aq) + H_2O(l)$$

If enough $H_3O^+$ is added, carbonic acid forms, which decomposes to $H_2O$ and $CO_2$, and the gas escapes the container:

$$HCO_3^-(aq) + H_3O^+(aq) \longrightarrow [H_2CO_3(aq)] + H_2O(l) \longrightarrow CO_2(g) + 2H_2O(l)$$

The net effect of adding $H_3O^+$ is a shift in the equilibrium position to the right, and more $CaCO_3$ dissolves:

$$CaCO_3(s) \rightleftharpoons Ca^{2+} + CO_3^{2-} \xrightarrow{H_3O^+} HCO_3 \xrightarrow{H_3O^+} [H_2CO_3] \longrightarrow CO_2(g) + H_2O + Ca^{2+}$$

In fact, this example illustrates a qualitative field test for carbonate minerals because the $CO_2$ bubbles vigorously (Figure 19.13).

In contrast, adding $H_3O^+$ to a saturated solution of a slightly soluble ionic compound with a strong-acid anion, such as AgCl, has no effect on its solubility:

$$AgCl(s) \rightleftharpoons Ag^+(aq) + Cl^-(aq)$$

The $Cl^-$ ion can coexist with high $[H_3O^+]$, so the equilibrium position is not affected.

**Figure 19.13** Test for the presence of a carbonate. When a carbonate mineral is treated with HCl, bubbles of $CO_2$ form.

---

**Sample Problem 19.9** | **Predicting the Effect on Solubility of Adding Strong Acid**

**Problem** Write balanced equations to explain whether addition of $H_3O^+$ from a strong acid affects the solubility of each ionic compound:
**(a)** Lead(II) bromide    **(b)** Copper(II) hydroxide    **(c)** Iron(II) sulfide

**Plan** We write the balanced dissolution equation and note the anion:
• Weak-acid anions react with $H_3O^+$ and increase solubility when strong acid is added.
• Strong-acid anions do not react with $H_3O^+$, so addition of strong acid has no effect.

**Solution** **(a)** $PbBr_2(s) \rightleftharpoons Pb^{2+}(aq) + 2Br^-(aq)$
No effect. $Br^-$ is the anion of HBr, a strong acid, so it does not react with $H_3O^+$.
**(b)** $Cu(OH)_2(s) \rightleftharpoons Cu^2(aq) + 2OH^-(aq)$ Increases solubility. $OH^-$ is the anion of $H_2O$, a very weak acid, so it reacts with the added $H_3O^+$:

$$OH^-(aq) + H_3O^+(aq) \longrightarrow 2H_2O(l)$$

**(c)** $FeS(s) + H_2O(l) \rightleftharpoons Fe^{2+}(aq) + HS^-(aq) + OH^-(aq)$ Increases solubility. The $S^{2-}$ ion reacts completely with water to form $HS^-$ and $OH^-$. The added $H_3O^+$ reacts with both of these weak-acid anions:

$$HS^-(aq) + H_3O^+(aq) \longrightarrow H_2S(aq) + H_2O(l)$$
$$OH^-(aq) + H_3O^+(aq) \longrightarrow 2H_2O(l)$$

**Follow-Up Problem 19.9** Write balanced equations to show how addition of $HNO_3(aq)$ affects the solubility of: **(a)** calcium fluoride; **(b)** zinc sulfide; **(c)** silver iodide.

---

## Applying Ionic Equilibria to the Formation of a Limestone Cave

Limestone caves and the remarkable structures within them provide striking evidence of the results of aqueous ionic equilibria involving carbonate rocks and the carbon dioxide and water that have flowed through them for many hundreds of millennia (Figure 19.14).

**The Cave-Forming Reactions** Limestone is mostly calcium carbonate ($CaCO_3$; $K_{sp} = 3.3 \times 10^{-9}$). Two key reactions help us understand how limestone caves form:

1. Gaseous $CO_2$ in air is in equilibrium with aqueous $CO_2$ in natural waters:

$$CO_2(g) \underset{}{\overset{H_2O(l)}{\rightleftharpoons}} CO_2(aq) \qquad \textbf{(equation 1)}$$

The concentration of aqueous $CO_2$ is proportional to the partial pressure of $CO_2(g)$ in contact with the water (Henry's law; Section 13.4):

$$[CO_2(aq)] \propto P_{CO_2}$$

Due to the continual release of $CO_2$ from within Earth (outgassing), $P_{CO_2}$ in soil-trapped air is *higher* than $P_{CO_2}$ in the atmosphere.

2. The reaction of $CO_2$ with water produces $H_3O^+$:

$$CO_2(aq) + 2H_2O(l) \rightleftharpoons H_3O^+(aq) + HCO_3^-(aq)$$

Thus, since $CaCO_3$ contains the anion of a weak acid, this formation of $H_3O^+$ increases the solubility of $CaCO_3$:

$$CaCO_3(s) + CO_2(aq) + H_2O(l) \rightleftharpoons Ca^{2+}(aq) + 2HCO_3^-(aq) \qquad \textbf{(equation 2)}$$

**Figure 19.14** Limestone cave in Nerja, Málaga, Spain.

**The Cave-Forming Process** Here is an overview of the process that forms most limestone caves:

1. As surface water trickles through cracks in the ground, it meets soil-trapped air with a high $P_{CO_2}$. As a result, $[CO_2(aq)]$ increases (equation 1 shifts to the right), and the solution becomes more acidic.
2. When this $CO_2$-rich water contacts $CaCO_3$, more $CaCO_3$ dissolves (equation 2 shifts to the right). As a result, more rock is carved out, more water flows in, and so on. Centuries pass, and a cave slowly begins to form.
3. Some of the aqueous solution, dilute $Ca(HCO_3)_2$, passes through the ceiling of the growing cave. As it drips, it meets air, which has a lower $P_{CO_2}$ than the soil, so some $CO_2(aq)$ comes out of solution (equation 1 shifts to the left).
4. Consequently, some $CaCO_3$ precipitates on the ceiling and on the floor below, where the drops land (equation 2 shifts to the left). After many decades, the ceiling bears a *stalactite*, while a spike, called a *stalagmite*, grows up from the floor. Eventually, they meet to form a column of precipitated limestone *(see chapter opener)*.

The same chemical process can lead to different shapes. Standing pools of $Ca(HCO_3)_2$ solution form limestone "lily pads" or "corals." Cascades of solution form delicate limestone "draperies" on a cave wall, with fabulous colors arising from trace metal ions, such as iron (reddish brown) or copper (bluish green).

## Predicting the Formation of a Precipitate: $Q_{sp}$ vs. $K_{sp}$

As in Chapter 17, here we compare the values of $Q_{sp}$ and $K_{sp}$ to see if a reaction has reached equilibrium and, if not, in which net direction it will move until it does. Using solutions of *soluble* salts that contain the ions of *slightly* soluble salts, we can calculate the ion concentrations and predict the result when we mix the solutions:

- If $Q_{sp} = K_{sp}$, the solution is saturated and no change will occur.
- If $Q_{sp} > K_{sp}$, a precipitate will form until the remaining solution is saturated.
- If $Q_{sp} < K_{sp}$, no precipitate will form because the solution is unsaturated.

**Sample Problem 19.10** | **Predicting Whether a Precipitate Will Form**

**Problem** A common laboratory method for preparing a precipitate is to mix solutions containing the component ions. Does a precipitate form when 0.100 L of 0.30 $M$ $Ca(NO_3)_2$ is mixed with 0.200 L of 0.060 $M$ NaF?

**Plan** First, we decide which slightly soluble salt could form, look up its $K_{sp}$ value in Appendix C, and write a dissolution equation and ion-product expression. To see whether mixing these solutions forms the precipitate, we find the initial ion concentrations by

Precipitation of $CaF_2$.

calculating the amount (mol) of each ion from its concentration and volume, and dividing by the *total* volume because each solution dilutes the other. Finally, we substitute these concentrations to calculate $Q_{sp}$, and compare $Q_{sp}$ with $K_{sp}$.

**Solution** The ions present are $Ca^{2+}$, $Na^+$, $F^-$, and $NO_3^-$. All sodium and all nitrate salts are soluble (Table 4.1, p. 145), so the only possibility is $CaF_2$ ($K_{sp} = 3.2\times10^{-11}$). Writing the equation and ion-product expression:

$$CaF_2(s) \rightleftharpoons Ca^{2+}(aq) + 2F^-(aq) \qquad Q_{sp} = [Ca^{2+}][F^-]^2$$

Calculating the ion concentrations:

$$\text{Amount (mol) of } Ca^{2+} = 0.30\ M\ Ca^{2+} \times 0.100\ L = 0.030\ \text{mol } Ca^{2+}$$

$$[Ca^{2+}]_{init} = \frac{0.030\ \text{mol } Ca^{2+}}{0.100\ L + 0.200\ L} = 0.10\ M\ Ca^{2+}$$

$$\text{Amount (mol) of } F^- = 0.060\ M\ F^- \times 0.200\ L = 0.012\ \text{mol } F^-$$

$$[F^-]_{init} = \frac{0.012\ \text{mol } F^-}{0.100\ L + 0.200\ L} = 0.040\ M\ F^-$$

Substituting into the ion-product expression and comparing $Q_{sp}$ with $K_{sp}$:

$$Q_{sp} = [Ca^{2+}]_{init}[F^-]^2_{init} = (0.10)(0.040)^2 = 1.6\times10^{-4}$$

Because $Q_{sp} > K_{sp}$, CaF$_2$ will precipitate until $Q_{sp} = 3.2\times10^{-11}$.

**Check** Make sure you round off and quickly check the math. For example, $Q_{sp} = (1\times10^{-1})(4\times10^{-2})^2 = 1.6\times10^{-4}$. With $K_{sp}$ so low, $CaF_2$ must have a low solubility, and given the sizable concentrations being mixed, we would expect $CaF_2$ to precipitate.

**Follow-Up Problem 19.10** As a result of mineral erosion and biological activity, phosphate ion is common in natural waters, where it often precipitates as insoluble salts such as $Ca_3(PO_4)_2$. If $[Ca^{2+}]_{init} = [PO_4^{3-}]_{init} = 1.0\times10^{-9}\ M$ in a given river, will $Ca_3(PO_4)_2$ precipitate? $K_{sp}$ of $Ca_3(PO_4)_2$ is $1.2\times10^{-29}$.

---

**Sample Problem 19.11**  **Using Molecular Scenes to Predict Whether a Precipitate Will Form**

**Problem** These four scenes represent solutions of silver (*gray*) and carbonate (*black and red*) ions above solid silver carbonate. (The solid, other ions, and water are not shown.)

1          2          3          4

**(a)** Which scene best represents the solution in equilibrium with the solid?
**(b)** In which, if any, other scene(s) will additional solid silver carbonate form?
**(c)** Explain how, if at all, addition of a small volume of concentrated strong acid affects the $[Ag^+]$ in scene 4 and the mass of solid present.

**Plan** **(a)** The solution of silver and carbonate ions in equilibrium with the solid ($Ag_2CO_3$) should have the same relative numbers of cations and anions as in the formula. We examine the scenes to see which has a ratio of 2 $Ag^+$ to 1 $CO_3^{2-}$. **(b)** A solid forms if the value of $Q_{sp}$ exceeds the $K_{sp}$. We write the dissolution equation and $Q_{sp}$ expression. Then we count ions to calculate $Q_{sp}$ in each scene and see which, if any, exceeds the value for the solution from part (a). **(c)** The $CO_3^{2-}$ ion reacts with added $H_3O^+$, so adding strong acid will shift the equilibrium to the right. We write the equations and determine how a shift to the right affects $[Ag^+]$ and the mass of solid $Ag_2CO_3$.

**Solution** **(a)** Scene 3 is the only one with an $Ag^+/CO_3^{2-}$ ratio of 2/1, as in the solid's formula.

**(b)** Calculating the ion products:

$$Ag_2CO_3(s) \rightleftharpoons 2Ag^+(aq) + CO_3^{2-}(aq) \qquad Q_{sp} = [Ag^+]^2[CO_3^{2-}]$$

Scene 1: $Q_{sp} = (2)^2(4) = 16$      Scene 2: $Q_{sp} = (3)^2(3) = 27$
Scene 3: $Q_{sp} = (4)^2(2) = 32$      Scene 4: $Q_{sp} = (3)^2(4) = 36$

Therefore, from scene 3, $K_{sp} = 32$; the $Q_{sp}$ value for  scene 4  is the only other one that equals or exceeds 32, so a precipitate of $Ag_2CO_3$ will form there.

**(c)** Writing the equations:

(1) $\qquad\qquad Ag_2CO_3(s) \rightleftharpoons 2Ag^+(aq) + CO_3^{2-}(aq)$

(2) $CO_3^{2-}(aq) + 2H_3O^+(aq) \longrightarrow [H_2CO_3(aq)] + 2H_2O(l) \longrightarrow 3H_2O(l) + CO_2(g)$

The $CO_2$ leaves as a gas, so adding $H_3O^+$ shifts the equilibrium position of reaction 2 to the right. This change lowers the $[CO_3^{2-}]$ in reaction 1, thereby causing more $CO_3^{2-}$ to form. As a result, more solid dissolves, which means that the  [Ag$^+$] increases  and the mass of $Ag_2CO_3$ decreases.

**Check** **(a)** In scene 1, the formula has two $CO_3^{2-}$ per formula unit, not two $Ag^+$. **(b)** Even though scene 4 has fewer $Ag^+$ ions than scene 3, its $Q_{sp}$ value is higher and exceeds the $K_{sp}$.

**Follow-Up Problem 19.11**   The following scenes represent solutions of nickel(II) (*black*) and hydroxide (*red and blue*) ions that are above solid nickel(II) hydroxide. (For clarity, the solid, other ions, and water are not shown.)

   **1**              **2**              **3**

**(a)** Which scene best depicts the solution at equilibrium with the solid?
**(b)** In which, if any, other scene(s) will additional solid form?
**(c)** Will addition of a small amount of concentrated strong acid or strong base affect the mass of solid present in any scene? Explain.

# Separating Ions by Selective Precipitation and Simultaneous Equilibria

Let's consider two ways to separate one ion from another by reacting them with a given precipitating ion to form compounds with different solubilities.

**Selective Precipitation** In the process of **selective precipitation,** a solution of one precipitating ion is added to a solution of two ionic compounds until the $Q_{sp}$ of the *more soluble* compound is almost equal to its $K_{sp}$. This method ensures that the $K_{sp}$ of the *less soluble* compound is exceeded as much as possible. As a result, the maximum amount of the less soluble compound precipitates, but none of the more soluble compound does.

**Sample Problem 19.12**  **Separating Ions by Selective Precipitation**

**Problem** A solution consists of $0.20\ M$ $MgCl_2$ and $0.10\ M$ $CuCl_2$. Calculate the $[OH^-]$ that would separate the metal ions. $K_{sp}$ of $Mg(OH)_2$ is $6.3 \times 10^{-10}$; $K_{sp}$ of $Cu(OH)_2$ is $2.2 \times 10^{-20}$.

**Plan** Because both compounds have 1/2 ratios of cation/anion (see p. 786), when we compare their $K_{sp}$ values, we find that $Mg(OH)_2$ is about $10^{10}$ times more soluble than $Cu(OH)_2$; thus, $Cu(OH)_2$ precipitates first. We write the dissolution equations and ion-product expressions. We are given both cation concentrations, so we solve for the $[OH^-]$ that gives a saturated solution of $Mg(OH)_2$, because this $[OH^-]$ will precipitate the most $Cu^{2+}$. Then, we calculate the $[Cu^{2+}]$ remaining to see if the separation was accomplished.

**Solution**  Writing the equations and ion-product expressions:

$$Mg(OH)_2(s) \rightleftharpoons Mg^{2+}(aq) + 2OH^-(aq) \quad K_{sp} = [Mg^{2+}][OH^-]^2 = 6.3 \times 10^{-10}$$

$$Cu(OH)_2(s) \rightleftharpoons Cu^{2+}(aq) + 2OH^-(aq) \quad K_{sp} = [Cu^{2+}][OH^-]^2 = 2.2 \times 10^{-20}$$

Calculating the $[OH^-]$ that gives a saturated $Mg(OH)_2$ solution:

$$[OH^-] = \sqrt{\frac{K_{sp}}{[Mg^{2+}]}} = \sqrt{\frac{6.3 \times 10^{-10}}{0.20}} = \boxed{5.6 \times 10^{-5} \, M}$$

This is the maximum $[OH^-]$ that will *not* precipitate $Mg^{2+}$ ion.
Calculating the $[Cu^{2+}]$ remaining in the solution with this $[OH^-]$:

$$[Cu^{2+}] = \frac{K_{sp}}{[OH^-]^2} = \frac{2.2 \times 10^{-20}}{(5.6 \times 10^{-5})^2} = 7.0 \times 10^{-12} \, M$$

Since the initial $[Cu^{2+}]$ is 0.10 $M$, virtually all the $Cu^{2+}$ ion is precipitated.

**Check**  Rounding, we find that $[OH^-]$ seems right: $\sim \sqrt{(6 \times 10^{-10})/0.2} = 5 \times 10^{-5}$. The $[Cu^{2+}]$ remaining also seems correct: $(200 \times 10^{-22})/(5 \times 10^{-5})^2 = 8 \times 10^{-12}$.

**Follow-Up Problem 19.12**  A solution is 0.050 $M$ $BaCl_2$ and 0.025 $M$ $CaCl_2$. What concentration of $SO_4^{2-}$ will separate the cations in solution? $K_{sp}$ of $BaSO_4$ is $1.1 \times 10^{-10}$, and $K_{sp}$ of $CaSO_4$ is $2.4 \times 10^{-5}$.

**Simultaneous Equilibria**  Sometimes two or more equilibrium systems are controlled simultaneously to separate one metal ion from another as their sulfides, using $HS^-$ as the precipitating ion. We control the $[HS^-]$ in order to exceed the $K_{sp}$ value of one metal sulfide but not the other, and we do so by shifting $H_2S$ dissociation through adjustments of $[H_3O^+]$:

$$H_2S(aq) + H_2O(l) \rightleftharpoons H_3O^+(aq) + HS^-(aq)$$

These interactions are controlled in the following way:

- If we add strong acid, the high $[H_3O^+]$ shifts $H_2S$ dissociation to the left, which decreases $[HS^-]$, so the *less* soluble sulfide precipitates.
- If we add strong base, the low $[H_3O^+]$ shifts $H_2S$ dissociation to the right, which increases $[HS^-]$, so the *more* soluble sulfide precipitates.

Thus, we shift one equilibrium system ($H_2S$ dissociation) by adjusting a second ($H_2O$ ionization) to control a third (metal sulfide solubility).

As the Chemical Connections essay demonstrates, the principles of ionic equilibria often help us understand the chemical basis of complex environmental problems and may provide ways to solve them.

## Summary of Section 19.3

- Only as a first approximation does the dissolved portion of a slightly soluble salt dissociate completely into ions.
- In a saturated solution, dissolved ions and the undissolved solid salt are in equilibrium. The product of the ion concentrations, each raised to the power of its subscript in the formula, has a constant value ($Q_{sp} = K_{sp}$).
- The value of $K_{sp}$ can be obtained from the solubility, and vice versa.
- Adding a common ion lowers a compound's solubility.
- Adding $H_3O^+$ (lowering pH) increases a compound's solubility if the anion of the compound is also that of a weak acid.
- Limestone caves result from shifts in the $CaCO_3/CO_2$ equilibrium system.
- An ionic solid forms if $Q_{sp} > K_{sp}$ when solutions that each contain one of the ions are mixed.
- Ions are precipitated selectively from a solution of two compounds by adding a precipitating ion until the $K_{sp}$ of one compound is exceeded as much as possible without exceeding the $K_{sp}$ of the other. An extension of this approach uses simultaneous control of three equilibrium systems to separate metal ions as their sulfides.
- Lakes bounded by limestone-rich soils form buffer systems that prevent acidification.

Acid rain, the deposition of acids in wet form as rain, snow, or fog or in dry form as solid particles, is a global environmental problem. It has been observed in the United States, Canada, Mexico, the Amazon basin, Europe, Russia, many parts of Asia, and even at the North and South Poles. Let's see how it arises and how to prevent some of its harmful effects.

## Origins of Acid Rain

The strong acids $H_2SO_4$ and $HNO_3$ cause the greatest concern, so let's see how they form (Figure B19.1):

1. *Sulfuric acid.* Sulfur dioxide ($SO_2$), formed mostly by the burning of high-sulfur coal, forms sulfurous acid ($H_2SO_3$) in contact with water. The atmospheric pollutants hydrogen peroxide ($H_2O_2$) and ozone ($O_3$) dissolve in the water in clouds and oxidize the sulfurous acid to sulfuric acid:

$$H_2O_2(aq) + H_2SO_3(aq) \longrightarrow H_2SO_4(aq) + H_2O(l)$$

Alternatively, $SO_2$ is oxidized by atmospheric hydroxyl radicals (HO·) to sulfur trioxide ($SO_3$), which forms $H_2SO_4$ with water.

2. *Nitric acid.* Nitrogen oxides ($NO_x$) form from $N_2$ and $O_2$ during high-temperature combustion in car and truck engines and electric power plants. Once formed, NO forms $NO_2$ and $HNO_3$ in a process that creates smog (p. 547). At night, $NO_x$ is converted to $N_2O_5$, which reacts with water to form $HNO_3$:

$$N_2O_5(g) + H_2O(l) \longrightarrow 2HNO_3(aq)$$

Ammonium salts, deposited as $NH_4HSO_4$ or $NH_4NO_3$, produce $HNO_3$ in soil through biochemical oxidation.

## The pH of Acid Rain

Normal rainwater is weakly acidic from the reaction of atmospheric $CO_2$ with water (see Problem 19.142):

$$CO_2(g) + 2H_2O(l) \rightleftharpoons H_3O^+(aq) + HCO_3^-(aq)$$

Yet, as long ago as 1984, rainfall in the United States had already reached an average pH of 4.2, an increase of about 25 times as much $H_3O^+$. Rain in Wheeling, West Virginia, has had a pH of 1.8, lower than the pH of lemon juice. And rain in industrial parts of Sweden once had a pH of 2.7, about the same as vinegar.

## Effects of Acid Rain

Some fish and shellfish die at pH values between 4.5 and 5.0. The young of most species are generally more vulnerable. At pH 5, most fish eggs cannot hatch. With tens of thousands of rivers and lakes around the world becoming or already acidified, the loss of freshwater fish became a major concern long ago.

In addition, acres of forest have been harmed by the acid, which removes nutrients and releases toxic substances from the soil. The aluminosilicates that make up most soils are extremely insoluble in water. Through a complex series of simultaneous equilibria, contact with water at pH < 5 causes these materials to release some bound $Al^{3+}$, which is toxic to fish and plants. At the

*(continued)*

**Figure B19.1 Formation of acidic precipitation.** A complex interplay of human activities, atmospheric chemistry, and environmental distribution leads to acidic precipitation and its harmful effects.

same time, acid rain dissolves $Ca^{2+}$ and $Mg^{2+}$ ions from the soil, which are nutrients for plants and animals.

Marble and limestone (both primarily $CaCO_3$) in buildings and monuments react with sulfuric acid to form gypsum ($CaSO_4 \cdot 2H_2O$), which flakes off. Ironically, the same process that destroys these structures rescues lakes that are bounded by limestone-rich soil. Limestone dissolves sufficiently in lake water to form an $HCO_3^-/CO_3^{2-}$ buffer capable of absorbing the incoming $H_3O^+$ and maintaining a mildly basic pH:

$$CO_3^{2-}(aq) + H_3O^+(aq) \rightleftharpoons HCO_3^-(aq) + H_2O(l)$$

Acidified lakes and rivers that are in contact with granite and other weathering-resistant bedrock can be remediated by *liming* (treating with limestone). This approach is expensive and only a stopgap because the lakes are acidic again within several years.

## Preventing Acid Rain

Effective prevention of acid rain has to address the sources of the sulfur and nitrogen pollutants:

1. *Sulfur pollutants.* As was pointed out earlier (Chemical Connections, p. 249), the principal means of minimizing sulfur dioxide release is by "scrubbing" power-plant emissions with limestone in both dry and wet form. Another method reduces $SO_2$ with methane, coal, or $H_2S$, and the mixture is converted catalytically to sulfur, which is sold as a byproduct:

$$16H_2S(g) + 8SO_2(g) \xrightarrow{\text{catalyst}} 3S_8(s) + 16H_2O(l)$$

Although low-sulfur coal is rare and expensive to mine, coal can be converted into gaseous and liquid low-sulfur fuels. The sulfur is removed (as $H_2S$) in an acid-gas scrubber after gasification.

2. *Nitrogen pollutants.* Through the use of a catalytic converter in an auto exhaust system, $NO_x$ species are reduced to $N_2$. In power plant emissions, $NO_x$ is decreased by adjusting conditions and by treating hot stack gases with ammonia in the presence of a heterogeneous catalyst:

$$4NO(g) + 4NH_3(g) + O_2(g) \xrightarrow{\text{catalyst}} 4N_2(g) + 6H_2O(g)$$

Reducing power-plant emissions in North America and Europe has increased the pH of rainfall and some surface waters. Lime (CaO) is routinely used to react with acid rain falling on croplands. Further progress is expected under current legislation, but, in much of eastern North America and northern Europe, additional measures are needed for full recovery.

### Problems

**B19.1** An environmental technician collects a sample of rainwater. Back in the lab, her pH meter isn't working, so she uses indicator solutions to estimate the pH. A piece of litmus paper turns red, indicating acidity, so she divides the sample into thirds and obtains the following results: thymol blue turns yellow; bromphenol blue turns green; and methyl red turns red. Estimate the pH of the rainwater.

**B19.2** A lake that has a surface area of 10.0 acres (1 acre = $4.840 \times 10^3$ yd²) receives 1.00 in. of rain of pH 4.20. (Assume that the acidity of the rain is due to a strong, monoprotic acid.)
(a) How many moles of $H_3O^+$ are in the rain falling on the lake?
(b) If the lake is unbuffered and its average depth is 10.0 ft before the rain, find the pH after the rain has been mixed with lake water. (Assume the initial pH is 7.00, and ignore runoff from the surrounding land.)
(c) If the lake contains hydrogen carbonate ions ($HCO_3^-$), what mass of $HCO_3^-$ would neutralize the acid in the rain?

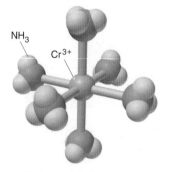

**Figure 19.15** $Cr(NH_3)_6^{3+}$, a typical complex ion.

## 19.4 • EQUILIBRIA INVOLVING COMPLEX IONS

A third kind of aqueous ionic equilibrium involves a type of ion we mentioned briefly in Section 18.9. A *simple ion,* such as $Na^+$ or $CH_3COO^-$, consists of one or a few bonded atoms, with an excess or deficit of electrons. A **complex ion** consists of a central metal ion covalently bonded to two or more anions or molecules, called **ligands.** Hydroxide, chloride, and cyanide ions are examples of ionic ligands; water, carbon monoxide, and ammonia are some molecular ligands. In the complex ion $Cr(NH_3)_6^{3+}$, for example, the central $Cr^{3+}$ is surrounded by six $NH_3$ ligands (Figure 19.15). Hydrated metal ions are complex ions with water as ligands (Section 18.6). In Chapter 23, we discuss the transition metals and the structures and properties of the numerous complex ions they form. Here, we focus on equilibria of hydrated ions with ligands other than water.

# Formation of Complex Ions

When a salt dissolves in water, a complex ion forms, with water as ligands around the metal ion. In many cases, when we treat this hydrated cation with a solution of another ligand, the bound water molecules are replaced by the other ligand. For example, a hydrated $M^{2+}$ ion, $M(H_2O)_4^{2+}$, forms the ammoniated ion, $M(NH_3)_4^{2+}$, in aqueous $NH_3$:

$$M(H_2O)_4^{2+}(aq) + 4NH_3(aq) \rightleftharpoons M(NH_3)_4^{2+}(aq) + 4H_2O(l)$$

At equilibrium, this system is expressed by a ratio of concentration terms whose form follows that of any other equilibrium expression:

$$K_c = \frac{[M(NH_3)_4^{2+}][H_2O]^4}{[M(H_2O)_4^{2+}][NH_3]^4}$$

Once again, because the concentration of water is essentially constant in aqueous reactions, we incorporate it into $K_c$ and obtain the expression for a new equilibrium constant called the **formation constant, $K_f$:**

$$K_f = \frac{K_c}{[H_2O]^4} = \frac{[M(NH_3)_4^{2+}]}{[M(H_2O)_4^{2+}][NH_3]^4}$$

At the molecular level, depicted in Figure 19.16, the actual process is stepwise, with ammonia molecules replacing water molecules one at a time. This process yields a series of intermediate species, each with its own formation constant:

$$M(H_2O)_4^{2+}(aq) + NH_3(aq) \rightleftharpoons M(H_2O)_3(NH_3)^{2+}(aq) + H_2O(l)$$

$$K_{f1} = \frac{[M(H_2O)_3(NH_3)^{2+}]}{[M(H_2O)_4^{2+}][NH_3]}$$

$$M(H_2O)_3(NH_3)^{2+}(aq) + NH_3(aq) \rightleftharpoons M(H_2O)_2(NH_3)_2^{2+}(aq) + H_2O(l)$$

$$K_{f2} = \frac{[M(H_2O)_2(NH_3)_2^{2+}]}{[M(H_2O)_3(NH_3)^{2+}][NH_3]}$$

$$M(H_2O)_2(NH_3)_2^{2+}(aq) + NH_3(aq) \rightleftharpoons M(H_2O)(NH_3)_3^{2+}(aq) + H_2O(l)$$

$$K_{f3} = \frac{[M(H_2O)(NH_3)_3^{2+}]}{[M(H_2O)_2(NH_3)_2^{2+}][NH_3]}$$

$$M(H_2O)(NH_3)_3^{2+}(aq) + NH_3(aq) \rightleftharpoons M(NH_3)_4^{2+}(aq) + H_2O(l)$$

$$K_{f4} = \frac{[M(NH_3)_4^{2+}]}{[M(H_2O)(NH_3)_3^{2+}][NH_3]}$$

**Figure 19.16** The stepwise exchange of $NH_3$ for $H_2O$ in $M(H_2O)_4^{2+}$. The molecular views show the first exchange and the fully ammoniated ion.

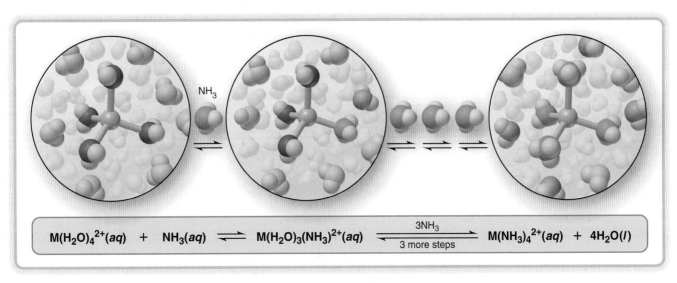

$$M(H_2O)_4^{2+}(aq) + NH_3(aq) \rightleftharpoons M(H_2O)_3(NH_3)^{2+}(aq) \xrightleftharpoons[\text{3 more steps}]{3NH_3} M(NH_3)_4^{2+}(aq) + 4H_2O(l)$$

**Table 19.4 Formation Constants ($K_f$) of Some Complex Ions at 25°C**

| Complex Ion | $K_f$ |
|---|---|
| $Ag(CN)_2^-$ | $3.0\times10^{20}$ |
| $Ag(NH_3)_2^+$ | $1.7\times10^7$ |
| $Ag(S_2O_3)_2^{3-}$ | $4.7\times10^{13}$ |
| $AlF_6^{3-}$ | $4\times10^{19}$ |
| $Al(OH)_4^-$ | $3\times10^{33}$ |
| $Be(OH)_4^{2-}$ | $4\times10^{18}$ |
| $CdI_4^{2-}$ | $1\times10^6$ |
| $Co(OH)_4^{2-}$ | $5\times10^9$ |
| $Cr(OH)_4^-$ | $8.0\times10^{29}$ |
| $Cu(NH_3)_4^{2+}$ | $5.6\times10^{11}$ |
| $Fe(CN)_6^{4-}$ | $3\times10^{35}$ |
| $Fe(CN)_6^{3-}$ | $4.0\times10^{43}$ |
| $Hg(CN)_4^{2-}$ | $9.3\times10^{38}$ |
| $Ni(NH_3)_6^{2+}$ | $2.0\times10^8$ |
| $Pb(OH)_3^-$ | $8\times10^{13}$ |
| $Sn(OH)_3^-$ | $3\times10^{25}$ |
| $Zn(CN)_4^{2-}$ | $4.2\times10^{19}$ |
| $Zn(NH_3)_4^{2+}$ | $7.8\times10^8$ |
| $Zn(OH)_4^{2-}$ | $3\times10^{15}$ |

The *sum* of the equations gives the overall equation, so the *product* of the individual formation constants gives the overall formation constant:

$$K_f = K_{f1} \times K_{f2} \times K_{f3} \times K_{f4}$$

Recall that *all complex ions are Lewis adducts* (Section 18.9). The metal ion acts as a Lewis acid (accepts an electron pair), and the ligand acts as a Lewis base (donates an electron pair). In the formation of $M(NH_3)_4^{2+}$, the $K_f$ for each step is much larger than 1 because ammonia is a stronger Lewis base than water. Therefore, if we add excess ammonia to the $M(H_2O)_4^{2+}$ solution, nearly all the $M^{2+}$ ions exist as $M(NH_3)_4^{2+}(aq)$.

Table 19.4 (and Appendix C) shows $K_f$ values of some complex ions. Notice that they are all $10^6$ or greater, which means that these ions form readily from the hydrated ion. Because of this behavior, some uses of complex-ion formation are to retrieve a metal from its ore, eliminate a toxic or unwanted metal ion from a solution, or convert a metal ion to a different form, as Sample Problem 19.13 shows for the zinc ion.

---

**Sample Problem 19.13** | **Calculating the Concentration of a Complex Ion**

**Problem** An industrial chemist converts $Zn(H_2O)_4^{2+}$ to the more stable $Zn(NH_3)_4^{2+}$ by mixing 50.0 L of 0.0020 $M$ $Zn(H_2O)_4^{2+}$ and 25.0 L of 0.15 $M$ $NH_3$. What is the $[Zn(H_2O)_4^{2+}]$ at equilibrium? $K_f$ of $Zn(NH_3)_4^{2+}$ is $7.8\times10^8$.

**Plan** We write the equation and the $K_f$ expression and use a reaction table to calculate the equilibrium concentrations. To set up the table, we must first find $[Zn(H_2O)_4^{2+}]_{init}$ and $[NH_3]_{init}$. We are given the individual volumes and molar concentrations, so we find the number of moles and divide by the *total* volume because the solutions are mixed. With the large excess of $NH_3$ and the high $K_f$, we assume that almost all the $Zn(H_2O)_4^{2+}$ is converted to $Zn(NH_3)_4^{2+}$. Because $[Zn(H_2O)_4^{2+}]$ at equilibrium is very small, we use $x$ to represent it.

**Solution** Writing the equation and the $K_f$ expression:

$$Zn(H_2O)_4^{2+}(aq) + 4NH_3(aq) \rightleftharpoons Zn(NH_3)_4^{2+}(aq) + 4H_2O(l)$$

$$K_f = \frac{[Zn(NH_3)_4^{2+}]}{[Zn(H_2O)_4^{2+}][NH_3]^4}$$

Finding the initial reactant concentrations:

$$[Zn(H_2O)_4^{2+}]_{init} = \frac{50.0\ L \times 0.0020\ M}{50.0\ L + 25.0\ L} = 1.3\times10^{-3}\ M$$

$$[NH_3]_{init} = \frac{25.0\ L \times 0.15\ M}{50.0\ L + 25.0\ L} = 5.0\times10^{-2}\ M$$

Setting up a reaction table: We assume that nearly all the $Zn(H_2O)_4^{2+}$ is converted to $Zn(NH_3)_4^{2+}$, so we set up the table with $x = [Zn(H_2O)_4^{2+}]$ at equilibrium. Because 4 mol of $NH_3$ is needed per mole of $Zn(H_2O)_4^{2+}$, the change in $[NH_3]$ is

$$[NH_3]_{reacted} \approx 4(1.3\times10^{-3}\ M) = 5.2\times10^{-3}\ M \quad \text{and} \quad [Zn(NH_3)_4^{2+}] \approx 1.3\times10^{-3}\ M$$

| Concentration ($M$) | $Zn(H_2O)_4^{2+}(aq)$ | + | $4NH_3(aq)$ | $\rightleftharpoons$ | $Zn(NH_3)_4^{2+}(aq)$ | + | $4H_2O(l)$ |
|---|---|---|---|---|---|---|---|
| Initial | $1.3\times10^{-3}$ | | $5.0\times10^{-2}$ | | 0 | | — |
| Change | $\sim(-1.3\times10^{-3})$ | | $\sim(-5.2\times10^{-3})$ | | $\sim(+1.3\times10^{-3})$ | | — |
| Equilibrium | $x$ | | $4.5\times10^{-2}$ | | $1.3\times10^{-3}$ | | — |

Solving for $x$, the $[Zn(H_2O)_4^{2+}]$ remaining at equilibrium:

$$K_f = \frac{[Zn(NH_3)_4^{2+}]}{[Zn(H_2O)_4^{2+}][NH_3]^4} = 7.8\times10^8 \approx \frac{1.3\times10^{-3}}{x(4.5\times10^{-2})^4}$$

$$x = [Zn(H_2O)_4^{2+}] \approx 4.1\times10^{-7}\ M$$

**Check** The $K_f$ is large, so we expect the $[Zn(H_2O)_4^{2+}]$ remaining to be very low.

**Follow-Up Problem 19.13**  Cyanide ion is toxic because it forms stable complex ions with the $Fe^{3+}$ ion in certain proteins involved in cellular energy production. To study this effect, a biochemist mixes 25.5 mL of $3.1 \times 10^{-2}$ $M$ $Fe(H_2O)_6^{3+}$ with 35.0 mL of 1.5 $M$ NaCN. What is the final $[Fe(H_2O)_6^{3+}]$? $K_f$ of $Fe(CN)_6^{3-}$ is $4.0 \times 10^{43}$.

## Complex Ions and the Solubility of Precipitates

In Section 19.3, you saw that $H_3O^+$ increases the solubility of a slightly soluble ionic compound if its anion is that of a weak acid. Similarly, *a ligand increases the solubility of a slightly soluble ionic compound if it forms a complex ion with the cation*. For example, iron(II) sulfide is very slightly soluble:

$$FeS(s) + H_2O(l) \rightleftharpoons Fe^{2+}(aq) + HS^-(aq) + OH^-(aq) \qquad K_{sp} = 8 \times 10^{-16}$$

When we add some 1.0 $M$ NaCN, the $CN^-$ ions act as ligands and react with the small amount of $Fe^{2+}(aq)$ to form the complex ion $Fe(CN)_6^{4-}$:

$$Fe^{2+}(aq) + 6CN^-(aq) \rightleftharpoons Fe(CN)_6^{4-}(aq) \qquad K_f = 3 \times 10^{35}$$

To see the effect of complex-ion formation on the solubility of FeS, we add the equations and, therefore, multiply their equilibrium constants:

$$FeS(s) + 6CN^-(aq) + H_2O(l) \rightleftharpoons Fe(CN)_6^{4-}(aq) + HS^-(aq) + OH^-(aq)$$
$$K_{overall} = K_{sp} \times K_f = (8 \times 10^{-16})(3 \times 10^{35}) = 2 \times 10^{20}$$

The overall dissociation of FeS into ions increased by more than a factor of $10^{35}$ in the presence of the ligand.

---

**Sample Problem 19.14**  |  **Calculating the Effect of Complex-Ion Formation on Solubility**

**Problem**  In black-and-white film developing *(see photo)*, excess AgBr is removed from a film negative with "hypo," an aqueous solution of sodium thiosulfate ($Na_2S_2O_3$), which forms the complex ion $Ag(S_2O_3)_2^{3-}$. Calculate the solubility of AgBr in **(a)** $H_2O$; **(b)** 1.0 $M$ hypo. $K_f$ of $Ag(S_2O_3)_2^{3-}$ is $4.7 \times 10^{13}$ and $K_{sp}$ of AgBr is $5.0 \times 10^{-13}$.

**Plan**  **(a)** After writing the equation and the ion-product expression, we use the given $K_{sp}$ to solve for $S$, the molar solubility of AgBr. **(b)** In hypo, $Ag^+$ forms a complex ion with $S_2O_3^{2-}$, which shifts the equilibrium and dissolves more AgBr. We write the complex-ion equation and add it to the equation for dissolving AgBr to obtain the overall equation for dissolving AgBr in hypo. We multiply $K_{sp}$ by $K_f$ to find $K_{overall}$. To find the solubility of AgBr in hypo, we set up a reaction table, with $S = [Ag(S_2O_3)_2^{3-}]$, substitute into the expression for $K_{overall}$, and solve for $S$.

Developing an image in "hypo."

**Solution**  **(a)** Solubility in water. Writing the equation for the saturated solution and the ion-product expression:

$$AgBr(s) \rightleftharpoons Ag^+(aq) + Br^-(aq) \qquad K_{sp} = [Ag^+][Br^-]$$

Solving for solubility ($S$) directly from the equation: We know that

$$S = [AgBr]_{dissolved} = [Ag^+] = [Br^-]$$

Thus,

$$K_{sp} = [Ag^+][Br^-] = S^2 = 5.0 \times 10^{-13}$$

so

$$S = \boxed{7.1 \times 10^{-7} \ M}$$

**(b)** Solubility in 1.0 $M$ hypo. Writing the overall equation:

$$AgBr(s) \rightleftharpoons \cancel{Ag^+(aq)} + Br^-(aq)$$
$$\underline{\cancel{Ag^+(aq)} + 2S_2O_3^{2-}(aq) \rightleftharpoons Ag(S_2O_3)_2^{3-}(aq)}$$
$$AgBr(s) + 2S_2O_3^{2-}(aq) \rightleftharpoons Ag(S_2O_3)_2^{3-}(aq) + Br^-(aq)$$

Calculating $K_{overall}$:

$$K_{overall} = \frac{[Ag(S_2O_3)_2^{3-}][Br^-]}{[S_2O_3^{2-}]^2} = K_{sp} \times K_f = (5.0 \times 10^{-13})(4.7 \times 10^{13}) = 24$$

Setting up a reaction table, with $S = [AgBr]_{dissolved} = [Ag(S_2O_3)_2{}^{3-}]$:

| Concentration (M) | AgBr(s) | + 2S$_2$O$_3^{2-}$(aq) | $\rightleftharpoons$ Ag(S$_2$O$_3$)$_2^{3-}$(aq) | + Br$^-$(aq) |
|---|---|---|---|---|
| Initial | — | 1.0 | 0 | 0 |
| Change | — | $-2S$ | $+S$ | $+S$ |
| Equilibrium | — | $1.0 - 2S$ | $S$ | $S$ |

Substituting the values into the expression for $K_{overall}$ and solving for $S$:

$$K_{overall} = \frac{[Ag(S_2O_3)_2{}^{3-}][Br^-]}{[S_2O_3{}^{2-}]^2} = \frac{S^2}{(1.0\,M - 2S)^2} = 24$$

Taking the square root of both sides gives

$$\frac{S}{1.0\,M - 2S} = \sqrt{24} = 4.9 \quad \text{so} \quad S = 4.9\,M - 9.8S \quad \text{and} \quad 10.8S = 4.9\,M$$

$$[Ag(S_2O_3)_2{}^{3-}] = S = \boxed{0.45\,M}$$

**Check** **(a)** From the number of ions in the formula of AgBr, we know that $S = \sqrt{K_{sp}}$, so the order of magnitude seems right: $\sim \sqrt{10^{-14}} \approx 10^{-7}$. **(b)** The $K_{overall}$ seems correct: the exponents cancel, and $5 \times 5 = 25$. Most importantly, the answer makes sense because the photographic process requires the remaining AgBr to be washed off the film and the large $K_{overall}$ confirms that. We can check $S$ by rounding and working backward to find $K_{overall}$: from the reaction table, we find that

$$[(S_2O_3)^{2-}] = 1.0\,M - 2S = 1.0\,M - 2(0.45\,M) = 1.0\,M - 0.90\,M = 0.1\,M$$

so $K_{overall} \approx (0.45)^2/(0.1)^2 = 20$, within rounding of the calculated value.

**Follow-Up Problem 19.14**  How does the solubility of AgBr in 1.0 $M$ NH$_3$ compare with its solubility in 1.0 $M$ hypo? $K_f$ of Ag(NH$_3$)$_2{}^+$ is $1.7 \times 10^7$.

## Complex Ions of Amphoteric Hydroxides

Many of the same metals that form amphoteric oxides (Chapter 8, p. 316) also form slightly soluble *amphoteric hydroxides*. These compounds dissolve very little in water, but they dissolve to a much greater extent in both acidic and basic solutions. Aluminum hydroxide is one of several examples:

$$Al(OH)_3(s) \rightleftharpoons Al^{3+}(aq) + 3OH^-(aq)$$

It is insoluble in water ($K_{sp} = 3 \times 10^{-34}$), but

- It dissolves in acid because H$_3$O$^+$ reacts with the OH$^-$ anion (Sample Problem 19.9b),

$$3H_3O^+(aq) + 3OH^-(aq) \longrightarrow 6H_2O(l)$$

giving the overall equation

$$Al(OH)_3(s) + 3H_3O^+(aq) \longrightarrow Al^{3+}(aq) + 6H_2O(l)$$

- It dissolves in base through the formation of a complex ion:

$$Al(OH)_3(s) + OH^-(aq) \longrightarrow Al(OH)_4{}^-(aq)$$

Let's look more closely at this behavior. When we dissolve a soluble aluminum salt, such as Al(NO$_3$)$_3$, in water and then slowly add a strong base, a white precipitate first forms and then dissolves as more base is added. What reactions are occurring? The formula for the hydrated Al$^{3+}$ ion is Al(H$_2$O)$_6{}^{3+}$(aq). It acts as a weak polyprotic acid and reacts with added OH$^-$ ions in a stepwise manner. In each step, one of the bound H$_2$O molecules loses a proton and becomes a bound OH$^-$ ion, so the number of bound H$_2$O molecules is reduced by 1:

$$Al(H_2O)_6{}^{3+}(aq) + OH^-(aq) \rightleftharpoons Al(H_2O)_5OH^{2+}(aq) + H_2O(l)$$

$$Al(H_2O)_5OH^{2+}(aq) + OH^-(aq) \rightleftharpoons Al(H_2O)_4(OH)_2{}^+(aq) + H_2O(l)$$

$$Al(H_2O)_4(OH)_2{}^+(aq) + OH^-(aq) \rightleftharpoons Al(H_2O)_3(OH)_3(s) + H_2O(l)$$

After three protons have been removed from each $Al(H_2O)_6^{3+}$, the white precipitate has formed, which is the insoluble hydroxide $Al(H_2O)_3(OH)_3(s)$, often written more simply as $Al(OH)_3(s)$. Now you can see that the precipitate actually consists of the hydrated $Al^{3+}$ ion with an $H^+$ removed from each of three bound $H_2O$ molecules (Figure 19.17, *center*). Addition of $H_3O^+$ protonates the $OH^-$ ions and re-forms the hydrated $Al^{3+}$ ion (Figure 19.17, *left*).

Further addition of $OH^-$ removes a fourth $H^+$ and the precipitate dissolves as the soluble ion $Al(H_2O)_2(OH)_4^-(aq)$ forms (Figure 19.17, *right*), which we usually write with the formula $Al(OH)_4^-(aq)$:

$$Al(H_2O)_3(OH)_3(s) + OH^-(aq) \rightleftharpoons Al(H_2O)_2(OH)_4^-(aq) + H_2O(l)$$

In other words, this complex ion is not created by ligands substituting for bound water molecules but through an acid-base reaction in which added $OH^-$ ions titrate bound water molecules.

Several other slightly soluble hydroxides, including those of cadmium, chromium(III), cobalt(III), lead(II), tin(II), and zinc, are amphoteric and exhibit similar reactions:

$$Zn(H_2O)_2(OH)_2(s) + OH^-(aq) \rightleftharpoons Zn(H_2O)(OH)_3^-(aq) + H_2O(l)$$

In contrast, the slightly soluble hydroxides of iron(II), iron(III), and calcium dissolve in acid, but do *not* dissolve in base, because the three remaining bound water molecules are not acidic enough to lose any of their protons:

$$Fe(H_2O)_3(OH)_3(s) + 3H_3O^+(aq) \longrightarrow Fe(H_2O)_6^{3+}(aq) + 3H_2O(l)$$

$$Fe(H_2O)_3(OH)_3(s) + OH^-(aq) \longrightarrow \text{no reaction}$$

This difference in solubility in base between $Al(OH)_3$ and $Fe(OH)_3$ is the key to an important separation step in the production of aluminum metal, so we'll consider it again in Section 22.4.

**Figure 19.17 The amphoteric behavior of aluminum hydroxide.** When solid $Al(OH)_3$ is treated with $H_3O^+$ (*left*) or with $OH^-$ (*right*), it dissolves as a result of the formation of soluble complex ions.

$$3H_2O(l) + Al(H_2O)_6^{3+}(aq) \xleftarrow{3H_3O^+} Al(H_2O)_3(OH)_3(s) \xrightarrow{OH^-} Al(H_2O)_2(OH)_4^-(aq) + H_2O(l)$$

## ■ Summary of Section 19.4

- A complex ion consists of a central metal ion covalently bonded to two or more negatively charged or neutral ligands. Its formation is described by a formation constant, $K_f$.
- A hydrated metal ion is a complex ion with water molecules as ligands. Other ligands (stronger Lewis bases) can displace the water in a stepwise process. In most cases, the $K_f$ value of each step is large, so the fully substituted complex ion forms almost completely with excess ligand.
- Adding a solution containing a ligand increases the solubility of an ionic precipitate if the cation forms a complex ion with the ligand.
- Amphoteric metal hydroxides dissolve in acid and base due to reactions that involve complex ions.

# CHAPTER REVIEW GUIDE

**Learning Objectives**  Relevant section (§) and/or sample problem (SP) numbers appear in parentheses.

### Understand These Concepts

1. How the presence of a common ion suppresses a reaction that forms it (§19.1)
2. Why the concentrations of buffer components must be high to minimize the change in pH from addition of small amounts of $H_3O^+$ or $OH^-$ (§19.1)
3. How buffer capacity depends on buffer concentration and on the $pK_a$ of the acid component; why buffer range is within $\pm 1$ pH unit of the $pK_a$ (§19.1)
4. The nature of an acid-base indicator as a conjugate acid-base pair with differently colored acidic and basic forms (§19.2)
5. The distinction between equivalence point and end point in an acid-base titration (§19.2)
6. Why the shapes of strong acid–strong base, weak acid–strong base, and weak base–strong acid titration curves differ (§19.2)
7. How the pH at the equivalence point is determined by the species present; why the pH at the midpoint of the buffer region equals the $pK_a$ of the acid (§19.2)
8. How the titration curve of a polyprotic acid has a buffer region and equivalence point for each ionizable proton (§19.2)
9. How a slightly soluble ionic compound reaches equilibrium in water, expressed by an equilibrium (solubility-product) constant, $K_{sp}$ (§19.3)
10. Why incomplete dissociation of an ionic compound leads to approximate calculated values for $K_{sp}$ and solubility (§19.3)
11. Why a common ion in a solution decreases the solubility of its compounds (§19.3)
12. How pH affects the solubility of a compound that contains a weak-acid anion (§19.3)
13. How precipitate formation depends on the relative values of $Q_{sp}$ and $K_{sp}$ (§19.3)
14. How selective precipitation and simultaneous equilibria are used to separate ions (§19.3)
15. How complex-ion formation is stepwise and expressed by an overall equilibrium (formation) constant, $K_f$ (§19.4)

16. Why addition of a ligand increases the solubility of a compound whose metal ion forms a complex ion (§19.4)
17. How the aqueous chemistry of amphoteric hydroxides involves precipitation, complex-ion formation, and acid-base equilibria (§19.4)

### Master These Skills

1. Using stoichiometry and equilibrium problem-solving techniques to calculate the effect of added $H_3O^+$ or $OH^-$ on buffer pH (SP 19.1)
2. Using the Henderson-Hasselbalch equation to calculate buffer pH (§19.1)
3. Using molecular scenes to depict buffers (SP 19.2)
4. Choosing the components of a buffer with a given pH and calculating their quantities (SP 19.3)
5. Calculating the pH at any point in an acid-base titration (§19.2 and SP 19.4)
6. Choosing an appropriate indicator based on the pH at various points in a titration (§19.2)
7. Writing $K_{sp}$ expressions for slightly soluble ionic compounds (SP 19.5)
8. Using $K_{sp}$ values to compare solubilities for compounds with the same total number of ions (§19.3)
9. Calculating a $K_{sp}$ value from solubility data (SP 19.6)
10. Calculating solubility from a $K_{sp}$ value (SP 19.7)
11. Calculating the decrease in solubility caused by the presence of a common ion (SP 19.8)
12. Predicting the effect of added $H_3O^+$ on solubility (SP 19.9)
13. Using ion concentrations to calculate $Q_{sp}$ and compare it with $K_{sp}$ to predict whether a precipitate forms (SPs 19.10, 19.11)
14. Comparing $K_{sp}$ values in order to separate ions by selective precipitation (SP 19.12)
15. Calculating the concentration of metal ion remaining after addition of excess ligand forms a complex ion (SP 19.13)
16. Using an overall equilibrium constant ($K_{sp} \times K_f$) to calculate the effect of complex-ion formation on solubility (SP 19.14)

## Key Terms    Page numbers appear in parentheses.

**Section 19.1**
acid-base buffer (765)
common-ion effect (766)
Henderson-Hasselbalch
 equation (770)
buffer capacity (770)
buffer range (771)

**Section 19.2**
acid-base titration curve (774)
equivalence point (775)
end point (776)

**Section 19.3**
solubility-product constant
 ($K_{sp}$) (783)
selective precipitation (791)

**Section 19.4**
complex ion (794)
ligand (794)
formation constant ($K_f$) (795)

## Key Equations and Relationships    Page numbers appear in parentheses.

**19.1** Finding the pH from known concentrations of a conjugate acid-base pair (Henderson-Hasselbalch equation) (770):

$$pH = pK_a + \log\left(\frac{[\text{base}]}{[\text{acid}]}\right)$$

**19.2** Defining the equilibrium condition for a saturated solution of a slightly soluble compound, $M_pX_q$, composed of $M^{n+}$ and $X^{z-}$ ions (783):

$$Q_{sp} = [M^{n+}]^p[X^{z-}]^q = K_{sp}$$

## Brief Solutions to Follow-Up Problems

**19.1** (a) Before addition:
Assuming $x$ is small enough to be neglected,
$[HF] = 0.50\,M$    and    $[F^-] = 0.45\,M$
$[H_3O^+] = K_a \times \dfrac{[HF]}{[F^-]} \approx (6.8\times10^{-4})\left(\dfrac{0.50}{0.45}\right) = 7.6\times10^{-4}\,M$
    pH = 3.12
(b) After addition of 0.40 g of NaOH (0.010 mol of NaOH) to 1.0 L of buffer,
$[HF] = 0.49\,M$    and    $[F^-] = 0.46\,M$
$[H_3O^+] \approx (6.8\times10^{-4})\left(\dfrac{0.49}{0.46}\right) = 7.2\times10^{-4}\,M$; pH = 3.14

**19.2** (a) Strong base would convert HB to B$^-$, thereby making the ratio closer to 1.
(b)

**19.3** $[H_3O^+] = 10^{-pH} = 10^{-4.25} = 5.6\times10^{-5}$
$[C_6H_5COOH] = \dfrac{[H_3O^+][C_6H_5COO^-]}{K_a}$
$= \dfrac{(5.6\times10^{-5})(0.050)}{6.3\times10^{-5}} = 0.044\,M$

Mass (g) of $C_6H_5COOH$
$= 5.0\text{ L soln} \times \dfrac{0.044\text{ mol }C_6H_5COOH}{1\text{ L soln}} \times \dfrac{122.12\text{ g }C_6H_5COOH}{1\text{ mol }C_6H_5COOH}$
$= 27\text{ g }C_6H_5COOH$

Dissolve 27 g of $C_6H_5COOH$ in 4.9 L of 0.050 $M$ $C_6H_5COONa$ and add solution to make 5.0 L. Adjust pH to 4.25 with strong acid or base.

**19.4** (a) $[H_3O^+] \approx \sqrt{(2.3\times10^{-9})(0.2000)} = 2.1\times10^{-5}\,M$
    pH = 4.68

(b) $[H_3O^+] = K_a \times \dfrac{[HBrO]}{[BrO^-]} = (2.3\times10^{-9})(1) = 2.3\times10^{-9}\,M$
    pH = 8.64

(c)
$[BrO^-] = \dfrac{\text{amount (mol) of }BrO^-}{\text{total volume (L)}} = \dfrac{0.004000\text{ mol}}{0.06000\text{ L}} = 0.06667\,M$
$K_b$ of $BrO^- = \dfrac{K_w}{K_a \text{ of HBrO}} = 4.3\times10^{-6}$
$[H_3O^+] = \dfrac{K_w}{\sqrt{K_b \times [BrO^-]}}$
$\approx \dfrac{1.0\times10^{-14}}{\sqrt{(4.3\times10^{-6})(0.06667)}} = 1.9\times10^{-11}\,M$
    pH = 10.72

## Brief Solutions to Follow-Up Problems (continued)

(d) Amount (mol) of $OH^-$ added = 0.008000 mol
Volume (L) of $OH^-$ soln = 0.08000 L

$$[OH^-] = \frac{\text{amount (mol) of } OH^- \text{ unreacted}}{\text{total volume (L)}}$$

$$= \frac{0.008000 \text{ mol} - 0.004000 \text{ mol}}{(0.02000 + 0.08000) \text{ L}} = 0.04000 \text{ } M$$

$$[H_3O^+] = \frac{K_w}{[OH^-]} = 2.5 \times 10^{-13}$$

$$pH = 12.60$$

(e)

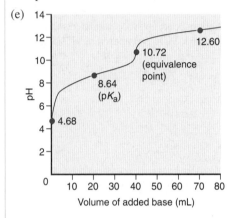

**19.5** (a) $K_{sp} = [Ca^{2+}][SO_4^{2-}]$
(b) $K_{sp} = [Cr^{3+}]^2[CO_3^{2-}]^3$
(c) $K_{sp} = [Mg^{2+}][OH^-]^2$
(d) $K_{sp} = [As^{3+}]^2[HS^-]^3[OH^-]^3$

**19.6** $[CaF_2] = \dfrac{1.5 \times 10^{-4} \text{ g } CaF_2}{10.0 \text{ mL soln}} \times \dfrac{1000 \text{ mL}}{1 \text{ L}} \times \dfrac{1 \text{ mol } CaF_2}{78.08 \text{ g } CaF_2}$

$$= 1.9 \times 10^{-4} \text{ } M$$

$$CaF_2(s) \rightleftharpoons Ca^{2+}(aq) + 2F^-(aq)$$

$[Ca^{2+}] = 1.9 \times 10^{-4} \text{ } M$ and $[F^-] = 3.8 \times 10^{-4} \text{ } M$

$$K_{sp} = [Ca^{2+}][F^-]^2 = (1.9 \times 10^{-4})(3.8 \times 10^{-4})^2 = 2.7 \times 10^{-11}$$

**19.7** From the reaction table, $[Mg^{2+}] = S$ and $[OH^-] = 2S$

$$K_{sp} = [Mg^{2+}][OH^-]^2 = 4S^3 = 6.3 \times 10^{-10}; \; S = 5.4 \times 10^{-4} \text{ } M$$

**19.8** (a) In water: $K_{sp} = [Ba^{2+}][SO_4^{2-}] = S^2 = 1.1 \times 10^{-10}$
$S = 1.0 \times 10^{-5}$
(b) In 0.10 $M$ $Na_2SO_4$: $[SO_4^{2-}] = 0.10 \text{ } M$

$$K_{sp} = 1.1 \times 10^{-10} \approx S \times 0.10; \; S = 1.1 \times 10^{-9} \text{ } M$$

$S$ decreases in presence of the common ion $SO_4^{2-}$.

**19.9** (a) Increases solubility.

$$CaF_2(s) \rightleftharpoons Ca^{2+}(aq) + 2F^-(aq)$$

$$F^-(aq) + H_3O^+(aq) \longrightarrow HF(aq) + H_2O(l)$$

(b) Increases solubility.

$$ZnS(s) + H_2O(l) \rightleftharpoons Zn^{2+}(aq) + HS^-(aq) + OH^-(aq)$$

$$HS^-(aq) + H_3O^+(aq) \longrightarrow H_2S(aq) + H_2O(l)$$

$$OH^-(aq) + H_3O^+(aq) \longrightarrow 2H_2O(l)$$

(c) No effect. $I^-(aq)$ is the conjugate base of strong acid HI.

**19.10** $Ca_3(PO_4)_2(s) \rightleftharpoons 3Ca^{2+}(aq) + 2PO_4^{3-}(aq)$

$$Q_{sp} = [Ca^{2+}]^3[PO_4^{3-}]^2 = (1.0 \times 10^{-9})^5 = 1.0 \times 10^{-45}$$

$Q_{sp} < K_{sp}$, so $Ca_3(PO_4)_2$ will not precipitate.

**19.11** (a) Scene 3 has the same relative numbers of ions as in the formula.
(b) Based on $Ni(OH)_2(s) \rightleftharpoons Ni^{2+}(aq) + 2OH^-(aq)$ and $Q_{sp} = [Ni^{2+}][OH^-]^2$, the ion products are $(3)(4)^2 = 48$ in scene 1; $(4)(2)^2 = 16$ in scene 2; and $(2)(4)^2 = 32 = K_{sp}$ in scene 3. $Q_{sp}$ of scene 1 exceeds $K_{sp}$ of scene 3.
(c) Addition of acid will decrease mass of $Ni(OH)_2(s)$ by reacting with $OH^-$, thereby causing more solid to dissolve; addition of base will increase mass of $Ni(OH)_2(s)$ due to common-ion effect.

**19.12** Both are 1/1 salts, and $K_{sp}$ values show $CaSO_4$ is more soluble:

$$[SO_4^{2-}] = \frac{K_{sp}}{[Ca^{2+}]} = \frac{2.4 \times 10^{-5}}{0.025} = 9.6 \times 10^{-4} \text{ } M$$

**19.13** $[Fe(H_2O)_6^{3+}]_{init} = \dfrac{(0.0255 \text{ L})(3.1 \times 10^{-2} \text{ } M)}{0.0255 \text{ L} + 0.0350 \text{ L}}$

$$= 1.3 \times 10^{-2} \text{ } M$$

Similarly, $[CN^-]_{init} = 0.87 \text{ } M$. From the reaction table,

$$K_f = \frac{[Fe(CN)_6^{3-}]}{[Fe(H_2O)_6^{3+}][CN^-]^6} = 4.0 \times 10^{43} \approx \frac{1.3 \times 10^{-2}}{x(0.79)^6}$$

$$x = [Fe(H_2O)_6^{3+}] \approx 1.3 \times 10^{-45}$$

**19.14** $AgBr(s) + 2NH_3(aq) \rightleftharpoons Ag(NH_3)_2^+(aq) + Br^-(aq)$

$$K_{overall} = K_{sp} \text{ of AgBr} \times K_f \text{ of } Ag(NH_3)_2^+$$

$$= 8.5 \times 10^{-6}$$

From the reaction table, $\dfrac{S}{1.0 - 2S} = \sqrt{8.5 \times 10^{-6}} = 2.9 \times 10^{-3}$

$$S = [Ag(NH_3)_2^+] = 2.9 \times 10^{-3} \text{ } M$$

Solubility is greater in 1.0 $M$ hypo than in 1.0 $M$ $NH_3$.

# PROBLEMS

Problems with **colored** numbers are answered in Appendix E and worked in detail in the Student Solutions Manual. Problem sections match those in the text and provide the numbers of relevant sample problems. Most offer Concept Review Questions, Skill-Building Exercises (grouped in pairs covering the same concept), and Problems in Context. The Comprehensive Problems are based on material from any section or previous chapter.

*Note:* Unless stated otherwise, all of the problems for this chapter refer to aqueous solutions at 298 K (25°C).

## Equilibria of Acid-Base Buffer Systems
(Sample Problems 19.1 to 19.3)

### Concept Review Questions

**19.1** What is the purpose of an acid-base buffer?

**19.2** How do the acid and base components of a buffer function? Why are they often a conjugate acid-base pair of a weak acid?

**19.3** What is the common-ion effect? How is it related to Le Châtelier's principle? Explain with equations that include HF and NaF.

**19.4** The scenes below depict solutions of the same $HA/A^-$ buffer (with counterions and water molecules omitted for clarity). (a) Which solution has the greatest buffer capacity? (b) Explain how the pH ranges of the buffers compare. (c) Which solution can react with the largest amount of added strong acid?

**19.5** What is the difference between buffers with high and low capacities? Will adding 0.01 mol of HCl produce a greater pH change in a buffer with a high or a low capacity? Explain.

**19.6** Which of these factors influence buffer capacity? How?
(a) Conjugate acid-base pair
(b) pH of the buffer
(c) Concentration of buffer components
(d) Buffer range
(e) $pK_a$ of the acid component

**19.7** What is the relationship between the buffer range and the buffer-component concentration ratio?

**19.8** A chemist needs a pH 3.5 buffer. Should she use NaOH with formic acid ($K_a = 1.8 \times 10^{-4}$) or with acetic acid ($K_a = 1.8 \times 10^{-5}$)? Why? What is the disadvantage of choosing the other acid? What is the role of the NaOH?

**19.9** State and explain the relative change in the pH and in the buffer-component concentration ratio, [NaA]/[HA], for each of the following additions:
(a) Add 0.1 *M* NaOH to the buffer
(b) Add 0.1 *M* HCl to the buffer
(c) Dissolve pure NaA in the buffer
(d) Dissolve pure HA in the buffer

**19.10** Does the pH increase or decrease, and does it do so to a large or small extent, with each of the following additions?

(a) 5 drops of 0.1 *M* NaOH to 100 mL of 0.5 *M* acetate buffer
(b) 5 drops of 0.1 *M* HCl to 100 mL of 0.5 *M* acetate buffer
(c) 5 drops of 0.1 *M* NaOH to 100 mL of 0.5 *M* HCl
(d) 5 drops of 0.1 *M* NaOH to distilled water

### Skill-Building Exercises (grouped in similar pairs)

**19.11** What are the $[H_3O^+]$ and the pH of a propanoic acid–propanoate buffer that consists of 0.35 *M* $CH_3CH_2COONa$ and 0.15 *M* $CH_3CH_2COOH$ ($K_a$ of propanoic acid = $1.3 \times 10^{-5}$)?

**19.12** What are the $[H_3O^+]$ and the pH of a benzoic acid–benzoate buffer that consists of 0.33 *M* $C_6H_5COOH$ and 0.28 *M* $C_6H_5COONa$ ($K_a$ of benzoic acid = $6.3 \times 10^{-5}$)?

**19.13** What are the $[H_3O^+]$ and the pH of a buffer that consists of 0.55 *M* $HNO_2$ and 0.75 *M* $KNO_2$ ($K_a$ of $HNO_2$ = $7.1 \times 10^{-4}$)?

**19.14** What are the $[H_3O^+]$ and the pH of a buffer that consists of 0.20 *M* HF and 0.25 *M* KF ($K_a$ of HF = $6.8 \times 10^{-4}$)?

**19.15** Find the pH of a buffer that consists of 0.45 *M* HCOOH and 0.63 *M* HCOONa ($pK_a$ of HCOOH = 3.74).

**19.16** Find the pH of a buffer that consists of 0.95 *M* HBrO and 0.68 *M* KBrO ($pK_a$ of HBrO = 8.64).

**19.17** Find the pH of a buffer that consists of 1.3 *M* sodium phenolate ($C_6H_5ONa$) and 1.2 *M* phenol ($C_6H_5OH$) ($pK_a$ of phenol = 10.00).

**19.18** Find the pH of a buffer that consists of 0.12 *M* boric acid ($H_3BO_3$) and 0.82 *M* sodium borate ($NaH_2BO_3$) ($pK_a$ of boric acid = 9.24).

**19.19** Find the pH of a buffer that consists of 0.25 *M* $NH_3$ and 0.15 *M* $NH_4Cl$ ($pK_b$ of $NH_3$ = 4.75).

**19.20** Find the pH of a buffer that consists of 0.50 *M* methylamine ($CH_3NH_2$) and 0.60 *M* $CH_3NH_3Cl$ ($pK_b$ of $CH_3NH_2$ = 3.35).

**19.21** A buffer consists of 0.22 *M* $KHCO_3$ and 0.37 *M* $K_2CO_3$. Carbonic acid is a diprotic acid with $K_{a1} = 4.5 \times 10^{-7}$ and $K_{a2} = 4.7 \times 10^{-11}$. (a) Which $K_a$ value is more important to this buffer? (b) What is the buffer pH?

**19.22** A buffer consists of 0.50 *M* $NaH_2PO_4$ and 0.40 *M* $Na_2HPO_4$. Phosphoric acid is a triprotic acid ($K_{a1} = 7.2 \times 10^{-3}$, $K_{a2} = 6.3 \times 10^{-8}$, and $K_{a3} = 4.2 \times 10^{-13}$). (a) Which $K_a$ value is most important to this buffer? (b) What is the buffer pH?

**19.23** What is the component concentration ratio, [$Pr^-$]/[HPr], of a buffer that has a pH of 5.44 ($K_a$ of HPr = $1.3 \times 10^{-5}$)?

**19.24** What is the component concentration ratio, [$NO_2^-$]/[$HNO_2$], of a buffer that has a pH of 2.95 ($K_a$ of $HNO_2$ = $7.1 \times 10^{-4}$)?

**19.25** What is the component concentration ratio, [$BrO^-$]/[HBrO], of a buffer that has a pH of 7.95 ($K_a$ of HBrO = $2.3 \times 10^{-9}$)?

**19.26** What is the component concentration ratio, [$CH_3COO^-$]/[$CH_3COOH$], of a buffer that has a pH of 4.39 ($K_a$ of $CH_3COOH$ = $1.8 \times 10^{-5}$)?

**19.27** A buffer containing 0.2000 *M* of acid, HA, and 0.1500 *M* of its conjugate base, $A^-$, has a pH of 3.35. What is the pH after 0.0015 mol of NaOH is added to 0.5000 L of this solution?

**19.28** A buffer that contains 0.40 $M$ base, B, and 0.25 $M$ of its conjugate acid, $BH^+$, has a pH of 8.88. What is the pH after 0.0020 mol of HCl is added to 0.25 L of this solution?

**19.29** A buffer that contains 0.110 $M$ HY and 0.220 $M$ $Y^-$ has a pH of 8.77. What is the pH after 0.0015 mol of $Ba(OH)_2$ is added to 0.350 L of this solution?

**19.30** A buffer that contains 1.05 $M$ B and 0.750 $M$ $BH^+$ has a pH of 9.50. What is the pH after 0.0050 mol of HCl is added to 0.500 L of this solution?

**19.31** A buffer is prepared by mixing 204 mL of 0.452 $M$ HCl and 0.500 L of 0.400 M sodium acetate. (See Appendix C.) (a) What is the pH? (b) How many grams of KOH must be added to 0.500 L of the buffer to change the pH by 0.15 units?

**19.32** A buffer is prepared by mixing 50.0 mL of 0.050 M sodium bicarbonate and 10.7 mL of 0.10 M NaOH. (See Appendix C.) (a) What is the pH? (b) How many grams of HCl must be added to 25.0 mL of the buffer to change the pH by 0.07 units?

**19.33** Choose specific acid-base conjugate pairs to make the following buffers: (a) pH $\approx$ 4.5; (b) pH $\approx$ 7.0. (See Appendix C.)

**19.34** Choose specific acid-base conjugate pairs to make the following buffers: (a) $[H_3O^+] \approx 1 \times 10^{-9}\ M$; (b) $[OH^-] \approx 3 \times 10^{-5}\ M$. (See Appendix C.)

**19.35** Choose specific acid-base conjugate pairs to make the following buffers: (a) pH $\approx$ 3.5; (b) pH $\approx$ 5.5. (See Appendix C.)

**19.36** Choose specific acid-base conjugate pairs to make the following buffers: (a) $[OH^-] \approx 1 \times 10^{-6}\ M$; (b) $[H_3O^+] \approx 4 \times 10^{-4}\ M$. (See Appendix C.)

**Problems in Context**

**19.37** An industrial chemist studying bleaching and sterilizing prepares several hypochlorite buffers. Find the pH of (a) 0.100 $M$ HClO and 0.100 $M$ NaClO; (b) 0.100 $M$ HClO and 0.150 $M$ NaClO; (c) 0.150 $M$ HClO and 0.100 $M$ NaClO; (d) 1.0 L of the solution in part (a) after 0.0050 mol of NaOH has been added.

**19.38** Oxoanions of phosphorus are buffer components in blood. For a $KH_2PO_4/Na_2HPO_4$ solution with pH = 7.40 (pH of normal arterial blood), what is the buffer-component concentration ratio?

## Acid-Base Titration Curves
(Sample Problem 19.4)

**Concept Review Questions**

**19.39** How can you estimate the pH range of an indicator's color change? Why do some indicators have two separate pH ranges?

**19.40** Why does the color change of an indicator take place over a range of about 2 pH units?

**19.41** Why doesn't the addition of an acid-base indicator affect the pH of the test solution?

**19.42** What is the difference between the end point of a titration and the equivalence point? Is the equivalence point always reached first? Explain.

**19.43** The scenes below depict the relative concentrations of $H_3PO_4$, $H_2PO_4^-$, and $HPO_4^{2-}$ during a titration with aqueous NaOH, but they are out of order. (Phosphate groups are purple, hydrogens are blue, and $Na^+$ ions and water molecules are not shown.) (a) List the scenes in the correct order. (b) What is the pH in the correctly ordered second scene (see Appendix C)? (c) If it requires 10.00 mL of the NaOH solution to reach this scene, how much more is needed to reach the last scene?

**19.44** Explain how strong acid–strong base, weak acid–strong base, and weak base–strong acid titrations using the same concentrations differ in terms of (a) the initial pH and (b) the pH at the equivalence point. (The component in italics is in the flask.)

**19.45** What species are in the buffer region of a weak acid–strong base titration? How are they different from the species at the equivalence point? How are they different from the species in the buffer region of a weak base–strong acid titration?

**19.46** Why is the center of the buffer region of a weak acid–strong base titration significant?

**19.47** How does the titration curve of a monoprotic acid differ from that of a diprotic acid?

**Skill-Building Exercises** (grouped in similar pairs)

**19.48** The indicator cresol red has $K_a = 3.5 \times 10^{-9}$. Over what approximate pH range does it change color?

**19.49** The indicator ethyl red has $K_a = 3.8 \times 10^{-6}$. Over what approximate pH range does it change color?

**19.50** Use Figure 19.5 to find an indicator for these titrations:
(a) 0.10 $M$ HCl with 0.10 $M$ NaOH
(b) 0.10 $M$ HCOOH (Appendix C) with 0.10 $M$ NaOH

**19.51** Use Figure 19.5 to find an indicator for these titrations:
(a) 0.10 $M$ $CH_3NH_2$ (Appendix C) with 0.10 $M$ HCl
(b) 0.50 $M$ HI with 0.10 $M$ KOH

**19.52** Use Figure 19.5 to find an indicator for these titrations:
(a) 0.5 $M$ $(CH_3)_2NH$ (Appendix C) with 0.5 $M$ HBr
(b) 0.2 $M$ KOH with 0.2 $M$ $HNO_3$

**19.53** Use Figure 19.5 to find an indicator for these titrations:
(a) 0.25 $M$ $C_6H_5COOH$ (Appendix C) with 0.25 $M$ KOH
(b) 0.50 $M$ $NH_4Cl$ (Appendix C) with 0.50 $M$ NaOH

**19.54** Calculate the pH during the titration of 40.00 mL of 0.1000 $M$ HCl with 0.1000 $M$ NaOH solution after the following additions of base:
(a) 0 mL        (b) 25.00 mL    (c) 39.00 mL    (d) 39.90 mL
(e) 40.00 mL    (f) 40.10 mL    (g) 50.00 mL

**19.55** Calculate the pH during the titration of 30.00 mL of 0.1000 $M$ KOH with 0.1000 $M$ HBr solution after the following additions of acid:
(a) 0 mL        (b) 15.00 mL    (c) 29.00 mL    (d) 29.90 mL
(e) 30.00 mL    (f) 30.10 mL    (g) 40.00 mL

**19.56** Find the pH during the titration of 20.00 mL of 0.1000 $M$ butanoic acid, $CH_3CH_2CH_2COOH$ ($K_a = 1.54 \times 10^{-5}$),

with 0.1000 $M$ NaOH solution after the following additions of titrant:
(a) 0 mL          (b) 10.00 mL     (c) 15.00 mL     (d) 19.00 mL
(e) 19.95 mL     (f) 20.00 mL     (g) 20.05 mL     (h) 25.00 mL

**19.57** Find the pH during the titration of 20.00 mL of 0.1000 $M$ triethylamine, $(CH_3CH_2)_3N$ ($K_b = 5.2 \times 10^{-4}$), with 0.1000 $M$ HCl solution after the following additions of titrant:
(a) 0 mL          (b) 10.00 mL     (c) 15.00 mL     (d) 19.00 mL
(e) 19.95 mL     (f) 20.00 mL     (g) 20.05 mL     (h) 25.00 mL

**19.58** Find the pH of the equivalence point(s) and the volume (mL) of 0.0372 $M$ NaOH needed to reach the point(s) in titrations of
(a) 42.2 mL of 0.0520 $M$ $CH_3COOH$
(b) 28.9 mL of 0.0850 $M$ $H_2SO_3$ (two equivalence points)

**19.59** Find the pH of the equivalence point(s) and the volume (mL) of 0.0588 $M$ KOH needed to reach the point(s) in titrations of
(a) 23.4 mL of 0.0390 $M$ $HNO_2$
(b) 17.3 mL of 0.130 $M$ $H_2CO_3$ (two equivalence points)

**19.60** Find the pH of the equivalence point(s) and the volume (mL) of 0.125 $M$ HCl needed to reach the point(s) in titrations of
(a) 65.5 mL of 0.234 $M$ $NH_3$
(b) 21.8 mL of 1.11 $M$ $CH_3NH_2$

**19.61** Find the pH of the equivalence point(s) and the volume (mL) of 0.447 $M$ $HNO_3$ needed to reach the point(s) in titrations of
(a) 2.65 L of 0.0750 $M$ pyridine ($C_5H_5N$)
(b) 0.188 L of 0.250 $M$ ethylenediamine ($H_2NCH_2CH_2NH_2$)

## Equilibria of Slightly Soluble Ionic Compounds
(Sample Problems 19.5 to 19.12)

### Concept Review Questions

**19.62** The molar solubility ($S$) of $M_2X$ is $5 \times 10^{-5}$ $M$. Find $S$ of each ion. How do you set up the calculation to find $K_{sp}$? What assumption must you make about the dissociation of $M_2X$ into ions? Why is the calculated $K_{sp}$ higher than the actual value?

**19.63** Why does pH affect the solubility of $BaF_2$ but not of $BaCl_2$?

**19.64** A list of $K_{sp}$ values like that in Appendix C can be used to compare the solubility of silver chloride directly with that of silver bromide but not with that of silver chromate. Explain.

**19.65** In a gaseous equilibrium, the reverse reaction occurs when $Q_c > K_c$. What occurs in aqueous solution when $Q_{sp} > K_{sp}$?

### Skill-Building Exercises (grouped in similar pairs)

**19.66** Write the ion-product expressions for (a) silver carbonate; (b) barium fluoride; (c) copper(II) sulfide.

**19.67** Write the ion-product expressions for (a) iron(III) hydroxide; (b) barium phosphate; (c) tin(II) sulfide.

**19.68** Write the ion-product expressions for (a) calcium chromate; (b) silver cyanide; (c) nickel(II) sulfide.

**19.69** Write the ion-product expressions for (a) lead(II) iodide; (b) strontium sulfate; (c) cadmium sulfide.

**19.70** The solubility of silver carbonate is 0.032 $M$ at 20°C. Calculate its $K_{sp}$.

**19.71** The solubility of zinc oxalate is $7.9 \times 10^{-3}$ $M$ at 18°C. Calculate its $K_{sp}$.

**19.72** The solubility of silver dichromate at 15°C is $8.3 \times 10^{-3}$ g/100 mL solution. Calculate its $K_{sp}$.

**19.73** The solubility of calcium sulfate at 30°C is 0.209 g/100 mL solution. Calculate its $K_{sp}$.

**19.74** Find the molar solubility of $SrCO_3$ ($K_{sp} = 5.4 \times 10^{-10}$) in (a) pure water and (b) 0.13 $M$ $Sr(NO_3)_2$.

**19.75** Find the molar solubility of $BaCrO_4$ ($K_{sp} = 2.1 \times 10^{-10}$) in (a) pure water and (b) $1.5 \times 10^{-3}$ $M$ $Na_2CrO_4$.

**19.76** Calculate the molar solubility of $Ca(IO_3)_2$ in (a) 0.060 $M$ $Ca(NO_3)_2$ and (b) 0.060 $M$ $NaIO_3$. (See Appendix C.)

**19.77** Calculate the molar solubility of $Ag_2SO_4$ in (a) 0.22 $M$ $AgNO_3$ and (b) 0.22 $M$ $Na_2SO_4$. (See Appendix C.)

**19.78** Which compound in each pair is more soluble in water?
(a) Magnesium hydroxide or nickel(II) hydroxide
(b) Lead(II) sulfide or copper(II) sulfide
(c) Silver sulfate or magnesium fluoride

**19.79** Which compound in each pair is more soluble in water?
(a) Strontium sulfate or barium chromate
(b) Calcium carbonate or copper(II) carbonate
(c) Barium iodate or silver chromate

**19.80** Which compound in each pair is more soluble in water?
(a) Barium sulfate or calcium sulfate
(b) Calcium phosphate or magnesium phosphate
(c) Silver chloride or lead(II) sulfate

**19.81** Which compound in each pair is more soluble in water?
(a) Manganese(II) hydroxide or calcium iodate
(b) Strontium carbonate or cadmium sulfide
(c) Silver cyanide or copper(I) iodide

**19.82** Write equations to show whether the solubility of either of the following is affected by pH: (a) AgCl; (b) $SrCO_3$.

**19.83** Write equations to show whether the solubility of either of the following is affected by pH: (a) CuBr; (b) $Ca_3(PO_4)_2$.

**19.84** Write equations to show whether the solubility of either of the following is affected by pH: (a) $Fe(OH)_2$; (b) CuS.

**19.85** Write equations to show whether the solubility of either of the following is affected by pH: (a) $PbI_2$; (b) $Hg_2(CN)_2$.

**19.86** Does any solid $Cu(OH)_2$ form when 0.075 g of KOH is dissolved in 1.0 L of $1.0 \times 10^{-3}$ $M$ $Cu(NO_3)_2$?

**19.87** Does any solid $PbCl_2$ form when 3.5 mg of NaCl is dissolved in 0.250 L of 0.12 $M$ $Pb(NO_3)_2$?

**19.88** Does any solid $Ba(IO_3)_2$ form when 7.5 mg of $BaCl_2$ is dissolved in 500. mL of 0.023 $M$ $NaIO_3$?

**19.89** Does any solid $Ag_2CrO_4$ form when $2.7 \times 10^{-5}$ g of $AgNO_3$ is dissolved in 15.0 mL of $4.0 \times 10^{-4}$ $M$ $K_2CrO_4$?

### Problems in Context

**19.90** When blood is donated, sodium oxalate solution is used to precipitate $Ca^{2+}$, which triggers clotting. A 104-mL sample of blood contains $9.7 \times 10^{-5}$ g $Ca^{2+}$/mL. A technologist treats the sample with 100.0 mL of 0.1550 $M$ $Na_2C_2O_4$. Calculate $[Ca^{2+}]$ after the treatment. (See Appendix C for $K_{sp}$ of $CaC_2O_4 \cdot H_2O$.)

**19.91** A 50.0-mL volume of 0.50 $M$ Fe(NO$_3$)$_3$ is mixed with 125 mL of 0.25 $M$ Cd(NO$_3$)$_2$.
(a) If aqueous NaOH is added, which ion precipitates first? (See Appendix C.)
(b) Describe how the metal ions can be separated using NaOH.
(c) Calculate the [OH$^-$] that will accomplish the separation.

## Equilibria Involving Complex Ions
(Sample Problems 19.13 and 19.14)

### Concept Review Questions

**19.92** How can a metal cation be at the center of a complex anion?

**19.93** Write equations to show the stepwise reaction of Cd(H$_2$O)$_4^{2+}$ in an aqueous solution of KI to form CdI$_4^{-2}$. Show that $K_{f(overall)} = K_{f1} \times K_{f2} \times K_{f3} \times K_{f4}$.

**19.94** Consider the dissolution of PbS in water:

$$PbS(s) + H_2O(l) \rightleftharpoons Pb^{2+}(aq) + HS^-(aq) + OH^-(aq)$$

Adding aqueous NaOH causes more PbS to dissolve. Does this violate Le Châtelier's principle? Explain.

### Skill-Building Exercises (grouped in similar pairs)

**19.95** Write a balanced equation for the reaction of Hg(H$_2$O)$_4^{2+}$ in aqueous KCN.

**19.96** Write a balanced equation for the reaction of Zn(H$_2$O)$_4^{2+}$ in aqueous NaCN.

**19.97** Write a balanced equation for the reaction of Ag(H$_2$O)$_2^+$ in aqueous Na$_2$S$_2$O$_3$.

**19.98** Write a balanced equation for the reaction of Al(H$_2$O)$_6^{3+}$ in aqueous KF.

**19.99** What is [Ag$^+$] when 25.0 mL each of 0.044 $M$ AgNO$_3$ and 0.57 $M$ Na$_2$S$_2$O$_3$ are mixed [$K_f$ of Ag(S$_2$O$_3$)$_2^{3-}$ = 4.7×10$^{13}$]?

**19.100** Potassium thiocyanate, KSCN, is often used to detect the presence of Fe$^{3+}$ ions in solution through the formation of the red Fe(H$_2$O)$_5$SCN$^{2+}$ (or, more simply, FeSCN$^{2+}$). What is [Fe$^{3+}$] when 0.50 L each of 0.0015 $M$ Fe(NO$_3$)$_3$ and 0.20 $M$ KSCN are mixed? $K_f$ of FeSCN$^{2+}$ = 8.9×10$^2$.

**19.101** Find the solubility of Cr(OH)$_3$ in a buffer of pH 13.0 [$K_{sp}$ of Cr(OH)$_3$ = 6.3×10$^{-31}$; $K_f$ of Cr(OH)$_4^-$ = 8.0×10$^{29}$].

**19.102** Find the solubility of AgI in 2.5 $M$ NH$_3$ [$K_{sp}$ of AgI = 8.3×10$^{-17}$; $K_f$ of Ag(NH$_3$)$_2^+$ = 1.7×10$^7$].

**19.103** When 0.84 g of ZnCl$_2$ is dissolved in 245 mL of 0.150 $M$ NaCN, what are [Zn$^{2+}$], [Zn(CN)$_4^{2-}$], and [CN$^-$][$K_f$ of Zn(CN)$_4^{2-}$ = 4.2×10$^{19}$]?

**19.104** When 2.4 g of Co(NO$_3$)$_2$ is dissolved in 0.350 L of 0.22 $M$ KOH, what are [Co$^{2+}$], [Co(OH)$_4^{2-}$], and [OH$^-$] [$K_f$ of Co(OH)$_4^{2-}$ = 5×10$^9$]?

## Comprehensive Problems

**19.105** What volumes of 0.200 $M$ HCOOH and 2.00 $M$ NaOH would make 500. mL of a buffer with the pH of one made from 475 mL of 0.200 $M$ benzoic acid and 25 mL of 2.00 $M$ NaOH?

**19.106** A microbiologist is preparing a medium on which to culture $E. coli$ bacteria. She buffers the medium at pH 7.00 to minimize the effect of acid-producing fermentation. What volumes of equimolar aqueous solutions of K$_2$HPO$_4$ and KH$_2$PO$_4$ must she combine to make 100. mL of the pH 7.00 buffer?

**19.107** As an FDA physiologist, you need 0.700 L of formic acid–formate buffer with a pH of 3.74. (a) What is the required buffer-component concentration ratio? (b) How do you prepare this solution from stock solutions of 1.0 $M$ HCOOH and 1.0 $M$ NaOH? (c) What is the final concentration of HCOOH in this solution?

**19.108** Tris(hydroxymethyl)aminomethane [(HOCH$_2$)$_3$CNH$_2$], known as TRIS, is a weak base used in biochemical experiments to make buffer solutions in the pH range of 7 to 9. A certain TRIS buffer has a pH of 8.10 at 25°C and a pH of 7.80 at 37°C. Why does the pH change with temperature?

**19.109** Water flowing through pipes of carbon steel must be kept at pH 5 or greater to limit corrosion. If an 8.0×10$^3$ lb/hr water stream contains 10 ppm sulfuric acid and 0.015% acetic acid, how many pounds per hour of sodium acetate trihydrate must be added to maintain that pH?

**19.110** Gout is caused by an error in metabolism that leads to a buildup of uric acid in body fluids, which is deposited as slightly soluble sodium urate (C$_5$H$_3$N$_4$O$_3$Na) in the joints. If the extracellular [Na$^+$] is 0.15 $M$ and the solubility of sodium urate is 0.085 g/100. mL, what is the minimum urate ion concentration (abbreviated [Ur$^-$]) that will cause a deposit of sodium urate?

**19.111** In the process of cave formation (p. 788), the dissolution of CO$_2$ (equation 1) has a $K_{eq}$ of 3.1×10$^{-2}$, and the formation of aqueous Ca(HCO$_3$)$_2$ (equation 2) has a $K_{eq}$ of 1×10$^{-12}$. The fraction by volume of atmospheric CO$_2$ is 3×10$^{-4}$. (a) Find [CO$_2$(aq)] in equilibrium with atmospheric CO$_2$. (b) Determine [Ca$^{2+}$] arising from (equation 2) given current levels of atmospheric CO$_2$. (c) Calculate [Ca$^{2+}$] if atmospheric CO$_2$ doubles.

**19.112** Phosphate systems form essential buffers in organisms. Calculate the pH of a buffer made by dissolving 0.80 mol of NaOH in 0.50 L of 1.0 $M$ H$_3$PO$_4$.

**19.113** The solubility of KCl is 3.7 $M$ at 20°C. Two beakers contain 100. mL of saturated KCl solution: 100. mL of 6.0 $M$ HCl is added to the first beaker and 100. mL of 12 $M$ HCl to the second. (a) Find the ion-product constant of KCl at 20°C. (b) What mass, if any, of KCl will precipitate from each beaker?

**19.114** It is possible to detect NH$_3$ gas over 10$^{-2}$ $M$ NH$_3$. To what pH must 0.15 $M$ NH$_4$Cl be raised to form detectable NH$_3$?

**19.115** Manganese(II) sulfide is one of the compounds found in the nodules on the ocean floor that may eventually be a primary source of many transition metals. The solubility of MnS is 4.7×10$^{-4}$ g/100 mL solution. Estimate the $K_{sp}$ of MnS.

**19.116** The normal pH of blood is 7.40 ± 0.05 and is controlled in part by the H$_2$CO$_3$/HCO$_3^-$ buffer system.
(a) Assuming that the $K_a$ value for carbonic acid at 25°C applies to blood, what is the [H$_2$CO$_3$]/[HCO$_3^-$] ratio in normal blood?
(b) In a condition called $acidosis$, the blood is too acidic. What is the [H$_2$CO$_3$]/[HCO$_3^-$] ratio in a patient whose blood pH is 7.20?

**19.117** A bioengineer preparing cells for cloning bathes a small piece of rat epithelial tissue in a TRIS buffer (see Problem 19.108). The buffer is made by dissolving 43.0 g of TRIS (p$K_b$ = 5.91) in enough 0.095 $M$ HCl to make 1.00 L of solution. What is the molarity of TRIS and the pH of the buffer?

**19.118** Sketch a qualitative curve for the titration of ethylenediamine, H$_2$NCH$_2$CH$_2$NH$_2$, with 0.1 $M$ HCl.

**19.119** A solution contains 0.10 $M$ ZnCl$_2$ and 0.020 $M$ MnCl$_2$. Given the following information, how would you adjust the pH to separate the ions as their sulfides ([$H_2S$] of a saturated aqueous solution at 25°C = 0.10 $M$; $K_w$ = 1.0×10⁻¹⁴ at 25°C)?

$$MnS + H_2O \rightleftharpoons Mn^{2+} + HS^- + OH^- \qquad K_{sp} = 3×10^{-11}$$
$$ZnS + H_2O \rightleftharpoons Zn^{2+} + HS^- + OH^- \qquad K_{sp} = 2×10^{-22}$$
$$H_2S + H_2O \rightleftharpoons H_3O^+ + HS^- \qquad K_{a1} = 9×10^{-8}$$

**19.120** Amino acids [general formula $NH_2CH(R)COOH$] can be considered polyprotic acids. In many cases, the R group contains additional amine and carboxyl groups.
(a) Can an amino acid dissolved in pure water have a protonated COOH group and an unprotonated $NH_2$ group ($K_a$ of COOH group = 4.47×10⁻³; $K_b$ of $NH_2$ group = 6.03×10⁻⁵)? Use glycine, $NH_2CH_2COOH$, to explain why.
(b) Calculate [$^+NH_3CH_2COO^-$]/[$^+NH_3CH_2COOH$] at pH 5.5.
(c) The R group of lysine is $-CH_2CH_2CH_2CH_2NH_2$ (p$K_b$ = 3.47). Draw the structure of lysine at pH 1, physiological pH (~7), and pH 13.
(d) The R group of glutamic acid is $-CH_2CH_2COOH$ (p$K_a$ = 4.07). Of the forms of glutamic acid that are shown below, which predominates at (1) pH 1, (2) physiological pH (~7), and (3) pH 13?

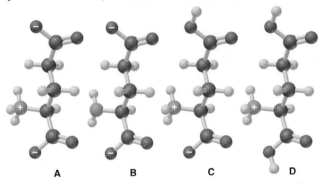

**A**      **B**      **C**      **D**

**19.121** The scene at right depicts a saturated solution of $MCl_2(s)$ in the presence of dilute aqueous NaCl; each sphere represents 1.0×10⁻⁶ mol of ion, and the volume is 250.0 mL (solid $MCl_2$ is shown as green chunks; $Na^+$ ions and water molecules are not shown). (a) Calculate the $K_{sp}$ of $MCl_2$. (b) If $M(NO_3)_2(s)$ is added, is there an increase, decrease, or no change in the number of $Cl^-$ particles? In $K_{sp}$? In mass of $MCl_2(s)$?

**19.122** Tooth enamel consists of hydroxyapatite, $Ca_5(PO_4)_3OH$ ($K_{sp}$ = 6.8×10⁻³⁷). Fluoride ion added to drinking water reacts with $Ca_5(PO_4)_3OH$ to form the more tooth decay–resistant fluorapatite, $Ca_5(PO_4)_3F$ ($K_{sp}$ = 1.0×10⁻⁶⁰). Fluoridated water has dramatically decreased cavities among children. Calculate the solubility of $Ca_5(PO_4)_3OH$ and of $Ca_5(PO_4)_3F$ in water.

**19.123** The acid-base indicator ethyl orange turns from red to yellow over the pH range 3.4 to 4.8. Estimate $K_a$ for ethyl orange.

**19.124** Use the values obtained in Problem 19.54 to sketch a curve of [$H_3O^+$] vs. mL of added titrant. Are there advantages or disadvantages to viewing the results in this form? Explain.

**19.125** Instrumental acid-base titrations use a pH meter to monitor the changes in pH and volume. The equivalence point is found from the volume at which the curve has the steepest slope.
(a) Use the data in Figure 19.7 (p. 775) to calculate the slope ($\Delta pH/\Delta V$) for all pairs of adjacent points and to calculate the average volume ($V_{avg}$) for each interval.
(b) Plot $\Delta pH/\Delta V$ vs. $V_{avg}$ to find the steepest slope, and thus the volume at the equivalence point. (For example, the first pair of

points gives $\Delta pH$ = 0.22, $\Delta V$ = 10.00 mL; hence, $\Delta pH/\Delta V$ = 0.022 mL⁻¹, and $V_{avg}$ = 5.00 mL.)

**19.126** What is the pH of a solution of 6.5×10⁻⁹ mol of $Ca(OH)_2$ in 10.0 L of water [$K_{sp}$ of $Ca(OH)_2$ = 6.5×10⁻⁶]?

**19.127** Muscle physiologists study the accumulation of lactic acid [$CH_3CH(OH)COOH$] during exercise. Food chemists study its occurrence in sour milk, beer, wine, and fruit. Industrial microbiologists study its formation by various bacterial species from carbohydrates. A biochemist prepares a lactic acid–lactate buffer by mixing 225 mL of 0.85 $M$ lactic acid ($K_a$ = 1.38×10⁻⁴) with 435 mL of 0.68 $M$ sodium lactate. What is the buffer pH?

**19.128** A student wants to dissolve the maximum amount of $CaF_2$ ($K_{sp}$ = 3.2×10⁻¹¹) to make 1 L of aqueous solution.
(a) Into which of the following solvents should she dissolve the salt?

(I) Pure water          (II) 0.01 $M$ HF
(III) 0.01 $M$ NaOH      (IV) 0.01 $M$ HCl
(V) 0.01 $M$ $Ca(OH)_2$

(b) Which would dissolve the least amount of salt?

**19.129** A 500.-mL solution consists of 0.050 mol of solid NaOH and 0.13 mol of hypochlorous acid (HClO; $K_a$ = 3.0×10⁻⁸) dissolved in water.
(a) Aside from water, what is the concentration of each species that is present?
(b) What is the pH of the solution?
(c) What is the pH after adding 0.0050 mol of HCl to the flask?

**19.130** Calcium ion present in water supplies is easily precipitated as calcite ($CaCO_3$):

$$Ca^{2+}(aq) + CO_3^{2-}(aq) \rightleftharpoons CaCO_3(s)$$

Because the $K_{sp}$ decreases with temperature, heating hard water forms a calcite "scale," which clogs pipes and water heaters. Find the solubility of calcite in water (a) at 10°C ($K_{sp}$ = 4.4×10⁻⁹) and (b) at 30°C ($K_{sp}$ = 3.1×10⁻⁹).

**19.131** Calculate the molar solubility of $Hg_2C_2O_4$ ($K_{sp}$ = 1.75×10⁻¹³) in 0.13 $M$ $Hg_2(NO_3)_2$.

**19.132** Environmental engineers use alkalinity as a measure of the capacity of carbonate buffering systems in water samples:

Alkalinity (mol/L) = [$HCO_3^-$] + 2[$CO_3^{2-}$] + [$OH^-$] − [$H^+$]

Find the alkalinity of a water sample that has a pH of 9.5, 26.0 mg/L $CO_3^{2-}$, and 65.0 mg/L $HCO_3^-$.

**19.133** Human blood contains one buffer system based on phosphate species and one based on carbonate species. Assuming that blood has a normal pH of 7.4, what are the principal phosphate and carbonate species present? What is the ratio of the two phosphate species? (In the presence of the dissolved ions and other species in blood, $K_{a1}$ of $H_3PO_4$ = 1.3×10⁻², $K_{a2}$ = 2.3×10⁻⁷, and $K_{a3}$ = 6×10⁻¹²; $K_{a1}$ of $H_2CO_3$ = 8×10⁻⁷ and $K_{a2}$ = 1.6×10⁻¹⁰.)

**19.134** A 0.050 $M$ $H_2S$ solution contains 0.15 M $NiCl_2$ and 0.35 $M$ $Hg(NO_3)_2$. What pH is required to precipitate the maximum amount of HgS but none of the NiS? (See Appendix C.)

**19.135** Quantitative analysis of $Cl^-$ ion is often performed by a titration with silver nitrate, using sodium chromate as an indicator. As standardized $AgNO_3$ is added, both white AgCl and red $Ag_2CrO_4$ precipitate, but so long as some $Cl^-$ remains, the $Ag_2CrO_4$ redissolves as the mixture is stirred. When the red color is permanent, the equivalence point has been reached.

(a) Calculate the equilibrium constant for the reaction

$$2AgCl(s) + CrO_4^{2-}(aq) \rightleftharpoons Ag_2CrO_4(s) + 2Cl^-(aq)$$

(b) Explain why the silver chromate redissolves.
(c) If 25.00 cm³ of 0.1000 $M$ NaCl is mixed with 25.00 cm³ of 0.1000 $M$ AgNO₃, what is the concentration of Ag⁺ remaining in solution? Is this sufficient to precipitate any silver chromate?

**19.136** An ecobotanist separates the components of a tropical bark extract by chromatography. She discovers a large proportion of quinidine, a dextrorotatory isomer of quinine used for control of arrhythmic heartbeat. Quinidine has two basic nitrogens ($K_{b1} = 4.0 \times 10^{-6}$ and $K_{b2} = 1.0 \times 10^{-10}$). To measure the concentration, she carries out a titration. Because of the low solubility of quinidine, she first protonates both nitrogens with excess HCl and titrates the acidified solution with standardized base. A 33.85-mg sample of quinidine ($\mathcal{M} = 324.41$ g/mol) is acidified with 6.55 mL of 0.150 $M$ HCl.
(a) How many milliliters of 0.0133 $M$ NaOH are needed to titrate the excess HCl?
(b) How many additional milliliters of titrant are needed to reach the first equivalence point of quinidine dihydrochloride?
(c) What is the pH at the first equivalence point?

**19.137** Some kidney stones form by the precipitation of calcium oxalate monohydrate (CaC₂O₄·H₂O, $K_{sp} = 2.3 \times 10^{-9}$). The pH of urine varies from 5.5 to 7.0, and the average [Ca²⁺] in urine is $2.6 \times 10^{-3}$ $M$.
(a) If the [oxalic acid] in urine is $3.0 \times 10^{-13}$ $M$, will kidney stones form at pH = 5.5?
(b) At pH = 7.0?
(c) Vegetarians have a urine pH above 7. Are they more or less likely to form kidney stones?

**19.138** A biochemist needs a medium for acid-producing bacteria. The pH of the medium must not change by more than 0.05 pH units for every 0.0010 mol of H₃O⁺ generated by the organisms per liter of medium. A buffer consisting of 0.10 $M$ HA and 0.10 $M$ A⁻ is included in the medium to control its pH. What volume of this buffer must be included in 1.0 L of medium?

**19.139** A 35.00-mL solution of 0.2500 $M$ HF is titrated with a standardized 0.1532 $M$ solution of NaOH at 25°C.
(a) What is the pH of the HF solution before titrant is added?
(b) How many milliliters of titrant are required to reach the equivalence point?
(c) What is the pH at 0.50 mL before the equivalence point?
(d) What is the pH at the equivalence point?
(e) What is the pH at 0.50 mL after the equivalence point?

**19.140** Because of the toxicity of mercury compounds, mercury(I) chloride is used in antibacterial salves. The mercury(I) ion (Hg₂²⁺) consists of two bound Hg⁺ ions.
(a) What is the empirical formula of mercury(I) chloride?
(b) Calculate [Hg₂²⁺] in a saturated solution of mercury(I) chloride ($K_{sp} = 1.5 \times 10^{-18}$).
(c) A seawater sample contains 0.20 lb of NaCl per gallon. Find [Hg₂²⁺] if the seawater is saturated with mercury(I) chloride.
(d) How many grams of mercury(I) chloride are needed to saturate 4900 km³ of pure water (the volume of Lake Michigan)?
(e) How many grams of mercury(I) chloride are needed to saturate 4900 km³ of seawater?

**19.141** A 35.0-mL solution of 0.075 $M$ CaCl₂ is mixed with 25.0 mL of 0.090 M BaCl₂.

(a) If aqueous KF is added, which fluoride precipitates first?
(b) Describe how the metal ions can be separated using KF to form the fluorides.
(c) Calculate the fluoride ion concentration that will accomplish the separation.

**19.142** Even before the industrial age, rainwater was slightly acidic due to dissolved CO₂. Use the following data to calculate pH of unpolluted rainwater at 25°C: vol % in air of CO₂ = 0.033 vol %; solubility of CO₂ in pure water at 25°C and 1 atm = 88 mL CO₂/100 mL H₂O; $K_{a1}$ of H₂CO₃ = $4.5 \times 10^{-7}$.

**19.143** Seawater at the surface has a pH of about 8.5.
(a) Which of the following species has the highest concentration at this pH: H₂CO₃; HCO₃⁻; CO₃²⁻? Explain.
(b) What are the concentration ratios [CO₃²⁻]/[HCO₃⁻] and [HCO₃⁻]/[H₂CO₃] at this pH?
(c) In the deep sea, light levels are low, and the pH is around 7.5. Suggest a reason for the lower pH at the greater ocean depth. (*Hint:* Consider the presence or absence of plant and animal life, and the effects on carbon dioxide concentrations.)

**19.144** Ethylenediaminetetraacetic acid (abbreviated H₄EDTA) is a tetraprotic acid. Its salts are used to treat toxic metal poisoning by forming soluble complex ions that are then excreted. Because EDTA⁴⁻ also binds essential calcium ions, it is often administered as the calcium disodium salt. For example, when Na₂Ca(EDTA) is given to a patient, the [Ca(EDTA)]²⁻ ions react with circulating Pb²⁺ ions and the metal ions are exchanged:

$$[Ca(EDTA)]^{2-}(aq) + Pb^{2+}(aq) \rightleftharpoons$$
$$[Pb(EDTA)]^{2-}(aq) + Ca^{2+}(aq) \qquad K_c = 2.5 \times 10^7$$

A child has a dangerous blood lead level of 120 μg/100 mL. If the child is administered 100. mL of 0.10 $M$ Na₂Ca(EDTA), assuming the exchange reaction and excretion process are 100% efficient, what is the final concentration of Pb²⁺ in μg/100 mL blood? (Total blood volume is 1.5 L.)

**19.145** Buffers that are based on 3-morpholinopropanesulfonic acid (MOPS) are often used in RNA analysis. The useful pH range of a MOPS buffer is 6.5 to 7.9. Estimate the $K_a$ of MOPS.

**19.146** NaCl is purified by adding HCl to a saturated solution of NaCl (317 g/L). When 28.5 mL of 8.65 $M$ HCl is added to 0.100 L of saturated solution, what mass (g) of pure NaCl precipitates?

**19.147** Scenes A to D represent tiny portions of 0.10 $M$ aqueous solutions of a weak acid HA (red and blue; $K_a = 4.5 \times 10^{-5}$), its conjugate base A⁻(red), or a mixture of the two (only these species are shown):

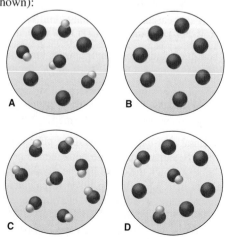

(a) Which scene(s) show(s) a buffer?

(b) What is the pH of each solution?

(c) Arrange the scenes in sequence, assuming that they represent stages in a weak acid–strong base titration.

(d) Which scene represents the titration at its equivalence point?

**19.148** Scenes A to C represent aqueous solutions of the slightly soluble salt MZ (only the ions of this salt are shown):

$$MZ(s) \rightleftharpoons M^{2+}(aq) + Z^{2-}(aq)$$

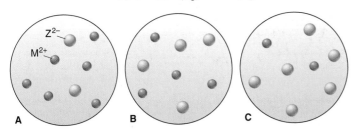

(a) Which scene represents the solution just after solid MZ is stirred thoroughly in distilled water?

(b) If each sphere represents $2.5 \times 10^{-6}\ M$ of ions, what is the $K_{sp}$ of MZ?

(c) Which scene represents the solution after $Na_2Z(aq)$ has been added?

(d) If $Z^{2-}$ is $CO_3^{2-}$, which scene represents the solution after the pH has been lowered?

**19.149** The solubility of Ag(I) in aqueous solutions containing different concentrations of $Cl^-$ is based on the following equilibria:

$$Ag^+(aq) + Cl^-(aq) \rightleftharpoons AgCl(s) \qquad K_{sp} = 1.8 \times 10^{-10}$$
$$Ag^+(aq) + 2Cl^-(aq) \rightleftharpoons AgCl_2^-(aq) \qquad K_f = 1.8 \times 10^5$$

When solid AgCl is shaken with a solution containing $Cl^-$, Ag(I) is present as both $Ag^+$ and $AgCl_2^-$. The solubility of AgCl is the sum of the concentrations of $Ag^+$ and $AgCl_2^-$.

(a) Show that $[Ag^+]$ in solution is given by

$$[Ag^+] = 1.8 \times 10^{-10} / [Cl^-]$$

and that $[AgCl_2^-]$ in solution is given by

$$[AgCl_2^-] = (3.2 \times 10^{-5})([Cl^-])$$

(b) Find the $[Cl^-]$ at which $[Ag^+] = [AgCl_2^-]$.

(c) Explain the shape of a plot of AgCl solubility vs. $[Cl^-]$.

(d) Find the solubility of AgCl at the $[Cl^-]$ of part (b), which is the minimum solubility of AgCl in the presence of $Cl^-$.

**19.150** EDTA binds metal ions to form complex ions (see Problem 19.144), so it is used to determine the concentrations of metal ions in solution:

$$M^{n+}(aq) + EDTA^{4-}(aq) \longrightarrow MEDTA^{n-4}(aq)$$

A 50.0-mL sample of $0.048\ M$ $Co^{2+}$ is titrated with $0.050\ M$ $EDTA^{4-}$. Find $[Co^{2+}]$ and $[EDTA^{4-}]$ after (a) 25.0 mL and (b) 75.0 mL of $EDTA^{4-}$ are added (log $K_f$ of $CoEDTA^{2-} = 16.31$).

# Thermodynamics: Entropy, Free Energy, and the Direction of Chemical Reactions

## Concepts and skills to review before you study this chapter

- internal energy, heat, and work (Section 6.1)
- state functions (Section 6.1) and standard states (Section 6.6)
- enthalpy, ΔH, and Hess's law (Sections 6.2 and 6.5)
- entropy and solution formation (Section 13.3)
- comparing Q and K to find reaction direction (Section 17.4)

In the last few chapters, we've examined some fundamental questions about change, whether chemical or physical: How fast does it occur? How far does it go toward completion? How are these aspects of the change affected by concentration and temperature? And we've explored these questions in systems ranging from the stratosphere to a limestone cave to the cells of your body.

It's now time to ask the most profound question of all: why does the change occur in the first place? Some changes seem to happen by themselves in one direction but not in the other. A candle burns in air and forms carbon dioxide and water vapor, but those products will never react to form candle wax and oxygen. A new steel shovel left outside slowly rusts, but put a rusty one outside and it won't become shiny. A cube of sugar dissolves in a cup of coffee after a few seconds of stirring, but stir for another millennium and the dissolved sugar won't form the cube again. Chemists speak of these types of changes as being *spontaneous*. Most release energy, but some absorb it.

The principles of thermodynamics were developed almost 200 years ago and soon applied to great new machines based on the steam engine (*photo*). But these principles apply, as far as we know, to every system in the universe and allow us to understand why a spontaneous change occurs.

**IN THIS CHAPTER...** We discuss *why* changes occur and how we can utilize them, by focusing on entropy and free energy and their relation to the direction of a spontaneous change.
- We discuss the need for a criterion to predict the direction of a spontaneous change.
- We review the first law of thermodynamics and see that it accounts for the energy of a change but not the direction.
- We see that the sign of the enthalpy change does not predict direction either.
- We find this criterion for predicting the direction of a spontaneous change in the second law of thermodynamics and its relation to entropy (S), a state function based on the natural tendency of a system's energy to become dispersed.
- We examine entropy changes for exothermic and endothermic changes.
- We develop the concept of free energy as a simplified criterion for spontaneous change and see how it relates to the work a system can do.
- We explore the key relationship between the free energy change of a reaction and its equilibrium constant.

## 20.1 • THE SECOND LAW OF THERMODYNAMICS: PREDICTING SPONTANEOUS CHANGE

A **spontaneous change** of a system is one that occurs under specified conditions without a continuous input of energy from outside the system. The freezing of water, for example, is spontaneous at 1 atm and −5°C. A spontaneous process, such as burning or falling, may need a little "push" to get started—a spark to ignite gasoline vapors in your car's engine, a shove to knock a book off your desk—but once the process begins, it supplies the energy to keep going. In contrast, a *nonspontaneous* change occurs only if the surroundings *continuously* supply the system with an input of energy. Under given conditions, *if a change is spontaneous in one direction, it is **not** spontaneous in the other.*

The term *spontaneous* does not mean *instantaneous* or reveal anything about how long a process takes to occur; it means that, given enough time, the process will happen by itself. Many processes are spontaneous but slow—ripening, rusting, and aging.

A *chemical reaction proceeding toward equilibrium is a spontaneous change.* Recall that we can predict the net direction of the reaction—its spontaneous direction—by comparing the reaction quotient ($Q$) with the equilibrium constant ($K$). But *why* is there a drive to attain equilibrium? And what determines the value of the equilibrium constant? And, most importantly, can we predict the direction of a spontaneous change in cases that are not as obvious as burning gasoline or falling books?

## The First Law of Thermodynamics Does Not Predict Spontaneous Change

Let's see whether energy changes can clarify the criterion for spontaneity. Recall from Chapter 6 that the first law of thermodynamics (law of conservation of energy) states that the internal energy ($E$) of a system, the sum of the kinetic and potential energies of its particles, changes when heat ($q$) and/or work ($w$) are absorbed or released:

$$\Delta E = q + w$$

Whatever is not part of the system (sys) is part of the surroundings (surr); thus, *the change in energy and, therefore, heat and/or work absorbed by the system is released by the surroundings,* and vice versa:

$$\Delta E_{sys} = -\Delta E_{surr} \quad \text{or} \quad (q + w)_{sys} = -(q + w)_{surr}$$

Since the system plus the surroundings is the universe (univ), it follows that *the total energy of the universe is constant, so the change in energy of the universe is zero:*[*]

$$\Delta E_{sys} + \Delta E_{surr} = 0 = \Delta E_{univ}$$

The first law accounts for the energy, but not the direction, of a process. When gasoline burns in a car engine, the first law states that the potential energy difference between the bonds in the fuel mixture and those in the exhaust gases is converted to the kinetic energy of the moving car and its parts plus the heat released to the environment. But, why doesn't the heat released in the engine convert exhaust fumes back into gasoline and oxygen? When an ice cube melts in your hand, the first law tells that energy from your hand is converted to kinetic energy as the solid changes to a liquid. But, why doesn't the pool of water in your cupped hand transfer the heat back to your hand and refreeze? Neither of these events violates the first law—if you measure the work and heat in each case, you find that energy is conserved—but these reverse changes never happen. That is, *the first law by itself does not predict the **direction** of a spontaneous change.*

## The Sign of $\Delta H$ Does Not Predict Spontaneous Change

Perhaps the sign of the enthalpy change ($\Delta H$), the heat gained or lost at constant pressure ($q_P$), is the criterion for spontaneity. If so, we expect exothermic processes ($\Delta H < 0$) to be spontaneous and endothermic processes ($\Delta H > 0$) nonspontaneous. Let's examine some examples to see if this is true.

1. *Spontaneous processes with $\Delta H < 0$.* All freezing and condensing processes are exothermic and spontaneous at certain conditions:

$$H_2O(l) \longrightarrow H_2O(s) \qquad \Delta H^\circ_{rxn} = -\Delta H^\circ_{fus} = -6.02 \text{ kJ } (1 \text{ atm}; T < 0°C)$$

All combustion reactions are spontaneous and exothermic:

$$CH_4(g) + 2O_2(g) \longrightarrow CO_2(g) + 2H_2O(g) \qquad \Delta H^\circ_{rxn} = -802 \text{ kJ}$$

Oxidation of iron and other metals occurs spontaneously and exothermically:

$$2Fe(s) + \tfrac{3}{2}O_2(g) \longrightarrow Fe_2O_3(s) \qquad \Delta H^\circ_{rxn} = -826 \text{ kJ}$$

---

[*]Any modern statement of conservation of energy must take into account mass-energy equivalence and the processes in stars, which convert enormous amounts of matter into energy. Thus, the total *mass-energy* of the universe is constant.

Ionic compounds form spontaneously and exothermically from their elements:

$$Na(s) + \tfrac{1}{2}Cl_2(g) \longrightarrow NaCl(s) \qquad \Delta H^\circ_{rxn} = -411 \text{ kJ}$$

However, in many cases, an exothermic process occurs spontaneously under one set of conditions, whereas the opposite, endothermic, process occurs spontaneously under another set.

2. *Spontaneous processes with* $\Delta H > 0$. All melting and vaporizing processes are endothermic *and* spontaneous at certain conditions:

$$H_2O(s) \longrightarrow H_2O(l) \qquad \Delta H^\circ_{rxn} = \Delta H^\circ_{fus} = +6.02 \text{ kJ } (1 \text{ atm}; T = 0°C)$$

At ordinary pressure water vaporizes spontaneously:

$$H_2O(l) \longrightarrow H_2O(g) \qquad \Delta H^\circ_{rxn} = \Delta H^\circ_{vap} = +44.0 \text{ kJ } (1 \text{ atm}; T = 100°C)$$

Most soluble salts dissolve endothermically *and* spontaneously:

$$NaCl(s) \xrightarrow{H_2O} Na^+(aq) + Cl^-(aq) \qquad \Delta H^\circ_{soln} = +3.9 \text{ kJ}$$

$$RbClO_3(s) \xrightarrow{H_2O} Rb^+(aq) + ClO_3^-(aq) \qquad \Delta H^\circ_{soln} = +47.7 \text{ kJ}$$

$$NH_4NO_3(s) \xrightarrow{H_2O} NH_4^+(aq) + NO_3^-(aq) \qquad \Delta H^\circ_{soln} = +25.7 \text{ kJ}$$

Even some endothermic reactions are spontaneous:

$$N_2O_5(s) \longrightarrow 2NO_2(g) + \tfrac{1}{2}O_2(g) \qquad \Delta H^\circ_{rxn} = +109.5 \text{ kJ}$$

$$Ba(OH)_2 \cdot 8H_2O(s) + 2NH_4NO_3(s) \longrightarrow$$
$$Ba^{2+}(aq) + 2NO_3^-(aq) + 2NH_3(aq) + 10H_2O(l) \qquad \Delta H^\circ_{rxn} = +62.3 \text{ kJ}$$

In the latter reaction, crystalline solids are mixed (Figure 20.1A) and the release of waters of hydration solvates the ions. The reaction mixture absorbs heat from the surroundings so quickly that the beaker freezes to a wet block (Figure 20.1B).

Given just these few examples, we see that, as for the first law, *the sign of* $\Delta H$ *by itself does not predict the* **direction** *of a spontaneous change.*

**Figure 20.1** A spontaneous endothermic reaction.

## Freedom of Particle Motion and Dispersal of Particle Energy

When we look closely at the previous examples of spontaneous *endothermic* processes, they have one major feature in common: in every case, the chemical entities—atoms, molecules, or ions—have more freedom of motion *after* the change. Put another way, after the change, the particles have a wider range of energy of motion (kinetic energy); we say that the energy has become more dispersed, distributed, or spread out:

- The phase changes convert a solid, in which motion is restricted, to a liquid, in which particles have more freedom to move around each other, and then to a gas, in which the particles have much greater freedom of motion. Thus, the energy of motion is more dispersed.
- Dissolving a salt changes a crystalline solid and a pure liquid into separate ions and solvent molecules moving and interacting, so their freedom of motion is greater and their energy of motion more dispersed.
- In the chemical reactions, *fewer* moles of crystalline solids produce *more* moles of gases and/or solvated ions, so once again, the freedom of motion of the particles increases and their energy of motion is more dispersed:

less freedom of particle motion $\longrightarrow$ more freedom of particle motion

localized energy of motion $\longrightarrow$ dispersed energy of motion

Phase change:                     solid $\longrightarrow$ liquid $\longrightarrow$ gas

Dissolving of salt:   crystalline solid + liquid $\longrightarrow$ ions in solution

Chemical change:          crystalline solids $\longrightarrow$ gases + ions in solution

*In thermodynamic terms, a change in the freedom of motion of particles in a system, that is, in the dispersal of their energy of motion, is a key factor affecting the* **direction** *of a spontaneous process.*

## Entropy and the Number of Microstates

Earlier, we discussed the quantized *electronic* energy levels of an atom (Chapter 7) and a molecule (Chapter 11), as well as the quantized *kinetic* energy levels—vibrational, rotational, and translational—of a molecule (see Tools of the Laboratory, p. 343). Now, we'll see that the energy state of a whole system of particles is quantized, too.

**Energy Dispersal and the Meaning of Entropy** Let's see why freedom of motion and dispersal of energy relate to spontaneous change:

- *Quantization of energy.* Picture a system of, say, 1 mol of $N_2$ gas and focus on one molecule. At any instant, it is moving through space (translating) at some speed and rotating at some frequency, and its atoms are vibrating at some frequency. In the next instant, the molecule collides with another or with the container, and these motional (kinetic) energy states change to different values. The complete quantum state of the molecule at any instant consists of its electronic states and these translational, rotational, and vibrational states. In this discussion, we focus on the latter three.
- *Number of microstates.* The energy of the other molecules is similarly quantized. Each quantized state of the system of molecules is called a *microstate,* and at any instant, the total energy of the system is dispersed throughout one microstate. In the next instant, it is dispersed throughout a different microstate. The number of microstates possible for a system of 1 mol of molecules is staggering, on the order of $10^{10^{23}}$.
- *Dispersal of energy.* At a given set of conditions, each microstate has the *same* total energy as any other. Therefore, each microstate is equally possible for the system, and the laws of probability say that, over time, all microstates are equally likely. The number of microstates for a system is the number of ways it can disperse (distribute or spread) its kinetic energy among the various motions of all its particles.

In 1877, the Austrian mathematician and physicist Ludwig Boltzmann related the number of microstates ($W$) to the **entropy ($S$)** of a system:

$$S = k \ln W \qquad (20.1)$$

where $k$, the *Boltzmann constant,* is the universal gas constant ($R$) divided by Avogadro's number ($N_A$), or $R/N_A$, and equals $1.38 \times 10^{-23}$ J/K. The term $W$ is the number of microstates, so it has no units; therefore, $S$ has units of joules/kelvin (J/K). Thus,

- A system with fewer microstates (smaller $W$) has *lower entropy (lower S)*.
- A system with more microstates (larger $W$) has *higher entropy (higher S)*.

For our earlier examples of endothermic processes,

lower entropy (fewer microstates) ⟶ higher entropy (more microstates)

| | |
|---|---|
| Phase change: | solid ⟶ liquid ⟶ gas |
| Dissolving of salt: | crystalline solid + liquid ⟶ ions in solution |
| Chemical change: | crystalline solids ⟶ gases + ions in solution |

(Recall from Chapter 13 that entropy is a factor in the formation of solutions.)

**Entropy as a State Function** If a change results in a greater number of microstates, there are more ways to disperse the energy of the system and the entropy increases:

$$S_{\text{more microstates}} > S_{\text{fewer microstates}}$$

If a change results in a lower number of microstates, the entropy decreases. Like internal energy ($E$) and enthalpy ($H$), *entropy is a state function,* so it depends only on the present state of the system, not on how it arrived at that state (see Chapter 6, p. 234). Therefore, the change in entropy of the system ($\Delta S_{\text{sys}}$) depends only on the *difference* between its final and initial values:

$$\Delta S_{\text{sys}} = S_{\text{final}} - S_{\text{initial}}$$

Like any state function, $\Delta S_{\text{sys}} > 0$ when its value increases during a change. For example, for the phase change when dry ice sublimes, the entropy increases:

$$CO_2(s) \longrightarrow CO_2(g) \qquad \Delta S_{\text{sys}} = S_{\text{final}} - S_{\text{initial}} = S_{\text{gaseous } CO_2} - S_{\text{solid } CO_2} > 0$$

And, $\Delta S_{sys} < 0$ when the entropy decreases, as when water vapor condenses:

$$H_2O(g) \longrightarrow H_2O(l) \qquad \Delta S_{sys} = S_{liquid\ H_2O} - S_{gaseous\ H_2O} < 0$$

As an example of a reaction during which entropy increases, consider the decomposition of dinitrogen tetraoxide (written as $O_2N{-}NO_2$):

$$O_2N{-}NO_2(g) \longrightarrow 2NO_2(g)$$

When the N—N bond in 1 mol of dinitrogen tetraoxide breaks, the 2 mol of $NO_2$ molecules have many more possible motions; thus, at any instant, the energy of the system is dispersed into any one of a larger number of microstates. Thus, the change in entropy of the system, which is the change in entropy of the reaction ($\Delta S_{rxn}$), goes up:

$$\Delta S_{sys} = \Delta S_{rxn} = S_{final} - S_{initial} = S_{products} - S_{reactants} = 2S_{NO_2} - S_{N_2O_4} > 0$$

**Quantitative Meaning of an Entropy Change** There are two approaches for quantifying an entropy change, but they give the same result. The first is based on the number of microstates possible for a system, and the second on the heat absorbed (or released) by the system. We'll examine both with a system of 1 mol of a gas expanding from 1 L to 2 L and behaving ideally, much as neon does at 298 K:

$$\text{1 mol neon (initial: 1 L and 298 K)} \longrightarrow \text{1 mol neon (final: 2 L and 298 K)}$$

1. *Quantifying* $\Delta S_{sys}$ *from the number of microstates.* Figure 20.2 shows two flasks connected by a stopcock—the right flask is evacuated, and the left flask contains 1 mol of neon. When we open the stopcock, the gas expands until each flask contains 0.5 mol—but *why?* Opening the stopcock increases the volume, which increases the number of translational energy levels the particles can occupy as they move to more locations. Thus, the number of microstates—and the entropy—increases.

**A**    1 mol        Evacuated       **B**   0.5 mol        0.5 mol

**Figure 20.2 Spontaneous expansion of a gas. A,** With the stopcock closed, the left flask contains 1 mol of Ne. **B,** With the stopcock open, the gas expands and each flask contains 0.5 mol of Ne.

Figure 20.3 presents this idea with particles on energy levels in a box of changeable volume. When the stopcock opens, there are more energy levels, and they are closer together on average, so more distributions of particles are possible.

In Figure 20.4 on the next page, the number of microstates is represented by the placement of particles in the left and/or right flasks:

- *One Ne atom.* At a given instant, an Ne atom in the left flask has its energy in one of some number ($W$) of microstates. Opening the stopcock increases the volume, which increases the number of possible locations and the number of translational energy levels. Thus, the system has $2^1$, or 2, times as many microstates available when the atom moves through both flasks (final state, $W_{final}$) as when it is confined to the left flask (initial state, $W_{initial}$).
- *Two Ne atoms.* For atoms A and B moving through both flasks, there are $2^2$, or 4, times as many microstates as when the atoms were initially in the left flask—some number of microstates with both A and B in the left, that many with A in the left and B in the right or with B in the left and A in the right, and that many with both in the right.
- *Three Ne atoms.* Add another atom, and there are $2^3$, or 8, times as many microstates when the stopcock is open.
- *Ten Ne atoms.* With 10 Ne atoms, there are $2^{10}$, or 1024, times as many microstates for the atoms in both flasks as there were for the 10 atoms in the left flask.
- *One mole of Ne atoms.* With 1 mol ($N_A$) of Ne, there are $2^{N_A}$ times as many microstates for the atoms in the larger volume ($W_{final}$) than in the smaller ($W_{initial}$):

$$\frac{W_{final}}{W_{initial}} = 2^{N_A}$$

**Figure 20.3 The entropy increase due to expansion of a gas.** Energy levels are shown as lines in a box of narrow width (*left*). Each distribution of energies for the 21 particles is one microstate. When the stopcock is opened, the box is wider (volume increases, *right*), and the particles have more energy levels available.

**Figure 20.4 Expansion of a gas and the increase in number of microstates.** Each set of particle locations represents a different microstate. When the volume increases (stopcock opens), the number of microstates is $2^n$, where $n$ is the number of particles.

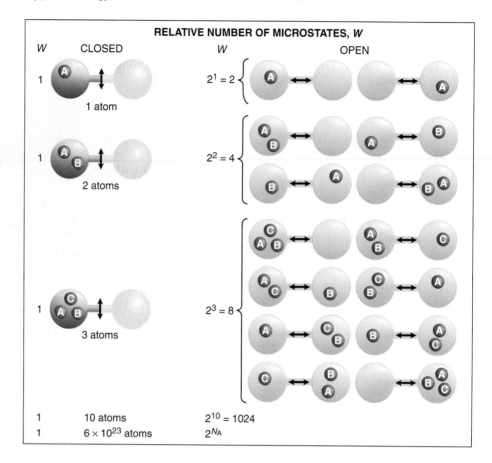

Now let's find $\Delta S_{sys}$ through the Boltzmann equation, $S = k \ln W$. From the properties of logarithms (Appendix A), we know that $\ln A - \ln B = \ln A/B$. Thus,

$$\Delta S_{sys} = S_{final} - S_{initial} = k \ln W_{final} - k \ln W_{initial} = k \ln \frac{W_{final}}{W_{initial}} = k \ln 2^{N_A}$$

Also, from Appendix A, $\ln A^y = y \ln A$; thus, with $k = R/N_A$, we have

$$\Delta S_{sys} = \frac{R}{N_A} \ln 2^{N_A} = \left(\frac{R}{N_A}\right) N_A \ln 2 = R \ln 2$$

$$= (8.314 \text{ J/mol·K})(0.693) = 5.76 \text{ J/mol·K}$$

2. *Quantifying $\Delta S_{sys}$ from the changes in heat.* Now we compare the $\Delta S_{sys}$ we just found for a gas expanding into an evacuated flask with the $\Delta S_{sys}$ for a gas that is heated and does work on the surroundings. This approach uses the relationship

$$\Delta S_{sys} = \frac{q_{rev}}{T} \qquad (20.2)$$

where $T$ is the temperature at which the heat change occurs and $q$ is the heat absorbed. The subscript "rev" refers to a *reversible process*, one that occurs in such tiny increments that the system remains at equilibrium and the direction of the change can be reversed by an *infinitesimal* reversal of conditions.

We'll approximate a reversible expansion by placing Ne gas in a piston-cylinder assembly within a heat reservoir (to maintain a constant $T$ of 298 K) and start by confining it to a volume of 1 L by the "pressure" of a beaker of sand on the piston (Figure 20.5). We remove one grain of sand (an "infinitesimal" decrease in pressure) with a pair of tweezers, and the gas expands a tiny amount, raising the piston and doing work, $-w$. Assuming Ne behaves ideally, it absorbs an equivalent tiny increment of heat, $q$, from the heat reservoir. With each grain of sand removed, the expanding gas absorbs another tiny increment of heat. This process simulates a reversible expansion because we can reverse it by putting back a grain of sand, which causes the surround-

**Figure 20.5 Simulating a reversible process.**

ings to do a tiny quantity of work compressing the gas, thus releasing a tiny quantity of heat to the reservoir.

If we continue this nearly reversible expansion to 2 L and use calculus to integrate the tiny increments of heat together, $q_{rev}$ is 1718 J. From Equation 20.2,

$$\Delta S_{sys} = \frac{q_{rev}}{T} = \frac{1718 \text{ J}}{298 \text{ K}} = 5.76 \text{ J/K}$$

This is the same value of $\Delta S_{sys}$ we obtained based on the number of microstates.

## Entropy and the Second Law of Thermodynamics

While it's true that the change in entropy determines the direction of a spontaneous process, we must consider more than the entropy change of the system. After all, some processes, such as ice melting, occur spontaneously and $\Delta S_{sys}$ goes up, while others, such as water freezing, occur spontaneously and $\Delta S_{sys}$ goes down. But when we consider *both* the system *and* its surroundings, we find that *all real processes occur spontaneously in the direction that increases the entropy of the universe (system plus surroundings).* This is one way to state the **second law of thermodynamics.**

The second law says that *either* the entropy change of the system *or* of the surroundings may be negative. But, for a process to be spontaneous, the *sum* of the two entropy changes must be positive. If the entropy of the system decreases, the entropy of the surroundings must increase even more to offset that decrease, so that the entropy of the universe (system *plus* surroundings) increases. A quantitative statement of the second law is, for any real spontaneous process,

$$\Delta S_{univ} = \Delta S_{sys} + \Delta S_{surr} > 0 \qquad \text{(20.3)}$$

## Standard Molar Entropies and the Third Law

Entropy and enthalpy are state functions, but their values differ in a fundamental way:

- For *enthalpy,* there is no zero point, so we can measure only *changes.*
- For *entropy,* there *is* a zero point, and we can determine *absolute* values by applying the **third law of thermodynamics:** *a perfect crystal has zero entropy at absolute zero: $S_{sys} = 0$ at 0 K.*

A "perfect" crystal means all the particles are aligned flawlessly. At absolute zero, the particles have minimum energy, so there is only one microstate. Thus, in Equation 20.1,

$$W = 1 \qquad \text{so} \qquad S = k \ln 1 = 0$$

When we warm the crystal to any temperature above 0 K, the total energy increases, so it can be dispersed into more than one microstate. Thus,

$$W > 1 \qquad \text{and} \qquad \ln W > 0 \qquad \text{so} \qquad S > 0$$

In principle, to find $S$ of a substance at a given temperature, we cool it as close to 0 K as possible. Then we heat it in small increments, dividing $q$ by $T$ to get the increase in $S$ for each increment, and add up all the entropy increases to the temperature of interest, usually 298 K. Therefore, $S$ of a substance at a given temperature is an *absolute* value. As with other thermodynamic variables,

- We compare entropy values for substances at the temperature of interest in their *standard states: 1 atm for gases, 1 M for solutions, and the pure substance in its most stable form for solids or liquids.*
- Because entropy is an *extensive* property—one that depends on the amount of substance—we specify the **standard molar entropy ($S°$),** in units of J/mol·K (or J $\text{mol}^{-1}$ $\text{K}^{-1}$). ($S°$ values at 298 K for many elements, compounds, and ions appear, with other thermodynamic variables, in Appendix B.)

## Predicting Relative $S°$ of a System

Let's see how the standard molar entropy of a substance is affected by several parameters: temperature, physical state, dissolution, and atomic size or molecular complexity. (Unless stated otherwise, the $S°$ values refer to the system at 298 K.)

**Temperature Changes** Temperature has the most important effect. For any substance, $S°$ *increases as the T rises,* as these values for copper metal show:

| $T$ (K): | 273 | 295 | 298 |
|---|---|---|---|
| $S°$: | 31.0 | 32.9 | 33.2 |

As heat is absorbed ($q > 0$), temperature, which is a measure of the average kinetic energy of the particles, increases. Recall that the kinetic energies of gas particles are distributed over a range, which becomes wider as $T$ rises (Figure 5.14); liquids and solids behave the same. Thus, at any instant, there are more microstates available in which the energy can be dispersed, so the entropy of the substance goes up. Figure 20.6 presents three ways to view the effect of temperature on entropy.

**Figure 20.6 Visualizing the effect of temperature on entropy. A,** Computer simulations show each particle in a crystal moving about its lattice position. Adding heat increases $T$ and the total energy, so the particles have greater freedom of motion, and their energy is more dispersed. Thus, $S$ increases. **B,** At any $T$, there is a range of occupied energy levels and, thus, a certain number of microstates. Adding heat increases the total energy (*area under curve*), so the range of occupied energy levels becomes greater, as does the number of microstates (higher $S$). **C,** A system of 21 particles occupy energy levels (*lines*) in a box whose height represents the total energy. When heat is added, the total energy increases (*box is higher*) *and* becomes more dispersed (*more lines*), so $S$ increases.

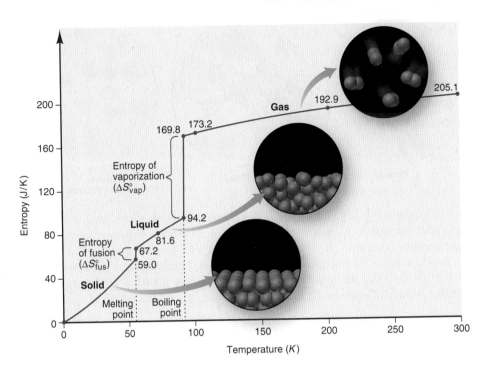

**Figure 20.7** The increase in entropy during phase changes from solid to liquid to gas.

**Physical States and Phase Changes** In melting or vaporizing, heat is absorbed ($q > 0$). The particles have more freedom of motion, and their energy is more dispersed. Thus, *$S°$ increases as the physical state of a substance changes from solid to liquid to gas:*

|           | Na       | H₂O      | C(graphite) |
|-----------|----------|----------|-------------|
| $S°$(s or l): | 51.4(s)  | 69.9(l)  | 5.7(s)      |
| $S°$(g):  | 153.6    | 188.7    | 158.0       |

Figure 20.7 plots entropy versus $T$ as solid $O_2$ is heated and changes to liquid and then to gas, with $S°$ values at various points; this behavior is typical of many substances. At the molecular scale, several stages occur:

- Particles in the solid vibrate about their positions but, on average, remain fixed. The energy of the solid is dispersed least, that is, has the fewest microstates, so the solid has the lowest entropy.
- As $T$ rises, the entropy increases gradually as the particles' kinetic energy increases.
- When the solid melts, the particles move much more freely between and around each other, so there is an abrupt increase in entropy ($\Delta S°_{fus}$).
- Further heating of the liquid increases the speed of the particles, and the entropy increases gradually.
- When the liquid vaporizes and becomes a gas, the particles undergo a much larger, abrupt entropy increase ($\Delta S°_{vap}$); *the increase in entropy from liquid to gas is much larger than from solid to liquid:* $\Delta S°_{vap} >> \Delta S°_{fus}$.
- Finally, with further heating of the gas, the entropy increases gradually.

**Dissolving a Solid or a Liquid in Water** Recall from Chapter 13 that, in general, entropy increases when a solute dissolves in a solvent: $S_{soln} > (S_{solute} + S_{solvent})$. But, when water is the solvent, the entropy may also depend on the nature of solute *and* solvent interactions and includes two opposing events:

|           | NaCl     | AlCl₃    | CH₃OH    |
|-----------|----------|----------|----------|
| $S°$(s or l): | 72.1(s)  | 167(s)   | 127(l)   |
| $S°$(aq): | 115.1    | −148     | 132      |

1. *For ionic solutes,* when the crystal dissolves in water, the ions have much more freedom of motion and their energy is dispersed into more microstates. That is, the entropy of the ions themselves is greater in the solution. However, some water molecules become arranged around the ions (Figure 20.8), which limits the molecules' freedom of

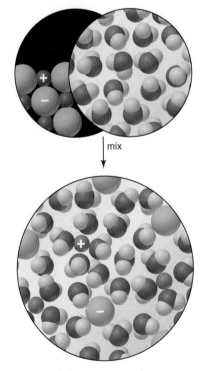

**Figure 20.8** The entropy change accompanying the dissolution of a salt. The entropy of a salt solution is usually *greater* than that of the solid and of water, but it is affected by water molecules becoming organized around each ion.

**Figure 20.9** The small increase in entropy when ethanol dissolves in water. Ethanol (**A**) and water (**B**) each have many H bonds to themselves. **C,** In solution, they form H bonds to each other, so their freedom of motion does not change significantly.

A Ethanol    B Water    C Solution of water and ethanol

motion (see also Figure 13.2, p. 479). In fact, around small, multiply charged ions, $H_2O$ molecules become so organized that their energy of motion becomes *less* dispersed. This negative portion of the total entropy change can lead to *negative* $S°$ values for the ions in solution. In the case of $AlCl_3$, the $Al^{3+}(aq)$ ion has such a negative $S°$ value ($-313$ J/mol·K) that when $AlCl_3$ dissolves in water, even though $S°$ of $Cl^-(aq)$ is positive, the entropy of aqueous $AlCl_3$ is lower than that of solid $AlCl_3$.*

2. *For molecular solutes,* the increase in entropy upon dissolving is typically much smaller than for ionic solutes. After all, for a solid such as glucose, there is no separation into ions, and for a liquid such as methanol or ethanol (Figure 20.9), there is no breakdown of a crystal structure. Furthermore, in these small alcohols and in pure water, the molecules form many H bonds, so there is relatively little change in their freedom of motion either before or after they are mixed.

**Dissolving a Gas in a Liquid** The particles in a gas already have so much freedom of motion—and, thus, such highly dispersed energy—that they lose some when they dissolve in a liquid or solid. Therefore, the entropy of a solution of a gas in a liquid or in a solid is always *less* than the entropy of the gas itself. For instance, when gaseous $O_2$ [$S°(g) = 205.0$ J/mol·K] dissolves in water, its entropy decreases considerably [$S°(aq) = 110.9$ J/mol·K] (Figure 20.10). When a gas dissolves in another gas, however, the entropy increases as a result of the separation and mixing of the molecules.

**Atomic Size or Molecular Complexity** Differences in $S°$ values for substances in the same phase are usually based on atomic size and molecular complexity.

1. *Within a periodic group,* energy levels become closer together for larger, heavier atoms, so the number of microstates, and thus the molar entropy, increases:

*Entropy of a gas is already so high that it decreases when the gas dissolves.*

**Figure 20.10** The entropy of a gas dissolved in a liquid.

|  | Li | Na | K | Rb | Cs |
|---|---|---|---|---|---|
| Atomic radius (pm): | 152 | 186 | 227 | 248 | 265 |
| Molar mass (g/mol): | 6.941 | 22.99 | 39.10 | 85.47 | 132.9 |
| $S°(s)$: | 29.1 | 51.4 | 64.7 | 69.5 | 85.2 |

The same trend of increasing entropy holds for similar compounds down a group:

|  | HF | HCl | HBr | HI |
|---|---|---|---|---|
| Molar mass (g/mol): | 20.01 | 36.46 | 80.91 | 127.9 |
| $S°(g)$: | 173.7 | 186.8 | 198.6 | 206.3 |

2. *For different forms of an element (allotropes),* the entropy is *higher* in the form that allows the atoms more freedom of motion. For example, $S°$ of graphite is 5.69 J/mol·K, whereas $S°$ of diamond is 2.44 J/mol·K. In graphite, covalent bonds extend within a two-dimensional sheet, and the sheets move past each other easily; in diamond, covalent bonds extend in three dimensions, allowing the atoms little movement (Table 12.6, p. 452).

---

*An $S°$ value for a hydrated ion can be negative because it is relative to the $S°$ value for the hydrated proton, $H^+(aq)$, which is assigned a value of 0. In other words, $Al^{3+}(aq)$ has a lower entropy than $H^+(aq)$.

3. *For compounds,* entropy increases with chemical complexity (that is, with number of atoms in the formula), and this trend holds for ionic and covalent substances:

| | NaCl | AlCl$_3$ | P$_4$O$_{10}$ | NO | NO$_2$ | N$_2$O$_4$ |
|---|---|---|---|---|---|---|
| S°(s): | 72.1 | 167 | 229 | | | |
| S°(g): | | | | 211 | 240 | 304 |

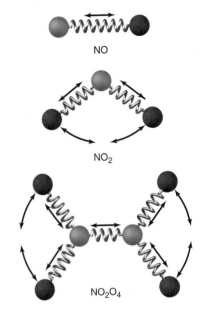

The trend is also based on the different types of motion. Thus, for example, among the nitrogen oxides listed, the number of different vibrational motions increases with the number of atoms in the molecule (Figure 20.11; see also p. 343).

For larger compounds, we also consider the motion of different parts of a molecule. A long hydrocarbon chain can rotate and vibrate in more ways than a short one, so *entropy increases with chain length.* A ring compound, such as cyclopentane (C$_5$H$_{10}$), has lower entropy than the corresponding chain compound, pentene (C$_5$H$_{10}$), because the ring structure restricts freedom of motion:

| | CH$_4$(g) | C$_2$H$_6$(g) | C$_3$H$_8$(g) | C$_4$H$_{10}$(g) | C$_5$H$_{10}$(g) | C$_5$H$_{10}$(cyclo, g) | C$_2$H$_5$OH(l) |
|---|---|---|---|---|---|---|---|
| S°: | 186 | 230 | 270 | 310 | 348 | 293 | 161 |

Remember, these trends hold only for *substances in the same physical state.* Gaseous methane (CH$_4$) has higher entropy than liquid ethanol (C$_2$H$_5$OH), even though ethanol molecules are more complex. When gases are compared with liquids, *the effect of physical state dominates the effect of molecular complexity.*

**Figure 20.11** Entropy, vibrational motion, and molecular complexity.

---

## Sample Problem 20.1 | Predicting Relative Entropy Values

**Problem** Choose the member with the higher entropy in each of the following pairs, and justify your choice [assume constant temperature, except in part (e)]:
(a) 1 mol of SO$_2$(g) or 1 mol of SO$_3$(g)
(b) 1 mol of CO$_2$(s) or 1 mol of CO$_2$(g)
(c) 3 mol of O$_2$(g) or 2 mol of O$_3$(g)
(d) 1 mol of KBr(s) or 1 mol of KBr(aq)
(e) Seawater at 2°C or at 23°C
(f) 1 mol of CF$_4$(g) or 1 mol of CCl$_4$(g)

**Plan** In general, particles with more freedom of motion have more microstates in which to disperse their kinetic energy, so they have higher entropy. We know that either raising temperature or having *more* particles increases entropy. We apply the general categories described in the text to choose the member with the higher entropy.

**Solution** (a) 1 mol of SO$_3$(g). For equal numbers of moles of substances with the same types of atoms in the same physical state, the more atoms in the molecule, the more types of motion available, and thus the higher the entropy.
(b) 1 mol of CO$_2$(g). For a given substance, entropy increases in the sequence $s < l < g$.
(c) 3 mol of O$_2$(g). The two samples contain the same number of oxygen atoms but different numbers of molecules. Despite the greater complexity of O$_3$, the greater number of molecules dominates because there are many more microstates possible for 3 mol of particles than for 2 mol.
(d) 1 mol of KBr(aq). The two samples have the same number of ions, but their motion is more limited and their energy less dispersed in the solid than in the solution.
(e) Seawater at 23°C. Entropy increases with rising temperature.
(f) 1 mol of CCl$_4$(g). For similar compounds, entropy increases with molar mass.

**Follow-Up Problem 20.1** Select the substance with the higher entropy in each of the following pairs, and give the reason for your choice (assume 1 mol of each at the same T):
(a) PCl$_3$(g) or PCl$_5$(g)
(b) CaF$_2$(s) or BaCl$_2$(s)
(c) Br$_2$(g) or Br$_2$(l)

## ◼ Summary of Section 20.1

- A change is spontaneous under specified conditions if it occurs without a continuous input of energy.
- Neither the first law of thermodynamics nor the sign of $\Delta H$ predicts the direction of a spontaneous change.
- Many spontaneous processes involve an increase in the freedom of motion of the system's particles and, thus, in the dispersal of the system's energy of motion.
- Entropy is a state function that measures the extent of energy dispersed into the number of microstates possible for a system. Each microstate consists of the quantized energy levels of the system at a given instant.
- The second law of thermodynamics states that, in a spontaneous process, the entropy of the universe (system plus surroundings) increases.
- Absolute entropy values can be found because perfect crystals have zero entropy at 0 K (third law of thermodynamics).
- Standard molar entropy, $S°$ (J/mol·K), is affected by temperature, phase changes, dissolution, and atomic size or molecular complexity.

# 20.2 • CALCULATING THE ENTROPY CHANGE OF A REACTION

Chemists are especially interested in learning how to predict the sign *and* calculate the value of the entropy change that occurs during a reaction.

## Entropy Changes in the System: Standard Entropy of Reaction ($\Delta S°_{rxn}$)

The **standard entropy of reaction, $\Delta S°_{rxn}$**, is the entropy change that occurs when all reactants and products are in their standard states.

**Predicting the Sign of $\Delta S°_{rxn}$** A deciding factor in predicting the sign of $\Delta S°_{rxn}$ is a change in the amount (mol) of gas, because gases have such great freedom of motion and, thus, high molar entropies: *if the number of moles of gas increases, $\Delta S°_{rxn}$ is positive; if the number decreases, $\Delta S°_{rxn}$ is negative.* Here are a few examples:

- *Increase in amount of gas.* When gaseous $H_2$ reacts with solid $I_2$ to form gaseous HI, the total number of moles of *substance* stays the same. Nevertheless, the sign of $\Delta S°_{rxn}$ is positive (entropy increases) because the number of moles of *gas* increases:

$$H_2(g) + I_2(s) \longrightarrow 2HI(g) \qquad \Delta S°_{rxn} = S°_{products} - S°_{reactants} > 0$$

- *Decrease in amount of gas.* When ammonia forms from its elements, 4 mol of gas produce 2 mol of gas, so $\Delta S°_{rxn}$ is negative (entropy decreases):

$$N_2(g) + 3H_2(g) \rightleftharpoons 2NH_3(g) \qquad \Delta S°_{rxn} = S°_{products} - S°_{reactants} < 0$$

- *No change in amount of gas, but change in structure.* When the amount (mol) of gas doesn't change, we *cannot* predict the sign of $\Delta S°_{rxn}$. But, a change in one of the structures can make it easier to predict the sign of $\Delta S°_{rxn}$. For example, when cyclopropane is heated to 500°C, the ring opens and propene forms. The chain has more freedom of motion than the ring, so $\Delta S°_{rxn}$ is positive:

$$\overset{\displaystyle CH_2}{\underset{\displaystyle H_2C-CH_2}{\diagup \diagdown}}(g) \xrightarrow{\Delta} CH_3-CH=CH_2(g) \qquad \Delta S° = S°_{products} - S°_{reactants} > 0$$

Keep in mind, however, that in general *we cannot predict the sign of the entropy change unless the reaction involves a change in number of moles of gas.*

**Calculating $\Delta S°_{rxn}$ from $S°$ Values** By applying Hess's law (Chapter 6), we combined $\Delta H°_f$ values to find $\Delta H°_{rxn}$. Similarly, we combine $S°$ values to find the standard entropy of reaction, $\Delta S°_{rxn}$:

$$\Delta S°_{rxn} = \Sigma m S°_{products} - \Sigma n S°_{reactants} \qquad (20.4)$$

where $m$ and $n$ are the amounts (mol) of products and reactants, respectively, given by the coefficients in the balanced equation. For the formation of ammonia, we have

$$\Delta S^{\circ}_{rxn} = [(2 \text{ mol NH}_3)(S^{\circ} \text{ of NH}_3)] - [(1 \text{ mol N}_2)(S^{\circ} \text{ of N}_2) + (3 \text{ mol H}_2)(S^{\circ} \text{ of H}_2)]$$

From Appendix B, we find the $S^{\circ}$ values:

$$\Delta S^{\circ}_{rxn} = [(2 \text{ mol})(193 \text{ J/mol·K})] - [(1 \text{ mol})(191.5 \text{ J/mol·K}) + (3 \text{ mol})(130.6 \text{ J/mol·K})]$$
$$= -197 \text{ J/K}$$

As we predicted from the decrease in number of moles of gas, $\Delta S^{\circ}_{rxn} < 0$.

---

### Sample Problem 20.2 · Calculating the Standard Entropy of Reaction, $\Delta S^{\circ}_{rxn}$

**Problem** Predict the sign of $\Delta S^{\circ}_{rxn}$, if possible, and calculate its value for the combustion of 1 mol of propane at 25°C:

$$C_3H_8(g) + 5O_2(g) \longrightarrow 3CO_2(g) + 4H_2O(l)$$

**Plan** From the change in the number of moles of gas (6 mol yields 3 mol), the entropy should decrease ($\Delta S^{\circ}_{rxn} < 0$). To find $\Delta S^{\circ}_{rxn}$, we apply Equation 20.4.

**Solution** Calculating $\Delta S^{\circ}_{rxn}$. Using Appendix B values,

$$\Delta S^{\circ}_{rxn} = [(3 \text{ mol CO}_2)(S^{\circ} \text{ of CO}_2) + (4 \text{ mol H}_2\text{O})(S^{\circ} \text{ of H}_2\text{O})]$$
$$- [(1 \text{ mol C}_3\text{H}_8)(S^{\circ} \text{ of C}_3\text{H}_8) + (5 \text{ mol O}_2)(S^{\circ} \text{ of O}_2)]$$
$$= [(3 \text{ mol})(213.7 \text{ J/mol·K}) + (4 \text{ mol})(69.9 \text{ J/mol·K})]$$
$$- [(1 \text{ mol})(269.9 \text{ J/mol·K}) + (5 \text{ mol})(205.0 \text{ J/mol·K})]$$
$$= -374 \text{ J/K}$$

**Check** $\Delta S^{\circ} < 0$, so our prediction is correct. Rounding gives $[3(200) + 4(70)] - [270 + 5(200)] = 880 - 1270 = -390$, close to the calculated value.

**Follow-Up Problem 20.2** Balance the following equations, predict the sign of $\Delta S^{\circ}_{rxn}$ if possible, and calculate its value at 25°C:
(a) $\text{NaOH}(s) + CO_2(g) \longrightarrow \text{Na}_2\text{CO}_3(s) + H_2O(l)$
(b) $\text{Fe}(s) + H_2O(g) \longrightarrow \text{Fe}_2\text{O}_3(s) + H_2(g)$

---

## Entropy Changes in the Surroundings: The Other Part of the Total

In the synthesis of ammonia, the combustion of propane, and many other spontaneous reactions, the entropy of the system decreases ($\Delta S^{\circ}_{rxn} < 0$). Remember that the second law dictates that, for a spontaneous process, a **decrease** in the entropy of the system is outweighed by an **increase** in the entropy of the surroundings. In this section, we examine the influence of the surroundings—in particular, the addition (or removal) of heat and the temperature at which this heat flow occurs—on the *total* entropy change.

**The Role of the Surroundings** In essence, the surroundings *add heat to or remove heat from the system.* That is, the surroundings function as an enormous heat source or heat sink, one so large that its temperature remains constant, even though its entropy changes. The surroundings participate in the two types of enthalpy changes as follows:

1. *In an exothermic change, heat released by the system is absorbed by the surroundings.* More heat increases the freedom of motion of the particles and makes the energy more dispersed, so the entropy of the surroundings increases:

   For an exothermic change:  $q_{sys} < 0$,  $q_{surr} > 0$,  and  $\Delta S_{surr} > 0$

2. *In an endothermic change, heat absorbed by the system is released by the surroundings.* Less heat reduces the freedom of motion of the particles and makes the energy less dispersed, so the entropy of the surroundings decreases:

   For an endothermic change:  $q_{sys} > 0$,  $q_{surr} < 0$,  and  $\Delta S_{surr} < 0$

**Temperature at Which Heat Is Transferred** The *temperature* of the surroundings at the time the heat is transferred also affects $\Delta S_{surr}$. Consider the effect of an exothermic reaction at a low or at a high temperature:

- At a low $T$, such as 20 K, there is little motion in the surroundings due to little energy. This means there are few energy levels in each microstate and few microstates in which to disperse the energy. Transferring a given quantity of heat to these surroundings causes a relatively large change in how much energy is dispersed.
- At a high $T$, such as 298 K, the surroundings have a large quantity of energy dispersed. There are more energy levels in each microstate and a greater number of microstates. Transferring the same given quantity of heat to these surroundings causes a relatively small change in how much energy is dispersed. ●

In other words, $\Delta S_{surr}$ is greater when heat is added at a lower $T$. Putting these ideas together, $\Delta S_{surr}$ *is directly related to an opposite change in the heat of the system ($q_{sys}$) and inversely related to the temperature at which the heat is transferred:*

$$\Delta S_{surr} = -\frac{q_{sys}}{T}$$

For a process at *constant pressure*, the heat ($q_P$) is $\Delta H$ (Section 6.2), so

$$\Delta S_{surr} = -\frac{\Delta H_{sys}}{T} \tag{20.5}$$

Thus, we find $\Delta S_{surr}$ by measuring $\Delta H_{sys}$ and $T$ at which the change takes place.

*The main point:* If a spontaneous reaction has a negative $\Delta S_{sys}$ (fewer microstates into which energy is dispersed), $\Delta S_{surr}$ must be positive enough (even more microstates into which energy is dispersed) for $\Delta S_{univ}$ to be positive (net increase in number of microstates to disperse the energy).

> **● A Checkbook Analogy for Heating the Surroundings** If you have $10 in your checking account, a $10 deposit represents a 100% increase in your net worth; that is, a given change to a low initial state has a large impact. If, however, you have a $1000 balance, a $10 deposit represents only a 1% increase. Thus, the same absolute change to a high initial state has a smaller impact.

---

### Sample Problem 20.3    Determining Reaction Spontaneity

**Problem** At 298 K, the formation of ammonia has a negative $\Delta S^{\circ}_{sys}$:

$$N_2(g) + 3H_2(g) \longrightarrow 2NH_3(g) \qquad \Delta S^{\circ}_{sys} = -197 \text{ J/K}$$

Calculate $\Delta S_{univ}$, and state whether the reaction occurs spontaneously at this temperature.

**Plan** For the reaction to occur spontaneously, $\Delta S_{univ} > 0$, so $\Delta S_{surr}$ must be greater than +197 J/K. To find $\Delta S_{surr}$, we need $\Delta H^{\circ}_{sys}$, which is the same as $\Delta H^{\circ}_{rxn}$. We use $\Delta H^{\circ}_f$ values from Appendix B to find $\Delta H^{\circ}_{rxn}$. Then, we divide $\Delta H^{\circ}_{rxn}$ by the given $T$ (298 K) to find $\Delta S_{surr}$. To find $\Delta S_{univ}$, we add the calculated $\Delta S_{surr}$ to the given $\Delta S^{\circ}_{sys}$ (−197 J/K).

**Solution** Calculating $\Delta H^{\circ}_{sys}$:

$$\Delta H^{\circ}_{sys} = \Delta H^{\circ}_{rxn}$$
$$= [(2 \text{ mol NH}_3)(-45.9 \text{ kJ/mol})] - [(3 \text{ mol H}_2)(0 \text{ kJ/mol}) + (1 \text{ mol N}_2)(0 \text{ kJ/mol})]$$
$$= -91.8 \text{ kJ}$$

Calculating $\Delta S_{surr}$:

$$\Delta S_{surr} = -\frac{\Delta H^{\circ}_{sys}}{T} = -\frac{-91.8 \text{ kJ} \times \dfrac{1000 \text{ J}}{1 \text{ kJ}}}{298 \text{ K}} = 308 \text{ J/K}$$

Determining $\Delta S_{univ}$:

$$\Delta S_{univ} = \Delta S^{\circ}_{sys} + \Delta S_{surr} = -197 \text{ J/K} + 308 \text{ J/K} = \boxed{111 \text{ J/K}}$$

$\Delta S_{univ} > 0$, so the reaction occurs spontaneously at 298 K *(see margin)*.

**Check** Rounding to check the math, we have

$$\Delta H^{\circ}_{rxn} \approx 2(-45 \text{ kJ}) = -90 \text{ kJ}$$
$$\Delta S_{surr} \approx -(-90,000 \text{ J})/300 \text{ K} = 300 \text{ J/K}$$
$$\Delta S_{univ} \approx -200 \text{ J/K} + 300 \text{ J/K} = 100 \text{ J/K}$$

Given the negative $\Delta H^{\circ}_{rxn}$, Le Châtelier's principle says that low $T$ favors NH$_3$ formation, so the answer is reasonable (see Section 17.6).

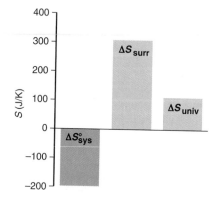

**Comment 1.** Because $\Delta H°$ has units of kJ, and $\Delta S$ has units of J/K, don't forget to convert kJ to J, or you'll introduce a large error.
**2.** This example highlights the distinction between thermodynamics and kinetics. $NH_3$ forms spontaneously, but so slowly that catalysts are required to achieve a practical rate.

**Follow-Up Problem 20.3** Does the oxidation of $FeO(s)$ to $Fe_2O_3(s)$ occur spontaneously at 298 K?

### Do Organisms Obey the Laws of Thermodynamics?
Taking the surroundings into account is crucial, not only for determining reaction spontaneity, as in Sample Problem 20.3, but also for understanding the relevance of thermodynamics to biology. Let's examine the first and second laws to see if they apply to living systems.

1. *Do organisms comply with the first law?* The chemical bond energy in food and oxygen is converted into the mechanical energy of jumping, flying, crawling, swimming, and countless other movements; the electrical energy of nerve conduction; the thermal energy of warming the body; and so forth. Many experiments have demonstrated that the total energy is conserved in these situations. Some of the earliest were performed by Lavoisier, who showed that "animal heat" was produced by slow, continual combustion. In experiments with guinea pigs, he invented a calorimeter to measure the heat released from intake of food and $O_2$ and output of $CO_2$ and water, and he included respiration in his new theory of combustion. Modern, room-sized calorimeters measure these and other variables to confirm the conservation of energy for an exercising human (Figure 20.12).

2. *Do organisms comply with the second law?* Mature humans are far more complex than the egg and sperm cells from which they develop, and modern organisms are far more complex than the one-celled ancestral specks from which they evolved. Are the growth of an organism and the evolution of life exceptions to the spontaneous tendency of natural processes to disperse their energy? For an organism to grow or a species to evolve, many moles of oxygen and nutrients—carbohydrates, proteins, and fats—undergo exothermic reactions to form many *more* moles of gaseous $CO_2$ and $H_2O$. Formation of these waste gases and the accompanying release of heat result in an enormous *increase* in the entropy of the surroundings. Thus, the localization of energy and synthesis of macromolecular structures required for the growth and evolution of organisms cause a far greater dispersal of energy and freedom of motion of small molecules in the environment. When system *and* surroundings are considered together, the entropy of the universe, as always, increases.

**Figure 20.12 A whole-body calorimeter.** In this room-sized apparatus, a person exercises while respiratory gases, energy input and output, and other physiological variables are monitored.

### The Entropy Change and the Equilibrium State
For a process approaching equilibrium, $\Delta S_{univ} > 0$. When the process reaches equilibrium, there is no further *net* change, $\Delta S_{univ} = 0$, because any entropy change in the system is balanced by an opposite entropy change in the surroundings:

At equilibrium:     $\Delta S_{univ} = \Delta S_{sys} + \Delta S_{surr} = 0$  so  $\Delta S_{sys} = -\Delta S_{surr}$

As an example, let's calculate $\Delta S_{univ}$ for the vaporization-condensation of 1 mol of water at 100°C (373 K),

$$H_2O(l; 373 \text{ K}) \rightleftharpoons H_2O(g; 373 \text{ K})$$

First, we find $\Delta S°_{sys}$ for the forward change (vaporization) of 1 mol of water:

$$\Delta S°_{sys} = \Sigma m S°_{products} - \Sigma n S°_{reactants} = S° \text{ of } H_2O(g; 373 \text{ K}) - S° \text{ of } H_2O(l; 373 \text{ K})$$
$$= 195.9 \text{ J/K} - 86.8 \text{ J/K} = 109.1 \text{ J/K}$$

As we expect, the entropy of the system increases ($\Delta S°_{sys} > 0$) as the liquid absorbs heat and changes to a gas.
For $\Delta S_{surr}$ of the vaporization step, we have

$$\Delta S_{surr} = -\frac{\Delta H°_{sys}}{T}$$

where $\Delta H^\circ_{sys} = \Delta H^\circ_{vap}$ at 373 K = 40.7 kJ/mol = $40.7 \times 10^3$ J/mol. For 1 mol of water, we have

$$\Delta S_{surr} = -\frac{\Delta H^\circ_{vap}}{T} = -\frac{40.7 \times 10^3 \text{ J}}{373 \text{ K}} = -109 \text{ J/K}$$

The surroundings lose heat, and the negative sign means that the entropy of the surroundings decreases. The two entropy changes have the same magnitude but opposite signs, so they cancel:

$$\Delta S_{univ} = 109 \text{ J/K} + (-109 \text{ J/K}) = 0$$

For the reverse change (condensation), $\Delta S_{univ}$ also equals zero, but $\Delta S^\circ_{sys}$ and $\Delta S_{surr}$ have signs opposite those for vaporization.

A similar treatment of a chemical change shows the same result: the entropy change of the forward reaction is *equal in magnitude but opposite in sign* to the entropy change of the reverse reaction. Thus, *when a system reaches equilibrium, neither the forward nor the reverse reaction is spontaneous,* and so there is no net reaction in either direction.

## Spontaneous Exothermic and Endothermic Change

No matter what its *enthalpy* change, a reaction occurs because the total *entropy* of the reacting system *and* its surroundings increases. There are two ways this can happen:

1. *In an exothermic reaction* ($\Delta H_{sys} < 0$), the heat released by the system increases the freedom of motion and dispersal of energy in the surroundings; thus, $\Delta S_{surr} > 0$.
- If the entropy of the products is *more* than that of the reactants ($\Delta S_{sys} > 0$), the total entropy change ($\Delta S_{sys} + \Delta S_{surr}$) will be positive (Figure 20.13A). For example, in the oxidation of glucose, an essential reaction for all higher organisms,

$$C_6H_{12}O_6(s) + 6O_2(g) \longrightarrow 6CO_2(g) + 6H_2O(g) + \textbf{\textit{heat}}$$

6 mol of gas yields 12 mol of gas; thus, $\Delta S_{sys} > 0$, $\Delta S_{surr} > 0$, and $\Delta S_{univ} > 0$.
- If the entropy of the products is *less* than that of the reactants ($\Delta S_{sys} < 0$), the entropy of the surroundings must increase even more ($\Delta S_{surr} >> 0$) to make the total $\Delta S$ positive (Figure 20.13B). For example, when calcium oxide and carbon dioxide form calcium carbonate, the amount (mol) of gas decreases from 1 to 0:

$$CaO(s) + CO_2(g) \longrightarrow CaCO_3(s) + \textbf{\textit{heat}}$$

However, even though the system's entropy goes down, the heat released increases the entropy of the surroundings even more; thus, $\Delta S_{sys} < 0$, but $\Delta S_{surr} >> 0$, so $\Delta S_{univ} > 0$.

2. *In an endothermic reaction* ($\Delta H_{sys} > 0$), the heat absorbed by the system decreases molecular freedom of motion and dispersal of energy in the surroundings; thus, $\Delta S_{surr} < 0$. Therefore, the only way an endothermic reaction can occur spontaneously is if $\Delta S_{sys}$ is positive and large enough to outweigh the negative $\Delta S_{surr}$ (Figure 20.13C).

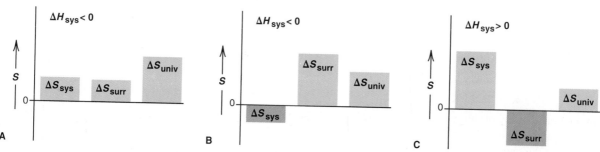

**Figure 20.13 Components of $\Delta S_{univ}$ for spontaneous reactions.** For a reaction to occur spontaneously, $\Delta S_{univ}$ must be positive. **A,** An exothermic reaction in which $\Delta S_{sys}$ increases; the size of $\Delta S_{surr}$ is not important. **B,** An exothermic reaction in which $\Delta S_{sys}$ decreases; $\Delta S_{surr}$ must be larger than $\Delta S_{sys}$. **C,** An endothermic reaction in which $\Delta S_{sys}$ increases; $\Delta S_{surr}$ must be smaller than $\Delta S_{sys}$.

- In the solution process for many ionic compounds, heat is absorbed to form the solution, so the entropy of the surroundings decreases ($\Delta S_{surr} < 0$). However, when the crystalline solid becomes freely moving ions, the entropy increase is so large ($\Delta S_{sys} >> 0$) that it outweighs the negative $\Delta S_{surr}$. Thus, $\Delta S_{univ}$ is positive.
- Spontaneous endothermic reactions are similar. Recall the reaction between barium hydroxide octahydrate and ammonium nitrate (Figure 20.1, p. 813),

$$\textit{heat} + Ba(OH)_2 \cdot 8H_2O(s) + 2NH_4NO_3(s) \longrightarrow$$
$$Ba^{2+}(aq) + 2NO_3^-(aq) + 2NH_3(aq) + 10H_2O(l)$$

3 mol of crystalline solids absorb heat from the surroundings ($\Delta S_{surr} < 0$) and yields 15 mol of dissolved ions and molecules, which have much more freedom of motion and, therefore, much greater entropy ($\Delta S_{sys} >> 0$).

## ■ Summary of Section 20.2

- The standard entropy of reaction, $\Delta S^\circ_{rxn}$, is calculated from $S^\circ$ values.
- When the amount (mol) of gas increases in a reaction, usually $\Delta S^\circ_{rxn} > 0$.
- $\Delta S_{surr}$ is related directly to $\Delta H^\circ_{sys}$ and inversely to the $T$ at which a change occurs.
- In a spontaneous change, the entropy of the system can decrease only if the entropy of the surroundings increases even more, so that $\Delta S_{univ} > 0$.
- The second law is obeyed in living systems when we consider system *plus* surroundings.
- For a system at equilibrium, $\Delta S_{univ} = 0$, so $\Delta S^\circ_{sys} = -\Delta S_{surr}$.
- Even if $\Delta S^\circ_{sys} < 0$, an exothermic reaction ($\Delta H^\circ_{rxn} < 0$) is spontaneous ($\Delta S_{univ} > 0$) if $\Delta S_{surr} >> 0$; an endothermic reaction ($\Delta H^\circ_{rxn} > 0$) is spontaneous only if $\Delta S^\circ_{sys} > \Delta S_{surr}$.

## 20.3 • ENTROPY, FREE ENERGY, AND WORK

By measuring both $\Delta S_{sys}$ *and* $\Delta S_{surr}$, we can predict whether a reaction will be spontaneous at a particular temperature. This section introduces *one* criterion for spontaneity that is determined by measuring the system only. The Gibbs free energy, or simply **free energy (G)**, combines the system's enthalpy and entropy:

$$G = H - TS$$

One of the greatest, and least recognized, American scientists, Josiah Willard Gibbs (1839–1903), established chemical thermodynamics as well as major principles of equilibrium and electrochemistry. Although the great European scientists of his time, James Clerk Maxwell and Henri Le Châtelier, realized Gibbs's achievements, he was not recognized by his American colleagues until nearly 50 years after his death!

### Free Energy Change and Reaction Spontaneity

*The free energy change ($\Delta G$) is a measure of the spontaneity of a process and of the useful energy available from it.*

**Deriving the Gibbs Equation**  Let's derive $\Delta G$ from the second law. By definition, the entropy change of the universe is the sum of the entropy changes of the system and the surroundings:

$$\Delta S_{univ} = \Delta S_{sys} + \Delta S_{surr}$$

At constant pressure,

$$\Delta S_{surr} = -\frac{\Delta H_{sys}}{T}$$

Substituting for $\Delta S_{surr}$ gives a relationship that relies solely on the system:

$$\Delta S_{univ} = \Delta S_{sys} - \frac{\Delta H_{sys}}{T}$$

Multiplying both sides by $-T$ gives

$$-T\Delta S_{univ} = \Delta H_{sys} - T\Delta S_{sys}$$

Using the Gibbs free energy relationship, $G = H - TS$, we obtain the *Gibbs equation* for the *change* in the free energy of the system ($\Delta G_{sys}$) at constant $T$ and $P$:

$$\Delta G_{sys} = \Delta H_{sys} - T\Delta S_{sys} \qquad (20.6)$$

Combining Equation 20.6 with the one preceding it shows that

$$-T\Delta S_{univ} = \Delta H_{sys} - T\Delta S_{sys} = \Delta G_{sys}$$

**Significance of the Sign of ΔG**  Let's see how the *sign* of $\Delta G$ tells if a reaction is spontaneous. According to the second law,

- $\Delta S_{univ} > 0$ for a spontaneous process
- $\Delta S_{univ} < 0$ for a nonspontaneous process
- $\Delta S_{univ} = 0$ for a process at equilibrium

Since the absolute temperature is always positive, for a spontaneous process,

$$T\Delta S_{univ} > 0 \qquad so \qquad -T\Delta S_{univ} < 0$$

From our derivation above, $\Delta G = -T\Delta S_{univ}$, so we have

- $\Delta G < 0$ for a spontaneous process
- $\Delta G > 0$ for a nonspontaneous process
- $\Delta G = 0$ for a process at equilibrium

## Calculating Standard Free Energy Changes

The *sign* of $\Delta G$ reveals *whether* a reaction is spontaneous, but the *magnitude* of $\Delta G$ tells *how* spontaneous it is. Because free energy ($G$) combines three state functions, $H$, $S$, and $T$, it is also a state function. As we do with enthalpy, we focus on the free energy *change* ($\Delta G$). As we do with other thermodynamic variables, to compare the free energy changes of different reactions, we calculate the **standard free energy change ($\Delta G°$)**, which occurs when all components of the system are in their standard states.

**Using the Gibbs Equation to Find ΔG°**  One way to calculate $\Delta G°$ is by writing the Gibbs equation (20.6) at standard state conditions and using Appendix B to find $\Delta H°_{sys}$ and $\Delta S°_{sys}$. Adapting the Gibbs equation, we have

$$\Delta G°_{sys} = \Delta H°_{sys} - T\Delta S°_{sys} \qquad (20.7)$$

This important relationship is used to find any one of these three variables, given the other two, as in Sample Problem 20.4.

---

**Sample Problem 20.4**   **Calculating $\Delta G°_{rxn}$ from Enthalpy and Entropy Values**

**Problem**  Potassium chlorate, a common oxidizing agent in fireworks (*see photo*) and matchheads, undergoes a solid-state disproportionation reaction when heated:

$$\overset{+5}{4KClO_3(s)} \xrightarrow{\Delta} \overset{+7}{3KClO_4(s)} + \overset{-1}{KCl(s)}$$

Use $\Delta H°_f$ and $S°$ values to calculate $\Delta G°_{sys}$ (which is $\Delta G°_{rxn}$) at 25°C for this reaction.

**Plan**  To solve for $\Delta G°$, we need values from Appendix B. We use $\Delta H°_f$ values to calculate $\Delta H°_{rxn}$ ($\Delta H°_{sys}$), use $S°$ values to calculate $\Delta S°_{rxn}$ ($\Delta S°_{sys}$), and then apply Equation 20.7.

**Solution**  Calculating $\Delta H°_{sys}$ from $\Delta H°_f$ values (with Equation 6.9):

$$\Delta H°_{sys} = \Delta H°_{rxn} = \Sigma m\Delta H°_{f(products)} - \Sigma n\Delta H°_{f(reactants)}$$

$$= [(3 \text{ mol } KClO_4)(\Delta H°_f \text{ of } KClO_4) + (1 \text{ mol } KCl)(\Delta H°_f \text{ of } KCl)]$$

$$- [(4 \text{ mol } KClO_3)(\Delta H°_f \text{ of } KClO_3)]$$

$$= [(3 \text{ mol})(-432.8 \text{ kJ/mol}) + (1 \text{ mol})(-436.7 \text{ kJ/mol})]$$

$$- [(4 \text{ mol})(-397.7 \text{ kJ/mol})]$$

$$= -144 \text{ kJ}$$

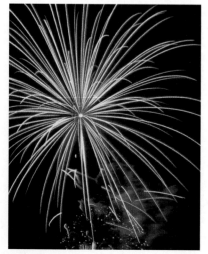
Fireworks explode spontaneously.

Calculating $\Delta S^{\circ}_{sys}$ from $S^{\circ}$ values (with Equation 20.4):

$$\Delta S^{\circ}_{sys} = \Delta S^{\circ}_{rxn} = \Sigma mS^{\circ}_{products} - \Sigma nS^{\circ}_{reactants}$$

$$= [(3 \text{ mol } KClO_4)(S^{\circ} \text{ of } KClO_4) + (1 \text{ mol } KCl)(S^{\circ} \text{ of } KCl)]$$
$$\quad - [(4 \text{ mol } KClO_3)(S^{\circ} \text{ of } KClO_3)]$$
$$= [(3 \text{ mol})(151.0 \text{ J/mol·K}) + (1 \text{ mol})(82.6 \text{ J/mol·K})]$$
$$\quad - [(4 \text{ mol})(143.1 \text{ J/mol·K})]$$
$$= -36.8 \text{ J/K}$$

Calculating $\Delta G^{\circ}_{sys}$ at 298 K:

$$\Delta G^{\circ}_{sys} = \Delta H^{\circ}_{sys} - T\Delta S^{\circ}_{sys} = -144 \text{ kJ} - \left[(298 \text{ K})(-36.8 \text{ J/K})\left(\frac{1 \text{ kJ}}{1000 \text{ J}}\right)\right] = \boxed{-133 \text{ kJ}}$$

**Check** Rounding to check the math:

$$\Delta H^{\circ} \approx [3(-433 \text{ kJ}) + (-440 \text{ kJ})] - [4(-400 \text{ kJ})] = -1740 \text{ kJ} + 1600 \text{ kJ} = -140 \text{ kJ}$$

$$\Delta S^{\circ} \approx [3(150 \text{ J/K}) + 85 \text{ J/K}] - [4(145 \text{ J/K})] = 535 \text{ J/K} - 580 \text{ J/K} = -45 \text{ J/K}$$

$$\Delta G^{\circ} \approx -140 \text{ kJ} - 300 \text{ K}(-0.04 \text{ kJ/K}) = -140 \text{ kJ} + 12 \text{ kJ} = -128 \text{ kJ}$$

**Comment** Recall from Section 20.1 that reaction spontaneity tells nothing about rate. Even though this reaction is spontaneous, the rate is very low in the solid. When $KClO_3$ is heated slightly above its melting point, the ions can move and the reaction occurs readily.

**Follow-Up Problem 20.4** Determine the standard free energy change at 298 K for the reaction $2NO(g) + O_2(g) \longrightarrow 2NO_2(g)$.

### Using Standard Free Energies of Formation to Find $\Delta G^{\circ}_{rxn}$

Another way to calculate $\Delta G^{\circ}_{rxn}$ is with values for the **standard free energy of formation ($\Delta G^{\circ}_f$)** of the components. Analogously to the standard enthalpy of formation, $\Delta H^{\circ}_f$ (Section 6.6), $\Delta G^{\circ}_f$ is the free energy change that occurs when 1 mol of compound is made *from its elements,* with all components in their standard states. Because free energy is a state function, we can apply Hess's law and combine $\Delta G^{\circ}_f$ values of reactants and products to calculate $\Delta G^{\circ}_{rxn}$, no matter how the reaction takes place:

$$\Delta G^{\circ}_{rxn} = \Sigma m\Delta G^{\circ}_{f(products)} - \Sigma n\Delta G^{\circ}_{f(reactants)} \qquad \text{(20.8)}$$

$\Delta G^{\circ}_f$ values have properties similar to $\Delta H^{\circ}_f$ values:

- $\Delta G^{\circ}_f$ of an element in its standard state is zero.
- An equation coefficient (*m* or *n* above) multiplies $\Delta G^{\circ}_f$ by that number.
- Reversing a reaction changes the sign of $\Delta G^{\circ}_f$.

Many $\Delta G^{\circ}_f$ values appear along with those for $\Delta H^{\circ}_f$ and $S^{\circ}$ in Appendix B.

### Sample Problem 20.5 | Calculating $\Delta G^{\circ}_{rxn}$ from $\Delta G^{\circ}_f$ Values

**Problem** Use $\Delta G^{\circ}_f$ values to calculate $\Delta G^{\circ}_{rxn}$ for the reaction in Sample Problem 20.4:

$$4KClO_3(s) \longrightarrow 3KClO_4(s) + KCl(s)$$

**Plan** We apply Equation 20.8 to calculate $\Delta G^{\circ}_{rxn}$.

**Solution** Applying Equation 20.8 with values from Appendix B:

$$\Delta G^{\circ}_{rxn} = \Sigma m\Delta G^{\circ}_{f(products)} - \Sigma n\Delta G^{\circ}_{f(reactants)}$$
$$= [(3 \text{ mol } KClO_4)(\Delta G^{\circ}_f \text{ of } KClO_4) + (1 \text{ mol } KCl)(\Delta G^{\circ}_f \text{ of } KCl)]$$
$$\quad - [(4 \text{ mol } KClO_3)(\Delta G^{\circ}_f \text{ of } KClO_3)]$$
$$= [(3 \text{ mol})(-303.2 \text{ kJ/mol}) + (1 \text{ mol})(-409.2 \text{ kJ/mol})]$$
$$\quad - [(4 \text{ mol})(-296.3 \text{ kJ/mol})] = \boxed{-134 \text{ kJ}}$$

**Check** Rounding to check the math:

$$\Delta G^{\circ}_{rxn} \approx [3(-300 \text{ kJ}) + 1(-400 \text{ kJ})] - 4(-300 \text{ kJ})$$
$$= -1300 \text{ kJ} + 1200 \text{ kJ} = -100 \text{ kJ}$$

**Comment** The slight discrepancy between this answer and the one obtained in Sample Problem 20.4 is due to rounding. As you can see, when $\Delta G_f^\circ$ values are available, this method is simpler arithmetically than the approach in Sample Problem 20.4.

**Follow-Up Problem 20.5** Use $\Delta G_f^\circ$ values to calculate the free energy change at 25°C for each of the following reactions:
**(a)** $2NO(g) + O_2(g) \longrightarrow 2NO_2(g)$ (from Follow-Up Problem 20.4)
**(b)** $2C(graphite) + O_2(g) \longrightarrow 2CO(g)$

## $\Delta G$ and the Work a System Can Do

Thermodynamics developed after the invention of the steam engine, a major advance that spawned a new generation of machines. Thus, some of the field's key ideas applied the relationships between the free energy change and the work a system can do:

- $\Delta G$ is the *maximum useful work* done *by* a system during a *spontaneous* process at constant $T$ and $P$:

$$\Delta G = w_{max} \qquad (20.9)$$

- $\Delta G$ is the *minimum work* done *to* a system to make a *nonspontaneous* process occur at constant $T$ and $P$.

The free energy change is the maximum work the system can *possibly* do. But the work it *actually* does is always less and depends on how the free energy is released. Let's consider the work done by an expanding gas, a car engine, and a battery.

1. *Work done by an expanding gas.* Suppose a gas at $V_{initial}$ is confined in a cylinder-piston assembly attached to a 1-kg weight (Figure 20.14A). The gas expands to some final volume, $V_{final}$, lifting the weight in one step and doing a certain quantity of work (Figure 20.14B). The expanding gas can do more work by lifting a 2-kg weight to one-half $V_{final}$ and then lifting a 1-kg weight to $V_{final}$; that is, doing the work in two steps. Lifting a 3-kg weight to one-third of $V_{final}$, a 2-kg weight to one-half $V_{final}$, and a 1-kg weight all the way to $V_{final}$, that is, in three steps, would do even more work. *As the number of steps increases, the quantity of work done by the gas increases.* Thus, the gas would do *close* to the maximum work if the weight were replaced by a container of sand that could be lifted by removing one grain at a time, that is, in a *very* high number of steps. (We described a similar method for finding the entropy change on p. 816.)

However, the *maximum* work is done by a spontaneous process *only if the work is carried out in an infinite number of steps,* that is, *reversibly.* Of course, in any *real* process, work is performed in a *finite* number of steps, that is, *irreversibly,* so *the maximum work is never done.* Any free energy not used for work is lost to the surroundings as heat. This "unharnessed" energy is a consequence of any real process.

2. *"Useful" work done by a car engine.* When gasoline (represented by octane, $C_8H_{18}$) is burned in a car engine,

$$C_8H_{18}(l) + \tfrac{25}{2}O_2(g) \longrightarrow 8CO_2(g) + 9H_2O(g)$$

a large amount of energy is released as heat ($\Delta H_{sys} < 0$), and because the number of moles of gas increases, the entropy of the system increases ($\Delta S_{sys} > 0$). Therefore, the reaction is spontaneous ($\Delta G_{sys} < 0$). The free energy released turns the wheels, moves the belts, plays the radio, and so on, all examples of "useful" work. However, only if the free energy is released *reversibly,* that is, in an infinite number of steps, can this reaction do the *maximum* useful work. In reality, the reaction occurs *irreversibly,* and much of the total free energy just warms the engine and the outside air, which increases the freedom of motion of the particles in the universe, in accord with the second law.

Gas at $V_{initial}$

**A**

Gas at $V_{final}$

**B**

**Figure 20.14** An expanding gas lifting a weight.

3. *"Useful" work done by a battery.* As you'll see in Chapter 21, a battery is essentially a packaged spontaneous redox reaction that releases free energy to the surroundings (flashlight, radio, motor, etc.). If we connect the battery terminals to each other through a short piece of wire, the free energy change is released all at once but does no work—it just heats wire and battery. But, if we connect the terminals to a motor, a significant portion of the free energy runs the motor, but some is still converted to heat. If we connect the battery to a more "efficient" device, one that discharges the free energy still more slowly, more of the energy does work and less is converted to heat. However, as with all systems, only when the battery discharges infinitely slowly can it do the maximum work.

*Efficiency* can be defined as the percentage of work output relative to the energy input. The range of efficiencies is very large: an incandescent bulb converts <7% of incoming electricity to light, the rest being given off as heat. At the other extreme, an electrical generator converts 95% of the incoming mechanical energy to electricity. Here are the efficiencies of some other devices: home oil furnace, 65%; hand-tool motor, 63%; liquid fuel rocket, 50%; car engine, <30%; compact fluorescent bulb, 18%; solar cell, ~15%.

Therefore, all engineers must face the fact that *no **real** process uses all the available free energy to do work because some is always "wasted" as heat.* Let's summarize the relationship between the free energy change of a reaction and the work it can do:

- A spontaneous reaction ($\Delta G_{sys} < 0$) will do work on the surroundings ($-w$). In any real machine, the actual work done is *always less than the maximum* because some of the $\Delta G$ is released as heat.
- A nonspontaneous reaction ($\Delta G_{sys} > 0$) will occur only if the surroundings do work on the system ($+w$). In any real machine, the actual work done on the system is *always more than the minimum* because some of the added free energy is wasted as heat.
- A reaction at equilibrium ($\Delta G_{sys} = 0$) can no longer do any work.

## The Effect of Temperature on Reaction Spontaneity

In most cases, the enthalpy contribution ($\Delta H$) to the free energy change ($\Delta G$) is much *larger* than the entropy contribution ($T\Delta S$). In fact, the reason most exothermic reactions are spontaneous is that the large negative $\Delta H$ makes $\Delta G$ negative. However, the *temperature of a reaction influences the magnitude of the $T\Delta S$ term,* so, for many reactions, the overall spontaneity depends on the temperature. From the signs of $\Delta H$ and $\Delta S$, we can predict how the temperature affects the sign of $\Delta G$. (The values we'll use below for the thermodynamic variables are standard state values, but we show them without the degree sign to emphasize that the relationships among $\Delta G$, $\Delta H$, and $\Delta S$ are valid at any conditions. Also, we assume that $\Delta H$ and $\Delta S$ change little with temperature, which is true as long as no phase change occurs.)

Let's examine the four combinations of positive and negative $\Delta H$ and $\Delta S$—two that are independent of temperature and two that are dependent on temperature:

- *Temperature-independent cases.* When $\Delta H$ and $\Delta S$ have *opposite* signs, the reaction occurs spontaneously either at all temperatures or at none (nonspontaneous).

  1. *Reaction is spontaneous at all temperatures:* $\Delta H < 0$, $\Delta S > 0$. Since $\Delta S$ is positive, $-T\Delta S$ is negative; thus, both contributions favor a negative $\Delta G$. Most combustion reactions are in this category. The decomposition of hydrogen peroxide, a common disinfectant, is also spontaneous at all temperatures:

$$2H_2O_2(l) \longrightarrow 2H_2O(l) + O_2(g)$$
$$\Delta H = -196 \text{ kJ} \quad \text{and} \quad \Delta S = 125 \text{ J/K}$$

  2. *Reaction is nonspontaneous at all temperatures:* $\Delta H > 0$, $\Delta S < 0$. Both contributions oppose spontaneity: $\Delta H$ is positive and $\Delta S$ is negative, so $-T\Delta S$ is positive; thus, $\Delta G$ is always positive. The formation of ozone from oxygen requires a continual energy input, so it is not spontaneous at any temperature:

$$3O_2(g) \longrightarrow 2O_3(g)$$
$$\Delta H = 286 \text{ kJ} \quad \text{and} \quad \Delta S = -137 \text{ J/K}$$

• *Temperature-dependent cases.* When $\Delta H$ and $\Delta S$ have the *same* sign, the relative magnitudes of $-T\Delta S$ and $\Delta H$ determine the sign of $\Delta G$. In these cases, the *direction of* the change in $T$ is crucial.

3. *Reaction becomes spontaneous as temperature increases:* $\Delta H > 0$ *and* $\Delta S > 0$. With a positive $\Delta H$, the reaction will occur spontaneously only when $-T\Delta S$ becomes large enough to make $\Delta G$ negative, which will happen as temperatures rise. For example,

$$2N_2O(g) + O_2(g) \longrightarrow 4NO(g)$$
$$\Delta H = 197.1 \text{ kJ} \quad \text{and} \quad \Delta S = 198.2 \text{ J/K}$$

The oxidation of $N_2O$ occurs spontaneously at any $T > 994$ K.

4. *Reaction becomes spontaneous as temperature decreases:* $\Delta H < 0$ *and* $\Delta S < 0$. Here, $\Delta H$ favors spontaneity, but $\Delta S$ does not ($-T\Delta S > 0$). The reaction will occur spontaneously only when $-T\Delta S$ becomes smaller than $\Delta H$, and this happens as temperatures drop. For example,

$$4Fe(s) + 3O_2(g) \longrightarrow 2Fe_2O_3(s)$$
$$\Delta H = -1651 \text{ kJ} \quad \text{and} \quad \Delta S = -549.4 \text{ J/K}$$

The production of iron(III) oxide occurs spontaneously at any $T < 3005$ K.

Table 20.1 summarizes these four possible combinations of $\Delta H$ and $\Delta S$, and Sample Problem 20.6 applies them.

**Table 20.1  Reaction Spontaneity and the Signs of $\Delta H$, $\Delta S$, and $\Delta G$**

| $\Delta H$ | $\Delta S$ | $-T\Delta S$ | $\Delta G$ | Description |
|---|---|---|---|---|
| − | + | − | − | Spontaneous at all $T$ |
| + | − | + | + | Nonspontaneous at all $T$ |
| + | + | − | + or − | Spontaneous at higher $T$; nonspontaneous at lower $T$ |
| − | − | + | + or − | Spontaneous at lower $T$; nonspontaneous at higher $T$ |

**Sample Problem 20.6    Using Molecular Scenes to Determine the Signs of $\Delta H$, $\Delta S$, and $\Delta G$**

**Problem** The following scenes represent a familiar phase change for water *(blue spheres):*

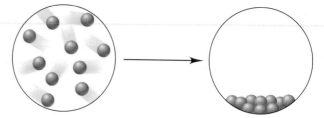

**(a)** What are the signs of $\Delta H$ and $\Delta S$ for this process? Explain.
**(b)** Is the process spontaneous at all $T$, no $T$, low $T$, or high $T$? Explain.

**Plan** **(a)** From the scenes, we determine any change in amount of gas, which indicates the sign of $\Delta S$, and any change in the freedom of motion of the particles, which indicates whether heat is absorbed or released, and thus the sign of $\Delta H$. **(b)** The question refers to the sign of $\Delta G$ (+ or −) at the different temperature possibilities, so we apply Equation 20.6 and refer to the previous text discussion and Table 20.1.

**Solution** **(a)** The scene represents the condensation of water vapor, so the amount of gas decreases dramatically, and the separated molecules give up energy as they come closer together. Therefore, $\Delta S < 0$ and $\Delta H < 0$. **(b)** With $\Delta S$ negative, the $-T\Delta S$ term is positive. In order for $\Delta G < 0$, the magnitude of $T$ must be small. Therefore, the process is spontaneous at low $T$.

**Check** The answer in part (b) seems reasonable based on our analysis in part (a). The answer makes sense because we know from everyday experience that water condenses spontaneously, and it does so at low temperatures.

**Follow-Up Problem 20.6** The following molecular scenes represent the gas-phase decomposition of $X_2Y_2$ to $X_2$ (*red*) and $Y_2$ (*blue*):

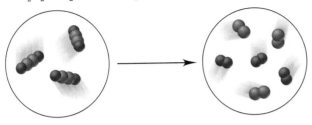

**(a)** What is the sign of $\Delta S$ for the reaction?
**(b)** If the reaction is spontaneous only above 325°C, what is the sign of $\Delta H$? Explain.

As you saw in Sample Problem 20.4, one way to calculate $\Delta G$ is from enthalpy and entropy changes. As long as phase changes don't occur, $\Delta H$ and $\Delta S$ usually change little with temperature, so we use their values at 298 K in Sample Problem 20.7 to examine the effect of $T$ on $\Delta G$ and, thus, on reaction spontaneity.

---

**Sample Problem 20.7** | **Determining the Effect of Temperature on $\Delta G$**

**Problem** A key step in the production of sulfuric acid is the oxidation of $SO_2(g)$ to $SO_3(g)$:
$$2SO_2(g) + O_2(g) \longrightarrow 2SO_3(g)$$
At 298 K, $\Delta G = -141.6$ kJ; $\Delta H = -198.4$ kJ; and $\Delta S = -187.9$ J/K.
**(a)** Use the data to decide if this reaction is spontaneous at 25°C, and predict how $\Delta G$ will change with increasing $T$.
**(b)** Assuming that $\Delta H$ and $\Delta S$ are constant with $T$ (no phase change occurs), is the reaction spontaneous at 900.°C?

**Plan** **(a)** We note the sign of $\Delta G$ to see if the reaction is spontaneous and the signs of $\Delta H$ and $\Delta S$ to see the effect of $T$. **(b)** We use Equation 20.7 to calculate $\Delta G$ from the given $\Delta H$ and $\Delta S$ at the higher $T$ (in K).

**Solution** **(a)** $\Delta G < 0$, so the reaction is spontaneous at 298 K: $SO_2$ and $O_2$ will form $SO_3$ spontaneously. With $\Delta S < 0$, the term $-T\Delta S > 0$, and this term will become more positive at higher $T$. Therefore, $\Delta G$ will become less negative, and the reaction less spontaneous, with increasing $T$.
**(b)** Calculating $\Delta G$ at 900.°C ($T = 273 + 900. = 1173$ K):
$$\Delta G = \Delta H - T\Delta S = -198.4 \text{ kJ} - [(1173 \text{ K})(-187.9 \text{ J/K})(1 \text{ kJ}/1000 \text{ J})] = 22.0 \text{ kJ}$$
$\Delta G > 0$, so the reaction is nonspontaneous at the higher $T$.

**Check** The answer in part (b) seems reasonable based on our prediction in part (a). The arithmetic seems correct, given considerable rounding:
$$\Delta G \approx -200 \text{ kJ} - [(1200 \text{ K})(-200 \text{ J/K})/1000 \text{ J}] = +40 \text{ kJ}$$

**Follow-Up Problem 20.7** A reaction is nonspontaneous at room temperature but *is* spontaneous at −40°C. What can you say about the signs and relative magnitudes of $\Delta H$, $\Delta S$, and $-T\Delta S$?

---

**The Temperature at Which a Reaction Becomes Spontaneous** As you've just seen, when the signs are the same for $\Delta H$ and $\Delta S$ of a reaction, it can be nonspontaneous at one temperature and spontaneous at another. The "crossover" temperature occurs when a positive $\Delta G$ switches to a negative $\Delta G$ because of the magnitude of the $-T\Delta S$ term. We find this temperature by setting $\Delta G$ equal to zero and solving for $T$:
$$\Delta G = \Delta H - T\Delta S = 0$$

Therefore,

$$\Delta H = T\Delta S \quad \text{and} \quad T = \frac{\Delta H}{\Delta S} \qquad \text{(20.10)}$$

Consider the reaction of copper(I) oxide with carbon. It does *not* occur at low temperature but does at high temperature and is used to extract copper from one of its ores:

$$Cu_2O(s) + C(s) \xrightarrow{\Delta} 2Cu(s) + CO(g)$$

We predict that this reaction has a positive $\Delta S$ because the number of moles of gas increases; in fact, $\Delta S = 165$ J/K. Furthermore, because the reaction is *non*spontaneous at lower temperatures, it must have a positive $\Delta H$; the actual value is 58.1 kJ. As the $-T\Delta S$ term becomes more negative with higher $T$, it eventually outweighs the positive $\Delta H$ term, so $\Delta G$ becomes negative and the reaction occurs spontaneously.

---

**Sample Problem 20.8**    **Finding the Temperature at Which a Reaction Becomes Spontaneous**

**Problem** At 25°C (298 K), the reduction of copper(I) oxide to copper is nonspontaneous ($\Delta G = 8.9$kJ). Calculate the temperature at which the reaction becomes spontaneous.

**Plan** As just discussed, we want the temperature at which $\Delta G$ crosses over from a positive to a negative value. We set $\Delta G$ equal to zero, and use Equation 20.10 to solve for $T$, using the $\Delta H$ (58.1 kJ) and $\Delta S$ (165 J/K) values from the text.

**Solution** From $\Delta G = \Delta H - T\Delta S = 0$, we have

$$T = \frac{\Delta H}{\Delta S} = \frac{58.1 \text{ kJ} \times \dfrac{1000 \text{ J}}{1 \text{ kJ}}}{165 \text{ J/K}} = \boxed{352 \text{ K}}$$

Thus, at any temperature above 352 K (79°C), which is a moderate temperature for extracting a metal from its ore, $\Delta G < 0$, so the reaction becomes spontaneous.

**Check** Rounding to quickly check the math gives

$$T = \frac{60000 \text{ J}}{150 \text{ J/K}} = 400 \text{ K}$$

which is close to the answer.

**Comment** Figure 20.15 shows that the line for $T\Delta S$ rises steadily (and thus the $-T\Delta S$ term becomes more negative) with increasing temperature. This line crosses the relatively constant $\Delta H$ line at 352 K. At any higher temperature, the $-T\Delta S$ term is greater than the $\Delta H$ term, so $\Delta G$ is negative.

**Follow-Up Problem 20.8** Use Appendix B values to find the temperature at which the following reaction becomes spontaneous (assume $\Delta H$ and $\Delta S$ are constant with $T$):

$$CaO(s) + CO_2(g) \longrightarrow CaCO_3(s)$$

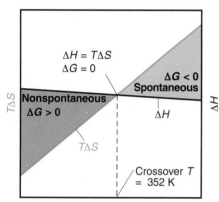

**Figure 20.15 The effect of temperature on reaction spontaneity.** At low $T$, $\Delta G > 0$ because $\Delta H$ dominates. At 352 K, $\Delta H = T\Delta S$, so $\Delta G = 0$. At any higher $T$, $\Delta G < 0$ because $-T\Delta S$ dominates.

## Coupling of Reactions to Drive a Nonspontaneous Change

In a complex, multistep reaction, we often see a nonspontaneous step driven by a spontaneous step. In such a **coupling of reactions,** *one step supplies enough free energy for the other to occur,* just as burning gasoline supplies enough free energy to move a car.

Look again at the reduction of copper(I) oxide by carbon. Previously, we found that the *overall* reaction becomes spontaneous at any temperature above 352 K. Dividing the reaction into two steps, however, we find that even at a higher temperature, such as 375 K, copper(I) oxide does not spontaneously decompose to its elements:

$$Cu_2O(s) \longrightarrow 2Cu(s) + \tfrac{1}{2}O_2(g) \qquad \Delta G_{375} = 140.0 \text{ kJ}$$

However, the oxidation of carbon to CO at 375 K is quite spontaneous:

$$C(s) + \tfrac{1}{2}O_2(g) \longrightarrow CO(g) \qquad \Delta G_{375} = -143.8 \text{ kJ}$$

Coupling these reactions means having the carbon in contact with the $Cu_2O$, which allows the reaction with the larger negative $\Delta G$ to "drive" the one with the smaller positive $\Delta G$. Adding the reactions together and canceling the common substance ($\frac{1}{2}O_2$) gives an overall reaction with a negative $\Delta G$:

$$Cu_2O(s) + C(s) \longrightarrow 2Cu(s) + CO(g) \qquad \Delta G_{375} = -3.8 \text{ kJ}$$

Many biochemical reactions are also nonspontaneous, including key steps in the synthesis of proteins and nucleic acids, the formation of fatty acids, the maintenance of ion balance, and the breakdown of nutrients. Driving a nonspontaneous step by coupling it to a spontaneous one is a life-sustaining strategy common to all organisms, as you'll see in the Chemical Connections essay *(next page)*.

## ◼ Summary of Section 20.3

- The sign of the free energy change, $\Delta G = \Delta H - T\Delta S$, is directly related to reaction spontaneity: a negative $\Delta G$ corresponds to a positive $\Delta S_{univ}$.
- We use the standard free energy of formation ($\Delta G_f^\circ$) to calculate $\Delta G_{rxn}^\circ$ at 298 K.
- The maximum work a system can do is never obtained from a real (irreversible) process because some free energy is always converted to heat.
- The magnitude of $T$ influences the spontaneity of a temperature-dependent reaction (same signs of $\Delta H$ and $\Delta S$) by affecting the size of $T\Delta S$. For such a reaction, the $T$ at which the reaction becomes spontaneous can be found by setting $\Delta G = 0$.
- A nonspontaneous reaction ($\Delta G > 0$) can be coupled to a more spontaneous one ($\Delta G \ll 0$) to make it occur. For example, in organisms, the hydrolysis of ATP drives many reactions with a positive $\Delta G$.

## 20.4 • FREE ENERGY, EQUILIBRIUM, AND REACTION DIRECTION

As you know from discussions in earlier chapters, the sign of $\Delta G$ is not the only way to predict reaction direction. In Chapter 17, we did so by comparing the values of the reaction quotient ($Q$) and the equilibrium constant ($K$). Recall that

- If $Q < K$ ($Q/K < 1$): reaction proceeds spontaneously to the right.
- If $Q > K$ ($Q/K > 1$): reaction proceeds spontaneously to the left.
- If $Q = K$ ($Q/K = 1$): reaction has attained equilibrium and no longer proceeds spontaneously in either direction.

It is easier to see the relation between these two ways to predict reaction spontaneity—the sign of $\Delta G$ and the magnitude of $Q/K$—when we compare the sign of the natural logarithm of $Q/K$ ($\ln Q/K$) with the sign of $\Delta G$ (refer to Appendix A if necessary):

- If $Q/K < 1$, then $\ln Q/K < 0$: reaction proceeds spontaneously to the right ($\Delta G < 0$).
- If $Q/K > 1$, then $\ln Q/K > 0$: reaction proceeds spontaneously to the left ($\Delta G > 0$).
- If $Q/K = 1$, then $\ln Q/K = 0$: reaction is at equilibrium ($\Delta G = 0$).

Note that the signs of $\Delta G$ and of $\ln Q/K$ are the same for a given direction; in fact, $\Delta G$ equals $\ln Q/K$ multiplied by the proportionality constant $RT$:

$$\Delta G = RT \ln \frac{Q}{K} = RT \ln Q - RT \ln K \qquad \textbf{(20.11)}$$

$Q$ represents the concentrations (or pressures) of a system's components at any time during the reaction, and $K$ represents these quantities at equilibrium. Therefore, Equation 20.11 says that $\Delta G$ is a measure of how different the concentrations at any time, $Q$, are from the concentrations at equilibrium, $K$:

- If $Q$ and $K$ are very different, the reaction releases (or absorbs) a *lot* of free energy.
- If $Q$ and $K$ are nearly the same, the reaction releases (or absorbs) relatively *little*.

Despite their incredible diversity, virtually all organisms use the same amino acids to make their proteins, the same nucleotides to make their nucleic acids, and the same carbohydrate (glucose) to provide energy.

In addition, *all organisms use the same spontaneous reaction to drive a variety of nonspontaneous ones*. This reaction is the hydrolysis of **adenosine triphosphate (ATP)** to adenosine diphosphate (ADP):*

$$ATP^{4-} + H_2O \rightleftharpoons ADP^{3-} + HPO_4^{2-} + H^+$$
$$\Delta G^{\circ'} = -30.5 \text{ kJ}$$

In the metabolic breakdown of glucose, for example, the first step, addition of $HPO_4^{2-}$ to glucose, is nonspontaneous:

$$\text{Glucose} + HPO_4^{2-} + H^+ \rightleftharpoons [\text{glucose phosphate}]^- + H_2O$$
$$\Delta G^{\circ'} = 13.8 \text{ kJ}$$

Coupling this nonspontaneous reaction to ATP hydrolysis makes the overall process spontaneous. If we add the two reactions, $HPO_4^{2-}$, $H^+$, and $H_2O$ cancel:

$$\text{Glucose} + ATP^{4-} \rightleftharpoons [\text{glucose phosphate}]^- + ADP^{3-}$$
$$\Delta G^{\circ'} = -16.7 \text{ kJ}$$

Coupling cannot occur if reactions are physically separated, so these reactions take place on an enzyme (Section 16.7) that simultaneously binds glucose and ATP, and the phosphate group of ATP that will be transferred lies next to the —OH group of glucose that will bind it (Figure B20.1).

The ADP produced in energy-releasing reactions combines with phosphate to regenerate ATP in energy-absorbing reactions catalyzed by other enzymes. Thus, there is a continuous cycling

*In biochemical systems, the standard-state concentration of $H^+$ is $10^{-7}$ $M$, not the usual 1 $M$, and the standard free energy change has the symbol $\Delta G^{\circ'}$.

**Figure B20.2** The cycling of metabolic free energy.

of ATP to ADP and back to ATP again to supply energy to the cells (Figure B20.2).

By examining the phosphate portions of ATP, ADP, and $HPO_4^{2-}$, we can see two basic chemical reasons why ATP hydrolysis supplies so much free energy (Figure B20.3):

1. *Charge repulsion.* At physiological pH (~7), the triphosphate group of ATP has four negative charges close together. This *high charge repulsion* is reduced in ADP (Figure B20.3, part A).

2. *Electron delocalization.* Once $HPO_4^{2-}$ is free, there is extensive delocalization and resonance stabilization of the π electrons (Figure B20.3, part B).

Thus, greater charge repulsion and less electron delocalization make ATP higher in energy (less stable) than the sum of the energies of ADP and $HPO_4^{2-}$. When ATP is hydrolyzed, some

**Figure B20.1** The coupling of a nonspontaneous reaction to the hydrolysis of ATP. Glucose lies next to ATP (shown as ADP—O—PO₃H) in the enzyme's active site. ADP (shown as ADP—OH) and glucose phosphate are released.

**Figure B20.3** ATP is a high-energy molecule.

of this additional energy is released and harnessed by the organism to drive metabolic reactions that could not otherwise take place.

## Problems

**B20.1** The oxidation of 1 mol of glucose supplies enough metabolic energy to form 36 mol of ATP. Oxidation of 1 mol of a typical dietary fat like tristearin ($C_{57}H_{116}O_6$) yields enough energy to form 458 mol of ATP. How many molecules of ATP can form per gram of (a) glucose; (b) tristearin?

**B20.2** Nonspontaneous processes like muscle contraction, protein synthesis, and nerve conduction are coupled to the spontaneous hydrolysis of ATP to ADP. ATP is then regenerated by coupling its synthesis to energy-yielding reactions such as

Creatine phosphate $\longrightarrow$ creatine + phosphate
$$\Delta G^{\circ\prime} = -43.1 \text{ kJ/mol}$$

ADP + phosphate $\longrightarrow$ ATP      $\Delta G^{\circ\prime} = +30.5$ kJ/mol

Find $\Delta G^{\circ\prime}$ for the overall reaction that regenerates ATP.

**The Standard Free Energy Change and the Equilibrium Constant** When we choose standard-state values for $Q$ (1 atm for gases, 1 $M$ for solutions, etc.) in Equation 20.11, $\Delta G$ becomes, by definition, $\Delta G^{\circ}$ and $Q$ equals 1:

$$\Delta G^{\circ} = RT \ln 1 - RT \ln K$$

Since $\ln 1 = 0$, the term $RT \ln Q$ drops out, which allows us to find the standard free energy change of a reaction ($\Delta G^{\circ}_{rxn}$) from its equilibrium constant, or vice versa:

$$\Delta G^{\circ} = -RT \ln K \qquad \text{(20.12)}$$

Table 20.2 shows that, due to their logarithmic relationship, a small change in $\Delta G^{\circ}$ causes a large change in $K$. Note just these two examples

- As $\Delta G^{\circ}$ becomes more positive, $K$ becomes smaller: if $\Delta G^{\circ} = +10$ kJ, $K$ is 0.02, so the product terms are $\frac{1}{50}$ the size of the reactant terms.
- As $\Delta G^{\circ}$ becomes more negative, $K$ becomes larger: if $\Delta G^{\circ} = -10$ kJ, the product terms are 50 times larger than the reactant terms.

### Table 20.2 The Relationship Between $\Delta G^{\circ}$ and $K$ at 298 K

| $\Delta G^{\circ}$ (kJ) | $K$ | Significance | |
|---|---|---|---|
| 200 | $9\times10^{-36}$ | Essentially no forward reaction; reverse reaction goes to completion | |
| 100 | $3\times10^{-18}$ | | |
| 50 | $2\times10^{-9}$ | | FORWARD REACTION |
| 10 | $2\times10^{-2}$ | | |
| 1 | $7\times10^{-1}$ | | |
| 0 | 1 | Forward and reverse reactions proceed to same extent | |
| −1 | 1.5 | | |
| −10 | $5\times10^{1}$ | | REVERSE REACTION |
| −50 | $6\times10^{8}$ | | |
| −100 | $3\times10^{17}$ | | |
| −200 | $1\times10^{35}$ | Forward reaction goes to completion; essentially no reverse reaction | |

**Finding the Free Energy Change Under Any Conditions** In reality, reactions rarely begin with all components in their standard states. By substituting the relationship between $\Delta G°$ and $K$ (Equation 20.12) into the expression for $\Delta G$ (Equation 20.11), we obtain a relationship that applies to *any starting concentrations:*

$$\Delta G = \Delta G° + RT \ln Q \tag{20.13}$$

Sample Problem 20.9 uses molecular scenes to explore these ideas, and Sample Problem 20.10 applies them in an important industrial reaction.

---

**Sample Problem 20.9** | **Using Molecular Scenes to Find $\Delta G$ for a Reaction at Nonstandard Conditions**

**Problem** These molecular scenes represent three mixtures in which $A_2$ (*black*) and $B_2$ (*green*) are forming AB. Each molecule represents 0.10 atm. The equation is

$$A_2(g) + B_2(g) \rightleftharpoons 2AB(g) \qquad \Delta G° = -3.4 \text{ kJ/mol}$$

1          2          3

**(a)** If mixture 1 is at equilibrium, calculate $K$.
**(b)** Which mixture has the most negative $\Delta G$, and which has the most positive?
**(c)** Is the reaction spontaneous at the standard state, that is, $P_{A_2} = P_{B_2} = P_{AB} = 1.0$ atm?

**Plan (a)** Mixture 1 is at equilibrium, so we first write the expression for $Q$ and then find the partial pressure of each substance from the numbers of molecules and calculate $K$.
**(b)** To find $\Delta G$, we apply Equation 20.13. We are given $\Delta G°$ ($-3.4$ kJ/mol) and know $R$ (8.314 J/mol·K) but we still need to find $T$. We calculate $T$ from Equation 20.12 using $K$ from part (a), and substitute the partial pressure of each substance (by counting particles) to get $Q$. **(c)** Since 1.0 atm is the standard state, we substitute them into $Q$ in Equation 20.13 and solve for $\Delta G$. Because they are standard state values, $\Delta G$ equals $\Delta G°$.

**Solution (a)** Writing the expression for $Q$ and calculating $K$:

$$A_2(g) + B_2(g) \rightleftharpoons 2AB(g) \qquad Q = \frac{P_{AB}^2}{P_{A_2} \times P_{B_2}} \qquad K = \frac{(0.40)^2}{(0.20)(0.20)} = 4.0$$

**(b)** Calculating $T$ from Equation 20.12 for use in Equation 20.13:

$$\Delta G° = -RT \ln K = -\frac{3.4 \text{ kJ}}{\text{mol}} = -\left(\frac{8.314 \text{ J}}{\text{mol·K}}\right) T \ln 4.0$$

$$T = \frac{\dfrac{-3.4 \text{ kJ}}{\text{mol}}\left(\dfrac{1000 \text{ J}}{1 \text{ kJ}}\right)}{-\left(\dfrac{8.314 \text{ J}}{\text{mol·K}}\right) \ln 4.0} = 295 \text{ K}$$

Calculating $\Delta G$ from Equation 20.13 for each reaction mixture:
Mixture 1:

$$\Delta G = \Delta G° + RT \ln Q = -3.4 \text{ kJ} + RT \ln 4.0$$

$$= -3.4 \text{ kJ} \left(\frac{1000 \text{ J}}{1 \text{ kJ}}\right) + \left(\frac{8.314 \text{ J}}{\text{mol·K}}\right)(295 \text{ K}) \ln 4.0$$

$$= -3400 \text{ J} + 3400 \text{ J} = 0.0 \text{ J}$$

Mixture 2:

$$\Delta G = -3.4 \text{ kJ} + RT \ln \frac{(0.20)^2}{(0.30)(0.30)}$$

$$= -3.4 \text{ kJ} \left(\frac{1000 \text{ J}}{1 \text{ kJ}}\right) + \left(\frac{8.314 \text{ J}}{\text{mol·K}}\right)(295 \text{ K}) \ln 0.44 = -5.4 \times 10^3 \text{ J}$$

Mixture 3:

$$\Delta G = -3.4 \text{ kJ/mol} + RT \ln \frac{(0.60)^2}{(0.10)(0.10)}$$

$$= -3.4 \text{ kJ/mol} \left(\frac{1000 \text{ J}}{1 \text{ kJ}}\right) + \left(\frac{8.314 \text{ J}}{\text{mol·K}}\right)(295 \text{ K}) \ln 36 = 5.4 \times 10^3 \text{ J}$$

Mixture 2 has the most negative $\Delta G$, and mixture 3 has the most positive $\Delta G$.

**(c)** Finding $\Delta G$ when $P_{A_2} = P_{B_2} = P_{AB} = 1.0$ atm:

$$\Delta G = \Delta G° + RT \ln Q = -3.4 \text{ kJ/mol} + RT \ln \frac{(1.0)^2}{(1.0)(1.0)}$$

$$= -3.4 \text{ kJ/mol} + RT \ln 1.0 = -3.4 \text{ kJ/mol}$$

Yes, the reaction is spontaneous when the components are in their standard states.

**Check** In (b), round to check the arithmetic; for example, for mixture 3, $\Delta G \approx -3000 \text{ J} + (8 \text{ J/mol·K})(300 \text{ K})4 \approx 7000 \text{ J}$, which is in the correct ballpark.

**Comment** **1.** By using the properties of logarithms, we didn't have to calculate $T$ and $\Delta G$ in (b). In mixture 2, $Q < 1$, so $\ln Q$ is negative, which makes $\Delta G$ more negative. Also, note that $Q(0.44) < K(4.0)$, so $\Delta G < 0$. In mixture 3, $Q > 1$ (and is greater than it is in mixture 1), so $\ln Q$ is positive, which makes $\Delta G$ positive. Also, $Q(36) > K(4.0)$, so $\Delta G > 0$.
**2.** In (b), the value of zero for $\Delta G$ of the equilibrium mixture (mixture 1) makes sense, because a system at equilibrium has released all of its free energy.

**Follow-Up Problem 20.9** The scenes below depict mixtures in which $X_2$ (*tan*) and $Y_2$ (*blue*) are forming $XY_2$. Each molecule represents 0.10 mol, and the volume is 1 L. The equation is $X_2(g) + 2Y_2(g) \rightleftharpoons 2XY_2(g)$; $\Delta G° = -1.3$ kJ/mol.

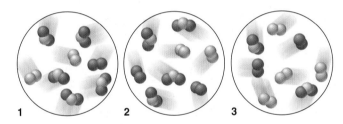

**(a)** If $K = 2$, which mixture is at equilibrium? **(b)** Rank the three mixtures from the lowest (most negative) $\Delta G$ to highest (most positive) $\Delta G$. **(c)** What is the sign of $\Delta G$ for the change that occurs as each nonequilibrium mixture approaches equilibrium?

**Sample Problem 20.10** **Calculating $\Delta G$ at Nonstandard Conditions**

**Problem** The oxidation of $SO_2(g)$, $2SO_2(g) + O_2(g) \longrightarrow 2SO_3(g)$, is too slow at 298 K to be useful in the manufacture of sulfuric acid, so the reaction is run at high $T$.
**(a)** Calculate $K$ at 298 K and at 973 K. ($\Delta G°_{298} = -141.6$ kJ/mol of reaction as written; using $\Delta H°$ and $\Delta S°$ values at 973 K, $\Delta G°_{973} = -12.12$ kJ/mol of reaction as written.)
**(b)** Two containers are filled with 0.500 atm of $SO_2$, 0.0100 atm of $O_2$, and 0.100 atm of $SO_3$; one is kept at 25°C and the other at 700.°C. In which direction, if any, will the reaction proceed to reach equilibrium at each temperature?
**(c)** Calculate $\Delta G$ for the system in part (b) at each temperature.

**Plan** **(a)** We know $\Delta G°$, $T$, and $R$, so we can calculate the $K$'s from Equation 20.12.
**(b)** To determine if a net reaction will occur, we find $Q$ from the given partial pressures and compare it with each $K$ from part (a). **(c)** These are *not* standard-state pressures, so we find $\Delta G$ at each $T$ with Equation 20.13 from the values of $\Delta G°$ (given) and $Q$ [from part (b)].

**Solution** **(a)** Calculating $K$ at the two temperatures:

$$\Delta G° = -RT \ln K$$

so

$$K = e^{-(\Delta G°/RT)}$$

At 298 K, the exponent is

$$-(\Delta G°/RT) = -\left(\dfrac{-141.6 \text{ kJ/mol} \times \dfrac{1000 \text{ J}}{1 \text{ kJ}}}{8.314 \text{ J/mol·K} \times 298 \text{ K}}\right) = 57.2$$

so

$$K = e^{-(\Delta G°/RT)} = e^{57.2} = \boxed{7 \times 10^{24}}$$

At 973 K, the exponent is

$$-(\Delta G°/RT) = -\left(\dfrac{-12.12 \text{ kJ/mol} \times \dfrac{1000 \text{ J}}{1 \text{ kJ}}}{8.314 \text{ J/mol·K} \times 973 \text{ K}}\right) = 1.50$$

so

$$K = e^{-(\Delta G°/RT)} = e^{1.50} = \boxed{4.5}$$

**(b)** Calculating the value of $Q$:

$$Q = \dfrac{P_{SO_3}^2}{P_{SO_2}^2 \times P_{O_2}} = \dfrac{0.100^2}{0.500^2 \times 0.0100} = 4.00$$

Because $Q < K$ at both temperatures, the denominator will decrease and the numerator will increase—more $SO_3$ will form—until $Q$ equals $K$. To reach equilibrium, the reaction will go far to the right at 298 K, and it will go slightly to the right at 973 K.

**(c)** Calculating $\Delta G$, the nonstandard free energy change, at 298 K:

$$\Delta G_{298} = \Delta G° + RT \ln Q$$

$$= -141.6 \text{ kJ/mol} + \left(8.314 \text{ J/mol·K} \times \dfrac{1 \text{ kJ}}{1000 \text{ J}} \times 298 \text{ K} \times \ln 4.00\right)$$

$$= \boxed{-138.2 \text{ kJ/mol}}$$

Calculating $\Delta G$ at 973 K:

$$\Delta G_{973} = \Delta G° + RT \ln Q$$

$$= -12.12 \text{ kJ/mol} + \left(8.314 \text{ J/mol·K} \times \dfrac{1 \text{ kJ}}{1000 \text{ J}} \times 973 \text{ K} \times \ln 4.00\right)$$

$$= \boxed{-0.9 \text{ kJ/mol}}$$

**Check** Note that in parts (a) and (c), we made the free energy units (kJ) consistent with the units in $R$ (J). For significant figures in addition and subtraction, we retain one digit to the right of the decimal place in part (c).

**Comment** For these starting gas pressures at 973 K, the process is barely spontaneous ($\Delta G = -0.9$ kJ/mol), so why use a higher temperature? As in the synthesis of $NH_3$ (Section 17.6), where the *yield* is greater at a lower temperature, this process is carried out at higher temperature *with a catalyst* to attain a higher *rate*. We discuss the details of the industrial production of sulfuric acid in Chapter 22.

**Follow-Up Problem 20.10**  At 298 K, hypobromous acid (HBrO) dissociates in water with a $K_a$ of $2.3 \times 10^{-9}$.
**(a)** Calculate $\Delta G°$ for the dissociation of HBrO.
**(b)** Calculate $\Delta G$ if $[H_3O^+] = 6.0 \times 10^{-4}$ $M$, $[BrO^-] = 0.10$ $M$, and $[HBrO] = 0.20$ $M$.

**Another Look at the Meaning of Spontaneity**  At this point, we introduce two terms related to *spontaneous* and *nonspontaneous*:

1. *Product-favored reaction.* For the general reaction

$$A \rightleftharpoons B \qquad K = [B]/[A] > 1$$

and therefore, the reaction proceeds largely from left to right (Figure 20.16A). From pure A to equilibrium, $Q < K$ and the curved *green* arrow in the figure indicates that the

**Figure 20.16 Free energy and the extent of reaction.** Each reaction proceeds spontaneously (*curved green arrows*) from reactants (A or C) or products (B or D) to the equilibrium mixture, at which point $\Delta G = 0$. After that, the reaction is nonspontaneous (*curved red arrows*).

**A,** For the product-favored reaction A $\rightleftharpoons$ B, $G_A^{\circ} > G_B^{\circ}$, so $\Delta G^{\circ} < 0$ and $K > 1$. **B,** For the reactant-favored reaction C $\rightleftharpoons$ D, $G_D^{\circ} > G_C^{\circ}$, so $\Delta G^{\circ} > 0$ and $K < 1$.

reaction is spontaneous ($\Delta G < 0$). From there on, the curved *red* arrow indicates that the reaction is nonspontaneous ($\Delta G > 0$). Similarly, from pure B to equilibrium, $Q > K$ and the reaction is also spontaneous ($\Delta G < 0$), but not thereafter. In either case, *free energy decreases until the reaction reaches a minimum at the equilibrium mixture:* $Q = K$ *and* $\Delta G = 0$. For the overall reaction A $\rightleftharpoons$ B (starting with all components in their standard states), $G_B^{\circ}$ is smaller than $G_A^{\circ}$, so $\Delta G^{\circ}$ is negative, which corresponds to $K > 1$. We call this a *product-favored* reaction because in its final state the system contains mostly product.

    2. *Reactant-favored reaction.* For the opposite reaction,

$$C \rightleftharpoons D \qquad K = [D]/[C] < 1$$

and the reaction proceeds slightly from left to right (Figure 20.16B). Here, too, whether we start with pure C or pure D, the reaction is spontaneous ($\Delta G < 0$) until equilibrium. In this case, however, the equilibrium mixture contains mostly C (the reactant), so we say the reaction is *reactant favored*. Here, $G_D^{\circ}$ is *larger* than $G_C^{\circ}$, so $\Delta G^{\circ}$ is *positive*, which corresponds to $K < 1$.

    Thus, "spontaneous" refers to that *portion* of a reaction in which the free energy decreases—from the starting mixture to the equilibrium mixture. A product-favored reaction goes predominantly, but *not* completely, toward product, and a reactant-favored reaction goes relatively little toward product (see Table 20.2).

## ■ Summary of Section 20.4

- Two ways of predicting reaction spontaneity are from the sign of $\Delta G$ or the value of $Q/K$. These variables are related to each other by $\Delta G = RT \ln Q/K$. When $Q = K$, $Q/K = 1$ and $\ln Q/K = 0$. Thus, the system is at equilibrium and can release no more free energy.
- Beginning with $Q$ at the standard state, the free energy change is $\Delta G^{\circ}$ and is related to the equilibrium constant: $\Delta G^{\circ} = -RT \ln K$.
- Any nonequilibrium mixture of reactants and products moves spontaneously ($\Delta G < 0$) toward the equilibrium mixture.
- A product-favored reaction goes predominantly toward product and, thus, has $K > 1$ and $\Delta G^{\circ} < 0$; a reactant-favored reaction has $K < 1$ and $\Delta G^{\circ} > 0$.

# CHAPTER REVIEW GUIDE

## Understand These Concepts

1. How the tendency of a process to occur by itself is distinct from how long it takes to occur (Introduction)
2. The distinction between a spontaneous and a nonspontaneous change (§20.1)
3. Why the first law of thermodynamics and the sign of $\Delta H°$ cannot predict the direction of a spontaneous process (§20.1)
4. How the entropy ($S$) of a system is defined by the number of microstates over which its energy is dispersed (§20.1)
5. How entropy is alternatively defined by the heat absorbed (or released) at constant $T$ in a reversible process (§20.1)
6. The criterion for spontaneity according to the second law of thermodynamics: that a change increases $S_{univ}$ (§20.1)
7. How absolute values of standard molar entropies ($S°$) can be obtained because the third law of thermodynamics provides a "zero point" (§20.1)
8. How temperature, physical state, dissolution, atomic size, and molecular complexity influence $S°$ values (§20.1)
9. How $\Delta S°_{rxn}$ is based on the difference between the summed $S°$ values for the reactants and those for products (§20.2)
10. How the surroundings add heat to or remove heat from the system and how $\Delta S_{surr}$ influences overall $\Delta S°_{rxn}$ (§20.2)
11. The relationship between $\Delta S_{surr}$ and $\Delta H_{sys}$ (§20.2)
12. How reactions proceed spontaneously toward equilibrium ($\Delta S_{univ} > 0$) but proceed no further at equilibrium ($\Delta S_{univ} = 0$) (§20.2)
13. How the free energy change ($\Delta G$) combines a system's entropy and enthalpy changes (§20.3)
14. How the expression for the free energy change is derived from the second law (§20.3)

15. The relationship between $\Delta G$ and the maximum work a system can perform and why this quantity of work is never performed in a real process (§20.3)
16. How temperature determines spontaneity for reactions in which $\Delta S$ and $\Delta H$ have the same sign (§20.3)
17. Why the temperature at which a reaction becomes spontaneous occurs when $\Delta G = 0$ (§20.3)
18. How a spontaneous change can be coupled to a nonspontaneous change to make it occur (§20.3)
19. How $\Delta G$ is related to the ratio of $Q$ to $K$ (§20.4)
20. The meaning of $\Delta G°$ and its relation to $K$ (§20.4)
21. The relation of $\Delta G$ to $\Delta G°$ and $Q$ (§20.4)
22. Why $G$ decreases, no matter what the starting concentrations, as the reacting system moves toward equilibrium (§20.4)

## Master These Skills

1. Predicting relative $S°$ values of systems (§20.1 and SP 20.1)
2. Calculating $\Delta S°_{rxn}$ for a chemical change (SP 20.2)
3. Finding reaction spontaneity from $\Delta S_{surr}$ and $\Delta H_{sys}$ (SP 20.3)
4. Calculating $\Delta G°_{rxn}$ from $\Delta H_f°$ and $S°$ values (SP 20.4)
5. Calculating $\Delta G°_{rxn}$ from $\Delta G_f°$ values (SP 20.5)
6. Predicting the signs of $\Delta H$, $\Delta S$, and $\Delta G$ (SP 20.6)
7. Calculating the effect of temperature on $\Delta G$ (SP 20.7)
8. Calculating the temperature at which a reaction becomes spontaneous (§20.3 and SP 20.8)
9. Calculating $K$ from $\Delta G°$ (§20.4 and SP 20.10)
10. Using $\Delta G°$ and $Q$ to calculate $\Delta G$ at any conditions (SPs 20.9, 20.10)

**Section 20.1**
spontaneous change (811)
entropy ($S$) (814)
second law of thermodynamics (817)
third law of thermodynamics (817)

standard molar entropy ($S°$) (817)

**Section 20.2**
standard entropy of reaction ($\Delta S°_{rxn}$) (822)

**Section 20.3**
free energy ($G$) (827)
standard free energy change ($\Delta G°$) (828)
standard free energy of formation ($\Delta G_f°$) (829)

coupling of reactions (834)
adenosine triphosphate (ATP) (836)

**20.1** Quantifying entropy in terms of the number of microstates ($W$) over which the energy of a system can be distributed (814):
$$S = k \ln W$$

**20.2** Quantifying the entropy change in terms of heat absorbed (or released) in a reversible process (816):
$$\Delta S_{sys} = \frac{q_{rev}}{T}$$

**20.3** Stating the second law of thermodynamics, for a spontaneous process (817):
$$\Delta S_{univ} = \Delta S_{sys} + \Delta S_{surr} > 0$$

**20.4** Calculating the standard entropy of reaction from the standard molar entropies of reactants and products (822):
$$\Delta S°_{rxn} = \Sigma m S°_{products} - \Sigma n S°_{reactants}$$

**20.5** Relating the entropy change in the surroundings to the enthalpy change of the system and the temperature (824):
$$\Delta S_{surr} = -\frac{\Delta H_{sys}}{T}$$

**20.6** Expressing the free energy change of the system in terms of its component enthalpy and entropy changes (Gibbs equation) (828):
$$\Delta G_{sys} = \Delta H_{sys} - T\Delta S_{sys}$$

**20.7** Calculating the standard free energy change from standard enthalpy and entropy changes (828):

$$\Delta G^\circ_{sys} = \Delta H^\circ_{sys} - T\Delta S^\circ_{sys}$$

**20.8** Calculating the standard free energy change from the standard free energies of formation (829):

$$\Delta G^\circ_{rxn} = \Sigma m\Delta G^\circ_{f(products)} - \Sigma n\Delta G^\circ_{f(reactants)}$$

**20.9** Relating the free energy change to the maximum work a process can perform (830):

$$\Delta G = w_{max}$$

**20.10** Finding the temperature at which a reaction becomes spontaneous (834):

$$T = \frac{\Delta H}{\Delta S}$$

**20.11** Expressing the free energy change in terms of $Q$ and $K$ (835):

$$\Delta G = RT \ln \frac{Q}{K} = RT \ln Q - RT \ln K$$

**20.12** Expressing the free energy change when $Q$ is at standard state conditions (837):

$$\Delta G^\circ = -RT \ln K$$

**20.13** Expressing the free energy change for nonstandard initial conditions (838):

$$\Delta G = \Delta G^\circ + RT \ln Q$$

## Brief Solutions to Follow-Up Problems

**20.1** (a) $PCl_5(g)$: higher molar mass and more complex molecule; (b) $BaCl_2(s)$: higher molar mass; (c) $Br_2(g)$: gases have more freedom of motion and dispersal of energy than liquids.

**20.2** (a) $2NaOH(s) + CO_2(g) \longrightarrow Na_2CO_3(s) + H_2O(l)$
$\Delta n_{gas} = -1$, so $\Delta S^\circ_{rxn} < 0$
$\Delta S^\circ_{rxn} = [(1 \text{ mol } H_2O)(69.9 \text{ J/mol·K})$
$\qquad + (1 \text{ mol } Na_2CO_3)(139 \text{ J/mol·K})]$
$\qquad - [(1 \text{ mol } CO_2)(213.7 \text{ J/mol·K})$
$\qquad + (2 \text{ mol } NaOH)(64.5 \text{ J/mol·K})]$
$\qquad = -134 \text{ J/K}$

(b) $2Fe(s) + 3H_2O(g) \longrightarrow Fe_2O_3(s) + 3H_2(g)$
$\Delta n_{gas} = 0$, so cannot predict sign of $\Delta S^\circ_{rxn}$
$\Delta S^\circ_{rxn} = [(1 \text{ mol } Fe_2O_3)(87.4 \text{ J/mol·K})$
$\qquad + (3 \text{ mol } H_2)(130.6 \text{ J/mol·K})]$
$\qquad - [(2 \text{ mol } Fe)(27.3 \text{ J/mol·K})$
$\qquad + (3 \text{ mol } H_2O)(188.7 \text{ J/mol·K})]$
$\qquad = -141.5 \text{ J/K}$

**20.3** $2FeO(s) + \frac{1}{2}O_2(g) \longrightarrow Fe_2O_3(s)$
$\Delta S^\circ_{sys} = (1 \text{ mol } Fe_2O_3)(87.4 \text{ J/mol·K})$
$\qquad - [(2 \text{ mol } FeO)(60.75 \text{ J/mol·K})$
$\qquad + (\frac{1}{2} \text{ mol } O_2)(205.0 \text{ J/mol·K})]$
$\qquad = -136.6 \text{ J/K}$
$\Delta H^\circ_{sys} = (1 \text{ mol } Fe_2O_3)(-825.5 \text{ kJ/mol})$
$\qquad - [(2 \text{ mol } FeO)(-272.0 \text{ kJ/mol}) + (\frac{1}{2} \text{ mol } O_2)(0 \text{ kJ/mol})]$
$\qquad = -281.5 \text{ kJ}$
$\Delta S_{surr} = -\dfrac{\Delta H^\circ_{sys}}{T} = -\dfrac{(-281.5 \text{ kJ} \times 1000 \text{ J/kJ})}{298 \text{ K}} = +945 \text{ J/K}$
$\Delta S_{univ} = \Delta S^\circ_{sys} + \Delta S_{surr} = -136.6 \text{ J/K} + 945 \text{ J/K}$
$\qquad = 808 \text{ J/K}$; reaction is spontaneous at 298 K.

**20.4** Using $\Delta H^\circ_f$ and $S^\circ$ values from Appendix B,
$\Delta H^\circ_{rxn} = -114.2 \text{ kJ}$ and $\Delta S^\circ_{rxn} = -146.5 \text{ J/K}$
$\Delta G^\circ_{rxn} = \Delta H^\circ_{rxn} - T\Delta S^\circ_{rxn}$
$\qquad = -114.2 \text{ kJ} - [(298 \text{ K})(-146.5 \text{ J/K})(1 \text{ kJ/1000 J})]$
$\qquad = -70.5 \text{ kJ}$

**20.5** (a) $\Delta G^\circ_{rxn} = (2 \text{ mol } NO_2)(51 \text{ kJ/mol})$
$\qquad - [(2 \text{ mol } NO)(86.60 \text{ kJ/mol})$
$\qquad + (1 \text{ mol } O_2)(0 \text{ kJ/mol})]$
$\qquad = -71 \text{ kJ}$

(b) $\Delta G^\circ_{rxn} = (2 \text{ mol } CO)(-137.2 \text{ kJ/mol}) - [(2 \text{ mol } C)(0 \text{ kJ/mol})$
$\qquad + (1 \text{ mol } O_2)(0 \text{ kJ/mol})]$
$\qquad = -274.4 \text{ kJ}$

**20.6** (a) More moles of gas are present after the reaction, so $\Delta S > 0$. (b) The problem says the reaction is spontaneous ($\Delta G < 0$) only above 325°C, which implies high $T$. If $\Delta S > 0$, $-T\Delta S < 0$, so $\Delta G$ will become negative at higher $T$ only if $\Delta H > 0$.

**20.7** $\Delta G$ becomes negative at lower $T$, so $\Delta H < 0$, $\Delta S < 0$, and $-T\Delta S > 0$. At lower $T$, the negative $\Delta H$ value becomes larger than the positive $-T\Delta S$ value.

**20.8**

$\Delta H = \Delta H^\circ_f \text{ CaCO}_3 - (\Delta H^\circ_f \text{ CaO} + \Delta H^\circ_f \text{ CO}_2)$
$\qquad = -1206.9 \text{ kJ} - (-635.1 \text{ kJ} - 393.5 \text{ kJ}) = -178.3 \text{ kJ}$
$\Delta S = S^\circ \text{ CaCO}_3 - (S^\circ \text{ CaO} + S^\circ \text{ CO}_2)$
$\qquad = 92.9 \text{ J/K} - (38.2 \text{ J/K} + 213.7 \text{ J/K}) = -159.0 \text{ J/K}$
$$T = \frac{\Delta H}{\Delta S} = \frac{-178.3 \text{ kJ} \times \dfrac{1000 \text{ J}}{1 \text{ kJ}}}{-159.0 \text{ J/K}} = 1121 \text{ K}$$

Reaction becomes spontaneous ($\Delta G < 0$) at any $T < 1121$ K.

**20.9** (a) Mixture 2 is at equilibrium.
(b) 3 (most negative) < 2 < 1 (most positive).
(c) Any reaction mixture moves spontaneously toward equilibrium, so both changes have a negative $\Delta G$.

**20.10** (a) $\Delta G^\circ = -RT \ln K = -8.314 \text{ J/mol·K} \times \dfrac{1 \text{ kJ}}{1000 \text{ J}} \times 298 \text{ K}$
$\qquad\qquad \times \ln (2.3 \times 10^{-9})$
$\qquad = 49 \text{ kJ/mol}$

(b) $Q = \dfrac{[H_3O^+][BrO^-]}{[HBrO]} = \dfrac{(6.0 \times 10^{-4})(0.10)}{0.20} = 3.0 \times 10^{-4}$

$\Delta G = \Delta G^\circ + RT \ln Q$
$\qquad = 49 \text{ kJ/mol}$
$\qquad\quad + \left[ 8.314 \text{ J/mol·K} \times \dfrac{1 \text{ kJ}}{1000 \text{ J}} \times 298 \text{ K} \times \ln (3.0 \times 10^{-4}) \right]$
$\qquad = 29 \text{ kJ/mol}$

## PROBLEMS

Problems with **colored** numbers are answered in Appendix E and worked in detail in the Student Solutions Manual. Problem sections match those in the text and provide the numbers of relevant sample problems. Most offer Concept Review Questions, Skill-Building Exercises (grouped in pairs covering the same concept), and Problems in Context. The Comprehensive Problems are based on material from any section or previous chapter.

*Note:* Unless stated otherwise, problems refer to systems at 298 K (25°C). Solving these problems may require values from Appendix B.

### The Second Law of Thermodynamics: Predicting Spontaneous Change
(Sample Problem 20.1)

**Concept Review Questions**

**20.1** Distinguish between the terms *spontaneous* and *instantaneous*. Give an example of a process that is spontaneous but very slow, and one that is very fast but not spontaneous.

**20.2** Distinguish between the terms *spontaneous* and *nonspontaneous*. Can a nonspontaneous process occur? Explain.

**20.3** State the first law of thermodynamics in terms of (a) the energy of the universe; (b) the creation or destruction of energy; (c) the energy change of system and surroundings. Does the first law reveal the direction of spontaneous change? Explain.

**20.4** State qualitatively the relationship between entropy and freedom of particle motion. Use this idea to explain why you will probably never (a) be suffocated because all the air near you has moved to the other side of the room; (b) see half the water in your cup of tea freeze while the other half boils.

**20.5** Why is $\Delta S_{vap}$ of a substance always larger than $\Delta S_{fus}$?

**20.6** How does the entropy of the surroundings change during an exothermic reaction? An endothermic reaction? Other than the examples in text, describe a spontaneous endothermic process.

**20.7** (a) What is the entropy of a perfect crystal at 0 K?
(b) Does entropy increase or decrease as the temperature rises?
(c) Why is $\Delta H_f^\circ = 0$ but $S^\circ > 0$ for an element?
(d) Why does Appendix B list $\Delta H_f^\circ$ values but not $\Delta S_f^\circ$ values?

**Skill-Building Exercises** (grouped in similar pairs)

**20.8** Which of the following processes are spontaneous?
(a) Water evaporates from a puddle. (b) A lion chases an antelope. (c) An isotope undergoes radioactive disintegration.

**20.9** Which of the following processes are spontaneous?
(a) Earth moves around the Sun. (b) A boulder rolls up a hill. (c) Sodium metal and chlorine gas form solid sodium chloride.

**20.10** Which of the following processes are spontaneous?
(a) Methane burns in air. (b) A teaspoonful of sugar dissolves in a cup of hot coffee. (c) A soft-boiled egg becomes raw.

**20.11** Which of the following processes are spontaneous?
(a) A satellite falls to Earth. (b) Water decomposes to $H_2$ and $O_2$ at 298 K and 1 atm. (c) Average car prices increase.

**20.12** Predict the sign of $\Delta S_{sys}$ for each process: (a) A piece of wax melts. (b) Silver chloride precipitates from solution. (c) Dew forms on a lawn in morning.

**20.13** Predict the sign of $\Delta S_{sys}$ for each process: (a) Gasoline vapors mix with air in a car engine. (b) Hot air expands. (c) Humidity condenses in cold air.

**20.14** Predict the sign of $\Delta S_{sys}$ for each process: (a) Alcohol evaporates. (b) A solid explosive converts to a gas. (c) Perfume vapors diffuse through a room.

**20.15** Predict the sign of $\Delta S_{sys}$ for each process: (a) A pond freezes in winter. (b) Atmospheric $CO_2$ dissolves in the ocean. (c) An apple tree bears fruit.

**20.16** Without using Appendix B, predict the sign of $\Delta S^\circ$ for
(a) $2K(s) + F_2(g) \longrightarrow 2KF(s)$
(b) $NH_3(g) + HBr(g) \longrightarrow NH_4Br(s)$
(c) $NaClO_3(s) \longrightarrow Na^+(aq) + ClO_3^-(aq)$

**20.17** Without using Appendix B, predict the sign of $\Delta S^\circ$ for
(a) $H_2S(g) + \frac{1}{2}O_2(g) \longrightarrow \frac{1}{8}S_8(s) + H_2O(g)$
(b) $HCl(aq) + NaOH(aq) \longrightarrow NaCl(aq) + H_2O(l)$
(c) $2NO_2(g) \longrightarrow N_2O_4(g)$

**20.18** Without using Appendix B, predict the sign of $\Delta S^\circ$ for
(a) $CaCO_3(s) + 2HCl(aq) \longrightarrow CaCl_2(aq) + H_2O(l) + CO_2(g)$
(b) $2NO(g) + O_2(g) \longrightarrow 2NO_2(g)$
(c) $2KClO_3(s) \longrightarrow 2KCl(s) + 3O_2(g)$

**20.19** Without using Appendix B, predict the sign of $\Delta S^\circ$ for
(a) $Ag^+(aq) + Cl^-(aq) \longrightarrow AgCl(s)$
(b) $KBr(s) \longrightarrow KBr(aq)$
(c) $CH_3CH{=}CH_2(g) \longrightarrow \underset{H_2C-CH_2(g)}{\overset{CH_2}{\diagup \diagdown}}$

**20.20** Predict the sign of $\Delta S$ for each process:
(a) $C_2H_5OH(g)$ (350 K and 500 torr) $\longrightarrow$ $C_2H_5OH(g)$ (350 K and 250 torr)
(b) $N_2(g)$ (298 K and 1 atm) $\longrightarrow N_2(aq)$ (298 K and 1 atm)
(c) $O_2(aq)$ (303 K and 1 atm) $\longrightarrow O_2(g)$ (303 K and 1 atm)

**20.21** Predict the sign of $\Delta S$ for each process:
(a) $O_2(g)$ (1.0 L at 1 atm) $\longrightarrow O_2(g)$ (0.10 L at 10 atm)
(b) $Cu(s)$ (350°C and 2.5 atm) $\longrightarrow Cu(s)$ (450°C and 2.5 atm)
(c) $Cl_2(g)$ (100°C and 1 atm) $\longrightarrow Cl_2(g)$ (10°C and 1 atm)

**20.22** Predict which substance has greater molar entropy. Explain.
(a) Butane $CH_3CH_2CH_2CH_3(g)$ or 2-butene $CH_3CH{=}CHCH_3(g)$
(b) $Ne(g)$ or $Xe(g)$   (c) $CH_4(g)$ or $CCl_4(l)$

**20.23** Predict which substance has greater molar entropy. Explain.
(a) $NO_2(g)$ or $N_2O_4(g)$   (b) $CH_3OCH_3(l)$ or $CH_3CH_2OH(l)$
(c) $HCl(g)$ or $HBr(g)$

**20.24** Predict which substance has greater molar entropy. Explain.
(a) $CH_3OH(l)$ or $C_2H_5OH(l)$   (b) $KClO_3(s)$ or $KClO_3(aq)$
(c) $Na(s)$ or $K(s)$

**20.25** Predict which substance has greater molar entropy. Explain.
(a) $P_4(g)$ or $P_2(g)$   (b) $HNO_3(aq)$ or $HNO_3(l)$
(c) $CuSO_4(s)$ or $CuSO_4 \cdot 5H_2O(s)$

**20.26** Without consulting Appendix B, arrange each group in order of *increasing* standard molar entropy ($S°$). Explain.
(a) Graphite, diamond, charcoal
(b) Ice, water vapor, liquid water
(c) $O_2$, $O_3$, O atoms

**20.27** Without consulting Appendix B, arrange each group in order of *increasing* standard molar entropy ($S°$). Explain.
(a) Glucose ($C_6H_{12}O_6$), sucrose ($C_{12}H_{22}O_{11}$), ribose ($C_5H_{10}O_5$)
(b) $CaCO_3$, $Ca + C + \frac{3}{2}O_2$, $CaO + CO_2$
(c) $SF_6(g)$, $SF_4(g)$, $S_2F_{10}(g)$

**20.28** Without consulting Appendix B, arrange each group in order of *decreasing* standard molar entropy ($S°$). Explain.
(a) $ClO_4^-(aq)$, $ClO_2^-(aq)$, $ClO_3^-(aq)$
(b) $NO_2(g)$, $NO(g)$, $N_2(g)$
(c) $Fe_2O_3(s)$, $Al_2O_3(s)$, $Fe_3O_4(s)$

**20.29** Without consulting Appendix B, arrange each group in order of *decreasing* standard molar entropy ($S°$). Explain.
(a) Mg metal, Ca metal, Ba metal
(b) Hexane ($C_6H_{14}$), benzene ($C_6H_6$), cyclohexane ($C_6H_{12}$)
(c) $PF_2Cl_3(g)$, $PF_5(g)$, $PF_3(g)$

**Calculating the Entropy Change of a Reaction**
(Sample Problems 20.2 and 20.3)
**Concept Review Questions**
**20.30** For the reaction depicted in the molecular scenes, X is red and Y is green.

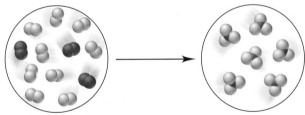

(a) Write a balanced equation.
(b) Determine the sign of $\Delta S$.
(c) Which species has the highest molar entropy?

**20.31** Describe the equilibrium condition in terms of the entropy changes of a system and its surroundings. What does this description mean about the entropy change of the universe?

**20.32** For the reaction $H_2O(g) + Cl_2O(g) \longrightarrow 2HClO(g)$, you know $\Delta S°_{rxn}$ and $S°$ of $HClO(g)$ and of $H_2O(g)$. Write an expression that can be used to determine $S°$ of $Cl_2O(g)$.

**Skill-Building Exercises** (grouped in similar pairs)
**20.33** For each reaction, predict the sign and find the value of $\Delta S°$:
(a) $3NO(g) \longrightarrow N_2O(g) + NO_2(g)$
(b) $3H_2(g) + Fe_2O_3(s) \longrightarrow 2Fe(s) + 3H_2O(g)$
(c) $P_4(s) + 5O_2(g) \longrightarrow P_4O_{10}(s)$

**20.34** For each reaction, predict the sign and find the value of $\Delta S°$:
(a) $3NO_2(g) + H_2O(l) \longrightarrow 2HNO_3(l) + NO(g)$
(b) $N_2(g) + 3F_2(g) \longrightarrow 2NF_3(g)$
(c) $C_6H_{12}O_6(s) + 6O_2(g) \longrightarrow 6CO_2(g) + 6H_2O(g)$

**20.35** Find $\Delta S°$ for the combustion of ethane ($C_2H_6$) to carbon dioxide and gaseous water. Is the sign of $\Delta S°$ as expected?

**20.36** Find $\Delta S°$ for the combustion of methane to carbon dioxide and liquid water. Is the sign of $\Delta S°$ as expected?

**20.37** Find $\Delta S°$ for the reaction of nitrogen monoxide with hydrogen to form ammonia and water vapor. Is the sign of $\Delta S°$ as expected?

**20.38** Find $\Delta S°$ for the combustion of ammonia to nitrogen dioxide and water vapor. Is the sign of $\Delta S°$ as expected?

**20.39** Find $\Delta S°$ for the formation of $Cu_2O(s)$ from its elements.

**20.40** Find $\Delta S°$ for the formation of $HI(g)$ from its elements.

**20.41** Find $\Delta S°$ for the formation of $CH_3OH(l)$ from its elements.

**20.42** Find $\Delta S°$ for the formation of $PCl_5(g)$ from its elements.

**Problems in Context**
**20.43** Sulfur dioxide is released in the combustion of coal. Scrubbers use aqueous slurries of calcium hydroxide to remove the $SO_2$ from flue gases. Write a balanced equation for this reaction and calculate $\Delta S°$ at 298 K [$S°$ of $CaSO_3(s) = 101.4$ J/mol·K].

**20.44** Oxyacetylene welding is used to repair metal structures, including bridges, buildings, and even the Statue of Liberty. Calculate $\Delta S°$ for the combustion of 1 mol of acetylene ($C_2H_2$).

**Entropy, Free Energy, and Work**
(Sample Problems 20.4 to 20.8)
**Concept Review Questions**
**20.45** What is the advantage of calculating free energy changes rather than entropy changes to determine reaction spontaneity?

**20.46** Given that $\Delta G_{sys} = -T\Delta S_{univ}$, explain how the sign of $\Delta G_{sys}$ correlates with reaction spontaneity.

**20.47** (a) Is an endothermic reaction more likely to be spontaneous at higher temperatures or lower temperatures? Explain.
(b) The change depicted below occurs at constant pressure. Explain your answers to each of the following: (1) What is the sign of $\Delta H$? (2) What is the sign of $\Delta S$? (3) What is the sign of $\Delta S_{surr}$? (4) How does the sign of $\Delta G$ vary with temperature?

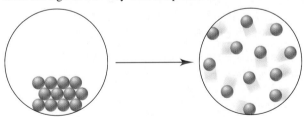

**20.48** With its components in their standard states, a certain reaction is spontaneous only at high $T$. What do you know about the signs of $\Delta H°$ and $\Delta S°$? Describe a process for which this is true.

**20.49** How can $\Delta S°$ be relatively independent of $T$ if $S°$ of each reactant and product increases with $T$?

**Skill-Building Exercises** (grouped in similar pairs)
**20.50** Calculate $\Delta G°$ for each reaction using $\Delta G°_f$ values:
(a) $2Mg(s) + O_2(g) \longrightarrow 2MgO(s)$
(b) $2CH_3OH(g) + 3O_2(g) \longrightarrow 2CO_2(g) + 4H_2O(g)$
(c) $BaO(s) + CO_2(g) \longrightarrow BaCO_3(s)$

**20.51** Calculate $\Delta G°$ for each reaction using $\Delta G_f°$ values:
(a) $H_2(g) + I_2(s) \longrightarrow 2HI(g)$
(b) $MnO_2(s) + 2CO(g) \longrightarrow Mn(s) + 2CO_2(g)$
(c) $NH_4Cl(s) \longrightarrow NH_3(g) + HCl(g)$

**20.52** Find $\Delta G°$ for the reactions in Problem 20.50 using $\Delta H_f°$ and $S°$ values.

**20.53** Find $\Delta G°$ for the reactions in Problem 20.51 using $\Delta H_f°$ and $S°$ values.

**20.54** Consider the oxidation of carbon monoxide:

$$CO(g) + \tfrac{1}{2}O_2(g) \longrightarrow CO_2(g)$$

(a) Predict the signs of $\Delta S°$ and $\Delta H°$. Explain.
(b) Calculate $\Delta G°$ by two different methods.

**20.55** Consider the combustion of butane gas:

$$C_4H_{10}(g) + \tfrac{13}{2}O_2(g) \longrightarrow 4CO_2(g) + 5H_2O(g)$$

(a) Predict the signs of $\Delta S°$ and $\Delta H°$. Explain.
(b) Calculate $\Delta G°$ by two different methods.

**20.56** For the gaseous reaction of xenon and fluorine to form xenon hexafluoride:
(a) Calculate $\Delta S°$ at 298 K ($\Delta H° = -402$ kJ/mol and $\Delta G° = -280.$ kJ/mol).
(b) Assuming that $\Delta S°$ and $\Delta H°$ change little with temperature, calculate $\Delta G°$ at 500. K.

**20.57** For the gaseous reaction of carbon monoxide and chlorine to form phosgene ($COCl_2$):
(a) Calculate $\Delta S°$ at 298 K ($\Delta H° = -220.$ kJ/mol and $\Delta G° = -206$ kJ/mol).
(b) Assuming that $\Delta S°$ and $\Delta H°$ change little with temperature, calculate $\Delta G°$ at 450. K.

**20.58** One reaction used to produce small quantities of pure $H_2$ is

$$CH_3OH(g) \rightleftharpoons CO(g) + 2H_2(g)$$

(a) Determine $\Delta H°$ and $\Delta S°$ for the reaction at 298 K.
(b) Assuming that these values are relatively independent of temperature, calculate $\Delta G°$ at 28°C, 128°C, and 228°C.
(c) What is the significance of the different values of $\Delta G°$?

**20.59** A reaction that occurs in the internal combustion engine is

$$N_2(g) + O_2(g) \rightleftharpoons 2NO(g)$$

(a) Determine $\Delta H°$ and $\Delta S°$ for the reaction at 298 K.
(b) Assuming that these values are relatively independent of temperature, calculate $\Delta G°$ at 100.°C, 2560.°C, and 3540.°C.
(c) What is the significance of the different values of $\Delta G°$?

**20.60** Use $\Delta H°$ and $\Delta S°$ values for the following process at 1 atm to find the normal boiling point of $Br_2$:

$$Br_2(l) \rightleftharpoons Br_2(g)$$

**20.61** Use $\Delta H°$ and $\Delta S°$ values to find the temperature at which these sulfur allotropes reach equilibrium at 1 atm:

$$S(rhombic) \rightleftharpoons S(monoclinic)$$

**Problems in Context**

**20.62** As a fuel, $H_2(g)$ produces only nonpolluting $H_2O(g)$ when it burns. Moreover, it combines with $O_2(g)$ in a fuel cell (Chapter 21) to provide electrical energy.
(a) Calculate $\Delta H°$, $\Delta S°$, and $\Delta G°$ per mole of $H_2$ at 298 K.
(b) Is the spontaneity of this reaction dependent on $T$? Explain.
(c) At what temperature does the reaction become spontaneous?

**20.63** The U.S. government requires automobile fuels to contain a renewable component. Fermentation of glucose from corn yields ethanol, which is added to gasoline to fulfill this requirement:

$$C_6H_{12}O_6(s) \longrightarrow 2C_2H_5OH(l) + 2CO_2(g)$$

Calculate $\Delta H°$, $\Delta S°$, and $\Delta G°$ for the reaction at 25°C. Is the spontaneity of this reaction dependent on $T$? Explain.

## Free Energy, Equilibrium, and Reaction Direction
(Sample Problems 20.9 and 20.10)

**Concept Review Questions**

**20.64** (a) If $K \ll 1$ for a reaction, what do you know about the sign and magnitude of $\Delta G°$? (b) If $\Delta G° \ll 0$ for a reaction, what do you know about the magnitude of $K$? Of $Q$?

**20.65** How is the free energy change of a process related to the work that can be obtained from the process? Is this quantity of work obtainable in practice? Explain.

**20.66** The scenes and the graph relate to the reaction of $X_2(g)$ (*black*) with $Y_2(g)$ (*orange*) to form $XY(g)$. (a) If reactants and products are in their standard states, what quantity is represented on the graph by $x$? (b) Which scene represents point 1? Explain. (c) Which scene represents point 2? Explain.

**20.67** What is the difference between $\Delta G°$ and $\Delta G$? Under what circumstances does $\Delta G = \Delta G°$?

**Skill-Building Exercises** (grouped in similar pairs)

**20.68** Calculate $K$ at 298 K for each reaction:
(a) $NO(g) + \tfrac{1}{2}O_2(g) \rightleftharpoons NO_2(g)$
(b) $2HCl(g) \rightleftharpoons H_2(g) + Cl_2(g)$
(c) $2C(graphite) + O_2(g) \rightleftharpoons 2CO(g)$

**20.69** Calculate $K$ at 298 K for each reaction:
(a) $MgCO_3(s) \rightleftharpoons Mg^{2+}(aq) + CO_3^{2-}(aq)$
(b) $2HCl(g) + Br_2(l) \rightleftharpoons 2HBr(g) + Cl_2(g)$
(c) $H_2(g) + O_2(g) \rightleftharpoons H_2O_2(l)$

**20.70** Calculate $K$ at 298 K for each reaction:
(a) $2H_2S(g) + 3O_2(g) \rightleftharpoons 2H_2O(g) + 2SO_2(g)$
(b) $H_2SO_4(l) \rightleftharpoons H_2O(l) + SO_3(g)$
(c) $HCN(aq) + NaOH(aq) \rightleftharpoons NaCN(aq) + H_2O(l)$

**20.71** Calculate $K$ at 298 K for each reaction:
(a) $SrSO_4(s) \rightleftharpoons Sr^{2+}(aq) + SO_4^{2-}(aq)$
(b) $2NO(g) + Cl_2(g) \rightleftharpoons 2NOCl(g)$
(c) $Cu_2S(s) + O_2(g) \rightleftharpoons 2Cu(s) + SO_2(g)$

**20.72** Use Appendix B to determine the $K_{sp}$ of $Ag_2S$.

**20.73** Use Appendix B to determine the $K_{sp}$ of $CaF_2$.

**20.74** For the reaction $I_2(g) + Cl_2(g) \rightleftharpoons 2ICl(g)$, calculate $K_p$ at 25°C [$\Delta G_f°$ of $ICl(g) = -6.075$ kJ/mol].

**20.75** For the reaction $CaCO_3(s) \rightleftharpoons CaO(s) + CO_2(g)$, calculate the equilibrium $P_{CO_2}$ at 25°C.

**20.76** The $K_{sp}$ of $PbCl_2$ is $1.7\times10^{-5}$ at 25°C. What is $\Delta G°$? Is it possible to prepare a solution that contains $Pb^{2+}(aq)$ and $Cl^-(aq)$, at their standard-state concentrations?

**20.77** The $K_{sp}$ of $ZnF_2$ is $3.0\times10^{-2}$ at 25°C. What is $\Delta G°$? Is it possible to prepare a solution that contains $Zn^{2+}(aq)$ and $F^-(aq)$ at their standard-state concentrations?

**20.78** The equilibrium constant for the reaction

$$2Fe^{3+}(aq) + Hg_2^{2+}(aq) \rightleftharpoons 2Fe^{2+}(aq) + 2Hg^{2+}(aq)$$

is $K_c = 9.1\times10^{-6}$ at 298 K.
(a) What is $\Delta G°$ at this temperature?
(b) If standard-state concentrations of the reactants and products are mixed, in which direction does the reaction proceed?
(c) Calculate $\Delta G$ when $[Fe^{3+}] = 0.20\ M$, $[Hg_2^{2+}] = 0.010\ M$, $[Fe^{2+}] = 0.010\ M$, and $[Hg^{2+}] = 0.025\ M$. In which direction will the reaction proceed to achieve equilibrium?

**20.79** The formation constant for the reaction

$$Ni^{2+}(aq) + 6NH_3(aq) \rightleftharpoons Ni(NH_3)_6^{2+}(aq)$$

is $K_f = 5.6\times10^8$ at 25°C.
(a) What is $\Delta G°$ at this temperature?
(b) If standard-state concentrations of the reactants and products are mixed, in which direction does the reaction proceed?
(c) Determine $\Delta G$ when $[Ni(NH_3)_6^{2+}] = 0.010\ M$, $[Ni^{2+}] = 0.0010\ M$, and $[NH_3] = 0.0050\ M$. In which direction will the reaction proceed to achieve equilibrium?

**Problems in Context**

**20.80** High levels of ozone ($O_3$) cause rubber to deteriorate, green plants to turn brown, and many people to have difficulty breathing.
(a) Is the formation of $O_3$ from $O_2$ favored at all $T$, no $T$, high $T$, or low $T$?
(b) Calculate $\Delta G°$ for this reaction at 298 K.
(c) Calculate $\Delta G$ at 298 K for this reaction in urban smog where $[O_2] = 0.21$ atm and $[O_3] = 5\times10^{-7}$ atm.

**20.81** A $BaSO_4$ slurry is ingested before the gastrointestinal tract is x-rayed because it is opaque to x-rays and defines the contours of the tract. $Ba^{2+}$ ion is toxic, but the compound is nearly insoluble. If $\Delta G°$ at 37°C (body temperature) is 59.1 kJ/mol for the process

$$BaSO_4(s) \rightleftharpoons Ba^{2+}(aq) + SO_4^{2-}(aq)$$

what is $[Ba^{2+}]$ in the intestinal tract? (Assume that the only source of $SO_4^{2-}$ is the ingested slurry.)

**Comprehensive Problems**

**20.82** According to advertisements, "a diamond is forever."
(a) Calculate $\Delta H°$, $\Delta S°$, and $\Delta G°$ at 298 K for the phase change

$$\text{Diamond} \longrightarrow \text{graphite}$$

(b) Given the conditions under which diamond jewelry is normally kept, argue for and against the statement in the ad.
(c) Given the answers in part (a), what would need to be done to make synthetic diamonds from graphite?
(d) Assuming $\Delta H°$ and $\Delta S°$ do not change with temperature, can graphite be converted to diamond spontaneously at 1 atm?

**20.83** Replace each question mark with the correct information:

| | $\Delta S_{rxn}$ | $\Delta H_{rxn}$ | $\Delta G_{rxn}$ | Comment |
|---|---|---|---|---|
| (a) | + | − | − | ? |
| (b) | ? | 0 | − | Spontaneous |
| (c) | − | + | ? | Not spontaneous |
| (d) | 0 | ? | − | Spontaneous |
| (e) | ? | 0 | + | ? |
| (f) | + | + | ? | $T\Delta S > \Delta H$ |

**20.84** Among the many complex ions of cobalt are the following:

$$Co(NH_3)_6^{3+}(aq) + 3en(aq) \rightleftharpoons Co(en)_3^{3+}(aq) + 6NH_3(aq)$$

where "en" stands for ethylenediamine, $H_2NCH_2CH_2NH_2$. Six Co—N bonds are broken and six Co—N bonds are formed in this reaction, so $\Delta H°_{rxn} \approx 0$; yet $K > 1$. What are the signs of $\Delta S°$ and $\Delta G°$? What drives the reaction?

**20.85** What is the change in entropy when 0.200 mol of potassium freezes at 63.7°C ($\Delta H_{fus} = 2.39$ kJ/mol)?

**20.86** Is each statement true or false? If false, correct it.
(a) All spontaneous reactions occur quickly.
(b) The reverse of a spontaneous reaction is nonspontaneous.
(c) All spontaneous processes release heat.
(d) The boiling of water at 100°C and 1 atm is spontaneous.
(e) If a process increases the freedom of motion of the particles of a system, the entropy of the system decreases.
(f) The energy of the universe is constant; the entropy of the universe decreases toward a minimum.
(g) All systems disperse their energy spontaneously.
(h) Both $\Delta S_{sys}$ and $\Delta S_{surr}$ equal zero at equilibrium.

**20.87** Hemoglobin carries $O_2$ from the lungs to tissue cells, where the $O_2$ is released. The protein is represented as Hb in its unoxygenated form and as Hb·$O_2$ in its oxygenated form. One reason CO is toxic is that it competes with $O_2$ in binding to Hb:

$$Hb·O_2(aq) + CO(g) \rightleftharpoons Hb·CO(aq) + O_2(g)$$

(a) If $\Delta G° \approx -14$ kJ at 37°C (body temperature), what is the ratio of [Hb·CO] to [Hb·$O_2$] at 37°C with $[O_2] = [CO]$?
(b) How is Le Châtelier's principle used to treat CO poisoning?

**20.88** Magnesia (MgO) is used for fire brick, crucibles, and furnace linings because of its high melting point. It is produced by decomposing magnesite ($MgCO_3$) at around 1200°C.
(a) Write a balanced equation for magnesite decomposition.
(b) Use $\Delta H°$ and S° values to find $\Delta G°$ at 298 K.
(c) Assuming $\Delta H°$ and $S°$ do not change with temperature, find the minimum temperature at which the reaction is spontaneous.
(d) Calculate the equilibrium $P_{CO_2}$ above $MgCO_3$ at 298 K.
(e) Calculate the equilibrium $P_{CO_2}$ above $MgCO_3$ at 1200 K.

**20.89** To prepare nuclear fuel, $U_3O_8$ ("yellow cake") is converted to $UO_2(NO_3)_2$, which is then converted to $UO_3$ and finally $UO_2$. The fuel is enriched (the proportion of the $^{235}U$ is increased) by a two-step conversion of $UO_2$ into $UF_6$, a volatile solid, followed by a gaseous-diffusion separation of the $^{235}U$ and $^{238}U$ isotopes:

$$UO_2(s) + 4HF(g) \longrightarrow UF_4(s) + 2H_2O(g)$$
$$UF_4(s) + F_2(g) \longrightarrow UF_6(s)$$

Calculate $\Delta G°$ for the overall process at 85°C:

| | $\Delta H°_f$ (kJ/mol) | $S°$ (J/mol·K) | $\Delta G°_f$ (kJ/mol) |
|---|---|---|---|
| $UO_2(s)$ | −1085 | 77.0 | −1032 |
| $UF_4(s)$ | −1921 | 152 | −1830. |
| $UF_6(s)$ | −2197 | 225 | −2068 |

**20.90** Methanol, a major industrial feedstock, is made by several catalyzed reactions, such as $CO(g) + 2H_2(g) \longrightarrow CH_3OH(l)$.
(a) Show that this reaction is thermodynamically feasible.
(b) Is it favored at low or at high temperatures?
(c) One concern about using $CH_3OH$ as an auto fuel is its oxidation in air to yield formaldehyde, $CH_2O(g)$, which poses a health hazard. Calculate $\Delta G°$ at 100.°C for this oxidation.

**20.91** (a) Write a balanced equation for the gaseous reaction between $N_2O_5$ and $F_2$ to form $NF_3$ and $O_2$. (b) Determine $\Delta G°_{rxn}$.

(c) Find $\Delta G_{rxn}$ at 298 K if $P_{N_2O_5} = P_{F_2} = 0.20$ atm, $P_{NF_3} = 0.25$ atm, and $P_{O_2} = 0.50$ atm.

**20.92** Consider the following reaction:

$$2NOBr(g) \rightleftharpoons 2NO(g) + Br_2(g) \qquad K = 0.42 \text{ at } 373 \text{ K}$$

Given that $S°$ of $NOBr(g) = 272.6$ J/mol·K and that $\Delta S_{rxn}°$ and $\Delta H_{rxn}°$ are constant with temperature, find
(a) $\Delta S_{rxn}°$ at 298 K      (b) $\Delta G_{rxn}°$ at 373 K
(c) $\Delta H_{rxn}°$ at 373 K      (d) $\Delta H_f°$ of NOBr at 298 K
(e) $\Delta G_{rxn}°$ at 298 K      (f) $\Delta G_f°$ of NOBr at 298 K

**20.93** Hydrogenation is the addition of $H_2$ to double (or triple) carbon-carbon bonds. Peanut butter and most commercial baked goods include hydrogenated oils. Find $\Delta H°$, $\Delta S°$, and $\Delta G°$ for the hydrogenation of ethene ($C_2H_4$) to ethane ($C_2H_6$) at 25°C.

**20.94** Styrene is produced by catalytic dehydrogenation of ethylbenzene at high temperature in the presence of superheated steam.
(a) Find $\Delta H_{rxn}°$, $\Delta G_{rxn}°$, and $\Delta S_{rxn}°$, given these data at 298 K:

| Compound | $\Delta H_f°$ (kJ/mol) | $\Delta G_f°$ (kJ/mol) | $S°$ (J/mol·K) |
|---|---|---|---|
| Ethylbenzene, $C_6H_5$—$CH_2CH_3$ | $-12.5$ | 119.7 | 255 |
| Styrene, $C_6H_5$—$CH$=$CH_2$ | 103.8 | 202.5 | 238 |

(b) At what temperature is the reaction spontaneous?
(c) What are $\Delta G_{rxn}°$ and $K$ at 600.°C?
(d) With 5.0 parts steam to 1.0 part ethylbenzene in the reactant mixture and the total pressure kept constant at 1.3 atm, what is $\Delta G$ at 50.% conversion, that is, when 50.% of the ethylbenzene has reacted?

**20.95** Propylene (propene; $CH_3CH$=$CH_2$) is used to produce polypropylene and many other chemicals. Although most is obtained from the cracking of petroleum, about 2% is produced by catalytic dehydrogenation of propane ($CH_3CH_2CH_3$):

$$CH_3CH_2CH_3 \xrightarrow{Pt/Al_2O_3} CH_3CH{=}CH_2 + H_2$$

Because this reaction is endothermic, heaters are placed between the reactor vessels to maintain the required temperature.
(a) If the molar entropy, $S°$, of propylene is 267.1 J/mol·K, find its entropy of formation, $S_f°$.
(b) Find $\Delta G_f°$ of propylene ($\Delta H_f°$ for propylene = 20.4 kJ/mol).
(c) Calculate $\Delta H_{rxn}°$ and $\Delta G_{rxn}°$ for the dehydrogenation.
(d) What is the theoretical yield of propylene at 580°C if the initial pressure of propane is 1.00 atm?
(e) Would the yield change if the reactor walls were permeable to $H_2$? Explain.
(f) At what temperature is the dehydrogenation spontaneous, with all substances in the standard state?

*Note:* Problems 20.96 and 20.97 relate to the thermodynamics of adenosine triphosphate (ATP). Refer to the Chemical Connections essay on pp. 836–837.

**20.96** Find $K$ for (a) the hydrolysis of ATP, (b) the dehydration-condensation to form glucose phosphate, and (c) the coupled reaction between ATP and glucose. (d) How does each $K$ change when $T$ changes from 25°C to 37°C?

**20.97** Energy from ATP hydrolysis drives many nonspontaneous cell reactions:

$$ATP^{4-}(aq) + H_2O(l) \rightleftharpoons ADP^{3-}(aq) + HPO_4{}^{2-}(aq) + H^+(aq)$$
$$\Delta G°' = -30.5 \text{ kJ}$$

Energy for the reverse process comes ultimately from glucose metabolism:

$$C_6H_{12}O_6(s) + 6O_2(g) \longrightarrow 6CO_2(g) + 6H_2O(l)$$

(a) Find $K$ for the hydrolysis of ATP at 37°C.
(b) Find $\Delta G_{rxn}°'$ for metabolism of 1 mol of glucose.
(c) How many moles of ATP can be produced by metabolism of 1 mol of glucose?
(d) If 36 mol of ATP is formed, what is the actual yield?

**20.98** From the following reaction and data, find (a) $S°$ of $SOCl_2$ and (b) $T$ at which the reaction becomes nonspontaneous:

$$SO_3(g) + SCl_2(l) \longrightarrow SOCl_2(l) + SO_2(g) \qquad \Delta G_{rxn}° = -75.2 \text{ kJ}$$

| | $SO_3(g)$ | $SCl_2(l)$ | $SOCl_2(l)$ | $SO_2(g)$ |
|---|---|---|---|---|
| $\Delta H_f°$ (kJ/mol) | $-396$ | $-50.0$ | $-245.6$ | $-296.8$ |
| $S°$ (J/mol·K) | 256.7 | 184 | — | 248.1 |

**20.99** Write equations for the oxidation of Fe and of Al. Use $\Delta G_f°$ to determine whether either process is spontaneous at 25°C.

**20.100** The molecular scene depicts a gaseous equilibrium mixture at 460°C for the reaction of $H_2$ (*blue*) and $I_2$ (*purple*) to form HI. Each molecule represents 0.010 mol and the container volume is 1.0 L. (a) Is $K_c$ >, =, or < 1? (b) Is $K_p$ >, =, or < $K_c$? (c) Calculate $\Delta G_{rxn}°$. (d) How would the value of $\Delta G_{rxn}°$ change if the purple molecules represented $H_2$ and the blue $I_2$? Explain.

**20.101** A key step in the metabolism of glucose for energy is the isomerization of glucose-6-phosphate (G6P) to fructose-6-phosphate (F6P): G6P $\rightleftharpoons$ F6P; $K = 0.510$ at 298 K.
(a) Calculate $\Delta G°$ at 298 K.
(b) Calculate $\Delta G$ when $Q$, the [F6P]/[G6P] ratio, equals 10.0.
(c) Calculate $\Delta G$ when $Q = 0.100$.
(d) Calculate $Q$ if $\Delta G = -2.50$ kJ/mol.

**20.102** A chemical reaction, such as HI forming from its elements, can reach equilibrium at many temperatures. In contrast, a phase change, such as ice melting, is in equilibrium at a given pressure only at the melting point. Each of the graphs below depicts $G_{sys}$ vs. extent of change. (a) Which graph depicts how $G_{sys}$ changes for the formation of HI? Explain. (b) Which graph depicts how $G_{sys}$ changes as ice melts at 1°C and 1 atm? Explain.

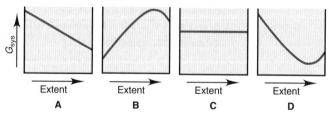

**20.103** When heated, the DNA double helix separates into two random-coil single strands. When cooled, the random coils reform the double helix: double helix $\rightleftharpoons$ 2 random coils.
(a) What is the sign of $\Delta S$ for the forward process? Why?
(b) Energy must be added to overcome H bonds and dispersion forces between the strands. What is the sign of $\Delta G$ for the forward process when $T\Delta S$ is smaller than $\Delta H$?
(c) Write an expression that shows $T$ in terms of $\Delta H$ and $\Delta S$ when the reaction is at equilibrium. (This temperature is called the *melting temperature* of the nucleic acid.)

**20.104** In the process of respiration, glucose is oxidized completely. In fermentation, $O_2$ is absent and glucose is broken down to ethanol and $CO_2$. Ethanol is oxidized to $CO_2$ and $H_2O$.
(a) Balance the following equations for these processes:
Respiration: $C_6H_{12}O_6(s) + O_2(g) \longrightarrow CO_2(g) + H_2O(l)$
Fermentation: $C_6H_{12}O_6(s) \longrightarrow C_2H_5OH(l) + CO_2(g)$
Ethanol oxidation: $C_2H_5OH(l) + O_2(g) \longrightarrow CO_2(g) + H_2O(l)$
(b) Calculate $\Delta G^\circ_{rxn}$ for respiration of 1.00 g of glucose.
(c) Calculate $\Delta G^\circ_{rxn}$ for fermentation of 1.00 g of glucose.
(d) Calculate $\Delta G^\circ_{rxn}$ for oxidation of the ethanol from part (c).

**20.105** Consider the formation of ammonia:
$$N_2(g) + 3H_2(g) \rightleftharpoons 2NH_3(g)$$
(a) Assuming that $\Delta H^\circ$ and $\Delta S^\circ$ are constant with temperature, find the temperature at which $K_p = 1.00$.
(b) Find $K_p$ at 400.°C, a typical temperature for $NH_3$ production.
(c) Given the lower $K_p$ at the higher temperature, why are these conditions used industrially?

**20.106** Kyanite, sillimanite, and andalusite all have the formula $Al_2SiO_5$. Each is stable under different conditions (see the graph at right). At the point where the three phases intersect:
(a) Which mineral, if any, has the lowest free energy?
(b) Which mineral, if any, has the lowest enthalpy?
(c) Which mineral, if any, has the highest entropy?
(d) Which mineral, if any, has the lowest density?

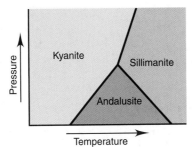

**20.107** Acetylene is produced commercially by the partial oxidation of methane. At 1500°C and pressures of 1–10 bar, the yield of acetylene is about 20%. The major side product is carbon monoxide, and some soot and carbon dioxide also form.
(a) At what temperature is the desired reaction spontaneous:
$$2CH_4 + \tfrac{1}{2}O_2 \longrightarrow C_2H_2 + 2H_2 + H_2O$$
(b) Acetylene can also be made by the reaction of its elements, carbon (graphite) and hydrogen. At what temperature is this formation reaction spontaneous?
(c) Why must this reaction mixture be immediately cooled?

**20.108** Synthesis gas, a mixture that includes the fuels CO and $H_2$, is used to produce liquid hydrocarbons and methanol. It is made at pressures up to 100 atm by oxidation of methane followed by the steam re-forming and water-gas shift reactions. Because the process is exothermic, temperatures reach 950–1100°C, and the conditions are such that the amounts of $H_2$, CO, $CO_2$, $CH_4$, and $H_2O$ leaving the reactor are close to the equilibrium amounts for the steam re-forming and water-gas shift reactions:
$$CH_4(g) + H_2O(g) \rightleftharpoons CO(g) + 3H_2(g) \quad \text{(steam re-forming)}$$
$$CO(g) + H_2O(g) \rightleftharpoons CO_2(g) + H_2(g) \quad \text{(water-gas shift)}$$
(a) At 1000.°C, what are $\Delta G^\circ$ and $\Delta H^\circ$ for the steam re-forming reaction and for the water-gas shift reaction?
(b) By doubling the steam re-forming step and adding it to the water-gas shift step, we obtain the following combined reaction:
$$2CH_4(g) + 3H_2O(g) \rightleftharpoons CO_2(g) + CO(g) + 7H_2(g)$$
Is this reaction spontaneous at 1000.°C in the standard state?
(c) Is it spontaneous at 98 atm and 50.% conversion (when 50.% of the starting materials have reacted)?
(d) Is it spontaneous at 98 atm and 90.% conversion?

# Electrochemistry: Chemical Change and Electrical Work

## Concepts and skills to review before you study this chapter

- redox terminology (Section 4.5)
- balancing redox reactions (Section 4.5)
- activity series of the metals (Section 4.6)
- trends in ionization energy (Section 8.4) and electronegativity (Section 9.5)
- free energy, work, and equilibrium (Sections 20.3 and 20.4)
- $Q$ vs. $K$ (Section 17.4) and $\Delta G$ vs. $\Delta G°$ (Section 20.4)

Thermodynamics has countless applications other than steam engines. In fact, probably within your reach right now are a laptop computer, MP3 player, cell phone, and/or camera, which represent one type of application. Metal-plated jewelry and silverware represent the other. These are a few of the objects you use every day that rely on a major field in applied thermodynamics—**electrochemistry,** the study of the relationship between chemical change and electrical work. We typically study this field with **electrochemical cells,** systems that incorporate a redox reaction to produce or utilize electrical energy.

**IN THIS CHAPTER . . .** We examine the essential features of electrochemical cells and quantify the relationship between free energy and electrical work.

- We review oxidation-reduction reactions and describe a method for balancing redox equations that take place in electrochemical cells.
- We highlight the key differences between the two types of electrochemical cells.
- We focus on voltaic cells, which release free energy to do electrical work, and see how they operate as a combination of two half-cells.
- We calculate the voltage, the cell's electrical potential, which is the sum of the voltages of the half-cells.
- We use half-cell voltages to determine the relative strengths of redox couples and write spontaneous redox equations.
- We examine the interdependence of the standard free energy change, the standard cell potential, and the equilibrium constant.
- We see how differences in concentration of the half-cells can be harnessed to generate electricity.
- We analyze the makeup and operation of the major types of batteries.
- We describe the problem of corrosion, which has key similarities to the operation of voltaic cells.
- We examine electrolytic cells, which absorb energy from an external source to do electrical work. We predict the products that form under different conditions and quantify the relation between charge and amount of subtance.
- We explore the redox system that generates energy in living cells.

## 21.1 • REDOX REACTIONS AND ELECTROCHEMICAL CELLS

In this section, we review the oxidation-reduction process and describe the *half-reaction method* of balancing redox reactions. Then we see how redox reactions are used in the two types of electrochemical cells.

### A Quick Review of Oxidation-Reduction Concepts

All electrochemical processes involve the *movement of electrons from one chemical species to another* in an oxidation-reduction (redox) reaction. In any redox process,

- *Oxidation* is the loss of electrons, and *reduction* is the gain of electrons. Oxidation and reduction occur *simultaneously.*
- The *oxidizing agent* does the oxidizing by *taking electrons* from the substance being oxidized. The *reducing agent* does the reducing by *giving electrons* to the substance being reduced.
- Therefore, *the oxidizing agent is reduced, and the reducing agent is oxidized.*

- The oxidized substance ends up with a *higher* (more positive or less negative) oxidation number (O.N.), and the reduced substance ends up with a *lower* (less positive or more negative) O.N.
- The total number of electrons gained by the atoms/ions of the oxidizing agent equals the total number lost by the atoms/ions of the reducing agent.

Figure 21.1 presents these ideas for the aqueous reaction between zinc metal and a strong acid. Be sure you can identify the oxidation and reduction parts of a redox process. You may want to review the full discussion in Section 4.5.

**Figure 21.1** A summary of redox terminology, as applied to the reaction of zinc with hydrogen ion.

| PROCESS | $\overset{0}{Zn}(s) + 2\overset{+1}{H^+}(aq) \longrightarrow \overset{+2}{Zn^{2+}}(aq) + \overset{0}{H_2}(g)$ | |
|---|---|---|
| **OXIDATION**<br>• One reactant loses electrons.<br>• Reducing agent is oxidized.<br><br>• Oxidation number increases. | Zinc **loses** electrons. Zinc is the reducing agent and becomes **oxidized**. The oxidation number of Zn **increases** from 0 to +2. | |
| **REDUCTION**<br>• Other reactant gains electrons.<br>• Oxidizing agent is reduced.<br><br>• Oxidation number decreases. | Hydrogen ion **gains** electrons. Hydrogen ion is the oxidizing agent and becomes **reduced**. The oxidation number of H **decreases** from +1 to 0. | |

## Half-Reaction Method for Balancing Redox Reactions

In Chapter 4, we mentioned two methods for balancing redox reactions but discussed only the oxidation-number method in detail. The other method, the **half-reaction method,** offers several advantages for studying electrochemistry:

- It *divides the overall redox reaction* into oxidation and reduction *half-reactions*, which reflect their actual physical separation in electrochemical cells.
- It is easier to apply to reactions in acidic or basic solution, which is common in cells.
- It (usually) does *not* require assigning O.N.s. (In cases where the half-reactions are not obvious, we assign O.N.s to determine which atoms undergo a change and write half-reactions with the species that contain those atoms.)

**Steps in the Half-Reaction Method** The balancing process begins with a "skeleton" ionic reaction that consists of only species that are oxidized and reduced. Here are the steps in the half-reaction method:

*Step 1.* Divide the skeleton reaction into two half-reactions, each of which contains the oxidized and reduced forms of one of the species: *if the oxidized form of a species is on the left side, the reduced form of that species is on the right, and vice versa.*
*Step 2.* Balance the atoms and charges in each half-reaction.
- Atoms are balanced *in this order:* atoms other than O and H, then O, then H.
- Charge is balanced by *adding* electrons ($e^-$) *to the left side in the reduction half-reaction* because the reactant gains them and *to the right side in the oxidation half-reaction* because the reactant loses them.
*Step 3.* If necessary, multiply one or both half-reactions by an integer so that

number of $e^-$ gained in reduction = number of $e^-$ lost in oxidation

*Step 4.* Add the balanced half-reactions, and include states of matter.
*Step 5.* Check that the atoms and charges are balanced.

Let's balance a redox reaction that occurs in acidic solution and then see how to balance one in basic solution in Sample Problem 21.1.

**Balancing Redox Reactions in Acidic Solution** For a reaction in acidic solution, $H_2O$ molecules and $H^+$ ions are present for the balancing. Even though we've usually used $H_3O^+$ to indicate the proton in water, we use $H^+$ in this chapter because it makes the balancing simpler. But, to make the point, we'll also balance this example with $H_3O^+$ to show that the only difference is in the number of water molecules.

The reaction between dichromate ion and iodide ion to form chromium(III) ion and solid iodine occurs in acidic solution (*see photo*). The skeleton ionic reaction is

$$Cr_2O_7^{2-}(aq) + I^-(aq) \longrightarrow Cr^{3+}(aq) + I_2(s) \quad [\text{acidic solution}]$$

*Step 1. Divide the reaction into half-reactions.* Each half-reaction contains the oxidized and reduced forms of one species:

$$Cr_2O_7^{2-} \longrightarrow Cr^{3+}$$
$$I^- \longrightarrow I_2$$

Dichromate ion (*left*) and iodide ion (*center*) form chromium(III) ion and solid iodine.

*Step 2. Balance atoms and charges in each half-reaction.* We use $H_2O$ to balance O, $H^+$ to balance H, and $e^-$ to balance charges.

- For the $Cr_2O_7^{2-}/Cr^{3+}$ half-reaction:
  a. *Balance atoms other than O and H.* We balance the two Cr on the left with a coefficient of 2 on the right:
  $$Cr_2O_7^{2-} \longrightarrow 2Cr^{3+}$$
  b. *Balance O atoms by adding $H_2O$ molecules.* Each $H_2O$ has one O atom, so we add seven $H_2O$ on the right to balance the seven O in $Cr_2O_7^{2-}$:
  $$Cr_2O_7^{2-} \longrightarrow 2Cr^{3+} + 7H_2O$$
  c. *Balance H atoms by adding $H^+$ ions.* Each $H_2O$ contains two H, and we added seven $H_2O$, so we add 14 $H^+$ ions on the left:
  $$14H^+ + Cr_2O_7^{2-} \longrightarrow 2Cr^{3+} + 7H_2O$$
  d. *Balance charge by adding electrons.* Each $H^+$ ion has a 1+ charge, and 14 $H^+$ plus $Cr_2O_7^{2-}$ gives 12+ on the left. Two $Cr^{3+}$ give 6+ on the right. There is an excess of 6+ on the left, so we add six $e^-$ on the left:
  $$6e^- + 14H^+ + Cr_2O_7^{2-} \longrightarrow 2Cr^{3+} + 7H_2O$$

This half-reaction is balanced. It is the *reduction* because electrons appear on the *left, as reactants:* $Cr_2O_7^{2-}$ gains electrons (is reduced), so $Cr_2O_7^{2-}$ is the *oxidizing agent.* The O.N. of Cr decreases from +6 on the left to +3 on the right.

- For the $I^-/I_2$ half-reaction:
  a. *Balance atoms other than O and H.* Two I atoms on the right require a coefficient of 2 on the left:
  $$2I^- \longrightarrow I_2$$
  b. *Balance O atoms with $H_2O$.* Not needed; there are no O atoms.
  c. *Balance H atoms with $H^+$.* Not needed; there are no H atoms.
  d. *Balance charge with $e^-$.* To balance the 2− on the left, we add two $e^-$ on the right:
  $$2I^- \longrightarrow I_2 + 2e^-$$

This half-reaction is balanced. It is the *oxidation* because electrons appear on the *right, as products:* the reactant $I^-$ loses electrons (is oxidized), so $I^-$ is the *reducing agent.* The O.N. of I increases from −1 to 0.

*Step 3. Multiply each half-reaction, if necessary, by an integer* so that the number of $e^-$ lost in the oxidation equals the number of $e^-$ gained in the reduction. Two $e^-$ are lost in the oxidation and six $e^-$ are gained in the reduction, so we multiply the oxidation by 3:

$$3(2I^- \longrightarrow I_2 + 2e^-)$$
$$6I^- \longrightarrow 3I_2 + 6e^-$$

*Step 4. Add the half-reactions,* canceling substances that appear on both sides, and include states of matter. In this example, only the electrons cancel:

$$6\cancel{e^-} + 14H^+ + Cr_2O_7^{2-} \longrightarrow 2Cr^{3+} + 7H_2O$$
$$6I^- \longrightarrow 3I_2 + 6\cancel{e^-}$$

$$\overline{6I^-(aq) + 14H^+(aq) + Cr_2O_7^{2-}(aq) \longrightarrow 3I_2(s) + 7H_2O(l) + 2Cr^{3+}(aq)}$$

*Step 5. Check that atoms and charges balance:*

Reactants (6I, 14H, 2Cr, 7O; 6+) $\longrightarrow$ products (6I, 14H, 2Cr, 7O; 6+)

**Using $H_3O^+$, Instead of $H^+$, to Balance H**  Now let's see what happens if we use $H_3O^+$ to supply H atoms, instead of $H^+$. In step 2 for the reduction half-reaction, balancing Cr atoms and balancing O atoms with $H_2O$ are the same as before, so we have

$$Cr_2O_7^{2-} \longrightarrow 2Cr^{3+} + 7H_2O$$

Now we use $H_3O^+$ to balance H atoms. Because each $H_3O^+$ is an $H^+$ bonded to an $H_2O$, we balance the 14 H on the right with 14 $H_3O^+$ on the left and immediately add 14 more $H_2O$ on the right:

$$14H_3O^+ + Cr_2O_7^{2-} \longrightarrow 2Cr^{3+} + 7H_2O + 14H_2O$$

Taking the sum of the $H_2O$ molecules on the right gives

$$14H_3O^+ + Cr_2O_7^{2-} \longrightarrow 2Cr^{3+} + 21H_2O$$

None of this affects the redox change, so balancing the charge still requires six $e^-$ on the left, and we obtain the balanced reduction half-reaction:

$$6e^- + 14H_3O^+ + Cr_2O_7^{2-} \longrightarrow 2Cr^{3+} + 21H_2O$$

Adding the balanced oxidation half-reaction gives the balanced redox equation:

$$6I^-(aq) + 14H_3O^+(aq) + Cr_2O_7^{2-}(aq) \longrightarrow 3I_2(s) + 21H_2O(l) + 2Cr^{3+}(aq)$$

Note that, as mentioned earlier, the only difference is the number of $H_2O$ molecules: 21 $H_2O$ instead of 7 $H_2O$. So, even though this approach uses $H_3O^+$, which is more accurate, only the number of water molecules changes and the balancing involves more steps. Therefore, we'll continue to use $H^+$ to balance H atoms.

**Balancing Redox Reactions in Basic Solution**  In acidic solution, $H_2O$ molecules and $H^+$ ions are available to balance a redox reaction, but in basic solution, $H_2O$ molecules and $OH^-$ ions are available.

We need only one additional step to balance a redox equation that takes place in basic solution. It appears after we balance the half-reactions *as if they occur in acidic solution* and are combined (step 4). At this point, *we add one OH⁻ to both sides of the equation* for every $H^+$ present. (This step is labeled "4 Basic" in Sample Problem 21.1.) The $OH^-$ added on the side with $H^+$ ions combine with them to form $H_2O$, while the $OH^-$ on the other side remain in the equation, and excess $H_2O$ is canceled.

**Sample Problem 21.1**  **Balancing a Redox Reaction in Basic Solution**

**Problem**  Permanganate ion reacts in basic solution with oxalate ion to form carbonate ion and solid manganese dioxide. Balance the skeleton ionic equation for the reaction between $NaMnO_4$ and $Na_2C_2O_4$ in basic solution:

$$MnO_4^-(aq) + C_2O_4^{2-}(aq) \longrightarrow MnO_2(s) + CO_3^{2-}(aq) \quad \text{[basic solution]}$$

**Plan**  We follow the numbered steps as described in text, and proceed through step 4 as if this reaction occurs in acidic solution. Then, we add the appropriate number of $OH^-$ ions and cancel excess $H_2O$ molecules (step 4 Basic).

**Solution**

1. Divide into half-reactions.

$$MnO_4^- \longrightarrow MnO_2 \qquad\qquad\qquad C_2O_4^{2-} \longrightarrow CO_3^{2-}$$

2. Balance.

  a. Atoms other than O and H,
    Not needed

  b. O atoms with $H_2O$,
$$MnO_4^- \longrightarrow MnO_2 + 2H_2O$$

  c. H atoms with $H^+$,
$$4H^+ + MnO_4^- \longrightarrow MnO_2 + 2H_2O$$

  d. Charge with $e^-$,
$$3e^- + 4H^+ + MnO_4^- \longrightarrow MnO_2 + 2H_2O$$
$$\text{[reduction]}$$

  a. Atoms other than O and H,
$$C_2O_4^{2-} \longrightarrow 2CO_3^{2-}$$

  b. O atoms with $H_2O$,
$$2H_2O + C_2O_4^{2-} \longrightarrow 2CO_3^{2-}$$

  c. H atoms with $H^+$,
$$2H_2O + C_2O_4^{2-} \longrightarrow 2CO_3^{2-} + 4H^+$$

  d. Charge with $e^-$,
$$2H_2O + C_2O_4^{2-} \longrightarrow 2CO_3^{2-} + 4H^+ + 2e^-$$
$$\text{[oxidation]}$$

3. Multiply each half-reaction, if necessary, by some integer to make $e^-$ lost equal $e^-$ gained.

$2(3e^- + 4H^+ + MnO_4^- \longrightarrow MnO_2 + 2H_2O)$          $3(2H_2O + C_2O_4^{2-} \longrightarrow 2CO_3^{2-} + 4H^+ + 2e^-)$
$6e^- + 8H^+ + 2MnO_4^- \longrightarrow 2MnO_2 + 4H_2O$          $6H_2O + 3C_2O_4^{2-} \longrightarrow 6CO_3^{2-} + 12H^+ + 6e^-$

4. Add half-reactions, and cancel substances appearing on both sides.
   The six $e^-$ cancel, eight $H^+$ cancel to leave four $H^+$ on the right, and four $H_2O$ cancel to leave two $H_2O$ on the left:

$$\cancel{6e^-} + \cancel{8}H^+ + 2MnO_4^- \longrightarrow 2MnO_2 + \cancel{4}H_2O$$
$$\underline{2\ \cancel{6}H_2O + 3C_2O_4^{2-} \longrightarrow 6CO_3^{2-} + 4\ \cancel{12}H^+ + \cancel{6e^-}}$$
$$2MnO_4^- + 2H_2O + 3C_2O_4^{2-} \longrightarrow 2MnO_2 + 6CO_3^{2-} + 4H^+$$

**4 Basic.** Add $OH^-$ to both sides to neutralize $H^+$, and cancel $H_2O$.
Adding four $OH^-$ to both sides forms four $H_2O$ on the right. Two of those cancel the two $H_2O$ on the left and leave two $H_2O$ on the right:

$2MnO_4^- + 2H_2O + 3C_2O_4^{2-} + 4OH^- \longrightarrow 2MnO_2 + 6CO_3^{2-} + [4H^+ + 4OH^-]$
$2MnO_4^- + \cancel{2H_2O} + 3C_2O_4^{2-} + 4OH^- \longrightarrow 2MnO_2 + 6CO_3^{2-} + 2\ \cancel{4}H_2O$

Including states of matter gives the final balanced equation:

$$2MnO_4^-(aq) + 3C_2O_4^{2-}(aq) + 4OH^-(aq) \longrightarrow 2MnO_2(s) + 6CO_3^{2-}(aq) + 2H_2O(l)$$

5. Check that atoms and charges balance.
$$(2Mn, 24O, 6C, 4H; 12-) \longrightarrow (2Mn, 24O, 6C, 4H; 12-)$$

**Comment** As a final step, let's see how to obtain the balanced *molecular* equation for this reaction. We note the amount (mol) of each anion in the balanced ionic equation and add the correct amount (mol) of spectator ions (in this case, $Na^+$, as given in the Problem statement) to obtain neutral compounds. The balanced molecular equation is

$2NaMnO_4(aq) + 3Na_2C_2O_4(aq) + 4NaOH(aq) \longrightarrow$
$\qquad\qquad\qquad\qquad 2MnO_2(s) + 6Na_2CO_3(aq) + 2H_2O(l)$

**Follow-Up Problem 21.1** Write a balanced molecular equation for the reaction between $KMnO_4$ and $KI$ in basic solution. The skeleton ionic reaction is

$$MnO_4^-(aq) + I^-(aq) \longrightarrow MnO_4^{2-}(aq) + IO_3^-(aq) \qquad [\text{basic solution}]$$

## An Overview of Electrochemical Cells

The fundamental difference between the two types of electrochemical cells is based on whether the overall redox reaction in the cell is spontaneous (free energy is released) or nonspontaneous (free energy is absorbed):

1. A **voltaic cell** (also called a **galvanic cell**) uses a *spontaneous* reaction ($\Delta G < 0$) to generate electrical energy. In the cell reaction, the difference in free energy between higher energy reactants and lower energy products is converted into electrical energy, which operates the load—flashlight, DVD player, car starter motor, and so forth. Thus, *the system does work on the surroundings*. All batteries contain voltaic cells.
2. An **electrolytic cell** uses electrical energy to drive a *nonspontaneous* reaction ($\Delta G > 0$). In the cell reaction, an external source supplies free energy to convert lower energy reactants into higher energy products. Thus, *the surroundings do work on the system*. Electroplating and the recovery of metals from ores utilize electrolytic cells.

The two types of cell have several features in common. Two **electrodes**, which conduct the electricity between cell and surroundings, are dipped into an **electrolyte**, a mixture of ions (usually in aqueous solution) that are involved in the reaction or that

**Figure 21.2** General characteristics of (**A**) voltaic cells and (**B**) electrolytic cells.

carry the charge (Figure 21.2). An electrode is identified as either **anode** or **cathode** depending on the half-reaction that takes place there:

- *The oxidation half-reaction occurs at the anode.* Electrons lost by the substance being oxidized (reducing agent) *leave the oxidation half-cell* at the anode.
- *The reduction half-reaction occurs at the cathode.* Electrons gained by the substance being reduced (oxidizing agent) *enter the reduction half-cell* at the cathode.

Note that, for reasons we discuss shortly, *the relative charges of the electrodes are* ***opposite in sign*** *in the two types of cell.*

● **Which Half-Reaction Occurs at Which Electrode?** Here are some memory aids to help you remember which half-reaction occurs at which electrode:
1. The words *anode* and *oxidation* start with vowels; the words *cathode* and *reduction* start with consonants.
2. Alphabetically, the *A* in anode comes before the *C* in cathode, and the *O* in oxidation comes before the *R* in reduction.
3. Look at the first syllables and use your imagination:
   ANode, OXidation; REDuction, CAThode
   ⟹ AN OX and a RED CAT

## ▌Summary of Section 21.1

- An oxidation-reduction (redox) reaction involves the transfer of electrons from a reducing agent to an oxidizing agent.
- The half-reaction method of balancing divides the overall reaction into half-reactions that are balanced separately and then recombined.
- There are two types of electrochemical cells. In a voltaic cell, a spontaneous reaction generates electricity and does work on the surroundings. In an electrolytic cell, the surroundings supply electricity that does work to drive a nonspontaneous reaction.
- In both types of cell, two electrodes dip into electrolyte solutions; oxidation occurs at the anode, and reduction occurs at the cathode.

# 21.2 • VOLTAIC CELLS: USING SPONTANEOUS REACTIONS TO GENERATE ELECTRICAL ENERGY

When you put a strip of zinc metal in a solution of $Cu^{2+}$ ion, the blue color of the solution fades and a brown-black crust of Cu metal forms on the Zn strip (Figure 21.3). During this spontaneous reaction, $Cu^{2+}$ ion is reduced to Cu metal, while Zn metal is oxidized to $Zn^{2+}$ ion. The overall reaction consists of two half-reactions:

$$Cu^{2+}(aq) + 2e^- \longrightarrow Cu(s) \qquad \text{[reduction]}$$
$$Zn(s) \longrightarrow Zn^{2+}(aq) + 2e^- \qquad \text{[oxidation]}$$
$$\overline{Zn(s) + Cu^{2+}(aq) \longrightarrow Zn^{2+}(aq) + Cu(s) \qquad \text{[overall reaction]}}$$

Let's examine this spontaneous reaction as the basis of a voltaic cell.

## Construction and Operation of a Voltaic Cell

Electrons are being transferred in the $Zn/Cu^{2+}$ reaction, but the system does not generate electrical energy because the oxidizing agent ($Cu^{2+}$) and the reducing agent (Zn) are in the *same* beaker. If, however, we physically separate the half-reactions and connect them by an external circuit, the electrons lost by the zinc travel through the circuit and produce an electric current as the copper ions gain them.

**Basis of the Voltaic Cell: Separation of Half-Reactions** In any voltaic cell, the components of each half-reaction are placed in a separate container, or **half-cell,** which

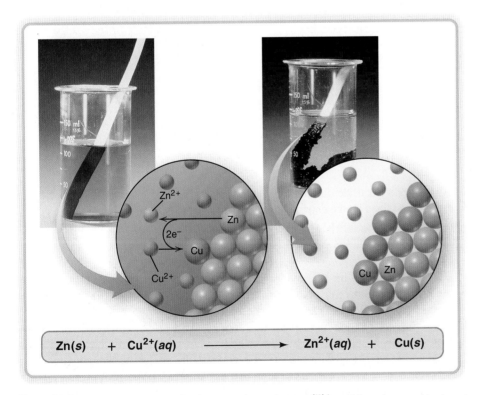

**Figure 21.3 The spontaneous reaction between zinc and copper(II) ion.** When zinc metal is placed in a solution of $Cu^{2+}$ ion (*left*), zinc is oxidized to $Zn^{2+}$, and $Cu^{2+}$ is reduced to copper metal (*right*). (The very finely divided Cu appears black.)

**Figure 21.4** A voltaic cell based on the zinc-copper reaction. **A,** In the anode half-cell (oxidation; *left*), two electrons from a Zn atom move through the Zn bar as the $Zn^{2+}$ ion enters the solution. In the cathode half-cell (reduction; *right*), the electrons reduce $Cu^{2+}$ ions to Cu atoms. **B,** After several hours, the Zn anode weighs less and the Cu cathode weighs more.

consists of one electrode dipping into an electrolyte solution (Figure 21.4A). The two half-cells are joined by the external circuit, and a voltmeter measures the voltage generated. A switch (not shown) closes (completes) or opens (breaks) the circuit. Here are some key points about the half-cells of the $Zn/Cu^{2+}$ voltaic cell:

1. *Oxidation half-cell (anode compartment, shown on the left).* The anode compartment consists of a bar of zinc (the anode) immersed in a $Zn^{2+}$ electrolyte (such as aqueous zinc sulfate, $ZnSO_4$). Zinc is the reactant in the oxidation half-reaction, and the bar loses electrons *and* conducts them *out* of this half-cell.

2. *Reduction half-cell (cathode compartment, shown on the right).* The cathode compartment consists of a bar of copper (the cathode) immersed in a $Cu^{2+}$ electrolyte [such as aqueous copper(II) sulfate, $CuSO_4$]. Copper is the product in the reduction half-reaction, and the bar conducts electrons *into* its half-cell, where $Cu^{2+}$ is reduced.

**Charges of the Electrodes** The charges of the electrodes are determined by the *source of electrons* and the *direction of electron flow* through the circuit. In this cell, Zn atoms are oxidized at the anode to $Zn^{2+}$ ions and electrons. The $Zn^{2+}$ ions enter the half-cell electrolyte, while the electrons move through the bar and into the wire. *The electrons flow left to right* through the wire to the cathode, where $Cu^{2+}$ ions in this electrolyte are reduced to Cu atoms. As the cell operates, electrons are continuously generated at the anode and consumed at the cathode. Therefore, the anode has an excess of electrons and the cathode has a deficit of electrons: *in any **voltaic** cell, the anode has a negative charge and the cathode has a positive charge.*

**Completing the Circuit with a Salt Bridge** A cell cannot operate unless the circuit is complete. The oxidation half-cell originally contains a neutral solution of $Zn^{2+}$ and $SO_4^{2-}$ ions, but as Zn atoms in the bar lose electrons, the $Zn^{2+}$ ions that form enter the solution and would give it a net positive charge. Similarly, in the reduction half-cell, the neutral solution of $Cu^{2+}$ and $SO_4^{2-}$ ions would develop a net negative charge as $Cu^{2+}$ ions leave the solution and form Cu atoms.

Such a charge imbalance between the half-cells would stop cell operation, and this situation is avoided by use of a **salt bridge.** It joins the half-cells and acts like a "liquid wire," allowing ions to flow through both compartments and complete the circuit. The salt bridge is an inverted U tube containing nonreacting ions, such as $Na^+$ and $SO_4^{2-}$, dissolved in a gel, which does not flow out of the tube but allows ions to diffuse into or out of the half-cells:

- *Maintaining a neutral reduction half-cell (right; cathode compartment).* As $Cu^{2+}$ ions change to Cu atoms, $Na^+$ ions move from the salt bridge into the electrolyte solution (and some $SO_4^{2-}$ ions move from the solution into the salt bridge).
- *Maintaining a neutral oxidation half-cell (left; anode compartment).* As Zn atoms change to $Zn^{2+}$ ions, $SO_4^{2-}$ ions move from the salt bridge into the electrolyte solution (and some $Zn^{2+}$ ions move from the solution into the salt bridge).

Thus, the wire and the salt bridge complete the circuit:

- *Electrons move left to right* through the wire.
- *Anions move right to left* through the salt bridge.
- *Cations move left to right* through the salt bridge.

**Active vs. Inactive Electrodes** The electrodes in the $Zn/Cu^{2+}$ cell are *active* because the metals themselves are components of the half-reactions. As the cell operates, the mass of the zinc bar gradually decreases, as the $[Zn^{2+}]$ in the anode half-cell increases. At the same time, the mass of the copper bar increases as the $[Cu^{2+}]$ in the cathode half-cell decreases and the ions form atoms that "plate out" on the electrode (Figure 21.4B).

In many cases, however, there are no reaction components that can be physically used as an electrode, so *inactive* electrodes are used. Most commonly, inactive electrodes are rods of *graphite* or *platinum*. In a voltaic cell based on the following half-reactions, for instance, the reacting species cannot be made into electrodes:

$$2I^-(aq) \longrightarrow I_2(s) + 2e^- \qquad [\text{anode; oxidation}]$$
$$MnO_4^-(aq) + 8H^+(aq) + 5e^- \longrightarrow Mn^{2+}(aq) + 4H_2O(l) \quad [\text{cathode; reduction}]$$

Each half-cell consists of an inactive electrode immersed in an electrolyte that contains *all the reactant species involved in that half-reaction* (Figure 21.5):

- In the *anode half-cell*, $I^-$ ions are oxidized to solid $I_2$, and the released electrons flow into the graphite electrode (C) and through the wire.
- From the wire, the electrons enter the graphite electrode in the *cathode half-cell* and reduce $MnO_4^-$ ions to $Mn^{2+}$ ions. (A $KNO_3$ salt bridge is used.)

**Diagram of a Voltaic Cell** As Figures 21.4A and 21.5 show, there are certain consistent features in the *diagram* of any voltaic cell:

- Components of the half-cells include electrode materials, electrolyte ions, and other species involved in the reaction.
- Electrode name (anode or cathode) and charge are shown. By convention, the anode compartment appears *on the left.*
- Each half-reaction and the overall cell reaction are given.
- Direction of electron flow in the external circuit is from left to right.
- Nature of ions and direction of ion flow in the salt bridge are shown, with cations moving right and anions moving left.

| Oxidation half-reaction |
| --- |
| $2I^-(aq) \longrightarrow I_2(s) + 2e^-$ |

| Reduction half-reaction |
| --- |
| $MnO_4^-(aq) + 8H^+(aq) + 5e^- \longrightarrow Mn^{2+}(aq) + 4H_2O(l)$ |

| Overall (cell) reaction |
| --- |
| $2MnO_4^-(aq) + 16H^+(aq) + 10I^-(aq) \longrightarrow 2Mn^{2+}(aq) + 5I_2(s) + 8H_2O(l)$ |

**Figure 21.5** A voltaic cell using inactive electrodes.

## Notation for a Voltaic Cell

A useful shorthand notation describes the components of a voltaic cell. The notation for the $Zn/Cu^{2+}$ cell is

$$Zn(s)\,|\,Zn^{2+}(aq)\,||\,Cu^{2+}(aq)\,|\,Cu(s)$$

Key parts of the notation are as follows:

- The components of the anode compartment (oxidation half-cell) are written *to the left* of the components of the cathode compartment (reduction half-cell).
- A double vertical line indicates the half-cells are physically separated.
- A single vertical line represents a phase boundary. For example, $Zn(s)\,|\,Zn^{2+}(aq)$ indicates that *solid* Zn is a *different* phase from *aqueous* $Zn^{2+}$.
- A comma separates the half-cell components that are in the *same* phase. For example, the notation for the voltaic cell shown in Figure 21.5 is

$$\text{graphite}\,|\,I^-(aq)\,|\,I_2(s)\,||\,MnO_4^-(aq),\,H^+(aq),\,Mn^{2+}(aq)\,|\,\text{graphite}$$

That is, in the cathode compartment, $MnO_4^-$, $H^+$, and $Mn^{2+}$ ions are in an aqueous solution with solid graphite immersed in it.

- If needed, the concentrations of dissolved components are given in parentheses; for example, if the concentrations of $Zn^{2+}$ and $Cu^{2+}$ are 1 $M$, we write

$$Zn(s)\,|\,Zn^{2+}(1\,M)\,||\,Cu^{2+}(1\,M)\,|\,Cu(s)$$

- Half-cell components usually appear in the same order as in the half-reaction, and electrodes appear at the far left (anode) and far right (cathode) of the notation.
- Ions in the salt bridge are not part of the reaction so they are not in the notation.

---

**Sample Problem 21.2** | **Describing a Voltaic Cell with Diagram and Notation**

**Problem** Draw a diagram, show balanced equations, and write the notation for a voltaic cell that consists of one half-cell with a Cr bar in a $Cr(NO_3)_3$ solution, another half-cell with an Ag bar in an $AgNO_3$ solution, and a $KNO_3$ salt bridge. Measurement indicates that the Cr electrode is negative relative to the Ag electrode.

**Plan** From the given contents of the half-cells, we write the half-reactions. To determine which is the anode compartment (oxidation) and which is the cathode (reduction), we note the relative electrode charges (which are based on the direction of the spontaneous redox reaction). Electrons are released into the anode during oxidation, so it has a negative charge. We are told that Cr is negative, so it is the anode and Ag is the cathode.

**Solution** Writing the balanced half-reactions. The Ag half-reaction consumes $e^-$:

$$Ag^+(aq) + e^- \longrightarrow Ag(s) \quad \text{[reduction; cathode]}$$

The Cr half-reaction releases $e^-$:

$$Cr(s) \longrightarrow Cr^{3+}(aq) + 3e^- \quad \text{[oxidation; anode]}$$

Writing the balanced overall cell equation. We triple the reduction half-reaction to balance $e^-$ and combine the half-reactions:

$$Cr(s) + 3Ag^+(aq) \longrightarrow Cr^{3+}(aq) + 3Ag(s)$$

Determining direction of electron and ion flow. The released $e^-$ in the Cr electrode (negative) flow through the external circuit to the Ag electrode (positive). As $Cr^{3+}$ ions enter the anode electrolyte, $NO_3^-$ ions enter from the salt bridge to maintain neutrality. As $Ag^+$ ions leave the cathode electrolyte and plate out on the Ag electrode, $K^+$ ions enter from the salt bridge to maintain neutrality. The cell diagram is shown in the margin. Writing the cell notation:

$$Cr(s)\,|\,Cr^{3+}(aq)\,||\,Ag^+(aq)\,|\,Ag(s)$$

**Check** Always be sure that the half-reactions and the cell reaction are balanced, the half-cells contain *all* components of the half-reactions, and the electron and ion flow are shown. You should be able to write the half-reactions from the cell notation as a check.

**Comment** The diagram of a voltaic cell relies on the *direction of the spontaneous reaction* to give the oxidation (anode; negative) and reduction (cathode; positive) half-reactions.

**Follow-Up Problem 21.2** In one compartment of a voltaic cell, a graphite rod dips into an acidic solution of $K_2Cr_2O_7$ and $Cr(NO_3)_3$; in the other compartment, a tin bar dips into a $Sn(NO_3)_2$ solution. A $KNO_3$ salt bridge joins them. The tin electrode is negative relative to the graphite. Diagram the cell and write the balanced equations and the cell notation.

## Why Does a Voltaic Cell Work?

What principles explain *how* the $Zn/Cu^{2+}$ cell reaction takes place and *why* electrons flow in the direction they do? Let's examine what is happening when the switch is open and no reaction is occurring. In each half-cell, the metal electrode is in equilibrium, with the metal ions in the electrolyte and the electrons within the metal:

$$Zn(s) \rightleftharpoons Zn^{2+}(aq) + 2e^- \text{(in Zn metal)}$$

$$Cu(s) \rightleftharpoons Cu^{2+}(aq) + 2e^- \text{(in Cu metal)}$$

Given the direction of the overall spontaneous reaction, Zn gives up its electrons more easily than Cu does; thus, Zn is a stronger reducing agent. Therefore, the equilibrium position of the Zn half-reaction lies farther to the right. We can think of the electrons in the Zn electrode as having a greater "pressure" than those in the Cu electrode, a greater potential energy (referred to as *electrical potential*) ready to "push" them through the circuit. Close the switch, and electrons flow from the Zn to the Cu electrode to equalize this difference in electrical potential. The flow disturbs the equilibrium at each electrode. The Zn half-reaction shifts to the right to restore the electrons flowing out, and the Cu half-reaction shifts to the left to remove the electrons flowing in. Thus, *the spontaneous reaction occurs as a result of the different abilities of these metals to give up their electrons.* ●

## ▌Summary of Section 21.2

- A voltaic cell consists of oxidation (anode) and reduction (cathode) half-cells, connected by a wire to conduct electrons and a salt bridge to maintain charge neutrality.
- Electrons move from the anode (left) to the cathode (right), while cations move from the salt bridge into the cathode half-cell and anions move from the salt bridge into the anode half-cell.
- The cell notation shows the species and their phases in each half-cell, as well as the direction of current flow.
- A voltaic cell operates because species in the two half-cells differ in the tendency to lose electrons (strength as a reducing agent).

● **Electron Flow and Water Flow**
Consider this analogy between electron "pressure" and water pressure. A U tube (cell) is separated into two arms (two half-cells) by a stopcock (switch), and the two arms contain water at different heights (the half-cells have different electrical potentials). Open the stopcock (close the switch), and the different heights (potential difference) become equal as water flows (electrons flow and current is generated).

## 21.3 • CELL POTENTIAL: OUTPUT OF A VOLTAIC CELL

A voltaic cell converts the free energy change of a spontaneous reaction into the kinetic energy of electrons moving through an external circuit (electrical energy). This electrical energy is proportional to the *difference in electrical potential between the two electrodes,* which is called the **cell potential ($E_{cell}$)**; it is also called the **voltage of the cell** or the **electromotive force (emf).**

Electrons flow spontaneously from the negative to the positive electrode, that is, toward the electrode with the more positive electrical potential. Thus, when the cell operates *spontaneously,* there is a *positive* cell potential:

$$E_{cell} > 0 \text{ for a spontaneous process} \tag{21.1}$$

- A *positive* $E_{cell}$ arises from a spontaneous reaction. The more positive it is, the more work the cell can do, and the farther the reaction proceeds to the right as written.
- A *negative* $E_{cell}$, on the other hand, is associated with a *nonspontaneous* cell reaction.
- If $E_{cell} = 0$, the reaction has reached equilibrium and the cell can do no more work. (We return to these ideas in Section 21.4.)

| Table **21.1** Voltages of Some Voltaic Cells | |
|---|---|
| **Voltaic Cell** | **Voltage (V)** |
| Common alkaline flashlight battery | 1.5 |
| Lead-acid car battery (6 cells ≈ 12 V) | 2.1 |
| Calculator battery (mercury) | 1.3 |
| Lithium-ion laptop battery | 3.7 |
| Electric eel (~5000 cells in 6-ft eel = 750 V) | 0.15 |
| Nerve of giant squid (across cell membrane) | 0.070 |

# Standard Cell Potentials

Cell potential refers to energy available to do the work of moving a charge between electrodes. The SI unit of electrical potential is the **volt (V),** and the SI unit of electrical charge is the **coulomb (C).** By definition, if two electrodes differ by 1 volt of electrical potential, 1 joule of energy is released (that is, 1 joule of work can be done) for each coulomb of charge that moves between the electrodes. That is,

$$1 \text{ V} = 1 \text{ J/C} \tag{21.2}$$

Table 21.1 lists the voltages of some commercial and natural voltaic cells.

The *measured* cell potential is affected by changes in concentration as the reaction proceeds and by energy losses from heating the cell and external circuit. Therefore, as with other thermodynamic quantities, to compare potentials of different cells, we obtain a **standard cell potential ($E^\circ_{cell}$),** which is measured at a specified temperature (usually 298 K) with no current flowing* and *all components in their standard states:* 1 atm for gases, 1 *M* for solutions, the pure solid for electrodes. For example, the zinc-copper cell produces 1.10 V when it operates at 298 K with $[Zn^{2+}] = [Cu^{2+}] = 1 M$ (Figure 21.6):

$$Zn(s) + Cu^{2+}(aq; 1 M) \longrightarrow Zn^{2+}(aq; 1 M) + Cu(s) \quad E^\circ_{cell} = 1.10 \text{ V}$$

Zn half-cell
(anode; oxidation)

Cu half-cell
(cathode; reduction)

**Figure 21.6** Measuring the standard cell potential of a zinc-copper cell.

**Standard Electrode (Half-Cell) Potentials** Just as each half-reaction makes up part of the overall reaction, the potential of each half-cell makes up a part of the overall cell potential. The **standard electrode potential ($E^\circ_{half-cell}$)** is the potential of a given half-reaction (electrode compartment) with all components in their standard states.

By convention (and as they appear in reference tables), *a standard electrode potential refers to the half-reaction written as a **reduction.*** For the zinc-copper reaction, both the zinc half-reaction ($E^\circ_{zinc}$, anode compartment) and the copper half-reaction ($E^\circ_{copper}$, cathode compartment) are written as reductions:

$$Zn^{2+}(aq) + 2e^- \longrightarrow Zn(s) \quad E^\circ_{zinc} (E^\circ_{anode}) \quad [\text{reduction}]$$
$$Cu^{2+}(aq) + 2e^- \longrightarrow Cu(s) \quad E^\circ_{copper} (E^\circ_{cathode}) \quad [\text{reduction}]$$

But, since the overall cell reaction involves the *oxidation* of zinc, not the *reduction* of $Zn^{2+}$, we reverse the zinc half-reaction:

$$Zn(s) \longrightarrow Zn^{2+}(aq) + 2e^- \quad [\text{oxidation}]$$
$$Cu^{2+}(aq) + 2e^- \longrightarrow Cu(s) \quad [\text{reduction}]$$

**Calculating $E^\circ_{cell}$ from $E^\circ_{half-cell}$** The overall redox reaction for the zinc-copper cell is the sum of its half-reactions:

$$Zn(s) + Cu^{2+}(aq) \longrightarrow Zn^{2+}(aq) + Cu(s)$$

Because electrons flow spontaneously from the negative to the positive electrode, the copper electrode (cathode) has a more positive $E^\circ_{half-cell}$ than the zinc electrode (anode). Arithmetically, to obtain a positive $E^\circ_{cell}$ for this spontaneous redox reaction, we must subtract $E^\circ_{zinc}$ from $E^\circ_{copper}$:

$$E^\circ_{cell} = E^\circ_{copper} - E^\circ_{zinc}$$

We can generalize this result for any voltaic cell: *the standard cell potential is the difference between the standard electrode potential of the cathode (reduction) half-cell and the standard electrode potential of the anode (oxidation) half-cell:*

$$E^\circ_{cell} = E^\circ_{cathode \text{ (reduction)}} - E^\circ_{anode \text{ (oxidation)}} \tag{21.3}$$

For a *spontaneous* reaction at standard conditions, this calculation gives $E^\circ_{cell} > 0$.

---

*The tiny current required to operate modern digital voltmeters makes a negligible difference in the value of $E^\circ_{cell}$.

**Determining $E^\circ_{\text{half-cell}}$ with the Standard Hydrogen Electrode** We want to determine the portion of $E^\circ_{\text{cell}}$ contributed by the anode half-cell (oxidation of Zn) and the portion contributed by the cathode half-cell (reduction of $Cu^{2+}$). But, how can we find potentials of the individual half-cells if we can measure only the potential of the overall cell?

Half-cell potentials, such as $E^\circ_{\text{zinc}}$ and $E^\circ_{\text{copper}}$, are *relative* to a standard reference half-cell, *which has a standard electrode potential defined as zero* ($E^\circ_{\text{reference}} \equiv 0.00 \text{ V}$). The **standard reference half-cell** is a **standard hydrogen electrode,** which consists of a platinum electrode that has $H_2$ gas at 1 atm bubbling through it and is immersed in 1 $M$ strong acid, $H^+(aq)$ [or $H_3O^+(aq)$]. Thus, the reference half-reaction is

$$2H^+(aq; 1 M) + 2e^- \rightleftharpoons H_2(g; 1 \text{ atm}) \qquad E^\circ_{\text{reference}} = 0.00 \text{ V}$$

To find an unknown standard electrode potential ($E^\circ_{\text{unknown}}$), we construct a voltaic cell consisting of this reference half-cell and the unknown half-cell. Since $E^\circ_{\text{reference}}$ is zero, the overall $E^\circ_{\text{cell}}$ gives $E^\circ_{\text{unknown}}$.

Depending on the unknown half-cell, the reference half-cell can be the anode or the cathode:

- When $H_2$ is oxidized, the reference half-cell is the anode, and so *reduction* occurs at the unknown half-cell:

$$E^\circ_{\text{cell}} = E^\circ_{\text{cathode}} - E^\circ_{\text{anode}} = E^\circ_{\text{unknown}} - E^\circ_{\text{reference}} = E^\circ_{\text{unknown}} - 0.00 \text{ V} = E^\circ_{\text{unknown}}$$

- When $H^+$ is reduced, the reference half-cell is the cathode, and so *oxidation* occurs at the unknown half-cell:

$$E^\circ_{\text{cell}} = E^\circ_{\text{cathode}} - E^\circ_{\text{anode}} = E^\circ_{\text{reference}} - E^\circ_{\text{unknown}} = 0.00 \text{ V} - E^\circ_{\text{unknown}} = -E^\circ_{\text{unknown}}$$

Figure 21.7 shows a voltaic cell that has the $Zn/Zn^{2+}$ half-reaction in one compartment and the $H^+/H_2$ (or $H_3O^+/H_2$) half-reaction in the other. The zinc electrode is negative relative to the hydrogen electrode, so we know that the zinc is being oxidized and is the anode. The measured $E^\circ_{\text{cell}}$ is +0.76 V (reaction is spontaneous), and we use this value to find the unknown standard electrode potential, $E^\circ_{\text{zinc}}$:

$$2H^+(aq) + 2e^- \longrightarrow H_2(g) \qquad\qquad E^\circ_{\text{reference}} = 0.00 \text{ V} \text{ [cathode; reduction]}$$
$$Zn(s) \longrightarrow Zn^{2+}(aq) + 2e^- \qquad\quad E^\circ_{\text{zinc}} = ? \text{ V} \quad \text{[anode; oxidation]}$$

$$\overline{Zn(s) + 2H^+(aq) \longrightarrow Zn^{2+}(aq) + H_2(g) \qquad E^\circ_{\text{cell}} = 0.76 \text{ V}}$$

$$E^\circ_{\text{cell}} = E^\circ_{\text{cathode}} - E^\circ_{\text{anode}} = E^\circ_{\text{reference}} - E^\circ_{\text{zinc}}$$
$$E^\circ_{\text{zinc}} = E^\circ_{\text{reference}} - E^\circ_{\text{cell}} = 0.00 \text{ V} - 0.76 \text{ V} = -0.76 \text{ V}$$

Oxidation half-reaction
$Zn(s) \longrightarrow Zn^{2+}(aq) + 2e^-$

Reduction half-reaction
$2H_3O^+(aq) + 2e^- \longrightarrow H_2(g) + 2H_2O(l)$

Overall (cell) reaction
$Zn(s) + 2H_3O^+(aq) \longrightarrow Zn^{2+}(aq) + H_2(g) + 2H_2O(l)$

**Figure 21.7 Determining an unknown $E^\circ_{\text{half-cell}}$ with the standard reference (hydrogen) electrode.** The magnified view of the hydrogen half-reaction (*right*) shows two $H_3O^+$ ions being reduced to two $H_2O$ molecules and an $H_2$ molecule, which enters the $H_2$ bubble.

Now we can return to the zinc-copper cell and use the measured $E°_{cell}$ (1.10 V) and the value we just found for $E°_{zinc}$ to calculate $E°_{copper}$:

$$E°_{cell} = E°_{cathode} - E°_{anode} = E°_{copper} - E°_{zinc}$$
$$E°_{copper} = E°_{cell} + E°_{zinc} = 1.10 \text{ V} + (-0.76 \text{ V}) = 0.34 \text{ V}$$

By continuing this process of constructing cells with one known and one unknown electrode potential, we find other standard electrode potentials.

---

**Sample Problem 21.3** **Calculating an Unknown $E°_{half-cell}$ from $E°_{cell}$**

**Problem** A voltaic cell houses the reaction between aqueous bromine and zinc metal:

$$Br_2(aq) + Zn(s) \longrightarrow Zn^{2+}(aq) + 2Br^-(aq) \qquad E°_{cell} = 1.83 \text{ V}$$

Calculate $E°_{bromine}$, given $E°_{zinc} = -0.76$ V.

**Plan** $E°_{cell}$ is positive, so the reaction is spontaneous as written. By dividing the reaction into half-reactions, we see that $Br_2$ is reduced and Zn is oxidized; thus, the zinc half-cell contains the anode. We use Equation 21.3 and the known $E°_{zinc}$ to find $E°_{unknown}$ ($E°_{bromine}$).

**Solution** Dividing the reaction into half-reactions:

$$Br_2(aq) + 2e^- \longrightarrow 2Br^-(aq) \qquad E°_{unknown} = E°_{bromine} = ? \text{ V}$$
$$Zn(s) \longrightarrow Zn^{2+}(aq) + 2e^- \qquad E°_{zinc} = -0.76 \text{ V}$$

Calculating $E°_{bromine}$:

$$E°_{cell} = E°_{cathode} - E°_{anode} = E°_{bromine} - E°_{zinc}$$
$$E°_{bromine} = E°_{cell} + E°_{zinc} = 1.83 \text{ V} + (-0.76 \text{ V}) = \boxed{1.07 \text{ V}}$$

**Check** A good check is to make sure that calculating $E°_{bromine} - E°_{zinc}$ gives $E°_{cell}$:
1.07 V − (−0.76 V) = 1.83 V.

**Comment** Keep in mind that, whichever half-cell potential is unknown, reduction is the cathode half-reaction and oxidation is the anode half-reaction. *Always* subtract $E°_{anode}$ from $E°_{cathode}$ to get $E°_{cell}$.

**Follow-Up Problem 21.3** A voltaic cell based on the reaction between aqueous $Br_2$ and vanadium(III) ions has $E°_{cell} = 1.39$ V:

$$Br_2(aq) + 2V^{3+}(aq) + 2H_2O(l) \longrightarrow 2VO^{2+}(aq) + 4H^+(aq) + 2Br^-(aq)$$

What is $E°_{vanadium}$, the standard electrode potential for the reduction of $VO^{2+}$ to $V^{3+}$?

---

## Relative Strengths of Oxidizing and Reducing Agents

We learn the relative strengths of oxidizing and reducing agents from measuring cell potentials. Three oxidizing agents just discussed are $Cu^{2+}$, $H^+$, and $Zn^{2+}$. We rank their relative oxidizing strengths by writing each half-reaction as a reduction (gain of electrons), with its corresponding standard electrode potential:

$$Cu^{2+}(aq) + 2e^- \longrightarrow Cu(s) \qquad E° = 0.34 \text{ V}$$
$$2H^+(aq) + 2e^- \longrightarrow H_2(g) \qquad E° = 0.00 \text{ V}$$
$$Zn^{2+}(aq) + 2e^- \longrightarrow Zn(s) \qquad E° = -0.76 \text{ V}$$

*The more positive the $E°$ value, the more readily the reaction (as written) occurs;* thus, $Cu^{2+}$ gains two $e^-$ more readily than $H^+$, which gains them more readily than $Zn^{2+}$:

• Strength as an oxidizing agent: $Cu^{2+} > H^+ > Zn^{2+}$.
• Strength as a reducing agent: $Zn > H_2 > Cu$.

By continuing this process with other half-cells, we create a list of reduction half-reactions in *decreasing* order of standard electrode potential (from most positive to most negative). Such a list, called an *emf series* or a *table of standard electrode potentials,* appears in Appendix D; a few examples are presented in Table 21.2. There are several key points to keep in mind:

## Table **21.2** Selected Standard Electrode Potentials (298 K)

| Half-Reaction | $E^{\circ}_{\text{half-cell}}$ (V) |
|---|---|
| $F_2(g) + 2e^- \rightleftharpoons 2F^-(aq)$ | +2.87 |
| $Cl_2(g) + 2e^- \rightleftharpoons 2Cl^-(aq)$ | +1.36 |
| $MnO_2(s) + 4H^+(aq) + 2e^- \rightleftharpoons Mn^{2+}(aq) + 2H_2O(l)$ | +1.23 |
| $NO_3^-(aq) + 4H^+(aq) + 3e^- \rightleftharpoons NO(g) + 2H_2O(l)$ | +0.96 |
| $Ag^+(aq) + e^- \rightleftharpoons Ag(s)$ | +0.80 |
| $Fe^{3+}(aq) + e^- \rightleftharpoons Fe^{2+}(aq)$ | +0.77 |
| $O_2(g) + 2H_2O(l) + 4e^- \rightleftharpoons 4OH^-(aq)$ | +0.40 |
| $Cu^{2+}(aq) + 2e^- \rightleftharpoons Cu(s)$ | +0.34 |
| $2H^+(aq) + 2e^- \rightleftharpoons H_2(g)$ | 0.00 |
| $N_2(g) + 5H^+(aq) + 4e^- \rightleftharpoons N_2H_5^+(aq)$ | −0.23 |
| $Fe^{2+}(aq) + 2e^- \rightleftharpoons Fe(s)$ | −0.44 |
| $Zn^{2+}(aq) + 2e^- \rightleftharpoons Zn(s)$ | −0.76 |
| $2H_2O(l) + 2e^- \rightleftharpoons H_2(g) + 2OH^-(aq)$ | −0.83 |
| $Na^+(aq) + e^- \rightleftharpoons Na(s)$ | −2.71 |
| $Li^+(aq) + e^- \rightleftharpoons Li(s)$ | −3.05 |

*Strength of oxidizing agent* (arrow pointing up, left side)

*Strength of reducing agent* (arrow pointing down, right side)

- All values are relative to the standard hydrogen (reference) electrode.
- Since the half-reactions are written as *reductions, reactants are oxidizing agents* and *products are reducing agents.*
- The more positive the $E^{\circ}_{\text{half-cell}}$, the more readily the half-reaction occurs, as written.
- Half-reactions are shown with an equilibrium arrow because each can occur as a reduction (at the cathode) or an oxidation (at the anode), depending on the $E^{\circ}_{\text{half-cell}}$ of the other half-reaction.
- As Appendix D (or Table 21.2) is arranged, the strength of the oxidizing agent (re-actant) *increases going up (bottom to top),* and the strength of the reducing agent (product) *increases going down (top to bottom).*

Thus, $F_2(g)$ is the strongest oxidizing agent (has the largest positive $E^{\circ}$), which means $F^-(aq)$ is the weakest reducing agent. Similarly, $Li^+(aq)$ is the weakest oxidizing agent (has the most negative $E^{\circ}$), which means $Li(s)$ is the strongest reducing agent: a *strong oxidizing agent forms a weak reducing agent,* and vice versa. Rely on your knowledge of the elements (Section 8.4) if you forget the ranking in the table:

- $F_2$ is very electronegative and occurs as $F^-$, so it is easily reduced (gains electrons) and must be a strong oxidizing agent (high, positive $E^{\circ}$).
- Li metal has a low ionization energy and occurs as $Li^+$, so it is easily oxidized (loses electrons) and must be a strong reducing agent (low, negative $E^{\circ}$).

## Writing Spontaneous Redox Reactions

*Every redox reaction is the sum of two half-reactions, so there is a reducing agent and an oxidizing agent on each side.* In the zinc-copper reaction, for instance, Zn and Cu are the reducing agents, and $Cu^{2+}$ and $Zn^{2+}$ are the oxidizing agents. The stronger oxidizing and reducing agents react spontaneously to form the weaker oxidizing and reducing agents:

$$\underset{\substack{\text{stronger} \\ \text{reducing agent}}}{Zn(s)} + \underset{\substack{\text{stronger} \\ \text{oxidizing agent}}}{Cu^{2+}(aq)} \longrightarrow \underset{\substack{\text{weaker} \\ \text{oxidizing agent}}}{Zn^{2+}(aq)} + \underset{\substack{\text{weaker} \\ \text{reducing agent}}}{Cu(s)}$$

Based on the order of the $E^{\circ}$ values in Appendix D, and as we just saw for the $Cu^{2+}/Cu$, $H^+/H_2$, and $Zn^{2+}/Zn$ redox pairs (or redox *couples*), *the stronger oxidizing agent (species on the left) has a half-reaction with a larger (more positive or less negative) $E^{\circ}$ value, and the stronger reducing agent (species on the right) has a half-reaction with a smaller (less positive or more negative) $E^{\circ}$ value.* Therefore, we can use Appendix D to choose a redox reaction for constructing a voltaic cell.

**Writing a Spontaneous Reaction with Appendix D** A spontaneous reaction ($E^\circ_{cell} > 0$) will occur between an oxidizing agent and any reducing agent that lies *below* it in the emf series, listed in Appendix D. In other words, *for a spontaneous reaction to occur, the half-reaction higher in the list proceeds at the cathode as written, and the half-reaction lower in the list proceeds at the anode in reverse.* This pairing ensures that the stronger oxidizing agent (higher on the left) and stronger reducing agent (lower on the right) will be the reactants. For example, two half-reactions in the order they appear in Appendix D are

$$Cl_2(g) + 2e^- \longrightarrow 2Cl^-(aq) \qquad E^\circ_{chlorine} = 1.36 \text{ V}$$
$$Ni^{2+}(aq) + 2e^- \longrightarrow Ni(s) \qquad E^\circ_{nickel} = -0.25 \text{ V}$$

We reverse the nickel half-reaction (lower in the list); note, however, that we do *not* reverse the sign of $E^\circ_{half\text{-}cell}$ because the minus sign in Equation 21.3 does that. Next, we have to be sure that $e^-$ lost equal $e^-$ gained. If they do not, we multiply one or both half-reactions by coefficients to accomplish this. In this case, they do, so we can skip this step. Adding the half-reactions and applying Equation 21.3 gives the balanced equation and $E^\circ_{cell}$:

$$Cl_2(g) + Ni(s) \longrightarrow Ni^{2+}(aq) + 2Cl^-(aq)$$
$$E^\circ_{cell} = E^\circ_{cathode} - E^\circ_{anode} = E^\circ_{chlorine} - E^\circ_{nickel} = 1.36 \text{ V} - (-0.25 \text{ V}) = 1.61 \text{ V}$$

**Writing a Spontaneous Reaction without Appendix D** Even when a list like Appendix D is not available, we can write a spontaneous redox reaction from a given pair of half-reactions. For example, here are two half-reactions:

$$Sn^{2+}(aq) + 2e^- \longrightarrow Sn(s) \qquad E^\circ_{tin} = -0.14 \text{ V}$$
$$Ag^+(aq) + e^- \longrightarrow Ag(s) \qquad E^\circ_{silver} = 0.80 \text{ V}$$

Two steps are required:

1. Reverse one of the half-reactions into an oxidation step so that the difference of the electrode potentials (cathode *minus* anode) gives a *positive* $E^\circ_{cell}$. (Remember that, as above, when we reverse the half-reaction, we do *not* reverse the sign of $E^\circ_{half\text{-}cell}$.)
2. Multiply by coefficients to make $e^-$ lost equal $e^-$ gained, add the rearranged half-reactions to get a balanced overall equation, and cancel species common to both sides.

We want the reactants to be the stronger oxidizing and reducing agents:

- The larger (more positive) $E^\circ$ value for the silver half-reaction means that $Ag^+$ is a stronger oxidizing agent (gains electrons more readily) than $Sn^{2+}$.
- The smaller (more negative) $E^\circ$ value for the tin half-reaction means that Sn is a stronger reducing agent (loses electrons more readily) than Ag.

*For step 1*, we reverse the tin half-reaction (but *not* the sign of $E^\circ_{tin}$):

$$Sn(s) \longrightarrow Sn^{2+}(aq) + 2e^- \qquad E^\circ_{tin} = -0.14 \text{ V}$$

because when we subtract $E^\circ_{half\text{-}cell}$ of the tin half-reaction (anode, oxidation) from $E^\circ_{half\text{-}cell}$ of the silver half-reaction (cathode, reduction), we get a positive $E^\circ_{cell}$:

$$0.80 \text{ V} - (-0.14 \text{ V}) = 0.94 \text{ V}$$

*For step 2, the number of electrons lost in the oxidation must equal the number gained in the reduction,* so we double the silver (reduction) half-reaction. Adding the half-reactions and applying Equation 21.3 gives

| | | |
|---|---|---|
| $2Ag^+(aq) + 2e^- \longrightarrow 2Ag(s)$ | $E^\circ_{silver} = 0.80 \text{ V}$ | [reduction] |
| $Sn(s) \longrightarrow Sn^{2+}(aq) + 2e^-$ | $E^\circ_{tin} = -0.14 \text{ V}$ | [oxidation] |

$$Sn(s) + 2Ag^+(aq) \longrightarrow Sn^{2+}(aq) + 2Ag(s) \qquad E^\circ_{cell} = E^\circ_{silver} - E^\circ_{tin} = 0.94 \text{ V}$$

A *very important point* to note is that, when we double the coefficients of the silver half-reaction, we do *not* double its $E^\circ_{half\text{-}cell}$. *Changing the coefficients of a half-reaction does **not** change its $E^\circ_{half\text{-}cell}$* because a standard electrode potential is an *intensive* property, one that does *not* depend on the amount of substance. Let's see why. The potential is the *ratio* of energy to charge. When we change the coefficients to change the amounts, the energy *and* the charge change proportionately, so their ratio stays the same. (Similarly, density does not change with the amount of substance because the mass *and* the volume change proportionately.)

## Sample Problem 21.4    Writing Spontaneous Redox Reactions and Ranking Oxidizing and Reducing Agents by Strength

**Problem** **(a)** Combine the following three half-reactions into three balanced equations for spontaneous reactions (A, B, and C), and calculate $E^\circ_{cell}$ for each. **(b)** Rank the relative strengths of the oxidizing and reducing agents.

(1) $NO_3^-(aq) + 4H^+(aq) + 3e^- \longrightarrow NO(g) + 2H_2O(l)$     $E^\circ = 0.96$ V
(2) $N_2(g) + 5H^+(aq) + 4e^- \longrightarrow N_2H_5^+(aq)$     $E^\circ = -0.23$ V
(3) $MnO_2(s) + 4H^+(aq) + 2e^- \longrightarrow Mn^{2+}(aq) + 2H_2O(l)$     $E^\circ = 1.23$ V

**Plan** **(a)** To write the redox equations, we combine the possible pairs of half-reactions: (1) and (2) give reaction A, (1) and (3) give B, and (2) and (3) give C. They are all written as reductions, so the oxidizing agents appear as reactants and the reducing agents appear as products. In each pair, we reverse the half-reaction that has the smaller (less positive or more negative) $E^\circ$ value to an oxidation to obtain a positive $E^\circ_{cell}$. We make $e^-$ lost equal $e^-$ gained, without changing the $E^\circ$ value, add the half-reactions together, and then apply Equation 21.3 to find $E^\circ_{cell}$. **(b)** Because each reaction is spontaneous as written, the stronger oxidizing and reducing agents are the reactants. To obtain the overall ranking, we first rank the relative strengths within each equation and then compare them.

**Solution** **(a)** Combining half-reactions (1) and (2) gives equation (A). The $E^\circ$ value for half-reaction (1) is larger (more positive) than that for (2), so we reverse (2) to obtain a positive $E^\circ_{cell}$:

(1) $NO_3^-(aq) + 4H^+(aq) + 3e^- \longrightarrow NO(g) + 2H_2O(l)$     $E^\circ = 0.96$ V
(rev 2)     $N_2H_5^+(aq) \longrightarrow N_2(g) + 5H^+(aq) + 4e^-$     $E^\circ = -0.23$ V

To make $e^-$ lost equal $e^-$ gained, we multiply (1) by four and the reversed (2) by three; then add half-reactions and cancel appropriate numbers of common species ($H^+$ and $e^-$):

$4NO_3^-(aq) + 16H^+(aq) + 12e^- \longrightarrow 4NO(g) + 8H_2O(l)$     $E^\circ = 0.96$ V
$3N_2H_5^+(aq) \longrightarrow 3N_2(g) + 15H^+(aq) + 12e^-$     $E^\circ = -0.23$ V
_____

(A) $3N_2H_5^+(aq) + 4NO_3^-(aq) + H^+(aq) \longrightarrow 3N_2(g) + 4NO(g) + 8H_2O(l)$
$E^\circ_{cell} = 0.96$ V $- (-0.23$ V$) = 1.19$ V

Combining half-reactions (1) and (3) gives equation (B). Half-reaction (1) has a smaller $E^\circ$, so it is reversed:

(rev 1)     $NO(g) + 2H_2O(l) \longrightarrow NO_3^-(aq) + 4H^+(aq) + 3e^-$     $E^\circ = 0.96$ V
(3) $MnO_2(s) + 4H^+(aq) + 2e^- \longrightarrow Mn^{2+}(aq) + 2H_2O(l)$     $E^\circ = 1.23$ V

We multiply reversed (1) by two and (3) by three, then add and cancel:

$2NO(g) + 4H_2O(l) \longrightarrow 2NO_3^-(aq) + 8H^+(aq) + 6e^-$     $E^\circ = 0.96$ V
$3MnO_2(s) + 12H^+(aq) + 6e^- \longrightarrow 3Mn^{2+}(aq) + 6H_2O(l)$     $E^\circ = 1.23$ V
_____

(B) $3MnO_2(s) + 4H^+(aq) + 2NO(g) \longrightarrow 3Mn^{2+}(aq) + 2H_2O(l) + 2NO_3^-(aq)$
$E^\circ_{cell} = 1.23$ V $- 0.96$ V $= 0.27$ V

Combining half-reactions (2) and (3) gives equation (C). Half-reaction (2) has a smaller $E^\circ$, so it is reversed:

(rev 2)     $N_2H_5^+(aq) \longrightarrow N_2(g) + 5H^+(aq) + 4e^-$     $E^\circ = -0.23$ V
(3) $MnO_2(s) + 4H^+(aq) + 2e^- \longrightarrow Mn^{2+}(aq) + 2H_2O(l)$     $E^\circ = 1.23$ V

We multiply reaction (3) by two, add the half-reactions, and cancel:

$N_2H_5^+(aq) \longrightarrow N_2(g) + 5H^+(aq) + 4e^-$     $E^\circ = -0.23$ V
$2MnO_2(s) + 8H^+(aq) + 4e^- \longrightarrow 2Mn^{2+}(aq) + 4H_2O(l)$     $E^\circ = 1.23$ V
_____

(C) $N_2H_5^+(aq) + 2MnO_2(s) + 3H^+(aq) \longrightarrow N_2(g) + 2Mn^{2+}(aq) + 4H_2O(l)$
$E^\circ_{cell} = 1.23$ V $- (-0.23$ V$) = 1.46$ V

**(b)** Ranking the oxidizing and reducing agents within each equation:

Equation (A)    Oxidizing agents: $NO_3^- > N_2$     Reducing agents: $N_2H_5^+ > NO$
Equation (B)    Oxidizing agents: $MnO_2 > NO_3^-$     Reducing agents:    $NO > Mn^{2+}$
Equation (C)    Oxidizing agents: $MnO_2 > N_2$     Reducing agents: $N_2H_5^+ > Mn^{2+}$

Determining the overall ranking of oxidizing and reducing agents. Comparing the relative strengths from the three balanced equations gives

Oxidizing agents: $MnO_2 > NO_3^- > N_2$
Reducing agents: $N_2H_5^+ > NO > Mn^{2+}$

**Check**  As always, check that atoms and charges balance on both sides of the equation. A good way to check the ranking and equations is to list the given half-reactions in order of decreasing $E°$ value:

$$MnO_2(s) + 4H^+(aq) + 2e^- \longrightarrow Mn^{2+}(aq) + 2H_2O(l) \qquad E° = 1.23 \text{ V}$$
$$NO_3^-(aq) + 4H^+(aq) + 3e^- \longrightarrow NO(g) + 2H_2O(l) \qquad E° = 0.96 \text{ V}$$
$$N_2(g) + 5H^+(aq) + 4e^- \longrightarrow N_2H_5^+(aq) \qquad E° = -0.23 \text{ V}$$

Then the oxidizing agents (reactants) decrease in strength going down the list, so the reducing agents (products) decrease in strength going up. Moreover, each of the three spontaneous reactions (A, B, and C) should combine a reactant with a product that is lower down on this list.

**Follow-Up Problem 21.4**    Is the following reaction spontaneous as written?

$$3Fe^{2+}(aq) \longrightarrow Fe(s) + 2Fe^{3+}(aq)$$

If not, write the equation for the spontaneous reaction, calculate $E°_{cell}$, and rank the three species of iron in order of decreasing reducing strength.

## Explaining the Activity Series of the Metals

In Chapter 4, we discussed the activity series of the metals (see Figure 4.20, p. 165), which ranks metals by their ability to "displace" one another from aqueous solution. Now you'll see *why* this displacement occurs, as well as why many, but not all, metals react with acid to form $H_2$, and why a few metals form $H_2$ even in water.

1. *Metals that can displace $H_2$ from acid.* The standard hydrogen half-reaction represents the reduction of $H^+$ ions from an acid to $H_2$:

$$2H^+(aq) + 2e^- \longrightarrow H_2(g) \qquad E° = 0.00 \text{ V}$$

To see which metals reduce $H^+$ (referred to as "displacing $H_2$") from acids, choose a metal, write its half-reaction as an oxidation, combine this half-reaction with the hydrogen half-reaction, and see if $E°_{cell}$ is positive. We find that the metals Li through Pb, those that lie *below* the standard hydrogen (reference) half-reaction in Appendix D, give a positive $E°_{cell}$ when reducing $H^+$. Iron, for example, reduces $H^+$ from an acid to $H_2$:

$$\begin{array}{ll} Fe(s) \longrightarrow Fe^{2+}(aq) + 2e^- & E° = -0.44 \text{ V} \quad \text{[anode; oxidation]} \\ \underline{2H^+(aq) + 2e^- \longrightarrow H_2(g)} & \underline{E° = 0.00 \text{ V} \quad \text{[cathode; reduction]}} \\ Fe(s) + 2H^+(aq) \longrightarrow H_2(g) + Fe^{2+}(aq) & E°_{cell} = 0.00 \text{ V} - (-0.44 \text{ V}) = 0.44 \text{ V} \end{array}$$

The lower the metal in the list, the stronger it is as a reducing agent; therefore, *if $E°_{cell}$ for the reduction of $H^+$ is more positive with metal A than with metal B, metal A is a stronger reducing agent than metal B and a more **active** metal.*

2. *Metals that cannot displace $H_2$ from acid.* For metals that are *above* the standard hydrogen (reference) half-reaction, the $E°_{cell}$ is negative when we reverse the metal half-reaction, so the reaction does not occur. For example, the coinage metals—copper, silver, and gold, which are in Group 1B(11)—are not strong enough reducing agents to reduce $H^+$ from acids:

$$\begin{array}{ll} Ag(s) \longrightarrow Ag^+(aq) + e^- & E° = 0.80 \text{ V} \quad \text{[anode; oxidation]} \\ \underline{2H^+(aq) + 2e^- \longrightarrow H_2(g)} & \underline{E° = 0.00 \text{ V} \quad \text{[cathode; reduction]}} \\ 2Ag(s) + 2H^+(aq) \longrightarrow 2Ag^+(aq) + H_2(g) & E°_{cell} = 0.00 \text{ V} - 0.80 \text{ V} = -0.80 \text{ V} \end{array}$$

The *higher* the metal in the list, the *more negative* is its $E°_{cell}$ for the reduction of $H^+$ to $H_2$, the *lower* is its reducing strength, and the *less active* it is. Thus, gold is less active than silver, which is less active than copper.

3. *Metals that can displace $H_2$ from water.* Metals active enough to reduce $H_2O$ lie below that half-reaction:

$$2H_2O(l) + 2e^- \longrightarrow H_2(g) + 2OH^-(aq) \qquad E = -0.42 \text{ V}$$

(The value shown here is the *nonstandard* electrode potential because, in pure water, $[OH^-]$ is $1.0 \times 10^{-7}$ $M$, not the standard-state value of 1 $M$.) For example, consider the reaction of sodium in water (with the $Na^+/Na$ half-reaction reversed and doubled):

$$
\begin{array}{lll}
2Na(s) \longrightarrow 2Na^+(aq) + 2e^- & E° = -2.71 \text{ V} & \text{[anode; oxidation]} \\
2H_2O(l) + 2e^- \longrightarrow H_2(g) + 2OH^-(aq) & E = -0.42 \text{ V} & \text{[cathode; reduction]} \\
\hline
2Na(s) + 2H_2O(l) \longrightarrow 2Na^+(aq) + H_2(g) + 2OH^-(aq) & &
\end{array}
$$

$$E_{cell} = -0.42 \text{ V} - (-2.71 \text{ V}) = 2.29 \text{ V}$$

The alkali metals [Group 1A(1)] and the larger alkaline earth metals [Group 2A(2)] can reduce water (displace $H_2$ from $H_2O$). Calcium is shown doing this in Figure 21.8.

4. *Metals that displace other metals from solution.* We can also predict whether one metal can reduce the aqueous ion of another metal. Any metal that is lower in the list in Appendix D can reduce the ion of a metal that is higher up, and thus displace that metal from solution. For example, zinc can displace iron from solution:

$$
\begin{array}{lll}
Zn(s) \longrightarrow Zn^{2+}(aq) + 2e^- & E° = -0.76 \text{ V} & \text{[anode; oxidation]} \\
Fe^{2+}(aq) + 2e^- \longrightarrow Fe(s) & E° = -0.44 \text{ V} & \text{[cathode; reduction]} \\
\hline
Zn(s) + Fe^{2+}(aq) \longrightarrow Zn^{2+}(aq) + Fe(s) & E°_{cell} = -0.44 \text{ V} - (-0.76 \text{ V}) = 0.32 \text{ V} &
\end{array}
$$

This particular reaction has tremendous economic importance in protecting iron from rusting, as we'll discuss in Section 21.6.

A common incident involving the reducing power of metals occurs from biting down with a filled tooth on a scrap of aluminum foil left on a piece of food. The foil acts as an active anode ($E°_{aluminum} = -1.66$ V), saliva as the electrolyte, and the filling (usually a silver/tin/mercury alloy) as an inactive cathode as $O_2$ is reduced to water. The circuit between the foil and the filling creates a current that is sensed as pain by the nerve of the tooth (Figure 21.9).

| Oxidation half-reaction |
| $Ca(s) \longrightarrow Ca^{2+}(aq) + 2e^-$ |

| Reduction half-reaction |
| $2H_2O(l) + 2e^- \longrightarrow H_2(g) + 2OH^-(aq)$ |

| Overall (cell) reaction |
| $Ca(s) + 2H_2O(l) \longrightarrow Ca(OH)_2(aq) + H_2(g)$ |

**Figure 21.8** The reaction of calcium in water.

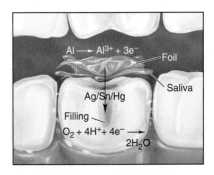

**Figure 21.9** A dental "voltaic cell."

## ■ Summary of Section 21.3

- The output of a cell is the cell potential ($E_{cell}$), measured in volts (1 V = 1 J/C).
- With all substances in their standard states, the output is the standard cell potential ($E°_{cell}$).
- $E°_{cell} > 0$ for a spontaneous reaction at standard-state conditions.
- By convention, a standard electrode potential ($E°_{half-cell}$) refers to the *reduction* half-reaction.
- $E°_{cell}$ equals $E°_{half-cell}$ of the cathode *minus* $E°_{half-cell}$ of the anode.
- Using a standard hydrogen (reference) electrode ($E°_{reference} = 0$ V), $E°_{half-cell}$ values can be measured and used to rank oxidizing (or reducing) agents.
- Spontaneous redox reactions combine stronger oxidizing and reducing agents to form weaker reducing and oxidizing agents, respectively.
- A metal can reduce another species ($H^+$, $H_2O$, or an ion of another metal) if $E°_{cell}$ for the overall reaction is positive.

## 21.4 • FREE ENERGY AND ELECTRICAL WORK

In this section, we examine the relationship of useful work, free energy, and the equilibrium constant in the context of electrochemical cells and see the effect of concentration on cell potential.

### Standard Cell Potential and the Equilibrium Constant

The signs of $\Delta G$ and $E_{cell}$ are *opposite* for a spontaneous reaction: a *negative* free energy change ($\Delta G < 0$; Section 20.3) and a *positive* cell potential ($E_{cell} > 0$). These two indicators of spontaneity are proportional to each other:

$$\Delta G \propto -E_{cell}$$

Let's determine this proportionality constant. The electrical work done ($w$, in joules) is the product of the potential ($E_{cell}$, in volts) and the charge that flows (in coulombs). Since $E_{cell}$ is measured with no current flowing and, thus, no energy lost as heat, it is the maximum voltage possible and, thus, the maximum work possible ($w_{max}$).* Work done *by* the cell *on* the surroundings has a negative sign:

$$w_{max} = -E_{cell} \times \text{charge}$$

The maximum work done *on* the surroundings is equal to $\Delta G$ (Equation 20.9, p. 830):

$$w_{max} = \Delta G = -E_{cell} \times \text{charge}$$

The charge that flows through the cell equals the amount (mol) of electrons transferred ($n$) times the charge of 1 mol of electrons (which has the symbol $F$):

$$\text{Charge} = \text{amount (mol) of e}^- \times \frac{\text{charge}}{\text{mol e}^-} \quad \text{or} \quad \text{charge} = nF$$

The charge of 1 mol of electrons is the **Faraday constant ($F$),** named for Michael Faraday, the 19th-century British scientist who pioneered the study of electrochemistry:

$$F = \frac{96{,}485 \text{ C}}{\text{mol e}^-}$$

Because 1 V = 1 J/C, we have 1 C = 1 J/V, and

$$F = 9.65 \times 10^4 \, \frac{\text{J}}{\text{V} \cdot \text{mol e}^-} \quad \text{(3 sf)} \tag{21.4}$$

Substituting for charge, the proportionality constant is $nF$:

$$\Delta G = -nFE_{cell} \tag{21.5}$$

And, when all components are in their standard states, we have

$$\Delta G° = -nFE°_{cell} \tag{21.6}$$

Using this relationship, we can relate the standard cell potential to the equilibrium constant of the redox reaction. Recall from Equation 20.12 that

$$\Delta G° = -RT \ln K$$

Substituting for $\Delta G°$ from Equation 21.6 gives

$$-nFE°_{cell} = -RT \ln K$$

Solving for $E°_{cell}$ gives

$$E°_{cell} = \frac{RT}{nF} \ln K \tag{21.7}$$

Figure 21.10 summarizes the interconnections among the standard free energy change, the equilibrium constant, and the standard cell potential. In Chapter 20, we determined $K$ from $\Delta G°$, which we found either from $\Delta H°$ and $\Delta S°$ values or from $\Delta G°_f$ values. Now, for redox reactions, we have a direct experimental method for determining $K$ *and* $\Delta G°$: measure $E°_{cell}$.

In calculations, we adjust Equation 21.7 as follows:

- Substitute 8.314 J/(mol rxn·K) for the constant $R$.
- Substitute $9.65 \times 10^4$ J/(V·mol e⁻) for the constant $F$.
- Substitute 298.15 K for $T$, keeping in mind that the cell can run at other temperatures.
- Multiply by 2.303 to convert natural to common (base-10) logarithms. This conversion shows that a *10-fold change in K makes $E°_{cell}$ change by 1*.

Thus, when $n$ moles of e⁻ are transferred per mole of reaction based on the balanced equation, we have

$$E°_{cell} = \frac{RT}{nF} \ln K = 2.303 \times \frac{8.314 \, \frac{\cancel{J}}{\text{mol rxn} \cdot \cancel{K}} \times 298.15 \, \cancel{K}}{\frac{n \, \cancel{\text{mol e}^-}}{\text{mol rxn}} \left( 9.65 \times 10^4 \, \frac{\cancel{J}}{\text{V} \cdot \cancel{\text{mol e}^-}} \right)} \log K$$

*Recall from Chapter 20 that only a reversible process can do maximum work. For no current to flow and the process to be reversible, $E_{cell}$ must be opposed by an equal potential in the measuring circuit: if the opposing potential is infinitesimally smaller, the cell reaction goes forward; if it is infinitesimally larger, the reaction goes backward.

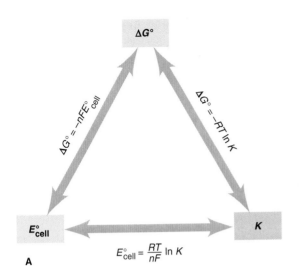

**Figure 21.10** The interrelationship of $\Delta G°$, $E°_{cell}$, and $K$. **A,** Any one parameter can be used to find the other two. **B,** The signs of $\Delta G°$ and $E°_{cell}$ determine reaction direction.

| Reaction Parameters at the Standard State | | | |
|---|---|---|---|
| $\Delta G°$ | $K$ | $E°_{cell}$ | Reaction at standard-state conditions |
| <0 | >1 | >0 | Spontaneous |
| 0 | 1 | 0 | At equilibrium |
| >0 | <1 | <0 | Nonspontaneous |

**B**

And this becomes

$$E°_{cell} = \frac{0.0592 \text{ V}}{n} \log K \quad \text{or} \quad \log K = \frac{nE°_{cell}}{0.0592 \text{ V}} \quad \text{(at 298.15 K)} \quad \textbf{(21.8)}$$

**Sample Problem 21.5** | **Calculating $K$ and $\Delta G°$ from $E°_{cell}$**

**Problem** Lead can displace silver from solution, and silver occurs in trace amounts in some ores of lead:

$$Pb(s) + 2Ag^+(aq) \longrightarrow Pb^{2+}(aq) + 2Ag(s)$$

As a consequence, silver is a valuable byproduct in the industrial extraction of lead from its ores. Calculate $K$ and $\Delta G°$ at 298.15 K for this reaction.

**Plan** We divide the spontaneous redox equation into the half-reactions and use values from Appendix D to calculate $E°_{cell}$. Then, we substitute this result into Equation 21.8 to find $K$ and into Equation 21.6 to find $\Delta G°$.

**Solution** Writing the half-reactions with their $E°$ values:

(1)     $Ag^+(aq) + e^- \longrightarrow Ag(s)$     $E° = 0.80 \text{ V}$
(2)   $Pb^{2+}(aq) + 2e^- \longrightarrow Pb(s)$     $E° = -0.13 \text{ V}$

Calculating $E°_{cell}$: We double (1), reverse (2), add the half-reactions, and subtract $E°_{lead}$ from $E°_{silver}$:

$$2Ag^+(aq) + 2e^- \longrightarrow 2Ag(s) \qquad\qquad E° = 0.80 \text{ V}$$
$$Pb(s) \longrightarrow Pb^{2+}(aq) + 2e^- \qquad\qquad E° = -0.13 \text{ V}$$

$$\overline{Pb(s) + 2Ag^+(aq) \longrightarrow Pb^{2+}(aq) + 2Ag(s) \qquad E°_{cell} = 0.80 \text{ V} - (-0.13 \text{ V}) = 0.93 \text{ V}}$$

Calculating $K$ with Equations 21.7 and 21.8: The adjusted half-reactions show that 2 mol of $e^-$ are transferred per mole of reaction as written, so $n = 2$. Then, performing the substitutions for $R$ and $F$ that we just discussed, changing to common logarithms, and running the cell at 25°C (298.15 K), we have

$$E°_{cell} = \frac{RT}{nF} \ln K = \frac{0.0592 \text{ V}}{2} \log K = 0.93 \text{ V}$$

So,         $\log K = \dfrac{0.93 \text{ V} \times 2}{0.0592 \text{ V}} = 31.42$     and     $K = 2.6 \times 10^{31}$

Calculating $\Delta G°$ (Equation 21.6):

$$\Delta G° = -nFE°_{cell} = -\frac{2 \text{ mol } e^-}{\text{mol rxn}} \times \frac{96.5 \text{ kJ}}{\text{V·mol } e^-} \times 0.93 \text{ V} = -1.8 \times 10^2 \text{ kJ/mol rxn}$$

**Check** The three variables are consistent with the reaction being spontaneous at standard-state conditions: $E^\circ_{cell} > 0$, $\Delta G^\circ < 0$, and $K > 1$. Be sure to round and check the order of magnitude: to find $\Delta G^\circ$, for instance, $\Delta G^\circ \approx -2 \times 100 \times 1 = -200$, so the overall math seems right. Another check would be to obtain $\Delta G^\circ$ directly from its relation with $K$:

$$\Delta G^\circ = -RT \ln K = -8.314 \text{ J/mol rxn·K} \times 298.15 \text{ K} \times \ln (2.6 \times 10^{31})$$
$$= -1.8 \times 10^5 \text{ J/mol rxn} = -1.8 \times 10^2 \text{ kJ/mol rxn}$$

**Follow-Up Problem 21.5** When cadmium metal reduces $Cu^{2+}$ in solution, $Cd^{2+}$ forms in addition to copper metal. Given that $\Delta G^\circ = -143$ kJ/mol rxn, calculate $K$ at 25°C. What is $E^\circ_{cell}$ of a voltaic cell that uses this reaction?

## The Effect of Concentration on Cell Potential

So far, we've considered cells at standard-state conditions, but most cells don't start with those concentrations, and even if they did, concentrations change as the cell operates. Moreover, in all batteries, reactant concentrations are far from the standard state.

To determine $E_{cell}$, the cell potential under *nonstandard* conditions, we'll derive an expression for the relation between $E_{cell}$ and concentration based on the relation between $\Delta G$ and concentration. Recall from Chapter 20 (Equation 20.13) that

$$\Delta G = \Delta G^\circ + RT \ln Q$$

$\Delta G$ is related to $E_{cell}$ and $\Delta G^\circ$ to $E^\circ_{cell}$ (Equations 21.5 and 21.6), so we substitute for them and get

$$-nFE_{cell} = -nFE^\circ_{cell} + RT \ln Q$$

Dividing both sides by $-nF$, we obtain the equation developed by the great German chemist Walther Hermann Nernst when he was only 25 years old. (In his career, which culminated in the 1920 Nobel Prize, he also formulated the third law of thermodynamics and established the concept of the solubility product.) The **Nernst equation** says that $E_{cell}$ depends on $E^\circ_{cell}$ *and* a term for the potential at any ratio of concentrations:

$$E_{cell} = E^\circ_{cell} - \frac{RT}{nF} \ln Q \tag{21.9}$$

How do changes in $Q$ affect cell potential? From Equation 21.9, we see that

- When $Q < 1$ and thus [reactant] > [product], $\ln Q < 0$, so $E_{cell} > E^\circ_{cell}$.
- When $Q = 1$ and thus [reactant] = [product], $\ln Q = 0$, so $E_{cell} = E^\circ_{cell}$.
- When $Q > 1$ and thus [reactant] < [product], $\ln Q > 0$, so $E_{cell} < E^\circ_{cell}$.

As before, to obtain a form for calculations, we substitute known values of $R$ and $F$, operate the cell at 298.15 K, and convert to common (base-10) logarithms:

$$E_{cell} = E^\circ_{cell} - \frac{RT}{nF} \ln Q$$

$$= E^\circ_{cell} - 2.303 \times \frac{8.314 \dfrac{\cancel{J}}{\text{mol rxn·K}} \times 298.15 \text{ K}}{\dfrac{n \cancel{\text{ mol e}^-}}{\text{mol rxn}} \left( 9.65 \times 10^4 \dfrac{\cancel{J}}{\text{V·}\cancel{\text{mol e}^-}} \right)} \log Q$$

We obtain:

$$E_{cell} = E^\circ_{cell} - \frac{0.0592 \text{ V}}{n} \log Q \quad \text{(at 298.15 K)} \tag{21.10}$$

Remember that the expression for $Q$ contains only those species with concentrations (and/or pressures) that can vary; thus, solids do not appear, even when they are the electrodes. For example, in the reaction between cadmium and silver ion, the Cd and Ag electrodes do not appear in the expression for $Q$:

$$Cd(s) + 2Ag^+(aq) \longrightarrow Cd^{2+}(aq) + 2Ag(s) \qquad Q = \frac{[Cd^{2+}]}{[Ag^+]^2}$$

## Sample Problem 21.6 Using the Nernst Equation to Calculate $E_{cell}$

**Problem** In a test of a new reference electrode, a chemist constructs a voltaic cell consisting of a $Zn/Zn^{2+}$ half-cell and an $H_2/H^+$ half-cell under the following conditions:

$$[Zn^{2+}] = 0.010\ M \qquad [H^+] = 2.5\ M \qquad P_{H_2} = 0.30\ atm$$

Calculate $E_{cell}$ at 298.15 K.

**Plan** To apply the Nernst equation and determine $E_{cell}$, we must know $E°_{cell}$ and $Q$. We write the spontaneous reaction and calculate $E°_{cell}$ from standard electrode potentials (Appendix D). To have consistent units, we convert the given pressure to molarity with the ideal gas law and find $Q$. Then we substitute into Equation 21.10.

**Solution** Determining the cell reaction and $E°_{cell}$:

| | |
|---|---|
| $2H^+(aq) + 2e^- \longrightarrow H_2(g)$ | $E° = 0.00\ V$ |
| $Zn(s) \longrightarrow Zn^{2+}(aq) + 2e^-$ | $E° = -0.76\ V$ |
| $2H^+(aq) + Zn(s) \longrightarrow H_2(g) + Zn^{2+}(aq)$ | $E°_{cell} = 0.00\ V - (-0.76\ V) = 0.76\ V$ |

Converting pressure to molarity: $PV = nRT$, or

$$\frac{n}{V} = \frac{P}{RT} = \frac{0.30\ atm}{0.0821\ \dfrac{atm \cdot L}{mol \cdot K} \times 298.15\ K} = 1.2 \times 10^{-2}\ mol/L = 0.012\ M$$

Calculating $Q$:

$$Q = \frac{[H_2] \times [Zn^{2+}]}{[H^+]^2} = \frac{0.012 \times 0.010}{2.5^2} = 1.9 \times 10^{-5}$$

Solving for $E_{cell}$ at 25°C (298.15 K), with $n = 2$:

$$E_{cell} = E°_{cell} - \frac{0.0592\ V}{n} \log Q$$

$$= 0.76\ V - \left[\frac{0.0592\ V}{2} \log (1.9 \times 10^{-5})\right] = 0.76\ V - (-0.14\ V) = \boxed{0.90\ V}$$

**Check** After you check the arithmetic, reason through the answer: $E_{cell} > E°_{cell}$ (0.90 > 0.76) because the log $Q$ term was negative, which is consistent with $Q < 1$.

**Follow-Up Problem 21.6** Consider a voltaic cell based on the following reaction: $Fe(s) + Cu^{2+}(aq) \longrightarrow Fe^{2+}(aq) + Cu(s)$. If $[Cu^{2+}] = 0.30\ M$, what must $[Fe^{2+}]$ be to increase $E_{cell}$ by 0.25 V above $E°_{cell}$ at 25°C?

## Changes in Potential During Cell Operation

As with any voltaic cell, the potential of the zinc-copper cell changes during cell operation because the concentrations of the components do. With both of the other components solids, the only variables are $[Cu^{2+}]$ and $[Zn^{2+}]$:

$$Zn(s) + Cu^{2+}(aq) \longrightarrow Zn^{2+}(aq) + Cu(s) \qquad Q = \frac{[Zn^{2+}]}{[Cu^{2+}]}$$

In this section, we follow the potential as the zinc-copper cell operates.

1. *Starting point of cell operation.* The positive $E°_{cell}$ (1.10 V) means that this reaction proceeds *spontaneously* to the right at standard-state conditions, $[Zn^{2+}] = [Cu^{2+}] = 1\ M$ ($Q = 1$). However, if we start the cell when $[Zn^{2+}] < [Cu^{2+}]$ ($Q < 1$), for example, $[Zn^{2+}] = 1.0 \times 10^{-4}\ M$ and $[Cu^{2+}] = 2.0\ M$, the cell potential starts out *higher* than the standard cell potential:

$$E_{cell} = E°_{cell} - \frac{0.0592\ V}{2} \log \frac{[Zn^{2+}]}{[Cu^{2+}]} = 1.10\ V - \left(\frac{0.0592\ V}{2} \log \frac{1.0 \times 10^{-4}}{2.0}\right)$$

$$= 1.10\ V - \left[\frac{0.0592\ V}{2}(-4.30)\right] = 1.10\ V + 0.127\ V = 1.23\ V$$

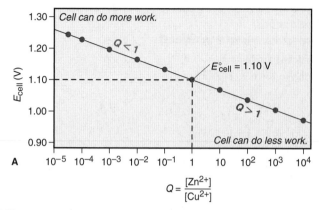

$$Q = \frac{[Zn^{2+}]}{[Cu^{2+}]}$$

**Figure 21.11** The relation between $E_{cell}$ and log $Q$ for the zinc-copper cell. **A,** A plot of $E_{cell}$ vs. $Q$ (on a logarithmic scale) decreases linearly. When $Q < 1$ (*left*), the cell does relatively more work. When $Q = 1$, $E_{cell} = E°_{cell}$. When $Q > 1$ (*right*), the cell does relatively less work. **B,** A summary of the changes in $E_{cell}$ as this or any voltaic cell operates. ($[Zn^{2+}]$ is [P] for [product], and $[Cu^{2+}]$ is [R] for [reactant].)

2. *Key stages during cell operation.* Using Equation 21.10, we identify four key stages of operation. Figure 21.11A shows the first three. The main point is that *as the cell operates, its potential decreases.* As $[Zn^{2+}]$ increases and $[Cu^{2+}]$ decreases, $Q$ becomes larger, the $[(0.0592 \text{ V}/n) \log Q]$ term becomes less negative (more positive), and $E_{cell}$ decreases:

*Stage 1.* $E_{cell} > E°_{cell}$ when $Q < 1$: When the cell begins operation, $[Cu^{2+}] > [Zn^{2+}]$, so $(0.0592 \text{ V}/n) \log Q < 0$ and $E_{cell} > E°_{cell}$.

*Stage 2.* $E_{cell} = E°_{cell}$ when $Q = 1$: At the point when $[Cu^{2+}] = [Zn^{2+}]$, $Q = 1$, so $(0.0592 \text{ V}/n) \log Q = 0$ and $E_{cell} = E°_{cell}$.

*Stage 3.* $E_{cell} < E°_{cell}$ when $Q > 1$: As the $[Zn^{2+}]/[Cu^{2+}]$ ratio continues to increase, $(0.0592 \text{ V}/n) \log Q > 0$, so $E_{cell} < E°_{cell}$.

*Stage 4.* $E_{cell} = 0$ when $Q = K$: Eventually, $(0.0592 \text{ V}/n) \log Q$ becomes so large that it equals $E°_{cell}$, which means that $E_{cell}$ is zero. This occurs *when the system reaches **equilibrium:** no more free energy is released, so the cell can do no more work.* At this point, we say that a battery is "dead."

Figure 21.11B summarizes these four key stages during operation of a voltaic cell.

3. *Q/K and the work the cell can do.* At equilibrium, Equation 21.10 becomes

$$0 = E°_{cell} - \left(\frac{0.0592 \text{ V}}{n}\right) \log K, \quad \text{which rearranges to} \quad E°_{cell} = \frac{0.0592 \text{ V}}{n} \log K$$

Note that this result is identical to Equation 21.8, which we obtained from $\Delta G°$. Solving for $K$ of the zinc-copper cell ($E°_{cell} = 1.10 \text{ V}$),

$$\log K = \frac{2 \times E°_{cell}}{0.0592 \text{ V}} \quad \text{so} \quad K = 10^{(2 \times 1.10 \text{ V})/0.0592 \text{ V}} = 10^{37.16} = 1.4 \times 10^{37}$$

As you can see, this cell does work until $[Zn^{2+}]/[Cu^{2+}]$ is *very* high.

The three relations between initial $Q/K$ and $E_{cell}$ are:

- If $Q/K < 1$, $E_{cell}$ is positive for the reaction *as written*. The smaller $Q/K$ is, the greater the value of $E_{cell}$, and the more electrical work the cell can do.
- If $Q/K = 1$, $E_{cell} = 0$. The cell is at equilibrium and can no longer do work.
- If $Q/K > 1$, $E_{cell}$ is negative for the reaction as written. The reverse reaction will take place, and the cell will do work until $Q/K$ equals 1 at equilibrium.

## Concentration Cells

If you mix a concentrated solution of a substance with a dilute solution of it, the final solution has an intermediate concentration. A **concentration cell** employs this simple, spontaneous change to generate electrical energy. The two solutions are in separate half-cells, so they do not mix, but their concentrations become equal as the cell operates.

**Finding $E_{cell}$ for a Concentration Cell**  Suppose a voltaic cell has the $Cu/Cu^{2+}$ half-reaction in both compartments. The cell reaction is the sum of identical half-reactions, written in opposite directions. The *standard* cell potential, $E°_{cell}$, is zero because the *standard* electrode potentials are both based on 1 $M$ $Cu^{2+}$, so they cancel. *In a concentration cell, however, the concentrations are different.* Thus, even though $E°_{cell}$ is still zero, the *nonstandard* cell potential, $E_{cell}$, depends on the *ratio of concentrations,* so it is *not* zero.

For the final concentration to be equal, a concentration cell must have the dilute solution in the anode compartment and the concentrated solution in the cathode compartment. For example, let's use 0.10 $M$ $Cu^{2+}$ in the anode half-cell and 1.0 $M$ $Cu^{2+}$, a 10-fold higher concentration, in the cathode half-cell (Figure 21.12A):

$$Cu(s) \longrightarrow Cu^{2+}(aq; 0.10\ M) + 2e^- \quad [\text{anode; oxidation}]$$
$$Cu^{2+}(aq; 1.0\ M) + 2e^- \longrightarrow Cu(s) \quad [\text{cathode; reduction}]$$

The overall cell reaction is the sum of the half-reactions:

$$Cu^{2+}(aq; 1.0\ M) \longrightarrow Cu^{2+}(aq; 0.10\ M) \quad E_{cell} = ?$$

The cell potential at the initial concentrations of 0.10 $M$ (dilute) and 1.0 $M$ (concentrated), with $n = 2$, is obtained from the Nernst equation:

$$E_{cell} = E°_{cell} - \frac{0.0592\ V}{2} \log \frac{[Cu^{2+}]_{dil}}{[Cu^{2+}]_{conc}} = 0\ V - \left( \frac{0.0592\ V}{2} \log \frac{0.10\ M}{1.0\ M} \right)$$

$$= 0\ V - \left[ \frac{0.0592\ V}{2} (-1.00) \right] = 0.0296\ V$$

Since $E°_{cell}$ is zero, $E_{cell}$ depends entirely on the $[(0.0592\ V/n) \log Q]$ term.

**How a Concentration Cell Works**  Let's see what is happening as this cell operates:

- In the anode (dilute) half-cell, Cu atoms in the electrode give up electrons and the resulting $Cu^{2+}$ ions enter the solution and make it *more* concentrated.
- In the cathode (concentrated) half-cell, $Cu^{2+}$ ions gain the electrons and the resulting Cu atoms plate out on the electrode, which makes that solution *less* concentrated.

As in any voltaic cell, $E_{cell}$ decreases until equilibrium is attained, which happens when $[Cu^{2+}]$ is the same in both half-cells (Figure 21.12B). The same final concentration would result if we mixed the two solutions, but no electrical work would be done.

Oxidation half-reaction
$Cu(s) \longrightarrow Cu^{2+}(aq; 0.10\ M) + 2e^-$

Reduction half-reaction
$Cu^{2+}(aq; 1.0\ M) + 2e^- \longrightarrow Cu(s)$

Overall (cell) reaction
$Cu^{2+}(aq; 1.0\ M) \longrightarrow Cu^{2+}(aq; 0.10\ M)$

**A**

**B**

**Figure 21.12** A concentration cell based on the $Cu/Cu^{2+}$ half-reaction. **A,** $E_{cell} > 0$ as long as the half-cell *concentrations* are different. **B,** Half-cell concentrations are equal (same color), and the sizes of the electrodes (exaggerated for clarity) are different.

## Sample Problem 21.7 Calculating the Potential of a Concentration Cell

**Problem** A concentration cell consists of two $Ag/Ag^+$ half-cells. In half-cell A, the electrolyte is 0.010 $M$ $AgNO_3$; in half-cell B, it is $4.0 \times 10^{-4}$ $M$ $AgNO_3$. What is the cell potential at 298.15 K?

**Plan** The standard half-cell reactions are identical, so $E^\circ_{cell}$ is zero, and we find $E_{cell}$ from the Nernst equation. Half-cell A has a higher $[Ag^+]$, so $Ag^+$ ions are reduced and plate out on electrode A. In half-cell B, Ag atoms of the electrode are oxidized and $Ag^+$ ions enter the solution. As in all voltaic cells, reduction occurs at the cathode, so it is positive.

**Solution** Writing the spontaneous reaction: The $[Ag^+]$ decreases in half-cell A and increases in half-cell B, so the spontaneous reaction is

$$Ag^+(aq; 0.010\ M)\ [\text{half-cell A}] \longrightarrow Ag^+(aq; 4.0 \times 10^{-4}\ M)\ [\text{half-cell B}]$$

Calculating $E_{cell}$, with $n = 1$:

$$E_{cell} = E^\circ_{cell} - \frac{0.0592\ \text{V}}{1} \log \frac{[Ag^+]_{dil}}{[Ag^+]_{conc}} = 0\ \text{V} - \left(0.0592\ \text{V} \log \frac{4.0 \times 10^{-4}}{0.010}\right)$$

$$= \boxed{0.0828\ \text{V}}$$

**Follow-Up Problem 21.7** A concentration cell is built using two $Au/Au^{3+}$ half-cells. In half-cell A, $[Au^{3+}] = 7.0 \times 10^{-4}$ $M$, and in half-cell B, $[Au^{3+}] = 2.5 \times 10^{-2}$ $M$. What is $E_{cell}$, and which electrode is negative?

**Applications of Concentration Cells** The principle of a concentration cell has many applications. Here, we'll discuss three:

1. *The pH meter.* The most important laboratory application of this principle is in measuring $[H^+]$. If we construct a concentration cell in which the cathode compartment is the standard hydrogen electrode and the anode compartment has the same apparatus dipping into a solution of unknown $[H^+]$, the half-reactions and overall reaction are

$$H_2(g; 1\ \text{atm}) \longrightarrow 2H^+(aq; \text{unknown}) + 2e^- \quad [\text{anode; oxidation}]$$
$$\underline{2H^+(aq; 1\ M) + 2e^- \longrightarrow H_2(g; 1\ \text{atm})} \quad\quad\quad [\text{cathode; reduction}]$$
$$2H^+(aq; 1\ M) \longrightarrow 2H^+(aq; \text{unknown}) \quad E_{cell} = ?$$

$E^\circ_{cell}$ is zero, but $E_{cell}$ is *not* because the half-cells differ in $[H^+]$. From the Nernst equation, with $n = 2$, we have

$$E_{cell} = E^\circ_{cell} - \frac{0.0592\ \text{V}}{2} \log \frac{[H^+]^2_{unknown}}{[H^+]^2_{standard}}$$

Substituting 1 $M$ for $[H^+]_{standard}$ and 0 V for $E^\circ_{cell}$ gives

$$E_{cell} = 0\ \text{V} - \frac{0.0592\ \text{V}}{2} \log \frac{[H^+]^2_{unknown}}{1^2} = -\frac{0.0592\ \text{V}}{2} \log [H^+]^2_{unknown}$$

Because $\log x^2 = 2 \log x$ (see Appendix A), we obtain

$$E_{cell} = -\left[\frac{0.0592\ \text{V}}{2} (2 \log [H^+]_{unknown})\right] = -0.0592\ \text{V} \times \log [H^+]_{unknown}$$

Substituting $-\log [H^+] = \text{pH}$, we have

$$E_{cell} = 0.0592\ \text{V} \times \text{pH}$$

Thus, by measuring $E_{cell}$, we can find the pH.

For routine lab measurement of pH, a concentration cell made of two hydrogen electrodes is too bulky and difficult to maintain. Instead, we use a pH meter (Figure 21.13A). In a common, but older, design, two separate electrodes dip into the solution being tested:

GLASS ELECTRODE
Pt
REFERENCE (CALOMEL) ELECTRODE

AgCl on Ag on Pt
1 *M* HCl
Thin glass membrane
Test solution pH = ?

Hg
Paste of Hg₂Cl₂ in Hg
KCl solution
Porous ceramic plug

**A**

GLASS ELECTRODE
REFERENCE (CALOMEL) ELECTRODE

Test solution pH = ?

**B**

**Figure 21.13 Laboratory measurement of pH. A,** An older style pH meter includes a glass electrode (*left*) and a reference calomel electrode (*right*). **B,** Modern pH meters use a combination electrode.

- The *glass electrode* consists of an Ag/AgCl half-reaction immersed in HCl solution (usually 1.000 *M*) and enclosed by a thin (~0.05 mm) membrane made of a glass that is very sensitive to H⁺ ions.
- The *reference electrode,* usually a *saturated calomel electrode,* consists of a platinum wire immersed in calomel ($Hg_2Cl_2$) paste, liquid Hg, and saturated KCl solution.

The glass electrode monitors the solution's [H⁺] relative to its own fixed internal [H⁺], and the instrument converts the potential difference between the glass and reference electrodes into a measure of pH. In modern instruments, a *combination* electrode that houses both electrodes in one tube is used (Figure 21.13B).

*2. Measuring ions selectively.* The pH electrode is one type of *ion-selective (or ion-specific) electrode.* These are designed with specialized membranes to selectively measure certain ion concentrations in a mixture of many, as in natural waters and soils. Biologists implant a tiny ion-selective electrode in a single cell to study ion channels and receptors. Recent advances allow measurement in the femtomolar ($10^{-15}$ *M*) range. Table 21.3 shows a few of the ions studied.

*3. Concentration cells in nerves.* A nerve cell membrane is imbedded with enzyme "gates" that use the energy of one-third of the body's ATP to create an ion gradient of low [Na⁺] and high [K⁺] inside and high [Na⁺] and low [K⁺] outside. As a result of these differences, the outside of a nerve cell is more positive than the inside. (The 1997 Nobel Prize in chemistry was shared by Jens C. Skou for elucidating this mechanism.) When the nerve membrane is stimulated, an electrical impulse is created as Na⁺ ions rush in spontaneously and the inside becomes more positive than the outside. This event is followed by K⁺ ions spontaneously rushing out, and the outside becomes more positive again; the whole process takes about 0.002 s! These large changes in charge in one membrane region stimulate the neighboring region and the electrical impulse moves along the cell (Figure 21.14).

**Table 21.3 Some Ions Measured with Ion-Specific Electrodes**

| Species Detected | Typical Sample |
|---|---|
| $NH_3/NH_4^+$ | Industrial wastewater, seawater |
| $CO_2/HCO_3^-$ | Blood, groundwater |
| F⁻ | Drinking water, urine, soil, industrial stack gases |
| Br⁻ | Grain, plant tissue |
| I⁻ | Milk, pharmaceuticals |
| $NO_3^-$ | Soil, fertilizer, drinking water |
| K⁺ | Blood serum, soil, wine |
| H⁺ | Laboratory solutions, soil, natural waters |

## Summary of Section 21.4

- A spontaneous process has a negative $\Delta G$ and a positive $E_{cell}$, $\Delta G = -nFE_{cell}$. The $\Delta G$ of the cell reaction represents the maximum electrical work the cell can do.
- The standard free energy change, $\Delta G°$, is related to $E°_{cell}$ and to $K$.
- For nonstandard conditions, the Nernst equation shows that $E_{cell}$ depends on $E°_{cell}$ and a correction term based on $Q$. $E_{cell}$ is high when $Q$ is small (high [reactant]), and it decreases as the cell operates. At equilibrium, $\Delta G$ and $E_{cell}$ are zero, which means that $Q = K$.
- Concentration cells have identical half-reactions, but solutions of differing concentration. They generate electrical energy as the concentrations become equal.
- Ion-specific electrodes, such as the pH electrode, measure the concentration of one species.
- The principle of the concentration cell—spontaneous movement of ions across a concentration gradient—creates an electrical impulse in a nerve cell.

**Figure 21.14 Minimicroanalysis.** A microelectrode records electrical impulses of a single neuron in a monkey's visual cortex.

# 21.5 • ELECTROCHEMICAL PROCESSES IN BATTERIES

Because of their compactness and mobility, batteries play a major role in everyday life, and in our increasingly wireless world, that role is growing. In general, a **battery** consists of self-contained voltaic cells arranged in series (plus-to-minus-to-plus, and so on), so that their individual voltages are added. In this section, we examine the three categories of batteries—primary, secondary, and fuel cells (flow batteries).

## Primary (Nonrechargeable) Batteries

A *primary battery* cannot be recharged, so it is discarded when the cell reaction has reached equilibrium, that is, when the battery is "dead." We'll discuss the alkaline battery, mercury and silver "button" batteries, and the primary lithium battery.

**Alkaline Battery** Invented in the 1860s, the common dry cell—the precursor of today's ubiquitous alkaline battery—was a familiar item into the 1970s. The anode is a zinc can that houses a mixture of $MnO_2$ and a weakly acidic electrolyte paste, consisting of $NH_4Cl$, $ZnCl_2$, $H_2O$, and starch. Powdered graphite improves conductivity, and the cathode is a graphite rod. Even today, the cathode half-reaction is not completely understood, but we know that it involves the reduction of $MnO_2(s)$ to $Mn_2O_3(s)$ and an acid-base reaction between $NH_4^+$ and $OH^-$. At a high current drain, this reaction yields $NH_3$ gas, which can cause a large voltage drop. Moreover, because the zinc anode reacts with the acidic $NH_4^+$, dry cells have a short shelf life.

The alkaline battery avoids these drawbacks. The same electrode materials, zinc and manganese dioxide, are used, but the electrolyte is a basic paste of KOH and water (Figure 21.15). The half-reactions are essentially the same, but KOH eliminates buildup of $NH_3$ gas and maintains the Zn electrode:

*Anode (oxidation):* $\quad\quad\quad\quad Zn(s) + 2OH^-(aq) \longrightarrow ZnO(s) + H_2O(l) + 2e^-$

*Cathode (reduction):* $\quad MnO_2(s) + 2H_2O(l) + 2e^- \longrightarrow Mn(OH)_2(s) + 2OH^-(aq)$

*Overall (cell) reaction:*

$$Zn(s) + MnO_2(s) + H_2O(l) \longrightarrow ZnO(s) + Mn(OH)_2(s) \quad E_{cell} = 1.5\ V$$

The alkaline battery powers portable radios, toys, flashlights, and so on, is safe, and comes in many sizes. It has no voltage drop, a longer shelf life, and better performance than the dry cell in terms of power capability and stored energy.

**Figure 21.15** Alkaline battery.

Positive button
Steel case
Zn (anode)
$MnO_2$ in KOH paste
Graphite rod (cathode)
Absorbent/separator
Negative end cap

**Mercury and Silver (Button) Batteries** Both mercury and silver batteries use a zinc container as the anode (reducing agent) in a basic medium. The mercury battery employs HgO as the oxidizing agent, the silver uses $Ag_2O$, and both use a steel can

Anode cap
Cathode can
Zn in KOH gel (anode, −)
Gasket
Separator
Pellets of $Ag_2O$ in graphite (cathode, +)

**Figure 21.16** Silver button battery.

around the cathode. The solid reactants are compacted with KOH and separated with moist paper. The half-reactions are

*Anode (oxidation):* $\quad Zn(s) + 2OH^-(aq) \longrightarrow ZnO(s) + H_2O(l) + 2e^-$

*Cathode (reduction) (mercury):* $HgO(s) + H_2O(l) + 2e^- \longrightarrow Hg(l) + 2OH^-(aq)$

*Cathode (reduction) (silver):* $\quad Ag_2O(s) + H_2O(l) + 2e^- \longrightarrow 2Ag(s) + 2OH^-(aq)$

*Overall (cell) reaction (mercury):*

$$Zn(s) + HgO(s) \longrightarrow ZnO(s) + Hg(l) \qquad E_{cell} = 1.3\ V$$

*Overall (cell) reaction (silver):*

$$Zn(s) + Ag_2O(s) \longrightarrow ZnO(s) + 2Ag(s) \qquad E_{cell} = 1.6\ V$$

Both cells are manufactured as button-sized batteries. The mercury cell is used in calculators and the silver cell (Figure 21.16) in watches, cameras, heart pacemakers, and hearing aids because of its very steady output. Disadvantages are the toxicity of discarded mercury and the high cost of silver.

**Primary Lithium Batteries** The primary lithium battery is also widely used in watches and implanted medical products, and more recently in numerous remote-control devices. It offers an extremely high energy/mass ratio, producing 1 mol of $e^-$ (1 $F$) from less than 7 g of metal ($\mathcal{M}$ of Li = 6.941 g/mol). The anode is lithium foil in a nonaqueous electrolyte. The cathode is one of several metal oxides in which lithium ions lie between oxide layers. Some pacemakers have a silver vanadium oxide (SVO; $AgV_2O_{5.5}$) cathode and can provide power (1.5 to 3.5 V) for several years, but at a low rate because energy storage is limited (Figure 21.17). The half-reactions are

*Anode (oxidation):* $\quad 3.5Li(s) \longrightarrow 3.5Li^+ + 3.5e^-$

*Cathode (reduction):* $\quad AgV_2O_{5.5} + 3.5Li^+ + 3.5e^- \longrightarrow Li_{3.5}AgV_2O_{5.5}$

*Overall (cell) reaction:* $\quad AgV_2O_{5.5} + 3.5Li(s) \longrightarrow Li_{3.5}AgV_2O_{5.5}$

Heart pacemaker

Feedthrough pin (+)
Stainless steel case (−)
Insulative seal
Multiplate cell stack
Electrolyte fill hole
Cathode lead bridge
Polypropylene separator
Lithium (anode)
SVO (cathode)

**Figure 21.17** Lithium battery.

## Secondary (Rechargeable) Batteries

In contrast to a primary battery, a *secondary battery* is *rechargeable;* when it runs down, *electrical energy is supplied to reverse the cell reaction* and form more reactant. In other words, in a secondary battery, the voltaic cells are periodically converted to electrolytic cells to restore *nonequilibrium* concentrations of the cell components. We'll discuss the common car battery, the nickel–metal hydride battery, and the lithium-ion battery, a secondary lithium battery.

**Lead-Acid Battery** A typical lead-acid car battery has six cells connected in series, each of which delivers about 2.1 V for a total of about 12 V. Each cell contains two lead grids packed with high-surface-area (spongy) Pb in the anode and high-surface-area $PbO_2$ in the cathode. The grids are immersed in a solution of ~4.5 $M$ $H_2SO_4$. Fiberglass sheets between the grids prevent shorting due to physical contact (Figure 21.18).

1. *Discharging.* When the cell discharges as a voltaic cell, it generates electrical energy:

*Anode (oxidation):* $\quad Pb(s) + HSO_4^-(aq) \longrightarrow PbSO_4(s) + H^+ + 2e^-$

*Cathode (reduction):*

$$PbO_2(s) + 3H^+(aq) + HSO_4^-(aq) + 2e^- \longrightarrow PbSO_4(s) + 2H_2O(l)$$

Cathode (positive): lead grids filled with $PbO_2$
Anode (negative): similar grids filled with spongy lead
$H_2SO_4$ electrolyte

**Figure 21.18** Lead-acid battery.

Both half-reactions form $Pb^{2+}$ ions, one through oxidation of Pb, the other through reduction of $PbO_2$. The $Pb^{2+}$ forms $PbSO_4(s)$ at both electrodes by reacting with $HSO_4^-$.

*Overall (cell) reaction (discharge):*

$$PbO_2(s) + Pb(s) + 2H_2SO_4(aq) \longrightarrow 2PbSO_4(s) + 2H_2O(l) \qquad E_{cell} = 2.1 \text{ V}$$

2. *Recharging.* When the cell recharges as an electrolytic cell, it uses electrical energy and the half-cell and overall reactions are reversed.

*Overall (cell) reaction (recharge):*

$$2PbSO_4(s) + 2H_2O(l) \longrightarrow PbO_2(s) + Pb(s) + 2H_2SO_4(aq)$$

Car and truck owners have relied on the lead-acid battery for over a century to provide the large burst of current needed to start the engine—and to do it in hot and cold weather for years. The main problems with the lead-acid battery are loss of capacity due to corrosion of the positive (Pb) grid, detachment of the active material due to normal mechanical bumping, and formation of large $PbSO_4$ crystals that hinder recharging.

**Nickel–Metal Hydride (Ni-MH) Battery** Concerns about the toxicity of cadmium in the nickel-cadmium (nicad) battery have led to its replacement by the nickel–metal hydride battery. The anode half-reaction oxidizes the hydrogen absorbed within a metal alloy (such as $LaNi_5$; designated M) in a basic (KOH) electrolyte, while nickel(III) in the form of NiO(OH) is reduced at the cathode (Figure 21.19):

*Anode (oxidation):* $\qquad\qquad MH(s) + OH^-(aq) \longrightarrow M(s) + H_2O(l) + e^-$

*Cathode (reduction):* $NiO(OH)(s) + H_2O(l) + e^- \longrightarrow Ni(OH)_2(s) + OH^-(aq)$

*Overall (cell) reaction:* $\quad MH(s) + NiO(OH)(s) \longrightarrow M(s) + Ni(OH)_2(s)$

$$E_{cell} = 1.4 \text{ V}$$

The cell reaction is reversed during recharging. The Ni-MH battery is common in cordless razors, camera flash units, and power tools. It is lightweight, has high power, and is nontoxic, but it discharges significantly during storage.

**Figure 21.19** Nickel–metal hydride battery.

**Lithium-Ion Battery** The secondary lithium-ion battery has an anode of Li atoms that lie between sheets of graphite (designated $Li_xC_6$). The cathode is a lithium metal oxide, such as $LiMn_2O_4$ or $LiCoO_2$, and a typical electrolyte is 1 $M$ $LiPF_6$ in an organic solvent, such as dimethyl carbonate mixed with methylethyl carbonate. Electrons flow through the circuit, while solvated $Li^+$ ions flow from anode to cathode within the cell (Figure 21.20). The cell reactions are

*Anode (oxidation):* $\qquad\qquad\qquad\qquad\qquad Li_xC_6 \longrightarrow xLi^+ + xe^- + C_6(s)$

*Cathode (reduction):* $Li_{1-x}Mn_2O_4(s) + xLi^+ + xe^- \longrightarrow LiMn_2O_4(s)$

*Overall (cell) reaction:* $\quad Li_xC_6 + Li_{1-x}Mn_2O_4(s) \longrightarrow LiMn_2O_4(s) + C_6(s)$

$$E_{cell} = 3.7 \text{ V}$$

The cell reaction is reversed during recharging. The lithium-ion battery powers countless laptop computers, cell phones, and camcorders. Its key drawbacks are cost and flammability of the organic solvent.

**Figure 21.20** Lithium-ion battery.

# Fuel Cells

In contrast to primary and secondary batteries, a **fuel cell,** sometimes called a *flow battery,* is not self-contained. The reactants (usually a fuel and oxygen) enter the cell, and the products leave, *generating electricity through controlled combustion* of the fuel. The fuel does not burn because, as in other voltaic cells, the half-reactions are separated, and the electrons move through an external circuit.

The most common fuel cell being developed for use in cars is the *proton exchange membrane (PEM) cell,* which uses $H_2$ as the fuel and has an operating temperature of around 80°C (Figure 21.21). The cell reactions are

*Anode (oxidation):* $\qquad\qquad\qquad 2H_2(g) \longrightarrow 4H^+(aq) + 4e^-$

*Cathode (reduction):* $\quad O_2(g) + 4H^+(aq) + 4e^- \longrightarrow 2H_2O(g)$

*Overall (cell) reaction:* $\qquad 2H_2(g) + O_2(g) \longrightarrow 2H_2O(g) \qquad E_{cell} = 1.2$ V

**Figure 21.21** Hydrogen fuel cell.

**How $H_2$ Fuel Cells Work**  Reaction rates are lower in fuel cells than in other batteries, so an *electrocatalyst* is used to decrease the activation energy (Section 16.7). The PEM cell's electrodes are made of a nanocomposite consisting of a Pt-based catalyst deposited on graphite. These are embedded in a polymer electrolyte membrane having a perfluoroethylene backbone ($-[F_2C-CF_2]_n-$) with attached sulfonic acid groups ($RSO_3^-$) that play a key role in ferrying protons from anode to cathode.

- *At the anode,* two $H_2$ molecules adsorb onto the catalyst and are split and oxidized. From each $H_2$, two $e^-$ travel through the wire to the cathode, while two $H^+$ are hydrated and migrate through the electrolyte as $H_3O^+$.

- *At the cathode,* an $O_2$ molecule is believed to adsorb onto the catalyst, which provides an $e^-$ to form $O_2^-$. One $H_3O^+$ donates its $H^+$ to the $O_2^-$, forming $HO_2$ (that is, HO—O). The O—O bond stretches and breaks as another $H_3O^+$ gives its $H^+$ and the catalyst provides another $e^-$: the first $H_2O$ has formed. In similar fashion, a third $H^+$ and $e^-$ attach to the freed O atom to form OH, and a fourth $H^+$ and $e^-$ are transferred to form the second $H_2O$. Both water molecules desorb and leave the cell.

**Applications of Fuel Cells**  Hydrogen fuel cells have been used for years to provide electricity *and* water during space flights. Similar ones have begun to supply electric power for residential needs, and every major car manufacturer has a fuel-cell prototype. Fuel cells produce no pollutants and convert about 75% of a fuel's bond energy into power, compared to 40% for a coal-fired power plant and 25% for a gasoline engine.

## ■ Summary of Section 21.5

- Batteries are voltaic cells arranged in series and are classified as primary (e.g., alkaline, mercury, silver, and lithium), secondary (e.g., lead-acid, nickel–metal hydride, and lithium-ion), or fuel cells.
- Supplying electricity to a rechargeable (secondary) battery reverses the redox reaction, re-forming reactant.
- Fuel cells generate a current through the controlled oxidation of a fuel such as $H_2$.

# 21.6 • CORROSION: AN ENVIRONMENTAL VOLTAIC CELL

If you think all spontaneous electrochemical processes are useful, consider the problem of **corrosion,** which causes tens of billions of dollars of damage to cars, ships, buildings, and bridges each year. This natural process, which oxidizes metals to their oxides and sulfides, shares similarities with the operation of a voltaic cell. We focus on the corrosion of iron, but many metals, such as copper and silver, also corrode.

## The Corrosion of Iron

The most common and economically destructive form of corrosion is the rusting of iron. About 25% of the steel produced in the United States each year is for replacing steel in which the iron has corroded. Rust is *not* a direct product of the reaction between iron and oxygen but arises through a complex electrochemical process. Let's look at the facts of iron corrosion and then use the features of a voltaic cell to explain them:

Fact 1.  Iron does not rust in dry air; moisture must be present.
Fact 2.  Iron does not rust in air-free water; oxygen must be present.
Fact 3.  Iron loss and rust formation occur at *different* places on the *same* object.
Fact 4.  Iron rusts more quickly at low pH (high $[H^+]$).
Fact 5.  Iron rusts more quickly in ionic solutions.
Fact 6.  Iron rusts more quickly in contact with a less active metal (such as Cu) and more slowly in contact with a more active metal (such as Zn).

Two separate redox processes occur during corrosion:

1. *The loss of iron.* Picture the surface of a piece of iron (Figure 21.22). A strain, ridge, or dent in contact with water is typically the site of iron loss (fact 1). This site is called an *anodic region* because the following half-reaction occurs there:

$$Fe(s) \longrightarrow Fe^{2+}(aq) + 2e^- \qquad [\text{anodic region; oxidation}]$$

Once the iron atoms lose electrons, the damage to the object has been done, and a pit forms where the iron is lost.

The freed electrons move through the external circuit—the piece of iron itself— until they reach a region of relatively high $[O_2]$ (fact 2), usually the air near the edge of a water droplet that surrounds the newly formed pit. At this *cathodic region*, the electrons released from the iron atoms reduce $O_2$:

$$O_2(g) + 4H^+(aq) + 4e^- \longrightarrow 2H_2O(l) \qquad [\text{cathodic region; reduction}]$$

**Figure 21.22 The corrosion of iron.**
**A,** False-color close-up view of an iron surface. Corrosion usually occurs at a surface irregularity. **B,** A small area of the surface, showing the steps in the corrosion process.

③ *The $Fe^{2+}$ migrates through the drop and reacts with $O_2$ and $H_2O$ to form rust.*

$\frac{3}{2} O_2$  Water droplet

$n\,H_2O$  $2H_2O$

$2Fe^{2+}$

② *Electrons at the Fe (inactive) cathode reduce $O_2$ to $H_2O$.*

Rust
$Fe_2O_3 \cdot nH_2O$

$4H^+$  $O_2$

$2Fe \longrightarrow 2Fe^{2+} + 4e^-$  pit  $4e^-$  **(cathodic region)**
**(anodic region)**

**IRON BAR**

① *Oxidation of Fe forms a pit and yields electrons, which travel through the metal.*

This portion of the corrosion process (the sum of these two half-reactions) occurs without any rust forming:

$$2Fe(s) + O_2(g) + 4H^+(aq) \longrightarrow 2Fe^{2+}(aq) + 2H_2O(l) \quad [\text{overall}]$$

2. *The rusting process.* Rust forms in another redox reaction. The $Fe^{2+}$ ions formed at the anodic region disperse through the water and react with $O_2$, often away from the pit, to form the $Fe^{3+}$ in rust (fact 3). The overall reaction for this step is

$$2Fe^{2+}(aq) + \tfrac{1}{2}O_2(g) + (2 + n)H_2O(l) \longrightarrow Fe_2O_3 \cdot nH_2O(s) + 4H^+(aq)$$

[The coefficient $n$ for $H_2O$ appears because rust, $Fe_2O_3 \cdot nH_2O$, has a variable number of waters of hydration.] The rust deposit is incidental to the real damage, which is the loss of iron that weakens the strength of the object. Adding the two previous equations gives the overall equation for the loss and rusting of iron:

$$2Fe(s) + \tfrac{3}{2}O_2(g) + nH_2O(l) + \cancel{4H^+(aq)} \longrightarrow Fe_2O_3 \cdot nH_2O(s) + \cancel{4H^+(aq)}$$

Other species (2 $Fe^{2+}$ and $2H_2O$) also cancel, but we showed the canceled $H^+$ ions to emphasize that they act as a catalyst: they speed the process as they are used up in one step and created in another. For this reason, rusting is faster at low pH (high $[H^+]$) (fact 4). Ionic solutions speed rusting by improving the conductivity of the aqueous medium near the anodic and cathodic regions (fact 5). The effect of ions is especially evident on ocean-going vessels (Figure 21.23) and on the underbodies and around the wheel wells of cars driven in cold climates, where salts are used to melt ice on slippery roads. (We discuss fact 6 in the next subsection.)

Thus, in some key ways, corrosion resembles the operation of a voltaic cell:

- Anodic and cathodic regions are physically separated.
- The regions are connected via an external circuit through which the electrons travel.
- In the anodic region, iron behaves like an active electrode, whereas in the cathodic region, it is inactive.
- The moisture surrounding the pit functions somewhat like an electrolye and salt bridge, a solution of ions and a means for them to move and keep the solution neutral.

**Figure 21.23 Enhanced corrosion at sea.**
The high ion concentration of seawater enhances the corrosion of iron in hulls and anchors.

## Protecting Against the Corrosion of Iron

Corrosion is prevented by eliminating corrosive factors. Washing road salt off auto bodies removes ions. Painting an object keeps out $O_2$ and moisture. Plating chromium on plumbing fixtures is a more permanent method, as is "blueing" of gun barrels and other steel objects, in which a coating of $Fe_3O_4$ (magnetite) is bonded to the surface.

The final point regarding corrosion (fact 6) concerns the relative activity of other metals in contact with iron. The essential idea is that *iron functions as both anode and cathode in the rusting process, but it is lost only at the anode.* Thus,

1. *Corrosion increases when iron behaves more like the anode.* When iron is in contact with a *less* active metal (weaker reducing agent), such as copper, it loses electrons more readily (its anodic function is enhanced; Figure 21.24A). For example, when iron plumbing is connected directly to copper plumbing, the iron pipe corrodes rapidly. Nonconducting rubber or plastic spacers are placed between the metals to avoid this problem.

**A Enhanced corrosion**

**B Cathodic protection**

**Figure 21.24 The effect of metal-metal contact on the corrosion of iron. A,** Fe in contact with Cu corrodes faster. **B,** Fe in contact with Zn does not corrode. The process is known as *cathodic protection.*

**Figure 21.25 The use of a sacrificial anode to prevent iron corrosion.** In cathodic protection, an active metal, such as zinc, magnesium, or aluminum, acts as the anode and is sacrificed instead of the iron.

2. *Corrosion decreases when iron behaves more like the cathode.* In *cathodic protection,* the most effective way to prevent corrosion, iron makes contact with a *more* active metal (stronger reducing agent), such as zinc. The iron becomes the cathode and remains intact, while the zinc acts as the anode and loses electrons (Figure 21.24B). Coating steel with a "sacrificial" layer of zinc is called *galvanizing.* In addition to blocking physical contact with $H_2O$ and $O_2$, the zinc (or other active metal) is "sacrificed" (oxidized) instead of the iron. Sacrificial anodes are used under water and underground to protect iron and steel pipes, tanks, oil rigs, and so on. Magnesium and aluminum are often used because they are much more active than iron and, thus, act as the anode (Figure 21.25). Moreover, they form adherent oxide coatings, which slow their own corrosion.

## Summary of Section 21.6

- Corrosion damages metal structures through a natural electrochemical process.
- Iron corrosion occurs in the presence of oxygen and moisture and is increased by high $[H^+]$, high [ion], or contact with a less active metal, such as Cu.
- Fe is oxidized and $O_2$ is reduced in one redox reaction, while $Fe^{2+}$ is oxidized and $O_2$ is reduced to form rust (hydrated form of $Fe_2O_3$) in another redox reaction that often takes place at a different location.
- Because Fe functions as both anode and cathode in the corrosion process, an iron object can be protected by physically covering it or by joining it to a more active metal (such as Zn, Mg, or Al), which acts as the anode in place of the Fe.

## 21.7 • ELECTROLYTIC CELLS: USING ELECTRICAL ENERGY TO DRIVE NONSPONTANEOUS REACTIONS

In contrast to a voltaic cell, which generates electrical energy from a spontaneous reaction, *an electrolytic cell requires electrical energy from an external source to drive a nonspontaneous redox reaction.* We discuss industrial electrolysis in Chapter 22.

### Construction and Operation of an Electrolytic Cell

Let's see how an electrolytic cell operates by constructing one from a voltaic cell. Consider a tin-copper voltaic cell (Figure 21.26A). The Sn anode will gradually be oxidized to $Sn^{2+}$ ions, which enter the electrolyte, and the $Cu^{2+}$ ions will gradually be reduced and plate out on the Cu cathode because the cell reaction is spontaneous in that direction:

*For the voltaic cell,*

$$Sn(s) \longrightarrow Sn^{2+}(aq) + 2e^- \qquad \text{[anode; oxidation]}$$
$$Cu^{2+}(aq) + 2e^- \longrightarrow Cu(s) \qquad \text{[cathode; reduction]}$$
$$\overline{Sn(s) + Cu^{2+}(aq) \longrightarrow Sn^{2+}(aq) + Cu(s) \qquad E°_{cell} = 0.48 \text{ V and } \Delta G° = -93 \text{ kJ}}$$

Therefore, the *reverse* cell reaction is *non*spontaneous and never happens on its own. But, we can make it happen by supplying an electric potential *greater than* $E°_{cell}$ from an external source. In effect, we convert the voltaic cell into an electrolytic cell—anode becomes cathode, and cathode becomes anode (Figure 21.26B):

*For the electrolytic cell,*

$$Cu(s) \longrightarrow Cu^{2+}(aq) + 2e^- \qquad \text{[anode; oxidation]}$$
$$Sn^{2+}(aq) + 2e^- \longrightarrow Sn(s) \qquad \text{[cathode; reduction]}$$
$$\overline{Cu(s) + Sn^{2+}(aq) \longrightarrow Cu^{2+}(aq) + Sn(s) \qquad E°_{cell} = -0.48 \text{ V and } \Delta G° = 93 \text{ kJ}}$$

In an electrolytic cell, as in a voltaic cell, *oxidation takes place at the anode and reduction takes place at the cathode.* Note, however, that *the direction of electron flow and the signs of the electrodes are reversed.*

To understand these differences, we focus on the *cause* of the electron flow:

- In a voltaic cell, electrons are generated *in* the anode, so it is *negative,* and *removed from* the cathode, so it is *positive.*
- In an electrolytic cell, an external power source supplies electrons *to* the cathode, so it is *negative,* and removes them *from* the anode, so it is *positive.*

**Figure 21.26** The tin-copper reaction as the basis of a voltaic and an electrolytic cell. **A,** The spontaneous reaction between Sn and $Cu^{2+}$ generates 0.48 V in a voltaic cell. **B,** If more than 0.48 V is supplied, the nonspontaneous (reverse) reaction between Cu and $Sn^{2+}$ occurs. Note the changes in electrode charges and direction of electron flow.

A rechargeable battery is a voltaic cell when it is discharging and an electrolytic cell when it is recharging. Let's compare these two functions in a lead-acid car battery (Figure 21.27; also see pp. 879–880):

- In the discharge mode (voltaic cell), oxidation occurs at electrode I, thus making the *negative* electrode the anode and the *positive* electrode (electrode II) the cathode.
- In the recharge mode (electrolytic cell), reduction occurs at electrode I, making the *negative* electrode the cathode and the *positive* electrode (electrode II) the anode.

Table 21.4 on the next page summarizes the processes and signs in the two types of cells.

**Figure 21.27** The processes occurring during the discharge (*top*) and recharge (*bottom*) of a lead-acid battery.

**Table 21.4 Comparison of Voltaic and Electrolytic Cells**

| Cell Type | $\Delta G$ | $E_{cell}$ | Electrode | | |
| | | | Name | Process | Sign |
| --- | --- | --- | --- | --- | --- |
| Voltaic | <0 | >0 | Anode | Oxidation | − |
| Voltaic | <0 | >0 | Cathode | Reduction | + |
| Electrolytic | >0 | <0 | Anode | Oxidation | + |
| Electrolytic | >0 | <0 | Cathode | Reduction | − |

## Predicting the Products of Electrolysis

**Electrolysis** is the splitting (lysing) of a substance by the input of electrical energy and is often used to decompose a compound into its elements, as you'll see for chlorine, aluminum, copper, and several others in Chapter 22. Water was first electrolyzed to $H_2$ and $O_2$ in 1800, and the process is still used to produce these gases in ultrahigh purity. The electrolyte in an electrolytic cell can be the pure compound (such as $H_2O$ or a molten salt), a mixture of molten salts, or an aqueous solution of a salt. As you'll see, the products depend on atomic properties and several other factors.

**Electrolysis of Pure Molten Salts** If the salt is pure, predicting the products is straightforward: *the cation will be reduced and the anion oxidized.* The electrolyte is the molten salt itself, and the ions are attracted by the oppositely charged electrodes.

Consider the electrolysis of molten (fused) calcium chloride. The two species present are $Ca^{2+}$ and $Cl^-$, so $Ca^{2+}$ ion is reduced and $Cl^-$ ion is oxidized:

$$
\begin{array}{ll}
2Cl^-(l) \longrightarrow Cl_2(g) + 2e^- & [\text{anode; oxidation}] \\
\underline{Ca^{2+}(l) + 2e^- \longrightarrow Ca(s)} & [\text{cathode; reduction}] \\
Ca^{2+}(l) + 2Cl^-(l) \longrightarrow Ca(s) + Cl_2(g) & [\text{overall}]
\end{array}
$$

Calcium is prepared industrially this way, as are several other active metals, such as Na and Mg, and the halogens $Cl_2$ and $Br_2$.

**Electrolysis of Mixed Molten Salts** More typically, the electrolyte is a mixture of molten salts being electrolyzed to obtain one of the metals. How can we tell which species will react at which electrode? The general rule for all electrolytic cells is that *the more easily oxidized species (stronger reducing agent) reacts at the anode, and the more easily reduced species (stronger oxidizing agent) reacts at the cathode.*

Unfortunately, for molten salts, we *cannot* use $E°$ values to tell the relative strength of the oxidizing and reducing agents, because they refer to the reduction of the *aqueous ion to the free element,* $M^{n+}(aq) + ne^- \longrightarrow M(s)$, under standard-state conditions. Instead, we use periodic trends of atomic properties to predict which ion gains or loses electrons more easily (Sections 8.3 and 9.5).

| Sample Problem 21.8 | Predicting the Electrolysis Products of a Molten Salt Mixture |
| --- | --- |

**Problem** A chemical engineer melts a naturally occurring mixture of NaBr and $MgCl_2$ and decomposes it in an electrolytic cell. Predict the substance formed at each electrode, and write balanced half-reactions and the overall cell reaction.

**Plan** We have to determine which metal and nonmetal will form more easily at the electrodes. We list the ions as oxidizing or reducing agents.
• If a metal holds its electrons *more* tightly than another, it has a higher ionization energy (IE). Thus, as a cation, it gains electrons more easily, so it is the stronger oxidizing agent and is reduced at the cathode.

- If a nonmetal holds its electrons *less* tightly than another, it has a lower electronegativity (EN). Thus, as an anion, it loses electrons more easily, so it is the stronger reducing agent and is oxidized at the anode.

**Solution**  Listing the ions as oxidizing or reducing agents:

The possible oxidizing agents are $Na^+$ and $Mg^{2+}$.

The possible reducing agents are $Br^-$ and $Cl^-$.

Determining the cathode product (more easily reduced cation): Mg is to the right of Na in Period 3. IE increases from left to right, so it is harder to remove $e^-$ from Mg. Thus, $Mg^{2+}$ has a greater attraction for $e^-$ and is more easily reduced (stronger oxidizing agent):

$$Mg^{2+}(l) + 2e^- \longrightarrow Mg(l) \qquad \text{[cathode; reduction]}$$

Determining the anode product (more easily oxidized anion): Br is below Cl in Group 7A(17). EN decreases down the group, so Br accepts $e^-$ less readily. Thus, $Br^-$ loses its $e^-$ more easily, so it is more easily oxidized (stronger reducing agent):

$$2Br^-(l) \longrightarrow Br_2(g) + 2e^- \qquad \text{[anode; oxidation]}$$

Writing the overall cell reaction:

$$Mg^{2+}(l) + 2Br^-(l) \longrightarrow Mg(l) + Br_2(g) \qquad \text{[overall]}$$

**Comment**  The cell temperature must be high enough to keep the salt mixture molten. In this case, the temperature is greater than the melting point of Mg, so it appears as a liquid in the equation, and greater than the boiling point of $Br_2$, so it appears as a gas.

**Follow-Up Problem 21.8**  A sample of $AlBr_3$ contaminated with KF is melted and electrolyzed. Determine the electrode products, and write the overall cell reaction.

**Electrolysis of Water and Nonstandard Half-Cell Potentials**  Before we analyze the electrolysis products of aqueous salt solutions, let's examine the electrolysis of water itself. Very pure water is difficult to electrolyze because few ions are present to conduct a current. However, if we add a small amount of a salt that cannot be electrolyzed (such as $Na_2SO_4$), electrolysis proceeds rapidly. An electrolytic cell with separate compartments for $H_2$ and $O_2$ is used (Figure 21.28). At the anode, water is oxidized; note the oxidation number (O.N.) of O changes from $-2$ to $0$:

$$2H_2O(l) \longrightarrow O_2(g) + 4H^+(aq) + 4e^- \qquad E = 0.82\ V \qquad \text{[anode; oxidation]}$$

At the cathode, water is reduced; note the O.N. of H changes from $+1$ to $0$:

$$2H_2O(l) + 2e^- \longrightarrow H_2(g) + 2OH^-(aq) \qquad E = -0.42\ V \qquad \text{[cathode; reduction]}$$

Doubling the cathode half-reaction to make $e^-$ loss equal $e^-$ gain, adding the half-reactions (which involves combining the $H^+$ and $OH^-$ into $H_2O$ and canceling $e^-$ and excess $H_2O$), and calculating $E_{cell}$ gives the overall reaction:

$$2H_2O(l) \longrightarrow 2H_2(g) + O_2(g) \qquad E_{cell} = -0.42\ V - 0.82\ V = -1.24\ V \ \text{[overall]}$$

Notice that these electrode potentials are *not* standard electrode potentials (and not designated with $E°$). The $[H^+]$ and $[OH^-]$ are $1.0\times10^{-7}\ M$ rather than the standard-state value of $1\ M$. These $E$ values are obtained by applying the Nernst equation. For example, the calculation for the anode potential (with $n = 4$) is

$$E_{cell} = E°_{cell} - \frac{0.0592\ V}{4} \log(P_{O_2} \times [H^+]^4)$$

The standard potential for the *oxidation* of water is $-1.23\ V$ (from Appendix D) and $P_{O_2} \approx 1$ atm in the half-cell, so we have

$$E_{cell} = -1.23\ V - \left\{ \frac{0.0592\ V}{4} \times [\log 1 + 4 \log (1.0\times10^{-7})] \right\} = -0.82\ V$$

In aqueous ionic solutions, $[H^+]$ and $[OH^-]$ are also approximately $10^{-7}\ M$, so we use these nonstandard $E_{cell}$ values to predict electrode products.

| Oxidation half-reaction |
| --- |
| $2H_2O(l) \longrightarrow O_2(g) + 4H^+(aq) + 4e^-$ |

| Reduction half-reaction |
| --- |
| $2H_2O(l) + 2e^- \longrightarrow H_2(g) + 2OH^-(aq)$ |

| Overall (cell) reaction |
| --- |
| $2H_2O(l) \longrightarrow 2H_2(g) + O_2(g)$ |

**Figure 21.28** The electrolysis of water. Twice as much $H_2$ forms as $O_2$.

**Electrolysis of Aqueous Salt Solutions and the Effect of Overvoltage** Aqueous salt solutions are mixtures of ions *and* water, so we have to compare the various electrode potentials to predict the electrode products.

1. *Predicting the electrode products.* When two half-reactions are possible at an electrode,
- *The reduction with the less negative (more positive) electrode potential occurs.*
- *The oxidation with the less positive (more negative) electrode potential occurs.*

What happens, for instance, when a solution of potassium iodide is electrolyzed?
- The possible *oxidizing agents* are $K^+$ and $H_2O$; their reduction half-reactions are

$$K^+(aq) + e^- \longrightarrow K(s) \qquad\qquad E° = -2.93 \text{ V}$$
$$2H_2O(l) + 2e^- \longrightarrow H_2(g) + 2OH^-(aq) \qquad E = -0.42 \text{ V} \qquad [\text{reduction}]$$

The less *negative* electrode potential for water means that it is much easier to reduce than $K^+$, so $H_2$ forms at the cathode.
- The possible *reducing agents* are $I^-$ and $H_2O$; their oxidation half-reactions are

$$2I^-(aq) \longrightarrow I_2(s) + 2e^- \qquad\qquad E° = 0.53 \text{ V} \qquad [\text{oxidation}]$$
$$2H_2O(l) \longrightarrow O_2(g) + 4H^+(aq) + 4e^- \qquad E = 0.82 \text{ V}$$

The less *positive* electrode potential for $I^-$ means that it is easier to oxidize than $H_2O$, so $I_2$ forms at the anode.

2. *The effect of overvoltage.* The products predicted from a comparison of electrode potentials are not always the actual products. For gases to be produced at metal electrodes, additional voltage is required. This increment above the expected voltage is the **overvoltage.** It is 0.4 to 0.6 V for $H_2(g)$ or $O_2(g)$ and is due to the large activation energy (Section 16.5) needed to form gases at the electrode.

Overvoltage has major practical significance. A multibillion-dollar example is the industrial production of chlorine from concentrated NaCl solution. Water is easier to reduce than $Na^+$, so $H_2$ forms at the cathode, even *with* an overvoltage of 0.6 V:

$$Na^+(aq) + e^- \longrightarrow Na(s) \qquad\qquad E° = -2.71 \text{ V}$$
$$2H_2O(l) + 2e^- \longrightarrow H_2(g) + 2OH^-(aq) \qquad E = -0.42 \text{ V} (\approx -1 \text{ V with overvoltage})$$
$$[\text{reduction}]$$

But $Cl_2$ *does* form at the anode, even though the electrode potentials *themselves* would lead us to predict that $O_2$ should form:

$$2H_2O(l) \longrightarrow O_2(g) + 4H^+(aq) + 4e^- \qquad E = 0.82 \text{ V} (\sim 1.4 \text{ V with overvoltage})$$
$$2Cl^-(aq) \longrightarrow Cl_2(g) + 2e^- \qquad\qquad E° = 1.36 \text{ V} \qquad [\text{oxidation}]$$

An overvoltage of $\sim$0.6 V for $O_2$ makes $Cl_2$ the product that is easier to form. Keeping $[Cl^-]$ high also favors this step. Thus, $Cl_2$, one of the 10 most heavily produced chemicals, is formed from plentiful natural sources of aqueous sodium chloride (Chapter 22).

3. *A summary: which product at which electrode.* Experiments have shown the elements that can be prepared electrolytically from aqueous solutions of their salts:
- Cations of less active metals, including gold, silver, copper, chromium, platinum, and cadmium, *are* reduced to the metal.
- Cations of more active metals, including those in Groups 1A(1) and 2A(2) and Al from 3A(13), *are not* reduced. Water is reduced to $H_2$ and $OH^-$ instead.
- Anions that *are* oxidized, because of overvoltage from $O_2$ formation, include the halides ($[Cl^-]$ must be high), except for $F^-$.
- Anions that *are not* oxidized include $F^-$ and common oxoanions, such as $SO_4^{2-}$, $CO_3^{2-}$, $NO_3^-$, and $PO_4^{3-}$, because the central nonmetal in these oxoanions is already in its highest oxidation state. Water is oxidized to $O_2$ and $H^+$ instead.

| Sample Problem 21.9 | Predicting the Electrolysis Products of Aqueous Salt Solutions |
|---|---|

**Problem** What products form at which electrode during the electrolysis of aqueous solutions of the following salts?
**(a)** KBr      **(b)** $AgNO_3$      **(c)** $MgSO_4$

**Plan** We identify the reacting ions and compare their electrode potentials with those of water, taking the 0.4 to 0.6 V overvoltage into account. The reduction half-reaction with the less negative electrode potential occurs at the cathode, and the oxidation half-reaction with the less positive electrode potential occurs at the anode.

**Solution**

**(a)**

$$K^+(aq) + e^- \longrightarrow K(s) \qquad\qquad E° = -2.93 \text{ V}$$

$$2H_2O(l) + 2e^- \longrightarrow H_2(g) + 2OH^-(aq) \qquad E = -0.42 \text{ V}$$

Despite the overvoltage, which makes $E$ for the reduction of water between $-0.8$ and $-1.0$ V, $H_2O$ is still easier to reduce than $K^+$, so $H_2(g)$ forms at the cathode.

$$2Br^-(aq) \longrightarrow Br_2(l) + 2e^- \qquad\qquad E° = 1.07 \text{ V}$$

$$2H_2O(l) \longrightarrow O_2(g) + 4H^+(aq) + 4e^- \qquad E = 0.82 \text{ V}$$

Because of the overvoltage, which makes $E$ for the oxidation of water between 1.2 and 1.4 V, $Br^-$ is easier to oxidize than water, so $Br_2(l)$ forms at the anode (*see photo*).

Electrolysis of aqueous KBr.

**(b)**

$$Ag^+(aq) + e^- \longrightarrow Ag(s) \qquad\qquad E° = 0.80 \text{ V}$$

$$2H_2O(l) + 2e^- \longrightarrow H_2(g) + 2OH^-(aq) \qquad E = -0.42 \text{ V}$$

As the cation of an inactive metal, $Ag^+$ is a better oxidizing agent than $H_2O$, so $Ag(s)$ forms at the cathode. $NO_3^-$ cannot be oxidized, because N is already in its highest ($+5$) oxidation state. Thus, $O_2(g)$ forms at the anode:

$$2H_2O(l) \longrightarrow O_2(g) + 4H^+(aq) + 4e^-$$

**(c)**

$$Mg^{2+}(aq) + 2e^- \longrightarrow Mg(s) \qquad E° = -2.37 \text{ V}$$

Like $K^+$ in part (a), $Mg^{2+}$ cannot be reduced in the presence of water, so $H_2(g)$ forms at the cathode. The $SO_4^{2-}$ ion cannot be oxidized because S is in its highest ($+6$) oxidation state. Thus, $H_2O$ is oxidized, and $O_2(g)$ forms at the anode:

$$2H_2O(l) \longrightarrow O_2(g) + 4H^+(aq) + 4e^-$$

**Follow-Up Problem 21.9** Write half-reactions for the products you predict will form in the electrolysis of aqueous $AuBr_3$.

## Stoichiometry of Electrolysis: The Relation Between Amounts of Charge and Products

Since charge flowing through an electrolytic cell yields products at the electrodes, it makes sense that the more charge that flows, the more product that forms. In fact, this relationship was first determined experimentally by Michael Faraday and is referred to as *Faraday's law of electrolysis: the amount of substance produced at each electrode is directly proportional to the quantity of charge flowing through the cell.*

Each balanced half-reaction shows the amounts (mol) of reactant, electrons, and product involved in the change, so it contains the information we need to answer such questions as "How much material will form from a given quantity of charge?" or, conversely, "How much charge is needed to produce a given amount of material?" To apply Faraday's law,

1. Balance the half-reaction to find the amount (mol) of electrons needed per mole of product.
2. Use the Faraday constant ($F = 9.65 \times 10^4$ C/mol e⁻) to find the quantity of charge.
3. Use the molar mass to find the charge needed for a given mass of product.

**Measuring Current to Find Charge** We cannot measure charge directly, but we *can* measure *current,* the charge flowing per unit time. The SI unit of current is the **ampere (A),** which is defined as a charge of 1 coulomb flowing through a conductor in 1 second:

$$1 \text{ ampere} = 1 \text{ coulomb/second} \quad \text{or} \quad 1 \text{ A} = 1 \text{ C/s} \qquad \textbf{(21.11)}$$

Thus, the current multiplied by the time gives the charge:

$$\text{Current} \times \text{time} = \text{charge} \quad \text{or} \quad \text{A} \times \text{s} = \frac{\text{C}}{\text{s}} \times \text{s} = \text{C}$$

Therefore, by measuring the current *and* the time during which the current flows, we find the charge, which relates to the amount of product (Figure 21.29).

**Figure 21.29** A summary diagram for the stoichiometry of electrolysis.

**Problems Involving Stoichiometry of Electrolysis** Problems based on Faraday's law often ask you to calculate current, mass of material, or time. As we said, the electrode half-reaction provides the key to solving these problems because it is related to the mass for a certain quantity of charge.

Here is a typical problem in practical electrolysis: how long does it take to produce 3.0 g of $Cl_2(g)$ by electrolysis of aqueous NaCl using a power supply with a current of 12 A? The problem asks for the time needed to produce a certain mass, so let's first relate mass to amount (mol) of electrons to find the charge needed. Then, we'll relate the charge to the current to find the time.

The half-reaction tells us that 2 mol of electrons are lost to form 1 mol of $Cl_2$ and we'll use this relationship as a conversion factor:

$$2Cl^-(aq) \longrightarrow Cl_2(g) + 2e^-$$

We convert the given mass of $Cl_2$ to amount of $Cl_2$, use the conversion factor from the half-reaction, and multiply by the Faraday constant to find the total charge:

$$\text{Charge (C)} = 3.0 \text{ g Cl}_2 \times \frac{1 \text{ mol Cl}_2}{70.90 \text{ g Cl}_2} \times \frac{2 \text{ mol e}^-}{1 \text{ mol Cl}_2} \times \frac{9.65 \times 10^4 \text{ C}}{1 \text{ mol e}^-} = 8.2 \times 10^3 \text{ C}$$

Now we use the relationship between charge and current to find the time needed:

$$\text{Time(s)} = \frac{\text{charge (C)}}{\text{current (A, or C/s)}} = 8.2 \times 10^3 \text{ C} \times \frac{1 \text{ s}}{12 \text{ C}} = 6.8 \times 10^2 \text{ s} \ (\sim 11 \text{ min})$$

Note that the entire calculation follows Figure 21.29 until the last step, which asks for the time that the given current must flow:

grams of $Cl_2 \Longrightarrow$ moles of $Cl_2 \Longrightarrow$ moles of e⁻ $\Longrightarrow$ coulombs $\Longrightarrow$ seconds

Sample Problem 21.10 applies these ideas in an important industrial setting.

## Sample Problem 21.10   Applying the Relationship Among Current, Time, and Amount of Substance

**Problem** A technician plates a faucet with 0.86 g of Cr metal by electrolysis of aqueous $Cr_2(SO_4)_3$. If 12.5 min is allowed for the plating, what current is needed?

**Plan** To find the current, we divide charge by time, so we need to find the charge. We write the half-reaction for $Cr^{3+}$ reduction to get the amount (mol) of $e^-$ transferred per mole of Cr. To find the charge, we convert the mass of Cr needed (0.86 g) to amount (mol) of Cr. Then, we use the Faraday constant ($9.65\times10^4$ C/mol $e^-$) to find the charge and divide by the time (12.5 min, converted to seconds) to obtain the current (see the road map).

**Solution** Writing the balanced half-reaction:

$$Cr^{3+}(aq) + 3e^- \longrightarrow Cr(s)$$

Combining steps to find amount (mol) of $e^-$ transferred for mass of Cr needed:

$$\text{Amount (mol) of } e^- \text{ transferred} = 0.86 \text{ g Cr} \times \frac{1 \text{ mol Cr}}{52.00 \text{ g Cr}} \times \frac{3 \text{ mol } e^-}{1 \text{ mol Cr}} = 0.050 \text{ mol } e^-$$

Calculating the charge:

$$\text{Charge (C)} = 0.050 \text{ mol } e^- \times \frac{9.65\times10^4 \text{ C}}{1 \text{ mol } e^-} = 4.8\times10^3 \text{ C}$$

Calculating the current:

$$\text{Current (A)} = \frac{\text{charge (C)}}{\text{time (s)}} = \frac{4.8\times10^3 \text{ C}}{12.5 \text{ min}} \times \frac{1 \text{ min}}{60 \text{ s}} = 6.4 \text{ C/s} = \boxed{6.4 \text{ A}}$$

**Check** Rounding gives

$$(\sim 0.9 \text{ g})(1 \text{ mol Cr/50 g})(3 \text{ mol } e^-/1 \text{ mol Cr}) = 5\times10^{-2} \text{ mol } e^-$$

then

$$(5\times10^{-2} \text{ mol } e^-)(\sim 1\times10^5 \text{ C/mol } e^-) = 5\times10^3 \text{ C}$$

and

$$(5\times10^3 \text{ C/12 min})(1 \text{ min/60 s}) = 7 \text{ A}$$

**Comment** For the sake of introducing Faraday's law, we neglected some details about actual electroplating. In practice, electroplating chromium is only 30% to 40% efficient and must be run at a specific temperature range for the plate to appear bright. Nearly 10,000 metric tons ($2\times10^8$ mol) of chromium are used annually for electroplating.

**Follow-Up Problem 21.10** Using a current of 4.75 A, how many minutes does it take to plate a sculpture with 1.50 g of Cu from a $CuSO_4$ solution?

**Road Map**

Mass (g) of Cr needed

↓ divide by $\mathcal{M}$ (g/mol)

Amount (mol) of Cr needed

↓ 3 mol $e^-$ = 1 mol Cr

Amount (mol) of $e^-$ transferred

↓ 1 mol $e^-$ = $9.65\times10^4$ C

Charge (C)

↓ divide by time (convert min to s)

Current (A)

---

The following Chemical Connections essay links several themes of this chapter to the generation of energy in a living cell.

## ▮ Summary of Section 21.7

- An electrolytic cell uses electrical energy to drive a nonspontaneous reaction.
- Oxidation occurs at the anode and reduction at the cathode, but the direction of electron flow and the charges of the electrodes are opposite those in voltaic cells.
- When two products can form at each electrode, the more easily oxidized substance reacts at the anode and the more easily reduced substance reacts at the cathode.
- The reduction or oxidation of water takes place at nonstandard conditions.
- Overvoltage causes the actual voltage required to be unexpectedly high (especially for gases, such as $H_2$ and $O_2$) and can affect the electrode product that forms.
- The amount of product that forms depends on the quantity of charge flowing through the cell, which is related to the time the charge flows and the current.
- Biological redox systems combine aspects of voltaic, concentration, and electrolytic cells to convert bond energy in food into electrochemical potential and then into the bond energy of ATP.

Biological cells apply the principles of electrochemical cells to generate energy. The complex multistep process can be divided into two parts:

1. Bond energy in food generates an electrochemical potential.
2. The potential creates the bond energy of ATP (see Chemical Connections, pp. 836–837).

These steps are part of the *electron-transport chain* (ETC), which lies on the inner membranes of *mitochondria,* the subcellular particles that produce energy (Figure B21.1).

The ETC is a series of large molecules (mostly proteins), each of which contains a *redox couple* (the oxidized and reduced forms of a species), such as $Fe^{3+}/Fe^{2+}$, that passes electrons along the chain. At three points, large potential differences supply enough free energy to convert adenosine diphosphate (ADP) into ATP.

## Bond Energy to Electrochemical Potential

Cells utilize the energy in food by releasing it in controlled steps rather than all at once. The reaction that ultimately powers the ETC is the oxidation of hydrogen to form water: $H_2 + \frac{1}{2}O_2 \longrightarrow H_2O$. But, instead of $H_2$ gas, which does not occur in organisms, the hydrogen takes the form of two $H^+$ ions and two $e^-$. The biological oxidizing agent $NAD^+$ (*n*icotinamide *a*denine *d*inucleotide) acquires these protons and electrons in the process of oxidizing molecules in food. To show this process, we use this half-reaction (without canceling an $H^+$ on both sides):

$$NAD^+(aq) + 2H^+(aq) + 2e^- \longrightarrow NADH(aq) + H^+(aq)$$

At the mitochondrial inner membrane, the NADH and $H^+$ transfer the two $e^-$ to the first redox couple of the ETC and release the

two $H^+$. The electrons are transported down the chain of redox couples, where they finally reduce $O_2$. The overall process, with standard electrode potentials,* is

$$NADH(aq) + H^+(aq) \longrightarrow NAD^+(aq) + 2H^+(aq) + 2e^-$$
$$E^{\circ\prime} = -0.315 \text{ V}$$
$$\frac{1}{2}O_2(aq) + 2e^- + 2H^+(aq) \longrightarrow H_2O(l) \qquad E^{\circ\prime} = 0.815 \text{ V}$$

---

$$NADH(aq) + H^+(aq) + \frac{1}{2}O_2(aq) \longrightarrow NAD^+(aq) + H_2O(l)$$
$$E^{\circ\prime}_{\text{overall}} = 0.815 \text{ V} - (-0.315 \text{ V}) = 1.130 \text{ V}$$

Thus, for every 2 mol of $e^-$, 1 mol of NADH enters the ETC, and the free-energy equivalent of 1.13 V is available:

$$\Delta G^{\circ\prime} = -nFE^{\circ\prime}$$
$$= -(2 \text{ mol } e^-/\text{mol NADH})(96.5 \text{ kJ/V·mol } e^-)(1.130 \text{ V})$$
$$= -218 \text{ kJ/mol NADH}$$

Note that this aspect of the process functions like a voltaic cell: a spontaneous reaction, the reduction of $O_2$ to $H_2O$, is used to generate a potential. In contrast to the operation of a voltaic cell, this process occurs in many small steps. Figure B21.2 is a highly simplified diagram showing the three steps in the ETC that generate a high enough potential to form ATP from ADP.

Each step consists of several components, in which electrons are passed from one redox couple to the next. Since most of the ETC components are iron-containing proteins, the redox change consists of the oxidation of $Fe^{2+}$ to $Fe^{3+}$ in one

---

*In biological systems, standard potentials are designated $E^{\circ\prime}$ and the standard states include a pH of 7.0 ($[H^+] = 1 \times 10^{-7} M$).

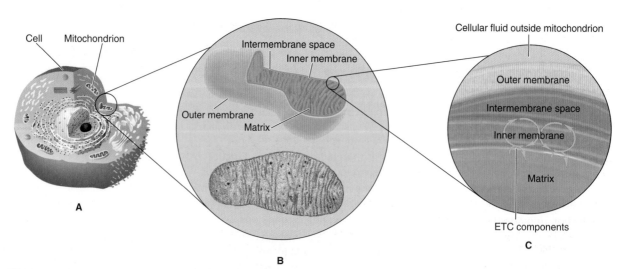

**Figure B21.1  The mitochondrion. A,** Mitochondria are subcellular particles outside the cell nucleus. **B,** They have a smooth outer membrane and a highly folded inner membrane, shown schematically and in an electron micrograph. **C,** The components of the electron-transport chain are attached to the inner membrane.

**Figure B21.2** The main energy-yielding steps in the electron-transport chain (ETC). At the three points shown, $E^{\circ\prime}$ (or $\Delta G^{\circ\prime}$) is large enough to form ATP from ADP. (A complex consists of many components; Q is a large organic molecule; Cyt stands for a cytochrome, a protein that contains a metal-ion redox couple.)

**Figure B21.3** Coupling electron transport to proton transport to ATP synthesis. Electrons are transported along the ETC (*curved yellow arrows*). Protons pumped into the intermembrane space create an [H$^+$] difference that generates a potential across the inner membrane. When that difference is large enough, H$^+$ flows back into the inner space, and the free energy drives the formation of ATP.

component accompanied by the reduction of $Fe^{3+}$ to $Fe^{2+}$ in the other:

$$Fe^{2+} \text{ (in A)} + Fe^{3+} \text{ (in B)} \longrightarrow Fe^{3+} \text{ (in A)} + Fe^{2+} \text{ (in B)}$$

In other words, metal ions bound within the ETC proteins are the actual species undergoing the redox reactions.

## Electrochemical Potential to Bond Energy

Formation of ATP requires a lot of energy:

$$ADP^{3-}(aq) + HPO_4^{2-}(aq) + H^+(aq) \longrightarrow$$
$$ATP^{4-}(aq) + H_2O(l)$$

$$\Delta G^{\circ\prime} = 30.5 \text{ kJ/mol}$$

Note that, at each of the three points in Figure B21.2, the free energy *released* exceeds the 30.5 kJ needed to form 1 mol of ATP. Thus, as in an electrolytic cell, an electrochemical potential is supplied to drive a nonspontaneous reaction.

We've followed the flow of *electrons* through the ETC. To see how electrochemical potential is converted to bond energy in ATP, we focus on the released *protons*. The free energy released at the three key steps is used to force the H$^+$ ions into the intermembrane space; as a result, [H$^+$] of the intermembrane space becomes higher than [H$^+$] of the matrix (Figure B21.3). This part of the process uses the free energy released by the three steps to *create an H$^+$ concentration cell across the membrane.*

When the [H$^+$] difference across the membrane reaches a "trigger" point of about 2.5-fold, H$^+$ ions spontaneously flow back through the membrane (in effect, closing the switch and allowing the concentration cell to operate). The free energy released in this spontaneous process drives the nonspontaneous ATP formation via an enzyme-catalyzed mechanism.

Thus, the mitochondrion uses the "electron-motive force" of redox couples on the membrane to generate a "proton-motive force" across the membrane, which converts a potential difference into bond energy.

## Problems

**B21.1** In the final steps of the ETC, there is a large protein complex containing iron and copper ions that interact with each other.
(a) Write balanced equations for the one-electron half-reactions of $Fe^{3+}$ and of $Cu^+$.
(b) Write a balanced overall equation for this redox reaction.

**B21.2** As the ETC proceeds, a difference in [H$^+$] develops across the inner mitochondrial membrane. The "proton-motive force," which is used to form ATP, is based largely on this difference and is equivalent to an electrical potential of 0.224 V. What is the free energy change (in kJ/mol) associated with the "proton-motive force"?

# CHAPTER REVIEW GUIDE

**Learning Objectives** Relevant section (§) and/or sample problem (SP) numbers appear in parentheses.

## Understand These Concepts

1. The meanings of *oxidation* and *reduction;* why an oxidizing agent is reduced and a reducing agent is oxidized (§21.1 and §4.5)
2. How the half-reaction method is used to balance redox reactions in acidic or basic solution (§21.1)
3. The distinction between voltaic and electrolytic cells in terms of the sign of $\Delta G$ (§21.1)
4. How voltaic cells use a spontaneous reaction to release electrical energy (§21.2)
5. The physical makeup of a voltaic cell: arrangement and composition of half-cells, relative charges of electrodes, and purpose of a salt bridge (§21.2)
6. How the difference in reducing strength of the electrodes determines the direction of electron flow (§21.2)
7. The correspondence between a positive $E_{cell}$ and a spontaneous cell reaction (§21.3)
8. The usefulness and significance of standard electrode potentials ($E^{\circ}_{half-cell}$) (§21.3)
9. How $E^{\circ}_{half-cell}$ values are combined to give $E^{\circ}_{cell}$ (§21.3)
10. How the standard reference electrode is used to find an unknown $E^{\circ}_{half-cell}$ (§21.3)
11. How an emf series (e.g., Table 21.2 or Appendix D) is used to write spontaneous redox reactions (§21.3)
12. How the relative reactivity of a metal is determined by its reducing power and is related to the negative of its $E^{\circ}_{half-cell}$ (§21.3)
13. How $E_{cell}$ (the nonstandard cell potential) is related to $\Delta G$ (maximum work) and the charge (moles of electrons times the Faraday constant) flowing through the cell (§21.4)
14. The interrelationship of $\Delta G^{\circ}$, $E^{\circ}_{cell}$, and $K$ (§21.4)
15. How $E_{cell}$ changes as the cell operates ($Q$ changes) (§21.4)
16. Why a voltaic cell can do work until $Q = K$ (§21.4)
17. How a concentration cell does work until the half-cell concentrations are equal (§21.4)
18. The distinction between primary (nonrechargeable) and secondary (rechargeable) batteries and the nature of fuel cells (§21.5)

19. How corrosion occurs and is prevented; the similarities between a corroding metal and a voltaic cell (§21.6)
20. How electrolytic cells use nonspontaneous redox reactions driven by an external source of electricity (§21.7)
21. How atomic properties (ionization energy and electronegativity) determine the products of the electrolysis of molten salt mixtures (§21.7)
22. How the electrolysis of water influences the products of aqueous electrolysis; the importance of overvoltage (§21.7)
23. The relationship between the quantity of charge flowing through the cell and the amount of product formed (§21.7)

## Master These Skills

1. Balancing redox reactions by the half-reaction method (§21.1 and SP 21.1)
2. Diagramming and notating a voltaic cell (§21.2 and SP 21.2)
3. Combining $E^{\circ}_{half-cell}$ values to obtain $E^{\circ}_{cell}$ (§21.3)
4. Using $E^{\circ}_{cell}$ and a known $E^{\circ}_{half-cell}$ to find an unknown $E^{\circ}_{half-cell}$ (SP 21.3)
5. Manipulating half-reactions to write a spontaneous redox reaction and calculate its $E^{\circ}_{cell}$ (SP 21.4)
6. Ranking the relative strengths of oxidizing and reducing agents in a redox reaction (SP 21.4)
7. Predicting whether a metal can displace hydrogen or another metal from solution (§21.3)
8. Using the interrelationship of $\Delta G^{\circ}$, $E^{\circ}_{cell}$, and $K$ to calculate one of the three given the other two (§21.4 and SP 21.5)
9. Using the Nernst equation to calculate the nonstandard cell potential ($E_{cell}$) (SP 21.6)
10. Calculating $E_{cell}$ of a concentration cell (SP 21.7)
11. Predicting the products of the electrolysis of a mixture of molten salts (SP 21.8)
12. Predicting the products of the electrolysis of aqueous salt solutions (SP 21.9)
13. Calculating the current (or time) needed to produce a given amount of product by electrolysis (SP 21.10)

## Key Terms Page numbers appear in parentheses.

electrochemistry (851)
electrochemical cell (851)

**Section 21.1**
half-reaction method (852)
voltaic (galvanic) cell (855)
electrolytic cell (855)
electrode (855)
electrolyte (855)
anode (856)
cathode (856)

**Section 21.2**
half-cell (857)
salt bridge (859)

**Section 21.3**
cell potential ($E_{cell}$) (861)
voltage (861)
electromotive force (emf) (861)
volt (V) (862)
coulomb (C) (862)

standard cell potential ($E^{\circ}_{cell}$) (862)
standard electrode (half-cell) potential ($E^{\circ}_{half-cell}$) (862)
standard reference half-cell (standard hydrogen electrode) (863)

**Section 21.4**
Faraday constant ($F$) (870)
Nernst equation (872)
concentration cell (874)

**Section 21.5**
battery (878)
fuel cell (881)

**Section 21.6**
corrosion (882)

**Section 21.7**
electrolysis (886)
overvoltage (888)
ampere (A) (890)

## Key Equations and Relationships    Page numbers appear in parentheses.

**21.1** Relating sponteneity of a process to the sign of the cell potential (861):

$$E_{cell} > 0 \text{ for a spontaneous process}$$

**21.2** Relating electric potential to energy and charge in SI units (862):

$$\text{Potential} = \text{energy/charge} \quad \text{or} \quad 1\text{ V} = 1\text{ J/C}$$

**21.3** Relating standard cell potential to standard electrode potentials in a voltaic cell (862):

$$E°_{cell} = E°_{cathode \ (reduction)} - E°_{anode \ (oxidation)}$$

**21.4** Defining the Faraday constant (870):

$$F = 9.65 \times 10^4 \ \frac{J}{V \cdot mol \ e^-} \quad (3 \text{ sf})$$

**21.5** Relating the free energy change to the cell potential (870):

$$\Delta G = -nFE_{cell}$$

**21.6** Finding the standard free energy change from the standard cell potential (870):

$$\Delta G° = -nFE°_{cell}$$

**21.7** Finding the equilibrium constant from the standard cell potential (870):

$$E°_{cell} = \frac{RT}{nF} \ln K$$

**21.8** Substituting known values of $R$, $F$, and $T$ into Equation 21.7 and converting to common logarithms (871):

$$E°_{cell} = \frac{0.0592 \text{ V}}{n} \log K \quad \text{or} \quad \log K = \frac{nE°_{cell}}{0.0592 \text{ V}} \quad \text{(at 298.15 K)}$$

**21.9** Calculating the nonstandard cell potential (Nernst equation) (872):

$$E_{cell} = E°_{cell} - \frac{RT}{nF} \ln Q$$

**21.10** Substituting known values of $R$, $F$, and $T$ into the Nernst equation and converting to common logarithms (872):

$$E_{cell} = E°_{cell} - \frac{0.0592 \text{ V}}{n} \log Q \quad \text{(at 298.15 K)}$$

**21.11** Relating current to charge and time (890):

$$\text{Current (A)} = \text{charge (C)/time (s)} \quad \text{and} \quad 1\text{ A} = 1\text{ C/s}$$

## Brief Solutions to Follow-Up Problems

**21.1** $6KMnO_4(aq) + 6KOH(aq) + KI(aq) \longrightarrow$
$$6K_2MnO_4(aq) + KIO_3(aq) + 3H_2O(l)$$

**21.2**
$$Sn(s) \longrightarrow Sn^{2+}(aq) + 2e^-$$
$$\text{[anode; oxidation]}$$
$$6e^- + 14H^+(aq) + Cr_2O_7^{2-}(aq) \longrightarrow 2Cr^{3+}(aq) + 7H_2O(l)$$
$$\text{[cathode; reduction]}$$

$$3Sn(s) + Cr_2O_7^{2-}(aq) + 14H^+(aq) \longrightarrow$$
$$3Sn^{2+}(aq) + 2Cr^{3+}(aq) + 7H_2O(l) \quad \text{[overall]}$$

Cell notation:
$$Sn(s) \mid Sn^{2+}(aq) \parallel H^+(aq), Cr_2O_7^{2-}(aq), Cr^{3+}(aq) \mid graphite$$

**21.3** $Br_2(aq) + 2e^- \longrightarrow 2Br^-(aq) \quad E°_{bromine} = 1.07 \text{ V}$
$$\text{[cathode]}$$
$$2V^{3+}(aq) + 2H_2O(l) \longrightarrow 2VO^{2+}(aq) + 4H^+(aq) + 2e^-$$
$$E°_{vanadium} = ? \quad \text{[anode]}$$

$$E°_{vanadium} = E°_{bromine} - E°_{cell} = 1.07 \text{ V} - 1.39 \text{ V} = -0.32 \text{ V}$$

**21.4** $Fe^{2+}(aq) + 2e^- \longrightarrow Fe(s) \quad\quad E° = -0.44 \text{ V}$
$$\underline{2[Fe^{2+}(aq) \longrightarrow Fe^{3+}(aq) + e^-] \quad E° = 0.77 \text{ V}}$$
$$3Fe^{2+}(aq) \longrightarrow 2Fe^{3+}(aq) + Fe(s)$$

$$E°_{cell} = -0.44 \text{ V} - 0.77 \text{ V} = -1.21 \text{ V}$$

The reaction is nonspontaneous. The spontaneous reaction is
$$2Fe^{3+}(aq) + Fe(s) \longrightarrow 3Fe^{2+}(aq) \quad E°_{cell} = 1.21 \text{ V}$$
$$Fe > Fe^{2+} > Fe^{3+}$$

**21.5** $Cd(s) + Cu^{2+}(aq) \longrightarrow Cd^{2+}(aq) + Cu(s)$
$$\Delta G° = -RT \ln K = -8.314 \text{ J/mol rxn·K} \times 298 \text{ K} \times \ln K$$
$$= -143 \text{ kJ/mol rxn}; K = 1.2 \times 10^{25}$$

$$E°_{cell} = \frac{0.0592 \text{ V}}{2} \log (1.2 \times 10^{25}) = 0.742 \text{ V}$$

**21.6** $\quad\quad Fe(s) \longrightarrow Fe^{2+}(aq) + 2e^- \quad E° = -0.44 \text{ V}$
$$\underline{Cu^{2+}(aq) + 2e^- \longrightarrow Cu(s) \quad\quad E° = 0.34 \text{ V}}$$
$$Fe(s) + Cu^{2+}(aq) \longrightarrow Fe^{2+}(aq) + Cu(s) \quad E°_{cell} = 0.78 \text{ V}$$
So $E_{cell} = 0.78 \text{ V} + 0.25 \text{ V} = 1.03 \text{ V}$

$$1.03 \text{ V} = 0.78 \text{ V} - \frac{0.0592 \text{ V}}{2} \log \frac{[Fe^{2+}]}{[Cu^{2+}]}$$

$$\frac{[Fe^{2+}]}{[Cu^{2+}]} = 3.6 \times 10^{-9}$$
$$[Fe^{2+}] = 3.6 \times 10^{-9} \times 0.30 \ M = 1.1 \times 10^{-9} \ M$$

**21.7** $Au^{3+}(aq; 2.5 \times 10^{-2} \ M) \text{ [B]} \longrightarrow$
$$Au^{3+}(aq; 7.0 \times 10^{-4} \ M) \text{ [A]}$$

$$E_{cell} = 0 \text{ V} - \left( \frac{0.0592 \text{ V}}{3} \times \log \frac{7.0 \times 10^{-4}}{2.5 \times 10^{-2}} \right) = 0.0306 \text{ V}$$

The electrode in A is negative, so it is the anode.

**21.8** Oxidizing agents: $K^+$ and $Al^{3+}$.
Reducing agents: $F^-$ and $Br^-$.
Al is above and to the right of K in the periodic table, so it has a higher IE:
$$Al^{3+}(l) + 3e^- \longrightarrow Al(s) \quad \text{[cathode; reduction]}$$
Br is below F in Group 7A(17), so it has a lower EN:
$$2Br^-(l) \longrightarrow Br_2(g) + 2e^- \quad \text{[anode; oxidation]}$$
$$2Al^{3+}(l) + 6Br^-(l) \longrightarrow 2Al(s) + 3Br_2(g) \quad \text{[overall]}$$

## Brief Solutions to Follow-Up Problems (continued)

**21.9** The reduction with the more positive electrode potential is $Au^{3+}(aq) + 3e^- \longrightarrow Au(s)$; $E° = 1.50$ V [cathode; reduction] Because of overvoltage, $O_2$ will not form at the anode, so $Br_2$ will form:

$2Br^-(aq) \longrightarrow Br_2(l) + 2e^-$; $E° = 1.07$ V   [cathode; oxidation]

**21.10** $Cu^{2+}(aq) + 2e^- \longrightarrow Cu(s)$; therefore,

2 mol $e^-$/1 mol Cu = 2 mol $e^-$/63.55 g Cu

$$\text{Time (min)} = 1.50 \text{ g Cu} \times \frac{2 \text{ mol } e^-}{63.55 \text{ g Cu}}$$

$$\times \frac{9.65 \times 10^4 \text{ C}}{1 \text{ mol } e^-} \times \frac{1 \text{ s}}{4.75 \text{ C}} \times \frac{1 \text{ min}}{60 \text{ s}} = 16.0 \text{ min}$$

## PROBLEMS

Problems with **colored** numbers are answered in Appendix E and worked in detail in the Student Solutions Manual. Problem sections match those in the text and provide the numbers of relevant sample problems. Most offer Concept Review Questions, Skill-Building Exercises (grouped in pairs covering the same concept), and Problems in Context. The Comprehensive Problems are based on material from any section or previous chapter.

*Note:* Unless stated otherwise, all problems refer to systems at 298 K (25°C).

### Redox Reactions and Electrochemical Cells
(Sample Problem 21.1)

#### Concept Review Questions

**21.1** Define *oxidation* and *reduction* in terms of electron transfer and change in oxidation number.

**21.2** Why must an electrochemical process involve a redox reaction?

**21.3** Can one half-reaction in a redox process take place independently of the other? Explain.

**21.4** Water is used to balance O atoms in the half-reaction method. Why can't $O^{2-}$ ions be used instead?

**21.5** During the redox balancing process, what step is taken to ensure that $e^-$ loss equals $e^-$ gain?

**21.6** How are protons removed when balancing a redox reaction in basic solution?

**21.7** Are spectator ions used to balance the half-reactions of a redox reaction? At what stage might spectator ions enter the balancing process?

**21.8** Which type of electrochemical cell has $\Delta G_{sys} < 0$? Which type shows an increase in free energy?

**21.9** Which statements are true? Correct any that are false.
(a) In a voltaic cell, the anode is negative relative to the cathode.
(b) Oxidation occurs at the anode of a voltaic or electrolytic cell.
(c) Electrons flow into the cathode of an electrolytic cell.
(d) In a voltaic cell, the surroundings do work on the system.
(e) A metal that plates out of an electrolytic cell appears on the cathode.
(f) The cell electrolyte provides a solution of mobile electrons.

#### Skill-Building Exercises (grouped in similar pairs)
**21.10** Consider the following balanced redox reaction:

$16H^+(aq) + 2MnO_4^-(aq) + 10Cl^-(aq) \longrightarrow$
$$2Mn^{2+}(aq) + 5Cl_2(g) + 8H_2O(l)$$

(a) Which species is being oxidized?
(b) Which species is being reduced?
(c) Which species is the oxidizing agent?
(d) Which species is the reducing agent?
(e) From which species to which does electron transfer occur?
(f) Write the balanced molecular equation, with $K^+$ and $SO_4^{2-}$ as the spectator ions.

**21.11** Consider the following balanced redox reaction:
$2CrO_2^-(aq) + 2H_2O(l) + 6ClO^-(aq) \longrightarrow$
$$2CrO_4^{2-}(aq) + 3Cl_2(g) + 4OH^-(aq)$$
(a) Which species is being oxidized?
(b) Which species is being reduced?
(c) Which species is the oxidizing agent?
(d) Which species is the reducing agent?
(e) From which species to which does electron transfer occur?
(f) Write the balanced molecular equation, with $Na^+$ as the spectator ion.

**21.12** Balance the following skeleton reactions and identify the oxidizing and reducing agents:
(a) $ClO_3^-(aq) + I^-(aq) \longrightarrow I_2(s) + Cl^-(aq)$ [acidic]
(b) $MnO_4^-(aq) + SO_3^{2-}(aq) \longrightarrow$
$$MnO_2(s) + SO_4^{2-}(aq) \text{ [basic]}$$
(c) $MnO_4^-(aq) + H_2O_2(aq) \longrightarrow Mn^{2+}(aq) + O_2(g)$ [acidic]

**21.13** Balance the following skeleton reactions and identify the oxidizing and reducing agents:
(a) $O_2(g) + NO(g) \longrightarrow NO_3^-(aq)$ [acidic]
(b) $CrO_4^{2-}(aq) + Cu(s) \longrightarrow Cr(OH)_3(s) + Cu(OH)_2(s)$ [basic]
(c) $AsO_4^{3-}(aq) + NO_2^-(aq) \longrightarrow$
$$AsO_2^-(aq) + NO_3^-(aq) \text{ [basic]}$$

**21.14** Balance the following skeleton reactions and identify the oxidizing and reducing agents:
(a) $Cr_2O_7^{2-}(aq) + Zn(s) \longrightarrow Zn^{2+}(aq) + Cr^{3+}(aq)$ [acidic]
(b) $Fe(OH)_2(s) + MnO_4^-(aq) \longrightarrow$
$$MnO_2(s) + Fe(OH)_3(s) \text{ [basic]}$$
(c) $Zn(s) + NO_3^-(aq) \longrightarrow Zn^{2+}(aq) + N_2(g)$ [acidic]

**21.15** Balance the following skeleton reactions and identify the oxidizing and reducing agents:
(a) $BH_4^-(aq) + ClO_3^-(aq) \longrightarrow H_2BO_3^-(aq) + Cl^-(aq)$ [basic]
(b) $CrO_4^{2-}(aq) + N_2O(g) \longrightarrow Cr^{3+}(aq) + NO(g)$ [acidic]
(c) $Br_2(l) \longrightarrow BrO_3^-(aq) + Br^-(aq)$ [basic]

**21.16** Balance the following skeleton reactions and identify the oxidizing and reducing agents:

(a) $Sb(s) + NO_3^-(aq) \longrightarrow Sb_4O_6(s) + NO(g)$ [acidic]

(b) $Mn^{2+}(aq) + BiO_3^-(aq) \longrightarrow$
$$MnO_4^-(aq) + Bi^{3+}(aq) \text{ [acidic]}$$

(c) $Fe(OH)_2(s) + Pb(OH)_3^-(aq) \longrightarrow$
$$Fe(OH)_3(s) + Pb(s) \text{ [basic]}$$

**21.17** Balance the following skeleton reactions and identify the oxidizing and reducing agents:

(a) $NO_2(g) \longrightarrow NO_3^-(aq) + NO_2^-(aq)$ [basic]

(b) $Zn(s) + NO_3^-(aq) \longrightarrow Zn(OH)_4^{2-}(aq) + NH_3(g)$ [basic]

(c) $H_2S(g) + NO_3^-(aq) \longrightarrow S_8(s) + NO(g)$ [acidic]

**21.18** Balance the following skeleton reactions and identify the oxidizing and reducing agents:

(a) $As_4O_6(s) + MnO_4^-(aq) \longrightarrow$
$$AsO_4^{3-}(aq) + Mn^{2+}(aq) \text{ [acidic]}$$

(b) $P_4(s) \longrightarrow HPO_3^{2-}(aq) + PH_3(g)$ [acidic]

(c) $MnO_4^-(aq) + CN^-(aq) \longrightarrow MnO_2(s) + CNO^-(aq)$ [basic]

**21.19** Balance the following skeleton reactions and identify the oxidizing and reducing agents:

(a) $SO_3^{2-}(aq) + Cl_2(g) \longrightarrow SO_4^{2-}(aq) + Cl^-(aq)$ [basic]

(b) $Fe(CN)_6^{3-}(aq) + Re(s) \longrightarrow$
$$Fe(CN)_6^{4-}(aq) + ReO_4^-(aq) \text{ [basic]}$$

(c) $MnO_4^-(aq) + HCOOH(aq) \longrightarrow$
$$Mn^{2+}(aq) + CO_2(g) \text{ [acidic]}$$

**Problems in Context**

**21.20** In many residential water systems, the aqueous $Fe^{3+}$ concentration is high enough to stain sinks and turn drinking water light brown. The iron content is analyzed by first reducing the $Fe^{3+}$ to $Fe^{2+}$ and then titrating with $MnO_4^-$ in acidic solution. Balance the skeleton reaction of the titration step:

$$Fe^{2+}(aq) + MnO_4^-(aq) \longrightarrow Mn^{2+}(aq) + Fe^{3+}(aq)$$

**21.21** *Aqua regia*, a mixture of concentrated $HNO_3$ and HCl, was developed by alchemists as a means to "dissolve" gold. The process is a redox reaction with this simplified skeleton reaction:

$$Au(s) + NO_3^-(aq) + Cl^-(aq) \longrightarrow AuCl_4^-(aq) + NO_2(g)$$

(a) Balance the reaction by the half-reaction method.
(b) What are the oxidizing and reducing agents?
(c) What is the function of HCl in aqua regia?

## Voltaic Cells: Using Spontaneous Reactions to Generate Electrical Energy
(Sample Problem 21.2)

**Concept Review Questions**

**21.22** Consider the following general voltaic cell:

Identify the (a) anode, (b) cathode, (c) salt bridge, (d) electrode at which $e^-$ leave the cell, (e) electrode with a positive charge, and (f) electrode that gains mass as the cell operates (assuming that a metal plates out).

**21.23** Why does a voltaic cell not operate unless the two compartments are connected through an external circuit?

**21.24** What purpose does the salt bridge serve in a voltaic cell, and how does it accomplish this purpose?

**21.25** What is the difference between an active and an inactive electrode? Why are inactive electrodes used? Name two substances commonly used for inactive electrodes.

**21.26** When a piece of metal A is placed in a solution containing ions of metal B, metal B plates out on the piece of A.
(a) Which metal is being oxidized?
(b) Which metal is being displaced?
(c) Which metal would you use as the anode in a voltaic cell incorporating these two metals?
(d) If bubbles of $H_2$ form when B is placed in acid, will they form if A is placed in acid? Explain.

**Skill-Building Exercises** (grouped in similar pairs)

**21.27** A voltaic cell is constructed with an $Sn/Sn^{2+}$ half-cell and a $Zn/Zn^{2+}$ half-cell. The zinc electrode is negative.
(a) Write balanced half-reactions and the overall reaction.
(b) Diagram the cell, labeling electrodes with their charges and showing the directions of electron flow in the circuit and of cation and anion flow in the salt bridge.

**21.28** A voltaic cell is constructed with an $Ag/Ag^+$ half-cell and a $Pb/Pb^{2+}$ half-cell. The silver electrode is positive.
(a) Write balanced half-reactions and the overall reaction.
(b) Diagram the cell, labeling electrodes with their charges and showing the directions of electron flow in the circuit and of cation and anion flow in the salt bridge.

**21.29** Consider the following voltaic cell:

(a) In which direction do electrons flow in the external circuit?
(b) In which half-cell does oxidation occur?
(c) In which half-cell do electrons enter the cell?
(d) At which electrode are electrons consumed?
(e) Which electrode is negatively charged?
(f) Which electrode decreases in mass during cell operation?
(g) Suggest a solution for the cathode electrolyte.
(h) Suggest a pair of ions for the salt bridge.
(i) For which electrode could you use an inactive material?
(j) In which direction do anions within the salt bridge move to maintain charge neutrality?
(k) Write balanced half-reactions and the overall cell reaction.

**21.30** Consider the following voltaic cell:

(a) In which direction do electrons flow in the external circuit?
(b) In which half-cell does reduction occur?
(c) In which half-cell do electrons leave the cell?
(d) At which electrode are electrons generated?
(e) Which electrode is positively charged?
(f) Which electrode increases in mass during cell operation?
(g) Suggest a solution for the anode electrolyte.
(h) Suggest a pair of ions for the salt bridge.
(i) For which electrode could you use an inactive material?
(j) In which direction do cations within the salt bridge move to maintain charge neutrality?
(k) Write balanced half-reactions and the overall cell reaction.

**21.31** A voltaic cell is constructed with an $Fe/Fe^{2+}$ half-cell and an $Mn/Mn^{2+}$ half-cell. The iron electrode is positive.
(a) Write balanced half-reactions and the overall reaction.
(b) Diagram the cell, labeling electrodes with their charges and showing the directions of electron flow in the circuit and of cation and anion flow in the salt bridge.

**21.32** A voltaic cell is constructed with a $Cu/Cu^{2+}$ half-cell and an $Ni/Ni^{2+}$ half-cell. The nickel electrode is negative.
(a) Write balanced half-reactions and the overall reaction.
(b) Diagram the cell, labeling electrodes with their charges and showing the directions of electron flow in the circuit and of cation and anion flow in the salt bridge.

**21.33** Write the cell notation for the voltaic cell that incorporates each of the following redox reactions:
(a) $Al(s) + Cr^{3+}(aq) \longrightarrow Al^{3+}(aq) + Cr(s)$
(b) $Cu^{2+}(aq) + SO_2(g) + 2H_2O(l) \longrightarrow$
$$Cu(s) + SO_4^{2-}(aq) + 4H^+(aq)$$

**21.34** Write a balanced equation from each cell notation:
(a) $Mn(s) \,|\, Mn^{2+}(aq) \,\|\, Cd^{2+}(aq) \,|\, Cd(s)$
(b) $Fe(s) \,|\, Fe^{2+}(aq) \,\|\, NO_3^-(aq) \,|\, NO(g) \,|\, Pt(s)$

## Cell Potential: Output of a Voltaic Cell
(Sample Problems 21.3 and 21.4)

### Concept Review Questions

**21.35** How is a standard reference electrode used to determine unknown $E°_{half-cell}$ values?

**21.36** What does a negative $E°_{cell}$ indicate about a redox reaction? What does it indicate about the reverse reaction?

**21.37** The standard cell potential is a thermodynamic state function. How are $E°$ values treated similarly to $\Delta H°$, $\Delta G°$, and $S°$ values? How are they treated differently?

### Skill-Building Exercises (grouped in similar pairs)

**21.38** In basic solution, $Se^{2-}$ and $SO_3^{2-}$ ions react spontaneously:
$2Se^{2-}(aq) + 2SO_3^{2-}(aq) + 3H_2O(l) \longrightarrow$
$$2Se(s) + 6OH^-(aq) + S_2O_3^{2-}(aq) \qquad E°_{cell} = 0.35 \text{ V}$$
(a) Write balanced half-reactions for the process.
(b) If $E°_{sulfite}$ is $-0.57$ V, calculate $E°_{selenium}$.

**21.39** In acidic solution, $O_3$ and $Mn^{2+}$ ion react spontaneously:
$O_3(g) + Mn^{2+}(aq) + H_2O(l) \longrightarrow$
$$O_2(g) + MnO_2(s) + 2H^+(aq) \qquad E°_{cell} = 0.84 \text{ V}$$
(a) Write the balanced half-reactions.
(b) Using Appendix D to find $E°_{ozone}$, calculate $E°_{manganese}$.

**21.40** Use the emf series (Appendix D) to arrange the species.
(a) In order of *decreasing* strength as *oxidizing* agents: $Fe^{3+}$, $Br_2$, $Cu^{2+}$

(b) In order of *increasing* strength as *oxidizing* agents: $Ca^{2+}$, $Cr_2O_7^{2-}$, $Ag^+$

**21.41** Use the emf series (Appendix D) to arrange the species.
(a) In order of *decreasing* strength as *reducing* agents: $SO_2$, $PbSO_4$, $MnO_2$
(b) In order of *increasing* strength as *reducing* agents: Hg, Fe, Sn

**21.42** Balance each skeleton reaction, calculate $E°_{cell}$, and state whether the reaction is spontaneous:
(a) $Co(s) + H^+(aq) \longrightarrow Co^{2+}(aq) + H_2(g)$
(b) $Mn^{2+}(aq) + Br_2(l) \longrightarrow MnO_4^-(aq) + Br^-(aq)$ [acidic]
(c) $Hg_2^{2+}(aq) \longrightarrow Hg^{2+}(aq) + Hg(l)$

**21.43** Balance each skeleton reaction, calculate $E°_{cell}$, and state whether the reaction is spontaneous:
(a) $Cl_2(g) + Fe^{2+}(aq) \longrightarrow Cl^-(aq) + Fe^{3+}(aq)$
(b) $Mn^{2+}(aq) + Co^{3+}(aq) \longrightarrow MnO_2(s) + Co^{2+}(aq)$ [acidic]
(c) $AgCl(s) + NO(g) \longrightarrow$
$$Ag(s) + Cl^-(aq) + NO_3^-(aq) \text{ [acidic]}$$

**21.44** Balance each skeleton reaction, calculate $E°_{cell}$, and state whether the reaction is spontaneous:
(a) $Ag(s) + Cu^{2+}(aq) \longrightarrow Ag^+(aq) + Cu(s)$
(b) $Cd(s) + Cr_2O_7^{2-}(aq) \longrightarrow Cd^{2+}(aq) + Cr^{3+}(aq)$
(c) $Ni^{2+}(aq) + Pb(s) \longrightarrow Ni(s) + Pb^{2+}(aq)$

**21.45** Balance each skeleton reaction, calculate $E°_{cell}$, and state whether the reaction is spontaneous:
(a) $Cu^+(aq) + PbO_2(s) + SO_4^{2-}(aq) \longrightarrow$
$$PbSO_4(s) + Cu^{2+}(aq) \text{ [acidic]}$$
(b) $H_2O_2(aq) + Ni^{2+}(aq) \longrightarrow O_2(g) + Ni(s)$ [acidic]
(c) $MnO_2(s) + Ag^+(aq) \longrightarrow MnO_4^-(aq) + Ag(s)$ [basic]

**21.46** Use the following half-reactions to write three spontaneous reactions, calculate $E°_{cell}$ for each reaction, and rank the strengths of the oxidizing and reducing agents:
(1) $Al^{3+}(aq) + 3e^- \longrightarrow Al(s) \qquad E° = -1.66 \text{ V}$
(2) $N_2O_4(g) + 2e^- \longrightarrow 2NO_2^-(aq) \qquad E° = 0.867 \text{ V}$
(3) $SO_4^{2-}(aq) + H_2O(l) + 2e^- \longrightarrow SO_3^{2-}(aq) + 2OH^-(aq)$
$$E° = 0.93 \text{ V}$$

**21.47** Use the following half-reactions to write three spontaneous reactions, calculate $E°_{cell}$ for each reaction, and rank the strengths of the oxidizing and reducing agents:
(1) $Au^+(aq) + e^- \longrightarrow Au(s) \qquad E° = 1.69 \text{ V}$
(2) $N_2O(g) + 2H^+(aq) + 2e^- \longrightarrow N_2(g) + H_2O(l)$
$$E° = 1.77 \text{ V}$$
(3) $Cr^{3+}(aq) + 3e^- \longrightarrow Cr(s) \qquad E° = -0.74 \text{ V}$

**21.48** Use the following half-reactions to write three spontaneous reactions, calculate $E°_{cell}$ for each reaction, and rank the strengths of the oxidizing and reducing agents:
(1) $2HClO(aq) + 2H^+(aq) + 2e^- \longrightarrow Cl_2(g) + 2H_2O(l)$
$$E° = 1.63 \text{ V}$$
(2) $Pt^{2+}(aq) + 2e^- \longrightarrow Pt(s) \qquad E° = 1.20 \text{ V}$
(3) $PbSO_4(s) + 2e^- \longrightarrow Pb(s) + SO_4^{2-}(aq) \qquad E° = -0.31 \text{ V}$

**21.49** Use the following half-reactions to write three spontaneous reactions, calculate $E°_{cell}$ for each reaction, and rank the strengths of the oxidizing and reducing agents:
(1) $I_2(s) + 2e^- \longrightarrow 2I^-(aq) \qquad E° = 0.53 \text{ V}$
(2) $S_2O_8^{2-}(aq) + 2e^- \longrightarrow 2SO_4^{2-}(aq) \qquad E° = 2.01 \text{ V}$
(3) $Cr_2O_7^{2-}(aq) + 14H^+(aq) + 6e^- \longrightarrow$
$$2Cr^{3+}(aq) + 7H_2O(l) \qquad E° = 1.33 \text{ V}$$

## Problems in Context

**21.50** When metal A is placed in a solution of a salt of metal B, the surface of metal A changes color. When metal B is placed in acid solution, gas bubbles form on the surface of the metal. When metal A is placed in a solution of a salt of metal C, no change is observed in the solution or on the surface of metal A. Will metal C cause formation of $H_2$ when placed in acid solution? Rank metals A, B, and C in order of *decreasing* reducing strength.

**21.51** When a clean iron nail is placed in an aqueous solution of copper(II) sulfate, the nail becomes coated with a brownish black material.
(a) What is the material coating the iron?
(b) What are the oxidizing and reducing agents?
(c) Can this reaction be made into a voltaic cell?
(d) Write the balanced equation for the reaction.
(e) Calculate $E°_{cell}$ for the process.

## Free Energy and Electrical Work
(Sample Problems 21.5 to 21.7)

### Concept Review Questions

**21.52** (a) How do the relative magnitudes of $Q$ and $K$ relate to the signs of $\Delta G$ and $E_{cell}$? Explain.
(b) Can a cell do work when $Q/K > 1$ or $Q/K < 1$? Explain.

**21.53** A voltaic cell consists of $A/A^+$ and $B/B^+$ half-cells, where A and B are metals and the A electrode is negative. The initial $[A^+]/[B^+]$ is such that $E_{cell} > E°_{cell}$.
(a) How do $[A^+]$ and $[B^+]$ change as the cell operates?
(b) How does $E_{cell}$ change as the cell operates?
(c) What is $[A^+]/[B^+]$ when $E_{cell} = E°_{cell}$? Explain.
(d) Is it possible for $E_{cell}$ to be less than $E°_{cell}$? Explain.

**21.54** Explain whether $E_{cell}$ of a voltaic cell will increase or decrease with each of the following changes:
(a) Decrease in cell temperature
(b) Increase in [active ion] in the anode compartment
(c) Increase in [active ion] in the cathode compartment
(d) Increase in pressure of a gaseous reactant in the cathode compartment

**21.55** In a concentration cell, is the more concentrated electrolyte in the cathode or the anode compartment? Explain.

### Skill-Building Exercises (grouped in similar pairs)

**21.56** What is the value of the equilibrium constant for the reaction between each pair at 25°C?
(a) Ni(*s*) and $Ag^+(aq)$          (b) Fe(*s*) and $Cr^{3+}(aq)$

**21.57** What is the value of the equilibrium constant for the reaction between each pair at 25°C?
(a) Al(*s*) and $Cd^{2+}(aq)$          (b) $I_2(s)$ and $Br^-(aq)$

**21.58** What is the value of the equilibrium constant for the reaction between each pair at 25°C?
(a) Ag(*s*) and $Mn^{2+}(aq)$          (b) $Cl_2(g)$ and $Br^-(aq)$

**21.59** What is the value of the equilibrium constant for the reaction between each pair at 25°C?
(a) Cr(*s*) and $Cu^{2+}(aq)$          (b) Sn(*s*) and $Pb^{2+}(aq)$

**21.60** Calculate $\Delta G°$ for each of the reactions in Problem 21.56.

**21.61** Calculate $\Delta G°$ for each of the reactions in Problem 21.57.

**21.62** Calculate $\Delta G°$ for each of the reactions in Problem 21.58.

**21.63** Calculate $\Delta G°$ for each of the reactions in Problem 21.59.

**21.64** What are $E°_{cell}$ and $\Delta G°$ of a redox reaction at 25°C for which $n = 1$ and $K = 5.0\times10^4$?

**21.65** What are $E°_{cell}$ and $\Delta G°$ of a redox reaction at 25°C for which $n = 1$ and $K = 5.0\times10^{-6}$?

**21.66** What are $E°_{cell}$ and $\Delta G°$ of a redox reaction at 25°C for which $n = 2$ and $K = 65$?

**21.67** What are $E°_{cell}$ and $\Delta G°$ of a redox reaction at 25°C for which $n = 2$ and $K = 0.065$?

**21.68** A voltaic cell consists of a standard reference half-cell and a $Cu/Cu^{2+}$ half-cell. Calculate $[Cu^{2+}]$ when $E_{cell}$ is 0.22 V.

**21.69** A voltaic cell consists of an $Mn/Mn^{2+}$ half-cell and a $Pb/Pb^{2+}$ half-cell. Calculate $[Pb^{2+}]$ when $[Mn^{2+}]$ is 1.4 *M* and $E_{cell}$ is 0.44 V.

**21.70** A voltaic cell with $Ni/Ni^{2+}$ and $Co/Co^{2+}$ half-cells has the following initial concentrations: $[Ni^{2+}] = 0.80$ *M*; $[Co^{2+}] = 0.20$ *M*.
(a) What is the initial $E_{cell}$?
(b) What is $[Ni^{2+}]$ when $E_{cell}$ reaches 0.03 V?
(c) What are the equilibrium concentrations of the ions?

**21.71** A voltaic cell with $Mn/Mn^{2+}$ and $Cd/Cd^{2+}$ half-cells has the following initial concentrations: $[Mn^{2+}] = 0.090$ *M*; $[Cd^{2+}] = 0.060$ *M*.
(a) What is the initial $E_{cell}$?
(b) What is $E_{cell}$ when $[Cd^{2+}]$ reaches 0.050 *M*?
(c) What is $[Mn^{2+}]$ when $E_{cell}$ reaches 0.055 V?
(d) What are the equilibrium concentrations of the ions?

**21.72** A concentration cell consists of two $H_2/H^+$ half-cells. Half-cell A has $H_2$ at 0.95 atm bubbling into 0.10 *M* HCl. Half-cell B has $H_2$ at 0.60 atm bubbling into 2.0 *M* HCl. Which half-cell houses the anode? What is the voltage of the cell?

**21.73** A concentration cell consists of two $Sn/Sn^{2+}$ half-cells, A and B. The electrolyte in A is 0.13 *M* $Sn(NO_3)_2$. The electrolyte in B is 0.87 *M* $Sn(NO_3)_2$. Which half-cell houses the cathode? What is the voltage of the cell?

## Electrochemical Processes in Batteries

### Concept Review Questions

**21.74** What is the direction of electron flow with respect to the anode and the cathode in a battery? Explain.

**21.75** In the everyday batteries used for flashlights, toys, etc., no salt bridge is evident. What is used in these cells to separate the anode and cathode compartments?

**21.76** Both a D-sized and an AAA-sized alkaline battery have an output of 1.5 V. What property of the cell potential allows this to occur? What is different about these two batteries?

### Problems in Context

**21.77** Many common electrical devices require the use of more than one battery.
(a) How many alkaline batteries must be placed in series to light a flashlight with a 6.0-V bulb?
(b) What is the voltage requirement of a camera that uses six silver batteries?
(c) How many volts can a car battery deliver if two of its anode/cathode cells are shorted?

## Corrosion: An Environmental Voltaic Cell

### Concept Review Questions

**21.78** During reconstruction of the Statue of Liberty, Teflon spacers were placed between the iron skeleton and the copper plates that cover the statue. What purpose do these spacers serve?

**21.79** Why do steel bridge-supports rust at the waterline but not above or below it?

**21.80** After the 1930s, chromium replaced nickel for corrosion resistance and appearance on car bumpers and trim. How does chromium protect steel from corrosion?

**21.81** Which of the following metals are suitable for use as sacrificial anodes to protect against corrosion of underground iron pipes? If any are not suitable, explain why:
(a) Aluminum      (b) Magnesium      (c) Sodium      (d) Lead
(e) Nickel      (f) Zinc      (g) Chromium

## Electrolytic Cells: Using Electrical Energy to Drive Nonspontaneous Reactions

(Sample Problems 21.8 to 21.10)

### Concept Review Questions

*Note:* Unless stated otherwise, assume that the electrolytic cells in the following problems operate at 100% efficiency.

**21.82** Consider the following general electrolytic cell:

(a) At which electrode does oxidation occur?
(b) At which electrode does elemental M form?
(c) At which electrode are electrons being released by ions?
(d) At which electrode are electrons entering the cell?

**21.83** A voltaic cell consists of $Cr/Cr^{3+}$ and $Cd/Cd^{2+}$ half-cells with all components in their standard states. After 10 minutes of operation, a thin coating of cadmium metal has plated out on the cathode. Describe what will happen if you attach the negative terminal of a dry cell (1.5 V) to the cell cathode and the positive terminal to the cell anode.

**21.84** Why are $E_{half-cell}$ values for the oxidation and reduction of water different from $E°_{half-cell}$ values for the same processes?

**21.85** In an aqueous electrolytic cell, nitrate ions never react at the anode, but nitrite ions do. Explain.

**21.86** How does overvoltage influence the products in the electrolysis of aqueous salts?

### Skill-Building Exercises (grouped in similar pairs)

**21.87** In the electrolysis of molten NaBr,
(a) What product forms at the anode?
(b) What product forms at the cathode?

**21.88** In the electrolysis of molten $BaI_2$,
(a) What product forms at the negative electrode?
(b) What product forms at the positive electrode?

**21.89** In the electrolysis of a molten mixture of KI and $MgF_2$, identify the product that forms at the anode and at the cathode.

**21.90** In the electrolysis of a molten mixture of CsBr and $SrCl_2$, identify the product that forms at the negative electrode and at the positive electrode.

**21.91** In the electrolysis of a molten mixture of NaCl and $CaBr_2$, identify the product that forms at the anode and at the cathode.

**21.92** In the electrolysis of a molten mixture of RbF and $CaCl_2$, identify the product that forms at the negative electrode and at the positive electrode.

**21.93** Identify the elements that can be prepared by electrolysis of their aqueous salts: copper, barium, aluminum, bromine.

**21.94** Identify the elements that can be prepared by electrolysis of their aqueous salts: strontium, gold, tin, chlorine.

**21.95** Identify the elements that can be prepared by electrolysis of their aqueous salts: lithium, iodine, zinc, silver.

**21.96** Identify the elements that can be prepared by electrolysis of their aqueous salts: fluorine, manganese, iron, cadmium.

**21.97** What product forms at each electrode in the aqueous electrolysis of the following salts: (a) LiF; (b) $SnSO_4$?

**21.98** What product forms at each electrode in the aqueous electrolysis of the following salts: (a) $ZnBr_2$; (b) $Cu(HCO_3)_2$?

**21.99** What product forms at each electrode in the aqueous electrolysis of the following salts: (a) $Cr(NO_3)_3$; (b) $MnCl_2$?

**21.100** What product forms at each electrode in the aqueous electrolysis of the following salts: (a) $FeI_2$; (b) $K_3PO_4$?

**21.101** Electrolysis of molten $MgCl_2$ is the final production step in the isolation of magnesium from seawater by the Dow process (Section 22.4). Assuming that 45.6 g of Mg metal forms,
(a) How many moles of electrons are required?
(b) How many coulombs are required?
(c) How many amps will produce this amount in 3.50 h?

**21.102** Electrolysis of molten NaCl in a Downs cell is the major isolation step in the production of sodium metal (Section 22.4). Assuming that 215 g of Na metal forms,
(a) How many moles of electrons are required?
(b) How many coulombs are required?
(c) How many amps will produce this amount in 9.50 h?

**21.103** How many grams of radium can form by passing 235 C through an electrolytic cell containing a molten radium salt?

**21.104** How many grams of aluminum can form by passing 305 C through an electrolytic cell containing a molten aluminum salt?

**21.105** How many seconds does it take to deposit 65.5 g of Zn on a steel gate when 21.0 A is passed through a $ZnSO_4$ solution?

**21.106** How many seconds does it take to deposit 1.63 g of Ni on a decorative drawer handle when 13.7 A is passed through a $Ni(NO_3)_2$ solution?

### Problems in Context

**21.107** A professor adds $Na_2SO_4$ to water to facilitate its electrolysis in a lecture demonstration. (a) What is the purpose of the $Na_2SO_4$? (b) Why is the water electrolyzed instead of the salt?

**21.108** Subterranean brines in parts of the United States are rich in iodides and bromides and serve as an industrial source of these elements. In one recovery method, the brines are evaporated to dryness and then melted and electrolyzed. Which halogen is more likely to form from this treatment? Why?

**21.109** Zinc plating (galvanizing) is an important means of corrosion protection. Although the process is done customarily by dipping the object into molten zinc, the metal can also be electroplated from aqueous solutions. How many grams of zinc can be deposited on a steel tank from a $ZnSO_4$ solution when a 0.855-A current flows for 2.50 days?

## Comprehensive Problems

**21.110** The $MnO_2$ used in alkaline batteries can be produced by an electrochemical process of which one half-reaction is

$$Mn^{2+}(aq) + 2H_2O(l) \longrightarrow MnO_2(s) + 4H^+(aq) + 2e^-$$

If a current of 25.0 A is used, how many hours are needed to produce 1.00 kg of $MnO_2$? At which electrode is the $MnO_2$ formed?

**21.111** Car manufacturers are developing engines that use $H_2$ as fuel. In Iceland, Sweden, and other parts of Scandinavia, where hydroelectric plants produce inexpensive electric power, the $H_2$ can be made industrially by the electrolysis of water.
(a) How many coulombs are needed to produce $3.5 \times 10^6$ L of $H_2$ gas at 12.0 atm and 25°C? (Assume the ideal gas law applies.)
(b) If the coulombs are supplied at 1.44 V, how many joules are produced?
(c) If the combustion of oil yields $4.0 \times 10^4$ kJ/kg, what mass of oil must be burned to yield the number of joules in part (b)?

**21.112** The overall cell reaction occurring in an alkaline battery is

$$Zn(s) + MnO_2(s) + H_2O(l) \longrightarrow ZnO(s) + Mn(OH)_2(s)$$

(a) How many moles of electrons flow per mole of reaction?
(b) If 4.50 g of zinc is oxidized, how many grams of manganese dioxide and of water are consumed?
(c) What is the total mass of reactants consumed in part (b)?
(d) How many coulombs are produced in part (b)?
(e) In practice, voltaic cells of a given capacity (coulombs) are heavier than the calculation in part (c) indicates. Explain.

**21.113** An inexpensive and accurate method of measuring the quantity of electricity flowing through a circuit is to pass it through a solution of a metal ion and weigh the metal deposited. A silver electrode immersed in an $Ag^+$ solution weighs 1.7854 g before the current has passed and weighs 1.8016 g after the current has passed. How many coulombs have passed?

**21.114** Brass, an alloy of copper and zinc, can be produced by simultaneously electroplating the two metals from a solution containing their 2+ ions. If 65.0% of the total current is used to plate copper, while 35.0% goes to plating zinc, what is the mass percent of copper in the brass?

**21.115** A thin circular-disk earring 4.00 cm in diameter is plated with a coating of gold 0.25 mm thick from an $Au^{3+}$ bath.
(a) How many days does it take to deposit the gold on one side of one earring if the current is 0.013 A (d of gold = 19.3 g/cm³)?
(b) How many days does it take to deposit the gold on both sides of the pair of earrings?
(c) If the price of gold is $1210 per troy ounce (31.10 g), what is the total cost of the gold plating?

**21.116** (a) How many minutes does it take to form 10.0 L of $O_2$ measured at 99.8 kPa and 28°C from water if a current of 1.3 A passes through the electrolytic cell? (b) What mass of $H_2$ forms?

**21.117** Trains powered by electricity, including subways, use direct current. One conductor is the overhead wire (or "third rail" for subways), and the other is the rails upon which the wheels run. The rails are on supports in contact with the ground. To minimize corrosion, should the overhead wire or the rails be connected to the positive terminal? Explain.

**21.118** A silver button battery used in a watch contains 0.75 g of zinc and can run until 80% of the zinc is consumed.
(a) How many days can the battery run at a current of 0.85 microamps ($10^{-6}$ amps)?
(b) When the battery dies, 95% of the $Ag_2O$ has been consumed. How many grams of Ag were used to make the battery?
(c) If Ag costs $23.00 per troy ounce (31.10 g), what is the cost of the Ag consumed each day the watch runs?

**21.119** Like any piece of apparatus, an electrolytic cell operates at less than 100% efficiency. A cell depositing Cu from a $Cu^{2+}$ bath operates for 10 h with an average current of 5.8 A. If 53.4 g of copper is deposited, at what efficiency is the cell operating?

**21.120** Commercial electrolysis is performed on both molten NaCl and aqueous NaCl solutions. Identify the anode product, cathode product, species reduced, and species oxidized for the (a) molten electrolysis and (b) aqueous electrolysis.

**21.121** To examine the effect of ion removal on cell voltage, a chemist constructs two voltaic cells, each with a standard hydrogen electrode in one compartment. One cell also contains a $Pb/Pb^{2+}$ half-cell; the other contains a $Cu/Cu^{2+}$ half-cell.
(a) What is $E°$ of each cell at 298 K?
(b) Which electrode in each cell is negative?
(c) When $Na_2S$ solution is added to the $Pb^{2+}$ electrolyte, solid PbS forms. What happens to the cell voltage?
(d) When sufficient $Na_2S$ is added to the $Cu^{2+}$ electrolyte, CuS forms and $[Cu^{2+}]$ drops to $1 \times 10^{-16}$ M. Find the cell voltage.

**21.122** Electrodes used in electrocardiography are disposable, and many incorporate silver. The metal is deposited in a thin layer on a small plastic "button," and then some is converted to AgCl:

$$Ag(s) + Cl^-(aq) \rightleftharpoons AgCl(s) + e^-$$

(a) If the surface area of the button is 2.0 cm² and the thickness of the silver layer is $7.5 \times 10^{-6}$ m, calculate the volume (in cm³) of Ag used in one electrode.
(b) The density of silver metal is 10.5 g/cm³. How many grams of silver are used per electrode?
(c) If Ag is plated on the button from an $Ag^+$ solution with a current of 12.0 mA, how many minutes does the plating take?
(d) If bulk silver costs $23.00 per troy ounce (31.10 g), what is the cost (in cents) of the silver in one disposable electrode?

**21.123** Commercial aluminum production is done by electrolysis of a bath containing $Al_2O_3$ dissolved in molten $Na_3AlF_6$. Why isn't it done by electrolysis of an aqueous $AlCl_3$ solution?

**21.124** Comparing the standard electrode potentials ($E°$) of the Group 1A(1) metals Li, Na, and K with the negative of their first ionization energies reveals a discrepancy:

Ionization process reversed: $M^+(g) + e^- \rightleftharpoons M(g)$ $(-IE)$

Electrode reaction: $M^+(aq) + e^- \rightleftharpoons M(s)$ $(E°)$

| Metal | −IE (kJ/mol) | $E°$ (V) |
|-------|--------------|----------|
| Li | −520 | −3.05 |
| Na | −496 | −2.71 |
| K | −419 | −2.93 |

Note that the electrode potentials do not decrease smoothly down the group, as the ionization energies do. You might expect that if it is more difficult to remove an electron from an atom to form a gaseous ion (larger IE), then it would be less difficult to add an electron to an aqueous ion to form an atom (smaller $E°$), yet $Li^+(aq)$ is *more* difficult to reduce than $Na^+(aq)$. Applying Hess's law, use an approach similar to a Born-Haber cycle to break down the process occurring at the electrode into three steps and label the energy involved in each step. How can you account for the discrepancy?

**21.125** In Appendix D, standard electrode potentials range from about $+3$ to $-3$ V. Thus, it might seem possible to use a half-cell from each end of this range to construct a cell with a voltage of approximately 6 V. However, most commercial aqueous voltaic cells have $E°$ values of 1.5 to 2 V. Why are there no aqueous cells with significantly higher potentials?

**21.126** Tin is used to coat "tin" cans used for food storage. If the tin is scratched and the iron of the can exposed, will the iron corrode more or less rapidly than if the tin were not present? Inside the can, the tin itself is coated with a clear varnish. Explain.

**21.127** Commercial electrolytic cells for producing aluminum operate at 5.0 V and 100,000 A.
(a) How long does it take to produce exactly 1 metric ton (1000 kg) of aluminum?
(b) How much electrical power (in kilowatt-hours, kW·h) is used [1 W = 1 J/s; 1 kW·h = $3.6 \times 10^3$ kJ]?
(c) If electricity costs $0.123 per kW·h and cell efficiency is 90.%, what is the cost of electricity to produce exactly 1 lb of aluminum?

**21.128** Magnesium bars are connected electrically to underground iron pipes to serve as sacrificial anodes.
(a) Do electrons flow from the bar to the pipe or the reverse?
(b) A 12-kg Mg bar is attached to an iron pipe, and it takes 8.5 yr for the Mg to be consumed. What is the average current flowing between the Mg and the Fe during this period?

**21.129** Bubbles of $H_2$ form when metal D is placed in hot $H_2O$. No reaction occurs when D is placed in a solution of a salt of metal E, but D is discolored and coated immediately when placed in a solution of a salt of metal F. What happens if E is placed in a solution of a salt of metal F? Rank metals D, E, and F in order of *increasing* reducing strength.

**21.130** In addition to reacting with gold (see Problem 21.21), aqua regia is used to bring other precious metals into solution. Balance the skeleton equation for the reaction with Pt:

$$Pt(s) + NO_3^-(aq) + Cl^-(aq) \longrightarrow PtCl_6^{2-}(aq) + NO(g)$$

**21.131** The following reactions are used in batteries:

I     $2H_2(g) + O_2(g) \longrightarrow 2H_2O(l)$     $E_{cell} = 1.23$ V

II     $Pb(s) + PbO_2(s) + 2H_2SO_4(aq) \longrightarrow$
$\qquad\qquad 2PbSO_4(s) + 2H_2O(l)$     $E_{cell} = 2.04$ V

III  $2Na(l) + FeCl_2(s) \longrightarrow 2NaCl(s) + Fe(s)$     $E_{cell} = 2.35$ V

Reaction I is used in fuel cells, II in the automobile lead-acid battery, and III in an experimental high-temperature battery for powering electric vehicles. The aim is to obtain as much work as possible from a cell, while keeping its weight to a minimum.
(a) In each cell, find the moles of electrons transferred and $\Delta G$.
(b) Calculate the ratio, in kJ/g, of $w_{max}$ to mass of reactants for each of the cells. Which has the highest ratio, which the lowest, and why? (*Note:* For simplicity, ignore the masses of cell components that do not appear in the cell as reactants, including electrode materials, electrolytes, separators, cell casing, wiring, etc.)

**21.132** A current is applied to two electrolytic cells in series. In the first, silver is deposited; in the second, a zinc electrode is consumed. How much Ag is plated out if 1.2 g of Zn dissolves?

**21.133** You are investigating a particular chemical reaction. State all the types of data available in standard tables that enable you to calculate the equilibrium constant for the reaction at 298 K.

**21.134** In an electric power plant, personnel monitor the $O_2$ content of boiler feed water to prevent corrosion of the boiler tubes. Why does Fe corrode faster in steam and hot water than in cold water?

**21.135** A voltaic cell using $Cu/Cu^{2+}$ and $Sn/Sn^{2+}$ half-cells is set up at standard conditions, and each compartment has a volume of 345 mL. The cell delivers 0.17 A for 48.0 h. (a) How many grams of $Cu(s)$ are deposited? (b) What is the $[Cu^{2+}]$ remaining?

**21.136** The $E_{half-cell}$ for the reduction of water is very different from the $E°_{half-cell}$ value. Calculate the $E_{half-cell}$ value when $H_2$ is in its standard state.

**21.137** From the skeleton equations below, create a list of balanced half-reactions in which the strongest oxidizing agent is on top and the weakest is on the bottom:

$$U^{3+}(aq) + Cr^{3+}(aq) \longrightarrow Cr^{2+}(aq) + U^{4+}(aq)$$
$$Fe(s) + Sn^{2+}(aq) \longrightarrow Sn(s) + Fe^{2+}(aq)$$
$$Fe(s) + U^{4+}(aq) \longrightarrow \text{no reaction}$$
$$Cr^{3+}(aq) + Fe(s) \longrightarrow Cr^{2+}(aq) + Fe^{2+}(aq)$$
$$Cr^{2+}(aq) + Sn^{2+}(aq) \longrightarrow Sn(s) + Cr^{3+}(aq)$$

**21.138** You are given the following three half-reactions:
(1) $Fe^{3+}(aq) + e^- \rightleftharpoons Fe^{2+}(aq)$
(2) $Fe^{2+}(aq) + 2e^- \rightleftharpoons Fe(s)$
(3) $Fe^{3+}(aq) + 3e^- \rightleftharpoons Fe(s)$
(a) Use $E°_{half-cell}$ values for (1) and (2) to find $E°_{half-cell}$ for (3).
(b) Calculate $\Delta G°$ for (1) and (2) from their $E°_{half-cell}$ values.
(c) Calculate $\Delta G°$ for (3) from (1) and (2).
(d) Calculate $E°_{half-cell}$ for (3) from its $\Delta G°$.
(e) What is the relationship between the $E°_{half-cell}$ values for (1) and (2) and the $E°_{half-cell}$ value for (3)?

**21.139** Use the half-reaction method to balance the equation for the conversion of ethanol to acetic acid in acid solution:

$$CH_3CH_2OH + Cr_2O_7^{2-} \longrightarrow CH_3COOH + Cr^{3+}$$

**21.140** When zinc is refined by electrolysis, the desired half-reaction at the cathode is

$$Zn^{2+}(aq) + 2e^- \longrightarrow Zn(s)$$

A competing reaction, which lowers the yield, is the formation of hydrogen gas:

$$2H^+(aq) + 2e^- \longrightarrow H_2(g)$$

If 91.50% of the current flowing results in zinc being deposited, while 8.50% produces hydrogen gas, how many liters of $H_2$, measured at STP, form per kilogram of zinc?

**21.141** A chemist designs an ion-specific probe for measuring $[Ag^+]$ in an NaCl solution saturated with AgCl. One half-cell has an Ag-wire electrode immersed in the unknown AgCl-saturated NaCl solution. It is connected through a salt bridge to the other half-cell, which has a calomel reference electrode [a platinum wire immersed in a paste of mercury and calomel $(Hg_2Cl_2)$] in a saturated KCl solution. The measured $E_{cell}$ is 0.060 V.
(a) Given the following standard half-reactions, calculate $[Ag^+]$.
Calomel:  $Hg_2Cl_2(s) + 2e^- \longrightarrow$
$$2Hg(l) + 2Cl^-(aq) \qquad E° = 0.24 \text{ V}$$
Silver:  $Ag^+(aq) + e^- \longrightarrow Ag(s) \qquad E° = 0.80$ V
(*Hint:* Assume $[Cl^-]$ is so high that it is essentially constant.)

**(b)** A mining engineer wants an ore sample analyzed with the $Ag^+$-selective probe. After pretreating the ore sample, the chemist measures the cell voltage as 0.53 V. What is $[Ag^+]$?

**21.142** Use Appendix D to calculate the $K_{sp}$ of AgCl.

**21.143** Black-and-white photographic film is coated with silver halides. Because silver is expensive, the manufacturer monitors the $Ag^+$ content of the waste stream, $[Ag^+]_{waste}$, from the plant with an $Ag^+$-selective electrode at 25°C. A stream of known $Ag^+$ concentration, $[Ag^+]_{standard}$, is passed over the electrode in turn with the waste stream and the data recorded by a computer.
**(a)** Write the equations relating the nonstandard cell potential to the standard cell potential and $[Ag^+]$ for each solution.
**(b)** Combine these into a single equation to find $[Ag^+]_{waste}$.
**(c)** Rewrite the equation from part (b) to find $[Ag^+]_{waste}$ in ng/L.
**(d)** If $E_{waste}$ is 0.003 V higher than $E_{standard}$, and the standard solution contains 1000. ng/L, what is $[Ag^+]_{waste}$?
**(e)** Rewrite the equation in part (b) to find $[Ag^+]_{waste}$ for a system in which $T$ changes and $T_{waste}$ and $T_{standard}$ may be different.

**21.144** Calculate the $K_f$ of $Ag(NH_3)_2^+$ from

$$Ag^+(aq) + e^- \rightleftharpoons Ag(s) \qquad E° = 0.80 \text{ V}$$
$$Ag(NH_3)_2^+(aq) + e^- \rightleftharpoons Ag(s) + 2NH_3(aq) \qquad E° = 0.37 \text{ V}$$

**21.145** Even though the toxicity of cadmium has become a concern, nickel-cadmium (nicad) batteries are still used commonly in many devices. The overall cell reaction is

$$Cd(s) + 2NiO(OH)(s) + 2H_2O(l) \longrightarrow$$
$$2Ni(OH)(s) + Cd(OH)_2(s)$$

A certain nicad battery weighs 18.3 g and has a capacity of 300. mA·h (that is, the cell can store charge equivalent to a current of 300. mA flowing for 1 h).
**(a)** What is the capacity of this cell in coulombs?
**(b)** What mass of reactants is needed to deliver 300. mA·h?
**(c)** What percentage of the cell mass consists of reactants?

**21.146** The zinc-air battery is a less expensive alternative to silver batteries for use in hearing aids. The cell reaction is

$$2Zn(s) + O_2(g) \longrightarrow 2ZnO(s)$$

A new battery weighs 0.275 g. The zinc accounts for exactly $\frac{1}{10}$ of the mass, and the oxygen does not contribute to the mass because it is supplied by the air.
**(a)** How much electricity (in C) can the battery deliver?
**(b)** How much free energy (in J) is released if $E_{cell}$ is 1.3 V?

**21.147** Use Appendix D to create an activity series of Mn, Fe, Ag, Sn, Cr, Cu, Ba, Al, Na, Hg, Ni, Li, Au, Zn, and Pb. Rank these metals in order of decreasing reducing strength, and divide them into three groups: those that displace $H_2$ from water, those that displace $H_2$ from acid, and those that cannot displace $H_2$.

**21.148** Both Ti and V are reactive enough to displace $H_2$ from water. The difference in their $E°_{half-cell}$ values is 0.43 V. Given

$$V(s) + Cu^{2+}(aq) \longrightarrow V^{2+}(aq) + Cu(s) \quad \Delta G° = -298 \text{ kJ/mol}$$

use Appendix D to calculate the $E°_{half-cell}$ values for V and Ti.

**21.149** For the reaction
$$S_4O_6^{2-}(aq) + 2I^-(aq) \longrightarrow I_2(s) + S_2O_3^{2-}(aq)$$
$$\Delta G° = 87.8 \text{ kJ/mol}$$

**(a)** Identify the oxidizing and reducing agents. **(b)** Calculate $E°_{cell}$. **(c)** For the reduction half-reaction, write a balanced equation, give the oxidation number of each element, and calculate $E°_{half-cell}$.

**21.150** Two concentration cells are prepared, both with 90.0 mL of 0.0100 $M$ $Cu(NO_3)_2$ and a Cu bar in each half-cell.
**(a)** In the first concentration cell, 10.0 mL of 0.500 $M$ $NH_3$ is added to one half-cell; the complex ion $Cu(NH_3)_4^{2+}$ forms, and $E_{cell}$ is 0.129 V. Calculate $K_f$ for the formation of the complex ion.
**(b)** Calculate $E_{cell}$ when an additional 10.0 mL of 0.500 $M$ $NH_3$ is added.
**(c)** In the second concentration cell, 10.0 mL of 0.500 $M$ NaOH is added to one half-cell; the precipitate $Cu(OH)_2$ forms ($K_{sp} = 2.2 \times 10^{-20}$). Calculate $E°_{cell}$.
**(d)** What would the molarity of NaOH have to be for the addition of 10.0 mL to result in an $E°_{cell}$ of 0.340 V?

**21.151** Two voltaic cells are to be joined so that one will run the other as an electrolytic cell. In the first cell, one half-cell has Au foil in 1.00 $M$ $Au(NO_3)_3$, and the other half-cell has a Cr bar in 1.00 $M$ $Cr(NO_3)_3$. In the second cell, one half-cell has a Co bar in 1.00 $M$ $Co(NO_3)_2$, and the other half-cell has a Zn bar in 1.00 $M$ $Zn(NO_3)_2$.
**(a)** Calculate $E°_{cell}$ for each cell.
**(b)** Calculate the total potential if the two cells are connected as voltaic cells in series.
**(c)** When the electrode wires are switched in one of the cells, which cell will run as the voltaic cell and which as the electrolytic cell?
**(d)** Which metal ion is being reduced in each cell?
**(e)** If 2.00 g of metal plates out in the voltaic cell, how much metal ion plates out in the electrolytic cell?

**21.152** A voltaic cell has one half-cell with a Cu bar in a 1.00 $M$ $Cu^{2+}$ salt, and the other half-cell with a Cd bar in the same volume of a 1.00 $M$ $Cd^{2+}$ salt. (a) Find $E°_{cell}$, $\Delta G°$, and $K$. (b) As the cell operates, $[Cd^{2+}]$ increases; find $E_{cell}$ and $\Delta G$ when $[Cd^{2+}]$ is 1.95 $M$. (c) Find $E_{cell}$, $\Delta G$, and $[Cu^{2+}]$ at equilibrium.

**21.153** Gasoline is a mixture of hydrocarbons, but the heat released when it burns is close to that of octane, $C_8H_{18}(l)$ ($\Delta H°_f = -250.1$ kJ/mol). As an alternative to gasoline, research is underway to use $H_2$ from the electrolysis of water in fuel cells to power cars.
**(a)** Calculate $\Delta H°$ when 1.00 gal of gasoline ($d = 0.7028$ g/mL) burns to produce carbon dioxide gas and water vapor.
**(b)** How many liters of $H_2$ at 25°C and 1.00 atm must burn to produce this quantity of energy?
**(c)** How long would it take to produce this amount of $H_2$ by electrolysis with a current of $1.00 \times 10^3$ A at 6.00 V?
**(d)** How much power in kilowatt·hours (kW·h) is required to generate this amount of $H_2$? (1 W = 1 J/s, 1 J = 1 C·V, and 1 kW·h = $3.6 \times 10^6$ J.)
**(e)** If the cell is 88.0% efficient and electricity costs $0.123 per kW·h, what is the cost of producing the amount of $H_2$ equivalent to 1.00 gal of gasoline?

**21.154** If the $E_{cell}$ of the following cell is 0.915 V, what is the pH in the anode compartment?

$$Pt(s) \mid H_2(1.00 \text{ atm}) \mid H^+(aq) \parallel Ag^+(0.100 \text{ } M) \mid Ag(s)$$

# The Elements in Nature and Industry

## Concepts and skills to review before you study this chapter

- trends in atomic properties (Sections 8.3, 8.4, 9.2, and 9.5)
- catalysts and reaction rate (Section 16.7)
- Le Châtelier's principle (Section 17.6)
- acid-base equilibria (Sections 18.3 and 18.9)
- solubility and complex-ion equilibria (Sections 19.3 and 19.4)
- temperature and reaction spontaneity (Section 20.3)
- free energy and equilibrium (Section 20.4)
- standard electrode potentials (Section 21.3)
- electrolysis of molten salts and aqueous salt solutions (Section 21.7)

**22**

Today, wearing jewelry made of a precious metal such as gold or silver studded with diamonds, emeralds, or rubies is considered a sign of wealth. But, in the mid-19th century, wealthy women proudly wore jewelry fabricated from aluminum (*photo*), at the time considered more precious than gold or silver. In fact, a prized bar of aluminum was displayed beside the French crown jewels at the 1855 Exposition Universelle in Paris! Now, aluminum is so inexpensive that it is used to make millions of soft drink cans, which are often thrown away. This change was the result of applying chemical principles to a real-life problem: how can we efficiently extract an element from its source in nature and use it?

In this chapter, we return to the periodic table to consider practical questions about the elements: how much of the element is present in nature, in what form does it occur, how do organisms affect its distribution, and how do we isolate it for our own use? We'll apply concepts of kinetics, equilibrium, thermodynamics, and electrochemistry from previous chapters to explain some major chemical processes in nature and industry.

**IN THIS CHAPTER . . .** We examine the distribution of elements on Earth, the intertwining natural cycles in which certain elements take part, and the methods we have developed to extract, purify, and utilize them.
- We identify the abundances and sources of elements in the various regions of Earth.
- We consider how three essential elements—carbon, nitrogen, and phosphorus—cycle through the environment and focus on how humans influence these processes.
- We focus on the isolation and purification of metals, discussing general redox and metallurgical procedures for extracting an element from its ore.
- We examine in detail the isolation and uses of seven key elements: sodium, potassium, iron, copper, aluminum, magnesium, and hydrogen.
- We take a close look at two of the most important processes in chemical manufacturing: the production of sulfuric acid and the isolation of chlorine.

## 22.1 • HOW THE ELEMENTS OCCUR IN NATURE

To begin our examination of how we use the elements, let's take inventory of our elemental stock—the distribution and relative amounts of the elements on Earth, especially that thin outer portion of the planet that we can reach.

### Earth's Structure and the Abundance of the Elements

Any attempt to isolate an element must begin with a knowledge of its **abundance,** the amount of the element in a particular region of the natural world. The abundances of the elements result from details of our planet's evolution.

**Formation and Layering of Earth** About 4.5 billion years ago, vast clouds of cold gases and interstellar debris from exploded older stars gradually coalesced into the Sun and planets. At first, Earth was a cold, solid sphere of uniformly distributed elements and simple compounds. In the next billion years or so, heat from radioactive decay and continuous meteor impacts raised the planet's temperature to around $10^4$ K, sufficient to form an enormous molten mass. Any remaining gaseous elements, such as the cosmically abundant hydrogen and helium, were ejected into space.

**Figure 22.1** The layered internal structure of Earth.

As Earth cooled, chemical and physical processes resulted in its **differentiation,** the formation of regions of different composition and density. Differentiation gave Earth an internal structure consisting of three layers (Figure 22.1):

- The dense **core** ($d = 10$–$15$ g/cm$^3$) is composed of a molten outer core and a solid Moon-sized inner core. Remarkably, the inner core is nearly as hot as the surface of the Sun and spins within the molten outer core slightly faster than Earth itself does!
- The thick, homogeneous **mantle** lying around the core has an overall average density of 4–6 g/cm$^3$.
- A thin, homogeneous **crust** lies on top of the mantle. The average density of the crust, on which all the comings and goings of life take place, is 2.8 g/cm$^3$.

Table 22.1 compares the abundance of some key elements in the universe, the whole Earth (actually core plus mantle only, which account for more than 99% of Earth's mass), and Earth's three regions. (Because the deepest terrestrial sampling can penetrate only a few kilometers into the crust, some of these data represent extrapolations from meteor samples and from seismic studies of earthquakes.) Several points stand out:

- Cosmic and whole-Earth abundances are very different, particularly for H and He; these two elements account for the majority of the mass of the universe but are not abundant in elemental form on Earth.
- The elements O, Si, Fe, and Mg are abundant both cosmically and on Earth. Together, they account for more than 90% of Earth's mass.
- The core is particularly rich in the dense Group 8B(8) through 8B(10) metals: Co, Ni, and especially Fe, the most abundant element in the whole Earth.

| Element | Universe | Earth | Crust | Mantle | Core |
|---------|----------|-------|-------|--------|------|
| O | 1.07 | 29.5 | 49.5 | 43.7 | — |
| Si | 0.06 | 15.2 | 25.7 | 21.6 | — |
| Al | — | 1.1 | 7.5 | 1.8 | — |
| Fe | 0.19 | 34.6 | 4.7 | 13.3 | 88.6 |
| Ca | 0.007 | 1.1 | 3.4 | 2.1 | — |
| Mg | 0.06 | 12.7 | 2.8 | 16.6 | — |
| Na | — | 0.6 | 2.6 | 0.8 | — |
| K | — | 0.07 | 2.4 | 0.2 | — |
| H | 73.9 | — | 0.87 | — | — |
| Ti | — | 0.05 | 0.58 | 0.18 | 0.01 |
| Cl | — | — | 0.19 | — | — |
| P | — | — | 0.12 | — | — |
| Mn | — | — | 0.09 | — | — |
| C | 0.46 | — | 0.08 | — | — |
| S | 0.04 | 1.9 | 0.06 | >2 | — |
| Ni | 0.006 | 2.4 | 0.008 | 0.3 | 8.5 |
| Co | — | 0.13 | 0.003 | 0.04 | 0.6 |
| He | 24.0 | — | — | — | — |

*A missing abundance value indicates either that reliable data are not available or that the value is less than 0.001% by mass.

- Crustal abundances are very different from whole-Earth abundances. The crust makes up only 0.4% of Earth's mass, but has the largest share of nonmetals, metalloids, and light, active metals: Al, Ca, Na, and K. The mantle contains much smaller proportions of these, and the core has none. Oxygen is the most abundant element in the crust and mantle but is absent from the core.

These differences in Earth's major layers arose from the effects of thermal energy. When Earth was molten, gravity and convection caused more dense materials to sink and less dense materials to rise, yielding several compositional *phases:*

- Most of the Fe sank to form the core, or *iron phase.*
- In the light outer phase, oxygen combined with Si, Al, Mg, and some Fe to form silicates, the material of rocks. This *silicate phase* later separated into the mantle and crust.
- The *sulfide phase,* intermediate in density and insoluble in the other two, consisted mostly of iron sulfide and mixed with parts of the silicate phase above and the iron phase below.
- The thin, primitive atmosphere, probably a mixture of water vapor (which gave rise to the oceans), carbon monoxide, and nitrogen (or ammonia), was produced by *outgassing* (the expulsion of trapped gases).

The distribution of the remaining elements (discussed here using only the new periodic-table group numbers) was controlled by their chemical affinity for one of the three phases. In general terms, as Figure 22.2 shows:

- Elements with low or high electronegativity—active metals (those in Groups 1 through 5, Cr, and Mn) and nonmetals (O, lighter members of Groups 13 to 15, and all of Group 17)—tended to congregate in the silicate phase as ionic compounds.
- Metals with intermediate electronegativities (many from Groups 6 to 10) dissolved in the iron phase.
- Lower-melting transition metals and many metals and metalloids in Groups 11 to 16 became concentrated in the sulfide phase.

**Figure 22.2** Geochemical differentiation of the elements.

**The Impact of Life on Crustal Abundances** At present, the crust is the only physically accessible portion of Earth, so only crustal abundances have practical significance. The crust is divided into the **lithosphere** (the solid region of the crust), **hydrosphere** (the liquid region), and **atmosphere** (the gaseous region). Over billions of years, weathering and volcanic upsurges have dramatically altered the composition of the crust. The **biosphere,** which consists of the living systems that have inhabited the planet, has been another *major influence on crustal element composition and distribution.*

When the earliest rocks were forming and the ocean basins were filling with water, binary inorganic molecules in the atmosphere were reacting to form first simple, and then more complex, organic molecules. The energy for these (mostly) endothermic changes was supplied by lightning, solar radiation, geologic heating, and meteoric impact. In an amazingly short period of time, probably no more than 500 million years, the first organisms appeared. It took less than another billion years for these to evolve into simple algae that could derive metabolic energy from photosynthesis, converting $CO_2$ and $H_2O$ into organic molecules and releasing $O_2$ as a byproduct.

Let's look at some of the essential ways the evolution of organisms affected the chemistry of the crust:

1. Due to photosynthesis, the atmosphere gradually became richer in $O_2$ over the 300 million years following the emergence of algae. Thus, *oxidation became the major source of free energy in the crust and biosphere.* As a result of this oxidizing environment, the predominating Fe(II)-containing minerals were oxidized to Fe(III)-containing minerals, such as hematite, $Fe_2O_3$, shown in Figure 22.3A in ancient banded-iron formations (red beds). The increase in oxygen also led to an explosion of $O_2$-utilizing life forms, a few of which evolved into the organisms of today. Figure 22.3B shows a fossil of one of the multicellular organisms whose appearance coincided with the increase in $O_2$.

**Figure 22.3** Ancient effects of an $O_2$-rich atmosphere.

**A   Banded-iron formations containing $Fe_2O_3$**

**B   Fossil of early multicellular organism**

2. The $K^+$ concentration of the oceans is much lower than the $Na^+$ concentration. Forming over eons from outgassed water vapor condensing into rain and streaming over the land, the oceans became complex ionic solutions of dissolved minerals with 30 times as much $Na^+$ as $K^+$. One reason for this is that plants require $K^+$ for growth, so they absorbed dissolved $K^+$ that would otherwise have washed down to the sea.

3. There are enormous subterranean deposits of organic carbon, formed when ancient plants, buried deeply and decomposing under high pressure and temperature in the absence of free $O_2$, gradually turned into coal or when animals buried under similar conditions turned into petroleum. Crustal deposits of this organic carbon still provide the fuels that move our cars, heat our homes, and electrify our cities.

4. Carbon and oxygen, together with calcium, the fifth most abundant element in the crust, occurs in vast sedimentary deposits all over the world as limestone, dolomite (*see photo*), marble, and chalk, the fossilized skeletal remains of countless early marine organisms.

Table 22.2 compares selected elemental abundances in the whole crust, the three crustal regions, and the human body, a representative portion of the biosphere. Note the quantities of the four major elements of life—O, C, H, and N. Oxygen is either the first or second most abundant element in all cases. The biosphere contains large amounts of carbon in its biomolecules and large amounts of hydrogen as water. Nitrogen is abundant in the atmosphere as free $N_2$ and in organisms as part of their proteins. Phosphorus and sulfur also occur in high amounts in organisms.

Dolomite Mountains, Italy.

| Table **22.2** Abundances of Selected Elements in the Crust, Its Regions, and the Human Body as Representative of the Biosphere (Mass %) | | | | | |
|---|---|---|---|---|---|
| | | **Crustal Regions** | | | |
| **Element** | **Crust** | **Lithosphere** | **Hydrosphere** | **Atmosphere** | **Human** |
| O | 49.5 | 45.5 | 85.8 | 23.0 | 65.0 |
| C | 0.08 | 0.018 | — | 0.01 | 18.0 |
| H | 0.87 | 0.15 | 10.7 | 0.02 | 10.0 |
| N | 0.03 | 0.002 | — | 75.5 | 3.0 |
| P | 0.12 | 0.11 | — | — | 1.0 |
| Mg | 1.9 | 2.76 | 0.13 | — | 0.50 |
| K | 2.4 | 1.84 | 0.04 | — | 0.34 |
| Ca | 3.4 | 4.66 | 0.05 | — | 2.4 |
| S | 0.06 | 0.034 | — | — | 0.26 |
| Na | 2.6 | 2.27 | 1.1 | — | 0.14 |
| Cl | 0.19 | 0.013 | 2.1 | — | 0.15 |
| Fe | 4.7 | 6.2 | — | — | 0.005 |
| Zn | 0.013 | 0.008 | — | — | 0.003 |
| Cr | 0.02 | 0.012 | — | — | $3\times10^{-6}$ |
| Co | 0.003 | 0.003 | — | — | $3\times10^{-6}$ |
| Cu | 0.007 | 0.007 | — | — | $4\times10^{-4}$ |
| Mn | 0.09 | 0.11 | — | — | $1\times10^{-4}$ |
| Ni | 0.008 | 0.010 | — | — | $3\times10^{-6}$ |
| V | 0.015 | 0.014 | — | — | $3\times10^{-6}$ |

One striking difference among the lithosphere, hydrosphere, and biosphere (human) is in the abundances of the transition metals vanadium through zinc. Their relatively insoluble oxides and sulfides make them much scarcer in water than on land. Yet organisms, which evolved in the seas, developed the ability to concentrate the trace amounts of these elements present in their aqueous environment. In every case, the biological concentration is at least 100-fold, with Mn increasing about 1000-fold, and Cu, Zn, and Fe even more. Each of these elements performs an essential role in living systems (see Chemical Connections, pp. 968–969).

## Sources of the Elements

Given an element's abundance in a region of the crust, we must determine its **occurrence,** or **source,** the form(s) in which the element exists. Practical considerations often determine the commercial source. Oxygen, for example, is abundant in all three crustal regions, but the atmosphere is its primary industrial source because it occurs there as the free element. Nitrogen and the noble gases (except helium) are also obtained from the atmosphere. Several other elements occur uncombined, formed in large deposits by prehistoric biological action, such as sulfur in caprock salt domes and nearly pure carbon in coal. The relatively unreactive elements gold and platinum also occur in an uncombined (*native*) state.

The overwhelming majority of elements, however, occur in **ores,** natural compounds or mixtures from which an element can be extracted economically (*see photo*): *the financial costs of mining, isolating, and purifying must be considered when choosing a process to obtain an element.*

Figure 22.4 *(next page)* shows the most useful sources of the elements. Note that elements with the same types of ores tend to be grouped together in the periodic table:

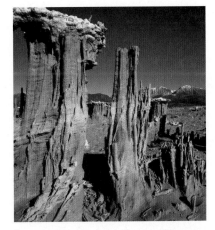

Deposit of borate (tufa), the ore of boron.

- Alkali metal halides are ores for both of their component groups of elements, Group 1A(1) and Group 7A(17).
- Group 2A(2) metals occur as carbonates in the marble and limestone of mountain ranges, although magnesium is very abundant in seawater (making that the preferred source, as we discuss later).

**Figure 22.4** Sources of the elements.

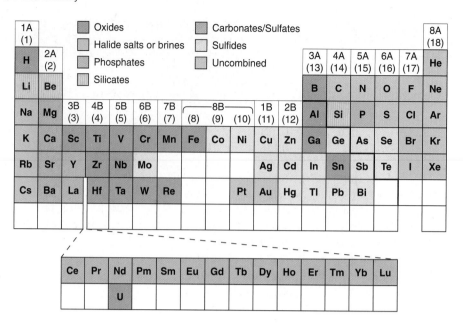

- Even though many elements occur as silicates, most of these compounds are very stable thermodynamically. Thus, the cost that would be required to process them prohibits their use—aside from silicon, only lithium and beryllium are obtained from their silicates.
- The ores of most industrially important metals are either oxides, which dominate the left half of the transition series, or sulfides, which dominate the right half of the transition series and a few of the main groups beyond.

The reasons for the prominence of oxide and sulfide ores of metallic elements are complex and include weathering processes, selective precipitation, and relative solubilities. Certain atomic properties are relevant as well. Metals toward the left side of the periodic table have lower ionization energies and electronegativities, so they tend to give up electrons or hold them loosely in bonds. The $O^{2-}$ ion is small enough to approach a metal cation closely, which results in a high lattice energy for the oxide. In contrast, metals toward the right side have higher ionization energies and electronegativities. Thus, they tend to form bonds that are more covalent, which suits the larger, more polarizable $S^{2-}$ ion.

## ▌Summary of Section 22.1

- As the young Earth cooled, the elements became differentiated into a dense metallic core, a silicate-rich mantle, and a low-density crust.
- High abundances of light metals, metalloids, and nonmetals are concentrated in the crust, which consists of three regions: lithosphere (solid), hydrosphere (liquid), and atmosphere (gaseous).
- The biosphere (living systems) profoundly affected crustal chemistry by producing free $O_2$, and thus an oxidizing environment.
- Some elements occur in their native state, but most are combined in ores. The ores of most important metallic elements are oxides or sulfides.

## 22.2 • THE CYCLING OF ELEMENTS THROUGH THE ENVIRONMENT

The distributions of many elements change at widely differing rates. The physical, chemical, and biological paths that atoms of an element take through regions of the crust constitute the element's **environmental cycle.** In this section, we consider the cycles for carbon, nitrogen, and phosphorus and highlight the effects of humans on them.

# The Carbon Cycle

Carbon is one of a handful of elements that appear in all three portions of Earth's crust. In the lithosphere, it occurs in elemental form as graphite and diamond, in fully oxidized form in carbonate minerals, in fully reduced form in petroleum hydrocarbons, and in complex mixtures, such as coal and living matter. In the hydrosphere, it occurs in living matter, in carbonate minerals formed by the action of coral-reef organisms, and in dissolved $CO_2$ and related oxoanions. In the atmosphere, it occurs principally in gaseous $CO_2$, a minor but essential component that exists in equilibrium with the aqueous fraction.

**Key Interactions Within the Cycle** Figure 22.5 depicts the complex interplay of sources and the effect of the biosphere on carbon's environmental cycle. It provides an estimate of the size of each source and, where possible, the amount of carbon moving annually between sources. Note these key points:

- The portions of the cycle are linked by the atmosphere—one link between oceans and air, the other between land and air. The $2.6 \times 10^{12}$ metric tons of $CO_2$ in air cycles through the oceans and atmosphere about once every 300 years but spends a much longer time in carbonate minerals.

**Figure 22.5 The carbon cycle.** Numbers in boxes refer to the size of the source; numbers along arrows refer to the annual movement of the element from source to source. Values are in $10^9$ metric tons of C (1 metric ton = 1000 kg = 1.1 tons).

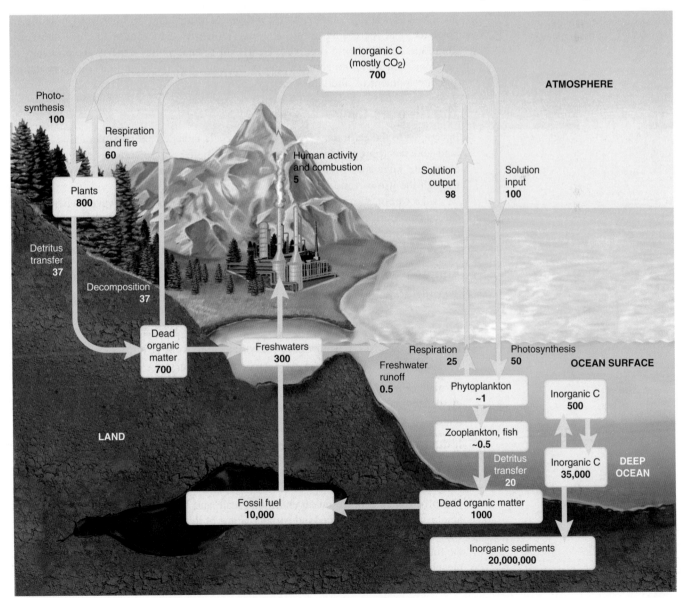

- Atmospheric $CO_2$ accounts for only 0.003% of crustal carbon but moves the element through the other regions. A $CO_2$ molecule spends, on average, 3.5 years in the atmosphere.
- The land and oceans are in contact with the largest sources of carbon, immobilized as carbonates, coal, and oil in rocky sediment beneath the soil.
- *Photosynthesis, respiration,* and *decomposition* are major factors in the cycle. **Fixation** is the process of converting a gaseous substance into a condensed form. Via photosynthesis, marine plankton and terrestrial plants use sunlight to fix atmospheric $CO_2$ into carbohydrates. Plants release $CO_2$ by respiration at night and, much more slowly, when they decompose. Animals eat the plants and release $CO_2$ by respiration and decomposition.
- Fires and volcanoes also release $CO_2$ into the air.

**Buildup of $CO_2$ and Global Warming** For hundreds of millions of years, the cycle has maintained a relatively constant amount of atmospheric $CO_2$, resulting in a relatively constant planetary temperature range. But over the past century and a half, especially since World War II, atmospheric $CO_2$ has increased. The principal cause is the combustion of coal, wood, and oil as fuel and for the decomposition of limestone to make cement, coupled with the clearing of forest and jungle for lumber, paper, and agriculture. And the principal effect is climate change. The 1990s and 2000s were the hottest decades ever recorded, and abundant evidence is showing that these activities have led to global warming through the greenhouse effect (see Chemical Connections, pp. 249–251). Higher temperatures, alterations in dry and rainy seasons, melting of polar ice, and increasing ocean acidity, with associated changes in carbonate equilibria, are already being observed. Nearly all science policy experts are pressing for programs that combine conservation of carbon-based fuels, an end to deforestation, and development of alternative energy sources.

## The Nitrogen Cycle

In contrast to the carbon cycle, the nitrogen cycle includes a *direct* interaction between land and sea (Figure 22.6). All nitrites and nitrates are soluble, so rain and runoff contribute huge amounts of nitrogen to lakes, rivers, and oceans. Human activity, through the use of fertilizer, plays a major role in this cycle.

Like carbon dioxide, atmospheric nitrogen must be fixed. However, whereas $CO_2$ can be incorporated by plants in either its gaseous or aqueous form, the great stability of $N_2$ prevents plants from using it directly. Fixation of $N_2$ requires a great deal of energy and occurs through atmospheric, industrial, and biological processes.

**Atmospheric Fixation** Lightning causes the high-temperature endothermic reaction of $N_2$ and $O_2$ to form NO, which is then oxidized by ozone exothermically to $NO_2$:

$$N_2(g) + O_2(g) \longrightarrow 2NO(g) \qquad \Delta H° = 180.6 \text{ kJ}$$
$$NO(g) + O_3(g) \longrightarrow NO_2(g) + O_2(g) \qquad \Delta H° = -200.1 \text{ kJ}$$

During the day, $NO_2$ reacts with hydroxyl radical to form $HNO_3$:

$$NO_2(g) + HO·(g) \longrightarrow HNO_3(g)$$

At night, a multistep reaction between $NO_2$ and ozone is involved. In either case, rain dissociates the nitric acid, and $NO_3^-(aq)$ enters both sea and land to be utilized by plants.

**Industrial Fixation** Most human-caused fixation occurs industrially during ammonia synthesis via the Haber process (Chapter 17, pp. 706–707):

$$N_2(g) + 3H_2(g) \rightleftharpoons 2NH_3(g)$$

The process takes place on an enormous scale and $NH_3$ ranks first, on a mole basis, among compounds produced industrially. Some of this $NH_3$ is converted to $HNO_3$ in the Ostwald process (Chapter 14, p. 548), but most is used as fertilizer, either directly or in the form of urea and ammonium salts (sulfate, phosphate, and nitrate), which enter the biosphere when taken up by plants (*see below*).

**Figure 22.6 The nitrogen cycle.** Numbers in boxes are in $10^9$ metric tons of N and refer to the size of the source; numbers along arrows are in $10^6$ metric tons of N and refer to the annual movement of the element between sources.

In recent decades, high-temperature combustion in electric power plants and in car, truck, and plane engines has become an important contributor to total fixed nitrogen. High engine operating temperatures mimic lightning to form NO from the air taken in to burn the hydrocarbon fuel. The NO in exhaust gases reacts to form nitric acid in the atmosphere, which adds to the nitrate load that reaches the ground.

The overuse of fertilizers *and* automobiles presents an increasingly serious water pollution problem in many areas. Leaching of the land by rain causes nitrate from fertilizer use and vehicle operation to enter lakes, rivers, and coastal estuaries and cause *eutrophication,* the depletion of $O_2$ and the death of aquatic animal life from excessive algal and plant growth and decomposition. Excess nitrate also spoils nearby drinkable water.

**Biological Fixation** The biological fixation of atmospheric $N_2$ occurs in blue-green algae and in nitrogen-fixing bacteria that live on the roots of leguminous plants (such as peas, alfalfa, and clover). These microbial processes dwarf the previous two, fixing more than seven times as much nitrogen as the atmosphere and six times as much as industry. Root bacteria fix $N_2$ by enzymatically reducing it to $NH_3$ and $NH_4^+$. Enzymes in other soil bacteria catalyze the multistep oxidation of $NH_4^+$ to $NO_2^-$ and finally $NO_3^-$, which the plants reduce again to make proteins. When the plants die, still other soil bacteria oxidize the proteins to $NO_3^-$.

Animals eat the plants, break down the plant proteins to make their own proteins, and excrete nitrogenous wastes, such as urea $[(H_2N)_2C{=}O]$. The nitrogen in the proteins is released when the animals die and decompose, and is converted by soil bacteria to $NO_2^-$ and $NO_3^-$ again. This central pool of inorganic nitrate has three main fates: some enters marine and terrestrial plants, some enters the enormous sediment store of mineral nitrates, and some is reduced by denitrifying bacteria to $NO_2^-$ and then reduced further to $N_2O$ and $N_2$, which re-enter the atmosphere to complete the cycle.

## The Phosphorus Cycle

Virtually all the mineral sources of phosphorus contain the phosphate group, $PO_4^{3-}$. The most commercially important ores are **apatites,** compounds of general formula $Ca_5(PO_4)_3X$, where X is usually F, Cl, or OH. The cycling of phosphorus through the environment involves three interlocking subcycles (Figure 22.7). Two rapid biological cycles—a land-based cycle (*yellow arrows in figure*) completed in a matter of years and a water-based cycle (*blue arrows*) completed in weeks to years—are superimposed on an inorganic cycle (*purple arrows*) that takes millions of years to complete. Unlike the carbon and nitrogen cycles, the phosphorus cycle has no gaseous component and thus does *not* involve the atmosphere.

**The Inorganic Cycle** Although most phosphorus occurs in phosphate rock formed when Earth's lithosphere solidified, a sizeable amount has come from outer space in meteorites. About 100 metric tons of meteorites enter Earth's atmosphere every day, and with an average P content of 0.1% by mass, they have contributed about $10^{11}$ metric tons of phosphorus to the crust over Earth's lifetime. The most important components of phosphate rock are nearly insoluble phosphate salts:

$$K_{sp} \text{ of } Ca_3(PO_4)_2 \approx 10^{-29}$$
$$K_{sp} \text{ of } Ca_5(PO_4)_3OH \approx 10^{-51}$$
$$K_{sp} \text{ of } Ca_5(PO_4)_3F \approx 10^{-60}$$

Weathering slowly leaches phosphates from the soil and carries the ions through rivers to the sea. Plants in the land-based biological cycle speed this process. In the ocean, some phosphate is absorbed by organisms in the water-based biological cycle, but the majority is precipitated again by $Ca^{2+}$ ion and deposited on the continental shelf. Geologic activity lifts the continental shelves, returning the phosphate to the land.

**The Land-Based Biological Cycle** The biological cycles involve the incorporation of phosphate into organisms (biomolecules, bones, teeth, and so forth) and the release of phosphate through their excretion and decomposition. In the land-based cycle, plants continually remove phosphate from the inorganic cycle. Recall that there are three phosphate oxoanions, which exist in equilibrium in aqueous solution:

$$H_2PO_4^- \rightleftharpoons HPO_4^{2-} \rightleftharpoons PO_4^{3-}$$
$$+ H^+ \qquad + H^+$$

**Figure 22.7** The phosphorus cycle.

In topsoil, phosphates occur as insoluble compounds of $Ca^{2+}$, $Fe^{3+}$, and $Al^{3+}$. Because they can absorb only the water-soluble dihydrogen phosphate, plants have evolved the ability to secrete acids near their roots to convert the insoluble salts gradually into the soluble ion:

$$Ca_3(PO_4)_2(s; \text{soil}) + 4H^+(aq; \text{secreted by plants}) \longrightarrow$$
$$3Ca^{2+}(aq) + 2H_2PO_4^-(aq; \text{absorbed by plants})$$

Animals that eat the plants excrete soluble phosphate, which is used by newly growing plants. As plants and animals excrete, die, and decompose, some phosphate is washed into rivers and the oceans. Most of the 2 million metric tons of phosphate that washes from land to sea each year comes from this biological source. Thus, the biosphere greatly increases the movement of phosphate from lithosphere to hydrosphere.

**The Water-Based Biological Cycle**  Various phosphate oxoanions continually enter the aquatic environment. Studies that incorporate trace amounts of radioactive phosphorus into $H_2PO_4^-$ and monitor its uptake show that, within 1 minute, 50% of the ion is taken up by photosynthetic algae, which use it to synthesize their biomolecules (denoted by the top curved arrow in the following equation, which shows the overall process):

$$106CO_2(g) + 16NO_3^-(aq) + H_2PO_4^-(aq) + 122H_2O(l) + 17H^+(aq) \overset{\text{synthesis}}{\underset{\text{decomposition}}{\rightleftharpoons}}$$
$$C_{106}H_{263}O_{110}N_{16}P(aq; \text{in algal cell fluid}) + 138O_2(g)$$

(The complex formula on the right represents the total composition of algal biomolecules, not some particular compound.)

As on land, animals eat the plants and are eaten by other animals, and they all excrete phosphate, die, and decompose (denoted by the bottom curved arrow in the preceding equation). Some of the released phosphate is used by other aquatic organisms, and some returns to the land when fish-eating animals (mostly humans and birds) excrete phosphate, die, and decompose. In addition, some aquatic phosphate precipitates with $Ca^{2+}$, sinks to the seabed, and returns to the long-term mineral deposits of the inorganic cycle.

**Human Effects on Phosphorus Movement**  From prehistoric through preindustrial times, these interlocking phosphorus cycles were balanced. Modern human activity, however, alters the movement of phosphorus considerably. Annually, we use more than 100 million tons of phosphate rock. Figure 22.8 shows the major end products, with box height proportional to the mass % of phosphate rock used annually. Removal

**Figure 22.8**  Industrial uses of phosphorus.

of phosphate rock has minimal influence on the inorganic cycle, but the end products have unbalanced the two biological cycles.

The imbalance arises from our overuse of *soluble phosphate fertilizers,* such as $Ca(H_2PO_4)_2$ and $NH_4H_2PO_4$, the end products of about 85% of phosphate rock mined. Some fertilizer finds its way into rivers, lakes, and oceans to enter the water-based cycle. Much larger pollution sources, however, are the crops grown with the fertilizer and the detergents made from phosphate rock. The great majority of this phosphate arrives eventually in cities as crops, as animals that were fed crops, and as consumer products, such as the tripolyphosphates in detergents. Human garbage, excrement, wash water with detergents, and industrial wastewater containing phosphate are carried through sewers to the aquatic system. This human contribution equals the natural contribution—another 2 million metric tons of phosphate per year. The increased concentration in rivers and lakes causes eutrophication, which robs the water of $O_2$ so that it cannot support life. Such "dead" rivers and lakes are no longer usable for fishing, drinking, or recreation.

A century ago, in 1912, Lake Zurich in Switzerland had been choked with algae and become devoid of fish. Treatment with $FeCl_3$ precipitated enough phosphate to gradually return the lake to its natural state. Soluble aluminum compounds have the same effect:

$$FeCl_3(aq) + PO_4^{3-}(aq) \longrightarrow FePO_4(s) + 3Cl^-(aq)$$

$$KAl(SO_4)_2 \cdot 12H_2O(aq) + PO_4^{3-}(aq) \longrightarrow AlPO_4(s) + K^+(aq) + 2SO_4^{2-}(aq) + 12H_2O(l)$$

## ▌ Summary of Section 22.2

- The environmental distribution of many elements changes cyclically with time and is affected in major ways by organisms.
- Carbon occurs in all three regions of Earth's crust, with atmospheric $CO_2$ linking the other two regions. Photosynthesis and decomposition of organisms alter the amount of carbon in the land and oceans. Human activity has increased atmospheric $CO_2$, leading to climate change.
- Nitrogen is fixed by lightning, by industry, and primarily by microorganisms. When plants or animals decompose, bacteria convert proteins to nitrites and nitrates and eventually to $N_2$, which returns to the atmosphere. Through extensive use of fertilizers, humans have added excess nitrogen to freshwaters.
- The phosphorus cycle has no gaseous component. Inorganic phosphates leach slowly into land and water, where biological cycles interact. When plants and animals decompose, they release phosphate to natural waters, where it is then absorbed by other plants and animals. Through overuse of phosphate fertilizers and detergents, humans double the amount of phosphorus entering the aqueous environment.

| Table **22.3** Common Mineral Sources of Some Elements | |
|---|---|
| **Element** | **Mineral, Formula** |
| Al | Gibbsite (in bauxite), $Al(OH)_3$ |
| Ba | Barite, $BaSO_4$ |
| Be | Beryl, $Be_3Al_2Si_6O_{18}$ |
| Ca | Limestone, $CaCO_3$ |
| Fe | Hematite, $Fe_2O_3$ |
| Hg | Cinnabar, $HgS$ |
| Na | Halite, $NaCl$ |
| Pb | Galena, $PbS$ |
| Sn | Cassiterite, $SnO_2$ |
| Zn | Sphalerite, $ZnS$ |

## 22.3 • METALLURGY: EXTRACTING A METAL FROM ITS ORE

**Metallurgy** is the branch of materials science concerned with the extraction and utilization of metals. In this section, we discuss the general procedures for isolating metals and, occasionally, the nonmetals that are found in their ores. The extraction process applies one or more of these three types of metallurgy:

- *Pyrometallurgy* uses heat to obtain the metal.
- *Electrometallurgy* employs an electrochemical step.
- *Hydrometallurgy* relies on the metal's aqueous solution chemistry.

The extraction of an element begins with *mining the ore.* Most ores consist of mineral and gangue. The **mineral** contains the element; it is defined as a naturally occurring, homogeneous, crystalline inorganic solid, with a well-defined composition. The **gangue** is the portion of the ore with no commercial value, such as sand, rock, and clay. Table 22.3 lists the common mineral sources of some metals.

**Figure 22.9** Steps in metallurgy.

Humans have been removing metals for thousands of years, so most of the concentrated sources are gone, and, in many cases, ores contain very low mass percents of a metal. The general procedure for extracting most metals (and many nonmetals) involves a few basic steps, described in the upcoming subsections (Figure 22.9).

## Pretreating the Ore

Following a crushing, grinding, or pulverizing step, which can be very expensive, pretreatment uses some physical or chemical difference to separate mineral from gangue. The following are common pretreatment techniques:

- *Magnetic attraction.* For magnetic minerals, such as magnetite ($Fe_3O_4$), a magnet can remove the mineral and leave the gangue behind.
- *Density separation.* When large density differences exist, a *cyclone separator* blows high-pressure air through the pulverized mixture to separate the particles. The lighter silicate-rich gangue is blown away, while the denser mineral-rich particles hit the walls of the separator and fall through the open bottom (Figure 22.10).
- *Flotation.* In **flotation,** an oil-detergent mixture is stirred with the pulverized ore in water to form a slurry (Figure 22.11). The surfaces of mineral and of gangue become wet to different extents with water and detergent. Rapid mixing with air produces an oily, mineral-rich froth that floats, while the silicate particles sink. Skimming, followed by solvent removal, isolates the concentrated mineral fraction.
- *Leaching.* Some metals are extracted by a hydrometallurgical process known as **leaching,** usually accomplished via formation of a complex ion. The modern extraction of gold is a good example of this technique. In the past, prospectors panned for gold (*see photo*), a process that relies on the very large density difference between gold and sand. In the leaching process, the crushed ore, which often contains as little as 25 ppm of gold, is contained in a plastic-lined pool, treated with a cyanide ion

Panning for gold.

Lighter particles (gangue)

Pulverized ore

Upward-moving air stream

Heavier particles (mineral)

**Figure 22.10** The cyclone separator.

Stirrer

Ore and oil-detergent mixture

Compressed air

Froth of detergent-coated mineral

Gangue (rock, sand)

**Figure 22.11** The flotation process.

solution, and aerated. In the presence of $CN^-$, the $O_2$ in air oxidizes gold metal to gold(I) ion, $Au^+$, which forms the soluble complex ion, $Au(CN)_2^-$:

$$4Au(s) + O_2(g) + 8CN^-(aq) + 2H_2O(l) \longrightarrow 4Au(CN)_2^-(aq) + 4OH^-(aq)$$

(This method is controversial because cyanide enters streams and lakes, where it poisons fish and birds.)

## Converting Mineral to Element

After the mineral has been freed of debris and concentrated, it may undergo several chemical steps during its conversion to the element.

**Converting the Mineral to Another Compound** First, the mineral is often converted to another compound, one that has different solubility properties, is easier to reduce, or is free of an impurity. Conversion to an oxide is common because oxides can be reduced easily. Carbonates are heated to convert them to the oxide:

$$CaCO_3(s) \xrightarrow{\Delta} CaO(s) + CO_2(g)$$

Metal sulfides, such as ZnS, can be converted to oxides by **roasting** in air:

$$2ZnS(s) + 3O_2(g) \xrightarrow{\Delta} 2ZnO(s) + 2SO_2(g)$$

In most countries, hydrometallurgical methods are now used to avoid the atmospheric release of $SO_2$ from roasting. One way of processing copper, for example, is by bubbling air through an acidic slurry of insoluble $Cu_2S$, which completes both the pretreatment and conversion steps:

$$2Cu_2S(s) + 5O_2(g) + 4H^+(aq) \longrightarrow 4Cu^{2+}(aq) + 2SO_4^{2-}(aq) + 2H_2O(l)$$

**Converting Compound to Element Through Chemical Redox** The next step converts the new mineral form (usually an oxide) to the free element by either chemical or electrochemical redox methods. Let's consider the chemical methods first. In these processes, a reducing agent reacts directly with the compound. The most common reducing agents are carbon, hydrogen, and a more active metal.

1. *Reduction with carbon.* Because of its low cost and ready availability, carbon, in the form of coke (a porous residue from incomplete combustion of coal) or charcoal, is a common reducing agent. Heating an oxide with a reducing agent such as coke to obtain the metal is called **smelting.** Many metal oxides, such as zinc oxide and tin(IV) oxide, are smelted with carbon to free the metal, which then may need to be condensed and solidified:

$$ZnO(s) + C(s) \longrightarrow Zn(g) + CO(g)$$
$$SnO_2(s) + 2C(s) \longrightarrow Sn(l) + 2CO(g)$$

Several nonmetals that occur with positive oxidation states in minerals can be reduced with carbon as well. Phosphorus, for example, is produced from calcium phosphate:

$$2Ca_3(PO_4)_2(s) + 10C(s) + 6SiO_2(s) \longrightarrow 6CaSiO_3(s) + 10CO(g) + P_4(s)$$

(Metallic calcium is a much stronger reducing agent than carbon, so it is not formed.)

- *Thermodynamic considerations.* Thermodynamic principles explain why carbon is often such an effective reducing agent. Consider the standard free energy change ($\Delta G^\circ$) for the reduction of tin(IV) oxide:

$$SnO_2(s) + 2C(s) \longrightarrow Sn(s) + 2CO(g) \qquad \Delta G^\circ = 245 \text{ kJ at } 25°C \text{ (298 K)}$$

The magnitude and sign of $\Delta G^\circ$ indicate a highly *non*spontaneous reaction at standard-state conditions and 25°C. However, because solid C becomes gaseous CO, the standard molar entropy change is very positive ($\Delta S^\circ \approx 380$ J/K). Therefore, *the $-T\Delta S^\circ$ term of $\Delta G^\circ$ becomes more negative with higher temperature* (Section 20.3). As the temperature increases, $\Delta G^\circ$ decreases, and at a high enough temperature, the reaction becomes spontaneous ($\Delta G^\circ < 0$). At 1000°C (1273 K), for example, $\Delta G^\circ = -62.8$ kJ. The actual process is carried out at a temperature of around 1250°C (1523 K), so $\Delta G^\circ$ is even more negative. In effect, the nonspontaneous reduction of $SnO_2$ is coupled to the spontaneous oxidation of C.

- *Multistep nature of the process.* As you know, overall reactions often mask several intermediate steps. For instance, the reduction of tin(IV) oxide involves formation of tin(II) oxide:

$$SnO_2(s) + C(s) \longrightarrow \cancel{SnO(s)} + CO(g)$$
$$\cancel{SnO(s)} + C(s) \longrightarrow Sn(l) + CO(g)$$

[Molten tin (mp = 232 K) is obtained at this temperature.] The second step may even be composed of others, in which CO, not C, is the actual reducing agent:

$$SnO(s) + \cancel{CO(g)} \longrightarrow Sn(l) + \cancel{CO_2(g)}$$
$$\cancel{CO_2(g)} + C(s) \rightleftharpoons \cancel{2CO(g)}$$

Other pyrometallurgical processes are similarly complex. For instance, shortly you'll see that the overall reaction for the smelting of iron is

$$2Fe_2O_3(s) + 3C(s) \longrightarrow 4Fe(l) + 3CO_2(g)$$

However, the actual process is a multistep one with CO as the reducing agent. The advantage of CO over C is the far greater contact the gaseous reducing agent can make with the other reactant, which speeds the process.

2. *Reduction with hydrogen.* For oxides of some metals, especially some members of Groups 6B(6) and 7B(7), reduction with carbon forms metal carbides that are difficult to convert further, so hydrogen is used as the reducing agent instead, especially for less active metals, such as tungsten:

$$WO_3(s) + 3H_2(g) \longrightarrow W(s) + 3H_2O(g)$$

One step in the purification of the metalloid germanium also uses hydrogen:

$$GeO_2(s) + 2H_2(g) \longrightarrow Ge(s) + 2H_2O(g)$$

3. *Reduction with a more active metal.* If a metal also forms an undesirable hydride, its oxide is reduced by a more active metal. In the *thermite reaction,* aluminum powder reduces the metal oxide in a spectacular exothermic reaction to give the molten metal (Figure 22.12). The reaction for chromium is

$$Cr_2O_3(s) + 2Al(s) \longrightarrow 2Cr(l) + Al_2O_3(s) \qquad \Delta H° \ll 0$$

Reduction by an active metal is also used when the new mineral is not an oxide. In the extraction of gold, after the pretreatment by leaching, the gold(I) complex ion is reduced with zinc:

$$2Au(CN)_2^-(aq) + Zn(s) \longrightarrow 2Au(s) + Zn(CN)_4^{2-}(aq)$$

In some cases, an active metal, such as calcium, is used to recover an even more active metal, such as rubidium, from its molten salt:

$$Ca(l) + 2RbCl(l) \longrightarrow CaCl_2(l) + 2Rb(g)$$

A similar process (detailed in Section 22.4) is used to recover sodium.

4. A variation uses the opposite process because, just as *reduction* of a mineral is used to obtain the metal, *oxidation* of a mineral can be used to obtain a nonmetal. A stronger oxidizing agent removes electrons from the nonmetal anion to give the free nonmetal, as in the production of iodine from concentrated brines:

$$2I^-(aq) + Cl_2(g) \longrightarrow 2Cl^-(aq) + I_2(s)$$

**Figure 22.12** The thermite reaction.

## Converting Compound to Element Through Electrochemical Redox

In these processes, the minerals are converted to the elements in an electrolytic cell (Section 21.7). Sometimes, the *pure* mineral, in the form of the molten halide or oxide, is used to prevent unwanted side reactions. The cation is reduced to the metal at the cathode, and the anion is oxidized to the nonmetal at the anode:

$$BeCl_2(l) \longrightarrow Be(s) + Cl_2(g)$$

High-purity hydrogen gas is prepared by electrochemical reduction:

$$2H_2O(l) \longrightarrow 2H_2(g) + O_2(g)$$

Specially designed cells separate the products to prevent recombination. An inexpensive source of electricity is essential for large-scale methods. The current and voltage requirements depend on the electrochemical potential and any overvoltage (Section 21.7).

**Figure 22.13** The redox step in converting a mineral to the element.

Uncombined in nature

Reduction of molten halide (or oxide) electrolytically

Reduction of halide with active metal (e.g., Na, Mg, Ca)

Reduction of oxide/halide with Al or $H_2$

Reduction of oxide with C (coke or charcoal)

Oxidation of anion (or oxoanion) chemically and/or electrolytically

Figure 22.13 shows the most common redox step used in obtaining each free element from its mineral.

## Refining and Alloying the Element

After being isolated, the element typically still contains impurities, so it must be refined to purify it further. Then, metallic elements are often alloyed to improve their properties.

**Refining (Purifying) the Element** Refining is often carried out by one of three common methods:

1. *Electrorefining.* An electrolytic cell is employed in **electrorefining,** in which the *impure metal acts as the anode and the pure metal as the cathode.* As the reaction proceeds, the anode disintegrates, and the metal ions are reduced to deposit on the cathode. In some cases, impurities that fall beneath the anode are the source of several valuable and less abundant elements.

2. *Distillation.* Metals with relatively low boiling points, such as zinc and mercury, are refined by *distillation.*

3. *Zone refining.* In the process of **zone refining,** a rod of an impure metal or metalloid (such as silicon) is passed slowly through a heating coil in an inert atmosphere. The first narrow zone of the impure solid melts, and as the next zone melts, the dissolved impurites from the first zone lower the freezing point, so the solvent (purer solid of first zone) refreezes. The process continues, zone by zone, for the entire rod. After several passes through the coil, in which each zone's impurities move into the adjacent zone, the refrozen solid at the end of the rod becomes extremely pure (Figure 22.14). Metalloids used in electronic semiconductors, such as silicon and germanium, are zone refined to greater than 99.999999% purity.

**Figure 22.14** Zone refining of silicon.

**Alloying the Purified Element** An **alloy** is a metal-like mixture consisting of solid phases of two or more pure elements (a solid solution) or, in some cases, distinct intermediate phases (these alloys are sometimes referred to as *intermetallic compounds*) that are so finely divided they can only be distinguished microscopically. Alloying a metal with other metals (and, in some cases, nonmetals) is done to alter the metal's melting point and to enhance properties such as luster, conductivity, malleability, ductility, and strength.

## Table 22.4 Some Important Alloys and Their Composition

| Name | Composition (Mass %) | Uses |
|---|---|---|
| **Mostly Fe** | | |
| Stainless steel | 73–79 Fe, 14–18 Cr, 7–9 Ni | Cutlery, instruments |
| Nickel steel | 96–98 Fe, 2–4 Ni | Cables, gears |
| High-speed steels | 80–94 Fe, 14–20 W (or 6–12 Mo) | Cutting tools |
| **Mostly Cu** | | |
| Bronzes | 70–95 Cu, 1–25 Zn, 1–18 Sn | Statues, castings |
| Brasses | 50–80 Cu, 20–50 Zn | Plating, ornamental objects |
| **Mostly precious metals** | | |
| Sterling silver | 92.5 Ag, 7.5 Cu | Jewelry, tableware |
| 14-Carat gold | 58 Au, 4–28 Ag, 14–28 Cu | Jewelry |
| 18-Carat white gold | 75 Au, 12.5 Ag, 12.5 Cu | Jewelry |
| Dental amalgam | 69 Ag, 18 Sn, 12 Cu, 1 Zn (dissolved in Hg) | Dental fillings |
| **Other** | | |
| Permalloy | 78 Ni, 22 Fe | Ocean cables |
| Typical tin solder | 67 Pb, 33 Sn | Electrical connections |

Iron is used only when alloyed. In pure form, it is soft and corrodes easily. However, when alloyed with carbon and other metals, such as Mo for hardness and Cr and Ni for corrosion resistance, it forms various steels. Copper stiffens when zinc is added to make brass. Mercury solidifies when alloyed with sodium, and vanadium becomes extremely tough with some carbon added. Table 22.4 shows the composition and uses of some common alloys.

The simplest alloys, called *binary alloys,* contain only two elements, which can combine in two ways:

- *The added element enters interstices,* spaces between the parent metal atoms in its crystal structure (Section 12.6). In vanadium carbide, for instance, carbon atoms occupy holes of a face-centered cubic vanadium unit cell (Figure 22.15A).
- The *added element substitutes for atoms of the parent.* In many types of brass, for example, relatively few zinc atoms substitute randomly for copper atoms in the face-centered cubic copper unit cell (see Figure 13.4A, p. 482). On the other hand, β-brass is an intermediate phase that crystallizes as the Zn/Cu ratio approaches 1/1 in a structure with a central Zn atom surrounded by eight Cu atoms (Figure 22.15B). In one alloy of copper and gold, Cu atoms occupy the faces of a face-centered cube, and Au atoms lie at the corners (Figure 22.15C).

**A  Vanadium carbide**

**B  β - Brass**

**C  Cu₃Au**

**Figure 22.15** Three binary alloys.

Atomic properties, including size, electron configuration, and number of valence electrons, determine which metals form stable alloys. For example, transition metals from the left half of the *d* block [Groups 3B(3) to 5B(5)] often form alloys with metals from the right half [Groups 8B(9) to 1B(11)]: electron-poor Zr, Nb, and Ta form strong alloys with electron-rich Ir, Pt, or Au; an example is the very stable $ZrPt_3$.

## ■ Summary of Section 22.3

- Metallurgy involves mining an ore, separating it from debris, pretreating it to concentrate the mineral source, converting the mineral to another compound that is easier to process further, reducing this compound to the metal, purifying the metal, and in many cases, alloying it to obtain a more useful material.

## 22.4 • TAPPING THE CRUST: ISOLATION AND USES OF SELECTED ELEMENTS

The isolation process depends on the physical and chemical properties of the source; thus, we isolate an element that occurs uncombined in the air differently from one dissolved in the sea or one found in a rocky ore. In this section, we detail methods for recovering some important elements.

### Producing the Alkali Metals: Sodium and Potassium

The alkali metals are among the most reactive elements and thus are always found as ions in nature, either in solid minerals or in aqueous solution. In fact, they are so reactive that, in the laboratory, the free elements must be protected from contact with air (usually by being stored under mineral oil) to prevent their immediate oxidation and to minimize the possibility of fires. The two most important alkali metals are sodium and potassium. Their abundant, water-soluble compounds are used throughout industry and research, and the $Na^+$ and $K^+$ ions are essential to organisms.

**Industrial Production of Sodium and Potassium** Different methods are employed in the industrial production of these two metals:

Evaporative salt beds near San Francisco Bay.

1. *Production of sodium.* The sodium ore is *halite* (largely NaCl), which is obtained either by evaporation of concentrated salt solutions called *brines* (*see photo*) or by mining vast salt deposits formed from the evaporation of prehistoric seas. The Cheshire salt field in Britain, for example, is 60 km by 24 km by 400 m thick and contains more than 90% NaCl. Other large deposits occur in New Mexico, Michigan, New York, and Kansas.

The brine is evaporated and the solid crushed and fused (melted) for use in an electrolytic apparatus called the **Downs cell** (Figure 22.16). To reduce heating costs, the NaCl (mp = 801°C) is mixed with $1\frac{1}{2}$ parts $CaCl_2$ to form a mixture that melts at only 580°C. Reduction of the metal ions to Na and Ca takes place at a cylindrical steel cathode, with the molten metals floating on the denser molten salt mixture. As they rise through a short collecting pipe, the liquid Na is siphoned off, while a higher melting Na/Ca alloy solidifies and falls back into the molten electrolyte. Chloride ions are oxidized to $Cl_2$ gas at a large anode within an inverted cone-shaped chamber that separates the metals from the $Cl_2$ to prevent their explosive recombination. The $Cl_2$ is purified and sold as a valuable byproduct.

2. *Production of potassium.* Sylvite (mostly KCl) is the major ore of potassium. The metal is too soluble in molten KCl to be obtained by a method similar to that used for sodium. Instead, chemical reduction of $K^+$ ions by Na is based on atomic properties and the nature of equilibrium systems. An Na atom is smaller than a K atom, so it holds its outer electron more tightly: $IE_1$ of Na = 496 kJ/mol; $IE_1$ of K = 419 kJ/mol. Thus, based on this atomic property, Na would not be effective at reducing

Inlet for NaCl

$Cl_2(g)$

Molten Na

Molten electrolyte
(NaCl/CaCl$_2$, 2/3)

Na(*l*)

(−)

Na/Ca alloy

(+)

Anode (oxidation)

$2Cl^-(l) \longrightarrow Cl_2(g) + 2e^-$

Cathode (reduction)

$2Na^+(l) + 2e^- \longrightarrow 2Na(l)$

**Figure 22.16** The Downs cell for production of sodium.

$K^+$. However, the reduction is carried out at 850°C, which is above the boiling point of K, so the equilibrium mixture contains *gaseous* K:

$$Na(l) + K^+(l) \rightleftharpoons Na^+(l) + K(g)$$

As the K gas is removed, Le Châtelier's principle predicts that the system shifts to produce more K. The gas is then condensed and purified by fractional distillation. The same general method (with Ca as the reducing agent) is used to produce rubidium and cesium.

**Uses of Sodium and Potassium** The compounds of Na and K (and indeed, of all the alkali metals) have many more uses than the elements themselves. Nevertheless, there are some interesting uses of the metals that take advantage of their strong reducing power:

1. *Uses of sodium.* Large amounts of Na were used as an alloy with lead to make gasoline antiknock additives, such as tetraethyllead:

$$4C_2H_5Cl(g) + 4Na(s) + Pb(s) \longrightarrow (C_2H_5)_4Pb(l) + 4NaCl(s)$$

The toxic effects of environmental lead have limited this use to aviation fuel in the United States. Moreover, although leaded gasoline is still used in several developing countries, the global market for tetraethyllead is declining more than 15% annually.

If certain types of nuclear reactors, called *breeder reactors* (Chapter 24), become a practical way to generate energy in the United States, Na production would increase enormously. Its low melting point, viscosity, and absorption of neutrons, combined with its high thermal conductivity and heat capacity, make it perfect for cooling the reactor and exchanging heat to the steam generator.

2. *Uses of potassium.* The major use of potassium at present is in an alloy with sodium for use as a heat exchanger in chemical and nuclear reactors. Another application relies on production of its superoxide, which it forms by direct contact with $O_2$:

$$K(s) + O_2(g) \longrightarrow KO_2(s)$$

Firefighter with $KO_2$ breathing mask.

This material is employed as an emergency source of $O_2$ in breathing masks for miners, divers, submarine crews, and firefighters (*see photo*):

$$4KO_2(s) + 4CO_2(g) + 2H_2O(g) \longrightarrow 4KHCO_3(s) + 3O_2(g)$$

## The Indispensable Three: Iron, Copper, and Aluminum

Their innumerable applications make iron (in the form of steel), copper, and aluminum indispensable materials of our industrial society.

**Metallurgy of Iron** Although people have practiced iron smelting for more than 3000 years, it was only about 240 years ago that iron assumed its current dominant role. In 1773, an inexpensive process to convert coal to carbon in the form of coke was discovered, and the coke process made iron smelting cheap and efficient and led to large-scale iron production, which ushered in the Industrial Revolution.

Modern society rests, quite literally, on the various alloys of iron known as **steel.** Although steel production has grown enormously since the 18th century, the process of recovering iron from its ores still employs *reduction by carbon in a blast furnace.* The most abundant minerals of iron are listed in Table 22.5. Only the first four are used for steelmaking, because traces of sulfur from the sulfide minerals make the steel brittle.

The conversion from ore to metal involves a series of redox and acid-base reactions that appear simple, even though their detailed chemistry is not completely understood even today. A modern **blast furnace** (Figure 22.17) is a tower about 14 m wide by 40 m high, made of brick. The *charge,* which usually consists of hematite, coke, and limestone, is fed through the top. More coke is burned in air at the bottom. The charge falls and meets a *blast* of rapidly rising hot air created by the burning coke:

$$2C(s) + O_2(g) \longrightarrow 2CO(g) + \textit{\textbf{heat}}$$

| Table 22.5 | Important Minerals of Iron |
|---|---|
| **Mineral Type** | **Mineral, Formula** |
| Oxide | Hematite, $Fe_2O_3$ |
| | Magnetite, $Fe_3O_4$ |
| | Ilmenite, $FeTiO_3$ |
| Carbonate | Siderite, $FeCO_3$ |
| Sulfide | Pyrite, $FeS_2$ |
| | Pyrrhotite, $FeS$ |

Charge (ore, limestone, coke)

Waste gases (CO, $CO_2$, $NO_2$)

200°C    Raw materials preheated
Partial reduction of iron ore
$3Fe_2O_3(s) + CO(g) \longrightarrow 2Fe_3O_4(s) + CO_2(g)$
$Fe_3O_4(s) + CO(g) \longrightarrow 3FeO(s) + CO_2(g)$
$CaCO_3(s) \longrightarrow CaO(s) + CO_2(g)$

700°C    Final reduction
$C(s) + CO_2(g) \longrightarrow 2CO(g)$
$FeO(s) + CO(g) \longrightarrow Fe(l) + CO_2(g)$

1200°C    Melting of impure Fe and slag

1500°C    Phosphates and silicates reduced;
P, Si, and other impurities enter molten Fe

2000°C    $2C(s) + O_2(g) \longrightarrow 2CO(g)$

Airblast ~900°C

Slag

Hearth

Human

Molten Fe (pig iron)

**Figure 22.17** The major reactions in a blast furnace.

At the bottom of the furnace, the temperature exceeds 2000°C, while at the top, it reaches only 200°C. Because the blast of hot air passes through the entire furnace in only 10 s, the various gas-solid reactions do *not* reach equilibrium, and many intermediate products form. As a result, different stages of the overall reaction process occur at different heights:

1. In the upper part of the furnace (200°C to 700°C), the charge is preheated, and a *partial reduction* occurs. The hematite ($Fe_2O_3$) is reduced to magnetite ($Fe_3O_4$) and then to iron(II) oxide (FeO) by CO, which is the actual reducing agent. Carbon dioxide is formed as well. Limestone ($CaCO_3$) also decomposes to form $CO_2$ and the basic oxide CaO.
2. Lower down, at 700°C to 1200°C, a *final reduction* step occurs, as some of the coke reduces $CO_2$ to form more CO, which reduces the FeO to Fe.
3. At temperatures between 1200°C and 1500°C, the iron melts and drips to the bottom of the furnace. Acidic silica particles from the gangue react with the CaO in a Lewis acid-base reaction to form a molten waste product called **slag:**

$$CaO(s) + SiO_2(s) \longrightarrow CaSiO_3(l)$$

The slag drips down and floats on the denser iron.
4. Some unwanted reactions occur between 1500°C and 2000°C. Any remaining phosphates and silicates are reduced to P and Si, and some Mn and traces of S dissolve into the molten iron along with carbon. The resulting impure product is called *pig iron* and contains about 3% to 4% C. A small amount of pig iron is used to make *cast iron,* but most is purified and alloyed to make various kinds of steel.

**From Pig Iron to Steel** Pig iron is converted to steel in a separate furnace by means of the **basic-oxygen process** (Figure 22.18). High-pressure $O_2$ is blown over and through the molten iron, so that impurities (C, Si, P, Mn, and S) are oxidized rapidly. The highly negative standard enthalpies of formation of their oxides ($\Delta H_f^\circ$ of $CO_2$ = $-394$ kJ/mol and $\Delta H_f^\circ$ of $SiO_2$ = $-911$ kJ/mol) raise the temperature, which speeds the reaction. A lime (CaO) flux is added, which converts the oxides to a molten slag [primarily $CaSiO_3$ and $Ca_3(PO_4)_2$] that is decanted from the molten steel. The product is **carbon steel,** which contains 1% to 1.5% C and other impurities. It is alloyed with metals that prevent corrosion and increase its strength or flexibility.

**Figure 22.18** The basic-oxygen process for making steel.

Mining chalcopyrite.

**Isolation of Copper** After many centuries of being mined to make bronze and brass, copper ores have become much less plentiful and rich in copper (*see photo*). Despite this, more than 2.5 billion pounds of copper is produced in the United States annually. The most common ore is chalcopyrite, $CuFeS_2$, a mixed sulfide of FeS and CuS. Most remaining deposits contain less than 0.5% Cu by mass. To "win" this small amount of copper requires several metallurgical steps:

1. *Flotation.* The low copper content in chalcopyrite must be enriched by removing the iron. The first step is pretreatment by flotation (see Figure 22.11, p. 917), which concentrates the ore to around 15% Cu by mass.

2. *Roasting.* The next step in many processing plants is a controlled roasting step, which oxidizes the FeS but not the CuS:

$$2FeCuS_2(s) + 3O_2(g) \longrightarrow 2CuS(s) + 2FeO(s) + 2SO_2(g)$$

3. *Heating with sand.* To remove the FeO and convert the CuS to a more convenient form, the mixture is heated to 1100°C with sand and more of the concentrated ore. Several reactions occur in this step. The FeO reacts with sand to form a molten slag:

$$FeO(s) + SiO_2(s) \longrightarrow FeSiO_3(l)$$

The CuS is thermodynamically unstable at the elevated temperature and decomposes to yield $Cu_2S$, which is drawn off as a liquid.

4. *Smelting.* In the final smelting step, the $Cu_2S$ is roasted in air, which converts some of it to $Cu_2O$:

$$2Cu_2S(s) + 3O_2(g) \longrightarrow 2Cu_2O(s) + 2SO_2(g)$$

The two copper(I) compounds then react, with sulfide ion acting as the reducing agent:

$$Cu_2S(s) + 2Cu_2O(s) \longrightarrow 6Cu(l) + SO_2(g)$$

The copper obtained at this stage is usable for plumbing, but it must be purified further for electrical applications by removing the unwanted Fe and Ni as well as the valuable byproducts Ag, Au, and Pt.

**Electrorefining of Copper** Achieving the desired 99.99% purity needed for wiring (copper's most important use) is accomplished by *electrorefining,* which involves the oxidation of Cu and the formation of $Cu^{2+}$ ions in solution, followed by their reduction and the plating out of Cu metal (Figure 22.19). The impure copper obtained from smelting is cast into plates to be used as anodes, and cathodes are made from already

**Figure 22.19** The electrorefining of copper.

purified copper. The electrodes are immersed in acidified $CuSO_4$ solution, and a voltage is applied that accomplishes two tasks simultaneously:

- Copper and the more active impurities (Fe, Ni) are oxidized to their cations, while the less active ones (Ag, Au, Pt) are not. As the anode slabs react, these unoxidized metals fall off as valuable "anode mud" and are purified separately. Sale of the precious metals in the anode mud nearly offsets the cost of electricity to operate the cell, making Cu wire inexpensive.
- Because Cu is much less active than the Fe and Ni impurities, $Cu^{2+}$ ions are reduced at the cathode, but $Fe^{2+}$ and $Ni^{2+}$ ions remain in solution:

$$Cu^{2+}(aq) + 2e^- \longrightarrow Cu(s) \qquad E° = 0.34 \text{ V}$$
$$Ni^{2+}(aq) + 2e^- \longrightarrow Ni(s) \qquad E° = -0.25 \text{ V}$$
$$Fe^{2+}(aq) + 2e^- \longrightarrow Fe(s) \qquad E° = -0.44 \text{ V}$$

**Isolation of Aluminum** Aluminum is the most abundant metal in Earth's crust by mass and the third most abundant element (after O and Si). It is found in numerous aluminosilicate minerals, such as feldspars, micas, and clays, and in the rare gems garnet, beryl, spinel, and turquoise. Corundum, pure aluminum oxide ($Al_2O_3$), is extremely hard; mixed with traces of transition metals, it exists as ruby and sapphire. Impure $Al_2O_3$ is used in sandpaper and other abrasives.

Through eons of weathering, certain clays became *bauxite,* the major ore of aluminum. This mixed oxide-hydroxide occurs in enormous surface deposits in Mediterranean and tropical regions (*see photo*), but with world aluminum production near 100 million tons annually, it may someday be scarce. In addition to hydrated $Al_2O_3$ (about 75%), industrial-grade bauxite also contains $Fe_2O_3$, $SiO_2$, and $TiO_2$, which are removed during the extraction. The overall two-step process combines hydro- and electrometallurgical techniques:

Mining bauxite.

1. *Isolating $Al_2O_3$ from bauxite.* After mining, bauxite is pretreated by boiling in 30% NaOH in the *Bayer process,* which involves acid-base, solubility, and complex-ion equilibria. The acidic $SiO_2$ and the amphoteric $Al_2O_3$ dissolve in the base, but the basic $Fe_2O_3$ and $TiO_2$ do not:

$$SiO_2(s) + 2NaOH(aq) + 2H_2O(l) \longrightarrow Na_2Si(OH)_6(aq)$$
$$Al_2O_3(s) + 2NaOH(aq) + 3H_2O(l) \longrightarrow 2NaAl(OH)_4(aq)$$
$$Fe_2O_3(s) + NaOH(aq) \longrightarrow \text{no reaction}$$
$$TiO_2(s) + NaOH(aq) \longrightarrow \text{no reaction}$$

Further heating precipitates the $Na_2Si(OH)_6$ as an aluminosilicate, which is filtered out with the insoluble $Fe_2O_3$ and $TiO_2$ ("red mud").

Acidifying the filtrate precipitates $Al^{3+}$ as $Al(OH)_3$. Recall that the aluminate ion, $Al(OH)_4^-(aq)$, is actually the complex ion $Al(H_2O)_2(OH)_4^-$ (see Figure 19.17, p. 799). Weakly acidic $CO_2$ is added to produce a small amount of $H^+$ ion, which reacts with this complex ion to form $Al(H_2O)_3(OH)_3$. Cooling supersaturates the solution, and the solid that forms is filtered out:

$$CO_2(g) + H_2O(l) \rightleftharpoons H^+(aq) + HCO_3^-(aq)$$
$$Al(H_2O)_2(OH)_4^-(aq) + H^+(aq) \longrightarrow Al(H_2O)_3(OH)_3(s)$$

[Recall that we usually write $Al(H_2O)_3(OH)_3$ more simply as $Al(OH)_3$.]

Drying at high temperature converts the hydroxide to the oxide:

$$2Al(H_2O)_3(OH)_3(s) \xrightarrow{\Delta} Al_2O_3(s) + 9H_2O(g)$$

2. *Converting $Al_2O_3$ to the free metal: the Hall-Heroult process.* Aluminum is an active metal, much too strong a reducing agent to be formed at the cathode from aqueous solution (Section 21.7), so the oxide itself is electrolyzed.

The melting point of $Al_2O_3$ is very high (2030°C), so it is dissolved in molten *cryolite* ($Na_3AlF_6$) to give a mixture that electrolyzes at ~1000°C. Using cryolite provides a major energy (and, thus, cost) savings, but the only sizeable cryolite mines cannot supply enough of the mineral, so production of synthetic cryolite has become a major subsidiary industry in aluminum manufacture.

The electrolytic step, called the *Hall-Heroult process,* takes place in a graphite-lined furnace, with the lining itself acting as the cathode. Anodes of graphite dip into the molten $Al_2O_3$-$Na_3AlF_6$ mixture (Figure 22.20). The cell typically operates at a moderate voltage of 4.5 V, but with an enormous current flow of $1.0 \times 10^5$ to $2.5 \times 10^5$ A.

The process is complex and its details are still not entirely known. The specific reactions shown below are among several other possibilities. Molten cryolite contains several ions (including $AlF_6^{3-}$, $AlF_4^-$, and $F^-$), which react with $Al_2O_3$ to form fluoro-oxy ions (including $AlOF_3^{2-}$, $Al_2OF_6^{2-}$, and $Al_2O_2F_4^{2-}$) that dissolve in the mixture. For example,

$$2Al_2O_3(s) + 2AlF_6^{3-}(l) \longrightarrow 3Al_2O_2F_4^{2-}(l)$$

Al forms at the cathode (reduction), shown here with $AlF_6^{3-}$ as reactant:

$$AlF_6^{3-}(l) + 3e^- \longrightarrow Al(l) + 6F^-(l) \qquad \text{[cathode; reduction]}$$

The graphite anodes are oxidized and form carbon dioxide gas. Using one of the fluoro-oxy species as an example, the anode reaction is

$$Al_2O_2F_4^{2-}(l) + 8F^-(l) + C(\text{graphite}) \longrightarrow 2AlF_6^{3-}(l) + CO_2(g) + 4e^-$$

$$\text{[anode; oxidation]}$$

Thus, the *graphite anodes themselves are consumed* in this half-reaction and must be replaced frequently.

Combining the three previous equations and making sure that $e^-$ gained at the cathode equal $e^-$ lost at the anode gives the overall reaction:

$$2Al_2O_3(\text{in } Na_3AlF_6) + 3C(\text{graphite}) \longrightarrow 4Al(l) + 3CO_2(g) \qquad \text{[overall (cell) reaction]}$$

3. *Energy considerations.* The Hall-Heroult process uses an enormous quantity of energy: aluminum production accounts for more than 5% of total U.S. electrical usage. The most basic reason for such high energy consumption is the electron configuration of Al ($[Ne]\ 3s^2 3p^1$). Each $Al^{3+}$ ion needs $3e^-$ to form an Al atom, and the atomic mass of Al is so low (~27 g/mol) that 1 mol of $e^-$ (96,500 C) produces only 9 g of Al. An aluminum-air battery can turn this disadvantage around. Once produced, Al represents a concentrated form of electrical energy that can deliver a high output per gram: 1 mol of $e^-$ for every 9 g of Al consumed in the battery.

**Figure 22.20** The electrolytic cell in the manufacture of aluminum.

Graphite rods
Anodes (+): $Al_2O_3F_4^{2-} + 8F^- + C \longrightarrow 2AlF_6^{3-} + CO_2 + 4e^-$

$Al_2O_3$ dissolved in molten $Na_3AlF_6$

Bubbles of $CO_2$

Molten Al

(−)    (+)

**Power source**

Graphite furnace lining
Cathode (−): $AlF_6^{3-} + 3e^- \longrightarrow Al + 6F^-$

**Uses and Recycling of Aluminum** Aluminum is a superb decorative, functional, and structural metal. It is lightweight, attractive, easy to work, and forms strong alloys. Although Al is very active, it does not corrode readily because of an adherent oxide layer that forms rapidly in air and prevents more $O_2$ from penetrating. Nevertheless, when it is in contact with less active metals such as Fe, Cu, and Pb, aluminum becomes the anode in a voltaic-like arrangement and deteriorates rapidly (Section 21.6). To prevent this, aluminum objects are often *anodized,* that is, made to act as the anode in an electrolytic cell that coats them with an oxide layer. The object is immersed in a 20% $H_2SO_4$ bath and connected to a graphite cathode:

$$6H^+(aq) + 6e^- \longrightarrow 3H_2(g) \qquad \text{[cathode; reduction]}$$
$$\underline{2Al(s) + 3H_2O(l) \longrightarrow Al_2O_3(s) + 6H^+(aq) + 6e^-} \qquad \text{[anode; oxidation]}$$
$$2Al(s) + 3H_2O(l) \longrightarrow Al_2O_3(s) + 3H_2(g) \qquad \text{[overall (cell) reaction]}$$

The $Al_2O_3$ layer deposited is typically from 10 $\mu$ to 100 $\mu$ thick, depending on the object's intended use. Figure 22.21 presents a breakdown of the many uses of aluminum.

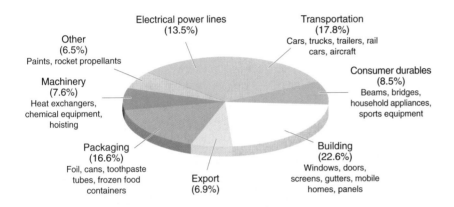

Other
(6.5%)
Paints, rocket propellants

Electrical power lines
(13.5%)

Transportation
(17.8%)
Cars, trucks, trailers, rail
cars, aircraft

Consumer durables
(8.5%)
Beams, bridges,
household appliances,
sports equipment

Machinery
(7.6%)
Heat exchangers,
chemical equipment,
hoisting

Packaging
(16.6%)
Foil, cans, toothpaste
tubes, frozen food
containers

Export
(6.9%)

Building
(22.6%)
Windows, doors,
screens, gutters, mobile
homes, panels

**Figure 22.21** The many familiar and essential uses of aluminum.

More than 4.0 billion pounds (1.8 million metric tons) of aluminum cans and packaging are discarded each year—a waste of one of the most useful materials in the world *and* the energy used to make it. A quick calculation of the energy needed to prepare 1 mol of Al from *purified* $Al_2O_3$, compared with the energy needed for recycling, conveys a clear message. For the overall cell reaction in the Hall-Heroult process, $\Delta H° = 2272$ kJ and $\Delta S° = 635.4$ J/K. If we consider *only* the standard free energy change of the reaction at 1000.°C, for 1 mol of Al, we obtain

$$\Delta G° = \Delta H° - T\Delta S° = \frac{2272 \text{ kJ}}{4 \text{ mol Al}} - \left(1273 \text{ K} \times \frac{0.6354 \text{ kJ/K}}{4 \text{ mol Al}}\right) = 365.8 \text{ kJ/mol Al}$$

The molar mass of Al is nearly 2.5 times the mass of a soft-drink or beer can, so the electrolysis step requires nearly 150 kJ of energy for each can!

When aluminum is recycled, the major energy input (which is for melting the cans and foil) has been calculated as ~26 kJ/mol Al. The ratio of these energy inputs is

$$\frac{\text{Energy to recycle 1 mol Al}}{\text{Energy for electrolysis of 1 mol Al}} = \frac{26 \text{ kJ}}{365.8 \text{ kJ}} = 0.071$$

Based on just these portions of the process, recycling uses about 7% as much energy as electrolysis. Recent energy estimates for the entire manufacturing process (including mining, pretreating, maintaining operating conditions, electrolyzing, and so forth) are about 6000 kJ/mol Al, which means recycling requires less than 1% as much energy as manufacturing. The economic advantages, not to mention the environmental ones, are obvious, and recycling of aluminum has become common in the United States (*see photo*).

Crushed aluminum cans ready for recycling.

## Mining the Sea for Magnesium

As terrestrial sources of certain elements become scarce or too costly to mine, the oceans will become an important source. In fact, despite the abundant distribution of magnesium on land, it is already obtained from the sea.

**Isolation of Magnesium** The *Dow process* for isolating magnesium from the sea involves steps similar to those used for rocky ores (Figure 22.22):

1. *Mining.* Intake of seawater and straining the debris are the "mining" steps. No pretreatment is needed.

2. *Converting to mineral.* The dissolved $Mg^{2+}$ ion is converted to the mineral $Mg(OH)_2$ with $Ca(OH)_2$, which is generated on-site (at the plant). Seashells ($CaCO_3$) are crushed, decomposed with heat to CaO, and mixed with water to make slaked lime [$Ca(OH)_2$]. This is pumped into the intake tank to precipitate the $Mg^{2+}$ as the hydroxide ($K_{sp} \approx 10^{-9}$):

$$Ca(OH)_2(aq) + Mg^{2+}(aq) \longrightarrow Mg(OH)_2(s) + Ca^{2+}(aq)$$

3. *Converting to compound.* The solid $Mg(OH)_2$ is filtered and mixed with excess HCl, which is also made on-site, to form aqueous $MgCl_2$:

$$Mg(OH)_2(s) + 2HCl(aq) \longrightarrow MgCl_2(aq) + 2H_2O(l)$$

The water is evaporated in stages to give solid, hydrated $MgCl_2 \cdot nH_2O$.

4. *Electrochemical redox.* Heating above 700°C drives off the water of hydration and melts the $MgCl_2$. Electrolysis gives chlorine gas and the molten metal, which floats on the denser molten salt:

$$MgCl_2(l) \longrightarrow Mg(l) + Cl_2(g)$$

The $Cl_2$ that forms is recycled to make the HCl used in step 3.

**Figure 22.22** The Dow process for isolation of elemental Mg from seawater.

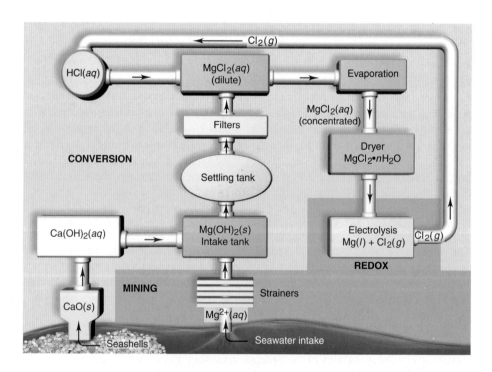

**Uses of Magnesium** Magnesium is the lightest structural metal available (about one-half the density of Al and one-fifth that of steel). Although Mg is quite reactive, it forms an extremely adherent, high-melting oxide layer (MgO); thus, it finds many uses in metal alloys and can be machined into any form. Magnesium alloys occur in everything from aircraft bodies to camera bodies, and from luggage to auto engine blocks. The pure metal is a strong reducing agent, which makes it useful for sacrificial anodes (Section 21.6) and in the metallurgical extraction of other metals, such as Be, Ti, Zr, Hf, and U. For example, titanium, an essential component of jet engines (*see photo*), is made from its major ore, ilmenite, in two steps:

(1) $2FeTiO_3(s) + 7Cl_2(g) + 6C(s) \longrightarrow 2TiCl_4(l) + 2FeCl_3(s) + 6CO(g)$

(2)         $TiCl_4(l) + 2Mg(l) \longrightarrow Ti(s) + 2MgCl_2(l)$

Jet engine assembly.

## The Sources and Uses of Hydrogen

Although hydrogen accounts for 90% of the atoms in the universe, it makes up only 15% of the atoms in Earth's crust. Moreover, hydrogen exists elsewhere in the universe mostly as $H_2$ molecules and free H atoms, but virtually all hydrogen in the crust is combined with other elements, either oxygen in natural waters or carbon in biomass, petroleum, and coal.

**Industrial Production of Hydrogen** Hydrogen gas ($H_2$) is produced on an industrial scale worldwide: 250,000 metric tons ($3\times10^{12}$ L at STP; equivalent to $\sim1\times10^{11}$ mol) are produced annually in the United States alone. All production methods are energy intensive, so the choice is determined by energy costs. In Scandinavia, where hydroelectric power is plentiful, electrolysis is used; on the other hand, where natural gas from oil refineries is plentiful, as in the United States and Great Britain, thermal methods are used.

1. *Electrolysis.* Very pure $H_2$ is prepared through electrolysis of water with Pt (or Ni) electrodes:

$$2H_2O(l) + 2e^- \longrightarrow H_2(g) + 2OH^-(aq) \qquad E = -0.42 \text{ V} \quad \text{[cathode; reduction]}$$
$$\underline{H_2O(l) \longrightarrow \tfrac{1}{2}O_2(g) + 2H^+(aq) + 2e^- \quad E = 0.82 \text{ V} \qquad \text{[anode; oxidation]}}$$
$$H_2O(l) \longrightarrow H_2(g) + \tfrac{1}{2}O_2(g) \qquad E_{cell} = -0.42 \text{ V} - 0.82 \text{ V} = -1.24 \text{ V}$$

Overvoltage makes the cell potential about $-2$ V (Section 21.7). Therefore, under typical operating conditions, it takes about 400 kJ of energy to produce 1 mol of $H_2$:

$$\Delta G = -nFE = (-2 \text{ mol e}^-)\left(\frac{96.5 \text{ kJ}}{\text{V·mol e}^-}\right)(-2 \text{ V}) = 4\times10^2 \text{ kJ/mol } H_2$$

High-purity $O_2$ is a valuable byproduct of this process that offsets some of the costs of isolating $H_2$.

2. *Thermal methods.* The most common thermal methods use water and a simple alkane like methane, which has the highest H/C ratio of any hydrocarbon. The reactants are heated to around 1000°C over a nickel-based catalyst in the endothermic *steam-reforming process:*

$$CH_4(g) + H_2O(g) \longrightarrow CO(g) + 3H_2(g) \qquad \Delta H° = 206 \text{ kJ}$$

Heat is supplied by burning methane. To generate more $H_2$, the product mixture (called *water gas*) is heated with steam at 400°C over an iron or cobalt oxide catalyst in the exothermic *water-gas shift reaction,* and the CO reacts (see also p. 249):

$$H_2O(g) + CO(g) \rightleftharpoons CO_2(g) + H_2(g) \qquad \Delta H° = -41 \text{ kJ}$$

The reaction mixture is recycled several times, which decreases the CO to around 0.2% by volume. Passing the mixture through liquid water removes the more soluble $CO_2$ (solubility = 0.034 mol/L) from the $H_2$ (solubility < 0.001 mol/L). Calcium oxide can also be used to remove $CO_2$ by formation of $CaCO_3$. By removing $CO_2$, these steps shift the equilibrium position to the right and produce $H_2$ that is about 98% pure. To filter out nearly all molecules larger than $H_2$ and attain greater purity (~99.9%), the gas mixture is passed through a *synthetic zeolite.* This material is an aluminosilicate whose framework of polyhedra contains small cavities of various sizes that trap some molecules and allow others to pass through.

**Industrial Uses of Hydrogen** Typically, a plant produces $H_2$ to make some other product. More than 95% of $H_2$ produced industrially is consumed in ammonia or petrochemical facilities.

1. *Ammonia synthesis.* In a plant that synthesizes $NH_3$, the reactant gases, $N_2$ and $H_2$, are formed through a series of reactions that involve methane.

Here is a typical reaction series in an ammonia plant:

- The steam-reforming reaction is performed with excess $CH_4$, which depletes the reaction mixture of $H_2O$:

$$CH_4(g; \text{excess}) + H_2O(g) \longrightarrow CO(g) + 3H_2(g)$$

- An excess of the product mixture ($CH_4$, CO, and $H_2$) is burned in an amount of air ($N_2 + O_2$) that is insufficient for complete combustion, but is enough to consume the $O_2$, heat the mixture to 1100°C, and form additional $H_2O$:

$$4CH_4(g; \text{excess}) + 7O_2(g) \longrightarrow 2CO_2(g) + 2CO(g) + 8H_2O(g)$$
$$2H_2(g; \text{excess}) + O_2(g) \longrightarrow 2H_2O(g)$$
$$2CO(g; \text{excess}) + O_2(g) \longrightarrow 2CO_2(g)$$

- Any remaining $CH_4$ reacts by the steam-reforming reaction, the remaining CO reacts by the water-gas shift reaction ($H_2O + CO \rightleftharpoons CO_2 + H_2$) to form more $H_2$, and then the $CO_2$ is removed with CaO.

- The amounts are carefully adjusted to produce a final mixture that contains a 1/3 ratio of $N_2$ (from the added air) to $H_2$ (with traces of $CH_4$, Ar, and CO). This mixture is used directly in the synthesis of ammonia (Section 17.6).

2. *Hydrogenation.* A second major use of $H_2$ is *hydrogenation* of C=C bonds in liquid oils to form C—C bonds in solid fats and margarine. The process uses $H_2$ in contact with transition metal catalysts, such as powdered nickel (see Figure 16.25, p. 662). Solid fats are also used in commercial baked goods. Look at the list of ingredients on most packages of bread, cake, and cookies, and you'll see the "partially hydrogenated vegetable oils" made by this process.

3. *Bulk chemicals and energy production.* Hydrogen is also essential in the manufacture of numerous "bulk" chemicals, those produced in large amounts because they have many further uses. One application that has been gaining great attention is the production of methanol. In this process, carbon monoxide reacts with hydrogen over a copper–zinc oxide catalyst:

$$CO(g) + 2H_2(g) \xrightarrow{\text{Cu-ZnO catalyst}} CH_3OH(l)$$

Methanol is already being used as a gasoline additive. As less expensive sources become available, hydrogen will be used increasingly in fuel cells on a major scale (Section 21.5).

**Production and Uses of Deuterium; Kinetic Isotope Effect** In addition to ordinary hydrogen ($^1H$), or protium, there are two other naturally occurring isotopes of significantly lower abundance. Deuterium ($^2H$ or D), has one neutron, and rare, radioactive tritium ($^3H$ or T) has two. Like $H_2$, both occur as diatomic molecules: $D_2$ (or $^2H_2$), and $T_2$ (or $^3H_2$). Table 22.6 compares some of their molecular and physical properties. As you can see, the heavier the isotope is and, thus, the higher the molar mass of the molecule, the higher the melting point, boiling point, and heats of phase change.

Because hydrogen is so light, the relative difference in mass of its isotopes is enormous compared with that of isotopes of other common elements. For example, $^2H$ has 2 times the mass of $^1H$, whereas $^{13}C$ has only 1.08 times the mass of $^{12}C$. *The mass difference leads to different bond energies, which affect reactivity.* As a result, an H atom bonded to a given atom vibrates at a higher frequency than a D atom does, so the bond to H is higher in energy. Thus, *it is weaker and easier to break.* Therefore, any reaction that includes breaking a bond to H or D in the rate-determining step occurs *faster with H than with D.* This phenomenon, called a *kinetic isotope effect,* is also used to isolate deuterium.

Deuterium and its compounds are produced from $D_2O$ (heavy water), which is present as a minor component (0.016 mol %) in normal water and is isolated on the multiton scale by *electrolytic enrichment.* Due to the kinetic isotope effect, there is a

| Table **22.6** | Some Molecular and Physical Properties of Diatomic Protium, Deuterium, and Tritium | | |
|---|---|---|---|
| **Property** | **H$_2$** | **D$_2$** | **T$_2$** |
| Molar mass (g/mol) | 2.016 | 4.028 | 6.032 |
| Bond length (pm) | 74.14 | 74.14 | 74.14 |
| Melting point (K) | 13.96 | 18.73 | 20.62 |
| Boiling point (K) | 20.39 | 23.67 | 25.04 |
| $\Delta H^{\circ}_{fus}$ (kJ/mol) | 0.117 | 0.197 | 0.250 |
| $\Delta H^{\circ}_{vap}$ (kJ/mol) | 0.904 | 1.226 | 1.393 |
| Bond energy (kJ/mol at 298 K) | 432 | 443 | 447 |

*higher rate of bond breaking for O—H bonds compared to O—D bonds,* and thus a higher rate of electrolysis of H$_2$O compared with D$_2$O.

For example, with Pt electrodes, H$_2$O is electrolyzed about 14 times faster than D$_2$O. As some of the liquid decomposes to the elemental gases, the remainder becomes enriched in D$_2$O. Thus, by the time the volume of water has been reduced to 1/20,000 of its original volume, the remaining water is around 99% D$_2$O. By combining samples and repeating the electrolysis, more than 99.9% D$_2$O is obtained.

Deuterium gas is produced by electrolysis of D$_2$O or by any of the chemical reactions that produce hydrogen gas from water, such as

$$2Na(s) + 2D_2O(l) \longrightarrow 2Na^+(aq) + 2OD^-(aq) + D_2(g)$$

Compounds containing deuterium (or tritium) are produced from reactions that give rise to the corresponding hydrogen-containing compound; for example,

$$SiCl_4(l) + 2D_2O(l) \longrightarrow SiO_2(s) + 4DCl(g)$$

Compounds with acidic protons undergo hydrogen/deuterium exchange:

$$CH_3COOH(l) + D_2O(l; excess) \longrightarrow CH_3COOD(l) + DHO(l; small amount)$$

We discuss the natural and synthetic formation of tritium in Chapter 24.

## ■ Summary of Section 22.4

Production highlights of key elements are as follows:

- Na is isolated by electrolysis of molten NaCl in the Downs process; Cl$_2$ is a byproduct.
- K is produced by reduction with Na in a thermal process.
- Fe is produced through a multistep high-temperature process in a blast furnace. The crude pig iron is converted to carbon steel in the basic-oxygen process and then alloyed with other metals to make different steels.
- Cu is produced by concentration of the ore through flotation, reduction to the metal by smelting, and purification by electrorefining. The metal has extensive electrical and plumbing uses.
- Al is extracted from bauxite by pretreating the ore with concentrated base, followed by electrolysis of the product Al$_2$O$_3$ mixed with molten cryolite. Al alloys are widely used in homes and industry. The total energy required to extract Al from its ore is over 100 times that needed for recycling it.
- The Mg$^{2+}$ in seawater is converted to Mg(OH)$_2$ and then to MgCl$_2$, which is electrolyzed to obtain the metal; Mg forms strong, lightweight alloys.
- H$_2$ is produced by electrolysis of water or in the formation of gaseous fuels from hydrocarbons. It is used in NH$_3$ production, in hydrogenation of vegetable oils, and in energy production. The isotopes of hydrogen differ significantly in atomic mass and thus in the rate at which their bonds to other atoms break (kinetic isotope effect). This difference is used to obtain D$_2$O from water.

# 22.5 • CHEMICAL MANUFACTURING: TWO CASE STUDIES

In this final section, we examine the interplay of theory and practice in two of the most important processes in the inorganic chemical industry: the contact process for the production of sulfuric acid, and the chlor-alkali process for the production of chlorine.

## Sulfuric Acid, the Most Important Chemical

Considering its countless uses, sulfuric acid is produced throughout the world on a gigantic scale—more than 150 million tons a year. The modern **contact process** is based on the *catalyzed oxidation of SO₂*. Here are the key steps.

1. *Obtaining sulfur.* In most countries today, the production of sulfuric acid starts with the production of elemental sulfur, often by the *Claus process,* in which the $H_2S$ in "sour" natural gas is chemically separated and then oxidized:

$$2H_2S(g) + 2O_2(g) \xrightarrow{\text{low temperature}} \tfrac{1}{8}S_8(g) + SO_2(g) + 2H_2O(g)$$

$$2H_2S(g) + SO_2(g) \xrightarrow{\text{Fe}_2\text{O}_3 \text{ catalyst}} \tfrac{3}{8}S_8(g) + 2H_2O(g)$$

Where natural deposits of the element are found, sulfur is obtained by a nonchemical method called the *Frasch process.* A hole is drilled to the deposit, and superheated water (about 160°C) is pumped down two outer concentric pipes to melt the sulfur (Figure 22.23A). Then, a combination of the hydrostatic pressure in an outermost pipe and the pressure of compressed air sent through a narrow inner pipe forces the sulfur to the surface (Figure 22.23B and C). The costs of drilling, pumping, and supplying water ($5 \times 10^6$ gallons per day) are balanced somewhat by the purity of the product (~99.7% sulfur).

2. *From sulfur to sulfur dioxide.* The sulfur is burned in air to form $SO_2$:

$$\tfrac{1}{8}S_8(s) + O_2(g) \longrightarrow SO_2(g) \qquad \Delta H° = -297 \text{ kJ}$$

Some $SO_2$ is also obtained by roasting metal sulfide ores and from the Claus process. About 90% of processed sulfur is used in making sulfur dioxide for production of sulfuric acid. Indeed, this end product is so important that a nation's level of sulfur production is a reliable indicator of its overall industrial capacity: the United States, Canada, China, Russia, Japan, and Germany are the top six sulfur producers.

3. *From sulfur dioxide to trioxide.* The *contact process* oxidizes $SO_2$ to $SO_3$:

$$SO_2(g) + \tfrac{1}{2}O_2(g) \rightleftharpoons SO_3(g) \qquad \Delta H° = -99 \text{ k}$$

The reaction is *exothermic* and very *slow* at room temperature. From Le Châtelier's principle (Section 17.6), the yield of $SO_3$ can be increased by (1) changing the temperature, (2) increasing the pressure (more moles of gas are on the left than on the right), or (3) adjusting the concentrations (adding excess $O_2$ and removing $SO_3$). In this case, the pressure effect is small and economically not worth exploiting. Let's examine the other two effects:

- *Effect of changing the temperature.* Adding heat (raising the temperature) increases the frequency and energy of $SO_2$-$O_2$ collisions and thus increases the *rate* of $SO_3$ formation. However, because the formation is exothermic, removing heat (lowering the temperature) shifts the equilibrium position to the right and thus increases the *yield* of $SO_3$. This is a classic situation that calls for use of a catalyst. By lowering the activation energy, *a catalyst allows equilibrium to be reached more quickly and at a lower temperature;* thus, rate *and* yield are optimized (Section 16.7). The catalyst in the contact process is $V_2O_5$ on inert silica, which is active between 400°C and 600°C.

disulfuric acid

**C**

**Figure 22.23** The Frasch process for mining elemental sulfur.

- *Effect of changing the concentration.* Providing an excess of $O_2$ in the form of a 5/1 mixture of air to $SO_2$, which is about 1/1 $O_2$ to $SO_2$, supplies about twice as much $O_2$ as in the balanced equation. The mixture is passed over catalyst beds in four stages, and the $SO_3$ is removed to favor more $SO_3$ formation. The overall yield of $SO_3$ is 99.5%.

4. *From sulfur trioxide to acid.* Sulfur trioxide is the anhydride of sulfuric acid. However, $SO_3$ cannot be added to water because, at the operating temperature, it would first meet water vapor, which catalyzes its polymerization to $(SO_3)_x$, and results in a smoke of solid particles that yields little acid (reaction 1). To avoid this, previously formed $H_2SO_4$ absorbs the $SO_3$ (reaction 2) and forms pyrosulfuric acid (or disulfuric acid, $H_2S_2O_7$; *see margin*), which is then hydrolyzed with sufficient water (reaction 3):

$$(1) \qquad SO_3(g) + H_2O(l) \longrightarrow H_2SO_4(l) \text{ [low yield]}$$
$$(2) \qquad SO_3(g) + H_2SO_4(l) \longrightarrow H_2S_2O_7(l)$$
$$(3) \qquad H_2S_2O_7(l) + H_2O(l) \longrightarrow 2H_2SO_4(l)$$

The industrial uses of sulfuric acid are legion, as Figure 22.24 on the next page indicates.

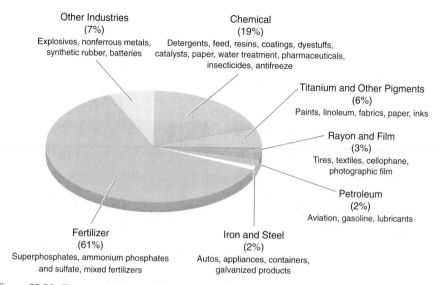

**Figure 22.24** The many indispensable applications of sulfuric acid.

Sulfuric acid is remarkably inexpensive (about $150/ton), largely because each step in the process is exothermic—burning S ($\Delta H° = -297$ kJ/mol), oxidizing $SO_2$ ($\Delta H° = -99$ kJ/mol), hydrating $SO_3$ ($\Delta H° = -132$ kJ/mol)—and the heat is a valuable byproduct. Three-quarters of the heat is sold as steam, and the rest of it is used to pump gases through the plant. A typical plant making 825 tons of $H_2SO_4$ per day produces enough steam to generate $7\times10^6$ watts of electric power.

## The Chlor-Alkali Process

Chlorine is produced and used in amounts many times greater than all the other halogens combined, ranking among the top 10 chemicals produced in the United States. The **chlor-alkali process,** which forms the basis of one of the largest inorganic chemical industries, *electrolyzes concentrated aqueous NaCl to produce $Cl_2$,* and several other important chemicals are also produced. There are three versions of this process.

**Diaphragm-Cell Method** As you learned in Section 21.7, the electrolysis of aqueous NaCl does not yield both of the component elements. Because of the overvoltage, $Cl^-$ ions rather than $H_2O$ molecules are oxidized at the anode. However, $Na^+$ ions are not reduced at the cathode because the half-cell potential ($-2.71$ V) is much more negative than that for reduction of $H_2O$ ($-0.42$ V), even with the normal overvoltage (around $-0.6$ V). Therefore, the half-reactions for electrolysis of aqueous NaCl are

$$2Cl^-(aq) \longrightarrow Cl_2(g) + 2e^- \qquad\qquad E° = 1.36 \text{ V} \quad \text{[anode; oxidation]}$$
$$\underline{2H_2O(l) + 2e^- \longrightarrow 2OH^-(aq) + H_2(g) \qquad\qquad E \approx -1.0 \text{ V} \quad \text{[cathode; reduction]}}$$
$$2Cl^-(aq) + 2H_2O(l) \longrightarrow 2OH^-(aq) + H_2(g) + Cl_2(g) \qquad E_{cell} = -1.0 \text{ V} - 1.36 \text{ V} = -2.4 \text{ V}$$

To obtain commercially meaningful amounts of $Cl_2$, however, a voltage almost twice this value and a current in excess of $3\times10^4$ A are used.

When we include the spectator ion $Na^+$, the total ionic equation shows another important product made by the process:

$$2Na^+(aq) + 2Cl^-(aq) + 2H_2O(l) \longrightarrow 2Na^+(aq) + 2OH^-(aq) + H_2(g) + Cl_2(g)$$

As Figure 22.25 shows, the sodium salts in the cathode compartment exist as an aqueous mixture of NaCl and NaOH; the NaCl is removed by fractional crystallization. Thus, in this version of the chlor-alkali process, which uses an *asbestos diaphragm* to separate the anode and cathode compartments, electrolysis of NaCl brines yields $Cl_2$, $H_2$, and industrial-grade NaOH, an important base. Like other reactive products, $H_2$

**Figure 22.25** A diaphragm cell for the chlor-alkali process.

and $Cl_2$ are kept apart to prevent explosive recombination. Note the higher liquid level in the anode (*left*) compartment. This slight hydrostatic pressure difference minimizes backflow of NaOH, which prevents the disproportionation reactions of $Cl_2$ that occur in the presence of $OH^-$ (Section 14.9), such as

$$Cl_2(g) + 2OH^-(aq) \longrightarrow Cl^-(aq) + ClO^-(aq) + H_2O(l)$$

**Mercury-Cell Method** If high-purity NaOH is desired, a slightly different version, called the *chlor-alkali mercury-cell process,* is employed. Mercury is used as the cathode, which creates such a large overvoltage for reduction of $H_2O$ to $H_2$ that the process *does* favor reduction of $Na^+$. The sodium dissolves in the mercury to form sodium amalgam, Na(Hg). In the mercury-cell version, the half-reactions are

$$2Cl^-(aq) \longrightarrow Cl_2(g) + 2e^- \qquad \text{[anode; oxidation]}$$

$$2Na^+(aq) + 2e^- \xrightarrow{\text{Hg}} 2Na(Hg) \qquad \text{[cathode; reduction]}$$

To obtain sodium hydroxide, the sodium amalgam is pumped out of the system and treated with $H_2O$, which is reduced by the Na:

$$2Na(Hg) + 2H_2O(l) \xrightarrow{-\text{Hg}} 2Na^+(aq) + 2OH^-(aq) + H_2(g)$$

The mercury released in this step is recycled back to the electrolysis bath. Therefore, *the products are the same in both versions,* but the purity of NaOH from the mercury-cell method is much higher.

The mercury-cell method is being steadily phased out because, as the mercury is recycled, small amounts are lost in the industrial wastewater. On average, 200 g of Hg is lost per ton of $Cl_2$ produced. In the 1980s, annual U.S. production via the mercury-cell method was 2.75 million tons of $Cl_2$; thus, during that decade, 550,000 kg of mercury, a toxic heavy metal, was flowing into U.S. waterways each year!

**Membrane-Cell Method** The *chlor-alkali membrane-cell process* replaces the diaphragm with a polymeric membrane to separate the cell compartments. The membrane allows only cations to move through it and only from anode to cathode compartments. Thus, as $Cl^-$ ions are removed at the anode through oxidation to $Cl_2$, $Na^+$ ions in the anode compartment move through the membrane to the cathode compartment and form an NaOH solution. In addition to forming purer NaOH than the older diaphragm-cell method, the membrane-cell method uses less electricity and eliminates the problem of Hg pollution. As a result, it has been adopted throughout much of the industrialized world.

## ▌Summary of Section 22.5

- Sulfuric acid production starts with the extraction of sulfur, either by the oxidation of $H_2S$ or the mining of sulfur deposits. The sulfur is roasted to $SO_2$ and oxidized to $SO_3$ by the catalyzed contact process, which optimizes the yield at lower temperatures. Absorption of the $SO_3$ into $H_2SO_4$, followed by hydration, forms sulfuric acid.

- In the diaphragm-cell chlor-alkali process, aqueous NaCl is electrolyzed to form $Cl_2$, $H_2$, and low-purity NaOH. The mercury-cell method produces high-purity NaOH but has been almost completely phased out because of mercury pollution. The membrane-cell method requires less electricity and does not use Hg.

# CHAPTER REVIEW GUIDE

## Learning Objectives  Relevant section (§) and/or sample problem (SP) numbers appear in parentheses.

### Understand These Concepts

1. How gravity, thermal convection, and elemental properties led to the silicate, sulfide, and iron phases and the predominance of certain elements in Earth's crust, mantle, and core (§22.1)
2. How organisms affect crustal abundances of elements, especially oxygen, carbon, calcium, and some transition metals; the onset of oxidation as an energy source (§22.1)
3. How atomic properties influence which elements have oxide ores and which have sulfide ores (§22.1)
4. The central role of $CO_2$ and the importance of photosynthesis, respiration, and decomposition in the carbon cycle (§22.2)
5. The central role of $N_2$ and the importance of atmospheric, industrial, and biological fixation in the nitrogen cycle (§22.2)
6. The absence of a gaseous component, the interactions of the inorganic and biological cycles, and the impact of humans on the phosphorus cycle (§22.2)
7. How pyro-, electro-, and hydrometallurgical processes are employed to extract a metal from its ore; the importance of the reduction step from compound to metal; refining and alloying processes (§22.3)

8. Functioning of the Downs cell for Na production and the application of Le Châtelier's principle for K production (§22.4)
9. How iron ore is reduced in a blast furnace and how pig iron is purified by the basic-oxygen process (§22.4)
10. How Fe is removed from copper ore and impure Cu is electrorefined (§22.4)
11. The importance of amphoterism in the Bayer process for isolating $Al_2O_3$ from bauxite; the significance of cryolite in the electrolytic step; the energy advantage of Al recycling (§22.4)
12. The steps in the Dow process for the extraction of Mg from seawater (§22.4)
13. How $H_2$ production, whether by chemical or electrolytic means, is tied to $NH_3$ production (§22.4)
14. How the kinetic isotope effect is applied to produce deuterium (§22.4)
15. How the Frasch process is used to obtain sulfur from natural deposits (§22.5)
16. The importance of equilibrium and kinetic factors in $H_2SO_4$ production (§22.5)
17. How overvoltage allows electrolysis of aqueous NaCl to form $Cl_2$ gas in the chlor-alkali process; coproduction of NaOH; comparison of diaphragm-cell, mercury-cell, and membrane-cell methods (§22.5)

## Key Terms  Page numbers appear in parentheses.

**Section 22.1**
abundance (905)
differentiation (906)
core (906)
mantle (906)
crust (906)
lithosphere (907)
hydrosphere (907)
atmosphere (907)
biosphere (907)

occurrence (source) (909)
ore (909)

**Section 22.2**
environmental cycle (910)
fixation (912)
apatites (914)

**Section 22.3**
metallurgy (916)
mineral (916)
gangue (916)

flotation (917)
leaching (917)
roasting (918)
smelting (918)
electrorefining (920)
zone refining (920)
alloy (920)

**Section 22.4**
Downs cell (922)
steel (924)

blast furnace (924)
slag (925)
basic-oxygen process (925)
carbon steel (925)

**Section 22.5**
contact process (934)
chlor-alkali process (936)

# PROBLEMS

Problems with **colored** numbers are answered in Appendix E and worked in detail in the Student Solutions Manual. Problem sections match those in the text and offer Concept Review Questions and Problems in Context. The Comprehensive Problems are based on material from any section or previous chapter.

## How the Elements Occur in Nature

### Concept Review Questions

**22.1** Hydrogen is by far the most abundant element cosmically. In interstellar space, it exists mainly as $H_2$. In contrast, on Earth, it exists very rarely as $H_2$ and is ninth in abundance in the crust. Why is hydrogen so abundant in the universe? Why is hydrogen so rare as a diatomic gas in Earth's atmosphere?

**22.2** Metallic elements can be recovered from ores that are oxides, carbonates, halides, or sulfides. Give an example of each type.

**22.3** The location of elements in the regions of Earth has enormous practical importance. (a) Define *differentiation*, and explain which physical property of a substance is primarily responsible for this process. (b) What are the four most abundant elements in the crust? (c) Which element is abundant in the crust and mantle but not the core?

**22.4** How does the position of a metal in the periodic table relate to whether it occurs primarily as an oxide or as a sulfide?

### Problems in Context

**22.5** What material is the source for commercial production of each of the following elements: (a) aluminum; (b) nitrogen; (c) chlorine; (d) calcium; (e) sodium?

**22.6** Aluminum is widely distributed throughout the world in the form of aluminosilicates. What property of these minerals prevents them from being a source of aluminum?

**22.7** Describe two ways in which the biosphere has influenced the composition of Earth's crust.

## The Cycling of Elements Through the Environment

### Concept Review Questions

**22.8** Use atomic and molecular properties to explain why life is based on carbon rather than some other element, such as silicon.

**22.9** Define *fixation*. Name two elements that undergo environmental fixation. What natural forms of them are fixed?

**22.10** Carbon dioxide enters the atmosphere by natural processes and from human activity. Why is the latter a cause of concern?

**22.11** Diagrams of environmental cycles are simplified to omit minor contributors. For example, the production of lime from limestone is not shown in the cycle for carbon (Figure 22.5, p. 911). Which labeled category in the figure includes this process? Name two other processes that contribute to this category.

**22.12** Describe three pathways for the utilization of atmospheric nitrogen. Is human activity a significant factor? Explain.

**22.13** Why don't the N-containing species in Figure 22.6 (p. 913) include rings or long chains with N—N bonds?

**22.14** (a) Which region of Earth's crust is not involved in the phosphorus cycle? (b) Name two roles organisms play in the cycle.

## Problems in Context

**22.15** Nitrogen fixation requires a great deal of energy because the $N_2$ bond is strong. (a) How do the processes of atmospheric and industrial fixation reflect this energy requirement? (b) How do the thermodynamics of the two processes differ? (*Hint:* Examine the respective heats of formation.) (c) In view of the mild conditions for biological fixation, what must be the source of the "great deal of energy"? (d) What would be the most obvious environmental result of a low activation energy for $N_2$ fixation?

**22.16** The following steps are *unbalanced* half-reactions involved in the nitrogen cycle. Balance each half-reaction to show the number of electrons lost or gained, and state whether it is an oxidation or a reduction (all occur in acidic conditions):
(a) $N_2(g) \longrightarrow NO(g)$
(b) $N_2O(g) \longrightarrow NO_2(g)$
(c) $NH_3(aq) \longrightarrow NO_2^-(aq)$
(d) $NO_3^-(aq) \longrightarrow NO_2^-(aq)$
(e) $N_2(g) \longrightarrow NO_3^-(aq)$

**22.17** The use of silica to form slag in the production of phosphorus from phosphate rock was introduced by Robert Boyle more than 300 years ago. When fluorapatite $[Ca_5(PO_4)_3F]$ is used in phosphorus production, most of the fluorine atoms appear in the slag, but some end up in the toxic and corrosive gas $SiF_4$.
(a) If 15% by mass of the fluorine in 100. kg of $Ca_5(PO_4)_3F$ forms $SiF_4$, what volume of this gas is collected at 1.00 atm and the industrial furnace temperature of 1450.°C?
(b) In some facilities, the $SiF_4$ is used to produce sodium hexafluorosilicate ($Na_2SiF_6$) which is sold for water fluoridation:
$$2SiF_4(g) + Na_2CO_3(s) + H_2O(l) \longrightarrow$$
$$Na_2SiF_6(aq) + SiO_2(s) + CO_2(g) + 2HF(aq)$$
How many cubic meters of drinking water can be fluoridated to a level of 1.0 ppm of $F^-$ using the $SiF_4$ produced in part (a)?

**22.18** An impurity sometimes found in $Ca_3(PO_4)_2$ is $Fe_2O_3$, which is removed during the production of phosphorus as *ferrophosphorus* ($Fe_2P$). (a) Why is this impurity troubling from an economic standpoint? (b) If 50. metric tons of crude $Ca_3(PO_4)_2$ contains 2.0% $Fe_2O_3$ by mass and the overall yield of phosphorus is 90.%, how many metric tons of $P_4$ can be isolated?

## Metallurgy: Extracting a Metal from Its Ore

### Concept Review Questions

**22.19** Define: (a) ore; (b) mineral; (c) gangue; (d) brine.

**22.20** Define: (a) roasting; (b) smelting; (c) flotation; (d) refining.

**22.21** What factors determine which reducing agent is selected for producing a specific metal?

**22.22** Use atomic properties to explain the reduction of a less active metal by a more active one: (a) in aqueous solution; (b) in the molten state. Give a specific example of each process.

**22.23** What class of element is obtained by oxidation of a mineral? What class of element is obtained by reduction of a mineral?

### Problems in Context

**22.24** Which set of elements gives each of the following alloys: (a) brass; (b) stainless steel; (c) bronze; (d) sterling silver?
1. Cu, Ag      2. Cu, Sn, Zn      3. Ag, Au
4. Fe, Cr, Ni      5. Fe, V      6. Cu, Zn

## Tapping the Crust: Isolation and Uses of Selected Elements

### Concept Review Questions

**22.25** How are each of the following involved in iron metallurgy: (a) slag; (b) pig iron; (c) steel; (d) basic-oxygen process?

**22.26** What are the distinguishing features of each extraction process: pyrometallurgy, electrometallurgy, and hydrometallurgy? Explain briefly how the types of metallurgy are used in the production of (a) Fe; (b) Na; (c) Au; (d) Al.

**22.27** What property allows copper to be purified in the presence of iron and nickel impurities? Explain.

**22.28** Why is cryolite used in the electrolysis of aluminum oxide?

**22.29** (a) What is a kinetic isotope effect?
(b) Do compounds of hydrogen exhibit a relatively large or small kinetic isotope effect? Explain.
(c) Carbon compounds also exhibit a kinetic isotope effect. How do you expect it to compare in magnitude with that for hydrogen compounds? Why?

**22.30** How is Le Châtelier's principle involved in the production of elemental potassium?

### Problems in Context

**22.31** Elemental Li and Na are prepared by electrolysis of a molten salt, whereas K, Rb, and Cs are prepared by chemical reduction.
(a) In general terms, explain why the alkali metals cannot be prepared by electrolysis of their aqueous salt solutions.
(b) Use ionization energies (see the Family Portraits, pp. 529 and 532) to explain why calcium should *not* be able to isolate Rb from molten RbX (X = halide).
(c) Use physical properties to explain why calcium *is* used to isolate Rb from molten RbX.
(d) Can Ca be used to isolate Cs from molten CsX? Explain.

**22.32** A Downs cell operating at 77.0 A produces 31.0 kg of Na.
(a) What volume of $Cl_2(g)$ is produced at 1.0 atm and 540.°C?
(b) How many coulombs were passed through the cell?
(c) How long did the cell operate?

**22.33** (a) In the industrial production of iron, what is the reducing substance loaded into the blast furnace?
(b) In addition to furnishing the reducing power, what other function does this substance serve?
(c) What is the formula of the active reducing agent in the process?
(d) Write equations for the stepwise reduction of $Fe_2O_3$ to iron in the furnace.

**22.34** One of the substances loaded into a blast furnace is limestone, which produces lime in the furnace.
(a) Give the chemical equation for the reaction forming lime.
(b) Explain the purpose of lime in the furnace. The term *flux* is often used as a label for a substance acting as the lime does. What is the derivation of this word, and how does it relate to the function of the lime?
(c) Write a chemical equation describing the action of lime flux.

**22.35** The last step in the Dow process for the production of magnesium metal involves electrolysis of molten $MgCl_2$.
(a) Why isn't the electrolysis carried out with aqueous $MgCl_2$? What are the products of this aqueous electrolysis?
(b) Do the high temperatures required to melt $MgCl_2$ favor products or reactants? (*Hint:* Consider the $\Delta H_f^\circ$ of $MgCl_2$.)

**22.36** Iodine is the only halogen that occurs in a positive oxidation state, in $NaIO_3$ impurities within Chile saltpeter, $NaNO_3$.
(a) Is this mode of occurrence consistent with iodine's location in the periodic table? Explain.
(b) In the production of $I_2$, $IO_3^-$ reacts with $HSO_3^-$:

$$IO_3^-(aq) + HSO_3^-(aq) \longrightarrow$$
$$HSO_4^-(aq) + SO_4^{2-}(aq) + H_2O(l) + I_2(s) \quad \text{[unbalanced]}$$

Identify the oxidizing and reducing agents.
(c) If 0.78 mol % of an $NaNO_3$ deposit is $NaIO_3$, how much $I_2$ (in g) can be obtained from 1.000 ton (2000. lb) of the deposit?

**22.37** Selenium is prepared by the reaction of $H_2SeO_3$ with gaseous $SO_2$.
(a) What redox process does the sulfur dioxide undergo? What is the oxidation state of sulfur in the product?
(b) Given that the reaction occurs in acidic aqueous solution, what is the formula of the sulfur-containing species?
(c) Write the balanced redox equation for the process.

**22.38** $F_2$ and $Cl_2$ are produced by electrolytic oxidation, whereas $Br_2$ and $I_2$ are produced by chemical oxidation of the halide ions in a concentrated aqueous solution (brine) by a more electronegative halogen. Give two reasons why $Cl_2$ isn't prepared this way.

**22.39** Silicon is prepared by the reduction of $K_2SiF_6$ with Al. Write the equation for this reaction. (*Hint:* Can $F^-$ be oxidized in this reaction? Can $K^+$ be reduced?)

**22.40** What is the mass percent of iron in each of the following iron ores: $Fe_2O_3$, $Fe_3O_4$, $FeS_2$?

**22.41** Phosphorus is one of the impurities present in pig iron that is removed in the basic-oxygen process. Assuming phosphorus is present as P atoms, write equations for its oxidation and subsequent reaction in the basic slag.

**22.42** The final step in the smelting of $FeCuS_2$ is
$$Cu_2S(s) + 2Cu_2O(s) \longrightarrow 6Cu(l) + SO_2(g)$$
(a) Give the oxidation states of copper in $Cu_2S$, $Cu_2O$, and Cu.
(b) What are the oxidizing and reducing agents in this reaction?

**22.43** Use equations to show how acid-base properties are used to separate $Fe_2O_3$ and $TiO_2$ from $Al_2O_3$ in the Bayer process.

**22.44** A piece of Al with a surface area of 2.5 $m^2$ is anodized to produce a film of $Al_2O_3$ that is 23 μm ($23 \times 10^{-6}$ m) thick. (a) How many coulombs flow through the cell in this process (assume that the density of the $Al_2O_3$ layer is 3.97 $g/cm^3$)? (b) If it takes 18 min to produce this film, what current must flow through the cell?

**22.45** The production of $H_2$ gas by the electrolysis of water typically requires about 400 kJ of energy per mole.
(a) Use the relationship between work and cell potential (Section 21.4) to calculate the minimum work needed to form 1.0 mol of $H_2$ gas at a cell potential of 1.24 V.
(b) What is the energy efficiency of the cell operation?
(c) Find the cost of producing 500. mol of $H_2$ if electricity is $0.06 per kilowatt·hour (1 watt·second = 1 joule).

**22.46** (a) What are the components of the reaction mixture following the water-gas shift reaction? (b) Explain how zeolites are used to purify the $H_2$ formed.

**22.47** Metal sulfides are often first converted to oxides by roasting in air and then reduced with carbon to produce the metal. Why aren't the metal sulfides reduced directly by carbon to yield $CS_2$? Give a thermodynamic analysis of both processes for ZnS.

## Chemical Manufacturing: Two Case Studies

### Concept Review Questions

**22.48** Explain in detail why a catalyst is used to produce $SO_3$.

**22.49** Among the exothermic steps in the manufacture of sulfuric acid is the process of hydrating $SO_3$. (a) Write two chemical reactions that show this process. (b) Why is the direct reaction of $SO_3$ with water not feasible?

**22.50** Why is commercial $H_2SO_4$ so inexpensive?

**22.51** (a) What are the three commercial products formed in the chlor-alkali process?
(b) State an advantage and a disadvantage of the mercury-cell method for this process.

### Problems in Context

**22.52** Consider the reaction of $SO_2$ to form $SO_3$ at standard conditions.
(a) Calculate $\Delta G°$ at 25°C. Is the reaction spontaneous?
(b) Why is the reaction not performed at 25°C?
(c) Is the reaction spontaneous at 500.°C? (Assume $\Delta H°$ and $\Delta S°$ are constant with changing $T$.)
(d) Compare $K$ at 500.°C and at 25°C.
(e) What is the highest $T$ at which the reaction is spontaneous?

**22.53** If a chlor-alkali cell used a current of $3 \times 10^4$ A, how many pounds of $Cl_2$ would be produced in a typical 8-h operating day?

**22.54** The products of the chlor-alkali process, $Cl_2$ and NaOH, are kept separated.
(a) Why is this necessary when $Cl_2$ is the desired product?
(b) $ClO^-$ or $ClO_3^-$ may form by disproportionation of $Cl_2$ in basic solution. What determines which product forms?
(c) What mole ratio of $Cl_2$ to $OH^-$ will produce $ClO^-$? $ClO_3^-$?

### Comprehensive Problems

**22.55** The key step in the manufacture of sulfuric acid is the oxidation of sulfur dioxide in the presence of a catalyst, such as $V_2O_5$. At 727°C, 0.010 mol of $SO_2$ is injected into an empty 2.00-L container ($K_p = 3.18$).
(a) What is the equilibrium pressure of $O_2$ that is needed to maintain a 1/1 mole ratio of $SO_3$ to $SO_2$?
(b) What is the equilibrium pressure of $O_2$ needed to maintain a 95/5 mole ratio of $SO_3$ to $SO_2$?

**22.56** Tetraphosphorus decaoxide ($P_4O_{10}$) is made from phosphate rock and used as a drying agent in the laboratory.
(a) Write a balanced equation for its reaction with water.
(b) What is the pH of a solution formed from the addition of 8.5 g of $P_4O_{10}$ in sufficient water to form 0.750 L? (See Table 18.5, p. 738, for additional information.)

**22.57** Heavy water ($D_2O$) is used to make deuterated chemicals.
(a) What major species, aside from the starting compounds, do you expect to find in a solution of $CH_3OH$ and $D_2O$?
(b) Write equations to explain how these various species arise. (*Hint:* Consider the autoionization of both components.)

**22.58** A blast furnace uses $Fe_2O_3$ to produce 8400. t of Fe per day.
(a) What mass of $CO_2$ is produced each day?
(b) Compare this amount of $CO_2$ with that produced by 1.0 million automobiles, each burning 5.0 gal of gasoline a day. Assume that gasoline has the formula $C_8H_{18}$ and a density of 0.74 g/mL, and that it burns completely. (Note that U.S. gasoline consumption is over $4 \times 10^8$ gal/day.)

**22.59** A major use of $Cl_2$ is in the manufacture of vinyl chloride, the monomer of poly(vinyl chloride). The two-step sequence for formation of vinyl chloride is depicted below.

(a) Write a balanced equation for each step.
(b) Write the overall equation.
(c) What type of organic reaction is shown in step 1?
(d) What type of organic reaction is shown in step 2?
(e) If each molecule depicted in the initial reaction mixture represents 0.15 mol of substance, what mass (in g) of vinyl chloride forms?

**22.60** In the production of magnesium, $Mg(OH)_2$ is precipitated by using $Ca(OH)_2$, which itself is "insoluble." (a) Use $K_{sp}$ values to show that $Mg(OH)_2$ can be precipitated from seawater in which $[Mg^{2+}]$ is initially 0.052 $M$. (b) If the seawater is saturated with $Ca(OH)_2$, what fraction of the $Mg^{2+}$ is precipitated?

**22.61** Step 1 of the Ostwald process for nitric acid production is

$$4NH_3(g) + 5O_2(g) \xrightarrow{\text{Pt/Rh catalyst}} 4NO(g) + 6H_2O(g)$$

An unwanted side reaction for this step is

$$4NH_3(g) + 3O_2(g) \longrightarrow 2N_2(g) + 6H_2O(g)$$

(a) Calculate $K_p$ for these two $NH_3$ oxidations at 25°C.
(b) Calculate $K_p$ for these two $NH_3$ oxidations at 900.°C.
(c) The Pt/Rh catalyst is one of the most efficient in the chemical industry, achieving 96% yield in 1 millisecond of contact with the reactants. However, at normal operating conditions (5 atm and 850°C), about 175 mg of Pt is lost per metric ton (t) of $HNO_3$ produced. If the annual U.S. production of $HNO_3$ is $1.01 \times 10^7$ t and the market price of Pt is \$1557/troy oz, what is the annual cost of the lost Pt (1 kg = 32.15 troy oz)?
(d) Because of the high price of Pt, a filtering unit composed of ceramic fiber is often installed, which recovers as much as 75% of the lost Pt. What is the value of the Pt captured by a recovery unit with 72% efficiency?

**22.62** Several transition metals are prepared by reduction of the metal halide with magnesium. Titanium is prepared by the Kroll method, in which ore (ilmenite) is converted to the gaseous chloride, which is then reduced to Ti metal by molten Mg (see p. 931). Assuming yields of 84% for step 1 and 93% for step 2, and an excess of the other reactants, what mass of Ti metal can be prepared from 21.5 metric tons of ilmenite?

**22.63** The production of $S_8$ from the $H_2S(g)$ found in natural gas deposits occurs through the Claus process (Section 22.5):
(a) Use these two unbalanced steps to write an overall balanced equation for this process:
(1) $H_2S(g) + O_2(g) \longrightarrow S_8(g) + SO_2(g) + H_2O(g)$
(2) $H_2S(g) + SO_2(g) \longrightarrow S_8(g) + H_2O(g)$
(b) Write the overall reaction with $Cl_2$ as the oxidizing agent instead of $O_2$. Use thermodynamic data to show whether $Cl_2(g)$ can be used to oxidize $H_2S(g)$.
(c) Why is oxidation by $O_2$ preferred to oxidation by $Cl_2$?

**22.64** Acid mine drainage (AMD) occurs when geologic deposits containing pyrite ($FeS_2$) are exposed to oxygen and moisture. AMD is generated in a multistep process catalyzed by acidophilic (acid-loving) bacteria. Balance each step and identify those that increase acidity:

(1) $FeS_2(s) + O_2(g) \longrightarrow Fe^{2+}(aq) + SO_4^{2-}(aq)$

(2) $Fe^{2+}(aq) + O_2(g) \longrightarrow Fe^{3+}(aq) + H_2O(l)$

(3) $Fe^{3+}(aq) + H_2O(l) \longrightarrow Fe(OH)_3(s) + H^+(aq)$

(4) $FeS_2(s) + Fe^{3+}(aq) \longrightarrow Fe^{2+}(aq) + SO_4^{2-}(aq)$

**22.65** Below 912°C, pure iron crystallizes in a body-centered cubic structure (ferrite) with $d = 7.86$ g/cm$^3$; from 912°C to 1394°C, it adopts a face-centered cubic structure (austenite) with $d = 7.40$ g/cm$^3$. Both types of iron form interstitial alloys with carbon. The maximum amount of carbon is 0.0218 mass% in ferrite and 2.08 mass% in austenite. Calculate the density of each alloy.

**22.66** Why isn't nitric acid produced by oxidizing $N_2$ as follows?

(1) $\qquad\qquad N_2(g) + 2O_2(g) \longrightarrow 2NO_2(g)$

(2) $\qquad 3NO_2(g) + H_2O(l) \longrightarrow 2HNO_3(aq) + NO(g)$

(3) $\qquad\quad \dfrac{2NO(g) + O_2(g) \longrightarrow 2NO_2(g)}{}$

$\quad 3N_2(g) + 6O_2(g) + 2H_2O(l) \longrightarrow 4HNO_3(aq) + 2NO(g)$

(*Hint:* Evaluate the thermodynamics of each step.)

**22.67** Before the development of the Downs cell, the Castner cell was used for the industrial production of Na metal. The Castner cell was based on the electrolysis of molten NaOH.
(a) Write balanced cathode and anode half-reactions for this cell.
(b) A major problem with this cell was that the water produced at one electrode diffused to the other and reacted with the Na. If all the water produced reacted with Na, what would be the maximum efficiency of the Castner cell expressed as moles of Na produced per mole of electrons flowing through the cell?

**22.68** When gold ores are leached with $CN^-$ solutions, gold forms a complex ion, $Au(CN)_2^-$. (a) Find $E_{cell}$ for the oxidation in air ($P_{O_2} = 0.21$) of Au to $Au^+$ in basic (pH 13.55) solution with $[Au^+] = 0.50$ $M$. Is the reaction $Au^+(aq) + e^- \longrightarrow Au(s)$, $E° = 1.68$ V, spontaneous? (b) How does formation of the complex ion change $E°$ so that the oxidation can be accomplished?

**22.69** Nitric oxide occurs in the tropospheric nitrogen cycle, but it destroys ozone in the stratosphere.
(a) Write equations for its reaction with ozone and for the reverse reaction.
(b) Given that the forward and reverse steps are first order in each component, write general rate laws for them.
(c) Calculate $\Delta G°$ for this reaction at 280. K, the average temperature in the stratosphere. (Assume that the $\Delta H°$ and $S°$ values in Appendix B do not change with temperature.)
(d) What ratio of rate constants is consistent with $K$ at this temperature?

**22.70** A key part of the carbon cycle is the fixation of $CO_2$ by photosynthesis to produce carbohydrates and oxygen gas.
(a) Using the formula $(CH_2O)_n$ to represent a carbohydrate, write a balanced equation for the photosynthetic reaction.
(b) If a tree fixes 48 g of $CO_2$ per day, what volume of $O_2$ gas measured at 1.0 atm and 78°F does the tree produce per day?
(c) What volume of air (0.035 mol % $CO_2$) at the same conditions contains this amount of $CO_2$?

**22.71** Farmers use ammonium sulfate as a fertilizer. In the soil, nitrifying bacteria oxidize $NH_4^+$ to $NO_3^-$, a groundwater contaminant that causes methemoglobinemia ("blue baby" syndrome). The World Health Organization standard for maximum $[NO_3^-]$ in groundwater is 45 mg/L. A farmer adds 210. kg of $(NH_4)_2SO_4$ to a field and 37% is oxidized to $NO_3^-$. What is the groundwater $[NO_3^-]$ (in mg/L) if 1000. m$^3$ of the water is contaminated?

**22.72** The key reaction (unbalanced) in the manufacture of synthetic cryolite for aluminum electrolysis is

$HF(g) + Al(OH)_3(s) + NaOH(aq) \longrightarrow Na_3AlF_6(aq) + H_2O(l)$

Assuming a 95.6% yield of dried, crystallized product, what mass (in kg) of cryolite can be obtained from the reaction of 365 kg of $Al(OH)_3$, 1.20 m$^3$ of 50.0% by mass aqueous NaOH ($d = 1.53$ g/mL), and 265 m$^3$ of gaseous HF at 305 kPa and 91.5°C? (Assume that the ideal gas law holds.)

**22.73** Because of their different molar masses, $H_2$ and $D_2$ effuse at different rates (Section 5.5).
(a) If it takes 16.5 min for 0.10 mol of $H_2$ to effuse, how long does it take for 0.10 mol of $D_2$ to do so in the same apparatus at the same $T$ and $P$?
(b) How many effusion steps does it take to separate an equimolar mixture of $D_2$ and $H_2$ to 99 mol % purity?

**22.74** The disproportionation of CO to graphite and $CO_2$ is thermodynamically favored but slow.
(a) What does this mean in terms of the magnitudes of the equilibrium constant ($K$), rate constant ($k$), and activation energy ($E_a$)?
(b) Write a balanced equation for the disproportionation of CO.
(c) Calculate $K_c$ at 298 K. (d) Calculate $K_p$ at 298 K.

**22.75** The overall cell reaction for aluminum production is

$2Al_2O_3(\text{in } Na_3AlF_6) + 3C(\text{graphite}) \longrightarrow 4Al(l) + 3CO_2(g)$

(a) Assuming 100% efficiency, how many metric tons (t) of $Al_2O_3$ are consumed per metric ton of Al produced?
(b) Assuming 100% efficiency, how many metric tons of the graphite anode are consumed per metric ton of Al produced?
(c) Actual conditions in an aluminum plant require 1.89 t of $Al_2O_3$ and 0.45 t of graphite per metric ton of Al. What is the percent yield of Al with respect to $Al_2O_3$?
(d) What is the percent yield of Al with respect to graphite?
(e) What volume of $CO_2$ (in m$^3$) is produced per metric ton of Al at operating conditions of 960.°C and exactly 1 atm?

**22.76** World production of chromite ($FeCr_2O_4$), the main ore of chromium, was $1.97 \times 10^7$ metric tons in 2006. To isolate chromium, a mixture of chromite and sodium carbonate is heated in air to form sodium chromate, iron(III) oxide, and carbon dioxide. The sodium chromate is dissolved in water, and this solution is acidified with sulfuric acid to produce the less soluble sodium dichromate. The sodium dichromate is filtered out and reduced with carbon to produce chromium(III) oxide, sodium carbonate, and carbon monoxide. The chromium(III) oxide is then reduced to chromium with aluminum metal.
(a) Write balanced equations for each step.
(b) What mass of chromium (in kg) could be prepared from the 2006 world production of chromite?

**22.77** Like heavy water ($D_2O$), so-called "semi-heavy water" (HDO) undergoes H/D exchange. The molecular scenes depict an initial mixture of HDO and $H_2$ reaching equilibrium.

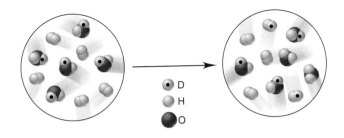

(a) Write the balanced equation for the reaction.
(b) Is the value of $K$ greater or less than 1?
(c) If each molecule depicted represents 0.10 $M$, calculate $K$.

**22.78** Even though most metal sulfides are sparingly soluble in water, their solubilities differ by several orders of magnitude. This difference is sometimes used to separate the metals by controlling the pH. Use the following data to find the pH at which you can separate 0.10 $M$ $Cu^{2+}$ and 0.10 $M$ $Ni^{2+}$:

Saturated $H_2S$ = 0.10 $M$

$K_{a1}$ of $H_2S$ = $9\times10^{-8}$      $K_{a2}$ of $H_2S$ = $1\times10^{-17}$
$K_{sp}$ of NiS = $1.1\times10^{-18}$      $K_{sp}$ of CuS = $8\times10^{-34}$

**22.79** Ores with as little as 0.25% by mass of copper are used as sources of the metal. (a) How many kilograms of such an ore would be needed for another Statue of Liberty, which contains $2.0\times10^5$ lb of copper? (b) If the mineral in the ore is chalcopyrite ($FeCuS_2$), what is the mass % of chalcopyrite in the ore?

**22.80** How does acid rain affect the leaching of phosphate into groundwater from terrestrial phosphate rock? Calculate the solubility of $Ca_3(PO_4)_2$ in each of the following:
(a) Pure water, pH 7.0 (Assume that $PO_4^{3-}$ does not react with water.)
(b) Moderately acidic rainwater, pH 4.5 (*Hint:* Assume that all the phosphate exists in the form that predominates at this pH.)

**22.81** The lead(IV) oxide used in car batteries is prepared by coating the electrode plate with PbO and then oxidizing it to lead dioxide ($PbO_2$). Despite its name, $PbO_2$ has a nonstoichiometric ratio of lead to oxygen of about 1/1.98. In fact, the holes in the $PbO_2$ crystal structure due to missing O atoms are responsible for the oxide's conductivity.

(a) What is the mole % of O missing from the $PbO_2$ structure?
(b) What is the molar mass of the nonstoichiometric compound?

**22.82** Chemosynthetic bacteria reduce $CO_2$ by "splitting" $H_2S(g)$ instead of the $H_2O(g)$ used by photosynthetic organisms. Compare the free energy change for splitting $H_2S$ with that for splitting $H_2O$. Is there an advantage to using $H_2S$ instead of $H_2O$?

**22.83** Silver has a face-centered cubic structure with a unit cell edge length of 408.6 pm. Sterling silver is a substitutional alloy that contains 7.5% copper atoms. Assuming the unit cell remains the same, find the density of silver and of sterling silver.

**22.84** Earth's mass is estimated to be $5.98\times10^{24}$ kg, and titanium represents 0.05% by mass of this total. (a) How many moles of Ti are present? (b) If half of the Ti is found as ilmenite ($FeTiO_3$), what mass of ilmenite is present? (c) If the airline and auto industries use $1.00\times10^5$ tons of Ti per year, how many years would it take to use up all the Ti (1 ton = 2000 lb)?

**22.85** In 1790, Nicolas Leblanc found a way to form $Na_2CO_3$ from NaCl. His process, now obsolete, consisted of three steps:

$$2NaCl(s) + H_2SO_4\,(aq) \longrightarrow Na_2SO_4(aq) + 2HCl(g)$$
$$Na_2SO_4(s) + 2C(s) \longrightarrow Na_2S(s) + 2CO_2(g)$$
$$Na_2S(s) + CaCO_3(s) \longrightarrow Na_2CO_3(s) + CaS(s)$$

(a) Write a balanced overall equation for the process.
(b) Calculate the $\Delta H_f^\circ$ of CaS if $\Delta H_{rxn}^\circ$ is 351.8 kJ/mol.
(c) Is the overall process spontaneous at standard-state conditions and 298 K?
(d) How many grams of $Na_2CO_3$ form from 250. g of NaCl if the process is 73% efficient?

**22.86** Limestone ($CaCO_3$) is the second most abundant mineral on Earth after $SiO_2$. For many uses, it is first decomposed thermally to quicklime (CaO). MgO is prepared similarly from $MgCO_3$.
(a) At what $T$ is each decomposition spontaneous?
(b) Quicklime reacts with $SiO_2$ to form a slag ($CaSiO_3$), a byproduct of steelmaking. In 2010, the total steelmaking capacity of the U.S. steel industry was 2,236,000 tons per week, but only 84% of this capacity was utilized. If 50. kg of slag is produced per ton of steel, what mass (in kg) of limestone was used to make slag in 2010?

# Transition Elements and Their Coordination Compounds

## Concepts and skills to review before you study this chapter

- properties of light (Section 7.1)
- electron shielding of nuclear charge (Section 8.1)
- electron configuration, ionic size, and magnetic behavior (Sections 8.2 to 8.5)
- valence bond theory (Section 11.1)
- constitutional, geometric, and optical isomerism (Section 15.2)

- Lewis acid-base concepts (Section 18.9)
- complex-ion formation (Section 19.4)
- redox behavior and standard electrode potentials (Section 21.3)

Though almost at the end of the text, we still haven't discussed the majority of the elements *and* some of the most familiar. The **transition elements** (*transition metals*) make up the *d* block (B groups) and *f* block (*inner transition elements*) (Figure 23.1) and have crucial uses in industry and biology.

Aside from essential copper and iron (Chapter 22), some other indispensable transition elements are chromium (plumbing fixtures; *photo*), gold and silver (jewelry and electronics), platinum (catalytic converters), titanium (bicycle and aircraft parts), nickel (coins and catalysts), and zinc (batteries), to mention a few of the better known ones. There are also the lesser known zirconium (nuclear-reactor liners), vanadium (axles and crankshafts), molybdenum (boiler plates), tantalum (organ-replacement parts), palladium (telephone-relay contacts)—the list goes on and on.

Transition metal cations occupy the centers of many complex ions. In addition to providing fundamental insights into bonding and structure, these species play vital roles in organisms *and* give color to gems—$Cr^{3+}$ ions make emeralds green and rubies red, and a mixture of $Fe^{2+}$, $Fe^{3+}$, and $Ti^{4+}$ ions makes sapphires blue.

**Figure 23.1** The transition elements (*d* block) and inner transition elements (*f* block) in the periodic table.

**IN THIS CHAPTER . . .** We focus on the transition metals and their properties, and especially on the bonding and structure of their coordination compounds.

- We discuss key atomic, physical, and chemical properties of transition and inner transition elements—with attention to the effects of filling inner sublevels—and contrast them with properties of the main-group elements.
- For most of the chapter, we concentrate on the nomenclature, structure, and isomerism of transition elements' coordination compounds, species that contain complex ions.
- We use valence bond theory to explain the bonding and molecular shape of complex ions.
- We use crystal field theory to explain the colors and magnetic properties of coordination compounds, which relate directly to structure.
- We end with some examples of transition metal ions in biochemistry.

# 23.1 • PROPERTIES OF THE TRANSITION ELEMENTS

The transition elements differ considerably in physical and chemical behavior from the main-group elements:

- *All transition elements are metals,* whereas main-group elements in each period change from metal to nonmetal.
- *Many transition metal compounds are colored and paramagnetic,* whereas most main-group ionic compounds are colorless and diamagnetic.

We first discuss electron configurations of the atoms and ions, and then examine key properties of transition elements to see how they contrast with the same properties among the main-group elements.

## Electron Configurations of the Transition Metals and Their Ions

As with all the elements, the properties of the transition elements and their compounds arise largely from the electron configurations of their atoms (Section 8.2) and ions (Section 8.4). As Figure 23.1 shows, *d*-block (B-group) elements occur in four series that lie within Periods 4 through 7 between the last *ns*-block element [Group 2A(2)] and the first *np*-block element [Group 3A(13)]. Each of the four series contains ten elements based on the filling of five *d* orbitals, for a total of 40 transition elements. Lying between the first and second members of the series in Periods 6 and 7 are the inner transition elements, in which *f* orbitals are filled. Several points are important to review:

1. *Electron configurations of the atoms.* Despite several exceptions, in general, the *condensed* ground-state electron configuration for the atoms in each *d*-block series is

$$[\text{noble gas}]\, ns^2(n-1)d^x, \text{ with } n = 4 \text{ to } 7 \text{ and } x = 1 \text{ to } 10$$

In Periods 6 and 7, the condensed configuration includes the *f* sublevel:

$$[\text{noble gas}]\, ns^2(n-2)f^{14}(n-1)d^x, \text{ with } n = 6 \text{ or } 7$$

The *partial* (valence-level) electron configuration for the *d*-block elements excludes the noble gas core and the filled inner *f* sublevel:

$$ns^2(n-1)d^x$$

**Figure 23.2 The Period 4 transition metals.** The ten elements appear in periodic-table order.

Scandium, Sc; 3B(3)

Titanium, Ti; 4B(4)

Vanadium, V; 5B(5)

Chromium, Cr; 6B(6)

Manganese, Mn; 7B(7)

## Table 23.1 Orbital Occupancy of the Period 4 Transition Metals

| Element | 4s | 3d | 4p | Unpaired Electrons |
|---|---|---|---|---|
| Sc | ↑↓ | ↑         |       | 1 |
| Ti | ↑↓ | ↑ ↑       |       | 2 |
| V | ↑↓ | ↑ ↑ ↑     |       | 3 |
| Cr | ↑ | ↑ ↑ ↑ ↑ ↑ |       | 6 |
| Mn | ↑↓ | ↑ ↑ ↑ ↑ ↑ |       | 5 |
| Fe | ↑↓ | ↑↓ ↑ ↑ ↑ ↑ |       | 4 |
| Co | ↑↓ | ↑↓ ↑↓ ↑ ↑ ↑ |       | 3 |
| Ni | ↑↓ | ↑↓ ↑↓ ↑↓ ↑ ↑ |       | 2 |
| Cu | ↑ | ↑↓ ↑↓ ↑↓ ↑↓ ↑↓ |       | 1 |
| Zn | ↑↓ | ↑↓ ↑↓ ↑↓ ↑↓ ↑↓ |       | 0 |

2. *Filling pattern in Period 4.* The first (Period 4) transition series consists of scandium (Sc) through zinc (Zn) (Figure 23.2, starting on p. 946, and Table 23.1). Scandium has the electron configuration $[Ar] \, 4s^2 3d^1$, and the addition of one electron at a time first half-fills, then fills, the $3d$ orbitals to zinc. Recall that chromium and copper are exceptions to this pattern: the $4s$ and $3d$ orbitals in Cr are half-filled to give $[Ar] \, 4s^1 3d^5$, and the $4s$ orbital in Cu is half-filled to give $[Ar] \, 4s^1 3d^{10}$. These exceptions are due to the relative energies of the $4s$ and $3d$ sublevels as electrons are added and the unusual stability of half-filled and filled sublevels (see Figure 8.26, p. 319).

3. *Electron configurations of the ions.* Transition metal ions form through *the loss of ns electrons before (n − 1)d electrons.* Thus, the electron configuration of $Ti^{2+}$ is $[Ar] \, 3d^2$, *not* $[Ar] \, 4s^2$, and $Ti^{2+}$ is referred to as a $d^2$ ion. Ions of different metals with the same configuration often have similar properties. For example, $Mn^{2+}$ and $Fe^{3+}$ are $d^5$ ions: both have pale colors in solution and form complex ions with similar magnetic properties.

Table 23.1 shows partial orbital box diagrams for the Period 4 elements. In general for all periods, the number of *unpaired* electrons (or half-filled orbitals) *increases in the first half* of the series and, when pairing begins, *decreases in the second half.* A key point to note in upcoming discussions is that the electron configuration of the *atom* (O.N. = 0) correlates with the physical properties of the *element*, whereas the electron configuration of the *ion* (and other species of higher O.N.) correlates with the chemical properties of the *compounds.*

Iron, Fe; 8B(8)

Cobalt, Co; 8B(9)

Nickel, Ni; 8B(10)

Copper, Cu; 1B(11)

Zinc, Zn; 2B(12)

**Sample Problem 23.1** **Writing Electron Configurations of Transition Metal Atoms and Ions**

**Problem** Write *condensed* electron configurations for the following: **(a)** Zr; **(b)** $V^{3+}$; **(c)** $Mo^{3+}$. (Assume that elements in higher periods behave like those in Period 4.)

**Plan** We locate the element in the periodic table and count its position in the respective transition series. These elements are in Periods 4 and 5, so the general configuration is [noble gas] $ns^2(n-1)d^x$. For the ions, we recall that $ns$ electrons are lost first.

**Solution** **(a)** Zr is the second element in the 4*d* series: [Kr] $5s^24d^2$.
**(b)** V is the third element in the 3*d* series: [Ar] $4s^23d^3$. In forming $V^{3+}$, three electrons are lost (two 4*s* and one 3*d*), so $V^{3+}$ is a $d^2$ ion: [Ar] $3d^2$.
**(c)** Mo lies below Cr in Group 6B(6), so we expect the same exception as for Cr. Thus, Mo is [Kr] $5s^14d^5$. To form the ion, Mo loses the one 5*s* and two of the 4*d* electrons, so $Mo^{3+}$ is a $d^3$ ion: [Kr] $4d^3$.

**Check** Figure 8.10 (p. 305) shows we're correct for the atoms. Be sure that charge plus number of *d* electrons in the ion equals the sum of outer *s* and *d* electrons in the atom.

**Follow-Up Problem 23.1** Write *partial* electron configurations (no noble-gas core or filled inner sublevels) for the following: **(a)** $Ag^+$; **(b)** $Cd^{2+}$; **(c)** $Ir^{3+}$.

## Atomic and Physical Properties of the Transition Elements

Properties of the transition elements contrast in several ways with properties of the main-group elements.

**Trends Across a Period** Consider the variations in atomic size, electronegativity, and ionization energy across Period 4 (Figure 23.3):

**A Atomic radius (pm)**

- *Atomic size.* Atomic size decreases overall across the period (Figure 23.3A). There is a smooth, steady decrease across the main groups because the electrons are added to *outer* orbitals, which shield the increasing nuclear charge poorly. This decrease is not steady in the transition series, where *atomic size decreases at first but then remains relatively constant.* The reason is that the *d* electrons fill *inner* orbitals, so they shield outer electrons very efficiently, and so, the outer 4*s* electrons are *not* pulled closer.

**B Electronegativity**

- *Electronegativity (EN).* Electronegativity generally increases across the period, but, once again, the main groups show a steady, steep increase between the metal potassium (0.8) and the nonmetal bromine (2.8), whereas the transition elements have *relatively constant EN* (Figure 23.3B), consistent with their relatively constant size. The transition elements all have intermediate electronegativity values, much like the large, metallic members of Groups 3A(13) to 5A(15).

**C First ionization energy (kJ/mol)**

**Figure 23.3** Trends in key atomic properties of Period 4 elements. Atomic radius **(A)**, electronegativity **(B)**, and first ionization energy **(C)** of all Period 4 elements are shown as heights of posts, with darker shading for the transition series.

- *Ionization energy ($IE_1$).* The ionization energies of the Period 4 main-group elements rise steeply from left to right, more than tripling from potassium (419 kJ/mol) to krypton (1351 kJ/mol), as electrons become more difficult to remove from the poorly shielded, increasing nuclear charge. In the transition metals, $IE_1$ *values increase relatively little* because the inner 3*d* electrons shield more effectively (Figure 23.3C). [Recall from Section 8.3 that the drop at Group 3A(13) occurs because it is relatively easy to remove the first electron from the outer *np* orbital.]

**Trends Within a Group** Vertical trends for transition elements are also different from main-group trends.

1. *Atomic size.* As expected, atomic size increases from Period 4 to 5, as it does for the main-group elements, but there is virtually *no size increase from Period 5 to 6* (Figure 23.4A). Since the lanthanides, with their buried 4*f* sublevel, appear between the 4*d* (Period 5) and 5*d* (Period 6) series, an element in Period 6 is separated from the one

**A**

**B**

**C**

**D**

Group numbers

**Figure 23.4 Vertical trends in key properties within the transition elements.** The trends are unlike those for the main-group elements in several ways: **A,** The second and third members of a transition metal group are nearly the same size. **B,** Electronegativity increases down a transition group. **C,** First ionization energies are highest at the bottom of a transition group. **D,** Densities increase down a transition group because mass increases faster than volume.

above it by 32 elements (ten 4*d*, six 5*p*, two 6*s*, and fourteen 4*f* orbitals) instead of just 18. The extra shrinkage from the increase in nuclear charge due to 14 additional protons is called the **lanthanide contraction.** By coincidence, this size *decrease* is about equal to the normal *increase* between periods, so Periods 5 and 6 transition elements have about the same atomic sizes.

2. *Electronegativity.* The vertical trend in electronegativity is opposite the decreasing trend in the main groups. Electronegativity *increases* from Period 4 to Period 5, but there is no further increase in Period 6 (Figure 23.4B). The heavier elements, especially gold (EN = 2.4), become quite electronegative, with values higher than most metalloids and even some nonmetals (e.g., EN of Te and of P = 2.1). (In fact, with very electropositive cesium EN = 0.7, gold forms the saltlike CsAu.) Although atomic size increases slightly from top to bottom in a group, the nuclear charge increases much more. Therefore, the heavier transition metals form bonds with more covalent character because they attract electrons more strongly than do main-group metals.

3. *Ionization energy.* The small increase in size combined with the large increase in nuclear charge also explains why *IE₁ values generally increase* down a transition group (Figure 23.4C). This trend also runs counter to the main group trend, where heavier members are so much larger that the outer electron is easier to remove.

4. *Density.* Atomic size, and therefore volume, is inversely related to density. Across a period, densities increase, then level off, and finally dip a bit at the end of a series (Figure 23.4D). Down a transition group, densities increase dramatically because atomic volumes change little from Period 5 to 6, but atomic masses increase significantly. As a result, the Period 6 series contains some of the densest elements known: tungsten, rhenium, osmium, iridium, platinum, and gold have densities about 20 times that of water and twice that of lead.

## Chemical Properties of the Transition Elements

Like their atomic and physical properties, the chemical properties of transition elements are very different from those of main-group elements. We examine key properties in the Period 4 series and then see how behavior changes within a group.

**Figure 23.5 Aqueous oxoanions of transition elements. A,** Mn can have the +2 ($Mn^{2+}$, *left*), the +6 ($MnO_4^{2-}$, *middle*), or the +7 oxidation state ($MnO_4^-$, *right*). **B,** The +5 state in $VO_4^{3-}$ (*left*), the +6 in $Cr_2O_7^{2-}$ (*middle*), and the +7 in $MnO_4^-$ (*right*).

**Multiple Oxidation States** One of the most characteristic chemical properties of the transition metals is the occurrence of *multiple oxidation states;* main-group metals, display one or, at most, two states. For example, vanadium has two common oxidation states, chromium and manganese have three (Figure 23.5A), and many others are seen less often (Table 23.2). Since the $ns$ and $(n-1)d$ electrons are so close in energy, transition elements can use all or most of these electrons in bonding.

*The highest oxidation state of elements in Groups 3B(3) through 7B(7) equals the group number.* These states are seen when the elements combine with highly electronegative oxygen or fluorine. For instance, Figure 23.5B shows vanadium as vanadate ion ($VO_4^{3-}$; O.N. of V = +5), chromium as dichromate ($Cr_2O_7^{2-}$; O.N. of Cr = +6), and manganese as permanganate ($MnO_4^-$; O.N. of Mn = +7).

Elements in Groups 8B(8), 8B(9), and 8B(10) exhibit fewer oxidation states, and the highest state is less common and never equal to the group number. For example, we never encounter iron in the +8 state and only rarely in the +6 state. The +2 and +3 states are the most common ones for iron* and cobalt, and the +2 state is most common for nickel, copper, and zinc. *The +2 oxidation state is common because $ns^2$ electrons are readily lost.*

| Table 23.2 | Oxidation States and *d*-Orbital Occupancy of the Period 4 Transition Metals* | | | | | | | | | |
|---|---|---|---|---|---|---|---|---|---|---|
| **Oxidation State** | **3B (3) Sc** | **4B (4) Ti** | **5B (5) V** | **6B (6) Cr** | **7B (7) Mn** | **8B (8) Fe** | **8B (9) Co** | **8B (10) Ni** | **1B (11) Cu** | **2B (12) Zn** |
| 0 | $d^1$ | $d^2$ | $d^3$ | $d^5$ | $d^5$ | $d^6$ | $d^7$ | $d^8$ | $d^{10}$ | $d^{10}$ |
| +1 | | | $d^3$ | $d^5$ | $d^5$ | $d^6$ | $d^7$ | $d^8$ | $d^{10}$ | |
| +2 | | $d^2$ | $d^3$ | $d^4$ | $d^5$ | $d^6$ | $d^7$ | $d^8$ | $d^9$ | $d^{10}$ |
| +3 | $d^0$ | $d^1$ | $d^2$ | $d^3$ | $d^4$ | $d^5$ | $d^6$ | $d^7$ | $d^8$ | |
| +4 | | $d^0$ | $d^1$ | $d^2$ | $d^3$ | $d^4$ | $d^5$ | $d^6$ | | |
| +5 | | | $d^0$ | $d^1$ | $d^2$ | | $d^4$ | | | |
| +6 | | | | $d^0$ | $d^1$ | $d^4$ | | | | |
| +7 | | | | | $d^0$ | | | | | |

*The most important orbital occupancies are in color.

**Metallic Behavior, Oxide Acidity, and Valence-State Electronegativity** Atomic size and oxidation state have a major effect on the nature of bonding in transition metal compounds. Like the metals in Groups 3A(13), 4A(14), and 5A(15), the transition elements in their *lower* oxidation states behave chemically more like metals. That is, *ionic bonding is more prevalent for the lower oxidation states, and covalent bonding is more prevalent for the higher states.* For example, at room temperature, $TiCl_2$ (O.N. = +2) is an ionic solid, whereas $TiCl_4$ (O.N. = +4) is a molecular liquid (see also Figure 14.11, p. 540). In the higher oxidation states, the atoms have higher charge densities, so they polarize the electron clouds of the nonmetal ions more strongly and the bonding becomes more covalent. For the same reason, the oxides become less basic (more acidic) as the oxidation state increases: TiO is weakly basic in water, whereas $TiO_2$ is amphoteric (reacts with both acid and base).

Why does oxide acidity increase with oxidation state? And, in addition to forming oxides, how can a metal like chromium or manganese form an oxoanion? The answers involve a type of "effective" electronegativity called *valence-state electronegativity,* which also has numerical values. A metal atom in a positive oxidation state has a greater attraction for the bonded electrons, that is, a higher electronegativity, than in its zero oxidation state. Thus, for example, the electronegativity of elemental chromium

*Iron *seems* to have unusual oxidation states in magnetite ($Fe_3O_4$) and pyrite ($FeS_2$), but it doesn't. In magnetite, one-third of the metal ions are $Fe^{2+}$ and two-thirds are $Fe^{3+}$, which gives a 1/1 ratio of $FeO/Fe_2O_3$ and a formula of $Fe_3O_4$. Pyrite contains $Fe^{2+}$ combined with the disulfide ion, $S_2^{2-}$.

is 1.6, close to that of aluminum (1.5), another active metal. For chromium(III), the value increases to 1.7, still characteristic of a metal. But, for chromium(VI), the value is 2.3, close to values of some nonmetals, such as phosphorus (2.1) and sulfur (2.5). Thus, like P in $PO_4^{3-}$ and S in $SO_4^{2-}$, Cr in $CrO_4^{2-}$ is covalently bonded at the center of an oxoanion of a relatively strong acid, $H_2CrO_4$, and manganese(VII) in $MnO_4^-$ behaves similarly in the strong acid $HMnO_4$.

**Reducing Strength** Table 23.3 shows the standard electrode potentials of the Period 4 transition metals in their +2 oxidation state in acid solution. Note that, in general, reducing strength decreases across the series. All the Period 4 transition metals, except copper, are active enough to reduce $H^+$ from aqueous acid to form hydrogen gas. In contrast to the rapid reaction at room temperature of the Group 1A(1) and 2A(2) metals with water, however, most transition metals have an oxide coating that allows rapid reaction only with hot water or steam.

**Color and Magnetism of Compounds** *Most main-group ionic compounds are colorless* because the metal ion has a filled outer level (noble gas electron configuration). With only much higher energy orbitals available to receive an excited electron, the ion does not absorb visible light. In contrast, electrons in a partially filled $d$ sublevel can absorb visible wavelengths and move to slightly higher energy orbitals. As a result, *many transition metal compounds have striking colors.* Exceptions are the compounds of scandium, titanium(IV), and zinc, which are colorless because their metal ions have either an empty $d$ sublevel ($Sc^{3+}$ or $Ti^{4+}$: [Ar] $3d^0$) or a filled one ($Zn^{2+}$: [Ar] $3d^{10}$) (Figure 23.6).

Magnetic properties are also related to sublevel occupancy (Section 8.5). *Most main-group metal ions are diamagnetic* for the same reason they are colorless: all their electrons are paired. In contrast, *many transition metal compounds are paramagnetic because of their unpaired $d$ electrons.* Transition metal ions with a $d^0$ or $d^{10}$ configuration are also colorless and diamagnetic.

| Table **23.3** Standard Electrode Potentials of Period 4 $M^{2+}$ Ions | |
|---|---|
| **Half-Reaction** | $E°$ (V) |
| $Ti^{2+}(aq) + 2e^- \rightleftharpoons Ti(s)$ | $-1.63$ |
| $V^{2+}(aq) + 2e^- \rightleftharpoons V(s)$ | $-1.19$ |
| $Cr^{2+}(aq) + 2e^- \rightleftharpoons Cr(s)$ | $-0.91$ |
| $Mn^{2+}(aq) + 2e^- \rightleftharpoons Mn(s)$ | $-1.18$ |
| $Fe^{2+}(aq) + 2e^- \rightleftharpoons Fe(s)$ | $-0.44$ |
| $Co^{2+}(aq) + 2e^- \rightleftharpoons Co(s)$ | $-0.28$ |
| $Ni^{2+}(aq) + 2e^- \rightleftharpoons Ni(s)$ | $-0.25$ |
| $Cu^{2+}(aq) + 2e^- \rightleftharpoons Cu(s)$ | $0.34$ |
| $Zn^{2+}(aq) + 2e^- \rightleftharpoons Zn(s)$ | $-0.76$ |

**Figure 23.6** Colors of representative compounds of the Period 4 transition metals. Staggered from left to right, the compounds are scandium oxide *(white)*, titanium(IV) oxide *(white)*, vanadyl sulfate dihydrate *(light blue)*, sodium chromate *(yellow)*, manganese(II) chloride tetrahydrate *(light pink)*, potassium ferricyanide *(red-orange)*, cobalt(II) chloride hexahydrate *(violet)*, nickel(II) nitrate hexahydrate *(green)*, copper(II) sulfate pentahydrate *(blue)*, and zinc sulfate heptahydrate *(white)*.

**Chemical Behavior Within a Group** The *increase* in reactivity going down a group of main-group metals due to the *decrease* in $IE_1$ does *not* occur going down a group of transition metals. The chromium (Cr) group [6B(6)] shows a typical pattern (Table 23.4). $IE_1$ *increases* down the group, which makes the two heavier members *less* reactive than the lightest one. Chromium is also a much stronger reducing agent than molybdenum (Mo) or tungsten (W), as shown by the standard electrode potentials.

| Table **23.4** Some Properties of Group 6B(6) Elements | | | |
|---|---|---|---|
| **Element** | **Atomic Radius (pm)** | **$IE_1$ (kJ/mol)** | **$E°$ (V) for $M^{3+}(aq) \mid M(s)$** |
| Cr | 128 | 653 | $-0.74$ |
| Mo | 139 | 685 | $-0.20$ |
| W | 139 | 770 | $-0.11$ |

The similarity in atomic size of members of Periods 5 and 6 leads to similar chemical behavior, which has some important consequences. Because Mo and W compounds behave similarly, their ores often occur together in nature, which makes the elements very difficult to separate from each other. The same situation occurs with zirconium and hafnium in Group 4B(4) and with niobium and tantalum in Group 5B(5).

## ■ Summary of Section 23.1

- All transition elements are metals.
- Atoms of the *d*-block elements have $(n - 1)d$ orbitals being filled, and their ions have an empty *ns* orbital.
- Unlike the trends for the main-group elements, atomic size, electronegativity, and first ionization energy change relatively little across a transition series. Because of the lanthanide contraction, atomic size changes little from Period 5 to 6 in a transition metal group; thus, electronegativity, first ionization energy, and density *increase* down such a group.
- Transition metals typically have several oxidation states, with the +2 state most common. The elements exhibit less metallic behavior in their higher states, as they have higher valence-state electronegativity.
- Most Period 4 transition metals are active enough to reduce hydrogen ion from acid solution.
- Many transition metal compounds are colored and paramagnetic because the metal ion has unpaired *d* electrons.
- In contrast to main-group metals, reactivity decreases down a transition group.

## 23.2 • THE INNER TRANSITION ELEMENTS

The 14 **lanthanides**—cerium (Ce; $Z = 58$) through lutetium (Lu; $Z = 71$)—and the 14 **actinides** below them—thorium (Th; $Z = 90$) through lawrencium (Lr; $Z = 103$)—are called **inner transition elements** because their seven inner $4f$ or $5f$ orbitals are being filled.

### The Lanthanides

The lanthanides are also known as the *rare earth elements,* but many are not rare: cerium (Ce), for instance, ranks 26th in abundance (by mass %), or five times more abundant than lead. All the lanthanides are silvery, high-melting metals.

As with other transition elements, atomic properties vary little across the period. As a result, chemical properties are so similar that the two ores of lanthanides, ceria and yttria, are mixtures of compounds of all 14 of them. This natural co-occurrence arises because the elements exist as $M^{3+}$ ions of very similar radii. Most lanthanides have the ground-state electron configuration [Xe] $6s^2 4f^x 5d^0$, where $x$ varies across the series. The three exceptions (Ce, Gd, and Lu) have a single electron in one of their $5d$ orbitals: cerium ([Xe] $6s^2 4f^1 5d^1$) forms a stable 4+ ion with an empty ($f^0$) sublevel, and the $Gd^{3+}$ and $Lu^{3+}$ ions have a stable half-filled ($f^7$) or filled ($f^{14}$) sublevel.

Lanthanide compounds are used in tinted glass, electronic devices (magnets, batteries, and lasers), and high-quality camera lenses, but two industrial applications account for over 60% of the total usage. In gasoline refining, catalysts used to "crack" hydrocarbons into smaller molecules are 5% by mass rare earth oxides. In steelmaking, a mixture of lanthanides, called *misch metal,* removes carbon impurities from molten iron and steel. Recently, shortages of some lanthanides has caused concern for many electronic applications.

### Sample Problem 23.2    Finding the Number of Unpaired Electrons

**Problem** The alloy $SmCo_5$ forms a permanent magnet because both samarium and cobalt have unpaired electrons. How many unpaired electrons are in Sm ($Z = 62$)?

**Plan** We write the condensed electron configuration of Sm and then, using Hund's rule and the aufbau principle, place the electrons in a partial orbital diagram and count the unpaired electrons.

**Solution** Samarium is the eighth element after Xe. Two electrons go into the $6s$ sublevel. In general, the $4f$ sublevel fills before the $5d$ (among the lanthanides, only Ce, Gd, and Lu have $5d$ electrons), so the remaining electrons go into the $4f$. Thus, the condensed configuration of Sm is $[Xe]\,6s^2 4f^6$. There are seven $f$ orbitals, so each of the six $f$ electrons enters a separate orbital:

| ↑↓ | ↑ ↑ ↑ ↑ ↑ ↑ | | |
|---|---|---|---|
| $6s$ | $4f$ | $5d$ | $6p$ |

Thus, Sm has   six unpaired electrons.

**Check** Six $4f\ e^-$ plus two $6s\ e^-$ plus the 54 $e^-$ in Xe gives 62, the atomic number of Sm.

**Follow-Up Problem 23.2** How many unpaired electrons are in the $Er^{3+}$ ion?

## The Actinides

*All actinides are radioactive.* Like the lanthanides, they have very similar physical and chemical properties. Thorium and uranium occur in nature, but the transuranium elements, those with $Z$ greater than 92, have been synthesized in particle accelerators (Section 24.3). The actinides are silvery and chemically reactive and, like the lanthanides, form highly colored compounds. The actinides and lanthanides have similar outer-electron configurations. Although the $+3$ oxidation state is characteristic of the actinides, as it is for the lanthanides, other states also occur. For example, uranium exhibits $+3$ through $+6$ states, with the $+6$ state the most prevalent; thus, the most common oxide of uranium is $UO_3$.

### ▪ Summary of Section 23.2

- There are two series of inner transition elements. The lanthanides ($4f$ series) have a common $+3$ oxidation state and exhibit very similar properties.
- The actinides ($5f$ series) are radioactive. All actinides have a $+3$ oxidation state; several, including uranium, have higher states as well.

## 23.3 • COORDINATION COMPOUNDS

The most distinctive feature of transition metal chemistry is the common occurrence of **coordination compounds** (or *complexes*). These species contain at least one **complex ion,** which consists of *a central metal cation bonded to molecules and/or anions called **ligands** (see margin).* To maintain charge neutrality, the complex ion is associated with **counter ions.** In the coordination compound $[Co(NH_3)_6]Cl_3$ (Figure 23.7A, *next page*), the complex ion (in square brackets) is $[Co(NH_3)_6]^{3+}$, the six $NH_3$ molecules bonded to the $Co^{3+}$ are ligands, and the three $Cl^-$ ions are counter ions.

A coordination compound behaves like an electrolyte in water: the complex ion and counter ions separate, but the complex ion behaves like a polyatomic ion because *the ligands and central metal ion remain attached.* Thus, as Figure 23.7A shows, 1 mol of $[Co(NH_3)_6]Cl_3$ yields 1 mol of $[Co(NH_3)_6]^{3+}$ ions and 3 mol of $Cl^-$ ions. This section covers the structure, naming, and properties of complex ions.

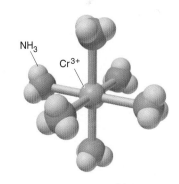

The complex ion $Cr(NH_3)_6{}^{3+}$ has a central $Cr^{3+}$ ion bonded to six $NH_3$ ligands.

### Complex Ions: Coordination Numbers, Geometries, and Ligands

A complex ion is described by the metal ion and the number and types of ligands attached to it. The ion's structure is related to coordination number and geometry.

**Coordination Numbers** The **coordination number** is the *number of ligand atoms* bonded directly to the central metal ion. It is *specific* for a given metal ion in a particular oxidation state and compound. The coordination number of the $Co^{3+}$ ion in $[Co(NH_3)_6]^{3+}$ is 6 because six ligand atoms (N of $NH_3$) are bonded to it. The coordination number of the $Pt^{2+}$ ion in many of its complexes is 4, whereas that of the $Pt^{4+}$ ion in its complexes is 6. Copper(II) may have a coordination number of 2, 4, or 6 in different

**Figure 23.7 Components of a coordination compound.** Coordination compounds are shown as models (*top*), wedge-bond perspective drawings (*middle*), and formulas (*bottom*). **A,** $[Co(NH_3)_6]Cl_3$ dissolves in water. The six ligands remain bound in the complex ion. **B,** $[Pt(NH_3)_4]Br_2$ has four $NH_3$ ligands and two $Br^-$ counter ions.

complex ions. In general, *the most common coordination number in complex ions is 6,* but 2 and 4 are often seen, and some higher ones are known.

**Geometries** The geometry (shape) depends on *the coordination number and the metal ion.* Table 23.5 shows the geometries for coordination numbers 2, 4, and 6. A complex ion whose metal ion has a coordination number of 2, such as $[Ag(NH_3)_2]^+$, is *linear*. The coordination number 4 gives rise to either of two geometries. Most $d^8$ metal ions form *square planar* complex ions (Figure 23.7B). The $d^{10}$ ions form *tetrahedral* complex ions. A coordination number of 6 results in an *octahedral* geometry, as shown by $[Co(NH_3)_6]^{3+}$ (Figure 23.7A). Note the similarity with some of the molecular shapes in VSEPR theory (Section 10.2).

| Table 23.5 Coordination Numbers and Shapes of Some Complex Ions | | |
|---|---|---|
| **Coordination Number** | **Shape** | **Examples** |
| 2 | Linear | $[CuCl_2]^-$, $[Ag(NH_3)_2]^+$, $[AuCl_2]^-$ |
| 4 | Square planar | $[Ni(CN)_4]^{2-}$, $[PdCl_4]^{2-}$, $[Pt(NH_3)_4]^{2+}$, $[Cu(NH_3)_4]^{2+}$ |
| 4 | Tetrahedral | $[Cu(CN)_4]^{3-}$, $[Zn(NH_3)_4]^{2+}$, $[CdCl_4]^{2-}$, $[MnCl_4]^{2-}$ |
| 6 | Octahedral | $[Ti(H_2O)_6]^{3+}$, $[V(CN)_6]^{4-}$, $[Cr(NH_3)_4Cl_2]^+$, $[Mn(H_2O)_6]^{2+}$, $[FeCl_6]^{3-}$, $[Co(en)_3]^{3+}$ |

**Ligands** The ligands of complex ions are *molecules or anions* with one or more **donor atoms.** Each *donates a lone pair of electrons* to the metal ion, thus forming a covalent bond. Because they must have at least one lone pair, donor atoms often come from Group 5A(15), 6A(16), or 7A(17).

## Table **23.6** Some Common Ligands in Coordination Compounds

| Ligand Type | Examples |
|---|---|

**Monodentate**

$H_2\ddot{O}\!:$ water    $:\!\ddot{\underset{..}{F}}\!:^-$ fluoride ion    $[:\!C\!\equiv\!N\!:]^-$ cyanide ion    $[:\!\ddot{O}\!-\!H]^-$ hydroxide ion

$:\!NH_3$ ammonia    $:\!\ddot{\underset{..}{Cl}}\!:^-$ chloride ion    $[:\!\ddot{S}\!=\!C\!=\!\ddot{N}\!:]^-$ thiocyanate ion    $[:\!\ddot{O}\!-\!N\!=\!\ddot{O}\!:]^-$ nitrite ion

**Bidentate**

$H_2C\!-\!CH_2$ with $H_2\ddot{N}$ and $\ddot{N}H_2$ — ethylenediamine (en)

$\left[\begin{array}{c} :\!\ddot{O}: \quad :\!\ddot{O}: \\ C\!-\!C \\ :\!\ddot{O}: \quad :\!\ddot{O}: \end{array}\right]^{2-}$ — oxalate ion

**Polydentate**

$H_2C\!-\!CH_2\ \ CH_2\!-\!CH_2$ with $H_2\ddot{N}$, $\ddot{N}H$, $\ddot{N}H_2$ — diethylenetriamine

$\left[:\!\ddot{O}\!-\!\overset{\overset{\displaystyle :O:}{\|}}{P}\!-\!\ddot{O}\!-\!\overset{\overset{\displaystyle :O:}{\|}}{P}\!-\!\ddot{O}\!-\!\overset{\overset{\displaystyle :O:}{\|}}{P}\!-\!\ddot{O}:\right]^{5-}$ — triphosphate ion

ethylenediaminetetraacetate ion (EDTA$^{4-}$)

Ligands are classified in terms of their number of donor atoms, or "teeth":

- *Monodentate* (Latin, "one-toothed") ligands bond through a single donor atom.
- *Bidentate* ligands have two donor atoms, each of which bonds to the metal ion.
- *Polydentate* ligands have more than two donor atoms.

Bidentate and polydentate ligands give rise to *rings* in the complex ion. For instance, ethylenediamine (abbreviated *en*) has a chain of four atoms (:N—C—C—N:), so it forms a five-membered ring, with the two electron-donating N atoms bonding to the metal ion. Such ligands seem to grab the metal ion like claws, so a complex ion that contains them is also called a **chelate** (pronounced "KEY-late"; Greek *chela*, "crab's claw"). With its six donor atoms, the ethylenediaminetetraacetate (EDTA$^{4-}$) ion forms very stable complexes with metal ions. This property makes EDTA useful in treating *heavy-metal poisoning*. Ingested by the patient, the EDTA$^{4-}$ ion removes lead (*see margin*) and other heavy-metal ions from the blood and other body fluids.

Table 23.6 shows some common ligands in coordination compounds. Note that each ligand has one or more donor atoms (colored type), each with a lone pair of electrons to donate and form a covalent bond to the metal ion.

$[Pb(EDTA)]^{2-}$

## Formulas and Names of Coordination Compounds

The combination of ions in a coordination compound is the key to writing its formula and name. A coordination compound can consist of a complex cation with simple anionic counter ions, a complex anion with simple cationic counter ions, or even a complex cation with complex anion as counter ion.

**Determining the Charge of the Metal Ion** To know the number of cations and anions, we must know the ion charges, and we use basic arithmetic to find them:

- For a compound with a *complex anion,* say, $K_2[Co(NH_3)_2Cl_4]$, we know that the $K^+$ ions balance the charge of the complex anion, which contains two $NH_3$ molecules and four $Cl^-$ ions as ligands. The two $NH_3$ are neutral, the four $Cl^-$ have a total charge of 4−, and the entire complex ion must have a charge of 2− to balance the two $K^+$. The charge of the central metal ion is

$$\text{Charge of complex ion} = \text{Charge of metal ion} + \text{total charge of ligands}$$
$$2- = \text{Charge of metal ion} + [(2 \times 0) + (4 \times 1-)]$$

So,    Charge of metal ion = (2−) − (4−) = 2+; that is, $Co^{2+}$

• For a compound with a *complex cation,* say $[Co(NH_3)_4Cl_2]Cl$, the complex ion is $[Co(NH_3)_4Cl_2]^+$ and one $Cl^-$ is the counter ion. The four $NH_3$ ligands are neutral, the two $Cl^-$ ligands have a total charge of $2-$, and the complex cation has a charge of $1+$, so the central metal ion must be $Co^{3+}$:

Charge of metal ion = charge of complex ion − total charge of ligands

$$= \quad 1+ \quad - [(4 \times 0) + (2 \times 1-)] = 3+$$

**Rules for Writing Formulas** There are three rules for writing formulas of coordination compounds (the first two are the same as those for the formula of any ionic compound):

1. *The cation is written before the anion.*
2. *The charge of the cation(s) is balanced by the charge of the anion(s).*
3. *For the complex ion, neutral ligands are written before anionic ligands, and the formula of the whole ion is placed in brackets.*

**Rules for Naming Coordination Compounds** Originally named after their discoverer or color, coordination compounds are named systematically with a set of rules. Let's see how to name $[Co(NH_3)_4Cl_2]Cl$. As we go through the naming steps, refer to Tables 23.7 and 23.8:

**Table 23.7 Names of Some Neutral and Anionic Ligands**

| Neutral | | Anionic | |
|---|---|---|---|
| **Name** | **Formula** | **Name** | **Formula** |
| Aqua | $H_2O$ | Fluoro | $F^-$ |
| Ammine | $NH_3$ | Chloro | $Cl^-$ |
| Carbonyl | $CO$ | Bromo | $Br^-$ |
| Nitrosyl | $NO$ | Iodo | $I^-$ |
| | | Hydroxo | $OH^-$ |
| | | Cyano | $CN^-$ |

**Table 23.8 Names of Some Metal Ions in Complex Anions**

| Metal | Name in Anion |
|---|---|
| Iron | Ferrate |
| Copper | Cuprate |
| Lead | Plumbate |
| Silver | Argentate |
| Gold | Aurate |
| Tin | Stannate |

1. *The cation is named before the anion.* Thus, we name the $[Co(NH_3)_4Cl_2]^+$ ion before the $Cl^-$ ion.
2. *Within the complex ion, the ligands are named in alphabetical order **before** the metal ion.* In the $[Co(NH_3)_4Cl_2]^+$ ion, four $NH_3$ and two $Cl^-$ are named before $Co^{3+}$.
3. *Neutral ligands generally have the molecule name,* but there are a few exceptions (Table 23.7). *Anionic ligands drop the -ide and add -o after the root name;* thus, the anion name *fluoride* for an $F^-$ ion becomes the ligand name *fluoro.* The two ligands in $[Co(NH_3)_4Cl_2]^+$ are *ammine* ($NH_3$) and *chloro* ($Cl^-$) with *ammine* coming before *chloro* alphabetically.
4. *A numerical prefix indicates the number of ligands of a particular type.* For example, *tetra*ammine denotes *four* $NH_3$, and *di*chloro denotes *two* $Cl^-$. Other prefixes are *tri-, penta-,* and *hexa-.* But prefixes do *not* affect the alphabetical order: *tetraammine* comes before *dichloro.* For ligand names that include a numerical prefix (such as ethylene*di*amine), we use *bis* (2), *tris* (3), or *tetrakis* (4) to indicate the number of such ligands, followed by the ligand name in parentheses. For example, a complex ion that has two ethylenediamine ligands has *bis(ethylenediamine)* in its name.
5. *The oxidation state of the metal ion has a Roman numeral (in parentheses) only if the metal ion can have more than one state.* Since cobalt can have $+2$ and $+3$ states, we add a III to name the complex ion. Thus, the compound is

tetraamminedichlorocobalt(III) chloride

The only typographical space in the name comes between cation and anion.

6. *If the complex ion is an anion, we drop the ending of the metal name and add -ate.* Thus, the name for $K[Pt(NH_3)Cl_5]$ is potassium amminepentachloroplatinate(IV). There is one $K^+$ counter ion, so the complex anion has a charge of $1-$. The five $Cl^-$ ligands have a total charge of $5-$, so Pt must be in the $+4$ oxidation state. For some metals, we use the Latin root with the *-ate* ending (Table 23.8). For example, the name for $Na_4[FeBr_6]$ is sodium hexabromoferrate(II).

**Sample Problem 23.3** Writing Names and Formulas of Coordination Compounds

**Problem (a)** What is the systematic name of $Na_3[AlF_6]$?
**(b)** What is the systematic name of $[Co(en)_2Cl_2]NO_3$?
**(c)** What is the formula of tetraamminebromochloroplatinum(IV) chloride?
**(d)** What is the formula of hexaamminecobalt(III) tetrachloroferrate(III)?

**Plan** We use the rules that were presented above and Tables 23.7 and 23.8.

**Solution (a)** The complex ion is $[AlF_6]^{3-}$. There are six *(hexa-)* $F^-$ ions *(fluoro)* as ligands, so we have *hexafluoro*. The complex ion is an anion, so the ending of the metal ion (aluminum) must be changed to *-ate:* hexafluoroaluminate. Aluminum has only the +3 oxidation state, so we do *not* use a Roman numeral. The positive counter ion is named first and separated from the anion by a space:  sodium hexafluoroaluminate.
**(b)** Listed alphabetically, there are two $Cl^-$ *(dichloro)* and two en [*bis(ethylenediamine)*] as ligands. The complex ion is a cation, so the metal name is unchanged, but we specify its oxidation state because cobalt can have several. One $NO_3^-$ balances the 1+ cation charge. With 2− for two $Cl^-$ and 0 for two en, the metal must be *cobalt(III)*. The word *nitrate* follows a space:  dichlorobis(ethylenediamine)cobalt(III) nitrate.
**(c)** The central metal ion is written first, followed by the neutral ligands and then (in alphabetical order) by the negative ligands. *Tetraammine* is four $NH_3$, *bromo* is one $Br^-$, *chloro* is one $Cl^-$, and *platinate(IV)* is $Pt^{4+}$, so the complex ion is $[Pt(NH_3)_4BrCl]^{2+}$. Its 2+ charge is the sum of 4+ for $Pt^{4+}$, 0 for four $NH_3$, 1− for one $Br^-$, and 1− for one $Cl^-$. To balance the 2+ charge, we need two $Cl^-$ counter ions:  $[Pt(NH_3)_4BrCl]Cl_2$.
**(d)** This compound consists of two different complex ions. In the cation, *hexaammine* is six $NH_3$ and *cobalt(III)* is $Co^{3+}$, so the cation is $[Co(NH_3)_6]^{3+}$. The 3+ charge is the sum of 3+ for $Co^{3+}$ and 0 for six $NH_3$. In the anion, *tetrachloro* is four $Cl^-$, and *ferrate(III)* is $Fe^{3+}$, so the anion is $[FeCl_4]^-$. The 1− charge is the sum of 3+ for $Fe^{3+}$ and 4− for four $Cl^-$. In the neutral compound, one 3+ cation must be balanced by three 1− anions:  $[Co(NH_3)_6][FeCl_4]_3$.

**Check** Reverse the process to be sure you obtain the name or formula in the problem.

**Follow-Up Problem 23.3   (a)** What is the name of $[Cr(H_2O)_5Br]Cl_2$?
**(b)** What is the formula of barium hexacyanocobaltate(III)?

## Isomerism in Coordination Compounds

**Isomers** are compounds with the same chemical formula but different properties. Recall the discussion of isomerism in organic compounds (Section 15.2); coordination compounds exhibit the same two broad categories—constitutional isomers and stereoisomers.

**Constitutional Isomers: Atoms Connected Differently** Compounds with the same formula, but with the atoms connected differently, are **constitutional (structural) isomers.** Coordination compounds exhibit two types:

1. **Coordination isomers** occur when the composition of the complex ion, but not of the compound, is different. This type of isomerism occurs in two ways:
- *Exchange of ligand and counter ion.* For example, in $[Pt(NH_3)_4Cl_2](NO_2)_2$, the $Cl^-$ ions are the ligands, and the $NO_2^-$ ions are counter ions; in $[Pt(NH_3)_4(NO_2)_2]Cl_2$, the roles are reversed. A common test to see whether $Cl^-$ is a ligand or a counter ion is to treat a solution of the compound with $AgNO_3$; the $Cl^-$ counter ion will form a white precipitate of AgCl, but the $Cl^-$ ligand won't. Thus, a solution of $[Pt(NH_3)_4Cl_2](NO_2)_2$ does not form AgCl because $Cl^-$ is bound to the metal ion, but a $[Pt(NH_3)_4(NO_2)_2]Cl_2$ solution forms 2 mol of AgCl per mole of compound.
- *Exchange of ligands.* This type of isomerism occurs in compounds consisting of two complex ions. For example, in $[Cr(NH_3)_6][Co(CN)_6]$ and $[Co(NH_3)_6][Cr(CN)_6]$, $NH_3$ is a ligand of $Cr^{3+}$ in one compound and of $Co^{3+}$ in the other.

2. **Linkage isomers** occur when the composition of the complex ion is the same but the ligand donor atom is different. Some ligands can bind to the metal ion through *either of two donor atoms.* For example, the nitrite ion can bind through the N atom (*nitro,*

$O_2N:$) or either of the O atoms (*nitrito,* ONO:) to give linkage isomers, such as penta-ammine*nitro*cobalt(III) chloride $[Co(NH_3)_5(NO_2)]Cl_2$ and pentaammine*nitrito*cobalt(III) chloride $[Co(NH_3)_5(ONO)]Cl_2$ (Figure 23.8).

**Figure 23.8** A pair of linkage (constitutional) isomers.

*Nitro* isomer, $[Co(NH_3)_5(NO_2)]Cl_2$          *Nitrito* isomer, $[Co(NH_3)_5(ONO)]Cl_2$

Other examples of ligands that have more than one donor atom are the cyanate ion, which can attach via the O atom (*cyanato,* NCO:) or the N atom (*isocyanato,* OCN:), and the thiocyanate ion, which can attach via the S atom or the N atom:

nitrite          cyanate          thiocyanate

**Stereoisomers: Atoms Arranged Differently in Space** **Stereoisomers** are compounds that have the same atomic connections but different spatial arrangements of the atoms. *Geometric* and *optical* isomers, which we discussed for organic compounds, occur with coordination compounds as well:

1. **Geometric isomers** (also called ***cis-trans* isomers** and *diastereomers*) occur when atoms or groups of atoms are arranged differently in space relative to the central metal ion. For example, the square planar $[Pt(NH_3)_2Cl_2]$ has two arrangements, which give rise to two different compounds (Figure 23.9A). The isomer with identical ligands *next* to each other is *cis*-diamminedichloroplatinum(II), and the one with identical ligands *across* from each other is *trans*-diamminedichloroplatinum(II).

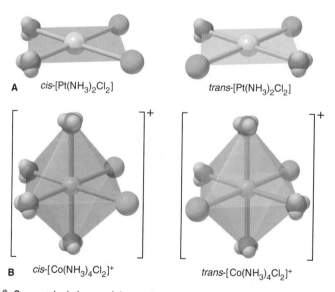

**A**   *cis*-$[Pt(NH_3)_2Cl_2]$          *trans*-$[Pt(NH_3)_2Cl_2]$

**B**   *cis*-$[Co(NH_3)_4Cl_2]^+$          *trans*-$[Co(NH_3)_4Cl_2]^+$

**Figure 23.9** Geometric (*cis-trans*) isomerism. **A,** The *cis* and *trans* isomers of $[Pt(NH_3)_2Cl_2]$. **B,** The *cis* and *trans* isomers of $[Co(NH_3)_4Cl_2]^+$. The colored shapes indicate the actual colors of the species.

These isomers have remarkably different biological behaviors. In the mid-1960s, Barnett Rosenberg and his colleagues found that *cis*-[Pt(NH₃)₂Cl₂] (cisplatin) was an antitumor agent. It and several closely related platinum(II) complexes are still used to treat certain types of cancer. In contrast, *trans*-[Pt(NH₃)₂Cl₂] has no antitumor effect. Cisplatin may work by becoming oriented within a cancer cell such that a donor atom on each DNA strand can replace a Cl⁻ ligand, and it binds the platinum(II) strongly, preventing DNA replication (Section 15.6).

Octahedral complexes also exhibit *cis-trans* isomerism (Figure 23.9B). The *cis* isomer of the [Co(NH₃)₄Cl₂]⁺ ion has the two Cl⁻ ligands at any two adjacent positions of the ion's octahedral shape, whereas the *trans* isomer has these ligands across from each other.

2. **Optical isomers** (also called *enantiomers*) occur when a molecule and its mirror image cannot be superimposed (see Figures 15.8 to 15.10, pp. 580–581). Unlike other types of isomers, which have distinct physical properties, optical isomers are physically identical except for *the direction in which they rotate the plane of polarized light*. Many octahedral complex ions show optical isomerism, which we can determine by rotating one isomer and seeing if it is superimposable on the other isomer (its mirror image). For example, in Figure 23.10A, the two structures (I and II) of *cis*-[Co(en)₂Cl₂]⁺, the *cis*-dichlorobis(ethylenediamine)cobalt(III) ion, are mirror images of each other. Rotate structure I 180° around a vertical axis, and you obtain III. The Cl⁻ ligands of III match those of II, but the en ligands do not: II and III (which is I rotated) are not superimposable: they are optical isomers. One isomer is designated *d*-[Co(en)₂Cl₂]⁺ and the other is *l*-[Co(en)₂Cl₂]⁺, depending on whether it rotates polarized light to the right (*d*- for "dextro-") or to the left (*l*- for "levo-"). (The *d*- or *l*- designation can only be determined by experiment.)

In contrast, as shown in Figure 23.10B, the two structures of the *trans*-dichlorobis(ethylenediamine)cobalt(III) ion are *not* optical isomers: rotate I 90° around a vertical axis and you obtain III, which *is* superimposable on II.

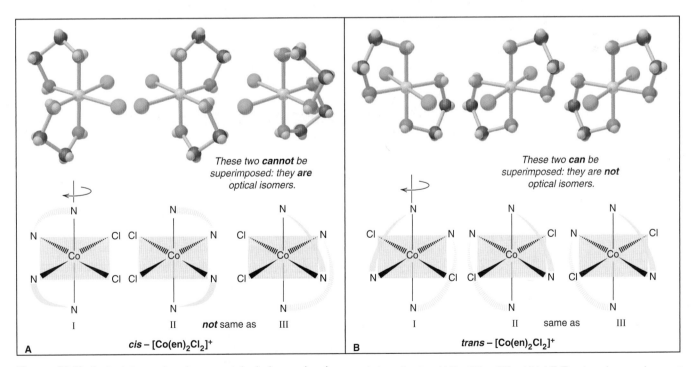

**Figure 23.10** Optical isomerism in an octahedral complex ion. **A,** Structure I and its mirror image, structure II, are optical isomers of *cis*-[Co(en)₂Cl₂]⁺. (The curved wedges represent the bidentate ligand ethylenediamine, H₂N—CH₂—CH₂—NH₂.) **B,** The *trans* isomer does *not* have optical isomers.

**Figure 23.11** Important types of isomerism in coordination compounds.

Figure 23.11 is an overview of the most common types of isomerism in coordination compounds.

---

**Sample Problem 23.4** Determining the Type of Stereoisomerism

**Problem** Draw stereoisomers for each of the following and state the type of isomerism:
**(a)** [Pt(NH$_3$)$_2$Br$_2$] (square planar) **(b)** [Cr(en)$_3$]$^{3+}$ (en = H$_2$ÑCH$_2$CH$_2$ÑH$_2$)

**Plan** We determine the geometry around each metal ion and the nature of the ligands. If there are different ligands that can be placed in different positions relative to each other, geometric (cis-trans) isomerism occurs. Then, we see whether the mirror image of an isomer is superimposable on the original. If it is *not*, optical isomerism also occurs.

**Solution (a)** The square planar Pt(II) complex has two different monodentate ligands. Each pair of ligands can lie next to or across from each other (*see margin*). Thus, geometric isomerism occurs. Each isomer *is* superimposable on a mirror image of itself, so there is no optical isomerism.
**(b)** Ethylenediamine (en) is a bidentate ligand. The Cr$^{3+}$ has a coordination number of 6 and an octahedral geometry, like Co$^{3+}$. The three bidentate ligands are identical, so there is no geometric isomerism. However, the complex ion has a nonsuperimposable mirror image (*see margin*). Thus, optical isomerism occurs.

**Follow-Up Problem 23.4** What stereoisomers, if any, are possible for the [Co(NH$_3$)$_2$(en)Cl$_2$]$^+$ ion?

---

**▌ Summary of Section 23.3**

- Coordination compounds consist of a complex ion and charge-balancing counter ions. The complex ion has a central metal ion bonded to neutral and/or anionic ligands, which have one or more donor atoms that each have a lone pair of electrons.
- The most common complex-ion geometry is octahedral (six ligand atoms bonding).
- Formulas and names of coordination compounds follow systematic rules.
- Coordination compounds can exhibit constitutional isomerism (coordination and linkage) and stereoisomerism (geometric and optical).

---

# 23.4 • THEORETICAL BASIS FOR THE BONDING AND PROPERTIES OF COMPLEXES

In this section, we consider valence bond theory and crystal field theory, which address different features of complexes: how metal-ligand bonds form, why certain geometries are preferred, and why complexes are brightly colored and often paramagnetic.

# Applying Valence Bond Theory to Complex Ions

*Valence bond (VB) theory,* which helped explain bonding and structure in main-group compounds (Section 11.1), is also used to describe bonding in complex ions. In the formation of a complex ion, the *filled* ligand orbital overlaps an *empty* metal-ion orbital: *the ligand (Lewis base) donates an electron pair, and the metal ion (Lewis acid) accepts it to form a covalent bond in the complex ion (Lewis adduct)* (Section 18.9). A bond in which one atom contributes both electrons is a **coordinate covalent bond;** once formed, it is identical to any covalent single bond.

Recall that the VB concept of hybridization proposes mixing particular combinations of *s, p,* and *d* orbitals to obtain sets of hybrid orbitals, which have specific geometries. For coordination compounds, the model proposes that *the type of metal-ion orbital hybridization determines the geometry of the complex ion.* Let's discuss orbital combinations that lead to octahedral, square planar, and tetrahedral geometries.

**Octahedral Complexes** The hexaamminechromium(III) ion, $[Cr(NH_3)_6]^{3+}$, is an *octahedral complex* (Figure 23.12). The six lowest-energy, *empty* orbitals of the $Cr^{3+}$ ion—two $3d$, one $4s$, and three $4p$—mix and become six equivalent $d^2sp^3$ hybrid orbitals that point toward the corners of an octahedron.* Six $NH_3$ molecules donate lone pairs from their N atoms to form six metal-ligand bonds. Three unpaired $3d$ electrons of the central $Cr^{3+}$ ion ([Ar] $3d^3$) remain in unhybridized orbitals and make the complex ion paramagnetic.

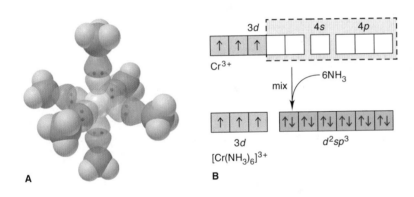

**Figure 23.12** Hybrid orbitals and bonding in the octahedral $[Cr(NH_3)_6]^{3+}$ ion. **A,** Orbital contour depiction of $Cr(NH_3)_6^{3+}$. **B,** Partial orbital diagrams depict formation of six $d^2sp^3$ hybrid orbitals, which are filled with six $NH_3$ lone pairs (*red*).

**Square Planar Complexes** Metal ions with a $d^8$ configuration usually form *square planar complexes* (Figure 23.13). In the $[Ni(CN)_4]^{2-}$ ion, for example, the model proposes that one $3d$, one $4s$, and two $4p$ orbitals of $Ni^{2+}$ mix and form four $dsp^2$ hybrid orbitals, which point to the corners of a square and accept one electron pair from each of four $CN^-$ ligands.

A look at the ground-state electron configuration of the $Ni^{2+}$ ion, however, raises a key question: how can the $Ni^{2+}$ ion ([Ar] $3d^8$) offer an empty $3d$ orbital for accepting a lone pair, if its eight $3d$ electrons lie in three filled and two half-filled orbitals?

---

*Note the distinction between hybrid-orbital designations here and in Chapter 11. Both designations give the orbitals in energy order. In $[Cr(NH_3)_6]^{3+}$, the $3d$ orbitals have a *lower n* value than the $4s$ and $4p$ orbitals, so the hybrid orbitals are $d^2sp^3$. But, for $SF_6$, the $3d$ orbitals have the *same n* value as the $3s$ and $3p$ orbitals of S, so the designation is $sp^3d^2$.

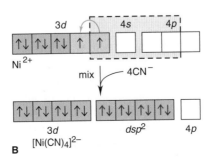

**Figure 23.13** Hybrid orbitals and bonding in the square planar $[Ni(CN)_4]^{2-}$ ion. **A,** Contour depiction of $[Ni(CN)_4]^{2-}$. **B,** Two lone $3d$ electrons pair up, which frees one $3d$ orbital for hybridization. Four $dsp^2$ orbitals are filled with lone pairs (*red*) from four $CN^-$ ligands.

Apparently, in the $d^8$ configuration of $Ni^{2+}$, electrons in the half-filled orbitals *pair up* and leave one $3d$ orbital empty. This explanation is consistent with the fact that the complex is diamagnetic (no unpaired electrons). Moreover, it means that the energy *gained* by using a $3d$ orbital for bonding in the hybrid orbital is greater than the energy *required* to overcome repulsions from pairing the $3d$ electrons.

**Tetrahedral Complexes**  Metal ions that have a filled $d$ sublevel, such as $Zn^{2+}$ ([Ar]$3d^{10}$), often form diamagnetic *tetrahedral complexes* (Figure 23.14). In the $[Zn(OH)_4]^{2-}$ ion, for example, VB theory proposes that the lowest *empty* $Zn^{2+}$ orbitals—one $4s$ and three $4p$—mix to become four $sp^3$ hybrid orbitals that point to the corners of a tetrahedron and are occupied by lone pairs, one from each of four $OH^-$ ligands.

**Figure 23.14** Hybrid orbitals and bonding in the tetrahedral $[Zn(OH)_4]^{2-}$ ion. **A,** Contour depiction of $[Zn(OH)_4]^{2-}$. **B,** Formation and filling of four $sp^3$ hybrid orbitals.

## Crystal Field Theory

The VB model is easy to picture and rationalizes bonding and shape, but it treats the orbitals as little more than empty "slots" for accepting electron pairs. Moreover, it gives no insight into the colors of these compounds and sometimes predicts their magnetic properties incorrectly. In contrast, **crystal field theory** provides little insight about metal-ligand bonding, but it explains color and magnetism by highlighting the *effect on d-orbital energies of the metal ion as the ligands approach.* Before we discuss the theory, let's consider why a substance is colored.

**What Is Color?**  White light consists of all wavelengths ($\lambda$) in the visible range (Section 7.1) and can be dispersed into colors of a narrower wavelength range. Objects appear colored in white light because they absorb only certain wavelengths: an opaque object *reflects* the other wavelengths, and a clear one *transmits* them. If an object absorbs all visible wavelengths, it appears black; if it reflects all, it appears white.

Each color has a *complementary* color; for example, green and red are complementary colors. Figure 23.15 shows these relationships on an artist's color wheel in which complementary colors are wedges opposite each other. A mixture of complementary colors absorbs all visible wavelengths and appears black.

An object has a particular color for one of two reasons:

- It reflects (or transmits) light of *that* color. Thus, if an object absorbs all wavelengths *except* green, the reflected (or transmitted) light is seen as green.
- It absorbs light of the *complementary* color. Thus, if the object absorbs only red, the *complement* of green, the remaining mixture of reflected (or transmitted) wavelengths is also seen as green.

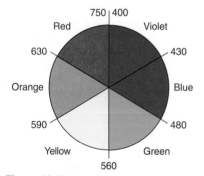

**Figure 23.15** An artist's wheel. Colors, with approximate wavelength ranges (in nm), are shown as wedges.

Table 23.9 lists the color absorbed and the resulting color observed. The relation between absorbed and observed colors is demonstrated by the seasonal colors of deciduous trees. In the spring and summer, leaves contain high concentrations of the photosynthetic pigment *chlorophyll* and lower concentrations of other pigments called *xanthophylls.* Chlorophyll absorbs strongly in the blue and red regions, reflecting mostly green. In the fall, photosynthesis slows, so the leaf no longer makes chlorophyll. The green fades as the chlorophyll decomposes, revealing the xanthophylls

| Table **23.9** Relation Between Absorbed and Observed Colors | | | |
|---|---|---|---|
| **Absorbed Color** | **λ (nm)** | **Observed Color** | **λ (nm)** |
| Violet | 400 | Green-yellow | 560 |
| Blue | 450 | Yellow | 600 |
| Blue-green | 490 | Red | 620 |
| Yellow-green | 570 | Violet | 410 |
| Yellow | 580 | Dark blue | 430 |
| Orange | 600 | Blue | 450 |
| Red | 650 | Green | 520 |

Foliage changing color in autumn.

that were present but masked by the chlorophyll. Xanthophylls absorb green and blue strongly, reflecting bright yellows and reds (*see photo*).

### Splitting of *d* Orbitals in an Octahedral Field of Ligands

The crystal field model explains that the properties of complexes result from the splitting of *d*-orbital energies, which arises from *electrostatic attractions between the metal cation and the negative charge of the ligands*. This negative charge is either partial, as in a polar covalent ligand like $NH_3$, or full, as in an anionic ligand like $Cl^-$. Picture six ligands approaching a metal ion along the mutually perpendicular *x*, *y*, and *z* axes, which forms an octahedral arrangement (Figure 23.16A). Let's follow the orientation of ligand and orbital and how the approach affects orbital energies.

1. *Orientation of ligand and metal ion orbitals.* As ligands approach, their electron pairs repel electrons in the five *d* orbitals of the metal ion. In the isolated ion, the *d* orbitals have different orientations but *equal* energies. But, in the negative field of ligands, the *d* electrons are *repelled unequally because of their different orbital orientations.* The ligands moving *along* the *x*, *y*, and *z* axes approach
- *Directly toward* the lobes of the $d_{x^2-y^2}$ and $d_{z^2}$ orbitals (Figure 23.16B and C).
- *Between* the lobes of the $d_{xy}$, $d_{xz}$, and $d_{yz}$ orbitals (Figure 23.16D to F).

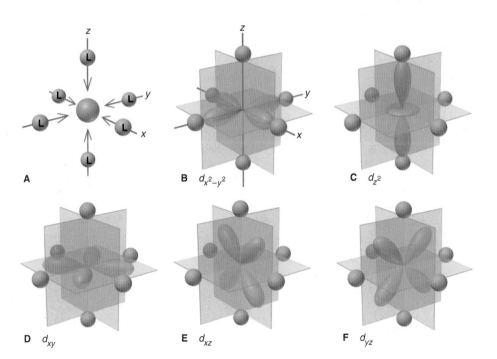

**Figure 23.16** The five *d* orbitals in an octahedral field of ligands. **A,** Ligands approach along the *x*, *y*, and *z* axes. **B** and **C,** The $d_{x^2-y^2}$ and $d_{z^2}$ orbitals point *directly* at some of the ligands. **D** to **F,** The $d_{xy}$, $d_{xz}$, and $d_{yz}$ orbitals point *between* the ligands.

**Figure 23.17** Splitting of *d*-orbital energies in an octahedral field of ligands.

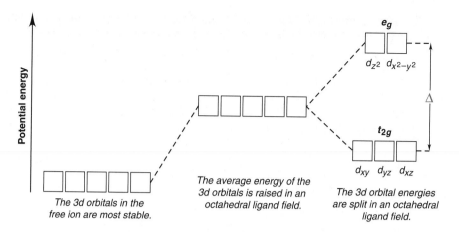

The 3d orbitals in the free ion are most stable.

The average energy of the 3d orbitals is raised in an octahedral ligand field.

The 3d orbital energies are split in an octahedral ligand field.

**Figure 23.18** The effect of ligands and splitting energy orbital occupancy.

**2.** *Effect on d-orbital energies.* As a result of these different orientations, electrons in the $d_{x^2-y^2}$ and $d_{z^2}$ orbitals experience *stronger* repulsions than electrons in the $d_{xy}$, $d_{xz}$, and $d_{yz}$ orbitals do. An energy diagram shows that the five *d* orbitals are most stable in the free ion and their *average* energy is higher in the ligand field. But *the orbital energies split, with two d orbitals higher in energy and three lower* (Figure 23.17):

- The two higher energy orbitals are $e_g$ **orbitals** and arise from the $d_{x^2-y^2}$ and $d_{z^2}$.
- The three lower energy orbitals are $t_{2g}$ **orbitals** and arise from the $d_{xy}$, $d_{xz}$, and $d_{yz}$.

**3.** *The crystal field effect.* This splitting of orbital energies is called the *crystal field effect,* and the energy difference between $e_g$ and $t_{2g}$ orbitals is the **crystal field splitting energy ($\Delta$).** Different ligands create crystal fields of different strength:

- **Strong-field ligands** lead to a *larger* splitting energy (larger $\Delta$).
- **Weak-field ligands** lead to a *smaller* splitting energy (smaller $\Delta$).

For instance, $H_2O$ is a weak-field ligand, and $CN^-$ is a strong-field ligand (Figure 23.18). Note the different orbital occupancies; we discuss the reason for these differences shortly.

**Explaining the Colors of Transition Metal Complexes** The color of a coordination compound is determined by $\Delta$ of its complex ion. When the ion absorbs radiant energy, electrons can move from the lower energy $t_{2g}$ level to the higher $e_g$ level. Recall from Chapter 7 that the *difference* between two atomic energy levels is equal to the energy (and inversely related to the wavelength) of the absorbed photon:

$$\Delta E_{electron} = E_{photon} = h\nu = hc/\lambda$$

Consider the $[Ti(H_2O)_6]^{3+}$ ion, which appears purple in aqueous solution (Figure 23.19). Hydrated $Ti^{3+}$ has its one *d* electron in one of the three lower energy $t_{2g}$ orbitals. The energy difference ($\Delta$) between the $t_{2g}$ and $e_g$ orbitals in this ion corresponds to photons between the green and yellow range. When white light shines on the solution, these colors of light are absorbed, and the electron jumps to one of the $e_g$ orbitals. Red, blue, and violet light are transmitted, so the solution appears purple.

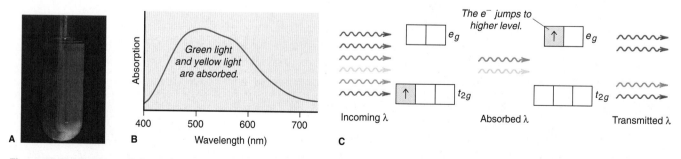

**Figure 23.19** The color of $[Ti(H_2O)_6]^{3+}$. **A,** The hydrated $Ti^{3+}$ ion is purple. **B,** An absorption spectrum shows that green light and yellow light are absorbed and other wavelengths are transmitted. **C,** An orbital diagram depicts the colors absorbed when the *d* electron jumps to the higher level.

Absorption spectra can show the wavelengths absorbed by (1) a metal ion with different ligands and (2) different metal ions with the same ligand. Such data allow us to relate the energy of the absorbed light to $\Delta$ and make two key observations:

- *For a given ligand,* color depends on the *oxidation state of the metal ion.* In Figure 23.20A, aqueous $[V(H_2O)_6]^{2+}$ (*left*) is violet and $[V(H_2O)_6]^{3+}$ (*right*) is yellow.
- *For a given metal ion,* color depends on the *ligand.* A single ligand substitution can affect the wavelengths absorbed and, thus, the color (Figure 23.20B).

**The Spectrochemical Series**  The fact that color depends on the ligand allows us to create a **spectrochemical series,** which ranks the ability of a ligand to split *d*-orbital energies (Figure 23.21). Using this series, we can predict the *relative* magnitude of $\Delta$ for a series of octahedral complexes of a *given* metal ion. Although we cannot predict the actual color of a given complex, we can determine whether a complex will absorb longer or shorter wavelengths than other complexes in the series.

**Figure 23.20 Effects of oxidation state and ligand on color. A,** Solutions of two hydrated vanadium ions: O.N. of V is +2 (*left*); O.N. of V is +3 (*right*). **B,** A change in one ligand can influence the color. $[Cr(NH_3)_6]^{3+}$ is yellow (*left*), and $[Cr(NH_3)_5Cl]^{2+}$ is purple (*right*).

$$I^- < Cl^- < F^- < OH^- < H_2O < SCN^- < NH_3 < en < NO_2^- < CN^- < CO$$

WEAKER FIELD          STRONGER FIELD

SMALLER $\Delta$          LARGER $\Delta$

LONGER $\lambda$          SHORTER $\lambda$

**Figure 23.21 The spectrochemical series.** As $\Delta$ increases, shorter wavelengths (higher energies) of light must be absorbed to excite electrons. For reference, water is a weak-field ligand.

---

**Sample Problem 23.5**  **Ranking Crystal Field Splitting Energies ($\Delta$) for Complex Ions of a Metal**

**Problem**  Rank $[Ti(H_2O)_6]^{3+}$, $[Ti(CN)_6]^{3-}$, and $[Ti(NH_3)_6]^{3+}$ in terms of $\Delta$ and of the energy of visible light absorbed.

**Plan**  The formulas show that Ti has an oxidation state of $+3$ in the three ions. From Figure 23.21, we rank the ligands by crystal field strength: the stronger the ligand, the greater the splitting, and the higher the energy of light absorbed.

**Solution**  The ligand field strength is in the order $CN^- > NH_3 > H_2O$, so the relative size of $\Delta$ and energy of light absorbed is

$$Ti(CN)_6^{3-} > Ti(NH_3)_6^{3+} > Ti(H_2O)_6^{3+}$$

**Follow-Up Problem 23.5**  Which complex ion absorbs visible light of higher energy, $[V(H_2O)_6]^{3+}$ or $[V(NH_3)_6]^{3+}$?

---

**Explaining the Magnetic Properties of Transition Metal Complexes**  Splitting of energy levels gives rise to magnetic properties based on the number of *unpaired* electrons in the metal ion's *d* orbitals. Based on Hund's rule, electrons occupy orbitals of equal energy one at a time. When all lower energy orbitals are half-filled,

- The next electron can enter a half-filled orbital and pair up by overcoming a repulsive *pairing energy* ($E_{pairing}$).
- The next electron can enter an empty, higher energy orbital by overcoming $\Delta$.

Thus, *the relative sizes of $E_{pairing}$ and $\Delta$ determine the occupancy of d orbitals,* which determines the number of unpaired electrons and, thus, magnetic behavior of the ion.

**Figure 23.22** High-spin and low-spin octahedral complex ions of $Mn^{2+}$.
**A,** Free $Mn^{2+}$ has five unpaired electrons.
**B,** Bonded to a weak-field ligand, $Mn^{2+}$ still has five unpaired electrons (high-spin complex). **C,** Bonded to a strong-field ligand, $Mn^{2+}$ has one unpaired electron (low-spin complex).

**No field**

Maximum number of unpaired electrons

**A  Free $Mn^{2+}$ ion**

**Weak-field ligand**

High-spin complex

$E_{pairing} > \Delta$

**B  $[Mn(H_2O)_6]^{2+}$**

**Strong-field ligand**

Low-spin complex

$E_{pairing} < \Delta$

**C  $[Mn(CN)_6]^{4-}$**

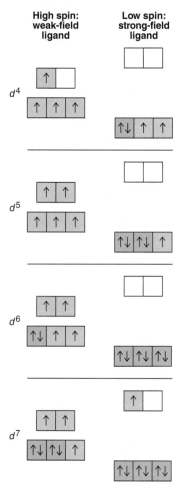

**High spin: weak-field ligand**     **Low spin: strong-field ligand**

$d^4$

$d^5$

$d^6$

$d^7$

**Figure 23.23** Orbital occupancy for high-spin and low-spin octahedral complexes of $d^4$ through $d^7$ metal ions.

As an example, the isolated $Mn^{2+}$ ion ([Ar] $3d^5$) has five unpaired electrons of equal energy (Figure 23.22A). In an octahedral field of ligands, orbital occupancy is affected by the ligand in one of two ways:

- *Weak-field ligands and high-spin complexes.* Weak-field ligands, such as $H_2O$ in $[Mn(H_2O)_6]^{2+}$, cause a *small* splitting energy, so it takes *less* energy for $d$ electrons to jump to the $e_g$ set and stay unpaired than to pair up in the $t_{2g}$ set (Figure 23.22B). Thus, for weak-field ligands, $E_{pairing} > \Delta$. Therefore, *the number of unpaired electrons in the complex ion is the **same** as in the free ion:* weak-field ligands create **high-spin complexes,** those with the *maximum* number of unpaired electrons.
- *Strong-field ligands and low-spin complexes.* In contrast, strong-field ligands, such as $CN^-$ in $[Mn(CN)_6]^{4-}$, cause a *large* splitting energy, so it takes *more* energy for electrons to jump to the $e_g$ set than to pair up in the $t_{2g}$ set (Figure 23.22C). Thus, for strong-field ligands, $E_{pairing} < \Delta$. Therefore, *the number of unpaired electrons in the complex ion is **less** than in the free ion.* Strong-field ligands create **low-spin complexes,** those with *fewer* unpaired electrons.

Orbital diagrams for $d^1$ through $d^9$ ions in octahedral complexes show that high-spin *and* low-spin options are possible only for $d^4$, $d^5$, $d^6$, and $d^7$ ions (Figure 23.23). With three $t_{2g}$ orbitals available, $d^1$, $d^2$, and $d^3$ ions always form high-spin complexes because there is no need to pair up. Similarly, $d^8$ and $d^9$ ions always form high-spin complexes because the $t_{2g}$ set is filled with six electrons, so the $e_g$ orbitals *must* have either two ($d^8$) or one ($d^9$) unpaired electron(s).

**Sample Problem 23.6**   **Identifying High-Spin and Low-Spin Complex Ions**

**Problem** Iron(II) forms a complex in hemoglobin. For each of the two octahedral complex ions $[Fe(H_2O)_6]^{2+}$ and $[Fe(CN)_6]^{4-}$, draw an energy diagram showing orbital splitting, predict the number of unpaired electrons, and identify the ion as low spin or high spin.

**Plan** The $Fe^{2+}$ electron configuration shows the number of $d$ electrons, and the spectrochemical series (Figure 23.21) shows the relative ligand strengths. We draw energy diagrams and separate the $t_{2g}$ and $e_g$ orbital sets more for the strong-field ligand. Then we add electrons, noting that a weak-field ligand gives the *maximum* number of unpaired electrons and a high-spin complex, whereas a strong-field ligand gives the *minimum* number of unpaired electrons and a low-spin complex.

**Solution** $Fe^{2+}$ has the [Ar]$3d^6$ configuration. $H_2O$ produces smaller splitting than $CN^-$. The energy diagrams are shown at left. The $[Fe(H_2O)_6]^{2+}$ ion has four unpaired electrons (high spin), and the $[Fe(CN)_6]^{4-}$ ion has no unpaired electrons (low spin).

**Comment 1.** $H_2O$ is a weak-field ligand, so it forms high-spin complexes. **2.** We cannot confidently predict the spin of a complex without having actual values for $\Delta$ and $E_{pairing}$. **3.** Cyanide ions and carbon monoxide are toxic because they bind to the iron complexes in proteins involved in cellular energy (Chemical Connections, pp. 892 and 968).

**Follow-Up Problem 23.6** How many unpaired electrons do you expect for $[Mn(CN)_6]^{3-}$? Is this a high-spin or low-spin complex ion?

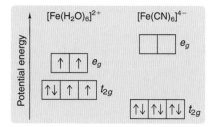

$[Fe(H_2O)_6]^{2+}$                  $[Fe(CN)_6]^{4-}$

Potential energy

$e_g$                                  $e_g$

$t_{2g}$                                $t_{2g}$

**Crystal Field Splitting in Tetrahedral and Square Planar Complexes** Four ligands around a metal ion also cause $d$-orbital splitting, but the magnitude and pattern of the splitting depend on whether the ligands approach from a tetrahedral or a square planar orientation.

1. *Tetrahedral complexes.* When the ligands approach from the corners of a tetrahedron, none of the five $d$ orbitals is directly in their paths (Figure 23.24A). Thus, the overall attraction of ligand and metal ion is weaker, so the splitting of $d$-orbital energies is *less* in a tetrahedral than an octahedral complex with the same ligands:

$$\Delta_{\text{tetrahedral}} < \Delta_{\text{octahedral}}$$

Repulsions are minimized when the ligands approach the $d_{xy}$, $d_{xz}$, and $d_{yz}$ orbitals closer than they do the $d_{x^2 - y^2}$ and $d_{z^2}$ orbitals. This situation is the *opposite of the octahedral case,* so the relative $d$-orbital energies are reversed: the $d_{xy}$, $d_{xz}$, and $d_{yz}$ orbitals become *higher* in energy than the $d_{x^2 - y^2}$ and $d_{z^2}$ orbitals. *Only high-spin tetrahedral complexes are known* because the magnitude of $\Delta$ is so small.

2. *Square planar complexes.* The effects of the ligand field in the square planar case are easier to picture if we imagine starting with an octahedral geometry and then removing the two ligands along the $z$-axis (Figure 23.24B). With no $z$-axis interactions present, any $d$ orbital with a $z$-axis component has lower energy, with the $d_{z^2}$ orbital decreasing most, and the $d_{xz}$ and $d_{yz}$, also decreasing. In contrast, the two $d$ orbitals in the $xy$-plane interact strongly with the ligands, and because the $d_{x^2 - y^2}$ orbital has its lobes *on* the axes, its energy is highest. The $d^8$ metal ions, such as $[PdCl_4]^{2-}$, form square planar complexes. They are *low spin* and usually *diamagnetic* because the four pairs of $d$ electrons fill the four lowest-energy orbitals.

In addition to their important chemical applications, complexes of the transition elements play vital roles in living systems, as the following Chemical Connections essay describes.

## ■ Summary of Section 23.4

- According to valence bond theory, complex ions have coordinate covalent bonds between ligands (Lewis bases) and metal ions (Lewis acids).
- Ligand lone pairs occupy hybridized metal-ion oribitals, leading to the characteristic shapes of complex ions.
- In crystal field theory, the surrounding field of ligands splits the metal ion's $d$-orbital energies. The crystal field splitting energy ($\Delta$) depends on the charge of the metal ion and the crystal field strength of the ligands.
- $\Delta$ influences the color (energy of the photons absorbed) and paramagnetism (number of unpaired $d$ electrons). Strong-field ligands create a large $\Delta$ and produce low-spin complexes that absorb light of higher energy (shorter wavelength); the reverse is true of weak-field ligands.
- Several transition metals, including iron and zinc, are essential dietary components in trace amounts because they are crucial to the biochemical function of key proteins.

**Figure 23.24** Splitting of $d$-orbital energies. **A,** The pattern of splitting by a tetrahedral field of ligands is the opposite of the octahedral pattern. **B,** Splitting by a square planar field of ligands decreases the energies of $d_{xz}$, $d_{yz}$, and especially $d_{z^2}$ orbitals relative to the octahedral pattern.

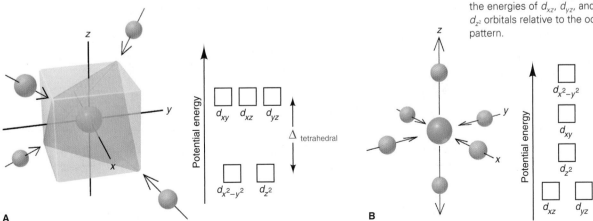

iving things consist primarily of water and complex organic compounds made of four *building-block elements* C, O, H, and N. They also contain seven other elements, known as *macro-nutrients* because they occur in fairly high concentrations (in order of atomic number) Na, Mg, P, S, Cl, K, and Ca. In addition, organisms contain a large number of elements in low concentrations, and most of these *micro*nutrients, or *trace elements,* are transition metals.

With the exception of scandium and titanium, all Period 4 transition elements are essential to organisms (Table B23.1, *facing page*), and plants also require molybdenum (from Period 5). A transition metal ion typically lies next to a protein chain covalently bonded to surrounding amino acid R groups whose N and O atoms act as ligands. Despite the complexity of biomolecules, the principles of bonding and *d*-orbital splitting are the same as in simple inorganic systems. In this discussion, we focus on iron and zinc.

## Iron and the Heme Group

Iron plays a crucial role in oxygen transport in all vertebrates. The oxygen-transporting protein hemoglobin (Figure B23.1A) consists of four folded protein chains called *globins,* each cradling the iron-containing complex *heme,* which is derived from a metal ion and the tetradentate ring ligand *porphin.* Iron(II) lies at the center of the plane of the porphin ring, bonded to four N lone pairs to form a square planar complex. When heme is bound in hemoglobin (Figure B23.1B), the complex is *octahedral,* with the fifth ligand an N atom from a nearby amino acid (histidine), and the sixth an O atom from either $O_2$ (as shown) or $H_2O$.

Hemoglobin exists in two forms, depending on the sixth ligand:

- *In the lungs,* where $[O_2]$ is high, heme binds $O_2$ to form *oxyhemoglobin,* which is transported in the arteries to tissues. $O_2$ is a strong-field ligand, so the $d^6$ $Fe^{2+}$ ion is part of a low-spin complex. Because of the relatively large *d*-orbital splitting, oxyhemoglobin absorbs blue (high-energy) light, so arterial blood is bright red.

- *At the tissues,* where $[O_2]$ is low, $O_2$ is released and replaced by $H_2O$ to form *deoxyhemoglobin,* which is transported in the veins back to the lungs. Since $H_2O$ is a weak-field ligand, $Fe^{2+}$ is part of a high-spin complex. Because of the relatively small *d*-orbital splitting, deoxyhemoglobin absorbs red (low-energy) light, so venous blood is dark, purplish red.

The relative position of $Fe^{2+}$ in the plane of the porphin ring also depends on the sixth ligand. Bound to $O_2$, $Fe^{2+}$ is *in* the porphin plane; bound to $H_2O$, it moves *out of* the plane slightly. This tiny (~60 pm) change due to release or binding of $O_2$ influences the shape of the globin chain. And this change in shape alters the shape of the next globin chain, triggering the release or attachment of *its* $O_2$, and so on, to the other two globin chains. This "cooperation" of the four globin chains allows hemoglobin to rapidly pick up $O_2$ from the lungs and unload it in the tissues.

Heme binding of $O_2$ is an equilibrium process. Carbon monoxide is toxic because it binds to $Fe^{2+}$ about 200 times more tightly than $O_2$ does; each CO eliminates that heme group from

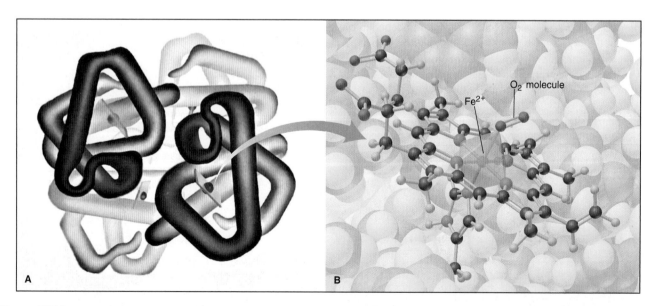

**Figure B23.1 Hemoglobin and the octahedral complex in heme.** **A,** Hemoglobin consists of four protein chains, each with a bound heme. (Illustration by Irving Geis. Rights owned by Howard Hughes Medical Institute. Not to be used without permission.) **B,** In oxyhemoglobin, the octahedral complex in heme has an $O_2$ molecule as the sixth ligand for iron(II).

| Table B23.1 Some Transition Metal Trace Elements in Humans | | |
|---|---|---|
| **Element** | **Biomolecule Containing Element** | **Function of Biomolecule** |
| Vanadium | Protein (?) | Redox couple in fat metabolism (?) |
| Chromium | Glucose tolerance factor | Glucose utilization |
| Manganese | Isocitrate dehydrogenase | Cell respiration |
| Iron | Hemoglobin and myoglobin | Oxygen transport |
|  | Cytochrome *c* | Cell respiration; ATP formation |
|  | Catalase | Decomposition of $H_2O_2$ |
| Cobalt | Cobalamin (vitamin $B_{12}$) | Development of red blood cells |
| Copper | Ceruloplasmin | Hemoglobin synthesis |
|  | Cytochrome oxidase | Cell respiration; ATP formation |
| Zinc | Carbonic anhydrase | Elmination of $CO_2$ |
|  | Carboxypeptidase A | Protein digestion |
|  | Alcohol dehydrogenase | Metabolism of ethanol |

functioning. Like $O_2$, CO is a strong-field ligand and produces a bright red, "healthy" look in the poisoned individual. Because binding is reversible, breathing high concentrations of $O_2$ displaces CO from the heme:

$$\text{heme}-CO + O_2 \rightleftharpoons \text{heme}-O_2 + CO$$

Porphin is a very common biological ligand. Chlorophyll has $Mg^{2+}$ and vitamin $B_{12}$ has $Co^{3+}$ at the center of a very similar ring system. Heme itself is found not only in hemoglobin, but also in proteins called *cytochromes* that are involved in energy metabolism (see Chemical Connections, pp. 892–893).

## Zinc and the Enzyme Active Site

The zinc ion occurs at the active sites of several enzymes. With its $d^{10}$ configuration, $Zn^{2+}$ forms tetrahedral complexes with the N atoms of three amino acid groups at three positions, and the fourth position is free to interact with the molecule undergoing reaction (Figure B23.2). In its role as Lewis acid, $Zn^{2+}$ accepts a lone pair from the reactant as a step in the catalytic process. Consider the enzyme carbonic anhydrase, which catalyzes the reaction between $H_2O$ and $CO_2$ during respiration:

$$CO_2(g) + H_2O(l) \rightleftharpoons H^+(aq) + HCO_3^-\ (aq)$$

The $Zn^{2+}$ at the active site binds three histidine N atoms, and O of the reactant $H_2O$ is the fourth donor atom. By withdrawing electron density from the O—H bonds, the $Zn^{2+}$ makes the $H_2O$ acidic enough to lose a proton. In the rate-determining step, the bound $OH^-$ ion is attracted to the partially positive C of $CO_2$ much more strongly than the lone pair of a free water molecule would be; thus, the reaction rate is higher. One reason $Cd^{2+}$ is toxic is that it competes with $Zn^{2+}$ for the carbonic anhydrase active site.

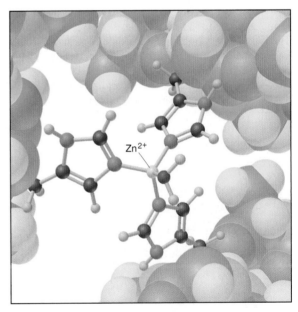

**Figure B23.2** The tetrahedral $Zn^{2+}$ complex in carbonic anhydrase.

## Problems

**B23.1** (a) Identify each compound's central metal ion and give its oxidation state: chlorophyll, heme, and vitamin $B_{12}$. (b) What similarity in structure do these compounds have?

**B23.2** Suggest a structural reason why carbonic anhydrase synthesized with $Ni^{2+}$, $Fe^{2+}$, or $Mn^{2+}$ in place of $Zn^{2+}$ has less catalytic efficiency.

# CHAPTER REVIEW GUIDE

## Understand These Concepts

1. The positions of the $d$- and $f$-block elements and the general forms of their atomic and ionic electron configurations (§23.1)
2. How atomic size, ionization energy, and electronegativity vary across a period and down a group of transition elements and how these trends differ from those of the main-group elements; why the densities of Period 6 transition elements are so high (§23.1)
3. Why the transition elements often have multiple oxidation states and why the +2 state is common (§23.1)
4. Why metallic behavior (prevalence of ionic bonding and basic oxides) decreases as oxidation state increases; how valence-state electronegativity explains metal atoms in oxoanions (§23.1)
5. Why many transition metal compounds are colored and paramagnetic (§23.1)
6. The common +3 oxidation state of lanthanides and the similarity in their $M^{3+}$ radii; the radioactivity of actinides (§23.2)
7. The coordination numbers, geometries, and ligand structures of complex ions (§23.3)
8. How coordination compounds are named and their formulas written (§23.3)
9. The types of constitutional isomerism (coordination and linkage) and stereoisomerism (geometric and optical) of coordination compounds (§23.3)
10. How valence bond theory uses hybridization to account for the shapes of octahedral, square planar, and tetrahedral complexes (§23.4)
11. How crystal field theory explains that approaching ligands cause $d$-orbital energies to split (§23.4)
12. How the relative crystal field strength of ligands (spectrochemical series) affects the $d$-orbital splitting energy ($\Delta$) (§23.4)
13. How the magnitude of $\Delta$ accounts for the energy of light absorbed and, thus, the color of a complex (§23.4)
14. How the relative sizes of pairing energy and $\Delta$ determine the occupancy of $d$ orbitals and, thus, the magnetic properties of complexes (§23.4)
15. How $d$-orbital splitting in tetrahedral and square planar complexes differs from that in octahedral complexes (§23.4)

## Master These Skills

1. Writing electron configurations of transition metal atoms and ions (SP 23.1)
2. Using a partial orbital diagram to determine the number of unpaired electrons in a transition-metal atom or ion (SP 23.2)
3. Recognizing the structural components of complex ions (§23.3)
4. Naming and writing formulas of coordination compounds (SP 23.3)
5. Determining the type of stereoisomerism in complexes (SP 23.4)
6. Correlating a complex ion's shape with the number and type of hybrid orbitals of the central metal ion (§23.4)
7. Using the spectrochemical series to rank complex ions in terms of $\Delta$ and the energy of light absorbed (SP 23.5)
8. Using the spectrochemical series to determine if a complex ion is high or low spin (SP 23.6)

## Key Terms Page numbers appear in parentheses.

transition elements (945)

**Section 23.1**
lanthanide contraction (949)

**Section 23.2**
lanthanides (952)
actinides (952)
inner transition elements (952)

**Section 23.3**
coordination compound (953)
complex ion (953)

ligand (953)
counter ion (953)
coordination number (953)
donor atom (954)
chelate (955)
isomer (957)
constitutional (structural) isomers (957)
coordination isomers (957)
linkage isomers (957)
stereoisomers (958)

geometric *(cis-trans)* isomers (958)
optical isomers (959)

**Section 23.4**
coordinate covalent bond (961)
crystal field theory (962)
$e_g$ orbital (964)

$t_{2g}$ orbital (964)
crystal field splitting energy ($\Delta$) (964)
strong-field ligand (964)
weak-field ligand (964)
spectrochemical series (965)
high-spin complex (966)
low-spin complex (966)

## Brief Solutions to Follow-Up Problems

**23.1** (a) $Ag^+$: $4d^{10}$
(b) $Cd^{2+}$: $4d^{10}$
(c) $Ir^{3+}$: $5d^6$

**23.2** Three; $Er^{3+}$ is [Xe] $4f^{11}$:

| | | | | | | | | | | | | | | |
|---|---|---|---|---|---|---|---|---|---|---|---|---|---|---|
| | ↑↓ | ↑↓ | ↑↓ | ↑↓ | ↑ | ↑ | ↑ | | | | | | | |

$6s$　　　　　　$4f$　　　　　　　　　$5d$　　　　　　$6p$

**23.3** (a) Pentaaquabromochromium(III) chloride; (b) $Ba_3[Co(CN)_6]_2$

**23.4** Two sets of *cis-trans* isomers, and the two *cis* isomers are optical isomers.

**23.5** Both metal ions are $V^{3+}$; in terms of ligand field energy, $NH_3 > H_2O$, so $[V(NH_3)_6]^{3+}$ absorbs light of higher energy.

**23.6** The metal ion is $Mn^{3+}$: $[Ar]\,3d^4$.

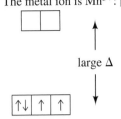

Two unpaired *d* electrons; low-spin complex

# PROBLEMS

Problems with **colored** numbers are answered in Appendix E and worked in detail in the Student Solutions Manual. Problem sections match those in the text and provide the numbers of relevant sample problems. Most offer Concept Review Questions, Skill-Building Exercises (grouped in pairs covering the same concept), and Problems in Context. The Comprehensive Problems are based on material from any section or previous chapter.

*Note:* In these problems, the term *electron configuration* refers to the condensed, ground-state electron configuration.

## Properties of the Transition Elements
(Sample Problem 23.1)

### Concept Review Questions

**23.1** How is the *n* value of the *d* sublevel of a transition element related to the period number of the element?

**23.2** Write the general electron configuration of a transition element (a) in Period 5; (b) in Period 6.

**23.3** What is the general rule concerning the order in which electrons are removed from a transition metal atom to form an ion? Give an example from Group 5B(5). Name two types of measurements used to study electron configurations of ions.

**23.4** What is the maximum number of unpaired *d* electrons that an atom or ion can possess? Give an example of an atom and an ion that have this number.

**23.5** How does the variation in atomic size across a transition series contrast with the change across the main-group elements of the same period? Why?

**23.6** (a) What is the lanthanide contraction? (b) How does it affect atomic size down a group of transition elements? (c) How does it influence the densities of the Period 6 transition elements?

**23.7** (a) What is the range in electronegativity across the first ($3d$) transition series? (b) What is the range across Period 4 of main-group elements? (c) Explain the difference.

**23.8** (a) Explain the major difference between the number of oxidation states of most transition elements and that of most main-group elements. (b) Why is the +2 oxidation state so common among transition elements? (c) What is valence-state electronegativity? Is the electronegativity of Cr different in CrO, $Cr_2O_3$, and $CrO_3$? Explain.

**23.9** (a) What behavior distinguishes paramagnetic and diamagnetic substances? (b) Why are paramagnetic ions common among transition elements but not main-group elements? (c) Why are colored solutions of metal ions common among transition elements but not main-group elements?

### Skill-Building Exercises (grouped in similar pairs)

**23.10** Using the periodic table to locate each element, write the electron configuration of (a) V; (b) Y; (c) Hg.

**23.11** Using the periodic table to locate each element, write the electron configuration of (a) Ru; (b) Cu; (c) Ni.

**23.12** Using the periodic table to locate each element, write the electron configuration of (a) Os; (b) Co; (c) Ag.

**23.13** Using the periodic table to locate each element, write the electron configuration of (a) Zn; (b) Mn; (c) Re.

**23.14** Give the electron configuration and the number of unpaired electrons for (a) $Sc^{3+}$; (b) $Cu^{2+}$; (c) $Fe^{3+}$; (d) $Nb^{3+}$.

**23.15** Give the electron configuration and the number of unpaired electrons for: (a) $Cr^{3+}$; (b) $Ti^{4+}$; (c) $Co^{3+}$; (d) $Ta^{2+}$.

**23.16** What is the highest oxidation state for (a) Ta; (b) Zr; (c) Mn?

**23.17** What is the highest oxidation state for (a) Nb; (b) Y; (c) Tc?

**23.18** Which transition metals have a maximum O.N. of +6?

**23.19** Which transition metals have a maximum O.N. of +4?

**23.20** In which compound does Cr exhibit greater metallic behavior, $CrF_2$ or $CrF_6$? Explain.

**23.21** $VF_5$ is a liquid that boils at 48°C, whereas $VF_3$ is a solid that melts above 800°C. Explain this difference in properties.

**23.22** Is it more difficult to oxidize Cr or Mo? Explain.

**23.23** Is $MnO_4^-$ or $ReO_4^-$ a stronger oxidizing agent? Explain.

**23.24** Which oxide, $CrO_3$ or CrO, is more acidic in water? Why?

**23.25** Which oxide, $Mn_2O_3$ or $Mn_2O_7$, is more basic in water? Why?

**Problems in Context**

**23.26** The green patina of Cu-alloy roofs results from corrosion in the presence of $O_2$, $H_2O$, $CO_2$, and sulfur compounds. The other members of Group 1B(11), Ag and Au, do not form a patina. Corrosion of Cu and Ag in the presence of sulfur compounds leads to a black tarnish, but Au does not tarnish. This pattern is different from that in Group 1A(1), where ease of oxidation *increases* down the group. Explain these different group patterns.

**The Inner Transition Elements**
(Sample Problem 23.2)

**Concept Review Questions**

**23.27** What atomic property of the lanthanides leads to their remarkably similar chemical properties?

**23.28** (a) What is the maximum number of unpaired electrons in a lanthanide ion? (b) How does this number relate to occupancy of the $4f$ subshell?

**23.29** Which of the actinides are radioactive?

**Skill-Building Exercises** (grouped in similar pairs)

**23.30** Give the electron configuration of (a) La; (b) $Ce^{3+}$; (c) Es; (d) $U^{4+}$.

**23.31** Give the electron configuration of (a) Pm; (b) $Lu^{3+}$; (c) Th; (d) $Fm^{3+}$.

**23.32** Only a few lanthanides show an oxidation state other than +3. Two of these, europium (Eu) and terbium (Tb), are found near the middle of the series, and their unusual oxidation states can be associated with a half-filled $f$ subshell. (a) Write the electron configurations of $Eu^{2+}$, $Eu^{3+}$, and $Eu^{4+}$. Why is $Eu^{2+}$ a common ion, whereas $Eu^{4+}$ is unknown? (b) Write the electron configurations of $Tb^{2+}$, $Tb^{3+}$, and $Tb^{4+}$. Would you expect Tb to show a +2 or a +4 oxidation state? Explain.

**23.33** Cerium (Ce) and ytterbium (Yb) exhibit some oxidation states in addition to +3. (a) Write the electron configurations of $Ce^{2+}$, $Ce^{3+}$, and $Ce^{4+}$. (b) Write the electron configurations of $Yb^{2+}$, $Yb^{3+}$, and $Yb^{4+}$. (c) In addition to the 3+ ions, the ions $Ce^{4+}$ and $Yb^{2+}$ are stable. Suggest a reason for this stability.

**Problems in Context**

**23.34** Which lanthanide has the maximum number of unpaired electrons in both its atom and 3+ ion? Give the number of unpaired electrons in the atom and ion.

**Coordination Compounds**
(Sample Problems 23.3 and 23.4)

**Concept Review Questions**

**23.35** Describe the makeup of a complex ion, including the nature of the ligands and their interaction with the central metal ion. Explain how a complex ion can be positive or negative and how it occurs as part of a neutral coordination compound.

**23.36** What electronic feature must a donor atom of a ligand have?

**23.37** What is the coordination number of a metal ion in a complex ion? How does it differ from oxidation number?

**23.38** What structural feature is characteristic of a chelate?

**23.39** What geometries are associated with the coordination numbers 2, 4, and 6?

**23.40** What are the coordination numbers of cobalt(III), platinum(II), and platinum(IV) in complexes?

**23.41** How is a complex ion a Lewis adduct?

**23.42** What does the ending *-ate* signify in a complex ion name?

**23.43** In what order are the metal ion and ligands given in the name of a complex ion?

**23.44** Is a linkage isomer a type of constitutional isomer or stereoisomer? Explain.

**Skill-Building Exercises** (grouped in similar pairs)

**23.45** Give systematic names for the following formulas:
(a) $[Ni(H_2O)_6]Cl_2$   (b) $[Cr(en)_3](ClO_4)_3$   (c) $K_4[Mn(CN)_6]$

**23.46** Give systematic names for the following formulas:
(a) $[Co(NH_3)_4(NO_2)_2]Cl$   (b) $[Cr(NH_3)_6][Cr(CN)_6]$
(c) $K_2[CuCl_4]$

**23.47** What are the charge and coordination number of the central metal ion(s) in each compound of Problem 23.45?

**23.48** What are the charge and coordination number of the central metal ion(s) in each compound of Problem 23.46?

**23.49** Give systematic names for the following formulas:
(a) $K[Ag(CN)_2]$   (b) $Na_2[CdCl_4]$   (c) $[Co(NH_3)_4(H_2O)Br]Br_2$

**23.50** Give systematic names for the following formulas:
(a) $K[Pt(NH_3)Cl_5]$   (b) $[Cu(en)(NH_3)_2][Co(en)Cl_4]$
(c) $[Pt(en)_2Br_2](ClO_4)_2$

**23.51** What are the charge and coordination number of the central metal ion(s) in each compound of Problem 23.49?

**23.52** What are the charge and coordination number of the central metal ion(s) in each compound of Problem 23.50?

**23.53** Give formulas corresponding to the following names:
(a) Tetraamminezinc sulfate
(b) Pentaamminechlorochromium(III) chloride
(c) Sodium bis(thiosulfato)argentate(I)

**23.54** Give formulas corresponding to the following names:
(a) Dibromobis(ethylenediamine)cobalt(III) sulfate
(b) Hexaamminechromium(III) tetrachlorocuprate(II)
(c) Potassium hexacyanoferrate(II)

**23.55** What is the coordination number of the metal ion and the number of individual ions per formula unit in each of the compounds in Problem 23.53?

**23.56** What is the coordination number of the metal ion and the number of individual ions per formula unit in each of the compounds in Problem 23.54?

**23.57** Give formulas corresponding to the following names:
(a) Hexaaquachromium(III) sulfate
(b) Barium tetrabromoferrate(III)
(c) Bis(ethylenediamine)platinum(II) carbonate

**23.58** Give formulas corresponding to the following names:
(a) Potassium tris(oxalato)chromate(III)
(b) Tris(ethylenediamine)cobalt(III) pentacyanoiodomanganate(II)
(c) Diamminediaquabromochloroaluminum nitrate

**23.59** Give the coordination number of the metal ion and the number of ions per formula unit in each compound in Problem 23.57.

**23.60** Give the coordination number of the metal ion and the number of ions per formula unit in each compound in Problem 23.58.

**23.61** Which of these ligands can participate in linkage isomerism: (a) $NO_2^-$; (b) $SO_2$; (c) $NO_3^-$? Explain with Lewis structures.

**23.62** Which of these ligands can participate in linkage isomerism: (a) $SCN^-$; (b) $S_2O_3^{2-}$ (thiosulfate); (c) $HS^-$? Explain with Lewis structures.

**23.63** For any of the following that can exist as isomers, state the type of isomerism and draw the structures:
(a) $[Pt(CH_3NH_2)_2Br_2]$   (b) $[Pt(NH_3)_2FCl]$   (c) $[Pt(H_2O)(NH_3)FCl]$

**23.64** For any of the following that can exist as isomers, state the type of isomerism and draw the structures:
(a) $[Zn(en)F_2]$   (b) $[Zn(H_2O)(NH_3)FCl]$   (c) $[Pd(CN)_2(OH)_2]^{2-}$

**23.65** For any of the following that can exist as isomers, state the type of isomerism and draw the structures:
(a) $[PtCl_2Br_2]^{2-}$   (b) $[Cr(NH_3)_5(NO_2)]^{2+}$   (c) $[Pt(NH_3)_4I_2]^{2+}$

**23.66** For any of the following that can exist as isomers, state the type of isomerism and draw the structures:
(a) $[Co(NH_3)_5Cl]Br_2$       (b) $[Pt(CH_3NH_2)_3Cl]Br$
(c) $[Fe(H_2O)_4(NH_3)_2]^{2+}$

**Problems in Context**

**23.67** Chromium(III), like cobalt(III), has a coordination number of 6 in many of its complex ions. Before Alfred Werner, in the 1890s, established the idea of a complex ion, coordination compounds had traditional formulas. Compounds are known that have the traditional formula $CrCl_3 \cdot nNH_3$, where $n = 3$ to 6. Which of the compounds has an electrical conductivity in aqueous solution similar to that of an equimolar NaCl solution?

**23.68** When $MCl_4(NH_3)_2$ is dissolved in water and treated with $AgNO_3$, 2 mol of AgCl precipitates immediately for each mole of $MCl_4(NH_3)_2$. Give the coordination number of M in the complex.

**23.69** Palladium, like its group neighbor platinum, forms four-coordinate Pd(II) and six-coordinate Pd(IV) complexes. Write formulas for the complexes with these compositions:
(a) $PdK(NH_3)Cl_3$ (b) $PdCl_2(NH_3)_2$ (c) $PdK_2Cl_6$ (d) $Pd(NH_3)_4Cl_4$

**Theoretical Basis for the Bonding and Properties of Complexes**
(Sample Problems 23.5 and 23.6)

**Concept Review Questions**

**23.70** (a) What is a coordinate covalent bond?
(b) Is it involved when $FeCl_3$ dissolves in water? Explain.
(c) Is it involved when HCl gas dissolves in water? Explain.

**23.71** According to valence bond theory, what set of orbitals is used by a Period 4 metal ion in forming (a) a square planar complex; (b) a tetrahedral complex?

**23.72** A metal ion uses $d^2sp^3$ orbitals when forming a complex. What is its coordination number and the shape of the complex?

**23.73** A complex in solution absorbs green light. What is the color of the solution?

**23.74** In terms of the theory of color absorption, explain two ways that a solution can be blue.

**23.75** (a) What is the crystal field splitting energy ($\Delta$)?
(b) How does it arise for an octahedral field of ligands?
(c) How is it different for a tetrahedral field of ligands?

**23.76** What is the distinction between a weak-field ligand and a strong-field ligand? Give an example of each.

**23.77** Is a complex with the same number of unpaired electrons as the free gaseous metal ion termed high spin or low spin?

**23.78** How do the relative magnitudes of $E_{pairing}$ and $\Delta$ affect the paramagnetism of a complex?

**23.79** Why are there both high-spin and low-spin octahedral complexes but only high-spin tetrahedral complexes?

**Skill-Building Exercises** (grouped in similar pairs)

**23.80** Give the number of $d$ electrons ($n$ of $d^n$) for the central metal ion in (a) $[TiCl_6]^{2-}$; (b) $K[AuCl_4]$; (c) $[RhCl_6]^{3-}$.

**23.81** Give the number of $d$ electrons ($n$ of $d^n$) for the central metal ion in (a) $[Cr(H_2O)_6](ClO_3)_2$; (b) $[Mn(CN)_6]^{2-}$; (c) $[Ru(NO)(en)_2Cl]Br$.

**23.82** How many $d$ electrons ($n$ of $d^n$) are in the central metal ion in (a) $Ca[IrF_6]$; (b) $[HgI_4]^{2-}$; (c) $[Co(EDTA)]^{2-}$?

**23.83** How many $d$ electrons ($n$ of $d^n$) are in the central metal ion in (a) $[Ru(NH_3)_5Cl]SO_4$; (b) $Na_2[Os(CN)_6]$; (c) $[Co(NH_3)_4CO_3I]$?

**23.84** Sketch the orientation of the orbitals relative to the ligands in an octahedral complex to explain the splitting and the relative energies of the $d_{xy}$ and the $d_{x^2 - y^2}$ orbitals.

**23.85** The two $e_g$ orbitals are identical in energy in an octahedral complex but have different energies in a square planar complex, with the $d_{z^2}$ orbital being much lower in energy than the $d_{x^2 - y^2}$. Explain with orbital sketches.

**23.86** Which of these ions *cannot* form both high- and low-spin octahedral complexes: (a) $Ti^{3+}$; (b) $Co^{2+}$; (c) $Fe^{2+}$; (d) $Cu^{2+}$?

**23.87** Which of these ions *cannot* form both high- and low-spin octahedral complexes: (a) $Mn^{3+}$; (b) $Nb^{3+}$; (c) $Ru^{3+}$; (d) $Ni^{2+}$?

**23.88** Draw orbital-energy splitting diagrams and use the spectrochemical series to show the orbital occupancy for each of the following (assuming that $H_2O$ is a weak-field ligand):
(a) $[Cr(H_2O)_6]^{3+}$       (b) $[Cu(H_2O)_4]^{2+}$       (c) $[FeF_6]^{3-}$

**23.89** Draw orbital-energy splitting diagrams and use the spectrochemical series to show the orbital occupancy for each of the following (assuming that $H_2O$ is a weak-field ligand):
(a) $[Cr(CN)_6]^{3-}$       (b) $[Rh(CO)_6]^{3+}$       (c) $[Co(OH)_6]^{4-}$

**23.90** Draw orbital-energy splitting diagrams and use the spectrochemical series to show the orbital occupancy for each of the following (assuming that $H_2O$ is a weak-field ligand):
(a) $[MoCl_6]^{3-}$       (b) $[Ni(H_2O)_6]^{2+}$       (c) $[Ni(CN)_4]^{2-}$

**23.91** Draw orbital-energy splitting diagrams and use the spectrochemical series to show the orbital occupancy for each of the following (assuming that $H_2O$ is a weak-field ligand):
(a) $[Fe(C_2O_4)_3]^{3-}$ ($C_2O_4^{2-}$ creates a weaker field than $H_2O$ does.)
(b) $[Co(CN)_6]^{4-}$       (c) $[MnCl_6]^{4-}$

**23.92** Rank the following in order of *increasing* $\Delta$ and energy of light absorbed: $[Cr(NH_3)_6]^{3+}$, $[Cr(H_2O)_6]^{3+}$, $[Cr(NO_2)_6]^{3-}$.

**23.93** Rank the following in order of *decreasing* $\Delta$ and energy of light absorbed: $[Cr(en)_3]^{3+}$, $[Cr(CN)_6]^{3-}$, $[CrCl_6]^{3-}$.

**23.94** A complex, $ML_6^{2+}$, is violet. The same metal forms a complex with another ligand, Q, that creates a weaker field. What color might $MQ_6^{2+}$ be expected to show? Explain.

**23.95** $[Cr(H_2O)_6]^{2+}$ is violet. Another $CrL_6$ complex is green. Can ligand L be $CN^-$? Can it be $Cl^-$? Explain.

**Problems in Context**

**23.96** Octahedral $[Ni(NH_3)_6]^{2+}$ is paramagnetic, whereas planar $[Pt(NH_3)_4]^{2+}$ is diamagnetic, even though both metal ions are $d^8$ species. Explain.

**23.97** The hexaaqua complex $[Ni(H_2O)_6]^{2+}$ is green, whereas the hexaammonia complex $[Ni(NH_3)_6]^{2+}$ is violet. Explain.

**23.98** Three of the complex ions that are formed by $Co^{3+}$ are $[Co(H_2O)_6]^{3+}$, $[Co(NH_3)_6]^{3+}$, and $[CoF_6]^{3-}$. These ions have the observed colors (listed in arbitrary order) yellow-orange, green, and blue. Match each complex with its color. Explain.

**Comprehensive Problems**

**23.99** When neptunium (Np) and plutonium (Pu) were discovered, the periodic table did not include the actinides, so these elements were placed in Groups 7B(7) and 8B(8). When americium (Am) and curium (Cm) were synthesized, they were placed in Groups 8B(9) and 8B(10). However, during chemical isolation procedures, Glenn Seaborg and his colleagues, who had synthesized these elements, could not find their compounds among other compounds of members of the same groups, which led Seaborg to suggest they were part of a new inner transition series.
(a) How do the electron configurations of these elements support Seaborg's suggestion?
(b) The highest fluorides of Np and Pu are hexafluorides, as is the highest fluoride of uranium. How does this chemical evidence support the placement of Np and Pu as *inner* transition elements rather than transition elements?

**23.100** How many different formulas are there for octahedral complexes with a metal M and four ligands A, B, C, and D? Give the number of isomers for each formula and describe the isomers.

**23.101** At one time, it was common to write the formula for copper(I) chloride as $Cu_2Cl_2$, instead of CuCl, analogously to $Hg_2Cl_2$ for mercury(I) chloride. Use electron configurations to explain why $Hg_2Cl_2$ and CuCl are both correct.

**23.102** For the compound $[Co(en)_2Cl_2]Cl$, give:
(a) The coordination number of the metal ion
(b) The oxidation number of the central metal ion
(c) The number of individual ions per formula unit
(d) The moles of AgCl that precipitate when 1 mol of compound is dissolved in water and treated with $AgNO_3$

**23.103** Hexafluorocobaltate(III) ion is a high-spin complex. Draw the orbital-energy splitting diagram for its $d$ orbitals.

**23.104** A salt of each of the ions in Table 23.3 (p. 951) is dissolved in water. A Pt electrode is immersed in each solution and connected to a 0.38-V battery. All of the electrolytic cells are run for the same amount of time with the same current.
(a) In which cell(s) will a metal plate out? Explain.
(b) Which cell will plate out the least mass of metal? Explain.

**23.105** Criticize and correct the following statement: strong-field ligands always give rise to low-spin complexes.

**23.106** Two major bidentate ligands used in analytical chemistry are bipyridyl (bipy) and *ortho*-phenanthroline (*o*-phen):

bipyridyl                     *o*-phenanthroline

Draw structures and discuss the possibility of isomers for
(a) $[Pt(bipy)Cl_2]$       (b) $[Fe(o\text{-}phen)_3]^{3+}$
(c) $[Co(bipy)_2F_2]^+$    (d) $[Co(o\text{-}phen)(NH_3)_3Cl]^{2+}$

**23.107** In many species, a transition metal has an unusually high or low oxidation state. Write balanced equations for the following and find the oxidation state of the transition metal in the product:
(a) Iron(III) ion reacts with hypochlorite ion in basic solution to form ferrate ion ($FeO_4^{2-}$), $Cl^-$, and water.
(b) Potassium hexacyanomanganate(II) reacts with K metal to form $K_6[Mn(CN)_6]$.
(c) Heating sodium superoxide ($NaO_2$) with $Co_3O_4$ produces $Na_4CoO_4$ and $O_2$ gas.
(d) Vanadium(III) chloride reacts with Na metal under a CO atmosphere to produce $Na[V(CO)_6]$ and NaCl.
(e) Barium peroxide reacts with nickel(II) ions in basic solution to produce $BaNiO_3$.
(f) Bubbling CO through a basic solution of cobalt(II) ion produces $[Co(CO)_4]^-$, $CO_3^{2-}$, and water.
(g) Heating cesium tetrafluorocuprate(II) with $F_2$ gas under pressure gives $Cs_2CuF_6$.
(h) Heating tantalum(V) chloride with Na metal produces NaCl and $Ta_6Cl_{15}$, in which half of the Ta is in the +2 state.
(i) Potassium tetracyanonickelate(II) reacts with hydrazine ($N_2H_4$) in basic solution to form $K_4[Ni_2(CN)_6]$ and $N_2$ gas.

**23.108** Draw a Lewis structure with lowest formal charges for $MnO_4^-$.

**23.109** The coordination compound $[Pt(NH_3)_2(SCN)_2]$ displays two types of isomerism. Name the types and give names and structures for the six possible isomers.

**23.110** An octahedral complex with three different ligands (A, B, and C) can have formulas with three different ratios of the ligands:
$[MA_4BC]^{n+}$,   such as $[Co(NH_3)_4(H_2O)Cl]^{2+}$
$[MA_3B_2C]^{n+}$,   such as $[Cr(H_2O)_3Br_2Cl]$
$[MA_2B_2C_2]^{n+}$,   such as $[Cr(NH_3)_2(H_2O)_2Br_2]^+$
For each example, give the name, state the type(s) of isomerism present, and draw all isomers.

**23.111** In $[Cr(NH_3)_6]Cl_3$, the $[Cr(NH_3)_6]^{3+}$ ion absorbs visible light in the blue-violet range, and the compound is yellow-orange. In $[Cr(H_2O)_6]Br_3$, the $[Cr(H_2O)_6]^{3+}$ ion absorbs visible light in the red range, and the compound is blue-gray. Explain these differences in light absorbed and color of the compound.

**23.112** The actinides Pa, U, and Np form a series of complex ions, such as the anion in the compound $Na_3[UF_8]$, in which the central metal ion has an unusual geometry and oxidation state. In the crystal structure, the complex ion can be pictured as resulting from interpenetration of simple cubic arrays of uranium and fluoride ions.
(a) What is the coordination number of the metal ion in the complex ion? (b) What is the oxidation state of uranium in the compound?
(c) Sketch the complex ion.

**23.113** Consider the square planar complex shown at right. Which of the structures A–F are geometric isomers of it?

**A**   **B**   **C**

**D**   **E**   **F**

**23.114** Several coordination isomers, with both Co and Cr as 3+ ions, have the molecular formula $CoCrC_6H_{18}N_{12}$. (a) Give the name and formula of the isomer in which the Co complex ion has six $NH_3$ groups. (b) Give the name and formula of the isomer in which the Co complex ion has one CN and five $NH_3$ groups.

**23.115** A shortcut to finding optical isomers is to see if the complex has a *plane of symmetry*—a plane passing through the metal atom such that every atom on one side of the plane is matched by an identical one at the same distance from the plane on the other side. Any planar complex has a plane of symmetry, since all atoms lie in one plane. Use this approach to determine whether these exist as optical isomers: (a) $[Zn(NH_3)_2Cl_2]$ (tetrahedral); (b) $[Pt(en)_2]^{2+}$; (c) *trans*-$[PtBr_4Cl_2]^{2-}$; (d) *trans*-$[Co(en)_2F_2]^+$; (e) *cis*-$[Co(en)_2F_2]^+$.

**23.116** Alfred Werner (see Problem 23.67) prepared two compounds by heating a solution of $PtCl_2$ with triethyl phosphine, $P(C_2H_5)_3$, which is a ligand for Pt. Both compounds have, by mass, Pt, 38.8%; Cl, 14.1%; C, 28.7%; P, 12.4%; and H, 6.02%. Write formulas, structures, and systematic names for the two isomers.

**23.117** Some octahedral complexes have distorted shapes. In some, two metal-ligand bonds that are 180° apart are shorter than the other four. In $[Cu(NH_3)_6]^{2+}$, for example, two Cu—N bonds are 207 pm long, and the other four are 262 pm long. (a) Calculate the longest distance between two N atoms in this complex. (b) Calculate the shortest distance between two N atoms.

**23.118** The effect of entropy on reactions appears in the stabilities of certain complexes. (a) In terms of number of product particles, predict which of the following will be favored in terms of $\Delta S^\circ_{rxn}$:

$[Cu(NH_3)_4]^{2+}(aq) + 4H_2O(l) \longrightarrow$
$[Cu(H_2O)_4]^{2+}(aq) + 4NH_3(aq)$

$[Cu(H_2NCH_2CH_2NH_2)_2]^{2+}(aq) + 4H_2O(l) \longrightarrow$
$[Cu(H_2O)_4]^{2+}(aq) + 2en(aq)$

(b) Given that the Cu—N bond strength is approximately the same in both complexes, which complex will be more stable with respect to ligand exchange in water? Explain.

**23.119** You know the following about a coordination compound:
(1) The partial empirical formula is $KM(CrO_4)Cl_2(NH_3)_4$.
(2) It has A (red) and B (blue) crystal forms.
(3) When 1.0 mol of A or B reacts with 1.0 mol of $AgNO_3$, 0.50 mol of a red precipitate forms immediately.
(4) After the reaction in (3), 1.0 mol of A reacts very slowly with 1.0 mol of silver oxalate ($Ag_2C_2O_4$) to form 2.0 mol of a white precipitate. (Oxalate can displace other ligands.)
(5) After the reaction in (3), 1.0 mol of B does not react further with 1.0 mol of $AgNO_3$.

From this information, determine the following:
(a) The coordination number of M
(b) The group(s) bonded to M ionically and covalently
(c) The stereochemistry of the red and blue forms

**23.120** The extent of crystal field splitting is often determined from spectra. (a) Given the wavelength ($\lambda$) of maximum absorption, find the crystal field splitting energy ($\Delta$), in kJ/mol, for each of the following complex ions:

| Ion | $\lambda$ (nm) | Ion | $\lambda$ (nm) |
|---|---|---|---|
| $[Cr(H_2O)_6]^{3+}$ | 562 | $[Fe(H_2O)_6]^{2+}$ | 966 |
| $[Cr(CN)_6]^{3-}$ | 381 | $[Fe(H_2O)_6]^{3+}$ | 730 |
| $[CrCl_6]^{3-}$ | 735 | $[Co(NH_3)_6]^{3+}$ | 405 |
| $[Cr(NH_3)_6]^{3+}$ | 462 | $[Rh(NH_3)_6]^{3+}$ | 295 |
| $[Ir(NH_3)_6]^{3+}$ | 244 | | |

(b) Write a spectrochemical series for the ligands in Cr complexes.
(c) Use the Fe data to state how oxidation state affects $\Delta$. (d) Use the Co, Rh, and Ir data to state how period number affects $\Delta$.

**23.121** Ionic liquids have many applications in engineering and materials science. The dissolution of the metavanadate ion in chloroaluminate ionic liquids has been studied:

$$VO_3^- + AlCl_4^- \longrightarrow VO_2Cl_2^- + AlOCl_2^-$$

(a) What is the oxidation number of V and Al in each ion?
(b) In reactions of $V_2O_5$ with HCl, acid concentration affects the product. At low acid concentration, $VO_2Cl_2^-$ and $VO_3^-$ form:

$$V_2O_5 + HCl \longrightarrow VO_2Cl_2^- + VO_3^- + H^+$$

At high acid concentration, $VOCl_3$ forms:

$$V_2O_5 + HCl \longrightarrow VOCl_3 + H_2O$$

Balance each equation, and state which, if either, is a redox process.
(c) What mass of $VO_2Cl_2^-$ or $VOCl_3$ can form from 12.5 g of $V_2O_5$ and the appropriate concentration of acid?

**23.122** The orbital occupancies for the $d$ orbitals of several complex ions are diagrammed below.

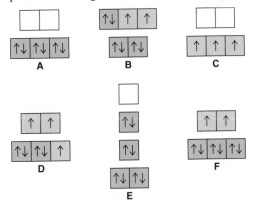

(a) Which diagram corresponds to the orbital occupancy of the cobalt ion in $[Co(CN)_6]^{3-}$?
(b) If diagram D depicts the orbital occupancy of the cobalt ion in $[CoF_6]^n$, what is the value of $n$?
(c) $[NiCl_4]^{2-}$ is paramagnetic and $[Ni(CN)_4]^{2-}$ is diamagnetic. Which diagrams correspond to the orbital occupancies of the nickel ions in these species?
(d) Diagram C shows the orbital occupancy of $V^{2+}$ in the octahedral complex $VL_6$. Can you determine whether L is a strong- or weak-field ligand? Explain.

# Nuclear Reactions and Their Applications

## Concepts and skills to review before you study this chapter

- discovery of the atomic nucleus (Section 2.4)
- protons, neutrons, mass number, and the $^A_Z X$ notation (Section 2.5)
- half-life and first-order reaction rate (Section 16.4)

You might find it hard to believe that uranium within the fuel pellets used in nuclear power reactors has any measureable behavior in common with ordinary bananas, but both exhibit **radioactivity,** the spontaneous disintegration of an unstable nucleus by emission of radiation. A very small percentage of unstable potassium atoms in a banana are the source of its tiny amount of radioactivity. In fact, as we'll discuss, many everyday materials exhibit radioactivity. For example, the trees that produce Brazil nuts have such deep root systems that the nuts have 1000 times more radium than the next most radioactive food. (Despite these facts, the levels of radioactivity in bananas and Brazil nuts are miniscule and present no health risk.)

Up to this point, we have focused on the atom's electrons, treating the nucleus as their electrostatic anchor and examining the effect of its positive charge on atomic properties and, ultimately, chemical behavior. In this chapter, we *will* focus on the atom's tiny, dense core, which is held together by the strongest force in the universe. Scientists studying the structure and behavior of the nucleus see enormous potential as well as great mystery and wonder.

But society is ambivalent about some applications of nuclear research. The promise of abundant energy and treatments for disease is offset by the threat of nuclear waste contamination, reactor accidents, and unimaginable destruction from nuclear war or terrorism. Can the power of the nucleus be harnessed for our benefit, or are the risks too great? By studying this chapter, you'll learn the principles that can help you consider this vital question knowledgably.

The changes that occur in atomic nuclei differ strikingly from chemical changes. In chemical reactions, electrons are shared or transferred to form *compounds,* while nuclei remain unchanged. In nuclear reactions, the roles are reversed: electrons take part much less often, while nuclei undergo changes that, in nearly every case, form different *elements.* Nuclear reactions are often accompanied by energy changes a million times greater than those for chemical reactions, energy changes so large that changes in mass *are* detectable. Moreover, nuclear reaction yields and rates are *not* subject to the effects of pressure, temperature, and catalysis that chemical reactions are. Table 24.1 summarizes these general differences.

### Table 24.1 Comparison of Chemical and Nuclear Reactions

| Chemical Reactions | Nuclear Reactions |
|---|---|
| 1. One substance is converted into another, but atoms never change identity. | 1. Atoms of one element typically are converted into atoms of another element. |
| 2. Electrons in orbitals are involved as bonds break and form; nuclear particles do not take part. | 2. Protons, neutrons, and other nuclear particles are involved; electrons in orbitals take part much less often. |
| 3. Reactions are accompanied by relatively small changes in energy and no measurable changes in mass. | 3. Reactions are accompanied by relatively large changes in energy and measurable changes in mass. |
| 4. Reaction rates are influenced by temperature, concentration, catalysts, and the compound in which an element occurs. | 4. Reaction rates depend on number of nuclei, but are not affected by temperature, catalysts, or, except on rare occasions, the compound in which an element occurs. |

**IN THIS CHAPTER ...** We survey the field of nuclear chemistry, examining radioactive nuclei and their decay processes, especially the effects and applications of radioactivity and the interconversion of matter and energy.

- We investigate nuclear stability to determine why some nuclei are stable and others are not and undergo radioactive decay.
- We learn how radioactivity is detected and how the kinetics of decay is applied.
- We see how nuclei synthesized in particle accelerators have extended the periodic table.
- We consider the effects of radioactive emissions on matter, especially living tissue, and focus on some major uses of radioisotopes in science, technology, and medicine.
- We discuss the mass difference that arises when a nucleus forms from its subatomic particles and the energy that is equivalent to this difference.
- We explore current and future attempts to harness the energy released when heavy nuclei split and lighter ones fuse.
- Finally, we look at the nuclear processes in stars that continue to create chemical elements.

## 24.1 • RADIOACTIVE DECAY AND NUCLEAR STABILITY

A stable nucleus remains intact indefinitely, but *the great majority of nuclei are unstable.* An unstable nucleus exhibits radioactivity, spontaneously decaying by emitting radiation. In Section 24.2, you'll see that each type of unstable nucleus has its own characteristic *rate* of radioactive decay. In this section, we cover important terms and notation for nuclei, discuss some key events in the discovery of radioactivity, define the types of emission, and describe various modes of radioactive decay and how to predict which occurs for a given nucleus.

### The Components of the Nucleus: Terms and Notation

Recall from Chapter 2 that the nucleus contains essentially all the atom's mass but is only about $10^{-5}$ times its radius (or $10^{-15}$ times its volume), making the nucleus incredibly dense: about $10^{14}$ g/mL. ● *Protons* and *neutrons,* the elementary particles that make up the nucleus, are called **nucleons.** A **nuclide** is a nucleus with a particular composition, that is, with specific numbers of the two types of nucleons. Most elements occur in nature as a mixture of **isotopes,** atoms with the characteristic number of protons of the element but different numbers of neutrons. Each isotope of an element thus has a different nuclide. For example, oxygen has three naturally occurring isotopes—the most abundant contains eight protons and eight neutrons, whereas the least abundant contains eight protons and nine neutrons.

The relative mass and charge of a particle—nucleon, elementary particle, or nuclide—is described by the notation $^{A}_{Z}X$, where X is the *symbol* for the particle, $A$ is the *mass number,* or the total number of nucleons, and $Z$ is the *charge* of the particle; for nuclei, $A$ is the *sum of protons and neutrons* and $Z$ is the *number of protons* (atomic number). In this notation, the three subatomic elementary particles are

$$^{0}_{-1}e \text{ (electron), } ^{1}_{1}p \text{ (proton), and } ^{1}_{0}n \text{ (neutron)}$$

(A proton is also sometimes represented as $^{1}_{1}H^{+}$.) The number of neutrons ($N$) in a nucleus is the mass number ($A$) minus the atomic number ($Z$): $N = A - Z$. The two naturally occurring stable isotopes of chlorine, for example, have 17 protons ($Z = 17$), but one has 18 neutrons ($^{35}_{17}Cl$, also written $^{35}Cl$) and the other has 20 ($^{37}_{17}Cl$, or $^{37}Cl$). Nuclides can also be designated with the element name followed by the mass number, for example, chlorine-35 and chlorine-37. In naturally occurring samples of an element or its compounds, *the isotopes of the element are present in specific proportions* that vary only very slightly. Thus, in a sample of sodium chloride (or any Cl-containing substance), 75.77% of the Cl atoms are chlorine-35 and the remaining 24.23% are chlorine-37.

● **Big Atom, Massive Core** If you could strip the electrons from the atoms in an object and compress the nuclei together, the object would lose only a fraction of a percent of its mass, but it would shrink to 0.0000000000001% ($10^{-13}$%) of its volume!

To understand this chapter, it's very important that you are comfortable with nuclear notations, so please take a moment to review Sample Problem 2.4 (pp. 49–50) and Problems 2.39 to 2.46 (p. 76).

## The Discovery of Radioactivity and the Types of Emissions

In 1896, the French physicist Antoine-Henri Becquerel accidentally discovered that uranium minerals, even when wrapped in paper and stored in the dark, emit a penetrating radiation that can expose a photographic plate. Becquerel also found that the radiation creates an electric discharge in air, thus providing a means for measuring its intensity.

Two years later, a young doctoral student named Marie Sklodowska Curie began a search for other minerals that behaved in this way. She found that thorium minerals also emit radiation and, most importantly, that *the intensity of the radiation is directly proportional to the concentration of the element in the mineral, not to the formula of the mineral or compound.* Curie named the emissions *radioactivity* and showed that they are *unaffected by temperature, pressure, or other physical and chemical conditions.*

After months of painstaking chemical work, Curie and her husband, physicist Pierre Curie, isolated two new elements from pitchblende, the principal ore of uranium: polonium (Po; $Z = 84$), the most metallic member of Group 6A(16), and radium (Ra; $Z = 88$), the heaviest alkaline earth metal.

Then, starting with several tons of pitchblende residues from which the uranium had been extracted and working arduously for four years, Curie isolated 0.1 g of radium chloride, which she melted and electrolyzed to obtain pure metallic radium. Curie is the only person to have received two Nobel Prizes in science, one in physics for her research into radioactivity, and the other in chemistry for her discoveries of polonium and radium.

During the next few years, Henri Becquerel, the Curies, and P. Villard in France and Ernest Rutherford and his coworkers in England studied the nature of radioactive emissions. A key finding was the observation of Rutherford and his colleague Frederick Soddy that elements other than radium were formed when radium decayed. In 1902, they proposed that radioactive emission results in the change of one element into another. This explanation seemed like a return to alchemy and was met with disbelief and ridicule. We now know it to be true: *when a nuclide of one element decays, it emits radiation and usually changes into a nuclide of a different element.*

There are three natural types of radioactive emission:

- **Alpha particles** (symbolized α, $_2^4$α, or $_2^4$He$^{2+}$) are identical to helium-4 nuclei.
- **Beta particles** (symbolized β, β$^-$, or sometimes $_{-1}^{0}$β) are high-speed electrons. (The emission of electrons from the nucleus may seem strange, but as you'll see shortly, they result from a nuclear reaction.)
- **Gamma rays** (symbolized γ, or sometimes $_0^0$γ) are very high-energy photons.

Figure 24.1 illustrates the behavior of these emissions in an electric field: the positively charged α particles curve to a small extent toward the negative plate, the negatively charged β particles curve to a greater extent toward the positive plate (because they have lower mass), and the uncharged γ rays are not affected by the electric field.

**Figure 24.1** How the three types of radioactive emissions behave in an electric field.

## Modes of Radioactive Decay; Balancing Nuclear Equations

*When a nuclide decays, it forms a nuclide of lower energy, and the excess energy is carried off by the emitted radiation and the recoiling nucleus.* The decaying, or reactant, nuclide is called the *parent;* the product nuclide is called the *daughter.* Nuclides can decay in several ways. As each of the major modes of decay is introduced (summarized in Table 24.2 on the next page), we'll show examples of that mode and apply the key principle used to balance nuclear reactions: *the total Z (charge, number of protons) and the total A (sum of protons and neutrons) of the reactants equal those of the products:*

$$\text{Total } _Z^A \text{ Reactants} = \text{Total } _Z^A \text{ Products} \qquad (24.1)$$

**Table 24.2 Modes of Radioactive Decay***

| Mode | Emission | Decay Process | Change in A | Z | N |
|---|---|---|---|---|---|
| α Decay | $\alpha(^4_2\text{He}^{2+})$ | α expelled | −4 | −2 | −2 |
| β⁻ Decay† | $\beta^-(^{\,0}_{-1}\beta)$ | nucleus with $x\text{p}^+$ and $y\text{n}^0$ → nucleus with $(x+1)\text{p}^+$ and $(y-1)\text{n}^0$ + $^{\,0}_{-1}\beta$ β⁻ expelled | 0 | +1 | −1 |
| | Net: | $^1_0\text{n}$ in nucleus → $^1_1\text{p}$ in nucleus + $^{\,0}_{-1}\beta$ β⁻ expelled | | | |
| Positron (β⁺) emission† | $\beta^+(^{\,0}_{1}\beta)$ | nucleus with $x\text{p}^+$ and $y\text{n}^0$ → nucleus with $(x-1)\text{p}^+$ and $(y+1)\text{n}^0$ + $^{\,0}_{1}\beta$ β⁺ expelled | 0 | −1 | +1 |
| | Net: | $^1_1\text{p}$ in nucleus → $^1_0\text{n}$ in nucleus + $^{\,0}_{1}\beta$ β⁺ expelled | | | |
| Electron (e⁻) capture (EC)† | x-ray | low-energy orbital; nucleus with $x\text{p}^+$ and $y\text{n}^0$ → nucleus with $(x-1)\text{p}^+$ and $(y+1)\text{n}^0$ | 0 | −1 | +1 |
| | Net: | $^{\,0}_{-1}\text{e}$ absorbed from low-energy orbital + $^1_1\text{p}$ in nucleus → $^1_0\text{n}$ in nucleus | | | |
| Gamma (γ) emission | γ | excited nucleus → stable nucleus + γ γ photon radiated | 0 | 0 | 0 |

*Nuclear chemists consider β⁻ decay, positron emission, and electron capture to be three decay modes of the more general process known as beta decay (see text).

†Neutrinos ($\nu$) or antineutrinos ($\bar{\nu}$) are also formed during the three modes of beta decay. Although we will not include them in other equations in the chapter, keep in mind that antineutrinos are always expelled during β⁻ decay, and neutrinos are expelled during β⁺ emission and e⁻ capture.

1. **Alpha (α) decay** involves the loss of an α particle from a nucleus. For each α particle emitted by the parent, *A decreases by 4 and Z decreases by 2* in the daughter. Every element beyond bismuth (Bi; $Z = 83$) is radioactive and exhibits α decay, which is *the most common means for a heavy, unstable nucleus to become more stable*. For example, radium undergoes α decay to yield radon (Rn; $Z = 86$):

$$^{226}_{88}\text{Ra} \longrightarrow {}^{222}_{86}\text{Rn} + {}^{4}_{2}\alpha$$

Note that the *A* value for Ra equals the sum of the *A* values for Rn and α ($226 = 222 + 4$), and that the *Z* value for Ra equals the sum of the *Z* values for Rn and α ($88 = 86 + 2$).

2. **Beta (β) decay** is a more general class of radioactive decay that includes three modes: β⁻ decay, β⁺ emission, and electron capture.

- **β⁻ decay** (or *negatron emission*) occurs through the ejection of a β⁻ particle from the nucleus. This change does not involve expulsion of a β⁻ particle that was in the nucleus; rather, *a neutron is converted into a proton, which remains in the nucleus, and a β⁻ particle, which is expelled immediately:*

$$^{1}_{0}\text{n} \longrightarrow {}^{1}_{1}\text{p} + {}^{0}_{-1}\beta$$

As always, the totals of the *A* and the *Z* values for reactant and products are equal. Radioactive nickel-63 becomes stable copper-63 through β⁻ decay:

$$^{63}_{28}\text{Ni} \longrightarrow {}^{63}_{29}\text{Cu} + {}^{0}_{-1}\beta$$

Another example is the β⁻ decay of carbon-14, used in radiocarbon dating:

$$^{14}_{6}\text{C} \longrightarrow {}^{14}_{7}\text{N} + {}^{0}_{-1}\beta$$

Note that *β⁻ decay results in a product nuclide with the same A but with Z one higher (one more proton) than in the reactant nuclide.* In other words, an atom of the element with the next *higher* atomic number is formed. Although equations in this chapter do not include it, a neutral particle called an antineutrino ($\overline{\nu}$) is also emitted during β⁻ decay. The mass of the antineutrino is thought to be much less than $10^{-4}$ times that of an electron.

- **Positron (β⁺) emission** is the emission of a β⁺ particle from the nucleus. A key idea of modern physics is that most fundamental particles have corresponding *antiparticles* with the same mass but opposite charge. The **positron** is the antiparticle of the electron. Positron emission occurs through a process in which *a proton in the nucleus is converted into a neutron, and a positron is expelled:*

$$^{1}_{1}p \longrightarrow {}^{1}_{0}n + {}^{0}_{1}\beta$$

Also emitted during this process is a *neutrino* ($\nu$), the antiparticle of the antineutrino. In terms of the effect on *A* and *Z, positron emission has the opposite effect of β⁻ decay: the daughter has the same A but Z is one lower (one fewer proton) than the parent.* Thus, an atom of the element with the next *lower* atomic number forms. Carbon-11, a synthetic radioisotope, decays to a stable boron isotope through β⁺ emission:

$$^{11}_{6}\text{C} \longrightarrow {}^{11}_{5}\text{B} + {}^{0}_{1}\beta$$

- **Electron (e⁻) capture (EC)** occurs when the nucleus interacts with an electron in a low atomic energy level. The net effect is that *a proton is transformed into a neutron:*

$$^{1}_{1}\text{p} + {}^{0}_{-1}\text{e} \longrightarrow {}^{1}_{0}\text{n}$$

(We use the symbol "e" to distinguish an orbital electron from a beta particle, β.) The orbital vacancy is quickly filled by an electron that moves down from a higher energy level, and that process continues through still higher energy levels, with x-ray photons and neutrinos carrying off the energy difference in each step. Radioactive iron forms stable manganese through electron capture:

$$^{55}_{26}\text{Fe} + {}^{0}_{-1}\text{e} \longrightarrow {}^{55}_{25}\text{Mn} + h\nu \quad \text{(x-rays and neutrinos)}$$

Even though the processes are different, *electron capture has the same net effect as positron emission: Z lower by 1, A unchanged.*

3. **Gamma (γ) emission** involves the radiation of high-energy γ photons (also called γ rays) from an excited nucleus. Just as an atom in an excited *electronic*

state reduces its energy by emitting photons, usually in the UV and visible ranges (see Section 7.2), a nucleus in an excited state lowers its energy by emitting γ photons, which are of much higher energy (much shorter wavelength) than UV photons. Many nuclear processes leave the nucleus in an excited state, so γ *emission accompanies many other (mostly β) types of decay.* Several γ photons of different energies can be emitted from an excited nucleus as it returns to the ground state. Some of Marie Curie's experiments involved the release of γ rays, such as

$$^{215}_{84}\text{Po} \longrightarrow ^{211}_{82}\text{Pb} + ^4_2\alpha \text{ (several } \gamma \text{ emitted)}$$

Gamma emission often accompanies β⁻ decay:

$$^{99}_{43}\text{Tc} \longrightarrow ^{99}_{44}\text{Ru} + ^0_{-1}\beta \text{ (several } \gamma \text{ emitted)}$$

Because γ rays have no mass or charge, γ *emission does not change A or Z.* Two gamma rays are emitted when a particle and an antiparticle annihilate each other. In the medical technique known as *positron-emission tomography* (which we discuss in Section 24.5), a positron and an electron annihilate each other (with all *A* and *Z* values shown):

$$^0_1\beta + ^0_{-1}e \longrightarrow 2^0_0\gamma$$

---

**Sample Problem 24.1**   **Writing Equations for Nuclear Reactions**

**Problem** Write balanced equations for the following nuclear reactions:
**(a)** Naturally occurring thorium-232 undergoes α decay.
**(b)** Zirconium-86 undergoes electron capture.

**Plan** We first write a skeleton equation that includes the mass numbers, atomic numbers, and symbols of all the particles on the correct sides of the equation, showing the unknown product particle as $^A_Z\text{X}$. Then, because the total of mass numbers and the total of charges on the left side and the right side must be equal, we solve for *A* and *Z*, and use *Z* to determine X from the periodic table.

**Solution (a)** Writing the skeleton equation, with the α particle as a product:

$$^{232}_{90}\text{Th} \longrightarrow ^A_Z\text{X} + ^4_2\alpha$$

Solving for *A* and *Z* and balancing the equation: For *A*, 232 = *A* + 4, so *A* = 228. For *Z*, 90 = *Z* + 2, so *Z* = 88. From the periodic table, we see that the element with *Z* = 88 is radium (Ra). Thus, the balanced equation is

$$^{232}_{90}\text{Th} \longrightarrow ^{228}_{88}\text{Ra} + ^4_2\alpha$$

**(b)** Writing the skeleton equation, with the captured electron as a reactant:

$$^{86}_{40}\text{Zr} + ^0_{-1}e \longrightarrow ^A_Z\text{X}$$

Solving for *A* and *Z* and balancing the equation: For *A*, 86 + 0 = *A*, so *A* = 86. For *Z*, 40 + (−1) = *Z*, so *Z* = 39. The element with *Z* = 39 is yttrium (Y), so we have

$$^{86}_{40}\text{Zr} + ^0_{-1}e \longrightarrow ^{86}_{39}\text{Y}$$

**Check** Always read across superscripts and then across subscripts, with the yield arrow as an equal sign, to check your arithmetic. In part (a), for example, 232 = 228 + 4, and 90 = 88 + 2.

**Follow-Up Problem 24.1** Write a balanced equation for the reaction in which a nuclide undergoes β⁻ decay and changes to cesium-133.

---

## Nuclear Stability and the Mode of Decay

Can we predict how, and whether, an unstable nuclide will decay? Our knowledge of the nucleus is much less complete than that of the whole atom, but some patterns emerge by observing naturally occurring nuclides.

### The Band of Stability   Two key factors determine the stability of a nuclide:

1. The number of neutrons (*N*), the number of protons (*Z*), and their ratio (*N/Z*), which we calculate from *(A − Z)/Z*. This factor relates primarily to nuclides that undergo one of the three modes of β decay.

2. The total mass of the nuclide, which mostly relates to nuclides that undergo α decay.

Figure 24.2A is a plot of number of neutrons vs. number of protons for all stable nuclides. Note the following:

- The points form a narrow **band of stability** that gradually curves above the line for $N = Z$ ($N/Z = 1$).
- The only stable nuclides with $N/Z < 1$ are $^1_1H$ and $^3_2He$.
- Many lighter nuclides with $N = Z$ are stable, such as $^4_2He$, $^{12}_6C$, $^{16}_8O$, and $^{20}_{10}Ne$; the heaviest of these is $^{40}_{20}Ca$. Thus, for lighter nuclides, one neutron for each proton ($N = Z$) is enough to provide stability.
- The $N/Z$ ratio of stable nuclides gradually increases as $Z$ increases. For example, for $^{56}_{26}Fe$, $N/Z = 1.15$; for $^{107}_{47}Ag$, $N/Z = 1.28$; for $^{184}_{74}W$, $N/Z = 1.49$, and, finally, for $^{209}_{83}Bi$, $N/Z = 1.52$. Thus, for heavier stable nuclides, $N > Z$ ($N/Z > 1$), and $N$ increases faster than $Z$. As we discuss below, and show in Figure 24.2B, if $N/Z$ of a nuclide is either too high (above the band) or not high enough (below the band), the nuclide is unstable and undergoes one of the three modes of beta decay.
- All nuclides with $Z > 83$ are unstable.* This means that all nuclides with a higher $Z$—the largest members of main groups 1A(1) through 8A(18), actinium and the actinides ($Z = 89$–103), and the other elements of the fourth (6d) transition series ($Z = 104$–112)—are radioactive, and, as we point out below, undergo α decay.

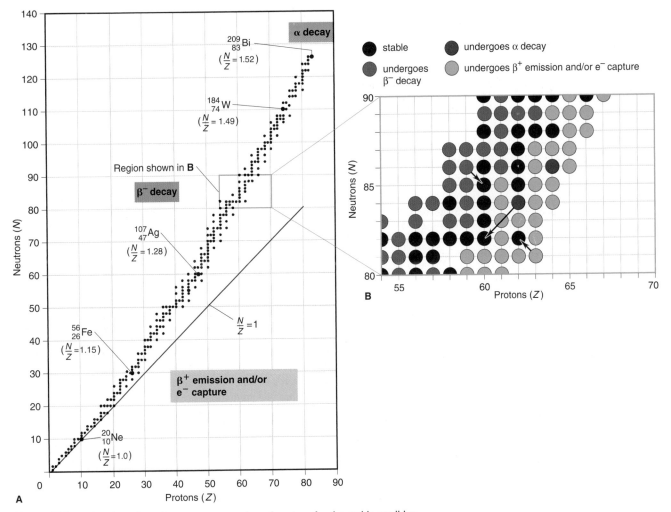

**Figure 24.2** A plot of number of neutrons vs. number of protons for the stable nuclides.

**Table 24.3 Number of Stable Nuclides for Elements 48 to 54***

| Element | Atomic No. (Z) | No. of Nuclides |
|---------|---------------|-----------------|
| Cd | 48 | 8 |
| In | 49 | 2 |
| Sn | 50 | 10 |
| Sb | 51 | 2 |
| Te | 52 | 8 |
| I | 53 | 1 |
| Xe | 54 | 9 |

*Even Z shown in boldface.

**Table 24.4 An Even-Odd Breakdown of the Stable Nuclides**

| Z | N | No. of Nuclides |
|------|------|-----------------|
| Even | Even | 157 |
| Even | Odd | 53 |
| Odd | Even | 50 |
| Odd | Odd | 4 |
| | TOTAL | 264 |

**Stability and Nuclear Structure** Given that protons are positively charged and neutrons are uncharged, the first question to ask is what holds the nucleus together? Nuclear scientists answer this question and explain the importance of $N$ and $Z$ values in terms of two opposing forces: Electrostatic repulsive forces between protons would break the nucleus apart if not for an attractive force called the **strong force,** which exists between all nucleons (protons and neutrons). This force is 137 times stronger than the repulsive force but *operates only over the short distances within the nucleus.* Thus, the *attractive* strong force overwhelms the much weaker *repulsive* electrostatic force and keeps the nucleus together.

The oddness or evenness of $N$ and $Z$ values is related to some important patterns of nuclear stability. Two interesting points become apparent when we classify the known stable nuclides:

1. Elements with an even $Z$ (number of protons) usually have a larger number of stable nuclides than elements with an odd $Z$. Table 24.3 demonstrates this point for cadmium ($Z = 48$) through xenon ($Z = 54$).
2. Well over half the stable nuclides have *both* even $N$ and even $Z$ (Table 24.4). Only four nuclides with odd $N$ and odd $Z$ are stable: $^2_1H$, $^6_3Li$, $^{10}_5B$, and $^{14}_7N$.

One model of nuclear structure that attempts to explain the stability of even values of $N$ and $Z$ postulates that protons and neutrons lie in *nucleon energy levels,* and that greater stability results from the *pairing of spins* of like nucleons. (Note the analogy to electron energy levels and the stability from pairing of electron spins.)

Just as noble gases—with 2, 10, 18, 36, 54, and 86 electrons—are exceptionally stable because they have filled *electron* levels, nuclides with $N$ or $Z$ values of 2, 8, 20, 28, 50, 82 (and $N = 126$) are exceptionally stable. These so-called *magic numbers* are thought to correspond to the numbers of protons or neutrons in filled *nucleon* levels. A few examples are $^{50}_{22}Ti$ ($N = 28$), $^{88}_{38}Sr$ ($N = 50$), and the ten stable nuclides of tin ($Z = 50$). Some extremely stable nuclides have two magic numbers: $^4_2He$, $^{16}_8O$, $^{40}_{20}Ca$, and $^{208}_{82}Pb$ ($N = 126$).

---

**Sample Problem 24.2 Predicting Nuclear Stability**

**Problem** Which of the following nuclides would you predict to be stable and which radioactive: **(a)** $^{18}_{10}Ne$; **(b)** $^{32}_{16}S$; **(c)** $^{236}_{90}Th$; **(d)** $^{123}_{56}Ba$? Explain.

**Plan** In order to evaluate the stability of each nuclide, we determine the $N$ and $Z$ values, the $N/Z$ ratio from $(A - Z)/Z$, the value of $Z$, stable $N/Z$ ratios (from Figure 24.2A), and whether $Z$ and $N$ are even or odd.

**Solution (a)** Radioactive. This nuclide has $N = 8$ ($18 - 10$) and $Z = 10$, so $N/Z = \dfrac{18 - 10}{10} = 0.8$. Except for hydrogen-1 and helium-3, no nuclides with $N < Z$ are stable; despite its even $N$ and $Z$, this nuclide has too few neutrons to be stable.

**(b)** Stable. This nuclide has $N = Z = 16$, so $N/Z = 1.0$. With $Z < 20$ and even $N$ and $Z$, this nuclide is most likely stable.

**(c)** Radioactive. This nuclide has $Z = 90$, and every nuclide with $Z > 83$ is radioactive.

**(d)** Radioactive. This nuclide has $N = 67$ and $Z = 56$, so $N/Z = 1.20$. For $Z$ values of 55 to 60, Figure 24.2A shows $N/Z \geq 1.3$, so this nuclide has too few neutrons to be stable.

**Check** By consulting a table of isotopes, such as the one in the *CRC Handbook of Chemistry and Physics,* we find that our predictions are correct.

**Follow-Up Problem 24.2** Why is $^{31}_{15}P$ stable but $^{30}_{15}P$ unstable?

---

*In 2003, French nuclear physicists discovered that $^{209}_{83}Bi$ actually undergoes $\alpha$ decay, but the half-life is $1.9 \times 10^{19}$ yr, about a billion times longer than the estimated age of the universe. Bismuth ($Z = 83$) can thus be considered stable.

**Predicting the Mode of Decay** An unstable nuclide generally decays in a mode that shifts its $N/Z$ ratio toward the band of stability. This fact is illustrated in Figure 24.2B, which expands the small region of $Z = 54$ to 70 in Figure 24.2A to show the stable *and* many of the unstable nuclides in that region, as well as their modes of decay. Note the following points:

1. *Neutron-rich nuclides.* Nuclides with too many neutrons for stability (a high $N/Z$) lie above the band of stability. They undergo $\beta^-$ *decay,* which converts a neutron into a proton, thus reducing the value of $N/Z$.
2. *Proton-rich nuclides.* Nuclides with too many protons for stability (a low $N/Z$) lie below the band. They undergo $\beta^+$ *emission* and/or $e^-$ *capture,* both of which convert a proton into a neutron, thus increasing the value of $N/Z$. (The rate of $e^-$ capture increases with $Z$, so $\beta^+$ emission is more common among lighter elements and $e^-$ capture more common among heavier elements.)
3. *Heavy nuclides.* Nuclides with $Z > 83$ (shown in Figure 24.2A) are too heavy to be stable and undergo $\alpha$ *decay,* which reduces their $Z$ and $N$ values by two units per emission.

   With the information in Figure 24.2, predicting the mode of decay of an unstable nuclide means just comparing its $N/Z$ ratio with those in the nearby region of the band of stability. But, even without Figure 24.2, we can often make an educated guess about mode of decay. The atomic mass of an element is the weighted average of its naturally occurring isotopes. Therefore,

- The mass number $A$ of a *stable* nuclide will be relatively close to the atomic mass.
- If an *unstable* nuclide of an element (given $Z$) has an $A$ value much higher than the atomic mass, it is neutron rich and will probably decay by $\beta^-$ emission.
- If, on the other hand, the unstable nuclide has an $A$ value much lower than the atomic mass, it is proton rich and will probably decay by $\beta^+$ emission and/or $e^-$ capture.

   In the next sample problem, we predict the mode of decay of some unstable nuclides.

---

**Sample Problem 24.3** | **Predicting the Mode of Nuclear Decay**

**Problem** Use the atomic mass of the element to predict the mode(s) of decay of the following radioactive nuclides: (a) $^{12}_{5}B$; (b) $^{234}_{92}U$; (c) $^{81}_{33}As$; (d) $^{127}_{57}La$.

**Plan** If the nuclide is too heavy to be stable ($Z > 83$), it undergoes $\alpha$ decay. For other cases, we use the $Z$ value to obtain its atomic mass from the periodic table. If the mass number of the nuclide is higher than the atomic mass, the nuclide has too many neutrons: $N$ too high $\Rightarrow \beta^-$ decay. If the mass number is lower than the atomic mass, the nuclide has too many protons: $Z$ too high $\Rightarrow \beta^+$ emission and/or $e^-$ capture.

**Solution** (a) This nuclide has $Z = 5$, which is boron (B), and the atomic mass is 10.81. The nuclide's $A$ value of 12 is significantly higher than its atomic mass, so this nuclide is neutron rich. It will probably undergo $\beta^-$ decay.
(b) This nuclide has $Z = 92$, so it will undergo $\alpha$ decay and decrease its total mass.
(c) This nuclide has $Z = 33$, which is arsenic (As), and the atomic mass is 74.92. The $A$ value of 81 is much higher, so this nuclide is neutron rich and will probably undergo $\beta^-$ decay.
(d) This nuclide has $Z = 57$, which is lanthanum (La), and the atomic mass is 138.9. The $A$ value of 127 is much lower, so this nuclide is proton rich and will probably undergo $\beta^+$ emission and/or $e^-$ capture.

**Check** To confirm our predictions in (a), (c), and (d), let's compare each nuclide's $N/Z$ ratio to those in the band of stability. (a) This nuclide has $N = 7$ and $Z = 5$, so $N/Z = 1.40$, which is too high for this region of the band, so it will undergo $\beta^-$ decay. (c) This nuclide has $N = 48$ and $Z = 33$, so $N/Z = 1.45$, which is too high for this region of the band, so it undergoes $\beta^-$ decay. (d) This nuclide has $N = 70$ and $Z = 57$, so $N/Z = 1.23$, which is too low for this region of the band, so it undergoes $\beta^+$ emission and/or $e^-$ capture. Our predictions based on $N/Z$ *values* were the same as those based on atomic mass.

**Comment** Both possible modes of decay are observed for the nuclide in part (d).

**Follow-Up Problem 24.3** Use the $A$ value for the nuclide and the atomic mass in the periodic table to predict the mode of decay of **(a)** $^{61}_{26}Fe$; **(b)** $^{241}_{95}Am$.

**Figure 24.3** The $^{238}U$ decay series.

**Decay Series** A parent nuclide may undergo a series of decay steps before a stable daughter nuclide forms. The succession of steps is called a **decay series,** or **disintegration series,** and is typically depicted on a gridlike display. Figure 24.3 shows the decay series from uranium-238 to lead-206. Numbers of neutrons ($N$) are plotted against numbers of protons ($Z$) to form the grid, which displays a series of $\alpha$ and $\beta^-$ decays. The typical zigzag pattern arises because $N > Z$, which means that $\alpha$ decay, which reduces both $N$ and $Z$ by two units, decreases $Z$ slightly more than it does $N$. Therefore, $\alpha$ decays result in neutron-rich daughters, which undergo $\beta^-$ decay to gain more stability. Note that a given nuclide can undergo both modes of decay. (Gamma emission accompanies many of these steps but does not affect the type of nuclide.)

The series in Figure 24.3 is one of three that occur in nature. All end with isotopes of lead whose nuclides all have one ($Z = 82$) or two ($N = 126$, $Z = 82$) magic numbers. A second series begins with uranium-235 and ends with lead-207, and a third begins with thorium-232 and ends with lead-208. (Neptunium-237 began a fourth series, but its half-life is so much less than the age of Earth that only traces of it remain today.)

## Summary of Section 24.1

- To become more stable, a radioactive nuclide may emit $\alpha$ particles ($^4_2He^{2+}$; helium-4 nuclei), $\beta$ particles ($\beta^-$ or $^0_{-1}\beta$; high-speed electrons), positrons ($\beta^+$ or $^0_1\beta$), or $\gamma$ rays (high-energy photons) or may capture an orbital electron ($^0_{-1}e$).
- A narrow band of neutron-to-proton ratios ($N/Z$) includes those of all the stable nuclides.
- Even values of $N$ and $Z$ are associated with stable nuclides, as are certain "magic numbers" of neutrons and protons.
- By comparing a nuclide's mass number with the atomic mass and its $N/Z$ ratio with those in the band of stability, we can predict that, in general, neutron-rich nuclides undergo $\beta^-$ decay and proton-rich nuclides undergo $\beta^+$ emission and/or $e^-$ capture. Heavy nuclides ($Z > 83$) undergo $\alpha$ decay.
- Three naturally occurring decay series all end in isotopes of lead.

# 24.2 • THE KINETICS OF RADIOACTIVE DECAY

Both chemical and nuclear systems tend toward maximum stability. Just as the concentrations in a chemical system change in a predictable direction to give a stable equilibrium ratio, the type and number of nucleons in an unstable nucleus change in a predictable direction to give a stable $N/Z$ ratio. As you know, however, the tendency of a chemical system to become more stable tells nothing about how long that process will take, and the same holds true for nuclear systems. In this section, we first see how radioactivity is detected and measured and then examine the kinetics of nuclear change; later, we'll examine the energetics of nuclear change.

## Detection and Measurement of Radioactivity

Radioactive emissions interact with surrounding atoms. To determine the rate of nuclear decay, we measure radioactivity by observing the effects of these interactions over time. Because these effects can be electrically amplified billions of times, it is

**Figure 24.4** Detection of radioactivity by an ionization counter.

possible to detect the decay of a single nucleus. Ionization counters and scintillation counters are two devices used to measure radioactive emissions.

**Ionization Counters** An *ionization counter* detects radioactive emissions as they ionize a gas. Ionization produces free electrons and gaseous cations, which are attracted to electrodes that conduct a current to a recording device. The most common type of ionization counter is a **Geiger-Müller counter** (Figure 24.4). It consists of a tube filled with an argon-methane mixture; the tube housing acts as the cathode, and a thin wire in the center of the tube acts as the anode. Emissions from the sample enter the tube through a thin window and strike argon atoms, producing $Ar^+$ ions that migrate toward the cathode and free electrons that are accelerated toward the anode. These electrons collide with other argon atoms and free more electrons in an *avalanche effect*. The current created is amplified and appears as a meter reading and/or an audible click. An initial release of 1 electron can release $10^{10}$ electrons in a microsecond, giving the Geiger-Müller counter great sensitivity.

**Scintillation Counters** In a **scintillation counter,** radioactive emissions are detected by their ability to excite atoms and cause them to emit light. The light-emitting substance in the counter, called a *phosphor,* is coated onto part of a *photomultiplier tube,* a device that increases the original electrical signal. Incoming radioactive particles strike the phosphor, which emits photons. Each photon, in turn, strikes a cathode, releasing an electron through the photoelectric effect (Section 7.1). This electron hits other portions of the tube that release increasing numbers of electrons, and the resulting current is recorded. Liquid scintillation counters employ an organic mixture that contains a phosphor and a solvent (Figure 24.5). This "cocktail" dissolves the radioactive sample *and* emits pulses of light when excited by the emission. The number of pulses is proportional to the concentration of the radioactive substance. These counters are often used to measure $\beta^-$ emissions from dissolved biological samples, particularly those containing compounds of $^3H$ and $^{14}C$.

**Figure 24.5** A scintillation "cocktail" in tubes to be placed in the counter.

## The Rate of Radioactive Decay

*Radioactive nuclei decay at a characteristic rate,* regardless of the chemical substance in which they occur. The *decay rate,* or **activity ($\mathscr{A}$),** of a radioactive sample is the change in number of nuclei ($\mathscr{N}$) divided by the change in time ($t$). As with chemical reaction rates (Section 16.2), because the number of nuclei is *decreasing,* a minus sign precedes the expression to obtain a positive decay rate:

$$\text{Decay rate } (\mathscr{A}) = -\frac{\Delta \mathscr{N}}{\Delta t}$$

The SI unit of radioactivity is the **becquerel (Bq),** defined as one disintegration per second (d/s): 1 Bq = 1 d/s. A much larger and more common unit of radioactivity is the **curie (Ci),** which was originally defined as the number of disintegrations per second in 1 g of radium-226, but is now a fixed quantity:

$$1 \text{ Ci} = 3.70 \times 10^{10} \text{ d/s} \tag{24.2}$$

Because the curie is so large, the millicurie (mCi) and microcurie ($\mu$Ci) are commonly seen. The radioactivity of a sample is often given as a *specific activity,* the decay rate per gram.

An activity is meaningful only when we consider the large number of nuclei in a macroscopic sample. Suppose there are $1 \times 10^{15}$ radioactive nuclei of a particular type in a sample and they decay at a rate of 10% per hour. Although any particular nucleus in the sample might decay in a microsecond or in a million hours, the *average* of all decays results in 10% of the entire collection of nuclei disintegrating each hour. During the first hour, 10% of the *original* number, or $1 \times 10^{14}$ nuclei, will decay. During the next hour, 10% of the remaining $9 \times 10^{14}$ nuclei, or $9 \times 10^{13}$ nuclei, will decay. During the next hour, 10% of those remaining will decay, and so forth. Thus, for a large collection of radioactive nuclei, *the number decaying per unit time is proportional to the number present:*

$$\text{Decay rate } (\mathscr{A}) \propto \mathscr{N} \qquad \text{or} \qquad \mathscr{A} = k\mathscr{N}$$

where $k$ is called the **decay constant** and is characteristic of each type of nuclide. The larger the value of $k$, the higher is the decay rate: larger $k \Rightarrow$ higher $\mathscr{A}$.

Combining the two rate expressions just given, we obtain

$$\mathscr{A} = -\frac{\Delta \mathscr{N}}{\Delta t} = k\mathscr{N} \tag{24.3}$$

Note that the activity depends only on $\mathscr{N}$ raised to the first power (and on the constant value of $k$). Therefore, *radioactive decay is a first-order process* (Section 16.4), but with respect to the *number* of nuclei rather than their concentration.

**Half-Life of Radioactive Decay** Decay rates are also commonly expressed in terms of the fraction of nuclei that decay over a given time interval. The **half-life ($t_{1/2}$)** of a nuclide has the same meaning as for a chemical change (Section 16.4) and can be expressed in terms of number of nuclei, mass of radioactive substance, and activity:

- *Number of nuclei.* Half-life is the time it takes for half the nuclei in a sample to decay—*the number of nuclei remaining is halved after each half-life.* Figure 24.6 shows the decay of carbon-14, which has a half-life of 5730 years, in terms of number of $^{14}$C nuclei remaining:

$$^{14}_{6}\text{C} \longrightarrow {}^{14}_{7}\text{N} + {}^{0}_{-1}\beta$$

- *Mass.* As $^{14}$C decays, the mass of $^{14}$C decreases while the mass of $^{14}$N increases. If we start with 1.0 g of $^{14}$C, half that mass of $^{14}$C (0.50 g) will be left after 5730 years, half of that mass (0.25 g) after another 5730 years, and so on.
- *Activity.* The activity depends on the number of nuclei, so the activity is halved after each succeeding half-life.

We determine the half-life of a nuclear reaction from its rate constant. Rearranging Equation 24.3 and integrating over time gives an expression for finding the number of nuclei remaining, $\mathscr{N}_t$, after a given time $t$:

$$\ln \frac{\mathscr{N}_t}{\mathscr{N}_0} = -kt \qquad \text{or} \qquad \mathscr{N}_t = \mathscr{N}_0 e^{-kt} \qquad \text{and} \qquad \ln \frac{\mathscr{N}_0}{\mathscr{N}_t} = kt \tag{24.4}$$

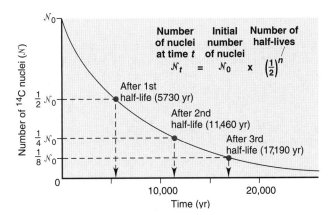

**Figure 24.6** Decrease in number of $^{14}C$ nuclei over time.

where $\mathcal{N}_0$ is the number of nuclei at $t = 0$. (Note the similarity to Equation 16.4, p. 642.) To calculate the half-life ($t_{1/2}$), we set $\mathcal{N}_t$ equal to $\frac{1}{2}\mathcal{N}_0$ and solve for $t_{1/2}$:

$$\ln \frac{\mathcal{N}_0}{\frac{1}{2}\mathcal{N}_0} = kt_{1/2} \quad \text{so} \quad t_{1/2} = \frac{\ln 2}{k} \qquad (24.5)$$

Exactly analogous to the half-life of a first-order chemical change, *this half-life is **not** dependent on the number of nuclei and is inversely related to the decay constant:*

large $k \Rightarrow$ short $t_{1/2}$    and    small $k \Rightarrow$ long $t_{1/2}$

The decay constants and half-lives of radioactive nuclides vary over a very wide range, even for the nuclides of a given element (Table 24.5).

**Table 24.5** Decay Constants ($k$) and Half-Lives ($t_{1/2}$) of Beryllium Isotopes

| Nuclide | $k$ | $t_{1/2}$ |
|---|---|---|
| $^{7}_{4}Be$ | $1.30 \times 10^{-2}$/day | 53.3 days |
| $^{8}_{4}Be$ | $1.0 \times 10^{16}$/s | $6.7 \times 10^{-17}$ s |
| $^{9}_{4}Be$ | Stable | |
| $^{10}_{4}Be$ | $4.3 \times 10^{-7}$/yr | $1.6 \times 10^{6}$ yr |
| $^{11}_{4}Be$ | $5.02 \times 10^{-2}$/s | 13.8 s |

---

## Sample Problem 24.4 | Finding the Number of Radioactive Nuclei

**Problem** Strontium-90 is a radioactive byproduct of nuclear reactors that behaves biologically like calcium, the element above it in Group 2A(2). When $^{90}Sr$ is ingested by mammals, it is found in their milk and eventually in the bones of those drinking the milk. If a sample of $^{90}Sr$ has an activity of $1.2 \times 10^{12}$ d/s, what are the activity and the fraction of nuclei that have decayed after 59 yr ($t_{1/2}$ of $^{90}Sr$ = 29 yr)?

**Plan** The fraction of nuclei that have decayed is the change in number of nuclei, expressed as a fraction of the starting number. The activity of the sample ($\mathcal{A}$) is proportional to the number of nuclei ($\mathcal{N}$), so we know that

$$\text{Fraction decayed} = \frac{\mathcal{N}_0 - \mathcal{N}_t}{\mathcal{N}_0} = \frac{\mathcal{A}_0 - \mathcal{A}_t}{\mathcal{A}_0}$$

We are given $\mathcal{A}_0$ ($1.2 \times 10^{12}$ d/s), so we find $\mathcal{A}_t$ from the integrated form of the first-order rate equation (Equation 24.4), in which $t$ is 59 yr. To solve that equation, we first need $k$, which we can calculate from the given $t_{1/2}$ (29 yr).

**Solution** Calculating the decay constant $k$:

$$t_{1/2} = \frac{\ln 2}{k} \quad \text{so} \quad k = \frac{\ln 2}{t_{1/2}} = \frac{0.693}{29 \text{ yr}} = 0.024 \text{ yr}^{-1}$$

Applying Equation 24.4 to calculate $\mathcal{A}_t$, the activity remaining at time $t$:

$$\ln \frac{\mathcal{N}_0}{\mathcal{N}_t} = \ln \frac{\mathcal{A}_0}{\mathcal{A}_t} = kt \quad \text{or} \quad \ln \mathcal{A}_0 - \ln \mathcal{A}_t = kt$$

So,     $\ln \mathcal{A}_t = -kt + \ln \mathcal{A}_0 = -(0.024 \text{ yr}^{-1} \times 59 \text{ yr}) + \ln (1.2 \times 10^{12} \text{ d/s})$
$\ln \mathcal{A}_t = -1.4 + 27.81 = 26.4$

$$\boxed{\mathcal{A}_t = 2.9 \times 10^{11} \text{ d/s}}$$

(All the data contain two significant figures, so we retained two in the answer.) Calculating the fraction decayed:

$$\text{Fraction decayed} = \frac{\mathcal{A}_0 - \mathcal{A}_t}{\mathcal{A}_0} = \frac{1.2 \times 10^{12} \text{ d/s} - 2.9 \times 10^{11} \text{ d/s}}{1.2 \times 10^{12} \text{ d/s}} = \boxed{0.76}$$

**Check** The answer is reasonable: $t$ is about 2 half-lives, so $\mathcal{A}_t$ should be about $\frac{1}{4}\mathcal{A}_0$, or about $0.3 \times 10^{12}$; therefore, the activity should have decreased by about $\frac{3}{4}$.

**Comment 1.** A useful substitution of Equation 24.4 for finding $\mathcal{A}_t$, the activity at time $t$, is $\mathcal{A}_t = \mathcal{A}_0\, e^{-kt}$.

**2.** Another way to find the fraction of activity (or nuclei) remaining incorporates the number of half-lives $(t/t_{1/2})$. By combining Equations 24.4 and 24.5 and substituting $(\ln 2)/t_{1/2}$ for $k$, we obtain

$$\ln \frac{\mathcal{N}_0}{\mathcal{N}_t} = \left(\frac{\ln 2}{t_{1/2}}\right)t = \frac{t}{t_{1/2}} \ln 2 = \ln 2^{t/t_{1/2}}$$

Inverting the ratio gives

$$\ln \frac{\mathcal{N}_t}{\mathcal{N}_0} = \ln \left(\frac{1}{2}\right)^{t/t_{1/2}}$$

Taking the antilog gives

$$\text{Fraction remaining} = \frac{\mathcal{N}_t}{\mathcal{N}_0} = \left(\frac{1}{2}\right)^{t/t_{1/2}} = \left(\frac{1}{2}\right)^{59/29} = 0.24$$

So,

$$\text{Fraction decayed} = 1.00 - 0.24 = 0.76$$

**Follow-Up Problem 24.4** Sodium-24 $(t_{1/2} = 15\ \text{h})$ is used to study blood circulation. If a patient is injected with an aqueous solution of $^{24}\text{NaCl}$ whose activity is $2.5 \times 10^9$ d/s, how much of the activity is present in the patient's body and excreted fluids after 4.0 days?

## Radioisotopic Dating

The historical record fades rapidly with time and virtually disappears for events of more than a few thousand years ago. Much knowledge of prehistory comes from **radioisotopic dating,** which uses **radioisotopes** to determine the ages of objects. This technique supplies data in fields such as art history, archeology, geology, and paleontology.

The technique of *radiocarbon dating,* for which the American chemist Willard F. Libby won the Nobel Prize in chemistry in 1960, is based on measuring the amounts of $^{14}\text{C}$ and $^{12}\text{C}$ in materials of biological origin. The accuracy of the method falls off after about six half-lives of $^{14}\text{C}$ $(t_{1/2} = 5730\ \text{yr})$, so it is used to date objects up to about 36,000 years old.

Here is how radiocarbon dating works:

1. High-energy cosmic rays, consisting mainly of protons, enter the atmosphere from outer space and initiate a cascade of nuclear reactions, some of which produce neutrons that bombard ordinary $^{14}\text{N}$ atoms to form $^{14}\text{C}$:

$$^{14}_{7}\text{N} + ^{1}_{0}\text{n} \longrightarrow {}^{14}_{6}\text{C} + {}^{1}_{1}\text{p}$$

Through the competing processes of formation and radioactive decay, the amount of $^{14}\text{C}$ in the atmosphere has remained nearly constant.*

2. The $^{14}\text{C}$ atoms combine with $O_2$, diffuse throughout the lower atmosphere, and enter the total carbon pool as gaseous $^{14}\text{CO}_2$ and aqueous $\text{H}^{14}\text{CO}_3^-$. They mix with ordinary $^{12}\text{CO}_2$ and $\text{H}^{12}\text{CO}_3^-$, reaching a constant $^{12}\text{C}/^{14}\text{C}$ ratio of about $10^{12}/1$.

3. The $CO_2$ is taken up by plants during photosynthesis, and then taken up and excreted by animals that eat the plants. Thus, the $^{12}\text{C}/^{14}\text{C}$ ratio of a living organism is the same as the ratio in the environment.

4. When an organism dies, it no longer absorbs or releases $CO_2$, so the $^{12}\text{C}/^{14}\text{C}$ ratio steadily increases because *the amount of $^{14}C$ decreases as it decays:*

$$^{14}_{6}\text{C} \longrightarrow {}^{14}_{7}\text{N} + {}^{0}_{-1}\beta$$

The difference between the $^{12}\text{C}/^{14}\text{C}$ ratio in a dead organism and the ratio in living organisms reflects the time elapsed since the organism died.

---

*Cosmic ray intensity does vary slightly with time, which affects the amount of atmospheric $^{14}\text{C}$. From $^{14}\text{C}$ activity in ancient trees, we know the amount fell slightly about 3000 years ago to current levels. Recently, nuclear testing and fossil fuel combustion have also altered the fraction of $^{14}\text{C}$ slightly. Taking these factors into account improves the accuracy of the dating method.

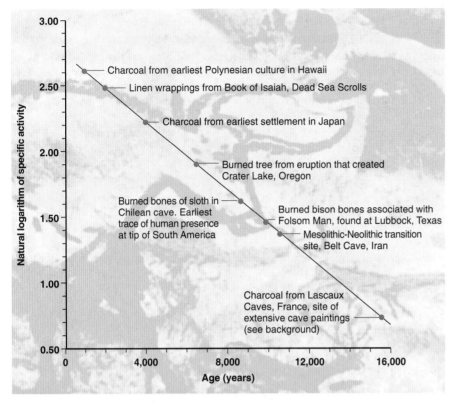

Figure 24.7 Ages of several objects determined by radiocarbon dating.

As you saw in Sample Problem 24.4, the first-order rate equation can be expressed in terms of a ratio of activities:

$$\ln \frac{\mathcal{N}_0}{\mathcal{N}_t} = \ln \frac{\mathcal{A}_0}{\mathcal{A}_t} = kt$$

We use this expression in radiocarbon dating, where $\mathcal{A}_0$ is the activity in a living organism and $\mathcal{A}_t$ is the activity in the object whose age is unknown. Solving for $t$ gives the age of the object:

$$t = \frac{1}{k} \ln \frac{\mathcal{A}_0}{\mathcal{A}_t} \tag{24.6}$$

A useful graphical method in radioisotopic dating shows a plot of the natural logarithm of the specific activity vs. time, which gives a straight line with a slope of $-k$, the negative of the decay constant. Using such a plot and measuring the $^{14}C$ specific activity of an object, we can determine its age; several examples appear in Figure 24.7.

One well-known example of the use of radiocarbon dating was in the determination of the age of the Shroud of Turin (*see photo*). One of the holiest Christian relics, the shroud is a piece of linen that bears a faint image of a man's body and was thought to be the burial cloth used to wrap the body of Jesus Christ. However, three labs in Europe and the United States independently measured the $^{12}C/^{14}C$ ratio of a 50-mg piece of the linen and determined that the flax from which the cloth was made was grown between 1260 A.D. and 1390 A.D.

To determine the ages of more ancient objects or of objects that do not contain carbon, different radioisotopes are measured. For example, comparing the ratio of $^{238}U$ ($t_{1/2} = 4.5 \times 10^9$ yr) to its final decay product, $^{206}Pb$, in meteorites gives 4.7 billion years for the age of the Solar System, and therefore Earth. From this and other isotope ratios, such as $^{40}K/^{40}Ar$ ($t_{1/2}$ of $^{40}K = 1.3 \times 10^9$ yr) and $^{87}Rb/^{87}Sr$ ($t_{1/2}$ of $^{87}Rb = 4.9 \times 10^{10}$ yr), Moon rocks collected by Apollo astronauts have been dated at 4.2 billion years old.

The Shroud of Turin.

**Sample Problem 24.5** Applying Radiocarbon Dating

**Problem** The charred bones of a sloth in a cave in Chile represent the earliest evidence of human presence at the southern tip of South America. A sample of the bone has a specific activity of 5.22 disintegrations per minute per gram of carbon (d/min·g). If the $^{12}C/^{14}C$ ratio for living organisms results in a specific activity of 15.3 d/min·g, how old are the bones ($t_{1/2}$ of $^{14}C$ = 5730 yr)?

**Plan** We calculate $k$ from the given $t_{1/2}$ (5730 yr). Then we apply Equation 24.6 to find the age ($t$) of the bones, using the given activities of the bones ($\mathcal{A}_t$ = 5.22 d/min·g) and of a living organism ($\mathcal{A}_0$ = 15.3 d/min·g).

**Solution** Calculating $k$ for $^{14}C$ decay:

$$k = \frac{\ln 2}{t_{1/2}} = \frac{0.693}{5730 \text{ yr}} = 1.21 \times 10^{-4} \text{ yr}^{-1}$$

Calculating the age ($t$) of the bones:

$$t = \frac{1}{k} \ln \frac{\mathcal{A}_0}{\mathcal{A}_t} = \frac{1}{1.21 \times 10^{-4} \text{ yr}^{-1}} \ln \left( \frac{15.3 \text{ d/min·g}}{5.22 \text{ d/min·g}} \right) = 8.89 \times 10^3 \text{ yr}$$

The bones are about 8900 years old.

**Check** The activity of the bones is between $\frac{1}{2}$ and $\frac{1}{4}$ the activity of a living organism, so the age should be between one and two half-lives (5730 to 11,460 yr).

**Follow-Up Problem 24.5** A sample of wood from an Egyptian mummy case has a specific activity of 9.41 d/min·g. How old is the case?

## ■ Summary of Section 24.2

- Ionization and scintillation counters measure the number of emissions from a radioactive sample.
- The decay rate (activity) of a sample is proportional to the number of radioactive nuclei. Nuclear decay is a first-order process, so half-life is constant.
- Radioisotopic methods, such as $^{14}C$ dating, determine the age of an object by measuring the ratio of specific isotopes in it.

## 24.3 • NUCLEAR TRANSMUTATION: INDUCED CHANGES IN NUCLEI

The alchemists' dream of changing base metals into gold was never realized, but in the early 20$^{th}$ century, nuclear physicists *did* change one element into another. Research into **nuclear transmutation,** the *induced* conversion of the nucleus of one element into the nucleus of another, was closely linked to research into atomic structure and led to the discovery of the neutron and the production of artificial radioisotopes. Later, high-energy bombardment of nuclei in particle accelerators began the ongoing effort to create new nuclides and new elements, and, most recently, to understand fundamental questions of matter and energy.

### Early Transmutation Experiments; Nuclear Shorthand Notation

The first recognized transmutation occurred in 1919, when Ernest Rutherford showed that α particles emitted from radium bombarded atmospheric nitrogen to form a proton and oxygen-17:

$$^{14}_{7}\text{N} + ^{4}_{2}\alpha \longrightarrow ^{1}_{1}\text{p} + ^{17}_{8}\text{O}$$

By 1926, experimenters had found that α bombardment transmuted most elements with low atomic numbers to the next higher element, with ejection of a proton.

A shorthand notation used specifically for nuclear transmutation reactions shows the reactant (target) nucleus to the left and the product nucleus to the right of a set of parentheses, within which a comma separates the projectile particle from the ejected particle(s):

> reactant nucleus (particle in, particle(s) out) product nucleus    **(24.7)**

Using this notation, we write the previous reaction as $^{14}$N ($\alpha$,p) $^{17}$O.

An unexpected finding in a transmutation experiment led to *the discovery of the neutron*. When lithium, beryllium, and boron were bombarded with $\alpha$ particles, they emitted highly penetrating radiation that could not be deflected by a magnetic or electric field. Unlike $\gamma$ radiation, these emissions were massive enough to eject protons from the substances they penetrated. In 1932, James Chadwick, a student of Rutherford, proposed that the emissions consisted of neutral particles with a mass similar to that of a proton, which he named *neutrons*. He received the Nobel Prize in physics in 1935 for his discovery.

In 1933, Irene and Frederic Joliot-Curie (*see photo*), daughter and son-in-law of Marie and Pierre Curie, created the first artificial radioisotope, phosphorus-30. When they bombarded aluminum foil with $\alpha$ particles, phosphorus-30 and neutrons were formed:

$$^{27}_{13}\text{Al} + {}^{4}_{2}\alpha \longrightarrow {}^{1}_{0}\text{n} + {}^{37}_{15}\text{P} \quad \text{or} \quad {}^{27}\text{Al}(\alpha,\text{n})\,{}^{30}\text{P}$$

Since then, other techniques for producing artificial radioisotopes have been developed. In fact, the majority of the nearly 1000 known radionuclides have been produced artificially.

The Joliot-Curies in their laboratory.

## Particle Accelerators and the Transuranium Elements

During the 1930s and 1940s, researchers probing the nucleus bombarded elements with neutrons, $\alpha$ particles, protons, and **deuterons** (nuclei of the stable hydrogen isotope deuterium, $^{2}$H). Neutrons are especially useful as projectiles because they have no charge and thus are not repelled as they approach a target nucleus. The other particles are all positive, so early researchers found it difficult to give them enough energy to overcome their repulsion by the target nuclei. Beginning in the 1930s, however, **particle accelerators** were invented to impart high kinetic energies to particles by placing them in an electric field, usually in combination with a magnetic field. In the simplest and earliest design, protons are introduced at one end of a tube and attracted to the other end by a potential difference.

**Linear Accelerator** A major advance was the *linear accelerator*, a series of separated tubes of increasing length that, through a source of alternating voltage, change their charge from positive to negative in synchrony with the movement of the particle through them (Figure 24.8).

A proton, for example, exits the first tube just when that tube becomes positive and the next tube negative. Repelled by the first tube and attracted by the second, the proton accelerates across the gap between them. The process is performed in stages to achieve high particle energies without having to apply a single high voltage. A 40-ft linear accelerator with 46 tubes, built in California after World War II, accelerated protons to speeds several million times faster than earlier accelerators.

**Figure 24.8** Schematic diagram of a linear accelerator.

Path of proton beam

Proton or other ion source

Alternating voltage sources

+/−    −/+

Evacuated chamber

Magnet (top magnet not shown)

"Dees"

Target

**Figure 24.9** Schematic diagram of a cyclotron.

A small section of the Large Hadron Collider.

**Other Early Particle Accelerators** The *cyclotron* (Figure 24.9), invented by E. O. Lawrence in 1930, applies the principle of the linear accelerator but uses electromagnets to give the particle a spiral path to save space. The magnets lie within an evacuated chamber above and below two "dees," open, D-shaped electrodes that act like the tubes in the linear design. The particle is accelerated as it passes from one dee, which is momentarily positive, to the other, which is momentarily negative. Its speed and path radius increase until it is deflected toward the target nucleus.

The *synchrotron* uses a synchronously increasing magnetic field to make the particle's path circular rather than spiral.

**Powerful Modern Accelerators** Some very powerful accelerators used to study the physics of high-energy particle collisions include both a linear section and a synchrotron section. The *tevatron* at the Fermi Lab near Chicago has a circumference of 3.9 miles and can accelerate particles to an energy slightly less than $1 \times 10^{12}$ electron volts (1 TeV) before colliding them together.

The world's most powerful accelerator is the Large Hadron Collider (LHC) near Geneva, Switzerland (*photo*). The first successful collision of protons in the LHC was achieved in early 2010. When operating at peak capacity, the LHC will accelerate protons to an energy of 7 TeV as they travel around the main ring at a speed of 11,000 revolutions per second, attaining a final speed about 99.99% of the speed of light before colliding with other protons. Physicists are eager to study the results of these high-energy subatomic collisions for information on the nature of matter and the early universe.

**Synthesis of Transuranium Elements** Scientists use accelerators for many applications, from producing radioisotopes used in medical applications to studying the fundamental nature of matter. Perhaps the most specific application for chemists is the synthesis of **transuranium elements,** those with atomic numbers higher than uranium, the heaviest naturally occurring element. Some reactions that were used to form several of these elements appear in Table 24.6. The transuranium elements include the remaining actinides ($Z = 93$ to $103$), in which the $5f$ sublevel is filled, and the elements in the fourth transition series ($Z = 104$ to $112$), in which the $6d$ sublevel is filled, and the remaining elements in the $7p$ sublevel ($Z = 113$ to $118$).

Conflicting claims of discovery by scientists in the United States and the former Soviet Union led to controversies about names for some of the more recently synthesized elements. To provide interim names until the disputes could be settled, the International Union of Pure and Applied Chemistry (IUPAC) adopted a system that

| Table **24.6** Formation of Some Transuranium Nuclides* | | | | | |
|---|---|---|---|---|---|
| **Reaction** | | | | | **Half-life of Product** |
| $^{239}_{94}\text{Pu}$ | $+$ $2^1_0\text{n}$ | $\longrightarrow$ | $^{241}_{95}\text{Am}$ | $+$ $^{0}_{-1}\beta$ | 432 yr |
| $^{239}_{94}\text{Pu}$ | $+$ $^4_2\alpha$ | $\longrightarrow$ | $^{242}_{96}\text{Cm}$ | $+$ $^1_0\text{n}$ | 163 days |
| $^{241}_{95}\text{Am}$ | $+$ $^4_2\alpha$ | $\longrightarrow$ | $^{243}_{97}\text{Bk}$ | $+$ $2^1_0\text{n}$ | 4.5 h |
| $^{242}_{96}\text{Cm}$ | $+$ $^4_2\alpha$ | $\longrightarrow$ | $^{245}_{98}\text{Cf}$ | $+$ $^1_0\text{n}$ | 45 min |
| $^{253}_{99}\text{Es}$ | $+$ $^4_2\alpha$ | $\longrightarrow$ | $^{256}_{101}\text{Md}$ | $+$ $^1_0\text{n}$ | 76 min |
| $^{243}_{95}\text{Am}$ | $+$ $^{18}_8\text{O}$ | $\longrightarrow$ | $^{256}_{103}\text{Lr}$ | $+$ $5^1_0\text{n}$ | 28 s |

*Like chemical reactions, nuclear reactions may occur in several steps. For example, the first reaction here is actually an overall process that occurs in three steps:
(1) $^{239}_{94}\text{Pu} + ^1_0\text{n} \longrightarrow ^{240}_{94}\text{Pu}$  (2) $^{240}_{94}\text{Pu} + ^1_0\text{n} \longrightarrow ^{241}_{94}\text{Pu}$  (3) $^{241}_{94}\text{Pu} \longrightarrow ^{241}_{95}\text{Am} + ^{0}_{-1}\beta$

uses the atomic number as the basis for a Latin name. Thus, for example, element 104 was named unnilquadium (un = 1, nil = 0, quad = 4, ium = metal suffix), with the symbol Unq. After much compromise, IUPAC has finalized these names: 104, rutherfordium (Rf); 105, dubnium (Db); 106, seaborgium (Sg); 107, bohrium (Bh); 108, hassium (Hs); 109, meitnerium (Mt); 110, darmstadtium (Ds); 111, roentgenium (Rg); and 112, copernicium (Cn). Elements with atomic numbers 113 and higher have not yet been named.

## ■ Summary of Section 24.3

- One nucleus can be transmuted to another through bombardment with high-energy particles.
- Accelerators increase the kinetic energy of particles in nuclear bombardment experiments and are used to produce transuranium elements and radioisotopes for medical use.

## 24.4 • EFFECTS OF NUCLEAR RADIATION ON MATTER

In 1986, an accident at the Chernobyl nuclear facility in the former Soviet Union released radioactivity that, according to the World Health Organization, will cause thousands of cancer deaths. In the same year, isotopes used in medical treatment emitted radioactivity that prevented thousands of cancer deaths. In this section and Section 24.5, we examine radioactivity's harmful and beneficial effects.

The key to both of these effects is that *nuclear changes cause chemical changes in surrounding matter.* In other words, even though the nucleus of an atom may undergo a reaction with little or no involvement of the atom's electrons, the emissions from that reaction *do* affect the electrons of nearby atoms.

Virtually all radioactivity causes **ionization** in surrounding matter, as the emissions collide with atoms and dislodge electrons:

$$\text{Atom} \xrightarrow{\text{ionizing radiation}} \text{ion}^+ + e^-$$

From each ionization event, a cation and a free electron result, and the number of such *cation-electron pairs* produced is directly related to the energy of the incoming **ionizing radiation.**

Many applications of ionizing radiation depend not only on the ionizing event itself, but also on secondary processes. For example, in a Geiger-Müller counter, the free electron of the cation-electron pair often collides with another atom, which ejects a second electron, and in a scintillation counter, the initial ionization eventually results in the emission of light. In nuclear power plants (Section 24.7), the initial process as well as several secondary processes cause the release of heat that makes steam to create electricity.

### Effects of Ionizing Radiation on Living Tissue

Ionizing radiation has a destructive effect on living tissue, and if the ionized atom is part of a key biological macromolecule or cell membrane, the results can be devastating to the cell and perhaps the organism.

The danger from a radionuclide depends on three factors: the type of radiation, its half-life, and, most importantly, its biological behavior. For example, both $^{235}U$ and $^{239}Pu$ emit $\alpha$ particles and have long half-lives, but uranium is rapidly excreted by the body, whereas plutonium behaves like calcium and, thus, is incorporated into bones and teeth. One of the most dangerous radionuclides is $^{90}Sr^{2+}$ (formed during a nuclear explosion) because it behaves very similarly to $Ca^{2+}$ and is absorbed rapidly by bones. Let's first see how to measure radiation dose and then look in more detail at the damaging power of ionizing radiation.

**Units of Radiation Dose and Its Effects** To measure the effects of ionizing radiation, we need a unit for radiation dose. Units of radioactive decay, such as the becquerel and curie, measure the number of decay events in a given time but not their energy or absorption by matter. However, the number of cation-electron pairs produced in a given amount of living tissue *is* a measure of the energy absorbed by the tissue. The SI unit for such energy absorption is the **gray (Gy)**; it is equal to 1 joule of energy absorbed per kilogram of body tissue: 1 Gy = 1 J/kg. A more widely used unit is the **rad (*r*adiation-*a*bsorbed *d*ose),** which is one-hundredth as much:

$$1 \text{ rad} = 0.01 \text{ J/kg} = 0.01 \text{ Gy}$$

To measure actual tissue damage, we must account for differences in the strength of the radiation, the exposure time, and the type of tissue. To do this, we multiply the number of rads by a *relative biological effectiveness* (RBE) factor, which depends on the effect a given type of radiation has on a given tissue or body part. The product is the **rem (*r*oentgen *e*quivalent for *m*an),** the unit of radiation dosage equivalent to a given amount of tissue damage in a human:

$$\text{no. of rems} = \text{no. of rads} \times \text{RBE}$$

Doses are often expressed in millirems ($10^{-3}$ rem). The SI unit for dosage equivalent is the **sievert (Sv).** It is defined in the same way as the rem but with absorbed dose in grays; thus, 1 rem = 0.01 Sv.

**Penetrating Power of Emissions** The effect on living tissue of a radiation dose depends on the penetrating power *and* ionizing ability of the radiation. Since water is the main component of living tissue, penetrating power is often measured in terms of the depth of water that stops 50% of incoming radiation. In Figure 24.10, the average values of the penetrating distances are shown in actual size for the three common types of emissions. Note, in general, that *penetrating power is inversely related to the mass, charge, and energy of the emission.* In other words, if a particle interacts strongly with matter, it penetrates only slightly, and vice versa:

1. *Alpha particles.* Alpha particles are massive and highly charged, which means that they interact with matter most strongly of the three common emissions. As a result, they penetrate so little that a piece of paper, light clothing, or the outer layer of skin can stop α radiation from an external source. However, if ingested, an α emitter can cause grave localized internal damage through extensive ionization. For example, in the early 20th century, wristwatch and clock dials were painted by hand with paint containing radium so they would glow in the dark. To write numbers clearly, the women who applied the paint "tipped" fine brushes repeatedly between their lips. Small amounts of ingested $^{226}\text{Ra}^{2+}$ were incorporated into their bones along with normal $\text{Ca}^{2+}$, which led to numerous cases of bone fracture and jaw cancer.

2. *Beta particles and positrons.* Beta particles (β⁻) and positrons (β⁺) have less charge and much less mass than α particles, so they interact less strongly with matter. Even though a given particle has less chance of causing ionization, a β⁻ (or β⁺) emitter is a more destructive external source because the particles penetrate deeper. Specialized heavy clothing or a thick (0.5 cm) piece of metal is required to stop these particles. The relative danger from α and β⁻ emissions is shown by the poisoning of two former Russian intelligence agents. In 1957, an agent was poisoned by thallium-204, a β⁻ emitter, but he survived because β⁻ particles do relatively little radiation damage. In contrast, in 2006, another agent was poisoned with polonium-210, an α emitter, and died in three weeks because of the much greater radiation damage.

3. *Gamma rays.* Neutral, massless γ rays interact least with matter and, thus, penetrate most. A block of lead several inches thick is needed to stop them. Therefore, an external γ ray source is the most dangerous because the energy can ionize many layers of living tissue.

The extent of interaction with matter is variable for emitted *neutrons,* which are neutral and massive. Outside a nucleus, neutrons decay with a half-life of 10.6 min into a proton and an electron (and an antineutrino). With energies ranging from very low to very high, they may be scattered or captured by interaction with nuclei.

α (~0.03 mm)

β (~2 mm)

γ (~10 cm)

**Figure 24.10** Penetrating power of radioactive emissions.

**Molecular Interactions** How does the damage take place on the molecular level? When ionizing radiation interacts with molecules, it causes the *loss of an electron from a bond or a lone pair.* The resulting charged species go on to form **free radicals,** molecular or atomic species with one or more unpaired electrons, which, as you know, are very reactive (Section 10.1, p. 370). They form electron pairs by attacking bonds in other molecules, often forming more free radicals.

When $\gamma$ radiation strikes living tissue, for instance, the most likely molecule to absorb it is water, yielding an electron and a water ion-radical:

$$H_2O + \gamma \longrightarrow H_2O\bullet^+ + e^-$$

The products collide with other water molecules to form more free radicals:

$$H_2O\bullet^+ + H_2O \longrightarrow H_3O^+ + \bullet OH \quad \text{and} \quad e^- + H_2O \longrightarrow H\bullet + OH^-$$

These free radicals attack more $H_2O$ and surrounding biomolecules, whose bonding and structure are intimately connected with their function (Section 15.6).

The double bonds in membrane lipids are highly susceptible to free-radical attack:

$$H\bullet + RCH{=}CHR' \longrightarrow RCH_2{-}\overset{\bullet}{C}HR'$$

In this reaction, one electron of the $\pi$ bond forms a C—H bond between one of the double-bonded carbons and the H•, and the other electron resides on the other carbon to form a free radical. Changes to lipid structure cause damage that results in leakage through cell membranes and destruction of the protective fatty tissue around organs. Changes to critical bonds in enzymes lead to their malfunction as catalysts of metabolic reactions. Changes in the nucleic acids and proteins that govern the rate of cell division can cause cancer. Genetic damage and mutations may occur when bonds in the DNA of sperm and egg cells are altered by free radicals.

## Sources of Ionizing Radiation

We are continuously exposed to ionizing radiation from natural and artificial sources (Table 24.7, *next page*). Indeed, life evolved in the presence of natural ionizing radiation, called **background radiation.** The same radiation that alters bonds in DNA and causes harmful mutations also causes beneficial ones that allow species to evolve.

Background radiation has several natural sources:

- *Cosmic radiation* increases with altitude because of decreased absorption by the atmosphere. Thus, people in Denver absorb twice as much cosmic radiation as people in Los Angeles; even a jet flight involves measurable absorption.
- Thorium and uranium minerals are present in rocks and soil. Radon, the heaviest noble gas [Group 8A(18)], is a radioactive product of uranium and thorium decay. Its concentration in the air we breathe is related to the presence of trace minerals in building materials and to the uranium content of local soil and rocks (Figure 24.11). Once it enters the body, radon poses a serious potential hazard as it decays to radioactive nuclides of Po, Pb, and Bi, through $\alpha$, $\beta^-$, and $\gamma$ emissions. The emissions damage lung tissue, and the heavy-metal atoms formed aggravate the problem. Recent EPA estimates indicate that radon contributes to 15% of annual lung cancer deaths.
- About 150 g of $K^+$ ions is dissolved in the water in the tissues of an average adult, and 0.0118% of these ions are radioactive $^{40}K$. The presence of these substances and of atmospheric $^{14}CO_2$ makes *all* food (including bananas and Brazil nuts; see beginning of chapter), water, clothing, and building materials slightly radioactive.

The largest artificial source of radiation, and the one that is easiest to control, is from medical diagnostic techniques, especially x-rays. The radiation dosage from nuclear testing and radioactive waste disposal is miniscule for most people, but exposures for those living near test sites or disposal areas may be much higher.

## Assessing the Risk from Ionizing Radiation

How much radiation is too much? To answer this question, we must ask several others: How strong is the exposure? How long is the exposure? Which tissue is exposed? Are children affected? One reason we lack clear data to answer

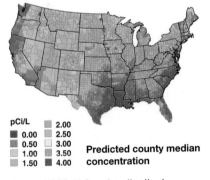

| pCi/L | |
|---|---|
| ■ 0.00 | ■ 2.00 |
| ■ 0.50 | □ 2.50 |
| □ 1.00 | □ 3.00 |
| □ 1.50 | ■ 3.50 |
| | ■ 4.00 |

**Predicted county median concentration**

**Figure 24.11** U.S. radon distribution.

**Table 24.7  Typical Radiation Doses from Natural and Artificial Sources**

| Source of Radiation | Average Adult Exposure |
|---|---|
| **Natural** | |
| Cosmic radiation | 30–50 mrem/yr |
| Radiation from the ground | |
|    From clay soil and rocks | ~25–170 mrem/yr |
|    In wooden houses | 10–20 mrem/yr |
|    In brick houses | 60–70 mrem/yr |
|    In concrete (cinder block) houses | 60–160 mrem/yr |
| Radiation from the air (mainly radon) | |
|    Outdoors, average value | 20 mrem/yr |
|    In wooden houses | 70 mrem/yr |
|    In brick houses | 130 mrem/yr |
|    In concrete (cinder block) houses | 260 mrem/yr |
| Internal radiation from minerals in tap water and daily intake of food ($^{40}K$, $^{14}C$, Ra) | ~40 mrem/yr |
| **Artificial** | |
| Diagnostic x-ray methods | 0.04–0.2 rad/film |
|    Lung (local) | 1.5–3 rad/film |
|    Kidney (local) | ≤1 rad/film |
|    Dental (dose to the skin) | Locally ≤ 10,000 rad |
| Therapeutic radiation treatment | |
| Other sources | |
|    Jet flight (4 h) | ~1 mrem |
|    Nuclear testing | <4 mrem/yr |
|    Nuclear power industry | <1 mrem/yr |
| **Total average value** | 100–200 mrem/yr |

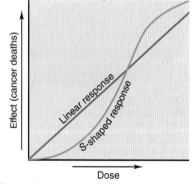

**Figure 24.12** Two models of radiation risk.

these questions is that scientific ethical standards forbid the intentional exposure of humans in an experimental setting. However, accidentally exposed radiation workers and Japanese atomic bomb survivors have been studied extensively. Table 24.8 summarizes the immediate effects on humans of an acute single dose of ionizing radiation to the whole body. The severity of the effects increases with dose; a dose of 500 rem will kill about 50% of the exposed population within a month.

Most data come from laboratory animals, whose biological systems may differ greatly from ours. Nevertheless, studies with mice and dogs show that lesions and cancers appear after massive whole-body exposure, with rapidly dividing cells affected first. In an adult animal, these are cells of the bone marrow, organ linings, and reproductive organs, but many other tissues are affected in an immature animal or fetus. Studies in both animals and humans show an increase in the incidence of cancer from either a high, single exposure or a low, chronic exposure.

Two current models of radiation risk are shown in Figure 24.12:

• The *linear response model* proposes that radiation effects, such as cancer risks, accumulate over time regardless of dose and that populations should not be exposed to any radiation above background levels.

• The *S-shaped response model* implies there is a threshhold above which the effects are more significant: very low risk at low dose and high risk at high dose.

Reliable data on genetic effects of radiation are few. Studies on fruit flies show a linear increase in genetic defects with both dose and exposure time. However, in the mouse, whose genetic system is obviously much more similar to ours than is the fruit fly's, a total dose given over a long period created one-third as many genetic defects as the same dose given over a short period. Therefore, rate of exposure is a

**Table 24.8 Acute Effects of a Single Dose of Whole-Body Irradiation**

| Dose (rem) | Effect | Lethal Dose | |
| --- | --- | --- | --- |
| | | Population (%) | No. of Days |
| 5–20 | Possible late effect; possible chromosomal aberrations | — | — |
| 20–100 | Temporary reduction in white blood cells | — | — |
| 50+ | Temporary sterility in men (100+ rem = 1-yr duration) | — | — |
| 100–200 | "Mild radiation sickness": vomiting, diarrhea, tiredness in a few hours Reduction in infection resistance Possible bone growth retardation in children | — | — |
| 300+ | Permanent sterility in women | — | — |
| 500 | "Serious radiation sickness": marrow/intestine destruction | 50–70 | 30 |
| 400–1000 | Acute illness, early deaths | 60–95 | 30 |
| 3000+ | Acute illness, death in hours to days | 100 | 2 |

key factor. The children of atomic bomb survivors show higher-than-normal childhood cancer rates, implying that their parents' reproductive systems were affected.

## ▌ Summary of Section 24.4

- All radioactive emissions cause ionization.
- The effect of ionizing radiation on living matter depends on the quantity of energy absorbed and the extent of ionization in a given type of tissue. Radiation dose for the human body is measured in rem.
- Ionization forms free radicals, some of which proliferate and destroy biomolecular function.
- All organisms are exposed to varying quantities of natural ionizing radiation.
- Studies show that either a large acute dose or a chronic small dose is harmful.

# 24.5 • APPLICATIONS OF RADIOISOTOPES

Radioisotopes are powerful tools for studying processes in biochemistry, medicine, materials science, environmental studies, and many other scientific and industrial fields. Such uses depend on the fact that *isotopes of an element exhibit **very** similar chemical and physical behavior.* In other words, except for having a less stable nucleus, a radioisotope has nearly the same properties as a nonradioactive isotope of that element.* For example, the fact that $^{14}CO_2$ is utilized by a plant in the same way as $^{12}CO_2$ forms the basis of radiocarbon dating.

## Radioactive Tracers

Just think how useful it could be to follow a substance through a complex process or from one region of a system to another. A tiny amount of a radioisotope mixed with

---

*Although this statement is generally correct, differences in isotopic mass *can* influence bond strengths and therefore reaction rates. Such behavior is called a *kinetic isotope effect* and is particularly important for isotopes of hydrogen—$^1H$, $^2H$, and $^3H$—because their masses differ by such large proportions. Section 22.4 discussed how the kinetic isotope effect is employed in the industrial production of heavy water, $D_2O$.

a large amount of the stable isotope can act as a **tracer,** a chemical "beacon" emitting radiation that signals the presence of the substance.

**Reaction Pathways** Tracers are used to identify simple and complex reaction pathways.

1. *Inorganic systems: the periodate-iodide reaction.* One well-studied example is the reaction between periodate and iodide ions:

$$IO_4^-(aq) + 2I^-(aq) + H_2O(l) \longrightarrow I_2(s) + IO_3^-(aq) + 2OH^-(aq)$$

Is $IO_3^-$ the result of $IO_4^-$ reduction or $I^-$ oxidation? When we add "cold" (nonradioactive) $IO_4^-$ to a solution of $I^-$ that contains some "hot" (radioactive, indicated in red) $^{131}I^-$, we find that the $I_2$ is radioactive, not the $IO_3^-$:

$$IO_4^-(aq) + 2\,^{131}I^-(aq) + H_2O(l) \longrightarrow \,^{131}I_2(s) + IO_3^-(aq) + 2OH^-(aq)$$

These results show that $IO_3^-$ forms through the reduction of $IO_4^-$, and that $I_2$ forms through the oxidation of $I^-$. To confirm this pathway, we add $IO_4^-$ containing some $^{131}IO_4^-$ to a solution of $I^-$. As we expected, the $IO_3^-$ is radioactive, not the $I_2$:

$$^{131}IO_4^-(aq) + 2I^-(aq) + H_2O(l) \longrightarrow I_2(s) + \,^{131}IO_3^-(aq) + 2OH^-(aq)$$

Thus, tracers act like "handles" we can "hold" to follow the changing reactants.

2. *Biochemical pathways: photosynthesis.* Far more complex pathways can be followed with tracers as well. The photosynthetic pathway, the most essential and widespread metabolic process on Earth, in which energy from sunlight is used to form the chemical bonds of glucose, has an overall reaction that looks quite simple:

$$6CO_2(g) + 6H_2O(l) \xrightarrow[\text{chlorophyll}]{\text{light}} C_6H_{12}O_6(s) + 6O_2(g)$$

However, the actual process is extremely complex: 13 enzyme-catalyzed steps are required to incorporate each C atom from $CO_2$, so the six $CO_2$ molecules incorporated to form a molecule of $C_6H_{12}O_6$ require six repetitions of the pathway. Melvin Calvin and his coworkers took seven years to determine the pathway, using $^{14}C$ in $CO_2$ as the tracer and chromatography as the means of separating the products formed after different times of light exposure. Calvin won the Nobel Prize in chemistry in 1961 for this remarkable achievement.

**Physiological Studies** Tracers are used in many studies of physiological function. Some recent studies examine challenges of living in outer space. In an animal study of red blood cell loss during extended space flight, blood plasma volume was measured with $^{125}I$-labeled albumin (a blood protein), and red blood cells labeled with $^{51}Cr$ as a trace substitute for Fe were used to assess survival of blood cells. In another study, blood flow in skin under long periods of microgravity was monitored using injected $^{133}Xe$.

**Material Flow** Tracers are used in studies of solid surfaces and the flow of materials. Metal atoms hundreds of layers deep within a solid have been shown to exchange with metal ions from the surrounding solution within a matter of minutes. Chemists and engineers use tracers to study material movement in semiconductor chips, paint, and metal plating, in detergent action, and in the process of corrosion, to mention just a few of many applications.

Hydrologic engineers use tracers to study the volume and flow of large bodies of water. By following radionuclides that formed during atmospheric nuclear bomb tests ($^3H$ in $H_2O$, $^{90}Sr^{2+}$, and $^{137}Cs^+$), scientists have mapped the flow of water from land to lakes and streams to oceans. They also use tracers to study the surface and deep ocean currents that circulate around the globe, the mechanisms of hurricane formation, and the mixing of the troposphere and stratosphere. Industries employ tracers to study material flow during manufacturing processes, such as the flow of ore pellets in smelting kilns, the paths of wood chips and bleach in paper mills, the diffusion of fungicide into lumber, and in a particularly important application, the porosity and leakage of oil and gas wells in geological formations.

**Activation Analysis**  Another use of tracers is in *neutron activation analysis* (NAA). In this method, neutrons bombard a nonradioactive sample, converting a small fraction of its atoms to radioisotopes, which exhibit characteristic decay patterns, such as γ-ray spectra, that reveal the elements present. Unlike chemical analysis, NAA leaves the sample virtually intact, so the method can be used to determine the composition of a valuable object or a very small sample. For example, a painting thought to be a 16th-century Dutch masterpiece was shown through NAA to be a 20th-century forgery, because a microgram-sized sample of its pigment contained much less silver and antimony than the pigments used by the Dutch masters. Forensic chemists use NAA to detect traces of ammunition on a suspect's hand or traces of arsenic in the hair of a victim of poisoning.

Automotive engineers employ NAA and γ-ray detectors to measure friction and wear of moving parts without having to take the engine apart. For example, when a steel surface that has been neutron-activated to form some radioactive $^{59}Fe$ moves against a second steel surface, the amount of radioactivity on the second surface indicates the amount of material rubbing off. The radioactivity appearing in a lubricant placed between the surfaces can demonstrate the lubricant's ability to reduce wear.

**Medical Diagnosis**  The largest use of radioisotopes is in medical science. In fact, over 25% of U.S. hospital admissions are for diagnoses based on data from radioisotopes. Tracers with half-lives of a few minutes to a few days are employed to observe specific organs and body parts. For example, a healthy thyroid gland incorporates dietary $I^-$ into iodine-containing hormones at a known rate. To assess thyroid function, the patient drinks a solution containing a trace amount of $Na^{131}I$; the thyroid gland absorbs $^{131}I^-$ ions, which undergo $\beta^-$ decay, and the emissions produce an image of the gland (Figure 24.13A). Technetium-99 ($Z = 43$) is also used for imaging the thyroid (Figure 24.13B), as well as the heart, lungs, and liver. Technetium does not occur naturally, so the radioisotope (actually a metastable form, $^{99m}Tc$) is prepared from radioactive molybdenum just before use:

$$^{99}_{42}Mo \longrightarrow {}^{99m}_{43}Tc + {}^{0}_{-1}\beta$$

Tracers are also used to measure physiological processes, such as blood flow. The rate at which the heart pumps blood, for example, can be observed by injecting $^{59}Fe$, which becomes incorporated into the hemoglobin of blood cells. Several radioisotopes used in medical diagnosis are listed in Table 24.9.

*Positron-emission tomography (PET)* is a powerful imaging method for observing brain structure and function. A biological substance is synthesized with one of its atoms replaced by an isotope that emits positrons. The substance is injected into a patient's bloodstream, from which it is taken up into the brain. The isotope emits positrons, each of which annihilates a nearby electron. In this process, two γ photons are emitted simultaneously 180° from each other:

$$^{0}_{1}\beta + {}^{0}_{-1}e \longrightarrow 2{}^{0}_{0}\gamma$$

| Table **24.9** Some Radioisotopes Used as Medical Tracers | |
|---|---|
| **Isotope** | **Body Part or Process** |
| $^{11}C$, $^{18}F$, $^{13}N$, $^{15}O$ | PET studies of brain, heart |
| $^{60}Co$, $^{192}Ir$ | Cancer therapy |
| $^{64}Cu$ | Metabolism of copper |
| $^{59}Fe$ | Blood flow, spleen |
| $^{67}Ga$ | Tumor imaging |
| $^{123}I$, $^{131}I$ | Thyroid |
| $^{111}In$ | Brain, colon |
| $^{42}K$ | Blood flow |
| $^{81m}Kr$ | Lung |
| $^{99m}Tc$ | Heart, thyroid, liver, lung, bone |
| $^{201}Tl$ | Heart muscle |
| $^{90}Y$ | Cancer, arthritis |

**Figure 24.13**  The use of radioisotopes to image the thyroid gland. **A**, This $^{131}I$ scan shows an asymmetric image that is indicative of disease. **B**, A $^{99}Tc$ scan of a healthy thyroid.

**Figure 24.14** PET and brain activity.
These PET scans show brain activity in a normal person (*left*) and in a patient with Alzheimer's disease (*right*). Red and yellow indicate relatively high activity within a region.

An array of detectors around the patient's head pinpoints the sites of γ emission, and the image is analyzed by computer. Two of the isotopes used are $^{15}O$, injected as $H_2^{15}O$ to measure blood flow, and $^{18}F$ bonded to a glucose analog to measure glucose uptake, which is an indicator of energy metabolism. Among many fascinating PET findings are those that show how changes in blood flow and glucose uptake accompany normal or abnormal brain activity (Figure 24.14). Also, substances incorporating $^{11}C$ and $^{15}O$ are being investigated using PET to learn how molecules interact with and move along the surface of a catalyst.

## Additional Applications of Ionizing Radiation

Many other uses of radioisotopes involve higher-energy ionizing radiation.

- *Radiation therapy.* Cancer cells divide more rapidly than normal cells, so radioisotopes that interfere with cell division kill more cancer cells than normal ones. Implants of $^{198}Au$ or of $^{90}Sr$, which decays to the γ-emitting $^{90}Y$, have been used to destroy pituitary and breast tumor cells, and γ rays from $^{60}Co$ have been used to destroy tumors of the brain and other body parts.
- *Destruction of microbes.* Irradiation of food increases shelf life by killing microorganisms that cause rotting or spoilage (Figure 24.15), but the practice is controversial. Advocates point to the benefits of preserving fresh foods, grains, and seeds for long periods, whereas opponents suggest that irradiation might lower the food's nutritional content or produce harmful byproducts. Irradiation also provides a way to destroy newer, more resistant bacterial strains that survive the increasing use of the more common antibiotics in animal feed. The United Nations has approved irradiation for potatoes, wheat, chicken, and strawberries, and, in 2003, the U.S. Food and Drug Administration approved it as well.
- *Insect control.* Ionizing radiation has been used to control harmful insects. Captured males are sterilized by radiation and released to mate, thereby reducing the number of offspring. This method has been used to control the Mediterranean fruit fly in California and disease-causing insects, such as the tsetse fly and malarial mosquito, in other parts of the world.
- *Power for spacecraft instruments.* A nonharmful use of ionizing radiation relies on its secondary processes. Most spacecraft use solar energy to provide power for instruments. In deep-space missions, when solar energy is too weak, however, a radioisotope heater unit (RHU) has been used. It consists of a $^{238}PuO_2$ fuel pellet the size of a pencil eraser that is clad within a multilayered graphite and metal shell a little smaller than a flashlight battery. The whole RHU weighs only 40 g.

Nonirradiated          Irradiated

**Figure 24.15** The increased shelf life of irradiated food.

## ■ Summary of Section 24.5

- Radioisotopic tracers have been used to study reaction mechanisms, material flow, elemental composition, and medical conditions.
- Ionizing radiation has been used in devices that destroy cancer tissue, kill organisms that spoil food, control insect populations, and power spacecraft instruments.

# 24.6 • THE INTERCONVERSION OF MASS AND ENERGY

Most of the nuclear processes we've considered so far have involved radioactive decay, in which a nucleus emits one or a few small particles or photons to become a more stable, slightly lighter nucleus. Two other nuclear processes cause much greater mass changes. In nuclear **fission,** a heavy nucleus splits into two much lighter nuclei, emitting several small particles at the same time. In nuclear **fusion,** the opposite process occurs: two lighter nuclei combine to form a heavier one. Both fission and fusion release enormous quantities of energy. Let's take a look at the origins of this energy by first examining the change in mass that accompanies the breakup of a nucleus into its nucleons and then considering the energy that is equivalent to this mass change.

## The Mass Difference Between a Nucleus and Its Nucleons

For most of the 20th century, we have known that mass and energy are interconvertible. The separate mass and energy conservation laws are combined to state that *the total quantity of mass-energy in the universe is constant.* Therefore, when *any* reacting system releases or absorbs energy, it also loses or gains mass.

**Mass Difference and Chemical Reactions** The interconversion of mass and energy is not important for chemical reactions because the energy changes involved in breaking or forming chemical bonds are so small that the mass changes are negligible. For example, when 1 mol of water breaks up into its atoms, heat is absorbed and we have:

$$H_2O(g) \longrightarrow 2H(g) + O(g) \qquad \Delta H^\circ_{rxn} = 2 \times BE \text{ of } O{-}H = 934 \text{ kJ}$$

We find the mass that is equivalent to this energy from *Einstein's equation:*

$$E = mc^2 \quad \text{or} \quad \Delta E = \Delta mc^2 \quad \text{so} \quad \Delta m = \frac{\Delta E}{c^2} \qquad \textbf{(24.8)}$$

where $\Delta m$ is the mass difference between reactants and products:

$$\Delta m = m_{products} - m_{reactants}$$

Substituting the enthalpy of reaction (in J/mol) for $\Delta E$ and the numerical value for $c$ ($2.9979 \times 10^8$ m/s), we obtain

$$\Delta m = \frac{9.34 \times 10^5 \text{ J/mol}}{(2.9979 \times 10^8 \text{ m/s})^2} = 1.04 \times 10^{-11} \text{ kg/mol} = 1.04 \times 10^{-8} \text{ g/mol}$$

(Units of kg/mol are obtained because the joule includes the kilogram: $1 \text{ J} = 1 \text{ kg·m}^2/\text{s}^2$.) The mass of 1 mol of $H_2O$ molecules (reactant) is about 10 ng *less* than the combined masses of 2 mol of H atoms and 1 mol of O atoms (products), a change difficult to measure with even the most sophisticated balance. Such minute mass changes when bonds break or form allow us to assume that, for all practical purposes, mass is conserved in *chemical* reactions.

**Mass Difference and Nuclear Reactions** The much larger mass change that accompanies a *nuclear* process is related to the enormous energy required to bind the nucleus together from its parts. In an analogy with the calculation above involving the water molecule, consider the change in mass that occurs when one $^{12}C$ nucleus breaks apart into its nucleons—six protons and six neutrons:

$$^{12}C \longrightarrow 6^1_1p + 6^1_0n$$

We calculate this mass difference in a special way. By combining the mass of six H *atoms* and six neutrons and then subtracting the mass of one $^{12}C$ *atom,* the masses of the electrons cancel: six $e^-$ (in six $^1H$ atoms) cancel six $e^-$ (in one $^{12}C$ atom). The mass of one $^1H$ atom is 1.007825 amu, and the mass of one neutron is 1.008665 amu, so

$$\text{Mass of six } ^1H \text{ atoms} = 6 \times 1.007825 \text{ amu} = 6.046950 \text{ amu}$$

$$\underline{\text{Mass of six neutrons} = 6 \times 1.008665 \text{ amu} = 6.051990 \text{ amu}}$$

$$\text{Total mass} = 12.098940 \text{ amu}$$

The mass of the reactant, one $^{12}$C atom, is 12 amu (exactly). The mass difference ($\Delta m$) we obtain is the total mass of the nucleons minus the mass of the nucleus:

$$\Delta m = 12.098940 \text{ amu} - 12.000000 \text{ amu}$$

$$= 0.098940 \text{ amu}/^{12}\text{C} = 0.098940 \text{ g/mol } ^{12}\text{C}$$

Two key points emerge from these calculations:

- *The mass of the nucleus is **less** than the combined masses of its nucleons:* there is *always* a mass decrease when nucleons form a nucleus.
- The mass change of this nuclear process ($9.89 \times 10^{-2}$ g/mol) is nearly 10 million times that of the chemical process ($10.4 \times 10^{-9}$ g/mol) we saw earlier and *can* be observed on any laboratory balance.

## Nuclear Binding Energy and the Binding Energy per Nucleon

Einstein's equation for the relation between mass and energy allows us to find the energy equivalent of any mass change. For 1 mol of $^{12}$C, after converting grams to kilograms, we have

$$\Delta E = \Delta mc^2 = (9.8940 \times 10^{-5} \text{ kg/mol})(2.9979 \times 10^8 \text{ m/s})^2$$

$$= 8.8921 \times 10^{12} \text{ J/mol} = 8.8921 \times 10^9 \text{ kJ/mol}$$

This quantity of energy is called the **nuclear binding energy** for carbon-12, and the positive value means *energy is absorbed*. This is the energy required to break 1 mol of $^{12}$C atoms into neutrons and hydrogen atoms. Thus, the *nuclear binding energy* is the energy to *break 1 mol of nuclei into individual nucleons:*

$$\text{Nucleus} + \text{nuclear binding energy} \longrightarrow \text{nucleons}$$

Thus, the nuclear binding energy is qualitatively analogous to the sum of bond energies of a covalent compound or the lattice energy of an ionic compound. But, quantitatively, nuclear binding energies are typically several million times greater.

**The Electron Volt as the Unit of Binding Energy** We use joules to express the binding energy per mole of nuclei, but the joule is much too large a unit to express the binding energy of a single nucleus. Instead, nuclear scientists use the **electron volt (eV),** the energy an electron acquires when it moves through a potential difference of 1 volt:

$$1 \text{ eV} = 1.602 \times 10^{-19} \text{ J}$$

Binding energies are commonly expressed in millions of electron volts, that is, in *mega–electron volts* (MeV):

$$1 \text{ MeV} = 10^6 \text{ eV} = 1.602 \times 10^{-13} \text{ J}$$

A particularly useful factor converts the atomic mass unit to its energy equivalent in electron volts:

$$1 \text{ amu} = 931.5 \times 10^6 \text{ eV} = 931.5 \text{ MeV} \qquad \textbf{(24.9)}$$

Earlier we found the mass change when $^{12}$C breaks apart into its nucleons to be 0.098940 amu. The binding energy per $^{12}$C nucleus, expressed in MeV, is

$$\frac{\text{Binding energy}}{^{12}\text{C nucleus}} = 0.098940 \text{ amu} \times \frac{931.5 \text{ MeV}}{1 \text{ amu}} = 92.16 \text{ MeV}$$

We can compare the stability of nuclides of different elements by determining the *binding energy per nucleon*. For $^{12}$C, we have

$$\text{Binding energy per nucleon} = \frac{\text{binding energy}}{\text{no. of nucleons}} = \frac{92.16 \text{ MeV}}{12 \text{ nucleons}} = 7.680 \text{ MeV/nucleon}$$

---

**Sample Problem 24.6**  Calculating the Binding Energy per Nucleon

**Problem** Iron-56 is an extremely stable nuclide. Compute the binding energy per nucleon for $^{56}$Fe and compare it with that for $^{12}$C (mass of $^{56}$Fe atom = 55.934939 amu; mass of $^1$H atom = 1.007825 amu; mass of neutron = 1.008665 amu).

**Plan** Iron-56 has 26 protons and 30 neutrons. We calculate the mass difference, $\Delta m$, when the nucleus forms by subtracting the given mass of one $^{56}$Fe atom from the sum of the masses of 26 $^{1}$H atoms and 30 neutrons. To find the binding energy per nucleon, we multiply $\Delta m$ by the equivalent in MeV (931.5 MeV/amu) and divide by the number of nucleons (56).

**Solution** Calculating the mass difference, $\Delta m$:

$$\text{Mass difference} = \left[(26 \times \text{mass } ^{1}\text{H atom}) + (30 \times \text{mass neutron})\right] - \text{mass } ^{56}\text{Fe atom}$$

$$= \left[(26)(1.007825 \text{ amu}) + (30)(1.008665 \text{ amu})\right] - 55.934939 \text{ amu}$$

$$= 0.52846 \text{ amu}$$

Calculating the binding energy per nucleon:

$$\text{Binding energy per nucleon} = \frac{0.52846 \text{ amu} \times 931.5 \text{ MeV/amu}}{56 \text{ nucleons}} = 8.790 \text{ MeV/nucleon}$$

An $^{56}$Fe nucleus would require more energy per nucleon to break up into its nucleons than would $^{12}$C (7.680 MeV/nucleon), so $^{56}$Fe is more stable than $^{12}$C.

**Check** The answer is consistent with the great stability of $^{56}$Fe. Given the number of decimal places in the values, rounding to check the math is useful only to find a *major* error. The number of nucleons (56) is an exact number, so we retain four significant figures.

**Follow-Up Problem 24.6** Uranium-235 is an essential component of the fuel in nuclear power plants. Calculate the binding energy per nucleon for $^{235}$U. Is this nuclide more or less stable than $^{12}$C (mass of $^{235}$U atom = 235.043924 amu)?

## Fission or Fusion: Means of Increasing the Binding Energy per Nucleon

Calculations similar to those in Sample Problem 24.6 for other nuclides show that the binding energy per nucleon varies considerably. The essential point is that *the greater the binding energy per nucleon, the more stable the nuclide is.*

Figure 24.16 shows a plot of the binding energy per nucleon vs. mass number. It provides information about nuclide stability and the two possible processes nuclides can undergo to form more stable nuclides. Most nuclides with fewer than 10 nucleons have a relatively small binding energy per nucleon. The $^{4}$He nucleus is an exception—it is stable enough to be emitted intact as an $\alpha$ particle. Above $A = 12$, the binding energy per nucleon varies from about 7.6 to 8.8 MeV.

The most important observation is that *the binding energy per nucleon peaks at elements with $A \approx 60$.* In other words, nuclides become more stable with increasing mass number up to around 60 nucleons and then become less stable with higher numbers of nucleons. The existence of a peak of stability suggests that there are two ways nuclides can increase their binding energy per nucleon:

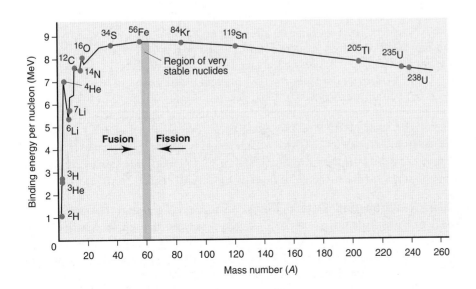

**Figure 24.16** The variation in binding energy per nucleon.

- *Fission.* A heavier nucleus can *split into lighter ones (closer to A ≈ 60)* by undergoing fission. The product nuclei have greater binding energy per nucleon (are more stable) than the reactant nucleus, and the difference in *energy is released.* Nuclear power plants generate energy through fission, as do atomic bombs (Section 24.7).
- *Fusion.* Lighter nuclei, on the other hand, can *combine to form a heavier one (closer to A ≈ 60)* by undergoing fusion. Once again, the product is more stable than the reactants, and *energy is released.* The Sun and other stars generate energy through fusion, as do thermonuclear (hydrogen) bombs. In these examples and in all current research efforts for developing fusion as a useful energy source, hydrogen nuclei fuse to form the very stable helium-4 nucleus.

In Section 24.7, we examine fission and fusion and their applications.

### ▌Summary of Section 24.6

- The mass of a nucleus is less than the sum of the masses of its nucleons. The energy equivalent to this mass difference is the nuclear binding energy, often expressed in units of MeV.
- The binding energy per nucleon is a measure of nuclide stability and varies with the number of nucleons. Nuclides with $A ≈ 60$ are most stable.
- Lighter nuclides join (fusion) or heavier nuclides split (fission) to create more stable products.

---

## 24.7 • APPLICATIONS OF FISSION AND FUSION

Of the many beneficial applications of nuclear reactions, the greatest is the potential for abundant quantities of energy, which is based on the multimillion-fold increase in energy yield of nuclear reactions over chemical reactions. Our experience with nuclear energy from power plants in the late 20th century, however, has shown that we must improve ways to tap this energy source safely and economically and deal with the waste generated. In this section, we discuss how fission and fusion occur and how we are applying them.

### The Process of Nuclear Fission

During the mid-1930s, Enrico Fermi and coworkers bombarded uranium ($Z = 92$) with neutrons in an attempt to synthesize transuranium elements. Many of the unstable nuclides produced were tentatively identified as having $Z > 92$, but other scientists were skeptical. Four years later, the German chemist Otto Hahn and his associate F. Strassmann showed that one of these unstable nuclides was an isotope of barium ($Z = 56$). The Austrian physicist Lise Meitner, a coworker of Hahn, and her nephew Otto Frisch proposed that barium resulted from the *splitting* of the uranium nucleus into *smaller* nuclei, a process that they called *fission* as an analogy to cell division in biology. Element 109 was named *meitnerium* in honor of this extraordinary physicist who proposed the correct explanation of nuclear fission and discovered the element protactinium (Pa; $Z = 91$) as well as numerous radioisotopes.

The $^{235}$U nucleus can split in many different ways, giving rise to various daughter nuclei, but all routes have the same general features. Figure 24.17 depicts one of these fission patterns. Neutron bombardment results in a highly excited $^{236}$U nucleus, which splits apart in $10^{-14}$ s. The products are two nuclei of unequal mass, two to four neutrons (average of 2.4), and a large quantity of energy. A single $^{235}$U nucleus releases $3.5 \times 10^{-11}$ J when it splits; 1 mol of $^{235}$U (about $\frac{1}{2}$ lb) releases $2.1 \times 10^{13}$ J— a billion times as much energy as burning $\frac{1}{2}$ lb of coal (about $2 \times 10^4$ J)!

**Chain Reaction and Critical Mass** We harness the energy of nuclear fission, much of which eventually appears as heat, by means of a **chain reaction** (Figure 24.18): the few neutrons that are released by the fission of one nucleus collide with other fissionable nuclei and cause them to split, releasing more neutrons, and so on,

**Figure 24.17** Fission of $^{235}$U caused by neutron bombardment.

in a self-sustaining process (with each step shown as a vertical dashed line). In this manner, the energy released increases rapidly because each fission event in a chain reaction releases about two-and-a-half times as much energy as the preceding one.

Whether a chain reaction occurs depends on the mass (and thus the volume) of the fissionable sample. If the piece of uranium is large enough, the product neutrons strike another fissionable nucleus *before* flying out of the sample, and a chain reaction takes place. The mass required to achieve a chain reaction is called the **critical mass.** If the sample has less than the critical mass (a *subcritical mass*), too many product neutrons leave the sample before they collide with and cause the fission of another $^{235}$U nucleus, and thus a chain reaction does not occur.

**Figure 24.18** A chain reaction involving fission of $^{235}$U.

TNT explosive

Separated subcritical masses

**Figure 24.19** An atomic bomb based on $^{235}U$.

**Uncontrolled Fission: The Atomic Bomb** An uncontrolled chain reaction can be adapted to make an extremely powerful explosive, as several of the world's leading atomic physicists hypothesized just prior to World War II. In August 1939, Albert Einstein wrote the president of the United States, Franklin Delano Roosevelt, to this effect, warning of the danger of allowing the Nazi government to develop this power first. It was this concern that led to the Manhattan Project, an enormous scientific effort to develop a bomb based on nuclear fission, which was initiated in 1941.* In August 1945, the United States detonated two atomic bombs over Japan, and the horrible destructive power of these bombs was a major factor in the surrender of the Japanese a few days later.

In an atomic bomb, small explosions of trinitrotoluene (TNT) bring subcritical masses of fissionable material together to exceed the critical mass, and the ensuing chain reaction brings about the explosion (Figure 24.19). The proliferation of nuclear power plants, which use fissionable materials to generate energy for electricity, has increased concern that more countries (and unscrupulous individuals) may have access to such material for making bombs. Since the devastating terrorist attacks of September 11, 2001 in the United States, this concern has been heightened.

**Controlled Fission: Nuclear Energy Reactors** Like a coal-fired power plant, *a nuclear power plant generates heat to produce steam, which turns a turbine attached to an electric generator.* But a nuclear plant has the potential to produce electric power much more cleanly than by the combustion of coal.

1. *Operation of a nuclear power plant.* Heat generation takes place in the **reactor core** of a nuclear plant (Figure 24.20). The core contains the *fuel rods,* which consist of fuel enclosed in tubes of a corrosion-resistant zirconium alloy. The fuel is uranium(IV) oxide ($UO_2$) that has been *enriched* from 0.7% $^{235}U$, the natural abundance of this fissionable isotope, to the 3% to 4% $^{235}U$ required to sustain a chain reaction in a practical volume. (Enrichment of nuclear fuel is the most important application of Graham's law, see p. 210.) Sandwiched between the fuel rods are movable *control rods* made of cadmium or boron (or, in nuclear submarines, hafnium), substances that absorb neutrons very efficiently. When the control rods are lowered between the fuel rods, the chain reaction slows because fewer neutrons are available to bombard uranium atoms; when they are raised, the chain reaction speeds up. Neutrons that leave the fuel-rod assembly collide with a *reflector,* usually made of a beryllium alloy, which absorbs very few neutrons. Reflecting the neutrons back to the fuel rods speeds the chain reaction.

Flowing around the fuel and control rods in the reactor core is the *moderator,* a substance that slows the neutrons, making them much better at causing fission than the fast ones emerging directly from the fission event. In most modern reactors, the moderator also acts as the *coolant,* the fluid that transfers the released heat to the steam-producing region. *Light-water reactors* use $H_2O$ as the moderator because $^1H$ absorbs neutrons to some extent; in heavy-water reactors, $D_2O$ is used. The advantage of $D_2O$ is that it absorbs very few neutrons, leaving more available for fission, so heavy-water reactors can use uranium that has been *less enriched.* As the coolant flows around the encased fuel, pumps circulate it through coils that transfer its heat to the water reservoir. Steam formed in the reservoir turns the turbine that runs the generator. The steam then enters a condenser, where water from a lake or river is used to cool it back to liquid that is returned to the water reservoir. Often (although not shown here), large cooling towers aid in this step (see Figure 13.20, p. 493).

---

*For an excellent scientific and historical account of the development of the atomic bomb, see R. Rhodes, *The Making of the Atomic Bomb,* New York, Simon and Schuster, 1986.

**Figure 24.20** A light-water nuclear reactor.

2. *Breeder reactors.* Because $^{235}U$ is not an abundant isotope, the *breeder reactor* was designed to consume one type of nuclear fuel as it produces another. Outside the moderator, fuel rods are surrounded by natural $U_3O_8$, which contains 99.3% *nonfissionable* $^{238}U$ atoms. As neutrons formed during $^{235}U$ fission escape the fuel rod, they collide with $^{238}U$, transmuting it into $^{239}Pu$, another fissionable nucleus:

$$^{238}_{92}U + {}^{1}_{0}n \longrightarrow {}^{239}_{92}U \qquad (t_{1/2} \text{ of } {}^{239}_{92}U = 23.5 \text{ min})$$

$$^{239}_{92}U \longrightarrow {}^{239}_{93}Np + {}^{0}_{-1}\beta \qquad (t_{1/2} \text{ of } {}^{239}_{93}Np = 2.35 \text{ days})$$

$$^{239}_{93}Np \longrightarrow {}^{239}_{94}Pu + {}^{0}_{-1}\beta \qquad (t_{1/2} \text{ of } {}^{239}_{94}Pu = 2.4\times10^4 \text{ yr})$$

Although breeder reactors can make fuel as they operate, they are difficult and expensive to build, and $^{239}Pu$ is extremely toxic and long lived. Breeder reactors are not used in the United States, although several are operating in Europe and Japan.

3. *Power plant accidents and other concerns.* Some major accidents at nuclear plants have caused decidedly negative public reactions. In 1979, malfunctions of coolant pumps and valves at the Three-Mile Island facility in Pennsylvania led to melting of some of the fuel and damage to the reactor core, but the release of only a very small amount (about 1 Ci) of radioactive gases into the atmosphere. In 1986, a million times as much radioactivity (1 MCi) was released when a cooling system failure at the Chernobyl plant in Ukraine caused a much greater melting of fuel and an uncontrolled reaction. High-pressure steam and ignited graphite moderator rods caused the reactor building to explode and expel radioactive debris. Carried by prevailing winds, the radioactive particles contaminated vegetables and milk in much of Europe. And, as we said earlier, health officials have evidence that thousands of people living near the accident have already developed or may eventually develop cancer from radiation exposure. The design of the Chernobyl plant was particularly unsafe because, unlike reactors in the United States and western Europe, the reactor was not contained in a massive, concrete building.*

4. *Current use of nuclear power.* Despite potential safety problems, nuclear power remains an important source of electricity. In the late 1990s, nearly every European country employed nuclear power, and it is the major power source in some countries—Sweden creates 50% of its electricity this way and France almost 80%. Currently, the United States obtains about 20% of its electricity from nuclear power, and Canada slightly less. As our need for energy grows and climate change from fossil-fuel consumption worsens, safer reactors are being designed and are likely to be built.

5. *Thermal pollution and waste disposal.* However, even a smoothly operating plant has certain inherent problems. The problem of *thermal pollution* is common to all power plants. Water used to condense the steam is several degrees warmer when returned to its source, which can harm aquatic organisms (Section 13.4). A more serious problem is *nuclear waste disposal.* Many of the fission products formed in nuclear reactors have long half-lives, and no satisfactory plan for their permanent disposal has yet been devised. Proposals to place the waste in containers and bury them in deep bedrock cannot possibly be field-tested for the thousands of years the material will remain harmful. Leakage of radioactive material into groundwater is a danger, and earthquakes can occur even in geologically stable regions. It remains to be seen whether we can operate fission reactors *and* dispose of the waste safely and economically.

## The Promise of Nuclear Fusion

Nuclear fusion in the Sun is the ultimate source of nearly all the energy—and chemical elements—on Earth. In fact, *all the elements heavier than hydrogen were formed in fusion and decay processes within stars,* as the next Chemical Connections essay describes.

Much research is being devoted to making nuclear fusion a practical, direct source of energy on Earth. To understand the advantages of fusion, let's consider one of the most discussed fusion reactions, in which deuterium and tritium react:

$$^2_1H + {}^3_1H \longrightarrow {}^4_2He + {}^1_0n$$

This reaction produces $1.7 \times 10^9$ kJ/mol, an enormous quantity of energy with no radioactive byproducts. Moreover, the reactant nuclei are relatively easy to come by.

---

*An even greater release of radioactivity (1.1 MCi), involving several radionuclides including the extremely dangerous $^{90}$Sr, occurred in 1957 in Kyshtym, a town in the South Ural Mountains of Russia. As a result, radioactivity spread globally, but the accident was kept secret by the former Soviet government until 1980.

Vacuum container
for plasma          Plasma      Magnets

**Figure 24.21** The tokamak design for magnetic containment of a fusion plasma.

We obtain deuterium from the electrolysis of water (Section 22.4). In nature, tritium forms through the cosmic (neutron) irradiation of $^{14}N$:

$$^{14}_{7}N + ^{1}_{0}n \longrightarrow ^{3}_{1}H + ^{12}_{6}C$$

However, this process results in a natural abundance of only $10^{-7}\%$ $^{3}H$. More practically, tritium is produced in nuclear accelerators by bombarding lithium-6 or by surrounding the fusion reactor itself with material containing lithium-6:

$$^{6}_{3}Li + ^{1}_{0}n \longrightarrow ^{3}_{1}H + ^{4}_{2}He$$

Thus, in principle, fusion *seems* promising and may represent an ideal source of power. However, some extremely difficult technical problems remain. Fusion requires enormous energy in the form of heat to give the positively charged nuclei enough kinetic energy to force themselves together. The fusion of deuterium and tritium, for example, occurs at practical rates at about $10^{8}$ K, a temperature hotter than the Sun's core! How can such conditions be achieved? Two current research approaches have promise. In one, atoms are stripped of their electrons at high temperatures, which results in a gaseous *plasma,* a neutral mixture of positive nuclei and electrons. Because of the extreme temperatures needed for fusion, no *material* can contain the plasma. The most successful approach to date has been to enclose the plasma within a magnetic field. The *tokamak* design has a donut-shaped container in which a helical magnetic field confines the plasma and prevents it from contacting the walls (Figure 24.21). Scientists at the Princeton University Plasma Physics facility have achieved some success in generating energy from fusion this way. In another approach, the high temperature is reached by using many focused lasers to compress and heat the fusion reactants. In any event, one or more major breakthroughs are needed before fusion will be a practical, everyday source of energy.

## ■ Summary of Section 24.7

- In nuclear fission, neutron bombardment causes a nucleus to split into two smaller nuclei and release neutrons that split other nuclei, giving rise to a chain reaction.
- A nuclear power plant controls the rate of the chain reaction to produce heat that creates steam, which is used to generate electricity.
- Potential hazards, such as radiation leaks, thermal pollution, and disposal of nuclear waste, remain current concerns.
- Nuclear fusion holds great promise as a source of clean abundant energy, but it requires extremely high temperatures and is not yet practical.
- The elements were formed through a complex series of nuclear reactions in evolving stars.

How did the universe begin? Where did matter come from? How were the elements formed? The most accepted model proposes that a sphere of unimaginable properties—diameter of $10^{-28}$ cm, density of $10^{96}$ g/mL (density of a nucleus $\approx$ $10^{14}$ g/mL), and temperature of $10^{32}$ K—exploded in a "Big Bang," for reasons not yet known, and distributed its contents through the void of space. Cosmologists consider this moment the beginning of time.

One second later, the universe was an expanding mixture of neutrons, protons, and electrons, denser than rock and hotter than an exploding hydrogen bomb (about $10^{10}$ K). In the next few minutes, it became a gigantic fusion reactor creating the first atomic nuclei other than $^1H$: $^2H$, $^3He$, and $^4He$. After 10 min, more than 25% of the mass of the universe existed as $^4He$, and only about 0.025% as $^2H$. About 100 million years later, or about 15 billion years ago, gravitational forces pulled this cosmic mixture into primitive, contracting stars.

This account of the origin of the universe is based on the observation of spectra from the Sun, other stars, nearby galaxies, and cosmic (interstellar) dust. Spectral analysis of planets and chemical analysis of Earth and Moon rocks, meteorites, and cosmic-ray particles furnish data about isotope abundance. From these, a model has been developed for **stellar nucleosynthesis,** the creation of the elements in stars. The overall process occurs in several stages during a star's evolution, and the entire sequence of steps occurs only in very massive stars, having 10 to 100 times the mass of the Sun. Each step involves a contraction of the volume of the star that results in higher temperature and yields heavier nuclei. Such events are forming elements in stars today. The key stages in the process are shown in Figure B24.1 and described below:

1. *Hydrogen burning produces He.* The initial contraction of a star heats its core to about $10^7$ K, at which point a fusion process called *hydrogen burning* begins. Through three possible reactions (one is shown below), helium nuclei are produced from the abundant protons:

$$4\,^1_1H \longrightarrow\, ^4_2He + 2\,^0_1\beta + 2\nu + energy$$

2. *Helium burning produces C, O, Ne, and Mg.* After several billion years of hydrogen burning, about 10% of the $^1H$ is consumed, and the star contracts further. The $^4He$ forms a dense core, hot enough ($2\times10^8$ K) to fuse $^4He$ nuclei. The energy released during *helium burning* expands the remaining $^1H$ into a vast envelope: the star becomes a *red giant,* more than 100 times its original diameter. Within its core, pairs of $^4He$ nuclei ($\alpha$ particles) fuse into unstable $^8Be$ nuclei ($t_{1/2} = 7\times10^{-17}$ s), which play the role of an activated complex in chemical reactions. A $^8Be$ nucleus collides with another $^4He$ to form $^{12}C$. Then, further fusion with $^4He$ creates nuclei up to $^{24}Mg$:

$$^{12}C \xrightarrow{\ \alpha\ } {}^{16}O \xrightarrow{\ \alpha\ } {}^{20}Ne \xrightarrow{\ \alpha\ } {}^{24}Mg$$

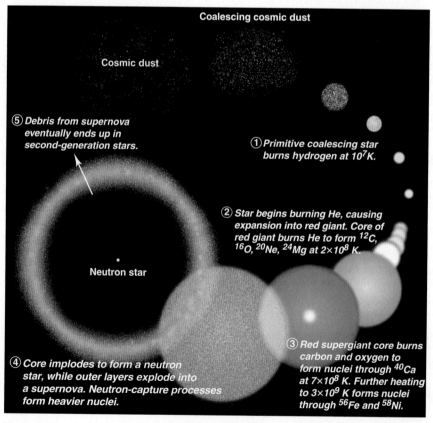

**Figure B24.1** Element synthesis in the life cycle of a star.

3. *Elements through Fe and Ni form.* For another 10 million years, $^4$He is consumed, and the heavier nuclei created form a core. This core contracts and heats, expanding the star into a *supergiant.* Within the hot core ($7 \times 10^8$ K), *carbon and oxygen burning* occur:

$$^{12}\text{C} + {}^{12}\text{C} \longrightarrow {}^{23}\text{Na} + {}^{1}\text{H}$$
$$^{12}\text{C} + {}^{16}\text{O} \longrightarrow {}^{28}\text{Si} + \gamma$$

Absorption of $\alpha$ particles forms nuclei up to $^{40}$Ca:

$$^{12}\text{C} \overset{\alpha}{\longrightarrow} {}^{16}\text{O} \overset{\alpha}{\longrightarrow} {}^{20}\text{Ne} \overset{\alpha}{\longrightarrow} {}^{24}\text{Mg} \overset{\alpha}{\longrightarrow}$$
$$^{28}\text{Si} \overset{\alpha}{\longrightarrow} {}^{32}\text{S} \overset{\alpha}{\longrightarrow} {}^{36}\text{Ar} \overset{\alpha}{\longrightarrow} {}^{40}\text{Ca}$$

Further contraction and heating to a temperature of $3 \times 10^9$ K allow reactions in which nuclei release neutrons, protons, and $\alpha$ particles and then recapture them. As a result, nuclei with lower binding energies supply nucleons to create those with higher binding energies. In stars of moderate mass, less than 10 times the mass of the Sun, this process stops at iron-56 and nickel-58, the nuclei with the highest binding energies.

4. *Heavier elements form.* In very massive stars, the next stage is the most spectacular. With all the fuel consumed, the core collapses within a second. Many Fe and Ni nuclei break down into neutrons and protons. Protons capture electrons to form neutrons, and the entire core forms an incredibly dense *neutron star.* (An Earth-sized star that became a neutron star would fit in the Houston Astrodome!) As the core implodes, the outer layers explode in a *supernova,* which expels material throughout space. A supernova occurs an average of every few hundred years in each galaxy or once every second somewhere in the universe. The heavier elements are formed during supernova events and are found in *second-generation stars,* those that coalesce from interstellar $^1$H and $^4$He and the debris of exploded first-generation stars.

Heavier elements form through *neutron-capture* processes. In the *s-process* (*slow* neutron-capture process), a nucleus captures a neutron, sometime over a period of 10 to 1000 years. If the resulting nucleus is unstable, it undergoes $\beta^-$ decay to form the next element, as in this conversion of $^{68}$Zn to $^{70}$Ge:

$$^{68}\text{Zn} \overset{n}{\longrightarrow} {}^{69}\text{Zn} \overset{\beta^-}{\longrightarrow} {}^{69}\text{Ga} \overset{n}{\longrightarrow} {}^{70}\text{Ga} \overset{\beta^-}{\longrightarrow} {}^{70}\text{Ge}$$

The stable isotopes of most heavy elements up to $^{209}$Bi form by the s-process.

Less stable isotopes and those with $A$ greater than 230 cannot form by the s-process because their half-lives are too short. These form by the *r-process* (*rapid* neutron-capture process) during the fury of the supernova. Many neutron captures, followed by many $\beta^-$ decays, occur in a second, as when $^{56}$Fe is converted to $^{79}$Br:

$$^{56}_{26}\text{Fe} + 23\,^1_0\text{n} \longrightarrow {}^{79}_{26}\text{Fe} \longrightarrow {}^{79}_{35}\text{Br} + 9\,^{0}_{-1}\beta$$

We know from the heavy elements present in the Sun that it is at least a second-generation star presently undergoing hydrogen burning. Together with its planets, it was formed from the dust of exploded stars about $4.6 \times 10^9$ years ago. This means that many of the atoms on Earth, including some within you, came from exploded stars and are older than the Solar System itself!

Any theory of element formation must be consistent with the element abundances we observe (Section 22.1). Although local compositions, such as those of Earth and the Sun, differ, and mineral grains in meteorites may have abnormal isotopic compositions, large regions of the universe have, on average, similar compositions. Scientists believe element forming reaches a dynamic equilibrium, resulting in *relatively constant amounts of the isotopes.*

## Problems

**B24.1** Compare the *s-* and *r*-processes in stellar nucleosynthesis in terms of rate, number of neutrons absorbed, and types of isotopes formed.

**B24.2** The overall reaction taking place during hydrogen burning in a young star is

$$4\,^1_1\text{H} \longrightarrow {}^4_2\text{He} + 2\,^0_1\beta + 2\nu + \text{energy}$$

How much energy (in MeV) is released per He nucleus formed? Per mole of He formed? (Masses of atoms: $^1_1$H atom = 1.007825 amu; $^4_2$He atom = 4.00260 amu; mass of positron = $5.48580 \times 10^{-4}$ amu.)

**B24.3** Cosmologists modeling the origin of the elements postulate nuclides with very short half-lives. One of these short-lived nuclides, $^8$Be ($t_{1/2} = 7 \times 10^{-17}$ s), is thought to play a key role in stellar nucleosynthesis by fusing with $^4$He to form $^{12}$C. Another model proposes the simultaneous fusion of three $^4$He nuclei to form $^{12}$C. Comment on the validity of this alternative mechanism.

**B24.4** The *s*-process produces isotopes of elements up to $^{209}$Bi. This process is terminated when $^{209}$Bi captures a neutron to produce $^{210}$Bi, which subsequently undergoes $\beta^-$ decay to produce nuclide A, which then decays by emitting an $\alpha$ particle to form nuclide B. This nuclide captures three neutrons to produce nuclide C, which undergoes $\beta^-$ decay to produce nuclide D, starting the cycle again. Write balanced nuclear equations for the formation of nuclides A through D.

# CHAPTER REVIEW GUIDE

## Learning Objectives    Relevant section (§) and/or sample problem (SP) numbers appear in parentheses.

### Understand These Concepts

1. How nuclear changes differ, in general, from chemical changes (Introduction)
2. The meanings of *radioactivity, nucleon, nuclide,* and *isotope* (§24.1)
3. Characteristics of three types of radioactive emissions: $\alpha$, $\beta$, and $\gamma$ (§24.1)
4. The various modes of radioactive decay and how each changes the values of $A$ and $Z$ (§24.1)
5. How the $N/Z$ ratio, the even-odd nature of $N$ and $Z$, and magic numbers correlate with nuclear stability (§24.1)
6. How an unstable nuclide's mass number or $N/Z$ ratio correlates with its mode of decay (§24.1)
7. How a decay series combines numerous decay steps and ends with a stable nuclide (§24.1)
8. How ionization and scintillation counters detect and measure radioactivity (§24.2)
9. Why radioactive decay is a first-order process; the meanings of *decay rate* and *specific activity* (§24.2)
10. The meaning of *half-life* in the context of radioactive decay (§24.2)
11. How the specific activity of an isotope in an object is used to determine the object's age (§24.2)
12. How particle accelerators and reactors are used to synthesize new nuclides (§24.3)
13. The units of radiation dose; the effects on living tissue of various dosage levels; the inverse relationship between the mass and charge of an emission and its penetrating power (§24.4)
14. How ionizing radiation creates free radicals that damage tissue; sources and risks of ionizing radiation (§24.4)
15. How radioisotopes are used in research, analysis, and medical diagnosis (§24.5)
16. Why the mass of a nucleus is less than the total mass of its nucleons and how this mass difference is related to the nuclear binding energy (§24.6)
17. How nuclear stability is related to binding energy per nucleon (§24.6)
18. How heavy nuclides undergo fission and lighter ones undergo fusion to increase the binding energy per nucleon (§24.6)
19. The current application of fission and potential application of fusion to produce energy (§24.7)

### Master These Skills

1. Expressing the mass and charge of a particle with the $_{Z}^{A}X$ notation (§24.1; see also §2.5)
2. Using changes in the values of $A$ and $Z$ to write and balance nuclear equations (SP 24.1)
3. Using the $N/Z$ ratio, the even-odd nature of $N$ and $Z$, and the presence of magic numbers to predict nuclear stability (SP 24.2)
4. Using the atomic mass of the element or the $N/Z$ ratio to predict the mode of decay of an unstable nuclide (SP 24.3)
5. Converting units of radioactivity (§24.2)
6. Calculating specific activity, decay constant, half-life, and number of nuclei (§24.2 and SP 24.4)
7. Estimating the age of an object from the specific activity and half-life of carbon-14 (SP 24.5)
8. Writing notations and balancing equations for nuclear transmutation (§24.3)
9. Calculating radiation dose and converting units (§24.4)
10. Calculating the mass difference between a nucleus and its nucleons and the energy equivalent (§24.6)
11. Calculating the binding energy per nucleon and using it to compare stabilities of nuclides (SP 24.6)

## Key Terms    Page numbers appear in parentheses.

radioactivity (977)

**Section 24.1**
nucleon (978)
nuclide (978)
isotope (978)
alpha ($\alpha$) particle (979)
beta ($\beta$) particle (979)
gamma ($\gamma$) ray (979)
alpha ($\alpha$) decay (981)
beta ($\beta$) decay (981)
$\beta^{-}$ decay (981)
positron ($\beta^{+}$) emission (981)
positron (981)
electron ($e^{-}$) capture (EC) (981)
gamma ($\gamma$) emission (982)

band of stability (983)
strong force (984)
decay (disintegration) series (986)

**Section 24.2**
Geiger-Müller counter (987)
scintillation counter (987)
activity ($\mathscr{A}$) (988)
becquerel (Bq) (988)
curie (Ci) (988)
decay constant (988)
half-life ($t_{1/2}$) (988)
radioisotopic dating (990)
radioisotope (990)

**Section 24.3**
nuclear transmutation (992)

deuteron (993)
particle accelerator (993)
transuranium element (994)

**Section 24.4**
ionization (995)
ionizing radiation (995)
gray (Gy) (996)
rad (*radiation-absorbed dose*) (996)
rem (*roentgen equivalent for man*) (996)
sievert (Sv) (996)
free radical (997)
background radiation (997)

**Section 24.5**
tracer (1000)

**Section 24.6**
fission (1003)
fusion (1003)
nuclear binding energy (1004)
electron volt (eV) (1004)

**Section 24.7**
chain reaction (1006)
critical mass (1007)
reactor core (1008)
stellar nucleosynthesis (1012)

## Key Equations and Relationships    Page numbers appear in parentheses.

**24.1** Balancing a nuclear equation (979):

$$\text{Total } A_{\text{Total } Z}\text{Reactants} = \text{Total } A_{\text{Total } Z}\text{Products}$$

**24.2** Defining the unit of radioactivity (curie, Ci) (988):

$$1 \text{ Ci} = 3.70 \times 10^{10} \text{ disintegrations per second (d/s)}$$

**24.3** Expressing the decay rate (activity) for radioactive nuclei (988):

$$\text{Decay rate } (\mathcal{A}) = -\frac{\Delta \mathcal{N}}{\Delta t} = k\mathcal{N}$$

**24.4** Finding the number of nuclei remaining after a given time, $\mathcal{N}_t$ (988):

$$\ln \frac{\mathcal{N}_t}{\mathcal{N}_0} = -kt \quad \text{or} \quad \mathcal{N}_t = \mathcal{N}_0 e^{-kt}$$

**24.5** Finding the half-life of a radioactive nuclide (989):

$$t_{1/2} = \frac{\ln 2}{k}$$

**24.6** Calculating the time to reach a given specific activity (age of an object in radioisotopic dating) (991):

$$t = \frac{1}{k} \ln \frac{\mathcal{A}_0}{\mathcal{A}_t}$$

**24.7** Writing a transmutation in shorthand notation (993):

reactant nucleus (particle in, particle(s) out) product nucleus

**24.8** Adapting Einstein's equation to calculate mass difference and/or nuclear binding energy (1003):

$$\Delta m = \frac{\Delta E}{c^2} \quad \text{or} \quad \Delta E = \Delta mc^2$$

**24.9** Relating the atomic mass unit to its energy equivalent in MeV (1004):

$$1 \text{ amu} = 931.5 \times 10^6 \text{ eV} = 931.5 \text{ MeV}$$

## Brief Solutions to Follow-Up Problems

**24.1** $^{133}_{54}\text{Xe} \longrightarrow ^{133}_{55}\text{Cs} + ^{0}_{-1}\beta$

**24.2** $^{31}\text{P}$ has an even $N$ (16), but $^{30}\text{P}$ has both $N$ and $Z$ odd. $^{31}\text{P}$ also has a slightly higher $N/Z$ ratio that is closer to the band of stability.

**24.3** (a) $Z = 26$ is iron (Fe), and the atomic mass is 55.85. The $A$ value of 61 is higher: $\beta^-$ decay; (b) $Z > 83$, which is too high for stability: $\alpha$ decay

**24.4** $\ln \mathcal{A}_t = -kt + \ln \mathcal{A}_0$

$$= -\left(\frac{\ln 2}{15 \text{ h}} \times 4.0 \text{ days} \times \frac{24 \text{ h}}{1 \text{ day}}\right) + \ln (2.5 \times 10^9)$$

$$= 17.20$$

$$\mathcal{A} = 3.0 \times 10^7 \text{ d/s}$$

**24.5** $t = \frac{1}{k} \ln \frac{\mathcal{A}_0}{\mathcal{A}_t} = \frac{5730 \text{ yr}}{\ln 2} \ln \left(\frac{15.3 \text{ d/min} \cdot \text{g}}{9.41 \text{ d/min} \cdot \text{g}}\right)$

$$= 4.02 \times 10^3 \text{ yr}$$

The mummy case is about 4000 years old.

**24.6** $^{235}\text{U}$ has 92 $^1_1\text{p}$ and 143 $^1_0\text{n}$.

$\Delta m = [(92 \times 1.007825 \text{ amu}) + (143 \times 1.008665 \text{ amu})]$

$\quad\quad - 235.043924 \text{ amu}$

$\quad = 1.9151 \text{ amu}$

$$\frac{\text{Binding energy}}{\text{nucleon}} = \frac{1.9151 \text{ amu} \times \dfrac{931.5 \text{ MeV}}{1 \text{ amu}}}{235 \text{ nucleons}}$$

$$= 7.591 \text{ MeV/nucleon}$$

Therefore, $^{235}\text{U}$ is less stable than $^{12}\text{C}$.

## PROBLEMS

Problems with **colored** numbers are answered in Appendix E and worked in detail in the Student Solutions Manual. Problem sections match those in the text and provide the numbers of relevant sample problems. Most offer Concept Review Questions, Skill-Building Exercises (grouped in pairs covering the same concept), and Problems in Context. The Comprehensive Problems are based on material from any section or previous chapter.

### Radioactive Decay and Nuclear Stability
(Sample Problems 24.1 to 24.3)

**Concept Review Questions**

**24.1** How do chemical and nuclear reactions differ in
(a) Magnitude of the energy change?
(b) Effect on rate of increasing temperature?

(c) Effect on rate of higher reactant concentration?
(d) Effect on yield of higher reactant concentration?

**24.2** Sulfur has four naturally occurring stable isotopes. The one with the lowest mass number is sulfur-32, which is also the most abundant (95.02%).
(a) What percentage of the S atoms in a matchhead are $^{32}\text{S}$?
(b) The isotopic mass of $^{32}\text{S}$ is 31.972070 amu. Is the atomic mass of S larger, smaller, or equal to this mass? Explain.

**24.3** What led Marie Curie to draw the following conclusions?
(a) Radioactivity is a property of the element and not the compound in which it is found. (b) A highly radioactive element, aside from uranium, occurs in pitchblende.

**24.4** Which of the following produce an atom of a *different* element: (a) $\alpha$ decay; (b) $\beta^-$ decay; (c) $\gamma$ emission; (d) $\beta^+$ emission;

(e) $e^-$ capture? Show how $Z$ and $N$ change, if at all, with each process.

**24.5** Why is $_2^3\text{He}$ stable, but $_2^2\text{He}$ has never been detected?

**24.6** How do the modes of decay differ for a neutron-rich nuclide and a proton-rich nuclide?

**24.7** Why might it be difficult to use only a nuclide's $N/Z$ ratio to predict whether it will decay by $\beta^+$ emission or by $e^-$ capture? What other factor is important?

**Skill-Building Exercises** (grouped in similar pairs)

**24.8** Write balanced nuclear equations for the following:
(a) Alpha decay of $_{92}^{234}\text{U}$
(b) Electron capture by neptunium-232
(c) Positron emission by $_7^{12}\text{N}$

**24.9** Write balanced nuclear equations for the following:
(a) $\beta^-$ decay of sodium-26
(b) $\beta^-$ decay of francium-223
(c) Alpha decay of $_{83}^{212}\text{Bi}$

**24.10** Write balanced nuclear equations for the following:
(a) $\beta^-$ emission by magnesium-27
(b) $\beta^+$ emission by $_{12}^{23}\text{Mg}$
(c) Electron capture by $_{46}^{103}\text{Pd}$

**24.11** Write balanced nuclear equations for the following:
(a) $\beta^-$ decay of silicon-32
(b) Alpha decay of polonium-218
(c) Electron capture by $_{49}^{110}\text{In}$

**24.12** Write balanced nuclear equations for the following:
(a) Formation of $_{22}^{48}\text{Ti}$ through positron emission
(b) Formation of silver-107 through electron capture
(c) Formation of polonium-206 through $\alpha$ decay

**24.13** Write balanced nuclear equations for the following:
(a) Formation of $_{95}^{241}\text{Am}$ through $\beta^-$ decay
(b) Formation of $_{89}^{228}\text{Ac}$ through $\beta^-$ decay
(c) Formation of $_{83}^{203}\text{Bi}$ through $\alpha$ decay

**24.14** Write balanced nuclear equations for the following:
(a) Formation of $^{186}\text{Ir}$ through electron capture
(b) Formation of francium-221 through $\alpha$ decay
(c) Formation of iodine-129 through $\beta^-$ decay

**24.15** Write balanced nuclear equations for the following:
(a) Formation of $^{52}\text{Mn}$ through positron emission
(b) Formation of polonium-215 through $\alpha$ decay
(c) Formation of $^{81}\text{Kr}$ through electron capture

**24.16** Which nuclide(s) would you predict to be stable? Why?
(a) $_8^{20}\text{O}$ (b) $_{27}^{59}\text{Co}$ (c) $_3^9\text{Li}$

**24.17** Which nuclide(s) would you predict to be stable? Why?
(a) $_{60}^{146}\text{Nd}$ (b) $_{48}^{114}\text{Cd}$ (c) $_{42}^{88}\text{Mo}$

**24.18** Which nuclide(s) would you predict to be stable? Why?
(a) $^{127}\text{I}$ (b) tin-106 (c) $^{68}\text{As}$

**24.19** Which nuclide(s) would you predict to be stable? Why?
(a) $^{48}\text{K}$ (b) $^{79}\text{Br}$ (c) argon-32

**24.20** What is the most likely mode of decay for each?
(a) $_{92}^{238}\text{U}$ (b) $_{24}^{48}\text{Cr}$ (c) $_{25}^{50}\text{Mn}$

**24.21** What is the most likely mode of decay for each?
(a) $_{47}^{111}\text{Ag}$ (b) $_{17}^{41}\text{Cl}$ (c) $_{44}^{110}\text{Ru}$

**24.22** What is the most likely mode of decay for each?
(a) $^{15}\text{C}$ (b) $^{120}\text{Xe}$ (c) $^{224}\text{Th}$

**24.23** What is the most likely mode of decay for each?
(a) $^{106}\text{In}$ (b) $^{141}\text{Eu}$ (c) $^{241}\text{Am}$

**24.24** Why is $_{24}^{52}\text{Cr}$ the most stable isotope of chromium?

**24.25** Why is $_{20}^{40}\text{Ca}$ the most stable isotope of calcium?

**Problems in Context**

**24.26** $^{237}\text{Np}$ is the parent nuclide of a decay series that starts with $\alpha$ emission, followed by $\beta^-$ emission, and then two more $\alpha$ emissions. Write a balanced nuclear equation for each step.

**24.27** Why is helium found in deposits of uranium and thorium ores? What kind of radioactive emission produces it?

**24.28** In a natural decay series, how many $\alpha$ and $\beta^-$ emissions per atom of uranium-235 result in an atom of lead-207?

## The Kinetics of Radioactive Decay
(Sample Problems 24.4 and 24.5)

**Concept Review Questions**

**24.29** What electronic process is the basis for detecting radioactivity in (a) a scintillation counter; (b) a Geiger-Müller counter?

**24.30** What is the reaction order of radioactive decay? Explain.

**24.31** After 1 minute, three radioactive nuclei remain from an original sample of six. Is it valid to conclude that $t_{1/2}$ equals 1 minute? Is this conclusion valid if the original sample contained $6 \times 10^{12}$ nuclei and $3 \times 10^{12}$ remain after 1 minute? Explain.

**24.32** Radioisotopic dating depends on the constant rate of decay and formation of various nuclides in a sample. How is the proportion of $^{14}\text{C}$ kept relatively constant in living organisms?

**Skill-Building Exercises** (grouped in similar pairs)

**24.33** What is the specific activity (in Ci/g) if 1.65 mg of an isotope emits $1.56 \times 10^6$ $\alpha$ particles per second?

**24.34** What is the specific activity (in Ci/g) if 2.6 g of an isotope emits $4.13 \times 10^8$ $\beta^-$ particles per hour?

**24.35** What is the specific activity (in Bq/g) if 8.58 µg of an isotope emits $7.4 \times 10^4$ $\alpha$ particles per minute?

**24.36** What is the specific activity (in Bq/g) if 1.07 kg of an isotope emits $3.77 \times 10^7$ $\beta^-$ particles per minute?

**24.37** If one-trillionth of the atoms of a radioactive isotope disintegrate each day, what is the decay constant of the process?

**24.38** If $2.8 \times 10^{-10}\%$ of the atoms of a radioactive isotope disintegrate in 1.0 yr, what is the decay constant of the process?

**24.39** If $1.00 \times 10^{-12}$ mol of $^{135}\text{Cs}$ emits $1.39 \times 10^5$ $\beta^-$ particles in 1.00 yr, what is the decay constant?

**24.40** If $6.40 \times 10^{-9}$ mol of $^{176}\text{W}$ emits $1.07 \times 10^{15}$ $\beta^+$ particles in 1.00 h, what is the decay constant?

**24.41** The isotope $_{83}^{212}\text{Bi}$ has a half-life of 1.01 yr. What mass (in mg) of a 2.00-mg sample will remain after $3.75 \times 10^3$ h?

**24.42** The half-life of radium-226 is $1.60 \times 10^3$ yr. How many hours will it take for a 2.50-g sample to decay to the point where 0.185 g of the isotope remains?

**24.43** A rock contains 270 μmol of $^{238}U$ ($t_{1/2} = 4.5 \times 10^9$ yr) and 110 μmol of $^{206}Pb$. Assuming that all the $^{206}Pb$ comes from decay of the $^{238}U$, estimate the rock's age.

**24.44** A fabric remnant from a burial site has a $^{14}C/^{12}C$ ratio of 0.735 of the original value. How old is the fabric?

**Problems in Context**

**24.45** Due to decay of $^{40}K$, cow's milk has a specific activity of about $6 \times 10^{-11}$ mCi per milliliter. How many disintegrations of $^{40}K$ nuclei are there per minute in an 8.0-oz glass of milk?

**24.46** Plutonium-239 ($t_{1/2} = 2.41 \times 10^4$ yr) represents a serious nuclear waste hazard. If seven half-lives are required to reach a tolerable level of radioactivity, how long must $^{239}Pu$ be stored?

**24.47** A rock that contains $3.1 \times 10^{-15}$ mol of $^{232}Th$ ($t_{1/2} = 1.4 \times 10^{10}$ yr) has $9.5 \times 10^4$ fission tracks, each track representing the fission of one atom of $^{232}Th$. How old is the rock?

**24.48** A volcanic eruption melts a large chunk of rock, and all gases are expelled. After cooling, $^{40}_{18}Ar$ accumulates from the ongoing decay of $^{40}_{19}K$ in the rock ($t_{1/2} = 1.25 \times 10^9$ yr). When a piece of rock is analyzed, it is found to contain 1.38 mmol of $^{40}K$ and 1.14 mmol of $^{40}Ar$. How long ago did the rock cool?

## Nuclear Transmutation: Induced Changes in Nuclei

**Concept Review Questions**

**24.49** Irene and Frederic Joliot-Curie converted $^{27}_{13}Al$ to $^{30}_{15}P$ in 1933. Why was this transmutation significant?

**24.50** Early workers mistakenly thought neutron beams were γ radiation. Why? What evidence led to the correct conclusion?

**24.51** Why must the electrical polarity of the tubes in a linear accelerator be reversed at very short time intervals?

**24.52** Why does bombardment with protons usually require higher energies than bombardment with neutrons?

**Skill-Building Exercises** (grouped in similar pairs)

**24.53** Determine the missing species in these transmutations, and write a full nuclear equation from the shorthand notation:
(a) $^{10}B$ (α,n) __
(b) $^{28}Si$ (d,__) $^{29}P$ (where d is a deuteron, $^2H$)
(c) __ (α,2n) $^{244}Cf$

**24.54** Name the unidentified species, and write each transmutation process in shorthand notation: (a) gamma irradiation of a nuclide yields a proton, a neutron, and $^{29}Si$; (b) bombardment of $^{252}Cf$ with $^{10}B$ yields five neutrons and a nuclide; (c) bombardment of $^{238}U$ with a particle yields three neutrons and $^{239}Pu$.

**Problems in Context**

**24.55** Elements 104, 105, and 106 have been named rutherfordium (Rf), dubnium (Db), and seaborgium (Sg), respectively. These elements are synthesized from californium-249 by bombarding with carbon-12, nitrogen-15, and oxygen-18 nuclei, respectively. Four neutrons are formed in each reaction as well. (a) Write balanced nuclear equations for the formation of these elements. (b) Write the equations in shorthand notation.

## Effects of Nuclear Radiation on Matter

**Concept Review Questions**

**24.56** The effects on matter of γ rays and α particles differ. Explain.

**24.57** What is a cation-electron pair, and how does it form?

**24.58** Why is ionizing radiation more harmful to children than adults?

**24.59** Why is ·OH more dangerous than OH$^-$ in an organism?

**Skill-Building Exercises** (grouped in similar pairs)

**24.60** A 135-lb person absorbs $3.3 \times 10^{-7}$ J of energy from radioactive emissions. (a) How many rads does she receive? (b) How many grays (Gy) does she receive?

**24.61** A 3.6-kg laboratory animal receives a single dose of $8.92 \times 10^{-4}$ Gy. (a) How many rads did the animal receive? (b) How many joules did the animal absorb?

**24.62** A 70.-kg person exposed to $^{90}Sr$ absorbs $6.0 \times 10^5$ β$^-$ particles, each with an energy of $8.74 \times 10^{-14}$ J. (a) How many grays does the person receive? (b) If the RBE is 1.0, how many millirems is this? (c) What is the equivalent dose in sieverts (Sv)?

**24.63** A laboratory rat weighs 265 g and absorbs $1.77 \times 10^{10}$ β$^-$ particles, each with an energy of $2.20 \times 10^{-13}$ J. (a) How many rads does the animal receive? (b) What is this dose in Gy? (c) If the RBE is 0.75, what is the equivalent dose in Sv?

**Problems in Context**

**24.64** If 2.50 pCi [1 pCi (picocurie) = $1 \times 10^{-12}$ Ci] of radioactivity from $^{239}Pu$ is emitted in a 95-kg human for 65 h, and each disintegration has an energy of $8.25 \times 10^{-13}$ J, how many grays does the person receive?

**24.65** A small region of a cancer patient's brain is exposed for 24.0 min to 475 Bq of radioactivity from $^{60}Co$ for treatment of a tumor. If the brain mass exposed is 1.858 g and each β$^-$ particle emitted has an energy of $5.05 \times 10^{-14}$ J, what is the dose in rads?

## Applications of Radioisotopes

**Concept Review Questions**

**24.66** What two ways are radioactive tracers used in organisms?

**24.67** Why is neutron activation analysis (NAA) useful to art historians and criminologists?

**24.68** Positrons cannot penetrate matter more than a few atomic diameters, but positron emission of radiotracers can be monitored in medical diagnosis. Explain.

**24.69** A steel part is treated to form some iron-59. Oil used to lubricate the part emits 298 β$^-$ particles (with the energy characteristic of $^{59}Fe$) per minute per milliliter of oil. What other information would you need to calculate the rate of removal of the steel from the part during use?

**Problems in Context**

**24.70** The oxidation of methanol to formaldehyde can be accomplished by reaction with chromic acid:

$$6H^+(aq) + 3CH_3OH(aq) + 2H_2CrO_4(aq) \longrightarrow$$
$$3CH_2O(aq) + 2Cr^{3+}(aq) + 8H_2O(l)$$

The reaction can be studied with the stable isotope tracer $^{18}O$ and mass spectrometry. When a small amount of $CH_3^{18}OH$ is present in the alcohol reactant, $CH_2^{18}O$ forms. When a small amount of $H_2Cr^{18}O_4$ is present, $H_2^{18}O$ forms. Does chromic acid or methanol supply the O atom to the aldehyde? Explain.

## The Interconversion of Mass and Energy
(Sample Problem 24.6)

*Note:* Data for problems in this section: mass of $^1H$ atom = 1.007825 amu; mass of neutron = 1.008665 amu.

**Concept Review Questions**

**24.71** Many scientists at first reacted skeptically to Einstein's equation, $E = mc^2$. Why?

**24.72** How does a change in mass arise when a nuclide forms from nucleons?

**24.73** When a nucleus forms from nucleons, is energy absorbed or released? Why?

**24.74** What is the binding energy per nucleon? Why is the binding energy per nucleon, rather than per nuclide, used to compare nuclide stability?

**Skill-Building Exercises** (grouped in similar pairs)

**24.75** A $^3$H nucleus decays with an energy of 0.01861 MeV. Convert this energy into (a) electron volts; (b) joules.

**24.76** Arsenic-84 decays with an energy of $1.57 \times 10^{-15}$ kJ per nucleus. Convert this energy into (a) eV; (b) MeV.

**24.77** How many joules are released when 1.5 mol of $^{239}$Pu decays, if each nucleus releases 5.243 MeV?

**24.78** How many MeV are released per nucleus when $3.2 \times 10^{-3}$ mol of chromium-49 releases $8.11 \times 10^5$ kJ?

**24.79** Oxygen-16 is one of the most stable nuclides. The mass of a $^{16}$O atom is 15.994915 amu. Calculate the binding energy (a) per nucleon in MeV; (b) per atom in MeV; (c) per mole in kJ.

**24.80** Lead-206 is the end product of $^{238}$U decay. One $^{206}$Pb atom has a mass of 205.974440 amu. Calculate the binding energy (a) per nucleon in MeV; (b) per atom in MeV; (c) per mole in kJ.

**24.81** Cobalt-59 is the only stable isotope of this transition metal. One $^{59}$Co atom has a mass of 58.933198 amu. Calculate the binding energy (a) per nucleon in MeV; (b) per atom in MeV; (c) per mole in kJ.

**24.82** Iodine-131 is one of the most important isotopes used in the diagnosis of thyroid cancer. One atom has a mass of 130.906114 amu. Calculate the binding energy (a) per nucleon in MeV; (b) per atom in MeV; (c) per mole in kJ.

**Problems in Context**

**24.83** The $^{80}$Br nuclide decays either by $\beta^-$ decay or by electron capture. (a) What is the product of each process? (b) Which process releases more energy? (Masses of atoms: $^{80}$Br = 79.918528 amu; $^{80}$Kr = 79.916380 amu; $^{80}$Se = 79.916520 amu; neglect the mass of electrons involved because these are atomic, not nuclear, masses.)

**Applications of Fission and Fusion**

**Concept Review Questions**

**24.84** What is the minimum number of neutrons from each fission event that must be absorbed by other nuclei for a chain reaction to be sustained?

**24.85** In what main way is fission different from radioactive decay? Are all fission events in a chain reaction identical? Explain.

**24.86** What is the purpose of enrichment in the preparation of fuel rods? How is it accomplished?

**24.87** Describe the nature and purpose of these components of a nuclear reactor: (a) control rods; (b) moderator; (c) reflector.

**24.88** State an advantage and a disadvantage of heavy-water reactors compared to light-water reactors.

**24.89** What are the expected advantages of fusion reactors over fission reactors?

**24.90** Why is iron the most abundant element in Earth's core?

**Problems in Context**

**24.91** The reaction that will probably power the first commercial fusion reactor is

$$^3_1\text{H} + {}^2_1\text{H} \longrightarrow {}^4_2\text{He} + {}^1_0\text{n}$$

How much energy would be produced per mole of reaction? (Masses of atoms: $^3_1$H = 3.01605 amu; $^2_1$H = 2.0140 amu; $^4_2$He = 4.00260 amu; mass of $^1_0$n = 1.008665 amu.)

**Comprehensive Problems**

**24.92** Some $^{243}_{95}$Am was present when Earth formed, but it all decayed in the next billion years. The first three steps in this decay series are emissions of an $\alpha$ particle, a $\beta^-$ particle, and another $\alpha$ particle. What other isotopes were present on the young Earth in a rock that contained some $^{243}_{95}$Am?

**24.93** Curium-243 undergoes $\alpha$ decay to plutonium-239:

$$^{243}\text{Cm} \longrightarrow {}^{239}\text{Pu} + \alpha$$

(a) Find the change in mass, $\Delta m$ (in kg). (Masses: $^{243}$Cm = 243.0614 amu; $^{239}$Pu = 239.0522 amu; $^4$He = 4.0026 amu; 1 amu = $1.661 \times 10^{-24}$ g.)
(b) Find the energy released in joules.
(c) Find the energy released in kJ/mol of reaction, and comment on the difference between this value and a typical heat of reaction for a chemical change, which is a few hundred kJ/mol.

**24.94** Plutonium "triggers" for nuclear weapons were manufactured at the Rocky Flats plant in Colorado. An 85-kg worker inhaled a dust particle containing 1.00 μg of $^{239}_{94}$Pu, which resided in his body for 16 h ($t_{1/2}$ of $^{239}$Pu = $2.41 \times 10^4$ yr; each disintegration released 5.15 MeV). (a) How many rads did he receive? (b) How many grays?

**24.95** Archeologists removed some charcoal from a Native American campfire, burned it in $O_2$, and bubbled the $CO_2$ formed into $Ca(OH)_2$ solution (limewater). The $CaCO_3$ that precipitated was filtered and dried. If 4.58 g of the $CaCO_3$ had a radioactivity of 3.2 d/min, how long ago was the campfire?

**24.96** A 5.4-μg sample of $^{226}$RaCl$_2$ has a radioactivity of $1.5 \times 10^5$ Bq. Calculate $t_{1/2}$ of $^{226}$Ra.

**24.97** How many rads does a 65-kg human receive each year from the approximately $10^{-8}$ g of $^{14}_6$C naturally present in her body ($t_{1/2}$ = 5730 yr; each disintegration releases 0.156 MeV)?

**24.98** A sample of AgCl emits 175 nCi/g. A saturated solution prepared from the solid emits $1.25 \times 10^{-2}$ Bq/mL due to radioactive Ag$^+$ ions. What is the molar solubility of AgCl?

**24.99** The scene below depicts a neutron bombarding $^{235}$U:

$$^1_0 + {}^{235}_{92} \longrightarrow {}^{144}_{55} + ? + 2{}^1_0$$

(a) Is this an example of fission or of fusion? (b) Identify the other nuclide formed. (c) What is the most likely mode of decay of the nuclide with Z = 55?

**24.100** What fraction of the $^{235}$U ($t_{1/2} = 7.0 \times 10^8$ yr) created when Earth was formed would remain after $2.8 \times 10^9$ yr?

**24.101** $^{238}$U ($t_{1/2} = 4.5 \times 10^9$ yr) begins a decay series that ultimately forms $^{206}$Pb. The scene below depicts the relative number of $^{238}$U atoms (red) and $^{206}$Pb atoms (green) in a mineral. If all the Pb comes from $^{238}$U, calculate the age of the sample.

**24.102** Technetium-99m is a metastable nuclide used in numerous cancer diagnostic and treatment programs. It is prepared just before use because it decays rapidly through γ emission:

$$^{99m}\text{Tc} \longrightarrow {}^{99}\text{Tc} + \gamma$$

Use the data below to determine (a) the half-life of $^{99m}$Tc; (b) the percentage of the isotope that is lost if it takes 2.0 h to prepare and administer the dose.

| Time (h) | γ Emission (photons/s) |
|----------|------------------------|
| 0 | 5000. |
| 4 | 3150. |
| 8 | 2000. |
| 12 | 1250. |
| 16 | 788 |
| 20 | 495 |

**24.103** How many curies are produced by 1.0 mol of $^{40}$K ($t_{1/2} = 1.25 \times 10^9$ yr)? How many becquerels?

**24.104** The fraction of a radioactive isotope remaining at time $t$ is $(\frac{1}{2})^{t/t_{1/2}}$, where $t_{1/2}$ is the half-life. If the half-life of carbon-14 is 5730 yr, what fraction of carbon-14 in a piece of charcoal remains after (a) 10.0 yr; (b) $10.0 \times 10^3$ yr; (c) $10.0 \times 10^4$ yr? (d) Why is radiocarbon dating more reliable for the fraction remaining in part (b) than that in part (a) or in part (c)?

**24.105** The isotopic mass of $^{210}_{86}$Rn is 209.989669 amu. When this nuclide decays by electron capture, it emits 2.368 MeV. What is the isotopic mass of the resulting nuclide?

**24.106** Exactly 0.1 of the radioactive nuclei in a sample decay per hour. Thus, after $n$ hours, the fraction of nuclei remaining is $(0.900)^n$. Find the value of $n$ equal to one half-life.

**24.107** In neutron activation analysis (NAA), stable isotopes are bombarded with neutrons. Depending on the isotope and the energy of the neutron, various emissions are observed. What are the products when the following neutron-activated species decay? Write an overall equation in shorthand notation for the reaction starting with the stable isotope before neutron activation.
(a) $^{52}_{23}$V* $\longrightarrow$ [β$^-$ emission]     (b) $^{64}_{29}$Cu* $\longrightarrow$ [β$^+$ emission]
(c) $^{28}_{13}$Al* $\longrightarrow$ [β$^-$ emission]

**24.108** In the 1950s, radioactive material was spread over the land from aboveground nuclear tests. A woman drinks some contaminated milk and ingests 0.0500 g of $^{90}$Sr, which is taken up by bones and teeth and not eliminated. (a) How much $^{90}$Sr ($t_{1/2} = 29$ yr) is present in her body after 10 yr? (b) How long will it take for 99.9% of the $^{90}$Sr to decay?

**24.109** The scene below represents a reaction (with neutrons gray and protons purple) that occurs during the lifetime of a star. (a) Write a balanced nuclear equation for the reaction. (b) If the mass difference is $7.7 \times 10^{-2}$ amu, find the energy (kJ) released.

**24.110** What volume of radon will be produced per hour at STP from 1.000 g of $^{226}$Ra ($t_{1/2} = 1599$ yr; 1 yr = 8766 h; mass of one $^{226}$Ra atom = 226.025402 amu)?

**24.111** $^{90}$Kr ($t_{1/2} = 32$ s) is used to study respiration. How soon after being made must a sample be administered to the patient if the activity must be at least 90% of the original activity?

**24.112** Which isotope in each pair is more stable? Why?
(a) $^{140}_{55}$Cs or $^{133}_{55}$Cs     (b) $^{79}_{35}$Br or $^{78}_{35}$Br
(c) $^{28}_{12}$Mg or $^{24}_{12}$Mg     (d) $^{14}_{7}$N or $^{18}_{7}$N

**24.113** A bone sample containing strontium-90 ($t_{1/2} = 29$ yr) emits $7.0 \times 10^4$ β$^-$ particles per month. How long will it take for the emission to decrease to $1.0 \times 10^4$ particles per month?

**24.114** The 23$^{rd}$-century starship *Enterprise* uses a substance called "dilithium crystals" as its fuel.
(a) Assuming this material is the result of fusion, what is the product of the fusion of two $^6$Li nuclei?
(b) How much energy is released per kilogram of dilithium formed? (Mass of one $^6$Li atom is 6.015121 amu.)
(c) When four $^1$H atoms fuse to form $^4$He, how many positrons are released?
(d) To determine the energy potential of the fusion processes in parts (b) and (c), compare the changes in mass per kilogram of dilithium and of $^4$He.
(e) Compare the change in mass per kilogram in part (b) to that for the formation of $^4$He by the method used in current fusion reactors (see p. 1010). (For masses, see Problem 24.91.)
(f) Using early 21$^{st}$-century fusion technology, how much tritium can be produced per kilogram of $^6$Li in the following reaction: $^6_3$Li + $^1_0$n $\longrightarrow$ $^4_2$He + $^3_1$H? When this amount of tritium is fused with deuterium, what is the change in mass? How does this quantity compare with the use of dilithium in part (b)?

**24.115** Uranium and radium are found in many rocky soils throughout the world. Both undergo radioactive decay, and one of the products is radon-222, the heaviest noble gas ($t_{1/2} = 3.82$ days). Inhalation of this gas contributes to many lung cancers. According to Environmental Protection Agency recommendations, the level of radioactivity from radon in homes should not exceed 4.0 pCi/L of air.
(a) What is the safe level of radon in Bq/L of air?
(b) A home has a radon measurement of 41.5 pCi/L. The owner vents the basement in such a way that no more radon enters the living area. What is the activity of the radon remaining in the room air (in Bq/L) after 9.5 days?
(c) How many more days does it take to reach the EPA recommended level?

**24.116** Nuclear disarmament could be accomplished if weapons were not "replenished." The tritium in warheads decays to helium with a half-life of 12.26 yr and must be replaced or the weapon is useless. What fraction of the tritium is lost in 5.50 yr?

**24.117** A decay series starts with the synthetic isotope $^{239}_{92}$U. The first four steps are emissions of a $\beta^-$ particle, another $\beta^-$, an $\alpha$ particle, and another $\alpha$. Write a balanced nuclear equation for each step. Which natural series could start by this sequence?

**24.118** How long can a 54-lb child be exposed to 1.0 mCi of radiation from $^{222}$Rn before accumulating 1.0 mrad if the energy of each disintegration is 5.59 MeV?

**24.119** An earthquake in the area of present-day San Francisco is to be dated by measuring the $^{14}$C activity ($t_{1/2} = 5730$ yr) of parts of a tree uprooted during the event. The tree parts have an activity of 12.9 d/min·g C, and a living tree has an activity of 15.3 d/min·g C. How long ago did the earthquake occur?

**24.120** Were organisms a billion years ago exposed to more or less ionizing radiation than similar organisms today? Explain.

**24.121** Tritium ($^3$H; $t_{1/2} = 12.26$ yr) is continually formed in the upper troposphere by interaction of solar particles with nitrogen. As a result, natural waters contain a small amount of tritium. Two samples of wine are analyzed, one known to be made in 1941 and another made earlier. The water in the 1941 wine has 2.23 times as much tritium as the water in the other. When was the other wine produced?

**24.122** Even though plutonium-239 ($t_{1/2} = 2.41 \times 10^4$ yr) is one of the main fission fuels, it is still a radiation hazard present in spent uranium fuel from nuclear power plants. How many years does it take for 99% of the plutonium-239 in spent fuel to decay?

**24.123** Carbon from the remains of an extinct Australian marsupial, called *Diprotodon*, has a specific activity of 0.61 pCi/g. Modern carbon has a specific activity of 6.89 pCi/g. How long ago did the *Diprotodon* apparently become extinct?

**24.124** The reaction that allows for radiocarbon dating is the continual formation of carbon-14 in the upper atmosphere:

$$^{14}_{7}N + ^{1}_{0}n \longrightarrow ^{14}_{6}C + ^{1}_{1}H$$

What is the energy change associated with this process in eV/reaction and in kJ/mol reaction? (Masses of atoms: $^{14}_{7}$N = 14.003074 amu; $^{14}_{6}$C = 14.003241 amu; $^{1}_{1}$H = 1.007825 amu; mass of $^{1}_{0}$n = 1.008665 amu.)

**24.125** What is the nuclear binding energy of a lithium-7 nucleus in units of kJ/mol and eV/nucleus? (Mass of a lithium-7 atom = 7.016003 amu.)

**24.126** Gadolinium-146 undergoes electron capture. Identify the product, and use Figure 24.2 to find the modes of decay and the other two nuclides in the series below:

$$^{146}_{64} \xrightarrow{EC} ? \xrightarrow{?} ? \xrightarrow{?} ?$$

**24.127** Using 21$^{st}$-century technology, hydrogen fusion requires temperatures around $10^8$ K. But, lower initial temperatures are used if the hydrogen is compressed. In the late 24$^{th}$ century, the starship *Leinad* uses such methods to fuse hydrogen at $10^6$ K.
(a) What is the kinetic energy of an H atom at $1.00 \times 10^6$ K?
(b) How many H atoms are heated to $1.00 \times 10^6$ K from the energy of one H and one anti-H atom annihilating each other?
(c) If these H atoms fuse into $^4$He atoms (with the loss of two positrons per $^4$He formed), how much energy (in J) is generated?
(d) How much more energy is generated by the fusion in (c) than by the hydrogen-antihydrogen collision in (b)?
(e) Should the captain of the *Leinad* change the technology and produce $^3$He (mass = 3.01603 amu) instead of $^4$He?

**24.128** A metastable (excited) form of $^{50}$Sc changes to its stable form by emitting $\gamma$ radiation with a wavelength of 8.73 pm. What is the change in mass of 1 mol of the isotope when it undergoes this change?

**24.129** A sample of cobalt-60 ($t_{1/2} = 5.27$ yr), a powerful $\gamma$ emitter used to treat cancer, was purchased by a hospital on March 1, 2007. The sample must be replaced when its activity reaches 70.% of the original value. On what date must it be replaced?

**24.130** Uranium-233 decays to thorium-229 by $\alpha$ decay, but the emissions have different energies and products: 83% emit an $\alpha$ particle with energy of 4.816 MeV and give $^{229}$Th in its ground state; 15% emit an $\alpha$ particle of 4.773 MeV and give $^{229}$Th in excited state I; and 2% emit a lower energy $\alpha$ particle and give $^{229}$Th in the higher excited state II. Excited state II emits a $\gamma$ ray of 0.060 MeV to reach excited state I. (a) Find the $\gamma$-ray energy and wavelength that would convert excited state I to the ground state. (b) Find the energy of the $\alpha$ particle that would convert $^{233}$U to excited state II.

**24.131** Uranium-238 undergoes a slow decay step ($t_{1/2} = 4.5 \times 10^9$ yr) followed by a series of fast steps to form the stable isotope $^{206}$Pb. Thus, on a time scale of billions of years, $^{238}$U effectively decays "directly" to $^{206}$Pb, and the relative amounts of these isotopes are used to find the age of some rocks. Two students derive equations relating number of half-lives ($n$) since the rock formed to the amounts of the isotopes:

Student 1: $\quad (\frac{1}{2})^n = \dfrac{^{238}_{92}U}{^{206}_{82}Pb}$

Student 2: $\quad (\frac{1}{2})^n = \dfrac{^{238}_{92}U}{^{238}_{92}U + ^{206}_{82}Pb}$

(a) Which equation is correct, and why?
(b) If a rock contains exactly twice as much $^{238}$U as $^{206}$Pb, what is its age in years?

**24.132** In the naturally occurring thorium-232 decay series, the steps emit this sequence of particles: $\alpha$, $\beta^-$, $\beta^-$, $\alpha$, $\alpha$, $\alpha$, $\alpha$, $\beta^-$, $\beta^-$, and $\alpha$. Write a balanced equation for each step.

**24.133** At death, a nobleman in ancient Egypt was mummified and his body contained $1.4 \times 10^{-3}$ g of $^{40}$K ($t_{1/2} = 1.25 \times 10^9$ yr), $1.2 \times 10^{-8}$ g of $^{14}$C ($t_{1/2} = 5730$ yr), and $4.8 \times 10^{-14}$ g of $^3$H ($t_{1/2} = 12.26$ yr). Which nuclide would give the most accurate estimate of the mummy's age? Explain.

**24.134** Assuming that many radioactive nuclides can be considered safe after 20 half-lives, how long will it take for each of the following nuclides to be safe: (a) $^{242}$Cm ($t_{1/2} = 163$ days); (b) $^{214}$Po ($t_{1/2} = 1.6 \times 10^{-4}$ s); (c) $^{232}$Th ($t_{1/2} = 1.39 \times 10^{10}$ yr)?

**24.135** An ancient sword has a blade from the early Roman Empire, around 100 AD, but the wooden handle, inlaid wooden decorations, leather ribbon, and leather sheath have different styles. Given the following activities, estimate the age of each part. Which part was made near the time of the blade ($t_{1/2}$ of $^{14}$C = 5730 yr; $\mathcal{A}_0 = 15.3$ d/min·g)?

| Part | $\mathcal{A}_t$ (d/min·g) |
|---|---|
| Handle | 10.1 |
| Inlaid wood | 13.8 |
| Ribbon | 12.1 |
| Sheath | 15.0 |

**24.136** The starship *Voyager*, like many other vessels of the newly designed 24$^{th}$-century fleet, uses antimatter as fuel.

(a) How much energy is released when 1.00 kg each of antimatter and matter annihilate each other?

(b) When the antimatter is atomic antihydrogen, a small amount of it is mixed with excess atomic hydrogen (gathered from interstellar space during flight). The annihilation releases so much heat that the remaining hydrogen nuclei fuse to form $^4$He. If each hydrogen-antihydrogen collision releases enough heat to fuse $1.00 \times 10^5$ hydrogen atoms, how much energy (in kJ) is released per kilogram of antihydrogen?

(c) Which produces more energy per kilogram of antihydrogen, the procedure in part (a) or that in part (b)?

**24.137** Use Einstein's equation, the mass in grams of 1 amu, and the relation between electron volts and joules to find the energy equivalent (in MeV) of a mass difference of 1 amu.

**24.138** Determine the age of a rock containing 0.065 g of uranium-238 ($t_{1/2} = 4.5 \times 10^9$ yr) and 0.023 g of lead-206. (Assume all the lead-206 came from $^{238}$U decay.)

**24.139** Plutonium-242 decays to uranium-238 by emission of an $\alpha$ particle with an energy of 4.853 MeV. The $^{238}$U that forms is unstable and emits a $\gamma$ ray ($\lambda = 0.02757$ nm). (a) Write balanced equations for these reactions. (b) What would be the energy of the $\alpha$ particle if $^{242}$Pu decayed directly to the more stable $^{238}$U?

**24.140** Seaborgium-263 (Sg), the first isotope of element 106 synthesized, was made, together with four neutrons, by bombarding californium-249 with oxygen-18. It then underwent a series of decays starting with three $\alpha$ emissions. Write balanced equations for the synthesis and the three $\alpha$ emissions of $^{263}$Sg.

**24.141** Some nuclear power plants use plutonium-239, which is produced in breeder reactors. The rate-determining step is the second $\beta^-$ emission. How long does it take to make 1.00 kg of $^{239}$Pu if the reaction is complete when the product is 90.% $^{239}$Pu?

**24.142** A random-number generator can be used to simulate the probability of a given atom decaying over a given time. For example, the formula "=RAND()" in the Excel spreadsheet returns a random number between 0 and 1; thus, for one radioactive atom and a time of one half-life, a number less than 0.5 means the atom decays and a number greater than 0.5 means it doesn't.

(a) Place the "=RAND()" formula in cells A1 to A10 of an Excel spreadsheet. In cell B1, place "=IF(A1<0.5, 0, 1)." This formula returns 0 if A1 is <0.5 (the atom decays) and 1 if A1 is >0.5 (the atom does not decay). Place analogous formulas in cells B2 to B10 (using the "Fill Down" procedure in Excel). To determine the number of atoms remaining after one half-life, sum cells B1 to B10 by placing "=SUM(B1:B10)" in cell B12. To create a new set of random numbers, click on an empty cell (e.g., B13) and hit "Delete." Perform 10 simulations, each time recording the total number of atoms remaining. Do half of the atoms remain after each half-life? If not, why not?

(b) Increase the number of atoms to 100 by placing suitable formulas in cells A1 to A100, B1 to B100, and B102. Perform 10 simulations, and record the number of atoms remaining each time. Are these results more realistic for radioactive decay? Explain.

**24.143** In the following Excel-based simulation, the fate of 256 atoms is followed over five half-lives. Set up formulas in columns A and B, as in Problem 24.142, and simulate the fate of the sample of 256 atoms over one half-life. Cells B1 to B256 should contain 1 or 0. In cell C1, enter "=IF(B1=0, 0, RAND())." This returns 0 if the original atom decayed in the previous half-life or a random number between 0 and 1 if it did not. Fill the formula in C1 down to cell C256. Column D should have formulas similar to those in B, but with modified references, as should columns F, H, and J. Columns E, G, and I should have formulas similar to those in C, but with modified references. In cell B258, enter "=SUM(B1:B256)." This records the number of atoms remaining after the first half-life. Put formulas in cells D258, F258, H258, and J258 to record atoms remaining after subsequent half-lives.

(a) Ideally, how many atoms should remain after each half-life?

(b) Make a table of the atoms remaining after each half-life in four separate simulations. Compare these outcomes to the ideal outcome. How would you make the results more realistic?

**24.144** Representations of three nuclei (with neutrons gray and protons purple) are shown below. Nucleus 1 is stable, but 2 and 3 are not. (a) Write the symbol for each isotope. (b) What is (are) the most likely mode(s) of decay for 2 and 3?

1          2          3

# Common Mathematical Operations in Chemistry

In addition to basic arithmetic and algebra, four mathematical operations are used frequently in general chemistry: manipulating logarithms, using exponential notation, solving quadratic equations, and graphing data. Each is discussed briefly below.

---

## MANIPULATING LOGARITHMS

### Meaning and Properties of Logarithms

A *logarithm* is an exponent. Specifically, if $x^n = A$, we can say that the logarithm to the base $x$ of the number $A$ is $n$, and we can denote it as

$$\log_x A = n$$

Because logarithms are exponents, they have the following properties:

$$\log_x 1 = 0$$
$$\log_x (A \times B) = \log_x A + \log_x B$$
$$\log_x \frac{A}{B} = \log_x A - \log_x B$$
$$\log_x A^y = y \log_x A$$

### Types of Logarithms

Common and natural logarithms are used in chemistry and the other sciences.

1. For *common* logarithms, the base ($x$ in the examples above) is 10, but they are written without specifying the base; that is, $\log_{10} A$ is written more simply as $\log A$; thus, the notation *log* means base 10. The common logarithm of 1000 is 3; in other words, you must raise 10 to the 3rd power to obtain 1000:

$$\log 1000 = 3 \qquad \text{or} \qquad 10^3 = 1000$$

Similarly, we have

$$\log 10 = 1 \qquad \text{or} \qquad 10^1 = 10$$
$$\log 1{,}000{,}000 = 6 \qquad \text{or} \qquad 10^6 = 1{,}000{,}000$$
$$\log 0.001 = -3 \qquad \text{or} \qquad 10^{-3} = 0.001$$
$$\log 853 = 2.931 \qquad \text{or} \qquad 10^{2.931} = 853$$

The last example illustrates an important point about significant figures with all logarithms: *the number of significant figures in the number equals the number of digits to the right of the decimal point in the logarithm.* That is, the number 853 has three significant figures, and the logarithm 2.931 has three digits to the right of the decimal point.

To find a common logarithm with an electronic calculator, enter the number and press the LOG button.

2. For *natural* logarithms, the base is the number $e$, which is 2.71828 . . . , and $\log_e A$ is written ln $A$; thus, the notation *ln* means base $e$. The relationship between the common and natural logarithms is easily obtained:

$$\log 10 = 1 \qquad \text{and} \qquad \ln 10 = 2.303$$

Therefore, we have

$$\ln A = 2.303 \log A$$

To find a natural logarithm with an electronic calculator, enter the number and press the LN button. If your calculator does not have an LN button, enter the number, press the LOG button, and multiply by 2.303.

## Antilogarithms

The *antilogarithm* is the base raised to the logarithm:

antilogarithm (antilog) of $n$ is $10^n$

Using two of the earlier examples, the antilog of 3 is 1000, and the antilog of 2.931 is 853. To obtain the antilog with a calculator, enter the number and press the $10^x$ button. Similarly, to obtain the natural antilogarithm, enter the number and press the $e^x$ button. [On some calculators, enter the number and first press INV and then the LOG (or LN) button.]

## USING EXPONENTIAL (SCIENTIFIC) NOTATION

Many quantities in chemistry are very large or very small. For example, in the conventional way of writing numbers, the number of gold atoms in 1 gram of gold is

59,060,000,000,000,000,000,000 atoms (to four significant figures)

As another example, the mass in grams of one gold atom is

0.0000000000000000000003272 g (to four significant figures)

Exponential (scientific) notation provides a much more practical way of writing such numbers. In exponential notation, we express numbers in the form

$$A \times 10^n$$

where $A$ (the coefficient) is greater than or equal to 1 and less than 10 (that is, $1 \leq A < 10$), and $n$ (the exponent) is an integer.

If the number we want to express in exponential notation is larger than 1, the exponent is positive ($n > 0$); if the number is smaller than 1, the exponent is negative ($n < 0$). The size of $n$ tells the number of places the decimal point (in conventional notation) must be moved to obtain a coefficient $A$ greater than or equal to 1 and less than 10 (in exponential notation). In exponential notation, 1 gram of gold contains $5.906 \times 10^{22}$ atoms, and each gold atom has a mass of $3.272 \times 10^{-22}$ g.

## Changing Between Conventional and Exponential Notation

In order to use exponential notation, you must be able to convert to it from conventional notation, and vice versa.

1. To change a number from conventional to exponential notation, move the decimal point to the left for numbers equal to or greater than 10 and to the right for numbers between 0 and 1:

   75,000,000 changes to $7.5 \times 10^7$ (decimal point 7 places to the left)
   0.006042 changes to $6.042 \times 10^{-3}$ (decimal point 3 places to the right)

2. To change a number from exponential to conventional notation, move the decimal point the number of places indicated by the exponent to the right for numbers with positive exponents and to the left for numbers with negative exponents:

   $1.38 \times 10^5$ changes to 138,000 (decimal point 5 places to the right)
   $8.41 \times 10^{-6}$ changes to 0.00000841 (decimal point 6 places to the left)

3. An exponential number with a coefficient greater than 10 or less than 1 can be changed to the standard exponential form by converting the coefficient to the standard form and adding the exponents:

$$582.3 \times 10^6 \text{ changes to } 5.823 \times 10^2 \times 10^6 = 5.823 \times 10^{(2+6)} = 5.823 \times 10^8$$
$$0.0043 \times 10^{-4} \text{ changes to } 4.3 \times 10^{-3} \times 10^{-4} = 4.3 \times 10^{[(-3)+(-4)]} = 4.3 \times 10^{-7}$$

## Using Exponential Notation in Calculations

In calculations, you can treat the coefficient and exponents separately and apply the properties of exponents (see earlier section on logarithms).

1. To multiply exponential numbers, multiply the coefficients, add the exponents, and reconstruct the number in standard exponential notation:

$$(5.5 \times 10^3)(3.1 \times 10^5) = (5.5 \times 3.1) \times 10^{(3+5)} = 17 \times 10^8 = 1.7 \times 10^9$$
$$(9.7 \times 10^{14})(4.3 \times 10^{-20}) = (9.7 \times 4.3) \times 10^{[14+(-20)]} = 42 \times 10^{-6} = 4.2 \times 10^{-5}$$

2. To divide exponential numbers, divide the coefficients, subtract the exponents, and reconstruct the number in standard exponential notation:

$$\frac{2.6 \times 10^6}{5.8 \times 10^2} = \frac{2.6}{5.8} \times 10^{(6-2)} = 0.45 \times 10^4 = 4.5 \times 10^3$$

$$\frac{1.7 \times 10^{-5}}{8.2 \times 10^{-8}} = \frac{1.7}{8.2} \times 10^{[(-5)-(-8)]} = 0.21 \times 10^3 = 2.1 \times 10^2$$

3. To add or subtract exponential numbers, change all numbers so that they have the same exponent, then add or subtract the coefficients:

$$(1.45 \times 10^4) + (3.2 \times 10^3) = (1.45 \times 10^4) + (0.32 \times 10^4) = 1.77 \times 10^4$$
$$(3.22 \times 10^5) - (9.02 \times 10^4) = (3.22 \times 10^5) - (0.902 \times 10^5) = 2.32 \times 10^5$$

## SOLVING QUADRATIC EQUATIONS

A *quadratic equation* is one in which the highest power of $x$ is 2. The general form of a quadratic equation is

$$ax^2 + bx + c = 0$$

where $a$, $b$, and $c$ are numbers. For given values of $a$, $b$, and $c$, the values of $x$ that satisfy the equation are called *solutions* of the equation. We calculate $x$ with the quadratic formula:

$$x = \frac{-b \pm \sqrt{b^2 - 4ac}}{2a}$$

We commonly require the quadratic formula when solving for some concentration in an equilibrium problem. For example, we might have an expression that is rearranged into the quadratic equation

$$4.3x^2 + 0.65x - 8.7 = 0$$
$$\phantom{4.3x^2 +}\text{a}\phantom{+00}\text{b}\phantom{000}\text{c}$$

Applying the quadratic formula, with $a = 4.3$, $b = 0.65$, and $c = -8.7$, gives

$$x = \frac{-0.65 \pm \sqrt{(0.65)^2 - 4(4.3)(-8.7)}}{2(4.3)}$$

The "plus or minus" sign ($\pm$) indicates that there are always two possible values for $x$. In this case, they are

$$x = 1.3 \quad \text{and} \quad x = -1.5$$

In any real physical system, however, only one of the values will have any meaning. For example, if $x$ were $[H_3O^+]$, the negative value would give a negative concentration, which has no physical meaning.

# GRAPHING DATA IN THE FORM OF A STRAIGHT LINE

Visualizing changes in variables by means of a graph is used throughout science. In many cases, it is most useful if the data can be graphed in the form of a straight line. Any equation will appear as a straight line if it has, or can be rearranged to have, the following general form:

$$y = mx + b$$

where $y$ is the dependent variable (typically plotted along the vertical axis), $x$ is the independent variable (typically plotted along the horizontal axis), $m$ is the slope of the line, and $b$ is the intercept of the line on the $y$ axis. The intercept is the value of $y$ when $x = 0$:

$$y = m(0) + b = b$$

The slope of the line is the change in $y$ for a given change in $x$:

$$\text{Slope } (m) = \frac{y_2 - y_1}{x_2 - x_1} = \frac{\Delta y}{\Delta x}$$

The *sign* of the slope tells the *direction* of the line. If $y$ increases as $x$ increases, $m$ is positive, and the line slopes upward with higher values of $x$; if $y$ decreases as $x$ increases, $m$ is negative, and the line slopes downward with higher values of $x$. The *magnitude* of the slope indicates the *steepness* of the line. A line with $m = 3$ is three times as steep ($y$ changes three times as much for a given change in $x$) as a line with $m = 1$.

Consider the linear equation $y = 2x + 1$. A graph of this equation is shown in Figure A.1. In practice, you can find the slope by drawing a right triangle to the line, using the line as the hypotenuse. Then, one leg gives $\Delta y$, and the other gives $\Delta x$. In the figure, $\Delta y = 8$ and $\Delta x = 4$.

At several places in the text, an equation is rearranged into the form of a straight line in order to determine information from the slope and/or the intercept. For example, in Chapter 16, we obtained the following expression:

$$\ln \frac{[A]_0}{[A]_t} = kt$$

Based on the properties of logarithms, we have

$$\ln [A]_0 - \ln [A]_t = kt$$

Rearranging into the form of an equation for a straight line gives

$$\ln [A]_t = -kt + \ln [A]_0$$
$$\phantom{\ln [A]_t}y\ \ =\ mx\ +\ \ b$$

Thus, a plot of $\ln [A]_t$ vs. $t$ is a straight line, from which you can see that the slope is $-k$ (the negative of the rate constant) and the intercept is $\ln [A]_0$ (the natural logarithm of the initial concentration of A).

At many other places in the text, linear relationships occur that were not shown in graphical terms. For example, the conversion of temperature scales in Chapter 1 can also be expressed in the form of a straight line:

$$°F = \tfrac{9}{5}°C + 32$$
$$\phantom{°F}y = mx\ + b$$

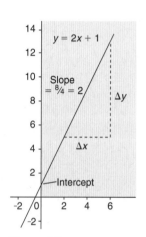

**Figure A.1**

# Standard Thermodynamic Values for Selected Substances*

| Substance or Ion | $\Delta H^\circ_f$ (kJ/mol) | $\Delta G^\circ_f$ (kJ/mol) | $S^\circ$ (J/mol·K) | Substance or Ion | $\Delta H^\circ_f$ (kJ/mol) | $\Delta G^\circ_f$ (kJ/mol) | $S^\circ$ (J/mol·K) |
|---|---|---|---|---|---|---|---|
| $e^-(g)$ | 0 | 0 | 20.87 | $CaCO_3(s)$ | −1206.9 | −1128.8 | 92.9 |
| Aluminum | | | | $CaO(s)$ | −635.1 | −603.5 | 38.2 |
| $Al(s)$ | 0 | 0 | 28.3 | $Ca(OH)_2(s)$ | −986.09 | −898.56 | 83.39 |
| $Al^{3+}(aq)$ | −524.7 | −481.2 | −313 | $Ca_3(PO_4)_2(s)$ | −4138 | −3899 | 263 |
| $AlCl_3(s)$ | −704.2 | −628.9 | 110.7 | $CaSO_4(s)$ | −1432.7 | −1320.3 | 107 |
| $Al_2O_3(s)$ | −1676 | −1582 | 50.94 | Carbon | | | |
| Barium | | | | $C(graphite)$ | 0 | 0 | 5.686 |
| $Ba(s)$ | 0 | 0 | 62.5 | $C(diamond)$ | 1.896 | 2.866 | 2.439 |
| $Ba(g)$ | 175.6 | 144.8 | 170.28 | $C(g)$ | 715.0 | 669.6 | 158.0 |
| $Ba^{2+}(g)$ | 1649.9 | − | − | $CO(g)$ | −110.5 | −137.2 | 197.5 |
| $Ba^{2+}(aq)$ | −538.36 | −560.7 | 13 | $CO_2(g)$ | −393.5 | −394.4 | 213.7 |
| $BaCl_2(s)$ | −806.06 | −810.9 | 126 | $CO_2(aq)$ | −412.9 | −386.2 | 121 |
| $BaCO_3(s)$ | −1219 | −1139 | 112 | $CO_3^{2-}(aq)$ | −676.26 | −528.10 | −53.1 |
| $BaO(s)$ | −548.1 | −520.4 | 72.07 | $HCO_3^-(aq)$ | −691.11 | 587.06 | 95.0 |
| $BaSO_4(s)$ | −1465 | −1353 | 132 | $H_2CO_3(aq)$ | −698.7 | −623.42 | 191 |
| Boron | | | | $CH_4(g)$ | −74.87 | −50.81 | 186.1 |
| $B(\beta$-rhombo-hedral$)$ | 0 | 0 | 5.87 | $C_2H_2(g)$ | 227 | 209 | 200.85 |
| | | | | $C_2H_4(g)$ | 52.47 | 68.36 | 219.22 |
| $BF_3(g)$ | −1137.0 | −1120.3 | 254.0 | $C_2H_6(g)$ | −84.667 | −32.89 | 229.5 |
| $BCl_3(g)$ | −403.8 | −388.7 | 290.0 | $C_3H_8(g)$ | −105 | −24.5 | 269.9 |
| $B_2H_6(g)$ | 35 | 86.6 | 232.0 | $C_4H_{10}(g)$ | −126 | −16.7 | 310 |
| $B_2O_3(s)$ | −1272 | −1193 | 53.8 | $C_6H_6(l)$ | 49.0 | 124.5 | 172.8 |
| $H_3BO_3(s)$ | −1094.3 | −969.01 | 88.83 | $CH_3OH(g)$ | −201.2 | −161.9 | 238 |
| Bromine | | | | $CH_3OH(l)$ | −238.6 | −166.2 | 127 |
| $Br_2(l)$ | 0 | 0 | 152.23 | $HCHO(g)$ | −116 | −110 | 219 |
| $Br_2(g)$ | 30.91 | 3.13 | 245.38 | $HCOO^-(aq)$ | −410 | −335 | 91.6 |
| $Br(g)$ | 111.9 | 82.40 | 174.90 | $HCOOH(l)$ | −409 | −346 | 129.0 |
| $Br^-(g)$ | −218.9 | − | − | $HCOOH(aq)$ | −410 | −356 | 164 |
| $Br^-(aq)$ | −120.9 | −102.82 | 80.71 | $C_2H_5OH(g)$ | −235.1 | −168.6 | 282.6 |
| $HBr(g)$ | −36.3 | −53.5 | 198.59 | $C_2H_5OH(l)$ | −277.63 | −174.8 | 161 |
| Cadmium | | | | $CH_3CHO(g)$ | −166 | −133.7 | 266 |
| $Cd(s)$ | 0 | 0 | 51.5 | $CH_3COOH(l)$ | −487.0 | −392 | 160 |
| $Cd(g)$ | 112.8 | 78.20 | 167.64 | $C_6H_{12}O_6(s)$ | −1273.3 | −910.56 | 212.1 |
| $Cd^{2+}(aq)$ | −72.38 | −77.74 | −61.1 | $C_{12}H_{22}O_{11}(s)$ | −2221.7 | −1544.3 | 360.24 |
| $CdS(s)$ | −144 | −141 | 71 | $CN^-(aq)$ | 151 | 166 | 118 |
| Calcium | | | | $HCN(g)$ | 135 | 125 | 201.7 |
| $Ca(s)$ | 0 | 0 | 41.6 | $HCN(l)$ | 105 | 121 | 112.8 |
| $Ca(g)$ | 192.6 | 158.9 | 154.78 | $HCN(aq)$ | 105 | 112 | 129 |
| $Ca^{2+}(g)$ | 1934.1 | − | − | $CS_2(g)$ | 117 | 66.9 | 237.79 |
| $Ca^{2+}(aq)$ | −542.96 | −553.04 | −55.2 | $CS_2(l)$ | 87.9 | 63.6 | 151.0 |
| $CaF_2(s)$ | −1215 | −1162 | 68.87 | $CH_3Cl(g)$ | −83.7 | −60.2 | 234 |
| $CaCl_2(s)$ | −795.0 | −750.2 | 114 | $CH_2Cl_2(l)$ | −117 | −63.2 | 179 |

*All values at 298 K.

(*continued*)

| Substance or Ion | $\Delta H^\circ_f$ (kJ/mol) | $\Delta G^\circ_f$ (kJ/mol) | $S^\circ$ (J/mol·K) | Substance or Ion | $\Delta H^\circ_f$ (kJ/mol) | $\Delta G^\circ_f$ (kJ/mol) | $S^\circ$ (J/mol·K) |
|---|---|---|---|---|---|---|---|
| $CHCl_3(l)$ | −132 | −71.5 | 203 | $Fe^{2+}(aq)$ | −87.9 | −84.94 | 113 |
| $CCl_4(g)$ | −96.0 | −53.7 | 309.7 | $FeCl_2(s)$ | −341.8 | −302.3 | 117.9 |
| $CCl_4(l)$ | −139 | −68.6 | 214.4 | $FeCl_3(s)$ | −399.5 | −334.1 | 142 |
| $COCl_2(g)$ | −220 | −206 | 283.74 | $FeO(s)$ | −272.0 | −251.4 | 60.75 |
| Cesium | | | | $Fe_2O_3(s)$ | −825.5 | −743.6 | 87.400 |
| $Cs(s)$ | 0 | 0 | 85.15 | $Fe_3O_4(s)$ | −1121 | −1018 | 145.3 |
| $Cs(g)$ | 76.7 | 49.7 | 175.5 | Lead | | | |
| $Cs^+(g)$ | 458.5 | 427.1 | 169.72 | $Pb(s)$ | 0 | 0 | 64.785 |
| $Cs^+(aq)$ | −248 | −282.0 | 133 | $Pb^{2+}(aq)$ | 1.6 | −24.3 | 21 |
| $CsF(s)$ | −554.7 | −525.4 | 88 | $PbCl_2(s)$ | −359 | −314 | 136 |
| $CsCl(s)$ | −442.8 | −414 | 101.18 | $PbO(s)$ | −218 | −198 | 68.70 |
| $CsBr(s)$ | −395 | −383 | 121 | $PbO_2(s)$ | −276.6 | −219.0 | 76.6 |
| $CsI(s)$ | −337 | −333 | 130 | $PbS(s)$ | −98.3 | −96.7 | 91.3 |
| Chlorine | | | | $PbSO_4(s)$ | −918.39 | −811.24 | 147 |
| $Cl_2(g)$ | 0 | 0 | 223.0 | Lithium | | | |
| $Cl(g)$ | 121.0 | 105.0 | 165.1 | $Li(s)$ | 0 | 0 | 29.10 |
| $Cl^-(g)$ | −234 | −240 | 153.25 | $Li(g)$ | 161 | 128 | 138.67 |
| $Cl^-(aq)$ | −167.46 | −131.17 | 55.10 | $Li^+(g)$ | 687.163 | 649.989 | 132.91 |
| $HCl(g)$ | −92.31 | −95.30 | 186.79 | $Li^+(aq)$ | −278.46 | −293.8 | 14 |
| $HCl(aq)$ | −167.46 | −131.17 | 55.06 | $LiF(s)$ | −616.9 | −588.7 | 35.66 |
| $ClO_2(g)$ | 102 | 120 | 256.7 | $LiCl(s)$ | −408 | −384 | 59.30 |
| $Cl_2O(g)$ | 80.3 | 97.9 | 266.1 | $LiBr(s)$ | −351 | −342 | 74.1 |
| Chromium | | | | $LiI(s)$ | −270 | −270 | 85.8 |
| $Cr(s)$ | 0 | 0 | 23.8 | Magnesium | | | |
| $Cr^{3+}(aq)$ | −1971 | — | — | $Mg(s)$ | 0 | 0 | 32.69 |
| $CrO_4^{2-}(aq)$ | −863.2 | −706.3 | 38 | $Mg(g)$ | 150 | 115 | 148.55 |
| $Cr_2O_7^{2-}(aq)$ | −1461 | −1257 | 214 | $Mg^{2+}(g)$ | 2351 | — | — |
| Copper | | | | $Mg^{2+}(aq)$ | −461.96 | −456.01 | 118 |
| $Cu(s)$ | 0 | 0 | 33.1 | $MgCl_2(s)$ | −641.6 | −592.1 | 89.630 |
| $Cu(g)$ | 341.1 | 301.4 | 166.29 | $MgCO_3(s)$ | −1112 | −1028 | 65.86 |
| $Cu^+(aq)$ | 51.9 | 50.2 | −26 | $MgO(s)$ | −601.2 | −569.0 | 26.9 |
| $Cu^{2+}(aq)$ | 64.39 | 64.98 | −98.7 | $Mg_3N_2(s)$ | −461 | −401 | 88 |
| $Cu_2O(s)$ | −168.6 | −146.0 | 93.1 | Manganese | | | |
| $CuO(s)$ | −157.3 | −130 | 42.63 | $Mn(s, \alpha)$ | 0 | 0 | 31.8 |
| $Cu_2S(s)$ | −79.5 | −86.2 | 120.9 | $Mn^{2+}(aq)$ | −219 | −223 | −84 |
| $CuS(s)$ | −53.1 | −53.6 | 66.5 | $MnO_2(s)$ | −520.9 | −466.1 | 53.1 |
| Fluorine | | | | $MnO_4^-(aq)$ | −518.4 | −425.1 | 190 |
| $F_2(g)$ | 0 | 0 | 202.7 | Mercury | | | |
| $F(g)$ | 78.9 | 61.8 | 158.64 | $Hg(l)$ | 0 | 0 | 76.027 |
| $F^-(g)$ | −255.6 | −262.5 | 145.47 | $Hg(g)$ | 61.30 | 31.8 | 174.87 |
| $F^-(aq)$ | −329.1 | −276.5 | −9.6 | $Hg^{2+}(aq)$ | 171 | 164.4 | −32 |
| $HF(g)$ | −273 | −275 | 173.67 | $Hg_2^{2+}(aq)$ | 172 | 153.6 | 84.5 |
| Hydrogen | | | | $HgCl_2(s)$ | −230 | −184 | 144 |
| $H_2(g)$ | 0 | 0 | 130.6 | $Hg_2Cl_2(s)$ | −264.9 | −210.66 | 196 |
| $H(g)$ | 218.0 | 203.30 | 114.60 | $HgO(s)$ | −90.79 | −58.50 | 70.27 |
| $H^+(aq)$ | 0 | 0 | 0 | Nitrogen | | | |
| $H^+(g)$ | 1536.3 | 1517.1 | 108.83 | $N_2(g)$ | 0 | 0 | 191.5 |
| Iodine | | | | $N(g)$ | 473 | 456 | 153.2 |
| $I_2(s)$ | 0 | 0 | 116.14 | $N_2O(g)$ | 82.05 | 104.2 | 219.7 |
| $I_2(g)$ | 62.442 | 19.38 | 260.58 | $NO(g)$ | 90.29 | 86.60 | 210.65 |
| $I(g)$ | 106.8 | 70.21 | 180.67 | $NO_2(g)$ | 33.2 | 51 | 239.9 |
| $I^-(g)$ | −194.7 | — | — | $N_2O_4(g)$ | 9.16 | 97.7 | 304.3 |
| $I^-(aq)$ | −55.94 | −51.67 | 109.4 | $N_2O_5(g)$ | 11 | 118 | 346 |
| $HI(g)$ | 25.9 | 1.3 | 206.33 | $N_2O_5(s)$ | −43.1 | 114 | 178 |
| Iron | | | | $NH_3(g)$ | −45.9 | −16 | 193 |
| $Fe(s)$ | 0 | 0 | 27.3 | $NH_3(aq)$ | −80.83 | 26.7 | 110 |
| $Fe^{3+}(aq)$ | −47.7 | −10.5 | −293 | $N_2H_4(l)$ | 50.63 | 149.2 | 121.2 |

(continued)

| Substance or Ion | $\Delta H^\circ_f$ (kJ/mol) | $\Delta G^\circ_f$ (kJ/mol) | $S^\circ$ (J/mol·K) | Substance or Ion | $\Delta H^\circ_f$ (kJ/mol) | $\Delta G^\circ_f$ (kJ/mol) | $S^\circ$ (J/mol·K) |
|---|---|---|---|---|---|---|---|
| $NO_3^-(aq)$ | −206.57 | −110.5 | 146 | $AgF(s)$ | −203 | −185 | 84 |
| $HNO_3(l)$ | −173.23 | −79.914 | 155.6 | $AgCl(s)$ | −127.03 | −109.72 | 96.11 |
| $HNO_3(aq)$ | −206.57 | −110.5 | 146 | $AgBr(s)$ | −99.51 | −95.939 | 107.1 |
| $NF_3(g)$ | −125 | −83.3 | 260.6 | $AgI(s)$ | −62.38 | −66.32 | 114 |
| $NOCl(g)$ | 51.71 | 66.07 | 261.6 | $AgNO_3(s)$ | −45.06 | 19.1 | 128.2 |
| $NH_4Cl(s)$ | −314.4 | −203.0 | 94.6 | $Ag_2S(s)$ | −31.8 | −40.3 | 146 |
| **Oxygen** | | | | **Sodium** | | | |
| $O_2(g)$ | 0 | 0 | 205.0 | $Na(s)$ | 0 | 0 | 51.446 |
| $O(g)$ | 249.2 | 231.7 | 160.95 | $Na(g)$ | 107.76 | 77.299 | 153.61 |
| $O_3(g)$ | 143 | 163 | 238.82 | $Na^+(g)$ | 609.839 | 574.877 | 147.85 |
| $OH^-(aq)$ | −229.94 | −157.30 | −10.54 | $Na^+(aq)$ | −239.66 | −261.87 | 60.2 |
| $H_2O(g)$ | −241.826 | −228.60 | 188.72 | $NaF(s)$ | −575.4 | −545.1 | 51.21 |
| $H_2O(l)$ | −285.840 | −237.192 | 69.940 | $NaCl(s)$ | −411.1 | −384.0 | 72.12 |
| $H_2O_2(l)$ | −187.8 | −120.4 | 110 | $NaBr(s)$ | −361 | −349 | 86.82 |
| $H_2O_2(aq)$ | −191.2 | −134.1 | 144 | $NaOH(s)$ | −425.609 | −379.53 | 64.454 |
| **Phosphorus** | | | | $Na_2CO_3(s)$ | −1130.8 | −1048.1 | 139 |
| $P_4(s, white)$ | 0 | 0 | 41.1 | $NaHCO_3(s)$ | −947.7 | −851.9 | 102 |
| $P(g)$ | 314.6 | 278.3 | 163.1 | $NaI(s)$ | −288 | −285 | 98.5 |
| $P(s, red)$ | −17.6 | −12.1 | 22.8 | **Strontium** | | | |
| $P_2(g)$ | 144 | 104 | 218 | $Sr(s)$ | 0 | 0 | 54.4 |
| $P_4(g)$ | 58.9 | 24.5 | 280 | $Sr(g)$ | 164 | 110 | 164.54 |
| $PCl_3(g)$ | −287 | −268 | 312 | $Sr^{2+}(g)$ | 1784 | — | — |
| $PCl_3(l)$ | −320 | −272 | 217 | $Sr^{2+}(aq)$ | −545.51 | −557.3 | −39 |
| $PCl_5(g)$ | −402 | −323 | 353 | $SrCl_2(s)$ | −828.4 | −781.2 | 117 |
| $PCl_5(s)$ | −443.5 | — | | $SrCO_3(s)$ | −1218 | −1138 | 97.1 |
| $P_4O_{10}(s)$ | −2984 | −2698 | 229 | $SrO(s)$ | −592.0 | −562.4 | 55.5 |
| $PO_4^{3-}(aq)$ | −1266 | −1013 | −218 | $SrSO_4(s)$ | −1445 | −1334 | 122 |
| $HPO_4^{2-}(aq)$ | −1281 | −1082 | −36 | **Sulfur** | | | |
| $H_2PO_4^-(aq)$ | −1285 | −1135 | 89.1 | $S(rhombic)$ | 0 | 0 | 31.9 |
| $H_3PO_4(aq)$ | −1277 | −1019 | 228 | $S(monoclinic)$ | 0.3 | 0.096 | 32.6 |
| **Potassium** | | | | $S(g)$ | 279 | 239 | 168 |
| $K(s)$ | 0 | 0 | 64.672 | $S_2(g)$ | 129 | 80.1 | 228.1 |
| $K(g)$ | 89.2 | 60.7 | 160.23 | $S_8(g)$ | 101 | 49.1 | 430.211 |
| $K^+(g)$ | 514.197 | 481.202 | 154.47 | $S^{2-}(aq)$ | 41.8 | 83.7 | 22 |
| $K^+(aq)$ | −251.2 | −282.28 | 103 | $HS^-(aq)$ | −17.7 | 12.6 | 61.1 |
| $KF(s)$ | −568.6 | −538.9 | 66.55 | $H_2S(g)$ | −20.2 | −33 | 205.6 |
| $KCl(s)$ | −436.7 | −409.2 | 82.59 | $H_2S(aq)$ | −39 | −27.4 | 122 |
| $KBr(s)$ | −394 | −380 | 95.94 | $SO_2(g)$ | −296.8 | −300.2 | 248.1 |
| $KI(s)$ | −328 | −323 | 106.39 | $SO_3(g)$ | −396 | −371 | 256.66 |
| $KOH(s)$ | −424.8 | −379.1 | 78.87 | $SO_4^{2-}(aq)$ | −907.51 | −741.99 | 17 |
| $KClO_3(s)$ | −397.7 | −296.3 | 143.1 | $HSO_4^-(aq)$ | −885.75 | −752.87 | 126.9 |
| $KClO_4(s)$ | −432.75 | −303.2 | 151.0 | $H_2SO_4(l)$ | −813.989 | −690.059 | 156.90 |
| **Rubidium** | | | | $H_2SO_4(aq)$ | −907.51 | −741.99 | 17 |
| $Rb(s)$ | 0 | 0 | 69.5 | **Tin** | | | |
| $Rb(g)$ | 85.81 | 55.86 | 169.99 | $Sn(white)$ | 0 | 0 | 51.5 |
| $Rb^+(g)$ | 495.04 | — | — | $Sn(gray)$ | 3 | 4.6 | 44.8 |
| $Rb^+(aq)$ | −246 | −282.2 | 124 | $SnCl_4(l)$ | −545.2 | −474.0 | 259 |
| $RbF(s)$ | −549.28 | — | — | $SnO_2(s)$ | −580.7 | −519.7 | 52.3 |
| $RbCl(s)$ | −435.35 | −407.8 | 95.90 | **Titanium** | | | |
| $RbBr(s)$ | −389.2 | −378.1 | 108.3 | $Ti(s)$ | 0 | 0 | 30.7 |
| $RbI(s)$ | −328 | −326 | 118.0 | $TiCl_4(l)$ | −804.2 | −737.2 | 252.3 |
| **Silicon** | | | | $TiO_2(s)$ | −944.0 | −888.8 | 50.6 |
| $Si(s)$ | 0 | 0 | 18.0 | **Zinc** | | | |
| $SiF_4(g)$ | −1614.9 | −1572.7 | 282.4 | $Zn(s)$ | 0 | 0 | 41.6 |
| $SiO_2(s)$ | −910.9 | −856.5 | 41.5 | $Zn(g)$ | 130.5 | 94.93 | 160.9 |
| **Silver** | | | | $Zn^{2+}(aq)$ | −152.4 | −147.21 | −106.5 |
| $Ag(s)$ | 0 | 0 | 42.702 | $ZnO(s)$ | −348.0 | −318.2 | 43.9 |
| $Ag(g)$ | 289.2 | 250.4 | 172.892 | $ZnS(s, zinc blende)$ | −203 | −198 | 57.7 |
| $Ag^+(aq)$ | 105.9 | 77.111 | 73.93 | | | | |

# Equilibrium Constants for Selected Substances

## Dissociation (Ionization) Constants ($K_a$) of Selected Acids

| Name and Formula | Lewis Structure† | $K_{a1}$ | $K_{a2}$ | $K_{a3}$ |
|---|---|---|---|---|
| Acetic acid $CH_3COOH$ | | $1.8 \times 10^{-5}$ | | |
| Acetylsalicylic acid $CH_3COOC_6H_4COOH$ | | $3.6 \times 10^{-4}$ | | |
| Adipic acid $HOOC(CH_2)_4COOH$ | | $3.8 \times 10^{-5}$ | $3.8 \times 10^{-6}$ | |
| Arsenic acid $H_3AsO_4$ | | $6 \times 10^{-3}$ | $1.1 \times 10^{-7}$ | $3 \times 10^{-12}$ |
| Ascorbic acid $H_2C_6H_6O_6$ | | $1.0 \times 10^{-5}$ | $5 \times 10^{-12}$ | |
| Benzoic acid $C_6H_5COOH$ | | $6.3 \times 10^{-5}$ | | |
| Carbonic acid $H_2CO_3$ | | $4.5 \times 10^{-7}$ | $4.7 \times 10^{-11}$ | |
| Chloroacetic acid $ClCH_2COOH$ | | $1.4 \times 10^{-3}$ | | |
| Chlorous acid $HClO_2$ | | $1.1 \times 10^{-2}$ | | |

*All values at 298 K, except for acetylsalicylic acid, which is at 37°C (310 K) in 0.15 $M$ NaCl.
†Acidic (ionizable) proton(s) shown in red. Structures have lowest formal charges. Benzene rings show one resonance form.

(*continued*)

## Dissociation (Ionization) Constants ($K_a$) of Selected Acids

| Name and Formula | Lewis Structure[†] | $K_{a1}$ | $K_{a2}$ | $K_{a3}$ |
|---|---|---|---|---|
| Citric acid<br>$HOOCCH_2C(OH)(COOH)CH_2COOH$ | | $7.4 \times 10^{-4}$ | $1.7 \times 10^{-5}$ | $4.0 \times 10^{-7}$ |
| Formic acid<br>$HCOOH$ | | $1.8 \times 10^{-4}$ | | |
| Glyceric acid<br>$HOCH_2CH(OH)COOH$ | | $2.9 \times 10^{-4}$ | | |
| Glycolic acid<br>$HOCH_2COOH$ | | $1.5 \times 10^{-4}$ | | |
| Glyoxylic acid<br>$HC(O)COOH$ | | $3.5 \times 10^{-4}$ | | |
| Hydrocyanic acid<br>$HCN$ | | $6.2 \times 10^{-10}$ | | |
| Hydrofluoric acid<br>$HF$ | | $6.8 \times 10^{-4}$ | | |
| Hydrosulfuric acid<br>$H_2S$ | | $9 \times 10^{-8}$ | $1 \times 10^{-17}$ | |
| Hypobromous acid<br>$HBrO$ | | $2.3 \times 10^{-9}$ | | |
| Hypochlorous acid<br>$HClO$ | | $2.9 \times 10^{-8}$ | | |
| Hypoiodous acid<br>$HIO$ | | $2.3 \times 10^{-11}$ | | |
| Iodic acid<br>$HIO_3$ | | $1.6 \times 10^{-1}$ | | |
| Lactic acid<br>$CH_3CH(OH)COOH$ | | $1.4 \times 10^{-4}$ | | |
| Maleic acid<br>$HOOCCH{=}CHCOOH$ | | $1.2 \times 10^{-2}$ | $4.7 \times 10^{-7}$ | |

*(continued)*

## Dissociation (Ionization) Constants ($K_a$) of Selected Acids (*continued*)

| Name and Formula | Lewis Structure[†] | $K_{a1}$ | $K_{a2}$ | $K_{a3}$ |
|---|---|---|---|---|
| Malonic acid HOOCCH$_2$COOH | | $1.4 \times 10^{-3}$ | $2.0 \times 10^{-6}$ | |
| Nitrous acid HNO$_2$ | | $7.1 \times 10^{-4}$ | | |
| Oxalic acid HOOCCOOH | | $5.6 \times 10^{-2}$ | $5.4 \times 10^{-5}$ | |
| Phenol C$_6$H$_5$OH | | $1.0 \times 10^{-10}$ | | |
| Phenylacetic acid C$_6$H$_5$CH$_2$COOH | | $4.9 \times 10^{-5}$ | | |
| Phosphoric acid H$_3$PO$_4$ | | $7.2 \times 10^{-3}$ | $6.3 \times 10^{-8}$ | $4.2 \times 10^{-13}$ |
| Phosphorous acid HPO(OH)$_2$ | | $3 \times 10^{-2}$ | $1.7 \times 10^{-7}$ | |
| Propanoic acid CH$_3$CH$_2$COOH | | $1.3 \times 10^{-5}$ | | |
| Pyruvic acid CH$_3$C(O)COOH | | $2.8 \times 10^{-3}$ | | |
| Succinic acid HOOCCH$_2$CH$_2$COOH | | $6.2 \times 10^{-5}$ | $2.3 \times 10^{-6}$ | |
| Sulfuric acid H$_2$SO$_4$ | | Very large | $1.0 \times 10^{-2}$ | |
| Sulfurous acid H$_2$SO$_3$ | | $1.4 \times 10^{-2}$ | $6.5 \times 10^{-8}$ | |

(*continued*)

# Dissociation (Ionization) Constants ($K_b$) of Selected Amine Bases

| Name and Formula | Lewis Structure[†] | $K_{b1}$ | $K_{b2}$ |
|---|---|---|---|
| Ammonia $NH_3$ | | $1.76\times10^{-5}$ | |
| Aniline $C_6H_5NH_2$ | | $4.0\times10^{-10}$ | |
| Diethylamine $(CH_3CH_2)_2NH$ | | $8.6\times10^{-4}$ | |
| Dimethylamine $(CH_3)_2NH$ | | $5.9\times10^{-4}$ | |
| Ethanolamine $HOCH_2CH_2NH_2$ | | $3.2\times10^{-5}$ | |
| Ethylamine $CH_3CH_2NH_2$ | | $4.3\times10^{-4}$ | |
| Ethylenediamine $H_2NCH_2CH_2NH_2$ | | $8.5\times10^{-5}$ | $7.1\times10^{-8}$ |
| Methylamine $CH_3NH_2$ | | $4.4\times10^{-4}$ | |
| tert-Butylamine $(CH_3)_3CNH_2$ | | $4.8\times10^{-4}$ | |
| Piperidine $C_5H_{10}NH$ | | $1.3\times10^{-3}$ | |
| n-Propylamine $CH_3CH_2CH_2NH_2$ | | $3.5\times10^{-4}$ | |

[†]Blue type indicates the basic nitrogen and its lone pair.

*(continued)*

## Dissociation (Ionization) Constants ($K_b$) of Selected Amine Bases (*continued*)

| Name and Formula | Lewis Structure[†] | $K_{b1}$ | $K_{b2}$ |
|---|---|---|---|
| Isopropylamine $(CH_3)_2CHNH_2$ | | $4.7\times10^{-4}$ | |
| 1,3-Propylenediamine $H_2NCH_2CH_2CH_2NH_2$ | | $3.1\times10^{-4}$ | $3.0\times10^{-6}$ |
| Pyridine $C_5H_5N$ | | $1.7\times10^{-9}$ | |
| Triethylamine $(CH_3CH_2)_3N$ | | $5.2\times10^{-4}$ | |
| Trimethylamine $(CH_3)_3N$ | | $6.3\times10^{-5}$ | |

## Dissociation (Ionization) Constants ($K_a$) of Some Hydrated Metal Ions

| Free Ion | Hydrated Ion | $K_a$ |
|---|---|---|
| $Fe^{3+}$ | $Fe(H_2O)_6{}^{3+}(aq)$ | $6\times10^{-3}$ |
| $Sn^{2+}$ | $Sn(H_2O)_6{}^{2+}(aq)$ | $4\times10^{-4}$ |
| $Cr^{3+}$ | $Cr(H_2O)_6{}^{3+}(aq)$ | $1\times10^{-4}$ |
| $Al^{3+}$ | $Al(H_2O)_6{}^{3+}(aq)$ | $1\times10^{-5}$ |
| $Cu^{2+}$ | $Cu(H_2O)_6{}^{2+}(aq)$ | $3\times10^{-8}$ |
| $Pb^{2+}$ | $Pb(H_2O)_6{}^{2+}(aq)$ | $3\times10^{-8}$ |
| $Zn^{2+}$ | $Zn(H_2O)_6{}^{2+}(aq)$ | $1\times10^{-9}$ |
| $Co^{2+}$ | $Co(H_2O)_6{}^{2+}(aq)$ | $2\times10^{-10}$ |
| $Ni^{2+}$ | $Ni(H_2O)_6{}^{2+}(aq)$ | $1\times10^{-10}$ |

## Formation Constants ($K_f$) of Some Complex Ions

| Complex Ion | $K_f$ |
|---|---|
| $Ag(CN)_2{}^-$ | $3.0\times10^{20}$ |
| $Ag(NH_3)_2{}^+$ | $1.7\times10^7$ |
| $Ag(S_2O_3)_2{}^{3-}$ | $4.7\times10^{13}$ |
| $AlF_6{}^{3-}$ | $4\times10^{19}$ |
| $Al(OH)_4{}^-$ | $3\times10^{33}$ |
| $Be(OH)_4{}^{2-}$ | $4\times10^{18}$ |
| $CdI_4{}^{2-}$ | $1\times10^6$ |
| $Co(OH)_4{}^{2-}$ | $5\times10^9$ |
| $Cr(OH)_4{}^-$ | $8.0\times10^{29}$ |
| $Cu(NH_3)_4{}^{2+}$ | $5.6\times10^{11}$ |
| $Fe(CN)_6{}^{4-}$ | $3\times10^{35}$ |
| $Fe(CN)_6{}^{3-}$ | $4.0\times10^{43}$ |
| $Hg(CN)_4{}^{2-}$ | $9.3\times10^{38}$ |
| $Ni(NH_3)_6{}^{2+}$ | $2.0\times10^8$ |
| $Pb(OH)_3{}^-$ | $8\times10^{13}$ |
| $Sn(OH)_3{}^-$ | $3\times10^{25}$ |
| $Zn(CN)_4{}^{2-}$ | $4.2\times10^{19}$ |
| $Zn(NH_3)_4{}^{2+}$ | $7.8\times10^8$ |
| $Zn(OH)_4{}^{2-}$ | $3\times10^{15}$ |

## Solubility-Product Constants ($K_{sp}$) of Slightly Soluble Ionic Compounds

| Name, Formula | $K_{sp}$ | Name, Formula | $K_{sp}$ |
|---|---|---|---|
| **Carbonates** | | Cobalt(II) hydroxide, $Co(OH)_2$ | $1.3 \times 10^{-15}$ |
| Barium carbonate, $BaCO_3$ | $2.0 \times 10^{-9}$ | Copper(II) hydroxide, $Cu(OH)_2$ | $2.2 \times 10^{-20}$ |
| Cadmium carbonate, $CdCO_3$ | $1.8 \times 10^{-14}$ | Iron(II) hydroxide, $Fe(OH)_2$ | $4.1 \times 10^{-15}$ |
| Calcium carbonate, $CaCO_3$ | $3.3 \times 10^{-9}$ | Iron(III) hydroxide, $Fe(OH)_3$ | $1.6 \times 10^{-39}$ |
| Cobalt(II) carbonate, $CoCO_3$ | $1.0 \times 10^{-10}$ | Magnesium hydroxide, $Mg(OH)_2$ | $6.3 \times 10^{-10}$ |
| Copper(II) carbonate, $CuCO_3$ | $3 \times 10^{-12}$ | Manganese(II) hydroxide, $Mn(OH)_2$ | $1.6 \times 10^{-13}$ |
| Lead(II) carbonate, $PbCO_3$ | $7.4 \times 10^{-14}$ | Nickel(II) hydroxide, $Ni(OH)_2$ | $6 \times 10^{-16}$ |
| Magnesium carbonate, $MgCO_3$ | $3.5 \times 10^{-8}$ | Zinc hydroxide, $Zn(OH)_2$ | $3 \times 10^{-16}$ |
| Mercury(I) carbonate, $Hg_2CO_3$ | $8.9 \times 10^{-17}$ | **Iodates** | |
| Nickel(II) carbonate, $NiCO_3$ | $1.3 \times 10^{-7}$ | Barium iodate, $Ba(IO_3)_2$ | $1.5 \times 10^{-9}$ |
| Strontium carbonate, $SrCO_3$ | $5.4 \times 10^{-10}$ | Calcium iodate, $Ca(IO_3)_2$ | $7.1 \times 10^{-7}$ |
| Zinc carbonate, $ZnCO_3$ | $1.0 \times 10^{-10}$ | Lead(II) iodate, $Pb(IO_3)_2$ | $2.5 \times 10^{-13}$ |
| **Chromates** | | Silver iodate, $AgIO_3$ | $3.1 \times 10^{-8}$ |
| Barium chromate, $BaCrO_4$ | $2.1 \times 10^{-10}$ | Strontium iodate, $Sr(IO_3)_2$ | $3.3 \times 10^{-7}$ |
| Calcium chromate, $CaCrO_4$ | $1 \times 10^{-8}$ | Zinc iodate, $Zn(IO_3)_2$ | $3.9 \times 10^{-6}$ |
| Lead(II) chromate, $PbCrO_4$ | $2.3 \times 10^{-13}$ | **Oxalates** | |
| Silver chromate, $Ag_2CrO_4$ | $2.6 \times 10^{-12}$ | Barium oxalate dihydrate, $BaC_2O_4 \cdot 2H_2O$ | $1.1 \times 10^{-7}$ |
| **Cyanides** | | Calcium oxalate monohydrate, $CaC_2O_4 \cdot H_2O$ | $2.3 \times 10^{-9}$ |
| Mercury(I) cyanide, $Hg_2(CN)_2$ | $5 \times 10^{-40}$ | Strontium oxalate monohydrate, | |
| Silver cyanide, $AgCN$ | $2.2 \times 10^{-16}$ | $SrC_2O_4 \cdot H_2O$ | $5.6 \times 10^{-8}$ |
| **Halides** | | **Phosphates** | |
| *Fluorides* | | Calcium phosphate, $Ca_3(PO_4)_2$ | $1.2 \times 10^{-29}$ |
| Barium fluoride, $BaF_2$ | $1.5 \times 10^{-6}$ | Magnesium phosphate, $Mg_3(PO_4)_2$ | $5.2 \times 10^{-24}$ |
| Calcium fluoride, $CaF_2$ | $3.2 \times 10^{-11}$ | Silver phosphate, $Ag_3PO_4$ | $2.6 \times 10^{-18}$ |
| Lead(II) fluoride, $PbF_2$ | $3.6 \times 10^{-8}$ | **Sulfates** | |
| Magnesium fluoride, $MgF_2$ | $7.4 \times 10^{-9}$ | Barium sulfate, $BaSO_4$ | $1.1 \times 10^{-10}$ |
| Strontium fluoride, $SrF_2$ | $2.6 \times 10^{-9}$ | Calcium sulfate, $CaSO_4$ | $2.4 \times 10^{-5}$ |
| *Chlorides* | | Lead(II) sulfate, $PbSO_4$ | $1.6 \times 10^{-8}$ |
| Copper(I) chloride, $CuCl$ | $1.9 \times 10^{-7}$ | Radium sulfate, $RaSO_4$ | $2 \times 10^{-11}$ |
| Lead(II) chloride, $PbCl_2$ | $1.7 \times 10^{-5}$ | Silver sulfate, $Ag_2SO_4$ | $1.5 \times 10^{-5}$ |
| Silver chloride, $AgCl$ | $1.8 \times 10^{-10}$ | Strontium sulfate, $SrSO_4$ | $3.2 \times 10^{-7}$ |
| *Bromides* | | **Sulfides** | |
| Copper(I) bromide, $CuBr$ | $5 \times 10^{-9}$ | Cadmium sulfide, $CdS$ | $1.0 \times 10^{-24}$ |
| Silver bromide, $AgBr$ | $5.0 \times 10^{-13}$ | Copper(II) sulfide, $CuS$ | $8 \times 10^{-34}$ |
| *Iodides* | | Iron(II) sulfide, $FeS$ | $8 \times 10^{-16}$ |
| Copper(I) iodide, $CuI$ | $1 \times 10^{-12}$ | Lead(II) sulfide, $PbS$ | $3 \times 10^{-25}$ |
| Lead(II) iodide, $PbI_2$ | $7.9 \times 10^{-9}$ | Manganese(II) sulfide, $MnS$ | $3 \times 10^{-11}$ |
| Mercury(I) iodide, $Hg_2I_2$ | $4.7 \times 10^{-29}$ | Mercury(II) sulfide, $HgS$ | $2 \times 10^{-50}$ |
| Silver iodide, $AgI$ | $8.3 \times 10^{-17}$ | Nickel(II) sulfide, $NiS$ | $3 \times 10^{-16}$ |
| **Hydroxides** | | Silver sulfide, $Ag_2S$ | $8 \times 10^{-48}$ |
| Aluminum hydroxide, $Al(OH)_3$ | $3 \times 10^{-34}$ | Tin(II) sulfide, $SnS$ | $1.3 \times 10^{-23}$ |
| Cadmium hydroxide, $Cd(OH)_2$ | $7.2 \times 10^{-15}$ | Zinc sulfide, $ZnS$ | $2.0 \times 10^{-22}$ |
| Calcium hydroxide, $Ca(OH)_2$ | $6.5 \times 10^{-6}$ | | |

# Standard Electrode (Half-Cell) Potentials*

| Half-Reaction | $E°$ (V) |
|---|---|
| $F_2(g) + 2e^- \rightleftharpoons 2F^-(aq)$ | +2.87 |
| $O_3(g) + 2H^+(aq) + 2e^- \rightleftharpoons O_2(g) + H_2O(l)$ | +2.07 |
| $Co^{3+}(aq) + e^- \rightleftharpoons Co^{2+}(aq)$ | +1.82 |
| $H_2O_2(aq) + 2H^+(aq) + 2e^- \rightleftharpoons 2H_2O(l)$ | +1.77 |
| $PbO_2(s) + 3H^+(aq) + HSO_4^-(aq) + 2e^- \rightleftharpoons PbSO_4(s) + 2H_2O(l)$ | +1.70 |
| $Ce^{4+}(aq) + e^- \rightleftharpoons Ce^{3+}(aq)$ | +1.61 |
| $MnO_4^-(aq) + 8H^+(aq) + 5e^- \rightleftharpoons Mn^{2+}(aq) + 4H_2O(l)$ | +1.51 |
| $Au^{3+}(aq) + 3e^- \rightleftharpoons Au(s)$ | +1.50 |
| $Cl_2(g) + 2e^- \rightleftharpoons 2Cl^-(aq)$ | +1.36 |
| $Cr_2O_7^{2-}(aq) + 14H^+(aq) + 6e^- \rightleftharpoons 2Cr^{3+}(aq) + 7H_2O(l)$ | +1.33 |
| $MnO_2(s) + 4H^+(aq) + 2e^- \rightleftharpoons Mn^{2+}(aq) + 2H_2O(l)$ | +1.23 |
| $O_2(g) + 4H^+(aq) + 4e^- \rightleftharpoons 2H_2O(l)$ | +1.23 |
| $Br_2(l) + 2e^- \rightleftharpoons 2Br^-(aq)$ | +1.07 |
| $NO_3^-(aq) + 4H^+(aq) + 3e^- \rightleftharpoons NO(g) + 2H_2O(l)$ | +0.96 |
| $2Hg^{2+}(aq) + 2e^- \rightleftharpoons Hg_2^{2+}(aq)$ | +0.92 |
| $Hg_2^{2+}(aq) + 2e^- \rightleftharpoons 2Hg(l)$ | +0.85 |
| $Ag^+(aq) + e^- \rightleftharpoons Ag(s)$ | +0.80 |
| $Fe^{3+}(aq) + e^- \rightleftharpoons Fe^{2+}(aq)$ | +0.77 |
| $O_2(g) + 2H^+(aq) + 2e^- \rightleftharpoons H_2O_2(aq)$ | +0.68 |
| $MnO_4^-(aq) + 2H_2O(l) + 3e^- \rightleftharpoons MnO_2(s) + 4OH^-(aq)$ | +0.59 |
| $I_2(s) + 2e^- \rightleftharpoons 2I^-(aq)$ | +0.53 |
| $O_2(g) + 2H_2O(l) + 4e^- \rightleftharpoons 4OH^-(aq)$ | +0.40 |
| $Cu^{2+}(aq) + 2e^- \rightleftharpoons Cu(s)$ | +0.34 |
| $AgCl(s) + e^- \rightleftharpoons Ag(s) + Cl^-(aq)$ | +0.22 |
| $SO_4^{2-}(aq) + 4H^+(aq) + 2e^- \rightleftharpoons SO_2(g) + 2H_2O(l)$ | +0.20 |
| $Cu^{2+}(aq) + e^- \rightleftharpoons Cu^+(aq)$ | +0.15 |
| $Sn^{4+}(aq) + 2e^- \rightleftharpoons Sn^{2+}(aq)$ | +0.13 |
| $2H^+(aq) + 2e^- \rightleftharpoons H_2(g)$ | 0.00 |
| $Pb^{2+}(aq) + 2e^- \rightleftharpoons Pb(s)$ | −0.13 |
| $Sn^{2+}(aq) + 2e^- \rightleftharpoons Sn(s)$ | −0.14 |
| $N_2(g) + 5H^+(aq) + 4e^- \rightleftharpoons N_2H_5^+(aq)$ | −0.23 |
| $Ni^{2+}(aq) + 2e^- \rightleftharpoons Ni(s)$ | −0.25 |
| $Co^{2+}(aq) + 2e^- \rightleftharpoons Co(s)$ | −0.28 |
| $PbSO_4(s) + H^+(aq) + 2e^- \rightleftharpoons Pb(s) + HSO_4^-(aq)$ | −0.31 |
| $Cd^{2+}(aq) + 2e^- \rightleftharpoons Cd(s)$ | −0.40 |
| $Fe^{2+}(aq) + 2e^- \rightleftharpoons Fe(s)$ | −0.44 |
| $Cr^{3+}(aq) + 3e^- \rightleftharpoons Cr(s)$ | −0.74 |
| $Zn^{2+}(aq) + 2e^- \rightleftharpoons Zn(s)$ | −0.76 |
| $2H_2O(l) + 2e^- \rightleftharpoons H_2(g) + 2OH^-(aq)$ | −0.83 |
| $Mn^{2+}(aq) + 2e^- \rightleftharpoons Mn(s)$ | −1.18 |
| $Al^{3+}(aq) + 3e^- \rightleftharpoons Al(s)$ | −1.66 |
| $Mg^{2+}(aq) + 2e^- \rightleftharpoons Mg(s)$ | −2.37 |
| $Na^+(aq) + e^- \rightleftharpoons Na(s)$ | −2.71 |
| $Ca^{2+}(aq) + 2e^- \rightleftharpoons Ca(s)$ | −2.87 |
| $Sr^{2+}(aq) + 2e^- \rightleftharpoons Sr(s)$ | −2.89 |
| $Ba^{2+}(aq) + 2e^- \rightleftharpoons Ba(s)$ | −2.90 |
| $K^+(aq) + e^- \rightleftharpoons K(s)$ | −2.93 |
| $Li^+(aq) + e^- \rightleftharpoons Li(s)$ | −3.05 |

*All values at 298 K. Written as reductions; $E°$ value refers to all components in their standard states: 1 $M$ for dissolved species; 1 atm pressure for the gas behaving ideally; the pure substance for solids and liquids.

# Answers to Selected Problems

## Chapter 1

**1.2** Gas molecules fill the entire container; the volume of a gas is the volume of the container. Solids and liquids have a definite volume. The volume of the container does not affect the volume of a solid or liquid. (a) gas (b) liquid (c) liquid **1.4** Physical property: a characteristic shown by a substance itself, without any interaction with or change into other substances. Chemical property: a characteristic of a substance that appears as it interacts with, or transforms into, other substances. (a) Color (yellow-green and silvery to white) and physical state (gas and metal to crystals) are physical properties. The interaction between chlorine gas and sodium metal is a chemical property. (b) Color and magnetism are physical properties. No chemical changes. **1.6**(a) Physical change; there is only a temperature change. (b) Chemical change; the change in appearance indicates an irreversible chemical change. (c) Physical change; there is only a change in size, not composition. (d) Chemical change; the wood (and air) become different substances with different compositions. **1.8**(a) fuel (b) wood **1.13** Lavoisier measured the total mass of the reactants and products, not just the mass of the solids. The total mass of the reactants and products remained constant. His measurements showed that a gas was involved in the reaction. He called this gas *oxygen* (one of his key discoveries). **1.16** A well-designed experiment must have the following essential features: (1) There must be at least two variables that are expected to be related; (2) there must be a way to control all the variables, so that only one at a time may be changed; (3) the results must be reproducible. **1.19**(a) $(2.54 \text{ cm})^2/(1 \text{ in})^2$ and $(1 \text{ m})^2/(100 \text{ cm})^2$ (b) $(1000 \text{ m})^2/(1 \text{ km})^2$ and $(100 \text{ cm})^2/(1 \text{ m})^2$ (c) $(1.609 \times 10^3 \text{ m/mi})$ and $(1 \text{ h}/3600 \text{ s})$ (d) $(1000 \text{ g}/2.205 \text{ lb})$ and $(3.531 \times 10^{-5} \text{ ft}^3/\text{cm}^3)$ **1.21** An extensive property depends on the amount of material present. An intensive property is the same regardless of how much material is present. (a) extensive property (b) intensive property (c) extensive property (d) intensive property **1.23**(a) increases (b) remains the same (c) decreases (d) increases (e) remains the same **1.26** 1.43 nm **1.28** $3.94 \times 10^3$ in **1.30**(a) $2.07 \times 10^{-9}$ km$^2$ (b) \$10.43 **1.32** Answers will vary, depending on the person's mass. **1.34**(a) $5.52 \times 10^3$ kg/m$^3$ (b) 345 lb/ft$^3$ **1.36**(a) $2.56 \times 10^{-9}$ mm$^3$ (b) $10^{-10}$ L **1.38**(a) 9.626 cm$^3$ (b) 64.92 g **1.40** 2.70 g/cm$^3$ **1.42**(a) 20.°C; 293 K (b) 109 K; −263°F (c) −273°C; −460.°F **1.45**(a) $2.47 \times 10^{-7}$ m (b) 67.6 Å **1.52**(a) none (b) none (c) 0.041$\underline{0}$ (d) 4.$\underline{0100}\times10^4$ **1.54**(a) 0.00036 (b) 35.83 (c) 22.5 **1.56** $6 \times 10^2$ **1.58**(a) 1.34 m (b) 21,621 mm$^3$ (c) 443 cm **1.60**(a) $1.310000\times10^5$ (b) $4.7\times10^{-4}$ (c) $2.10006\times10^5$ (d) $2.1605\times10^3$ **1.62**(a) 5550 (b) 10,070. (c) 0.000000885 (d) 0.003004 **1.64**(a) $8.025\times10^4$ (b) $1.0098\times10^{-3}$ (c) $7.7\times10^{-11}$

**1.66**(a) $4.06\times10^{-19}$ J (b) $1.61\times10^{24}$ molecules (c) $1.82\times10^5$ J/mol **1.68**(a) Height measured, not exact. (b) Planets counted, exact. (c) Number of grams in a pound is not a unit definition, not exact. (d) Definition of "millimeter," exact. **1.70** $7.50 \pm 0.05$ cm **1.72**(a) I$_{avg}$ = 8.72 g; II$_{avg}$ = 8.72 g; III$_{avg}$ = 8.50 g; IV$_{avg}$ = 8.56 g; sets I and II are most accurate. (b) Set III is the most precise, but is the least accurate. (c) Set I has the best combination of high accuracy and high precision. (d) Set IV has both low accuracy and low precision. **1.74**(a)

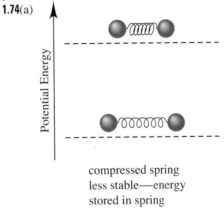

compressed spring
less stable—energy
stored in spring

(b)

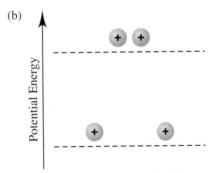

two charges near each other
less stable—repulsion of like
charges

**1.76** 7.7/1 **1.78**(a) density = 0.21 g/L, will float (b) $CO_2$ is denser than air, will sink (c) density = 0.30 g/L, will float (d) $O_2$ is denser than air, will sink (e) density = 1.38 g/L, will sink (f) 0.55 g for empty ball; 0.50 g for ball filled with hydrogen **1.80**(a) $8.0\times10^{12}$ g (b) $4.1\times10^5$ m$^3$ (c) $9.5\times10^{13}$ dollars **1.82**(a) −195.79°C (b) −320.42°F (c) 5.05 L **1.83**(a) 2.6 m/s (b) 16 km (c) 12:45 pm **1.85** freezing point = −3.7°X; boiling point = 63.3°X **1.86** $2.3\times10^{25}$ g oxygen; $1.4\times10^{25}$ g silicon; $5\times10^{15}$ g ruthenium and rhodium

## Chapter 2

**Answers to Boxed Reading Problems: B2.1** (a) 5 peaks  (b) *m/e* ratio of heaviest particle = 74; *m/e* ratio of lightest particle = 35  **B2.3** (a) Since salt dissolves in water and pepper does not, add water to mixture and filter to remove solid pepper. Evaporate water to recover solid salt.  (d) Heat the mixture; the ethanol will boil off (distill), while the sugar will remain behind.

• **2.1** Compounds contain different types of atoms; there is only one type of atom in an element. **2.4**(a) The presence of more than one element makes pure calcium chloride a compound. (b) There is only one kind of atom, so sulfur is an element. (c) The presence of more than one compound makes baking powder a mixture.  (d) The presence of more than one type of atom means cytosine cannot be an element. The specific, not variable, arrangement means it is a compound. **2.12**(a) elements, compounds, and mixtures  (b) compounds  (c) compounds  **2.14**(a) Law of definite composition: the composition is the same regardless of its source.  (b) Law of mass conservation: the total quantity of matter does not change.  (c) Law of multiple proportions: two elements can combine to form two different compounds that have different proportions of those elements.  **2.16**(a) No, the percent by mass of each element in a compound is fixed.  (b) Yes, the *mass* of each element in a compound depends on the amount of compound.  **2.18** The two experiments demonstrate the law of definite composition. The unknown compound decomposes the same way both times. The experiments also demonstrate the law of conservation of mass since the total mass before reaction equals the total mass after reaction.  **2.20**(a) 1.34 g F  (b) 0.514 Ca; 0.486 F (c) 51.4 mass % Ca; 48.6 mass % F  **2.22**(a) 0.603  (b) 322 g Mg **2.24** $3.498 \times 10^6$ g Cu; $1.766 \times 10^6$ g S  **2.26** compound 1: 0.905 S/Cl; compound 2: 0.451 S/Cl; ratio: 2.00/1.00 **2.29** Coal A **2.31** Dalton postulated that atoms of an element are identical and that compounds result from the chemical combination of specific ratios of different elements.  **2.32** If you know the ratio of any two quantities and the value of one of them, the other can always be calculated; in this case, the charge and the mass/charge ratio were known.  **2.36** The atomic number is the number of protons in an atom's nucleus. When the atomic number changes, the identity of the element changes. The mass number is the total number of protons and neutrons in the nucleus. The identity of an element is based on the number of protons, not the number of neutrons. The mass number can vary (by a change in number of neutrons) without changing the identity of the element.  **2.39** All three isotopes have 18 protons and 18 electrons. Their respective mass numbers are 36, 38, and 40, with the respective numbers of neutrons being 18, 20, and 22.  **2.41**(a) These have the same number of protons and electrons, but different numbers of neutrons; same Z.  (b) These have the same number of neutrons, but different numbers of protons and electrons; same N. (c) These have different numbers of protons, neutrons, and electrons; same A.

**2.43**(a) $^{38}_{18}Ar$  (b) $^{55}_{25}Mn$   (c) $^{109}_{47}Ag$
**2.45**(a) $^{48}_{22}Ti$           (b) $^{79}_{34}Se$                    (c) $^{11}_{5}B$

**2.47** 69.72 amu  **2.49** $^{35}Cl$ = 75.774%, $^{37}Cl$ = 24.226% **2.52**(a) In the modern periodic table, the elements are arranged in order of increasing atomic number.  (b) Elements in a group (or family) have similar chemical properties.  (c) Elements can be classified as metals, metalloids, or nonmetals.  **2.55** The alkali metals [Group 1A(1)] are metals and readily lose one electron to form cations; the halogens [Group 7A(17)] are nonmetals and readily gain one electron to form anions. **2.56**(a) germanium; Ge; 4A(14); metalloid  (b) phosphorus; P; 5A(15); nonmetal  (c) helium; He; 8A(18); nonmetal (d) lithium; Li; 1A(1); metal  (e) molybdenum; Mo; 6B(6); metal  **2.58**(a) Ra; 88  (b) Si; 14  (c) Cu; 63.55 amu  (d) Br; 79.90 amu  **2.60** Atoms of these two kinds of substances will form ionic bonds, in which one or more electrons are transferred from the metal atom to the nonmetal atom to form a cation and an anion, respectively.  **2.63** Coulomb's law states the energy of attraction in an ionic bond is directly proportional to the product of charges and inversely proportional to the distance between charges. The product of charges in MgO [(2+) (2−)] is greater than that in LiF [(1+) (1−)]. Thus, MgO has stronger ionic bonding.  **2.66** The Group 1A(1) elements form cations, and the Group 7A(17) elements form anions.  **2.68** Each potassium atom loses one electron to form an ion with a 1+ charge. Each sulfur atom gains two electrons to form an ion with a 2− charge. Two potassiums, losing one electron each, are required for each sulfur, which gains two electrons. The oppositely charged ions attract each other to form an ionic solid, $K_2S$.  **2.70** $K^+$; $I^-$  **2.72**(a) oxygen; 17; 6A(16); 2  (b) fluorine; 19; 7A(17); 2  (c) calcium; 40; 2A(2); 4 **2.74** Lithium forms the $Li^+$ ion; oxygen forms the $O^{2-}$ ion. Number of $O^{2-}$ ions = $4.2 \times 10^{21}$ $O^{2-}$ ions.  **2.76** NaCl **2.78** The subscripts in a formula give the numbers of ions in a formula unit of the compound. The subscripts indicate that there are two $F^-$ ions for each $Mg^{2+}$ ion. Using this information and the mass of each element, we can calculate percent mass of each element in the compound.  **2.80** The two samples are similar in that both contain 20 billion oxygen atoms and 20 billion hydrogen atoms. They differ in that they contain different types of molecules: $H_2O_2$ molecules in the hydrogen peroxide sample, and $H_2$ and $O_2$ molecules in the mixture. In addition, the mixture contains 20 billion molecules (10 billion $H_2$ and 10 billion $O_2$), while the hydrogen peroxide sample contains 10 billion molecules.  **2.84**(a) $Na_3N$, sodium nitride (b) SrO, strontium oxide  (c) $AlCl_3$, aluminum chloride **2.86**(a) $MgF_2$, magnesium fluoride  (b) ZnS, zinc sulfide (c) $SrCl_2$, strontium chloride  **2.88**(a) $SnCl_4$  (b) iron(III) bromide

(c) CuBr  (d) manganese(III) oxide  **2.90**(a) cobalt(II) oxide
(b) $Hg_2Cl_2$  (c) lead(II) acetate trihydrate  (d) $Cr_2O_3$
**2.92**(a) BaO  (b) $Fe(NO_3)_2$  (c) MgS  **2.94**(a) $H_2SO_4$; sulfuric
acid  (b) $HIO_3$; iodic acid  (c) HCN; hydrocyanic acid
(d) $H_2S$; hydrosulfuric acid  **2.96**(a) ammonium ion, $NH_4^+$;
ammonia, $NH_3$  (b) magnesium sulfide, MgS; magnesium
sulfite, $MgSO_3$; magnesium sulfate, $MgSO_4$  (c) hydrochloric
acid, HCl; chloric acid, $HClO_3$; chlorous acid, $HClO_2$
(d) cuprous bromide, CuBr; cupric bromide, $CuBr_2$  **2.98** Disulfur tetrafluoride, $S_2F_4$  **2.100**(a) calcium chloride  (b) copper(I)
oxide  (c) stannic fluoride  (d) hydrochloric acid  **2.102**(a) 12
oxygen atoms; 342.2 amu  (b) 9 hydrogen atoms; 132.06 amu
(c) 8 oxygen atoms; 344.6 amu  **2.104**(a) $(NH_4)_2SO_4$; 132.15 amu
(b) $NaH_2PO_4$; 119.98 amu  (c) $KHCO_3$; 100.12 amu
**2.106**(a) 108.02 amu  (b) 331.2 amu  (c) 72.08 amu
**2.108**(a) $SO_3$; sulfur trioxide; 80.07 amu  (b) $C_3H_8$; propane;
44.09 amu  **2.112** Separating the components of a mixture
requires physical methods only; that is, no chemical changes
(no changes in composition) take place, and the components
maintain their chemical identities and properties throughout.
Separating the components of a compound requires a chemical
change (change in composition).  **2.115**(a) compound  (b) homogeneous mixture  (c) heterogeneous mixture  (d) homogeneous
mixture  (e) homogeneous mixture  **2.117**(a) filtration
(b) chromatography  **2.119**(a) fraction of volume = $5.2 \times 10^{-13}$
(b) mass of nucleus = $6.64466 \times 10^{-24}$ g; fraction of mass =
0.999726  **2.120** strongest ionic bonding: MgO; weakest ionic
bonding: RbI  **2.124**(a) I = NO; II = $N_2O_3$; III = $N_2O_5$  (b) I has
1.14 g O per 1.00 g N; II, 1.71 g O; III, 2.86 g O  **2.128**(a) $Cl^-$,
1.898 mass %; $Na^+$, 1.056 mass %; $SO_4^{2-}$, 0.265 mass %;
$Mg^{2+}$, 0.127 mass %; $Ca^{2+}$, 0.04 mass %; $K^+$, 0.038 mass %;
$HCO_3^-$, 0.014 mass %  (b) 30.72%  (c) Alkaline earth metal
ions, total mass % = 0.17%; alkali metal ions, total mass % =
1.094%  (d) Anions (2.177 mass %) make up a larger mass
fraction than cations (1.26 mass %).  **2.131** Molecular formula,
$C_4H_6O_4$; molecular mass, 118.09 amu; 40.68% by mass C;
5.122% by mass H; 54.20% by mass O  **2.134**(a) Formulas and
masses in amu: $^{15}N_2{}^{18}O$, 48; $^{15}N_2{}^{16}O$, 46; $^{14}N_2{}^{18}O$, 46; $^{14}N_2{}^{16}O$,
44; $^{15}N^{14}N^{18}O$, 47; $^{15}N^{14}N^{16}O$, 45  (b) $^{15}N_2{}^{18}O$, least common;
$^{14}N_2{}^{16}O$, most common  **2.136** 58.091 amu  **2.138** nitroglycerin,
39.64 mass % NO; isoamyl nitrate, 22.54 mass % NO
**2.139** 0.370 lb C; 0.0222 lb H; 0.423 lb O; 0.185 lb N
**2.144**(1) chemical change  (2) physical change  (3) chemical
change  (4) chemical change  (5) physical change

## Chapter 3

**3.2**(a) 12 mol C atoms  (b) $1.445 \times 10^{25}$ C atoms  **3.7**(a) left
(b) left  (c) left  (d) neither  **3.8**(a) 121.64 g/mol
(b) 76.02 g/mol  (c) 106.44 g/mol  (d) 152.00 g/mol
**3.10**(a) 134.7 g/mol  (b) 175.3 g/mol  (c) 342.17 g/mol
(d) 125.84 g/mol  **3.12**(a) $1.1 \times 10^2$ g $KMnO_4$  (b) 0.188 mol O
atoms  (c) $1.5 \times 10^{20}$ O atoms  **3.14**(a) 9.73 g $MnSO_4$  (b) 44.6 mol
$Fe(ClO_4)_3$  (c) $1.74 \times 10^{21}$ N atoms  **3.16**(a) $1.56 \times 10^3$ g
$Cu_2CO_3$  (b) 0.0725 g $N_2O_5$  (c) 0.644 mol $NaClO_4$; $3.88 \times 10^{23}$
formula units $NaClO_4$  (d) $3.88 \times 10^{23}$ $Na^+$ ions; $3.88 \times 10^{23}$

$ClO_4^-$ ions; $3.88 \times 10^{23}$ Cl atoms; $1.55 \times 10^{24}$ O atoms
**3.18**(a) 6.375 mass % H  (b) 71.52 mass % O  **3.20**(a) 0.1252
mass fraction C  (b) 0.3428 mass fraction O  **3.23**(a) 0.9507 mol
cisplatin  (b) $3.5 \times 10^{24}$ H atoms  **3.25**(a) 195 mol rust
(b) 195 mol $Fe_2O_3$  (c) $2.18 \times 10^4$ g Fe  **3.27** $CO(NH_2)_2 >$
$NH_4NO_3 > (NH_4)_2SO_4 > KNO_3$  **3.28**(a) 883 mol PbS
(b) $1.88 \times 10^{25}$ Pb atoms  **3.32**(b) From the mass percent, determine the empirical formula. Add up the total number of atoms
in the empirical formula, and divide that number into the total
number of atoms in the molecule. The result is the multiplier
that converts the empirical formula into the molecular formula.

### Road Map

(c) Find the empirical formula from the mass percents. Compare the number of atoms given for the one element to the
number in the empirical formula. Multiply the empirical formula by the factor that is needed to obtain the given number
of atoms for that element.

### Road Map

First three steps are the same as in road map for part (b).

(e) Count the numbers of the various types of atoms in the
structural formula and put these into a molecular formula.

### Road Map

**3.34**(a) $CH_2$; 14.03 g/mol  (b) $CH_3O$; 31.03 g/mol  (c) $N_2O_5$;
108.02 g/mol  (d) $Ba_3(PO_4)_2$; 601.8 g/mol  (e) $TeI_4$; 635.2 g/mol
**3.36** Disulfur dichloride; SCl; 135.04 g/mol  **3.38**(a) $C_3H_6$
(b) $N_2H_4$  (c) $N_2O_4$  (d) $C_5H_5N_5$  **3.40**(a) $Cl_2O_7$  (b) $SiCl_4$
(c) $CO_2$  **3.42**(a) $NO_2$  (b) $N_2O_4$  **3.44**(a) 1.20 mol F  (b) 24.0 g M

(c) calcium **3.47** $C_{21}H_{30}O_5$　**3.49** $C_{10}H_{20}O$　**3.50** A balanced equation provides information on the identities of reactants and products, the physical states of reactants and products, and the molar ratios by which reactants form products.　**3.53** b

**3.54**(a) $16Cu(s) + S_8(s) \longrightarrow 8Cu_2S(s)$

(b) $P_4O_{10}(s) + 6H_2O(l) \longrightarrow 4H_3PO_4(l)$

(c) $B_2O_3(s) + 6NaOH(aq) \longrightarrow 2Na_3BO_3(aq) + 3H_2O(l)$

(d) $4CH_3NH_2(g) + 9O_2(g) \longrightarrow$
$$4CO_2(g) + 10H_2O(g) + 2N_2(g)$$

**3.56**(a) $2SO_2(g) + O_2(g) \longrightarrow 2SO_3(g)$

(b) $Sc_2O_3(s) + 3H_2O(l) \longrightarrow 2Sc(OH)_3(s)$

(c) $H_3PO_4(aq) + 2NaOH(aq) \longrightarrow Na_2HPO_4(aq) + 2H_2O(l)$

(d) $C_6H_{10}O_5(s) + 6O_2(g) \longrightarrow 6CO_2(g) + 5H_2O(g)$

**3.58**(a) $4Ga(s) + 3O_2(g) \longrightarrow 2Ga_2O_3(s)$

(b) $2C_6H_{14}(l) + 19O_2(g) \longrightarrow 12CO_2(g) + 14H_2O(g)$

(c) $3CaCl_2(aq) + 2Na_3PO_4(aq) \longrightarrow$
$$Ca_3(PO_4)_2(s) + 6NaCl(aq)$$

**3.64** Balance the equation for the reaction: $aA + bB \longrightarrow cC$. Since A is the limiting reactant, A is used to determine the amount of C. Divide the mass of A by its molar mass to obtain the number of moles of A. Use the molar ratio from the balanced equation to find the number of moles of C. Multiply the number of moles of C by its molar mass to obtain the mass of C.

**Road Map**

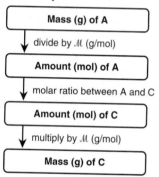

**3.66**(a) 0.455 mol $Cl_2$　(b) 32.3 g $Cl_2$　**3.68**(a) $1.42 \times 10^3$ mol $KNO_3$　(b) $1.43 \times 10^5$ g $KNO_3$　**3.70** 195.8 g $H_3BO_3$; 19.16 g $H_2$　**3.72** $2.60 \times 10^3$ g $Cl_2$

**3.74**(a) $I_2(s) + Cl_2(g) \longrightarrow 2ICl(s)$
$ICl(s) + Cl_2(g) \longrightarrow ICl_3(s)$

(b) $I_2(s) + 3Cl_2(g) \longrightarrow 2ICl_3(s)$

(c) $1.33 \times 10^3$ g $I_2$

**3.76**(a) 0.105 mol CaO　(b) 0.175 mol CaO　(c) calcium (d) 5.88 g CaO　**3.78** 1.36 mol $HIO_3$, 239 g $HIO_3$; 44.9 g $H_2O$ in excess　**3.80** 4.40 g $CO_2$; 4.80 g $O_2$ in excess　**3.82** 12.2 g $Al(NO_2)_3$, no $NH_4Cl$, 48.7 g $AlCl_3$, 30.7 g $N_2$, 39.5 g $H_2O$　**3.84** 50.%　**3.86** 90.5%　**3.88** 24.0 g $CH_3Cl$　**3.90**(a) 39.7 g $CF_4$　**3.91** A　**3.95**(a) C　(b) B　(c) C　(d) B　**3.98** No, instructions should read: "Take 100.0 mL of the 10.0 $M$ solution and, with stirring, add water until the total volume is 1000. mL."

**3.99**(a) 7.85 g $Ca(C_2H_3O_2)_2$　(b) 0.254 $M$ KI　(c) 124 mol NaCN　**3.101**(a) 4.65 g $K_2SO_4$　(b) 0.0653 $M$ $CaCl_2$　(c) $1.11 \times 10^{20}$ $Mg^{2+}$ ions　**3.103**(a) 0.0617 $M$ KCl　(b) 0.00363 $M$ $(NH_4)_2SO_4$ (c) 0.138 $M$ $Na^+$　**3.105**(a) 987 g $HNO_3$/L　(b) 15.7 $M$ $HNO_3$　**3.107** 845 mL　**3.109** 0.88 g $BaSO_4$　**3.112**(a) Instructions: Be

sure to wear goggles to protect your eyes! Pour approximately 2.0 gal of water into the container. Add to the water, slowly and with mixing, 0.90 gal of concentrated HCl. Dilute to 3.0 gal with more water.

(b) 22.6 mL　**3.117** $x = 3$　**3.118** ethane > propane > cetyl palmitate > ethanol > benzene　**3.123**(a) $Fe_2O_3(s) + 3CO(g) \longrightarrow 2Fe(s) + 3CO_2(g)$　(b) $3.39 \times 10^7$ g CO　**3.125** 89.8%　**3.127**(a) $2AB_2 + B_2 \longrightarrow 2AB_3$　(b) $AB_2$　(c) 5.0 mol $AB_3$ (d) 0.5 mol $B_2$　**3.129** B, C, and D have the same empirical formula, $C_2H_4O$; 44.05 g/mol　**3.130** 44.3%　**3.133**(a) C (b) B　(c) D　**3.140**(a) 586 g $CO_2$　(b) 10.5% $CH_4$ by mass　**3.142** 10/0.66/1.0　**3.147**(a) 192.12 g/mol; $C_6H_8O_7$ (b) 0.549 mol

**3.148**(a) $N_2(g) + O_2(g) \longrightarrow 2NO(g)$
$2NO(g) + O_2(g) \longrightarrow 2NO_2(g)$
$3NO_2(g) + H_2O(g) \longrightarrow 2HNO_3(aq) + NO(g)$

(b) $2N_2(g) + 5O_2(g) + 2H_2O(g) \longrightarrow 4HNO_3(aq)$

(c) $6.07 \times 10^3$ t $HNO_3$

**3.149** A　**3.151**(a) 0.039 g heme　(b) $6.3 \times 10^{-5}$ mol heme (c) $3.5 \times 10^{-3}$ g Fe　(d) $4.1 \times 10^{-2}$ g hemin　**3.153**(a) 46.65 mass % N in urea; 31.98 mass % N in arginine; 21.04 mass % N in ornithine　(b) 28.45 g N　**3.155** 29.54%　**3.157**(a) 89.3% (b) 1.47 g ethylene　**3.159**(a) 125 g salt　(b) 65.6 L $H_2O$

## Chapter 4

**4.2** Ionic or polar covalent compounds　**4.3** Ions must be present, and they come from ionic compounds or from electrolytes such as acids and bases.　**4.6** B　**4.10**(a) Benzene is likely to be insoluble in water because it is nonpolar and water is polar. (b) Sodium hydroxide, an ionic compound, is likely to be very soluble in water.　(c) Ethanol ($CH_3CH_2OH$) is likely to be soluble in water because the alcohol group (—OH) is very polar, like the water molecule.　(d) Potassium acetate, an ionic compound, is likely to be very soluble in water.

**4.12**(a) Yes, CsBr is a soluble salt.　(b) Yes, HI is a strong acid. **4.14**(a) 0.64 mol　(b) 0.242 mol　(c) $1.18 \times 10^{-4}$ mol **4.16**(a) 3.0 mol　(b) $7.57 \times 10^{-5}$ mol　(c) 0.148 mol **4.18**(a) 0.058 mol $Al^{3+}$; $3.5 \times 10^{22}$ $Al^{3+}$ ions; 0.18 mol $Cl^-$; $1.1 \times 10^{23}$ $Cl^-$ ions　(b) $4.62 \times 10^{-4}$ mol $Li^+$; $2.78 \times 10^{20}$ $Li^+$ ions; $2.31 \times 10^{-4}$ mol $SO_4^{2-}$; $1.39 \times 10^{20}$ $SO_4^{2-}$ ions (c) $1.50 \times 10^{-2}$ mol $K^+$; $9.02 \times 10^{21}$ $K^+$ ions; $1.50 \times 10^{-2}$ mol $Br^-$; $9.02 \times 10^{21}$ $Br^-$ ions　**4.20**(a) 0.35 mol $H^+$　(b) $6.3 \times 10^{-3}$ mol $H^+$ (c) 0.22 mol $H^+$　**4.24** Spectator ions do not appear in a net ionic equation because they are not involved in the reaction and serve only to balance charges.　**4.28** Assuming that the left beaker contains $AgNO_3$ (because it has gray $Ag^+$ ions), the right must contain NaCl. Then, $NO_3^-$ is blue, $Na^+$ is brown, and $Cl^-$ is green.

Molecular equation: $AgNO_3(aq) + NaCl(aq) \longrightarrow$
$$AgCl(s) + NaNO_3(aq)$$

Total ionic equation: $Ag^+(aq) + NO_3^-(aq) + Na^+(aq) + Cl^-(aq) \longrightarrow AgCl(s) + Na^+(aq) + NO_3^-(aq)$

Net ionic equation: $Ag^+(aq) + Cl^-(aq) \longrightarrow AgCl(s)$

**4.29**(a) Molecular: $Hg_2(NO_3)_2(aq) + 2KI(aq) \longrightarrow$
$$Hg_2I_2(s) + 2KNO_3(aq)$$

Total ionic: $Hg_2^{2+}(aq) + 2NO_3^-(aq) + 2K^+(aq) +$
$2I^-(aq) \longrightarrow Hg_2I_2(s) + 2K^+(aq) + 2NO_3^-(aq)$

Net ionic: $Hg_2^{2+}(aq) + 2I^-(aq) \longrightarrow Hg_2I_2(s)$

Spectator ions are $K^+$ and $NO_3^-$.

(b) Molecular: $FeSO_4(aq) + Sr(OH)_2(aq) \longrightarrow$
$Fe(OH)_2(s) + SrSO_4(s)$

Total ionic: $Fe^{2+}(aq) + SO_4^{2-}(aq) + Sr^{2+}(aq) +$
$2OH^-(aq) \longrightarrow Fe(OH)_2(s) + SrSO_4(s)$

Net ionic: This is the same as the total ionic equation, because there are no spectator ions.

**4.31**(a) No precipitate will form.  (b) A precipitate will form because silver ions, $Ag^+$, and bromide ions, $Br^-$, will combine to form a solid salt, silver bromide, AgBr. The ammonium and nitrate ions do not form a precipitate.

Molecular: $NH_4Br(aq) + AgNO_3(aq) \longrightarrow$
$AgBr(s) + NH_4NO_3(aq)$

Total ionic: $NH_4^+(aq) + Br^-(aq) + Ag^+(aq) + NO_3^-(aq) \longrightarrow$
$AgBr(s) + NH_4^+(aq) + NO_3^-(aq)$

Net ionic: $Ag^+(aq) + Br^-(aq) \longrightarrow AgBr(s)$

**4.33**(a)  No precipitate will form.

(b) $BaSO_4$ will precipitate.

Molecular: $(NH_4)_2SO_4(aq) + BaCl_2(aq) \longrightarrow$
$BaSO_4(s) + 2NH_4Cl(aq)$

Total ionic: $2NH_4^+(aq) + SO_4^{2-}(aq) + Ba^{2+}(aq)$
$+ 2Cl^-(aq) \longrightarrow BaSO_4(s) + 2NH_4^+(aq) + 2Cl^-(aq)$

Net ionic: $SO_4^{2-}(aq) + Ba^{2+}(aq) \longrightarrow BaSO_4(s)$

**4.35** $0.0354\ M\ Pb^{2+}$  **4.37**(a) $PbSO_4$  (b) $Pb^{2+}(aq) +$
$SO_4^{2-}(aq) \longrightarrow PbSO_4(s)$  (c) 1.5 g $PbSO_4$  **4.39** Potassium carbonate, $K_2CO_3$  **4.41** 2.206 mass % $Cl^-$  **4.47**(a) Formation of a gas, $SO_2(g)$, and of a nonelectrolyte (water) will cause the reaction to go to completion.  (b) Formation of a precipitate $Ba_3(PO_4)_2(s)$, and of a nonelectrolyte (water) will cause the reaction to go to completion.

**4.49**(a) Molecular equation: $KOH(aq) + HBr(aq) \longrightarrow$
$KBr(aq) + H_2O(l)$

Total ionic equation: $K^+(aq) + OH^-(aq) + H^+(aq)$
$+ Br^-(aq) \longrightarrow K^+(aq) + Br^-(aq) + H_2O(l)$

Net ionic equation: $OH^-(aq) + H^+(aq) \longrightarrow H_2O(l)$

The spectator ions are $K^+(aq)$ and $Br^-(aq)$.

(b) Molecular equation: $NH_3(aq) + HCl(aq) \longrightarrow$
$NH_4Cl(aq)$

Total ionic equation: $NH_3(aq) + H^+(aq) + Cl^-(aq) \longrightarrow$
$NH_4^+(aq) + Cl^-(aq)$

$NH_3$, a weak base, is written in the molecular (undissociated) form. HCl, a strong acid, is written as dissociated ions. $NH_4Cl$ is a soluble compound because all ammonium compounds are soluble.

Net ionic equation: $NH_3(aq) + H^+(aq) \longrightarrow NH_4^+(aq)$

$Cl^-$ is the only spectator ion.

**4.51** Total ionic equation: $CaCO_3(s) + 2H^+(aq) + 2Cl^-(aq) \longrightarrow$
$Ca^{2+}(aq) + 2Cl^-(aq) + H_2O(l) + CO_2(g)$

Net ionic equation: $CaCO_3(s) + 2H^+(aq) \longrightarrow$
$Ca^{2+}(aq) + H_2O(l) + CO_2(g)$

**4.53** $0.05839\ M\ CH_3COOH$  **4.64**(a) S has O.N. $= +6$ in $SO_4^{2-}$ (i.e., $H_2SO_4$) and O.N. $= +4$ in $SO_2$, so S has been

reduced (and $I^-$ oxidized); $H_2SO_4$ acts as an oxidizing agent.  (b) The oxidation numbers remain constant throughout; $H_2SO_4$ transfers an $H^+$ to $F^-$ to produce HF, so it acts as an acid.  **4.66**(a) $+4$  (b) $+3$  (c) $+4$  (d) $-3$  **4.68**(a) $-1$
(b) $+2$  (c) $-3$  (d) $+3$  **4.70**(a) $-3$  (b) $+5$  (c) $+3$
**4.72**(a) $+6$  (b) $+3$  (c) $+7$  **4.74**(a) $MnO_4^-$ is the oxidizing agent; $H_2C_2O_4$ is the reducing agent.  (b) Cu is the reducing agent; $NO_3^-$ is the oxidizing agent.  **4.76**(a) Oxidizing agent is $NO_3^-$; reducing agent is Sn.  (b) Oxidizing agent is $MnO_4^-$; reducing agent is $Cl^-$.

**4.78**(a) $8HNO_3(aq) + K_2CrO_4(aq) + 3Fe(NO_3)_2(aq) \longrightarrow$
$2KNO_3(aq) + 3Fe(NO_3)_3(aq) + Cr(NO_3)_3(aq) + 4H_2O(l)$
Oxidizing agent is $K_2CrO_4$; reducing agent is $Fe(NO_3)_2$.

(b) $8HNO_3(aq) + 3C_2H_6O(l) + K_2Cr_2O_7(aq) \longrightarrow$
$2KNO_3(aq) + 3C_2H_4O(l) + 7H_2O(l) + 2Cr(NO_3)_3(aq)$
Oxidizing agent is $K_2Cr_2O_7$; reducing agent is $C_2H_6O$.

(c) $6HCl(aq) + 2NH_4Cl(aq) + K_2Cr_2O_7(aq) \longrightarrow$
$2KCl(aq) + 2CrCl_3(aq) + N_2(g) + 7H_2O(l)$
Oxidizing agent is $K_2Cr_2O_7$; reducing agent is $NH_4Cl$.

(d) $KClO_3(aq) + 6HBr(aq) \longrightarrow$
$3Br_2(l) + 3H_2O(l) + KCl(aq)$
Oxidizing agent is $KClO_3$; reducing agent is HBr.

**4.80**(a) $4.54 \times 10^{-3}$ mol $MnO_4^-$  (b) 0.0113 mol $H_2O_2$
(c) 0.386 g $H_2O_2$  (d) 2.61 mass % $H_2O_2$  (e) $H_2O_2$
**4.86** A combination reaction that is also a redox reaction is $2Mg(s) + O_2(g) \longrightarrow 2MgO(s)$. A combination reaction that is not a redox reaction is $CaO(s) + H_2O(l) \longrightarrow Ca(OH)_2(aq)$.
**4.87**(a) $Ca(s) + 2H_2O(l) \longrightarrow$
$Ca(OH)_2(aq) + H_2(g)$; displacement

(b) $2NaNO_3(s) \longrightarrow 2NaNO_2(s) + O_2(g)$; decomposition

(c) $C_2H_2(g) + 2H_2(g) \longrightarrow C_2H_6(g)$; combination
**4.89**(a) $2Sb(s) + 3Cl_2(g) \longrightarrow 2SbCl_3(s)$; combination

(b) $2AsH_3(g) \longrightarrow 2As(s) + 3H_2(g)$; decomposition

(c) $Zn(s) + Fe(NO_3)_2(aq) \longrightarrow$
$Zn(NO_3)_2(aq) + Fe(s)$; displacement
**4.91**(a) $Sr(s) + Br_2(l) \longrightarrow SrBr_2(s)$

(b) $2Ag_2O(s) \xrightarrow{\Delta} 4Ag(s) + O_2(g)$

(c) $Mn(s) + Cu(NO_3)_2(aq) \longrightarrow Mn(NO_3)_2(aq) + Cu(s)$
**4.93**(a) $N_2(g) + 3H_2(g) \longrightarrow 2NH_3(g)$

(b) $2NaClO_3(s) \xrightarrow{\Delta} 2NaCl(s) + 3O_2(g)$

(c) $Ba(s) + 2H_2O(l) \longrightarrow Ba(OH)_2(aq) + H_2(g)$
**4.95**(a) $2Cs(s) + I_2(s) \longrightarrow 2CsI(s)$

(b) $2Al(s) + 3MnSO_4(aq) \longrightarrow Al_2(SO_4)_3(aq) + 3Mn(s)$

(c) $2SO_2(g) + O_2(g) \longrightarrow 2SO_3(g)$

(d) $2C_4H_{10}(g) + 13O_2(g) \longrightarrow 8CO_2(g) + 10H_2O(g)$

(e) $2Al(s) + 3Mn^{2+}(aq) \longrightarrow 2Al^{3+}(aq) + 3Mn(s)$
**4.97** 315 g $O_2$; 3.95 kg Hg  **4.99**(a) $O_2$ is in excess.
(b) 0.117 mol $Li_2O$  (c) 0 g Li, 3.49 g $Li_2O$, and 4.63 g $O_2$
**4.101** 67.2 mass % $KClO_3$  **4.103** 2.79 kg Fe  **4.104** 99.9 g compound B, which is $FeCl_2$  **4.108** The reaction is
$2NO + Br_2 \rightleftharpoons 2NOBr$, which can proceed in either direction. If NO and $Br_2$ are placed in a container, they will react to form NOBr, and NOBr will decompose to form NO and $Br_2$. Eventually, the concentrations of NO, $Br_2$, and NOBr

adjust so that the rates of the forward and reverse reactions become equal, and equilibrium is reached.
**4.110**(a)     $Fe(s) + 2H^+(aq) \longrightarrow Fe^{2+}(aq) + H_2(g)$
O.N.:   0      +1                  +2        0
(b) $3.1\times10^{21}$ $Fe^{2+}$ ions
**4.112** 5.11 g $C_2H_5OH$; 24.9 L $CO_2$
**4.114**(a) $Ca^{2+}(aq) + C_2O_4^{2-}(aq) \longrightarrow CaC_2O_4(s)$
(b) $5H_2C_2O_4(aq) + 2MnO_4^-(aq) + 6H^+(aq) \longrightarrow$
$10CO_2(g) + 2Mn^{2+}(aq) + 8H_2O(l)$
(c) $KMnO_4$  (d) $H_2C_2O_4$  (e) 55.06 mass % $CaCl_2$
**4.117** 2.809 mass % $CaMg(CO_3)_2$  **4.119**(a) Step 1: oxidizing agent is $O_2$; reducing agent is $NH_3$. Step 2: oxidizing agent is $O_2$; reducing agent is NO. Step 3: oxidizing agent is $NO_2$; reducing agent is $NO_2$.  (b) $1.2\times10^4$ kg $NH_3$  **4.123** 627 L air
**4.125** 0.75 kg $SiO_2$; 0.26 kg $Na_2CO_3$; 0.18 kg $CaCO_3$
**4.128**(a) 4 mol $IO_3^-$  (b) 12 mol $I_2$; $IO_3^-$ is oxidizing agent and $I^-$ is reducing agent.  (c) 12.87 mass % thyroxine
**4.131** $3.0\times10^{-3}$ mol $CO_2$  (b) 0.11 L $CO_2$  **4.133**(a) $C_7H_5O_4Bi$
(b) $C_{21}H_{15}O_{12}Bi_3$  (c) $Bi(OH)_3(s) + 3HC_7H_5O_3(aq) \longrightarrow$
$Bi(C_7H_5O_3)_3(s) + 3H_2O(l)$  (d) 0.490 mg $Bi(OH)_3$
**4.135**(a) Ethanol: $C_2H_5OH(l) + 3O_2(g) \longrightarrow 2CO_2(g) + 3H_2O(l)$
Gasoline: $2C_8H_{18}(l) + 25O_2(g) \longrightarrow 16CO_2(g) + 18H_2O(g)$
(b) $2.50\times10^3$ g $O_2$  (c) $1.75\times10^3$ L $O_2$  (d) $8.38\times10^3$ L air
**4.137** yes

## Chapter 5

**Answers to Boxed Reading Problems: B5.1** The density of the atmosphere decreases with increasing altitude. High density causes more drag on the aircraft. At high altitudes, low density means that there are relatively few gas particles present to collide with the aircraft. **B5.3** 0.934 %, 7.10 torr

• **5.1**(a) The volume of the liquid remains constant, but the volume of the gas increases to the volume of the larger container. (b) The volume of the container holding the gas sample increases when heated, but the volume of the container holding the liquid sample remains essentially constant when heated. (c) The volume of the liquid remains essentially constant, but the volume of the gas is reduced. **5.6** 990 $cmH_2O$ **5.8**(a) 566 mmHg (b) 1.32 bar (c) 3.60 atm (d) 107 kPa **5.10** 0.9408 atm **5.12** 0.966 atm **5.18** At constant temperature and volume, the pressure of a gas is directly proportional to number of moles of the gas. **5.20**(a) Volume decreases to one-third of the original volume. (b) Volume increases by a factor of 3.0. (c) Volume increases by a factor of 4. **5.22**(a) Volume decreases by a factor of 2. (b) Volume increases by a factor of 1.48. (c) Volume decreases by a factor of 3. **5.24** $-144°C$ **5.26** 35.3 L **5.28** 0.085 mol $Cl_2$ **5.30** 1.16 g $ClF_3$ **5.33** yes **5.35** Beaker is inverted for $H_2$ and upright for $CO_2$. The molar mass of $CO_2$ is greater than the molar mass of air, which, in turn, has a greater molar mass than $H_2$. **5.39** 5.86 g/L **5.41** $1.78\times10^{-3}$ mol $AsH_3$; 3.48 g/L **5.43** 51.1 g/mol **5.45** 1.33 atm **5.47** 39.2 g $P_4$ **5.49** 41.2 g $PH_3$ **5.51** 0.0249 g Al **5.55** $C_5H_{12}$ **5.57**(a) 0.90 mol (b) 6.76 torr **5.58** 286 mL $SO_2$ **5.60** 0.0997 atm $SiF_4$ **5.65** At STP, the volume occupied by a mole of any gas is the same.

At the same temperature, all gases have the same average kinetic energy, resulting in the same pressure. **5.68**(a) $P_A > P_B > P_C$ (b) $E_A = E_B = E_C$ (c) $rate_A > rate_B > rate_C$ (d) total $E_A >$ total $E_B >$ total $E_C$ (e) $d_A = d_B = d_C$ (f) collision frequency in A > collision frequency in B > collision frequency in C **5.69** 13.21 **5.71**(a) curve 1 (b) curve 1 (c) curve 1; fluorine and argon have about the same molar mass **5.73** 14.9 min **5.75** 4 atoms per molecule **5.78** negative deviations; $N_2 < Kr < CO_2$ **5.80** At 1 atm; at lower pressures, the gas molecules are farther apart and intermolecular forces are less important. **5.83** $6.81\times10^4$ g/mol **5.86**(a) 22.1 atm (b) 20.9 atm **5.90**(a) 597 torr $N_2$; 159 torr $O_2$; 0.3 torr $CO_2$; 3.5 torr $H_2O$ (b) 74.9 mol % $N_2$; 13.7 mol % $O_2$; 5.3 mol % $CO_2$; 6.2 mol % $H_2O$ (c) $1.6\times10^{21}$ molecules $O_2$ **5.92**(a) $4\times10^2$ mL (b) 0.013 mol $N_2$ **5.93** 35.7 L $NO_2$ **5.98** $Al_2Cl_6$ **5.100** $1.52\times10^{-2}$ mol $SO_3$ **5.104**(a) $1.95\times10^3$ g Ni (b) $3.5\times10^4$ g Ni (c) 63 m³ CO **5.106**(a) 9 volumes of $O_2(g)$ (b) $CH_5N$ **5.109** The lungs would expand by a factor of 4.86; the diver can safely ascend 52.5 ft to a depth of 73 ft. **5.111** 6.07 g $H_2O_2$ **5.116** $6.53\times10^{-3}$ g $N_2$ **5.120**(a) xenon (b) water vapor (c) mercury vapor (d) water vapor **5.124** 17.2 g $CO_2$; 17.8 g Kr **5.130** Ne, 676 m/s; Ar, 481 m/s; He, $1.52\times10^3$ m/s **5.132**(a) 0.052 g (b) 1.1 mL **5.139**(a) 16.5 L $CO_2$ (b) $P_{H_2O} = 48.8$ torr; $P_{O_2} = P_{CO_2} = 3.7\times10^2$ torr **5.144** 332 steps **5.146** 1.4 **5.150** $P_{total} = 245$ torr; $P_{I_2} = 25.2$ torr

## Chapter 6

**Answers to Boxed Reading Problem: B6.2** (a) $2C(coal) + 2H_2O(g) \longrightarrow CH_4(g) + CO_2(g)$ (b) 12 kJ (c) $-3.30\times10^4$ kJ

• **6.4** Increase: eating food, lying in the sun, taking a hot bath. Decrease: exercising, taking a cold bath, going outside on a cold day. **6.6** The amount of the change in internal energy is the same for heater and air conditioner. Since both devices consume the same amount of electrical energy, the change in energy of the heater equals that of the air conditioner. **6.8** 0 J **6.10** $1.54\times10^3$ J **6.12**(a) $6.6\times10^7$ kJ (b) $1.6\times10^7$ kcal (c) $6.3\times10^7$ Btu **6.15** 8.8 h **6.17** Measuring the heat transfer at constant pressure is more convenient than measuring at constant volume. **6.19**(a) exothermic (b) endothermic (c) exothermic (d) exothermic (e) endothermic (f) endothermic (g) exothermic

**6.22**

**6.24**(a) Combustion of ethane: $2C_2H_6(g) + 7O_2(g) \longrightarrow 4CO_2(g) + 6H_2O(g) +$ heat

(b) Freezing of water: $H_2O(l) \longrightarrow H_2O(s)$ + heat

$$H \uparrow \begin{array}{l} \underline{\hspace{1cm}} H_2O(l) \text{ (initial)} \\ \qquad \downarrow \quad \Delta H = (-), \text{(exothermic)} \\ \underline{\hspace{1cm}} H_2O(s) \text{ (final)} \end{array}$$

**6.26**(a) $2CH_3OH(l) + 3O_2(g) \longrightarrow 2CO_2(g) + 4H_2O(g)$ + heat

$$H \uparrow \begin{array}{l} \underline{\hspace{1cm}} 2CH_3OH + 3O_2 \text{ (initial)} \\ \qquad \downarrow \quad \Delta H = (-), \text{(exothermic)} \\ \underline{\hspace{1cm}} 2CO_2 + 4H_2O \text{ (final)} \end{array}$$

(b) $\frac{1}{2}N_2(g) + O_2(g) + \text{heat} \longrightarrow NO_2(g)$

$$H \uparrow \begin{array}{l} \underline{\hspace{1cm}} NO_2 \text{ (final)} \\ \qquad \uparrow \quad \Delta H = (+), \text{(endothermic)} \\ \underline{\hspace{1cm}} \frac{1}{2}N_2 + O_2 \text{ (initial)} \end{array}$$

**6.28**(a) This is a phase change from the solid phase to the gas phase. Heat is absorbed by the system so $q_{sys}$ is positive (+). (b) The volume of the system is expanding as more moles of gas are present after the phase change than were present before the phase change. So the system has done work of expansion, and $w$ is negative. Since $\Delta E_{sys} = q + w$, $q$ is positive, and $w$ is negative, the sign of $\Delta E_{sys}$ cannot be predicted. It will be positive if $q > w$ and negative if $q < w$. (c) $\Delta E_{univ} = 0$. If the system loses energy, the surroundings gain an equal amount of energy. The sum of the energy of the system and the energy of the surroundings remains constant. **6.31** To determine the specific heat capacity of a substance, you need its mass, the heat added (or lost), and the change in temperature. **6.33** Heat capacity is the quantity of heat required to raise the temperature of an object 1 K. Specific heat capacity is the quantity of heat required to raise 1 g of a material by 1 K. Molar heat capacity is the quantity of heat required to raise the temperature of 1 mol of a substance by 1 K. **6.35** $6.9 \times 10^3$ J **6.37** 295°C **6.39** 77.5°C **6.41** 45°C **6.43** 36.6°C **6.50** The reaction has a positive $\Delta H$, because it requires the input of energy to break the oxygen-oxygen bond. **6.51** $\Delta H$ is negative; it is opposite in sign and half of the value for the vaporization of 2 mol of $H_2O$. **6.52**(a) exothermic (b) 20.2 kJ (c) $-4.2 \times 10^2$ kJ (d) $-15.7$ kJ **6.54**(a) $\frac{1}{2}N_2(g) + \frac{1}{2}O_2(g) \longrightarrow NO(g)$; $\Delta H = 90.29$ kJ (b) $-10.5$ kJ **6.56** $-1.88 \times 10^6$ kJ **6.60**(a) $C_2H_4(g) + 3O_2(g) \longrightarrow 2CO_2(g) + 2H_2O(l)$; $\Delta H_{rxn} = -1411$ kJ (b) 1.39 g $C_2H_4$ **6.64** $-110.5$ kJ **6.65** $-813.4$ kJ **6.67** $N_2(g) + 2O_2(g) \longrightarrow 2NO_2(g)$; $\Delta H_{overall} = 66.4$ kJ; equation 1 is A, equation 2 is B, and equation 3 is C. **6.69** 44.0 kJ **6.72** The standard enthalpy of reaction, $\Delta H_{rxn}^{\circ}$, is the enthalpy change for a reaction where all substances are in their standard states. The standard

enthalpy of formation, $\Delta H_f^{\circ}$, is the enthalpy change that accompanies the formation of one mole of a compound in its standard state from elements in their standard states.
**6.74**(a) $\frac{1}{2}Cl_2(g) + Na(s) \longrightarrow NaCl(s)$
(b) $H_2(g) + \frac{1}{2}O_2(g) \longrightarrow H_2O(g)$
(c) no changes
**6.75**(a) $Ca(s) + Cl_2(g) \longrightarrow CaCl_2(s)$
(b) $Na(s) + \frac{1}{2}H_2(g) + C(\text{graphite}) + \frac{3}{2}O_2(g) \longrightarrow$
$$NaHCO_3(s)$$
(c) $C(\text{graphite}) + 2Cl_2(g) \longrightarrow CCl_4(l)$
(d) $\frac{1}{2}H_2(g) + \frac{1}{2}N_2(g) + \frac{3}{2}O_2(g) \longrightarrow HNO_3(l)$
**6.77**(a) $-1036.9$ kJ (b) $-433$ kJ **6.79** $-157.3$ kJ/mol
**6.81**(a) 503.9 kJ (b) $-\Delta H_1 + 2\Delta H_2 = 504$ kJ
**6.82**(a) $C_{18}H_{36}O_2(s) + 26O_2(g) \longrightarrow 18CO_2(g) + 18H_2O(g)$
(b) $-10,488$ kJ (c) $-36.9$ kJ; $-8.81$ kcal (d) 8.81 kcal/g $\times 11.0$ g = 96.9 kcal **6.84**(a) initial = 23.6 L/mol; final = 24.9 L/mol (b) 187 J (c) $-1.2 \times 10^2$ J (d) $3.1 \times 10^2$ J (e) 310 J (f) $\Delta H = \Delta E + P\Delta V = \Delta E - w = (q + w) - w = q_P$ **6.93**(a) $1.1 \times 10^3$ J (b) $1.1 \times 10^8$ J (c) $1.3 \times 10^2$ mol $CH_4$ (d) \$0.0050/mol (e) \$0.85 **6.98**(a) $\Delta H_{rxn1}^{\circ} = -657.0$ kJ; $\Delta H_{rxn2}^{\circ} = 32.9$ kJ (b) $-106.6$ kJ **6.99**(a) $-6.81 \times 10^3$ J (b) $+243°C$ **6.100** $-22.2$ kJ **6.101**(a) 34 kJ/mol (b) $-757$ kJ **6.103**(a) $-1.25 \times 10^3$ kJ (b) $2.24 \times 10^3°C$

## Chapter 7

**Answers to Boxed Reading Problem: B7.1** (a) slope = $1.3 \times 10^4$/M; y-intercept = 0.00

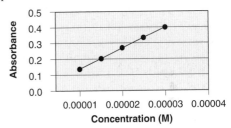

(b) diluted solution = $1.8 \times 10^{-5}$ M; original solution = $1.4 \times 10^{-4}$ M

• **7.2**(a) x-ray < ultraviolet < visible < infrared < microwave < radio waves (b) radio < microwave < infrared < visible < ultraviolet < x-ray
(c) radio < microwave < infrared < visible < ultraviolet < x-ray **7.7** 316 m; $3.16 \times 10^{11}$ nm; $3.16 \times 10^{12}$ Å **7.9** $2.5 \times 10^{-23}$ J **7.11** red < yellow < blue **7.13** $1.3483 \times 10^7$ nm; $1.3483 \times 10^8$ Å **7.16**(a) $1.24 \times 10^{15}$ s$^{-1}$; $8.21 \times 10^{-19}$ J (b) $1.4 \times 10^{15}$ s$^{-1}$; $9.0 \times 10^{-19}$ J **7.18** Bohr's key assumption was that the electron in an atom does not radiate energy while in a stationary state, and it can move to a different orbit only by absorbing or emitting a photon whose energy is equal to the difference in energy between two states. These differences in energy correspond to the wavelengths in the known line spectra for the hydrogen atom. A solar system model does not allow for the movement of electrons between levels. **7.20**(a) absorption (b) emission (c) emission (d) absorption **7.22** Yes, the predicted line spectra are accurate. The energies could be predicted from

$$E_n = \frac{-(Z^2)(2.18 \times 10^{-18} \text{ J})}{n^2}, \text{ where } Z \text{ is the atomic number for}$$

the atom or ion. The energy levels for $Be^{3+}$ will be greater by a factor of 16 ($Z = 4$) than those for the hydrogen atom. This means that the pattern of lines will be similar, but the lines will be at different wavelengths. **7.23** 434.17 nm **7.25** 1875.6 nm **7.27** $-2.76\times10^5$ J/mol **7.29** $d < a < c < b$ **7.31** $n = 4$ **7.37** Macroscopic objects do exhibit a wavelike motion, but the wavelength is too small for humans to perceive. **7.39**(a) $7.10\times10^{-37}$ m (b) $1\times10^{-35}$ m **7.41** $2.2\times10^{-26}$ m/s **7.43** $3.75\times10^{-36}$ kg **7.47** The total probability of finding the $1s$ electron in any distance $r$ from the H nucleus is greatest when the value of $r$ is 0.529 Å. The probability is greater for the $1s$ orbital. **7.48**(a) principal determinant of the electron's energy or distance from the nucleus (b) determines the shape of the orbital (c) determines the orientation of the orbital in three-dimensional space **7.49**(a) one (b) five (c) three (d) nine **7.51**(a) $m_l$: $-2, -1, 0, +1, +2$ (b) $m_l$: 0 (if $n = 1$, then $l = 0$) (c) $m_l$: $-3, -2, -1, 0, +1, +2, +3$
**7.53**(a)                          (b)

   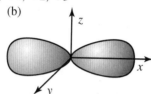

**7.55**

| Sublevel | Allowable $m_l$ values | No. of orbitals |
|---|---|---|
| (a) $d$ ($l = 2$) | $-2, -1, 0, +1, +2$ | 5 |
| (b) $p$ ($l = 1$) | $-1, 0, +1$ | 3 |
| (c) $f$ ($l = 3$) | $-3, -2, -1, 0, +1, +2, +3$ | 7 |

**7.57**(a) $n = 5$ and $l = 0$; one orbital (b) $n = 3$ and $l = 1$; three orbitals (c) $n = 4$ and $l = 3$; seven orbitals **7.59**(a) no; $n = 2, l = 1, m_l = -1; n = 2, l = 0, m_l = 0$ (b) allowed (c) allowed (d) no; $n = 5, l = 3, m_l = +3; n = 5, l = 2, m_l = 0$ **7.62**(a) $E = -(2.180\times10^{-18} \text{ J})(1/n^2)$. This is identical to the expression from Bohr's theory. (b) $3.028\times10^{-19}$ J (c) 656.1 nm **7.63**(a) The attraction of the nucleus for the electrons must be overcome. (b) The electrons in silver are more tightly held by the nucleus. (c) silver (d) Once the electron is freed from the atom, its energy increases in proportion to the frequency of the light. **7.66** $Li^{2+}$ **7.68**(a) $2 \longrightarrow 1$ (b) $5 \longrightarrow 2$ (c) $4 \longrightarrow 2$ (d) $3 \longrightarrow 2$ (e) $6 \longrightarrow 3$ **7.72**(a) $l = 1$ or 2 (b) $l = 1$ or 2 (c) $l = 3, 4, 5,$ or 6 (d) $l = 2$ or 3 **7.74**(a) $\Delta E =$

$$(-2.18\times10^{-18} \text{ J})\left(\frac{1}{\infty^2} - \frac{1}{n_{initial}^2}\right)Z^2\left(\frac{6.022\times10^{23}}{1 \text{ mol}}\right)$$

(b) $3.28\times10^7$ J/mol (c) 205 nm (d) 22.8 nm **7.76**(a) $5.293\times10^{-11}$ m (b) $5.293\times10^{-9}$ m **7.78** $6.4\times10^{27}$ photons **7.80**(a) no overlap (b) overlap (c) two (d) At longer wavelengths, the hydrogen spectrum begins to become a continuous band. **7.82**(a) $7.56\times10^{-18}$ J; $2.63\times10^{-8}$ m (b) $5.122\times10^{-17}$ J; $3.881\times10^{-9}$ m (c) $1.2\times10^{-18}$ J; $1.66\times10^{-7}$ m **7.84**(a) $1.87\times10^{-19}$ J (b) $3.58\times10^{-19}$ J **7.86**(a) red; green (b) 5.89 kJ (Sr); 5.83 kJ (Ba) **7.88**(a) This is

the wavelength of maximum absorbance, so it gives the highest sensitivity. (b) ultraviolet region (c) $1.93\times10^{-2}$ g vitamin A/g oil **7.92** $1.0\times10^{18}$ photons/s **7.95** $3s \longrightarrow 2p$; $3d \longrightarrow 2p$; $4s \longrightarrow 2p$; $3p \longrightarrow 2s$

## Chapter 8

**8.1** Elements are listed in the periodic table in an ordered, systematic way that correlates with a periodicity of their chemical and physical properties. The theoretical basis for the table in terms of atomic number and electron configuration does not allow for a "new element" between Sn and Sb. **8.3**(a) predicted atomic mass = 54.23 amu (b) predicted melting point = 6.3°C **8.6** The quantum number $m_s$ relates to just the electron; all the others describe the orbital. **8.9** Shielding occurs when electrons protect, or shield, other electrons from the full nuclear attraction. The effective nuclear charge is the nuclear charge an electron actually experiences. As the number of electrons, especially inner electrons, increases, the effective nuclear charge decreases. **8.11**(a) 6 (b) 10 (c) 2 **8.13**(a) 6 (b) 2 (c) 14 **8.16** Hund's rule states that electrons will occupy empty orbitals in a given sublevel (with parallel spins) before filling half-filled orbitals. The lowest energy arrangement has the maximum number of unpaired electrons with parallel spins.
N: $1s^2 2s^2 2p^3$

**8.18** Main-group elements from the same group have similar outer electron configurations, and the (old) group number equals the number of outer electrons. Outer electron configurations vary in a periodic manner within a period, with each succeeding element having an additional electron. **8.20** The maximum number of electrons in any energy level $n$ is $2n^2$, so the $n = 4$ energy level holds a maximum of $2(4^2) = 32$ electrons. **8.21**(a) $n = 5, l = 0, m_l = 0,$ and $m_s = +\frac{1}{2}$ (b) $n = 3, l = 1, m_l = +1,$ and $m_s = -\frac{1}{2}$ (c) $n = 5, l = 0, m_l = 0,$ and $m_s = +\frac{1}{2}$ (d) $n = 2, l = 1, m_l = +1,$ and $m_s = -\frac{1}{2}$
**8.23**(a) Rb: $1s^2 2s^2 2p^6 3s^2 3p^6 4s^2 3d^{10} 4p^6 5s^1$
(b) Ge: $1s^2 2s^2 2p^6 3s^2 3p^6 4s^2 3d^{10} 4p^2$
(c) Ar: $1s^2 2s^2 2p^6 3s^2 3p^6$
**8.25**(a) Cl: $1s^2 2s^2 2p^6 3s^2 3p^5$ (b) Si: $1s^2 2s^2 2p^6 3s^2 3p^2$
(c) Sr: $1s^2 2s^2 2p^6 3s^2 3p^6 4s^2 3d^{10} 4p^6 5s^2$
**8.27**(a) Ti: [Ar] $4s^2 3d^2$

| ↑↓ | ↑ | ↑ | | | | | | |
|---|---|---|---|---|---|---|---|---|
| 4s | 3d | | | | | 4p | | |

(b) Cl: [Ne] $3s^2 3p^5$

| ↑↓ | ↑↓ | ↑↓ | ↑ |
|---|---|---|---|
| 3s | 3p | | |

(c) V: [Ar] $4s^2 3d^3$

| ↑↓ | ↑ | ↑ | ↑ | | | | | |
|---|---|---|---|---|---|---|---|---|
| 4s | 3d | | | | | 4p | | |

**8.29**(a) Mn: [Ar] $4s^2 3d^5$

(b) P: [Ne] $3s^2 3p^3$

(c) Fe: [Ar] $4s^2 3d^6$

**8.31**(a) O; Group 6A(16); Period 2

(b) P; Group 5A(15); Period 3

**8.33**(a) Cl; Group 7A(17); Period 3

(b) As; Group 5A(15); Period 4

**8.35**(a) [Ar] $4s^2 3d^{10} 4p^1$; Group 3A(13)   (b) [He] $2s^2 2p^6$; Group 8A(18)

**8.37**

| | Inner Electrons | Outer Electrons | Valence Electrons |
|---|---|---|---|
| (a) O | 2 | 6 | 6 |
| (b) Sn | 46 | 4 | 4 |
| (c) Ca | 18 | 2 | 2 |
| (d) Fe | 18 | 2 | 8 |
| (e) Se | 28 | 6 | 6 |

**8.39**(a) B; Al, Ga, In, and Tl   (b) S; O, Se, Te, and Po   (c) La; Sc, Y, and Ac   **8.41**(a) C; Si, Ge, Sn, and Pb   (b) V; Nb, Ta, and Db   (c) P; N, As, Sb, and Bi

**8.43** Na (first excited state): $1s^2 2s^2 2p^6 3p^1$

**8.50** A high IE$_1$ and a very negative EA$_1$ suggest that the elements are halogens, in Group 7A(17), which form 1− ions.   **8.53**(a) K < Rb < Cs   (b) O < C < Be   (c) Cl < S < K   (d) Mg < Ca < K   **8.55**(a) Ba < Sr < Ca   (b) B < N < Ne   (c) Rb < Se < Br   (d) Sn < Sb < As   **8.57** $1s^2 2s^2 2p^1$ (boron, B)   **8.59**(a) Na   (b) Na   (c) Be   **8.61**(1) Metals conduct electricity; nonmetals do not. (2) Metal ions have a positive charge; nonmetal ions have a negative charge. (3) Metal oxides are mostly ionic and act as bases; nonmetal oxides are mostly covalent and act as acids.   **8.62** Metallic character increases down a group and decreases to the right across a period. These trends are the same as those for atomic size and opposite those for ionization energy.   **8.65** Possible ions are 2+ and 4+. The 2+ ions form by loss of the outermost two $p$ electrons; the 4+ ions form by loss of these and the outermost two $s$ electrons.   **8.69**(a) Rb   (b) Ra   (c) I   **8.71**(a) As   (b) P   (c) Be   **8.73** acidic solution; $SO_2(g) + H_2O(l) \longrightarrow H_2SO_3(aq)$

**8.75**(a) Cl$^-$: $1s^2 2s^2 2p^6 3s^2 3p^6$   (b) Na$^+$: $1s^2 2s^2 2p^6$   (c) Ca$^{2+}$: $1s^2 2s^2 2p^6 3s^2 3p^6$   **8.77**(a) Al$^{3+}$: $1s^2 2s^2 2p^6$   (b) S$^{2-}$: $1s^2 2s^2 2p^6 3s^2 3p^6$   (c) Sr$^{2+}$: $1s^2 2s^2 2p^6 3s^2 3p^6 4s^2$ $3d^{10} 4p^6$   **8.79**(a) 0   (b) 3   (c) 0   (d) 1   **8.81** a, b, and d   **8.83**(a) V$^{3+}$: [Ar] $3d^2$, paramagnetic   (b) Cd$^{2+}$: [Kr] $4d^{10}$, diamagnetic   (c) Co$^{3+}$: [Ar] $3d^6$, paramagnetic   (d) Ag$^+$: [Kr] $4d^{10}$, diamagnetic   **8.85** For palladium to be diamagnetic, all of its electrons must be paired. (a) You might first write the condensed electron configuration for Pd as [Kr] $5s^2 4d^8$. However, the partial orbital diagram is not consistent with diamagnetism.

(b) This is the only configuration that supports diamagnetism, [Kr] $4d^{10}$.

(c) Promoting an $s$ electron into the $d$ sublevel still leaves two electrons unpaired.

**8.87**(a) Li$^+$ < Na$^+$ < K$^+$   (b) Rb$^+$ < Br$^-$ < Se$^{2-}$   (c) F$^-$ < O$^{2-}$ < N$^{3-}$   **8.90** Ce: [Xe] $6s^2 4f^1 5d^1$; Ce$^{4+}$: [Xe]; Eu: [Xe] $6s^2 4f^7$; Eu$^{2+}$: [Xe] $4f^7$. Ce$^{4+}$ has a noble-gas configuration; Eu$^{2+}$ has a half-filled $f$ subshell.   **8.91**(a) Cl$_2$O, dichlorine monoxide   (b) Cl$_2$O$_3$, dichlorine trioxide   (c) Cl$_2$O$_5$, dichlorine pentaoxide   (d) Cl$_2$O$_7$, dichlorine heptaoxide   (e) SO$_3$, sulfur trioxide   (f) SO$_2$, sulfur dioxide   (g) N$_2$O$_5$, dinitrogen pentaoxide   (h) N$_2$O$_3$, dinitrogen trioxide   (i) CO$_2$, carbon dioxide   (j) P$_4$O$_{10}$, tetraphosphorus decaoxide   **8.94**(a) SrBr$_2$, strontium bromide   (b) CaS, calcium sulfide   (c) ZnF$_2$, zinc fluoride   (d) LiF, lithium fluoride   **8.95**(a) 2009 kJ/mol   (b) −549 kJ/mol   **8.97** All ions except Fe$^{8+}$ and Fe$^{14+}$ are paramagnetic; Fe$^+$ and Fe$^{3+}$ would be most attracted.

## Chapter 9

**Answers to Boxed Reading Problems: B9.1** The C=C bond shows absorption of IR at shorter wavelength (higher energy) because it is a stronger bond than C—C. The C≡C bond would show absorption at a shorter wavelength (higher energy) than the C=C bond since the triple bond has a larger bond energy than the double bond.   **B9.2** (a) 7460 nm (symmetric stretch), $1.50 \times 10^4$ nm (bending), 4260 nm (asymmetrical stretch)   (b) $2.66 \times 10^{-20}$ J (symmetric stretch), $1.33 \times 10^{-20}$ J (bending), $4.67 \times 10^{-20}$ J (asymmetrical stretch); bending requires the least amount of energy.

• **9.1**(a) Greater ionization energy decreases metallic character.   (b) Larger atomic radius increases metallic character.   (c) Higher number of outer electrons decreases metallic character.   (d) Larger effective nuclear charge decreases metallic character.   **9.4**(a) Cs   (b) Rb   (c) As   **9.6**(a) ionic   (b) covalent   (c) metallic   **9.8**(a) covalent   (b) ionic   (c) covalent   **9.10**(a) Rb·   (b) ·Ṡi·   (c) ·Ï:   **9.12**(a) ·Sr·   (b) :Ṗ·   (c) :Ṡ·   **9.14**(a) 6A(16); [noble gas] $ns^2 np^4$   (b) 3(A)13; [noble gas] $ns^2 np^1$   **9.20**(a) Ba$^{2+}$, [Xe]; Cl$^-$, [Ne] $3s^2 3p^6$, :C̈l:$^-$ ; BaCl$_2$

(b) $Sr^{2+}$, [Kr]; $O^{2-}$, [He] $2s^22p^6$, :Ö:$^{2-}$; SrO  (c) $Al^{3+}$, [Ne]; $F^-$, [He] $2s^22p^6$, :F̈:$^-$; $AlF_3$  (d) $Rb^+$, [Kr]; $O^{2-}$, [He] $2s^22p^6$, :Ö:$^{2-}$; $Rb_2O$.  **9.22**(a) 2A(2)  (b) 6A(16)  (c) 1A(1)  **9.24**(a) 3A(13)  (b) 2A(2)  (c) 6A(16)  **9.26**(a) BaS; the charge on each ion is twice the charge on the ions in CsCl.  (b) LiCl; $Li^+$ is smaller than $Cs^+$.  **9.28**(a) BaS; $Ba^{2+}$ is larger than $Ca^{2+}$.  (b) NaF; the charge on each ion is less than the charge on Mg and O.  **9.30** 788 kJ; the lattice energy for NaCl is less than that for LiF, because the $Na^+$ and $Cl^-$ ions are larger than $Li^+$ and $F^-$ ions.  **9.33** $-336$ kJ  **9.34** When two chlorine atoms are far apart, there is no interaction between them. As the atoms move closer together, the nucleus of each atom attracts the electrons of the other atom. The closer the atoms, the greater this attraction; however, the repulsions of the two nuclei and the electrons also increase at the same time. The final internuclear distance is the distance at which maximum attraction is achieved in spite of the repulsion.  **9.35** The bond energy is the energy required to break the bond between H atoms and Cl atoms in one mole of HCl molecules in the gaseous state. Energy is needed to break bonds, so bond breaking is always endothermic and $\Delta H°_{bond\ breaking}$ is positive. The quantity of energy needed to break the bond is released upon its formation, so $\Delta H°_{bond\ forming}$ has the same magnitude as $\Delta H°_{bond\ breaking}$ but is opposite in sign (always exothermic and negative).  **9.39**(a) I—I < Br—Br < Cl—Cl  (b) S—Br < S—Cl < S—H  (c) C—N < C=N < C≡N  **9.41**(a) C—O < C=O; the C=O bond (bond order = 2) is stronger than the C—O bond (bond order = 1).  (b) C—H < O—H; O is smaller than C so the O—H bond is shorter and stronger than the C—H bond.  **9.43** Less energy is required to break weak bonds.  **9.45** Both are one-carbon molecules. Since methane contains fewer carbon-oxygen bonds, it will have the greater heat of reaction per mole for combustion.  **9.47** $-168$ kJ  **9.49** $-22$ kJ  **9.50** $-59$ kJ  **9.51** Electronegativity increases from left to right and increases from bottom to top within a group. Fluorine and oxygen are the two most electronegative elements. Cesium and francium are the two least electronegative elements.  **9.53** The H—O bond in water is polar covalent. A nonpolar covalent bond occurs between two atoms with identical electronegativities. A polar covalent bond occurs when the atoms have differing electronegativities. Ionic bonds result from electron transfer between atoms.  **9.56**(a) Si < S < O  (b) Mg < As < P  **9.58**(a) N > P > Si  (b) As > Ga > Ca

**9.60**(a) N⟶B  (b) N⟶O  (c) C—S none  (d) S⟶O  (e) N⟶H  (f) Cl⟶O

**9.62** a, d, and e  **9.64**(a) nonpolar covalent  (b) ionic  (c) polar covalent  (d) polar covalent  (e) nonpolar covalent  (f) polar covalent; $SCl_2 < SF_2 < PF_3$

**9.66**(a) H—I < H—Br < H—Cl  (b) H—C < H—O < H—F  (c) S—Cl < P—Cl < Si—Cl

**9.69**(a) Shiny, conducts heat, conducts electricity, and is malleable.  (b) Metals lose electrons to form positive ions, and metals form basic oxides.  **9.73**(a) 800. kJ/mol, which is lower than the value in Table 9.2  (b) $-2.417\times10^4$ kJ  (c) 1690. g $CO_2$  (d) 65.2 L $O_2$  **9.75**(a) $-125$ kJ  (b) yes, since $\Delta H°_f$ is negative  (c) $-392$ kJ  (d) No, $\Delta H°_f$ for $MgCl_2$ is much more negative than that for MgCl.  **9.77**(a) 406 nm  (b) $2.93\times10^{-19}$ J  (c) $1.87\times10^4$ m/s  **9.80** C—Cl: $3.53\times10^{-7}$ m; bond in $O_2$: $2.40\times10^{-7}$ m  **9.81** $XeF_2$: 132 kJ/mol; $XeF_4$: 150. kJ/mol; $XeF_6$: 146 kJ/mol  **9.83**(a) The presence of the very electronegative fluorine atoms bonded to one of the carbons makes the C—C bond polar. This polar bond will tend to undergo heterolytic rather than homolytic cleavage. More energy is required to achieve heterolytic cleavage.  (b) 1420 kJ  **9.86** 13,286 kJ  **9.88** $8.70\times10^{14}$ s$^{-1}$; $3.45\times10^{-7}$ m; the ultraviolet region of the electromagnetic spectrum  **9.90**(a) $CH_3OCH_3(g)$: $-326$ kJ; $CH_3CH_2OH(g)$: $-369$ kJ  (b) The formation of gaseous ethanol is more exothermic.  (c) 43 kJ

## Chapter 10

**Answers to Boxed Reading Problem: B10.1** resonance form on the left: trigonal planar around C, trigonal pyramidal around N; resonance form on the right: trigonal planar around both C and N.

• **10.1** He cannot serve as a central atom because it does not bond. H cannot because it forms only one bond. Fluorine cannot because it needs only one electron to complete its valence level, and it does not have $d$ orbitals available to expand its valence level. Thus, it can bond to only one other atom.  **10.3** All the structures obey the octet rule except c and g.

**10.5**(a) :F̈—Si̇(—F̈:)—F̈: with F above  (b) :Cl̈—S̈e—Cl̈:  (c) :F̈—C(=O)—F̈:

**10.7**(a) :F̈—P̈(—F̈:)—F̈: with F below  (b) H—Ö—C(=O)—Ö—H  (c) :S̈=C=S̈:

**10.9**(a) [Ö=N=Ö]$^+$  (b) :Ö·—N(·F̈:)=Ö ↔ Ö=N(·F̈:)—Ö·

**10.11**(a) [:N̈=N=N̈:]$^-$ ↔ [:N̈—N≡N:]$^-$ ↔ [:N≡N—N̈:]$^-$  (b) [:Ö=N—Ö:]$^-$ ↔ [:Ö—N=Ö:]$^-$

**10.13**(a) :F̈—I(F̈:)(F̈:)—F̈: formal charges: I = 0, F = 0  (b) [H—Al(H)(H)—H]$^-$ formal charges: H = 0, Al = $-1$

**10.15**(a) [:C≡N:]$^-$ formal charges: C = $-1$, N = 0  (b) [:Cl̈—Ö:]$^-$ formal charges: Cl = 0, O = $-1$

**10.17**(a)

formal charges: Br = 0, doubly bonded O = 0, singly bonded O = −1 O.N.: Br = +5; O = −2

(b)

formal charges: S = 0, singly bonded O = −1, doubly bonded O = 0 O.N.: S = +4; O = −2

**10.19**(a) B has 6 valence electrons in $BH_3$, so the molecule is electron deficient. (b) As has an expanded valence level with 10 electrons. (c) Se has an expanded valence level with 10 electrons.

**10.21**(a) Br expands its valence level to 10 electrons. (b) I has an expanded valence level of 10 electrons. (c) Be has only 4 valence electrons in $BeF_2$, so the molecule is electron deficient.

**10.23**

**10.26** structure A **10.28** The molecular shape and the electron-group arrangement are the same when no lone pairs are present on the central atom. **10.30** tetrahedral, $AX_4$; trigonal pyramidal, $AX_3E$; bent or V shaped, $AX_2E_2$

**10.32**(a)

**10.34**(a) trigonal planar, bent, 120° (b) tetrahedral, trigonal pyramidal, 109.5° (c) tetrahedral, trigonal pyramidal, 109.5° **10.36**(a) trigonal planar, trigonal planar, 120° (b) trigonal planar, bent, 120° (c) tetrahedral, tetrahedral, 109.5° **10.38**(a) trigonal planar, $AX_3$, 120° (b) trigonal pyramidal, $AX_3E$, 109.5° (c) trigonal bipyramidal, $AX_5$, 90° and 120° **10.40**(a) bent, 109.5°, less than 109.5° (b) trigonal bipyramidal, 90° and 120°, angles are ideal (c) seesaw, 90° and 120°, less than ideal (d) linear, 180°, angle is ideal **10.42**(a) C: tetrahedral, 109.5°; O: bent, < 109.5° (b) N: trigonal planar, 120° **10.44**(a) C in $CH_3$: tetrahedral, 109.5°; C with C=O: trigonal planar, 120°; O with H: bent, < 109.5° (b) O: bent, < 109.5° **10.46** $OF_2 < NF_3 < CF_4 < BF_3 < BeF_2$ **10.48**(a) The C and N each have three groups, so the ideal angles are 120°; the O has four groups, so the ideal angle is

109.5°. The N and O have lone pairs, so the angles are less than ideal. (b) All central atoms have four pairs, so the ideal angles are 109.5°. The lone pairs on the O reduce this value. (c) The B has three groups and an ideal bond angle of 120°. All the O's have four groups (ideal bond angles of 109.5°), two of which are lone pairs that reduce the angle.

**10.51**

In the gas phase, $PCl_5$ is $AX_5$, so the shape is trigonal bipyramidal, and the bond angles are 120° and 90°. The $PCl_4^+$ ion is $AX_4$, so the shape is tetrahedral, and the bond angles are 109.5°. The $PCl_6^-$ ion is $AX_6$, so the shape is octahedral, and the bond angles are 90°. **10.52** Molecules are polar if they have polar bonds that are not arranged to cancel each other. A polar bond is present any time there is a bond between elements with differing electronegativities. **10.55**(a) $CF_4$ (b) BrCl and $SCl_2$ **10.57**(a) $SO_2$, because it is polar and $SO_3$ is not. (b) IF has a greater electronegativity difference between its atoms. (c) $SF_4$, because it is polar and $SiF_4$ is not. (d) $H_2O$ has a greater electronegativity difference between its atoms.

**10.59**

Yes, compound Y has a dipole moment.

**10.61**(a)

The single N—N bond (bond order = 1) is weaker and longer than the others. The triple bond (bond order = 3) is stronger and shorter than the others. The double bond (bond order = 2) has an intermediate strength and length.

(b) $\Delta H^\circ_{rxn} = -367$ kJ

**10.65**(a) formal charges: Al = −1, end Cl = 0, bridging Cl = +1; I = −1, end Cl = 0, bridging Cl = +1 (b) The iodine atoms are each $AX_4E_2$, and the shape around each is square planar. These square planar portions are adjacent, giving a planar molecule.

**10.70**

(a) In propylene oxide, the shape around each C is tetrahedral, with ideal angles of 109.5°. (b) The C that is not part of the three-membered ring should have close to the ideal angle. The atoms in the ring form an equilateral triangle, so the angles around the two C's in the ring are reduced from the ideal 109.5° to 60°. **10.75**(a) −1267 kJ/mol (b) −1226 kJ/mol (c) −1234.8 kJ/mol. The two answers differ by less than 10 kJ/mol. This is very good agreement since average bond energies were used to calculate answers a and b. (d) −37 kJ

**10.77** H—Ö—C—C—Ö—H
$\quad\quad\quad$ ‖ ‖
$\quad\quad$ :O: :O:

**10.80** $CH_4$: $-409$ kJ/mol $O_2$; $H_2S$: $-398$ kJ/mol $O_2$
**10.82**(a) The O in the OH species has only 7 valence electrons, which is less than an octet, and 1 electron is unpaired.
(b) 426 kJ   (c) 508 kJ   **10.84**(a) The F atoms will substitute at the axial positions first.   (b) $PF_5$ and $PCl_3F_2$
**10.86** $H_2C_2O_4$:

H—Ö     Ö—H
$\quad$ C—C
$\quad$ :O: :O:

$HC_2O_4^-$:

$$\left[ \begin{array}{c} :\ddot{O} \quad \ddot{O}—H \\ C—C \\ :O: :O: \end{array} \right]^- \longleftrightarrow \left[ \begin{array}{c} :\ddot{O} \quad \ddot{O}—H \\ C—C \\ :O: :O: \end{array} \right]^-$$

$C_2O_4^{2-}$:

$$\left[ \begin{array}{c} :\ddot{O} \quad \ddot{O}: \\ C—C \\ :O: :O: \end{array} \right]^{2-} \longleftrightarrow \left[ \begin{array}{c} :O \quad \ddot{O}: \\ C—C \\ :O: \ddot{O}: \end{array} \right]^{2-}$$

$$\longleftrightarrow \left[ \begin{array}{c} :\ddot{O} \quad \ddot{O}: \\ C—C \\ :O: :O: \end{array} \right]^{2-} \longleftrightarrow \left[ \begin{array}{c} :\ddot{O} \quad \ddot{O}: \\ C—C \\ :O: :O: \end{array} \right]^{2-}$$

In $H_2C_2O_4$, there are two shorter and stronger C=O bonds and two longer and weaker C—O bonds. In $HC_2O_4^-$, the carbon-oxygen bonds on the side retaining the H remain as one long, weak C—O and one short, strong C=O. The carbon-oxygen bonds on the other side of the molecule have resonance forms with a bond order of 1.5, so they are intermediate in length and strength. In $C_2O_4^{2-}$, all the carbon-oxygen bonds have a bond order of 1.5.   **10.90** 22 kJ   **10.91** Trigonal planar molecules are nonpolar, so $AY_3$ cannot be that shape. Trigonal pyramidal molecules and T-shaped molecules are polar, so $AY_3$ could have either of these shapes.   **10.95**(a) 339 pm   (b) 316 pm and 223 pm   (c) 270 pm

## Chapter 11

**11.1**(a) $sp^2$   (b) $sp^3d^2$   (c) $sp$   (d) $sp^3$   (e) $sp^3d$   **11.3** C has only $2s$ and $2p$ atomic orbitals, allowing for a maximum of four hybrid orbitals. Si has $3s$, $3p$, and $3d$ atomic orbitals, allowing it to form more than four hybrid orbitals.   **11.5**(a) six, $sp^3d^2$   (b) four, $sp^3$   **11.7**(a) $sp^2$   (b) $sp^2$   (c) $sp^2$   **11.9**(a) $sp^3$ (b) $sp^3$   (c) $sp^3$   **11.11**(a) Si: one $s$ and three $p$ atomic orbitals form four $sp^3$ hybrid orbitals.   (b) C: one $s$ and one $p$ atomic orbital forms two $sp$ hybrid orbitals.   (c) S: one $s$, three $p$, and one $d$ atomic orbital mix to form five $sp^3d$ hybrid orbitals.   (d) N: one $s$ and three $p$ atomic orbitals mix to form four $sp^3$ hybrid orbitals.   **11.13**(a) B ($sp^3 \longrightarrow sp^3$)   (b) A ($sp^2 \longrightarrow sp^3$)
**11.15** (a) ↑↓ | ↑ ↑ | $\longrightarrow$ | ↑ ↑ ↑ ↑ |
$\quad$ $4s$ $\quad$ $4p$ $\quad\quad\quad\quad$ $sp^3$

(b) ↑↓ | ↑ | $\longrightarrow$ | ↑ ↑ ↑ | ☐
$\quad$ $2s$ $\quad$ $2p$ $\quad\quad\quad\quad$ $sp^2$ $\quad\quad$ $2p$

(c) ↑↓ | ↑ ↑ | $\longrightarrow$ | ↑ ↑ ↑ | ☐ $+e^-$
$\quad$ $2s$ $\quad$ $2p$ $\quad\quad\quad\quad$ $sp^2$ $\quad\quad$ $2p$

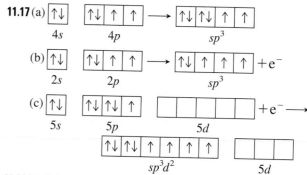

**11.17** (a) ↑↓ | ↑↓ ↑ ↑ | $\longrightarrow$ | ↑↓ ↑↓ ↑ ↑ |
$\quad$ $4s$ $\quad$ $4p$ $\quad\quad\quad\quad\quad$ $sp^3$

(b) ↑↓ | ↑↓ ↑ ↑ | $\longrightarrow$ | ↑↓ ↑ ↑ ↑ | $+e^-$
$\quad$ $2s$ $\quad$ $2p$ $\quad\quad\quad\quad\quad$ $sp^3$

(c) ↑↓ | ↑↓ ↑↓ ↑ | $\quad$ ☐☐☐☐☐ $+e^- \longrightarrow$
$\quad$ $5s$ $\quad$ $5p$ $\quad\quad\quad$ $5d$
$\quad\quad\quad\quad$ | ↑↓ ↑↓ ↑ ↑ ↑ ↑ | ☐☐☐
$\quad\quad\quad\quad\quad\quad$ $sp^3d^2$ $\quad\quad\quad$ $5d$

**11.20**(a) False. A double bond is one σ and one π bond.
(b) False. A triple bond consists of one σ and two π bonds.
(c) True   (d) True   (e) False. A π bond consists of a second pair of electrons after a σ bond has been previously formed.
(f) False. End-to-end overlap results in a bond with electron density along the bond axis.   **11.21**(a) Nitrogen uses $sp^2$ to form three σ bonds and one π bond.   (b) Carbon uses $sp$ to form two σ bonds and two π bonds.   (c) Carbon uses $sp^2$ to form three σ bonds and one π bond.
**11.23**(a) N: $sp^2$, forming 2 σ bonds and 1 π bond
$\quad$ :F̈—N̈=Ö:

(b) C: $sp^2$, forming 3 σ bonds and 1 π bond
$\quad$ :F̈ $\quad\quad$ F̈:
$\quad\quad$ C=C
$\quad$ :F̈ $\quad\quad$ F̈:

(c) C: $sp$, forming 2 σ bonds and 2 π bonds
$\quad$ :N≡C—C≡N:

**11.25** H $\quad\quad$ H $\quad\quad\quad$ $CH_3$ $\quad$ H
$\quad\quad$ C=C $\quad\quad\quad\quad\quad$ C=C
$\quad$ $CH_3$ $\quad$ $CH_3$ $\quad\quad$ H $\quad\quad$ $CH_3$
$\quad\quad$ *cis* $\quad\quad\quad\quad\quad\quad$ *trans*

The single bonds are all σ bonds. The double bond is one σ bond and one π bond.   **11.26** Four MOs form from the four $p$ atomic orbitals. The total number of MOs must equal the number of atomic orbitals.   **11.28**(a) Bonding MOs have lower energy than antibonding MOs. Lower energy means more stable.   (b) Bonding MOs do not have a nodal plane perpendicular to the bond.   (c) Bonding MOs have higher electron density between nuclei than antibonding MOs.   **11.30**(a) two   (b) two (c) four   **11.32**(a) A is $\pi^*_{2p}$, B is $\sigma_{2p}$, C is $\pi_{2p}$, and D is $\sigma^*_{2p}$.   (b) $\pi^*_{2p}$ (A), $\sigma_{2p}$ (B), and $\pi_{2p}$ (C) have at least one electron.   (c) $\pi^*_{2p}$ (A) has only one electron.   **11.34**(a) stable   (b) paramagnetic   (c) $(\sigma_{2s})^2(\sigma^*_{2s})^1$   **11.36**(a) $C_2^+ < C_2 <$ $C_2^-$   (b) $C_2^- < C_2 < C_2^+$   **11.40**(a) C (ring): $sp^2$; C (all others): $sp^3$; O (all): $sp^3$; N: $sp^3$   (b) 26   (c) 6   **11.42**(a) 17   (b) All carbons are $sp^2$; the ring N is $sp^2$, the other N's are $sp^3$.
**11.44**(a) B changes from $sp^2$ to $sp^3$.   (b) P changes from $sp^3$ to $sp^3d$.   (c) C changes from $sp$ to $sp^2$. Two electron groups surround C in $C_2H_2$, and three electron groups surround C in $C_2H_4$.   (d) Si changes from $sp^3$ to $sp^3d^2$.   (e) no change for S
**11.46** P: tetrahedral, $sp^3$; N: trigonal pyramid, $sp^3$; $C_1$ and $C_2$: tetrahedral, $sp^3$; $C_3$: trigonal planar, $sp^2$   **11.51**(a) B and D are present.   (b) Yes, $sp$ hybrid orbitals.   (c) Two sets of $sp$ orbitals,

four sets of $sp^2$ orbitals, and three sets of $sp^3$ orbitals.
**11.52** Through resonance, the C—N bond gains some double-bond character, which hinders rotation about that bond.

**11.55**(a) C in —CH₃: $sp^3$; all other C atoms: $sp^2$; O in two C—O bonds: $sp^3$; O in two C=O bonds: $sp^2$ (b) two (c) eight; one **11.56**(a) four (b) eight

## Chapter 12

**Answer to Boxed Reading Problem: B12.1** $1.76\times10^{-10}$ m

• **12.1** In a solid, the energy of attraction of the particles is greater than their energy of motion; in a gas, it is less. Gases have high compressibility and the ability to flow, while solids have neither. **12.4**(a) Because the intermolecular forces are only partially overcome when fusion occurs but need to be totally overcome in vaporization. (b) Because solids have greater intermolecular forces than liquids do. (c) $\Delta H_{vap} = -\Delta H_{cond}$ **12.5**(a) intermolecular (b) intermolecular (c) intramolecular (d) intramolecular **12.7**(a) condensation (b) fusion (c) vaporization **12.9** The gas molecules slow down as the gas is compressed. Therefore, much of the kinetic energy lost by the propane molecules is released to the surroundings. **12.13** At first, the vaporization of liquid molecules from the surface predominates, which increases the number of gas molecules and hence the vapor pressure. As more molecules enter the gas phase, more gas molecules hit the surface of the liquid and "stick" more frequently, so the condensation rate increases. When the vaporization and condensation rates become equal, the vapor pressure becomes constant. **12.14** As intermolecular forces increase, (a) critical temperature increases, (b) boiling point increases, (c) vapor pressure decreases, and (d) heat of vaporization increases. **12.18** because the condensation of the vapor supplies an additional 40.7 kJ/mol **12.19** $7.67\times10^3$ J **12.21** 0.777 atm **12.23** $2\times10^4$ J/mol
**12.25**

Solid ethylene is more dense than liquid ethylene. **12.28** 32 atm **12.32** O is smaller and more electronegative than Se; so the electron density on O is greater, which attracts H more strongly. **12.34** All particles (atoms and molecules) exhibit dispersion forces, but the total force is weak for small molecules.

Dipole-dipole forces between small polar molecules dominate the dispersion forces. **12.37**(a) hydrogen bonding (b) dispersion forces (c) dispersion forces **12.39**(a) dipole-dipole forces (b) dispersion forces (c) hydrogen bonding
**12.41**(a)

$$CH_3-CH-\ddot{O}:\cdots H-\underset{\underset{H}{|}}{\ddot{O}}-CH-CH_3$$
$$\underset{CH_3\ H}{}$$

(b)

**12.43**(a) dispersion forces (b) hydrogen bonding (c) dispersion forces **12.45**(a) I⁻ (b) CH₂=CH₂ (c) H₂Se. In (a) and (c) the larger particle has the higher polarizability. In (b), the less tightly held $\pi$ electron clouds are more easily distorted. **12.47**(a) C₂H₆; it is a smaller molecule exhibiting weaker dispersion forces than C₄H₁₀. (b) CH₃CH₂F; it has no H—F bonds, so it exhibits only dipole-dipole forces, which are weaker than the hydrogen bonds of CH₃CH₂OH. (c) PH₃; it has weaker intermolecular forces (dipole-dipole) than NH₃ (hydrogen bonding). **12.49**(a) HCl; it has dipole-dipole forces, and there are stronger ionic bonds in LiCl. (b) PH₃; it has dipole-dipole forces, and there is stronger hydrogen bonding in NH₃. (c) Xe; it exhibits weaker dispersion forces since its smaller size results in lower polarizability than the larger I₂ molecules. **12.51**(a) C₄H₈ (cyclobutane), because it is more compact than C₄H₁₀. (b) PBr₃; the dipole-dipole forces in PBr₃ are weaker than the ionic bonds in NaBr. (c) HBr; the dipole-dipole forces in HBr are weaker than the hydrogen bonds in water. **12.53** As atomic size decreases and electronegativity increases, the electron density of an atom increases. Thus, the attraction to an H atom on another molecule increases while its bonded H atom becomes more positive. Fluorine is the smallest of the three and the most electronegative, so the H bonds in hydrogen fluoride are the strongest. Oxygen is smaller and more electronegative than nitrogen, so H bonds in water are stronger than H bonds in ammonia. **12.57** The cohesive forces in water and mercury are stronger than the adhesive forces to the nonpolar wax on the floor. Weak adhesive forces result in spherical drops. The adhesive forces overcome the even weaker cohesive forces in the oil, and so the oil drop spreads out. **12.59** Surface tension is defined as the energy needed to increase the surface area by a given amount, so units of energy per area are appropriate. **12.61** CH₃CH₂CH₂OH < HOCH₂CH₂OH < HOCH₂CH(OH)CH₂OH.
More hydrogen bonding means more attraction between molecules, so more energy is needed to increase surface area. **12.63** HOCH₂CH(OH)CH₂OH > HOCH₂CH₂OH > CH₃CH₂CH₂OH. More hydrogen bonding means more attraction between molecules, so they flow less easily. **12.68** Water is a good solvent for polar and ionic substances and a poor solvent for nonpolar substances. Water is a polar molecule and dissolves polar substances because their intermolecular forces are of similar strength. **12.69** A single water molecule can form four H bonds. The two hydrogen atoms each form one H bond to oxygen atoms on neighboring water molecules. The two

lone pairs on the oxygen atom form H bonds with hydrogen atoms on two neighboring molecules. **12.72** Water exhibits strong capillary action, which allows it to be easily absorbed by the plant's roots and transported upward to the leaves. **12.78** simple cubic **12.81** The energy gap is the energy difference between the highest filled energy level (valence band) and the lowest unfilled energy level (conduction band). In conductors and superconductors, the energy gap is zero because the valence band overlaps the conduction band. In semiconductors, the energy gap is small. In insulators, the gap is large. **12.83** atomic mass and atomic radius **12.84**(a) face-centered cubic  (b) body-centered cubic  (c) face-centered cubic  **12.86**(a) The change in unit cell is from a sodium chloride structure in CdO to a zinc blende structure in CdSe.  (b) Yes, the coordination number of Cd changes from 6 in CdO to 4 in CdSe.  **12.88**(a) Nickel forms a metallic solid since it is a metal whose atoms are held together by metallic bonds. (b) Fluorine forms a molecular solid since the $F_2$ molecules are held together by dispersion forces.  (c) Methanol forms a molecular solid since the $CH_3OH$ molecules are held together by hydrogen bonds.  (d) Tin forms a metallic solid since it is a metal whose atoms are held together by metallic bonds. (e) Silicon is in the same group as carbon, so it exhibits similar bonding properties. Since diamond and graphite are both network covalent solids, it makes sense that Si forms a network covalent solid as well.  (f) Xe is an atomic solid since its individual atoms are held together by dispersion forces. **12.90** four **12.92**(a) four $Se^{2-}$ ions, four $Zn^{2+}$ ions  (b) 577.48 amu (c) $1.77\times10^{-22}$ cm³  (d) $5.61\times10^{-8}$ cm  **12.94**(a) insulator (b) conductor  (c) semiconductor **12.96**(a) Conductivity increases.  (b) Conductivity increases.  (c) Conductivity decreases.  **12.98** $1.68\times10^{-8}$ cm  **12.105** A substance whose properties are the same in all directions is isotropic; otherwise, the substance is anisotropic. Liquid crystals have a degree of order only in certain directions, so they are anisotropic. **12.111**(a) n-type semiconductor  (b) p-type semiconductor  **12.113** $n = 3.4\times10^3$  **12.115** 8.4 pm  **12.118**(a) 19.8 torr (b) 0.0485 g  **12.124** 259 K  **12.126**(a) $2.23\times10^{-2}$ atm (b) 6.23 L

**12.129**(a) furfuryl alcohol

2-furoic acid

(b) furfuryl alcohol    2-furoic acid

**12.130**(a) 49.3 metric tons $H_2O$  (b) $-1.11\times10^8$ kJ **12.131** 2.9 g/m³  **12.136**(a) 1.1 min  (b) 10. min (c)

**12.137** $2.98\times10^5$ g BN  **12.140** 45.98 amu

## Chapter 13

**Answers to Boxed Reading Problem: B13.1** (a) The colloidal particles in water generally have negatively charged surfaces and so repel each other, slowing the settling process. Cake alum, $Al_2(SO_4)_3$, is added to coagulate the colloids. The $Al^{3+}$ ions neutralize the negative surface charges and allow the particles to aggregate and settle.  (b) Water that contains large amounts of divalent cations (such as $Ca^{2+}$, and $Mg^{2+}$) is called hard water. During cleaning, these ions combine with the fatty-acid anions in soaps to produce insoluble deposits.  (c) In reverse osmosis, a pressure greater than the osmotic pressure is applied to the solution, forcing the water back through the membrane, leaving the ions behind.  (d) Chlorine may give the water an unpleasant odor, and can form carcinogenic chlorinated compounds.  (e) The high concentration of NaCl displaces the divalent and polyvalent ions from the ion-exchange resin.

**• 13.2** When a salt such as NaCl dissolves, ion-dipole forces cause the ions to separate, and many water molecules cluster around each ion in hydration shells. Ion-dipole forces bind the first shell to an ion. The water molecules in that shell form H bonds to others to create the next shell, and so on. **13.4** Sodium stearate is a more effective soap because the hydrocarbon chain in the stearate ion is longer than that in the acetate ion. The longer chain allows for more dispersion forces with grease molecules. **13.7** $KNO_3$ is an ionic compound and is therefore more soluble in water.  **13.9**(a) ion-dipole forces  (b) hydrogen bonding  (c) dipole–induced dipole forces **13.11**(a) hydrogen bonding  (b) dipole–induced dipole forces  (c) dispersion forces  **13.13**(a) $HCl(g)$, because the molecular interactions (dipole-dipole forces) in ether are like those in HCl but not like the ionic bonding in NaCl. (b) $CH_3CHO(l)$, because the molecular interactions with ether (dipole-dipole) can replace those between $CH_3CHO$, but not the H bonds in water.  (c) $CH_3CH_2MgBr(s)$, because the molecular interactions (dipole-dipole and dispersion forces) are greater than between ether and the ions in $MgBr_2$.  **13.16** Gluconic acid is soluble in water due to extensive hydrogen bonding by the —OH groups attached to five of its carbons. The dispersion forces in the nonpolar tail of caproic acid are more similar to the dispersion forces in hexane; thus, caproic acid is soluble in hexane. **13.18** The nitrogen-containing bases form H bonds to their complementary bases. The flat, N-containing bases stack above each other, which allows extensive dispersion forces. The exterior negatively charged sugar-phosphate chains form ion-dipole and H bonds with water molecules in the aqueous surroundings, which also stabilizes the structure. **13.21** Dispersion forces are present between the nonpolar tails of the lipid molecules within the bilayer. The polar heads interact with the aqueous surroundings through H bonds and ion-dipole forces. **13.25** The enthalpy changes needed to separate the solvent ($\Delta H_{\text{solvent}}$) and to mix the solvent and solute ($\Delta H_{\text{mix}}$) combine to give $\Delta H_{\text{solvation}}$. **13.29** very soluble, because a decrease in enthalpy and an increase in entropy both favor the formation of a solution

**13.30**

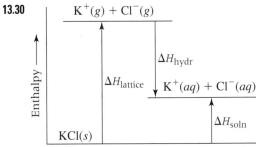

**13.32**(a) The volume of $Na^+$ is smaller. (b) $Sr^{2+}$ has a larger ionic charge and a smaller volume. (c) $Na^+$ is smaller than $Cl^-$. (d) $O^{2-}$ has a larger ionic charge with a similar ion volume. (e) $OH^-$ has a smaller volume than $SH^-$. (f) $Mg^{2+}$ has a smaller volume. (g) $Mg^{2+}$ has both a smaller volume and a larger ionic charge. (h) $CO_3^{2-}$ has both a smaller volume and a larger ionic charge. **13.34**(a) $Na^+$ (b) $Sr^{2+}$ (c) $Na^+$ (d) $O^{2-}$ (e) $OH^-$ (f) $Mg^{2+}$ (g) $Mg^{2+}$ (h) $CO_3^{2-}$ **13.36**(a) $-704$ kJ/mol (b) The $K^+$ ion contributes more because it is smaller and, therefore, has a greater charge density. **13.38**(a) increases (b) decreases (c) increases **13.41** Add a pinch of X to each solution. Addition of a "seed" crystal of solute to a supersaturated solution causes the excess solute to crystallize immediately, leaving behind a saturated solution. The solution in which the added X dissolves is the unsaturated solution. The solution in which the added X remains undissolved is the saturated solution. **13.44**(a) increase (b) decrease **13.46**(a) 0.102 g $O_2$ (b) 0.0214 g $O_2$ **13.49** 0.20 mol/L **13.52**(a) molarity and % w/v or % v/v (b) parts-by-mass (% w/w) (c) molality **13.54** With just this information, you can convert between molality and molarity, but you need to know the molar mass of the solvent to convert to mole fraction. **13.56**(a) 0.944 $M$ $C_{12}H_{22}O_{11}$ (b) 0.167 $M$ $LiNO_3$ **13.58**(a) 0.0749 $M$ NaOH (b) 0.36 $M$ $HNO_3$ **13.60**(a) Add 4.25 g $KH_2PO_4$ to enough water to make 365 mL of aqueous solution. (b) Add 125 mL of 1.25 $M$ NaOH to enough water to make 465 mL of solution. **13.62**(a) Weigh out 48.0 g KBr, dissolve it in about 1 L distilled water, and then dilute to 1.40 L with distilled water. (b) Measure 82.7 mL of the 0.264 $M$ $LiNO_3$ solution and add distilled water to make a total of 255 mL. **13.64**(a) 0.896 $m$ glycine (b) 1.21 $m$ glycerol **13.66** 4.48 $m$ $C_6H_6$ **13.68**(a) Add 2.39 g $C_2H_6O_2$ to

308 g $H_2O$. (b) Add 0.0508 kg of 52.0% $HNO_3$ by mass to 1.15 kg $H_2O$ to make 1.20 kg of 2.20% $HNO_3$ by mass. **13.70**(a) 0.29 (b) 58 mass % (c) 23 $m$ $C_3H_7OH$ **13.72** 42.6 g CsBr; mole fraction = $7.16\times10^{-3}$; 7.84% by mass **13.74** 5.11 $m$ $NH_3$; 4.53 $M$ $NH_3$; mole fraction = 0.0843 **13.76** 2.5 ppm $Ca^{2+}$; 0.56 ppm $Mg^{2+}$ **13.80** It conducts a "strong" current. A strong electrolyte dissociates completely into ions in solution. **13.82** The boiling point is higher and the freezing point is lower for the solution than for the solvent. **13.85** A dilute solution of an electrolyte behaves more ideally than a concentrated one. With increasing concentration, the effective concentration deviates from the molar concentration because of ionic attractions. Thus, 0.050 $m$ NaF has a boiling point closer to its predicted value. **13.88**(a) strong electrolyte (b) strong electrolyte (c) nonelectrolyte (d) weak electrolyte **13.90**(a) 0.6 mol of solute particles (b) 0.13 mol (c) $2\times10^{-4}$ mol (d) 0.06 mol **13.92**(a) $CH_3OH$ in $H_2O$ (b) $H_2O$ in $CH_3OH$ solution **13.94**(a) $\Pi_{II} < \Pi_{I} < \Pi_{III}$ (b) $bp_{II} < bp_{I} < bp_{III}$ (c) $fp_{III} < fp_{I} < fp_{II}$ (d) $vp_{III} < vp_{I} < vp_{II}$ **13.96** 23.4 torr **13.98** $-0.467°C$ **13.100** 79.5°C **13.102** $1.18\times10^4$ g $C_2H_6O_2$ **13.104**(a) NaCl: 0.173 $m$ and $i = 1.84$ (b) $CH_3COOH$: 0.0837 $m$ and $i = 1.02$ **13.107** 209 torr for $CH_2Cl_2$; 48.1 torr for $CCl_4$ **13.108** The fluid inside a bacterial cell is both a solution and a colloid. It is a solution of ions and small molecules and a colloid of large molecules (proteins and nucleic acids). **13.112** Soap micelles have nonpolar tails pointed inward and anionic heads pointed outward. The like charges on the heads of one micelle repel those on the heads of a neighboring micelle. This repulsion between micelles keeps them from coagulating. Soap is more effective in freshwater than in seawater because the divalent cations in seawater combine with the anionic heads to form a precipitate. **13.116** $3.4\times10^9$ L **13.120** 0.0°C: $4.53\times10^{-4}$ $M$ $O_2$; 20.0°C: $2.83\times10^{-4}$ $M$ $O_2$; 40.0°C: $2.00\times10^{-4}$ $M$ $O_2$ **13.122**(a) 89.9 g/mol (b) $C_2H_5O$; $C_4H_{10}O_2$ (c) Forms H bonds:

$$\text{HO}-\overset{\overset{\displaystyle H}{|}}{\underset{\underset{\displaystyle H}{|}}{C}}-\overset{\overset{\displaystyle H}{|}}{\underset{\underset{\displaystyle H}{|}}{C}}-\overset{\overset{\displaystyle H}{|}}{\underset{\underset{\displaystyle H}{|}}{C}}-\overset{\overset{\displaystyle H}{|}}{\underset{\underset{\displaystyle H}{|}}{C}}-\text{OH}$$

Does not form H bonds:

$$\text{H}-\overset{\overset{\displaystyle H}{|}}{\underset{\underset{\displaystyle H}{|}}{C}}-\text{O}-\overset{\overset{\displaystyle H}{|}}{\underset{\underset{\displaystyle H}{|}}{C}}-\text{O}-\overset{\overset{\displaystyle H}{|}}{\underset{\underset{\displaystyle H}{|}}{C}}-\overset{\overset{\displaystyle H}{|}}{\underset{\underset{\displaystyle H}{|}}{C}}-\text{H}$$

**13.126**(a) 9.45 g NaF (b) 0.0017 g $F^-$ **13.129**(a) 68 g/mol (b) $2.1\times10^2$ g/mol (c) The molar mass of $CaN_2O_6$ is 164.10 g/mol. This value is less than the $2.1\times10^2$ g/mol calculated when the compound is assumed to be a strong electrolyte and is greater than the 68 g/mol calculated when the compound is assumed to be a nonelectrolyte. Thus, the compound forms a nonideal solution because the ions interact but do not dissociate completely in solution. (d) $i = 2.4$ **13.133**(a) $1.82\times10^4$ g/mol (b) $3.41\times10^{-5}°C$ **13.134** $8.2\times10^5$ ng/L **13.138**(a) 0.02 (b) $5\times10^{-3}$ atm·L/mol (c) yes **13.140** Weigh 3.11 g of $NaHCO_3$ and dissolve in 247 g of water. **3.144** $M = m$

(kg solvent/L solution) = $m \times d_{solution}$. Thus, for very dilute solutions, molality $\times$ density = molarity. For an aqueous solution, the number of liters of solution is approximately the same as the kg of solvent because the density of water is close to 1 kg/L, so $m = M$. **13.146**(a) $2.5\times10^{-3}$ $M$ $SO_2$  (b) The base reacts with the sulfur dioxide to produce calcium sulfite. The reaction of sulfur dioxide makes "room" for more sulfur dioxide to dissolve. **13.151**(a) $7.83\times10^{-3}$ mol L·atm  (b) $4\times10^{-5}$ $M$  (c) $3\times10^{-6}$  (d) 1 ppm  **13.155**(a) 0.0212 mol/L·atm  (b) 8.86 ppm  (c) $k_H$: $C_6F_{14} > C_6H_{14} >$ ethanol $>$ water. To dissolve oxygen in a solvent, the solvent molecules must be moved apart to make room for the gas. The stronger the intermolecular forces in the solvent, the more difficult it is to separate solvent particles and the lower the solubility of the gas. In both $C_6F_{14}$ and $C_6H_{14}$ have weak dispersion forces, with $C_6F_{14}$ having the weaker forces due to the electronegative fluorine atoms repelling each other. In both ethanol and water, the molecules are held together by strong hydrogen bonds with those bonds being stronger in water, as the boiling point indicates. **13.157**(a) Yes, the phases of water can still coexist at some temperature and can therefore establish equilibrium.  (b) The triple point would occur at a lower pressure and lower temperature because the dissolved air would lower the vapor pressure of the solvent.  (c) Yes, this is possible because the gas-solid phase boundary exists below the new triple point.  (d) No; at both temperatures, the presence of the solute lowers the vapor pressure of the liquid.  **13.159**(a) $2.8\times10^{-4}$ g/mL  (b) 81 mL

## Chapter 14

**14.1** The outermost electron is attracted by a smaller effective nuclear charge in Li because of shielding by the inner electrons, and it is farther from the nucleus in Li. Both of these factors lead to a lower ionization energy for Li.
**14.3**(a) $NH_3$ will hydrogen bond.

:F̈—N̈—F̈:      H—N̈—H
     |              |
    :F̈:             H

(b) $CH_3CH_2OH$ will hydrogen bond.

     H   H              H  H
     |   |              |  |
  H—C—Ö—C—H       H—C—C—Ö—H
     |   |              |  |
     H   H              H  H

**14.5**(a) $2Al(s) + 6HCl(aq) \longrightarrow 2AlCl_3(aq) + 3H_2(g)$
(b) $LiH(s) + H_2O(l) \longrightarrow LiOH(aq) + H_2(g)$
**14.7**(a) $NaBH_4$: +1 for Na, +3 for B, $-1$ for H
$Al(BH_4)_3$: +3 for Al, +3 for B, $-1$ for H
$LiAlH_4$: +1 for Li, +3 for Al, $-1$ for H
(b) tetrahedral

$$\left[ \begin{array}{c} H \\ | \\ H-B-H \\ | \\ H \end{array} \right]^-$$

**14.10** For Groups 1A(1) to 4A(14), the number of covalent bonds equals the (old) group number. For Groups 5A(15) to 7A(17), it equals 8 minus the (old) group number. There are exceptions in Period 3 to Period 6 because it is possible for the 3A(13) to 7A(17) elements to use $d$ orbitals and form more bonds.  **14.13**(a) Group 3A(13) or 3B(3)  (b) If E is in Group 3B(3), the oxide will be more basic and the fluoride will be more ionic; if E is in Group 3A(13), the oxide will be more acidic and the fluoride will be more covalent.
**14.16**(a) reducing agent  (b) Alkali metals have relatively low ionization energies, which means they easily lose the outermost electron.
(c) $2Na(s) + 2H_2O(l) \longrightarrow 2Na^+(aq) + 2OH^-(aq) + H_2(g)$
$2Na(s) + Cl_2(g) \longrightarrow 2NaCl(s)$
**14.18** Density and ionic size increase down a group; the other three properties decrease down a group.
**14.20** $2Na(s) + O_2(g) \longrightarrow Na_2O_2(s)$
**14.22** $K_2CO_3(s) + 2HI(aq) \longrightarrow 2KI(aq) + H_2O(l) + CO_2(g)$
**14.26** Group 2A(2) metals have an additional valence electron to increase the strength of metallic bonding, which leads to higher melting points, higher boiling points, greater hardness, and greater density.
**14.27**(a) $CaO(s) + H_2O(l) \longrightarrow Ca(OH)_2(s)$
(b) $2Ca(s) + O_2(g) \longrightarrow 2CaO(s)$
**14.30**(a) $BeO(s) + H_2O(l) \longrightarrow$ no reaction
(b) $BeCl_2(l) + 2Cl^-(solvated) \longrightarrow BeCl_4^{2-}(solvated)$
Be behaves like other Group 2A(2) elements in reaction (b).
**14.33** The electron removed from Group 2A(2) atoms occupies the outer $s$ orbital, whereas in Group 3A(13) atoms, the electron occupies the outer $p$ orbital. For example, the electron configuration for Be is $1s^2 2s^2$ and for B it is $1s^2 2s^2 2p^1$. It is easier to remove the $p$ electron of B than an $s$ electron of Be, because the energy of a $p$ orbital is higher than that of the $s$ orbital of the same level. Even though atomic size decreases because of increasing $Z_{eff}$, IE decreases from 2A(2) to 3A(13).
**14.34**(a) Most atoms form stable compounds when they complete their outer shell (octet). Some compounds of Group 3A(13) elements, like boron, have only six electrons around the central atom. Having fewer than eight electrons is called *electron deficiency*.
(b) $BF_3(g) + NH_3(g) \longrightarrow F_3B—NH_3(g)$
$B(OH)_3(aq) + OH^-(aq) \longrightarrow B(OH)_4^-(aq)$
**14.36** $In_2O_3 < Ga_2O_3 < Al_2O_3$  **14.38** Apparent O.N., +3; actual O.N., +1. $\left[ :\ddot{I}—\ddot{I}—\ddot{I}: \right]^-$ The anion $I_3^-$ has the general formula $AX_2E_3$ and bond angles of 180°. $(Tl^{3+})(I^-)_3$ does not exist  because of the low strength of the Tl—I bond.
**14.43**(a) $B_2O_3(s) + 2NH_3(g) \longrightarrow 2BN(s) + 3H_2O(g)$
(b) $1.30\times10^2$ kJ  (c) 5.3 kg borax  **14.44** Basicity in water is greater for the oxide of a metal. Tin(IV) oxide is more basic in water than carbon dioxide because tin has more metallic character than carbon.  **14.46**(a) Ionization energy generally decreases down a group.  (b) The deviations (increases) from the expected trend are due to the presence of the first transition series between Si and Ge and of the lanthanides between Sn and Pb.  (c) Group 3A(13)  **14.49** Atomic size increases down a group. As atomic size increases, ionization energy decreases and so it is easier to form a positive ion. An atom that is easier to ionize exhibits greater metallic character.

**14.51**(a) 

$$\left[\begin{array}{c} :\overset{..}{O}: \quad :\overset{..}{O}: \\ :\overset{..}{O}-Si-\overset{..}{O}-Si-\overset{..}{O}: \\ :\overset{..}{O}: \quad :\overset{..}{O}: \\ :\overset{..}{O}-Si-\overset{..}{O}-Si-\overset{..}{O}: \\ :\overset{..}{O}: \quad :\overset{..}{O}: \end{array}\right]^{8-}$$

(b)

$$\begin{array}{cc} H \quad H \\ H-C-C-H \\ H-C-C-H \\ H \quad H \end{array}$$

**14.54**(a) diamond, C  (b) calcium carbonate, $CaCO_3$  (c) carbon dioxide, $CO_2$  (d) carbon monoxide, CO  (e) silicon, Si
**14.58**(a) −3 to +5  (b) For a group of nonmetals, the oxidation states range from the lowest, group number − 8, or 5 − 8 = −3 for Group 5A, to the highest, equal to the group number, or +5 for Group 5A.  **14.61** $H_3AsO_4 < H_3PO_4 < HNO_3$
**14.63**(a) $4As(s) + 5O_2(g) \longrightarrow 2As_2O_5(s)$
 (b) $2Bi(s) + 3F_2(g) \longrightarrow 2BiF_3(s)$
 (c) $Ca_3As_2(s) + 6H_2O(l) \longrightarrow 3Ca(OH)_2(s) + 2AsH_3(g)$
**14.65**(a) $N_2(g) + 2Al(s) \overset{\Delta}{\longrightarrow} 2AlN(s)$
 (b) $PF_5(g) + 4H_2O(l) \longrightarrow H_3PO_4(aq) + 5HF(g)$
**14.67** trigonal bipyramidal, with axial F atoms and equatorial Cl atoms;

$$:\overset{..}{C}l-P\begin{array}{c}\overset{:\overset{..}{F}:}{|} \quad \overset{..}{C}l: \\ | \\ \underset{:\overset{..}{F}:}{|} \quad \overset{..}{C}l: \end{array}$$

**14.71**(a) $\overset{..}{O}=\overset{..}{N}-\overset{..}{N}=\overset{..}{O}$  (b) $\overset{..}{O}=\overset{..}{N}-\overset{..}{O}=\overset{..}{N}:$
 (c)  :$\overset{..}{O}$:
$\overset{..}{O}=\overset{..}{N}-\overset{..}{O}=\overset{..}{N}$  (d) $[:N\equiv O:]^+$  $\left[\overset{..}{O}=N\underset{\underset{:\overset{..}{O}:}{}}{\overset{:\overset{..}{O}:}{}}\right]^-$

**14.73**(a) $2KNO_3(s) \overset{\Delta}{\longrightarrow} 2KNO_2(s) + O_2(g)$  (b) $4KNO_3(s) \overset{\Delta}{\longrightarrow} 2K_2O(s) + 2N_2(g) + 5O_2(g)$  **14.75**(a) Boiling point and conductivity vary in similar ways down both groups.  (b) Degree of metallic character and types of bonding vary in similar ways down both groups.  (c) Both P and S have allotropes, and both bond covalently with almost every other nonmetal.  (d) Both N and O are diatomic gases at normal temperatures and pressures.  (e) $O_2$ is a reactive gas, whereas $N_2$ is not. Nitrogen can have any of six oxidation states, whereas oxygen has two.
**14.77**(a) $NaHSO_4(aq) + NaOH(aq) \longrightarrow Na_2SO_4(aq) + H_2O(l)$
 (b) $S_8(s) + 24F_2(g) \longrightarrow 8SF_6(g)$
 (c) $FeS(s) + 2HCl(aq) \longrightarrow H_2S(g) + FeCl_2(aq)$
 (d) $Te(s) + 2I_2(s) \longrightarrow TeI_4(s)$
**14.79**(a) acidic  (b) acidic  (c) basic  (d) amphoteric  (e) basic
**14.81** $H_2O < H_2S < H_2Te$  **14.84**(a) $O_3$, ozone  (b) $SO_3$, sulfur trioxide  (c) $SO_2$, sulfur dioxide  (d) $H_2SO_4$, sulfuric acid  (e) $Na_2S_2O_3 \cdot 5H_2O$, sodium thiosulfate pentahydrate
**14.86** $S_2F_{10}(g) \longrightarrow SF_4(g) + SF_6(g)$; O.N. of S in $S_2F_{10}$ is +5; O.N. of S in $SF_4$ is +4; O.N. of S in $SF_6$ is +6.  **14.88**(a) −1, +1, +3, +5, +7  (b) The electron configuration for Cl is [Ne] $3s^2 3p^5$. By gaining one electron, Cl achieves an octet. By forming covalent bonds, Cl completes or expands its valence level by maintaining electron pairs in bonds or as lone pairs.  (c) Fluorine has only the −1 oxidation state because its small size and absence of $d$ orbitals prevent it from forming more than one covalent bond.  **14.90**(a) Cl—Cl bond is stronger

than Br—Br bond.  (b) Br—Br bond is stronger than I—I bond.  (c) Cl—Cl bond is stronger than F—F bond. The fluorine atoms are so small that electron-electron repulsion of the lone pairs decreases the strength of the bond.
**14.92**(a) $3Br_2(l) + 6OH^-(aq) \longrightarrow$
 $5Br^-(aq) + BrO_3^-(aq) + 3H_2O(l)$
 (b) $ClF_5(l) + 6OH^-(aq) \longrightarrow$
 $5F^-(aq) + ClO_3^-(aq) + 3H_2O(l)$
**14.93**(a) $2Rb(s) + Br_2(l) \longrightarrow 2RbBr(s)$
 (b) $I_2(s) + H_2O(l) \longrightarrow HI(aq) + HIO(aq)$
 (c) $Br_2(l) + 2I^-(aq) \longrightarrow I_2(s) + 2Br^-(aq)$
 (d) $CaF_2(s) + H_2SO_4(l) \longrightarrow CaSO_4(s) + 2HF(g)$
**14.95** $HIO < HBrO < HClO < HClO_2$  **14.99** $I_2 < Br_2 < Cl_2$, because $Cl_2$ is able to oxidize Re to the +6 oxidation state, $Br_2$ only to +5, and $I_2$ only to +4  **14.100** helium; argon
**14.102** Only dispersion forces hold atoms of noble gases together.  **14.106** $\Delta H_{soln} = -411$ kJ  **14.110**(a) Second ionization energies for alkali metals are so high because the electron being removed is from the next lower energy level and these are very tightly held by the nucleus. Also, the alkali metal would lose its noble gas electron configuration.
 (b) $2CsF_2(s) \longrightarrow 2CsF(s) + F_2(g)$; −405 kJ/mol
**14.112**(a) hyponitrous acid, $H_2N_2O_2$; nitroxyl, HNO
 (b) $H-\overset{..}{O}-\overset{..}{N}=\overset{..}{N}-\overset{..}{O}-H$    $H-\overset{..}{N}=\overset{..}{O}:$
 (c) In both species the shape is bent about the N atoms.
 (d) $\left[\underset{:\overset{..}{O}: \quad :\overset{..}{O}:}{\overset{\overset{..}{N}=\overset{..}{N}}{}}\right]^{2-}$     $\left[\begin{array}{c} :\overset{..}{O}: \\ \overset{..}{N}=N: \\ :\overset{..}{O}: \end{array}\right]^{2-}$
        *cis*                    *trans*

**14.116** 13 t  **14.118** In a disproportionation reaction, a substance acts as both a reducing agent and an oxidizing agent because atoms of an element within the substance attain both higher and lower oxidation states in the products. The disproportionation reactions are b, c, d, e, and f.  **14.120**(a) Group 5A(15)  (b) Group 7A(17)  (c) Group 6A(16)  (d) Group 1A(1)  (e) Group 3A(13)  (f) Group 8A(18)
**14.122** 117.2 kJ
**14.127** $\left[\overset{..}{O}=\overset{.}{N}-\overset{..}{O}:\right]^- \longleftrightarrow \left[:\overset{..}{O}-\overset{.}{N}=\overset{..}{O}\right]^-$
 $\overset{..}{O}=\overset{.}{N}-\overset{..}{O}: \longleftrightarrow :\overset{..}{O}-\overset{.}{N}=\overset{..}{O}$
 $\left[\overset{..}{O}=N=\overset{..}{O}\right]^+$
The nitronium ion ($NO_2^+$) has a linear shape because the central N atom has two surrounding electron groups, which achieve maximum repulsion at 180°. The nitrite ion ($NO_2^-$) bond angle is more compressed than the nitrogen dioxide ($NO_2$) bond angle because the lone pair of electrons takes up more space than the lone electron.  **14.129** $2.29 \times 10^4$ g $UF_6$
**14.133** $O^+$, $O^-$, and $O^{2+}$  **14.134**(a) 39.96 mass % in $CuHAsO_3$; As, 62.42 mass % in $(CH_3)_3As$  (b) 0.35 g $CuHAsO_3$

## Chapter 15

**Answers to Boxed Reading Problems: B15.1** butane, 2 peaks; 2-methylpropane, 2 peaks; pentane, 3 peaks; 2-methylbutane, 4 peaks; 2,2-dimethylpropane, 1 peak  **B15.2** 0.08 J/mol
**B15.4** ddATP: four complementary chain pieces; ddCTP: three complementary chain pieces

• **15.2**(a) Carbon's electronegativity is midway between the most metallic and most nonmetallic elements of Period 2. To attain a filled outer shell, carbon forms covalent bonds to other atoms in molecules, network covalent solids, and polyatomic ions.  (b) Since carbon has four valence shell electrons, it forms four covalent bonds to attain an octet.  (c) To reach the He electron configuration, a carbon atom must lose four electrons, requiring too much energy to form the $C^{4+}$ cation. To reach the Ne electron configuration, the carbon atom must gain four electrons, also requiring too much energy to form the $C^{4-}$ anion.  (d) Carbon is able to bond to itself extensively because its small size allows for close approach and great orbital overlap. The extensive orbital overlap results in a strong, stable bond.  (e) The C—C σ bond is short enough to allow sideways overlap of unhybridized $p$ orbitals of neighboring C atoms. The sideways overlap of $p$ orbitals results in the π bonds that are part of double and triple bonds.  **15.3**(a) H, O, N, P, S, and halogens  (b) Heteroatoms are atoms of any element other than carbon and hydrogen.  (c) More electronegative than C: N, O, F, Cl, and Br; less electronegative than C: H and P. Sulfur and iodine have the same electronegativity as carbon.  (d) Since carbon can bond to a wide variety of heteroatoms and to carbon atoms, it can form many different compounds.  **15.6** The C—H and C—C bonds are unreactive because electronegativities are close and the bonds are short. The C—I bond is somewhat reactive because it is long and weak. The C=O bond is reactive because oxygen is more electronegative than carbon and the electron-rich π bond makes it attract electron-poor atoms. The C—Li bond is also reactive because the bond polarity results in an electron-rich region around carbon and an electron-poor region around lithium.  **15.7**(a) An alkane and a cycloalkane are organic compounds that consist of carbon and hydrogen and have only single bonds. A cycloalkane has a ring of carbon atoms. An alkene is a hydrocarbon with at least one double bond. An alkyne is a hydrocarbon with at least one triple bond.  (b) alkane = $C_nH_{2n+2}$,  cycloalkane = $C_nH_{2n}$,  alkene = $C_nH_{2n}$,  alkyne = $C_nH_{2n-2}$  (c) Alkanes and cycloalkanes are saturated hydrocarbons.  **15.10** a, c, and f

**15.13**(a)

(b)

(c)

**15.15**(a)

(b) $CH_2=C-CH-CH_2-CH_3$
         |    |
        $CH_3$  $CH_3$

$CH_2=C-CH_2-CH-CH_3$
      |          |
     $CH_3$       $CH_3$

           $CH_3$
            |
$CH_2=CH-C-CH_2-CH_3$
            |
           $CH_3$

$CH_2=CH-CH-CH-CH_3$
          |   |
         $CH_3$  $CH_3$

         $CH_3$
          |
$CH_2=CH-CH_2-C-CH_3$
          |
         $CH_3$

$CH_2=CH-CH-CH_2-CH_3$
          |
         $CH_2-CH_3$

$CH_3-C=C-CH_2-CH_3$
      |   |
     $CH_3$  $CH_3$

$CH_3-C=CH-CH-CH_3$
      |        |
     $CH_3$     $CH_3$

$CH_3-CH=C-CH-CH_3$
          |   |
         $CH_3$  $CH_3$

                 $CH_3$
                  |
$CH_3-CH=CH-C-CH_3$
                  |
                 $CH_3$

$CH_3-CH=C-CH_2-CH_3$
          |
         $CH_2-CH_3$

(c) cyclopentane structures:

$CH_2$
$CH_2$  $CH-CH_2-CH_3$
$H_2C-CH_2$

$CH_2$
$CH_2$  $CH-CH_3$
$H_2C-CH-CH_3$

$CH_2$
$H_2C$  $CH-CH_3$
$H_3C-HC-CH_2$

$CH_2$  $CH_3$
$H_2C$  $C$
              $CH_3$
$H_2C-CH_2$

**15.17**(a)
         $CH_3$
          |
$CH_3-C-CH_2-CH_3$
          |
         $CH_3$

(b) $H_2C=CH-CH_2-CH_3$

(c) $HC\equiv C-CH-CH_3$
                |
               $CH_2$
                |
               $CH_3$

(d) Structure is correct.

**15.19**(a)
       $CH_3$
        |
$CH_3-CH-CH-CH_2-CH_2-CH_2-CH_2-CH_3$
             |
            $CH_3$

(b)
    $CH_2-CH_3$
   (cyclohexane ring numbered 1-6 with $CH_3$ at position 4)

(c) 3,4-dimethylheptane  (d) 2,2-dimethylbutane

**15.21**(a)
                        $CH_3$
                         |
$CH_3-CH_2-CH_2-CH-CH_2-CH_3$
Correct name is 3-methylhexane.

(b)
                   $CH_2-CH_3$
                    |
$CH_3-CH_2-CH_2-CH-CH_3$
Correct name is 3-methylhexane.

(c)
        $CH_3$
   (cyclohexane ring with $CH_3$)
Correct name is methylcyclohexane.

(d)
                 $CH_3$
                  |
$CH_3-CH_2-C-CH-CH_2-CH_2-CH_2-CH_3$
                  |   |
                 $CH_3$  $CH_2-CH_3$
Correct name is 4-ethyl-3,3-dimethyloctane.

**15.23**(a)
   H   H
    \ /
     C
    / \
H-C---C-CH_3
   |   |
   Cl  H

(b)
            H   $CH_3$
            |   |
$CH_3-CH_2-C---C-CH_3$
            |   |
           $CH_3$  H

**15.25**(a) 3-Bromohexane is optically active.
$CH_3-CH_2-CH-CH_2-CH_2-CH_3$
              |
              Br

(b) 3-Chloro-3-methylpentane is not optically active.
            $CH_3$
             |
$CH_3-CH_2-C-CH_2-CH_3$
             |
             Cl

(c) 1,2-Dibromo-2-methylbutane is optically active.
            $CH_3$
             |
$CH_2-C-CH_2-CH_3$
 |    |
 Br   Br

**15.27**(a)

  H        H              H        $CH_3$
   \      /                \      /
    C=C                     C=C
   /      \                /      \
$CH_3CH_2$   $CH_3$        $CH_3CH_2$   H

cis-2-pentene          trans-2-pentene

(b)
   H     H                H     $CH_3$
    \   /                  \   /
     C=C                    C=C
    /   \                  /   \
(cyclohexane) $CH_3$   (cyclohexane) H

cis-1-cyclohexylpropene   trans-1-cyclohexylpropene

(c) no geometric isomers

**15.29**(a) no geometric isomers

(b)
$CH_3-CH_2$    $CH_2-CH_3$      $CH_3-CH_2$      H
        \      /                      \        /
         C=C                           C=C
        /      \                      /        \
       H        H                    H          $CH_2-CH_3$

cis-3-hexene              trans-3-hexene

(c) no geometric isomers

(d)
   Cl     Cl                Cl      H
    \    /                   \     /
     C=C                      C=C
    /    \                   /     \
   H      H                 H       Cl

cis-1,2-dichloroethene     trans-1,2-dichloroethene

**15.31**

1,2-dichlorobenzene (o-dichlorobenzene)  1,3-dichlorobenzene (m-dichlorobenzene)  1,4-dichlorobenzene (p-dichlorobenzene)

**15.33**

**15.34**

cis-2-methyl-3-hexene  trans-2-methyl-3-hexene

The compound 2-methyl-2-hexene does not have *cis-trans* isomers. **15.38** $\pi$ bond **15.40**(a) elimination (b) addition **15.42**(a) $CH_3CH_2CH{=}CHCH_2CH_3 + H_2O \xrightarrow{H^+}$

$CH_3CH_2CH_2CH(OH)CH_2CH_3$

(b) $CH_3CHBrCH_3 + CH_3CH_2OK \longrightarrow$

$CH_3CH{=}CH_2 + CH_3CH_2OH + KBr$

(c) $CH_3CH_3 + 2Cl_2 \xrightarrow{hv} CHCl_2CH_3 + 2HCl$

**15.44**(a) oxidation (b) reduction (c) reduction **15.46**(a) oxidized (b) oxidized **15.49**(a) Methylethylamine is more soluble because it has the ability to form H bonds with water molecules. (b) 1-Butanol has a higher melting point because it can form intermolecular H bonds. (c) Propylamine has a higher boiling point because it contains N—H bonds that allow H bonding, and trimethylamine cannot form H bonds. **15.52** Both groups react by addition to the $\pi$ bond. The very polar $C{=}O$ bond attracts the electron-rich O of water to the partially positive C. There is no such polarity in the alkene, so either C atom can be attacked, and two products result.

$CH_3{-}CH_2{-}\underset{O}{C}{-}CH_2{-}CH_3 + H_2O \xrightarrow{H^+}$

$CH_3{-}CH_2{-}\underset{OH}{\overset{OH}{C}}{-}CH_2{-}CH_3$

$CH_3{-}CH_2{-}CH{=}CH{-}CH_3 + H_2O \xrightarrow{H^+}$

$CH_3{-}CH_2{-}\underset{OH}{CH}{-}CH_2{-}CH_3 + CH_3{-}CH_2{-}CH_2{-}\underset{OH}{CH}{-}CH_3$

**15.55** Esters and acid anhydrides form through dehydration-condensation reactions, and water is the other product. **15.57**(a) alkyl halide (b) nitrile (c) carboxylic acid (d) aldehyde

**15.59**(a) $CH_3{-}CH{=}CH{-}CH_2{-}OH$
alkene   alcohol

(b)
haloalkane   carboxylic acid

(c)
amide
alkene

(d) $N{\equiv}C{-}CH_2{-}C{-}CH_3$
nitrile   ketone

(e)
ester

**15.61** $H_3C{-}CH_2{-}CH_2{-}CH_2{-}CH_2{-}OH$
$H_3C{-}CH_2{-}CH_2{-}\underset{OH}{CH}{-}CH_3$

$H_3C{-}CH{-}\underset{OH}{CH}{-}CH_3$
$\;\;\;\;\;\;CH_3$

$H_3C{-}\underset{CH_3}{\overset{OH}{C}}{-}CH_2{-}CH_3$

$H_3C{-}CH_2{-}\underset{OH}{CH}{-}CH_2{-}CH_3$

$H_3C{-}CH{-}CH_2{-}CH_2{-}OH$
$\;\;\;\;\;\;CH_3$

$H_3C{-}CH_2{-}\underset{CH_3}{CH}{-}CH_2{-}OH$

$H_3C{-}\underset{CH_3}{\overset{CH_3}{C}}{-}CH_2{-}OH$

**15.63** $H_3C{-}CH_2{-}CH_2{-}CH_2{-}NH_2$
$H_3C{-}CH_2{-}\underset{NH_2}{CH}{-}CH_3$

$H_3C{-}\underset{CH_3}{CH}{-}CH_2{-}NH_2$

$H_3C{-}\underset{CH_3}{\overset{CH_3}{C}}{-}NH_2$

$H_3C{-}CH_2{-}\underset{H}{N}{-}CH_2{-}CH_3$

$H_3C{-}CH_2{-}CH_2{-}\underset{H}{N}{-}CH_3$

$H_3C{-}CH_2{-}\underset{CH_3}{N}{-}CH_3$

$H_3C{-}\underset{CH_3}{CH}{-}\underset{H}{N}{-}CH_3$

**15.65**(a) $CH_3{-}\underset{O}{C}{-}CH_2{-}CH_3$ (b) $CH_3{-}\underset{CH_3}{CH}{-}\underset{O}{C}{-}OH$

(c)

**15.67**(a) $CH_3{-}\overset{O}{C}{-}\underset{H}{N}{-}CH_3$

(b) $CH_3{-}CH_2{-}CH_2{-}\overset{O}{C}{-}O{-}\underset{CH_3}{CH}{-}CH_3$

(c) $H{-}\overset{O}{C}{-}O{-}CH_2{-}\underset{CH_3}{CH}{-}CH_3$

**15.69**(a) $CH_3{-}(CH_2)_4{-}\overset{O}{C}{-}OH$ and $HO{-}CH_2{-}CH_3$

(b) $\overset{O}{C}{-}OH$ and $HO{-}CH_2{-}CH_2{-}CH_3$

(c) $CH_3{-}CH_2{-}OH$ and $HO{-}\overset{O}{C}{-}CH_2{-}CH_2{-}$

**15.71**(a) $CH_3-CH_2-OH$

(b)

$$CH_3-CH_2-\overset{\overset{\displaystyle O}{\|}}{C}-O-CH_2-CH_3$$

$$CH_3-CH_2-\overset{\overset{\displaystyle C\equiv N}{|}}{CH}-CH_3$$

$$CH_3-CH_2-\overset{\overset{\displaystyle OH}{|}}{\underset{\underset{\displaystyle C=O}{|}}{CH}}-CH_3$$

**15.73**(a) propanoic acid  (b) ethylamine  **15.77** addition reactions and condensation reactions  **15.80** Dispersion forces strongly attract the long, unbranched chains of high-density polyethylene (HDPE). Low-density polyethylene (LDPE) has branching in the chains that prevents packing and weakens the attractions.  **15.82** An amine and a carboxylic acid react to form nylon; a carboxylic acid and an alcohol form a polyester.
**15.83**(a)

$$\left[\begin{matrix} H & H \\ -C-C- \\ H & Cl \end{matrix}\right]_n$$

(b)

$$\left[\begin{matrix} H & H \\ -C-C- \\ H & CH_3 \end{matrix}\right]_n$$

**15.87**(a) condensation  (b) addition  (c) condensation  (d) condensation  **15.89** The amino acid sequence in a protein determines its shape and structure, which determine its function.  **15.92** The DNA base sequence determines the RNA base sequence, which determines the protein amino acid sequence.
**15.93**(a)

$CH_3$

(b)

(c)

$CH_3$

**15.95**(a)

(b)

**15.97**(a) AATCGG  (b) TCTGTA  **15.99** ACAATGCCT; this sequence codes for three amino acids.  **15.101**(a) Both R groups are from cysteine, which can form a disulfide bond (covalent bond).  (b) Lysine and aspartic acid give a salt link.
(c) Asparagine and serine will hydrogen bond.  (d) Valine

and phenylalanine interact through dispersion forces.
**15.106**(a) Perform an acid-catalyzed dehydration of the alcohol followed by addition of $Br_2$.  (b) Oxidize 1 mol of ethanol to acetic acid, then react 1 mol of acetic acid with 1 mol of ethanol to form the ester.
**15.108**

$$H_2N-CH_2-CH_2-CH_2-CH_2-CH_2-NH_2$$
$$\text{cadaverine}$$

$$H_2N-CH_2-CH_2-CH_2-CH_2-NH_2$$
$$\text{putrescine}$$

$$Br-CH_2CH_2-Br + 2CN^- \longrightarrow$$
$$\qquad N\equiv C-CH_2CH_2-C\equiv N + 2Br^-$$

$$N\equiv C-CH_2CH_2-C\equiv N \xrightarrow{\text{reduction}}$$
$$\qquad H_2N-CH_2CH_2CH_2CH_2-NH_2$$

**15.109**(a)

(b) Carbon 1 is $sp^2$ hybridized.  Carbon 2 is $sp^3$ hybridized.  Carbon 3 is $sp^3$ hybridized.  Carbon 4 is $sp^2$ hybridized.  Carbon 5 is $sp^3$ hybridized.  Carbons 6 and 7 are $sp^2$ hybridized.
(c) Carbons 2, 3, and 5 are chiral centers, as they are each bonded to four different groups.
**15.113** The resonance structures show that the bond between carbon and nitrogen will have some double bond character that restricts rotation around the bond.

$$\overset{:O:}{\underset{}{\overset{\|}{-C-N-}}}\overset{H}{\underset{}{|}} \longleftrightarrow \overset{:\ddot{O}:^-}{\underset{}{-C=N-}}\overset{H}{\underset{+}{|}}$$

**15.116**(a) Hydrolysis requires the addition of water to break the peptide bonds.  (b) glycine, 4; alanine, 1; valine, 3; proline, 6; serine, 7; arginine, 49  (c) 10,700 g/mol  **15.117** When 2-butanone is reduced, equal amounts of both isomers are produced because the reaction does not favor the production of one over the other. The mixture is not optically active since the rotation of light to the right by one isomer cancels the rotation of light to the left by the other isomer.

## Chapter 16

### Answers to Boxed Reading Problems:
**B16.2**  (a) Step 1   $\cancel{NO(g)} + O_3(g) \longrightarrow \cancel{NO_2(g)} + O_2(g)$
Step 2   $\cancel{NO_2(g)} + O(g) \longrightarrow \cancel{NO(g)} + O_2(g)$
Overall   $O_3(g) + O(g) \longrightarrow 2O_2(g)$
(b) rate $= 3\times10^7$ molecule/s
**B16.3** (a) Step 1 with Cl will have the higher value for the $p$ factor.  Since Cl is a single atom, no matter how it collides with the ozone molecule, the two particles should react, if the collision has enough energy.  NO is a molecule. If the $O_3$ molecule collides with the N atom in the NO molecule, reaction can occur as a bond can form between N and O; if the $O_3$

molecule collides with the O atom in the NO molecule, reaction will not occur as the bond between N and O cannot form. The probability of a successful collision is smaller with NO.

(b)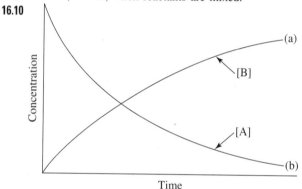

• **16.2** Reaction rate is proportional to concentration. An increase in pressure will increase the concentration, resulting in an increased rate. **16.3** The addition of water will lower the concentrations of all dissolved solutes, and the rate will decrease. **16.5** An increase in temperature increases the rate by increasing the number of collisions between particles, but more importantly, it increases the energy of collisions. **16.8**(a) The instantaneous rate is the rate at one point in time during the reaction. The average rate is the average over a period of time. On a graph of reactant concentration vs. time, the instantaneous rate is the slope of the tangent to the curve at any point. The average rate is the slope of the line connecting two points on the curve. The closer together the two points (the shorter the time interval), the closer the average rate is to the instantaneous rate. (b) The initial rate is the instantaneous rate at the point on the graph where $t = 0$, that is, when reactants are mixed.

**16.10**

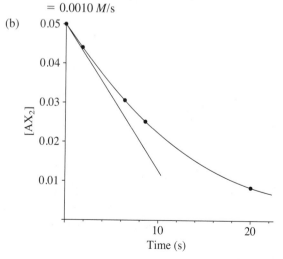

**16.12**(a) $\text{rate} = -\left(\dfrac{1}{2}\right)\dfrac{\Delta AX_2}{\Delta t}$

$= -\left(\dfrac{1}{2}\right)\dfrac{(0.0088\ M - 0.0500\ M)}{(20.0\ \text{s} - 0\ \text{s})}$

$= 0.0010\ M/s$

(b)

The initial rate is higher than the average rate because the rate decreases as reactant concentration decreases.

**16.14** $\text{rate} = -\dfrac{1}{2}\dfrac{\Delta[A]}{\Delta t} = \dfrac{\Delta[B]}{\Delta t} = \dfrac{\Delta[C]}{\Delta t}$; 4 mol/L·s

**16.16** $\text{rate} = -\dfrac{\Delta[A]}{\Delta t} = -\dfrac{1}{2}\dfrac{\Delta[B]}{\Delta t} = \dfrac{\Delta[C]}{\Delta t}$; 0.2 mol/L·s

**16.18** $2N_2O_5(g) \longrightarrow 4NO_2(g) + O_2(g)$

**16.21** $\text{rate} = -\dfrac{\Delta[N_2]}{\Delta t} = -\dfrac{1}{3}\dfrac{\Delta[H_2]}{\Delta t} = \dfrac{1}{2}\dfrac{\Delta[NH_3]}{\Delta t}$

**16.22**(a) $\text{rate} = -\dfrac{1}{3}\dfrac{\Delta[O_2]}{\Delta t} = \dfrac{1}{2}\dfrac{[\Delta O_3]}{\Delta t}$

(b) $1.45\times10^{-5}$ mol/L·s

**16.23**(a) $k$ is the rate constant, the proportionality constant in the rate law; it is reaction and temperature specific. (b) $m$ represents the order of the reaction with respect to [A], and $n$ represents the order of the reaction with respect to [B]. The order of a reactant does not necessarily equal its stoichiometric coefficient in the balanced equation. (c) $L^2/\text{mol}^2$·min **16.25**(a) Rate doubles. (b) Rate decreases by a factor of 4. (c) Rate increases by a factor of 9. **16.26** first order in $BrO_3^-$; first order in $Br^-$; second order in $H^+$; fourth order overall **16.28**(a) Rate doubles. (b) Rate is halved. (c) The rate increases by a factor of 16. **16.30** second order in $NO_2$; first order in Cl; third order overall **16.32**(a) Rate increases by a factor of 9. (b) Rate increases by a factor of 8. (c) Rate is halved. **16.34**(a) second order in A; first order in B (b) rate = $k[A]^2[B]$ (c) $5.00\times10^3$ $L^2/\text{mol}^2$·min **16.36**(a) $\text{time}^{-1}$ (b) L/mol·time (c) $L^2/\text{mol}^2$·time (d) $L^{3/2}/\text{mol}^{3/2}$·time **16.39**(a) first order (b) second order (c) zero order **16.41** 7 s **16.43**(a) $k = 0.0660$ $\text{min}^{-1}$ (b) 21.0 min

**16.45**(a)

| x-axis (time, s) | [NH₃] | y-axis (ln [NH₃]) |
|---|---|---|
| 0 | 4.000 M | 1.38629 |
| 1.000 | 3.986 M | 1.38279 |
| 2.000 | 3.974 M | 1.37977 |

$k = 3\times10^{-3}$ $\text{s}^{-1}$

(b) $t_{1/2} = 2\times10^2$ s

**16.47** No, other factors that affect the rate are the energy and orientation of the collisions. **16.50** Measure the rate constant at a series of temperatures and plot $\ln k$ versus $1/T$. The slope of the line equals $-E_a/R$. **16.53** No, reaction is reversible and will eventually reach a state where the forward and reverse rates are equal. When this occurs, there are no concentrations equal to zero. Since some reactants are reformed from EF, the

amount of EF will be less than $4\times10^{-5}$ mol. **16.54** At the same temperature, both reaction mixtures have the same average kinetic energy, but the reactant molecules do not have the same average velocity. The trimethylamine molecule has greater mass than the ammonia molecule, so trimethylamine molecules will collide less often with HCl. Moreover, the bulky groups bonded to nitrogen in trimethylamine mean that collisions with HCl having the correct orientation occur less frequently. Therefore, the rate of the reaction between $NH_3$ and HCl is higher. **16.55** 12 unique collisions **16.57** $2.96\times10^{-18}$ **16.59** $0.033$ s$^{-1}$
**16.61**(a)

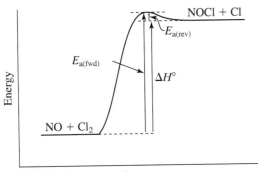

(b) $2.70\times10^2$ kJ/mol
(c) 

bond forming
A—B⋯⋯C⋯⋯D
bond breaking

**16.64**(a) Because the enthalpy change is positive, the reaction is endothermic.

(b) 3 kJ  (c) $:\ddot{Cl}\cdots\ddot{Cl}\cdots\ddot{N}{=}\ddot{O}:$

**16.65** The rate of an overall reaction depends on the rate of the slowest step. The rate of the overall reaction will be lower than the average of the individual rates because the average includes higher rates as well. **16.69** The probability of three particles colliding with one another with the proper energy and orientation is much less than the probability for two particles.
**16.70** No, the overall rate law must contain only reactants (no intermediates), and the overall rate is determined by the slow step.
**16.72**(a) $A(g) + B(g) + C(g) \longrightarrow D(g)$
(b) X and Y are intermediates.
(c)

| Step | Molecularity | Rate Law |
|---|---|---|
| $A(g) + B(g) \rightleftharpoons X(g)$ | bimolecular | $rate_1 = k_1[A][B]$ |
| $X(g) + C(g) \longrightarrow Y(g)$ | bimolecular | $rate_2 = k_2[X][C]$ |
| $Y(g) \longrightarrow D(g)$ | unimolecular | $rate_3 = k_3[Y]$ |

(d) yes  (e) yes  **16.74** The proposed mechanism is valid because the individual steps are chemically reasonable, they add to give the overall equation, and the rate law for the mechanism matches the observed rate law. **16.77** No. A catalyst changes the mechanism of a reaction to one with lower activation energy. Lower activation energy means a faster reaction. An increase in temperature does not influence the activation energy, but increases the fraction of collisions with sufficient energy to equal or exceed the activation energy. **16.78**(a) No. The spark provides energy that is absorbed by the $H_2$ and $O_2$ molecules to achieve the activation energy. (b) Yes. The powdered metal acts as a heterogeneous catalyst, providing a surface on which the oxygen-hydrogen reaction can proceed with a lower activation energy.
**16.83**(a) Water does not appear as a reactant in the rate-determining step.
(b) Step 1:  $rate_1 = k_1[(CH_3)_3CBr]$
Step 2:  $rate_2 = k_2[(CH_3)_3C^+]$
Step 3:  $rate_3 = k_3[(CH_3)_3COH_2^+]$
(c) $(CH_3)_3C^+$ and $(CH_3)_3COH_2^+$
(d) The rate-determining step is step 1. The rate law for this step agrees with the rate law observed with $k = k_1$.
**16.85** $4.61\times10^4$ J/mol  **16.89**(a) Rate increases 2.5 times. (b) Rate is halved.  (c) Rate decreases by a factor of 0.01. (d) Rate does not change.  **16.90** second order  **16.93** 57 yr
**16.96**(a) $0.21$ h$^{-1}$; $3.3$ h  (b) $6.6$ h  (c) If the concentration of sucrose is relatively low, the concentration of water remains nearly constant even with small changes in the amount of water. This gives an apparent zero-order reaction with respect to water. Thus, the reaction is first order overall because the rate does not change with changes in the amount of water.
**16.99**(a) $0.68$ M  (b) $0.57$  **16.102** 71 kPa  **16.106** $7.3\times10^3$ J/mol
**16.108**(a) $2.4\times10^{-15}$ M  (b) $2.4\times10^{-11}$ mol/L·s  **16.111**(a) 2.8 days
(b) 7.4 days  (c) 4.5 mol/m$^3$  **6.114**(a) $rate_1 = 1.7\times10^{-5}$ M s$^{-1}$; $rate_2 = 3.4\times10^{-5}$ M s$^{-1}$; $rate_3 = 3.4\times10^{-5}$ M s$^{-1}$  (b) zero order with respect to $S_2O_8^{2-}$; first order with respect to $I^-$
(c) $4.3\times10^{-4}$ s$^{-1}$  (d) $rate = (4.3\times10^{-4}$ s$^{-1})[KI]$
**16.117**(a) $7\times10^4$ cells/L  (b) $2.0\times10^1$ min  **16.120**(a) Use the Monod equation.

(b) $8.2\times10^3$ cells/m$^3$  (c) $8.4\times10^3$ cells/m$^3$
**16.125**(a) $8.0\times10^1$ s  (b) 59 s  (c) $2.6\times10^2$ s

# Chapter 17

**Answers to Boxed Reading Problem: B17.1** (a) Enzyme 3 (d) If F inhibited enzyme 6, then the second branch would not take place when enough F was made.

• **17.1** If the change is one of concentrations, it results temporarily in more products and less reactants. After equilibrium is re-established, $K_c$ remains unchanged because the ratio of products and reactants remains the same. **17.7** The equilibrium constant expression is $K = [O_2]$. If the temperature remains constant, $K$ remains constant. If the initial amount of $Li_2O_2$ present is sufficient to reach equilibrium, the amount of $O_2$ obtained will be constant.

**17.8**(a) $Q = \dfrac{[HI]^2}{[H_2][I_2]}$

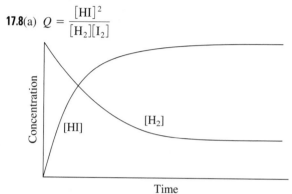

The value of $Q$ increases as a function of time until it reaches the value of $K$. (b) no **17.11** Yes. If $Q_1$ is for the formation of 1 mol $NH_3$ from $H_2$ and $N_2$, and $Q_2$ is for the formation of $NH_3$ from $H_2$ and 1 mol of $N_2$, then $Q_2 = Q_1^2$.

**17.12**(a) $4NO(g) + O_2(g) \rightleftharpoons 2N_2O_3(g)$;

$Q_c = \dfrac{[N_2O_3]^2}{[NO]^4[O_2]}$

(b) $SF_6(g) + 2SO_3(g) \rightleftharpoons 3SO_2F_2(g)$;

$Q_c = \dfrac{[SO_2F_2]^3}{[SF_6][SO_3]^2}$

(c) $2SClF_5(g) + H_2(g) \rightleftharpoons S_2F_{10}(g) + 2HCl(g)$;

$Q_c = \dfrac{[S_2F_{10}][HCl]^2}{[SClF_5]^2[H_2]}$

**17.14**(a) $2NO_2Cl(g) \rightleftharpoons 2NO_2(g) + Cl_2(g)$;

$Q_c = \dfrac{[NO_2]^2[Cl_2]}{[NO_2Cl]^2}$

(b) $2POCl_3(g) \rightleftharpoons 2PCl_3(g) + O_2(g)$;

$Q_c = \dfrac{[PCl_3]^2[O_2]}{[POCl_3]^2}$

(c) $4NH_3(g) + 3O_2(g) \rightleftharpoons 2N_2(g) + 6H_2O(g)$;

$Q_c = \dfrac{[N_2]^2[H_2O]^6}{[NH_3]^4[O_2]^3}$

**17.16**(a) 7.9 (b) $3.2\times10^{-5}$

**17.18**(a) $2Na_2O_2(s) + 2CO_2(g) \rightleftharpoons 2Na_2CO_3(s) + O_2(g)$;

$Q_c = \dfrac{[O_2]}{[CO_2]^2}$

(b) $H_2O(l) \rightleftharpoons H_2O(g)$;    $Q_c = [H_2O(g)]$

(c) $NH_4Cl(s) \rightleftharpoons NH_3(g) + HCl(g)$;    $Q_c = [NH_3][HCl]$

**17.20**(a) $2NaHCO_3(s) \rightleftharpoons Na_2CO_3(s) + CO_2(g) + H_2O(g)$;
$Q_c = [CO_2][H_2O]$

(b) $SnO_2(s) + 2H_2(g) \rightleftharpoons Sn(s) + 2H_2O(g)$;

$Q_c = \dfrac{[H_2O]^2}{[H_2]^2}$

(c) $H_2SO_4(l) + SO_3(g) \rightleftharpoons H_2S_2O_7(l)$;

$Q_c = \dfrac{1}{[SO_3]}$

**17.23**(a) (1)    $Cl_2(g) + F_2(g) \rightleftharpoons 2ClF(g)$
(2)    $2ClF(g) + 2F_2(g) \rightleftharpoons 2ClF_3(g)$
overall:    $Cl_2(g) + 3F_2(g) \rightleftharpoons 2ClF_3(g)$

(b) $Q_{overall} = Q_1 Q_2 = \dfrac{[ClF]^2}{[Cl_2][F_2]} \times \dfrac{[ClF_3]^2}{[ClF]^2[F_2]^2}$

$= \dfrac{[ClF_3]^2}{[Cl_2][F_2]^3}$

**17.25** $K_c$ and $K_p$ are equal when $\Delta n_{gas} = 0$. **17.26**(a) smaller (b) Assuming that $RT > 1$ ($T > 12.2$ K), $K_p > K_c$ if there are more moles of products than reactants at equilibrium, and $K_p < K_c$ if there are more moles of reactants than products. **17.27**(a) 3 (b) $-1$ (c) 3 **17.29**(a) 3.2 (b) 28.5 **17.31**(a) 0.15 (b) $3.6\times10^{-7}$ **17.33** The reaction quotient ($Q$) and equilibrium constant ($K$) are determined by the ratio [products]/[reactants]. When $Q < K$, the reaction proceeds to the right to form more products. **17.35** no; to the left **17.38** At equilibrium, equal concentrations of $CFCl_3$ and $HCl$ exist, regardless of starting reactant concentrations, because the product coefficients are equal. **17.40**(a) The approximation applies when the change in concentration from initial concentration to equilibrium concentration is so small that it is insignificant; this occurs when $K$ is small and initial concentration is large. (b) This approximation should not be used when the change in concentration is greater than 5%. This can occur when [reactant]$_{initial}$ is very small or when change in [reactant] is relatively large due to a large $K$. **17.41** 50.8

**17.43**

| Concentration ($M$) | $PCl_5(g)$ | $\rightleftharpoons$ | $PCl_3(g) + Cl_2(g)$ | |
|---|---|---|---|---|
| Initial | 0.075 | | 0 | 0 |
| Change | $-x$ | | $+x$ | $+x$ |
| Equilibrium | $0.075 - x$ | | $x$ | $x$ |

**17.45** 28 atm **17.47** 0.33 atm **17.49** $3.5\times10^{-3}$ $M$ **17.51** [HI] $= 0.0152$ $M$; [$I_2$] $= 0.00328$ $M$ **17.53** [$I_2$]$_{eq}$ $=$ [$Cl_2$]$_{eq}$ $= 0.0199$ $M$; [$ICl$]$_{eq}$ $= 0.0601$ $M$ **17.55** $6.01\times10^{-6}$ **17.58** Equilibrium position refers to the specific concentrations or pressures of reactants and products that exist at equilibrium, whereas equilibrium constant is the overall ratio of equilibrium concentrations or pressures. Equilibrium position changes as a result of a change in reactant and product concentrations. **17.59**(a) B, because the amount of product increases with temperature (b) A, because the lowest temperature will give the least product **17.63**(a) shifts toward products (b) shifts toward products (c) does not shift (d) shifts toward reactants **17.65**(a) more F and less $F_2$ (b) more $C_2H_2$ and $H_2$ and less $CH_4$ **17.67**(a) no effect (b) less $H_2$ and $O_2$ and more $H_2O$ **17.69**(a) no change (b) increase volume **17.71**(a) amount decreases (b) amounts increase (c) amounts increase  (d) amount decreases  **17.73** 2.0  **17.76**(a) lower temperature, higher pressure  (b) $Q$ decreases; no change in $K$  (c) Reaction rates are lower at lower temperatures, so a catalyst is used to speed up the reaction.  **17.78**(a) $P_{N_2} = 31$ atm; $P_{H_2} = 93$ atm; $P_{total} = 174$ atm  (b) $P_{N_2} = 18$ atm; $P_{H_2} = 111$ atm; $P_{total} = 179$ atm; not a valid argument  **17.81** 0.204 atm  **17.84**(a) $3\times10^{-3}$ atm  (b) high pressure; low temperature  (c) $2\times10^5$  (d) No, because water condenses at a higher temperature.  **17.87**(a) 0.016 atm  (b) $K_c = 5.6\times10^2$; $P_{O_2} = 0.16$ atm  **17.89** 12.5 g $CaCO_3$  **17.93** Both concentrations increased by a factor of 2.2.  **17.95**(a) $3.0\times10^{-14}$ atm  (b) 0.013 pg CO/L  **17.97**(a) 98.0%  (b) 99.0%  (c) $2.60\times10^5$ J/mol  **17.99**(a) $2CH_4(g) + O_2(g) + 2H_2O(g) \rightleftharpoons 2CO_2(g) + 6H_2(g)$  (b) $1.76\times10^{29}$  (c) $3.19\times10^{23}$  (d) 48 atm  **17.100**(a) $4.0\times10^{-21}$ atm  (b) $5.5\times10^{-8}$ atm  (c) 29 N atoms/L; $4.0\times10^{14}$ H atoms/L  (d) The more reasonable step is $N_2(g) + H(g) \longrightarrow NH(g) + N(g)$. With only 29 N atoms in 1.0 L, the first reaction would produce virtually no $NH(g)$ molecules. There are orders of magnitude more $N_2$ molecules than N atoms, so the second reaction is the more reasonable step.  **17.103**(a) $P_{N_2} = 0.780$ atm; $P_{O_2} = 0.210$ atm; $P_{NO} = 2.67\times10^{-16}$ atm  (b) 0.990 atm  (c) $K_c = K_p = 4.35\times10^{-31}$  **17.105**(a) $1.26\times10^{-3}$  (b) 794  (c) $-51.8$ kJ  (d) $1.2\times10^4$ J/mol  **17.109**(a) 1.52  (b) 0.9626 atm  (c) 0.2000 mol CO  (d) 0.01097 $M$

## Chapter 18

**18.2** All Arrhenius acids have H in their formula and produce hydronium ion ($H_3O^+$) in aqueous solution. All Arrhenius bases have OH in their formula and produce hydroxide ion ($OH^-$) in aqueous solution. Neutralization occurs when each $H_3O^+$ ion combines with an $OH^-$ ion to form two molecules of $H_2O$. Chemists found the reaction of any strong base with any strong acid always had a $\Delta H$ of $-56$ kJ/mol $H_2O$ produced.
**18.4** Strong acids and bases dissociate completely into ions when dissolved in water. Weak acids and bases dissociate only partially. The characteristic property of all weak acids is that a great majority of the acid molecules are undissociated.
**18.5** a, c, and d
**18.7** b and d
**18.9**(a) $K_a = \dfrac{[CN^-][H_3O^+]}{[HCN]}$

(b) $K_a = \dfrac{[CO_3^{2-}][H_3O^+]}{[HCO_3^-]}$

(c) $K_a = \dfrac{[HCOO^-][H_3O^+]}{[HCOOH]}$

**18.11**(a) $K_a = \dfrac{[NO_2^-][H_3O^+]}{[HNO_2]}$

(b) $K_a = \dfrac{[CH_3COO^-][H_3O^+]}{[CH_3COOH]}$

(c) $K_a = \dfrac{[BrO_2^-][H_3O^+]}{[HBrO_2]}$

**18.13** $CH_3COOH < HF < HIO_3 < HI$  **18.15**(a) weak acid  (b) strong base  (c) weak acid  (d) strong acid  **18.17**(a) strong base  (b) strong acid  (c) weak acid  (d) weak acid
**18.22**(a) The acid with the smaller $K_a$ ($4\times10^{-5}$) has the higher pH, because less dissociation yields fewer hydronium ions.  (b) The acid with the larger $pK_a$ (3.5) has the higher pH, because it has a smaller $K_a$ and, thus, lower $[H_3O^+]$.  (c) Lower concentration (0.01 $M$) contains fewer hydronium ions.  (d) A 0.1 $M$ weak acid solution contains fewer hydronium ions.  (e) The 0.01 $M$ base solution contains more hydroxide ions, so fewer hydronium ions.  (f) The solution that has pOH = 6.0 has the higher pH: pH = 14.0 − 6.0 = 8.0.
**18.23**(a) 12.05; basic  (b) 11.13; acidic  **18.25**(a) 2.212; acidic  (b) −0.708; basic
**18.27**(a) $[H_3O^+] = 1.4\times10^{-10}$ $M$, $[OH^-] = 7.1\times10^{-5}$ $M$, pOH = 4.15

(b) $[H_3O^+] = 2.7\times10^{-5}$ $M$, $[OH^-] = 3.7\times10^{-10}$ $M$, pH = 4.57

**18.29**(a) $[H_3O^+] = 1.7\times10^{-5}$ $M$, $[OH^-] = 5.9\times10^{-10}$ $M$, pOH = 9.23

(b) $[H_3O^+] = 4.5\times10^{-9}$ $M$, $[OH^-] = 2.2\times10^{-6}$ $M$, pH = 8.36

**18.31** $4.8\times10^{-4}$ mol $OH^-$/L  **18.33** $1.4\times10^{-4}$ mol $OH^-$
**18.36**(a) Rising temperature increases the value of $K_w$.  (b) $K_w = 2.5\times10^{-14}$; pOH = 6.80; $[OH^-] = 1.6\times10^{-7}$ $M$
**18.37** The Brønsted-Lowry theory defines acids as proton donors and bases as proton acceptors, while the Arrhenius definition looks at acids as containing ionizable hydrogen atoms and at bases as containing hydroxide ions. In both definitions, an acid produces $H_3O^+$ ions and a base produces $OH^-$ ions when added to water. Ammonia and carbonate ion are two Brønsted-Lowry bases that are not Arrhenius bases because they do not contain $OH^-$ ions. Brønsted-Lowry acids must contain an ionizable hydrogen atom in order to be proton donors, so a Brønsted-Lowry acid is also an Arrhenius acid.  **18.40** An amphiprotic species is one that can lose a proton to act as an acid or gain a proton to act as a base. The dihydrogen phosphate ion, $H_2PO_4^-$, is an example.
$H_2PO_4^-(aq) + OH^-(aq) \longrightarrow H_2O(l) + HPO_4^{2-}(aq)$
$H_2PO_4^-(aq) + HCl(aq) \longrightarrow H_3PO_4(aq) + Cl^-(aq)$
**18.41**(a) $H_3PO_4(aq) + H_2O(l) \rightleftharpoons H_2PO_4^-(aq) + H_3O^+(aq)$
$K_a = \dfrac{[H_3O^+][H_2PO_4^-]}{[H_3PO_4]}$
(b) $C_6H_5COOH(aq) + H_2O(l) \rightleftharpoons$
$C_6H_5COO^-(aq) + H_3O^+(aq)$
$K_a = \dfrac{[H_3O^+][C_6H_5COO^-]}{[C_6H_5COOH]}$
(c) $HSO_4^-(aq) + H_2O(l) \rightleftharpoons SO_4^{2-}(aq) + H_3O^+(aq)$
$K_a = \dfrac{[H_3O^+][SO_4^{2-}]}{[HSO_4^-]}$
**18.43**(a) $Cl^-$  (b) $HCO_3^-$  (c) $OH^-$  **18.45**(a) $NH_4^+$  (b) $NH_3$  (c) $C_{10}H_{14}N_2H^+$

**18.47**(a) $HCl + H_2O \rightleftharpoons Cl^- + H_3O^+$
     acid    base      base    acid
Conjugate acid-base pairs: $HCl/Cl^-$ and $H_3O^+/H_2O$
(b) $HClO_4 + H_2SO_4 \rightleftharpoons ClO_4^- + H_3SO_4^+$
    acid      base        base     acid
Conjugate acid-base pairs: $HClO_4/ClO_4^-$ and
$H_3SO_4^+/H_2SO_4$
(c) $HPO_4^{2-} + H_2SO_4 \rightleftharpoons H_2PO_4^- + HSO_4^-$
     base      acid        acid     base
Conjugate acid-base pairs: $H_2SO_4/HSO_4^-$ and
$H_2PO_4^-/HPO_4^{2-}$

**18.49**(a) $NH_3 + H_3PO_4 \rightleftharpoons NH_4^+ + H_2PO_4^-$
     base      acid       acid      base
Conjugate acid-base pairs: $H_3PO_4/H_2PO_4^-$ and $NH_4^+/NH_3$
(b) $CH_3O^- + NH_3 \rightleftharpoons CH_3OH + NH_2^-$
     base      acid       acid      base
Conjugate acid-base pairs: $NH_3/NH_2^-$ and
$CH_3OH/CH_3O^-$
(c) $HPO_4^{2-} + HSO_4^- \rightleftharpoons H_2PO_4^- + SO_4^{2-}$
     base      acid       acid      base
Conjugate acid-base pairs: $HSO_4^-/SO_4^{2-}$ and
$H_2PO_4^-/HPO_4^{2-}$

**18.51**(a) $OH^-(aq) + H_2PO_4^-(aq) \rightleftharpoons H_2O(l) + HPO_4^{2-}(aq)$
Conjugate acid-base pairs: $H_2PO_4^-/HPO_4^{2-}$ and $H_2O/OH^-$
(b) $HSO_4^-(aq) + CO_3^{2-}(aq) \rightleftharpoons$
                         $SO_4^{2-}(aq) + HCO_3^-(aq)$
Conjugate acid-base pairs: $HSO_4^-/SO_4^{2-}$ and
$HCO_3^-/CO_3^{2-}$

**18.53** $K_c > 1$: $HS^- + HCl \rightleftharpoons H_2S + Cl^-$
$K_c < 1$: $H_2S + Cl^- \rightleftharpoons HS^- + HCl$

**18.55** $K_c > 1$ for both a and b   **18.57** $K_c < 1$ for both a and b
**18.59**(a) A strong acid is 100% dissociated, so the acid concentration will be very different after dissociation. (b) A weak acid dissociates to a very small extent, so the acid concentration before and after dissociation is nearly the same. (c) same as b, but with the extent of dissociation greater (d) same as a
**18.60** No. HCl is a strong acid and dissociates to a greater extent than the weak acid $CH_3COOH$. The $K_a$ of the acid, not the concentration of $H_3O^+$, determines the strength of the acid. **18.63** $1.5 \times 10^{-5}$ **18.65** $[H_3O^+] = [NO_2^-] = 2.1 \times 10^{-2}$ $M$;
$[OH^-] = 4.8 \times 10^{-13}$ $M$ **18.67** $[H_3O^+] = [ClCH_2COO^-] =$
$0.041$ $M$; $[ClCH_2COOH] = 1.21$ $M$; pH = 1.39
**18.69**(a) $[H_3O^+] = 6.0 \times 10^{-3}$ $M$; pH = 2.22; $[OH^-] =$
$1.7 \times 10^{-12}$ $M$; pOH = 11.78 (b) $1.9 \times 10^{-4}$ **18.71** $2.2 \times 10^{-7}$
**18.73**(a) 2.37 (b) 11.53 **18.75**(a) 2.290 (b) 12.699 **18.77** 1.1%
**18.79** $[H_3O^+] = [HS^-] = 9 \times 10^{-5}$ $M$; pH = 4.0; $[OH^-] =$
$1 \times 10^{-10}$ $M$; pOH = 10.0; $[H_2S] = 0.10$ $M$; $[S^{2-}] =$
$1 \times 10^{-17}$ $M$ **18.82** 1.5% **18.83** All Brønsted-Lowry bases contain at least one lone pair of electrons, which binds an $H^+$ and allows the base to act as a proton acceptor.
**18.86**(a) $C_5H_5N(aq) + H_2O(l) \rightleftharpoons OH^-(aq) + C_5H_5NH^+(aq)$

$$K_b = \frac{[C_5H_5NH^+][OH^-]}{[C_5H_5N]}$$

(b) $CO_3^{2-}(aq) + H_2O(l) \rightleftharpoons OH^-(aq) + HCO_3^-(aq)$

$$K_b = \frac{[HCO_3^-][OH^-]}{[CO_3^{2-}]}$$

**18.88**(a) $HONH_2(aq) + H_2O(l) \rightleftharpoons OH^-(aq) + HONH_3^+(aq)$

$$K_b = \frac{[HONH_3^+][OH^-]}{[HONH_2]}$$

(b) $HPO_4^{2-}(aq) + H_2O(l) \rightleftharpoons H_2PO_4^-(aq) + OH^-(aq)$

$$K_b = \frac{[H_2PO_4^-][OH^-]}{[HPO_4^{2-}]}$$

**18.90** 11.79 **18.92** 11.45 **18.94**(a) $5.6 \times 10^{-10}$ (b) $2.5 \times 10^{-5}$
**18.96**(a) 12.04 (b) 10.77 **18.98**(a) 11.19 (b) 5.56
**18.100**(a) 8.78 (b) 4.66 **18.102** $[OH^-] = 5.5 \times 10^{-4}$ $M$; pH =
10.74 **18.104** As a nonmetal becomes more electronegative, the acidity of its binary hydride increases. The electronegative nonmetal attracts the electrons more strongly in the polar bond, shifting the electron density away from H, thus making $H^+$ more easily transferred to a water molecule to form $H_3O^+$.
**18.107** Chlorine is more electronegative than iodine, and $HClO_4$ has more oxygen atoms than HIO. **18.108**(a) $H_2SeO_4$
(b) $H_3PO_4$ (c) $H_2Te$ **18.110**(a) $H_2Se$ (b) $B(OH)_3$ (c) $HBrO_2$
**18.112**(a) 0.5 $M$ $AlBr_3$ (b) 0.3 $M$ $SnCl_2$ **18.114**(a) 0.2 $M$
$Ni(NO_3)_2$ (b) 0.35 $M$ $Al(NO_3)_3$ **18.117** NaF contains the anion of the weak acid HF, so $F^-$ acts as a base. NaCl contains the anion of the strong acid HCl.

**18.119**(a) $KBr(s) \xrightarrow{H_2O} K^+(aq) + Br^-(aq)$; neutral
(b) $NH_4I(s) \xrightarrow{H_2O} NH_4^+(aq) + I^-(aq)$
$NH_4^+(aq) + H_2O(l) \rightleftharpoons NH_3(aq) + H_3O^+(aq)$; acidic
(c) $KCN(s) \xrightarrow{H_2O} K^+(aq) + CN^-(aq)$
$CN^-(aq) + H_2O(l) \rightleftharpoons HCN(aq) + OH^-(aq)$; basic
**18.121**(a) $Na_2CO_3(s) \xrightarrow{H_2O} 2Na^+(aq) + CO_3^{2-}(aq)$
$CO_3^{2-}(aq) + H_2O(l) \rightleftharpoons$
                       $HCO_3^-(aq) + OH^-(aq)$; basic
(b) $CaCl_2(s) \xrightarrow{H_2O} Ca^{2+}(aq) + 2Cl^-(aq)$; neutral
(c) $Cu(NO_3)_2(s) \xrightarrow{H_2O} Cu^{2+}(aq) + 2NO_3^-(aq)$
$Cu(H_2O)_6^{2+}(aq) + H_2O(l) \rightleftharpoons$
                   $Cu(H_2O)_5OH^+(aq) + H_3O^+(aq)$; acidic
**18.123**(a) $SrBr_2(s) \xrightarrow{H_2O} Sr^{2+}(aq) + 2Br^-(aq)$; neutral
(b) $Ba(CH_3COO)_2(s) \xrightarrow{H_2O} Ba^{2+}(aq) + 2CH_3COO^-(aq)$
$CH_3COO^-(aq) + H_2O(l) \rightleftharpoons$
                   $CH_3COOH(aq) + OH^-(aq)$; basic
(c) $(CH_3)_2NH_2Br(s) \xrightarrow{H_2O} (CH_3)_2NH_2^+(aq) + Br^-(aq)$
$(CH_3)_2NH_2^+(aq) + H_2O(l) \rightleftharpoons$
                   $(CH_3)_2NH(aq) + H_3O^+(aq)$; acidic
**18.125**(a) $NH_4^+(aq) + H_2O(l) \rightleftharpoons NH_3(aq) + H_3O^+(aq)$
$PO_4^{3-}(aq) + H_2O(l) \rightleftharpoons HPO_4^{2-}(aq) + OH^-(aq)$;
$K_b > K_a$; basic
(b) $SO_4^{2-}(aq) + H_2O(l) \rightleftharpoons HSO_4^-(aq) + OH^-(aq)$;
$Na^+$ gives no reaction; basic
(c) $ClO^-(aq) + H_2O(l) \rightleftharpoons HClO(aq) + OH^-(aq)$;
$Li^+$ gives no reaction; basic

**18.127**(a) $Fe(NO_3)_2 < KNO_3 < K_2SO_3 < K_2S$
(b) $NaHSO_4 < NH_4NO_3 < NaHCO_3 < Na_2CO_3$
**18.129** Since both bases produce $OH^-$ ions in water, both bases appear equally strong. $CH_3O^-(aq) + H_2O(l) \longrightarrow OH^-(aq) + CH_3OH(aq)$ and $NH_2^-(aq) + H_2O(l) \longrightarrow OH^-(aq) + NH_3(aq)$. **18.131** Ammonia, $NH_3$, is a more basic solvent than $H_2O$. In a more basic solvent, weak acids such as HF act like strong acids and are 100% dissociated. **18.133** A Lewis acid is an electron-pair acceptor while a Brønsted-Lowry acid is a proton donor. The proton of a Brønsted-Lowry acid is a Lewis acid because it accepts an electron pair when it bonds with a base. All Lewis acids are not Brønsted-Lowry acids. A Lewis base is an electron-pair donor and a Brønsted-Lowry base is a proton acceptor. All Brønsted-Lowry bases are Lewis bases, and vice versa. **18.134**(a) No,
$Zn(H_2O)_6^{2+}(aq) + 6NH_3(aq) \rightleftharpoons Zn(NH_3)_6^{2+} + 6H_2O(l)$;
$NH_3$ is a weak Brønsted-Lowry base, but a strong Lewis base. (b) cyanide ion and water (c) cyanide ion **18.137**(a) Lewis acid (b) Lewis base (c) Lewis acid (d) Lewis base **18.139**(a) Lewis acid (b) Lewis base (c) Lewis base (d) Lewis acid **18.141**(a) Lewis acid: $Na^+$; Lewis base: $H_2O$ (b) Lewis acid: $CO_2$; Lewis base: $H_2O$ (c) Lewis acid: $BF_3$; Lewis base: $F^-$ **18.143**(a) Lewis (b) Brønsted-Lowry and Lewis (c) none (d) Lewis **18.146** $3.5\times10^{-8}$ to $4.5\times10^{-8}$ $M$ $H_3O^+$; $5.2\times10^{-7}$ to $6.6\times10^{-7}$ $M$ $OH^-$ **18.147**(a) Acids vary in the extent of dissociation depending on the acid-base character of the solvent. (b) Methanol is a weaker base than water since phenol dissociates less in methanol than in water.
(c) $C_6H_5OH(solvated) + CH_3OH(l) \rightleftharpoons$
$\qquad\qquad CH_3OH_2^+(solvated) + C_6H_5O^-(solvated)$
(d) $CH_3OH(l) + CH_3OH(l) \rightleftharpoons CH_3O^-(solvated)$
$\qquad + CH_3OH_2^+(solvated)$; $K = [CH_3O^-][CH_3OH_2^+]$
**18.120**(a) $SnCl_4$ is the Lewis acid; $(CH_3)_3N$ is the Lewis base (b) $5d$ **18.151** pH = 5.00, 6.00, 6.79, 6.98, 7.00 **18.157** $3\times10^{18}$ **18.160** 10.48 **18.162** 2.41 **18.164** amylase, $2\times10^{-7}$ $M$; pepsin, $1\times10^{-2}$ $M$; trypsin, $3\times10^{-10}$ $M$ **18.168** $1.47\times10^{-3}$ **18.170**(a) $Ca^{2+}$ does not react with water; $CH_3CH_2COO^-(aq) + H_2O(l) \rightleftharpoons CH_3CH_2COOH(aq) + OH^-(aq)$; basic (b) 9.08 **18.176** $4.5\times10^{-5}$ **18.179**(a) The concentration of oxygen is higher in the lungs, so the equilibrium shifts to the right. (b) In an oxygen-deficient environment, the equilibrium shifts to the left to release oxygen. (c) A decrease in $[H_3O^+]$ shifts the equilibrium to the right. More oxygen is absorbed, but it will be more difficult to remove the $O_2$. (d) An increase in $[H_3O^+]$ shifts the equilibrium to the left. Less oxygen is bound to Hb, but it will be easier to remove it. **18.181**(a) 1.012 $M$ (b) 0.004 $M$ (c) 0.4% **18.182**(a) 10.0 (b) The $pK_b$ for the 3° amine group is much smaller than that for the aromatic ring, thus the $K_b$ is significantly larger (yielding a much greater amount of $OH^-$). (c) 4.7 (d) 5.1

## Chapter 19

**Answers to Boxed Reading Problem: B19.2** (a) 65 mol (b) 6.28
(c) $4.0\times10^3$ g $HCO_3^-$

• **19.2** The acid component neutralizes added base, and the base component neutralizes added acid, so the pH of the buffer solution remains relatively constant. The components of a buffer do not neutralize one another because they are a conjugate acid-base pair. **19.7** The buffer range, the pH over which the buffer acts effectively, is greatest when the buffer-component concentration ratio is 1; the range decreases as this ratio deviates from 1. **19.9**(a) Ratio and pH increase; added $OH^-$ reacts with HA. (b) Ratio and pH decrease; added $H^+$ reacts with $A^-$. (c) Ratio and pH increase; added $A^-$ increases $[A^-]$. (d) Ratio and pH decrease; added HA increases [HA].
**19.11** $[H_3O^+] = 5.6\times10^{-6}$ $M$; pH = 5.25
**19.13** $[H_3O^+] = 5.2\times10^{-4}$ $M$; pH = 3.28 **19.15** 3.89
**19.17** 10.03 **19.19** 9.47 **19.21**(a) $K_{a2}$ (b) 10.55 **19.23** 3.6
**19.25** 0.20 **19.27** 3.37 **19.29** 8.82 **19.31**(a) 4.81 (b) 0.66 g KOH
**19.33**(a) $HOOC(CH_2)_4COOH/HOOC(CH_2)_4COO^-$ or $C_6H_5NH_3^+/C_6H_5NH_2$ (b) $H_2PO_4^-/HPO_4^{2-}$ or $H_2AsO_4^-/HAsO_4^{2-}$
**19.35**(a) $HOCH_2CH(OH)COOH/HOCH_2CH(OH)COO^-$ or $CH_3COOC_6H_4COOH/CH_3COOC_6H_4COO^-$
(b) $C_5H_5NH^+/C_5H_5N$ **19.38** 1.6 **19.40** To see a distinct color in a mixture of two colors, you need one to have about 10 times the intensity of the other. For this to be the case, the concentration ratio $[HIn]/[In^-]$ has to be greater than $10/1$ or less than $1/10$. This occurs when pH = $pK_a - 1$ or pH = $pK_a + 1$, respectively, giving a pH range of about 2 units.
**19.42** The equivalence point in a titration is the point at which the number of moles of base is stoichiometrically equivalent to the number of moles of acid. The endpoint is the point at which the added indicator changes color. If an appropriate indicator is selected, the endpoint is close to the equivalence point, but they are not usually the same. The pH at the endpoint, or color change, may precede or follow the pH at the equivalence point, depending on the indicator chosen.
**19.44**(a) initial pH: *strong acid*–strong base < *weak acid*–strong base < *weak base*–strong acid (b) pH at equivalence point: *weak base*–strong acid < *strong acid*–strong base < *weak acid*–strong base **19.46** At the center of the buffer region, the concentrations of weak acid and conjugate base are equal, so the pH = $pK_a$ of the acid. **19.48** pH range from 7.5 to 9.5 **19.50**(a) bromthymol blue (b) thymol blue or phenolphthalein **19.52**(a) methyl red (b) bromthymol blue **19.54**(a) 1.0000 (b) 1.6368 (c) 2.898 (d) 3.903 (e) 7.00 (f) 10.10 (g) 12.05 **19.56**(a) 2.91 (b) 4.81 (c) 5.29 (d) 6.09 (e) 7.41 (f) 8.76 (g) 10.10 (h) 12.05 **19.58**(a) 59.0 mL and 8.54 (b) 66.0 mL and 7.13, total 132.1 mL and 9.69 **19.60**(a) 123 mL and 5.17 (b) 194 mL and 5.80 **19.63** Fluoride ion is the conjugate base of a weak acid and reacts with $H_2O$: $F^-(aq) + H_2O(l) \rightleftharpoons HF(aq) + OH^-(aq)$. As the pH increases, the equilibrium shifts to the left and $[F^-]$ increases. As the pH decreases, the equilibrium shifts to the right and $[F^-]$ decreases. The changes in $[F^-]$ influence the solubility of $BaF_2$. Chloride ion is the conjugate base of a strong acid, so it does not react with water and its concentration is not influenced by pH. **19.65** The compound precipitates. **19.66**(a) $K_{sp} = [Ag^+]^2[CO_3^{2-}]$ (b) $K_{sp} = [Ba^{2+}][F^-]^2$ (c) $K_{sp} = [Cu^{2+}][HS^-][OH^-]$

**19.68**(a) $K_{sp} = [Ca^{2+}][CrO_4^{2-}]$  (b) $K_{sp} = [Ag^+][CN^-]$
(c) $K_{sp} = [Ni^{2+}][HS^-][OH^-]$  **19.70** $1.3\times10^{-4}$  **19.72** $2.8\times10^{-11}$
**19.74**(a) $2.3\times10^{-5}\ M$  (b) $4.2\times10^{-9}\ M$  **19.76**(a) $1.7\times10^{-3}\ M$
(b) $2.0\times10^{-4}\ M$  **19.78**(a) $Mg(OH)_2$  (b) $PbS$
(c) $Ag_2SO_4$  **19.80**(a) $CaSO_4$  (b) $Mg_3(PO_4)_2$  (c) $PbSO_4$
**19.82**(a) $AgCl(s) \rightleftharpoons Ag^+(aq) + Cl^-(aq)$. The chloride ion
is the anion of a strong acid, so it does not react with $H_3O^+$.
No change with pH.
(b) $SrCO_3(s) \rightleftharpoons Sr^{2+}(aq) + CO_3^{2-}(aq)$. The strontium ion is
the cation of a strong base, so pH will not affect its solubility.
The carbonate ion acts as a base:
$CO_3^{2-}(aq) + H_2O(l) \rightleftharpoons HCO_3^-(aq) + OH^-(aq)$; also
$CO_2(g)$ forms and escapes: $CO_3^{2-}(aq) + 2H_3O^+(aq) \longrightarrow$
$CO_2(g) + 3H_2O(l)$. Therefore, the solubility of $SrCO_3$
will increase with addition of $H_3O^+$ (decreasing pH).
**19.84**(a) $Fe(OH)_2(s) \rightleftharpoons Fe^{2+}(aq) + 2OH^-(aq)$. The $OH^-$ ion
reacts with added $H_3O^+$: $OH^-(aq) + H_3O^+(aq) \longrightarrow 2H_2O(l)$.
The added $H_3O^+$ consumes the $OH^-$, driving the equilibrium
toward the right to dissolve more $Fe(OH)_2$. Solubility
increases with addition of $H_3O^+$ (decreasing pH).
(b) $CuS(s) + H_2O(l) \rightleftharpoons Cu^{2+}(aq) + HS^-(aq) + OH^-(aq)$.
Both $HS^-$ and $OH^-$ are anions of weak acids, so both ions
react with added $H_3O^+$. Solubility increases with addition of
$H_3O^+$ (decreasing pH).  **19.86** yes  **19.88** yes  **19.91**(a) $Fe(OH)_3$
(b) The two metal ions are separated by adding just enough
NaOH to precipitate iron(III) hydroxide.  (c) $2.0\times10^{-7}\ M$
**19.94** No, because it indicates that a complex ion forms
between the lead ion and hydroxide ions:
$Pb^{2+}(aq) + nOH^-(aq) \rightleftharpoons Pb(OH)_n^{2-n}(aq)$
**19.95** $Hg(H_2O)_4^{2+}(aq) + 4CN^-(aq) \rightleftharpoons$
$$Hg(CN)_4^{2-}(aq) + 4H_2O(l)$$
**19.97** $Ag(H_2O)_2^+(aq) + 2S_2O_3^{2-}(aq) \rightleftharpoons$
$$Ag(S_2O_3)_2^{3-}(aq) + 2H_2O(l)$$
**19.99** $8.1\times10^{-15}\ M$  **19.101** $0.05\ M$  **19.103** $1.0\times10^{-16}\ M\ Zn^{2+}$;
$0.025\ M\ Zn(CN)_4^{2-}$; $0.049\ M\ CN^-$  **19.105** 0.035 L of $2.00\ M$
NaOH and 0.465 L of $0.200\ M$ HCOOH  **19.107**(a) 0.99
(b) assuming the volumes are additive: 0.468 L of $1.0\ M$
HCOOH and 0.232 L of $1.0\ M$ NaOH  (c) $0.34\ M$
**19.110** $1.3\times10^{-4}\ M$  **19.113**(a) 14  (b) 1 g from the second
beaker  **19.116**(a) 0.088  (b) 0.14  **19.117** $0.260\ M$ TRIS; pH =
8.53  **19.119** Lower the pH below 6.6  **19.123** $8\times10^{-5}$
**19.125**(a)

| V (mL) | pH | ΔpH/ΔV | $V_{avg}$ (mL) |
|---|---|---|---|
| 0.00 | 1.00 | | |
| 10.00 | 1.22 | 0.022 | 5.00 |
| 20.00 | 1.48 | 0.026 | 15.00 |
| 30.00 | 1.85 | 0.037 | 25.00 |
| 35.00 | 2.18 | 0.066 | 32.50 |
| 39.00 | 2.89 | 0.18 | 37.00 |
| 39.50 | 3.20 | 0.62 | 39.25 |
| 39.75 | 3.50 | 1.2 | 39.63 |
| 39.90 | 3.90 | 2.7 | 39.83 |
| 39.95 | 4.20 | 6 | 39.93 |
| 39.99 | 4.90 | 18 | 39.97 |

| V (mL) | pH | ΔpH/ΔV | $V_{avg}$ (mL) |
|---|---|---|---|
| 40.00 | 7.00 | 200 | 40.00 |
| 40.01 | 9.40 | 200 | 40.01 |
| 40.05 | 9.80 | 10 | 40.03 |
| 40.10 | 10.40 | 10 | 40.08 |
| 40.25 | 10.50 | 0.67 | 40.18 |
| 40.50 | 10.79 | 1.2 | 40.38 |
| 41.00 | 11.09 | 0.60 | 40.75 |
| 45.00 | 11.76 | 0.17 | 43.00 |
| 50.00 | 12.05 | 0.058 | 47.50 |
| 60.00 | 12.30 | 0.025 | 55.00 |
| 70.00 | 12.43 | 0.013 | 65.00 |
| 80.00 | 12.52 | 0.009 | 75.00 |

(b)

Maximum slope (equivalence point) is at $V_{avg} = 40.00$ mL.
**19.127** 4.05  **19.133** $H_2CO_3/HCO_3^-$ and $H_2PO_4^-/HPO_4^{2-}$;
$[HPO_4^{2-}]/[H_2PO_4^-] = 5.8$  **19.134** 3.8  **19.136**(a) 58.2 mL
(b) 7.85 mL  (c) 6.30  **19.138** 170 mL  **19.142** 5.68
**19.144** $3.9\times10^{-9}\ \mu g\ Pb^{2+}/100$ mL blood  **19.146** No NaCl will
precipitate.  **19.147**(a) A and D  (b) $pH_A = 4.35$; $pH_B = 8.67$;
$pH_C = 2.67$; $pH_D = 4.57$  (c) C, A, D, B  (d) B

## Chapter 20

**Answer to Boxed Reading Problem: B20.2** $-12.6$ kJ/mol

• **20.2** A spontaneous process occurs by itself, whereas a nonspontaneous process requires a continuous input of energy to
make it happen. It is possible to cause a nonspontaneous process to occur, but the process stops once the energy source is
removed. A reaction that is nonspontaneous under one set of
conditions may be spontaneous under a different set of conditions.  **20.5** The transition from liquid to gas involves a greater
increase in dispersal of energy and freedom of motion than
does the transition from solid to liquid.  **20.6** In an exothermic
reaction, $\Delta S_{surr} > 0$. In an endothermic reaction, $\Delta S_{surr} < 0$. A
chemical cold pack for injuries is an example of an application
using a spontaneous endothermic process.  **20.8** a, b, and c
**20.10** a and b  **20.12**(a) positive  (b) negative  (c) negative
**20.14**(a) positive  (b) positive  (c) positive  **20.16**(a) negative
(b) negative  (c) positive  **20.18**(a) positive  (b) negative
(c) positive  **20.20**(a) positive  (b) negative  (c) positive
**20.22**(a) Butane. The double bond in 2-butene restricts freedom
of rotation.  (b) $Xe(g)$. It has the greater molar mass.
(c) $CH_4(g)$. Gases have greater entropy than liquids.
**20.24**(a) $C_2H_5OH(l)$. It is a more complex molecule.

(b) $KClO_3(aq)$. Ions in solution have their energy more dispersed than those in a solid. (c) $K(s)$. It has a greater molar mass. **20.26**(a) Diamond $<$ graphite $<$ charcoal. Freedom of motion is least in the network solid; more freedom between graphite sheets; most freedom in amorphous solid. (b) Ice $<$ liquid water $<$ water vapor. Entropy increases as a substance changes from solid to liquid to gas. (c) O atoms $< O_2 < O_3$. Entropy increases with molecular complexity. **20.28**(a) $ClO_4^-(aq) > ClO_3^-(aq) > ClO_2^-(aq)$; decreasing molecular complexity (b) $NO_2(g) > NO(g) > N_2(g)$. $N_2$ has lower standard molar entropy because it consists of two of the same atoms; the other species have two different types of atoms. $NO_2$ is more complex than NO. (c) $Fe_3O_4(s) > Fe_2O_3(s) > Al_2O_3(s)$. $Fe_3O_4$ is more complex and more massive. $Fe_2O_3$ is more massive than $Al_2O_3$. **20.31** For a system at equilibrium, $\Delta S_{univ} = \Delta S_{sys} + \Delta S_{surr} = 0$. For a system moving to equilibrium, $\Delta S_{univ} > 0$. **20.32** $S^\circ_{Cl_2O(g)} = 2S^\circ_{HClO(g)} - S^\circ_{H_2O(g)} - \Delta S^\circ_{rxn}$ **20.33**(a) negative; $\Delta S^\circ = -172.4$ J/K (b) positive; $\Delta S^\circ = 141.6$ J/K (c) negative; $\Delta S^\circ = -837$ J/K **20.35** $\Delta S^\circ = 93.1$ J/K; yes, the positive sign of $\Delta S$ is expected because there is a net increase in the number of gas molecules. **20.37** $\Delta S^\circ = -311$ J/K; yes, the negative entropy change matches the decrease in moles of gas. **20.39** $-75.6$ J/K **20.41** $-242$ J/K **20.44** $-97.2$ J/K **20.46** A spontaneous process has $\Delta S_{univ} > 0$. Since the absolute temperature is always positive, $\Delta G_{sys}$ must be negative ($\Delta G_{sys} < 0$) for a spontaneous process. **20.48** $\Delta H^\circ$ is positive and $\Delta S^\circ$ is positive. Melting is an example. **20.49** The entropy changes little within a phase. As long as the substance does not change phase, the value of $\Delta S^\circ$ is relatively unaffected by temperature. **20.50**(a) $-1138.0$ kJ (b) $-1379.4$ kJ (c) $-224$ kJ **20.52**(a) $-1138$ kJ (b) $-1379$ kJ (c) $-226$ kJ **20.54**(a) Entropy decreases ($\Delta S^\circ$ is negative) because the number of moles of gas decreases. The combustion of CO releases energy ($\Delta H^\circ$ is negative). (b) $-257.2$ kJ or $-257.3$ kJ, depending on the method **20.56**(a) $-0.409$ kJ/mol·K (b) $-197$ kJ/mol **20.58**(a) $\Delta H^\circ_{rxn} = 90.7$ kJ; $\Delta S^\circ_{rxn} = 221$ J/K (b) At 28°C, $\Delta G^\circ = 24.3$ kJ; at 128°C, $\Delta G^\circ = 2.2$ kJ; at 228°C, $\Delta G^\circ = -19.9$ kJ (c) For the substances in their standard states, the reaction is nonspontaneous at 28°C, near equilibrium at 128°C, and spontaneous at 228°C. **20.60** $\Delta H^\circ = 30910$ J, $\Delta S^\circ = 93.15$ J/K, $T = 331.8$ K **20.62**(a) $\Delta H^\circ_{rxn} = -241.826$ kJ, $\Delta S^\circ_{rxn} = -44.4$ J/K, $\Delta G^\circ_{rxn} = -228.60$ kJ (b) Yes. The reaction will become nonspontaneous at higher temperatures. (c) The reaction is spontaneous below $5.45 \times 10^3$ K. **20.64**(a) $\Delta G^\circ$ is a relatively large positive value. (b) $K >> 1$. $Q$ depends on initial conditions, not equilibrium conditions. **20.67** The standard free energy change, $\Delta G^\circ$, applies when all components of the system are in their standard states; $\Delta G^\circ = \Delta G$ when all concentrations equal 1 $M$ and all partial pressures equal 1 atm. **20.68**(a) $1.7 \times 10^6$ (b) $3.89 \times 10^{-34}$ (c) $1.26 \times 10^{48}$ **20.70**(a) $6.57 \times 10^{173}$ (b) $4.46 \times 10^{-15}$ (c) $3.46 \times 10^4$ **20.72** $4.89 \times 10^{-51}$ **20.74** $3.36 \times 10^5$ **20.76** $2.7 \times 10^4$ J/mol; no **20.78**(a) $2.9 \times 10^4$ J/mol (b) The reverse direction, formation of reactants, is spontaneous, so the reaction proceeds to the left. (c) $7.0 \times 10^3$ J/mol; the reaction proceeds to the left to reach equilibrium. **20.80**(a) no $T$ (b) 163 kJ (c) $1 \times 10^2$ kJ/mol **20.83**(a) spontaneous (b) $+$ (c) $+$ (d) $-$ (e) $-$, not spontaneous (f) $-$ **20.87**(a) $2.3 \times 10^2$ (b) The treatment is to administer oxygen-rich air; increasing the concentration of oxygen shifts the equilibrium to the left, in the direction of $Hb \cdot O_2$. **20.89** $-370.$ kJ **20.91**(a) $2N_2O_5(g) + 6F_2(g) \longrightarrow 4NF_3(g) + 5O_2(g)$ (b) $\Delta G^\circ_{rxn} = -569$ kJ (c) $\Delta G_{rxn} = -5.60 \times 10^2$ kJ/mol **20.93** $\Delta H^\circ_{rxn} = -137.14$ kJ; $\Delta S^\circ_{rxn} = -120.3$ J/K; $\Delta G^\circ_{rxn} = -101.25$ kJ **20.101**(a) $1.67 \times 10^3$ J/mol (b) $7.37 \times 10^3$ J/mol (c) $-4.04 \times 10^3$ J/mol (d) 0.19 **20.105**(a) 465 K (b) $6.59 \times 10^{-4}$ (c) The reaction rate is higher at the higher temperature. The shorter time required (kinetics) overshadows the lower yield (thermodynamics).

## Chapter 21

**Answers to Boxed Reading Problem: B21.1** (a) reduction: $Fe^{3+} + e^- \longrightarrow Fe^{2+}$; oxidation: $Cu^+ \longrightarrow Cu^{2+} + e^-$ (b) Overall: $Fe^{3+} + Cu^+ \longrightarrow Fe^{2+} + Cu^{2+}$

• **21.1** Oxidation is the loss of electrons and results in a higher oxidation number; reduction is the gain of electrons and results in a lower oxidation number. **21.3** No, one half-reaction cannot take place independently because there is a transfer of electrons from one substance to another. If one substance loses electrons, another substance must gain them. **21.6** To remove $H^+$ ions from an equation, add an equal number of $OH^-$ ions to both sides to neutralize the $H^+$ ions and produce water. **21.8** Spontaneous reactions, for which $\Delta G_{sys} < 0$, take place in voltaic cells (also called galvanic cells). Nonspontaneous reactions, for which $\Delta G_{sys} > 0$, take place in electrolytic cells. **21.10**(a) $Cl^-$ (b) $MnO_4^-$ (c) $MnO_4^-$ (d) $Cl^-$ (e) from $Cl^-$ to $MnO_4^-$ (f) $8H_2SO_4(aq) + 2KMnO_4(aq) + 10KCl(aq) \longrightarrow$
$\qquad 2MnSO_4(aq) + 5Cl_2(g) + 8H_2O(l) + 6K_2SO_4(aq)$ **21.12**(a) $ClO_3^-(aq) + 6H^+(aq) + 6I^-(aq) \longrightarrow$
$\qquad\qquad Cl^-(aq) + 3H_2O(l) + 3I_2(s)$
Oxidizing agent is $ClO_3^-$ and reducing agent is $I^-$.
(b) $2MnO_4^-(aq) + H_2O(l) + 3SO_3^{2-}(aq) \longrightarrow$
$\qquad\qquad 2MnO_2(s) + 3SO_4^{2-}(aq) + 2OH^-(aq)$
Oxidizing agent is $MnO_4^-$ and reducing agent is $SO_3^{2-}$.
(c) $2MnO_4^-(aq) + 6H^+(aq) + 5H_2O_2(aq) \longrightarrow$
$\qquad\qquad 2Mn^{2+}(aq) + 8H_2O(l) + 5O_2(g)$
Oxidizing agent is $MnO_4^-$ and reducing agent is $H_2O_2$.
**21.14**(a) $Cr_2O_7^{2-}(aq) + 14H^+(aq) + 3Zn(s) \longrightarrow$
$\qquad\qquad 2Cr^{3+}(aq) + 7H_2O(l) + 3Zn^{2+}(aq)$
Oxidizing agent is $Cr_2O_7^{2-}$ and reducing agent is Zn.
(b) $MnO_4^-(aq) + 3Fe(OH)_2(s) + 2H_2O(l) \longrightarrow$
$\qquad\qquad MnO_2(s) + 3Fe(OH)_3(s) + OH^-(aq)$
Oxidizing agent is $MnO_4^-$ and reducing agent is $Fe(OH)_2$.
(c) $2NO_3^-(aq) + 12H^+(aq) + 5Zn(s) \longrightarrow$
$\qquad\qquad N_2(g) + 6H_2O(l) + 5Zn^{2+}(aq)$
Oxidizing agent is $NO_3^-$ and reducing agent is Zn.
**21.16**(a) $4NO_3^-(aq) + 4H^+(aq) + 4Sb(s) \longrightarrow$
$\qquad\qquad 4NO(g) + 2H_2O(l) + Sb_4O_6(s)$
Oxidizing agent is $NO_3^-$ and reducing agent is Sb.

(b) $5BiO_3^-(aq) + 14H^+(aq) + 2Mn^{2+}(aq) \longrightarrow$
$5Bi^{3+}(aq) + 7H_2O(l) + 2MnO_4^-(aq)$
Oxidizing agent is $BiO_3^-$ and reducing agent is $Mn^{2+}$.
(c) $Pb(OH)_3^-(aq) + 2Fe(OH)_2(s) \longrightarrow$
$Pb(s) + 2Fe(OH)_3(s) + OH^-(aq)$
Oxidizing agent is $Pb(OH)_3^-$ and reducing agent is $Fe(OH)_2$.

**21.18**(a) $5As_4O_6(s) + 8MnO_4^-(aq) + 18H_2O(l) \longrightarrow$
$20AsO_4^{3-}(aq) + 8Mn^{2+}(aq) + 36H^+(aq)$
Oxidizing agent is $MnO_4^-$ and reducing agent is $As_4O_6$.
(b) $P_4(s) + 6H_2O(l) \longrightarrow$
$2HPO_3^{2-}(aq) + 2PH_3(g) + 4H^+(aq)$
$P_4$ is both the oxidizing agent and the reducing agent.
(c) $2MnO_4^-(aq) + 3CN^-(aq) + H_2O(l) \longrightarrow$
$2MnO_2(s) + 3CNO^-(aq) + 2OH^-(aq)$
Oxidizing agent is $MnO_4^-$ and reducing agent is $CN^-$.

**21.21**(a) $Au(s) + 3NO_3^-(aq) + 4Cl^-(aq) + 6H^+(aq) \longrightarrow$
$AuCl_4^-(aq) + 3NO_2(g) + 3H_2O(l)$ (b) Oxidizing agent is $NO_3^-$ and reducing agent is Au. (c) HCl provides chloride ions that combine with the gold(III) ion to form the stable $AuCl_4^-$ ion. **21.22**(a) A (b) E (c) C (d) A (e) E (f) E
**21.25** An active electrode is a reactant or product in the cell reaction. An inactive electrode does not take part in the reaction and is present only to conduct a current. Platinum and graphite are commonly used as inactive electrodes. **21.26**(a) A (b) B (c) A (d) Hydrogen bubbles will form when metal A is placed in acid. Metal A is a better reducing agent than metal B, so if metal B reduces $H^+$ in acid, then metal A will also.
**21.27**(a) Oxidation: $Zn(s) \longrightarrow Zn^{2+}(aq) + 2e^-$
Reduction: $Sn^{2+}(aq) + 2e^- \longrightarrow Sn(s)$
Overall: $Zn(s) + Sn^{2+}(aq) \longrightarrow Zn^{2+}(aq) + Sn(s)$
(b)

**21.29**(a) left to right  (b) left  (c) right  (d) Ni  (e) Fe
(f) Fe  (g) 1 $M$ $NiSO_4$  (h) $K^+$ and $NO_3^-$  (i) neither  (j) from right to left
(k) Oxidation: $Fe(s) \longrightarrow Fe^{2+}(aq) + 2e^-$
Reduction: $Ni^{2+}(aq) + 2e^- \longrightarrow Ni(s)$
Overall: $Fe(s) + Ni^{2+}(aq) \longrightarrow Fe^{2+}(aq) + Ni(s)$
**21.31**(a) Reduction: $Fe^{2+}(aq) + 2e^- \longrightarrow Fe(s)$
Oxidation: $Mn(s) \longrightarrow Mn^{2+}(aq) + 2e^-$
Overall: $Fe^{2+}(aq) + Mn(s) \longrightarrow Fe(s) + Mn^{2+}(aq)$

(b)

**21.33**(a) $Al(s) \mid Al^{3+}(aq) \parallel Cr^{3+}(aq) \mid Cr(s)$
(b) $Pt(s) \mid SO_2(g) \mid SO_4^{2-}(aq), H^+(aq) \parallel Cu^{2+}(aq) \mid Cu(s)$
**21.36** A negative $E_{cell}^\circ$ indicates that the redox reaction is not spontaneous at the standard state, that is, $\Delta G^\circ > 0$. The reverse reaction is spontaneous with $E_{cell}^\circ > 0$. **21.37** Similar to other state functions, $E^\circ$ changes sign when a reaction is reversed. Unlike $\Delta G^\circ$, $\Delta H^\circ$, and $S^\circ$, $E^\circ$ (the ratio of energy to charge) is an intensive property. When the coefficients in a reaction are multiplied by a factor, the values of $\Delta G^\circ$, $\Delta H^\circ$, and $S^\circ$ are multiplied by that factor. However, $E^\circ$ does not change because both the energy and charge are multiplied by the factor and thus their ratio remains unchanged.
**21.38**(a) Oxidation: $Se^{2-}(aq) \longrightarrow Se(s) + 2e^-$
Reduction: $2SO_3^{2-}(aq) + 3H_2O(l) + 4e^- \longrightarrow$
$S_2O_3^{2-}(aq) + 6OH^-(aq)$
(b) $E_{anode}^\circ = E_{cathode}^\circ - E_{cell}^\circ = -0.57$ V $- 0.35$ V
$= -0.92$ V
**21.40**(a) $Br_2 > Fe^{3+} > Cu^{2+}$  (b) $Ca^{2+} < Ag^+ < Cr_2O_7^{2-}$
**21.42**(a) $Co(s) + 2H^+(aq) \longrightarrow Co^{2+}(aq) + H_2(g)$
$E_{cell}^\circ = 0.28$ V; spontaneous
(b) $2Mn^{2+}(aq) + 5Br_2(l) + 8H_2O(l) \longrightarrow$
$2MnO_4^-(aq) + 10Br^-(aq) + 16H^+(aq)$
$E_{cell}^\circ = -0.44$ V; not spontaneous
(c) $Hg_2^{2+}(aq) \longrightarrow Hg^{2+}(aq) + Hg(l)$
$E_{cell}^\circ = -0.07$ V; not spontaneous
**21.44**(a) $2Ag(s) + Cu^{2+}(aq) \longrightarrow 2Ag^+(aq) + Cu(s)$
$E_{cell}^\circ = -0.46$ V; not spontaneous
(b) $Cr_2O_7^{2-}(aq) + 3Cd(s) + 14H^+(aq) \longrightarrow$
$2Cr^{3+}(aq) + 3Cd^{2+}(aq) + 7H_2O(l)$
$E_{cell}^\circ = 1.73$ V; spontaneous
(c) $Pb(s) + Ni^{2+}(aq) \longrightarrow Pb^{2+}(aq) + Ni(s)$
$E_{cell}^\circ = -0.12$ V; not spontaneous
**21.46** $3N_2O_4(g) + 2Al(s) \longrightarrow 6NO_2^-(aq) + 2Al^{3+}(aq)$
$E_{cell}^\circ = 0.867$ V $- (-1.66$ V$) = 2.53$ V
$2Al(s) + 3SO_4^{2-}(aq) + 3H_2O(l) \longrightarrow$
$2Al^{3+}(aq) + 3SO_3^{2-}(aq) + 6OH^-(aq)$
$E_{cell}^\circ = 2.59$ V
$SO_4^{2-}(aq) + 2NO_2^-(aq) + H_2O(l) \longrightarrow$
$SO_3^{2-}(aq) + N_2O_4(g) + 2OH^-(aq)$
$E_{cell}^\circ = 0.06$ V
Oxidizing agents: $Al^{3+} < N_2O_4 < SO_4^{2-}$
Reducing agents: $SO_3^{2-} < NO_2^- < Al$

**21.48** $2HClO(aq) + Pt(s) + 2H^+(aq) \longrightarrow$
$$Cl_2(g) + Pt^{2+}(aq) + 2H_2O(l)$$
$E°_{cell} = 0.43$ V
$2HClO(aq) + Pb(s) + SO_4^{2-}(aq) + 2H^+(aq) \longrightarrow$
$$Cl_2(g) + PbSO_4(s) + 2H_2O(l)$$
$E°_{cell} = 1.94$ V
$Pt^{2+}(aq) + Pb(s) + SO_4^{2-}(aq) \longrightarrow Pt(s) + PbSO_4(s)$
$E°_{cell} = 1.51$ V
Oxidizing agents: $PbSO_4 < Pt^{2+} < HClO$
Reducing agents: $Cl_2 < Pt < Pb$
**21.50** yes; C > A > B **21.53** $A(s) + B^+(aq) \longrightarrow A^+(aq)$
$+ B(s)$ with $Q = [A^+]/[B^+]$. (a) $[A^+]$ increases and $[B^+]$
decreases. (b) $E_{cell}$ decreases. (c) $E_{cell} = E°_{cell} - (RT/nF)$
$\ln([A^+]/[B^+])$; $E_{cell} = E°_{cell}$ when $(RT/nF)\ln([A^+]/[B^+]) =$
0. This occurs when $\ln([A^+]/[B^+]) = 0$, that is, $[A^+]$ equals
$[B^+]$. (d) Yes, when $[A^+] > [B^+]$. **21.55** In a concentration
cell, the overall reaction decreases the concentration of the
more concentrated electrolyte because it is reduced in the
cathode compartment. **21.56**(a) $3 \times 10^{35}$ (b) $4 \times 10^{-31}$
**21.58**(a) $1 \times 10^{-67}$ (b) $6 \times 10^9$ **21.60**(a) $-2.03 \times 10^5$ J
(b) $1.74 \times 10^5$ J **21.62**(a) $3.82 \times 10^5$ J (b) $-5.6 \times 10^4$ J
**21.64** $E° = 0.28$ V; $\Delta G° = -2.7 \times 10^4$ J **21.66** $E°_{cell} = 0.054$ V;
$\Delta G° = -1.0 \times 10^4$ J **21.68** $8.8 \times 10^{-5}$ $M$ **21.70**(a) 0.05 V
(b) 0.50 $M$ (c) $[Co^{2+}] = 0.91$ $M$; $[Ni^{2+}] = 0.09$ $M$ **21.72** A;
0.083 V **21.74** Electrons flow from the anode, where oxidation
occurs, to the cathode, where reduction occurs. The electrons
always flow from the anode to the cathode no matter what
type of battery. **21.76** A D-sized alkaline battery is larger than
an AAA-sized one, so it contains greater amounts of the cell
components. The cell potential is an intensive property and
does not depend on the amounts of the cell components. The
total charge, however, does depend on the amount of cell components, so the D-sized battery produces more charge.
**21.78** The Teflon spacers keep the two metals separated so that
the copper cannot conduct electrons that would promote the
corrosion (rusting) of the iron skeleton. **21.81** Sacrificial anodes
are made of metals with $E°$ less than that of iron, $-0.44$ V, so
they are more easily oxidized than iron. Only b, f, and g will
work for iron: a will form an oxide coating that prevents further oxidation; c will react with groundwater quickly; d and e
are less easily oxidized than iron. **21.83** To reverse the reaction
requires 0.34 V with the cell in its standard state. A 1.5 V cell
supplies more than enough potential, so the Cd metal is oxidized to $Cd^{2+}$ and Cr metal plates out. **21.85** The oxidation
number of N in $NO_3^-$ is +5, the maximum O.N. for N. In the
nitrite ion, $NO_2^-$, the O.N. of N is +3, so nitrogen can be further oxidized. **21.87**(a) $Br_2$ (b) Na **21.89** $I_2$ gas forms at the
anode; magnesium (liquid) forms at the cathode. **21.91** Bromine gas forms at the anode; calcium metal forms at the cathode.
**21.93** copper and bromine **21.95** iodine, zinc, and silver
**21.97**(a) Anode: $2H_2O(l) \longrightarrow O_2(g) + 4H^+(aq) + 4e^-$
Cathode: $2H_2O(l) + 2e^- \longrightarrow H_2(g) + 2OH^-(aq)$
(b) Anode: $2H_2O(l) \longrightarrow O_2(g) + 4H^+(aq) + 4e^-$
Cathode: $Sn^{2+}(aq) + 2e^- \longrightarrow Sn(s)$
**21.99**(a) Anode: $2H_2O(l) \longrightarrow O_2(g) + 4H^+(aq) + 4e^-$

Cathode: $NO_3^-(aq) + 4H^+(aq) + 3e^- \longrightarrow$
$$NO(g) + 2H_2O(l)$$
(b) Anode: $2Cl^-(aq) \longrightarrow Cl_2(g) + 2e^-$
Cathode: $2H_2O(l) + 2e^- \longrightarrow H_2(g) + 2OH^-(aq)$
**21.101**(a) 3.75 mol $e^-$ (b) $3.62 \times 10^5$ C (c) 28.7 A
**21.103** 0.275 g Ra **21.105** $9.20 \times 10^3$ s **21.107**(a) The sodium and
sulfate ions conduct a current, facilitating electrolysis. Pure
water, which contains very low ($10^{-7}$ $M$) concentrations of $H^+$
and $OH^-$, conducts electricity very poorly. (b) The reduction
of $H_2O$ has a more positive half-potential than does the reduction of $Na^+$; the oxidation of $H_2O$ is the only reaction possible
because $SO_4^{2-}$ cannot be oxidized. Thus, it is easier to reduce
$H_2O$ than $Na^+$ and easier to oxidize $H_2O$ than $SO_4^{2-}$.
**21.109** 62.6 g Zn **21.111**(a) $3.3 \times 10^{11}$ C (b) $4.8 \times 10^{11}$ J
(c) $1.2 \times 10^4$ kg **21.114** 64.3 mass % Cu **21.115**(a) 8 days
(b) 32 days (c) $940 **21.118** (a) $2.4 \times 10^4$ days (b) 2.1 g
(c) $6.1 \times 10^{-5}$ dollars **21.121**(a) $Pb/Pb^{2+}$: $E°_{cell} = 0.13$ V;
$Cu/Cu^{2+}$: $E°_{cell} = 0.34$ V (b) The anode (negative electrode) is
Pb. The anode in the other cell is platinum in the standard
hydrogen electrode. (c) The precipitation of PbS decreases
$[Pb^{2+}]$, which increases the potential. (d) $-0.13$ V
**21.124** The three steps equivalent to the overall reaction
$M^+(aq) + e^- \longrightarrow M(s)$ are
(1) $M^+(aq) \longrightarrow M^+(g)$    $\Delta H$ is $-\Delta H_{hydration}$
(2) $M^+(g) + e^- \longrightarrow M(g)$   $\Delta H$ is $-IE$
(3) $M(g) \longrightarrow M(s)$       $\Delta H$ is $-\Delta H_{atomization}$
The energy for step 3 is similar for all three elements, so the
difference in energy for the overall reaction depends on the
values for $\Delta H_{hydration}$ and IE. The $Li^+$ ion has a much greater
hydration energy than $Na^+$ and $K^+$ because it is smaller, with
a larger charge density that holds the water molecules more
tightly. The energy required to remove the waters surrounding
$Li^+$ offsets the lower ionization energy, making the overall
energy for the reduction of lithium larger than expected.
**21.125** The very high and very low standard electrode potentials
involve extremely reactive substances, such as $F_2$ (a powerful
oxidizer) and Li (a powerful reducer). These substances react
directly with water because any aqueous cell with a voltage of
more than 1.23 V has the ability to electrolyze water into
hydrogen and oxygen.
**21.127**(a) $1.073 \times 10^5$ s (b) $1.5 \times 10^4$ kW·h (c) 0.92¢
**21.129** If metal E and a salt of metal F are mixed, the salt is
reduced, producing metal F because E has the greatest reducing strength of the three metals; F < D < E.
**21.131**(a) Cell I: 4 mol electrons; $\Delta G = -4.75 \times 10^5$ J
      Cell II: 2 mol electrons; $\Delta G = -3.94 \times 10^5$ J
      Cell III: 2 mol electrons; $\Delta G = -4.53 \times 10^5$ J
  (b) Cell I: $-13.2$ kJ/g
      Cell II: $-0.613$ kJ/g
      Cell III: $-2.63$ kJ/g
      Cell I has the highest ratio (most energy released per
      gram) because the reactants have very low mass,
      while Cell II has the lowest ratio because the reactants
      have large masses.
**21.135**(a) 9.7 g Cu (b) 0.56 $M$ $Cu^{2+}$

**21.137** $Sn^{2+}(aq) + 2e^- \longrightarrow Sn(s)$
$Cr^{3+}(aq) + e^- \longrightarrow Cr^{2+}(aq)$
$Fe^{2+}(aq) + 2e^- \longrightarrow Fe(s)$
$U^{4+}(aq) + e^- \longrightarrow U^{3+}(aq)$
**21.141** (a) $3.6 \times 10^{-9}$ $M$ (b) 0.3 $M$
**21.143** (a) Nonstandard cell:

$$E_{waste} = E°_{cell} - (0.0592 \text{ V}/1) \log [Ag^+]_{waste}$$

Standard cell:

$$E_{standard} = E°_{cell} - (0.0592 \text{ V}/1) \log [Ag^+]_{standard}$$

(b) $[Ag^+]_{waste} = \text{antilog}\left(\dfrac{E_{standard} - E_{waste}}{0.0592}\right)[Ag^+]_{standard}$

(c) $C_{Ag^+, waste} = \text{antilog}\left(\dfrac{E_{standard} - E_{waste}}{0.0592}\right)C_{Ag^+, standard}$,

where $C$ is concentration in ng/L
(d) 900 ng/L
(e) $[Ag^+]_{waste} =$

$$\text{antilog}\left[\frac{(E_{standard} - E_{waste})\dfrac{nF}{2.303R} + T_{standard}\log[Ag^+]_{standard}}{T_{waste}}\right]$$

**21.145** (a) $1.08 \times 10^3$ C (b) 0.629 g Cd, 1.03 g NiO(OH),
0.202 g $H_2O$; total mass of reactants = 1.86 g (c) 10.1%
**21.147** Li > Ba > Na > Al > Mn > Zn > Cr > Fe > Ni >
Sn > Pb > Cu > Ag > Hg > Au. Metals with potentials
lower than that of water (−0.83 V) can displace $H_2$ from
water: Li, Ba, Na, Al, and Mn. Metals with potentials lower
than that of hydrogen (0.00 V) can displace $H_2$ from acid: Li,
Ba, Na, Al, Mn, Zn, Cr, Fe, Ni, Sn, and Pb. Metals with
potentials greater than that of hydrogen (0.00 V) cannot displace $H_2$: Cu, Ag, Hg, and Au. **21.150** (a) $5.3 \times 10^{-11}$
(b) 0.20 V (c) 0.43 V (d) $8.2 \times 10^{-4}$ $M$ NaOH
**21.153** (a) $-1.18 \times 10^5$ kJ (b) $1.20 \times 10^4$ L (c) $9.43 \times 10^4$ s
(d) 157 kW·h (e) 22.0¢ **21.154** 2.94

## Chapter 22

**22.2** Fe from $Fe_2O_3$; Ca from $CaCO_3$; Na from NaCl; Zn from
ZnS **22.3** (a) Differentiation refers to the processes involved in
the formation of Earth into regions (core, mantle, and crust) of
differing composition. Substances separated according to their
densities, with the more dense material in the core and the less
dense in the crust. (b) O, Si, Al, and Fe (c) O **22.7** Plants
produced $O_2$, slowly increasing the oxygen concentration in the
atmosphere and creating an environment for oxidizing metals.
The oxygen-free decay of plant and animal material created
large fossil fuel deposits. **22.9** Fixation refers to the process of
converting a substance in the atmosphere into a form more
readily usable by organisms. Carbon and nitrogen; fixation of
carbon dioxide gas by plants and fixation of nitrogen gas by
nitrogen-fixing bacteria. **22.12** Atmospheric nitrogen is fixed by
three pathways: atmospheric, industrial, and biological. Atmospheric fixation requires high-temperature reactions (e.g., initiated by lightning) to convert $N_2$ into NO and other oxidized
species. Industrial fixation involves mainly the formation of
ammonia, $NH_3$, from $N_2$ and $H_2$. Biological fixation occurs in
nitrogen-fixing bacteria that live on the roots of legumes.

Human activity is an example of industrial fixation. It contributes about 17% of the fixed nitrogen. **22.14** (a) the atmosphere (b) Plants excrete acid from their roots to convert
$PO_4^{3-}$ ions into more soluble $H_2PO_4^-$ ions, which the plant
can absorb. Through excretion and decay, organisms return soluble phosphate compounds to the cycle. **22.17** (a) $1.1 \times 10^3$ L
(b) $4.2 \times 10^2$ $m^3$ **22.18** (a) The iron(II) ions form an insoluble salt,
$Fe_3(PO_4)_2$, that decreases the yield of phosphorus. (b) 8.8 t
**22.20** (a) Roasting consists of heating the mineral in air at high
temperatures to convert the mineral to the oxide. (b) Smelting
is the reduction of the metal oxide to the free metal using heat
and a reducing agent such as coke. (c) Flotation is a separation process in which the ore is removed from the gangue by
exploiting the difference in density in the presence of detergent. The gangue sinks to the bottom and the lighter ore-
detergent mix is skimmed off the top. (d) Refining is the final
step in the purification process to yield the pure metal.
**22.25** (a) Slag is a byproduct of steel-making and contains the
impurity $SiO_2$. (b) Pig iron is the impure product of iron metallurgy (containing 3–4% C and other impurities). (c) Steel
refers to iron alloyed with other elements to attain desirable
properties. (d) The basic-oxygen process is used to purify pig
iron and obtain carbon steel. **22.27** Iron and nickel are more
easily oxidized and less easily reduced than copper. They are
separated from copper in the roasting step and converted to
slag. In the electrorefining process, all three metals are in solution, but only $Cu^{2+}$ ions are reduced at the cathode to form
$Cu(s)$. **22.30** Le Châtelier's principle says that the system shifts
toward formation of K as the gaseous metal leaves the cell.
**22.31** (a) $E°_{half-cell}$ = −3.05 V, −2.93 V, and −2.71 V for $Li^+$,
$K^+$, and $Na^+$, respectively. In all of these cases, it is energetically more favorable to reduce $H_2O$ to $H_2$ than to reduce $M^+$
to M. (b) $2RbX + Ca \longrightarrow CaX_2 + 2Rb$, where $\Delta H =$
$IE_1(Ca) + IE_2(Ca) - 2IE_1(Rb)$ = 929 kJ/mol. Based on the
IEs and positive $\Delta H$ for the forward reaction, it seems more
reasonable that Rb metal will reduce $Ca^{2+}$ than the
reverse. (c) If the reaction is carried out at a temperature
greater than the boiling point of Rb, the product mixture will
contain gaseous Rb, which can be removed from the reaction
vessel; this would cause a shift in equilibrium to form more
Rb as product. (d) $2CsX + Ca \longrightarrow CaX_2 + 2Cs$, where
$\Delta H = IE_1(Ca) + IE_2(Ca) - 2IE_1(Cs)$ = 983 kJ/mol. This
reaction is more unfavorable than for Rb, but Cs has a lower
boiling point. **22.32** (a) $4.5 \times 10^4$ L (b) $1.30 \times 10^8$ C
(c) $1.69 \times 10^6$ s **22.35** (a) $Mg^{2+}$ is more difficult to reduce than
$H_2O$, so $H_2(g)$ would be produced instead of Mg metal.
$Cl_2(g)$ forms at the anode due to overvoltage. (b) The $\Delta H°_f$ of
$MgCl_2(s)$ is −641.6 kJ/mol. High temperature favors the
reverse (endothermic) reaction, the formation of magnesium
metal and chlorine gas. **22.37** (a) Sulfur dioxide is the reducing
agent and is oxidized to the +6 state ($SO_4^{2-}$). (b) $HSO_4^-(aq)$
(c) $H_2SeO_3(aq) + 2SO_2(g) + H_2O(l) \longrightarrow Se(s) +$
$2HSO_4^-(aq) + 2H^+(aq)$ **22.42** (a) O.N. for Cu: in $Cu_2S$, +1;
in $Cu_2O$, +1; in Cu, 0 (b) $Cu_2S$ is the reducing agent, and
$Cu_2O$ is the oxidizing agent. **22.44** (a) $1.3 \times 10^6$ C (b) $1.2 \times 10^3$ A

**22.47** $2ZnS(s) + C(graphite) \longrightarrow 2Zn(s) + CS_2(g)$; $\Delta G^{\circ}_{rxn} = 463$ kJ. Since $\Delta G^{\circ}_{rxn}$ is positive, this reaction is not spontaneous at standard-state conditions. $2ZnO(s) + C(s) \longrightarrow 2Zn(s) + CO_2(g)$; $\Delta G^{\circ}_{rxn} = 242.0$ kJ. This reaction is also not spontaneous, but is less unfavorable. **22.48** The formation of sulfur trioxide is very slow at ordinary temperatures. Increasing the temperature can speed up the reaction, but because the reaction is exothermic, increasing the temperature decreases the yield. Adding a catalyst increases the rate of the reaction, allowing a lower temperature to be used to enhance the yield. **22.51**(a) $Cl_2$, $H_2$, and NaOH (b) The mercury-cell method yields higher purity NaOH, but releases some Hg, which is released into the environment. **22.52**(a) $\Delta G^{\circ} = -142$ kJ; yes (b) The rate of the reaction is very low at 25°C. (c) $\Delta G^{\circ}_{500} = -53$ kJ, so the reaction is spontaneous. (d) $K_{25} = 7.8\times10^{24} > K_{500} = 3.8\times10^3$ (e) $1.05\times10^3$ K **22.53** $7\times10^2$ lb $Cl_2$ **22.56**(a) $P_4O_{10}(s) + 6H_2O(l) \longrightarrow 4H_3PO_4(l)$ (b) 1.52 **22.58**(a) $9.006\times10^9$ g $CO_2$ (b) The $4.3\times10^{10}$ g $CO_2$ produced by automobiles is much greater than that from the blast furnace. **22.60**(a) If $[OH^-] > 1.1\times10^{-4}$ $M$ (i.e., if pH $> 10.04$), $Mg(OH)_2$ will precipitate. (b) 1 (To the correct number of significant figures, all the magnesium precipitates.) **22.61**(a) $K_{25}$(step 1) $= 1\times10^{168}$; $K_{25}$(side rxn) $= 7\times10^{228}$ (b) $K_{900}$(step 1) $= 4.5\times10^{49}$; $K_{900}$(side rxn) $= 1.4\times10^{63}$ (c) $8.8\times10^7$ dollars (d) $6.4\times10^7$ dollars
**22.64**(1) $2H_2O(l) + 2FeS_2(s) + 7O_2(g) \longrightarrow$
$$2Fe^{2+}(aq) + 4SO_4^{2-}(aq) + 4H^+(aq)$$
increases acidity
(2) $4H^+(aq) + 4Fe^{2+}(aq) + O_2(g) \longrightarrow$
$$4Fe^{3+}(aq) + 2H_2O(l)$$
(3) $Fe^{3+}(aq) + 3H_2O(l) \longrightarrow Fe(OH)_3(s) + 3H^+(aq)$
increases acidity
(4) $8H_2O(l) + FeS_2(s) + 14Fe^{3+}(aq) \longrightarrow$
$$15Fe^{2+}(aq) + 2SO_4^{2-}(aq) + 16H^+(aq)$$
increases acidity

**22.65** density of ferrite: 7.86 g/cm$^3$; density of austenite: 7.55 g/cm$^3$
**22.67**(a) Cathode: $Na^+(l) + e^- \longrightarrow Na(l)$
Anode: $4OH^-(l) \longrightarrow O_2(g) + 2H_2O(g) + 4e^-$
(b) 50%
**22.70**(a) $nCO_2(g) + nH_2O(l) \longrightarrow (CH_2O)_n(s) + nO_2(g)$
(b) 27 L (c) $7.6\times10^4$ L **22.71** 73 mg/L **22.72** 891 kg $Na_3AlF_6$ **22.73**(a) 23.2 min (b) 14 effusion steps
**22.75**(a) 1.890 t $Al_2O_3$ (b) 0.3339 t C (c) 100% (d) 74% (e) $2.813\times10^3$ m$^3$ **22.80** Acid rain increases the leaching of phosphate into the groundwater, due to the protonation of $PO_4^{3-}$ to form $HPO_4^{2-}$ and $H_2PO_4^-$. As shown in calculations for parts (a) and (b), solubility of $Ca_3(PO_4)_2$ increases from $6.4\times10^{-7}$ $M$ (in pure water) to $1.1\times10^{-2}$ $M$ (in acidic rainwater). (a) $6.4\times10^{-7}$ $M$ (b) $1.1\times10^{-2}$ $M$ **22.81**(a) 1.00 mol % (b) 238.9 g/mol **22.83** density of silver $= 10.51$ g/cm$^3$; density of sterling silver $= 10.2$ g/cm$^3$

## Chapter 23

**Answer to Boxed Reading Problem: B23.2** Zinc ions prefer a tetrahedral environment. The other ions listed prefer other environments ($Ni^{2+}$ forms square planar complex ions while

$Fe^{2+}$ and $Mn^{2+}$ form octahedral complex ions). If these ions are placed in a tetrahedral environment in place of the zinc, they cannot function as well as zinc since the enzyme catalyst would have a different shape.

**• 23.2**(a) $1s^22s^22p^63s^23p^64s^23d^{10}4p^65s^24d^x$
(b) $1s^22s^22p^63s^23p^64s^23d^{10}4p^65s^24d^{10}5p^66s^24f^{14}5d^x$ **23.4** Five; examples are Mn, [Ar] $4s^23d^5$, and $Fe^{3+}$, [Ar] $3d^5$. **23.6**(a) The elements should increase in size as they increase in mass from Period 5 to Period 6. Because there are 14 inner transition elements in Period 6, the effective nuclear charge increases significantly; so the atomic size decreases, or "contracts." This effect is significant enough that $Zr^{4+}$ and $Hf^{4+}$ are almost the same size but differ greatly in atomic mass. (b) The atomic size increases from Period 4 to Period 5, but stays fairly constant from Period 5 to Period 6. (c) Atomic mass increases significantly from Period 5 to Period 6, but atomic radius (and thus volume) increases slightly, so Period 6 elements are very dense. **23.9**(a) A paramagnetic substance is attracted to a magnetic field, while a diamagnetic substance is slightly repelled by one. (b) Ions of transition elements often have half-filled $d$ orbitals whose unpaired electrons make the ions paramagnetic. Ions of main-group elements usually have a noble-gas configuration with no partially filled levels. (c) Some $d$ orbitals in the transition element ions are empty, which allows an electron from one $d$ orbital to move to a slightly higher energy one. The energy required for this transition is small and falls in the visible wavelength range. All orbitals are filled in ions of main-group elements, so enough energy would have to be added to move an electron to the next principal energy level, not just another orbital within the same energy level. This amount of energy is very large and much greater than the visible range of wavelengths.
**23.10**(a) $1s^22s^22p^63s^23p^64s^23d^3$
(b) $1s^22s^22p^63s^23p^64s^23d^{10}4p^65s^24d^1$ (c) [Xe] $6s^24f^{14}5d^{10}$
**23.12**(a) [Xe] $6s^24f^{14}5d^6$ (b) [Ar] $4s^23d^7$ (c) [Kr] $5s^14d^{10}$
**23.14**(a) [Ar], no unpaired electrons (b) [Ar] $3d^9$, one unpaired electron (c) [Ar] $3d^5$, five unpaired electrons (d) [Kr] $4d^2$, two unpaired electrons **23.16**(a) +5 (b) +4 (c) +7 **23.18** Cr, Mo, and W **23.20** in $CrF_2$, because the chromium is in a lower oxidation state **23.22** Atomic size increases slightly down a group of transition elements, but nuclear charge increases much more, so the first ionization energy generally increases. The reduction potential for Mo is lower, so it is more difficult to oxidize Mo than Cr. In addition, the ionization energy of Mo is higher than that of Cr, so it is more difficult to remove electrons from Mo. **23.24** $CrO_3$, with Cr in a higher oxidation state, yields a more acidic aqueous solution. **23.28**(a) seven (b) This corresponds to a half-filled $f$ subshell. **23.30**(a) [Xe] $6s^25d^1$ (b) [Xe] $4f^1$ (c) [Rn] $7s^25f^{11}$ (d) [Rn] $5f^2$
**23.32**(a) $Eu^{2+}$: [Xe] $4f^7$; $Eu^{3+}$: [Xe] $4f^6$; $Eu^{4+}$: [Xe] $4f^5$. The stability of the half-filled $f$ subshell makes $Eu^{2+}$ most stable. (b) $Tb^{2+}$: [Xe] $4f^9$; $Tb^{3+}$: [Xe] $4f^8$; $Tb^{4+}$: [Xe] $4f^7$. Tb should show a +4 oxidation state because that gives a half-filled subshell. **23.34** Gd has the electron configuration [Xe] $6s^24f^75d^1$ with eight unpaired electrons. $Gd^{3+}$ has seven unpaired electrons: [Xe] $4f^7$. **23.37** The coordination number

indicates the number of ligand atoms bonded to the metal ion. The oxidation number represents the number of electrons lost to form the ion. The coordination number is unrelated to the oxidation number. **23.39** 2, linear; 4, tetrahedral or square planar; 6, octahedral **23.42** The complex ion has a negative charge. **23.45**(a) hexaaquanickel(II) chloride (b) tris(ethylenediamine)chromium(III) perchlorate (c) potassium hexacyanomanganate(II) **23.47**(a) 2+, 6 (b) 3+, 6 (c) 2+, 6 **23.49**(a) potassium dicyanoargentate(I) (b) sodium tetrachlorocadmate(II) (c) tetraammineaquabromocobalt(III) bromide **23.51**(a) 1+, 2 (b) 2+, 4 (c) 3+, 6 **23.53**(a) [Zn(NH$_3$)$_4$]SO$_4$ (b) [Cr(NH$_3$)$_5$Cl]Cl$_2$ (c) Na$_3$[Ag(S$_2$O$_3$)$_2$] **23.55**(a) 4, two ions (b) 6, three ions (c) 2, four ions **23.57**(a) [Cr(H$_2$O)$_6$]$_2$(SO$_4$)$_3$ (b) Ba[FeBr$_4$]$_2$ (c) [Pt(en)$_2$]CO$_3$ **23.59**(a) 6, five ions (b) 4, three ions (c) 4, two ions **23.61**(a) The nitrite ion forms linkage isomers because it can bind to the metal ion through the lone pair on the N atom or any lone pair on either O atom.

$$[:\ddot{O}\!-\!\ddot{N}\!=\!\ddot{O}\,]^-$$

(b) Sulfur dioxide molecules form linkage isomers because the lone pair on the S atom or any lone pair on either O atom can bind the central metal ion.

$$\ddot{O}\!=\!\ddot{S}\!=\!\ddot{O}$$

(c) Nitrate ions have an N atom with no lone pair and three O atoms, all with lone pairs that can bind to the metal ion. But all of the O atoms are equivalent, so these ions do not form linkage isomers.

$$\left[\,:\ddot{O}\!-\!N\!=\!\ddot{O}\,\right]^-$$
$$\overset{|}{:\underset{}{\ddot{O}}:}$$

**23.63**(a) geometric isomerism

Br, Br / Pt \ CH$_3$NH$_2$, NH$_2$CH$_3$ — *cis*   and   Br, NH$_2$CH$_3$ / Pt \ CH$_3$NH$_2$, Br — *trans*

(b) geometric isomerism

H$_3$N, NH$_3$ / Pt \ Cl, F — *cis*   and   H$_3$N, F / Pt \ Cl, NH$_3$ — *trans*

(c) geometric isomerism

H$_2$O, NH$_3$ / Pt \ Cl, F   and   H$_2$O, NH$_3$ / Pt \ F, Cl   and   H$_2$O, F / Pt \ Cl, NH$_3$

**23.65**(a) geometric isomerism

[Cl, Cl / Pt \ Br, Br]$^{2-}$ — *cis*   and   [Cl, Br / Pt \ Br, Cl]$^{2-}$ — *trans*

(b) linkage isomerism

[NH$_3$; H$_3$N, NH$_3$ / Cr \ H$_3$N, NO$_2$; NH$_3$]$^{2+}$   and   [NH$_3$; H$_3$N, NH$_3$ / Cr \ H$_3$N, ONO; NH$_3$]$^{2+}$

(c) geometric isomerism

[NH$_3$; H$_3$N, I / Pt \ H$_3$N, I; NH$_3$]$^{2+}$ — *cis*   and   [NH$_3$; H$_3$N, I / Pt \ I, NH$_3$; NH$_3$]$^{2+}$ — *trans*

**23.67** The compound with the traditional formula is CrCl$_3$·4NH$_3$; the actual formula is [Cr(NH$_3$)$_4$Cl$_2$]Cl. **23.69**(a) K[Pd(NH$_3$)Cl$_3$] (b) [PdCl$_2$(NH$_3$)$_2$] (c) K$_2$[PdCl$_6$] (d) [Pd(NH$_3$)$_4$Cl$_2$]Cl$_2$ **23.71**(a) $dsp^2$ (b) $sp^3$ **23.74** absorption of orange or yellow light **23.75**(a) The crystal field splitting energy ($\Delta$) is the energy difference between the two sets of $d$ orbitals that result from electrostatic effects of ligands on a central transition metal atom. (b) In an octahedral field of ligands, the ligands approach along the $x$, $y$, and $z$ axes. The $d_{x^2-y^2}$ and $d_{z^2}$ orbitals are located *along* the $x$, $y$, and $z$ axes, so ligand interaction is higher in energy. The other orbital-ligand interactions are lower in energy because the $d_{xy}$, $d_{yz}$, and $d_{xz}$ orbitals are located *between* the $x$, $y$, and $z$ axes. (c) In a tetrahedral field of ligands, the ligands do not approach along the $x$, $y$, and $z$ axes. The ligand interaction is greater for the $d_{xy}$, $d_{yz}$, and $d_{xz}$ orbitals and lesser for the $d_{x^2-y^2}$ and $d_{z^2}$ orbitals. Therefore, the crystal field splitting is reversed, and the $d_{xy}$, $d_{yz}$, and $d_{xz}$ orbitals are higher in energy than the $d_{x^2-y^2}$ and $d_{z^2}$ orbitals. **23.78** If $\Delta$ is greater than $E_{\text{pairing}}$, electrons will pair their spins in the lower energy set of $d$ orbitals before entering the higher energy set of $d$ orbitals as unpaired electrons. If $\Delta$ is less than $E_{\text{pairing}}$, electrons will occupy the higher energy set of $d$ orbitals as unpaired electrons before pairing in the lower energy set of $d$ orbitals. **23.80**(a) no $d$ electrons (b) eight $d$ electrons (c) six $d$ electrons **23.82**(a) five (b) ten (c) seven

**23.84**

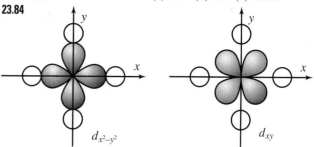

$d_{x^2-y^2}$   $d_{xy}$

In an octahedral field of ligands, the ligands approach along the $x$, $y$, and $z$ axes. The $d_{x^2-y^2}$ orbital is located along the $x$ and $y$ axes, so ligand interaction is greater. The $d_{xy}$ orbital is offset from the $x$ and $y$ axes by 90°, so ligand interaction is less. The greater interaction of the $d_{x^2-y^2}$ orbital results in its higher energy.

**23.86** a and d

**23.88**

(a)   (b)   (c)

**23.90**

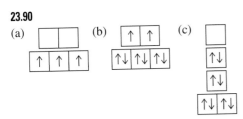

(a)  (b)  (c)

**23.92** $[Cr(H_2O)_6]^{3+} < [Cr(NH_3)_6]^{3+} < [Cr(NO_2)_6]^{3-}$

**23.94** A violet complex absorbs yellow-green light. The light absorbed by a complex with a weaker field ligand would be at a lower energy and higher wavelength. Light of lower energy than yellow-green light is yellow, orange, or red. The color observed would be blue or green. **23.97** The $H_2O$ ligand is weaker than the $NH_3$ ligand. The weaker field ligand results in a lower splitting energy and absorbs visible light of lower energy. The hexaaqua complex appears green because it absorbs red light. The hexaammine complex appears violet because it absorbs yellow light, which has higher energy (shorter $\lambda$) than red light. **23.101** $Hg^+$ is $[Xe]\, 6s^1 4f^{14} 5d^{10}$ and $Cu^+$ is $[Ar]\, 3d^{10}$. The mercury(I) ion has one electron in the $6s$ orbital that can form a covalent bond with the electron in the $6s$ orbital of another mercury(I) ion. In the copper(I) ion there are no electrons in the $s$ orbital, so these ions cannot bond with one another. **23.102**(a) 6  (b) +3  (c) two  (d) 1 mol **23.109** geometric (*cis-trans*) and linkage isomerism

*cis*-diamminedithiocyanatoplatinum(II)

*trans*-diamminedithiocyanatoplatinum(II)

*cis*-diamminediisothiocyanatoplatinum(II)

*trans*-diamminediisothiocyanatoplatinum(II)

*cis*-diammineisothiocyanatothiocyanatoplatinum(II)

*trans*-diammineisothiocyanatothiocyanatoplatinum(II)

**23.110** $[Co(NH_3)_4(H_2O)Cl]^{2+}$

tetraammineaquachlorocobalt(III) ion

2 geometric isomers

*cis*    *trans*

$[Cr(H_2O)_3Br_2Cl]$
triaquadibromochlorochromium(III)

3 geometric isomers

Br's are *trans*    Br's are *cis*    Br's and H₂O's are *cis*
H₂O's are *cis* and *trans*

$[Cr(NH_3)_2(H_2O)_2Br_2]^+$
diamminediaquadibromochromium(III) ion

6 isomers (5 geometric)

all ligands are *trans*    only NH₃ is *trans*    only Br is *trans*

only H₂O is *trans*    optical isomers
all three ligands are *cis*

**23.115**(a) no optical isomers  (b) no optical isomers  (c) no optical isomers  (d) no optical isomers  (e) optical isomers **23.116** $Pt[P(C_2H_5)_3]_2Cl_2$

*cis*-dichlorobis(triethylphosphine)platinum(II)

*trans*-dichlorobis(triethylphosphine)platinum(II)

**23.118**(a) The first reaction shows no change in the number of particles. In the second reaction, the number of reactant particles is greater than the number of product particles. A decrease in the number of particles means a decrease in entropy. Based on entropy change only, the first reaction is favored.  (b) The ethylenediamine complex will be more stable with respect to ligand exchange in water because the entropy change for that exchange is unfavorable (negative).

## Chapter 24

**Answers to Boxed Reading Problems: B24.1** In the s-process, a nucleus captures a neutron sometime over a long period of time. Then the nucleus emits a beta particle to form another element. The stable isotopes of most heavy elements up to $^{209}$Bi form by the s-process. The r-process very quickly forms less stable isotopes and those with A greater than 230 by multiple neutron captures, followed by multiple beta decays. **B24.3** The simultaneous fusion of three nuclei is a termolecular process. Termolecular processes have a very low probability of occurring. The bimolecular fusion of $^8$Be with $^4$He is more likely. **B24.4** $^{210}_{83}$Bi $\longrightarrow$ $^{0}_{-1}\beta$ + $^{210}_{84}$Po (nuclide A); $^{210}_{84}$Po $\longrightarrow$ $^4_2\alpha$ + $^{206}_{82}$Pb (nuclide B); $^{206}_{82}$Pb + $3^1_0$n $\longrightarrow$ $^{209}_{82}$Pb (nuclide C); $^{209}_{82}$Pb $\longrightarrow$ $^0_{-1}\beta$ + $^{210}_{83}$Bi (nuclide D)

• **24.1**(a) Chemical reactions are accompanied by relatively small changes in energy; nuclear reactions are accompanied by relatively large changes in energy. (b) Increasing temperature increases the rate of a chemical reaction but has no effect on a nuclear reaction. (c) Both chemical and nuclear reaction rates increase with higher reactant concentrations. (d) If the reactant is limiting in a chemical reaction, then more reactant produces more product and the yield increases. The presence of more radioactive reactant results in more decay product, so a higher reactant concentration increases the yield. **24.2**(a) 95.02% (b) The atomic mass is larger than the isotopic mass of $^{32}$S. Sulfur-32 is the lightest isotope. **24.4**(a) Z down by 2, N down by 2 (b) Z up by 1, N down by 1 (c) no change in Z or N (d) Z down by 1, N up by 1 (e) Z down by 1, N up by 1   A different element is produced in all cases except c. **24.6** A neutron-rich nuclide decays by beta (minus) decay. A neutron-poor nuclide undergoes positron decay or electron capture.
**24.8**(a) $^{234}_{92}$U $\longrightarrow$ $^4_2\alpha$ + $^{230}_{90}$Th (b) $^{232}_{93}$Np + $^0_{-1}$e $\longrightarrow$ $^{232}_{92}$U
(c) $^7_4$N $\longrightarrow$ $^0_{1}\beta$ + $^{12}_6$C  **24.10**(a) $^{27}_{12}$Mg $\longrightarrow$ $^0_{-1}\beta$ + $^{27}_{13}$Al
(b) $^{23}_{12}$Mg $\longrightarrow$ $^0_1\beta$ + $^{23}_{11}$Na (c) $^{103}_{46}$Pd + $^0_{-1}$e $\longrightarrow$ $^{103}_{45}$Rh
**24.12**(a) $^{48}_{23}$V $\longrightarrow$ $^{48}_{22}$Ti + $^0_1\beta$ (b) $^{107}_{48}$Cd + $^0_{-1}$e $\longrightarrow$ $^{107}_{47}$Ag
(c) $^{210}_{86}$Rn $\longrightarrow$ $^{206}_{84}$Po + $^4_2\alpha$  **24.14**(a) $^{186}_{78}$Pt + $^0_{-1}$e $\longrightarrow$ $^{186}_{77}$Ir
(b) $^{225}_{89}$Ac $\longrightarrow$ $^{221}_{87}$Fr + $^4_2\alpha$ (c) $^{129}_{52}$Te $\longrightarrow$ $^{129}_{53}$I + $^0_{-1}\beta$
**24.16**(a) Appears stable because its N and Z values are both magic numbers, but its N/Z ratio (1.50) is too high; it is unstable. (b) Appears unstable because its Z value is an odd number, but its N/Z ratio (1.19) is in the band of stability, so it is stable. (c) Unstable because its N/Z ratio is too high.
**24.18**(a) The N/Z ratio for $^{127}$I is 1.4; it is stable. (b) The N/Z ratio for $^{106}$Sn is 1.1; it is unstable because this ratio is too low. (c) The N/Z ratio is 1.1 for $^{68}$As. The ratio is within the range of stability, but the nuclide is most likely unstable because there are odd numbers of both protons and neutrons.
**24.20**(a) alpha decay (b) positron decay or electron capture (c) positron decay or electron capture  **24.22**(a) beta (minus) decay (b) positron decay or electron capture (c) alpha decay
**24.24** Stability results from a favorable N/Z ratio, even numbered N and/or Z, and the occurrence of magic numbers. The N/Z ratio of $^{52}$Cr is 1.17, which is within the band of stability. The fact that Z is even does not account for the variation in stability because all isotopes of chromium have the same Z.

However, $^{52}$Cr has 28 neutrons, so N is both an even number and a magic number for this isotope only. **24.28** seven α emissions and four β$^-$ emissions **24.31** No, it is not valid to conclude that $t_{1/2}$ equals 1 min because the number of nuclei is so small. Decay rate is an average rate and is only meaningful when the sample is macroscopic and contains a large number of nuclei. For the sample containing $6\times10^{12}$ nuclei, the conclusion is valid. **24.33** $2.56\times10^{-2}$ Ci/g **24.35** $1.4\times10^8$ Bq/g **24.37** $1\times10^{-12}$ day$^{-1}$ **24.39** $2.31\times10^{-7}$ yr$^{-1}$ **24.41** 1.49 mg **24.43** $2.2\times10^9$ yr **24.45** 30 dpm **24.47** $1.0\times10^6$ yr **24.50** Neither γ radiation nor neutron beams have charge, so neither is deflected by a magnetic or electric field. Neutron beams differ from γ radiation in that a neutron has a mass approximately equal to that of a proton. It was observed that a neutron beam induces the emission of protons from a substance; γ radiation does not cause such emission. **24.52** Protons are repelled from the target nuclei due to interaction with like (positive) charges. Higher energy is required to overcome the repulsion.
**24.53**(a) $^{10}_5$B + $^4_2\alpha$ $\longrightarrow$ $^1_0$n + $^{13}_7$N (b) $^{28}_{14}$Si + $^2_1$H $\longrightarrow$ $^1_0$n + $^{29}_{15}$P (c) $^{242}_{96}$Cm + $^4_2\alpha$ $\longrightarrow$ $2^1_0$n + $^{244}_{98}$Cf **24.58** Ionizing radiation is more dangerous to children because their rapidly dividing cells are more susceptible to radiation than adults' slowly dividing cells. **24.60**(a) $5.4\times10^{-7}$ rad (b) $5.4\times10^{-9}$ Gy **24.62**(a) $7.5\times10^{-10}$ Gy (b) $7.5\times10^{-5}$ mrem (c) $7.5\times10^{-10}$ Sv **24.65** $1.86\times10^{-3}$ rad **24.67** NAA does not destroy the sample, while chemical analyses do. Neutrons bombard a nonradioactive sample, inducing some atoms within the sample to be radioactive. The radioisotopes decay by emitting radiation characteristic of each isotope. **24.73** Energy is released when a nucleus forms from nucleons. The nuclear binding energy is the quantity of energy holding 1 mol of nuclei together. This energy must be absorbed to break up the nucleus into nucleons and is released when nucleons come together.
**24.75**(a) $1.861\times10^4$ eV (b) $2.981\times10^{-15}$ J **24.77** $7.6\times10^{11}$ J **24.79**(a) 7.976 MeV/nucleon (b) 127.6 MeV/atom (c) $1.231\times10^{10}$ kJ/mol **24.81**(a) 8.768 MeV/nucleon (b) 517.3 MeV/atom (c) $4.99\times10^{10}$ kJ/mol **24.85** Radioactive decay is a spontaneous process in which unstable nuclei emit radioactive particles and energy. Fission occurs as the result of high-energy bombardment of nuclei with small particles that cause the nuclei to break into smaller nuclides, radioactive particles, and energy. All fission events are not the same. The nuclei split in a number of ways to produce several different products. **24.88** The water serves to slow the neutrons so that they are better able to cause a fission reaction. Heavy water is a better moderator because it does not absorb neutrons as well as light water does; thus, more neutrons are available to initiate the fission process. However, $D_2O$ does not occur naturally in great abundance, so its production adds to the cost of a heavy-water reactor. **24.93**(a) $1.1\times10^{-29}$ kg (b) $9.9\times10^{-13}$ J (c) $5.9\times10^8$ kJ/mol; this is approximately 1 million times larger than a typical enthalpy of reaction. **24.95** $8.0\times10^3$ yr **24.98** $1.35\times10^{-5}$ M **24.100** $6.2\times10^{-2}$ **24.102**(a) 5.99 h (b) 21% **24.104**(a) 0.999 (b) 0.298 (c) $5.58\times10^{-6}$

(d) Radiocarbon dating is more reliable for the fraction in part (b) because a significant amount of $^{14}C$ has decayed and a significant amount remains. Therefore, a change in the amount of $^{14}C$ will be noticeable. For the fraction in part (a), very little $^{14}C$ has decayed, and for (c) very little $^{14}C$ remains. In either case, it will be more difficult to measure the change, so the error will be relatively large. **24.106** 6.58 h **24.110** $4.904 \times 10^{-9}$ L/h **24.113** 81 yr **24.115**(a) 0.15 Bq/L (b) 0.27 Bq/L (c) 3.3 d; a total of 12.8 d **24.118** 7.4 s **24.121** 1926

**24.124** $6.27 \times 10^5$ eV/reaction, $6.05 \times 10^7$ kJ/mol reaction **24.127**(a) $2.07 \times 10^{-17}$ J (b) $1.45 \times 10^7$ H atoms (c) $1.4960 \times 10^{-5}$ J (d) $1.4959 \times 10^{-5}$ J (e) No, the captain should continue using the current technology. **24.130**(a) 0.043 MeV, $2.9 \times 10^{-11}$ m (b) 4.713 MeV **24.134**(a) $3.26 \times 10^3$ d (b) $3.2 \times 10^{-3}$ s (c) $2.78 \times 10^{11}$ yr **24.136**(a) $1.80 \times 10^{17}$ J (b) $6.15 \times 10^{16}$ kJ (c) The procedure in part (b) produces more energy per kilogram of antihydrogen. **24.137** $9.316 \times 10^2$ MeV **24.141** 7.81 d

Numbers in parentheses refer to the page(s) on which a term is introduced and/or discussed.

# A

**absolute scale** (also *Kelvin scale*)   The preferred temperature scale in scientific work, which has absolute zero (0 K, or $-273.15°C$) as the lowest temperature. (23) [See also *kelvin (K)*.]

**absorption spectrum**   The spectrum produced when atoms absorb specific wavelengths of incoming light and become excited from lower to higher energy levels. (273)

**abundance**   The amount of an element in a particular region of the natural world. (905)

**accuracy**   The closeness of a measurement to the actual value. (29)

**acid**   In common laboratory terms, any species that produces $H^+$ ions when dissolved in water. (145) [See also *Arrhenius, Brønsted-Lowry,* and *Lewis acid-base definitions*.]

**acid anhydride**   A compound, usually formed by a dehydration-condensation reaction of an oxoacid, that yields two molecules of the acid when it reacts with water. (600)

**acid-base buffer** (also *buffer*)   A solution that resists changes in pH when a small amount of either strong acid or strong base is added. (765)

**acid-base indicator**   An organic molecule whose color is different in acid and in base and is used to monitor the equivalence point of a titration or the pH of a solution. (728)

**acid-base reaction**   Any reaction between an acid and a base. (145) (See also *neutralization reaction*.)

**acid-base titration curve**   A plot of the pH of a solution of acid (or base) versus the volume of base (or acid) added to the solution. (774)

**acid-dissociation (acid-ionization) constant ($K_a$)**   An equilibrium constant for the dissociation of an acid (HA) in $H_2O$ to yield the conjugate base ($A^-$) and $H_3O^+$:

$$K_a = \frac{[H_3O^+][A^-]}{[HA]} \qquad (722)$$

**actinides**   The Period 7 elements that constitute the second inner transition series (5*f* block), which includes thorium (Th; $Z = 90$) through lawrencium (Lr; $Z = 103$). (306, 952)

**activated complex**   (See *transition state*.)

**activation energy ($E_a$)**   The minimum energy with which molecules must collide to react. (649)

**active site**   The region of an enzyme formed by specific amino acid side chains at which catalysis occurs. (662)

**activity ($\mathcal{A}$)** (also *decay rate*)   The change in number of nuclei ($\mathcal{N}$) of a radioactive sample divided by the change in time ($t$). (988)

**activity series of the metals**   A listing of metals arranged in order of decreasing strength of the metal as a reducing agent in aqueous reactions. (165)

**actual yield**   The amount of product actually obtained in a chemical reaction. (112)

**addition polymer** (also *chain-reaction,* or *chain-growth, polymer*)   A polymer formed when monomers (usually containing C=C) combine through an addition reaction. (604)

**addition reaction**   A type of organic reaction in which atoms linked by a multiple bond become bonded to more atoms. (588)

**adduct**   The product of a Lewis acid-base reaction characterized by the formation of a new covalent bond. (751)

**adenosine triphosphate (ATP)**   A high-energy molecule that serves most commonly as a store and source of energy in organisms. (836)

**alcohol**   An organic compound (ending, *-ol*) that contains a $-\overset{|}{\underset{|}{C}}-\overset{..}{\underset{..}{O}}-H$ functional group. (591)

**aldehyde**   An organic compound (ending, *-al*) that contains the carbonyl functional group (C=$\overset{..}{\underset{..}{O}}$) in which the carbonyl C is also bonded to H. (597)

**alkane**   A hydrocarbon that contains only single bonds and no rings (general formula, $C_nH_{2n+2}$). (576)

**alkene**   A hydrocarbon that contains at least one C=C bond (general formula, $C_nH_{2n}$). (582)

**alkyl group**   A saturated hydrocarbon chain with one bond available. (588)

**alkyl halide**   (See *haloalkane*.)

**alkyne**   A hydrocarbon that contains at least one C≡C bond (general formula, $C_nH_{2n-2}$). (583)

**allotrope**   One of two or more crystalline or molecular forms of an element. In general, one allotrope is more stable than another at a particular pressure and temperature. (539)

**alloy**   A mixture with metallic properties that consists of solid phases of two or more pure elements, a solid-solid solution, or distinct intermediate phases. (354, 482, 921)

**alpha (α) decay**   A radioactive process in which an alpha particle is emitted from a nucleus. (981)

**alpha particle (α or $^4_2He^{2+}$)**   A positively charged particle, identical to a helium-4 nucleus, that is one of the common types of radioactive emissions. (979)

**amide**   An organic compound that contains the $-\overset{\overset{:O:}{\|}}{C}-\overset{|}{\underset{|}{N}}-$ functional group. (599)

**amine**   An organic compound (general formula, $-\overset{|}{\underset{|}{C}}-\overset{|}{\underset{|}{N}}-$) derived structurally by replacing one or more H atoms of ammonia with organic groups; a weak organic base. (594, 754)

**amino acid**   An organic compound [general formula, $H_2N-CH(R)-COOH$] with at least one carboxyl and one amine group on the same molecule; the monomer unit of a protein. (483, 608)

**amorphous solid**   A solid that has a poorly defined shape because it lacks extensive molecular-level ordering of its particles. (441)

**ampere (A)**   The SI unit of electric current; 1 ampere of current results when 1 coulomb flows through a conductor in 1 second. (890)

**amphoteric**   Able to act as either an acid or a base. (316)

**amplitude**   The height of the crest (or depth of the trough) of a wave; related to the intensity of the energy (brightness of the light). (262)

**angular momentum quantum number (*l*)**   An integer from 0 to $n - 1$ that is related to the shape of an atomic orbital. (281)

**anion** A negatively charged ion. (55)

**anode** The electrode at which oxidation occurs in an electro-chemical cell. Electrons are given up by the reducing agent and leave the cell at the anode. (856)

**antibonding MO** A molecular orbital formed when wave functions are subtracted from each other, which decreases electron density between the nuclei and leaves a node. Electrons occupying such an orbital destabilize the molecule. (406)

**apatite** A compound of general formula $Ca_5(PO_4)_3X$, where X is generally F, Cl, or OH; a source of phosphorus. (914)

**aqueous solution** A solution in which water is the solvent. (70)

**aromatic hydrocarbon** A compound of C and H with one or more rings of C atoms (often drawn with alternating C—C and C=C bonds), in which there is extensive delocalization of $\pi$ electrons. (584)

**Arrhenius acid-base definition** A model of acid-base behavior in which an acid is a substance that has H in its formula and dissoci-ates in water to yield $H_3O^+$, and a base is a substance that has OH in its formula and produces $OH^-$ in water. (720)

**Arrhenius equation** An equation that expresses the exponen-tial relationship between temperature and the rate constant: $k = Ae^{-E_a/RT}$. (649)

**atmosphere** The mixture of gases that extends from a planet's sur-face and eventually merges with outer space; the gaseous portion of Earth's crust. (212, 908) (For the unit, see *standard atmosphere*.)

**atom** The smallest particle of an element that retains the chem-ical nature of the element. A neutral, spherical entity composed of a positively charged central nucleus surrounded by one or more negatively charged electrons. (43)

**atomic mass** (also *atomic weight*) The average of the masses of the naturally occurring isotopes of an element weighted according to their abundances. (50)

**atomic mass unit (amu)** (also *dalton, Da*) A mass exactly equal to $\frac{1}{12}$ the mass of a carbon-12 atom. (50)

**atomic number (Z)** The unique number of protons in the nucleus of each atom of an element (equal to the number of electrons in the neutral atom). An integer that expresses the positive charge of a nucleus or subatomic particle in multiples of the electronic charge. (48)

**atomic orbital** (also *wave function*) A mathematical expression that describes the motion of the electron's matter-wave in terms of time and position in the region of the nucleus. The term is used qualitatively to mean the region of space in which there is a high probability of finding the electron. (279)

**atomic solid** A solid consisting of individual atoms held together by dispersion forces; the frozen noble gases are the only examples. (449)

**atomic symbol** (also *element symbol*) A one- or two-letter abbreviation for the English, Latin, or Greek name of an element. (49)

**atomic weight** (See *atomic mass*.)

**aufbau principle** The conceptual approach for building up atoms by adding one proton at a time to the nucleus and one electron around it to obtain the ground-state electron configurations of the elements. (299)

**autoionization** (also *self-ionization*) A reaction in which two mol-ecules of a substance react to give ions. The most important exam-ple is for water:

$$2H_2O(l) \rightleftharpoons H_3O^+(aq) + OH^-(aq) \qquad (724)$$

**average rate** The change in concentration of reactants (or prod-ucts) divided by a finite time period. (630)

**Avogadro's law** The gas law stating that, at fixed temperature and pressure, equal volumes of any ideal gas contain equal num-bers of particles, and, therefore, the volume of a gas is directly proportional to its amount (mol): $V \propto n$. (190)

**Avogadro's number** A number ($6.022 \times 10^{23}$ to four significant fig-ures) equal to the number of atoms in exactly 12 g of carbon-12; the number of atoms, molecules, or formula units in one mole of an element or compound. (83)

**axial group** An atom (or group) that lies above or below the tri-gonal plane of a trigonal bipyramidal molecule, or a similar struc-tural feature in a molecule. (377)

# B

**background radiation** Natural ionizing radiation, the most important form of which is cosmic radiation. (997)

**balancing coefficient** (also *stoichiometric coefficient*) A numerical multiplier of all the atoms in the formula immediately following it in a balanced chemical equation. (99)

**band of stability** The band of stable nuclides that appears on a plot of number of neutrons versus number of protons for all nuclides. (983)

**band theory** An extension of molecular orbital (MO) theory that explains many properties of metals and other solids, in par-ticular, the differences in electrical conductivity of conductors, semiconductors, and insulators. (452)

**barometer** A device used to measure atmospheric pressure. Most commonly, a tube open at one end, which is filled with mer-cury and inverted into a dish of mercury. (183)

**base** In common laboratory terms, any species that produces $OH^-$ ions when dissolved in water. (146) [See also *Arrhenius, Brønsted-Lowry,* and *Lewis acid-base definitions.*]

**base-dissociation (base-ionization) constant ($K_b$)** An equilibrium constant for the reaction of a base (B) with $H_2O$ to yield the con-jugate acid ($BH^+$) and $OH^-$:

$$K_b = \frac{[BH^+][OH^-]}{[B]} \qquad (740)$$

**base pair** Two complementary mononucleotide bases that are H bonded to each other; guanine (G) always pairs with cytosine (C), and adenine (A) always pairs with thymine (T) (or uracil, U). (613)

**base unit** (also *fundamental unit*) A unit that defines the stan-dard for one of the seven physical quantities in the International System of Units (SI). (17)

**basic-oxygen process** The method used to convert pig iron to steel, in which $O_2$ is blown over and through molten pig iron to oxidize impurities and decrease the content of carbon. (925)

**battery** A group of voltaic cells arranged in series; primary and secondary types are self-contained, but flow batteries are not. (878)

**becquerel (Bq)** The SI unit of radioactivity; 1 Bq = 1 d/s (disinte-gration per second). (988)

**bent shape** (also *V shape*) A molecular shape that arises when a central atom is bonded to two other atoms and has one or two lone pairs; occurs as the $AX_2E$ shape class (bond angle < 120°) in the trigonal planar arrangement and as the $AX_2E_2$ shape class (bond angle < 109.5°) in the tetrahedral arrangement. (375)

**beta (β) decay** A radioactive change that encompasses any of three specific processes— $\beta^-$ decay, $\beta^+$ emission, and $e^-$ capture. (981)

**beta ($\beta^-$) decay** A radioactive process in which a beta particle is emitted from a nucleus. (981)

**beta particle** ($\beta$, $\beta^-$, or $_{-1}^{0}\beta$) A negatively charged particle, identified as a high-speed electron, that is one of the common types of radioactive emissions. (979)

**bimolecular reaction** An elementary reaction involving the collision of two reactant species. (655)

**binary covalent compound** A compound that consists of atoms of two elements in which bonding occurs primarily through electron sharing. (65)

**binary ionic compound** A compound that consists of the oppositely charged ions of two elements. (55)

**biomass conversion** The process of applying chemical and biological methods to convert plant or animal matter into fuels. (249)

**biosphere** The living systems that inhabit Earth. (908)

**blast furnace** A tower-shaped furnace made of brick material in which intense heat and blasts of air are used to convert iron ore and coke to iron metal and carbon dioxide. (924)

**body-centered cubic unit cell** A unit cell in which a particle lies at each corner and in the center of a cube. (442)

**boiling point (bp or $T_b$)** The temperature at which the vapor pressure of a gas equals the external (atmospheric) pressure. (428)

**boiling point elevation ($\Delta T_b$)** The increase in the boiling point of a solvent caused by the presence of dissolved solute. (501)

**bond angle** The angle formed by the nuclei of two surrounding atoms with the nucleus of the central atom at the vertex. (374)

**bond energy (BE)** (also *bond enthalpy* or *bond strength*) The enthalpy change (always $>0$) accompanying the breakage of a given bond in 1 mol of gaseous molecules. (339)

**bond length** The distance between the nuclei of two bonded atoms. (340)

**bond order** The number of electron pairs shared by two bonded atoms. (339)

**bonding MO** A molecular orbital formed when wave functions are added to each other, which increases electron density between the nuclei. Electrons occupying such an orbital stabilize the molecule. (406)

**bonding pair** (also *shared pair*) An electron pair shared by two nuclei; the mutual attraction between the nuclei and the electron pair forms a covalent bond. (339)

**Born-Haber cycle** A series of hypothetical steps and their enthalpy changes that convert elements to an ionic compound; it is used to calculate the lattice energy. (333)

**Boyle's law** The gas law stating that, at constant temperature and amount of gas, the volume occupied by a gas is inversely proportional to the applied (external) pressure: $V \propto 1/P$. (187)

**branch** A side chain appended to a polymer backbone or longest sequence of atoms in an organic compound. (465)

**bridge bond** (also *three-center, two-electron bond*) A covalent bond in which three atoms are held together by two electrons. (536)

**Brønsted-Lowry acid-base definition** A model of acid-base behavior based on proton transfer, in which an acid and a base are defined, respectively, as species that donate and accept a proton. (729)

**buffer** (See *acid-base buffer.*)

**buffer capacity** A measure of the ability of a buffer to resist a change in pH; related to the total concentrations and relative proportions of buffer components. (770)

**buffer range** The pH range over which a buffer acts effectively. (771)

# C

**calibration** The process of correcting for systematic error of a measuring device by comparing it to a known standard. (29)

**calorie (cal)** A unit of energy defined as exactly 4.184 joules; originally defined as the heat needed to raise the temperature of 1 g of water 1°C (from 14.5°C to 15.5°C). (233)

**calorimeter** A device used to measure the heat released or absorbed by a physical or chemical process taking place within it. (239)

**capillarity** (or *capillary action*) A property that results in a liquid rising through a narrow space against the pull of gravity. (438)

**carbon steel** The steel that is produced by the basic-oxygen process, contains about 1% to 1.5% C and other impurities, and is alloyed with metals that prevent corrosion and increase strength. (925)

**carbonyl group** The $C{=}O$ grouping of atoms. (597)

**carboxylic acid** An organic compound (ending, *-oic acid*) that contains the $-\overset{\overset{\displaystyle :O:}{\|}}{C}-\overset{..}{O}H$ group. (599)

**catalyst** A substance or mixture that increases the rate of a reaction without being used up in the process. (660)

**catenation** The process by which atoms of an element bond to each other in chains; most common with carbon in organic compounds but also occurs with boron, silicon, sulfur, and several other elements. (572)

**cathode** The electrode at which reduction occurs in an electrochemical cell. Electrons enter the cell and are acquired by the oxidizing agent at the cathode. (856)

**cathode ray** The ray of light emitted by the cathode (negative electrode) in a gas discharge tube; travels in straight lines, unless deflected by magnetic or electric fields. (45)

**cation** A positively charged ion. (55)

**cell potential ($E_{cell}$)** (also *electromotive force,* or *emf; cell voltage*) The potential difference between the electrodes of an electrochemical cell when no current flows. (861)

**Celsius scale** (formerly *centigrade scale*) A temperature scale in which the freezing and boiling points of water are defined as 0°C and 100°C, respectively. (23)

**ceramic** A nonmetallic, nonpolymeric solid that is hardened by heating it to high temperatures and, in most cases, consists of silicate microcrystals suspended in a glassy cementing medium. (459)

**chain reaction** In nuclear fission, a self-sustaining process in which neutrons released by splitting of one nucleus cause other nuclei to split, which releases more neutrons, and so on. (1006)

**change in enthalpy ($\Delta H$)** The change in internal energy plus the product of the constant pressure and the change in volume: $\Delta H = \Delta E + P\Delta V$; the heat lost or gained at constant pressure: $\Delta H = q_P$. (235)

**charge density** The ratio of the charge of an ion to its volume. (489)

**Charles's law** The gas law stating that at constant pressure, the volume occupied by a fixed amount of gas is directly proportional to its absolute temperature: $V \propto T$. (188)

**chelate** A complex ion in which the metal ion is bonded to a bidentate or polydentate ligand. (955)

**chemical bond** The force that holds two atoms together in a molecule (or formula unit). (55)

**chemical change** (also *chemical reaction*) A change in which one or more substances are converted into one or more substances with different composition and properties. (4)

**chemical equation** A statement that uses chemical formulas to express the identities and quantities of the substances involved in a chemical or physical change. (98)

**chemical formula** A notation of atomic symbols and numerical subscripts that shows the type and number of each atom in a molecule or formula unit of a substance. (59)

**chemical kinetics** The study of the rates and mechanisms of reactions. (627)

**chemical property** A characteristic of a substance that appears as it interacts with, or transforms into, other substances. (4)

**chemical reaction** (See *chemical change.*)

**chemistry** The scientific study of matter and its properties, the changes it undergoes, and the energy associated with those changes. (4)

**chiral molecule** One that is not superimposable on its mirror image; an optically active molecule. In organic compounds, a chiral molecule typically contains a C atom bonded to four different groups (asymmetric C). (580)

**chlor-alkali process** An industrial method that electrolyzes concentrated aqueous NaCl and produces $Cl_2$, $H_2$, and NaOH. (936)

**chromatography** A separation technique in which a mixture is dissolved in a fluid (gas or liquid), and the components are separated through differences in adsorption to (or solubility in) a solid surface (or viscous liquid). (72)

***cis-trans* isomers** (See *geometric isomers.*)

**Clausius-Clapeyron equation** An equation that expresses the linear relationship between vapor pressure $P$ of a liquid and temperature $T$; in two-point form, it is

$$\ln \frac{P_2}{P_1} = \frac{-\Delta H_{vap}}{R}\left(\frac{1}{T_2} - \frac{1}{T_1}\right) \qquad (427)$$

**coal gasification** An industrial process for altering the large molecules in coal to sulfur-free gaseous fuels. (249)

**colligative property** A property of a solution that depends on the number, not the identity, of solute particles. (499) (See also *boiling point elevation, freezing point depression, osmotic pressure,* and *vapor pressure lowering.*)

**collision frequency** The average number of collisions per second that a particle undergoes. (211)

**collision theory** A model that explains reaction rate as based on the number, energy, and orientation of colliding particles. (648)

**colloid** A heterogeneous mixture in which a solute-like phase is dispersed throughout a solvent-like phase. (508)

**combustion** The process of burning in air, often with release of heat and light. (10)

**combustion analysis** A method for determining the formula of a compound from the amounts of its combustion products; used commonly for organic compounds. (95)

**common-ion effect** The shift in the position of an ionic equilibrium away from an ion involved in the process that is caused by the addition or presence of that ion. (766)

**complex** (See *coordination compound.*)

**complex ion** An ion consisting of a central metal ion bonded covalently to molecules and/or anions called ligands (792, 953)

**composition** The types and amounts of simpler substances that make up a sample of matter. (4)

**compound** A substance composed of two or more elements that are chemically combined in fixed proportions. (38)

**concentration** A measure of the quantity of solute dissolved in a given quantity of solution (or solvent). (114)

**concentration cell** A voltaic cell in which both compartments contain the same components but at different concentrations. (874)

**condensation** The process of a gas changing into a liquid. (420)

**condensation polymer** A polymer formed by monomers with two functional groups that are linked together in a dehydration-condensation reaction. (606)

**conduction band** In band theory, the empty, higher energy portion of the band of molecular orbitals into which electrons move when conducting heat and electricity. (453)

**conductor** A substance (usually a metal) that conducts an electric current well. (453)

**conjugate acid-base pair** Two species related to each other through the gain or loss of a proton; the acid has one more proton than its conjugate base. (729)

**constitutional isomers** (also *structural isomers*) Compounds with the same molecular formula but different arrangements of atoms. (579, 957)

**contact process** An industrial process for the manufacture of sulfuric acid based on the catalyzed oxidation of $SO_2$. (934)

**controlled experiment** An experiment that measures the effect of one variable at a time by keeping other variables constant. (12)

**conversion factor** A ratio of equivalent quantities that is equal to 1 and used to convert the units of a quantity. (13)

**coordinate covalent bond** A covalent bond formed when one atom donates both electrons to provide the shared pair and, once formed, is identical to any covalent single bond. (961)

**coordination compound** (also *complex*) A substance containing at least one complex ion and counter ion(s). (953)

**coordination isomers** Two or more coordination compounds with the same composition in which the complex ions have different ligand arrangements. (957)

**coordination number** In a crystal, the number of nearest neighbors surrounding a particle. (442) In a complex, the number of ligand atoms bonded to the central metal ion. (953)

**copolymer** A polymer that consists of two or more types of monomer. (465)

**core** The dense, innermost region of Earth. (906)

**core electrons** (See *inner electrons.*)

**corrosion** The natural redox process that results in unwanted oxidation of a metal. (882)

**coulomb (C)** The SI unit of electric charge. One coulomb is the charge of $6.242 \times 10^{18}$ electrons; one electron possesses a charge of $1.602 \times 10^{-19}$ C. (862)

**Coulomb's law** A law stating that the electrostatic energy between particles A and B is directly proportional to the product of their charges and inversely proportional to the distance between them:

$$\text{electrostatic energy} \propto \frac{\text{charge A} \times \text{charge B}}{\text{distance}} \qquad (335)$$

**counter ion** A simple ion associated with a complex ion in a coordination compound. (953)

**coupling of reactions** The pairing of reactions of which one releases enough free energy for the other to occur. (834)

**covalent bond** A type of bond in which atoms are bonded through the sharing of electrons; the mutual attraction of the nuclei and an electron pair that holds atoms together in a molecule. (58, 338)

**covalent bonding** The idealized bonding type that is based on localized electron-pair sharing between two atoms with little difference in their tendencies to lose or gain electrons (most commonly nonmetals). (330)

**covalent compound** A compound that consists of atoms bonded together by shared electron pairs. (55)

**covalent radius** One-half the shortest distance between nuclei of identical covalently bonded atoms. (308)

**critical mass** The minimum mass needed to achieve a chain reaction. (1007)

**critical point** The point on a phase diagram above which the vapor cannot be condensed to a liquid; the end of the liquid-gas curve. (429)

**crosslink** A branch that covalently joins one polymer chain to another. (465)

**crust** The thin, light, heterogeneous outer layer of Earth, which consists of gasous, liquid, and solid regions. (906)

**crystal defect** Any of a variety of disruptions in the regularity of a crystal structure. (455)

**crystal field splitting energy (Δ)** The difference in energy between two sets of metal-ion $d$ orbitals that results from electrostatic interactions with the surrounding ligands. (964)

**crystal field theory** A model that explains the color and magnetism of coordination compounds based on the effects of ligands on metal-ion $d$-orbital energies. (962)

**crystalline solid** Solid with a well-defined shape because of the orderly arrangement of the atoms, molecules, or ions. (441)

**crystallization** A technique used to separate and purify the components of a mixture through differences in solubility in which a component comes out of solution as crystals. (72)

**cubic closest packing** A crystal structure based on the face-centered cubic unit cell in which the layers have an *abcabc . . .* pattern. (444)

**cubic meter (m$^3$)** The SI-derived unit of volume. (18)

**curie (Ci)** The most common unit of radioactivity, defined as the number of nuclei disintegrating each second in 1 g of radium-226; 1 Ci = $3.70\times10^{10}$ d/s (disintegrations per second). (988)

**cyclic hydrocarbon** A hydrocarbon with one or more rings in its structure. (578)

# D

***d* orbital** An atomic orbital with $l = 2$. (286)

**dalton (Da)** A unit of mass identical to *atomic mass unit*. (50)

**Dalton's law of partial pressures** A gas law stating that, in a mixture of unreacting gases, the total pressure is the sum of the partial pressures of the individual gases: $P_{total} = P_1 + P_2 + \cdots$. (199)

**data** Pieces of quantitative information obtained by observation. (12)

**de Broglie wavelength** The wavelength of a moving particle obtained from the de Broglie equation: $\lambda = h/mu$. (276)

**decay constant** The rate constant $k$ for radioactive decay. (988)

**decay series** (also *disintegration series*) The succession of steps a parent nucleus undergoes as it decays into a stable daughter nucleus. (986)

**degree of polymerization (*n*)** The number of monomer repeat units in a polymer chain. (461)

**dehydration-condensation reaction** A reaction in which an $H_2O$ molecule is lost for every pair of OH groups that join. (550)

**delocalization** (See *electron-pair delocalization*.)

**density (*d*)** An intensive physical property of a substance at a given temperature and pressure, defined as the ratio of the mass to the volume: $d = m/V$. (22)

**deposition** The process of changing directly from gas to solid. (421)

**derived unit** Any of various combinations of the seven SI base units. (17)

**desalination** A process used to remove large amounts of ions from seawater, usually by reverse osmosis. (511)

**deuterons** Nuclei of the stable hydrogen isotope deuterium, $^2$H. (993)

**diagonal relationship** Physical and chemical similarities between a Period 2 element and one located diagonally down and to the right in Period 3. (533)

**diamagnetism** The tendency of a species not to be attracted (or to be slightly repelled) by a magnetic field as a result of its electrons being paired. (319)

**diastereomers** (See *geometric isomers*.)

**differentiation** The geochemical process of forming regions in Earth based on differences in composition and density. (906)

**diffraction** The phenomenon in which a wave striking the edge of an object bends around it. A wave passing through a slit as wide as its wavelength forms a circular wave. (264)

**diffusion** The movement of one fluid through another. (210)

**dimensional analysis** (also *factor-label method*) A calculation method in which arithmetic steps are accompanied by canceling units that represent physical dimensions. (15)

**dipole-dipole force** The intermolecular attraction between oppositely charged poles of nearby polar molecules. (432)

**dipole–induced dipole force** The intermolecular attraction between a polar molecule and the oppositely charged pole it induces in a nearby molecule. (478)

**dipole moment (μ)** A measure of molecular polarity; the magnitude of the partial charges on the ends of a molecule (in coulombs) times the distance between them (in meters). (383)

**disaccharide** An organic compound formed by a dehydration-condensation reaction between two simple sugars (monosaccharides). (607)

**disintegration series** (See *decay series*.)

**dispersion force** (also *London force*) The intermolecular attraction between all particles as a result of instantaneous polarizations of their electron clouds; the intermolecular force primarily responsible for the condensed states of nonpolar substances. (435)

**disproportionation** A reaction in which a given substance is both oxidized and reduced. (547)

**distillation** A separation technique in which a more volatile component of a mixture vaporizes and condenses separately from the less volatile components. (72)

**donor atom** An atom that donates a lone pair of electrons to form a covalent bond, usually from ligand to metal ion in a complex. (954)

**doping** Adding small amounts of other elements into the crystal structure of a semiconductor to enhance a specific property, usually conductivity. (455)

**double bond** A covalent bond that consists of two bonding pairs; two atoms sharing four electrons in the form of one $\sigma$ and one $\pi$ bond. (339)

**double helix** The two intertwined polynucleotide strands held together by H bonds that form the structure of DNA (deoxyribonucleic acid). (487, 612)

**Downs cell** An industrial apparatus that electrolyzes molten NaCl to produce sodium and chlorine. (923)

**dynamic equilibrium** The condition at which the forward and reverse reactions are taking place at the same rate, so there is no net change in the amounts of reactants or products. (167)

# E

**$e_g$ orbitals** The set of orbitals (composed of $d_{x^2-y^2}$ and $d_{z^2}$) that results when the energies of the metal-ion $d$ orbitals are split by a ligand field. This set is higher in energy than the other ($t_{2g}$) set in an octahedral field of ligands and lower in energy in a tetrahedral field. (964)

**effective collision** A collision in which the particles meet with sufficient energy and an orientation that allows them to react. (651)

**effective nuclear charge ($Z_{eff}$)** The nuclear charge an electron actually experiences as a result of shielding effects due to the presence of other electrons. (297)

**effusion** The process by which a gas escapes from its container through a tiny hole into an evacuated space. (209)

**elastomer** A polymeric material that can be stretched and springs back to its original shape when released. (465)

**electrochemical cell** A system that incorporates a redox reaction to produce or use electrical energy. (851)

**electrochemistry** The study of the relationship between chemical change and electrical work. (851)

**electrode** The part of an electrochemical cell that conducts the electricity between the cell and the surroundings. (855)

**electrolysis** The nonspontaneous lysing (splitting) of a substance, often to its component elements, by supplying electrical energy. (886)

**electrolyte** A substance that conducts a current when it dissolves in water. (137, 499) A mixture of ions, in which the electrodes of an electrochemical cell are immersed, that conducts a current. (855)

**electrolytic cell** An electrochemical system that uses electrical energy to drive a nonspontaneous chemical reaction ($\Delta G > 0$). (855)

**electromagnetic radiation** (also *electromagnetic energy* or *radiant energy*) Oscillating, perpendicular electric and magnetic fields moving simultaneously through space as waves and manifested as visible light, x-rays, microwaves, radio waves, and so on. (261)

**electromagnetic spectrum** The continuum of wavelengths of radiant energy. (262)

**electromotive force (emf)** (See *cell potential*.)

**electron ($e^-$)** A subatomic particle that possesses a unit negative charge ($-1.60218\times10^{-19}$ C) and occupies the space around the atomic nucleus. (48)

**electron affinity (EA)** The energy change (in kJ) accompanying the addition of one mole of electrons to one mole of gaseous atoms or ions. (314)

**electron capture (EC)** A type of radioactive decay in which a nucleus draws in an orbital electron, usually one from the lowest energy level, and releases energy. (981)

**electron cloud depiction** An imaginary representation of an electron's rapidly changing position around the nucleus over time. (280)

**electron configuration** The distribution of electrons within the orbitals of the atoms of an element; also the notation for such a distribution. (295)

**electron deficient** Referring to a bonded atom, such as Be or B, that has fewer than eight valence electrons. (369)

**electron density diagram** (also *electron probability density diagram*) The pictorial representation for a given energy sublevel of the quantity $\psi^2$ (the probability density of the electron lying within a particular tiny volume) as a function of $r$ (distance from the nucleus). (280)

**electron-pair delocalization** (also *delocalization*) The process by which electron density is spread over several atoms rather than remaining between two. (367)

**electron-sea model** A qualitative description of metallic bonding proposing that metal atoms pool their valence electrons into a delocalized "sea" of electrons in which the metal cores (metal ions) are submerged in an orderly array. (354)

**electron volt (eV)** The energy (in joules, J) that an electron acquires when it moves through a potential difference of 1 volt; 1 eV = $1.602\times10^{-19}$ J. (1004)

**electronegativity (EN)** The relative ability of a bonded atom to attract shared electrons. (349)

**electronegativity difference ($\Delta$EN)** The difference in electronegativities between the atoms in a bond. (351)

**electrorefining** An industrial, electrolytic purification process in which a sample of impure metal acts as the anode and a sample of the pure metal acts as the cathode. (921)

**element** The simplest type of substance with unique physical and chemical properties. An element consists of only one kind of atom, so it cannot be broken down into simpler substances. (38)

**element symbol** (See *atomic symbol*.)

**elementary reaction** (also *elementary step*) A simple reaction that describes a single molecular event in a proposed reaction mechanism. (655)

**elimination reaction** A type of organic reaction in which C atoms are bonded to fewer atoms in the product than in the reactant, which leads to multiple bonding. (589)

**emission spectrum** The line spectrum produced when excited atoms return to lower energy levels and emit photons characteristic of the element. (273)

**empirical formula** A chemical formula that shows the lowest relative number of atoms of each element in a compound. (92)

**enantiomers** (See *optical isomers*.)

**end point** The point in a titration at which the indicator changes color. (152, 776)

**endothermic process** A process that occurs with an absorption of heat from the surroundings and therefore an increase in the enthalpy of the system ($\Delta H > 0$). (237)

**energy** The capacity to do work, that is, to move matter. (8) [See also *kinetic energy* ($E_k$) and *potential energy* ($E_p$).]

**enthalpy ($H$)** A thermodynamic quantity that is the sum of the internal energy plus the product of the pressure and volume. (235)

**enthalpy diagram** A graphic depiction of the enthalpy change of a system. (237)

**enthalpy of formation ($\Delta H_f$)** (also *heat of formation*)  The enthalpy change occurring when 1 mol of a compound forms from its elements. When all components are in their standard states, this is called the *standard enthalpy of formation ($\Delta H_f^\circ$)*. (246)

**enthalpy of fusion**  (See *heat of fusion.*)

**enthalpy of hydration**  (See *heat of hydration.*)

**enthalpy of reaction ($\Delta H_{rxn}$)** (also *heat of reaction*)  The enthalpy change that occurs during a reaction. When all components are in their standard states, this is called the *standard enthalpy of reaction ($\Delta H_{rxn}^\circ$)*. (246)

**enthalpy of solution**  (See *heat of solution.*)

**enthalpy of sublimation**  (See *heat of sublimation.*)

**enthalpy of vaporization**  (See *heat of vaporization.*)

**entropy ($S$)**  A thermodynamic quantity related to the number of ways the energy of a system can be dispersed through the motions of its particles. (490, 814)

**environmental cycle**  The physical, chemical, and biological paths through which the atoms of an element move within Earth's crust. (911)

**enzyme**  A biological macromolecule (usually a protein) that acts as a catalyst. (662)

**enzyme-substrate complex (ES)**  The intermediate in an enzyme-catalyzed reaction, which consists of enzyme and substrate(s) and whose concentration determines the rate of product formation. (663)

**equatorial group**  An atom (or group) that lies in the trigonal plane of a trigonal bipyramidal molecule, or a similar structural feature in a molecule. (377)

**equilibrium constant ($K$)**  The value obtained when equilibrium concentrations are substituted into the reaction quotient. (679)

**equilibrium vapor pressure**  (See *vapor pressure.*)

**equivalence point**  The point in a titration when the number of moles of the added species is stoichiometrically equivalent to the original number of moles of the other species. (152, 775)

**ester**  An organic compound that contains the $-\overset{\displaystyle :O:}{\overset{\displaystyle \|}{C}}-\overset{..}{O}-\overset{|}{\underset{|}{C}}-$ group. (599)

**exact number**  A quantity, usually obtained by counting or based on a unit definition, that has no uncertainty associated with it and, therefore, contains as many significant figures as a calculation requires. (28)

**exchange reaction**  (See *metathesis reaction.*)

**excited state**  Any electron configuration of an atom or molecule other than the lowest energy (ground) state. (269)

**exclusion principle**  A principle developed by Wolfgang Pauli stating that no two electrons in an atom can have the same set of four quantum numbers. The principle arises from the fact that an orbital has a maximum occupancy of two electrons and their spins are paired. (297)

**exothermic process**  A process that occurs with a release of heat to the surroundings and therefore a decrease in the enthalpy of the system ($\Delta H < 0$). (236)

**expanded valence shell**  A valence level that can accommodate more than eight electrons by using available $d$ orbitals; occurs only with central nonmetal atoms from Period 3 or higher. (370)

**experiment**  A set of procedural steps that tests a hypothesis. (12)

**extensive property**  A property, such as mass, that depends on the quantity of substance present. (25)

# F

**face-centered cubic unit cell**  A unit cell in which a particle occurs at each corner and in the center of each face of a cube. (442)

**Faraday constant ($F$)**  The physical constant representing the charge of 1 mol of electrons: $F = 96{,}485$ C/mol e$^-$. (870)

**fatty acid**  A carboxylic acid that has a long hydrocarbon chain and is derived from a natural source. (599)

**filtration**  A method of separating the components of a mixture on the basis of differences in particle size. (72)

**first law of thermodynamics**  (See *law of conservation of energy.*)

**fission**  The process by which a heavier nucleus splits into lighter nuclei with the release of energy. (1003)

**fixation**  A chemical/biochemical process that converts a gaseous substance in the environment into a condensed form that can be used by organisms. (911)

**flame test**  A procedure for identifying the presence of metal ions in which a granule of a compound or a drop of its solution is placed in a flame to observe a characteristic color. (273)

**flotation**  A metallurgical process in which oil and detergent are mixed with pulverized ore in water to create a slurry that separates the mineral from the gangue. (917)

**formal charge**  The hypothetical charge on an atom in a molecule or ion, equal to the number of valence electrons minus the sum of all the unshared and half the shared valence electrons. (368)

**formation constant ($K_f$)**  An equilibrium constant for the formation of a complex ion from the hydrated metal ion and ligands. (794)

**formation equation**  An equation in which 1 mole of a compound forms from its elements. (246)

**formula mass**  The sum (in amu) of the atomic masses of a formula unit of a (usually ionic) compound. (66)

**formula unit**  The chemical unit of a compound that contains the relative numbers of the types of atoms or ions expressed in the chemical formula. (60)

**fossil fuel**  Any fuel, including coal, petroleum, and natural gas, derived from the products of the decay of dead organisms. (249)

**fraction by mass** (also *mass fraction*)  The portion of a compound's mass contributed by an element; the mass of an element in a compound divided by the mass of the compound. (41)

**fractional distillation**  A physical process involving numerous vaporization-condensation steps used to separate two or more volatile components. (505)

**free energy ($G$)**  A thermodynamic quantity that is the difference between the enthalpy and the product of the absolute temperature and the entropy: $G = H - TS$. (827)

**free energy change ($\Delta G$)**  The change in free energy that occurs during a reaction. (827)

**free radical**  A molecular or atomic species with one or more unpaired electrons, which typically make it very reactive. (370, 996)

**freezing**  The process of cooling a liquid until it solidifies. (420)

**freezing point depression ($\Delta T_f$)**  The lowering of the freezing point of a solvent caused by the presence of dissolved solute particles. (502)

**frequency ($\nu$)**  The number of cycles a wave undergoes per second, expressed in units of 1/second, or s$^{-1}$ [also called *hertz* (Hz)]; related inversely to wavelength. (261)

**frequency factor (*A*)** The product of the collision frequency *Z* and an orientation probability factor *p* that is specific for a reaction. (651)

**fuel cell** (also *flow battery*) A battery that is not self-contained and in which electricity is generated by the controlled oxidation of a fuel. (881)

**functional group** A specific combination of atoms, typically containing a carbon-carbon multiple bond and/or carbon-heteroatom bond, that reacts in a characteristic way no matter what molecule it occurs in. (573)

**fundamental unit** (See *base unit.*)

**fusion** (See *melting.*)

**fusion (nuclear)** The process by which light nuclei combine to form a heavier nucleus with the release of energy. (1003)

# G

**galvanic cell** (See *voltaic cell.*)

**gamma emission** The type of radioactive decay in which gamma rays are emitted from an excited nucleus. (981)

**gamma (γ) ray** A very high-energy photon. (979)

**gangue** In an ore, the debris, such as sand, rock, and clay, attached to the mineral. (917)

**gas** One of the three states of matter. A gas fills its container regardless of the shape because its particles are far apart. (6)

**Geiger-Müller counter** An ionization counter that detects radioactive emissions through their ionization of gas atoms within the instrument. (987)

**genetic code** The set of three-base sequences that is translated into specific amino acids during the process of protein synthesis. (613)

**geometric isomers** (also *cis-trans isomers* or *diastereomers*) Stereoisomers in which the molecules have the same connections between atoms but differ in the spatial arrangements of the atoms. The *cis* isomer has similar groups on the same side of a double bond; the *trans* isomer has them on opposite sides. (582, 958)

**Graham's law of effusion** A gas law stating that the rate of effusion of a gas is inversely proportional to the square root of its density (or molar mass):

$$\text{rate} \propto \frac{1}{\sqrt{\mathcal{M}}} \tag{209}$$

**gray (Gy)** The SI unit of absorbed radiation dose; 1 Gy = 1 J/kg tissue. (996)

**green chemistry** Field that is focused on developing methods to synthesize compounds efficiently and reduce or prevent the release of harmful products into the environment. (113)

**ground state** The electron configuration of an atom or ion that is lowest in energy. (269)

**group** A vertical column in the periodic table; elements in a group usually have the same outer electron configuration and, thus, similar chemical behavior. (53)

# H

**H bond** (See *hydrogen bond.*)

**Haber process** An industrial process used to form ammonia from its elements. (706)

**half-cell** A portion of an electrochemical cell in which a half-reaction takes place. (857)

**half-life ($t_{1/2}$)** In chemical processes, the time required for half the initial reactant concentration to be consumed. (644) In nuclear processes, the time required for half the initial number of nuclei in a sample to decay. (988)

**half-reaction method** A method of balancing redox reactions by treating the oxidation and reduction half-reactions separately. (852)

**haloalkane** (also *alkyl halide*) A hydrocarbon with one or more halogen atoms (X) in place of H; contains a $-\overset{|}{\underset{|}{C}}-\overset{..}{\underset{..}{X}}:$ group. (593)

**hard water** Water that contains large amounts of divalent cations, especially $Ca^{2+}$ and $Mg^{2+}$. (510)

**heat (*q*)** (also *thermal energy*) The energy transferred between objects because of a difference in their temperatures only. (23, 230)

**heat capacity** The quantity of heat required to change the temperature of an object by 1 K. (238)

**heat of formation** (See *enthalpy of formation.*)

**heat of fusion ($\Delta H_{fus}$)** (also *enthalpy of fusion*) The enthalpy change occurring when 1 mol of a solid substance melts; designated $\Delta H_{fus}^{\circ}$ at the standard state. (421)

**heat of hydration ($\Delta H_{hydr}$)** (also *enthalpy of hydration*) The enthalpy change occurring when 1 mol of a gaseous species (often an ion) is hydrated. The sum of the enthalpies from separating water molecules and mixing the gaseous species with them; designated $\Delta H_{hydr}^{\circ}$ at the standard state. (489)

**heat of reaction ($\Delta H_{rxn}$)** (See *enthalpy of reaction.*)

**heat of solution ($\Delta H_{soln}$)** (also *enthalpy of solution*) The enthalpy change occurring when a solution forms from solute and solvent. The sum of the enthalpies from separating solute and solvent substances and mixing them; designated $\Delta H_{soln}^{\circ}$ at the standard state. (488)

**heat of sublimation ($\Delta H_{subl}$)** (also *enthalpy of sublimation*) The enthalpy change occurring when 1 mol of a solid substance changes directly to a gas. The sum of the heats of fusion and vaporization; designated $\Delta H_{subl}^{\circ}$ at the standard state. (421)

**heat of vaporization ($\Delta H_{vap}$)** (also *enthalpy of vaporization*) The enthalpy change occurring when 1 mol of a liquid substance vaporizes; designated $\Delta H_{vap}^{\circ}$ at the standard state. (421)

**heating-cooling curve** A plot of temperature vs. time for a substance when heat is absorbed or released by the system at a constant rate. (422)

**Henderson-Hasselbalch equation** An equation for calculating the pH of a buffer system:

$$\text{pH} = \text{p}K_a + \log\left(\frac{[\text{base}]}{[\text{acid}]}\right) \tag{770}$$

**Henry's law** A law stating that the solubility of a gas in a liquid is directly proportional to the partial pressure of the gas above the liquid: $S_{gas} = k_H \times P_{gas}$. (494)

**Hess's law** A law stating that the enthalpy change of an overall process is the sum of the enthalpy changes of the individual steps. (244)

**heteroatom** Any atom in an organic compound other than C or H. (573)

**heterogeneous catalyst** A catalyst that occurs in a different phase from the reactants, usually a solid interacting with gaseous or liquid reactants. (661)

**heterogeneous mixture** A mixture that has one or more visible boundaries among its components. (70)

**hexagonal closest packing**  A crystal structure based on the hexagonal unit cell in which the layers have an *abab . . .* pattern. (444)

**high-spin complex**  Complex ion that has the same number of unpaired electrons as in the isolated metal ion; contains weak-field ligands. (966)

**homogeneous catalyst**  A catalyst (gas, liquid, or soluble solid) that exists in the same phase as the reactants. (660)

**homogeneous mixture** (also *solution*)  A mixture that has no visible boundaries among its components. (70)

**homologous series**  A series of organic compounds in which each member differs from the next by a —CH₂— (methylene) group. (576)

**homonuclear diatomic molecule**  A molecule composed of two identical atoms. (408)

**Hund's rule**  A principle stating that when orbitals of equal energy are available, the electron configuration of lowest energy has the maximum number of unpaired electrons with parallel spins. (300)

**hybrid orbital**  An atomic orbital postulated to form during bonding by the mathematical mixing of specific combinations of non-equivalent orbitals in a given atom. (396)

**hybridization**  A postulated process of orbital mixing to form hybrid orbitals. (396)

**hydrate**  A compound in which a specific number of water molecules are associated with each formula unit. (63)

**hydration**  Solvation in water. (489)

**hydration shell**  The oriented cluster of water molecules that surrounds an ion in aqueous solution. (478)

**hydrocarbon**  An organic compound that contains only H and C atoms. (574)

**hydrogen bond (H bond)**  A type of dipole-dipole force that arises between molecules that have an H atom bonded to a small, highly electronegative atom with lone pairs, usually N, O, or F. (432)

**hydrogenation**  The addition of hydrogen to a carbon-carbon multiple bond to form a carbon-carbon single bond. (662)

**hydrolysis**  Cleaving a molecule by reaction with water, in which one part of the molecule bonds to the water —OH and the other to the water H. (600)

**hydronium ion (H₃O⁺)**  A proton covalently bonded to a water molecule. (720)

**hydrosphere**  The liquid portion of Earth's crust. (908)

**hypothesis**  A testable proposal made to explain an observation. If inconsistent with experimental results, a hypothesis is revised or discarded. (12)

**I**

**ideal gas**  A hypothetical gas that exhibits linear relationships among volume, pressure, temperature, and amount (mol) at all conditions; approximated by simple gases at ordinary conditions. (186)

**ideal gas law** (also *ideal gas equation*)  An equation that expresses the relationships among volume, pressure, temperature, and amount (mol) of an ideal gas: $PV = nRT$. (191)

**ideal solution**  A solution whose vapor pressure equals the mole fraction of the solvent times the vapor pressure of the pure solvent; approximated only by very dilute solutions. (500) (See also *Raoult's law.*)

**indicator**  (See *acid-base indicator.*)

**induced-fit model**  A model of enzyme action that pictures the binding of the substrate as inducing the active site to change its shape and become catalytically active. (663)

**infrared (IR)**  The region of the electromagnetic spectrum between the microwave and visible regions. (262)

**infrared (IR) spectroscopy**  An instrumental technique for determining the types of bonds in a covalent molecule by measuring the absorption of IR radiation. (343)

**initial rate**  The instantaneous rate occurring as soon as the reactants are mixed, that is, at $t = 0$. (631)

**inner electrons** (also *core electrons*)  Electrons that fill all the energy levels of an atom except the valence level; electrons also present in atoms of the previous noble gas and any completed transition series. (306)

**inner transition elements**  The elements of the periodic table in which *f* orbitals are being filled; the lanthanides and actinides. (306, 952)

**instantaneous rate**  The reaction rate at a particular time, given by the slope of a tangent to a plot of reactant concentration vs. time. (631)

**insulator**  A substance (usually a nonmetal) that does not conduct an electric current. (453)

**integrated rate law**  A mathematical expression for reactant concentration as a function of time. (642)

**intensive property**  A property, such as density, that does not depend on the quantity of substance present. (25)

**interhalogen compound**  A compound consisting entirely of halogens. (558)

**intermolecular forces** (also *interparticle forces*)  The attractive and repulsive forces among the particles—molecules, atoms, or ions—in a sample of matter. (419)

**internal energy (E)**  The sum of the kinetic and potential energies of all the particles in a system. (230)

**ion**  A charged particle that forms from an atom (or covalently bonded group of atoms) when it gains or loses one or more electrons. (55)

**ion-dipole force**  The intermolecular attractive force between an ion and a polar molecule (dipole). (432)

**ion exchange**  A process of softening water by exchanging one type of ion (usually $Ca^{2+}$) for another (usually $Na^+$) by binding the ions on a specially designed resin. (511)

**ion–induced dipole force**  The attractive force between an ion and the dipole it induces in the electron cloud of a nearby nonpolar molecule. (478)

**ion pair**  A pair of ions that form a gaseous ionic molecule; sometimes formed when a salt boils. (337)

**ion-product constant for water (Kw)**  The equilibrium constant for the autoionization of water; equal to $1.0 \times 10^{-14}$ at 298 K.

$$K_w = [H_3O^+][OH^-] \qquad (724)$$

**ionic atmosphere**  A cluster of ions of net opposite charge surrounding a given ion in solution. (506)

**ionic bonding**  The idealized type of bonding based on the attraction of oppositely charged ions that arise through electron transfer between atoms with large differences in their tendencies to lose or gain electrons (typically metals and nonmetals). (330)

**ionic compound**  A compound that consists of oppositely charged ions. (55)

**ionic radius**  The size of an ion as measured by the distance between the nuclei of adjacent ions in a crystalline ionic compound. (320)

**ionic solid** A solid whose unit cell contains cations and anions. (449)

**ionization** In nuclear chemistry, the process by which a substance absorbs energy from high-energy radioactive particles and loses an electron to become ionized. (995)

**ionization energy (IE)** The energy (in kJ) required to remove completely one mole of electrons from one mole of gaseous atoms or ions. (311)

**ionizing radiation** The high-energy radiation from natural and artificial sources that forms ions in a substance by causing electron loss. (995)

**isoelectronic** Having the same number and configuration of electrons as another species. (317)

**isomer** One of two or more compounds with the same molecular formula but different properties, often as a result of different arrangements of atoms. (97, 579, 957)

**isotopes** Atoms of a given atomic number (that is, of a specific element) that have different numbers of neutrons and therefore different mass numbers. (49, 978)

**isotopic mass** The mass (in amu) of an isotope relative to the mass of carbon-12. (50)

# J

**joule ( J)** The SI unit of energy; $1 \text{ J} = 1 \text{ kg} \cdot \text{m}^2/\text{s}^2$. (233)

# K

**kelvin (K)** The SI base unit of temperature. The kelvin is the same size as the Celsius degree. (23)

**Kelvin scale** (See *absolute scale*.)

**ketone** An organic compound (ending, *-one*) that contains a carbonyl group bonded to two other C atoms, $-\overset{|}{\underset{|}{C}}-\overset{:O:}{\underset{}{\overset{||}{C}}}-\overset{|}{\underset{|}{C}}-$. (597)

**kilogram (kg)** The SI base unit of mass. (20)

**kinetic energy ($E_k$)** The energy an object has because of its motion. (8)

**kinetic-molecular theory** The model that explains gas behavior in terms of particles in random motion whose volumes and interactions are negligible. (204)

# L

**lanthanide contraction** The additional decrease in atomic and ionic size, beyond the expected trend, caused by the poor shielding of the increasing nuclear charge by *f* electrons in the elements following the lanthanides. (949)

**lanthanides** (also *rare earths*) The Period 6 (4*f*) series of inner transition elements, which includes cerium (Ce; $Z = 58$) through lutetium (Lu; $Z = 71$). (306, 952)

**lattice** The three-dimensional arrangement of points created by choosing each point to be at the same location within each particle of a crystal; thus, the lattice consists of all points with identical surroundings. (442)

**lattice energy ($\Delta H^\circ_{\text{lattice}}$)** The enthalpy change (always positive) that accompanies the separation of 1 mol of a solid ionic compound into gaseous ions. (333)

**law** (See *natural law*.)

**law of chemical equilibrium** (also *law of mass action*) The law stating that when a system reaches equilibrium at a given temperature, the ratio of quantities that make up the reaction quotient has a constant numerical value. (680)

**law of conservation of energy** (also *first law of thermodynamics*) A basic observation that the total energy of the universe is constant; thus, $\Delta E_{\text{universe}} = \Delta E_{\text{system}} + \Delta E_{\text{surroundings}} = 0$. (233)

**law of definite (or constant) composition** A mass law stating that, no matter what its source, a particular compound is composed of the same elements in the same parts (fractions) by mass. (41)

**law of mass action** (See *law of chemical equilibrium*.)

**law of mass conservation** A mass law stating that the total mass of substances does not change during a chemical reaction. (40)

**law of multiple proportions** A mass law stating that if elements A and B react to form two or more compounds, the different masses of B that combine with a fixed mass of A can be expressed as a ratio of small whole numbers. (42)

**Le Châtelier's principle** A principle stating that if a system in a state of equilibrium is disturbed, it will undergo a change that shifts its equilibrium position in a direction that reduces the effect of the disturbance. (698)

**leaching** A hydrometallurgical process that extracts a metal selectively, usually through formation of a complex ion. (918)

**level** (also *shell*) A specific energy state of an atom given by the principal quantum number *n*. (282)

**leveling effect** The inability of a solvent to distinguish the strength of an acid (or base) that is stronger than the conjugate acid (or conjugate base) of the solvent. (750)

**Lewis acid-base definition** A model of acid-base behavior in which acids and bases are defined, respectively, as species that accept and donate an electron pair. (751)

**Lewis electron-dot symbol** A notation in which the element symbol represents the nucleus and inner electrons, and surrounding dots represent the valence electrons. (331)

**Lewis structure** (also *Lewis formula*) A structural formula consisting of electron-dot symbols, with lines as bonding pairs and dots as lone pairs. (363)

**ligand** A molecule or anion bonded to a central metal ion in a complex ion. (792, 953)

**like-dissolves-like rule** An empirical observation stating that substances having similar kinds of intermolecular forces dissolve in each other. (478)

**limiting reactant** (also *limiting reagent*) The reactant that is consumed when a reaction occurs and, therefore, the one that determines the maximum amount of product that can form. (107)

**line spectrum** A series of separated lines of different colors representing photons whose wavelengths are characteristic of an element. (267) (See also *emission spectrum*.)

**linear arrangement** The geometric arrangement obtained when two electron groups maximize their separation around a central atom. (374)

**linear shape** A molecular shape formed by three atoms lying in a straight line, with a bond angle of $180°$ (shape class $AX_2$ or $AX_2E_3$). (374)

**linkage isomers** Coordination compounds with the same composition but with different ligand donor atoms linked to the central metal ion. (957)

**lipid** Any of a class of biomolecules, including fats, that are soluble in nonpolar solvents and not soluble in water. (600)

**lipid bilayer** An extended sheetlike double layer of phospholipid molecules that forms in water and has the charged heads of the molecules on the surfaces of the bilayer and the nonpolar tails within the interior. (485)

**liquid** One of the three states of matter. A liquid fills a container to the extent of its own volume and thus forms a surface. (5)

**liquid crystal** A substance that flows like a liquid but packs like a crystalline solid at the molecular level. (456)

**liter (L)** A non-SI unit of volume equivalent to 1 cubic decimeter $(0.001\ m^3)$. (18)

**lithosphere** The solid portion of Earth's crust. (908)

**lock-and-key model** A model of enzyme function that pictures the enzyme active site and the substrate as rigid shapes that fit together as a lock and key, respectively. (663)

**London force** (See *dispersion force*.)

**lone pair** (also *unshared pair*) An electron pair that is part of an atom's valence level but not involved in covalent bonding. (339)

**low-spin complex** Complex ion that has fewer unpaired electrons than in the free metal ion because of the presence of strong-field ligands. (966)

## M

**macromolecule** (See *polymer*.)

**magnetic quantum number ($m_l$)** An integer from $-l$ through 0 to $+l$ that specifies the orientation of an atomic orbital in the three-dimensional space about the nucleus. (281)

**manometer** A device used to measure the pressure of a gas in a laboratory experiment. (184)

**mantle** A thick homogeneous layer of Earth's internal structure that lies between the core and the crust. (906)

**mass** The quantity of matter an object contains. Balances are designed to measure mass. (20)

**mass-action expression** (See *reaction quotient*.)

**mass fraction** (See *fraction by mass*.)

**mass number ($A$)** The total number of protons and neutrons in the nucleus of an atom. (49)

**mass percent** (also *mass %* or *percent by mass*) The fraction by mass expressed as a percentage. (41) A concentration term [% (w/w)] expressed as the mass of solute dissolved in 100. parts by mass of solution. (496)

**mass spectrometry** An instrumental method for measuring the relative masses of particles in a sample by creating charged particles and separating them according to their mass-charge ratio. (50)

**matter** Anything that possesses mass and occupies volume. (4)

**mean free path** The average distance a molecule travels between collisions at a given temperature and pressure. (211)

**melting** (also *fusion*) The change of a substance from a solid to a liquid. (420)

**melting point (mp or $T_f$)** The temperature at which the solid and liquid forms of a substance are at equilibrium. (429)

**metabolic pathway** A biochemical reaction sequence that flows in one direction and has each reaction enzyme catalyzed. (708)

**metal** A substance or mixture that is relatively shiny and malleable and is a good conductor of heat and electricity. In reactions, metals tend to transfer electrons to nonmetals and form ionic compounds. (54)

**metallic bonding** An idealized type of bonding based on the attraction between metal ions and their delocalized valence electrons. (331) (See also *electron-sea model*.)

**metallic radius** One-half the shortest distance between the nuclei of adjacent individual atoms in a crystal of an element. (308)

**metallic solid** A solid whose individual atoms are held together by metallic bonding. (451)

**metalloid** (also *semimetal*) An element with properties between those of metals and nonmetals. (54)

**metallurgy** The branch of materials science concerned with the extraction and utilization of metals. (917)

**metathesis reaction** (also *double-displacement reaction*) A reaction in which atoms or ions of two compounds exchange bonding partners. (143)

**meter (m)** The SI base unit of length. The distance light travels in a vacuum in 1/299,792,458 second. (18)

**methanogenesis** The process of producing methane by anaerobic biodegradation of plant and animal waste. (249)

**milliliter (mL)** A volume (0.001 L) equivalent to 1 $cm^3$. (18)

**millimeter of mercury (mmHg)** A unit of pressure based on the difference in the heights of mercury in a barometer or manometer. Renamed the *torr* in honor of Torricelli. (185)

**mineral** The portion of an ore that contains the element of interest, a mineral is a naturally occurring, homogeneous, crystalline inorganic solid, with a well-defined composition. (917)

**miscible** Soluble in any proportion. (478)

**mixture** A group of two or more elements and/or compounds that are physically intermingled. (39)

**MO bond order** One-half the difference between the number of electrons in bonding and antibonding MOs. (407)

**model** (also *theory*) A simplified conceptual picture based on experiment that explains how a natural phenomenon occurs. (12)

**molality ($m$)** A concentration term expressed as number of moles of solute dissolved in 1000 g (1 kg) of solvent. (495)

**molar heat capacity ($C$)** The quantity of heat required to change the temperature of 1 mol of a substance by 1 K. (238)

**molar mass ($\mathcal{M}$)** The mass of 1 mol of entities (atoms, molecules, or formula units) of a substance, in units of g/mol. (84)

**molarity ($M$)** A concentration term expressed as the moles of solute dissolved in 1 L of solution. (114)

**mole (mol)** The SI base unit for amount of a substance. The amount that contains a number of objects equal to the number of atoms in exactly 12 g of carbon-12 (which is $6.022\times10^{23}$). (83)

**mole fraction ($X$)** A concentration term expressed as the ratio of moles of one component of a mixture to the total moles present. (200, 496)

**molecular equation** A chemical equation showing a reaction in solution in which reactants and products appear as intact, undissociated compounds. (140)

**molecular formula** A formula that shows the actual number of atoms of each element in a molecule of a compound. (68, 92)

**molecular mass** (also *molecular weight*) The sum (in amu) of the atomic masses of the elements in a molecule (or formula unit) of a compound. (66)

**molecular orbital (MO)** An orbital of given energy and shape that extends over a molecule and can be occupied by no more than two paired electrons. (405)

**molecular orbital (MO) diagram** A depiction of the relative energy and number of electrons in each MO, as well as the atomic orbitals from which the MOs form. (406)

**molecular orbital (MO) theory** A model that describes a molecule as a collection of nuclei and electrons in which the electrons occupy orbitals that extend over the entire molecule. (405)

**molecular polarity** The overall distribution of electronic charge in a molecule, determined by its shape and bond polarities. (383)

**molecular shape** The three-dimensional structure defined by the relative positions of the atomic nuclei in a molecule. (373)

**molecular solid** A solid held together by intermolecular forces between individual molecules. (449)

**molecular weight** (See *molecular mass*.)

**molecularity** The number of reactant particles involved in an elementary step. (655)

**molecule** A structure consisting of two or more atoms that are bound chemically and behave as an independent unit. (38)

**monatomic ion** An ion derived from a single atom. (55)

**monomer** A small molecule, linked covalently to others of the same or similar type to form a polymer; the repeat unit of the polymer. (461)

**mononucleotide** A monomer unit of a nucleic acid, consisting of an N-containing base, a sugar, and a phosphate group. (487, 611)

**monosaccharide** A simple sugar; a polyhydroxy ketone or aldehyde with three to nine C atoms. (607)

## N

**nanotechnology** The science and engineering of nanoscale (1–100 nm) systems. (466)

**natural law** (also *law*) A summary, often in mathematical form, of a universal observation. (12)

**Nernst equation** An equation stating that the voltage of an electrochemical cell under any conditions depends on the standard cell voltage and the concentrations of the cell components:

$$E_{cell} = E^\circ_{cell} - \frac{RT}{nF} \ln Q \qquad (872)$$

**net ionic equation** A chemical equation of a reaction in solution in which spectator ions have been eliminated to show the actual chemical change. (141)

**network covalent solid** A solid in which all the atoms are bonded covalently so that individual molecules are not present. (451)

**neutralization** Process that occurs when an $H^+$ ion from an acid combines with an $OH^-$ ion from a base to form $H_2O$. (720)

**neutralization reaction** An acid-base reaction that yields water and a solution of a salt; when the $H^+$ ions of a strong acid react with an equivalent amount of the $OH^-$ ions of a strong base, the solution is neutral. (145)

**neutron ($n^0$)** An uncharged subatomic particle found in the nucleus, with a mass slightly greater than that of a proton. (48)

**nitrile** An organic compound containing the $-C\equiv N:$ group. (603)

**node** A region of an orbital where the probability of finding the electron is zero. (285)

**nonbonding MO** A molecular orbital that is not involved in bonding. (412)

**nonelectrolyte** A substance whose aqueous solution does not conduct an electric current. (139, 499)

**nonmetal** An element that lacks metallic properties. In reactions, nonmetals tend to share electrons with each other to form covalent compounds or accept electrons from metals to form ionic compounds. (54)

**nonpolar covalent bond** A covalent bond between identical atoms such that the bonding pair is shared equally. (351)

**nuclear binding energy** The energy required to break 1 mole of nuclei of an element into individual nucleons. (1004)

**nuclear magnetic resonance (NMR) spectroscopy** An instrumental technique used to determine the molecular environment of a given type of nucleus, most often $^1H$, from its absorption of radio waves in a magnetic field. (586)

**nuclear transmutation** The induced conversion of one nucleus into another by bombardment with a particle. (992)

**nucleic acid** An unbranched polymer consisting of mononucleotides that occurs as two types, DNA and RNA (deoxyribonucleic and ribonucleic acids), which differ chemically in the nature of the sugar portion of the mononucleotides. (487, 611)

**nucleon** A subatomic particle found in the nucleus; a proton or neutron. (978)

**nucleus** The tiny central region of the atom that contains all the positive charge and essentially all the mass. (47)

**nuclide** A nuclear species with specified numbers of protons and neutrons. (978)

## O

**observation** A fact obtained with the senses, often with the aid of instruments. Quantitative observations provide data that can be compared. (12)

**occurrence** (also *source*) The form(s) in which an element exists in nature. (909)

**octahedral arrangement** The geometric arrangement obtained when six electron groups maximize their space around a central atom; when all six groups are bonding groups, the molecular shape is octahedral ($AX_6$; ideal bond angle = 90°). (378)

**octet rule** The observation that when atoms bond, they often lose, gain, or share electrons to attain a filled outer level of eight electrons (or two for H and Li). (331)

**optical isomers** (also *enantiomers*) A pair of stereoisomers consisting of a molecule and its mirror image that cannot be superimposed on each other. (580, 959)

**optically active** Able to rotate the plane of polarized light. (581)

**orbital diagram** A depiction of orbital occupancy in terms of electron number and spin shown by means of arrows in a series of small boxes, lines, or circles. (299)

**ore** A naturally occurring compound or mixture of compounds from which an element can be profitably extracted. (909)

**organic compound** A compound in which carbon is nearly always bonded to itself and to hydrogen, and often to other elements. (571)

**organometallic compound** An organic compound in which carbon has a polar covalent bond to a metal atom. (598)

**osmosis** The process by which solvent flows through a semipermeable membrane from a dilute to a concentrated solution. (503)

**osmotic pressure ($\Pi$)** The pressure that results from the ability of solvent, but not solute, particles to cross a semipermeable membrane. The pressure required to prevent the net movement of solvent across the membrane. (503)

**outer electrons** Electrons that occupy the highest energy level (highest $n$ value) and are, on average, farthest from the nucleus. (306)

**overall (net) equation** A chemical equation that is the sum of two or more balanced sequential equations in which a product of one becomes a reactant for the next. (106)

**overvoltage** The additional voltage, usually associated with gaseous products forming at an electrode, that is required above the standard cell voltage to accomplish electrolysis. (888)

**oxidation** The loss of electrons by a species, accompanied by an increase in oxidation number. (154)

**oxidation number (O.N.)** (also *oxidation state*)   A number equal to the magnitude of the charge an atom would have if its shared electrons were held completely by the atom that attracts them more strongly. (155)

**oxidation number method**   A method for balancing redox reactions in which the change in oxidation numbers is used to determine balancing coefficients. (158)

**oxidation-reduction reaction** (also *redox reaction*)   A process in which there is a net movement of electrons from one reactant (reducing agent) to another (oxidizing agent). (153)

**oxidation state**   (See *oxidation number.*)

**oxidizing agent**   The substance that accepts electrons in a reaction and undergoes a decrease in oxidation number. (154)

**oxoanion**   An anion in which an element is bonded to one or more oxygen atoms. (63)

# P

**p orbital**   An atomic orbital with $l = 1$. (285)

**packing efficiency**   The percentage of the available volume occupied by atoms, ions, or molecules in a unit cell. (444)

**paramagnetism**   The tendency of a species with unpaired electrons to be attracted by an external magnetic field. (319)

**partial ionic character**   An estimate of the actual charge separation in a bond (caused by the electronegativity difference of the bonded atoms) relative to complete separation. (351)

**partial pressure**   The portion of the total pressure contributed by a gas in a mixture of gases. (199)

**particle accelerator**   A device used to impart high kinetic energies to nuclear particles. (993)

**pascal (Pa)**   The SI unit of pressure; $1\ Pa = 1\ N/m^2$. (185)

**penetration**   The process by which an outer electron moves through the region occupied by the core electrons to spend part of its time closer to the nucleus; penetration increases the average effective nuclear charge for that electron. (298)

**percent by mass (mass %)**   (See *mass percent.*)

**percent yield (% yield)**   The actual yield of a reaction expressed as a percentage of the theoretical yield. (112)

**period**   A horizontal row of the periodic table. (53)

**periodic law**   A law stating that when the elements are arranged by atomic number, they exhibit a periodic recurrence of properties. (295)

**periodic table of the elements**   A table in which the elements are arranged by atomic number into columns (groups) and rows (periods). (53)

**pH**   The negative common logarithm of $[H_3O^+]$. (726)

**phase**   A physically distinct and homogeneous part of a system. (419)

**phase change**   A physical change from one phase to another, usually referring to a change in physical state. (420)

**phase diagram**   A diagram used to describe the stable phases and phase changes of a substance as a function of temperature and pressure. (429)

**photoelectric effect**   The observation that when monochromatic light of sufficient frequency shines on a metal, an electric current is produced. (266)

**photon**   A quantum of electromagnetic radiation. (266)

**photovoltaic cell**   A device capable of converting light directly into electricity. (251)

**physical change**   A change in which the physical form (or state) of a substance, but not its composition, is altered. (4)

**physical property**   A characteristic shown by a substance itself, without interacting with or changing into other substances. (4)

**pi ($\pi$) bond**   A covalent bond formed by sideways overlap of two atomic orbitals that has two regions of electron density, one above and one below the internuclear axis. (403)

**pi ($\pi$) MO**   A molecular orbital formed by combination of two atomic (usually *p*) orbitals whose orientations are perpendicular to the internuclear axis. (408)

**Planck's constant ($h$)**   A proportionality constant relating the energy and frequency of a photon, equal to $6.626 \times 10^{-34}$ J·s. (266)

**plastic**   A material that, when deformed, retains its new shape. (465)

**polar covalent bond**   A covalent bond in which the electron pair is shared unequally, so the bond has partially negative and partially positive poles. (351)

**polar molecule**   A molecule with an unequal distribution of charge as a result of its polar bonds and shape. (136)

**polarimeter**   A device used to measure the rotation of plane-polarized light by an optically active compound. (581)

**polarizability**   The ease with which a particle's electron cloud can be distorted. (434)

**polyatomic ion**   An ion in which two or more atoms are bonded covalently. (59)

**polymer** (also *macromolecule*)   An extremely large molecule that results from the covalent linking of many simpler molecular units (monomers). (461)

**polyprotic acid**   An acid with more than one ionizable proton. (737)

**polysaccharide**   A macromolecule composed of many simple sugars linked covalently. (607)

**positron ($\beta^+$)**   The antiparticle of an electron. (981)

**positron emission**   A type of radioactive decay in which a positron is emitted from a nucleus. (981)

**potential energy ($E_p$)**   The energy an object has as a result of its position relative to other objects or because of its composition. (8)

**precipitate**   The insoluble product of a precipitation reaction. (141)

**precipitation reaction**   A reaction in which two soluble ionic compounds form an insoluble product, a precipitate. (141)

**precision** (also *reproducibility*)   The closeness of a measurement to other measurements of the same phenomenon in a series of experiments. (28)

**pressure ($P$)**   The force exerted per unit of surface area. (183)

**pressure-volume work ($PV$ work)**   A type of work in which a volume change occurs against an external pressure. (235)

**principal quantum number ($n$)**   A positive integer that specifies the energy and relative size of an atomic orbital; a number that specifies an energy level in an atom. (281)

**probability contour**   A shape that defines the volume around an atomic nucleus within which an electron spends a given percentage of its time. (281)

**product**   A substance formed in a chemical reaction. (99)

**property**   A characteristic that gives a substance its unique identity. (4)

**protein**   A natural, linear polymer composed of any of about 20 types of amino acid monomers linked together by peptide bonds. (483, 608)

**proton ($p^+$)** A subatomic particle found in the nucleus that has a unit positive charge ($1.60218 \times 10^{-19}$ C). (48)

**proton acceptor** A substance that accepts an $H^+$ ion; a Brønsted-Lowry base. (729)

**proton donor** A substance that donates an $H^+$ ion; a Brønsted-Lowry acid. (729)

**pseudo–noble gas configuration** The $(n-1)d^{10}$ configuration of a $p$-block metal ion that has an empty outer energy level. (317)

## Q

**quantum** A packet of energy equal to $h\nu$. The smallest quantity of energy that can be emitted or absorbed. (266)

**quantum mechanics** The branch of physics that examines the wave motion of objects on the atomic scale. (279)

**quantum number** A number that specifies a property of an orbital or an electron. (266)

## R

**rad (radiation-absorbed dose)** The quantity of radiation that results in 0.01 J of energy being absorbed per kilogram of tissue; 1 rad = 0.01 J/kg tissue = $10^{-2}$ Gy. (996)

**radial probability distribution plot** The graphic depiction of the total probability distribution (sum of $\psi^2$) of an electron in the region near the nucleus. (280)

**radioactivity** The emissions resulting from the spontaneous disintegration of an unstable nucleus. (977)

**radioisotope** An isotope with an unstable nucleus that decays through radioactive emissions. (990)

**radioisotopic dating** A method for determining the age of an object based on the rate of decay of a particular radioactive nuclide relative to a stable nuclide. (990)

**radius of gyration ($R_g$)** A measure of the size of a coiled polymer chain, expressed as the average distance from the center of mass of the chain to its outside edge. (463)

**random coil** The shape adopted by most polymer chains and caused by random rotation about the bonds joining the repeat units. (462)

**random error** Error that occurs in all measurements (with its size depending on the measurer's skill and the instrument's precision) and results in values *both* higher and lower than the actual value. (29)

**Raoult's law** A law stating that the vapor pressure of solvent above a solution equals the mole fraction of solvent times the vapor pressure of pure solvent: $P_{solvent} = X_{solvent} \times P^{\circ}_{solvent}$. (500)

**rare earths** (See *lanthanides*.)

**rate constant ($k$)** The proportionality constant that relates reaction rate to reactant (and product) concentrations. (634)

**rate-determining step** (also *rate-limiting step*) The slowest step in a reaction mechanism and therefore the step that limits the overall rate. (656)

**rate law** (also *rate equation*) An equation that expresses the rate of a reaction as a function of reactant (and product) concentrations. (634)

**reactant** A starting substance in a chemical reaction. (99)

**reaction energy diagram** A graph that shows the potential energy of a reacting system as it progresses from reactants to products. (652)

**reaction intermediate** A substance that is formed and used up during the overall reaction and therefore does not appear in the overall equation. (657)

**reaction mechanism** A series of elementary steps that sum to the overall reaction and is consistent with the rate law. (655)

**reaction order** The exponent of a reactant concentration in a rate law that shows how the rate is affected by changes in that concentration. (634)

**reaction quotient ($Q$)** (also *mass-action expression*) A ratio of terms for a given reaction consisting of product concentrations multiplied together and divided by reactant concentrations multiplied together, each raised to the power of their balancing coefficient. The value of $Q$ changes until the system reaches equilibrium, at which point it equals $K$. (680)

**reaction rate** The change in the concentrations of reactants (or products) with time. (627)

**reactor core** The part of a nuclear reactor that contains the fuel rods and generates heat from fission. (1008)

**redox reaction** (See *oxidation-reduction reaction.*)

**reducing agent** The substance that donates electrons in a redox reaction and undergoes an increase in oxidation number. (154)

**reduction** The gain of electrons by a species, accompanied by a decrease in oxidation number. (154)

**refraction** A phenomenon in which a wave changes its speed and therefore its direction as it passes through a phase boundary into a different medium. (263)

**rem (roentgen equivalent for man)** The unit of radiation dosage for a human based on the product of the number of rads and a factor related to the biological tissue; 1 rem = $10^{-2}$ Sv. (996)

**reproducibility** (See *precision.*)

**resonance hybrid** The weighted average of the resonance structures of a molecule. (367)

**resonance structure** (also *resonance form*) One of two or more Lewis structures for a molecule that cannot be adequately depicted by a single structure. Resonance structures differ only in the position of bonding and lone electron pairs. (367)

**reverse osmosis** A process for preparing drinkable water that uses an applied pressure greater than the osmotic pressure to remove ions from an aqueous solution, typically seawater. (511)

**rms (root-mean-square) speed ($u_{rms}$)** The speed of a molecule having the average kinetic energy; very close to the most probable speed. (209)

**roasting** A pyrometallurgical process in which metal sulfides are converted to oxides. (918)

**round off** The process of removing digits based on a series of rules to obtain an answer with the proper number of significant figures (or decimal places). (27)

## S

**s orbital** An atomic orbital with $l = 0$. (284)

**salt** An ionic compound that results from an Arrhenius acid-base reaction after solvent is removed. (148)

**salt bridge** An inverted U tube containing a solution of a nonreacting electrolyte that connects the compartments of a voltaic cell and maintains neutrality by allowing ions to flow between compartments. (859)

**saturated hydrocarbon** A hydrocarbon in which each C is bonded to four other atoms. (576)

**saturated solution** A solution that contains the maximum amount of dissolved solute at a given temperature (prepared with undissolved solute present). (492)

**scanning tunneling microscopy** An instrumental technique that uses electrons moving across a minute gap to observe the topography of a surface on the atomic scale. (447)

**Schrödinger equation** An equation that describes how the electron matter-wave changes in space around the nucleus. Solutions of the equation provide allowable energy levels of the atom. (279)

**scientific method** A process of creative thinking and testing aimed at objective, verifiable discoveries of the causes of natural events. (12)

**scintillation counter** A device used to measure radioactivity through its excitation of atoms and their subsequent emission of light. (987)

**screening** (See *shielding.*)

**second (s)** The SI base unit of time. (25)

**second law of thermodynamics** A law stating that a process occurs spontaneously in the direction that increases the entropy of the universe. (817)

**seesaw shape** A molecular shape caused by the presence of one equatorial lone pair in a trigonal bipyramidal arrangement ($AX_4E$). (377)

**selective precipitation** The process of separating ions through differences in the solubility of their compounds with a given precipitating ion. (791)

**self-ionization** (See *autoionization.*)

**semiconductor** A substance whose electrical conductivity is poor at room temperature but increases significantly with rising temperature. (453)

**semimetal** (See *metalloid.*)

**semipermeable membrane** A membrane that allows solvent, but not solute, to pass through. (503)

**shared pair** (See *bonding pair.*)

**shell** (See *level.*)

**shielding** (also *screening*) The ability of other electrons, especially those occupying inner orbitals, to lessen the nuclear attraction for an outer electron. (297)

**SI unit** A unit composed of one or more of the base units of the Système International d'Unités, a revised metric system. (17)

**side reaction** An undesired chemical reaction that consumes some of the reactant and reduces the overall yield of the desired product. (112)

**sievert (Sv)** The SI unit of human radiation dosage; 1 Sv = 100 rem. (996)

**sigma ($\sigma$) bond** A type of covalent bond that arises through end-to-end orbital overlap and has most of its electron density along an imaginary line joining the nuclei. (403)

**sigma ($\sigma$) MO** A molecular orbital that is cylindrically symmetrical about an imaginary line that runs through the nuclei of the component atoms. (406)

**significant figures** The digits obtained in a measurement. The greater the number of significant figures, the greater the certainty of the measurement. (25)

**silicate** A type of compound found throughout rocks and soil and consisting of repeating —Si—O groupings and, in most cases, metal cations. (542)

**silicone** A type of synthetic polymer containing —Si—O repeat units, with organic groups and crosslinks. (542)

**simple cubic unit cell** A unit cell in which a particle occupies each corner of a cube. (442)

**single bond** A bond that consists of one electron pair. (339)

**slag** A molten waste product formed in a blast furnace by the reaction of acidic silica with a basic metal oxide. (925)

**smelting** Heating a mineral with a reducing agent, such as coke, to obtain a metal. (919)

**soap** The salt formed in a reaction between a fatty acid and a strong base, usually a Group 1A(1) or 2A(2) hydroxide. (485)

**solid** One of the three states of matter. A solid has a fixed shape that does not conform to the container shape. (5)

**solubility ($S$)** The maximum amount of solute that dissolves in a fixed quantity of a particular solvent at a specified temperature. (478)

**solubility-product constant ($K_{sp}$)** An equilibrium constant for a slightly soluble ionic compound dissolving in water. (783)

**solute** The substance that dissolves in the solvent. (114, 478)

**solution** (See *homogeneous mixture.*)

**solvated** Surrounded closely by solvent molecules. (136)

**solvation** The process of surrounding a solute particle with solvent particles. (489)

**solvent** The substance in which the solute(s) dissolve. (114, 478)

**source** (See *occurrence.*)

**$sp$ hybrid orbital** An orbital formed by the mixing of one $s$ and one $p$ orbital of a central atom. (396)

**$sp^2$ hybrid orbital** An orbital formed by the mixing of one $s$ and two $p$ orbitals of a central atom. (398)

**$sp^3$ hybrid orbital** An orbital formed by the mixing of one $s$ and three $p$ orbitals of a central atom. (398)

**$sp^3d$ hybrid orbital** An orbital formed by the mixing of one $s$, three $p$, and one $d$ orbital of a central atom. (399)

**$sp^3d^2$ hybrid orbital** An orbital formed by the mixing of one $s$, three $p$, and two $d$ orbitals of a central atom. (400)

**specific heat capacity ($c$)** The quantity of heat required to change the temperature of 1 gram of a material by 1 K. (238)

**spectator ion** An ion that is present as part of a reactant but is not involved in the chemical change. (141)

**spectrochemical series** A ranking of ligands in terms of their ability to split $d$-orbital energies. (965)

**spectrometry** Any instrumental technique that uses a portion of the electromagnetic spectrum to measure the atomic and molecular energy levels of a substance. (273)

**speed of light ($c$)** A fundamental constant giving the speed at which electromagnetic radiation travels in a vacuum: $c = 2.99792458 \times 10^8$ m/s. (262)

**spin quantum number ($m_s$)** A number, either $+\frac{1}{2}$ or $-\frac{1}{2}$, that indicates the direction of electron spin. (296)

**spontaneous change** A change that occurs by itself, that is, without an ongoing input of external energy. (811)

**square planar shape** A molecular shape ($AX_4E_2$) caused by the presence of two lone pairs at opposite vertices in an octahedral arrangement. (378)

**square pyramidal shape** A molecular shape ($AX_5E$) caused by the presence of one lone pair in an octahedral arrangement. (378)

**standard atmosphere (atm)** The average atmospheric pressure measured at sea level and 0°C, defined as $1.01325 \times 10^5$ Pa. (185)

**standard cell potential ($E^\circ_{cell}$)** The potential of a cell measured with all components in their standard states and no current flowing. (862)

**standard electrode potential ($E^\circ_{half-cell}$)** (also *standard half-cell potential*) The standard potential of a half-cell, with the half-reaction written as a reduction. (862)

**standard enthalpy of formation ($\Delta H^\circ_f$)** (also *standard heat of formation*) The enthalpy change occurring when 1 mol of a compound forms from its elements with all components in their standard states. (246)

**standard enthalpy of reaction ($\Delta H^\circ_{rxn}$)** (also *standard heat of reaction*) The enthalpy change that occurs during a reaction when all components are in their standard states. (246)

**standard entropy of reaction ($\Delta S^\circ_{rxn}$)** The entropy change that occurs when all components are in their standard states. (822)

**standard free energy change ($\Delta G^\circ$)** The free energy change that occurs when all components are in their standard states. (828)

**standard free energy of formation ($\Delta G^\circ_f$)** The standard free energy change that occurs when 1 mol of a compound is made from its elements with all components in their standard states. (829)

**standard half-cell potential** (See *standard electrode potential.*)

**standard heat of formation** (See *standard enthalpy of formation.*)

**standard heat of reaction** (See *standard enthalpy of reaction.*)

**standard hydrogen electrode** (See *standard reference half-cell.*)

**standard molar entropy ($S^\circ$)** The entropy of 1 mol of a substance in its standard state. (817)

**standard molar volume** The volume of 1 mol of an ideal gas at standard temperature and pressure: 22.4141 L. (190)

**standard reference half-cell** (also *standard hydrogen electrode*) A specially prepared platinum electrode immersed in 1 $M$ H$^+$($aq$) through which H$_2$ gas at 1 atm is bubbled. $E^\circ_{half-cell}$ is defined as 0 V. (863)

**standard state** A set of specifications used to compare thermodynamic data: 1 atm for gases behaving ideally, 1 $M$ for dissolved species, or the pure substance for liquids and solids. (246)

**standard temperature and pressure (STP)** The reference conditions for a gas:

$$0°C\ (273.15\ K)\ \text{and}\ 1\ atm\ (760\ torr) \qquad (190)$$

**state function** A property of the system determined by its current state, regardless of how it arrived at that state. (234)

**state of matter** One of the three physical forms of matter: solid, liquid, or gas. (5)

**stationary state** In the Bohr model, one of the allowable energy levels of the atom in which it does not release or absorb energy. (269)

**steel** An alloy of iron with small amounts of carbon and usually other metals. (924)

**stellar nucleosynthesis** The process by which elements are formed in the stars through nuclear fusion. (1012)

**stereoisomers** Molecules with the same connections of atoms but different orientations of groups in space. (580, 958) (See also *geometric isomers* and *optical isomers.*)

**stoichiometric coefficient** (See *balancing coefficient.*)

**stoichiometry** The study of the mass-mole-number relationships of chemical formulas and reactions. (83)

**strong-field ligand** A ligand that causes larger crystal field splitting energy and therefore is part of a low-spin complex. (964)

**strong force** An attractive force that exists between all nucleons and is many times stronger than the electrostatic repulsive force. (984)

**structural formula** A formula that shows the actual number of atoms, their relative placement, and the bonds between them. (68, 92)

**structural isomers** (See *constitutional isomers.*)

**sublevel** (also *subshell*) An energy substate of an atom within a level. Given by the $n$ and $l$ values, the sublevel designates the size and shape of the atomic orbitals. (282)

**sublimation** The process by which a solid changes directly into a gas. (421)

**substance** A type of matter, either an element or a compound, that has a fixed composition. (38)

**substitution reaction** An organic reaction that occurs when an atom (or group) from one reactant substitutes for one in another reactant. (589)

**substrate** A reactant that binds to the active site in an enzyme-catalyzed reaction. (662)

**superconductivity** The ability to conduct a current with no loss of energy to resistive heating. (454)

**supersaturated solution** An unstable solution in which more solute is dissolved than in a saturated solution. (492)

**surface tension** The energy required to increase the surface area of a liquid by a given amount. (437)

**surroundings** All parts of the universe other than the system being considered. (230)

**suspension** A heterogeneous mixture containing particles that are distinct from the surrounding medium. (508)

**synthetic natural gas (SNG)** A gaseous fuel mixture, mostly methane, formed from coal. (249)

**system** The defined part of the universe under study. (230)

**systematic error** A type of error producing values that are all either higher or lower than the actual value, often caused by faulty equipment or a consistent flaw in technique. (29)

# T

**$t_{2g}$ orbitals** The set of orbitals (composed of $d_{xy}$, $d_{yz}$, and $d_{xz}$) that results when the energies of the metal-ion $d$ orbitals are split by a ligand field. This set is lower in energy than the other ($e_g$) set in an octahedral field and higher in energy in a tetrahedral field. (964)

**T shape** A molecular shape caused by the presence of two equatorial lone pairs in a trigonal bipyramidal arrangement (AX$_3$E$_2$). (377)

**temperature ($T$)** A measure of how hot or cold a substance is relative to another substance. (23) A measure of the average kinetic energy of the particles in a sample. (208)

**tetrahedral arrangement** The geometric arrangement formed when four electron groups maximize their separation around a central atom; when all four groups are bonding groups, the molecular shape is tetrahedral (AX$_4$; ideal bond angle 109.5°). (375)

**theoretical yield** The amount of product predicted by the stoichiometrically equivalent molar ratio in the balanced equation. (112)

**theory** (See *model.*)

**thermochemical equation** A chemical equation that shows the heat involved for the amounts of substances specified. (242)

**thermochemistry** The branch of thermodynamics that focuses on the heat involved in chemical and physical change. (229)

**thermodynamics** The study of heat (thermal energy) and its interconversions. (229)

**thermometer** A device for measuring temperature that contains a fluid that expands or contracts within a graduated tube. (23)

**third law of thermodynamics** A law stating that the entropy of a perfect crystal is zero at 0 K. (817)

**titration** A method of determining the concentration of a solution by monitoring relative amounts during its reaction with a solution of known concentration. (152)

**torr** A unit of pressure identical to 1 mmHg. (185)

**total ionic equation** An equation for an aqueous reaction that shows all the soluble ionic substances dissociated into ions. (141)

**tracer** A radioisotope that signals the presence of the species of interest by radioactive emissions. (1000)

**transcription** The process of producing messenger RNA from DNA. (614)

**transition element** An element that occupies the *d* block of the periodic table; one whose *d* orbitals are being filled. (303, 945)

**transition state** (also *activated complex*) An unstable species formed in an effective collision of reactants that exists momentarily when the system is highest in energy and that can either form products or re-form reactants. (652)

**transition state theory** A model that explains how the energy of reactant collisions is used to form a high-energy transitional species that can change to reactant or product. (652)

**translation** The process by which messenger RNA specifies the sequence of amino acids and synthesizes proteins. (614)

**transuranium element** An element with atomic number higher than that of uranium (Z = 92). (994)

**trigonal bipyramidal arrangement** The geometric arrangement formed when five electron groups maximize their separation around a central atom. When all five groups are bonding groups, the molecular shape is trigonal bipyramidal ($AX_5$; ideal bond angles, axial-center-equatorial 90° and equatorial-center-equatorial 120°). (376)

**trigonal planar arrangement** The geometric arrangement formed when three electron groups maximize their separation around a central atom. When all three groups are bonding groups, the molecular shape is trigonal planar ($AX_3$; ideal bond angle 120°). (374)

**trigonal pyramidal shape** A molecular shape ($AX_3E$) caused by the presence of one lone pair in a tetrahedral arrangement. (376)

**triple bond** A covalent bond that consists of three bonding pairs, two atoms sharing six electrons; one σ and two π bonds. (339)

**triple point** The pressure and temperature at which three phases of a substance are in equilibrium. In a phase diagram, the point at which three phase-transition curves meet. (429)

**Tyndall effect** The scattering of light by a colloid. (509)

## U

**ultraviolet (UV)** Radiation in the region of the electromagnetic spectrum between the visible and the x-ray regions. (262)

**uncertainty** A characteristic of every measurement that results from the inexactness of the measuring device and the need to estimate when taking a reading. (25)

**uncertainty principle** The principle stated by Werner Heisenberg that it is impossible to know simultaneously the exact position and velocity of a particle; the principle becomes important only for particles of very small mass. (278)

**unimolecular reaction** An elementary reaction that involves the decomposition or rearrangement of a single particle. (655)

**unit cell** The smallest portion of a crystal that, if repeated in all three directions, gives the crystal. (442)

**universal gas constant ($R$)** A proportionality constant that relates the energy, amount of substance, and temperature of a system; $R = 0.0820578$ atm·L/mol·K = 8.31447 J/mol·K. (191)

**unsaturated hydrocarbon** A hydrocarbon with at least one carbon-carbon multiple bond; one in which at least two C atoms are bonded to fewer than four atoms. (582)

**unsaturated solution** A solution in which more solute can be dissolved at a given temperature. (492)

**unshared pair** (See *lone pair.*)

## V

**V shape** (See *bent shape.*)

**valence band** In band theory, the lower energy portion of the band of molecular orbitals, which is filled with valence electrons. (453)

**valence bond (VB) theory** A model that attempts to reconcile the shapes of molecules with those of atomic orbitals through the concepts of orbital overlap and hybridization. (395)

**valence electrons** The electrons involved in compound formation; in main-group elements, the electrons in the valence (outer) level. (306)

**valence-shell electron-pair repulsion (VSEPR) theory** A model explaining that the shapes of molecules and ions result from minimizing electron-pair repulsions around a central atom. (373)

**van der Waals constants** Experimentally determined positive numbers used in the van der Waals equation to account for the intermolecular attractions and molecular volume of real gases. (216)

**van der Waals equation** An equation that accounts for the behavior of real gases. (216)

**van der Waals radius** One-half of the shortest distance between the nuclei of identical nonbonded atoms. (431)

**vapor pressure** (also *equilibrium vapor pressure*) The pressure exerted by a vapor at equilibrium with its liquid in a closed system. (426)

**vapor pressure lowering ($\Delta P$)** The lowering of the vapor pressure of a solvent caused by the presence of dissolved solute particles. (499)

**vaporization** The process of changing from a liquid to a gas. (420)

**variable** A quantity that can have more than a single value. (12) (See also *controlled experiment.*)

**viscosity** A measure of the resistance of a liquid to flow. (439)

**volatility** The tendency of a substance to become a gas. (72)

**volt (V)** The SI unit of electric potential: 1 V = 1 J/C. (862)

**voltage** (See *cell potential.*)

**voltaic cell** (also *galvanic cell*) An electrochemical cell that uses a spontaneous redox reaction to generate electric energy. (855)

**volume ($V$)** The space occupied by a sample of matter. (18)

**volume percent [% (v/v)]** A concentration term defined as the volume of solute in 100. volumes of solution. (496)

## W

**wastewater** Used water, usually containing industrial and/or residential waste, that is treated before being returned to the environment. (511)

**water softening** The process of replacing the hard-water ions $Ca^{2+}$ and $Mg^{2+}$ with $Na^+$ ions. (510)

**wave function**   (See *atomic orbital*.)

**wave-particle duality**   The principle stating that both matter and energy have wavelike and particle-like properties. (277)

**wavelength ($\lambda$)**   The distance between any point on a wave and the corresponding point on the next wave, that is, the distance a wave travels during one cycle. (262)

**weak-field ligand**   A ligand that causes smaller crystal field splitting energy and therefore is part of a high-spin complex. (964)

**weight**   The force exerted by a gravitational field on an object that is directly proportional to its mass. (20)

**work ($w$)**   The energy transferred when an object is moved by a force. (231)

## X

**x-ray diffraction analysis**   An instrumental technique used to determine dimensions of a crystal structure by measuring the diffraction patterns caused by x-rays impinging on the crystal. (447)

## Z

**zone refining**   A process used to purify metals and metalloids in which impurities are removed from a bar of the element by concentrating them in a thin molten zone. (921)

## Chapter 1

Opener: © The McGraw-Hill Companies, Inc./John Thoeming Photographer; 1.1A: © Paul Morrell/Stone/Getty Images; 1.1B: © The McGraw-Hill Companies, Inc./Stephen Frisch Photographer; Table 1.1A: © The McGraw-Hill Companies, Inc./Stephen Frisch Photographer; Table 1.1B: © Ruth Melnick; Table 1.1C-E: © The McGraw-Hill Companies, Inc./Stephen Frisch Photographer; p. 7: Gallileo Project, SSI, University of Arizona; 1.4: © SSPL/The Image Works; 1.5A: © George Haling/Photo Researchers, Inc.; 1.5B: © Javier Soriano/AFP/Getty Images; 1.5C: © Kiselev Andrey Velerevich/Shutterstock.com; 1.5D: © ayazad/Shutterstock.com; 1.8A: © The McGraw-Hill Companies, Inc./Stephen Frisch Photographer; 1.8B: © BrandTech Scientific, Inc.; 1.13A-B: © The McGraw-Hill Companies, Inc./Stephen Frisch Photographer.

## Chapter 2

Opener: © Mark Schneider/Visuals Unlimited; Table 2.1(all), 2.2A-B: © The McGraw-Hill Companies, Inc./Stephen Frisch Photographer; 2.3(top): © Punchstock RF; 2.3(bottom): © Alexander Cherednichenko/Shutterstock.com; p. 45: © Roman Crochuk/Shutterstock.com; 2.10(all), 2.11A(both), 2.11E: © The McGraw-Hill Companies, Inc./Stephen Frisch Photographer; 2.16: © Mark Schneider/Visuals Unlimited; 2.19A-B: © The McGraw-Hill Companies, Inc./Stephen Frisch Photographer.

## Chapter 3

Opener: © Stepan Jezek/Shutterstock.com; 3.1, 3.7(all): © The McGraw-Hill Companies, Inc./Charles Winters Photographer; p. 104: © The McGraw-Hill Companies, Inc./Stephen Frisch Photographer; p. 105: © Richard Megna/Fundamental Photographs, NYC; 3.14A-D, 3.15(both): © The McGraw-Hill Companies, Inc./Stephen Frisch Photographer.

## Chapter 4

Opener: © Paul Avis/Stone Getty Images; 4.3A-C, 4.4(both): © The McGraw-Hill Companies, Inc./Stephen Frisch Photographer; 4.5: © The McGraw-Hill Companies, Inc./Richard Megna, Photographer; 4.6, 4.8A-B: © The McGraw-Hill Companies, Inc./Stephen Frisch Photographer; 4.10: © The McGraw-Hill Companies, Inc./Charles Winters Photographer; 4.11A-C, p. 158, 4.14(both), 4.15(all), 4.16(all), 4.17(all), 4.18, 4.19(both): © The McGraw-Hill Companies, Inc./Stephen Frisch Photographer.

## Chapter 5

Opener: © The McGraw-Hill Companies, Inc./John Thoeming Photographer; 5.1A-C, 5.2A-B: © The McGraw-Hill Companies, Inc./Stephen Frisch Photographer; 5.10: © The McGraw-Hill Companies, Inc./Charles Winters Photographer; p. 198: © Charles F. McCarthy/Shutterstock.com; p. 203: © The McGraw-Hill Companies, Inc./Stephen Frisch Photographer.

## Chapter 6

Opener: © The McGraw-Hill Companies, Inc./Charles Winters Photographer; 6.1: © The McGraw-Hill Companies, Inc./Stephen Frisch Photographer.

## Chapter 7

Opener: © Orla/Shutterstock.com; p. 264: © Anthony McAulay/Shutterstock.com; 7.5A: © Richard Megna/Fundamental Photographs, NYC; 7.6A: © Ravi/Shutterstock.com; 7.6B: © The McGraw-Hill Companies, Inc./Charles Winters Photographer; 7.6C: © Feng Yu/Shutterstock.com; B7.1A(both): © The McGraw-Hill Companies, Inc./Stephen Frisch Photographer; B7.1B: Washington DC Convention & Visitors Association; 7.13A-B: PSSC Physics © 1965, Education Development Center, Inc.; D.C. Heath & Company/Education Development Center, Inc.; 7.14: © Dennis Kunkel/Phototake.com.

## Chapter 8

CO8: © bbostjan/Shutterstock.com; 8.9A-B, 8.21(all), 8.23: © The McGraw-Hill Companies, Inc./Stephen Frisch Photographer.

## Chapter 9

Opener(crystal): © E. R. Degginger/Photo Researchers, Inc.; Opener(candle): © Dolgisch/Shutterstock.com; Opener(copper): © The McGraw-Hill Companies, Inc./Stephen Frisch Photographer; 9.6A-B, 9.9A, 9.10(all), 9.15, 9.26, 9.29: © The McGraw-Hill Companies, Inc./Stephen Frisch Photographer; p. 355: © Diane Hirsch/Fundamental Photographs, NYC.

## Chapter 10

Opener: © Jill Braaten; 10.2A(all), 10.6(both): © The McGraw-Hill Companies, Inc./Stephen Frisch Photographer.

## Chapter 11

11.23: © The McGraw-Hill Companies, Inc./Charles Winters Photographer.

## Chapter 12

Opener: © Cathleen Howland/Shutterstock.com; p. 420: © Christopher Meder Photography/Shutterstock.com; 12.1A: © dinadesign/Shutterstock.com; 12.1B: © Jill Birschbach Photo Services; 12.9: © The McGraw-Hill Companies, Inc./Richard Megna Photographer; p. 438(strider): © Nuridsany & Perennou /Photo Researchers, Inc.; p. 438(dew): © Rod Planck/Photo Researchers, Inc.; 12.21A-B: © The McGraw-Hill Companies, Inc./Stephen Frisch Photographer; 12.23B: © Scott Camazine/Photo Researchers, Inc.; 12.25A: © Jeffrey A. Scovil Photography (Wayne Thompson Minerals); 12.25B: © Mark Schneider/Visuals Unlimited; 12.25C: © Jeffrey A. Scovil Photography; 12.25D: © Jeffrey A. Scovil Photography (Francis Benjamin Collection); Page 444: © Bryan Busovicki/Shutterstock.com; B12.3: Courtesy National Institute of Standards and Technology; 12.43A: © J. R. Factor/Photo Researchers, Inc.; 12.43B: © James Dennis/Phototake.com; p. 465: © Ingram Publishing/Alamy; 12.49: Courtesy of Benoit Dubertret; 12.50: © & by permission from Ferrotec (USA) Corporation. May not be reproduced without written permission; 12.51: T. Sasaki/Rice University (Image courtesy of Rice University Office of Media Relations and Information).

## Chapter 13

Opener: © CNRI/Photo Researchers, Inc.; 13.4A: © Ruth Melnick; 13.4B: © Ingram Publishing/AGE Fotostock RF; 13.18A-C: © The McGraw-Hill Companies, Inc./Stephen Frisch Photographer; 13.20: © Photodisc/Getty RF; p. 494: © Peter Scoones/Photo Researchers, Inc.; 13.22A-C: © The McGraw-Hill Companies, Inc./Stephen Frisch Photographer; 13.29A-C: © David M. Phillips/Photo Researchers, Inc.; 13.30A: © Ed Degginger/Color-Pic; 13.30B: © Corbis RF; 13.31: © Earth Satellite Corporation/SPL/Photo Researchers, Inc.; B13.3A: © Robert Essel/Corbis.

## Chapter 14

Opener(left): © Joseph T. & Suzanne L. Collins/Photo Researchers, Inc.; Opener(right): © Joel Sartore/National Geographic Stock; Table 14.1, p. 529,

530(top & bottom), 532, 534, 536, 538: © The McGraw-Hill Companies, Inc./ Stephen Frisch Photographer; 14.10A: © Gordon Vrdoljak, UC Berkeley Electron Microscope Lab; 14.11A-B: © The McGraw-Hill Companies, Inc./ Stephen Frisch Photographer; 14.15 © Gontar/Shutterstock.com; Page 544: © The McGraw-Hill Companies, Inc./Stephen Frisch Photographer; p. 547: © Daniel Stein/iStockphoto.com; p. 551, 14.21: © The McGraw-Hill Companies, Inc./Stephen Frisch Photographer; p. 555(right): © Steve Cole/Getty RF; p. 556, 14.23B, p. 562: © The McGraw-Hill Companies, Inc./Stephen Frisch Photographer; 14.26: © Ed Degginger/Color-Pic.

## Chapter 15

Opener: © Georgy Markov/Shutterstock.com; 15.8: © Martin Bough/Fundamental Photographs, NYC; B15.4A: © Zephyr/Photo Researchers, Inc.; 15.14A-B: © The McGraw-Hill Companies, Inc./Richard Megna Photographer; p. 600: © Jill Braaten; 15.28: © The McGraw-Hill Companies, Inc./ Charles Winters Photographer; Page 608: © The McGraw-Hill Companies, Inc./Pat Watson Photographer; 15.32A: © J. Gross/SPL/Photo Researchers, Inc.; 15.32B: © Ed Degginger/Color-Pic; B15.7: © Courtesy of Orchid Cellmark.

## Chapter 16

Opener: © avatra images/Alamy; 16.2(explosion): © Crown Copyright/Health & Safety Lab./Photo Researchers, Inc.; 16.2(fruit, baby): © Ruth Melnick; 16.2(landscape): © Publiphoto/Photo Researchers, Inc.; 16.3A-B: © The McGraw-Hill Companies, Inc./Stephen Frisch Photographer; Page 629: © Roberta Schmidt/AFP/Getty Images; p. 649: © Sipa via AP Images; 16.24A-B: © 2009 Richard Megna, Fundamental Photographs, NYC; B16.1: NASA.

## Chapter 17

Opener: © Richard Megna, Fundamental Photographs, NYC; 17.1A-D: © The McGraw-Hill Companies, Inc./Stephen Frisch Photographer; Page 698: © AfriPics.com/Alamy.

## Chapter 18

Opener: © Jill Braaten; Table 18.1(acids, bases), 18.2, 18.6A-B: © The McGraw-Hill Companies, Inc./Stephen Frisch Photographer.

## Chapter 19

Opener: © Michael J. Thompson/Shutterstock.com; 19.1A-B, 19.2A-B, 19.6: © The McGraw-Hill Companies, Inc./Stephen Frisch Photographer; 19.11: © Jackie Lewin, Royal Free Hospital/Photo Researchers, Inc.; p. 785: © Jeffrey A. Scovil Photography; 19.12A-B: © The McGraw-Hill Companies, Inc./ Stephen Frisch Photographer; p.787: © CNRI/Science Source/Photo Researchers, Inc.; 19.13: © The McGraw-Hill Companies, Inc./Stephen Frisch Photographer; 19.14: © Ruth Melnick; p. 790: © The McGraw-Hill Companies, Inc./ Stephen Frisch Photographer; p. 797: © Phil Degginger/Color-Pic; 19.17: © The McGraw-Hill Companies, Inc./Stephen Frisch Photographer.

## Chapter 20

Opener: © Ian Clark/Image State/Photolibrary.com; 20.1A-B: © The McGraw-Hill Companies, Inc./Stephen Frisch Photographer; 20.12: © Vanderbilt University-Clinical Nutrition Research; p. 828: © PhotoDisc RF.

## Chapter 21

Opener: © ifong/Shutterstock.com; 21.1, 21.2, 21.3, 21.4B: © The McGraw-Hill Companies, Inc./Stephen Frisch Photographer; 21.6: © Richard Megna/ Fundamental Photographs, NYC; 21.8: © The McGraw-Hill Companies, Inc./ Stephen Frisch Photographer; 21.14: Photo © F. W. Goro; 21.15: © Jill Braaten; 21.16: © The McGraw-Hill Companies, Inc./Pat Watson Photographer; 21.17: Courtesy of the Guidant Corporation; 21.19: © The McGraw-Hill Companies, Inc./Stephen Frisch Photographer; 21.20: © AP/Wide World Photos; 21.22A: © Alfred Dias/Photo Researchers, Inc.; 21.23: © David Weintraub/Photo Researchers, Inc.; 21.27: © Jill Braaten; 21.28, p. 889: © The McGraw-Hill Companies, Inc./Stephen Frisch Photographer.

## Chapter 22

Opener: © Cooper-Hewitt, National Design Museum, Smithsonian Institution/ Art Resource, NY; 22.3A: © Doug Sherman/Geofile; 22.3B: © University of Cambridge, Department of Earth Sciences; p. 908: © Ruth Melnick; p. 909: © Robert Holmes/Corbis; p. 917: © Patrick W. Grace/Photo Researchers, Inc.; 22.12: © Richard Megna/Fundamental Photographs, NYC; p. 922: © Christine L. Case/Visuals Unlimited; p. 924: © Remi Benali; 22.18: Courtesy Bethlehem Steel Corporation; p. 926: © Lee Prince/Shutterstock.com; 22.19: © Tom Hollyman/Photo Researchers, Inc.; p. 927: © James L. Amos/ Peter Arnold, Inc./Photolibrary.com; p. 929: © Hank Morgan/Rainbow; p. 931: © Ken Whitmore/Getty Images; 22.23c: © Nathan Benn/Woodfin Camp & Associates.

## Chapter 23

Opener: © VanHart/Shutterstock.com; 23.2, 23.5A-B, 23.6: © The McGraw-Hill Companies, Inc./Stephen Frisch Photographer; 23.8: © Richard Megna/ Fundamental Photographs, NYC; p. 963: © Pete Turner/The Image Bank/ Getty Images; 23.19A: © The McGraw-Hill Companies, Inc./Pat Watson Photographer; 23.20A-B: © The McGraw-Hill Companies, Inc./Stephen Frisch Photographer.

## Chapter 24

Opener(bananas): © Goncharuk/Shutterstock.com; Opener(pellet): © Mitsubishi Nuclear Fuel Co., Ltd.; 24.4: © Hank Morgan/Rainbow; 24.5: © Meridian Biotechnologies Ltd.; p. 991: © Copyright 1978 by Vernon Miller. For use by permission for Business Wire via Getty Images; p. 993: © Hulton Archive/ Getty Images; p. 994: © Maximilien Brice/CERN; 24.13A: © Scott Camazine/Photo Researchers, Inc.; 24.13B: © T. Youssef/Custom Medical Stock Photo; 24.14: © Dr. Robert Friedland/SPL/Photo Researchers, Inc.; 24.15: © Dr. Dennis Olson/Meat Lab, Iowa State University, Ames, IA; 24.20: © Albert Copley/Visuals Unlimited; 24.21: © Dietmar Krause/Princeton Plasma Physics Lab.